CIVIL AIRCRAFT REGISTERS OF

UNITED KINGDOM AND IRELAND 2000

Thirty Sixth Year of Publication - Compiled and Edited by Barrie Womersley

© Air-Britain (Historians) Limited 2000

Published by: Air-Britain (Historians) Limited
Registered Office: 12 Lonsdale Gardens, Tunbridge Wells, Kent TN1 1PA
Sales Department: 19 Kent Road, Grays, Essex RM17 6DE
Membership Enquiries: (ABN) 1 Rose Cottages, 179 Penn Road, Hazlemere, Bucks HP15 7NE
Web-site: http://www.air-britain.com   Sales e-mail: mike@absales.demon.co.uk

Front Cover: Emerald's HS.748, G-BVOU, at Liverpool August 1998 (Denis Norman)

Rear Cover: Air Cavrel's Short SD.3.30, G-DACS, at Coventry October 1998 (Denis Norman)
                Rand Robinson KR-2, G-BUDF, at Kemble July 1999 (Chris Chatfield)

Printed in Great Britain by Bell and Bain Ltd., Glasgow   ISBN 0 85130 294 7
                                                                          ISSN 0264-5270

Thanks for your constructive comments made after my first edition became available in June 1999.

I feel that this latest volume is overshadowed, somewhat, by the emergence of our long awaited, and exceedingly complementary publication, "British Aircraft Registers - 1919 to 1999". This latest annual volume serves to continue the story and the official CAA information takes this on to 31st December 1999. Those of you who are not Air-Britain members and cannot wait another year will be able to keep up to date each month by subscribing to "Air-Britain News" and examining the "United Kingdom Register" section.

A short word about the methodology and background of producing this 36th edition: early books were compiled by typewriter, and a few gallons of Tippex, but recently word-processing techniques have been employed. The chosen software for many years was "Wordstar" but this year all the information has been processed through "Word 97". I hope this gives a more professional appearance. Consideration is being given to the use of Databases and Air-Britain's Monographs' Committee, who oversee all publications, are examining several formats for future publications, particularly registers. This will allow greater flexibility to compile and present tabular data.

As with so many previous editions Phil Butler has produced and compiled the British Glider Association information and, once again, Bernard Martin has ensured that the all relevant facts are included. He has continued to forward all necessary detail obtained from various Web-sites and e-mails especially upto October 1999 when I went on-line. It is self evident that a shared task can only help to ease that of the co-ordinating editor and this allows me more time to scrutinise the presented detail. To this end I am very grateful for all contributions and look to others who would wish to become involved in taking over the specific responsibility for preparing and maintaining any of the subsidiary Sections of this book.

Despite my wish to focus on core activities reflecting individual aircraft I have been asked by several members to re-introduce the listing of radio frequencies. I have introduced a cut-down version in tabular form and hope this satisfies those who always have a copy of this book with them when visiting airfields. Following comments I have reviewed the order and presentation again this year. The individual register blocks now tend to run continuously and so there are fewer highlights and a little less white space. Aircraft register information for the individual country feature initially and Glider data now closes the book. As requested the Aircraft Indices are unified and contain details of UK & Irish aircraft only. I am pleased to re-introduce CAA's UK statistical information this year and include the similar data, which failed to appear in 1999's edition. A brief analysis of totals shows that, despite the ever-growing restrictions, the overall trend is still upwards – some +1.7% with microlight numbers increasing by 3%.

I am grateful to Tony Smith who forwarded a copy of his Balloon names listing. Time has prevented me from re-introducing it this year. I would like to thank Barrie Taylor for his copious detail on microlight maufacturers and construction information. Many thanks to this year's contributors and to the continued support from the regular stalwarts. For this edition I would like to thank the following correspondents [as always in alphabetic order: David Buck, B J Burt, Les Bywaters, Phil Butler, Mike Cain, Peter Campbell/Cirrus Associates, Richard Cawsey, Chris Chatfield, Dennis Clement, Noel Collier, Terry Dann, Phil Dunnington, Malcolm Fillmore, Bill Fisher, Ray Fitton, David Fogwill, Wal Gandy, Dave Haines, Paul Hewins, Nigel Hitchman, Bob Kent, I D McKenzie, Bernard Martin, Tony Morris, Dave Partington Nigel Ponsford, Jeremy Parkin, Paul Rushton, Trevor Sexton, Mark Shortman, Mark Simmons, Graham Slack, Colin M Smith, Warren Smith, Steve Sowter, Jeff Spiers, Martyn Steggalls, Keith Tayles, Barrie V Taylor, Mervyn Thomas, Steve Thompson, Nigel Webb, David Wise, Robert Woodhams and, finally, to Angela for her tolerance.

Thanks are also due to those who send in relevant reports and material direct to A-B News editors. The deadline for the 2001 edition is 15th January 2001. Special appreciation to Graham Slack who provides valuable updates throughout the year. Once again, gratitude is owed to Alan Johnson, editor of the afore-mentioned "United Kingdom Register" section for supplying the official Civil Aviation Authority data and for stimulating me to re-introduce myself to the CAA in London to access their data-base.

Finally, I would like to dedicate this particular edition to John W R Taylor OBE, FRAeS who died in December 1999. His annual "ABC Civil Aircraft Markings" published by Ian Allan in the 1950s and 1960s inspired many aircraft enthusiasts. Therein lay the seeds of this book and the other 35 editions produced by Air-Britain (Historians) Ltd.

FEBRUARY 2000

BARRIE WOMERSLEY
19 The Pastures
Westwood
Bradford-on-Avon
Wilts BA15 2BH

E:MAIL: brw936@netscapeonline.co.uk

There are several purposes to this annual volume. The primary one is to list all aircraft on the current civil aircraft registers, giving full details of types and previous identities, registered ownership and/or operator, probable home base and certification of airworthiness status. This information reproduces, expands upon and amplifies the official country registers. However, we go well beyond that; included in the main text are all other known but no longer currently registered UK and Irish aircraft which, no matter where located, remain in a reasonably identifiable condition either under or pending rebuild, in museum or store, even if merely for spares use, or perhaps held for instructional, fire service or similar use. Many of the latter are also included in the "British Aircraft Registers - 1919 to 1999" volume. In addition many other active & civilian owned aircraft, including foreign registered and former military specimens based in the United Kingdom and Ireland with UK register potential, are also included so that there is a fully comprehensive guide to the British and Irish civil aviation scene.

On a secondary level we cater for the aviation specialist or historian who wants to know more about particular aircraft by providing detailed information such as non-standard engine power and reasons for the aircraft's non-airworthy state. As this book has developed over the years we have included more information aim to give details of significant happenings during the year to support the snapshot at the year-end.

A guide to the main text is as follows: -

Registration (Regn) Registrations are set out in alphabetical order, other than for the initial 1919/28 register. Aircraft no longer currently registered are marked "*". A few aircraft, either real or static reproductions are identified in fictitious UK civil marks for display purposes and are shown in the Index. Those marks which have been re-issued or re-allotted, particularly either if the first holder or allottee did not use the marks or they were not allocated at the time, are shown with the suffix (2) after the registration.

Type   We adopt the official type description as set down by the manufacturer or designer. Where there is doubt, reference is usually made to the relevant issue of "Jane's All the Worlds Aircraft". Indication is given if the manufacturer is a successor company or a licence builder - although not always if it is merely a sub-contractor. Under this column, we show engine types in parenthesis if the engine is non-standard and for all home-builds and microlights and for those vintage/classic aircraft where engines can vary. Additional explanatory notes show details of any unrepaired accidents and comments on the airframe's identity and where the true position is at variance with the official records.

Constructors' Number (C/N)   This is the manufacturers' serial number as generally quoted in the official register. Some aircraft have more than one c/n, for example homebuilds can have the builders' own reference number as well as an official sequential number allotted by the PFA and, on occasion, a manufacturers' plan or kit number. All are shown where known. Those homebuilds and microlights which have been registered without a c/n are identified by the CAA using owners' initials following by "01". These numbers are replaced if the correct C/N is identified. Although manufacturers often identify weightshift microlights with separate c/ns for the Trike unit and for the Wing respectively the CAA usually only registers the Wing C/N. For example, manufacturers Hornet, Mainair and Medway issue a composite C/N comprising both units. Both c/ns are identified, where known, with the C/N for the Trike unit preceding the Wing.

Previous Identities (P/I)   These are set out in reverse order with the most recent identity first. Those registrations shown in parenthesis were allotted but believed never officially used. The nationality of foreign military serials is indicated only where it may not be apparent. Manufacturers' test marks are given, where known, except in respect of where a standard generic mark has been used, such as for the Piper Company in the 1960s and some German motorgliders more recently.

Registration Date (Date)   This is the date of the original registration for those particular marks even where subsequently removed and restored.

Owner/Operator   This is the registered owner for current aircraft as recorded in CAA records. Where the operator is known to be different this is shown in parenthesis. Included under this column are details of the latest reported status, for example if the C of A is not current or the aircraft is known to be under repair plus details of any names and, in particular, any military colour schemes and marks worn. Some aircraft are shown as temporary un-registered ("Temp unregd"); this is where the CAA has not received an application from a new owner following a sale. Usually the CAA gives a period of discretion and if no response is received the Certificate is cancelled and the aircraft is not permitted to fly. Such action usually stimulates the new owner to produce the relevant documentation.

Probable Base   Information in the column is not guaranteed: there is no official information. Reports by readers visiting airfields and strips are perused to compile this column. When the location is uncertain the owner's hometown is shown in parenthesis. Aircraft change base frequently. Readers are reminded that the identification of a base, particularly if it is a private strip, is not an invitation to visit and in a number of cases visiting is actively discouraged because of previous abuses. Balloons and microlights are generally shown as being based at the owner's registered address unless an alternative is known. We recognise the need for privacy in this area and consequently not all information is published.

C of A Expiry   Information is taken from the monthly and annual details published by the CAA. The expiry date indicates the currency of the aircraft's Certificate and details of the suffix letters applied are set out below. Where Cs of A have expired or lapsed and aircraft have been reported since that date notes are given.

EDITORIAL NOTE

All information in the UK & Ireland Register, including that regarding the issue and status of UK Certificates of Airworthiness, is correct to 31st December 1999. Some additional allocations are incorporated to the mid February 2000. BGA information is current to 27th January 2000.

ABBREVIATIONS

A/c – Aircraft	AAC – Army Air Corps	Acft – Aircraft
AAIU – Aircraft Accident Investigation Unit	Assn - Association	BoBMF - Battle of Britain Memorial Flight
BMAA – British Microlight Aircraft Association	C of A – Certificate of Airworthiness	Cf/f - Cleared for first flight (PFA clearance)
c/s – Colour scheme	CC – County Council	Cont – Continental
DBF – Destroyed by fire	DRA – Defence Research Agency	Eng – Engineering
F/C – Flying Club	F/f – First flight	FAA – Fleet Air Arm
FB – Free Balloon	GC – Gliding Club	HAFB - (Hot-Air) Free Balloon
Intl – International	JEFTS – Joint Evaluation Flying Test School	
Lsg – Leasing	Ltd – Limited	Lyc – Lycoming
N/w – Nose-Wheel	NK – Not Known	NTU – Not taken up
PRC – Peoples' Republic of China	PWFU - Permanently WFU	qv – Which See
RAF - Royal Air Force	rep – Reproduction	R – Reservation
RFC – Royal Flying Corps	RN – Royal Navy	RNAS – Royal Naval Air Service
RTS – Reduced to spares	SAAC – Society of Amateur Aircraft Constructors	
SAR – Search and Rescue	t/a – Trustees of the Assets	TR - Trading As
t/s – Tail scheme	t/w – Tail-wheel	TWU - Tactical Weapons Unit
V-S – Vickers-Supermarine	WFU – Withdrawn from Use	

CERTIFICATES OF AIRWORTHINESS (C OF A) STATUS

The coding after the date of expiry indicates the C of A category. No code letter indicates a private category C of A of one or three year duration.

Others are: -

A	Aerial Work:	Normally indicating crop-spraying or banner towing/aerial advertising.
AC	Awaiting Certification	
E	Exemption:	Applicable only to microlights not subject to permit to fly status, no new issues are being made.
F	Ferry:	normally issued for two months, and commonly for overseas sale, or an unlicensed aircraft being flown to another airfield for overhaul.
NE	Non-Expiring:	Hot-Air balloons were, until recently, usually certified as such. The suffix in parenthesis indicates whether it is an Aerial Work, Private or Transport certificate. Non-Expiring exemptions were also given a few years ago to certain early Microlights. These are being progressively upgraded. Any without a date should, in reality, be considered to have lapsed. A few other N/E certificates are used for exports.
P	Permit to Fly:	Introduced in 1950 covering homebuilders, microlights and vintage aircraft - normally issued for one year
PF	Permit to Fly (Ferry):	Issued for one specific flight only - the aircraft need not be of a type that normally operates under a permit to fly.
P	Permit to Fly (Test):	Issued for varying periods of one, two or three months for test purposes leading usually to the issue of a full one year permit to fly. Only a few now seem to be issued.
S	Special:	Mainly lapsed now and replaced by permits to fly but sometimes still used for manufacturers trials aircraft, particularly for overseas demonstration.
T	Transport (Passenger):	Issued to any aircraft operated for hire or reward, usually for either One or Three years.
TC	Transport (Cargo):	As above, but aircraft restricted to carrying cargo for hire or reward. Few aircraft fall into this category.
X	Export:	Issued for limited period solely to facilitate delivery overseas.

SUMMARY OF AIRCRAFT ON THE UK REGISTER AT 1ST JANUARY 2000

CLASS (SEE NOTE 4)		TC(P)	TC(C)	AW	PTE	SPEC	PERMIT	NOT CURRENTLY CERTIFICATED	TOTAL
						CERTIFICATION STATUS			
1.	HEAVIER THAN AIR AIRCRAFT								
1.1	AEROPLANES								
1.1.1	MAXIMUM WEIGHT EXCEEDING 5700 KG	883	9	22	26	-	19	80	1039
1.1.2	MAXIMUM WEIGHT EXCEEDING 2730 KG BUT NOT EXCEEDING 5700 KG	154	-	12	59	-	72	97	394
1.1.3	MAXIMUM WEIGHT NOT EXCEEDING 2730 KG (SEE NOTE 1)	2025	-	23	2658	3	1309	2130	8148
1.1.4	MICROLIGHTS (INCLUDES SMALL LIGHT AEROPLANE)	-	-	-	-	-	1977	1522	3499
1.2	ROTORCRAFT								
1.2.1	HELICOPTERS	657	-	1	189	-	26	140	1013
1.2.2	GYROPLANES	-	-	-	-	-	58	186	244
1.3	GLIDERS (SEE NOTE 3)	-	-	-	-	-	-	7	7
2.	LIGHTER THAN AIR AIRCRAFT								
2.1	AIRSHIPS								
2.1.1	GAS FILLED AIRSHIPS	-	-	-	-	-	-	6	6
2.1.2	HOT AIR AIRSHIPS	-	-	14	-	-	-	22	36
2.2	FREE BALLOONS								
2.2.1	GAS FILLED BALLOONS	-	-	7	-	-	-	8	15
2.2.2	HOT AIR BALLOONS	215	-	586	38	1	-	890	1730
2.2.3	GAS/HOT AIR BALLOONS	-	-	1	-	-	-	11	12
2.2.4	MINIMUM LIFT BALLOONS	-	-	-	-	-	-	150	150
TOTALS		3934	9	666	2970	4	3461	5249	16293

SUMMARY OF AIRCRAFT ON THE UK REGISTER AT 4th JANUARY 1999

CLASS (SEE NOTE 4)		TC(P)	TC(C)	AW	PTE	SPEC	PERMIT	NOT CURRENTLY CERTIFICATED	TOTAL
						CERTIFICATION STATUS			
1.	HEAVIER THAN AIR AIRCRAFT								
1.1	AEROPLANES								
1.1.1	MAXIMUM WEIGHT EXCEEDING 5700 KG	828	7	23	22	-	32	68	978
1.1.2	MAXIMUM WEIGHT EXCEEDING 2730 KG BUT NOT EXCEEDING 5700 KG	151	1	14	57	-	76	95	394
1.1.3	MAXIMUM WEIGHT NOT EXCEEDING 2730 KG (SEE NOTE 1)	1944	-	22	2670	3	1236	2237	8112
1.1.4	MICROLIGHTS (SEE NOTE 2)	-	-	-	-	-	1917	1478	3395
1.2	ROTORCRAFT								
1.2.1	HELICOPTERS	615	-	1	195	-	19	150	980
1.2.2	GYROPLANES	-	-	-	-	-	62	203	265
1.3	GLIDERS (SEE NOTE 3)	-	-	-	-	-	-	7	7
2.	LIGHTER THAN AIR AIRCRAFT								
2.1	AIRSHIPS								
2.1.1	GAS FILLED AIRSHIPS	-	-	-	-	-	-	6	6
2.1.2	HOT AIR AIRSHIPS	-	-	12	-	-	-	22	34
2.2	FREE BALLOONS								
2.2.1	GAS FILLED BALLOONS	-	-	6	1	-	-	8	13
2.2.2	HOT AIR BALLOONS	224	-	529	33	-	-	883	1669
2.2.3	GAS/HOT AIR BALLOONS	-	-	1	-	-	-	11	12
2.2.4	MINIMUM LIFT BALLOONS	-	-	-	-	-	-	150	150
TOTALS		37604	8	608	2978	3	3342	5316	16015

NOTE 1 = Includes aeroplanes which are classified as self-launching motor gliders.

NOTE 2 = The criteria for classifying an aircraft as a microlight are specified in the British Civil Airworthiness Requirements (Section S). Originally this was 390kg limit but note change for 1999 with introduction of Small Light Aircraft ceiling of 450kg.

NOTE 3 = A glider may fly unregistered on any flight within the United Kingdom when not used for public transport or Aerial work.

NOTE 4 = Certification Status:

TC(P)	Transport (Passenger)	> 2730 kg
TC(C)	Transport (Cargo)	> 2730 to 5700 kg
AW	Aerial Work	> 5700 kg
Pte	Private	
Spec	Special	
Permit	Permit to Fly	
Not currently certificated		Aircraft awaiting certification, certification expired or withdrawn, or not subject to certification.

Examples of aircraft over 5700 kg Maximum Total Weight Authorised (MTWA) = Boeing 737 upwards, BAe 146, Jetstream 31
Examples of aircraft between 5700 & 2250 kg MTWA = Piper PA-23
Examples of aircraft 2250 kg MTWA or less = Auster D4, Mooney M20, Piper PA-30, Robinson R-22.

AIR-BRITAIN MEMBERSHIP

If you are not already a member of Air-Britain why not join now ?

Members can receive -

Discounts on Air-Britain Monographs.

Quarterly Air-Britain Digest
A4 magazine containing articles of current and historical aviation interest and comprehensive black & white and colour photographic coverage.

Monthly Air-Britain News
A5 size magazine, normally with 140 pages, includes complete coverage of UK civil and military aviation scene; comprehensive updates on virtually all overseas registers, including USA; sections on bizjets, bizprops and jet, turbine & piston commercial aircraft; full coverage of air displays, UK and overseas.

Quarterly - Archive and Aeromilitaria.
Historical A4 magazines packed with previously unpublished information and photos.

Access to our Information Services, Black and White Photo and Colour Slide Libraries, Air-Britain Travel to overseas airfields, museums and displays.

Access to our expanding Branch Network.

Basic Membership fee for 2000 is £33.00 (to include 4 X Air-Britain Digests and 12 X Air-Britain News).

VISA/MASTERCARD/DELTA/SWITCH accepted - please give full details of card number and expiry date.

To join or for more information please write to:-

Air-Britain Membership Department (Dept UK00)
1 Rose Cottages
179 Penn Road
Hazlemere
Bucks HP15 7NE

For samples of Air-Britain Digest and News please enclose £1.00; with samples of Aeromilitaria and Archive please forward £2.00.

SECTION 1

UNITED KINGDOM

The first permanent United Kingdom Register of Civil Aircraft was inaugurated on 31st July 1919 and ran until 29th July 1928 when the marks G-EBZZ had been issued. With the growth of international civil aviation new regulations came into place on 1st January 1929. The transition to a second series of registrations, commencing from G-AAAA onwards, was made with effect from 30th July 1928. Registrations were usually allocated in alphabetical sequence until the late 1970s although there have been several sporadic exceptions to this rule throughout the period.

The G-AAAA-AZZZ series were all allocated by mid 1972 and a new series G-BAAA commenced. This is still in use in conjunction with registrations allotted from other series extending from G-C... to G-Z... Many of the G-B... registrations, issued ahead of the alphabetical sequence, have now been subsumed within their proper sequence. In addition several special registration series have been isssued embracing: a) Balloons and Airships (G-FAAA-FAAZ) issued from 1920 to 1928. b) Model balloons (G-FYAA-FYZZ) issued from 1982 to 1997. c) specific alphanumeric marks for British Airways' Concordes (G-NxxAx) issued in 1979, and d) Microlights (G-MBAA-MBZZ, G-MGAA-MGZZ, G-MJAA-MJZZ, G-MMAA-MNZZ, G-MTAA-MTZZ & G-MYAA-MZZZ) issued from 1981 to 1998.

Regn	Type	C/n	P/I	Date	Owner/operator	Probable Base	CA Expy

G-EAAA – G-EAZZ

Regn	Type	C/n	P/I	Date	Owner/operator	Probable Base	CA Expy
G-EACN*	BAT FK.23 Bantam 1 (ABC Wasp)	FK23/15	K-123 F1654	29. 5.19	Aviodome/Early Birds Foundation (On rebuild 1992) Lelystad, The Netherlands		
G-EACQ*	Avro 534 Baby	534/1	VH-UCQ G-AUCQ/G-EACQ/K-131	29. 5.19	Queensland Cultural Centre Brisbane, Australia		
G-EAML*	Airco DH.6	-	C9449	8. 9.19	South African Air Force Museum (Components only) Pretoria, South Africa		18. 9.20
G-EAOU*	Vickers FB.27A Vimy IV	-	(A5-1) G-EAOU/F8630	23.10.19	Not known Adelaide, Australia (On display Airport Museum 9.96)		31.10.20
G-EAQM*	Airco DH.9 (AS Puma)	-	F1278	31.12.19	Australian War Memorial Canberra, Australia		1. 1.21
G-EASD	Avro 504L floatplane (Le Clerget 130hp)	E.5	S-AHAA S-AAP/G-EASD/(RAF)	26. 3.20	AJD Engineering Ltd Moat Farm, Milden (Stored 8.93 pending rebuild)		
G-EAVX	Sopwith Pup	PFA/101-10523	B1807	2.11.20	K.A.M.Baker (Winscombe, Somerset) (To carry "B1807/A7" in RFC c/s)		

(Claimed to be rebuild of original aircraft which was written-off at Hendon 21.7.21; status uncertain)

G-EBAA – G-EBZZ

Regn	Type	C/n	P/I	Date	Owner/operator	Probable Base	CA Expy
G-EBHX	DH.53 Humming Bird (ABC Scorpion II)	98	No.8 (Lympne 1923)	22. 9.23	The Shuttleworth Trust Old Warden "L'Oiseau-Mouche"		2. 7.95P
G-EBIA	R.A.F. SE-5A (Wolseley Viper 200hp)	654/2404	F904	26. 9.23	The Shuttleworth Trust Old Warden "D7000"/G-EBIA/F904 (As "F904/H" in 56 Sqdn RFC c/s)		14. 5.99P
G-EBIB*	R.A.F. SE-5A (Regd with c/n 688/2404)	687/2404	"F939" G-EBIB/F937	26. 9.23	The Science Museum (Flight Gallery) South Kensington, London		6. 6.35
G-EBIC*	R.A.F. SE-5A (Wolseley Viper 200hp)	688/2404	"B4563" G-EBIC/F938	26. 9.23	RAF Museum (As "F938") Hendon (Regd with c/n 687/2404; allocated 9208M)		3. 9.30
G-EBIR	DH.51 (ADC Renault 120hp)	102	VP-KAA G-KAA/G-EBIR	22. 1.24	The Shuttleworth Trust Old Warden "Miss Kenya"		18. 7.99P
G-EBJE*	Avro 504K	927		4. 1.26	RAF Museum (As "E449") Hendon		29. 9.34
	(Includes components of Avro 548A G-EBKN ex E449; allocated 9205M 1994)						
G-EBJG*	Parnall Pixie III	-	No.17/18 (Lympne 1924)	?. 9.24	Midland Air Museum Coventry (Components only remain for long term rebuild 4.96)		2.10.36
G-EBJO	ANEC II	2	No.7 (Lympne 1924)	17.7.24	The Shuttleworth Trust Old Warden (On rebuild 10.97)		30.11.35
G-EBKY	Sopwith Dove (Le Rhone 80hp) (Converted to Sopwith Pup) "N5184"/G-EBKY	w/o 3004/14	"N5180"	27. 3.25	The Shuttleworth Trust Old Warden (As "N6181" in 3 Sqdn RNAS c/s) "Happy"		9. 5.00P
G-EBLV	DH.60 Moth (Cirrus III)	188		22. 6.25	British Aerospace (Ops) Ltd Old Warden (On loan to The Shuttleworth Trust)		17. 6.00P
G-EBMB*	Hawker Cygnet I (Bristol Cherub III)	1	No.14 (Lympne 1925)	29. 7.25	RAF Museum Hendon		30.11.61
G-EBNV	English Electric S.1 Wren (ABC 398cc) (Composite aircraft - principally c/n 3 rebuilt 1955/56; as "No.4")	4	(BAPC11)	9. 4.26	The Shuttleworth Trust Old Warden		23.6.87P*
G-EBOV*	Avro 581E Avian	5116	No 9 (Lympne 1926)	7. 7.26	Queensland Cultural Centre Brisbane, Australia		30. 1.29
G-EBQP	DH.53 Humming Bird	114	J7326	?. 4.27	M.C.Russell Audley End		AC
	(On rebuild 3.97 based on wings ex Martin Monoplane G-AEYY; to carry "J7326")						

1

Regn	Type	C/n	P/I	Date	Owner/operator	Probable Base	CA Expy
G-EBWD	DH.60X Moth	552		2. 3.28	The Shuttleworth Trust	Old Warden	10. 4.00P
	(Cirrus Hermes 2)						
G-EBXU	DH.60X Moth Seaplane	627		2. 5.28	D.E.Cooper-Maguire	Findon, Worthing	13.12.00P
	(Crashed nr Rio De Janeiro 1930; provenance unconfirmed; restored 1998)						
G-EBYY*	Avro 617 Cierva C.8L Mk.2	-		21. 6.28	Musee de l'Air et de l'Espace		
	(AS Lynx 180hp)					Le Bourget, Paris	13. 7.29
G-EBZM*	Avro 594A Avian IIIA	R3/CN/160		3. 2.28	The Aeroplane Collection Ltd	Manchester	20. 1.38
	(Cirrus)				(On loan to Manchester Museum of Science & Industry)		

G-AAAA – G-AAZZ

Regn	Type	C/n	P/I	Date	Owner/operator	Probable Base	CA Expy
G-AAAH*	DH.60G Moth	804		30. 8.28	The Science Museum (Flight Gallery)		
					"Jason" South Kensington, London		23.12.30
	(A reproduction, allocated BAPC168, is displayed at the Yorkshire Air Museum - see SECTION 5)						
G-AACD*	DH.60M Moth	340		16.10.28		St.Ives, Huntingdon	8. 4.38
	(Gipsy I)			(Crashed Fen Ditton, Cambridge 24.6.37, rebuilt but stored in 1989)			
G-AACN*	Handley Page HP.39 Gugnunc	1	K1908	2.11.28	The Science Museum	Wroughton	19. 9.30
			G-AACN				
G-AADR(2)	Moth Corpn DH.60GM Moth	138	NC939M	2. 6.86	H.F.Moffatt	Woodlow Farm, Bosbury	16. 8.00P
	(Gipsy I)						
G-AAEG	DH.60G Moth	1027	D-EUPI	4. 2.29	J.Dixon	(Brensbach, Germany)	
			D-1599/G-AAEG		(On rebuild 1994 - provenance unconfirmed)		
G-AAHI	DH.60G Moth	1082		25. 5.29	N.J.W.Reid	Lee-on-Solent	30. 6.02P
	(Gipsy I) (Rebuilt from components remaining from G-AAWO rebuild)						
G-AAHY	DH.60M Moth	1362	HB-AFI	10. 5.29	D.J.Elliott	Thruxton	12. 8.00P
	(Gipsy I)		(CH-480)/G-AAHY		(Brooklands Flying Club c/s)		
G-AAIN	Parnall Elf II	2 & J.6		11. 6.29	The Shuttleworth Trust	Old Warden	30. 4.00P
	(ADC Cirrus Hermes 2)						
G-AALP*	Surrey Flying Services AL-1	AL-1		29. 8.29	Arden Family Trust (Stored 1.98)		
						Thorncross Farm, Caudleigh	17. 5.40
G-AALY	DH.60G Gipsy Moth	1175	F-AJKM	9. 9.29	K M Freeson	(Pulborough)	
G-AAMX(2)*	Moth Corpn DH.60GM Moth	125	NC926M	11. 9.86	RAF Museum	RAF Cosford	7. 5.94P
	(Gipsy II)				(Cancelled as WFU 19.8.95)		
G-AAMY	Moth Corpn DH.60GMW Moth	86	N585M	2. 5.80	Totalsure Ltd	(The Netherlands)	23. 6.00P
	(Wright Gipsy L320)		NC585M				
G-AANF(2)*	Moth Corpn DH.60GMW Moth	49	N298M	3. 2.87	C.Smith	Mandeville, New Zealand	17. 4.90P
	(Wright Gipsy 1)		N237K/NC237K		(Damaged nr Popham 8.8.89 and on rebuild 2.91)		
G-AANG(2)	Bleriot Type XI	14	(BAPC3)	29.11.81	The Shuttleworth Trust	Old Warden	
	(Anzani 25hp) (1910 original; no external marks)						
G-AANH(2)	Deperdussin Monoplane	43	(BAPC4)	29.10.81	The Shuttleworth Trust	Old Warden	14. 5.83P
	(Anzani Y 35hp) (Possibly c/n 143; no external marks)						
G-AANI(2)	Blackburn 1912 Monoplane No.9	725	(BAPC5)	29.10.81	The Shuttleworth Trust	Old Warden	18. 7.99P
	(Gnome 683 50hp)				(No external marks)		
G-AANJ(2)	LVG C.VI 4503	C7198/18		29.10.81	The Shuttleworth Trust	Old Warden	12. 5.00P
	(Benz 230hp)		"1594"/C7198/18		(As "7198/18" in German Air Force c/s; composite		
	aircraft including parts from LVG 1594: captured 1916/17 and allotted RFC serial "XG7")						
G-AANL(2)	DH.60M Moth	1446	OY-DEH	29. 6.81	P.L.Allwork	Hildon-le-Noble, Hants	29. 6.00P
	(Gipsy II)		RDAF S-357/S-107		(National Flying Services c/s; composite rebuild)		
G-AANM(2)	Bristol F.2B Fighter	"67626"	BAPC166	16. 7.87	Aero Vintage Ltd	St.Leonards-on-Sea	
	(RR Falcon)				(Exhibited at Museum, Sandown by 4.99: to carry "D7889")		
G-AANO(2)	Moth Corpn DH.60GMW Moth	165	N590N	3. 3.88	A.W. & M.E.Jenkins	Comberton, Cambridge	
			NC590N		(Composite rebuild 11.91)		
G-AANV(2)	Morane Saulnier DH.60M Moth	13	HB-OBU	8. 3.84	R A Seeley	Henstridge	14. 4.00P
	(Gipsy I)		CH-349/F-AJNY		(Stored 4.98)		
G-AAOK(2)	Curtiss-Wright Travel Air CW-12Q		N370N	18.11.81	Shipping & Airlines Ltd	Biggin Hill	18. 1.84P
	(Warner Scarab 145)	12Q-2026	NC370N/NC352M				
					(Damaged in gales Rijeka, Yugoslavia 21.10.83: - on rebuild 8.97)		
G-AAOR(2)	DH.60G Moth	1075	EC-AAO	15. 4.85	V.S.E.Norman	Sywell	4.10.99P
	(Gipsy I)		(Original identity uncertain and probably composite)				
G-AAPZ	Desoutter I	D.25		9. 8.31	The Shuttleworth Trust	Old Warden	AC
	(Cirrus Hermes)				(National Flying Services c/s)		
G-AAUP	Klemm L 25aI	145		19. 2.30	Janice I.Cooper t/a Newbury Aeroplane Co		
	(Salmson AD9)				(Stored 6.95) Denford Manor, Hungerford		21.11.84P
G-AAWO	DH.60G Moth	1235		2. 5.30	N.J.W.Reid & L.A.Fenwick	Lee-on-Solent	10. 2.00P
	(Gipsy 1) (Composite 1953 rebuild including parts of G-AAHI c/n 1082)						
G-AAXK*	Klemm L 25aI	182		?. 5.30	C.C.Russell-Vick	Orpington	29.11.60
					(Damaged White Waltham 3.62: stored 3.96)		
G-AAYX	Southern Martlet	202		14. 5.30	The Shuttleworth Trust	Old Warden	12. 4.49
	(Genet Major 1A)				(On long term rebuild 3.96)		

Regn	Type	C/n	P/I	Date	Owner/operator	Probable Base	CA Expy
G-AAZP	DH.80A Puss Moth (Gipsy Major)	2047	HL537	4. 6.30	R.P.Williams Denford Manor, Hungerford		30. 9.99
					G-AAZP/SU-AAC/G-AAZP "British Heritage"		

G-ABAA – G-ABZZ

Regn	Type	C/n	P/I	Date	Owner/operator	Probable Base	CA Expy
G-ABAA*	Avro 504K	-	"H2311" G-ABAA	11. 9.30	RAF Museum Manchester		11. 4.39
					(On loan to Manchester Museum of Science & Industry)		
G-ABAG	DH.60G Moth (Gipsy I)	1259		23. 6.30	The Shuttleworth Trust	Old Warden	30. 4.00P
G-ABBB*	Bristol 105A Bulldog IIA	7446	"K2227"	12. 6.30	RAF Museum	Hendon	
			G-ABBB/R-11/G-ABBB (As "K2227")				
G-ABDX	DH.60G Moth (Gipsy I)	1294	HB-UAS (CH-405)/G-ABDX	22. 8.30	M.D.Souch	Hill Farm, Durley	28. 7.99P
G-ABEV(2)	DH.60G Moth (Gipsy I)	1823	N4203E	10. 3.77	Wessex Aviation & Transport Ltd	Chalmington	
			G-ABEV/HB-OKI/CH-217				9.10.97P
G-ABLM*	Cierva C.24 (Gipsy III)	710		22. 4.31	The Science Museum Salisbury Hall, London Colney		16. 1.35
G-ABLS	DH.80A Puss Moth (Gipsy Major)	2164		7. 5.31	R.C.F.Bailey	Ludlow	26. 8.00P
G-ABMR*	Hawker Hart	H.H-1	"J9933" G-ABMR	28. 5.31	RAF Museum	Hendon	11. 6.57
					(As "J9941" in 57 Sqn c/s)		
G-ABNT	Civilian CAC.1 Coupe (Genet Major 1A) (C/n also quoted as 0.3)	0.2.3		10. 9.31	Shipping & Airlines Ltd	Biggin Hill	30. 9.99P
G-ABNX	Robinson Redwing 2 (Genet)	9		2. 7.31	J.A.Pothecary Newton Toney, Salisbury		21. 6.94P
					(Stored 8.97)		
G-ABOI*	Wheeler Slymph	AHW.1		17. 7.31	A.H.Wheeler	Coventry	
					(On loan to Midland Air Museum & dismantled components stored 4.96)		
G-ABOX(2)	Sopwith Pup (Le Rhone 80hp)	-	N5195	12. 9.84	C.M.D. & A.P. St.Cyrien		
					(On loan to Museum of Army Flying: as "N5195")	AAC Middle Wallop	22. 4.93P
G-ABSD	DH.60G Moth	1883	A7-96 VH-UTN/G-ABSD	21.11.31	M.E.Vaisey	Hemel Hempstead	
					(On rebuild following import from USA in 1985 as basket case: identity unconfirmed)		
G-ABTC*	Comper CLA.7 Swift (Pobjoy Niagara)	S.32/1		1. 1.32	P.Channon	Lelant, Cornwall	18. 7.84P
					"Spirit of Butler" (Stored since 7.84: cancelled by CAA 22.2.99)		
G-ABUS	Comper CLA.7 Swift (Pobjoy Niagara 3)	S.32/4		27. 2.32	R.C.F.Bailey	Ludlow	19. 6.79P
					(On rebuild 1989)		
G-ABVE	Arrow Active 2 (Gipsy III)	2		19. 3.32	J.D.Penrose	Old Warden	15. 4.00P
					(On loan to The Shuttleworth Trust)		
G-ABWP	Spartan Arrow 1 (Cirrus Hermes 2)	78		18. 5.32	R.E.Blain	Redhill	4. 9.99P
G-ABXL	Granger Archeopteryx (Cherub III)	3A		3. 6.32	The Shuttleworth Trust	Old Warden	22. 9.82P
G-ABYA*	DH.60G Moth (Gipsy I)	1906		7. 7.32	J.F.Moore	Biggin Hill	21. 5.73
					(Crashed Biggin Hill 21.5.72 & stored 2.95)		
G-ABYN*	Spartan Three-Seater II	102	EI-ABU	14. 9.32	Julie D Souch Mandeville, New Zealand		
					G-ABYN (On rebuild by Croydon Aviation Co 1995: cancelled by CAA 31.3.99)		
G-ABZB	DH.60GIII Moth Major	5011	SE-AIA G-ABZB	30. 8.32	R.Earl & B.Morris	Foley Farm, Berks	15. 8.00P

G-ACAA – G-ACZZ

Regn	Type	C/n	P/I	Date	Owner/operator	Probable Base	CA Expy
G-ACAA(2)	Bristol F.2B Fighter (RR Falcon)	- 7434	F4516	25.10.91	Patina Ltd	Duxford	AC
					(Op The Fighter Collection)		
	(Regd as "original" G-ACAA but in fact on rebuild 7.97 from various components including						
	ex Weston-on-the-Green fuselage frame/to carry "D8084/S")						
G-ACBH*	Blackburn B.2	4700/3	(2895M) G-ACBH	1.12.32	R.Coles t/a Coles Auto Supplies Temple Farm, West Hanningfield, Essex		27.11.41
	(Stored 1.96 for possible refurbishment/probably to be composite with G-ADFO c/n 5920/2 written off in 1940)						
G-ACCB	DH.83 Fox Moth	4042		24. 1.33	E.A.Gautrey	Nuneaton	20. 7.57
					(Crashed off Southport 25.9.56 & on rebuild 10.95)		
G-ACDA	DH.82A Tiger Moth	3175	BB724 G-ACDA	6. 2.33	B.D.Hughes	Rotary Farm, Hatch	26. 6.82
	(Crashed & burned out nr Cirencester 27.6.79 - rebuild probably composite with G-ANOR by Skysport 1.96)						
G-ACDC	DH.82A Tiger Moth	3177	BB726 G-ACDC	6. 2.33	The Tiger Club (1990) Ltd	Headcorn	15. 4.02T
					(Composite airframe after several major rebuilds)		
G-ACDI	DH.82A Tiger Moth (Composite rebuild)	3182	BB742 G-ACDI	6. 2.33	J.A.Pothecary Newton Toney, Salisbury		AC
G-ACDJ	DH.82A Tiger Moth	3183	BB729 G-ACDJ	6. 2.33	P.Henley Brickhouse Farm, Frogland Cross		8. 6.01

Regn	Type	C/n	P/I	Date	Owner/operator	Probable Base	CA Expy
G-ACEJ	DH.83 Fox Moth	4069		21. 4.33	Janice I.Cooper	Rendcomb	3.11.00
					t/a Newbury Aeroplane Co (Scottish Motor Traction c/s)		
G-ACET	DH.84 Dragon	6021	2779M AW171/G-ACET	21. 4.33	M.D.Souch (Hedge End, Southampton)		
					(On rebuild 1995; composite based on original wings)		
G-ACGR*	Percival Gull Four IIA (Gipsy Major I)	D.29		11. 5.33	Musee Royal de l'Armee Brussels, Belgium		20. 6.35
G-ACGT*	Avro 594B Avian IIIA	R3/CN/171	EI-AAB	8. 5.33	Yorkshire Light Acft Ltd	Leeds-Bradford	21. 7.39
					(On long term rebuild 1.97)		
G-ACGZ	DH.60G III Moth Major	5030	VT-AFW G-ACGZ	30. 5.33	N.H.Lemon	(Maidenhead)	
G-ACIT	DH.84 Dragon 1	6039		24. 7.33	The Science Museum	Wroughton	25. 5.74
					(Highland Airways c/s) "Aberdeen"		
G-ACLL	DH.85 Leopard Moth	7028	AW165 G-ACLL	16. 1.34	D.C.M. & V.M.Stiles	Jurby, IOM	6.12.95P
					(Stored 10.96)		
G-ACMA	DH.85 Leopard Moth	7042	BD148 G-ACMA	14. 3.34	S.J.Filhol	Headcorn	3. 2.94P
					(Stored 2.95)		
G-ACMD(2)	DH.82A Tiger Moth	3195	N182DH EC-AGB/Sp AF 33-5	20. 1.88	M.J.Bonnick	Rectory Farm, Abbotsley	27. 5.02
G-ACMN	DH.85 Leopard Moth	7050	X9381 G-ACMN	?. 4.34	Carolyn S.Grace	Duxford	18. 2.00
G-ACOJ(2)	DH.85 Leopard Moth	7035	F-AMXP	5. 6.87	A.J.Norman	Rendcomb	3. 9.01
	(Composite with wings from HB-OXO)				t/a Norman Aeroplane Trust		
G-ACSP	DH.88 Comet	1994	CS-AAJ G-ACSP/E-1	21. 8.34	K.Fern	Stoke-on-Trent	
					(On rebuild 10.96 based on some original components)		
G-ACSS	DH.88 Comet (Gipsy Queen 2)	1996	K5084 G-ACSS	4. 9.34	The Shuttleworth Trust "Grosvenor House"	Old Warden	2. 6.94P
	(a) Static rep built Australia for film purposes is owned by G Gaywood - see BAPC216 in SECTION 5)						
	(b) Second flying rep built in 1993 by Repeat Aircraft, Riverside CA, USA for Tom Wathen regd N88XD)						
G-ACTF	Comper CLA.7 Swift (Pobjoy Niagara 2)	S.32/9	VT-ADO	24. 5.34	The Shuttleworth Trust "The Scarlet Angel"	Old Warden	29. 4.99P
G-ACUS(2)	DH.85 Leopard Moth	7082	HB-OXA (G-ACUS)	17.11.77	A.J.Norman	Rendcomb	8.11.02
					t/a Norman Aeroplane Trust		
	(Composite including parts from HB-OXO (G-ACOL) c/n 7045)						
G-ACUU*	Avro 671 Cierva C.30A Autogiro (AS Civet)	726	(G-AIXE) HM580/G-ACUU	26. 6.34	Imperial War Museum - Skyfame Collection (As "HM580")	Duxford	30. 4.60
G-ACUX*	Short S.16 Scion 1	S.776	VH-UUP G-ACUX	26. 6.34	Ulster Folk & Transport Museum (As "VH-UUP")	Holywood, Belfast	-
G-ACVA*	Kay Gyroplane 33/1 (Pobjoy R 75hp)	1002		26. 6.34	Glasgow Museum of Transport Kelvin Hall, Glasgow		
G-ACWM*	Avro 671 Cierva C.30A Autogiro	715	(G-AHMK) AP506/G-ACWM	24. 7.34	E.D. Ap Rees	Weston-super-Mare	13. 7.40
					t/a The Helicopter Museum		
G-ACWP*	Avro 671 Cierva C.30A Autogiro	728	AP507 G-ACWP	24. 7.34	The Science Museum (Flight Gallery) South Kensington, London		6. 3.41
					(As "AP507/KX-P" in 529 Sqn c/s)		
G-ACXB(2)	DH.60GIII Moth Major	5098	EC-ABY	24. 1.89	D.F.Hodgkinson	(Gravesend)	
				EC-BAX/Sp AF 30-53/EC-YAY (On rebuild)			
G-ACXE	British Klemm L 25c1 Swallow	21		29.10.34	J.G.Wakeford	Bexhill-on-Sea	7. 4.40
					(On rebuild since 1989)		
G-ACYK*	Spartan Cruiser III	101		2. 5.35	Royal Museum of Scotland	East Fortune	2. 6.38
					(Crashed Largs, Ayrshire 14.1.38 & remains recovered 7.73)		
G-ACYR*	DH.89 Dragon Rapide	6261		15.10.34	Museo del Air	Cuatro Vientos, Spain	23. 8.47
G-ACZE	DH.89A Dragon Rapide	6264	G-AJGS	20.11.34	Wessex Aviation & Transport Ltd		
			G-ACZE/Z7266/G-ACZE (Stored 8.97)			Henstridge	18. 8.95

G-ADAA – G-ADZZ

Regn	Type	C/n	P/I	Date	Owner/operator	Probable Base	CA Expy
G-ADAH*	DH.89 Dragon Rapide	6278		30. 1.35	The Aeroplane Collection Ltd	Manchester	9. 6.47
	(On loan to Manchester Museum of Science & Industry; Allied Airways (Gandar Dower) c/s) "Pioneer"						
G-ADEV(2)	Avro 504K (Le Rhone 110hp)	R3/LE/61400	G-ACNB "E3404"	18. 4.84	The Shuttleworth Trust (As "H5199")	Old Warden	10. 4.99P
	(P/i not confirmed but, if c/n is correct, the full p/i is 3118M/BK892/G-ADEV/H5199)						
G-ADFV*	Blackburn B.2	5920/8	2893M G-ADFV	3. 4.35	J.Chillingworth	St.Ives, Huntingdon	26. 6.41
					(Forward fuselage for rebuild 4.96)		
G-ADGP	Miles M.2L Hawk Speed Six	160	(N ntu)	20. 5.35	R.A.Mills	(Wokingham)	22. 4.00P
G-ADGT	DH.82A Tiger Moth	3338	BB697 G-ADGT	23. 5.35	D.R. & Mrs M.Wood	Fowle Hall Farm, Paddock Wood, Kent	18. 8.97
G-ADGV	DH.82A Tiger Moth	3340	(D-E)	23. 5.35	K.J. & P.J.Whitehead		
			G-ADGV/(G-BACW)/BB694/G-ADGV			Whitchurch Hill, Reading	10. 6.02
G-ADHD(2)	DH.60GIII Moth Major	5105	EC-...	17. 2.88	M.E.Vaisey	Henlow	
			Sp AF 34-5/EC-W32 (Rebuild of ex Spanish components acquired from USA)				

Regn	Type	C/n	P/I	Date	Owner/operator	Probable Base	CA Expy
G-ADIA	DH.82A Tiger Moth	3368	BB747	13. 8.35	S.J.Beaty	Wold Lodge	20. 5.02
			G-ADIA				
G-ADJJ	DH.82A Tiger Moth	3386	BB819	29. 8.35	J.M.Presto	Great Eversden	20. 3.75
			G-ADJJ		(Stored 4.95)		
G-ADKC	DH.87B Hornet Moth	8064	X9445	27. 3.36	A.J.Davy	Redhill	30.11.01
			G-ADKC				
G-ADKK	DH.87B Hornet Moth	8033	W5749	9.11.35	R.G.Anniss	(Horsham)	7. 8.00
G-ADKL	DH.87B Hornet Moth	8035	F-BCJO	17.11.35	A.de Cadenet	Perigeux, France	29. 5.95
			G-ADKL/W5750/G-ADKL				
G-ADKM	DH.87B Hornet Moth	8037	W5751	12.11.35	L.V.Mayhead	Hedge End, Durley	6. 7.01
			G-ADKM				
G-ADLY	DH.87B Hornet Moth	8020	W9388	5.10.35	Totalsure Ltd	(The Netherlands)	3. 5.00P
			G-ADLY				
G-ADMT	DH.87B Hornet Moth	8093		8. 5.36	P.A.D.Swoffer "Curlew"	White Waltham	19. 5.01
G-ADMW*	Miles M.2H Hawk Major	177	DG590	30. 7.35	RAF Museum	Cardington	30. 7.65
			G-ADMW		(Allotted 8379M; as "DG590"; stored 1.96)		
G-ADND	DH.87B Hornet Moth	8097	W9385	4. 8.36	The Shuttleworth Trust	Old Warden	21. 7.00P
			G-ADND		(As "W9385/YG-L/3" of 502 Sqn)		
G-ADNE	DH.87B Hornet Moth	8089	X9325	10. 3.36	G-ADNE Ltd "Ariadne"	Oaksey Park	17. 3.00
			G-ADNE				
G-ADNL	Miles M.5 Sparrowhawk	239		12. 8.35	A.G.Dunkerley	(Bury, Lancs)	13. 5.58S
		(On rebuild from components discarded from reconstruction 1953 as M.77 Sparrowjet)					
G-ADNZ(2)	DH.82A Tiger Moth	85614	6948M	10.10.74	D.C.Wall	Swanton Morley	16. 7.00
			DE673		(As "DE673")		
G-ADOT*	DH.87B Hornet Moth	8027	X9326	1.11.35	De Havilland Aircraft Museum		
			G-ADOT			Salisbury Hall, London Colney	15.10.59
G-ADPC	DH.82A Tiger Moth	3393	BB852	24. 9.35	T.Groves	(Fareham)	22. 5.99
			G-ADPC		t/a G-ADPC Group (Composite rebuild)		
G-ADPJ	BAC Drone 2	7		21. 8.35	N.H.Ponsford	(Selby)	17. 5.55
	(Douglas Sprite)		(Crashed Leicester 3.4.55: on rebuild 12.99 using parts from G-AEJR c/n 22)				
G-ADPS	BA Swallow 2	410		4. 9.35	J.F.Hopkins	Watchford Farm, Yarcombe	8. 9.99P
	(Pobjoy Cataract 2)				(On overhaul 10.97)		
G-ADRA(2)	Pietenpol Air Camper	PFA/1514		10. 4.78	A.J.Mason	Hinton-in-The-Hedges	3. 4.00P
	(Continental A65)				"Edna May"		
G-ADRH(2)	DH.87B Hornet Moth	8038	F-AQBY	6. 8.82	R G Grocott	(Zurich, Switzerland)	
			HB-OBE		(Shipped to Gore, New Zealand for rebuild 5.91)		
G-ADRR(2)	Aeronca C.3	A.734	N17423	6. 9.88	S.J.Rudkin	(Westmoor Farm, Langham)	
			NC17423		(Stored Roughay Farm, Bishops Waltham 1992)		
G-ADSK	DH.87B Hornet Moth	8091	D-EJOM	9. 4 36	R.G.Grocott	(Banbury)	14. 3.70
			AP-AES/G-ADSK/AV952/G-ADSK		(On rebuild Gore, New Zealand 1993 from components)		
G-ADUR	DH.87B Hornet Moth	8085		10. 3.36	Wessex Aviation & Transport Ltd		
					(Stored 4.94)	Chalmington	7. 9.93
G-ADWJ	DH.82A Tiger Moth	3450	BB803	9.12.35	C.Adams	(Shobdon)	
			G-ADWJ		(On rebuild 3.96)		
G-ADWO*	DH.82A Tiger Moth	3455	BB807	9.12.35	Southampton Hall of Aviation Southampton		
			G-ADWO (As "BB807"; composite rebuild incl components from G-AOAC & AOJJ)				
G-ADXS*	Mignet HM.14 Pou-Du-Ciel	CLS.1		18.11.35	Storey Family	Shoreham	1.12.36
	(Scott Squirrel A2S)				"The Fleeing Fly" (On rebuild at Winthorpe 9.97)		
G-ADXT	DH.82A Tiger Moth	3436		9.12.35	J.R.Hanauer	Goodwood	3. 8.00T
	(Officially restored but is mainly a rebuild of various components)						
G-ADYS	Aeronca C.3 (Aeronca E113C)	A.600		21. 1.36	Janice I.Cooper	Rendcomb	18. 9.99P
					(London Air Park Flying Club c/s)		

G-AEAA – G-AEZZ

Regn	Type	C/n	P/I	Date	Owner/operator	Probable Base	CA Expy
G-AEBB	Mignet HM.14 Pou-Du-Ciel	KWO.1		24. 1.36	The Shuttleworth Trust	Old Warden	31. 5.39
G-AEBJ	Blackburn B.2	6300/8		4. 2.36	British Aerospace (Operations) Ltd		
	(Gipsy Major)					Brough	3. 7.00
G-AEDB	BAC Drone 2	13		18. 3.36	P.L.Kirk & R E Nerou	(Derby)	26. 5.87P
	(Cherub III) (Registered as BGA2731 31.3.81: composite with wings of G-AEJH & tail end of G-AEEN; stored 7.96)						
G-AEDU(2)	DH.90A Dragonfly	7526	N190DH	4. 6.79	A.J.Norman	Langham	18. 7.02
			G-AEDU/ZS-CTR/CR-AAB t/a Norman Aeroplane Trust				
G-AEEG	Miles M.3A Falcon Major	216	SE-AFN	14. 3.36	G.E.J.Spooner	(Colchester)	2. 7.00
			Fv913/SE-AFN/G-AEEG/U-20				
G-AEEH*	Mignet HM.14 Pou-Du-Ciel	EGD.1		13. 3.36	Cosford Aerospace Museum	RAF Cosford	15. 5.38
G-AEFG*	Mignet HM.14 Pou-Du-Ciel	JN.1	BAPC75	27. 3.36	N.H.Ponsford	(Selby)	31. 3.38
	(Scott Flying Squirrel)				(Rebuilt using 65% of original inc engine: on rebuild 1.00)		
G-AEFT	Aeronca C.3	A.610		17. 4.36	N.C.Chittenden	Kineton	27.10.99P
	(JAP J.99)						

Regn	Type	C/n	P/I	Date	Owner/operator	Probable Base	CA Expy
G-AEGV*	Mignet HM.14 Pou-Du-Ciel	EMAC.1		22. 4.36	Midland Air Museum	Coventry	26. 5.37
					(Rebuild with some original components)		
G-AEHM*	Mignet HM.14 Pou-Du-Ciel	HJD.1		30. 4.36	The Science Museum	Wroughton	
	(ABC Scorpion 35 hp)				"Blue Finch"		
G-AEJZ*	Mignet HM.14 Pou-Du-Ciel	TLC.1	BAPC120	9. 6.36	Bomber County Aviation Museum	Hemswell	
					(Stored 4.97)		
G-AEKR*	Mignet HM.14 Pou-Du-Ciel	CAC.1	BAPC121	26. 6.36	G.Claybourn	Doncaster Museum	22. 6.37
			(Rebuilt using some original components after damaged by fire at RAF Finningley 4.9.70)				
G-AEKV*	Kronfeld (BAC) Drone de luxe	30		13. 1.37	M.L.Beach	Brooklands Museum	6.10.60P
	(Allocated BGA.2510 5.79)				(WFU 14.1.99)		
G-AEKW*	Miles M.12 Mohawk	298	HM503	14. 7.36	L.Casey	Fort Union, Virginia, USA	1. 3.50
			G-AEKW/"G-AEKN"		(Crashed Spain 1.1.50, stored & now on rebuild)		
G-AELO	DH.87B Hornet Moth	8105	AW118	30. 7.36	M.J.Miller	Little Gransden	1. 5.00
			G-AELO				
G-AEML	DH.89 Dragon Rapide	6337	X9450	1. 9.36	Amanda Investments Ltd	Rendcomb	22. 5.02
			G-AEML		"Proteus"		
G-AEMY*	Mignet HM.14 Pou-Du-Ciel	NMB.1		25. 8.36	N.Ponsford	(Selby)	
					(Small parts stored 12.99)		
G-AENP(2)	Hawker Afghan Hind	41H/81902	(BAPC78)	29.10.81	The Shuttleworth Trust	Old Warden	30. 9.99P
	(Kestrel V)		R.Afghan AF		(As "K5414 "in 15 Sqdn c/s)		
G-AEOA	DH.80A Puss Moth	2184	ES921	1.10.36	A. & P.A.Wood t/a P & A Wood	Audley End	27. 6.95P
	(Gipsy Major)		G-AEOA/YU-PAX/UN-PAX				
G-AEOF(2)	Rearwin 8500 Sportster	462	N15863	1.12.81	Shipping & Airlines Ltd	Biggin Hill	5. 9.00P
	(Le Blond 5DF 85hp)		NC15863		(Stored 8.97)		
G-AEOH*	Mignet HM.14 Pou-Du-Ciel	RCS.1		15.10.36	Billy Dulles	Dieme, France	4.10.37
	(Praga B 40hp) (Reproduction using original wings/extant 1995)						
G-AEPH	Bristol F.2B Fighter	7575	D8096	13.11.36	The Shuttleworth Trust	Old Warden	1. 9.00P
	(RR Falcon 3)		G-AEPH/D8096		(Original c/n 3746, rebuilt c.1931: as "D8096/D")		
G-AERV*	Miles M.11A Whitney Straight	307	EM999	30.12.36	Not known (On rebuild 4.96)		9. 4.66
			G-AERV		Upper Ballinderry, Lisburn, Co.Antrim		
G-AESB(2)	Aeronca C.3	A.638	N15742	5. 8.88	R.J.M.Turnbull (On rebuild 1997)		
			NC15742		Rydinghurst Farm, Cranleigh		
G-AESE	DH.87B Hornet Moth	8108	W5775	13. 1.37	J.G.Green	White Ox Mead, Bath	4.10.01
			G-AESE		"Sheena"		
G-AESZ	Chilton DW.1	DW.1/1		?. 1.37	R.E.Nerou	Coventry	4. 8.53
	(Carden Ford 32hp)				(Long term rebuild project using some original components)		
G-AETA*	Caudron G.III	7487	OO-ELA	29. 1.37	RAF Museum	Hendon	
	(Anzani 90hp)				(As "(N)3066" in RNAS c/s)		
	(Also reported as either c/n 5019 or 5021; allotted "9203M" 1994)						
G-AETG*	Aeronca 100	AB.110		2.37	Not known	NK	9. 4.68
	(Crashed Booker 7.4.69 & on rebuild with parts from G-AEWV 4.96: fuselage at Clothall Common 1998:						
	since the remains of G-AEWV are at Brickhouse Farm, Frogland Cross and/or stored in the area, it is						
	surmised that these remains are almost certainly there including those from Roy Mills at Hanwell)						
G-AEUJ	Miles M.11A Whitney Straight	313		19. 2.37	R.E.Mitchell	RAF Cosford	4. 6.70
					(Stored 6.92)		
G-AEVS	Aeronca 100	AB.114		18. 5.37	A.M.Lindsay & N.H.Ponsford	Breighton	8. 7.00P
	(JAP J.99)				(Composite including parts of original G-AEXD)		
G-AEVZ	BA L.25c Swallow II	475		19. 3.37	B.R.Cox	Brickhouse Farm, Frogland Cross	15. 6.00P
	(Cirrus Minor)						
G-AEWV*	Aeronca 100	AB.117		5. 8.38	Not Known (Fuselage at Clothall Common 1998)		
G-AEXD	Aeronca 100	AB.124		1. 4.37	Mrs M.A. & R.W.Mills	Hanwell	20. 4.70P
	(JAP J.99)		(Mostly comprises parts of G-AESP after rebuild in 1958: on rebuild 1.91: sold & stored 1997)				
G-AEXF	Percival P.6 Mew Gull	E.22	ZS-AHM	18. 5.37	J.D.Penrose	Old Warden	18. 8.00P
	(Rebuilt with c/n PFA/13-10020)						
G-AEXT	Dart Kitten II	123		30. 4.37	A.J.Hartfield Marsh Hill Farm, Aylesbury		27. 6.00P
	(JAP J.99)						
G-AEXZ	Piper J/2 Cub	997		5. 2.38	J.R. & Mrs M.Dowson	Leicester	2.11.78S
	(Continental A75)				(On rebuild)		
G-AEYY*	Martin Monoplane	1	G-AAJK	6. 7.37	R.W.E.Lake, A.D.Raby & D.W.Brabham		3.11.39
	(See comments on G-EBQP; on long term rebuild 1989)				t/a Martin Monoplane Syndicate	Hitchin	
G-AEZF	Short S.16 Scion 2	PA.1008	M-5	18. 6.37	R.Jackson/Acebell Aviation Ltd	Redhill	5. 5.54
			O-BELA		(Noted 9.99 on rebuild)		
			G-AEZF				
G-AEZJ	Percival P.10 Vega Gull	K.65	SE-ALA	2. 7.37	R.A.J.Spurrell	White Waltham	10. 6.01
			D-IXWD/PH-ATH/G-AEZJ				
G-AEZX(2)	Bucker Bu.133C Jungmeister	1018	N5A	10. 5.88	A.J.E.Ditheridge	Moat Farm, Milden	27. 7.00P
			PP-TDP		(As "LG+03 in Luftwaffe c/s)		

G-AFAA – G-AFZZ

Regn	Type	C/n	P/I	Date	Owner/operator	Probable Base	CA Expy
G-AFAX	BA Eagle 2 (Gipsy Major)	138	VH-ACN G-AFAX	26.10.37	J.G.Green	White Ox Mead, Bath	4. 8.00
G-AFBS*	Miles M.14A Hawk Trainer 3	539	(G-AKKU) BB661/G-AFBS	17. 9.37	Imperial War Museum (On rebuild 1.99 - unmarked)	Duxford	25. 2.63
G-AFCL	BA L.25c Swallow II (Pobjoy Niagara 3)	462		3.11.37	A.M.Dowson (On loan to The Shuttleworth Trust)	Old Warden	12. 5.00P
G-AFDO(2)	Piper J3C-65 Cub (Frame No.2633)	2593	N21697 NC21697	7. 6.88	R.Wald Le Plessis-Belleville, France "Butter Cub"		27. 7.99P
G-AFEL(2)	Monocoupe 90A (Lambert R266)	A.782	N19432 NC19432	7. 6.82	M.Rieser	(Germany)	1. 8.00P
G-AFFD	Percival P.16A Q-Six	Q.21	(G-AIEY) X9407/G-AFFD	12. 2.38	B.D.Greenwood (On rebuild by Aeroservice IOM Ltd 6.96)	Ronaldsway	31. 8.56
G-AFFH	Piper J/2 Cub (Continental A40)	1166	EC-ALA G-AFFH	26. 3.38	M.J.Honeychurch (On rebuild 1997)	Devizes	29. 8.53
G-AFGC	BA L.25c Swallow II (Pobjoy Niagara 3)	467	BK893 G-AFGC	4. 4.38	Glenda E.Arden (Stored 1.98) Thorns Cross Farm, Chudleigh		20. 3.51
G-AFGD	BA L.25c Swallow II (Pobjoy Cataract 3)	469	BK897 G-AFGD	4. 4.38	A.T.Williams, B.Arden, C.A.Cook, J.Hughes & M.Barmby t/a South Wales Swallow Group Shobdon		22. 9.98P
G-AFGE	BA L.25c Swallow II (Pobjoy Niagara 2)	470	BK894 G-AFGE	4. 4.38	G.R.French Benson's Farm, Laindon "Maggie"		27. 7.98P
G-AFGH	Chilton DW.1 (Lycoming O-145-A2) (To be re-engined with Carden-Ford)	DW.1/2		20. 3.38	M.L. & G.L.Joseph Denford Manor, Hungerford (On rebuild by Newbury Aeroplane Co 6.95)		7. 7.83P
G-AFGI	Chilton DW.1 (Walter Mikron 2)	DW.1/3		30. 3.38	J.E. & K.A.A. McDonald White Waltham		21. 9.00P
G-AFGM(2)	Piper J/4A Cub Coupe	4-943	N26895 NC26895	30.12.81	A.J.P.Marshall	Carlisle	9.11.99P
G-AFGZ	DH.82A Tiger Moth	3700	G-AMHI BB759/G-AFGZ	9. 5.38	M.R.Paul & P.A.Shaw	Lee-on-Solent	23. 1.00
G-AFHA(2)	Mosscraft MA.1	MA.1/2		27. 2.67	C.V.Butler (Allesley, Coventry) (Small components only stored)		
G-AFHC*	BA L.25c Swallow II (Cirrus Minor)	486		17. 5.38	Arden Family Trust (Stored 1.98) Thorn Cross Farm, Chudleigh		20. 3.51
G-AFIN	Chrislea LC.1 Airguard	LC.1	BAPC203	7. 7.38	N H Wright (Bury St Edmunds) (On rebuild 12.99 using original wings, tailplane & metal fittings)		
G-AFIR	Luton LA-4 Minor (JAP J-99)	JSS.2		7. 7.38	A.J.Mason (Finmere) (Damaged nr Cobham 14.3.71 & on rebuild 1993)		30. 7.71
G-AFIU*	Parker CA-4 Parasol	CA-4		19.10.82	The Aeroplane Collection Manchester (A Luton Minor variant with reserved marks from 1938: stored 3.96: cancelled by CAA 31.3.99)		
G-AFJA	Taylor-Watkinson Dingbat (Carden-Ford 32hp)	DB.100		2. 8.38	K.Woolley (Berkswell, Coventry) (Damaged Headcorn 19.5.75 and partially rebuilt: stored 4.94)		23. 6.75S
G-AFJB	Foster-Wikner GM.1 Wicko (Gipsy Major 1)	5	DR613 G-AFJB	15. 8.38	J.Dibble (Southampton) (On rebuild 1999) (As "DR613")		12. 7.63
G-AFJR*	Tipsy Trainer 1	2		20. 8.38	Musee Royal de L'Armee Brussels (Stored 1992 for static rebuild with remains of G-AFRV)		10. 9.64
G-AFJU*	Miles M.17 Monarch	789	X9306 G-AFJU	25. 8.38	Acft Preservation Society of Scotland East Fortune		18. 5.64
G-AFJV(2)	Mosscraft MA.2	MA.2/2		27. 2.67	C.V.Butler (Allesley, Coventry) (Small components only stored)		
G-AFLW	Miles M.17 Monarch	792		2.11.38	N.I.Dalziel	White Waltham	30. 7.98
G-AFNG	DH.94 Moth Minor	94014	AW112 G-AFNG	2. 5.39	D.Saunders Galway, Ireland t/a The Gullwing Trust		21.10.98P
G-AFNI	DH.94 Moth Minor (Cabin)	94035	W7972 G-AFNI	11. 5.39	B.N.C. & C.M.Mogg (On rebuild 6.94) Bibberne Farm, Stalbridge		26. 5.67
G-AFOB	DH.94 Moth Minor	94018	X5117 G-AFOB	16. 5.39	Wessex Aviation & Transport Ltd (Stored 4.94) Chalmington		11. 5.93P
G-AFOJ	DH.94 Moth Minor (Cabin)	9407	E-1 E-0236/G-AFOJ	21. 7.39	R.M.Long Salisbury Hall, London Colney (On loan to de Havilland Aircraft Museum)		27. 8.69P
G-AFPN	DH.94 Moth Minor (Now regd with c/n 94016)	94044	X9297 G-AFPN	23. 5.39	J.W. & A.R.Davy	Redhill	9. 5.02
G-AFRZ	Miles M.17 Monarch	793	G-AIDE W6463/G-AFRZ	24. 3.39	R.E.Mitchell (Stored 6.92)	RAF Cosford	29. 6.70
G-AFSC	Tipsy Trainer 1 (Walter Mikron 2)	11		15. 7.39	G.A.Cull	Cheddington	21. 9.99P
G-AFSV	Chilton DW.1A (Train 45hp)	DW.1A/1		5. 4.39	R.E.Nerou (Coventry) (On rebuild 12.93)		12. 7.72S
G-AFSW*	Chilton DW.2	DW.2/1		6. 4.39	R.I.Souch Durley, Southampton (Fuselage box in poor condition: possibly beyond rebuild)		

Regn	Type	C/n	P/I	Date	Owner/operator	Probable Base	CA Expy
G-AFTA	Hawker Tomtit	30380	K1786	26. 4.39	The Shuttleworth Trust	Old Warden	21. 7.00P
	(Mongoose 3C)		G-AFTA/K1786		(As "K1786")		
G-AFTN*	Taylorcraft Plus C2	102	HL535	2. 5.39	Leicestershire C.C.Museums	Coalville	1.11.57
			G-AFTN		(On rebuild 10.97: cancelled by CAA 13.1.99)		
G-AFUP(2)	Luscombe 8A Master	1246	N25370	7. 6.88	R.Dispain	Chilbolton	12. 3.97P
	(Continental A65)		NC25370				
G-AFVE(2)	DH.82A Tiger Moth	83720	T7230	1. 2.78	P.A.Shaw & M.R.Paul	Lee-on-Solent	15. 4.01T
					(As "T7230")		
G-AFVN	Tipsy Trainer 1	12		15. 7.39	D.F.Lingard	Fenland	1. 3.00P
	(Walter Mikron 2)						
G-AFWH(2)	Piper J/4A Cub Coupe	4-1341	N33093	14. 1.82	O.T.Taylor	(Newark)	3. 5.00P
	(Continental A65)		NC33093				
G-AFWI	DH.82A Tiger Moth	82187	BB814	19. 7.39	E.Newbigin	Westbury-sub-Mendip	12. 8.00
			G-AFWI				
G-AFWT	Tipsy Trainer 1	13		1. 8.39	J.M.Lovell	Chilbolton	7. 2.00P
	(Walter Mikron 2)						
G-AFYD(2)	Luscombe 8AF Silvaire	1044	N25120	29. 7.75	J.D.Iliffe	Hampstead Norreys	13. 5.00
	(Continental C90)		NC25120				
G-AFYO(2)	Stinson HW-75 Model 105	7039	F-BGQP	25. 4.77	R.N.Wright		22. 7.00P
	(Continental C90)		NC22586		Red House Farm, Gedney Marsh, Holbeach		
				(Probably ex Fr.Mil with identity "22586")			
G-AFZA(2)	Piper J/4A Cub Coupe	4-873	N26198	27. 6.84	J.R.Hope Belle Vue Farm, Yarnscombe		3. 6.99P
	(Continental A65)		NC26198		t/a G-AFZA Group (Wingnuts Flying Club)		
G-AFZE*	Heath Parasol	PA.1		25. 8.39	Estate of K.C.D.St.Cyrien Horley, Surrey		10. 5.64P
	(Bristol Cherub III)				(Stored 11.93)		
G-AFZK(2)	Luscombe 8A Master	1042	N25118	24.10.88	M.G.Byrnes Walkeridge Farm, Overton		29. 5.97P
	(Continental A65)		NC25118				
G-AFZL(2)	Porterfield CP-50	581	N25401	18. 3.82	P.G.Lucas & S.H.Sharpe White Waltham		29. 6.00P
	(Continental A50)		NC25401		t/a The Skinny Bird Flyers		
G-AFZN(2)	Luscombe 8A Master	1186	N25279	5.10.81	A.L.Young	Henstridge	3. 6.00P
	(Continental A65)		NC25279				

G-AGAA – G-AGZZ

Regn	Type	C/n	P/I	Date	Owner/operator	Probable Base	CA Expy
G-AGAT(2)	Piper J3F-50 Cub	4062	N26126	17. 7.87	G.S.Williams	Cardiff	13. 6.99P
	(Franklin 4AC-150)		NC26126				
G-AGBN*	GAL.42 Cygnet 2	111	ES915	4.10.40	Royal Museum of Scotland	East Fortune	28.11.80P
			G-AGBN				
G-AGEG(2)	DH.82A Tiger Moth	82710	N9146	16. 8.82	A.J.Norman	Rendcomb	2. 5.01
			D-EDIL/R.Neth AF A-32/PH-UFK/A-32/R4769 t/a Norman Aeroplane Trust				
G-AGFT(2)	Avia FL.3	176	I-TOLB	21. 8.84	P.A.Smith	Leicester	21. 3.00P
	(CNA D4S)		MM.....		(As "W7" in Italian Co-Belligerent AF c/s)		
G-AGHB(2)*	Hawker Sea Fury FB.XI	41H-636336	CF-CHB	9. 5.74	C.Charleston	(USA)	22. 5.79P
			RAN WH589/WH589				
	(Damaged Munster, Germany 24.6.79; parts sold to USA & incorporated into rebuild as N4434P, with identity of WH589, further rebuild 3.94 using major sections of wreck plus original centre section of TF956, rear fuselage of R Neth Navy 10-14, ex 6-14/VX715 and parts from G-FURY/WJ244)						
G-AGHY(2)	DH.82A Tiger Moth	82292	N9181	17. 2.88	P.Groves	Stubbington	AC
	(Composite rebuild from ex Rollason airframe/components: now on further rebuild)						
G-AGIV(2)	Piper J3C-65 Cub (L-4J-PI)	12676	OO-AFI	13. 8.82	P.C. & F.M.Gill		
	(Frame No.12506)		OO-GBA/44-80380		Waits Farm, Belchamp Walter		13.12.99P
G-AGJG	DH.89A Dragon Rapide	6517	X7344	25.10.43	M.J. & D.J.T.Miller	Duxford	15.11.74
					(Long term rebuild 1.99: unmarked)		
G-AGLK	Taylorcraft Auster 5D	1137	RT475	25. 8.44	C R Harris	Biggin Hill	12. 2.01
G-AGMI(2)	Luscombe 8A Master	1569	N28827	15.11.88	P.R.Bush	RAF Kinloss	5. 4.94P
	(Continental A65)		NC28827		(Damaged Biggin Hill 26.3.94; on rebuild 5.95)		
G-AGNJ(2)	DH.82A Tiger Moth	660	VP-YOJ	21. 2.89	B.P., A.J. & P.J.Borsberry		
	(Australian built)		ZS-BGF/SAAF 2366		(On rebuild) Kidmore End, Reading		
G-AGNV*	Avro 685 York C.1	1223	"MW100"	20. 8.45	RAF Museum	RAF Cosford	6. 3.65
			"LV633"/G-AGNV/TS798		(As "TS798")		
G-AGOH*	Auster 5 J/1 Autocrat	1442		19. 4.45	Leicestershire CC Museums	Winthorpe	24. 8.95
					(On loan to Newark Air Museum)		
G-AGOS*	Reid & Sigrist RS.4 Desford Tnr	3	VZ728	?. 5.45	Leicester Museum of Science & Industry		
			G-AGOS		(As Bobsleigh "VZ728"; stored 4.96) Coalville		28.11.80P
G-AGOY	Miles M.48 Messenger 3	4690	EI-AGE	5. 6.45	P.A.Brook West Chiltington, Pulborough		25.11.53
			G-AGOY/HB-EIP/G-AGOY/U-0247		(On rebuild 4.92; to carry "U-0247")		
G-AGPG*	Avro 19 Srs.2	1212		15. 6.45	Manchester Museum of Science & Industry		
					(Stored 3.97)	Chadderton	13. 2.71
G-AGPK(2)	DH.82A Tiger Moth	86566	N657DH	27.10.88	Delta Aviation Ltd.	Sywell	21.12.01
			F-BGDN/Fr AF/PG657				

Regn	Type	C/n	P/I	Date	Owner/operator	Probable Base	CA Expy
G-AGRU*	Vickers V.657 Viking 1	112	VP-TAX G-AGRU	8. 5.46	British Airways plc (BEA c/s) "Vagrant"	Brooklands	9. 1.64
G-AGRW*	Vickers V.639 Viking 1	115		8. 5.46	Not known Vienna-Schwechat A/P, Austria		9. 7.68
G-AGSH	DH.89A Dragon Rapide 6	6884	EI-AJO G-AGSH/NR808	25. 7.45	Venom Jet Promotions Ltd (Philip Meeson) (BEA c/s) "Jemma Meeson"	Bournemouth	19. 6.01
G-AGTM	DH.89A Dragon Rapide 6 (Fuselage No.BCL89397)	6746	JY-ACL OD-ABP/G-AGTM/NF875	19. 9.45	Aviation Heritage Ltd (Dave Geddes)	Coventry	14.11.99T
G-AGTO	Auster 5 J/1 Autocrat	1822		2.10.45	M.J.Barnett & D.J.T.Miller (Unmarked frame noted 1.99)	Duxford	6. 9.97
G-AGTT	Auster 5 J/1 Autocrat	1826		2.10.45	R.Farrer (Bromham, Bedford) (Status uncertain)		11. 2.93
G-AGVG	Auster J/1U Workmaster	1858		7.12.45	S.J.Riddington (On overhaul 11.95)	Leicester	25. 4.76
G-AGVN	Auster 5 J/1 Autocrat	1873	EI-CKC G-AGVN	18. 1.46	G.H.Farrar	Abbeyshrule	21. 4.02
G-AGVV(2)	Piper J3C-65 Cub (L-4H-PI)	11163	F-BCZK Fr.AF/43-29872	19. 2.81	M.Molina-Ruano	(Malaga, Spain)	21. 7.00P
G-AGWE*	Avro 19 Srs.2	1286	TX201	28.12.45	Valiant Air Command Museum (Stored 6.94)	Tico, Florida, USA	5. 3.73
G-AGXN	Auster 5 J/1N Alpha	1963		22. 1.46	Gentleman's Aerial Touring Carriage Syndicate Ltd	Popham	14. 4.02
G-AGXU	Auster 5 J/1N Alpha	1969		24. 1.46	A.L.Tuttle	Spanhoe	11. 4.99
G-AGXV	Auster 5 J/1 Autocrat	1970		1. 2.46	B.S.Dowsett "Pamela IV"	Little Gransden	28. 8.00
G-AGYD	Auster 5 J/1N Alpha	1985		4. 2.46	P.R.Hodson (Damaged nr Felthorpe 25.11.90; on rebuild 4.94)	Little Gransden	24.11.90
G-AGYH	Auster 5 J/1N Alpha	1989		4. 2.46	W.R.V.Marklew (On rebuild)	(Barrow-in-Furness)	10.10.72S
G-AGYK	Auster 5 J/1 Autocrat	2002		4. 2.46	M.C.Hayes t/a Autocraft Syndicate (Stored 10.97)	Bidford	25. 5.96
G-AGYT	Auster 5 J/1N Alpha	1862		18. 1.46	P.J.Barrett (Lightwater, Surrey) (On overhaul 6.94)		27. 2.91
G-AGYU	DH.82A Tiger Moth	85265	DE208	10. 1.46	P.L.Jones (As "DE208": stored 10.96)	Ronaldsway	11. 8.01
G-AGYY(2)	Ryan ST3KR (PT-21-RY) (Kinner R56)	1167	N56792 41-1942	15. 6.83	J.J.van Egmond t/a Nostalgic Flying (As "27" in USAAC c/s) (Nijverdal, The Netherlands)		14. 7.00P
G-AGZZ(2)	DH.82A(Aust)Tiger Moth	T256 & 926	N3862 VH-BTU/VH-RNM/VH-BMY/A17-503	14. 5.82	G.C.P.Shea-Simonds	(Netheravon)	23. 4.01

G-AHAA — G-AHZZ

Regn	Type	C/n	P/I	Date	Owner/operator	Probable Base	CA Expy
G-AHAG	DH.89A Dragon Rapide	6926	RL944	31. 1.46	R.Jones t/a Southern Sailplanes (Stored 9.97)	Membury	15. 7.73
G-AHAL	Auster 5 J/1N Alpha	1870		31. 1.46	Wickenby Flying Club Ltd	Wickenby	7. 6.01T
G-AHAM	Auster 5 J/1 Autocrat	1885		21. 1.46	A.J.Twemlow	West Compton	24.10.02
G-AHAN(2)	DH.82A Tiger Moth	86553	N90406 F-BGDG/Fr.AF/PG644	31. 5.85	Tiger Associates Ltd	White Waltham	16. 6.01T
G-AHAP	Auster 5 J/1 Autocrat (Rover V-8 conversion)	1887		8. 2.46	F.J.Bellamy	Farley Farm, Winchester	20.2.91P*
G-AHAR*	Auster 5 J/1 Autocrat (Frame No.TAY347E/EJA304)	1888	F-BGRZ	7. 2.46	W.P.Miller (Fuselage frame for rebuild 8.98)	Mavis Enderby	
G-AHAT*	Auster 5 J/1N Alpha	1849	(HB-EOK)	11. 2.46	D.Burke (Crashed Old Sarum 31.8.74; open store 6.98)	Dumfries	6. 2.75
G-AHAU	Auster 5 J/1-160 Autocrat (Lycoming O-320)	1850	(HB-EOL)	11. 2.46	A.C.Webber, T.P.H.Wiseman & A.B.J.Young	Andreas, IoM	13. 4.00
G-AHAV*	Auster 5 J/1 Autocrat	1863	(HB-EOM)	13. 2.46	C.J.Freeman (Stored 4.96: cancelled by CAA 22.2.99)	Headcorn	21. 6.75
G-AHBL	DH.87B Hornet Moth	8135	P6786 CF-BFN	6. 2.46	H.D.Labouchere Blue Tile Farm, Langham		26.11.99
G-AHBM	DH.87B Hornet Moth	8126	P6785 CF-BFJ/(CF-BFO)/CF-BFJ	6. 2.46	P.A. & E.P.Gliddon	Redhill	21. 6.02
G-AHCK*	Auster 5 J/1N Alpha	1973		25. 3.46	Not known (Damaged Ingoldmells 14.9.93 stored 5.93)	Mavis Enderby	7. 5.94T
G-AHCL	Auster 5 J/1N Alpha	1977	G-OJVC G-AHCL	13. 5.46	Electronic Precision Ltd (On rebuild 8.92 with Lycoming O-320)	RAF Mona	10.10.91
G-AHCR	Gould-Taylorcraft Plus D Special 211 (Continental C90)		LB352	15. 4.46	D.E.H.Balmford & D.R.Shepherd Dunkeswell t/a Wagtail Flying Group		2. 9.00P
G-AHEC(2)	Luscombe 8A Silvaire (Continental A65)	3428	N72001 NC72001	28.10.88	S.P.Parsons	Rush Green	27. 1.00P

9

Regn	Type	C/n	P/I	Date	Owner/operator	Probable Base	CA Expy
G-AHED*	DH.89A Dragon Rapide 6	6944	RL962	27. 2.46	RAF Museum (In store 10.95)	RAF Cardington	17. 4.68
G-AHGD	DH.89A Dragon Rapide	6862	NR786	1. 4.46	R.Jones t/a Southern Sailplanes (Destroyed nr.Audley End 30.6.91; components for possible rebuild 1.92)	Membury	20. 9.92
G-AHGW	Taylorcraft Plus D	222	LB375	2. 9.46	C.V.Butler (Op Military Auster Flight: as "LB375")	Shenington	3. 5.96P
G-AHGZ	Taylorcraft Plus D	214	LB367	24. 4.46	M.Pocock (As LB367")	Old Sarum	13.10.02
G-AHHH	Auster 5 J/1N Alpha	2011	F-BAVR G-AHHH	11. 5.46	H.A.Jones	Brampton	31. 7.98P
G-AHHP*	Auster 5 J/1N Alpha	2019	G-SIME G-AHHP	11. 5.46	M.J.Bonnick Standalone Farm, Meppershall (On rebuild Meppershall 1992 following damage in mid-1980s: cancelled by CAA 22.2.99		8. 3.86
G-AHHT	Auster 5 J/1N Alpha	2022		11. 5.46	A.C.Barber & N.J.Hudson t/a Southdowns Auster Group Durleighmarsh Farm, Rogate, Petersfield		7. 5.01
G-AHHU*	Auster 5 J/1N Alpha	2023		11. 5.46	L.A.Groves & I.R.F.Hammond (Crashed at Soria, Spain 10.6.63 & on rebuild 12.91) t/a Crofton Aeroplane Services	Stubbington	12. 6.63
G-AHIP(2)	Piper J3C-65 Cub (L-4H-PI)	12122	OO-GEJ(2) OO-ALY/44-79826	3. 7.85	Veronica L.Tanner & K.F.Spragg (Frame No.11950; official c/n is 12008: see G-AJAD)	Wellesbourne Mountford	20. 7 00P
G-AHIZ	DH.82A Tiger Moth	86533	PG624	23. 4.46	CFG Flying Ltd (Regd with Fuselage No.4610)	Cambridge	1. 6.00T
G-AHKX	Avro 19 Srs.2	1333		18. 5.46	British Aerospace (Operations) Ltd (On rebuild 4.97 by Avro Heritage Society) Woodford		AC
G-AHKY*	Miles M.18 Srs.2	4426	HM545 U-0224/U-8	26. 4.46	Royal Scottish Museum/Museum of Flight	East Fortune	20. 9.89P
G-AHLI*	Taylorcraft E Auster III	540	NJ911	21. 5.46	G.A.Leathers (Cancelled by CAA 23.2.99; status unknown as owner emigrated to New Zealand)	(Orpington)	26. 4.73
G-AHLK	Taylorcraft E Auster III	700	NJ889	1. 5.46	E.T.Brackenbury	Leicester	21. 9.97
G-AHLT	DH.82A Tiger Moth	82247	N9128	2. 5.46	K.J.Jarvis	(Wheathampstead)	9. 4.00
G-AHMN	DH.82A Tiger Moth	82223	N6985	8. 5.46	The Museum of Army Flying (As "N6985")	AAC Middle Wallop	27. 5.02P
G-AHNR(2)	Taylorcraft BC-12D (Continental A65)	7204	N43545 NC43545	15.11.88	P.E.Hinkley Downland Farm, Redhill		2. 6.00P
G-AHOO(2)	DH.82A Tiger Moth	6940M	6940M EM967	6. 6.85	J.T. & A.D.Milsom (Marlborough/Crediton) (Regd with c/n 86149)		AC
G-AHPZ	DH.82A Tiger Moth	83794	T7280 EI-AFJ	22. 5.46	N.J.Wareing	(Chipping Norton)	5. 1.50
G-AHRI*	DH.104 Dove 1B	04008	4X-ARI G-AHRI	11. 7.46	Newark Air Museum	Winthorpe	
G-AHRO(2)	Cessna 140	8069	N89065 NC89065	25. 1.82	R.H.Screen	Manchester	14. 7.00
G-AHSA	Avro 621 Tutor (Lynx IVM)	-	K3215 G-AHSA/K3215	21. 6.46	The Shuttleworth Trust (As "K3215")	Old Warden	1. 5.00P
G-AHSD	Taylorcraft Plus D	182	LB323	1. 7.46	A.L.Hall-Carpenter (On rebuild 8.95)	(Thetford)	10. 9.62
G-AHSO	Auster 5 J/1N Alpha	2123		8. 8.46	W.P.Miller (On rebuild 8.98)	Mavis Enderby	6. 4.95T
G-AHSP	Auster 5 J/1 Autocrat	2134	F-BGRO G-AHSP	8. 8.46	R.M.Weeks	Earls Colne	21. 5.00
G-AHSS	Auster 5 J/1N Alpha	2136		8. 8.46	A.M.Roche	Swanton Morley	10. 3.00
G-AHST	Auster 5 J/1N Alpha	2137		8. 8.46	A.C.Frost Standalone Farm, Meppershall		3. 7.00
G-AHTE	Percival P.44 Proctor 5	Ae58		26. 6.46	D.K.Tregilgas Hill Farm, Nayland (On rebuild 7.99)		10. 8.61
G-AHTW*	Airspeed AS.40 Oxford 1	3083	V3388	6. 6.46	Imperial War Museum - Skyfame Collection (As "V3388")	Duxford	15.12.60
G-AHUF(2)	DH.82A Tiger Moth	86221	A2123 NL750	26. 2.85	First County Finance (UK) Ltd (As "T7997": see G-AOBH)	Shoreham	10.12.99
G-AHUG	Taylorcraft Plus D	153	LB282	5. 6.46	D.Nieman	(Thame)	12. 7.70
G-AHUI*	Miles M.38 Messenger 2A	6335		19. 7.46	Royal Berkshire Aviation Society (Fuselage stored off-site 11.93)	Woodley	4. 9.60
G-AHUJ*	Miles M.14A Hawk Trainer 3	1900	R1914	6. 6.46	Sir W.J.D.Roberts t/a Strathallan Acft Collection (As "R1914") (Cancelled as WFU 19.11.99)	Strathallan	9. 7.98P
G-AHUN(2)	Temco Globe GC-1B Swift (Lycoming IO-360)	3536	EC-AJK OO-KAY/NC77764	24. 7.86	R.J.Hamlett	North Weald	4. 8.95P
G-AHUV	DH.82A Tiger Moth	3894	N6593	24. 6.46	J.D.Gordon	Blair Atholl	10. 7.00
G-AHVG*	Percival P.28B Proctor 1	H.224	VH-AVG G-AHVG/BV658	17. 6.46	Warbirds Museum	Mildura, Australia	
G-AHVU	DH.82A Tiger Moth	84728	T6313	14. 8.46	R.A.L.Hubbard (As "T6313")	Meon	17. 3.00
G-AHVV	DH.82A Tiger Moth	86123	EM929	24. 6.46	R.Jones t/a Southern Sailplanes (First post restoration flight 16.1.00)	Lasham	2.11.73

Regn	Type	C/n	P/I	Date	Owner/operator	Probable Base	CA Expy
G-AHWJ	Taylorcraft Plus D	165	LB294	20. 6.46	M.D.Pitcher & S.D.Lee Ferndown, Hants		30. 6.71
					(On rebuild 1.97)		
G-AHWO*	Percival P.44 Proctor 5	Ae72	(EI-ALY)	22. 7.46	P.Bedford Celbridge, Co.Kildare		11. 3.61
			G-AHWO		(Crashed Collinstown, Dublin 5.5.59 & stored 4.96)		
G-AHXE	Taylorcraft Plus D	171	LB312	9. 7.46	Jenny M.C.Pothecary Old Sarum		14. 7.00P
					(As "LB312")		

G-AIAA – G-AIZZ

Regn	Type	C/n	P/I	Date	Owner/operator	Probable Base	CA Expy
G-AIBE*	Fairey Fulmar 2	F.3707	N1854	29. 7.46	Fleet Air Arm Museum RNAS Yeovilton		6. 7.59
			G-AIBE/N1854		(As "N1854")		
G-AIBH	Auster 5 J/1N Alpha	2113		19. 8.46	M.J.Bonnick Standalone Farm, Meppershall		18. 4.98
G-AIBM	Auster 5 J/1 Autocrat	2148		2. 9.46	D.G.Greatrex Thatcham		9.11.01
G-AIBR	Auster 5 J/1 Autocrat	2151		2. 9.46	K.L.Clarke (Horncastle)		24. 7.02T
G-AIBW	Auster 5 J/1N Alpha	2158		2. 9.46	W.B.Bateson Blackpool		4. 5.97T
G-AIBX	Auster 5 J/1 Autocrat	2159		2. 9.46	B.H.Beeston Little Gransden		29.11.02
					t/a The Wasp Flying Group		
G-AIBY	Auster 5 J/1 Autocrat	2160		2. 9.46	D.Morris Sherburn in Elmet		13. 4.81
					(Stored 6.97)		
G-AICX(2)	Luscombe 8A Silvaire	2568	N71141	27. 1.88	R.V.Smith Henstridge		3. 6.00P
	(Continental A65)		NC71141		"Easy Grace"		
G-AIDL	DH.89A Dragon Rapide 6	6968	TX310	23. 8.46	Atlantic Air Transport Ltd Coventry		13. 6.02T
					(Air Caernarfon c/s)		
G-AIDS	DH.82A Tiger Moth	84546	T6055	22. 8.46	K.D.Pogmore & T.Dann		16. 7.00
					"The Sorcerer" Bensons Farm, Laindon		
G-AIEK	Miles M.38 Messenger 2A	6339	U-9	27. 8.46	J.Buckingham New Farm, Felton, Bristol		13. 5.00
					(As "RG333" in 2 TAF Comm Sqn c/s)		
G-AIFZ	Auster 5 J/1N Alpha	2182		2.11.46	M.D.Anstey Rushett Farm, Chessington		20. 8.01
G-AIGD	Auster 5 J/1 Autocrat	2186		2.11.46	R.B.Webber Hayrish Farm, Okehampton		31. 8.99P
	(Officially regd incorrectly as J/1N Alpha)						
G-AIGF	Auster 5 J/1N Alpha	2188		5.11.46	A.R.C.Mathie (On overhaul 9.96) Wrexham		19. 5.85
G-AIGP*	Auster 5 J/1 Autocrat	2165		12.10.46	W.P.Miller Mavis Enderby		19. 6.72
	(Lycoming O-320)				(On rebuild 8.98)		
G-AIGR*	Auster 5 J/1N Alpha	2172		12.10.46	C.J. & D.J.Baker Carr Farm, Newark		25. 4.88T
	(Rebuilt 1953 with spare fuselage no. TAY/R/308G; damaged Cranfield 3.86; derelict frame stored 4.98)						
G-AIGT*	Auster 5 J/1N Alpha	2176		12.10.46	P.R. & J.S.Johnson (Bury St.Edmunds)		22.10.76S
					(Cancelled by CAA 23.2.99; status unknown)		
G-AIGU*	Auster 5 J/1N Alpha	2180		12.10.46	Not known (On rebuild 3.96) (Selby)		5. 9.74S
G-AIIH	Piper J3C-65 Cub (L-4H-PI)	11945	44-79649	14. 9.46	J.A.de Salis Oxford		25. 5.99P
G-AIJI*	Auster 5 J/1N Alpha	2307		15. 4.47	C.J.Baker Carr Farm, Newark		30. 4.76
					(Damaged Humberside 12.1.75; frame only for spares use 4.98)		
G-AIJK*	Auster 5 J/4	2067		13.11.46	Leicester Museum of Science & Industry		24. 8.68
					(On rebuild off-site 4.96) Coalville		
G-AIJM	Auster 5 J/4	2069	EI-BEU	13.11.46	N.Huxtable Cheddington, Bucks		28. 3.97
			G-AIJM		"Priscilla"		
					(Damaged nr Tring 5.1.97 & stored pending overhaul/repairs)		
G-AIJS*	Auster 5 J/4	2074		13.11.46	R.W.Brown Clothall Farm, Clothall Common		14.12.71
					(Stored 5.96)		
G-AIJT	Auster 5 J/4 Srs.100	2075		13.11.46	J.L.Thorogood Insch		5. 4.02
	(Continental O-200-A)				t/a The Aberdeen Auster Flying Group		
G-AIJZ*	Auster 5 J/1 Autocrat	2195		5.11.46	A.A.Marshall		17. 6.71
					Yeatsall Farm, Abbots Bromley		
					(Crashed Kingsland, Hereford 25.10.70 & frame stored 11.95)		
G-AIKE	Taylorcraft J Auster 5	1097	NJ728	15.11.46	C.J.Baker Carr Farm, Newark		3. 2.66
	(Frame No.TAY 2450)				(Crashed Luton 1.9.65 & dismantled 4.98)		
G-AIKR*	Airspeed AS.65 Consul	4338	PK286	25. 9.46	Canadian National Aeronautical Collection		14. 5.65
					Rockcliffe, Canada		
G-AILL*	Miles M.38 Messenger 2A	6341		14.11.46	Miles Aircraft Collection Woodley		11. 4.73
					(Major components stored off-site 3.96)		
G-AIPR	Auster 5 J/4	2084		9. 1.47	R.W. & Mrs M.A.Mills t/a The MPM Flying Group		27. 5.00P
					Church Farm, North Moreton		
G-AIPV	Auster 5 J/1 Autocrat	2203		9. 1.47	W.P.Miller "Buttercup" Mavis Enderby		8.12.01
G-AIRC	Auster 5 J/1 Autocrat	2215		13. 1.47	R.C.Tebbett Shobdon		16. 2.01
G-AIRI*	DH.82A Tiger Moth	3761	N5488	22.10.46	E.R.Goodwin Little Gransden		9.11.81
					(Stored 3.97)		
G-AIRK	DH.82A Tiger Moth	82336	N9241	22.10.46	R.C.Teverson, R.W.Marshall & C.E.McKinney		28. 5.01
					Waits Farm, Belchamp Walter		
G-AISA	Tipsy B Srs.1	17		24. 4.47	G.A.Cull Cheddington		16.12.98P
G-AISC	Tipsy B Srs.1	19		24. 4.47	D.R.Shepherd Cumbernauld		23. 5.79P
					t/a Wagtail Flying Group (Stored 6.98)		

Regn	Type	C/n	P/I	Date	Owner/operator	Probable Base	CA Expy
G-AISS(2)	Piper J3C-65 Cub (L-4H-PI) (Frame No.11904)	12077	D-ECAV SL-AAA/44-79781	3. 9.85	K.W.Wood & F.Watson	Insch	25. 6.97P
G-AIST	VS.300 Spitfire IA	WASP/20/2	AR213	25.10.46	Sheringham Aviation UK Ltd	Booker	6. 9.00P
	(As "AR213/PR-D" in 609 Sqdn c/s & "K9853/QV-H" in 19 Sqdn c/s)						
G-AISU*	VS.349 Spitfire LF.VB	CBAF.1061	AB910	25.10.46	Battle of Britain Mem Flt RAF Coningsby		
	(As "AB910/ZD-C" in 222 Sqn) "President Roosevelt"						
G-AISX	Piper J3C-85 Cub (L-4H-PI) (Frame No.11489)	11663	43-30372	28.10.46	A M Turney t/a Cubfly (Rebuilt with ex Spanish airframe)	Booker	20. 5.00P
G-AITB*	Airspeed AS.40 Oxford 1	-	MP425	1.11.46	RAF Museum	Hendon	24. 5.61
	(As "MP425" in 1536 BATF c/s)						
G-AITF*	Airspeed AS.40 Oxford 1	-	ED290	1.11.46	SAAF Museum Port Elizabeth, S.Africa		8. 6.60
	(On rebuild to flying condition 3.92)						
G-AIUA	Miles M.14A Hawk Trainer 3	2035	T9768	11.11.46	P.A.Brook West Chiltington, Pulborough		13. 7.67
	(Crashed Roborough 26.9.65 & stored 1995 with parts from G-ANWO)						
G-AIUL*	DH.89A Dragon Rapide 6	6837	NR749	8.11.46	I.Jones Ley Farm, Chirk		29. 9.67
	(On rebuild 7.97 with parts from G-AEMH/G-AKRN; parts possibly consumed since in rebuild of G-AJBJ: fuselage noted 3.98)						
G-AIVG*	Vickers V.610 Viking 1B	220		18.11.46	Musee National de l'Automobile		
	(Crashed Le Bourget 12.8.53 & fuselage stored 4.95) Mulhouse, France						12. 2.54
G-AIVW*	DH.82A Tiger Moth	83135	T5370	14.11.46	Robertsbridge Aviation Society Robertsbridge		20. 7.85
	(On long term rebuild 3.96 following write off nr Camber 27.8.82; mainly comprises airframe of G-ANLR (82111) ex N6856)						
G-AIXA	Taylorcraft Plus D	134	LB264	13. 1.47	C.W.Udale	Leicester	16. 2.00P
G-AIXJ	DH.82A Tiger Moth	85434	DE426	28.11.46	D.Green	Goodwood	13. 8.00
	(Probably composite airframe rebuilt by Newbury Aeroplane Co 1991)						
G-AIXN	Benes-Mraz M.1C Sokol	112	OK-BHA	22. 4.47	A.J.Wood	Breighton	13. 4.77
	(Status unknown)						
G-AIYG(2)	SNCAN Stampe SV-4B (Gipsy Major)	21	OO-CKZ F-BCKZ/Fr Mil	31. 8.89	L.Casteleyn Antwerp-Deurne, Belgium		12. 7.99
G-AIYR	DH.89A Dragon Rapide	6676	HG691	11.12.46	Fairmont Investments Ltd "Classic Lady" (Op by Classic Wings) Clacton/Duxford		29. 4.02T
G-AIYS	DH.85 Leopard Moth	7089	YI-ABI SU-ABM	16.12.46	Wessex Aviation & Transport Ltd Chalmington		7. 5.00
G-AIZE*	Fairchild F.24W-41A Argus 2	565	N9996F	18.12.46	RAF Museum	RAF Cosford	6. 8.66
	(On rebuild by Medway Aircraft Preservation Group of Rochester 11.97)						
G-AIZG*	VS.236 Walrus 1	6S/21840	EI-ACC IAC N-18/L2301	20.12.46	Fleet Air Arm Museum RNAS Yeovilton (As "L2301")		
G-AIZU	Auster 5 J/1 Autocrat	2228		31. 1.47	C.J. & J.G.B.Morley	Popham	19. 6.00
G-AIZY	Auster 5 J/1 Autocrat	2233		31. 1.47	B.J.Richards (Portskewett, Gwent)		20. 9.78S
	(Damaged Portskewett 8.89; on rebuild at Brunel Technical College, Ashley Down, Bristol 6.91)						

G-AJAA – G-AJZZ

Regn	Type	C/n	P/I	Date	Owner/operator	Probable Base	CA Expy
G-AJAC*	Auster 5 J/1N Alpha	2236		4. 2.47	N.J.Mortimore & H.A.Bridgman Watchford Farm, Yarcombe		8. 3.79
	(Crashed 14.5.78 & on rebuild 6.94; cancelled as WFU 28.1.99)						
G-AJAD(2)	Piper J3C-65 Cub (L-4H-PI) (Frame No.11835) (Regd with c/n 11700)	12008	OO-GEJ(1) 44-79712	26. 6.84	N.A.Rooney (Wymondham)		18. 4.00P
	(Airframe has original fuselage of OO-GEJ discarded in a rebuild in 1970s; OO-GEJ was rebuilt using Frame No. 11950 (c/n 12122) ex OO-ALY/44-79826 and is now G-AHIP; OO-ALY was then rebuilt from c/n 11709 ex OO-TON/43-30409)						
G-AJAE	Auster 5 J/1N Alpha	2237		4. 2.47	A.C.Ladd Romney Street Farm, Sevenoaks		20. 5.00
G-AJAJ	Auster 5 J/1N Alpha	2243		4. 2.47	R.B.Lawrence (Stored 5.97) Dunkeswell		18. 4.94
G-AJAM	Auster 5 J/2 Arrow	2371		8. 2.47	D.A.Porter Griffins Farm, Temple Bruer		28. 5.00P
G-AJAO(2)	Piper J3C-65 Cub (L-4H-PI) (Frame No.11990)	12162	OO-RAM ALAT/44-79866	17. 5.85	M.Stow Kearsley Farm, Peterlee		20.10.00P
G-AJAP(2)	Luscombe 8A Silvaire (Continental A65)	2305	N45778 NC45778	26. 1.89	R J Thomas Hamilton Farm, Bilsington		25. 5.00P
G-AJAS	Auster 5 J/1N Alpha	2319		14. 3.47	C.J.Baker Carr Farm, Newark		11. 4.90
	(On rebuild 4.98)						
G-AJBJ*	DH.89A Dragon Rapide	6765	NF894	20. 1.47	John Pierce Aviation Ltd Ley Farm, Chirk		14 .9.61T
	(Under rebuild 3.98)						
G-AJCP(2)	Rollason-Druine D.31 Turbulent (Ardem 4C02)	PFA/512		9. 2.59	B.R.Pearson Eaglescott t/a Turbulent Group (Stored 10.95)		4. 9.78S
G-AJDW*	Auster 5 J/1 Autocrat	2320		14. 3.47	D.R.Hunt Mavis Enderby		17.11.77
	(Being restored to Husky configuration 8.98 with wings of G-AVOD)						
G-AJDY*	Auster 5 J/1 Autocrat	2322		14. 3.47	Truck Panels Ltd Sywell		9. 7.71
	(On rebuild 7.95: cancelled by CAA 13.1.99)						
G-AJEB*	Auster 5 J/1N Alpha	2325		14. 3.47	The Aeroplane Collection Manchester		27. 3.69
	(On rebuild 11.96 at Manchester Museum of Science & Industry)						

Regn	Type	C/n	P/I	Date	Owner/operator	Probable Base	CA Expy
G-AJEE	Auster 5 J/1 Autocrat	2309		14. 3.47	A.R.Carillo De Albornoz (Stored 8.92)	Ronaldsway	10. 7.89
G-AJEH	Auster 5 J/1N Alpha	2312		14. 3.47	J.T.Powell-Tuck (Status uncertain)	(Pontypool)	28. 5.90
G-AJEI	Auster 5 J/1N Alpha	2313		14. 3.47	W.P.Miller	Mavis Enderby	13. 8.94T
	(Composite, rebuilt 1976, including fuselage of F-BFUT c/n 3357; original fuselage stored by Crofton Aeroplane Services, Stubbington 1.97)						
G-AJEM	Auster 5 J/1 Autocrat	2317	F-BFPB G-AJEM	14. 3.47	K.A.Jones (On rebuild 5.99)	Haverfordwest	18. 2.72
G-AJES(2)	Piper J3C-65 Cub (L-4H-PI) (Frame No.11602)	11776	OO-ACB 43-30485	21. 9.84	G.W.Jarvis (Penn, Wolverhampton) (As "330485/44/C" in USAAC c/s)		24. 7.00P
G-AJGJ	Taylorcraft J Auster 5	1147	RT486	31. 1.47	D.Gotts & E.J.Downing t/a Auster RT486 Flying Group (As "RT486/PF-A")	Old Sarum	19. 7.03
G-AJHJ*	Taylorcraft J Auster 5	1067	NJ676	10. 2.47	Arden Family Trust (Stored 1.98) Thorncross Farm, Chudleigh		27. 6.49
G-AJHS	DH.82A Tiger Moth	82121	N6866	12. 2.47	J.M.Voeten & H.Van Der Paauw (Op Vliegend Museum) Seppe, The Netherlands		18. 6.00
G-AJHU	DH.82A Tiger Moth	83900	T7471	12. 2.47	G.Valenti (As "T7471") (Parma, Italy)		23. 8.98T
G-AJIH	Auster 5 J/1 Autocrat	2318		2. 4.47	A.H.Diver (Stored 6.97)	Newtownards	19.11.94
G-AJIS	Auster 5 J/1N Alpha	2336		30. 4.47	J.D.Smith & J.M.Hodgson t/a Husthwaite Auster Group Baxby Manor, Husthwaite		3.12.99
G-AJIT	Auster 5 J/1 Kingsland (Continental O-200-A)	2337		30. 4.47	A.J.Kay t/a G-AJIT Group	Netherthorpe	14. 6.00P
G-AJIU	Auster 5 J/1 Autocrat	2338		30. 4.47	M.D.Greenhalgh	Netherthorpe	25. 6.99
G-AJIW	Auster 5 J/1N Alpha	2340		30. 4.47	Truman Aviation Ltd (On rebuild 7.99)	Nottingham	16.10.82
G-AJJS(2)	Cessna 120 (Continental O-200-A)	13047	8R-GBO VP-GBO/VP-TBO/N1106M/YV-T-CTA/NC2786N	7. 1.87	R.W.Marchant, I.D.Ranger & S.C.Parsons t/a Robhurst Flying Group	Headcorn	28. 3.00P
G-AJJT(2)	Cessna 120 (Continental C85)	12881	N2621N NC2621N	27. 1.88	J.S.Robson	Franklyns Field, Chewton Mendip	20. 9.00P
G-AJJU(2)	Luscombe 8E Silvaire (Continental C85)	2295	N45768 NC45768	10. 1.89	L.C.Moon	White Waltham	2. 9.00P
G-AJKB(2)	Luscombe 8E Silvaire (Continental C85)	3058	N71631 NC71631	4. 1.89	A.F.Hall & P.S.Hatwell	Priory Farm, Tibenham	23. 8.99P
G-AJLR*	Airspeed AS.65 Consul	5136	R6029	21. 5.47	Singapore Airlines (As "VR-SCD")	Singapore	23. 4.63
G-AJOA	DH.82A Tiger Moth	83167	T5424	29. 4.47	F.P.Le Coyte (As "T5424") Lotmead Farm, Wanborough, Swindon		22. 5.00
G-AJOC*	Miles M.38 Messenger 2A	6370		23. 4.47	Ulster Folk & Transport Museum (Stored 4.96) Holywood, Belfast		18. 5.72
G-AJOE	Miles M.38 Messenger 2A	6367		28. 4.47	J.Eagles & P.C.Kirby t/a Classic Messenger	Kemble	AC
G-AJON(2)	Aeronca 7AC Champion	7AC-2633	OO-TWH	3. 1.86	A.Biggs & J.L.Broad t/a Oscar November 92 Syndicate	Edge Hill	30. 6.00P
G-AJOZ*	Fairchild F.24W-41A Argus 1 (Ranger UC-61-FA)	347	FK338 42-32142	21. 4.47	The Aeroplane Collection Ltd	Woodhall Spa	15.12.63
	(Crashed Rennes, France 16.8.62; on loan to The Thorpe Camp Preservation Group; stored 3.96)						
G-AJPI	Fairchild F.24R-46A Argus 3 (UC-61A-FA)	851	HB614 43-14887	26. 4.47	T.H.Bishop (As "314887" in USAAF c/s)	Horsford, Norwich	30. 1.01
G-AJPZ*	Auster 5 J/1 Autocrat	2348	F-BFPE G-AJPZ	12. 5.47	W.Hamblen (Damaged Thruxton 2.3.84: on rebuild 2.96)	Sopley, Hants	14. 6.85
G-AJRB	Auster 5 J/1 Autocrat	2350		12. 5.47	N.Ravine	Sywell	29. 1.01
G-AJRC	Auster 5 J/1 Autocrat	2601		12. 5.47	Moira Barker Willyhow Farm, Scarborough		14. 7.02
G-AJRE	Auster 5 J/1 Autocrat	2603		12. 5.47	C.W.N. & A.A.M.Huke	Crowfield	5. 8.01
G-AJRH*	Auster 5 J/1N Alpha	2606		12. 5.47	Leicestershire CC Museums Charnwood Museum, Loughborough (Cancelled by CAA 18.1.99: on display 5.99)		5. 6.69
G-AJRS	Miles M.14A Hawk Trainer 3	1750	P6382 G-AJDR/G-AJRS/P6382	30. 4.47	The Shuttleworth Trust (As "P6382/C" in 16 EFTS c/s) (Composite aircraft which flew as "G-AJDR" 1.54/3.71)	Old Warden	21. 7.00P
G-AJSN*	Fairchild F.24W-41A Argus 2	849	HB612 43-14885	8. 5.47	V.Trimble (Damaged Cork 10.6.67 & stored 2.95)	Banbridge, Co.Down	9. 5.69T
G-AJTW	DH.82A Tiger Moth	82203	N6965	21. 5.47	J.A.Barker (As "N6965/FL-J") (Crashed landing Raydon near Ipswich 7.6.99 & extensively damaged)	Tibenham	9. 9.00
G-AJUD*	Auster 5 J/1 Autocrat	2614		5. 6.47	C.L.Sawyer (On rebuild 8.92: cancelled by CAA 31.3.99)	Camberley	18. 5.74
G-AJUE	Auster 5 J/1 Autocrat	2616		5. 6.47	P.H.B.Cole	Lavington, Devizes	31.10.02
G-AJUL	Auster 5 J/1N Alpha	2624		18. 6.47	M.J.Crees (On rebuild 12.90)	Halstead, Essex	11. 9.81
G-AJVE	DH.82A Tiger Moth	85814	DE943	28. 5.47	R.A.Gammons	(Letchworth)	10. 7.00
	(Composite 1981 rebuild including substantial parts of G-APGL c/n 86460/NM140)						

13

Regn	Type	C/n	P/I	Date	Owner/operator	Probable Base	CA Expy
G-AJVH*	Fairey Swordfish II	-	LS326		RN Historic Flight RNAS Yeovilton		
					(As "LS326/L2" in 836 Sqdn c/s)		
G-AJVT*	Taylorcraft J Auster 5	1495	TJ478	4. 6.47	S.Craggs (Frame/wings stored 5.86)		
						Lane House Farm, Burneston, Bedale	25. 8.70
G-AJWB	Miles M.38 Messenger 2A	6699		17. 6.47	G.E.J.Spooner (Colchester)		13.11.69
					(Crashed Doncaster, Yorks 23.3.70 & on rebuild 1996)		
G-AJXC*	Taylorcraft J Auster 5	1409	TJ343	11. 6.47	J.Graves Scotland Farm, Hook		2. 8.82
					(Damaged 16.10.87; stored 9.94; fuselage noted 4.99)		
G-AJXV	Taylorcraft G Auster 4	1065	F-BEEJ	8. 9.47	Barbara A.Farries Carr Farm, Newark		17.11.99
			G-AJXV/NJ695		(As "NJ695")		
G-AJXY	Taylorcraft G Auster 4	792	MT243	4. 5.48	P.D.Lowdon (Farnborough)		10.11.70
					(On rebuild 1993)		
G-AJYB	Auster 5 J/1N Alpha	847	MS974	3. 2.49	P.J.Shotbolt		
					· Ingthorpe Farm, Great Casterton, Lincs		25. 7.02

G-AKAA – G-AKZZ

Regn	Type	C/n	P/I	Date	Owner/operator	Probable Base	CA Expy
G-AKAT	Miles M.14A Hawk Trainer 3	2005	F-AZOR	2. 7.47	J.D.Haslam (As "T9738") Breighton		18. 7.00P
			G-AKAT/T9738				
G-AKAZ(2)	Piper J3C-65 Cub AN.1 & 8499		F-BFYL	19. 4.82	Jeanne R.Frazer Duxford		29. 2.00P
	(L-4A-PI) (Frame No.8616)		Fr Mil/42-36375		(As "H/57" in 83rd FS/78th FG USAAF c/s)		
G-AKBO	Miles M.38 Messenger 2A	6378		15. 7.47	B. du Cros Keevil		24. 5.00
G-AKDK*	Miles M.65 Gemini 1A	6469		22. 8.47	Danmarks Flyvemuseum		
	(For rebuild with parts from G-AJWA c/n 6290; stored 1992) Kongelunden, Billund, Denmark						27. 3.70
G-AKDN	DHC.1A Chipmunk 10	11		14. 8.47	D.S.Backhouse Old Buckenham		15.10.99
G-AKDW	DH.89A Dragon Rapide	6897	F-BCDB	25. 8.47	De Havilland Aircraft Museum Trust Ltd		
			G-AKDW		Salisbury Hall, London Colney		8. 5.59
			YI-ABD/NR833		"City of Winchester" (On rebuild 3.96)		
G-AKEK*	Miles M.65 Gemini 3A	6483		8. 9.47	M.Vaisey & T.Moore Rotary Farm, Hatch		22. 9.72
					t/a Gemini Wanderers (On long term rebuild 12.94)		
G-AKEL*	Miles M.65 Gemini 1A	6484		8. 9.47	Ulster Folk & Transport Museum		
					(Components only 4.96: for rebuild with G-AKGE) Holywood, Belfast		29. 4.72
G-AKEZ	Miles M.38 Messenger 2A	6707		27. 8.47	P.G.Lee (New Zealand)		15.11.68
					(As "RG333": sold 1997)		
G-AKGD*	Miles M.65 Gemini 1A	6492		11. 9.47	Royal Berkshire Aviation Society Woodley		14.11.66
					(Parts only stored off-site 3.96)		
G-AKGE*	Miles M.65 Gemini 3C	6488	EI-ALM	18.10.47	Ulster Folk & Transport Museum		
			G-AKGE		(Stored 4.96) Holywood, Belfast		7. 6.74
G-AKHP	Miles M.65 Gemini 1A	6519		3.10.47	P.G.Lee Earls Colne		28.10.99
G-AKHZ*	Miles M.65 Gemini 7	6527		21.10.47	Royal Berkshire Aviation Society Woodley		8. 1.64
	(Composite airframe with parts from G-ALMU, G-ALUG & G-AMME; on rebuild by Miles Aircraft Collection						
	for Museum of Berkshire Aviation 3.96)						
G-AKIB(2)	Piper J3C-90 Cub	12311	OO-RAY	18. 4.84	M.C.Bennett Bodmin		4. 8.00P
	(L-4H-PI) (Frame No.12139)		44-80015		(As "480015/M/44" in USAAC c/s)		
G-AKIF	DH.89A Dragon Rapide	6838	LN-BEZ	24. 9.47	Airborne Taxi Services Ltd		
			G-AKIF/NR750		Duxford/Booker		19. 8.00T
G-AKIN	Miles M.38 Messenger 2A	6728		19. 9.47	R.Spiller & Sons Ltd Sywell		3. 5.02
G-AKIS*	Miles M.38 Messenger 2A	6725		19. 9.47	Musee Royal de L'Armee Brussels		5. 8.70
					(Stored 1992)		
G-AKIU	Percival P.44 Proctor 5	Ae129		20. 2.48	Air Atlantique Ltd Coventry		24. 1.65
G-AKKB	Miles M.65 Gemini 1A	6537		28.10.47	J.Buckingham New Farm, Felton, Bristol		19. 9.98
					(Air Total c/s)		
G-AKKH	Miles M.65 Gemini 1A	6479	OO-CDO	23. 7.48	M.C.Russell Top Farm, Royston		21. 9.89T
					(Stored 7.96)		
G-AKKR*	Miles M.14A Hawk Trainer 3	1995	"T9967"	23. 6.48	Manchester Museum of Science & Industry		
	(P/I could be T9967 from 1943 rebuild) G-AKKR/T9708 (Allocated "8378M"; as "T9707") Manchester						10. 4.65
G-AKKY*	Miles M.14A Hawk Trainer 3	2078	T9841	23. 6.48	G.H.Johnson/Royal Berkshire Aviation Society		
	(Allocated BAPC44 to reflect rebuild status from various parts) (As "L6906") Woodley						6.11.64
G-AKLW*	Short SA.6 Sealand 1	SH.1571	(USA)	26.11.47	Ulster Folk & Transport Museum (Stored 4.98)		
			R Saudi AF/SU-AHY/G-AKLW		Holywood, Belfast		
G-AKOE	DH.89A Dragon Rapide 4	6601	X7484	3.12.47	J.E.Pierce Ley Farm, Chirk		25. 7.82
					(British Airways c/s; stored 3.98)		
G-AKOW	Taylorcraft J Auster 5	1579	PH-NAD	23.12.47	The Museum of Army Flying		
	(Regd with c/n TJ569A following Dutch rebuild) PH-NEG/G-AKOW/TJ569 (As "TJ569") AAC Middle Wallop						26. 6.82
G-AKPF	Miles M.14A Hawk Trainer 3	2228	V1075	27. 1.48	P.A.Brook Sandown		30. 8.96P
	(Magister I)				(As "V1075" in RAF c/s)		
	(Composite with fuselage of N3788/G-ANLT c/n 836 from 1955 rebuild)						
G-AKPI	Taylorcraft J Auster 5	1088	NJ703	27. 1.48	B.H.Hargrave Croft, Skegness		1.12.85
					(To J.Allen 1.91: stored 5.93: as "NJ703")		

14

Regn	Type	C/n	P/I	Date	Owner/operator	Probable Base	CA Expy
G-AKRP	DH.89A Rapide 4	6940	CN-TTO	26. 1.48	R.H. Ford	Sywell	12. 6.58
			(F-DAFS)/G-AKRP/RL958 c/o Fordaire Aviation Ltd (On rebuild 1999)				
G-AKRA(2)	Piper J3C-65 Cub	11255	I-FIVI	15. 6.84	W.R.Savin	(Cambridge)	
	(L-4H-PI) (Frame No.11080)		43-29964		(On rebuild 8.97)		
G-AKSY*	Taylorcraft J Auster 5D	1567	F-BGOO	10. 2.48	A.Brier	Ellerton, Yorks	
			G-AKSY/TJ534		(On rebuild 1992)		
G-AKSZ	Taylorcraft J Auster 5C	1503	F-BGPQ	10. 2.48	A.R.C.Mathie	Wrexham	9. 5.02
	(Gipsy Major 1)		G-AKSZ/TJ457				
G-AKTH(2)	Piper J3C-65 Cub (L-4J-PI)	13211	OO-AGL	14. 7.86	G.J.Harry, The Viscount Goschen		
	(Frame No.13041) (Regd with incorrect c/n 13047)		PH-UCR/45-4471			White Waltham	14. 4.00P
G-AKTI(2)	Luscombe 8A Silvaire	4101	N1374K	27. 5.87	M.W.Olliver	Old Sarum	20. 4.00P
	(Continental A65)		NC1374K				
G-AKTK(2)	Aeronca 11AC Chief	11AC-1017	N9379E	13. 3.89	R.W.Marshall, G.C.Jones & C.E.McKinney		
	(Continental A65)		NC9379E		Waits Farm, Belchamp Walter		10. 5.00P
G-AKTN(2)	Luscombe 8A Silvaire	3540	N77813	22. 7.88	D.Taylor	(Canvey Island)	1. 8.00P
	(Continental A65)		NC77813				
G-AKTO(2)	Aeronca 7BCM Champion	7AC-940	N8515X	19. 5.88	D.C.Murray	Lee-on-Solent	22. 9.99P
	(Continental A75) (Modified from 7AC standard 8.50)		N82311/NC82311				
G-AKTP(2)	PA-17 Vagabond	17-82	N4683H	24. 6.88	G.Campbell	Old Sarum	27. 5.00P
	(Continental C85)		NC4683H		t/a G-AKTP Flying Group		
G-AKTR(2)	Aeronca 7AC Champion	7AC-3017	N58312	19. 6.89	C.Fielder "Eddie"	New Farm, Felton	27. 7.96P
			NC58312				
G-AKTS(2)	Cessna 120	11875	N77434	26. 5.88	J.J.Boon "Southern Belle"	Popham	12. 5.00P
			NC77434				
G-AKTT(2)	Luscombe 8A Silvaire	3279	N71852	21. 7.88	S.J.Charters	Orton Grange, Carlisle	23. 6.92P
	(Continental A65)		NC71852		(Damaged Chelford, Cheshire 6.7.91 & on repair 1.96)		
G-AKUE(2)	DH.82A [OGMA] Tiger Moth	P.68	ZS-FZL	12. 2.86	D.F.Hodgkinson	(Gravesend)	6. 6.91
			CR-AGM/FAP...	(Damaged Bryngwyn Bach 2.1.89 & on rebuild Kemble 8.98)			
G-AKUF(2)	Luscombe 8F Silvaire	4794	N2067K	1. 8.88	A.G.Palmer	Wellesbourne Mountford	15. 7.00P
	(Continental C90)		NC2067K				
G-AKUG(2)	Luscombe 8A Silvaire	3689	N77962	21. 7.88	P Groves	Exton, Hants	9. 9.00P
	(Continental A65)		NC77962		t/a G-AKUG Group		
G-AKUH(2)	Luscombe 8E Silvaire	4644	N1917K	24.10.88	I.M.Bower	Leicester	27. 7.00P
	(Continental O-200-A)		NC1917K		"Lucy Too"		
G-AKUI(2)	Luscombe 8E Silvaire	2464	N45937	24.10.88	D.A.Sims	(Stoke-on-Trent)	17. 1.90P
	(Continental O-200-A)		NC45937				
G-AKUJ(2)	Luscombe 8E Silvaire	5282	N2555K	4. 8.88	R.Fraser & R.Carlton-Green	Coventry	18.10.00P
	(Continental C85)		NC2555K				
G-AKUK(2)	Luscombe 8A Silvaire	5793	N1166B	28.10.88	N.B.Brown	Leckhampstead Farm, Newbury	30. 6.98P
	(Continental A65)		NC1166B		t/a Leckhampstead Flying Group		
G-AKUL(2)	Luscombe 8A Silvaire	4189	N1462K	9. 2.89	E.A.Taylor	Southend	21. 5.90P
	(Continental A65)		NC1462K		(Rebuild complete 12.99)n		
G-AKUM(2)	Luscombe 8F Silvaire	6452	N2025B	17. 2.88	D A Young	(Enfield)	14. 9.00P
	(Continental C90)						
G-AKUN(2)	Piper J3C-85 Cub	6914	N38304	13. 1.89	W.R.Savin Cold Harbour Farm, Willingham		13. 1.99P
			NC38304				
G-AKUO(2)	Aeronca 11AC Chief	11AC-1376	N9730E	16. 1.89	S.Longstaff & K.Latham	White Waltham	28. 7.00P
			NC9730E		t/a KUO Flying Group		
G-AKUP(2)	Luscombe 8E Silvaire	5501	N2774K	9. 5.89	Melanie J.Willies (Stored 12.96)		
	(Lycoming O-320) (To be a floatplane)		NC2774K		Honeydon Farm, Colmworth, Bedford		
G-AKUR(2)	Cessna 140	13819	N1647V	26. 1.89	J.Greenaway & C.A.Davis	Popham	21. 9.95
			NC1647V				
G-AKUW	Chrislea CH.3 Srs.2 Super Ace	105		8. 3.48	D.R.Bean	Old Manor Farm, Anwick	29. 5.00P
G-AKVF	Chrislea CH.3 Srs.2 Super Ace	114	AP-ADT	8. 3.48	T.Pate	Kilkerran	17. 7.95P
			G-AKVF		(Stored 4.97)		
G-AKVM(2)	Cessna 120	13431	N3173N	10. 1.89	N.Wise & S.Walker		
			NC3173N		Croft-on-Tees, Darlington		11. 5.00P
G-AKVN(2)	Aeronca 11AC Chief	11AC-469	N3742B	13. 1.89	C.E.Ellis	Priory Farm, Tibenham	17. 3.00P
			NC3742B		t/a Breckland Aeronca Group		
G-AKVO(2)	Taylorcraft BC-12D	9845	N44045	10. 1.89	R.J.Whybrow & M.J.Steward t/a Albion Flyers		
	(Continental A65)		NC44045		Priory Farm, Tibenham		28. 9.99P
G-AKVP(2)	Luscombe 8A Silvaire	5549	N2822K	21. 7.88	J.M.Edis	Henlow	14. 4.00P
	(Continental A65)		NC2822K				
G-AKVR	Chrislea CH3 Srs.4 Skyjeep	125	VH-OLD	8. 3.48	D.R.Bean	Old Manor Farm, Alnwick	
			VH-RCD/VH-BRP/G-AKVR				
G-AKVZ	Miles M.38 Messenger 4B	6352	RH427	25. 6.48	Shipping & Airlines Ltd	Bigin Hill	24. 9.00
G-AKWS	Auster 5A-160	1237	RT610	1. 4.48	Fast Aerospace Ltd	Crowfield	26. 4.00
	(Lycoming O-320)				(As "RT610")		
G-AKWT*	Taylorcraft J Auster 5	998	MT360	1. 4.48	C.J.Baker	Carr Farm, Newark	22. 7.49
					(Crashed Nottingham 7.8.48: derelict frame stored 4.98)		

G-AKXP	Taylorcraft J Auster 5	1017	NJ633	13. 4.48	M.Pocock	Hedge End, Southampton	19.12.70
	(Crashed St.Mary's, Isles of Scilly 9.4.70: on long term rebuild by Classic Vintage Acft Services 6.95)						
G-AKXS	DH.82A Tiger Moth	83512	T7105	13. 4.48	P.A.Colman		
					Luxters Farm, Hambleden, Henley-on-Thames		23.10.99
G-AKZN*	Percival P.34A Proctor 3	K.386	Z7197	24. 5.48	RAF Museum	Hendon	29.11.63
			(8380M)		(As "Z7197")		

G-ALAA – G-ALZZ

G-ALAH*	Miles M.38 Messenger 4A	-	RH377	28. 5.48	Not known	Sabadella, Barcelona, Spain	18. 4.65
					(Stored 3.95)		
G-ALAX*	DH.89A Dragon Rapide	6930	RL948	27. 5.48	Durney Aeronautical Collection/D.Johnson		
			(Fuselage stored 1994 with components from G-AFRK, G-AHGC, G-AHJS & G-ASRJ) Andover					8. 3.67
G-ALBD	DH.82A Tiger Moth	84130	T7748	27. 5.48	C.H.Schoonbeek	(The Netherlands)	31.10.81
				(Damaged Leopoldsburg, Belgium 24.5.81 & stored pending rebuild)			
G-ALBJ	Taylorcraft J Auster 5	1831	TW501	3. 6.48	P.N.Elkington	Bloxholm, Sleaford	5. 8.00
G-ALBK	Taylorcraft J Auster 5	1273	RT644	3. 6.48	S.J.Wright & Co (Farmers) Ltd		
					Ropsley Heath Farm, Grantham		23.10.99
G-ALCK*	Percival P.34A Proctor 3	H.536	LZ766	18. 6.48	Imperial War Museum - Skyfame Collection		
					(As "LZ766")	Duxford	19. 6.63
G-ALCU*	DH.104 Dove 2B	04022	VT-CEH	3. 8.48	Midland Air Museum	Coventry	16. 3.73
G-ALDG*	Handley Page HP.81 Hermes 4	HP.81/8		27.10.49	Duxford Aviation Society	Duxford	9. 1.63
					(Fuselage only) (BOAC c/s) "Horsa"		
G-ALEH(2)	PA-17 Vagabond	17-87	N4689H	17. 8.81	A.D.Pearce	White Waltham	11. 3.00P
	(Continental A65)		NC4689H				
G-ALFA	Taylorcraft J Auster 5	1236	RT607	20.10.48	S.P.Barrett	Sturgate	24.11.01
					t/a Golf Alfa Auster Group		
	(P/i uncertain as c/n 1236 considered sold as HB-EOC 4.48; reported as c/n 826 (MS958) but doubtful)						
G-ALFT*	DH.104 Dove 6	04233		14.12.48	Air Atlantique Ltd	Caernarfon	13. 6.73
					(Under restoration 12.99)		
G-ALFU*	DH.104 Dove 6	04234		14.12.48	Duxford Aviation Society	Duxford	4. 6.71
G-ALGA(2)	PA-15 Vagabond	15-348	N4575H	3.12.86	D.A.Lord	Herrings Farm, Sussex	21. 2.00P
	(Lycoming O-145)		NC4575H				
G-ALIJ(2)	PA-17 Vagabond	17-166	N4866H	13. 2.87	A.S.Cowan	Popham	19. 3.00P
	(Continental A65)		NC4866H		t/a Popham Flying Group G-ALIJ		
G-ALIW(2)	DH.82A Tiger Moth	82901	N27WB	17. 8.81	D.I.M.Geddes & F.R.Curry	White Waltham	14. 8.00
			ZK-ATI/NZ899/R5006				
G-ALJF	Percival P.34A Proctor 3	K.427	Z7252	3. 3.49	J.F.Moore	Biggin Hill	26. 8.01
G-ALJL	DH.82A Tiger Moth	84726	T6311	7. 3.49	C.G.Clarke	Bursledon, Southampton	28. 9.50
					(On long term rebuild from components 11.92)		
G-ALLF	Slingsby T.30A Prefect	548	BGA.599	29. 3.49	J.F.Hopkins & K.M.Fresson	Parham Park	
			PH-1/BGA.599/G-ALLF/BGA.599				
G-ALNA	DH.82A Tiger Moth	85061	T6774	11. 4.49	R.J.Doughton	Dunkeswell	11.11.01T
					(Brooklands Aviation c/s)		
G-ALND	DH.82A Tiger Moth	82308	N9191	12. 4.49	J.T.Powell-Tuck	Abergavenny	11. 4.82
				(Crashed Panshanger 8.3.81 & on rebuild 3.96: as "N9191" in RN c/s)			
G-ALNV*	Taylorcraft J Auster 5	1216	RT578	21. 4.49	C.J.Baker	Carr Farm, Newark	4. 7.50
					(Frame stored 4.98)		
G-ALOD(2)	Cessna 140	14691	N2440V	14.10.83	J.R.Stainer	Bennington	11. 1.02
G-ALRH	EoN AP.8 Baby	EoN/B/005	BGA629	25. 5.49	P.D.Moran	Chipping	
			G-ALRH/BGA629		(Op by EoN Baby Syndicate on BGA CA)		
G-ALRI	DH.82A Tiger Moth	83350	ZK-BAB	2. 5.51	Wessex Aviation & Transport Ltd		
			G-ALRI/T5672		(As "T5672" in RAF c/s)	Chalmington	19. 8.94
G-ALSX*	Bristol 171 Sycamore 3	12892	G-48/1	17.11.50	E.D.Ap Rees	Weston-super-Mare	24. 9.65
			G-ALSX/VR-TBS/G-ALSX		t/a The Helicopter Museum		
G-ALTO(2)	Cessna 140	14253	N2040V	19. 1.82	J.P.Bell	Carlisle	25. 5.98
	(Continental C85)						
G-ALTW*	DH.82A Tiger Moth	84177	T7799	13. 6.49	A.Mangham	Hounslow Green, Essex	8. 6.70
					(Crashed Panshanger 5.11.69 & on rebuild 10.91)		
G-ALUC	DH.82A Tiger Moth	83094	R5219	28. 6.49	D.R. & Mrs M.Wood		
					Fowle Hall Farm, Paddock Wood, Kent		21. 9.01
G-ALVP*	DH.82A Tiger Moth	82711	R4770	26. 9.49	V. & R.Wheele	(Shoreham)	15. 2.61
					(Stored for rebuild)		
G-ALWB	DHC.1 Chipmunk 22A	C1/0100	OE-ABC	28.12.49	M.L. & J.M.Soper	Perth	18. 5.00
			G-ALWB				
G-ALWC	Douglas C-47A-25DK Dakota 4	13590	(F-GBOL)	10. 1.50	Ailes Anciennes Toulouse		
			KG723/42-93654		(Open storage 6.95)	Toulouse-Blagnac	6. 2.83A
G-ALWF*	Vickers 701 Viscount	5		2. 1.50	Duxford Aviation Society	Duxford	16. 4.72
					(BEA c/s) "RMA Sir John Franklin"		

Regn	Type	C/n	P/I	Date	Owner/operator	Probable Base	CA Expy
G-ALWS	DH.82A Tiger Moth	82415	N9328	24. 1.50	A.P.Beynon	Welshpool	
	(Regd with c/n 82413)				(On rebuild 5.98)		
G-ALWW	DH.82A Tiger Moth	86366	NL923	24. 1.50	D.E.Findon	Bidford	11. 3.00
					t/a Stratford-upon-Avon Tiger Moth Group		
G-ALXT*	DH.89A Dragon Rapide	6736	4R-AAI	24. 1.50	The Science Museum	Wroughton	
					CY-AAI/G-ALXT/NF865 (Railway A/S c/s) "Star of Scotia"		
G-ALXZ	Taylorcraft J Auster 5-150	1082	D-EGOF	2. 1.50	M.F.Cuming	Sackville Farm, Riseley	18. 7.99
	(Lycoming O-320) (Frame No.TAY24070)		PH-NER/G-ALXZ/NJ689				
G-ALYB*	Taylorcraft J Auster 5	1173	RT520	3. 2.50	South Yorkshire Aviation Museum		
					(On rebuild 5.97)	Home Farm, Firbeck	26. 5.63
G-ALYG	Taylorcraft J Auster 5D	835	MS968	14. 3.50	A.L.Young	Henstridge	19. 1.70
	(Regd with incorrect identity MT968; frame stored 4.98; for rebuild as Auster 5)						
G-ALYW*	DH.106 Comet 1	06009		18. 9.51	RAF Exhibition Unit	RAF St.Athan	14. 6.54
	(Fuselage converted to "Nimrod" exhibition airframe as "XV238")						
G-ALYX*	DH.106 Comet 1	06010		18. 9.51	Not known	Lasham	21. 7.54
	(Fuselage centre-section stored by DRA 3.93; possibly scrapped)						
G-ALZE*	Britten-Norman BN-1F	1		16. 3.50	Southampton Hall of Aviation Southampton		
G-ALZO*	Airspeed AS.57 Ambassador 2	5226	RJAF-108	5. 4.50	Duxford Aviation Society	Duxford	14. 5.72
			G-ALZO/(G-AMAD)		(On rebuild 1.99)		

G-AMAA – G-AMZZ

Regn	Type	C/n	P/I	Date	Owner/operator	Probable Base	CA Expy
G-AMAU*	Hawker Hurricane IIc	-	PZ865	1. 5.50	Battle of Britain Mem Flt	RAF Coningsby	
					(As "PZ865/Q" in RAFSEAC c/s)		
G-AMAW	Luton LA-4 Minor	JRC.1 & SA.I		29. 4.50	R.H.Coates	Breighton	6. 8.88P
	(Cherub III) (Known as Swalesong SA.I)				(Stored 12.00)		
G-AMBB	DH.82A Tiger Moth	85070	T6801	1. 5.50	J.Eagles	Oaksey Park	
	(Composite rebuild - parts to "G-MAZY" ? - see SECTION 4: on rebuild 6.95)						
G-AMCA	Douglas C-47B-30DK Dakota 3	16218/32966	KN487 44-76634	1. 6.50	Atlantic Air Transport Ltd	Coventry	10.12.00A
					(Op Air Atlantique) (Pollution Control c/s)		
G-AMCK	DH.82A Tiger Moth	84641	N65N	15. 6.50	D.L.Frankel	Redhill	8. 7.01
			C-GBBF/SLN-05/D-EGXY/HB-UAC/G-AMCK/T6193				
G-AMCM	DH.82A Tiger Moth	85295	DE249	14.12.50	B.C., J.I. & A.K.Cooper		
	(Regd with c/n "89259")					Denford Manor, Hungerford	28. 5.56
	(Crashed nr Somerton 25.9.55 & on long term rebuild from components)						
G-AMDA*	Avro 652A Anson 1	-	N4877	20. 7.50	Imperial War Museum - Skyfame Collection		
					(Unmarked)	Duxford	14.12.62
G-AMEN(2)	PA-18-95 Super Cub (L-18C-PI)	18-1998	(G-BJTR)	29.12.81	A.Lovejoy & W.Cook	Popham	10. 1.00P
			MM52-2398 "EI.71"/I-EIAM/MM52-2398/52-2398				
	(Frame No.18-1963; Italian rebuild c/n OMA.71-08)				t/a Sierra Golf Flying Group		
G-AMHF	DH.82A Tiger Moth	83026	R5144	6. 2.51	Wavendon Social Housing Ltd	Sywell	22. 8.00
	(Rebuilt with components from G-BABA ex 86584 ex F-BGDT/PG687) (Anthony West)						
G-AMHJ	Douglas C-47A-25DK Dakota 6	13468	SU-AZI	6. 2.51	Atlantic Air Transport Ltd	Coventry	5.12.00A
			G-AMHJ/ZS-BRW/KG651/42-108962		(Op Air Atlantique) (Pollution Control c/s)		
G-AMIU	DH.82A Tiger Moth	83228	T5495	9. 4.51	R. & Mrs J.L.Jones	Membury	9. 9.71
	(Crashed Booker 15.10.69 & stored 1.92)				t/a Southern Sailplanes		
G-AMKL*	Auster B.4	2983	XA177	3. 7.51	Not known	Carr Farm, Newark	
			G-AMKL/G-25-2				
			(On rebuild with new fuselage & some original components 4.98)				
G-AMKU	Auster 5 J/1B Aiglet	2721	ST-ABD	10. 7.51	P.G.Lipman Romney Street Farm, Sevenoaks		2. 7.00
			SN-ABD/G-AMKU				
G-AMLZ*	Percival P.50 Prince 6E	P.46	(VR-TBN)	23.11.51	Air Atlantique Ltd	Caernarfon	18. 6.71
			G-AMLZ		(Under restoration 12.99)		
G-AMMS	Auster J/5K Aiglet Trainer	2745		11.10.51	A.J.Large	Gloucestershire	19.10.98
G-AMNN	DH.82A Tiger Moth	86457	NM137	24.12.51	M.Thrower "Spirit of Pashley"	Shoreham	25. 6.00
					t/a Northbrook College of Aeronautical Engineering		
	(Composite from unidentified airframe; the original G-AMNN may have been absorbed into G-BPAJ)						
G-AMOG*	Vickers 701 Viscount	7	(G-AMNZ)	23. 5.52	RAF Museum	RAF Cosford	14. 6.77
					(BEA c/s) "RMA Robert Falcon Scott"		
G-AMPG(2)	PA-12 Super Cruiser	12-985	N2647M NC2647M	25. 3.85	R.Simpson	Preston Court, Ledbury	3.12.98P
G-AMPI(2)	SNCAN Stampe SV-4C	213	N6RA F-BCFX	13. 2.84	T.W.Harris,	(Hunstanton)	
G-AMPO	Douglas C-47B-30DK Dakota 3	16437/33185	LN-RTO	25. 2.52	Atlantic Air Transport Ltd	Coventry	29. 3.97A
	(Regd as c/n 33186/16438)		G-AMPO/KN566/44-76853		(Pollution Control c/s) (Open store 6.99)		
G-AMPP*	Douglas C-47B Dakota 3	15272/26717	XF756	4. 3.52	Not known	(France)	7. 2.71
			G-AMPP/KK136/43-49456		(As "G-AMSU" in Dan-Air c/s; to Euro-Disney 1993)		
G-AMPY	Douglas C-47B-15DK Dakota 3	15124/26569	(EI-BKJ)	8. 3.52	Dak Holdings Ltd	Coventry	5. 1.01A
			G-AMPY/N15751/		(Op Air Atlantique/Pollution Control)		
			G-AMPY/TF-FIO/G-AMPY/JY-ABE/G-AMPY/KK116/43-49308				

Regn	Type	C/n	P/I	Date	Owner/operator	Probable Base	CA Expy
G-AMPZ	Douglas C-47B-30DK Dakota 4	16124/32872	EI-BDT G-AMPZ/ TF-AIV/G-41-3-66/PH-RIC/G-AMPZ/OD-AEQ/G-AMPZ/KN442/44-76540	8. 3.52	Atlantic Air Transport Ltd (Op Air Atlantique)	Coventry	29. 4.01T
G-AMRA	Douglas C-47B-15DK Dakota 6	15290/26735	XE280 G-AMRA/KK151/43-49474	8. 3.52	Dak Holdings Ltd (Op Air Atlantique)	Coventry	11. 6.00T
G-AMRF	Auster J/5F Aiglet Trainer	2716	VT-DHA G-AMRF	20. 3.52	A.I.Topps	East Midlands	28.11.99
G-AMRK	Gloster Gladiator 1 (Bristol Mercury XXX)	-	L8032 "K8032"/G-AMRK/L8032 (As "423-Port/427-Starboard" in R.Nor AF c/s)	16. 5.52	The Shuttleworth Trust	Old Warden	16. 7.00P
G-AMSG	SIPA 903	77	OO-VBL F-BGHB	25.11.81	S.W.Markham	Valentine Farm, Odiham	8. 4.00P
G-AMSN	Douglas C-47B-35DK Dakota 4	16631/33379	N3455 G-AMSN/EI-BSI/SU-BFZ/G-AMSN/KN673/44-77047	28. 4.52	Aces High Ltd (Stored 6.98)	North Weald	3. 1.68
G-AMSV	Douglas C-47B-25DK Dakota 3	16072/32820	(F-BSGV) G-AMSV/KN397/44-76488	15. 5.52	Dak Holdings Ltd (Op Air Atlantique) (Pollution Control c/s)	Coventry	1. 7.01A
G-AMTA	Auster J/5F Aiglet Trainer	2780		24. 5.52	N.H.J.Cottrell	Headcorn	17. 7.00
G-AMTD*	Auster J/5F Aiglet Trainer	2783	EI-AVL G-AMTD	24. 5.52	Leicestershire Aero Club Ltd	Leicester	8.12.93T
	(Damaged Hayrish Farm, Okehampton 7.8.93; wings noted 5.96; cancelled as WFU 15.1.99)						
G-AMTF	DH.82A Tiger Moth	84207	ZK-AVE G-AMTF/T7842	11. 6.52	M.W.Zipfell (As "T-7842")	RAF Marham	19. 7.01
G-AMTK	DH.82A Tiger Moth	3982	N6709	18. 6.52	S.W.McKay & M.E.Vaisey (Stored 2.96)	(Berkhamsted)	27. 5.66
G-AMTM	Auster 5 J/1 Autocrat (Auster Aircraft rebuild - originally c/n 2622)	3101	G-AJUJ	3. 7.52	R.J.Stobo & D.A.Clewley	Oaklands Farm, Stonesfield, Oxon	16. 6.00P
G-AMTV	DH.82A Tiger Moth	3858	OO-SOE G-AMTV/N6545	5. 8.52	Medalbest Ltd	Old Sarum	1.10.00
G-AMUF	DHC.1 Chipmunk 21	C1/0832		2. 9.52	Redhill Tailwheel Flying Club Ltd	Redhill	24. 1.02
G-AMUI	Auster J/5F Aiglet Trainer	2790		29. 8.52	Deborah Hatelie (On rebuild 7.93)	(Liverpool)	15. 2.66T
G-AMUJ*	Auster J/5F Aiglet Trainer	2791		29. 8.52	C.J.Baker (Crashed nr Sleaford 8.6.60; remains expired 1999)	Carr Farm, Newark	5. 4.61
G-AMVD	Taylorcraft J Auster 5	1565	F-BGTF G-AMVD/TJ565	6.10.52	M.Hammond (As "TJ565")	Hardwick	6. 4.01
G-AMVP	Tipsy Junior (Walter Mikron 2)	J.111	OO-ULA	23.10.52	A.R.Wershat (Damaged Wroughton 4.7.93; under repair 12.95)	Sandown	22. 6.94P
G-AMVS	DH.82A Tiger Moth	82784	OO-SOJ G-AMVS/R4852	12.11.52	J.T.Powell-Tuck (On rebuild Shobdon 8.92)	(Pontypool)	21.12.53
G-AMYA(2)*	Zlin Z.381 Bestmann (Hirth HM504A)	461	OO-AVC OK-AVC	17. 6.87	K.Weeks/Fantasy of Flight Museum (As "AM+YA" in Luftwaffe c/s)	Polk City, Florida	21. 2.96P
G-AMYD	Auster J/5L Aiglet Trainer	2773		13. 2.53	G.H.Maskell	Duckend Farm, Wilstead, Bedford	4. 3.01
G-AMYJ	Douglas C-47B-25DK Dakota 6	15968/32716	SU-AZF G-AMYJ/XF747/G-AMYJ/KN353/44-76384	23. 2.53	Atlantic Air Transport Ltd (Pollution Control c/s) (Open store 6.99)	Coventry	4. 4.97A
G-AMYL(2)	PA-17 Vagabond (Continental C75)	17-30	N4613H NC4613H	24. 4.87	P.J.Penn-Sayer t/a The Fun Airplane Co "Yankee Lady"(Stored 9.97)	Scaynes Hill, Haywards Heath	20. 6.89P
G-AMZI	Auster J/5F Aiglet Trainer	3104		4. 5.53	J.F.Moore	Biggin Hill	29.12.00
G-AMZT	Auster J/5F Aiglet Trainer	3107		28. 5.53	D.Hyde, J.W.Saull & J.C.Hutchinson	Cranfield	25. 5.01
G-AMZU	Auster J/5F Aiglet Trainer	3108		28. 5.53	J.A.Longworth, A.R.M. & C.B.A.Eagle t/a Flying Flicks	White Waltham	11. 9.02

G-ANAA – G-ANZZ

Regn	Type	C/n	P/I	Date	Owner/operator	Probable Base	CA Expy
G-ANAF	Douglas C-47B-35DK Dakota 3	16688/33436	N170GP G-ANAF/KP220/44-77104	17. 6.53	Atlantic Air Transport Ltd (Op Air Atlantique for Racal)	Coventry	26. 2.01A
G-ANAP*	DH.104 Dove 6	04433		17. 7.53	Brunel Technical College (Instructional airframe 10.99)	Bristol	
G-ANCF*	Bristol 175 Britannia 308F	12922	5Y-AZP G-ANCF/LV-GJB/LV-PPJ/(G-ANCF)/G-14-1/G-18-4/(N6597C)/G-ANCF t/a Britannia Acft Preservation Trust	3. 1.58	R.Hargreaves (Stored 6.97)	Kemble	12. 1.81T
G-ANCS	DH.82A Tiger Moth	82824	R4907	12. 9.53	M.A.B.Mitchell	Wold Farm, Cambridge	8. 5.02
G-ANCX	DH.82A Tiger Moth	83719	T7229	15. 9.53	D.R.Wood	Fowle Hall Farm, Paddock Wood	28. 7.02
G-ANDE	DH.82A Tiger Moth	85957	EM726	23. 9.53	Montrose Aviation Ltd	Redhill	4. 2.00T
G-ANDM	DH.82A Tiger Moth	3946	EI-AGP G-ANDM/EI-AGROUP/G-ANDM/(G-ANDI)/N6642	23. 9.53	N.J.Stagg	Bristol	14. 8.00
G-ANDP	DH.82A Tiger Moth	82868	D-EBEC N9920F/G-ANDP/R4960	22. 9.53	A.H.Diver (Damaged mid 1995)	Newtownards	20. 7.01

Regn	Type	C/n	P/I	Date	Owner/operator	Probable Base	CA Expy
G-ANDX*	DH.104 Devon C.2 (Dove 7XC)	04435	XG496	28. 9.53	L.Richards	Newcastle	3.4.86P*
			G-ANDX		(Stored Newcastle 4.86: cancelled by CAA 21.1.99)		
G-ANEH	DH.82A Tiger Moth	82067	N6797	29. 9.53	G.J.Wells (As "N6797")(Henley-on-Thames)		6. 8.01
G-ANEJ*	DH.82A Tiger Moth	85592	DE638	1.10.53	Royal Malaysian Air Force Museum		
					(As "T7245" in RAF c/s) Sungei Besi Air Base, Kuala Lumpur		
G-ANEL	DH.82A Tiger Moth	82333	N9238	1.10.53	Chauffair Ltd	Redhill	17. 6.02
G-ANEM	DH.82A Tiger Moth	82943	EI-AGN	1.10.53	P.J.Benest	Hamstead Marshall	16. 7.02
			G-ANEM/R5042				
G-ANEN	DH.82A Tiger Moth	85418	OO-ACG	2.10.53	R.J.Jackson	Old Sarum	13. 4.02
			G-ANEN/DE410				
G-ANEW	DH.82A Tiger Moth	86458	NM138	6.10.53	A.L.Young (Stored 4.98)	Henstridge	18. 6.62T
G-ANEZ	DH.82A Tiger Moth	84218	T7849	20.10.53	C.D.J.Bland	Farley Farm, Winchester	14. 6.02P
G-ANFC	DH.82A Tiger Moth	85385	DE363	13.10.53	J.E.Pierce	Welshpool	11.11.99T
G-ANFH*	Westland WS.55 Whirlwind 1	WA.15		27.10.53	E.D. Ap Rees	Weston-super-Mare	17. 7.71
					t/a The Helicopter Museum (Open store 8.98)		
G-ANFI	DH.82A Tiger Moth	85577	DE623	16.10.53	G.P.Graham (As "DE623")	Shobdon	19.12.99
					(Tiger Moth "DE623" [D-EDON] displayed Auto Und Technik Museum, Sinsheim)		
G-ANFL	DH.82A Tiger Moth	84617	T6169	22.10.53	R.P.Whitby	Swanton Morley	23. 4.01
	(Built Morris Motors)				t/a IDA Flying Group		
G-ANFM	DH.82A Tiger Moth	83604	T5888	22.10.53	S.A.Brook, L.S.Mitton & J.Hartill		
					t/a Reading Flying Group	White Waltham	5. 8.01
G-ANFP	DH.82A Tiger Moth	82530	N9503	28.10.53	G D Horn	(Fordingbridge)	1. 7.63
G-ANFU*	Taylorcraft J Auster 5	1748	TW385	31.10.53	J.Stelling	Newcastle	17. 2.71
					t/a Newcastle Vehicle Museum		
	(On rebuild with frame from un-identified Auster 6 5.93; to be "NJ719" with ident of starboard wing ex G-AKPH)						
G-ANFV	DH.82A Tiger Moth	85904	DF155	1.12.53	R.A.L.Falconer	Shempston Farm, Elgin	4. 2.01
					(As "DF155")		
G-ANFW	DH.82A Tiger Moth	85660	DE730	5.11.53	G.M.K.Fraser	Duxford	21.12.01
	(Regd with Fuselage No.3737)				t/a Fraser Aviation (Stored 1.99)		
G-ANFY*	Thruxton Jackaroo	86349	NL906	13.11.53	B.Knock	Ashford, Kent	25. 5.68
					(Stored in poor condition 1.96)		
G-ANGK(2)	Cessna 140A	15396	N9675A	10. 3.89	D.W.Munday	Popham	21. 7.01
G-ANHK	DH.82A Tiger Moth	82442	F-BHIM	4.12.53	J.D.Iliffe	Hampstead Norreys	9. 2.00
			G-ANHK/N9372				
G-ANHR	Taylorcraft J Auster 5	759	MT192	5.12.53	C.G.Winch	Rushett Farm, Chessington	20. 7.86
					(On rebuild 6.96)		
G-ANHS	Taylorcraft G Auster 4	737	MT197	5.12.53	R.G.Tomlinson	Spanhoe	9. 9.00
					t/a Tango Uniform Group		
G-ANHU	Taylorcraft G Auster 4	799	EC-AXR	5.12.53	D.J.Baker	Carr Farm, Newark	22.10.66
			G-ANHU/MT255			(Dismantled 4.98)		
G-ANHW*	Taylorcraft J Auster 5D	1396	TJ320	5.12.53	C.J.Baker	Carr Farm, Newark	9. 3.70
					(Damaged Carlton Manor, Newark 1970: derelict fuselage 4.98)		
G-ANHX	Taylorcraft J Auster 5D	2064	TW519	5.12.53	D.J.Baker	Carr Farm, Newark	2.11.73
					(Crashed 28.3.70: dismantled 4.98)		
G-ANIE	Taylorcraft J Auster 5	1809	TW467	5.12.53	S.J.Partridge	Bassingbourn	20.10.02
					(Op Military Auster Flight as "TW467/ROD-F" in 664 Sqn c/s)		
G-ANIJ	Taylorcraft J Auster 5D	1680	TJ672	5.12.53	M.Pocock	Whitchurch, Hants	5. 5.71
					t/a Military Auster Flight as "TJ672/TS-D" in 657 Sqdn c/s; on rebuild 7.93)		
G-ANIS*	Taylorcraft J Auster 5	1429	TJ375	5.12.53	R.W.Hall t/a Halls Autospares		
					(Stored 6.97)	Longford, Ireland	19. 9.76
G-ANIX	DH.82A Tiger Moth	84764	D-EFTF	14. 4.55	J.M.Koch	Sandown	2. 7.00T
					(Op Island Aeroplane Co) (As "T6390" in RAF c/s)		
	(Composite rebuild of un-identified Tiger Moth Germany 1990/92 using documentation of D-ELOM, ex G-ANIX/T6390)						
G-ANJA	DH.82A Tiger Moth	82459	N9389	7.12.53	P.Aukland (As "N9389")	Seething	15. 2.02
G-ANJD	DH.82A Tiger Moth	84652	T6226	8.12.53	A.C.Ladd Romney Street Farm, Sevenoaks		6. 9.81
					(On rebuild 12.99)		
G-ANJK*	DH.82A Tiger Moth	84557	T6066	12.12.53	Not known Rhos-Y-Gilwen Farm, Rhos Hill		12. 5.85
					(As "T6066") (Stored 5.94)		
G-ANJV*	Westland WS-55 Whirlwind 3	WA.24	VR-BET	14.12.53	E.D.Ap Rees	Weston-super-Mare	
			G-ANJV			t/a The Helicopter Museum (Stored 5.97)		
G-ANKK	DH.82A Tiger Moth	83590	T5854	24.12.53	Patricia A.Cambridge	Pool Quay	18. 1.01
					t/a Halfpenny Green Tiger Group (As "T5854")		
G-ANKT	DH.82A Tiger Moth	85087	T6818	24.12.53	The Shuttleworth Trust	Old Warden	12. 8.00P
					(As "T6818/91")		
G-ANKV*	DH.82A Tiger Moth	84166	T7793	30.12.53	Westmead Business Group Croydon Airport		
	(Provenance uncertain; static rebuild by Acebell Aviation early 1994: as "T7793" in RAF c/s at Terminal Building)						
G-ANKZ	DH.82A Tiger Moth	3803	(N)	30.12.53	D.W.Graham	Sywell	15. 4.99
			F-BHIO/G-ANKZ/N6466 (As "N6466")				
G-ANLD	DH.82A Tiger Moth	85990	OO-DPA	30.12.53	K.Peters	Rushett Farm, Chessington	7.12.02
			G-ANLD/EM773				

Regn	Type	C/n	P/I	Date	Owner/operator	Probable Base	CA Expy
G-ANLH	DH.82A Tiger Moth (Fuselage No. MCO/DH.4623)	86546	N3744F OO-EVO/G-ANLH/PG637	4. 1.54	T.S.Warren & J.J.Woodhouse	Sandown	7. 5.00T
G-ANLS	DH.82A Tiger Moth	85862	DF113	7. 1.54	P.A.Gliddon Great Fryup, Egton, Whitby		26. 2.00
G-ANLU	Taylorcraft J Auster 5	1780	TW448	8. 1.54	B.H.Hargrave	Stubbington	8. 8.68
					(Stored by Crofton Aeroplane Services 1.95)		
G-ANLW	Westland WS.51 Srs.2 Widgeon	WA/H/133	"MD497" G-ANLW	23. 3.54	Sloane Helicopters Ltd	Sywell	27. 5.81A
					(Stored 8.97)		
G-ANLX	DH.82A Tiger Moth	84165	T7792	8. 1.54	B.J., P.B., A.J. & P.J.Borsberry		
					t/a Jack's Tiger Flying Group Kidmore End, Reading		11. 4.56
			(Crashed near Luton Airport 31.12.55; minor components held for composite rebuild)				
G-ANMO	DH.82A Tiger Moth	3255	F-BHIU G-ANMO/K4259	22. 1.54	E. & K.M.Lay (As "K4259/71")	White Waltham	10. 8.00
G-ANMV	DH.82A Tiger Moth	83745	F-BHAZ G-ANMV/T7404	22. 1.54	B.P.Sanders t/a Tigerfly (As "T7404/04")	Booker	26. 6.01T
G-ANMY	DH.82A Tiger Moth	85466	OO-SOL "OO-SOC"/G-ANMY/DE470	22. 1.54	R.Earl & B.Morris (As "DE470/16" in RAF c/s)	Oaksey Park	24. 8.01
G-ANNB	DH.82A Tiger Moth	84233	N6037 D-EGYN/G-ANNB/T6037	22. 1.54	G.M.Bradley (On rebuild Rothesay 4.92)	(Colchester)	12. 6.58
G-ANNE(2)	DH.82A Tiger Moth	"83814"		15. 4.94	C.R.Hardiman (On rebuild 3.96)	Shobdon	30. 5.58
	(Composite airframe, not likely to be connected with original G-ANNE, ex T7418, sold as OO-CCI/90-CCI/9Q-CCI)						
G-ANNG	DH.82A Tiger Moth	85504	DE524	22. 1.54	P.F.Walter	Farnborough	18. 5.01
G-ANNI	DH.82A Tiger Moth	85162	T6953	22. 1.54	A.R.Brett (As "T6953")	Hong Kong	27. 8.00
G-ANNK	DH.82A Tiger Moth	83804	F-BFDO G-ANNK/T7290	22. 1.54	Patricia J.Wilcox (On rebuild Cranfield 5.92)	(Northampton)	25. 9.87
G-ANNN	DH.82A Tiger Moth	84073	T5968	2. 2.54	H.C.Cox (On rebuild 1996)	(Bristol)	
G-ANOD	DH.82A Tiger Moth	84588	T6121	16. 2.54	Penelope G.Grafton Kidmore End, Reading		7. 2.60
					(Composite rebuild; on long term rebuild 6.94)		
G-ANOH	DH.82A Tiger Moth	86040	EM838	22. 2.54	N.Parkhouse	Great Massingham	14. 9.02T
G-ANOK*	SAAB 91C Safir	91311	SE-CAH	22. 4.54	A.F.Galt & Co Ltd (Stored 4.89)	Kirk Yetholm	5. 2.73
G-ANOM	DH.82A Tiger Moth	82086	N6837	2. 3.54	A.L.Creer (Crashed Fairoaks 17.12.61; on rebuild 12.95)	(Bristol)	3. 5.62T
G-ANON	DH.82A Tiger Moth	84270	T7909	4. 3.54	A.C.Mercer (As "T7909")	Sherburn in Elmet	4. 8.99
G-ANOO	DH.82A Tiger Moth	85409	DE401	11. 3.54	R.K.Packman	Compton Abbas	12. 9.02
G-ANOR	DH.82A Tiger Moth	85635	DE694	4. 3.54	R.Clifford (As "T6991": see G-ACDA)	(London NW3)	27. 1.01
G-ANOV*	DH.104 Dove 6	04445	G-5-16	11. 3.54	Royal Museum of Scotland/Museum of Flight (Civil Aviation Authority c/s) East Fortune		31. 5.75
G-ANPC*	DH.82A Tiger Moth	82858	R4950	19. 3.54	Irish Aviation Museum		
			(Crashed nr Loch Leven 2.1.67; stored 4.96) Castlemoate House, Dublin					2. 9.67
G-ANPE	DH.82A Tiger Moth	83738	G-IESH G-ANPE/F-BHAT/G-ANPE/T7397	27. 3.54	I.E.S.Hudleston	(Lymington)	22.11.02
G-ANPK	DH.82A Tiger Moth	3571	L6936	5. 4.54	D.E.Partridge	Great Waltham	10. 7.97T
			t/a The P & D Group (Damaged Jaywick Sands, Clacton 18.8.96; stored 1.97)				
G-ANRF	DH.82A Tiger Moth	83748	T5850	24. 5.54	C.D.Cyster	Glenrothes	24. 8.01
G-ANRM	DH.82A Tiger Moth	85861	DF112	8. 6.54	Fairmont Investments Ltd Clacton/Duxford (As "DF112")		28. 7.01T
G-ANRN	DH.82A Tiger Moth	83133	T5368	24. 5.54	J.J.V.Elwes	Rush Green	10. 8.00
G-ANRP	Taylorcraft J Auster 5	1789	TW439	21. 5.54	A.Brier (As "TW439")	Breighton	16.12.02
G-ANRX*	DH.82A Tiger Moth	3863	N6550	25. 5.54	De Havilland Aircraft Museum "Border City" Salisbury Hall, London Colney		20. 6.61
G-ANSM	DH.82A Tiger Moth	82909	R5014	3. 6.54	J.L.Bond	Redhill	23. 7.01
G-ANTE	DH.82A Tiger Moth	84891	T6562	20. 9.54	M.R.Keen (As "T6562")	Liverpool	7. 4.02T
G-ANTK*	Avro 685 York C1	-	MW232	23. 7.54	Duxford Aviation Society (On rebuild 1.99)	Duxford	29.10.64TC
G-ANUO*	DH.114 Heron 2D	14062		27. 9.54	Westmead Business Centre Croydon Airport (As "G-AOXL" in Morton Air Services c/s)		12. 9.86T
G-ANUW*	DH.104 Dove 6	04458		16. 5.55	Ross Aviation Services (Stored 2.97)	Fownhope, Hereford	22. 7.81
G-ANVU*	DH.104 Dove 1B	04082	VR-NAP	12.11.54	Flygvapenmuseum Malmen (Stored 1992) Malmslatt, Linkoping, Sweden		14. 9.77
G-ANWB*	DHC.1 Chipmunk 21	C1/0987	G-5-17	15. 2.55	G.Briggs (On rebuild 6.96: cancelled by CAA 26.2.99)	Blackpool	8. 3.91
G-ANWO	Miles M.14A Hawk Trainer 3	718	L8262	31.12.58	A.G.Dunkerley (Stored West Chiltington, Pulborough 11.92)	(Bury)	18. 4.63
G-ANWX*	Auster J/5L Aiglet Trainer	3131		25.11.54	D.Hodgkinson	Canterbury	2. 5.94
			"Shepherd's Delight" (Damaged Nayland 1.8.93; on rebuild 9.96)				
G-ANXB*	DH.114 Heron 1B	14048	G-5-14	3.12.54	Newark Air Museum	Winthorpe	25. 3.79
			(BEA Scottish Airways c/s) "Sir James Young Simpson"				

Regn	Type	C/n	P/I	Date	Owner/operator	Probable Base	CA Expy
G-ANXC	Auster J/5R Alpine	3135	5Y-UBD	4.12.54	R.B.Webber Trenchard Farm, Eggesford		2. 8.98
					VP-UBD/G-ANXC/(AP-AHG)/G-ANXC t/a Alpine Group		
G-ANXR	Percival P.31C Proctor 4	H.803	RM221	14.12.54	L.H.Oakins (As "RM221")	Biggin Hill	8. 6.00
G-ANZT	Thruxton Jackaroo	84176	T7798	4. 3.55	D.J.Neville & P.J.Dear	Rush Green	14. 8.02
G-ANZU	DH.82A Tiger Moth	3583	L6938	9. 3.55	P.A.Jackson (Stored 1994)		
						Brookfield Farm, Great Stukeley	17. 3.91
G-ANZZ	DH.82A Tiger Moth	85834	DE974	14. 3.55	J.I.B.Bennett & P.P.Amershi	(Hatfield)	28. 2.69T

G-AOAA – G-AOZZ

Regn	Type	C/n	P/I	Date	Owner/operator	Probable Base	CA Expy
G-AOAA	DH.82A Tiger Moth	85908	DF159	14. 3.55	R.C.P.Brookhouse	(Redhill)	8.12.91T
					(Damaged Redhill 4.6.89)		
G-AOBG*	Somers-Kendall SK-1	1		30. 3.55	A.J.E.Smith	Breighton	26. 6.58
					(WFU after engine turbine failure 11.7.57; stored 10.97)		
G-AOBH	DH.82A Tiger Moth	84350	T7997	31. 3.55	P.Nutley (As "NL750")	Thruxton	20. 2.00
	(Regd with c/n 83818 ex T7439; G-AOBH is marked as "NL750" which belongs to G-AHUF marked "T7997";						
	both Aero Club are registered to same owner)						
G-AOBO	DH.82A Tiger Moth	3810	N6473	23. 4.55	J.S. & J.V.Shaw	Cubert, Newquay	28. 9.69T
					(On rebuild 10.97)		
G-AOBU	Hunting Percival P.84 Jet Provost T.1 (XM129)		2. 5.55	T.J.Manna	Cranfield	27. 4.00P
		P84/6	G-AOBU/G-42-1		t/a Kennet Aviation (As "XD693/Z-Q" in RAF c/s)		
G-AOBV*	Auster J/5P Autocar	3171		9. 5.55	Not known (Stored 10.97) Cheshunt, Bucks		7. 4.71T
G-AOBX	DH.82A Tiger Moth	83653	T7187	26. 4.55	D.G.Ross	Uffley Common, Odiham	5.11.02
G-AOCP(2)*	Taylorcraft J Auster 5	1800	TW462	25. 5.56	C.J.Baker	Carr Farm, Newark	22. 6.68
					(WFU 22.6.68 fuselage stored 4.98)		
G-AOCR(2)	Taylorcraft J Auster 5D	1060	EI-AJS	25. 5.56	G.J.McDill	Park Farm, Eaton Bray	8. 9.01
			G-AOCR/NJ673		(As "NJ673")		
G-AOCU(2)	Taylorcraft J Auster 5	986	MT349	8. 6.56	S.J.Ball	Leicester	29. 1.01
G-AODA*	Westland WS.55 Whirlwind Srs.3		9Y-TDA	13. 5.55	The Helicopter Museum Weston-super-Mare		23. 8.91A
		WA/113	EP-HAC/G-AODA		(Bristow Helicopters c/s) "Dorado"		
G-AODT	DH.82A Tiger Moth	83109	R5250	4. 8.55	R.A.Harrowven	Tibenham	30. 4.01
G-AOEH	Aeronca 7AC Champion	7AC-2144	N79854	8. 9.55	R.A. & S.P.Smith	Crowfield	20. 9.97P
	(Continental A65)		OO-TWF				
G-AOEI	DH.82A Tiger Moth	82196	N6946	14. 9.55	CFG Flying Ltd	Cambridge	11. 7.02T
	(Regd with Fuselage No. MCO/DH3409, which should be c/n 85332 ex DE298, converted at Croydon as N524R 12.65						
	but ntu ?; a/c is probably a composite airframe)						
G-AOEL*	DH.82A Tiger Moth	82537	N9510	27. 9.55	Museum of Flight/Royal Museum of Scotland		
						East Fortune	18. 7.72
G-AOES	DH.82A Tiger Moth	84547	T6056	6.10.55	A.Twemlow & G.A.Cordery		
						Charity Farm, Baxterley	15. 6.02
					(Damaged Baxterley 26.9.99)		
G-AOET	DH.82A Tiger Moth	85650	DE720	7.10.55	Venom Jet Promotions Ltd (P.Meeson)		
						Oaklands Farm, East Tytherley	1.11.02
	(Tiger Moth frame quoted as "G-AOET" is stored by A.S.Topen, Cranfield)						
G-AOEX	Thruxton Jackaroo	86483	NM175	10.10.55	A.T.Christian Walkeridge Farm, Overton		3. 2.68T
					(On rebuild 5.90)		
G-AOFE	DHC.1 Chipmunk 22A	C1/0150	WB702	13. 9.56	E.J.F.McEntee Kirdford, Billingshurst		21. 9.01
					(As "WB702")		
G-AOFJ*	Auster Alpha 5	3401		3.10.56	R.Drew (Stored 8.98)	Perth	20. 9.79
G-AOFM	Auster J/5P Autocar	3178		16. 6.55	W.H.Dyozinski	White Waltham	22.10.00
G-AOFS	Auster J/5L Aiglet Trainer	3143	EI-ALN	28.10.55	P.N.A.Whitehead	Leicester	11. 4.01
			G-AOFS				
G-AOGA*	Miles M.75 Aries 1	75/1007	EI-ANB	9.11.55	The Irish Aviation Museum		
	(Damaged Cork 8.8.69; stored 4.96)		G-AOGA		Castlemoate House, Dublin		10.10.69
G-AOGE*	Percival P.34A Proctor 3	H.210	BV651	24.11.55	N.I.Dalziel	Biggin Hill	21. 5.84
					(Stored 8.97; cancelled by CAA 19.1.99)		
G-AOGI	DH.82A Tiger Moth	85922	(N)	14.12.55	W.J.Taylor	(Boston)	23. 8.91
			OO-SOA/G-AOGI/DF186		t/a Lincs Aerial Spraying Co (Stored Ingoldmells 10.92)		
G-AOGR	DH.82A Tiger Moth	84566	XL714	20. 1.56	M.I.Edwards	Swanton Morley	16. 9.96T
			G-AOGR/T6099		(As "XL714"; stored 5.99)		
G-AOGV	Auster J/5R Alpine	3302		2. 2.56	R.E.Heading (Stored 3.97)		17. 7.72
						Walnut Tree Farm, Thorney, Whittlesey	
G-AOHD*	Hunting Percival P.84 Jet Provost T.2	P84/12	A99-001	26. 3.56	Royal Australian AF Museum (Stored 1995)		
			G-AOHD			Point Cook, Victoria	10. 4.60
G-AOHL*	Vickers 802 Viscount	161		2. 1.56	London-Southend Airport Co Ltd	Southend	11. 4.80T
					(Fire Services trainer 5.99)		
G-AOHY	DH.82A Tiger Moth	3850	N6537	23. 2.56	M.Somerton-Rayner	AAC Middle Wallop	20. 8.60
					t/a Historic Aircraft Flight Reserve Collection (On rebuild 2.96)		
G-AOHZ	Auster J/5P Autocar	3252		28. 2.56	A.D.Hodgkinson	Dunkirk, Canterbury	24. 7.00T

Regn	Type	C/n	P/I	Date	Owner/operator	Probable Base	CA Expy
G-AOIL	DH.82A Tiger Moth	83673	XL716 G-AOIL/T7363	20. 8.56	T.C.Lawless (As "XL716")	Popham	17. 9.02
G-AOIM	DH.82A Tiger Moth	83536	T7109	27. 8.56	D.A.Hardiman	Shobdon	16. 8.00
G-AOIR	Thruxton Jackaroo	82882	R4972	13. 1.56	L.H.Smith & I.M.Oliver	Little Gransden	18. 3.02
G-AOIS	DH.82A Tiger Moth	83034	R5172	13. 1.56	J.K.Ellwood	Sherburn in Elmet	20. 5.01
G-AOIY	Auster J/5V-160 Autocar (Lycoming O-320)	3199		1. 3.56	J.B.Nicholson Watchford Farm, Yarncombe (On rebuild 3.98)		26. 8.90
G-AOJC*	Vickers 802 Viscount	152	(G-AOHC)	2. 1.56	Not known (Fuselage stored 7.96: BEA c/s)	Enstone	20. 1.77T
G-AOJD*	Vickers 802 Viscount	153	(G-AOHD)	2. 1.56	Jersey Airport Fire Service	Jersey	13. 6.77T
G-AOJH	DH.83C Fox Moth	FM.42	AP-ABO	29. 3.56	A.J.Norman t/a Norman Aeroplane Trust	Rendcomb	17.10.02
G-AOJJ	DH.82A Tiger Moth	85877	DF128	5. 4.56	E.Lay & T.J.Pegram t/a JJ Flying Group (As "DF128/RCO-U")	White Waltham	24. 7.00
G-AOJK	DH.82A Tiger Moth	82813	R4896	5. 4.56	D.E.Guck & P.W.Crispe	Halfpenny Green	18. 8.02
G-AOJR	DHC.1 Chipmunk 22	C1/0205	SE-BBS	9. 4.56	G J G-H Caubergs & N Marien OY-DFB/D-EGIM/G-AOJR/D-EGIM/G-AOJR/WB756 (Awirs-Flemalle, Belgium)		28. 7.02
G-AOJT*	DH.106 Comet 1XB	06020	F-BGNX	11. 5.56	De Havilland Aircraft Museum Salisbury Hall, London Colney (Fuselage only as "F-BGNX" in Air France c/s 3.96)		5. 7.56
G-AOJZ*	DHC.1 Chipmunk 21	C1/0181	"G-ASTD"	16.4.56	Air Service Training Ltd G-AOJZ/WB732 (Crashed nr Perth 31.5.56; instructional airframe 12.95)	Perth	13.11.66
G-AOKH*	Percival P.40 Prentice 1	PAC/212	VS251	11. 4.56	J.F.Moore (Stored 8.97)	Biggin Hill	2. 8.73
G-AOKL	Percival P.40 Prentice 1	PAC/208	VS610	13. 4.56	The Shuttleworth Trust (As "VS610/K-L")	Old Warden	20. 9.96
G-AOKO*	Percival P.40 Prentice 1	PAC/234	VS621	13. 4.56	Atlantic Air Transport Ltd (Derelict fuselage 6.99)	Coventry	23.10.72
G-AOKZ*	Percival P.40 Prentice 1	PAC/238	VS623	20. 4.56	Midland Air Museum (As "VS623")	Coventry	
G-AOLK	Percival P.40 Prentice 1	PAC/225	VS618	25. 4.56	A.Hilton	Southend	3.12.98
G-AOLU	Percival P.40 Prentice 1 (Regd with c/n 5830/3) B3/1A/PAC/283		VS356 G-AOLU/VS356	25. 4.56	N.J.Butler t/a Montrose Air Station Museum (On rebuild 8.95: as "VS356")	Montrose	8. 5.76
G-AORB(2)	Cessna 170B	20767	OO-SIZ N2615D	13. 2.84	A.R.Thompson Hawley Farm, Tadley t/a Hawley Farm Group		21. 2.00
G-AORG	DH.114 Heron 2	14101	XR441 G-AORG/G-5-16	1. 5.56	Duchess of Brittany (Jersey) Ltd Jersey (Jersey Airlines c/s) "Duchess of Brittany"		10. 2.01
G-AORW	DHC.1 Chipmunk 22A	C1/0130	WB682	28. 5.56	Bushfire Investments Ltd	(Jersey)	3.11.02
G-AOSF	DHC.1 Chipmunk 22	C1/0023	D-EIIZ	26. 6.56	D.Mercer Porta Westfalica, Germany G-AOSF/HB-TUA/G-AOSF/WB571 (As "WB571/34")		25.10.02
G-AOSK	DHC.1 Chipmunk 22A (Frame No.DHH/F/121)	C1/0178	WB726	26. 6.56	E.J.Leigh (As "WB726/E" in Cambridge UAS c/s)	Audley End	23.11.02
G-AOSO	DHC.1 Chipmunk 22	C1/0227	WD288	26. 6.56	The Earl of Suffolk & Berkshire & J.Hoerner (As "WD288") Charlton Park, Malmesbury		14. 9.00
G-AOSU	DHC.1 Chipmunk 22 (Lycoming O-360)	C1/0217	WB766	28. 6.56	T.Holloway t/a RAFGSA (Op Fulmar Gliding Club)	Inverness	29. 4.00
G-AOSY	DHC.1 Chipmunk 22	C1/0037	WB585	29. 6.56	Propshop Ltd (As "WB585/M")	Duxford	14. 6.02
	(Substantially rebuilt following accidents at Redbourne, Herts 4.59 & Blackbushe 8.87)						
G-AOTD	DHC.1 Chipmunk 22	C1/0040	WB588	30. 6.56	S.Piech (As "WB588/D" in Oxford UAS c/s)	Biggin Hill	7. 9.00
G-AOTF	DHC.1 Chipmunk 23 (Lycoming O-360)	C1/0015	WB563	2. 7.56	T.Holloway t/a RAFGSA (Op Clevelands Gliding Club)	RAF Dishforth	29. 6.01
G-AOTI*	DH.114 Heron 2D	14107	G-5-19	25. 7.56	De Havilland Aircraft Museum Salisbury Hall, London Colney		24. 6.87T
G-AOTK	Druine D.53 Turbi (Walter Mikron 3)	1 & PFA/230		1.11.56	J.I.B.Bennett & R.G.A.Willoughby t/a The TK Flying Group Whitehall Farm, Benington		8.12.99P
G-AOTR	DHC.1 Chipmunk 22	C1/0045	HB-TUH D-EGOG/G-AOTR/WB604	12. 7.56	M.R.Woogate	Aldergrove	12.11.99
G-AOTY	DHC.1 Chipmunk 22A	C1/0522	WG472	12. 7.56	A.A.Hodgson (As "WG472" in RAF c/s)	(Abergele)	28. 9.00T
G-AOUJ*	Fairey Ultralight Helicopter	F.9424	XJ928	1. 8.56	E.D.Ap Rees t/a The Helicopter Museum (To Cotswold Aircraft Restoration Group 1999)	Innsworth	29. 3.59
G-AOUO	DHC.1 Chipmunk 22 (Lycoming O-360)	C1/0179	WB730	10. 8.56	T.Holloway t/a RAFGSA	RAF Bicester	5. 8.00
G-AOUP	DHC.1 Chipmunk 22	C1/0180	WB731	10. 8.56	A.R.Harding	(Milden)	24.10.02
G-AOUR*	DH.82A Tiger Moth	86341	NL898	14. 8.56	Ulster Folk & Transport Museum (Crashed Newtownards 6.6.65; stored 4.96) Holywood, Belfast		19.11.66
G-AOVF*	Bristol 175 Britannia 312F	13237	9Q-CAZ G-AOVF	13. 2.57	RAF Museum (BOAC c/s)	RAF Cosford	

Regn	Type	C/n	P/I	Date	Owner/operator	Probable Base	CA Expy
G-AOVT*	Bristol 175 Britannia 312	13427		23. 6.58	Duxford Aviation Society (Monarch c/s)	Duxford	11. 3.75
G-AOVW	Taylorcraft J Auster 5	894	MT119	16.11.59	B.Marriott Ropsley Heath Farm, Grantham		28. 9.00
G-AOXG*	DH.82A Tiger Moth	83805	T7291	3.10.56	Fleet Air Arm Museum RNAS Yeovilton (Displayed as "G-ABUL")		
G-AOXN	DH.82A Tiger Moth	85958	EM727	31.10.56	S.L.G.Darch East Chinnock, Yeovil		21.12.01
G-AOZE*	Westland WS-51/2 Widgeon	WA/H/141	5N-ABW G-AOZE	11. 1.57	E.D. Ap Rees Weston-super-Mare t/a The Helicopter Museum (Under restoration 8.98)		
G-AOZH	DH.82A Tiger Moth	86449	NM129	18. 1.57	G J & S Wheele (As "K2572") Shoreham		28. 9.02
G-AOZL	Auster J/5Q Alpine	3202		5. 2.57	R.M.Weeks Earls Colne (On rebuild 12.99)		28. 5.88
G-AOZP	DHC.1 Chipmunk 22A	C1/0183	WB734	14. 2.57	H.Darlington Audley End		23. 4.99

G-APAA – G-APZZ

Regn	Type	C/n	P/I	Date	Owner/operator	Probable Base	CA Expy
G-APAF	Auster Alpha 5	3404	G-CMAL G-APAF	25. 3.57	J.E.Allen North Coates (As "TW511")		22. 7.02
G-APAH	Auster Alpha 5	3402		29. 3.57	T.J.Goodwin Hill Farm, Nayland		8. 4.00
G-APAL	DH.82A Tiger Moth	82102	N6847	3. 4.57	P.S. & R.A.Chapman Little Gransden (As "N6847")		24. 6.00
G-APAM	DH.82A Tiger Moth	3874	N6580	3. 4.57	R.P.Williams Denford Manor, Hungerford t/a Myth Group "Myth"		8. 7.01
G-APAO	DH.82A Tiger Moth	82845	R4922	3. 4.57	Fairmont Investments Ltd Duxford/Clacton (Op Classic Wings)		10. 8.02T
G-APAP	DH.82A Tiger Moth	83018	R5136	3. 4.57	J.Romain Duxford (Damaged Kingston Deverill 4.9.94; on rebuild 1.99)		27. 6.96
G-APAS*	DH.106 Comet 1A	06022	8351M XM823/G-APAS/G-5-23/F-BGNZ (BOAC c/s)	23. 5.57	RAF Museum RAF Cosford		
G-APBE	Auster Alpha 5	3403		7. 5.57	A.M.Edwards (Norwich)		28. 9.01
G-APBI	DH.82A Tiger Moth	86097	EM903	16. 5.57	A.Wood Halstead, Essex (Damaged Audley End 7.7.80; on rebuild 12.90)		19. 4.82
G-APBO	Druine D.53 Turbi (Continental C75)	PFA/229		3. 6.57	R.C.Hibberd (Devizes)		31. 8.00P
G-APBW	Auster Alpha 5A	3405		23. 5.57	N.Huxtable Cheddington, Bucks		26. 5.00
G-APCB	Auster J/5Q Alpine	3204		5. 6.57	A.A.Beswick & I.A.Freeman Thruxton		2. 4.99
G-APCC	DH.82A Tiger Moth	86549	PG640	11. 6.57	L.J.Rice Bishopstrow Farm, Warminster		12. 5.00
G-APDB*	DH.106 Comet 4	6403	9M-AOB G-APDB	2. 5.57	Duxford Aviation Society Duxford (Dan-Air c/s)		7.10.74
G-APEK*	V.953C Vanguard Merchantman	714		9. 9.57	Europe Aero Service Perpignan (Stored 6.95)		16.12.89F
G-APEP*	V.953C Vanguard Merchantman	719		9. 9.57	Brooklands Museum Brooklands (Hunting Cargo Airlines c/s) "Superb"		1.10.98T
G-APFA	Druine D.52 Turbi (Continental A65)	PFA/232		5. 2.57	F.J.Keitch Smiths Farm, Brixham		22. 9.92P
G-APFG*	Boeing 707-436	17708	N5094K	7. 8.59	Civil Aviation Authority (Fuselage used for fire suppression trials) Building Research Establishment, Cardington		24. 5.81T
G-APFJ*	Boeing 707-436	17711		7. 8.59	RAF Museum RAF Cosford (British Airtours c/s)		16. 2.82T
G-APFU	DH.82A Tiger Moth	86081	EM879	28. 8.57	Leisure Assets Ltd Goodwood		11. 4.00T
G-APGL	DH.82A Tiger Moth	86460	NM140	6. 9.57	K.A.Broomfield Charity Farm, Baxterley (Not previously converted; on rebuild 3.97: see G-AJVE)		
G-APHV*	Avro 652A Anson C.19 Srs.2	-	VM360	19. 9.57	Museum of Flight/Royal Museum of Scotland (As "VM360") East Fortune		15. 6.73
G-APIE	Tipsy Belfair (Walter Mikron 2)	535	(OO-TIE)	22.10.57	D.Beale Fenland		22. 5.00P
G-APIH	DH.82A Tiger Moth	82981	N111DH OY-DGJ/D-EMEX/G-APIH/R5086	25.10.57	K.Stewering (Borken-Gemen, Germany)		15. 5.00
G-APIK	Auster Alpha	3375		11.11.57	T P Hancock Leicester t/a G-APIK Flying Group		14.12.02
G-APIM*	Vickers 806 Viscount	412		19.11.57	Brooklands Museum Brooklands (British Air Ferries c/s) "Viscount Stephen Piercey"		19. 7.88T
G-APIT*	Percival P.40 Prentice T.1	PAC/016	VR192	28.11.57	Second World War Aircraft Preservation Society (As "VR192") Lasham		7. 9.67
G-APIU*	Percival P.40 Prentice T.1	PAC/024	VR200	28.11.57	Atlantic Air Transport Ltd Coventry (Spares use 5.96)		23. 3.67
G-APIY*	Percival P.40 Prentice T.1	PAC/075	VR249	28.11.57	Newark Air Museum Winthorpe (As "VR249/FA-EL" in RAFC c/s)		18. 3.67
G-APIZ	Rollason-Druine D.31 Turbulent (VW1600)	PFA/478		22.11.57	E J I Musty "Witch Lady" White Waltham		3. 8.00P

Regn	Type	C/n	P/I	Date	Owner/operator	Probable Base	CA Expy
G-APJB	Percival P.40 Prentice T.1	PAC/086	VR259	28.11.57	Atlantic Air Transport Ltd	Coventry	3. 8.00T
					(As "VR259/M" in 2 ASS c/s)		
G-APJJ*	Fairey Ultralight Helicopter	F.9428		4.12.57	Midland Air Museum	Coventry	1. 4.59
G-APJO	DH.82A Tiger Moth	86446	NM126	23.12.57	D.R. & Mrs M.Wood	Tunbridge Wells	27. 3.59
	(C/n quoted as "17712"; crashed Ross-on-Wye 5.8.58; on rebuild & may includes components from G-APJR)						
G-APJZ	Auster Alpha	3382	5N-ACY	3. 1.58	P.G.Lipman Romney Street Farm, Sevenoaks		15. 7.77
			(VR-NDR)/G-APJZ		(Damaged Thornicombe 10.11.75; on rebuild 8.90)		
G-APKH	DH.85 Leopard Moth	PPS.85/1/DH7131	AX858	23. 1.58	A R Tarleton	Bournemouth	16. 7.00P
			G-ACGS/PH-ALM/G-ACGS				
G-APKM*	Auster Alpha	3385		27. 1.58	D.E.A.Huggins	(Meriden, Coventry)	9. 1.89
					(Stored 4.90)		
G-APKN	Auster Alpha	3387		27. 1.58	P.R.Hodson	Felthorpe	9. 8.02
					t/a The Felthorpe Auster Group		
G-APKY	Hiller UH-12B	673	PH-NFL	4. 3.58	D.A.George	Sywell	7. 5.74S
					(Sloane Helicopters Ltd) (Stored 5.96)		
G-APLG	Auster J/5L Aiglet Trainer	3148		4. 3.58	G.R.W.Brown	Dumfries	26.10.68
					(On rebuild by Solway Aviation.Society for static display; cancelled by CAA 11.2.99)		
G-APLO	DHC.1 Chipmunk 22A	C1/0144	EI-AHU	1. 5.58	Lindholme Aircraft Ltd	Jersey	17. 9.00T
			WB696		(As "WD379/K" in Cambridge UAS c/s)		
G-APLU	DH.82A Tiger Moth	85094	VR-AAY	2. 4.58	R.A.Bishop & M.E.Vaisey	Rush Green	14. 8.01
			F-OBKK/G-APLU/T6825				
G-APMB*	DH.106 Comet 4B	6422		15. 4.58	Gatwick Handling Ltd	Gatwick	18. 5.79
					(Training airframe 8.98)		
G-APMH	Auster J/1U Workmaster	3502	F-OBOA	15. 4.58	J.L.Thorogood	Insch	19. 5.01
			G-APMH				
G-APML	Douglas C-47B-1DK Dakota 6	14175/25620	KJ836	17. 3.58	Dak Holdings Ltd	Coventry	27. 7.84T
			43-48359		(Op Air Atlantique)		
G-APMX	DH.82A Tiger Moth	85645	DE715	9. 5.58	G.A.Broughton	Popham	21.10.02
G-APMY*	PA-23-160 Apache	23-1258	EI-AJT	15. 5.58	W.Fern	Home Farm, Firbeck	1.11.81
					(On loan to South Yorkshire Aviation Museum)		
G-APNJ*	Cessna 310	35335	EI-AJY	2. 6.58	Northbrook College	Shoreham	28.11.74
			N3635D		(Instructional Airframe)		
G-APNS	Garland-Bianchi Linnet	001		17. 6.58	Paul Penn-Sayers Model Services Ltd (Stored 6.95)		
	(Continental C90)				Scaynes Hill, Haywards Heath		6.10.78S
G-APNT	Bellamy Currie Wot	HAC/3		18. 6.58	J.W.Salter "Airymouse"	Newtownards	28. 4.00P
	(Continental PC60) (Regd with c/n P.6,399)						
G-APNZ	Rollason-Druine D.31 Turbulent			17. 4.58	J.Knight	Hailsham	13.12.95P
	(Ardem 4C02)	PFA/482			(Damaged River Rother nr Iden 3.9.95: on rebuild)		
G-APOD	Tipsy Belfair	536	(OO-TIF)	16. 7.58	L.F.Potts	Dundee	23. 8.88P
	(Walter Mikron 2)				(Stored 2.98)		
G-APOI	Saunders-Roe Skeeter Srs.8	S2/5081		29. 7.58	Maj.F.F.Chamberlain	Otley, Ipswich	2. 8.00
G-APOL	Druine D.31 Turbulent	PFA/439		31. 7.58	A.Gregori & S.Tinker	Charterhall	18. 6.94P
	(Ardem 4C02)				(Damaged Charterhall 24.7.93; stored 8.99)		
G-APPA	DHC.1 Chipmunk 22	C1/0792	N5073E	11. 9.58	D.M.Squires	Wellesbourne Mountford	14. 7.85
			G-APPA/WP917		(On rebuild 7.97)		
G-APPL	Percival P.40 Prentice 1	PAC/013	VR189	7.10.58	Susan J.Saggers	Biggin Hill	11. 9.00
G-APPM	DHC.1 Chipmunk 22	C1/0159	WB711	14.10.58	Freston Aviation Ltd	Crowfield	22. 7.02
					(As "WB711")		
G-APPN	DH.82A Tiger Moth	83839	T7328	17.10.58	E.G.Waite-Roberts	(Basingstoke)	9. 6.65A
					(Crashed Mendlesham 14.7.64; rebuild provenance unconfirmed; on rebuild 6.96)		
G-APRF	Auster Alpha 5	3412	VR-LAF	8.12.58	W.B.Bateson	Blackpool	14.11.00
			G-APRF				
G-APRJ	Avro 694 Lincoln B.2	-	RF342	29.12.58	Aces High Ltd	North Weald	
			G-36-3/G-29-1/G-APRJ/RF342 (As "G-29-1")				
G-APRL*	AW.650 Argosy Srs.101	6652	N890U	2. 1.59	Midland Air Museum	Coventry	23. 3.87T
			N602Z/N6507R/G-APRL (Elan c/s) "Edna"				
G-APRO*	Auster 6		WJ370	21. 1.59	(To N370WJ 5.84: as "G-APRO" Massachusetts, USA 1999)		
G-APRR	CZL Super Aero 45 Srs.04	04-014	OK-KFQ	5. 1.59	R.H.Jowett	Ronaldsway	16. 2.96
G-APRS	Scottish Avn Twin Pioneer 3	561	G-BCWF	9. 1.59	Bravo Aviation Ltd (Op Atlantic Air Transport Ltd)		
			XT610/G-APRS/(PI-C430) (In ETPS c/s)			Coventry	1. 7.00T
G-APRT	Taylor JT.1 Monoplane	PFA/537		15. 1.59	D.A.Slater	Redhill	8. 4.02P
	(Ardem 4C02)						
G-APSA	Douglas DC-6A	45497	4W-ABQ	12. 2.59	Atlantic Air Transport Ltd	Coventry	11. 4.02T
			HZ-ADA/G-APSA/CF-MCK (Op by Air Atlantique)				
G-APSO	DH.104 Dove 5	04505	(N1046T)	16. 2.59	Cormack (Aircraft Services) Ltd		
			G-APSO		(On rebuild 1.00)	Cumbernauld	8. 7.78T
G-APSR	Auster J/1U Workmaster	3499	OO-HXA	22. 4.59	D & K Aero Services Ltd (Op P. De Liens)		
			G-APSR/VP-JCD/G-APSR/(F-OBHR)			Temploux, Belgium	30. 9.02A
G-APSY*	Bensen B-7Mc	JH/001 & 2		25. 2.59	J.Howell	Copthorne, Sussex	
					(Crashed Biggin Hill 19.9.59; stored)		

Regn	Type	C/n	P/I	Date	Owner/operator	Probable Base	CA Expy
G-APSZ*	Cessna 172	46472	N6372E	21. 5.59	Not known	Ronaldsway	4. 6.84
					(Damaged Barton 2.3.84; stored 4.91)		
G-APTP	PA-22-150 Tri-Pacer	22-5009	EI-AJN	20. 3.59	Comunica Industries International Ltd		
	(Modified to PA-20 Pacer configuration)					Roughay Farm, Bishops Waltham	20. 7.00
					(Damaged Roughay Farm 15.7.99)		
G-APTR	Auster Alpha	3392		15. 4.59	C.J. & D.J.Baker	Carr Farm, Newark	11. 4.87
					(Complete 4.98)		
G-APTU	Auster Alpha 5	3413		20. 4.59	A.J. & J.M.Davis	Sywell	8. 6.98
					t/a G-APTU Flying Group		
G-APTW*	Westland WS-51/2 Widgeon	WA/H/150		27. 4.59	North East Aircraft Museum	Usworth	26. 9.75
					(On display 5.97)		
G-APTY	Beechcraft G35 Bonanza	D-4789	EI-AJG	4. 6.59	G.E.Brennand	Blackpool	23. 1.99
G-APTZ	Rollason-Druine D.31 Turbulent	PFA/508		18. 3.59	Tiger Club (1990) Ltd	Headcorn	11. 5.00P
	(VW1600)						
G-APUD*	Bensen B-7Mc	1		11. 5.59	The Aeroplane Collection Ltd	Manchester	27. 9.60
					(On loan to Manchester Museum of Science & Industry)		
G-APUE	Orlican L-40 Meta-Sokol	150708	OK-NMB	2. 6.59	S.E. & M.J.Aherne	Top Farm, Royston	13. 5.00
G-APUK*	Auster 5 J/1 Autocrat	1843	5N-ADW	16. 6.59	P.L.Morley	(Yateley)	8.10.75
			VR-NDJ/G-APUK/D-EGEG/SE-ARA		(Stored 1995)		
G-APUP*	Sopwith Pup rep	B.5292 & PFA/1582	N5182	13. 2.59	RAF Museum	Hendon	28. 6.78
	(Le Rhone)				(Allocated 9213M 1994; as "N5182")		
G-APUR	PA-22-160 Tri-Pacer	22-6711		3. 7.59	L F Miller	(Dublin)	20. 8.01
G-APUW	Auster J/5V Srs.160 Autocar	3273		23. 6.59	E.A.J.Hibbard, D.Ball, P.L.Buckley & R.A.Partridge		
					t/a The Anglia Auster Syndicate		
						Hill Farm, Nayland	22. 5.00
G-APUY	Druine D.31 Turbulent	PFA/509		24. 6.59	C.Jones	(Stockport)	10. 6.86P
	(VW1300)				(On rebuild 1995; wings at Barton 12.97)		
G-APUZ	PA-24-250 Comanche	24-1094	N6000P	3. 7.59	R.R. & A.L.Stadie	Blackbushe	1.12.00
G-APVF	Putzer Elster B	006	D-EEQX	29.12.83	A.J.Robinson	Breighton	1. 7.98P
	(Continental O-200-A)		97+04/D-EJUH		(As "97+04" in Luftwaffe c/s)		
G-APVG	Auster J/5L Aiglet Trainer	3306	(ZK-BQW)	10. 7.59	R.Farrer	Cranfield	20. 3.00
G-APVN	Druine D.31 Turbulent	PFA/511		24. 7.59	R.Sherwin	Swanborough Farm, Lewes	24. 6.94P
	(VW1600)				(Stored 3.97)		
G-APVS	Cessna 170B	26156	N2512C	7. 8.59	N.Simpson "Stormin' Norman"	East Kirkby	23. 6.00
G-APVU	Orlican L-40 Meta-Sokol	150706	OK-NMI	21. 8.59	S.A. & M.J.Aherne	(St.Albans)	27. 6.79
					(Damaged Manchester 12.9.78; on rebuild 1993)		
G-APVV*	Mooney M.20A	1474	N8164E	30. 7.59	Newark Air Museum	Winthorpe	19. 9.81
					(Crashed at Barton 11.1.81; stored 4.97)		
G-APVZ	Rollason-Druine D.31 Turbulent			23. 7.59	I.D.Daniels	Maypole Farm, Chislet	1. 8.00P
	(Ardem 4C02)	PFA/545					
G-APWA	HPR.7 Dart Herald 100	149	PP-SDM	28. 9.59	Museum of Berkshire Aviation/The Herald Society		
			G-APWA/PP-SDM/PP-ASV/G-APWA (BEA c/s)			Woodley	6. 4.82T
G-APWJ*	HPR.7 Dart Herald 201	158		28. 9.59	Duxford Aviation Society	Duxford	21.12.85
					(Air UK c/s)		
G-APWL	EoN AP.10 460 Srs.1A	EoN/S/001	BGA.1172	2. 9.59	D.G.Andrew	Eaglescott	
			G-APWL/RAFGSA.268/G-APWL				
G-APWN*	Westland WS-55 Whirlwind 3	WA.298	VR-BER	8. 9.59	The Midland Air Museum	Coventry	17. 5.78
			G-APWN/5N-AGI/G-APWN (Bristow Helicopters c/s) "Skerries"				
G-APWP	Druine D.31 Turbulent	PFA/497		14. 9.59	C.F.Rogers	(Wheathamstead)	27. 6.67
					(Status uncertain)		
G-APWU*	Thurston Tawney Owl	TA.1		23. 9.59	Thurston Engineering Ltd	Stondon Massey	
					(Damaged Stapleford 22.4.60; stored for possible rebuild)		
G-APWY	Piaggio P.166	362		16.12.59	The Science Museum	Wroughton	14. 3.81
G-APWZ	Lancashire Aircraft EP-9 Prospector	42		5.11.59	G.B.Pearce	Washington, West Sussex	8. 6.01
					t/a Prospector Flying Group		
G-APXJ	PA-24-250 Comanche	24-291	VR-NDA	11.12.59	T.Wildsmith	Gamstom	15.11.02
G-APXR	PA-22-160 Tri-Pacer	22-7172		29. 1.60	A.Troughton	Armagh Field, Woodview	25.10.01
G-APXT	PA-22-150 Tri-Pacer	22-3854	N4545A	16. 2.60	J.W. & I.Daniels	Ashford, Middx	5. 7.87T
					(Damaged Southend 26.12.85 & on rebuild to PA-20 Pacer configuration)		
G-APXU	PA-22-150 Tri-Pacer	22-474	N1723A	10. 2.60	K.Hassell	Perth	20. 2.85
					"The Cloth Bomber" (On rebuild 6.98)		
G-APXW*	Lancashire Aircraft EP-9 Prospector	43		22.12.59	Museum of Army Flying	AAC Middle Wallop	22. 5.76
					(Composite rebuild from G-APWZ and others; as "XM819" in Army c/s)		
G-APXX*	DHA.3 Drover 2	5014	VH-EAS	15.12.59	Second World War Acft Preservation Society		
			VH-EAZ		(As "VH-FDT")	Lasham	
G-APXY	Cessna 150	17711	N7911E	15. 1.60	The Merlin Flying Club Ltd	Hucknall	24. 3.02T
G-APXZ*	Knight Twister	BKT-001 & PFA/1307		7. 1.60	N.H.Ponsford	Breighton	
					(Identity unconfirmed; incomplete frame stored 4.96)		
G-APYB	Tipsy T.66 Nipper 3	T66/S/39		28. 1.60	B.O.Smith	Yearby	12. 6.96P
	(VW1834)				(On rebuild 9.98)		

Regn	Type	C/n	P/I	Date	Owner/operator	Probable Base	CA Expy
G-APYD*	DH.106 Comet 4B	6438	SX-DAL G-APYD	21. 1.60	The Science Museum (Dan-Air c/s)	Wroughton	3. 8.79T
G-APYG	DHC.1 Chipmunk 22	C1/0060	OH-HCB WB619	11.11.60	E.J.I.Musty & P.A.Colman	White Waltham	14. 6.01
G-APYI	PA-22-135 Tri-Pacer	22-2218	N8031C	8. 2.60	B.T. & J.Cullen	Ballyboy, Co.Meath	26. 3.99
	(Modified to PA-20 Pacer configuration)						
G-APYN	PA-22-160 Tri-Pacer	22-6797	N2804Z	24. 2.60	S.J.Raw	Morgansfield, Fishburn	21. 6.02
G-APYT	Champion 7FC Tri-Traveler	7FC-387		9. 5.60	B.J.Anning	Watchford Farm, Yarcombe	20. 6.00P
G-APYU*	Champion 7FC Tri-Traveler	7FC-388		12. 5.60	R.W.Brown Clothall Farm, Clothall Common		6. 8.72
					(Crashed Old Warden 23.4.72; stored 5.96)		
G-APZJ	PA-18-150 Super Cub	18-7233		29. 1.60	R.Jones t/a Southern Sailplanes Membury		18.11.99
	(Rebuilt 1986 after accident 12.6.83 using un-identified new fuselage frame; original frame in open store Membury 1989)						
G-APZL	PA-22-160 Tri-Pacer	22-7054	EI-ALF	27. 1.60	R.T.Evans	Bristol	18.11.99
G-APZR*	Cessna 150	17861	N6461T	31. 3.60	Avtech Ltd	Biggin Hill	4. 4.81
	(Damaged Biggin Hill 14.1.81; front fuselage only used as engine test-bed 2.95)						
G-APZS	Cessna 175A	56677	N7977T	31. 3.60	G.A.Nash	Ham Street, Yeovilton	15. 8.95
	(Lycoming O-360)						
G-APZX	PA-22-150 Tri-Pacer	22-5181	N7420D	28. 4.60	Applied Signs Ltd	Tatenhill	10. 6.00
	(Modified to PA-20 Pacer configuration)						

G-ARAA – G-ARZZ

Regn	Type	C/n	P/I	Date	Owner/operator	Probable Base	CA Expy
G-ARAD	Phoenix Luton LA-5A Major PAL/1204 & PFA/836			29. 4.60	D.J.Bone & P.L.Jobes (Guisborough/Sunderland)		
	(Completed but not flown; stored Lennox Plunton, Borgue 3.94)						
G-ARAI	PA-22-160 Tri-Pacer	22-7421		17. 5.60	T.Richards & G.C.Winters	Oxenhope	17. 9.01
G-ARAM	PA-18-150 Super Cub	18-7312		17. 5.60	Fairmont Investments Ltd	Clacton	22. 6.02T
G-ARAN	PA-18-150 Super Cub	18-7307		28. 4.60	A.P.Docherty	Redhill	8. 6.01
G-ARAO	PA-18-95 Super Cub	18-7327		17. 5.60	R.G.Manton	(Great Missenden)	2. 4.01
	(As "607327/L/09" in USAAC c/s)						
G-ARAP*	Champion 7EC Traveler	7FC-394		12. 9.60	J.McGonagal	(Londonderry)	26. 6.82P
	(Damaged Eglinton 22. 9.81; on rebuild 12.92)						
G-ARAS	Champion 7FC Tri-Traveler	7FC-396		12. 9.60	G.J.Taylor t/a Alpha Sierra Flying Group	(Uttoxeter)	22. 6.00P
G-ARAT	Cessna 180C	50827	N9327T	18. 5.60	S.Peck	Eaglescott	19. 5.00
G-ARAU*	Cessna 150	17894	N6494T	29. 4.60	Colton Aviation Ltd	Little Staughton	14. 9.84T
	(Stored unmarked 9.96)						
G-ARAW	Cessna 182C Skylane	52843	N8943T	18. 5.60	M.& E.N.Ford	(Horsham)	1. 6.02T
G-ARAX	PA-22-150 Tri-Pacer	22-3830	N4523A	22. 4.60	P.J.Fahie	Old Sarum	14. 4.02
G-ARAY*	Avro 748 Srs.1A/200	1535	OY-DFV	21. 4.60	Not known	Lasham	16. 6.90T
	G-11/G-ARAY/PI-C784/G-ARAY/VP-LIO/G-ARAY/PP-VJQ/G-ARAY/YV-C-AMC/G-ARAY (WFU 10.89; fuselage Fire Services 12.95)						
G-ARAZ	DH.82A Tiger Moth	82867	R4959	25. 3.60	D.A.Porter Griffins Farm, Temple Bruer		13. 5.01
	(As "R4959/59" in RAF c/s)						
G-ARBC*	Cessna 310D	39234	N6934T	5. 9.60	Air Service Training Ltd	Perth	25. 6.77
	(On fire dump 12.95)						
G-ARBE	DH.104 Dove 8	04517		6. 5.60	M.Whale & M.W.A.Lunn	Kemble	3.10.02
G-ARBG	Tipsy T.66 Nipper 2	ABAC.1 & 57		11. 5.60	J.Horovitz & J.McLeod	Felthorpe	17. 8.84P
	(VW 1834)				t/a The Felthorpe Tipsy Group (Damaged Felthorpe 6.5.84; on rebuild 5.91)		
G-ARBH*	DH.104 Dove 1	04196	XY-ABS	14. 7.60	Not known (Stored 11.88) Zaragoza, Spain		5. 8.75
	(An unmarked Dove noted displayed within Malaga Airport Terminal 24.3.96 - is this the same ?)						
G-ARBM	Auster 5 J/1B Aiglet	2792	EI-AMO G-ARBM/VP-SZZ/VP-KKR	8. 6.60	B.V.Nabbs & C.Chaddock 	Scotland Farm, Hook	16. 4.00
G-ARBN*	PA-23-160 Apache	23-1385	EI-AKI (N3421P)	1. 6.60	Busy Bee Aviation Ltd	Sibson	25. 8.86T
	(Damaged Sibson 8.86; fuselage stored 9.99)						
G-ARBO	PA-24-250 Comanche	24-2117		15. 6.60	C.Matthews	(Guernsey)	27. 5.84
	(Damaged Morecambe Bay 27.4.83)						
G-ARBP	Tipsy T.66S Nipper 2	54		7. 6.60	F.W.Kirk	Seighford	21. 6.00P
	(VW1834)						
G-ARBS	PA-22-160 Tri-Pacer	22-6858	N2868Z	24. 8.60	S.D.Rowell "Greta" Valley Farm, Winwick		2.12.01
	(Modified to PA-20 Pacer configuration)						
G-ARBV	PA-22-160 Tri-Pacer	22-5836	N8633D	29. 6.60	E R O'Hara	Oaksey Park	2. 7.00
	(Rebuilt 1983/84 using fuselage of G-ARDP c/n 22-4254)				t/a G-ARBV Oaksey Pacers Group		
G-ARBZ	Rollason-Druine D.31 Turbulent	PFA/ 553		6. 5.60	G Richards & R Bishop	Headcorn	15.10.99P
	(Ardem 4C02)				(Damaged East Mersea, Essex 17.7.99; remains noted 10.99)		
G-ARCC	PA-22-150 Tri-Pacer	22-4006	N4853A	23. 6.60	A.S.Cowan t/a Popham Flying Group G-ARCC	Popham	11. 4.00
G-ARCF	PA-22-150 Tri-Pacer	22-4563	N5902D	28. 6.60	B.Southerland	East Winch	2. 5.99
G-ARCI*	Cessna 310D	39266	N6966T	21.10.60	Not known	Blackpool	25. 4.84
	(Damaged Sandtoft 22.8.86; open store 9.99)						

Regn	Type	C/n	P/I	Date	Owner/operator	Probable Base	CA Expy
G-ARCS	Auster D.6 Srs.180	3703		4. 7.60	E.A.Matty (Status uncertain) (Bewdley)		9. 8.93
G-ARCT	PA-18-95 Super Cub	18-7375	EI-AVE	6. 7.60	K.A.Kirk & C.M.Goodwin		
			G-ARCT			Dunnyvadden, Ballymena	21. 4.86
					(Damaged Mullaghmore 29.3.87; stored 1996)		
G-ARCV	Cessna 175A Skylark	56757	N8057T	7.11.60	R.Francis & C.Campbell	Sandtoft	6. 7.02
	(Continental O-300D)						
G-ARCW*	PA-23-160 Apache (Mod)	23-796	N2187P	7. 7.60	Not known Water Leisure Park, Skegness		8. 7.93
					(On rebuild 8.99)		
G-ARCX*	Armstrong-Whitworth Meteor NF.14	WM261		8. 9.60	Royal Museum of Scotland/Museum of Flight		
		AW.2163				East Fortune	20. 2.69S
G-ARDB	PA-24-250 Comanche	24-2166	PH-RON	15. 8.60	A.Scrase, C.Phelps & G.W.Simpson Booker		3. 4.01
			G-ARDB/N7019P		t/a Delta Bravo Acft Associates		
G-ARDD	Scintex CP.301C-1 Emeraude	549		4. 7.60	R.M.Shipp	Full Sutton	29. 6.98P
	(Rebuilt EMK Aeroplanes with c/n EMK.004)						
G-ARDE	DH.104 Dove 6	04469	I-TONY	15.11.60	T.E.Evans	Wellesbourne Mountford	25. 8.91
					"Sir Geoffrey de Havilland" (Stored 6.98)		
G-ARDG*	Lancashire Acft EP-9 Prospector 2	47		14. 7.60	G.Pearce/Museum of Army Flying		
	(Stored 7.93 with parts from G-APWZ & G-APXW)					Durrington, W.Sussex	
G-ARDJ	Auster D.6 Srs.180	3704		15. 7.60	R.E.Neal t/a RN Aviation (Leicester Airport)		
	(Damaged nr Leicester 30.5.86; on rebuild 5.98)					Leicester	7. 7.88T
G-ARDK*	Aero Commander 560F	560F-992-6		9. 1.61	Not known	Lisbon Airport	8.10.69
					(Regn CS-AJL NTU 10.72; open storage 3.95)		
G-ARDO	Jodel D.112	146	F-PBTE	22. 8.60	W.R.Prescott	Kilkeel, Co.Down	24.10.00P
	(Composite inc fuse G-AYEO [684] ex F-BIGG) F-BBTE/F-WBTE						
G-ARDS	PA-22-150 Caribbean	22-7154	N3214Z	4. 9.60	A.C.Donaldson & C.I.Lavery	Newtownards	31. 3.01
G-ARDT	PA-22-160 Tri-Pacer	22-6210	N9158D	15. 9.60	M.Henderson	Cheyne Farm	29. 6.02
G-ARDV	PA-22-160 Tri-Pacer	22-7487	EI-APA	28. 7.60	R.W. Christie	(Ballymena, NI)	2. 1.99
			G-ARDV		(Damaged at Ballymena 10.7.98)		
G-ARDX*	Auster 6A Tugmaster	1905	TW524	2. 8.60	A.A.Marshall		
	(Damaged Lasham 1.1.64; frame stored 3.96)					Yeatsall Farm, Abbots Bromley	29. 8.64A
G-ARDY	Tipsy T.66 Nipper 2	55		10. 8.60	M.J.A.Trudgill	RAF Linton-on-Ouse	12.12.00P
	(VW Martlet)						
G-ARDZ	SAN Jodel D.140A Mousquetaire	49		10.11.60	M.J.Wright Cherry Tree Farm, Monewden		29.11.91
					(Stored 9.97; cancelled by CAA 26.2.99)		
G-AREA	DH.104 Dove 8	04520		3. 8.60	De Havilland Aircraft Museum Trust Ltd		
					(Stored Hatfield 9.99) Salisbury Hall, London Colney		18. 9.87
G-AREB*	Cessna 175B Skylark	56818	N8118T	29.12.60	R.J.& J.Postlethwaite & J.E.Littler NK		6. 4.91
					(In a damaged condition pre 3.90; cancelled by CAA 9.3.99)		
G-AREH	DH.82A Tiger Moth	85287	(G-APYV)	4. 7.60	N.K.Geddes	Lochwinnoch	19. 4.66
		T6746M/DE241			(On long-term rebuild 5.94)		
G-AREI	Taylorcraft Auster III	518	9M-ALB	14.12.60	P.J.Stock	Petersfield	21. 4.00
			VR-RBM/VR-SCJ/MT438	(Op Military Auster Flt as "MT438" "Akyab" in SEAC c/s)			
G-AREL	PA-22-150 Caribbean	22-7284	N3344Z	14. 9.60	H.H.Cousins t/a Fenland Aerosvcs Fenland		22. 8.98
G-AREO	PA-18-150 Super Cub	18-7407		24. 8.60	DRA (Farnborough) Gliding Club Ltd		
						DRA Farnborough	31. 8.01
G-ARET	PA-22-160 Tri-Pacer	22-7590		2. 9.60	I.S.Runnalls Church Farm, North Moreton		20. 5.83T
					(On rebuild 5.99)		
G-AREV	PA-22-160 Tri-Pacer	22-6540	N9628D	25.10.60	D.J.Ash "Smart Cat"	Barton	19.10.00
G-AREX	Aeronca 15AC Sedan	15AC-61	CF-FNM	12. 9.60	R.J.M.Turnbull & P.Lowndes		
						Rydinghurst Farm, Cranleigh	25. 6.01
G-AREZ	Rollason-Druine D.31 Turbulent			22. 9.60	J.St.Clair-Quentin	(Ledbury)	19. 9.84P
	(Ardem 4C02)	PFA/561			(Status uncertain)		
G-ARFB	PA-22-150 Caribbean	22-7518	N3625Z	8. 9.60	C.T.Woodward, R.W.Hall & T.Lawton		
						Holly Meadow Farm, Bradley	29.12.99
G-ARFD	PA-22-160 Tri-Pacer	22-7565	N3667Z	8. 9.60	J.R.Dunnett Priory Farm, Tibenham		27. 1.01
G-ARFG	Cessna 175AX Skylark	56505	N7005E	15.11.60	P.K.Blair	Stapleford	22. 1.01
	(Rebuilt to Cessna 172 standard 1988)				t/a Foxtrot Golf Group		
G-ARFH	PA-24-250 Comanche	24-2240	N7087P	13.10.60	A.B.W.Taylor	(Fakenham)	13.11.00
G-ARFI	Cessna 150A	150-59100	N41836	1. 2.61	J.H.Fisher	Haverfordwest	26. 6.00
			G-ARFI/N7000X				
G-ARFL	Cessna 175B Skylark	175-56868	N8168T	2. 2.61	D.J.Mason	Denham	16. 2.00
G-ARFO	Cessna 150A	150-59174	N7074X	23. 3.61	M A Arterton	Little Snoring	21. 4.00T
G-ARFT	SAN Jodel DR.1050 Ambassadeur	170		27.10.60	R.Shaw	(Sowerby Bridge)	13.10.84
					(Damaged Prestwick 15.6.84; status uncertain)		
G-ARFV	Tipsy T.66 Nipper 2	44		5.10.60	W.Buchan,	Perth	3. 8.00P
	(VW 1834)						
G-ARGB*	Auster 6A	2593	VF635	12.10.60	C.J.Baker	Carr Farm, Newark	21. 6.74
					(Frame stored 4.98)		
G-ARGG	DHC.1 Chipmunk 22	C1/0247	WD305	19.10.60	B.Hook (As "WD305")	Coventry	21. 4.96
G-ARGI*	Auster 6A	2299	VF530	8.12.60	Not known	(Yorkshire)	4. 7.76
					(Bare frame Carr Farm 4.98 but status not known 1999)		

Regn	Type	C/n	P/I	Date	Owner/operator	Probable Base	CA Expy
G-ARGO	PA-22-108 Colt	22-8034		18. 1.61	M.J.Speakman	(Brigg)	27. 6.02
G-ARGV	PA-18-180 Super Cub	18-7559	N10F	20.12.60	Deeside Gliding Club (Aberdeenshire) Ltd		
					(Damaged Aboyne 23.8.96)	Aboyne	15. 3.02
G-ARGY	PA-22-160 Tri-Pacer	22-7620	G-JEST	20.12.60	G.K.Hare	Fenland	7.12.02
	(Modified to PA-20 configuration)		G-ARGY		(On rebuild 7.95)		
G-ARGZ	Rollason-Druine D.31 Turbulent			7.11.60	The Tiger Club (1990) Ltd	Headcorn	3.10.00P
	(VW 1600)	PFA/562					
G-ARHB	Forney F-1A Aircoupe	5733		17. 4.61	A.V.Rash & D.R.Wickes	Earls Colne	7.11.02
					t/a Aircoupe Hotel Bravo		
G-ARHC	Forney F-1A Aircoupe	5734		26. 5.61	A.P.Gardner	Little Gransden	28. 5.01
G-ARHF*	Forney F-1A Aircoupe	5737		26. 5.61	Not known (Stored 5.99)	Swanton Morley	10. 5.94
G-ARHI	PA-24-180 Comanche	24-2260		20.12.60	D.D.Smith	(Norwich)	31. 5.00
G-ARHL	PA-23-250 Aztec	27-402		3. 3.61	C.J.Freeman (On overhaul 1.96)	Headcorn	23.11.79
G-ARHM	Auster 6A	2515	VF557	5. 1.61	D.Hollowell, R.L.Wharmby & P.H.Hollowell		
						Finmere	9.12.01
G-ARHN	PA-22-150 Caribbean	22-7514	N3622Z	10. 1.61	D.B.Furniss & A.Munro	Gamston	1.10.99
	(Rebuilt with parts of G-ATXB - DBR 26.8.74)						
G-ARHP	PA-22-160 Tri-Pacer	22-7549	N3652Z	10. 1.61	R.N.Morgan		
					Boones Farm, High Garrett, Braintree		22. 5.00
G-ARHR	PA-22-150 Caribbean	22-7576	N3707Z	10. 1.61	A.R.Wyatt	Fowlmere	26.10.01
G-ARHW	DH.104 Dove 8	04512		10. 1.61	Pacelink Ltd	Fairoaks	5. 8.00
G-ARHX*	DH.104 Dove 8	04513		11. 1.61	North East Aircraft Museum	Usworth	8. 9.78
G-ARHZ	Rollason-Druine D.62A Condor			13.12.60	T.J.Goodwin	Hill Farm, Nayland	26. 7.95P
	(Continental O-200-A) PFA/247 & RAE/602				(Damaged Damyns Hall, Upminster 4.9.94)		
G-ARID	Cessna 172B Skyhawk	172-48209	N7709X	2. 2.61	L.M.Edwards	Sleap	14. 6.00
G-ARIE	PA-24-250 Comanche	24-1888	ZS-CNL	25. 5.61	R.C.Nichols t/a G-ARIE Group	Stapleford	21.12.01
G-ARIF	Ord-Hume O-H 7 Minor Coupe			22. 8.60	N.H.Ponsford	Wigan	
	(Modified Luton LA-4C Minor) O-H 7 & PAL/1401				(Stored incomplete 3.96)		
G-ARIH	Auster 6A	2463	TW591	23. 1.61	R.Tarder & J.J.Fisher t/a India Hotel Group		
		(As "TW591" in 664 (AOP) Sqdn c/s) Yeatsall Farm, Abbots Bromley						14. 6.01
G-ARIK	PA-22-150 Caribbean	22-7570	N3701Z	26. 1.61	C.J.Berry	Booker	26. 3.00
G-ARIL	PA-22-150 Caribbean	22-7574	N3705Z	26. 1.61	K.Knight	(Malvern)	21.12.01
G-ARIM	Druine D.31 Turbulent	PFA/510		27. 2.61	R M.White	Bishopton	
G-ARJB	DH.104 Dove 8	04518		29. 9.60	Cormack (Aircraft Services) Ltd		
					(Stored 3.99)	Cumbernauld	10.12.73T
G-ARJC	PA-22-108 Colt	22-8154		21. 3.61	F.W.H.Dulies (On rebuild)	(Stroud, Glos)	28.11.75
G-ARJE	PA-22-108 Colt	22-8184		29. 3.61	Touchdown Aviation Ltd	(Macclesfield)	29. 4.73
					(On rebuild 1993)		
G-ARJF*	PA-22-108 Colt	22-8199		23. 3.61	Not known	Stockton, Warminster	9. 2.80
					(On rebuild 6.93)		
G-ARJH	PA-22-108 Colt	22-8249		29. 3.61	A.Vine	Goodwood	7. 8.00
G-ARJR*	PA-23-160 Apache G	23-1966	N4447P	1. 3.61	Oxford Air Training School	Oxford	24.10.78
					(Instructional airframe 5.95)		
G-ARJS	PA-23-160 Apache G	23-1977		3. 3.61	Bencray Ltd	Blackpool	17.10.00T
					t/a Blackpool & Fylde Aero Club (Op Blackpool Air Charter)		
G-ARJT	PA-23-160 Apache G	23-1981		3. 3.61	Hiveland Ltd		
						Water Leisure Park, Skegness	29. 1.01T
G-ARJU	PA-23-160 Apache G	23-1984		3. 3.61	G.R.Manley	Andrewsfield	1. 8.99T
G-ARJV	PA-23-160 Apache G	23-1985		3. 3.61	Metham Aviation Ltd	Blackbushe	11.11.01
G-ARJZ	Rollason-Druine D.31 Turbulent			8. 2.61	C.J.Tilson	Great Massingham	4. 9.95P
	(VW1700)	PFA/564			(Stored 2.99)		
G-ARKG	Auster J/5G Cirrus Autocar	3061	AP-AHJ	22. 2.61	G.C.Milborrow	Spanhoe	18. 4.01
			VP-KKN				
G-ARKJ	Beechcraft N35 Bonanza	D-6736		5. 5.61	T.Cust	Sandtoft	2. 6.01
G-ARKK	PA-22-108 Colt	22-8290		12. 4.61	The Rochford Hundred Flying Group Ltd		
						Southend	9. 9.97
G-ARKM	PA-22-108 Colt	22-8313		12. 4.61	B.J.Thorogood	(Braintree)	14. 3.02
G-ARKN	PA-22-108 Colt	22-8327	N10F	9. 5.61	N.Rawlinson & J.M.Lilley	(Leek)	21. 7.02
G-ARKP	PA-22-108 Colt	22-8364		19. 5.61	C.J.& J.Freeman	Headcorn	27. 6.82T
					(On overhaul 4.96)		
G-ARKR	PA-22-108 Colt	22-8376		9. 5.61	Barbara J.M.Montegut	Booker	7. 5.02
G-ARKS	PA-22-108 Colt	22-8422		7. 6.61	R.A.Nesbitt-Dufort		
	(Lycoming O-320)					Bradleys Lawn, Heathfield	18.10.01
G-ARLG	Auster D.4/108	3606		4. 4.61	R.D.Helliar-Symons	Scotland Farm, Hook	8. 4.00P
					t/a Auster D4 Group		
G-ARLK	PA-24-250 Comanche	24-2433	EI-ALW	25. 5.61	Gibad Aviation Ltd	Stapleford	2. 4.02
			G-ARLK/N10F				
G-ARLO*	Beagle A.61 Terrier 1	2500	TW642	11. 4.61	S.C.Challis	Hedge End, Southampton	3.11.79
					t/a British Classic Aircraft Restorations		
	(Damaged off Shoreham 10.7.79; stored 3.96 for rebuild as Auster AOP.6)						

Regn	Type	C/n	P/I	Date	Owner/operator	Probable Base	CA Expy
G-ARLP	Beagle A.61 Terrier 1	3724(1)	VX123	11. 4.61	D.R.Whitby	(Fakenham)	31.10.91
					t/a Gemini Flying Group		
	(C/n officially quoted as 2573/VF631 which became G-ARLM(2)/G-ASDK; damaged Truleigh Farm, Edburton 4.8.91;						
	on rebuild 1992)						
G-ARLR	Beagle A.61 Terrier 2	3721 & B.601	VW996	11. 4.61	M. Palfreman	Bagby	9. 9.01
G-ARLU*	Cessna 172B	172-48502	N8002X	14. 6.61	Irish Air Corps	Baldonnel	6.10.78
					(Damaged 30.10.77; instructional airframe 8.93)		
G-ARLW	Cessna 172B Skyhawk	172-48499	N7999X	15. 6.61	South Lancashire Flyers Ltd	Barton	21. 3.91
					(Damaged Barton 20.2.90; open store 1.96; cancelled by CAA 21.1.99)		
G-ARLX	SAN Jodel D.140B Mousquetaire II	66		12. 4.61	M.J.Dunkerly	(Ouessant, France)	21. 6.01T
G-ARLY*	Auster J/5P Autocar	3271		14. 4.61	P.J.Elliott & G.Green	Not known	6. 6.71
	(On rebuild to D.6/180 standard using parts from Airedale/G-ARNR & J/5R/G-APAA wings;						
	sold in Switzerland 12.87; cancelled by CAA 25.2.99)						
G-ARLZ	Rollason-Druine D.31A Turbulent			7. 4.61	W.J.Hitchcock & R.J.K.Blech	Coventry	17. 8.99P
	(Ardem 4C02)	RAE/578			t/a Turb Group		
G-ARMA	PA-23-160 Apache G	23-1967	N4448P	8. 5.61	C J Hopewell	Sibson	22. 7.77
					(To Sibson 8.99 for restoration by Busy Bee Aviation)		
G-ARMB	DHC.1 Chipmunk 22A	C1/0099	WB660	26. 4.61	P.A.Layzell	Bunns Bank, Norfolk	20. 5.02
	(Fuselage No.DHB/F/25)				(As "WB660")		
G-ARMC	DHC.1 Chipmunk 22A	C1/0151	WB703	26. 4.61	J.T.H.Henderson	White Waltham	7. 6.02
					(As "WB703" in RAF c/s)		
G-ARMD	DHC.1 Chipmunk 22A	C1/0237	WD297	26. 4.61	D M Squires	Wellesbourne Mountford	
G-ARMF	DHC.1 Chipmunk 22A	C1/0394	WG322	26. 4.61	D.M.Squires	Wellesbourne Mountford	12.10.98
					(As "WZ868/H")		
G-ARMG	DHC.1 Chipmunk 22A	C1/0575	WK558	26. 4.61	A.D.Cook	Bidford	16.12.00
	(Fuselage No.DHB/F/460)				t/a The MG Group		
G-ARML	Cessna 175B Skylark	175-56995	N8295T	12. 7.61	R.W.Boote	RAF Lyneham	31. 3.02
G-ARMN	Cessna 175B Skylark	175-56994	N8294T	18. 8.61	G.A.Nash	Lower Wasing Farm, Brimpton	22. 5.02
G-ARMO	Cessna 172B Skyhawk	172-48560	N8060X	12. 6.61	G.M.Jones	Little Staughton	21. 3.02
G-ARMR	Cessna 172B Skyhawk	172-48566	N8066X	12. 6.61	Sunsaver Ltd	Barton	29. 7.00
G-ARMX*	Avro 748 Srs 1A/101	1538	VP-LVN	28. 4.61	Manchester Airport Fire Training Services		
			G-ARMX		(Fuselage on fire dump 4.97)	Manchester	18. 3.84T
G-ARMZ	Rollason-Druine D.31 Turbulent			2. 5.61	J.Mickleburgh & D.Clark	Headcorn	12.10.00P
	(VW1500)	PFA/565					
G-ARNA*	Mooney M.20B Mark 21	1806		26. 6.61	Not known	Casablanca-Anfa, Morocco	14. 8.81
					(Stored 3.94)		
G-ARNB	Auster J/5G Cirrus Autocar	3169	AP-AHL	18. 5.61	R.F.Tolhurst	Lenham, Maidstone	19. 2.77
			VP-KNL		(Status uncertain: possibly on rebuild 1995)		
G-ARND	PA-22-108 Colt	22-8484		6. 6.61	E.J.Clarke	Seighford	4. 8.99
G-ARNE	PA-22-108 Colt	22-8502		15. 6.61	T.D.L.Bowden	Knettishall	20. 4.01
G-ARNG	PA-22-108 Colt	22-8547		26. 6.61	S.S.Delwarte (On rebuild 8.97)	Shoreham	12.10.73
G-ARNH*	PA-22-108 Colt	22-8558		5. 9.61	Fenland & West Norfolk Aero Club Presvation Society		
	(Crashed 1.9.72; fuselage on rebuild 4.96) West Walton, Wisbech						20. 3.73
G-ARNI	PA-22-108 Colt	22-8575		26. 7.61	B.A.Drury	Rochester	15. 6.98T
G-ARNJ	PA-22-108 Colt	22-8587		3. 8.61	R.A.Keech	Woodvale	16. 1.00
G-ARNK	PA-22-108 Colt	22-8622		5. 9.61	N.G. & A.N.M.McDonald	RAF Coltishall	12.12.01
	(Modified to PA-20 configuration with Lycoming O-320 as "Super Colt")						
G-ARNL	PA-22-108 Colt	22-8625		3. 8.61	Miss J.A.Dodsworth	White Waltham	24. 7.00
G-ARNN	Globe GC-1B Swift	1272	VP-YMJ	11. 5.61	K.E.Sword	(Leicester)	11. 7.74
			VP-RDA/ZS-BMX/NC3279K (Crashed Hucknall 1.9.73: status unknown)				
G-ARNO*	Beagle A.61 Terrier 1	3722	VX113	8. 5.61	R.Webber	Hayrish Farm, Okehampton	19. 6.81
					(On rebuild 7.97)		
G-ARNP	Beagle A.109 Airedale	B.503		10. 5.61	S.T. & M.Isbister	Elstree/North Weald	13. 3.00
	(Original c/n A109-P1)						
G-ARNR*	Beagle A.109 Airedale	B.504		10. 5.61	Not known	Carr Farm, Newark	
	(Original c/n A109-P2)			(Cancelled as WFU 12.7.63: rear fuselage 4.98- remains expired 1999)			
G-ARNY	SAN Jodel D.117	595	F-BHXQ	13. 6.61	P.Jenkins	Inverness	15. 3.00P
G-ARNZ	Rollason-Druine D.31 Turbulent			28. 6.61	The Tiger Club (1990) Ltd	Headcorn	14. 9.00P
	(VW 1600)	PFA/579					
G-AROA	Cessna 172B Skyhawk	172-48628	N8128X	19. 9.61	D.E.Partridge	Rayne Hall Farm, Rayne	30. 7.00T
					t/a The D & P Group		
G-AROC	Cessna 175BX Skylark	175-56997	G-OTOW	2.10.61	A.J.Symms	High Ham	17.12.99
	(Modified to 172 configuration)		G-AROC/N8297T				
G-AROJ*	Beagle A.109 Airedale	B.508	HB-EUC	17. 5.61	C.J.Baker	Carr Farm, Newark	8. 1.76
			G-AROJ		(Dismantled 4.98)		
G-ARON	PA-22-108 Colt	22-8822		23.11.61	R.W.Curtis	(Warminster)	5. 7.01
G-AROO	Forney F.1A Aircoupe	5750	N25B	3.11.61	W.J.McMeekan	Newtownards	7. 6.01
G-AROW	SAN Jodel D.140B Mousquetaire II	71		13. 9.61	Mousquetaire Ltd	Redhill	9. 7.00T
G-AROY	Boeing-Stearman A75N1(PT-17) Kaydet	N56418	6. 6.61	W.A.Jordan	Little Gransden	12. 4.00
	(P&W R985)	75-4775	42-16612				

Regn	Type	C/n	P/I	Date	Owner/operator	Probable Base	CA Expy
G-ARPH*	DH.121 Trident 1C	2108		13. 4.61	RAF Museum (British Airways c/s)	RAF Cosford	8. 9.82
G-ARPK*	DH.121 Trident 1C	2111		13. 4.61	Manchester Airport Fire Sve	Manchester	17. 5.82
G-ARPO*	DH.121 Trident 1C	2116		13. 4.61	CAA Intnl Fire Training Centre	Teesside	12. 1.86
G-ARPP*	DH.121 Trident 1C	2117		13. 4.61	BAA Airport Fire Service	Glasgow	16. 2.86
G-ARPZ*	DH.121 Trident 1C	2128		13. 4.61	RFD Ltd (Escape systems test airframe)	Dunsfold	26. 1.86
G-ARRD	SAN Jodel DR.1051 Ambassadeur	274		20. 7.61	C.M.Fitton Watchford Farm, Yarcombe		28.11.00P
G-ARRE	SAN Jodel DR.1050 Ambassadeur	275		20. 7.61	A.Luty & M.P.Edwards	Barton	21. 4.02
G-ARRG*	Cessna 175B Skylark	175-56999	N8299T	5.10.61	Not known Little Staughton (Damaged Great Yarmouth 3.11.70; stored unmarked 4.99)		4. 5.73
G-ARRL	Auster 5 J/1N Alpha	2115	VP-KFK VP-KPF/VP-KFK/VP-UAK	13. 6.61	G.N.Smith & C.Webb	Headcorn	1. 7.99
G-ARRM*	Beagle B.206X	B.001		23. 6.61	Bristol Aero Collection (Stored 8.99)	Kemble	23.12.64S
G-ARRS	Menavia Piel CP.301A Emeraude	226	F-BIMA	29. 6.61	Julia P.Drake & N.W.Cawley Sturgate t/a ARSSY Aviation		7. 6.00P
G-ARRT	Wallis WA-116/Mc (McC 4318A)	2		28. 6.61	K.H.Wallis Reymerston Hall (Stored 5.99)		26. 5.83P
G-ARRU	Druine D.31 Turbulent (VW 1600)	PFA/502		28. 6.61	N.A.Morgan & J.Paget (Damaged Lamberhurst, Kent 8.7.96) Stoneacre Farm, Farthing Corner		27. 2.97P
G-ARRX	Auster 6A	2281	VF512	4. 7.61	J.E.D.Mackie "Peggy Too" Popham (As "VF512/PF-M" in 43 OTU c/s)		7. 6.00
G-ARRY	SAN Jodel D.140B Mousquetaire II	72		13. 9.61	Fictionview Ltd	Lichfield	25.10.01
G-ARRZ	Rollason-Druine D.31 Turbulent (Ardem 4C02)	PFA/580		21. 8.61	C.I.Jefferson "Tarzan" Hingham, Norfolk (Damaged Horley, Surrey 21.7.90; on rebuild 9.97)		21.12.90P
G-ARSB*	Cessna 150A	150-59337	N7237X	25. 9.61	Not known Little Staughton (Open storage 4.99)		10. 6.88
G-ARSG	Roe Triplane Type IV rep (ADC Cirrus III) (Also c/n TRI.1)	HAC.1	(BAPC1)	29.10.81	The Shuttleworth Trust Old Warden (No external marks)		2. 5.00P
G-ARSJ	Scintex CP.301C-2 Emeraude	581		28. 7.61	R.J.Lewis Garston Farm, Marshfield (On overhaul 6.96)		2. 7.93P
G-ARSL	Beagle A.61 Terrier 2	2539	VF581	13. 7.61	D.J.Colclough Hayrish Farm, Okehampton (As "VF581") (On rebuild 7.97)		30. 9.85A
G-ARSU	PA-22-108 Colt	22-8835	EI-AMI G-ARSU	23.11.61	D.P.Owen	Thruxton	15. 5.00
G-ARSW	PA-22-108 Colt	22-8858		23.11.61	M.J.Kirk t/a Entire Flying Group Cardiff		30. 1.97
G-ARSX	PA-22-160 Tri-Pacer	22-6712	N2907Z	8. 8.61	S.Hutchinson Rathfriland, Co.Down		19. 5.02
G-ARTH	PA-12 Super Cruiser	12-3278	EI-ADO	22. 9.61	R.I.Souch & B.J.Dunford Hall Farm, Durley		21. 4.95P
G-ARTJ*	Bensen B.8M (VW 1600)	7		22. 9.61	S.Russell Wilkieston Farm, Cupar (Stored 6.95)		
G-ARTL	DH.82A Tiger Moth (P/i is doubtful- if correct c/n is 83795)		"T7281"	22. 9.61	Fiona G.Clacherty (As "T7281" in RAF c/s) Great Fryup, Egton, Whitby		30. 4.00
G-ARTM*	Beagle A.61 Terrier 1	3723	WE536	9.10.61	C.J.Baker Carr Farm, Newark (Crashed Priory Farm, Turvey, Beds 28.5.70; on rebuild 4.98)		13.11.71
G-ARTT	Morane MS.880B Rallye Club	8		11.12.61	R.N.Scott (On rebuild 11.96)	Blackpool	29. 5.94
G-ARTY*	Cessna 150B	150-59482	N7382X	23. 2.62	Air Service Training Ltd Perth (Instructional airframe 5.96)		6.10.68
G-ARTZ(2)	McCandless M.4	M4/1		24.10.61	W.R.Partridge (Extant 10.95) St.Merryn		13.10.69P

(VW 1500) (Two Gyrocopters may have worn these marks - the prototype M.2 (650cc Triumph) is on display and un-marked)at the Ulster Folk & Transport Museum, Dublin

Regn	Type	C/n	P/I	Date	Owner/operator	Probable Base	CA Expy
G-ARUG	Auster J/5G Cirrus Autocar	3272		2. 1.62	D.P.H.Hulme	Biggin Hill	2. 3.00
G-ARUH	SAN Jodel DR.1050 Ambassadeur	284		5.12.61	B.A.H.LeGrange & R.C.Laverick Denham t/a PFA Flying Group No.272 (Stored 3.89)		4. 7.88
G-ARUI	Beagle A.61 Terrier 1	2529	VF571	9. 3.62	T.W.J.Dann	Southend	28.10.01
G-ARUL	LeVier Cosmic Wind (Continental O-200-A) (Rebuilt 1973 as c/n PFA/1511)	103	N22C	28.11.61	P.G.Kynsey "Ballerina" Duxford (Contains little of original as fuselage, wings & data plate for original held elsewhere)		4. 7.00P
G-ARUO	PA-24-180 Comanche	24-2427	N7251P	16. 1.62	J.B.W.Dore White Waltham t/a The Uniform Oscar Group		22. 8.00
G-ARUR*	PA-28-160 Cherokee	28-133		16. 1.62	M.Jarrett Crowland (Damaged nr Redhill 14.9.92; fuselage stored 8.97)		12.10.92
G-ARUV	Piel CP.301 Emeraude Srs. 1 (Continental C90)	PFA/700		2. 2.62	S.T. & J.A.Smoothy "Emma"	Langar	26.10.00P
G-ARUY	Auster J/1N Alpha	3394		2. 2.62	D Burnham	(Chelmsford)	7. 7.02
G-ARUZ	Cessna 175C Skylark	175-57080	N8380T	23. 2.62	S.R.Page & M.Lowe Cardiff t/a Cardiff Skylark Group		25. 3.00
G-ARVF*	Vickers VC-10-1101	808		16. 1.63	Flugausstellung L & P Junior Museum Hermeskeil, Germany		23.7.81

Regn	Type	C/n	P/I	Date	Owner/operator	Probable Base	CA Expy
G-ARVM*	Vickers VC-10-1101	815		16. 1.63	RAF Museum	RAF Cosford	5. 8.80
					(British Airways c/s)		
G-ARVN*	Servotec Rotorcraft Grasshopper 1 1			16. 2.63	E.D.Ap Rees	Weston-super-Mare	18. 5.63
					t/a The Helicopter Museum (Stored 8.97)		
		(Two airframes identified as G-ARVN; the other stored by J.Wilkie at Blackpool)					
G-ARVO	PA-18-95 Super Cub	18-7252	D-ENFI N3376Z	18. 1.83	Northamptonshire School of Flying Ltd.	Sywell	19.11.01T
G-ARVT	PA-28-160 Cherokee	28-379		21. 3.62	Red Rose Aviation Ltd	Liverpool	27. 4.01
G-ARVU	PA-28-160 Cherokee	28-410	PH-ONY G-ARVU	30. 3.62	P.F.G.Simms,J.Lamb & P.Barrett	Barton	9. 3.01
					t/a G-ARVU Flying Group		
G-ARVV	PA-28-160 Cherokee	28-451		11. 7.62	G.E.Hopkins	Shobdon	26.10.00
G-ARVZ	Rollason-Druine D.62B Condor	RAE/606		6.12.61	J.D.Jewitt	(Selby)	5. 5.00
G-ARWB	DHC.1 Chipmunk 22A	C1/0621	WK611	2. 1.62	P.G.Alston	Thruxton	29. 6.02
					t/a Thruxton Chipmunk Flying Group (As "WK611")		
G-ARWH*	Cessna 172C Skyhawk	172-49166	N1466Y	18. 4.62	Not known (Stored for spares 5.99) Stoneacre Farm, Farthing Corner		28. 4.86
G-ARWO	Cessna 172C Skyhawk	172-49187	N1487Y	10. 4.62	J.P.Stafford	Ashcroft Farm, Winsford	12.11.99
G-ARWR	Cessna 172C Skyhawk	172-49172	N1472Y	13. 4.62	M.McCann	Insch	18. 3.01
					t/a Devanha Flying Group		
G-ARWS	Cessna 175C Skylark	175-57102	N8502X	12. 4.62	B.A.I.Torrington	(Swansea)	28. 8.01
G-ARXC*	Beagle A.109 Airedale	B.510	EI-ATD G-ARXC	9. 4.62	C.J.Baker	Carr Farm, Newark	27. 6.76
					(Fuselage on rebuild 4.98)		
G-ARXD	Beagle A.109 Airedale	B.511		9. 4.62	D.Howden (Stored 6.95)	Banchory	13. 6.86
G-ARXG	PA-24-250 Comanche	24-3154		21. 2.62	R.F.Corstin	Fairoaks	13. 6.02
					t/a Fairoaks Comanche		
G-ARXH	Bell 47G	40	N120B NC120B	13. 2.62	A.B.Searle	Parklands, Northampton	6. 7.90
G-ARXN*	Cobelavia Tipsy T.66 Nipper 2	77		3. 7.62	I.Wood & C.E.Pickton	Hucknall	19. 8.80P
	(VW 1800)				t/a The Griffon Flying Group (Stored 5.96)		
G-ARXP	Phoenix Luton LA-4A Minor			23. 2.62	E.Evans	Bensons Farm, Laindon	17.10.95P
	(Walter Mikron 3) PAL/1119 & PFA/816				(Fuselage stored 7.99)		
G-ARXT	SAN Jodel DR.1050 Ambassadeur	355		14. 3.62	M.F.Coy	Wellesbourne Mountford	8.11.01
					t/a CJM Flying Group		
G-ARXU	Auster 6A	2295	VF526	5. 3.62	E.C.Tait & M.Pocock	AAC Middle Wallop	12. 9.02
					(As "VF526/T" in Army c/s)		
G-ARXW	Morane MS.885 Super Rallye	100		30. 3.62	A.F.Danton & A.Kennedy	Dunnamanagh, Londonderry	4. 5.01
G-ARYB*	DH.125 Srs.1	25002		1. 3.62	Midland Air Museum	Coventry	22. 1.68
G-ARYC*	DH.125 Srs.1	25003		1. 3.62	De Havilland Aircraft Museum (On rebuild 3.96) Salisbury Hall, London Colney		1. 8.73
G-ARYD*	Auster AOP.6	-	WJ358	8. 3.62	The Museum of Army Flying	AAC Middle Wallop	
					(As "WJ358")		
G-ARYF	PA-23-250 Aztec B	27-2065		11. 4.62	I.J.T.Branson	Biggin Hill	18. 6.99
G-ARYH	PA-22-160 Tri-Pacer	22-7039	N3102Z	9. 3.62	C.Watt	Crosland Moor	12. 5.02
G-ARYI	Cessna 172C	172-49260	N1560Y	13. 7.62	Joyce Rhodes	Blackburn	24. 7.00T
G-ARYK	Cessna 172C	172-49288	N1588Y	13. 7.62	G.W.Goodban	(Canterbury)	3. 7.00
G-ARYR	PA-28-180 Cherokee B	28-770		12. 7.62	R.P.Synge & C.S.Wilkinson	Turweston	27. 6.00
					t/a GARYR Flying Group		
G-ARYS	Cessna 172C Skyhawk	172-49291	N1591Y	13. 7.62	D.J.Squires, C.J & J.Hill	Coventry	13. 8.00
G-ARYV	PA-24-250 Comanche	24-2516	N7337P	17. 4.62	A.G.Wintle & D.C.Hanss	Elstree	10. 6.02
G-ARYZ	Beagle A.109 Airedale	B.512		9. 4.62	S.Barker t/a Rutland Aviation	Spanhoe	16.11.97
G-ARZB	Beagle-Wallis WA-116 Srs.1 Agile (McCulloch 4318A)	B.203	XR943 G-ARZB	18. 4.62	K.H.Wallis (Stored 5.99) Reymerston Hall	RAF Newton	29. 6.93P
					(Another Wallis owned by D.Worrall t/a James Bond Collectors Club, is displayed as "G-ARZB" in Planet Hollywood, Leicester Square, London, provenance unidentified)		
G-ARZD*	Cessna 172C	172-49389	N1689Y	22. 6.62	V.H.Bellamy	St.Just	23.10.77
					(Crashed St.Marys 28.5.77; stored 11.93)		
G-ARZE*	Cessna 172C	172-49388	N1688Y	22. 6.62	The Black Knights Parachute Centre	Bank End Farm, Cockerham	16. 3.77
		(Damaged Brawdy 11.9.76; training airframe 3.95)					
G-ARZN	Beechcraft N.35 Bonanza	D-6795	N215DM	23. 5.62	D.W.Mickleburgh	RAF Newton	25. 5.01
G-ARZW	Phoenix Currie Wot	1 & HAC/5		25. 5.62	B.R.Pearson	Eaglescott	7. 1.89P
	(Walter Mikron 3)				(Damaged nr Headcorn 12.2.88; on rebuild 9.99 as Pfalz D.VII scale rep)		
G-ARZX*	Cessna 150B	150-59642	N1242Y	13. 7.62	I.B.Osborn t/a Gate Flyers	Manston	5. 9.99
		(Damaged at Manston; sold by insurers & reduced to spares Caterham: cancelled by CAA 16.9.98)					

G-ASAA – G-ASZZ

Regn	Type	C/n	P/I	Date	Owner/operator	Probable Base	CA Expy
G-ASAA	Phoenix Luton LA-4A Minor (JAP J.99)	O-H/4		19. 4.62	J.W.Cudby	Netherthorpe	10. 2.00P

Regn	Type	C/n	P/I	Date	Owner/operator	Probable Base	CA Expy
G-ASAI	Beagle A.109 Airedale	B.516		26. 6.62	K.R. & R.I. & P.Howden	Banchory	20. 5.77S
					(On rebuild 6.95)		
G-ASAJ	Beagle A.61 Terrier 2	B.605	WE569	26. 6.62	R.Skingley	Bassingbourn	19. 8.01
	(Initially allocated c/n 3732)				t/a G-ASAJ Flying Group		
					(Op Military Auster Flt as Auster T.7 "WE569")		
G-ASAK	Beagle A.61 Terrier 2	B.604	WE591	26. 6.62	J.H.Oakins	Biggin Hill	8. 6.02
					(As "WE591/Y")		
G-ASAL(2)	Scottish Avn Bulldog Srs.120/124		(G-BBHF)	5. 9.73	Pioneer Flying Co Ltd	Prestwick	12. 5.00P
		BH120/239	G-31-17				
G-ASAN	Beagle A.61 Terrier 2	B.608	VX928	26. 6.62	R.J.Bentley	Haverfordwest	28. 6.96
					(On rebuild 4.97)		
G-ASAT	Morane MS.880B Rallye Club	178		21. 6.62	M.Cutovic	Croft Farm, Defford	8. 7.00
G-ASAU	Morane MS.880B Rallye Club	179		21. 6.62	T.C. & R.Edwards	Sibson	24. 4.00
G-ASAX	Beagle A.61 Terrier 2	B.609	TW533	12. 6.62	P.G. & F.M.Morris "The Jacobite Air Force"		1. 9.96
	(Converted from Auster 6 c/n 1911)				Cheyne Farm, Netherley, Aberdeen		
G-ASAZ	Hiller UH-12E-4	2070	N5372V	18. 6.62	Pan Air Ltd	Gamlingay	18.12.97T
					(Stored 4.99: as "XS165/37" in 705 Sqdn RN c/s)		
G-ASBA	Phoenix Currie Wot	AE.1 & PFA/3005		16. 8.62	M.A.Kaye	Presteigne	20. 9.94P
	(Continental C90)						
G-ASBB	Beechcraft 23 Musketeer	M-15		21. 6.62	E.J.Hammond	Cambridge	18.12.00
					t/a Five Musketeers Flying Group		
G-ASBH	Beagle A.109 Airedale	B.519		26. 6.62	D.T.Smollett		
						Bratton Clovelly, Okehampton	19. 2.99
G-ASBU*	Beagle A.61 Terrier 2		WE570	12. 7.62	G.Strathdee	Netherley, Aberdeen	5. 7.82
		3733(1) & B.613			(Damaged Netherley 12.8.80: stored for spares 12.95)		
G-ASBY	Beagle A.109 Airedale	B.523		23. 7.62	R.K.Wilson	Lydd	22.3.80
G-ASCC	Beagle E.3 Mk.11	B.701	(G-25-12)	23. 7.62	P.T.Bolton	South Lodge Farm, Widmerpool	16. 6.00P
			XP254		(As "XP254")		
G-ASCD*	Beagle A.61 Terrier 2	B.615	PH-SFT	23. 7.62	Yorkshire Air Museum	Elvington	26. 9.71
			G-ASCD/VW993		(As "TJ704/JA" in Royal Navy c/s)		
G-ASCM	Isaacs Fury II	PFA/2002/1B & 1		1. 8.62	M.M.Ward	(Hamburg)	16. 6.98P
	(Lycoming O-290) (PFA c/n is probably the builder's membership no.) (As "K2050" in pre-war RAF c/s)						
G-ASCT*	Bensen B.7Mc	DC.3		14. 8.62	The Helicopter Museum	Weston-super-Mare	11.11.66P
	(McCulloch 4318E)				(Stored dismantled 8.97)		
G-ASCU	PA-18A-150 Super Cub	18-6797	VP-JBL	31. 8.62	Farm Aviation Services Ltd	Stapleford	13. 9.02
G-ASCZ	Menavia Piel CP.301A Emeraude	233	F-BIMG	1.10.62	P.Johnson	Goodwood	18.10.99P
G-ASDA*	Beechcraft 65-80 Queen Air	LD-64		2.10.62	Biggin Hill Airport Fire Service		
					(Front section only)	Biggin Hill	8.11.79
G-ASDB*	Rollason-Druine D.31 Turbulent			23. 8.62	C.I.Jefferson	Hingham, Norfolk	11. 9.68P
	(Ardem 4C02)	PFA/1600			(Crashed Shoreham 11.8.68: stored 9.97)		
G-ASDF*	Edwards Helicopter	NAFE.1		17.10.62	J.Parkin	RAF Innsworth	
	(Modified Adams-Wilson Hobbycopter)				t/a Computair Consultants		
	(Originally regd as an Edwards Gyrocopter: based upon a Bensen B.8M c/n 9 registered as G-ARUN to the same initial owner (N.A.F.Edwards, Gillingham, Kent: cancelled 3.10.63 as PWFU: on long term rebuild 10.99)						
G-ASDK	Beagle A.61 Terrier 2	B.702	G-ARLM(2)	26.10.62	M.L.Rose	Sywell	5. 8.99
	(Converted from Auster AOP.6 c/n 2573)		G-ARLP(1)/VF631				
G-ASDL	Beagle A.61 Terrier 2	B.703	G-ARLN(2)	26.10.62	C.E.Mason	Marsh Hill Farm, Aylesbury	30. 5.00
	(Also c/ns 3727(1) & B.632(1))		WE558				
G-ASDO*	Beechcraft 95-A55 Baron	TC-401		5.11.62	RAF Northolt Fire Service	RAF Northolt	16. 4.83
G-ASDY	Beagle-Wallis WA-116/F	B.205	XR944	9.11.62	K.H.Wallis	Reymerston Hall	28.10.97P
	(Franklin 2A-120-B)		(G-ARZC(1))		(Noted 5.99)		
G-ASEA	Phoenix Luton LA-4A Minor	PAL/1154		14.11.62	J.Bradstock	RAF Wyton	16. 8.89P
	(JAP J.99) (Regd with c/n PFA/1154: c/n also quoted as PFA/1319 which is EAA Biplane G-AYFY)						
					(Damaged Mendlesham 8.4.89: wings at Waits Farm, Belchamp Walter 5/93: on rebuild 1.97)		
G-ASEB	Phoenix Luton LA-4A Minor	PAL/1149		26.11.62	S.R.P.Harper	Movenis, Co.Londonderry	29.10.82P
	(Lycoming O-145)				(On overhaul 4.96)		
G-ASEE*	Auster Alpha	3359	I-AGRI	1. 2.63	R.Harper	Spanhoe	1. 6.74S
					(Damaged RAE Bedford 9.2.74: stored 8.92)		
G-ASEF*	Auster 6A	-	VW985	17.12.62	Not known	RAF Bicester	19.12.66
					(Damaged Bicester 1966: stored 11.92)		
G-ASEG	Beagle A.61 Terrier 1	2506	VF548	17.12.62	M.J.Kirk	Llantwit Major	16. 7.98
					(As "VF548": damaged Haverfordwest 3.99)		
G-ASEO	PA-24-250 Comanche	24-3367	(G-ASDX)	23. 1.63	Eagle European Airways Ltd	Goodwood	21. 3.99
					(Op Osprey Aviation)		
G-ASEP	PA-23-235 Apache	27-541		28. 1.63	Air Warren Ltd	Denham	14.11.99
G-ASER*	PA-23-250 Aztec B	27-2283		28. 1.63	Not known	Smeeth, Kent	17. 8.74
					(Crashed Nigg Bay, Aberdeen 14.9.72: for recreational purposes 2.97)		
G-ASEU	Rollason-Druine D.62A Condor	RAE/607		12. 2.63	W.M.Grant	Inverness	19. 3.98P
G-ASFA	Cessna 172D Skyhawk	172-50182	N2582U	21. 2.63	D.Halfpenny	Maypole Farm,Chislet	3.11.00
G-ASFD	LET L-200A Morava	170808	OK-PHH	26. 2.63	M.Emery (Stored 7.95)	Guildford	12. 7.84T
G-ASFK	Auster J/5G Cirrus Autocar	3276		7. 3.63	T.D.G.Lancaster	Elmsett	20. 5.00

Regn	Type	C/n	P/I	Date	Owner/operator	Probable Base	CA Expy
G-ASFL	PA-28-180 Cherokee B	28-1170		7. 3.63	J.Simpson & D.Kennedy Lee-on-Solent		18.12.00
G-ASFR	Bolkow Bo.208C Junior	522	D-EGMO	12. 3.63	S.T.Dauncey (Stored 9.98) Yearby		29. 3.90P
G-ASFX	Druine D.31 Turbulent (VW1600)	PFA/513		18. 3.63	E.F.Clapham & W.B.S.Dobie Oldbury-on-Severn		8. 7.00P
G-ASGC*	BAC Super VC-10 Srs.1151	853		11. 4.63	Duxford Aviation Society Duxford (BOAC c/s)		20. 4.80
G-ASHD*	Brantly B.2A	314		2. 4.63	The Helicopter Museum Weston-super-Mare		5. 6.67
					(Crashed off Brightlingsea, Essex 19.2.67; components stored 5.97)		
G-ASHH*	PA-23-250 Aztec	27-63	N455SL N4557P	25. 3.63	Not known Sibson (Stored 5.98)		27. 9.85
G-ASHS	SNCAN Stampe SV-4C (G) (Gipsy Major)	265	F-BCFN	23. 4.63	Three Point Flying Ltd Rochester		25. 5.02T
	(Original fuselage used for spares in rebuild of G-AWEF 1980; rebuilt 1984 using fuselage of G-AZIR c/n 452 ex F-BCXR)						
G-ASHT	Rollason-Druine D.31 Turbulent (VW1600)	PFA/1610		23. 4.63	C.W.N.Huke RAF Coltishall		7.11.00P
G-ASHU	PA-15 Vagabond (Rotax 912UL)	15-46	N4164H NC4164H	1. 5.63	G.J.Romanes & T.J.Ventham Little Bredy "Calybe"		13. 7.00P
G-ASHV*	PA-23-250 Aztec B	27-2347	(N5281Y)	1. 5.63	Alderney Airport Fire Service Alderney (On fire dump 1.00)		22. 7.85T
G-ASHX	PA-28-180 Cherokee B	28-1266		3. 5.63	Powertheme Ltd Barton		29. 4.02
G-ASIB	Reims Cessna F.172D Skyhawk (Wichita c/n 50091)	0006	F-WLIR	9. 5.63	R.G.Jones & D.A.Smart RAF Mona t/a G-ASIB Flying Group		24. 2.01
G-ASII	PA-28-180 Cherokee B	28-1264		21. 5.63	T.R.Hart & Natocars Ltd Exeter		13. 6.01
G-ASIJ	PA-28-180 Cherokee B	28-1333		21. 5.63	G.R.Moore t/a G-ASIJ Group Andrewsfield		29.10.00T
G-ASIL	PA-28-180 Cherokee B	28-1350		21. 5.63	J.Dickenson & C.D.Powell Leicester		14. 6.01
G-ASIP*	Auster 6A	2549	VF608	22. 5.63	Cotswold Acft Restoration Group Kemble (Damaged Nympsfield 7.5.73; stored 6.97)		19. 7.73
G-ASIT	Cessna 180	32567	N7670A	24. 5.63	A. & P.A.Wood Audley End		8.12.00
G-ASIY	PA-25-235 Pawnee (Four blade propeller)	25-2446		30. 5.63	T.Holloway RAF Bicester t/a RAFGSA		18. 1.02
G-ASJL	Beechcraft H35 Bonanza	D-5132	N5582D	14. 6.63	R.H.B.Malim Shobdon		14. 6.02
G-ASJO	Beechcraft 23 Musketeer	M-518		18. 6.63	K A Boon t/a G-ASJO Syndicate Sandown		12. 2.01
G-ASJV	VS 361 Spitfire LF.IXB	CBAF.IX.552	OO-ARA	3. 7.63	Merlin Aviation Ltd Duxford		1. 5.99P
	Belgian AF SM-41/Fokker B-13/R Neth H-68/H-105/MH434						
	(Op by The Old Flying Machine Co; as "MH434/PK-K" in 316 Sqdn c/s)						
G-ASJY	Gardan GY-80-160 Horizon	13		9. 7.63	P.D.Bradbury & S.M.Derbyshire Bagby		24. 3.02
G-ASJZ	SAN Jodel D.117A	826	F-BITD	5. 7.63	W.J.Siertsema Church Farm, North Moreton		5. 5.00P
G-ASKC*	DH.98 Mosquito TT.35	TA719		8. 7.63	Imperial War Museum - Skyfame Collection (As "TA719") Duxford		18. 1.64S
G-ASKJ	Beagle A.61 Terrier 1	3730	(EI-AMC) VX926	16. 7.63	C.C.Irvine (Congleton)		7. 2.85
					(WFU following u/c collapse Redhill 20.6.84; on rebuild Gamlingay 1.96; to be restored in T.7 configuration as "VX926" in 664 Sqdn c/s)		
G-ASKK*	HPR.7 Dart Herald 211	161	PP-ASU G-ASKK/PI-C910/CF-MCK	17. 7.63	City of Norwich Aviation Museum Norwich		19. 5.85T
G-ASKL	SAN Jodel 150 Mascaret	27		18. 7.63	J.M.Graty Nuthampstead		18. 6.00P
G-ASKP	DH.82A Tiger Moth	3889	N6588	22. 7.63	The Tiger Club (1990) Ltd Headcorn		3. 3.00T
G-ASKT	PA-28-180 Cherokee B	28-1410		24. 7.63	A.A.Mattacks Biggin Hill		10. 9.02
G-ASKV	PA-25-235 Pawnee	25-2272	9Q-CHV G-ASKV/ST-ACW/G-ASKV/ST-ACF/G-ASKV/N6700Z	31. 7.63	Southdown Gliding Club Ltd Parham Park		22. 3.02
G-ASLH	Cessna 182F Skylane	182-54905	N3505U	19. 8.63	J.M.Powell & J.A.Horton Framlingham		22. 6.01T
G-ASLK	PA-25-235 Pawnee	25-2370	9Q-CFK G-ASLK/ST-ADT/G-ASLK/N6801Z	20. 8.63	Bristol Gliding Club (Pty) Ltd Nympsfield		14. 1.00
G-ASLL*	Cessna 336 Skymaster	336-0074	N1774Z	23. 8.63	Not known Farley Farm, Winchester (Fuselage cabin stored 3.92)		6. 1.74
G-ASLP*	Bensen B.7	11		3. 9.63	R Light & T Smith Stockport (Dismantled 2.99)		
G-ASLV	PA-28-235 Cherokee	28-10048		11. 9.63	I.L.Harding Sackville Farm, Riseley t/a Sackville Flying Group		13.12.98
G-ASLX	Menavia Piel CP.301A Emeraude	292	F-BISV	12. 9.63	D.Wallace Coonagh, Ireland		10. 2.02P
G-ASMA	PA-30-160 Twin Comanche (Modified to C/R status)	30-143		17. 9.63	A.J.Mew & M.F.Oliver White Waltham t/a Mike Alpha Group "Double Trouble"		5. 1.00
G-ASMC*	Hunting-Percival P.56 Provost T.1	PAC/F/417	XF908	19. 9.63	Not known Moenchengladbach, Germany (Stored 5.86)		14. 2.72S
G-ASME	Bensen B.8M (Arrow GT500R)	12		24. 9.63	R.M.Harris & R.T.Bennett Melrose Farm, Melbourne		11.12.00P
G-ASMF	Beechcraft D95A Travel Air	TD-565		26. 9.63	M.J.A.Hornblower Southend		3.10.02T
G-ASMJ	Reims Cessna F.172E (Wichita c/n 50584)	0029		25.10.63	A.J.G.Crawshaw Sherburn in Elmet		20. 5.01T
G-ASML	Phoenix Luton LA-4A Minor (VW1600)	PAL/1148 & PFA/802		28.10.63	D.Leggett Fenland t/a Fenland Strut Flying Group		20.12.99P

Regn	Type	C/n	P/I	Date	Owner/operator	Probable Base	CA Expy
G-ASMM	Rollason-Druine D.31 Turbulent			31.10.63	W.J. Browning	Redhill	10. 8.00P
	(Ardem 4C02)	PFA/1611			"Mouche Miel"		
G-ASMO*	PA-23-160 Apache G	23-1995	5N-AAU	30.10.63	Not known	Wallington Green	14. 7.99T
			5N-ADB/(N4473P)		(Stored 7.96)		
G-ASMS	Cessna 150A	150-59204	N7104X	18.11.63	P.P.Connor	Barton	3.11.00
G-ASMT	Fairtravel Linnet 2	004		20.11.63	A.F.Cashin	Maypole Farm, Chislet	27. 7.00P
G-ASMU*	Cessna 150D	150-60252	N4252U	26.11.63	Not known	(Moss-Side, Manchester)	3.11.85T
					(Damaged in gales Barton 13.2.89; on rebuild 1991)		
G-ASMV	Scintex CP.1310-C3 Super Emeraude			22.11.63	P.F.D.Waltham	Leicester	7.11.94
		919			(Stored 10.97)		
G-ASMW	Cessna 150D	150-60247	N4247U	26.11.63	Yorkshire Light Aircraft Ltd		
						Leeds-Bradford	4. 9.97T
G-ASMY	PA-23-160 Apache H	23-2032	N4309Y	3.12.63	R.D. & E.Forster	Swanton Morley	25.11.95T
					(Stored 5.99)		
G-ASMZ	Beagle A.61 Terrier 2	B.629	G-35-11	4.12.63	R.C.Burden	Bagby	20. 2.00
	(Conversion of Auster AOP.10 c/n 2285)		VF516		(As "VF516")		
G-ASNB	Auster 6A Tugmaster	3725(2)	VX118	6.12.63	S.Alexander	Bidford/Bickmarsh	14. 1.02
					(As "VX118")		
G-ASNC	Beagle D.5/180 Husky	3678		9.12.63	E.Brooks & R.Sharman	Crowland	16. 9.00
					t/a Peterborough & Spalding Gliding Club		
G-ASND	PA-23-250 Aztec	27-134	N4800P	10.12.63	J.R.Grange	Shoreham	23. 7.00T
G-ASNF	Ercoupe 415CD	4754	PH-NCF	11.12.63	C.R.Weldon	Dublin	2. 7.73
			NC94647				
	(Crashed Bodmin 15.6.73; on rebuild 1993 with major parts from OO-JPB c/n 4777)						
G-ASNG*	DH.104 Dove 6	04485	(EI-BJW)	16.12.63	Not known (On fire dump 8.93)	Waterford	18.11.80P
			G-ASNG/HB-LFF/G-ASNG/HB-LFF/G-ASNG/PH-IOM				
G-ASNI	Scintex CP.1310-C3 Super Emeraude			20.12.63	D.Chapman	Wickenby	22.12.02
		925					
G-ASNK	Cessna 205	205-0400	N8400Z	27.12.63	Justgold Ltd	Blackpool	18. 7.99T
					(Op Blackpool Air Centre)		
G-ASNN*	Cessna 182F Skylane	182-55012	N3612U	27.12.63	Manchester Free-Fall Parachute Club		
						Tilstock	3. 5.85
	(Damaged nr Whitchurch, Shropshire 5.1.85; para-trainer use 5.97)						
G-ASNU*	HS.125 Srs.1	25005	D-COMA	9. 1.64	Not known	Lagos, Nigeria	5. 1.84
			(D-CFKG)/G-ASNU		(Impounded at Lagos over ownership dispute)		
G-ASNW	Reims Cessna F.172E	0031		13. 1.64	B.M.Tremain	Draycott Farm, Chiseldon	5. 4.01
	(Wichita c/n 50613)				t/a G-ASNW Group		
G-ASNY*	Campbell-Bensen B.8M	RCA/203		15. 1.64	R Light & T.Smith	Stockport	16. 3.70P
	(McCulloch 4318A)				(On rebuild 2.99)		
G-ASOC	Auster 6A Tugmaster	2544	VF603	21. 1.64	R.J.McCarthy	Ashburn, Staffs	20.12.97
					t/a Auster 6 Group		
G-ASOH	Beechcraft 95-B55A Baron	TC-656		31. 1.64	G.S.Goodsir t/a GMD Group	Biggin Hill	18. 5.02
G-ASOI	Beagle A.61 Terrier 2	B.627	G-35-11	31. 1.64	N.K. & C.M.Geddes t/a Ranfurly Flying Group		
			WJ404		South Barnbeth Farm, Bridge of Weir		19. 6.98
G-ASOK	Reims Cessna F.172E	0057		31. 1.64	D.W.Disney	Egginton	6. 9.02
G-ASOL*	Bell 47D-1	4	N146B	31. 1.64	The Helicopter Museum	Weston-super-Mare	6. 9.71
					(Stored 8.97)		
G-ASOM	Beagle A.61 Terrier 2	B.622	G-JETS	3. 2.64	S.J.Tootell	Booker	15. 3.02
			G-ASOM/G-35-11/VF505				
G-ASON*	PA-30-160 Twin Comanche	30-312	(N7273Y)	4. 2.64	Not known (On rebuild 3.99)	Elstree	30.11.91T
G-ASOX	Cessna 205A	205-0556	N4856U	13. 2.64	A.Turnbull	Bournemouth	1. 8.92
					(On rebuild with Airtime/GT Aviation 1.99)		
G-ASPF	Jodel-Wassmer D.120 Paris-Nice	02	F-BFNP	26. 2.64	T.J.Bates	Dairy House Farm, Nantwich	19. 6.00P
G-ASPI	Reims Cessna F.172E	0050		26. 2.64	J.A.M.Anthony	Rochester	17. 4.00
					t/a Icarus Flying Group		
G-ASPK	PA-28-140 Cherokee	28-20051		28. 2.64	Westward Airways (Lands End) Ltd St.Just		30. 3.02T
G-ASPP	Bristol Boxkite rep BOX.1 & BM.7279		(BAPC2)	29.10.81	The Shuttleworth Trust "No.12A"		
	(Continental O-200-B)				(No external registration)	Old Warden	2. 5.99P
G-ASPS	Piper J3C-90 Cub	22809	N3571N	2. 3.64	A.J.Chalkley	Rhoshirwaun, Pwllheli	20. 5.00P
	(Frame No.21971)		NC3571N				
G-ASPU	Druine D.31 Turbulent	PFA/1623		4. 3.64	M.W.Bodger	(Burton-on-Trent)	16. 8.96P
	(VW1500)				(Damaged Hurst Green, E.Sussex 8.10.95)		
G-ASPV(2)	DH.82A Tiger Moth	84167	T7794	5. 3.64	B.S.Charters	Benson's Farm, Laindon	31. 8.97
	(Identity obscure - original G-ASPV sold to Norway 7.75 & rebuilt as LN-MAX)						
G-ASRB	Rollason-Druine D.62B Condor	RAE/608		11. 3.64	T.J.McRae & H.C.Palmer	Shoreham	1.11.98
G-ASRC	Rollason-Druine D.62C Condor	RAE/609		11. 3.64	O.R.Pluck	Monewden	15.12.99P
G-ASRH	PA-30-160 Twin Comanche	30-368		19. 3.64	Island Aviation & Travel Ltd	Chester	13. 3.99
G-ASRI*	PA-23-250 Aztec B	27-2352	N5287Y	24. 3.64	Witney Technical College	Witney	30. 8.87A
					(Instructional airframe 1.96)		
G-ASRK	Beagle A.109 Airedale	B.538		26. 3.64	R.K.Wilson	Lydd	2. 6.01

Regn	Type	C/n	P/I	Date	Owner/operator	Probable Base	CA Expy
G-ASRO	PA-30-160 Twin Comanche	30-395		31. 3.64	D.W.Blake	Halfpenny Green	27. 5.02
					t/a Five Star Flying Group		
G-ASRP*	SAN Jodel DR.1050 Ambassadeur	64	F-BITI	1. 4.64	S.Bishan	Stromness, Orkney	4.11.86
	(Ditched Swanbister Bay, Orkney 17.3.86; on rebuild 10.94; cancelled as WFU 20.1.99:						
	parts to Kingfisher G-BXBC project (qv)						
G-ASRR	Cessna 182G Skylane	182-55135	(G-CBIL)	2. 4.64	P.Ragg	(Schwaz, Austria)	5. 7.02P
			EI-ATF/G-ASRR/N3735U				
G-ASRT	SAN Jodel 150 Mascaret	45		6. 4.64	P.Turton (Status uncertain)	Welshpool	3. 6.94P
G-ASRW	PA-28-180 Cherokee B	28-1606		21. 4.64	MK Aero Support Ltd	Andrewsfield	8. 6.00T
G-ASSB*	PA-30-160 Twin Comanche	30-432		22. 4.64	Brooklands Technical College	Brooklands	11. 3.93T
					(Instructional airframe 3.94)		
G-ASSE	PA-22-108 Colt	22-9832	(N5961Z)	28. 4.64	A.Ingold	(Birmingham)	12. 6.00
					t/a G-ASSE Flying Group		
G-ASSF	Cessna 182G Skylane	182-55593	N2493R	5. 5.64	B.W.Wells	Baxterley	5. 3.01
G-ASSM*	HS.125 Srs 1/522	25010	5N-AMK	5. 5.64	The Science Museum (Flight Gallery)		
			G-ASSM			South Kensington, London	
G-ASSP	PA-30-160 Twin Comanche	30-458		7. 5.64	P.H.Tavener	Redhill	6. 1.00
G-ASSS	Cessna 172E	172-51467	N5567T	7. 5.64	D.H.N.Squires & P.R.March	Filton	27. 5.00
G-ASST	Cessna 150D	150-60630	N5930T	7. 5.64	F.R.H.Parker		
					Pear Tree Farm, Marsh Gibbon, Bicester		15. 7.01
G-ASSV	Kensinger KF	02	N23S	11. 5.64	C.I.Jefferson	Hingham, Norfolk	30. 7.69P
	(Continental C85)				(Crashed Halfpenny Green 2.7.69; on rebuild 9.97)		
G-ASSW	PA-28-140 Cherokee	28-20055		11. 5.64	W.G.R.Wunderlich	Biggin Hill	7. 5.01
G-ASSY	Druine D.31 Turbulent	PFA/586		12. 5.64	D.Silsbury	Dunkeswell	20. 4.84P
	(VW1500)						
G-ASTA	Druine D.31 Turbulent	152	F-PJGH	12. 5.64	P.A.Cooke	RAF Brize Norton	13.11.97P
	(Ardem 4C02)						
G-ASTG	Nord 1002 Pingouin II	183	F-BGKI	21. 5.64	L.M.Walton	Duxford	26.10.73S
			Fr.AF 183		(On rebuild by The Aircraft Restoration Co 1.99)		
G-ASTI	Auster 6A Tugmaster	3745	WJ359	27. 5.64	R.B.Webber	Tatenhill	21. 7.99P
					(To revert to AOP.6 c/s as "WJ359" in 1999)		
G-ASTL*	Fairey Firefly 1	F.5607	SE-BRD	1. 6.64	Imperial War Museum - Skyfame Collection		
			Z2033		"Evelyn Tentions"	Duxford	
					(As "Z2033/275/N" in 1771 Sqn RN c/s)		
G-ASTP*	Hiller UH-12C	1045	N9750C	4. 6.64	The Helicopter Museum	Weston-super-Mare	3. 7.82
					(Under restoration 8.98)		
G-ASUA*	Nord 1002 Pingouin	248	F-BFDY	23. 6.64	L.M.Walton	Long Sutton, Kings Lynn	28. 7.65
					(Crashed Elstree 30.7.64; in store)		
G-ASUB	Mooney M.20E Super 21	397	N7158U	24. 6.64	S.C.Coulbeck	North Coates	17.11.00
G-ASUD	PA-28-180 Cherokee B	28-1654		29. 6.64	S.J.Rogers & M.N.Petchey	Andrewsfield	23. 7.00
G-ASUE	Cessna 150D	150-60718	N6018T	30. 6.64	D.Huckle (Stored 6.94)	West Thurrock	1. 8.90
G-ASUG*	Beechcraft E18S-9700	BA-111	N575C	3. 7.64	Royal Museum of Scotland, Museum of Flight		
			N555CB/N24R		(Loganair c/s)	East Fortune	23. 7.75
G-ASUH*	Reims Cessna F.172E	0070		6. 7.64	Not known	Clacton	14. 4.78
					(Fuselage in open store 7.95)		
G-ASUI	Beagle A.61 Terrier 2	B.641	VF628	6. 7.64	R.J.Bentley	(Nenagh, Co Tipperary)	25.7.99
	(Conversion of Auster AOP.10 c/n 2570)						
G-ASUL	Cessna 182G Skylane	182-55077	N3677U	9. 7.64	Blackpool & Fylde Aero Club Ltd		
						Blackpool	27. 1.01
G-ASUP	Reims Cessna F.172E	0071		22. 7.64	P.T. & L.E.Trivett	Cardiff	8. 6.00
					t/a G-ASUP Air		
G-ASUR	Dornier Do.28A-1	3051	D-IBOM	28. 7.64	Not known	Thruxton	13. 4.00
G-ASUS	Jurca MJ.2E Tempete	PFA/2001		28. 7.64	D.G.Jones	Coventry	3. 8.00P
	(Continental O-200-A)						
G-ASVG	Rousseau Piel CP.301B Emeraude	109	F-BILV	7. 8.64	K.S.Woodard	Priory Farm, Tibenham	24. 5.00P
					"Emma II"		
G-ASVM	Reims Cessna F.172E	0077		11. 8.64	J.A.Furse	(Southwick)	30.12.99
					t/a Golf Victor Mike Flying Group		
G-ASVN	Cessna 206 Super Skywagon	206-0275	N5275U	12. 8.64	L.Rawson	Langar	21. 2.00
G-ASVO	HPR.7 Dart Herald 214	185	PP-SDG	13. 8.64	Dart Group plc	Bournemouth	14. 1.00T
			G-ASVO/G-8-3				
	(Stored 6.97: nose in place outside Terminal Building, Shoreham 5.99)						
G-ASVP	PA-25-235 Pawnee	25-2978		17. 8.64	Aquila Gliding Club Ltd		
						Hinton-in-The-Hedges	13. 4.02
G-ASVZ	PA-28-140 Cherokee	28-20357		24. 8.64	J.S. Garvey	(Telford)	3. 7.00
G-ASWB*	Beagle A.109 Airedale	B.543		25. 8.64	A.E.F.Bryant	(Nottingham)	27. 6.97
					(Cancelled by CAA 10.6.98)		
G-ASWF*	Beagle A.109 Airedale	B.537		26. 8.64	Not known	Carr Farm, Newark	27. 4.83
					(Dismantled 4.98)		
G-ASWH	Phoenix Luton LA.5A Major	PAL/1225		31. 8.64	J.T.Powell-Tuck	(Pontypool)	22. 6.78S
	(Walter Mikron 2)				(Damaged nr Turnworth, Dorset 3.7.77: on rebuild 1991)		

Regn	Type	C/n	P/I	Date	Owner/operator	Probable Base	CA Expy
G-ASWJ*	Beagle B.206 Srs.1	B.009	8449M G-ASWJ	9. 9.64	Midland Air Museum Ashley Down, Bristol (On loan to Brunel Technical College 11.95)		30. 1.75
G-ASWL	Reims Cessna F.172F	0087		10. 9.64	J.A.Clegg	(Swansea)	2. 7.00
G-ASWN	Bensen B.8M	14		15. 9.64	D.R.Shepherd (Not constructed)	(Prestwick)	
G-ASWP	Beechcraft A23 Musketeer II	M-587		22. 9.64	J.Holden & G.Benet (Damaged Sedlescombe 5.3.94; status uncertain)	(Hastings)	27. 4.95
G-ASWW	PA-30-160 Twin Comanche	30-556	N7531Y	1.10.64	R.Jenkins t/a RJ Motors	Bournemouth	1. 7.00
G-ASWX	PA-28-180 Cherokee C	28-1932		1.10.64	A.F.Dadds	Biggin Hill	16. 4.00
G-ASXC	SIPA 903 (Continental C90)	8	F-BEYK	6.10.64	M.K.Dartford & M.Cookson (Stored 4.95)	Andrewsfield	28. 7.94P
G-ASXD	Brantly B.2B	435		7.10.64	Lousada plc Crawley Park, Husborne Crawley, Bedford		28. 9.99
G-ASXF*	Brantly 305	1014		7.10.64	(Stored 7.98) Binfield, Bracknell		
G-ASXI	Cobelavia Tipsy T.66 Nipper 3 (Jabiru 2200A)	56	VH-CGH OO-KOC/(VH-CGC)	13.10.64	B.Dixon	Bagby	11. 2.00P
G-ASXJ	Phoenix Luton LA-4A Minor (Lycoming O-145)	PFA/801		14.10.64	M.R.Sallows Damyns Hall, Upminster "Pride & Joy"		18. 2.00P
G-ASXR	Cessna 210 Centurion	57532	5Y-KPW VP-KPW/N6532X	16.10.64	A.Schofield (On rebuild 12.97)	Barton	3. 1.93
G-ASXS	SAN Jodel DR.1050 Ambassadeur	133	F-BJNG	19.10.64	R.A.Hunter	Finmere	30. 6.00
G-ASXU	Jodel Wassmer D.120A Paris-Nice	196	F-BKAG	19.10.64	D.M.Garrett Croft Farm, Defford t/a The Jodel Group		7. 2.00P
G-ASXX*	Avro 683 Lancaster B.VII	-	WU-15 Fr.Navy/NX611	22.10.64	F.Panton/Lincolnshire Aviation Heritage Centre (Allocated 8375M)	East Kirkby	
	("NX611/LE-C"/630 Sqdn c/s "City of Sheffield" - Starboard & "NX611/DX-C"/57 Sqdn c/s "Just Jane" - Port)						
G-ASXY	SAN Jodel D.117A	914	F-BIVA	27.10.64	P.A., R.A.Davies & D.G.Claxton	Cardiff	21.12.00P
G-ASXZ	Cessna 182G Skylane	182-55738	N3238S	28.10.64	Last Refuge Ltd	(Wells)	14. 4.00
G-ASYD*	BAC One-Eleven 475AM	BAC.053		9.11.64	Brooklands Museum	Brooklands	13. 7.94
G-ASYG	Beagle A.61 Terrier 2	B.637	VX927	3.11.64	G.Rea (On rebuild 1.95)	Turweston	19. 2.70T
G-ASYJ	Beechcraft D95A Travel Air	TD-595	N8675Q	6.11.64	Crosby Aviation (Jersey) Ltd	Jersey	20. 9.01
G-ASYN*	Beagle A.61 Terrier 2	2288 & B.634	VF519	16.11.64	A.A.Marshall		
					(Damaged Netherthorpe 2.1.76; stored 2.96) Yeatsall Farm, Abbots Bromley		28. 3.76
G-ASYP	Cessna 150E	150-60794	N6094T	23.11.64	A.C.Melmore t/a Henlow Flying Group	RAF Henlow	28. 8.00
G-ASZB	Cessna 150E	150-61113	N3013J	16.12.64	R.J.Scott,	Blackbushe	1. 4.01
G-ASZD	Bolkow Bo.208A2 Junior	563	D-ENKI	16.12.64	M.J.Ayres	Full Sutton	23. 6.98P
G-ASZE	Beagle A.61 Terrier 2 (Conversion of Auster 6 c/n 2510)	B.636	VF552	17.12.64	P.J.Moore	RAF Leuchars	9. 8.02
G-ASZR	Fairtravel Linnet 2	005		5. 1.65	R.Palmer & D.Scott Swanborough Farm, Lewes		29. 3.00P
G-ASZS	Gardan GY-80-160 Horizon	70		6. 1.65	L.R.Burton Wellesbourne Mountford t/a ZS Group		5.11.01
G-ASZU	Cessna 150E	150-61152	N3052J	13. 1.65	T.H.Milburn	Cranfield	8. 4.02
G-ASZV	Tipsy T.66 Nipper 2 (VW1835)	45	5N-ADE ; 5N-ADY/VR-NDD	14. 1.65	R.L.Mitcham (Stored 3.97)	Little Gransden	23. 5.90P
G-ASZX	Beagle A.61 Terrier 1	3742	(SE-ELO) WJ368	18. 1.65	R.B.Webber (Damaged Verdun, France c.6.89; on rebuild 7.97)	(Crediton)	24. 2.90

G-ATAA – G-ATZZ

Regn	Type	C/n	P/I	Date	Owner/operator	Probable Base	CA Expy
G-ATAA*	PA-28-180 Cherokee C	28-2055	(OO-...) G-ATAA/(CN-...)/G-ATAA	26.11.69	D J D Richie, K H Brend & A Lewis t/a Brendair	Southend	16. 5.87
					(Damaged nr Melan, France; 12.9.86: wreck thought stored 1.89)		
G-ATAF	Reims Cessna F.172F	0135		25. 1.65	P.J.Thirtle	Humberside	6. 5.01
G-ATAG	CEA Jodel DR.1050 Ambassadeur	226	F-BKGG	25. 1.65	T.M.Dawes-Gamble	Oxford	4.10.02
G-ATAH*	Cessna 336 Skymaster	336-0007	N1707Z	26. 1.65	Not known Farley Farm, Winchester (Open storage 3.92)		5.12.76
G-ATAS	PA-28-180 Cherokee C	28-2137		4. 2.65	R Osborn t/a Atlas Group	(Ongar)	30. 7.00
G-ATAU	Rollason-Druine D.62B Condor	RAE/610		10. 2.65	M.A.Peare White Waltham t/a Golf Alpha Uniform Group		16.11.02
G-ATAV	Rollason-Druine D.62C Condor	RAE/611		10. 2.65	R.W.H.Watson (Stored 4.97)	Kilkerran	6. 8.94
G-ATBG	Nord 1002 Pingouin II	121	F-BGVX F-OTAN-5/Fr.Mil	24. 2.65	T.W.Harris Little Snoring (As "NJ+C11" in Luftwaffe c/s)		3. 6.98P
G-ATBH	CZL Aero 145	172015		24. 2.65	P.D.Aviram Kingston-upon-Thames (On rebuild 1997)		26.10.81
G-ATBI	Beechcraft A23 Musketeer II	M-696		26. 2.65	A.C.Dent, t/a Three Musketeers F/Group	Enstone	2. 6.00

Regn	Type	C/n	P/I	Date	Owner/operator	Probable Base	CA Expy
G-ATBJ	Sikorsky S-61N	61-269		12. 3.65	Brintel Helicopters Ltd	Aberdeen	2. 6.00T
		(Possibly ex N10043)			t/a British International Helicopters		
	[General Note: British Intl H/Cs & Bond H/Cs merged 9.99 to become Scotia Helicopter Services Ltd]						
G-ATBL	DH.60G Moth	1917	HB-OBA	2. 3.65	J.M.Greenland		
	(Gipsy I)		CH-353			Blackacre Farm, Holt, Wilts	23. 7.00P
G-ATBP	Alpavia Fournier RF3	59		11. 3.65	D.McNicholl	Inverness	19.10.02
G-ATBS	Druine D.31 Turbulent	PFA/1620		16. 3.65	D.R.Keene & J.A.Lear	Wheatley, Oxon	21.10.99P
	(VW1500)				"Fly Baby Fly"		
G-ATBU	Beagle A.61 Terrier 2	B.635	VF611	17. 3.65	D.M.Snape	(Derby)	2. 6.02
	(Conversion of Auster 6 c/n 2552)				t/a K9 Flying Group		
G-ATBW	Cobelavia Tipsy T.66 Nipper 2	52	OO-MAG	19. 3.65	S.C.M.Defries	Stapleford	6. 9.00P
	(VW1834/ACRO)				t/a Stapleford Nipper Group (Damaged landing Stapleford 7.2.99)		
G-ATBX	PA-20-135 Pacer	20-904	VP-KRX	19. 3.65	G.D. & P.M.Thomson		
			VR-TCH/VP-KKE			Wellesbourne Mountford	11. 5.02
G-ATBZ*	Westland Wessex 60 Srs.1	WA/461	G-17-4	22. 3.65	The Helicopter Museum	Weston-super-Mare	5.12.81
			G-ATBZ				
G-ATCC	Beagle A.109 Airedale	B.542		25. 3.65	J.R.Bowden	Biggin Hill	13.10.01
G-ATCD	Beagle D.5/180 Husky	3683		25. 3.65	D.J.O'Gorman	Enstone	12. 3.00
G-ATCE	Cessna U206 Super Skywagon	U206-0380	N2180F	25. 3.65	D.Turner & D.T.Hickling	Langar	25. 5.02
					t/a British Parachute Schools		
G-ATCJ	Phoenix Luton LA-4A Minor	PAL/1163 & PFA/812		5. 4.65	P.R.Diffey	(London Colney)	21. 3.00P
	(VW1600)						
G-ATCL	Victa Airtourer 100	93		5. 4.65	A.D.Goodall	Cardiff	13. 6.02
G-ATCN	Phoenix Luton LA-4A Minor	PAL/1118		7. 4.65	J.C.Gates & C.Neilson		
	(Lycoming O-145)				Comarques Farm, Thorpe-Le-Soken		26. 6.98P
G-ATCU	Cessna 337 Super Skymaster	337-0133	N2233X	22. 4.65	The Committee for Aerial Photography,		
					University of Cambridge	Cambridge	25. 4.02A
G-ATCX	Cessna 182H Skylane	182-55848	N3448S	26. 4.65	K.J.Fisher (See G-OLSC)	St.Merryn	14. 8.00
G-ATDA	PA-28-160 Cherokee	28-206	EI-AME	27. 4.65	J.Gosling	(Hereford)	27. 9.02
			(G-ARUV)		t/a Portway Aviation		
G-ATDB	SNCAN 1101 Noralpha	186	F-OTAN-6	27. 4.65	J.W.Hardie	Skelmorlie, Largs	22.11.78S
			Fr.Mil		(On rebuild 8.93)		
	(Nord 1101 as "F-OTAN-6" reported Barton 8.96 but believed to be G-BAYV)						
G-ATDN	Beagle A.61 Terrier 2	B.638	TW641	7. 5.65	Susan J.Saggers (As "TW641") Biggin Hill		8. 7.01T
	(Conversion of Auster 6 c/n 2499)						
G-ATDO	Bolkow Bo.208C Junior	576	D-EGZU	10. 5.65	H.Swift	Hill Farm, Marton, Hull	28. 3.00P
G-ATEF	Cessna 150E	150-61378	N3978U	25. 5.65	A.J.White & B.M. Scott	Blackbushe	8. 7.02
					t/a Swans Aviation		
G-ATEM	PA-28-180 Cherokee C	28-2329		26. 5.65	Chiltern Valley Aviation Ltd	Bovingdon	4. 2.01
G-ATEP*	EAA Biplane	PFA/1301		28. 5.65	E.L.Martin	Castle Farm, Guernsey	18. 6.73
	(Continental C75)				(Stored in poor condition 8.96)		
G-ATES*	PA-32-260 Cherokee Six	32-20		31. 5.65	Stirling Parachute Centre	NK	11. 6.83
	(Crashed nr Kinglassie 8.2.81; front fuselage used as para-trainer 9.92)						
G-ATET	PA-30-160 Twin Comanche	30-770	N230ET	31. 5.65	S.J.Gaveston	Biggin Hill	27. 2.00
G-ATEV	CEA Jodel DR.1050 Ambassadeur	18	F-BJHL	31. 5.65	M.G.Cookson (On rebuild 1997)	(Epping)	13. 8.71
G-ATEW	PA-30-160 Twin Comanche	30-719	N7640Y	3. 6.65	J.C.White	Newcastle	9. 6.01
					t/a Air Northumbria Group		
G-ATEX	Victa Airtourer 100	110	(VH-MTU)	3. 6.65	M.Dale	Rochester	12.10.02
					t/a The Medway Victa Group		
G-ATEZ	PA-28-140 Cherokee	28-21044		8. 6.65	EFI Aviation Ltd	Norwich	3.12.99T
G-ATFD	CEA Jodel DR.1050 Ambassadeur	311	F-BKIM	14. 6.65	V.Usher	Carr Farm, Newark	1. 3.97
G-ATFF	PA-23-250 Aztec C	27-2898	N5769Y	16. 6.65	Neatspin Ltd	Tatenhill	13. 8.01
G-ATFG*	Brantly B.2B	448		16. 6.65	Acft Preservation Society of Scotland		
	(Composite with parts from G-ASLO/G-AXSR; displayed Museum of Flight 3.96)					East Fortune	25. 3.85
G-ATFM	Sikorsky S-61N Mk.II	61-270	CF-OKY	21. 6.65	Brintel Helicopters Ltd	Sumburgh	1.10.00T
			(Possibly initially N10052)			t/a British International Helicopters		
G-ATFR	PA-25-150 Pawnee	25-135	OY-ADJ	28. 6.65	Borders (Milfield) Gliding Club Ltd		
						Milfield	17. 4.00
G-ATFV*	Agusta-Bell 47J-2A Ranger	2093	9J-ACX	1. 7.65	Not known	Ley Farm, Chirk	8. 8.92T
			G-ATFV/MM80417		(Stored 9.99)		
G-ATFW	Phoenix Luton LA-4A Minor	PFA/811		2. 7.65	P.A.Rose	(Walney)	2.12.97P
	(Lycoming O-145)						
G-ATFX*	Reims Cessna F.172G	0196		8. 7.65	Not known	Redhill	12. 2.92
	(Damaged Booker 25.1.90; displayed Town centre 7.97 for "Leprosy Awareness/Flight Aid" - all-red/no marks)						
G-ATFY	Reims Cessna F.172G	0199		8. 7.65	H.Cowan	Kilkeel, Co.Down	25. 5.01
G-ATGE	SAN Jodel DR.1050 Ambassadeur	114	F-BJJF	9. 7.65	L.S.& K.L.Johnson	Lodge Farm, Clacton	17. 2.01
G-ATGN*	Thorn K-800 Coal Gas Balloon	2		12. 7.65	British Balloon Museum & Library Newbury		
					"Eccles" (Stored)		
G-ATGO	Reims Cessna F.172G	0181		12. 7.65	W.J.Baker	Bristol	5. 5.01
G-ATGP	SAN Jodel DR.1050 Ambassadeur	122	F-BJNB	14. 7.65	G.W.Anderson & R.T.Bowden	Shobdon	4. 2.01T
					t/a Madley Flying Group		

Regn	Type	C/n	P/I	Date	Owner/operator	Probable Base	CA Expy
G-ATGY	Gardan GY-80-160 Horizon	121		20. 7.65	P.W.Gibberson	Birmingham	21. 8.99
G-ATGZ	Griffiths GH-4 Gyroplane	G.1		20. 7.65	R.W.J.Cripps	Spondon, Derby	
					(Stored Shardlow,Derby 7.91)		
G-ATHA*	PA-23-235 Apache	27-610	N4326Y	21. 7.65	Brunel Technical College		
						Ashley Down, Bristol	7. 6.86
					(Instructional airframe 6.91)		
G-ATHD	DHC.1 Chipmunk 22	C1/0837	WP971	26. 7.65	O.L.Cubitt & K.P.A.Lewis	Denham	30. 6.00
			G-ATHD/WP971		t/a Spartan Flying Group (As "WP971")		
G-ATHI*	PA-28-180 Cherokee C	28-2545		2. 8.65	Dublin Institute of Technology		
		(Crashed Castlebar, Co.Mayo 9.5.74; Instructional airframe 5.92)				Bolton St, Dublin	26.10.74
G-ATHK	Aeronca 7AC Champion	7AC-971	N82339	2. 8.65	T.P.McDonald, T.Crawley & E.Walker		
	(Continental A75)		NC82339			Crosland Moor	18. 4.00P
G-ATHM	Wallis WA-116/F	402 & 211	4R-ACK	3. 8.65	Wallis Autogyros Ltd	Reymerston Hall	23. 5.93P
	(Franklin 60hp) (C/n 213 quoted)		G-ATHM		(Stored 5.99)		
G-ATHN*	SNCAN 1101 Noralpha	84	F-BFUZ	5. 8.65	E.L.Martin	St.Peter Port, Guernsey	27. 6.75S
			Fr.Mil		(Stored 8.96)		
G-ATHR	PA-28-180 Cherokee C	28-2343	EI-AOT	11. 8.65	Britannia Airways Ltd	Henlow	10. 8.01T
					(Damaged Henlow 5.7.99)		
G-ATHT	Victa Airtourer 115	120		16. 8.65	D.A.Beese	Badminton	23.12.02
G-ATHU	Beagle A.61 Terrier 1	AUS/127/FM	7435M	16. 8.65	J.A.L.Irwin	Park Farm, Eaton Bray	7. 9.01
			WE539				
G-ATHV	Cessna 150F	150-62019	N8719S	16. 8.65	E.K.Robinson	Sherburn in Elmet	2. 2.00
					t/a Cessna Hotel Victor Group		
G-ATHX	SAN Jodel DR.100A Ambassadeur	74	F-OBMM	17. 8.65	W.R.Prescott	Kilkeel, Co.Down	2. 6.99
					t/a Mourne Flying Club		
G-ATHZ	Cessna 150F	150-61586	(EI-AOP)	20. 8.65	E. & R.D.Forster	Beccles	27.3.98T
			N6286R		(Op Norfolk & Norwich Aero Club)		
G-ATIA	PA-24-260 Comanche	24-4049	N8650P	20. 8.65	L.A.Brown	Leicester	16. 6.01
					t/a The India Alpha Partnership		
G-ATIC	CEA Jodel DR.1050 Ambassadeur	6	F-BJCJ	23. 8.65	R.E.Major	(St.Agnes, Cornwall)	1. 6.81
					(On overhaul 1993)		
G-ATID*	Cessna 337 Super Skymaster	337-0239	N6239F	24. 8.65	Not known	Stapleford	6. 1.97
					(Temp unregd 7.7.97: stored 5.98)		
G-ATIE*	Cessna 150F	150-61591	N6291R	24. 8.65	Staffordshire Sports Skydiving Club		
	(Crashed nr Shobdon 28.7.79; fuselage as para-trainer 4.97; status unknown) Chetwynd, Shropshire						7 .9.81
G-ATIG*	HPR.7 Dart Herald 214	177	PP-SDI	25. 8.65	Nordic Oil Services Ltd	Norwich	14.10.97T
			G-ATIG		(Stored 5.99)		
G-ATIN	SAN Jodel D.117	437	F-BHNV	8. 9.65	G.G.Simpson	Muirhouses Farm, Errol	18. 4.96P
					(Stored 4.97)		
G-ATIR	AIA Stampe SV-4C	1047	F-BNMC	9. 9.65	N.M.Bloom		
		G-ATIR/F-BMKQ/Aeronavale/F-BCDM/Aeronavale Abbot's Hill Farm, Hemel Hempstead					29. 6.00
G-ATIS	PA-28-160 Cherokee C	28-2713		9. 9.65	R.M.Jenner & J.H.Peploe		
						Draycott Farm, Chiseldon	8. 1.00
G-ATIZ	SAN Jodel D.117	636	F-BIBR	15. 9.65	D.K.Shipton	Deenethorpe	25. 5.00P
					(Damaged Leicester 30.6.95; sold as "wreck" 5.96: extant 3.99)		
G-ATJA	SAN Jodel DR.1050 Ambassadeur	378	F-BKHL	15. 9.65	D.A.Head & G.W.Cunningham	RAF Bicester	14. 9.99
					t/a Bicester Flying Group		
G-ATJC	Victa Airtourer 100	125		16. 9.65	Aviation West Ltd	Perth	18. 9.00T
G-ATJF*	PA-28-140 Cherokee	28-21283		20. 9.65	Not known	Sabadell, Spain	16. 6.82
					(Crashed Corcubion, Spain 29.8.79; fuselage stored 3.89)		
G-ATJG	PA-28-140 Cherokee	28-21299		20. 9.65	H.M.Wittmann	Rushett Farm, Chessington	21.10.02
G-ATJL	PA-24-260 Comanche	24-4203	N8752P	23. 9.65	M.J.Berry & T.R.Quinn	Blackbushe	20. 5.00
G-ATJM	Fokker DR.1 Triplane rep	002	N78001	23. 9.65	R.J.Lamplough	North Weald	10. 9.93P
	(Siemens SH-14A-165)		EI-APY/G-ATJM		(As "152/17": stored 10.97)		
G-ATJN	Dormois Jodel D.119	863	F-PINZ	23. 9.65	R.F.Bradshaw	Valley Farm, Winwick	27. 5.00P
G-ATJR*	PA-E23-250 Aztec C	27-3033	N5881Y	30. 9.65	Not known (Stored 11.98)	Manchester	23. 7.95
G-ATJT	Gardan GY-80-160 Horizon	108		4.10.65	N.Huxtable	Cheddington	23. 5.02
G-ATJV	PA-32-260 Cherokee Six	32-103	TF-GOS	7.10.65	Wingglider Ltd	Hibaldstow	17. 5.95
			G-ATJV		(Stored/dumped 6.99)		
G-ATKF	Cessna 150F	150-62386	N3586L	20.10.65	C.J.Freeman	Headcorn	10.7.00T
G-ATKG*	Hiller UH-12B	496		21.10.65	Not known	Maltby, Cleveland	28.11.69
			Thai AF 103		(Stored 1.96)		
G-ATKH	Phoenix Luton LA-4A Minor	PFA/809		25.10.65	H.E.Jenner	Brenchley, Kent	24. 6.92P
	(Lycoming O-145)				(Stored 1.96)		
G-ATKI	Piper J3C-75 Cub	17545	N70536	25.10.65	P.H.Wilmot-Allistone	Kemble	29. 4.94P
			NC70536		(Damaged Enstone 14.11.93: on rebuild 8.97)		
G-ATKT	Reims Cessna F.172G	0206		9.11.65	P.J.Megson	Goodwood	13. 2.02
G-ATKU	Reims Cessna F.172G	0232		9.11.65	Holdcroft Aviation Services Ltd	Popham	31. 1.95T
					(On rebuild 1.97)		
G-ATKX	SAN Jodel D.140C Mousquetaire III			19.11.65	A.J.White & G.A.Piper	Redhill	30. 3.01T
		163			(Op Acebell Aviation)		

Regn	Type	C/n	P/I	Date	Owner/operator	Probable Base	CA Expy
G-ATKZ	Cobelavia Tipsy T.66 Nipper 2 (VW1834)	72		24.11.65	M.W.Knights Blue Tile Farm, Hindolveston		2.12.00P
G-ATLA	Cessna 182J Skylane	182-56923	N2823F	24.11.65	J W & J T Whicher	(York)	26.10 02
G-ATLB	SAN Jodel DR.1050/M1 Excellence	78	F-BIVG	29.11.65	B.Lumb t/a La Petit Oiseau Syndicate	Breighton	24. 8.02
G-ATLH*	Fewsdale Tigercraft Gyroplane	F.T5		6.12.65	Not known (Under restoration 2.99)	Thornaby-on-Tees	
G-ATLM	Reims Cessna F.172G	0252		6.12.65	Air Fotos Aviation Ltd	Newcastle	3. 3.00T
G-ATLP	Bensen B.8M (McCulloch 4318F)	17		9.12.65	R.F.G.Moyle	(Penryn)	19. 5.97P
G-ATLT	Cessna U206A Super Skywagon	U206-0523	N4823F	13.12.65	A.I.M & A.J. Guest	Dunkeswell	6. 6.02T
G-ATLV	Jodel Wassmer D.120 Paris-Nice	224	F-BKNQ	15.12.65	L.S.Thorne Shenstone Hall Farm, Shenstone		8. 7.02P
G-ATLW	PA-28-180 Cherokee C	28-2877		17.12.65	R.D.Masters (Damaged Leicester 30.6.95)	Rush Green	13. 7.95
G-ATMC	Reims Cessna F.150F (Wichita c/n 62849)	0020		28.12.65	C.J. & E.J.Leigh	Audley End	5. 1.01
G-ATMH	Beagle D.5/180 Husky	3684		3. 1.66	Dorset Gliding Club Ltd	Gallows Hill	13. 8.00
G-ATMI	HS.748 Srs.2A/225	1592	VP-LIU	4. 1.66	Emerald Airways Ltd (Reed Aviation c/s) "Old Ben" G-ATMI/VP-LIU/G-ATMI/VP-LIU/G-ATMI/VP-LIU/G-ATMI	Liverpool	18. 5.00T
G-ATMJ	HS.748 Srs.2A/225	1593	VP-LAJ	4. 1.66	Emerald Airways Ltd G-ATMJ/6Y-JFJ/G-ATMJ	Exeter	7. 9.00T
G-ATML	Reims Cessna F.150F (Wichita c/n 62722)	0014		6. 1.66	G.I.Smith	Eddsfield	28. 9.01
G-ATMM	Reims Cessna F.150F (Wichita c/n 62775)	0016		6. 1.66	B.Powell	Headcorn	9. 6.01T
G-ATMT	PA-30-160 Twin Comanche	30-439	XW938	10. 1.66	Montagu-Smith & Co Ltd G-ATMT/N7385Y	Turweston	11. 7.02
G-ATMU	PA-23-160 Apache G	23-2000	N4478P	11. 1.66	P.K.Martin & R.W.Harris (Fuselage to Busy Bee Aviation 9.99 & stored outside)	Sibson	14. 4.90T
G-ATMW	PA-28-140 Cherokee	28-21486		11. 1.66	Bencray Ltd t/a Blackpool & Fylde Aero Club	Blackpool	27. 1.01T
G-ATMY	Cessna 150F	150-62642	SE-ETD N8542G	13. 1.66	J.A.Starbuck	Crosland Moor	20. 6.01
G-ATNB	PA-28-180 Cherokee C	28-3057		20. 1.66	G.Taylor	Woodford	31. 3.00
G-ATNE	Reims Cessna F.150F (Wichita c/n 63252)	0042		20. 1.66	N.H.Scott	Leicester	11. 9.00
G-ATNL	Reims Cessna F.150F (Wichita c/n 63652)	0066		25. 1.66	G.A.Lauf Draycott Farm, Chiseldon t/a G-ATNL Flying Group		4. 7.02
G-ATNV	PA-24-260 Comanche	24-4350	N8896P	28. 1.66	B.S.Reynolds (Stored 4.99)	Bourn	3. 7.93
G-ATOA	PA-23-160 Apache G	23-1954	N4437P	31. 1.66	K.A.Passmore (Derelict 8.99)	Stapleford	18.12.98
G-ATOD	Reims Cessna F.150F (Wichita c/n 62342)	0003		1. 2.66	J.H.A.Boyns, E.Watson & G.Bold	St.Just	6. 9.02
G-ATOE	Reims Cessna F.150F (Wichita c/n 63096)	0031		1. 2.66	J.A.Richardson	(London NW10)	25. 8.01
G-ATOF*	Reims Cessna F.150F (Wichita c/n 63582)	0063		1. 2.66	Air Service Training Ltd (Crashed nr Perth 25.11.71; on fire dump 2.96)	Perth	22. 7.73
G-ATOH	Rollason-Druine D.62B Condor	RAE/612		3. 2.66	T.A.Bridge t/a Three Spires Flying Group	Lichfield	11. 6.99P
G-ATOI	PA-28-140 Cherokee	28-21556		3. 2.66	R.W.Nash	RAF Brize Norton	27. 5.02
G-ATOJ	PA-28-140 Cherokee	28-21584		3. 2.66	A Flight Aviation Ltd	Prestwick	2. 7.00T
G-ATOK	PA-28-140 Cherokee	28-21612		3. 2.66	G.T.S.Done & P.R.Harrison White Waltham t/a ILC Flying Group		14.12.00
G-ATOL	PA-28-140 Cherokee	28-21626		3. 2.66	L.J.Nation & G.Alford t/a G-ATOL Flying Group	Cardiff	23. 1.98
G-ATOM	PA-28-140 Cherokee	28-21640		3. 2.66	A Flight Aviation Ltd	Prestwick	27. 8.01T
G-ATON	PA-28-140 Cherokee	28-21654		3. 2.66	R.G.Walters	Shobdon	13. 8.01
G-ATOO	PA-28-140 Cherokee	28-21668		3. 2.66	I.Wilson (On rebuild 7.99)	Carlisle	24. 9.84
G-ATOP	PA-28-140 Cherokee	28-21682		3. 2.66	P.R.Coombs t/a The Aero 80 Flying Group	Popham	16. 5.02
G-ATOR	PA-28-140 Cherokee	28-21696		3. 2.66	D.Palmer t/a Aligator Group	Shobdon	18. 5.00
G-ATOT	PA-28-180 Cherokee C	28-3061		3. 2.66	Totair Ltd "Totty"	Not known	22. 6.00T
G-ATOU	Mooney M.20E Super 21	961	N5946Q	3. 2.66	A.C. Mate t/a M20 Flying Group	Sherburn in Elmet	28. 5.00

Regn	Type	C/n	P/I	Date	Owner/operator	Probable Base	CA Expy
G-ATOY*	PA-24-260 Comanche B	24-4346	N8893P	7. 2.66	Royal Museum of Scotland/Museum of Flight "Myth Too"	East Fortune	
	(Crashed nr Elstree 6.3.79; fuselage displayed)						
G-ATOZ	Bensen B.8M	18		7. 2.66	N.C.White & W.Stark	Kingsmuir	18. 7.00P
	(Rotax 503)				(Substantially rebuilt in 1986, original airframe stored at Wimborne)		
G-ATPD	HS.125 Srs.1B/522	25085	5N-AGU G-ATPD	11. 2.66	Wessex Air (Holdings) Ltd	Bournemouth	14.10.98T
					(WFU 1997 - to Bournemouth Aviation Museum 1999)		
G-ATPN	PA-28-140 Cherokee	28-21899		18. 2.66	R.W.Harris, M.F.Hatt, P.E.Preston & A.Jahanfar (Op Southend Flying Club)	Southend	24. 3.02T
G-ATPT	Cessna 182J Skylane	182-57056	N2956F	22. 2.66	G.B.Scholes t/a Papa Tango Group	Elstree	11. 8.01
G-ATPV	Barritault JB.01 Minicab	01	F-PJKA	22. 2.66	C.F.O'Niell (Stored 6.97)	Newtownards	28. 4.99P
	(Continental C90) (Rebuild of GY-20 F-PHUC c/n A.155)						
G-ATRG	PA-18-180 Super Cub	18-7764	5B-CAB N4985Z	1. 3.66	Lasham Gliding Society Ltd	Lasham	31. 5.01
G-ATRI	Bolkow Bo.208C Junior	602	D-ECGY	3. 3.66	A.A.W.Stevens	Cumbernauld	22. 4.01
G-ATRK	Reims Cessna F.150F	0049	(G-ATNC)	4. 3.66	G.G. & J.G.Armstrong t/a Armstrong Aviation	Wigtown Baldoon	19. 8.02
	(Wichita c/n 63381)						
G-ATRL	Reims Cessna F.150F	0050		4. 3.66	S.S.Delwarte t/a G-ATRL Flying Group (Used in rebuild of G-AVHM)	Shoreham	21. 2.98
	(Wichita c/n 63382)						
G-ATRM	Reims Cessna F.150F	0053	(G-ATNJ)	4. 3.66	J.Redfearn	(Bishop Auckland)	29.11.00T
	(Wichita c/n 63454)						
G-ATRO	PA-28-140 Cherokee	28-21871		4. 3.66	F.E.Ward t/a 390th Flying Group	Framlingham	7. 7.00
G-ATRP*	PA-28-140 Cherokee	28-21885		4. 3.66	JRB Aviation Ltd	Southend	20. 9.84
	(Damaged Boughton Monchelsea 16.10.81; wreck stored 1.00)						
G-ATRR	PA-28-140 Cherokee	28-21892		4. 3.66	Marnham Investments Ltd (Op Manx Flyers Aero Club)	Ronaldsway	5.10.00T
G-ATRW	PA-32-260 Cherokee Six	32-360	N11C	8. 3.66	Moxley & Frankl Ltd & J.Pringle	Biggin Hill	11. 8.01
G-ATRX	PA-32-260 Cherokee Six	32-390		8. 3.66	J.W.Stow t/a The Comet Flying Group	Elstree	23. 8.01
G-ATSI	Bolkow Bo.208C Junior	605	D-EFNU	14. 3.66	M.R.Reynolds & R.S.Jordan t/a G-ATSI Group	Little Snoring	31. 1.00
G-ATSL	Reims Cessna F.172G	0260		16. 3.66	L.McMullin	Strandhill	18. 8.01
G-ATSM	Cessna 337A Super Skymaster	337-0434	N5334S	23. 3.66	I.J. & H.R.Jones t/a Landscape & Ground Maintenance	Thruxton	10. 7.97T
G-ATSR	Beechcraft M35 Bonanza	D-6236	EI-ALL	29. 3.66	D.G.Lewendon (Damaged Kingland Church 6.12.98)	Gloucestershire	28. 9.01
G-ATSX	Bolkow Bo.208C Junior	608	D-EJUC	7. 4.66	R.J.Campbell & M.H.Goley	Westbury-sub-Mendip	1. 7.02
G-ATSY	Wassmer WA.41 Super Baladou IV	117		12. 4.66	B.Turnbull t/a Baladou Flying Group	Newcastle	23.11.91
G-ATSZ	PA-30-160 Twin Comanche B	30-1002	EI-BPS (EI-BBS)/G-ATSZ/N7912Y	13. 4.66	Richardson Aviation Consultants Ltd	Exeter	6. 6.02
G-ATTB	Wallis WA-116/F	214		19. 4.66	D.A.Wallis (Noted 5.99: as "XR944")	Reymerston Hall	18. 5.98P
	(Franklin 2A) (Rebuild of WA-116 G-ARZC/XR944 c/n 204)						
G-ATTD	Cessna 182J Skylane	182-57229	N3129F	19. 4.66	M.Brennan, M.A.Griggs & P.J.Ackerley	Leicester	30. 4.01
G-ATTF	PA-28-140 Cherokee	28-21939		25. 4.66	D.H.Fear	Bembridge	10. 6.00
G-ATTG	PA-28-140 Cherokee	28-21943		25. 4.66	D.E.Spells (Stored 5.99)	Swanton Morley	3.10.92T
G-ATTI	PA-28-140 Cherokee	28-21951		24. 4.66	R.H.Rathbone t/a G-ATTI Flying Group	Bristol	14. 9 01T
	(Damaged Bembridge overnight 12/13.6.99 during unauthorised taxiing)						
G-ATTK	PA-28-140 Cherokee	28-21959		25. 4.66	D.J.E.Fairburn t/a The G-ATTK Flying Group	Southend	25. 2.01
G-ATTM	CEA Jodel DR.250 Srs.160	65		26. 4.66	R.W.Tomkinson	Seletar, Singapore	15.12.01
G-ATTN*	Piccard HAFB (62,000 cu ft)	15 & 1352		27. 4.66	The Science Museum "The Red Dragon" (Envelope/basket stored 6.94) South Kensington, London		
G-ATTR	Bolkow Bo.208C Junior	612	D-EHEH	28. 4.66	S.Luck	Rothwell Lodge Farm, Kettering	14. 8.00
G-ATTU*	PA-28-140 Cherokee	28-21987		2. 5.66	Not known	Geneva, Switzerland	4.10.93
	(Damaged in collision with AA-5A G-OCPL Elstree 27.6.92; to unknown hotel & displayed in foyer 1993)						
G-ATTV	PA-28-140 Cherokee	28-21991		2. 5.66	N.E.Leech t/a G-ATTV Group	Andrewsfield	19.11.01
G-ATTX	PA-28-180 Cherokee C	28-3390	PH-VDP (G-ATTX)	2. 5.66	IPAC Aviation Ltd	Earls Colne/Southend	11.11.99
G-ATUB	PA-28-140 Cherokee	28-21971		2. 5.66	R.H.Partington & M.J.Porter	Wombleton	18. 3.02
G-ATUD	PA-28-140 Cherokee	28-21979		2. 5.66	J.J.Ferguson	(Bideford)	19. 8.00T
G-ATUF	Reims Cessna F.150F	0040		4. 5.66	D.P.Williams "Honeysuckle"	Hill Farm, Nayland	27. 4.02
	(Wichita c/n 63229)						
G-ATUG	Rollason-Druine D.62B Condor	RAE/614		4. 5.66	R.Crosby	Watchford Farm, Yarcombe	17. 6.00P
G-ATUH	Tipsy T.66 Nipper 1	6	OO-NIF	4. 5.66	D.G.Spruce	Crosland Moor	17.11.00
	(VW1600)						
G-ATUI	Bolkow Bo.208C Junior	611	D-EHEF	4. 5.66	A.W.Wakefield	Conington	29. 6.02

Regn	Type	C/n	P/I	Date	Owner/operator	Probable Base	CA Expy
G-ATUL	PA-28-180 Cherokee C	28-3033	N9007J	6. 5.66	Kirkland Ltd	Ronaldsway	21. 6.02
G-ATVF	DHC.1 Chipmunk 22	C1/0265	WD327	25. 5.66	T.M.Holloway	RAF Syerston	9. 5.01
	(Lycoming AEIO-360) (Regd with Fuselage No. DHB/F/147)				t/a RAFGSA (Op Four Counties Gliding Club)		
G-ATVK	PA-28-140 Cherokee	28-22006		27. 5.66	H Hyde	Calais	6. 7.01T
G-ATVL	PA-28-140 Cherokee	28-22013		27. 5.66	White Waltham Airfield Ltd	White Waltham	8. 9.00T
					(Op West London Aero Services)		
G-ATVO	PA-28-140 Cherokee	28-22020		27. 5.66	G.R.Bright	(Biggleswade)	13. 2.00T
G-ATVP*	Vickers FB.5 Gunbus rep			31. 5.66	RAF Museum	Hendon	6. 5.69P
	(Gnome Monosoupape 100 hp) VAFA-01 & FB.5				(As "2345"/"Bombay(2)" in RFC c/s)		
G-ATVS	PA-28-180 Cherokee C	28-3041	N9014J	1. 6.66	S.M. Patterson	(London SW11)	23. 7.99
G-ATVW	Rollason-Druine D.62B Condor	RAE/615		7. 6.66	J.P.Coulter & J.Chidley	Nuthampstead	23. 5.01
					t/a Alpha One Flying Group		
G-ATVX	Bolkow Bo.208C Junior	615	D-EHER	9. 6.66	D.E.Thomas & R.G.Morris	Swansea	30.10.00P
					t/a D & G Aviation		
G-ATWA	SAN Jodel DR.1050 Ambassadeur	296	F-BKHA	10. 6.66	M.G.Binks t/a Jodel Syndicate	Popham	13.12.02
G-ATWB	SAN Jodel D.117	423	F-BHNH	10. 6.66	C.R.Isbell	Andrewsfield	1. 6.00P
					t/a Andrewsfield Whiskey Bravo Group		
G-ATWE*	GEMS MS.892A Rallye Commodore 150			13. 6.66	D.I.Murray	(Newport, Gwent)	15. 2.82
		10634	(Damaged nr Taunton 29.3.81; for rebuild 1989; cancelled by CAA 17.02.99)					
G-ATWJ	Reims Cessna F.172F	0095	EI-ANS	21. 6.66	C.J. & J.Freeman	Headcorn	30. 4.01T
					t/a Weald Air Services		
G-ATWR*	PA-30-160 Twin Comanche B	30-1134	N8025Y	30. 6.66	Not known	Wickenby	22.12.94T
					(Damaged Crosland Moor 14.9.93; stored 8.94)		
G-ATWS*	Phoenix Luton LA-4A Minor			30. 6.66	(On rebuild 4.97)	Barton	26. 3.69P
	PAL/1195 & PFA/818						
G-ATXA	PA-22-150 Tri-Pacer	22-3730	N4403A	8. 7.66	S.Hildrop	Top Farm, Royston	26. 4.01
	(Modified to PA-20 Super Pacer configuration)				(Damaged u/c & propeller Top Farm 11.10.98; under repair 5.99)		
G-ATXD	PA-30-160 Twin Comanche B	30-1166	N8053Y	12. 7.66	Jet Heritage Ltd	Fairoaks	16. 3.00T
G-ATXJ*	HP.137 Jetstream 300	200		15. 7.66	Cardiff-Wales Airport Fire Service		
	(Modified to Jetstream 41 mock-up & display unit)					Cardiff	8. 2.71
G-ATXM	PA-28-180 Cherokee C	28-2759	N8809J	19. 7.66	M.J.Stack	Stapleford	12.10.02
					t/a G-ATXM Flying Group		
G-ATXN	Mitchell-Procter Kittiwake 1			19. 7.66	P.A.Dawson	Shenington	24. 7.98P
	(Lycoming O-290)	1 & PFA/1306					
G-ATXO	SIPA 903	41	F-BGAP	19. 7.66	S.A. & D.C.Whitehead	Thruxton	29. 4.02P
					"La Pirouette"		
G-ATXX*	McCandless M.4	M4/3		27. 7.66	Ulster Folk & Transport Museum		
	(VW1600)					Holywood, Belfast	
G-ATXZ	Bolkow Bo.208C Junior	624	D-ELNE	28. 7.66	R.Bradbury	Tatenhill	23. 5.00P
					t/a Bradbury & ptnrs		
G-ATYM	Reims Cessna F.150G	0074		15. 8.66	J.F.Perry	Rochester	28. 9.92
					t/a J.F.Perry & Co (Stored 11.97)		
G-ATYN	Reims Cessna F.150G	0076		15. 8.66	J.S.Grant	North Coates	13.12.97
					(Damaged Stewton 30.6.95)		
G-ATYS	PA-28-180 Cherokee C	28-3296	N9226J	19. 8.66	E.Baker	Headcorn	21. 5.00
					t/a G-ATYS Flying Group		
G-ATZK	PA-28-180 Cherokee C	28-3128	D-EFUN	21. 9.66	B.H. & E.F.Austen	RAF Brize Norton	21.10.02T
			N9090J		t/a Austen Associates (Op RAF Brize Norton Flying Club)		
G-ATZM	Piper J3C-90 Cub	20868	N2092M	26. 9.66	R.W.Davison	Holywell	23. 6.00P
	(Frame No.21310)		NC2092M				
G-ATZO*	Beagle B.206 Srs.1	044	EI-APO	28. 9.66	Not known Coldwater, Michigan, USA		
			G-ATZO		(Sold to USA 12.81 but no regn issued; stored 7.91)		
G-ATZS	Wassmer WA.41 Super Baladou IV	128		30. 9.66	Temporal Songs Ltd & Anti Climb Guards Ltd		
						Biggin Hill	28.11.02
G-ATZY	Reims Cessna F.150G	0135		14.10.66	Fraggle Leasing Ltd	Aberdeen	1. 7.00T

G-AVAA – G-AVZZ

Regn	Type	C/n	P/I	Date	Owner/operator	Probable Base	CA Expy
G-AVAR	Reims Cessna F.150G	0122		27.10.66	J.A.Rees	Haverfordwest	7. 9.01T
					t/a Poyston Aviation		
G-AVAU	PA-30-160 Twin Comanche B	30-1328	N8230Y	8.11.66	Enrico Ermano Ltd	Fairoaks	19. 5.02
G-AVAW	Rollason-Druine D.62C Condor	RAE/617		10.11.66	S.Banyard	Tibenham	6. 5.00
					t/a Condor Aircraft Group		
G-AVAX	PA-28-180 Cherokee C	28-3798		11.11.66	J.J.Parkes	Halfpenny Green	30. 5.02
G-AVBG	PA-28-180 Cherokee C	28-3801		11.11.66	R.A.Cayless & R.D.B.Severn	White Waltham	13. 3.00
					t/a G-AVBG Flying Group		
G-AVBH	PA-28-180 Cherokee C	28-3802		11.11.66	T.R.Smith (Agricultural Machinery) Ltd		
						Shipdham	14. 5.00
G-AVBS	PA-28-180 Cherokee C	28-3938		14.11.66	A.G.Arthur	Perranporth	22. 6.01T

Regn	Type	C/n	P/I	Date	Owner/operator	Probable Base	CA Expy
G-AVBT	PA-28-180 Cherokee C	28-3945		14.11.66	J.F.Mitchell	Shoreham	26. 4.01T
G-AVBZ	Reims Cessna F.172H	0387		18.11.66	M.Byl	Crosland Moor	10. 4.00
G-AVCM	PA-24-260 Comanche B	24-4520	N9054P	5.12.66	Airbase Aircraft Ltd	Stapleford	16. 6.02
G-AVCS*	Beagle A.61 Terrier 1	-	WJ363	12.12.66	J.May	Ballynahinch, NI	28. 6.82
					(Damaged Finmere 18.10.81; on rebuild 11.95)		
G-AVCV	Cessna 182J Skylane	182-57492	N3492F	15.12.66	The University of Manchester Institute		
					of Science & Technology	Woodford	2. 2.01
G-AVCX	PA-30-160 Twin Comanche B	30-1302	N8185Y	16.12.66	T.Barge	Nottingham	18.11.00
G-AVDA	Cessna 182K Skylane	182-57959	N2759Q	16.12.66	F.W.Ellis & M.C.Burnett		
						Water Leisure Park, Skegness	17. 6.01
G-AVDB*	Cessna 310L	310L-0079	N2279F	20.12.66	Not known	NK	8. 7.79
					(Fuselage only stored 7.98: status unknown 12.99)		
G-AVDF*	Beagle B.121 Pup 1	B.121/001		28.12.66	D.Collings & J.Chillingworth		
					(On rebuild Cambridge Airport 4.96)	St.Ives, Cambs	22. 5.68
G-AVDG	Wallis WA-116 Srs.1 Agile	215		28.12.66	K.H.Wallis	Reymerston Hall	23. 5.92P
	(Rotax 532)				(Stored 5.99)		
G-AVDR*	Beechcraft 65-B80 Queen Air	LD-339	A40-CR	5. 1.67	Brunel Technical College		
			G-AVDR			Ashley Down, Bristol	30. 6.86T
					(Instructional airframe 6.91)		
G-AVDS*	Beechcraft 65-B80 Queen Air	LD-337	A40-CS	5. 1.67	Brunel Technical College	Filton	26. 8.77
			G-AVDS			(Dumped as "G-A" 11.99)		
G-AVDT	Aeronca 7AC Champion	7AC-6932	N3594E	5. 1.67	D.Cheney & G.Moore	(Newry, NI)	10. 7.90P
			NC3594E				
G-AVDV	PA-22-150 Tri-Pacer	22-3752	N4423A	5. 1.67	Suzanne C.Brooks		
	(Modifed to PA-20 Super Pacer configuration)					Wellcross Grange, Slinfold	25. 8.00
G-AVDY	Phoenix Luton LA-4A Minor			10. 1.67	M.Stoney	Stapleford	9. 8.00P
	(Lycoming O-145)	PAL/1183 & PFA/808					
G-AVEC	Reims Cessna F.172H	0405		13. 1.67	W.H.Ekin (Engineering) Co Ltd	Inverness	11. 5.02
G-AVEF	SAN Jodel 150 Mascaret	16	F-BLDK	19. 1.67	Heavy Install Ltd	Headcorn	26. 6.02T
G-AVEH	SIAI-Marchetti S.205-20R	346		20. 1.67	M.Jarrett, K.Fear & R.L.F.Darby		
					t/a EH Aviation	Crowland	11. 6.99
G-AVEM	Reims Cessna F.150G	0198		23. 1.67	T.D.& J.A.Warren		
						Rushett Farm, Chessington	24. 3.02
G-AVEN	Reims Cessna F.150G	0202		23. 1.67	N.J. Richardson	Southampton	3. 9.01
					t/a 150 Flying Group		
G-AVER	Reims Cessna F.150G	0206		23. 1.67	E.Atherden	Barton	17. 8.01
G-AVEU	Wassmer WA.41 Super Baladou IV	136		27. 1.67	G.J.Richardson	Little Staughton	10.12.01
G-AVEX	Rollason-Druine D.62B Condor	RAE/616		31. 1.67	J.Riley & M.Mordue	Hinton-in-The-Hedges	5.10.99P
G-AVEY	Phoenix Currie Super Wot			31. 1.67	B.J.Anning	Watchford Farm, Yarcombe	4. 8.00P
	(Pobjoy "R")	SE.100 & PFA/3006					
G-AVEZ*	HPR.7 Dart Herald 210	169	PP-ASW	31. 1.67	Norwich Airport Fire Service	Norwich	5. 1.81
			G-AVEZ/HB-AAH		(For rescue training)		
G-AVFB*	HS.121 Trident 2E	2141	5B-DAC	1. 2.67	Duxford Aviation Society	Duxford	30. 9.82
			G-AVFB		(BEA c/s)		
G-AVFE*	HS.121 Trident 2E	2144		1. 2.67	Belfast Airport Fire Service	Belfast	6. 5.85T
G-AVFG*	HS.121 Trident 2E	2146		1. 2.67	BAA Fire Service	Heathrow	2. 7.85T
					(For fire service use 12.99)		
G-AVFJ*	HS.121 Trident 2E	2149		1. 2.67	CAA International Fire Training Centre		
						Teesside	18. 9.83T
G-AVFK*	HS.121 Trident 2E	2150		1. 2.67	Not known	RAF Valley	15. 8.83T
					(For Fire Section use 6.96)		
G-AVFM*	HS.121 Trident 2E	2152		1. 2.67	Brunel Technical College	Bristol	2. 6.84T
					(Instructional airframe 10.99)		
G-AVFP	PA-28-140 Cherokee	28-22652		1. 2.67	Rebecca L.Howells	Barton	14. 7.02
G-AVFR	PA-28-140 Cherokee	28-22747		1. 2.67	J.B.Edgar & J.E.Brown		
					t/a VFR Flying Group	Newtownards	6. 4.02
G-AVFS	PA-32-300 Cherokee Six	32-40038		1. 2.67	Comed Aviation Ltd	Blackpool	12. 7.91
					(Damaged Crosland Moor 28.9.90; on rebuild 1.97)		
G-AVFU	PA-32-300 Cherokee Six	32-40182		1. 2.67	M.J.Hoodless	(Camberley)	30. 4.00
G-AVFX	PA-28-140 Cherokee	28-22757		1. 2.67	R.A.Irwin	Thruxton	7. 7.01
					t/a Wessex Flyers Group		
G-AVFZ	PA-28-140 Cherokee	28-22767		1. 2.67	C.J.Law	Yeovil	10. 9.01
					t/a G-AVFZ Flying Group		
G-AVGA	PA-24-260 Comanche B	24-4489	N9027P	31. 1.67	M.D.Crooks, J.R.Butterworth & V.R.Dennay		
					t/a Conram Aviation Group "C'est Si Bon"	RAF Wittering	21. 1.00
G-AVGC	PA-28-140 Cherokee	28-22777		31. 1.67	P.A.Hill	Popham	22. 4.01
G-AVGD	PA-28-140 Cherokee	28-22782		31. 1.67	S. & G.W.Jacobs	Sywell	25. 8.02
G-AVGE	PA-28-140 Cherokee	28-22787		31. 1.67	A.J.Cutler	Bournemouth	5. 4.01
G-AVGG*	PA-28-140 Cherokee	28-22797		31. 1.67	Yorkshire Light Acft Ltd	Duxford	3. 7.71
					(Crashed Papplewick, Notts 10.8.70; wrecked 1.99)		
G-AVGH*	PA-28-140 Cherokee	28-22802		31. 1.67	Not known (Wreck stored 1.97)	Cardiff	5.12.91T

Regn	Type	C/n	P/I	Date	Owner/operator	Probable Base	CA Expy
G-AVGI	PA-28-140 Cherokee	28-22822		31. 1.67	D.G.Smith & C.D.Barden	Barton	10. 8.01
					t/a Golf India Group		
G-AVGJ*	SAN Jodel DR.1050 Ambassadeur	265	F-BJYJ	31. 1.67	Not known	Enstone	22. 4.85
					(WFU with glue failure 1985; on rebuild off-site 6.95)		
G-AVGK	PA-28-180 Cherokee C	28-3639	N9516J	2. 2.67	N.K.Lamping & S.B.Smith	Liverpool	14.10.02T
					t/a Golf Kilo Flying Group		
G-AVGU*	Reims Cessna F.150G	0199		8. 2.67	Colton Aviation Ltd	Little Staughton	22. 7.84
					(Damaged Southend 25.5.83; stored dismantled 4.99)		
G-AVGY	Cessna 182K Skylane	182-58112	N3112Q	17. 2.67	R.M.C.Sears & R.N.Howgego	Stoke Ferry	24. 3.00
G-AVGZ	CEA Jodel DR.1050 Sicile	341	F-BKPR	14. 2.67	D.C.Webb (Stored 9.99)	Bagby	13. 7.97
G-AVHH	Reims Cessna F.172H	0337		20. 2.67	Avon Aviation Ltd	Bristol	10. 2.02T
					t/a The Bristol & Wessex Aeroplane Club		
G-AVHL	SAN Jodel DR.105A Ambassadeur	90	F-BIVY	23. 2.67	V.D.Long	Hethel	17. 7.00
G-AVHM	Reims Cessna F.150G	0181		24. 2.67	Thornhill Aviation Ltd & G.Baldock (Op Airbase)		
	(Rebuilt 1997 with fuselage from G-ATRL [0050]: old fuselage dumped Shoreham)					Shoreham	30.11.01T
G-AVHT	Beagle E.3 (Auster AOP.9M)	-	WZ711	1. 3.67	M.Somerton-Raynor	AAC Middle Wallop	29. 4.01
	(Lycoming O-360)				(As "WZ711")		
G-AVHY	Sportavia Fournier RF4D	4009		10. 3.67	J.Connolly	Yearby	10.11.00P
G-AVIA	Reims Cessna F.150G	0184		10. 3.67	Cheshire Air Training Services Ltd		
						Liverpool	22.10.00T
G-AVIB	Reims Cessna F.150G	0180		10. 3.67	Edinburgh Air Centre Ltd	Edinburgh	2. 4.00T
G-AVIC	Reims Cessna F.172H	0320	N17011	10. 3.67	Leeside Flying Ltd	(Bandon, Eire)	12. 2.01
G-AVID	Cessna 182K	182-57734	N2534Q	10. 3.67	Jaguar Aviation Ltd	Bristol	4. 7.99
G-AVII	Agusta-Bell 206B JetRanger II	8011		10. 3.67	Bristow Helicopters Ltd	North Denes	4. 1.01T
					"Brighton Belle"		
G-AVIL	Alon A.2 Aircoupe	A.5	N5471E	14. 3.67	M.J.Close	Headcorn	7. 6.01
					(As "VX147" in RAF c/s)		
G-AVIN	Socata MS.880B Rallye Club	884		14. 3.67	P.Bradley	Compton Abbas	25. 5.02
G-AVIP	Brantly B.2B	471		14. 3.67	N.J.R.Minchin Hill Top Farm, Hambleden		18.10.01
G-AVIS	Reims Cessna F.172H	0413		14. 3.67	C.J.Freeman	Headcorn	17. 9.01T
					(Op Weald Air Services)		
G-AVIT	Reims Cessna F.150G	0217		14. 3.67	I.B.Osborn t/a Invicta Flyers	Manston	2. 4.01
G-AVIZ	Scheibe SF-25A Motorfalke	4552	(D-KOFY)	21. 3.67	T.J.Wiltshire	Spilsby	19. 9.91
					t/a Splisby Gliding Trust		
G-AVJE	Reims Cessna F.150G	0219		29. 3.67	T.F.Fisher	Booker	7. 1.01
					t/a G-AVJE Syndicate		
G-AVJF	Reims Cessna F.172H	0393		31. 3.67	J.A. & G.M.Rees	Haverfordwest	15.12.00
G-AVJH*	Druine D.62 Condor	PFA/603		31. 3.67	J.Tempest Kings Cliffe, Peterborough		4.11.83P
	(Continental O-200-A)				(Crashed Nefyn, Gwynedd 31.7.83; on rebuild 12.95)		
G-AVJI	Reims Cessna F.172H	0442		31. 3.67	N.P.Bendle	Shoreham	29. 9.98
					t/a G-AVJI Group		
	(Damaged Croft Farm, Defford 28.10.95; to Northbrook College 2.96)						
G-AVJJ	PA-30-160 Twin Comanche B	30-1420	N8285Y	7. 4.67	A.H.Manser	Gloucestershire	14. 7.01T
G-AVJK	SAN Jodel DR.1050/M1 Excellence	453	F-BLJH	7. 4.67	M.H.Wylde	Long Marston	20. 7.02
G-AVJO	Fokker E.III rep			12. 4.67	Bianchi Aviation Film Services Ltd		
	PPS/FOK/1 & PPS/REP/6					Booker	13. 8.97P
	(Continental C85) (Regd as c/n PPS/FOK/6)			(Op Blue Max Movie A/c Museum: as "E.III 422/15" in German c/s)			
G-AVJV	Wallis WA-117 Srs.1	K/402/X		12. 4.67	K.H.Wallis	Reymerston Hall	21. 4.89P
	(RR Continental O-200-B)				(Used major components of G-ATCV c/n 301; stored 5.99)		
G-AVJW	Wallis WA-118/M Meteorite	K/502/X		12. 4.67	K.H.Wallis	Reymerston Hall	21. 4.83P
	(Meteor Alfa 1)						
	(Used major components of G-ATPW c/n 401; two gyrocopters may have carried marks G-AVJW; stored 5.99)						
G-AVKB	Brochet MB.50 Pipistrelle	02	F-PFAL	17. 4.67	B.H.Pickard	Earls Colne	30.10.96P
	(Walter Mikron 3)						
G-AVKD	Sportavia Fournier RF4D	4024		19. 4.67	R.E.Cross t/a Lasham RF4 Group	Lasham	9. 5.00P
G-AVKE*	Gadfly HDW-1	HDW-1		19. 4.67	E.D.Ap Rees	Weston-super-Mare	
	(Continental IO-340A)				t/a The Helicopter Museum (Stored 8.97)		
G-AVKG	Reims Cessna F.172H	0345		21. 4.67	Aerogroup 98 Ltd	Ronaldsway	12.10.00
	(Rebuilt with fuselage of G-AVDC c/n 0382 1986)						
G-AVKI	Slingsby Nipper T.66 RA.45 Srs.3			24. 4.67	J.M.Greenway	(Penkridge)	7. 8.91P
	(Ardem 4C02) (Tipsy c/n 31) S.102/1586						
G-AVKJ	Slingsby Nipper T.66 RA.45 Srs.3			24. 4.67	T.Dale	Breighton	21. 8.97P
	(VW1834) (Tipsy c/n 32) S.103/1587				t/a G-AVKJ Group (Damaged 18.6.97)		
G-AVKK	Slingsby Nipper T.66 RA.45 Srs.3		EI-BJH	24. 4.67	C.Watson	Newtownards	6. 4.00P
	(Ardem 4C02) (Tipsy c/n 74) S.104/1588 G-AVKK						
G-AVKL	PA-30-160 Twin Comanche B	30-1418	OY-DHL	25. 4.67	Bravo Aviation Ltd	Jersey	8. 6.02
			G-AVKL/N8284Y				
G-AVKM*	Rollason-Druine D.62B Condor	RAE/620		26. 4.67	M.Hobson	Cruden Bay, Peterhead	30. 6.82
					(Damaged Wilkieston Farm, Cupar 2/3.3.82; stored 2.96)		
G-AVKN	Cessna 401	401-0082	(N3282Q)	26. 4.67	Law Leasing Ltd	Rochester	23. 4.00
G-AVKP	Beagle A.109 Airedale	B.540	SE-EGA	26. 4.67	D.R.Williams	Spanhoe	28. 5.00

43

Regn	Type	C/n	P/I	Date	Owner/operator	Probable Base	CA Expy
G-AVKR	Bolkow Bo.208C Junior	648	D-EGRA	28. 4.67	C.W.Grant	Old Sarum	8.11.98
G-AVKZ*	PA-23-250 Aztec C	27-3658	N6448Y	3. 5.67	Not known (Stored 5.93)	Little Snoring	29.10.90T
G-AVLB	PA-28-140 Cherokee	28-23158		8. 5.67	M.Wilson	Little Gransden	2.12.00
G-AVLC	PA-28-140 Cherokee	28-23178		8. 5.67	NE Wales Institute of Higher Education		
						Welshpool	25. 9.98
G-AVLD	PA-28-140 Cherokee	28-23193		8. 5.67	S.H.A.Petter	White Waltham	5. 4.00
					t/a The West London Strut Flying Group		
G-AVLE	PA-28-140 Cherokee	28-23223		8. 5.67	G.E.Wright South Lodge Farm, Widnerpool		22.12.01
					t/a Video Security Services		
G-AVLF	PA-28-140 Cherokee	28-23268		8. 5.67	G.H.Hughesdon	White Waltham	9. 2.01
G-AVLG	PA-28-140 Cherokee	28-23358		8. 5.67	R.Friedlander & D.C.Raymond		
						Grateley, Andover	2. 7.00
G-AVLH	PA-28-140 Cherokee	28-23368		8. 5.67	M.B.Rothschild	Stapleford	18. 8.00
G-AVLI	PA-28-140 Cherokee	28-23388		8. 5.67	I.R.Richmond & C Baxter	Southend	1. 4.01
					t/a Lima India Aviation Club		
G-AVLJ	PA-28-140 Cherokee	28-23393	9H-AAZ	8. 5.67	Demeter Aviation Ltd	Luton	1. 8.02
			G-AVLJ				
G-AVLM	Beagle B.121 Pup 2	B121-003		8. 5.67	T.M. & D.A.Jones	Egginton	29. 4.69S
					(On rebuild 8.99)		
G-AVLN	Beagle B.121 Pup 2	B121-004		8. 5.67	C.A.Thorpe	Manston	19. 8.01
G-AVLO	Bolkow Bo.208C Junior	650	D-EGUC	8. 5.67	P.J.Swain Sandford Hall, Knockin		8. 6.00P
G-AVLR	PA-28-140 Cherokee	28-23288		9. 5.67	S.W.Slade t/a Group 140	Cambridge	19. 2.01
G-AVLW	Sportavia Fournier RF4D	4025		9. 5.67	J.W Scott	Bidford/Bickmarsh	1. 2.01
G-AVLY	Jodel Wassmer D.120A Paris-Nice	331		11. 5.67	N.V. de Candole		
						Boarsbarrow Farm, Bridport	29. 6.98P
G-AVMA	Socata GY-80-180 Horizon	196		12. 5.67	B.R.Hildick		
						Shenstone Hall Farm, Shenstone	8. 1.01
G-AVMB	Rollason-Druine D.62B Condor	RAE/621		12. 5.67	L.J.Dray Watchford Farm, Yarcombe		1. 9.00P
					"Spirit of Silver City"		
G-AVMD	Cessna 150G	150-65504	N2404J	16. 5.67	T.A.White t/a Bagby Aviation	Bagby	2. 8.01
G-AVMF	Reims Cessna F.150G	0203		17. 5.67	J.F.Marsh Newton Green, Sudbury		21. 7.00
G-AVMH	BAC One-Eleven 510ED	BAC.136		11. 5.67	European Aviation Ltd	Bournemouth	9. 2.01T
G-AVMI	BAC One-Eleven 510ED	BAC.137		11. 5.67	European Aviation Ltd	Filton	25. 1.01T
					"The Rome Express"		
G-AVMJ	BAC One-Eleven 510ED	BAC.138		11. 5.67	European Aviation Ltd	Bournemouth	17.11.94T
					(WFU 6.94; cabin trainer use 8.96)		
G-AVMK	BAC One-Eleven 510ED	BAC.139		11. 5.67	European Aviation Ltd	Stansted	8. 8.00T
					(Op Jersey European Airways) "The Paris Express"		
G-AVML	BAC One-Eleven 510ED	BAC.140		11. 5.67	European Aviation Ltd	Bournemouth	11. 4.01T
					(Op European VIP First)		
G-AVMM	BAC One-Eleven 510ED	BAC.141		11. 5.67	European Aviation Ltd	Bournemouth	26. 8.01T
					(Stored 11.99)		
G-AVMN	BAC One-Eleven 510ED	BAC.142		11. 5.67	European Aviation Ltd	Filton	21. 6.00T
					(Air Bristol c/s)		
G-AVMO*	BAC One-Eleven 510ED	BAC.143		11. 5.67	RAF Museum	RAF Cosford	3. 2.95T
					Cancelled as WFU 12.7.93 (British Airways c/s) "Lothian Region"		
G-AVMP	BAC One-Eleven 510ED	BAC.144		11. 5.67	European Aviation Ltd	Bournemouth	6. 4.01T
					"The Madrid Express"		
G-AVMR	BAC One-Eleven 510ED	BAC.145		11. 5.67	European Aviation Ltd	Bournemouth	23.10.94T
					(Stored 3.96)		
G-AVMS	BAC One-Eleven 510ED	BAC.146		11. 5.67	European Aviation Ltd	Bournemouth	26. 2.01T
					"The London Express"		
G-AVMT	BAC One-Eleven 510ED	BAC.147		11. 5.67	European Aviation Ltd	Bournemouth	25.11.00T
G-AVMU*	BAC One-Eleven 510ED	BAC.148		11. 5.67	Duxford Aviation Society	Duxford	8. 1.95T
					(British Airways c/s)		
G-AVMV	BAC One-Eleven 510ED	BAC.149		11. 5.67	European Aviation Ltd	Bournemouth	5. 4.93T
					(Stored 9.96)		
G-AVMW	BAC One-Eleven 510ED	BAC.150		11. 5.67	European Aviation Ltd	Shannon	4.10.00T
					(Op AB Airlines)		
G-AVMX	BAC One-Eleven 510ED	BAC.151	(5N-USE)	11. 5.67	European Aviation Ltd	Bournemouth	27. 5.93
			G-AVMX		(Stored 1.00)		
G-AVMY	BAC One-Eleven 510ED	BAC.152		11. 5.67	European Aviation Ltd	Bournemouth	28. 6.01T
G-AVMZ	BAC One-Eleven 510ED	BAC.153	(5N-OSA)	11. 5.67	European Aviation Ltd	Bournemouth	17.10.02T
			G-AVMZ				
G-AVNC	Reims Cessna F.150G	0200		18. 5.67	J.Turner	Popham	24. 3.01
G-AVNE*	Westland Wessex 60 Srs.1	WA/561	G-17-3	15. 5.67	The Helicopter Museum Weston-super-Mare		7. 2.83
					G-ANE/5N-AJL/G-AVIATIONE/9M-ASS/VH-BHC/PK-HBQ/G-AVIATIONE/(G-AVMC)		
					(As "G-17-3")		
G-AVNN	PA-28-180 Cherokee C	28-4049		26. 5.67	C.S.Mitchell Trenchard Farm, Eggesford		2. 3.00
G-AVNO	PA-28-180 Cherokee C	28-4105		26. 5.67	Allister Flight Ltd	Southend	22. 9.01T

44

Regn	Type	C/n	P/I	Date	Owner/operator	Probable Base	CA Expy
G-AVNP	PA-28-180 Cherokee C	28-4113		26. 5.67	R.W.Harris, P.E.Preston, M.F.Hatt & M.Jahanfar		
					(Op Southend Flying Club)	Southend	21.10.01T
G-AVNR	PA-28-180 Cherokee C	28-4121		26. 5.67	R.R.Livingstone	Biggin Hill	24. 9.01T
G-AVNS	PA-28-180 Cherokee C	28-4129		26. 5.67	E.Alexander	Andrewsfield	10. 6.00T
G-AVNU	PA-28-180 Cherokee C	28-4153		26. 5.67	O.Durrani	Lydd	11. 2.01T
G-AVNW	PA-28-180 Cherokee C	28-4210		26. 5.67	Len Smith's School & Sports Ltd	Fairoaks	2. 7.00T
G-AVNX	Sportavia Fournier RF4D	4026		26. 5.67	M.G.Woollard	Little Gransden	21. 1.99P
G-AVNZ	Sportavia Fournier RF4D	4030		26. 5.67	V.S.E.Norman	Rendcomb	9. 7.01
G-AVOA	SAN Jodel DR.1050 Ambassadeur	195	F-BJYY	31. 5.67	D.A.Willies	Anwick	7. 8.00
G-AVOC	CEA Jodel DR.221 Dauphin	67		2. 6.67	J.M.Graty	Nuthampstead	27. 1.02
G-AVOD*	Beagle D.5/180 Husky	3688		6. 6.67	W.P.Miller	Mavis Enderby	31. 7.92T
	(Crashed Crosland Moor 31.7.92; wings donated to J/1 G-AJDW 9.98: on rebuild 1999)						
G-AVOH	Rollason-Druine D.62B Condor	RAE/622		6. 6.67	Rankart Ltd	Hinton-in-The-Hedges	1.10.99T
G-AVOM	CEA Jodel DR.221 Dauphin	65		6. 6.67	M.A.T.Mountford	Maypole Farm, Chislet	29.10.00
G-AVOO	PA-18-180 Super Cub	18-8511		7. 6.67	London Gliding Club Pty Ltd	Dunstable	27. 3.00
					"Terry Mac"		
G-AVOZ	PA-28-180 Cherokee C	28-3711	N9574J	13. 6.67	P.Hoskins & R.Flavell	Booker	6. 7.01
					t/a Oscar Zulu Flying Group		
	(Damaged landing Gunton Park, Cromer 4.9.99)						
G-AVPC	Druine D.31 Turbulent	PFA/544		15. 6.67	S.A.Sharp	Wigtown Baldoon	28. 9.99P
	(VW1500)						
G-AVPD	Jodel D.9 Bebe	521/MAC.1/PFA/927		15. 6.67	S.W.McKay (Stored 2.96)	Berkhamsted	6. 6.75S
	(VW1500)						
G-AVPH	Reims Cessna F.150G	0197		20. 6.67	Zero 9 Flight Academy	Little Snoring	9. 4.86T
G-AVPI	Reims Cessna F.172H	0409		20. 6.67	R.W.Cope	Netherthorpe	30. 5.00
G-AVPJ	DH.82A Tiger Moth	86326	NL879	20. 6.67	Catherine C.Silk		
					Bericote Farm, Blackdown, Leamington Spa		13. 8.01
G-AVPK*	Socata MS.892A Rallye Commodore 150			20. 6.67	B.A.Bridgewater		
		10736			Shelsley Beauchamp, Worcester		10. 1.92
	(Stored 8.92: cancelled by CAA 13.4.99)						
G-AVPM	SAN Jodel D.117	593	F-BHXO	20. 6.67	J.C.Haynes	Breighton	13. 1.99P
G-AVPN*	HPR.7 Dart Herald 213	176	I-TIVB	22. 6.67	Yorkshire Air Museum	Elvington	14.12.99T
	G-AVPN/D-BIBI/(HB-AAK) (Channel Express c/s)						
G-AVPO	Hindustan HAL-26 Pushpak	PK-127	9M-AOZ	31. 3.83	J.A.Rimell Cherry Tree Farm, Monewden		28. 7.99P
	(Continental C90)		VT-DWL				
G-AVPR	PA-30-160 Twin Comanche B	30-1511	N8395Y	27. 6.67	J.O.Coundley Farley Farm, Winchester		15.12.02
G-AVPS	PA-30-160 Twin Comanche B	30-1548	N8393Y	27. 6.67	J.M.Bisco Farley Farm, Winchester		9. 8.02
G-AVPV	PA-28-180 Cherokee C	28-2705	9J-RBP	27. 6.67	S.Moore	Stapleford	4. 9.99
G-AVPY	PA-25-235 Pawnee C	25-4330	N4636Y	7. 7.67	Farm Aviation Services Ltd	Enstone	14.10.77S
	(Crashed Lower Radbourne Farm, Ladbroke, Warwicks 25.6.76; status uncertain)						
G-AVRK	PA-28-180 Cherokee C	28-4041		11. 7.67	J.Gama	Coventry	27. 2.00
G-AVRP	PA-28-140 Cherokee	28-23153		14. 7.67	M.H.Hoffman t/a Trent-199	Tatenhill	15. 5.00
G-AVRS	Socata GY-80-180 Horizon	224		14. 7.67	Air Venturas Ltd	Bagby	7. 8.00
	(Damaged landing Throstle Nest Farm, Cleveland 12.9.99)						
G-AVRT	PA-28-140 Cherokee	28-23143		17. 7.67	C.L.Hawkins Kings Farm, Thurrock		10. 2.02
G-AVRU	PA-28-180 Cherokee C	28-4025		17. 7.67	D.J.Rowell	Clacton	22. 3.02
					t/a G-AVRU Partnership		
G-AVRW	Barritault JB-01 Minicab			18. 7.67	D.J.Smith	Hucknall	19. 8.00P
	(Continental C90) OH-1549 & PFA/1800				t/a Kestrel Flying Group		
G-AVRY	PA-28-180 Cherokee C	28-4089		24. 7.67	Brigfast Ltd	Blackbushe	26. 3.00
G-AVRZ	PA-28-180 Cherokee C	28-4137		24. 7.67	Mantavia Group Ltd	Guernsey	27.10.02
G-AVSA	PA-28-180 Cherokee C	28-4184		24. 7.67	D.J.Royle & W.Beaty	Barton	5. 5.02
					t/a G-AVSA Flying Group		
G-AVSB	PA-28-180 Cherokee C	28-4191		24. 7.67	T.H.Lloyd	Denham	2. 5.02
G-AVSC	PA-28-180 Cherokee C	28-4193		24. 7.67	Medidata Ltd	White Waltham	17. 3.00T
G-AVSD	PA-28-180 Cherokee C	28-4195		24. 7.67	Landmate Ltd	Haverfordwest	18. 5.01
G-AVSE*	PA-28-180 Cherokee C	28-4196		24. 7.67	G.Cotrulia	Kemble	30. 4.00T
	(Cancelled by CAA 18.5.99)						
G-AVSF	PA-28-180 Cherokee C	28-4197		24. 7.67	S.E.Pick & D.A.Rham	Blackbushe	6. 4.01
					t/a a Monday Club		
G-AVSI	PA-28-140 Cherokee	28-23148		24. 7.67	C.M.Royle	White Waltham	21. 1.01
					t/a G-AVSI Flying Group		
G-AVSP	PA-28-180 Cherokee C	28-3952	(PJ-ACT)	8. 8.67	L.J.Jones	Dunkeswell	17. 9.00T
G-AVSR	Beagle D.5/180 Husky	3689		8. 8.67	A.L.Young	Henstridge	19.10.02A
G-AVSZ	Agusta-Bell 206B JetRanger	8032	VH-BEQ	8. 8.67	Burman Aviation Ltd	Newcastle/Cranfield	16. 6.99T
	PK-HBZ/VR-BCR/PK-HBD/VR-BCR/G-AVSZ						
G-AVTJ	PA-32-260 Cherokee Six	32-219	N3373W	14. 8.67	J.A.Carr	Dunkeswell	20.11.01T
	(Rebuilt using spare Frame No.32-860S)						
G-AVTL*	Brighton Ax7-65 HAFB	01		17. 8.67	British Balloon Museum	Newbury	
					"Bristol Belle"		

Regn	Type	C/n	P/I	Date	Owner/operator	Probable Base	CA Expy
G-AVTP	Reims Cessna F.172H	0458		17. 8.67	R.A.Lee & A.S.Watkins t/a Tango Papa Group	White Waltham	7. 4.01
G-AVTT	Ercoupe 415D (Continental C85)	4399	SE-BFZ NC3774H	21. 8.67	Wright Farm Eggs Ltd (Stored 9.98) Cherry Tree Farm, Monewden		20. 1.86
G-AVTV	Socata MS.893A Rallye Commodore 180	10725		24. 8.67	D.B.& M.E.Meeks	Feshiebridge	6. 8.00
G-AVUD	PA-30-160 Twin Comanche B	30-1515	N8422Y	5. 9.67	P.M.Fox t/a FM Aviation	Biggin Hill	6. 5.01
G-AVUG	Reims Cessna F.150H	0234		11. 9.67	R.K.Moody & V.J.Larkin t/a Skyways Flying Group	Netherthorpe	9. 6.02
G-AVUH	Reims Cessna F.150H	0244		11. 9.67	C.M.Chinn	North Coates	11. 8.00
G-AVUO	Phoenix Luton LA.4A Minor	PAL/1313		21. 9.67	M.E.Vaisey (Hemel Hempstead) (Not completed and parts used in construction of G-AXKH - possible long-term build project)		
G-AVUS	PA-28-140 Cherokee	28-24065	(G-AVUT)	25. 9.67	D.J.Hunter	Norwich	28.10.01T
G-AVUT	PA-28-140 Cherokee	28-24085		25. 9.67	Bencray Ltd t/a Blackpool & Fylde Aero Club	Blackpool	16. 4.01T
G-AVUU	PA-28-140 Cherokee	28-24100	(G-AVUS)	25. 9.67	R.W.Harris, A.Jahanfar, P.E.Preston & M.F.Hatt (Op Southend Flying Club)	Southend	28. 4.00T
G-AVUZ	PA-32-300 Cherokee Six	32-40302		29. 9.67	Ceesix Ltd	Jersey	23. 4.00
G-AVVC	Reims Cessna F.172H	0443		29. 9.67	A.Turnbull	(Bedlington)	21.10.01T
G-AVVF*	DH.104 Dove 8	04541		2.10.67	Not known (Wreck on fire dump 6.97)	Gloucestershire	11. 2.88
G-AVVI*	PA-30-160 Twin Comanche B	30-1613	EI-AVD G-AVVI/N8454Y	5.10.67	Not known (Damaged at Shipdham 7.4.91; on rebuild 8.93)	Shipdham	7. 3.94T
G-AVVJ	Socata MS.893A Rallye Commodore 180	10752		6.10.67	P.Etherington t/a AVVJ Group	Gamston	28. 7.02
G-AVVL	Reims Cessna F.150H	0257		6.10.67	N.E.Sams "Samurai"	Cranfield	11. 3.89T
	(Experimental Wankel MWAE 100R engine under development 7.97) t/a International Aerospace Engineering						
G-AVVO*	Avro 652A Anson C.19 Srs.2	34219	VL348	6.10.67	Newark Air Museum (As "VL348")	Winthorpe	
G-AVVW*	Reims Cessna F.150H	0258		19.10.67	Brunel Technical College Ashley Down, Bristol (Instructional airframe 6.91)		31. 5.82
G-AVWA	PA-28-140 Cherokee	28-23660		19.10.67	SFG Ltd	Old Buckenham	19.12.02T
G-AVWD	PA-28-140 Cherokee	28-23700		19.10.67	C.Bentley & G.J.Williams t/a Evelyn Air	Leeds-Bradford	6. 8.01T
G-AVWE*	PA-28-140 Cherokee	28-23720		19.10.67	Not known (On rebuild 11.97)	Blackpool	22. 4.82T
G-AVWG	PA-28-140 Cherokee	28-23760		19.10.67	Bencray Ltd t/a Blackpool & Fylde Aero Club	Blackpool	11. 8.91T
	(Damaged Tal y Fan, Conwy, Gwynedd 11.12.88; status uncertain - only wings remain 6.96)						
G-AVWI	PA-28-140 Cherokee	28-23800		19.10.67	Mrs.L.M.Middleton	Cranfield	23. 1.00
G-AVWJ	PA-28-140 Cherokee	28-23940		19.10.67	F.E.Telling	(Esher)	13. 8.01
G-AVWL	PA-28-140 Cherokee	28-24000		19.10.67	B.W.Griffiths & R.Fraser-Duthie t/a Bobev Aviation	Coventry	6. 9.01
G-AVWM	PA-28-140 Cherokee	28-24005		19.10.67	A.Jahanfar, P.E.Preston, M.F.Hatt & R.W.Harris (Op Southend Flying Club)	Southend	27. 5.01T
G-AVWN	PA-28R-180 Cherokee Arrow	28R-30170		19.10.67	Vawn Air Ltd	Jersey	10. 4.02
G-AVWO	PA-28R-180 Cherokee Arrow	28R-30205		19.10.67	R.G.Tweddle	White Waltham	9. 9.00
G-AVWR	PA-28R-180 Cherokee Arrow	28R-30242		19.10.67	S.J.French, G.A.Rogers, C.A.Bailey & R.J.Doughton	Dunkeswell	7. 5.00
G-AVWT	PA-28R-180 Cherokee Arrow	28R-30362		19.10.67	Cloudbase Aviation Ltd	Barton	14. 4.00
G-AVWU	PA-28R-180 Cherokee Arrow	28R-30380		19.10.67	Arrow Flyers Ltd	Booker	18. 5.01
G-AVWV	PA-28R-180 Cherokee Arrow	28R-30404		19.10.67	R.V.Thornton & R.Barron t/a Strathtay Flying Group	Perth	18. 6.02
G-AVWY	Sportavia Fournier RF4D	4031		26.10.67	P Turner (Weston-super-Mare) (On rebuild 9.99)		15. 4.90A
G-AVXA	PA-25-235 Pawnee C (Re-built using new frame)	25-4244	N4576Y	26.10.67	South Wales Gliding Club Ltd	Usk	5. 4.00
G-AVXC	Slingsby Nipper T.66 RA.45 Srs.3 (Ardem 4C02)	S.108/1605		26.10.67	D.S.T.Eggleton Waits Farm, Belchamp Walter		16. 5.00P
G-AVXD	Slingsby Nipper T.66 RA.45 Srs.3 (VW1834 Acro)	S.109/1606		26.10.67	D.A.Davidson	Shenington	31. 8.00P
G-AVXF	PA-28R-180 Cherokee Arrow	28R-30044		26.10.67	J.A.Lunness t/a JDR Arrow Group	Top Farm, Royston	4. 6.01
G-AVXI	HS.748 Srs.2A/238	1623		2.11.67	Emerald Airways Ltd (Radar Calibration Service titles: stored 5.99)	Southend	30. 8.98T
G-AVXJ	HS.748 Srs.2A/238	1624		2.11.67	Emerald Airways Ltd	Exeter	22. 8.98T
G-AVXW	Rollason-Druine D.62B Condor	RAE/625		3.11.67	A.J.Cooper	Rochester	30. 9.01
G-AVXY	Auster AOP.9 (Regd with c/n AUS/120)	B5/10-120	XK417	7.11.67	E.Wright South Lodge Farm, Widmerpool t/a Auster Nine Group (As "XK417" in Army c/s)		9. 7.00P

Regn	Type	C/n	P/I	Date	Owner/operator	Probable Base	CA Expy
G-AVYE*	HS.121 Trident 1E-140	2139		13.11.67	British Aerospace plc Hatfield		13. 7.82
					(Noted 9.99)		
G-AVYK	Beagle A.61 Terrier 3	B.642	WJ357	20.11.67	J.P.Roland (Stored 8.98) Aboyne		28. 8.93
G-AVYL	PA-28-180 Cherokee D	28-4622		24.11.67	I.Kerr Perth		23. 5.02
					t/a Cherokee G-AVYL Flying Group		
G-AVYM	PA-28-180 Cherokee D	28-4638		24.11.67	Carlisle Aviation (1985) Ltd Kirkbride		14. 5.01T
G-AVYP	PA-28-140 Cherokee	28-24211		24.11.67	K.Hobbs . Belfast		10. 2.01
					t/a Aldergrove Flight Training Centre		
G-AVYR	PA-28-140 Cherokee	28-24226		24.11.67	DR Flying Club Ltd Gloucestershire		18. 6.00
					(Dowty Rotol)		
G-AVYS	PA-28R-180 Cherokee Arrow	28R-30456		24.11.67	A.M.Playford Poplar Hall Farm, Elmsett		19. 1.00
G-AVYT	PA-28R-180 Cherokee Arrow	28R-30472		24.11.67	E.J.Booth & B.D.Tipler Blackpool		13. 5.00
G-AVYV	Jodel Wassmer D.120A Paris-Nice	252	F-BMAM	27.11.67	A.J.Sephton (Stored 4.96)		
					Brickhouse Farm, Frogland Cross		30. 8.93P
G-AVZB*	LET Z-37 Cmelak	04-08	OK-WKQ	30.11.67	The Science Museum Wroughton		5. 4.84A
G-AVZI	Bolkow Bo.208C Junior	673	D-EGZF	19.12.67	C.F.Rogers (Wheathampstead)		24. 7.76
					(Status uncertain)		
G-AVZN	Beagle B.121 Pup 1	B121-006		19.12.67	J.K.Healey Old Buckenham		28. 7.01
					t/a Shipdham Aviators Flying Group		
G-AVZP	Beagle B.121 Pup 1	B121-008		19.12.67	T.A.White Bagby		8. 6.01
G-AVZR	PA-28-180 Cherokee C	28-4114	N4779L	19.12.67	Lincoln Aero Club Ltd Sturgate		30. 4.00T
G-AVZU	Reims Cessna F.150H	0283		29.12.67	R.D. & E.Forster Beccles		1.12.02T
					(Op Norfolk & Norwich Aero Club)		
G-AVZV	Reims Cessna F.172H	0511		29.12.67	E.L. & D.S.Lightbown Crosland Moor		24. 7.00
G-AVZW	EAA Model P Biplane	PFA/1314		29.12.67	R.G.Maidment & G.R.Edmondson Fairoaks		9. 8.00P
	(Lycoming O-290)						
G-AVZX	Socata MS.880B Rallye Club	1165		29.12.67	T.C.Bayes Sturgate		19.11.02

G-AWAA – G-AWZZ

Regn	Type	C/n	P/I	Date	Owner/operator	Probable Base	CA Expy
G-AWAA*	Socata MS.880B Rallye Club	1174		29.12.67	P.A.Cairns St.Just		4. 8.91
					(Stored 10.95: cancelled by CAA 4.3.99)		
G-AWAC	Socata GY-80-180 Horizon	234		29.12.67	Gardan Party Ltd "Le Fantome" Popham		11. 6.01
G-AWAH	Beechcraft D55 Baron	TE-540		1. 1.68	B.J.S.Grey Duxford		4. 7.99
G-AWAJ	Beechcraft D55 Baron	TE-536		1. 1.68	Standard Hose Ltd Blackpool		12. 3.01
G-AWAS*	Campbell-Bensen B.8Mc	CA/307		5. 1.68	S.Modi (Stored)		
					Borgo San Laurenz, Florence, Italy		27. 4.70
G-AWAT	Rollason-Druine D.62B Condor	RAE/627		8. 1.68	Tamwood Ltd Shoreham		12. 3.01
G-AWAU*	Vickers FB.27A Vimy rep	VAFA-02	"H651"	8. 1.68	RAF Museum Hendon		4. 8.69
					(As "F8614") "Triple First"		
G-AWAW*	Reims Cessna F.150F	0037	OY-DKJ	5. 1.68	The Science Museum (Flight Laboratory)		
	(Wichita c/n 63167)				South Kensington, London		8. 6.92T
G-AWAX	Cessna 150D	15060153	OY-TRJ	5.1.68	H.H.Cousins Fenland		23. 7.99T
	(Tail-wheel conversion)		N4153U				
G-AWAZ	PA-28R-180 Cherokee Arrow	28R-30512		8. 1.68	R.Z.Staniszewski Barton		28. 4.02
G-AWBA	PA-28R-180 Cherokee Arrow	28R-30528		8. 1.68	A.Taplin & G.A.Dunster Stapleford		23. 1.00
					t/a March Flying Group		
G-AWBB	PA-28R-180 Cherokee Arrow	28R-30552		8. 1.68	M.D.Parker & J.Lowe Bourn		24. 6.02
G-AWBC	PA-28R-180 Cherokee Arrow	28R-30572		8. 1.68	Anglo Aviation (UK) Ltd Bournemouth		28.12.00
G-AWBE	PA-28-140 Cherokee	28-24266		8. 1.68	B.E.Boyle Edge Hill		28. 6.02
G-AWBG	PA-28-140 Cherokee	28-24286		8. 1.68	Westward Airways (Lands End) Ltd St.Just		23. 2.01T
G-AWBH	PA-28-140 Cherokee	28-24306		8. 1.68	Tour UK Travel Ltd Newcastle		16.10.01
					t/a G-AWBH Group		
G-AWBJ	Sportavia Fournier RF4D	4055		12. 1.68	J.M.Adams RAF Syerston		6. 4.00P
G-AWBM	Druine D.31A Turbulent	PFA/1647		17. 1.68	A.D.Pratt North Coates		20. 7.95P
	(VW1700)						
G-AWBN	PA-30-160 Twin Comanche B	30-1472	N8517Y	18. 1.68	Stourfield Investments Ltd Jersey		2.12.02
G-AWBS	PA-28-140 Cherokee	28-24331		22. 1.68	M.A.English & T.M.Brown Little Snoring		25.11.01
G-AWBT*	PA-30-160 Twin Comanche B	30-1668	N8508Y	22. 1.68	Cranfield University Cranfield		25. 3.89
					(Damaged Humberside 10.3.88; instructional airframe 7.99)		
G-AWBU	Morane-Saulnier Type N Rep	PPS/REP/7		22. 1.68	Personal Plane Services Ltd Booker		29. 7.97P
	(Continental C90)				(Blue Max Movie Aero Club Museum; as "MS824" in French AF c/s)		
G-AWBW*	Reims Cessna F.172H	0486		22. 1.68	Brunel Technical College		
	(Crashed Compton Abbas 20.5.73; instructional airframe 6.91) Ashley Down, Bristol						15. 5.75
G-AWBX	Reims Cessna F.150H	0286		22. 1.68	J.Meddings Tatenhill		20.12.02
G-AWCM	Reims Cessna F.150H	0281		25. 1.68	R.Garbett Halfpenny Green		14. 8.99T
G-AWCN	Reims Cessna FR.172E Rocket	0020		25. 1.68	Y.F.Herdman (Romford)		12. 7.01
G-AWCO*	Reims Cessna F.150H	0338		29. 1.68	Not known Biggin Hill		29. 8.75
					(Wreck in open storage 2.95)		

Regn	Type	C/n	P/I	Date	Owner/operator	Probable Base	CA Expy
G-AWCP	Reims Cessna F.150H	0354		29. 1.68	C.E.Mason	Shobdon	12. 2.00
	(Tail-wheel conversion)						
G-AWCR*	Piccard Ax6 HAFB	6204		29. 1.68	British Balloon Museum & Library		
					"London Pride 1"	Newbury	
G-AWDA	Slingsby Nipper T.66 RA.45 Srs.3			7. 2.68	J.A.Cheesbrough Hill Farm, Marton, Hull		16. 5.00P
	(Acro/VW1834)	S.117/1624					
G-AWDE*	Glos-Air Airtourer T.2	504		9. 2.68	Not known	St.Just	6. 8.76
					(Crashed Stapleford 23.3.75; fuselage in open store 8.96)		
G-AWDO	Druine D.31 Turbulent	PFA/1649		21. 2.68	R.N.Crosland	Deanland, Hailsham	16. 3.00P
	(VW1600)						
G-AWDP	PA-28-180 Cherokee D	28-4870		21. 2.68	B.H. & P.M.Illston	Norwich	7.12.01T
					(Op Norwich School of Flying)		
G-AWDR	Reims Cessna FR.172E Rocket	0004		21. 2.68	B.A.Wallace	Nuthampstead	2. 4.01
G-AWDU	Brantly B.2B	481		23. 2.68	B.M.Freeman	(Stourport-on-Severn)	22. 7.01
G-AWDW	Campbell-Bensen CB.8MS	DS.1330		26. 2.68	M.R.Langton	Berkhamsted	7.10.71P
	(McC.4318C)				(Stored - status uncertain)		
G-AWEF	SNCAN Stampe SV-4C	549	F-BDCT	29. 3.68	The Tiger Club (1990) Ltd	Headcorn	19.12.01T
	(Gipsy Major)						
G-AWEI	Rollason-Druine D.62B Condor	RAE/628		6. 3.68	M.J.Steer	Rushett Farm, Chessington	10.11.98T
G-AWEK	Sportavia Fournier RF4D	4071		6. 3.68	P.Barrett	(Lightwater)	23. 8.74
					(Crashed nr Chelsfield, Kent 25.10.72; stored Rendcomb 12.93)		
G-AWEL	Sportavia Fournier RF4D	4077		7. 3.68	A.B.Clymo	Halfpenny Green	3. 9.00P
G-AWEM	Sportavia Fournier RF4D	4078		7. 3.68	B.J.Griffin	Wickenby	11. 6.00P
G-AWEN*	SAN Jodel DR.1050 Ambassadeur	67	F-BIVD	8. 3.68	Not known	Crosland Moor	8.11.85
					(Crashed Crosland Moor 11.8.83; stored 3.93)		
G-AWEO*	Reims Cessna F.150H	0342		11. 3.68	Shobdon Acft Maintenance Ltd	Shobdon	30. 9.90T
					(Damaged Baginton 22.11.89; on rebuild 3.96)		
G-AWEP	Barritault JB-01 Minicab	PFA/1801		12. 3.68	J.A.Stewart & J.Taylor		
	(Continental C90)					Griffins Farm, Temple Bruer	19. 5.00P
G-AWES*	Cessna 150H	150-68626	N22933	20. 3.68	Yorkshire Light Aircraft Ltd		
					(WFU after gale damage Glenrothes 2.10.81; on rebuild 1.97)	Leeds-Bradford	5. 8.84
G-AWET	PA-28-180 Cherokee D	28-4871		21. 3.68	Broadland Flying Group Ltd Old Buckenham		30. 4.00
G-AWEV	PA-28-140 Cherokee	28-24460		21. 3.68	Norflight Ltd	Ludham	6. 1.01
G-AWEX	PA-28-140 Cherokee	28-24472		21. 3.68	R.A.Page	Coventry	16. 4.01
					t/a Sir W.G.Armstrong-Whitworth Flying Group		
G-AWEZ	PA-28R-180 Cherokee Arrow	28R-30592		21. 3.68	T.R.Leighton, R.G.E.Simpson & D.A.C.Clissett		
						Stapleford	7.12.02
G-AWFB	PA-28R-180 Cherokee Arrow	28R-30689		21. 3.68	Luke Aviation Ltd	Bristol	19.11.01
G-AWFC	PA-28R-180 Cherokee Arrow	28R-30670		21. 3.68	B.J.Hines	Bristol	16. 7.01
G-AWFD	PA-28R-180 Cherokee Arrow	28R-30669		21. 3.68	D.J.Hill	Andrewsfield	19. 5.02
G-AWFF	Reims Cessna F.150H	0280		25. 3.68	J.A.Hardiman	Shobdon	19. 9.02T
G-AWFH*	Reims Cessna F.150H	0274		25. 3.68	Cheshire Fire Brigade Training School		
	(Crashed Swanton Morley 16.12.79; now fitted with tail from G-AWTX; stored 12.93)					Winsford	17.12.81
G-AWFJ	PA-28R-180 Cherokee Arrow	28R-30688		26. 3.68	Parplon Ltd	Barton	7. 5.02
G-AWFN	Rollason-Druine D.62B Condor	RAE/629		27. 3.68	R.James	Shobdon	17. 6.00
G-AWFO	Rollason-Druine D.62B Condor	RAE/630		27. 3.68	R.E.Major	Porthtowan, Cornwall	12.10.00P
G-AWFP	Rollason-Druine D.62B Condor	RAE/631		27. 3.68	D.J.Taylor	Blackbushe	22. 5.01
					t/a Blackbushe Flying Club		
G-AWFR	Druine D.31 Turbulent			27. 3.68	J.R.Froud	(Edenbridge, Kent)	
		SU.001 & PFA/1652			(Under construction 1993)		
G-AWFT	Jodel D.9 Bebe	PFA/932		29. 3.68	W.H.Cole	Spilsted Farm, Sedlescombe	22. 7.69P
	(VW1200)				(Stored 8.94)		
G-AWFW	SAN Jodel D.117	599	PH-VRE	2. 4.68	F.H.Greenwell	Bishopton, Durham	17. 3.00P
			F-BHXU				
G-AWFZ	Beechcraft 19A Musketeer Sport		N2811B	3. 4.68	R.Sweet & B.D.Corbett	Booker	12. 5.94
		MB-323			(Stored 9.97)		
G-AWGA*	Beagle A.109 Airedale	B.535	EI-ATA	3. 4.68	Not known	(Greater Manchester)	3. 7.86
			G-AWGA/D-ENRU				
G-AWGD	Reims Cessna F.172H	0503		5. 4.68	D.Whitton & P.Storey	Sywell	18. 7.00T
G-AWGJ	Reims Cessna F.172H	0531		8. 4.68	J. & C.J.Freeman	Headcorn	7. 7.90T
					(Damaged Headcorn 16.10.87; wreck stored 1.96)		
G-AWGK	Reims Cessna F.150H	0347		8. 4.68	G.E.Allen	(Lincoln)	30. 4.01
G-AWGM*	Mitchell Kittiwake II 002 & PFA/1329			9. 4.68	M.K.Field	Astley, Shrewsbury	13.10.86P
	(Continental O-240-A)			(Damaged Halton 18.1.86; open store 9.95; cancelled by CAA 4.3.99)			
G-AWGN	Sportavia Fournier RF4D	4084		9. 4.68	R.H.Ashforth	Gloucestershire	9. 6.00
					t/a The Gloster Aero Group		
G-AWGR	Reims Cessna F.172H	0484		9. 4.68	Pauline A.Hallam	Barton	27. 5.01
G-AWGZ	Taylor JT.1 Monoplane			17. 4.68	R.L.Sambell	(Hinckley)	21. 6.93P
	(Ardem 4CO2)	M.1 & PFA/1406			(Damaged Sleap 14.7.92)		
G-AWHB	CASA C.2111D (He.111H-16)	049	B2I-57	14. 5.68	Aces High Ltd	North Weald	
	(Officially quoted as c/n 167 - ex B2I-37)				(As "6J+PR"; on rebuild 1.99)		

Regn	Type	C/n	P/I	Date	Owner/operator	Probable Base	CA Expy
G-AWHS*	Hispano HA.1112-Mil (DB.605D)	228	C4K-170	14. 5.68	Auto n Technik Museum Sinsheim, Germany (As "4+·" in Luftwaffe c/s)		
G-AWHX	Rollason Beta B.2	RAE/04	(G-ATEE)	17. 4.68	S.G.Jones "Vertigo" (On rebuild 3.91)	Membury	14. 6.87P
G-AWHY	Falconar F-11-3 (Continental C90)	PFA/1322	G-BDPB (G-AWHY)	17. 4.68	B.E.Smith Wellcross Grange, Slinford		17. 3.00P
G-AWIF*	Brookland Mosquito	3 & LC.1		17. 4.68	Not known	St.Merryn	7. 1.82P
G-AWII	VS.349 Spitfire LF.Vc	WASP/20/223	AR501	25. 4.68	The Shuttleworth Trust Old Warden (As "AR501/NN-A" in 310 Sqn c/s)		13. 5.00P
G-AWIJ*	VS.329 Spitfire F.IIA	CBAF.14	P7350	25.4.68	Battle of Britain Memorial Flight (As "P7350/BA-Y" in 277 Sqdn c/s) RAF Coningsby		
G-AWIO*	Brantly B.2B	483	G-OBPG G-AWIO	30. 4.68	Not known) (Temp unregd 29.11.95)	Rhyl	5. 8.95
G-AWIP	Phoenix Luton LA-4A Minor (Continental A65) PAL/1308 & PFA/830			30. 4.68	J.Houghton (Damaged nr Holme-on-Spalding Moor 20.7.88; status uncertain)	Sproatley	8. 5.89P
G-AWIR	Bushby-Long Midget Mustang (Continental O-200-A)	PFA/1315		30. 4.68	K.E.Sword (On overhaul 1991)	Leicester	6. 3.90P
G-AWIT	PA-28-180 Cherokee D	28-4987		30. 4.68	Cherry Orchard Aparthotel Ltd (Op Manx Flyers Aero Club) Ronaldsway		16. 6.02T
G-AWIV	Airmark TSR.3 PFA/1325 (Continental PC60)			30. 4.68	D.J. & F.M.Nunn "Stor"	St Just	31. 1.00P
G-AWIW	SNCAN Stampe SV-4B	532	F-BDCC	2. 5.68	R.E.Mitchell (On rebuild 3.95)	RAF Cosford	6. 5.73
G-AWJE	Slingsby Nipper T.66 RA.45 Srs.3 (VW1834)	S.121/1628		8. 5.68	T.S.Mosedale	Barton	6. 7.00P
G-AWJF*	Slingsby Nipper T.66 RA.45 Srs.3	S.122/1629		8. 5.68	S.Maric (Stored 6.95)	(Glasgow)	7. 6.88P
G-AWJV*	DH.98 Mosquito TT.35	-	TA634	21. 5.68	de Havilland Aircraft Museum (As "TA634/8K-K" in 571 Sqdn c/s) Salisbury Hall, London Colney		
G-AWJX	Moravan Zlin Z.526 Trener Master	1049		22. 5.68	Aerobatics International Ltd (Stored 3.99) Rushett Farm, Chessington		29. 5.85A
G-AWJY	Moravan Zlin Z.526 Trener Master	1050		22. 5.68	M.Gainza	White Waltham	29. 8.99
G-AWKD	PA-17 Vagabond (Continental A65)	17-192	F-BFMZ N4892H/NC4892H	27. 5.68	A.T. & Mrs.M.R.Dowie Scotland Farm, Hook		6. 9.00P
G-AWKM	Beagle B.121 Pup 1	B121-017		11. 6.68	D.M.G.Jenkins Bourne Park, Hurstbourne Tarrant (Damaged Swansea 7.91; stored wingless 8.99)		29. 6.84
G-AWKO	Beagle B.121 Pup 1	B121-019		11. 6.68	E.C.Felix	Elstree	23. 6.00T
G-AWKP*	CEA Jodel DR.253 Regent	130		14. 6.68	G.R.W.Wright t/a G-AWKP Group (Force landed Blackpool 8.6.98: cancelled by CAA 13.10.98)	Blackpool	1.10.98
G-AWKT	Socata MS.880B Rallye Club	1235		17. 6.68	D.G.Cochrane	Enniskillen	15.10.99
G-AWKX*	Beechcraft A65 Queen Air	LC-303		21. 6.68	Northbrook College (Instructional airframe 8.97)	Shoreham	25.10.89T
G-AWLA	Reims Cessna F.150H	0269	N13175	27. 6.68	T.A.White t/a Bagby Aviation	Bagby	28. 6.01T
G-AWLF	Reims Cessna F.172H	0536		27. 6.68	Gannet Aviation Ltd	Aldergrove	25.11.99
G-AWLG	SIPA 903	82	F-BGHG	27. 6.68	S.W.Markham Valentine Farm, Odiham (Stored 1997)		22. 8.79P
G-AWLI	PA-22-150 Tri-Pacer	22-5083	N7256D	1. 7.68	J.S.Lewery "Little Peach"	Shoreham	5. 6.02
G-AWLM*	Campbell-Bensen B.8MS (McCulloch 4318A)	CA/311	EI-ATE G-AWLM	8. 7.68	Not known (Stored 1992)	Haslemere, Surrey	20. 3.80P
G-AWLO	Boeing Stearman E75 (PT-13D) Kaydet (P&W R985)	75-5563	5Y-KRR VP-KRR/42-17400	9. 7.68	N.D.Pickard	Panshanger	7.10.01
G-AWLP	Mooney M.20F Executive 21	680200		9. 7.68	I.C.Lomax	Ottringham	7. 7.00
G-AWLR	Slingsby Nipper T.66 RA.45 Srs.3	S.125/1662		9. 7.68	T.D.Reid	Newtownards	17. 2.00P
G-AWLS	Slingsby Nipper T.66 RA.45 Srs.3	S.126/1663		9. 7.68	G.A.Dunster & B.Gallagher (Loughton, Essex) (Damaged Stapleford 14.1.88; on rebuild 1995)		25. 3.88P
G-AWLX*	Auster 5 J/2 Arrow	2378	F-BGJQ OO-ABZ	10. 7.68	W.J.Taylor (On rebuild 11.93)	RAF West Raynham	23. 4.70
G-AWLZ	Sportavia Fournier RF4D	4099		12. 7.68	J.H.Taylor t/a Nympsfield RF4 Group	Nympsfield	31. 1.00P
G-AWMD	Jodel.D.11 (Continental C90)	PFA/904		19. 7.68	D.A.Barr-Hamilton t/a Moby Dick Flying Group "Moby Dick"	Shobdon	8. 4.00P
G-AWMF	PA-18-180 Super Cub	18-8674	N4356Z	23. 7.68	Booker Gliding Club Ltd	Booker	26. 8.00
G-AWMI	AESL Airtourer T.2 (115)	505		24. 7.68	W.G.Jones t/a Airtourer Group	Cardiff	15.12.00
G-AWMN	Phoenix Luton LA-4A Minor (VW1800)	PFA/827		30. 7.68	B.J.Douglas	Newtownards	15. 7.00P
G-AWMP	Reims Cessna F.172H	0488		31. 7.68	R.J.D.Blois	Yoxford, Saxmundham	23.12.02

Regn	Type	C/n	P/I	Date	Owner/operator	Probable Base	CA Expy
G-AWMR	Druine D.31 Turbulent 43 & PFA/1661 (VW1390)			1. 8.68	M.J.Bond "Demelza"	Inverness	27. 9.00P
G-AWMT	Reims Cessna F.150H	0360		1. 8.68	Oilfield Expertise Ltd	Newtownards	24. 6.00
G-AWNP	Boeing 747-136	20952		18. 9.74	British Airways plc (For disposal 11.99)	(Roswell, USA)	12.12.01T
G-AWNT	BN-2A Islander	32		2. 8.68	Aerofilms Ltd	Cranfield	24. 3.01A
G-AWOA	Socata MS.880B Rallye Club	1258		2. 8.68	J.A.Rimmer	Sturgate	20.10.02
G-AWOE	Aero Commander 680E	753-41	N3844C	5. 8.68	J.M.Houlder t/a Elstree Flying Club	Elstree	13. 3.00
G-AWOF	PA-15 Vagabond (Continental C90)	15-227	F-BETF	6. 8.68	C.M.Hicks	Barton	29. 2.00P
G-AWOH	PA-17 Vagabond (Continental C90)	17-191	F-BFMY N4891H	6. 8.68	W.M.Haley, D.Ridley & R.H.Ryle t/a The High Flatts Flying Group High Flatts Farm, Chester-le-Street		2. 6.00P
G-AWOK*	Sussex Gas (Free) Balloon	SARD.1		7. 8.68	British Balloon Museum "Sardinia" (Stored)	Newbury	
G-AWOT	Reims Cessna F.150H	0389		14. 8.68	J.M.Montgomerie & J.Ferguson (Stored 4.97)	Kilkerran	13. 6.89
G-AWOU	Cessna 170B	25829	VQ-ZJA ZS-CKY/CR-ADU/N3185A	16. 8.68	S.Billington	White Waltham	27. 5.01
G-AWOX*	Westland Wessex 60 Srs.1	WA/686	G-17-2	28. 8.68	Paintball Adventure West		13. 1.83
	G-AWOX/5N-AJO/G-AWOX/9Y-TFB/G-AWOX/VH-BHE/G-AWOX/VR-BCV/G-AWOX/G-17-1 Kingswood, Bristol						
G-AWPH	Percival P.56 Provost T.1	PAC/F/003	WV420	6. 9.68	J.A.D.Bradshaw Three Mile Cross, Reading		8. 6.00P
G-AWPJ	Reims Cessna F.150H	0376		9. 9.68	W.J.Greenfield (Op Humberside Flying Club)	Humberside	24. 4.02T
G-AWPN	Shield Xyla 2 & PFA/1320 (Continental A65)			13. 9.68	K.R.Snell	Deanland, Hailsham	23. 6.00P
G-AWPP	Reims Cessna F.150H	0348		13. 9.68	K2 Aviation Ltd & R.S.Willcock Cranfield (Damaged landing Cranfield 3.2.99: fuselage only 7.99)		22. 7.01T
G-AWPS	PA-28-140 Cherokee	28-20196	5N-AEK	16. 9.68	A.R.Matthews	Sittles Farm, Alrewas	18. 9.00
G-AWPU	Reims Cessna F.150J	0411		18. 9.68	LAC (Enterprises) Ltd t/a Lancashire Aero Club	Barton	19.10.00T
G-AWPW	PA-12 Super Cruiser	12-3947	N78572 NC78572	23. 9.68	AK Leasing (Jersey) Ltd	Jersey	5. 4.01
G-AWPY	Campbell-Bensen B.8M	CA/314		20. 9.68	J.Jordan	Melrose Farm, Melbourne	
G-AWPZ	Andreasson BA-4B	1	SE-XBS	24. 9.68	J.M.Vening	Goodwood	12.10.00P
G-AWRK	Reims Cessna F.150J	0410		8.10.68	Systemroute Ltd	Shoreham	15. 7.00T
G-AWRP*	Cierva Rotorcraft CR.LTH.1 Grasshopper III	GB.1		14.10.68	The Helicopter Museum Weston-super-Mare		12. 5.72P
G-AWRS	Avro 652A Anson C.19/2	33785	TX213	14.10.68	North East Aircraft Museum (On rebuild 5.97)	Usworth	10. 8.73
G-AWRY	Hunting-Percival P.56 Provost T.1	XF836 PAC/F/339 8043M	29.10.81	Sylmar Aviation & Services Ltd (As "XF836/J-G") Lower Wasing Farm, Brimpton (Damaged nr Newbury 28.7.87; on rebuild 6.94)		22. 8.88P
G-AWSA*	Avro 652A Anson C.19/2	293483	N5054 G-AWSA/VL349	21.10.68	Norfolk & Suffolk Aviation Museum (As "VL349")	Flixton	
G-AWSH	Moravan Zlin Z.526 Trener Master	1052	OK-XRH G-AWSH	23.11.68	Aerobatics International Ltd	White Waltham	8.10.00
G-AWSL	PA-28-180 Cherokee D	28-4907		30.10.68	Fascia Services Ltd Kings Farm, Thurrock/Southend		23. 7.00
G-AWSM	PA-28-235 Cherokee C	28-11125		30.10.68	N.A.Wright t/a Aviation Projects	(London SW20)	9. 3.01T
G-AWSN	Rollason-Druine D.62B Condor	RAE/632		31.10.68	M.K.A.Blyth	Little Gransden	31. 8.00P
G-AWSP	Rollason-Druine D.62B Condor	RAE/634		31.10.68	R.Q. & A.S.Bond (Stored 10.97)	Enstone	23. 1.95
G-AWSS	Rollason-Druine D.62B Condor	RAE/636		31.10.68	N.J. & D.Butler (Stored 10.95)	Fordoun	19.10.94P
G-AWST	Rollason-Druine D.62B Condor	RAE/637		31.10.68	P.L.Clements Beeches Farm, South Scarle		7. 5.00P
G-AWSV*	Saro Skeeter AOP.12	S2/5107	XM553	31.10.68	Major M.Somerton-Rayner (As "XM553") AAC Middle Wallop		22. 2.95P
G-AWSW	Beagle D.5/180 Husky	3690	XW635 G-AWSW	4.11.68	C.Tyers t/a Windmill Aviation (As "XW635")	Spanhoe	18. 5.01T
G-AWTJ	Reims Cessna F.150J	0419		8.11.68	D.G.Williams	Headcorn	8.12.01T
G-AWTL	PA-28-180 Cherokee D	28-5068		12.11.68	E.Alexander	Andrewsfield	8. 6.01T
G-AWTS	Beechcraft 19A Musketeer Sport	MB-412	OO-BGN G-AWTS/N2763B	14.11.68	J.Holden & G.Benet	Lydd	15. 8.02T
G-AWTV	Beechcraft 19A Musketeer Sport	MB-424	N2770B	14.11.68	L.Mariscotti	Southend	17. 8.00
G-AWTX	Reims Cessna F.150J	0404		18.11.68	R.D. & E.Forster	Beccles	25. 6.95T
G-AWUA*	Cessna P206D Super Skylane	P206-0550	N8750Z	21.11.68	Not known (Damaged Thruxton 16.10.87; stored 6.96)	Blackpool	4.12.87
G-AWUB*	Gardan GY-201 Minicab	A.205	F-PERX	22.11.68	R.A.Yates (Fuselage stored 9.91)	Sibsey	23.10.80P
G-AWUE	SAN Jodel DR.1050 Ambassadeur	299	F-BKHE	22.11.68	K.W. & F.M.Wood (On rebuild 4.97)	Insch	AC

Regn	Type	C/n	P/I	Date	Owner/operator	Probable Base	CA Expy
G-AWUG	Reims Cessna F.150H	0299		25.11.68	Fraggle Leasing Ltd Edinburgh (Op Edinburgh Air Centre)		12. 9.99T
G-AWUH*	Reims Cessna F.150H	0307		25.11.68	Not known Farley Farm, Winchester (Fuselage stored 6.99)		16. 7.94T
G-AWUJ	Reims Cessna F.150H	0332		25.11.68	S.R.Hughes	Netherthorpe	3. 2.00
G-AWUK*	Reims Cessna F.150H	0344		25.11.68	Not known Oaksey Park (Crashed Shoreham 4.9.71; stored 4.95)		3. 9.73
G-AWUL	Reims Cessna F.150H	0346		25.11.68	C.A. & L.P.Green Drayton St.Leonard		20. 5.00
G-AWUN	Reims Cessna F.150H	0377		25.11.68	D.S.Paton	Sywell	12.11.01
G-AWUO	Reims Cessna F.150H	0380		25.11.68	S.Stevens t/a SAS Flying Group	Thruxton	2. 4.01
G-AWUT	Reims Cessna F.150J	0405		25.11.68	S.J.Black Sherburn in Elmet		18. 9.00
G-AWUU	Reims Cessna F.150J	0408	EI-BRA G-AWUU	25.11.68	A.L.Grey Armshold Farm, Kingston, Cambs		15. 6.97
G-AWUX	Reims Cessna F.172H	0577		25.11.68	D.K.& K.Brian, A.M.Martin & C.Kelly St.Just		27. 3.01
G-AWUZ	Reims Cessna F.172H	0587		25.11.68	G.F.Burling	Andrewsfield	26.10.01
G-AWVA	Reims Cessna F.172H	0597		25.11.68	Barton Air Ltd	Barton	21. 5.00
G-AWVB	SAN Jodel D.117	604	F-BIBA	26.11.68	H.Davies	Swansea	31. 5.00P
G-AWVC	Beagle B.121 Pup 1	B121-026	(OE-CUP)	27.11.68	J.H.Marshall & J.J.West	Sturgate	2. 7.01
G-AWVE	CEA Jodel DR.1050/M1 Sicile Record	612	F-BMPQ	27.11.68	E.A.Taylor	Southend	18. 5.00
G-AWVF	Hunting-Percival P.56 Provost T.1	XF877 PAC/F/375		28.11.68	Hunter Wing Ltd (As "XF877/J-X")	Sandown	24. 6.01P
G-AWVG	AESL Airtourer T2 (115)	513	OO-WIC G-AWVG	29.11.68	C.J.Scholfield Top Farm, Royston		30. 6.01
G-AWVN	Aeronca 7AC Champion	7AC-6005	N2426E NC2426E	4.12.68	P.K.Brown Rush Green t/a Champ Flying Group		15. 3.00P
G-AWVZ	Jodel D.112	898	F-PKVL	12.12.68	D.C.Stokes	East Pennard	10. 5.00
G-AWWE	Beagle B.121 Pup 2	B121-032	G-35-032	12.12.68	J.N.Randle	Coventry	10. 5.02
G-AWWI	SAN Jodel D.117	728	F-BIDU	13.12.68	W.J.Evans	Rhigos	1. 6.00P
G-AWWM	Gardan GY-201 Minicab	A.195	F-BFOQ	1. 1.69	P J Brayshaw Haddock Stone Farm, Markington		10.12.92P
G-AWWN	SAN Jodel DR.1050 Sicile	398	F-BLJA	8. 1.69	R.A.J.Hurst (Buntingford, Herts)		14. 6.01
G-AWWO	CEA Jodel DR.1050 Sicile	552	F-BLOI	8. 1.69	A.R.Grimshaw & J.Hodcroft Barton t/a The Whiskey Oscar Group		15. 5.00
G-AWWP	Aerosport Woody Pusher Mk.3	WA/163 & PFA/1323		7. 1.69	M.S.& Mrs R.D.Bird Pepperbox, Salisbury (Stored 6.93)		
G-AWWT	Druine D.31 Turbulent (VW1600)	PFA/1653		15. 1.69	E.L.Phillips Andrewsfield (Damaged Andrewsfield 7.10.96)		23. 4.97P
G-AWWU	Reims Cessna FR.172F Rocket	0111		15. 1.69	Westward Airways (Lands End) Ltd St.Just		16. 3.00T
G-AWWW	Cessna 401	401-0294	N8446F	19.12.68	Treble Whiskey Aviation Ltd Blackpool (Op Westair Flying Services)		3. 2.00T
G-AWXR	PA-28-180 Cherokee D	28-5171		24. 1.69	Aero Club de Portugal (Lisbon, Portugal)		14. 4.01
G-AWXS	PA-28-180 Cherokee D	28-5283		24. 1.69	J.A.Hardiman	Shobdon	3. 3.00T
G-AWXY	Morane MS.885 Super Rallye	5097	EI-AMG	29. 1.69	K.Henderson	Sandtoft	1. 2.97
G-AWXZ	SNCAN Stampe SV-4C	360	F-BHMZ Fr.Mil/F-BCOI	30. 1.69	Personal Plane Services Ltd Booker (Op Blue Max Movie A/c Museum)		10. 6.02A
G-AWYB	Reims Cessna FR.172F Rocket	0075		30. 1.69	C.W.Larkin Larkins Farm, Laindon North		17. 9.00
G-AWYJ	Beagle B.121 Pup 2	B121-038	G-35-038	10. 2.69	H.C.Taylor	Popham	27. 4.02
G-AWYL	CEA Jodel DR.253B Regent	143		11. 2.69	M.R.Elms	Rochester	9. 4.00
G-AWYO	Beagle B.121 Pup 1	B121-041	G-35-041	11. 2.69	B.R.C.Wild	Popham	5.12.02
G-AWYV	BAC One-Eleven 501EX	BAC.178		11. 2.69	European Aviation Ltd Birmingham (Op Maersk Air)		24. 6.01T
G-AWYX	Socata MS.880B Rallye Club	1311		11. 2.69	Marjorie J.Edwards Henstridge (Open storage 4.98)		27. 6.86
G-AWYY*	Slingsby T.57 Sopwith Camel F.1 rep (Clerget)	1701	"C1701" N1917H/G-AWYY	14. 2.69	Fleet Air Arm Museum RNAS Yeovilton (As "B6401")		1.9.85P*
G-AWZI*	HS.121 Trident 3B-101	2310		14. 1.69	Surrey County Fire Brigade HQ Reigate (Instructional airframe)		5. 8.85T
G-AWZJ*	HS.121 Trident 3B-101	2311		14. 1.69	Prestwick Fire Dept Prestwick (Noted 6.98)		12. 9.85T
G-AWZK*	HS.121 Trident 3B-101	2312		14. 1.69	British Airways plc Heathrow (Instructional airframe 12.99) (As "Windsor Collection")		14.10.86T
G-AWZM*	HS.121 Trident 3B-101	2314		14. 1.69	The Science Museum Wroughton (British Airways c/s)		13.12.85T
G-AWZO*	HS.121 Trident 3B-101	2316		14. 1.69	De Havilland Aircraft Museum Hatfield (Stored 9.99)		13. 2.86T
G-AWZS*	HS.121 Trident 3B-101	2319		14. 1.69	CAA International Fire Training Centre Teesside		9. 9.86T

Regn	Type	C/n	P/I	Date	Owner/operator	Probable Base	CA Expy
G-AWZU*	HS.121 Trident 3B-101	2321		14. 1.69	CAA Fire Service (Open storage 5.99)	Stansted	3. 7.85T
G-AWZX*	HS.121 Trident 3B-101	2324		14. 1.69	Gatwick Airport Ltd (Fire Services airframe)	Gatwick	30. 4.84T
G-AWZZ*	HS.121 Trident 3B-101	2326		14. 1.69	Birmingham Airport Fire Service (Training airframe 5.99)	Birmingham	21. 5.84T

G-AXAA – G-AXZZ

Regn	Type	C/n	P/I	Date	Owner/operator	Probable Base	CA Expy
G-AXAB	PA-28-140 Cherokee	28-20238	EI-AOA N6206W	17. 2.69	Bencray Ltd t/a Blackpool & Fylde Aero Club	Blackpool	9.10.00T
G-AXAK	Socata MS.880B Rallye Club	1304		20. 2.69	A.G.Foster	North Coates	23. 1.00
G-AXAN	DH.82A Tiger Moth (Official c/n EM720-85)	85951	F-BDMM Fr.AF/EM720	21. 2.69	M.E.Carrell (As "EM720")	Little Gransden	17. 3.99
G-AXAO*	Omega O-56 HAFB (Rebuilt as Western O-65 c/n 021)	02		25. 2.69	Not known "Alcofribas"	Gerrards Cross	19. 5.75S
G-AXAS	Wallis WA-116-T/Mc (Used major components from G-AVDH c/n 216)	217		25. 2.69	K.H.Wallis (Noted 5.99)	Reymerston Hall	15. 6.99P
G-AXAT	SAN Jodel D.117A	836	F-BITJ	26. 2.69	P.S.Wilkinson	Insch	22.12.99P
G-AXAU	PA-30-160 Twin Comanche C	30-1753	N8613Y	25. 2.69	Bartcourt Ltd (Stored 2.96)	Bournemouth	8. 3.86T
G-AXBF	Beagle D.5/180 Husky	3691	OE-DEW	17.10.84	C.M.Barnes	Garden Piece, Basingstoke	23. 6.00
G-AXBG	Bensen B.8M	RC.1		12. 3.69	R.Curtis	(Bury St.Edmunds)	
G-AXBH	Reims Cessna F.172H	0571		12. 3.69	D.F.Ranger	Popham	6. 3.00T
G-AXBJ	Reims Cessna F.172H	0573		12. 3.69	R.H.Bowers t/a Bravo Juliet Group	Leicester	27.11.00
G-AXBU*	Reims Cessna FR.172F Rocket	0073		12. 3.69	M.Hobson Cruden Bay, Peterhead (Crashed nr Priestland, Darvel 13.10.74; wreck in store 2.96)		23. 8.75
G-AXBW	DH.82A Tiger Moth	83595	6854M T5879	12. 3.69	Hunter Wing Ltd (As "T5879")	Frensham	15. 1.01
G-AXBZ	DH.82A Tiger Moth	86552	F-BGDF Fr.AF/PG643	14. 3.69	D.H.McWhir	Newtownards	6. 9.01
G-AXCA	PA-28R-200 Cherokee Arrow	28R-35053		18. 3.69	R.A.Symmonds	Southend	6. 3.00
G-AXCG	SAN Jodel D.117	510	PH-VRA F-BHXI	19. 3.69	C.A.White t/a The Charlie Golf Group	Andrewsfield	15. 6.00P
G-AXCI*	Bensen B.8M	CEW.1		20. 3.69	Not known (Stored 9.93)	Lichfield	
G-AXCL	Socata MS.880B Rallye Club	1321		25. 3.69	P.P.Loucas	Seething	9. 7.00
G-AXCM	Socata MS.880B Rallye Club	1322		25. 3.69	D.C.Maniford	Croft Farm, Defford	23. 7.01
G-AXCN*	Socata MS.880B Rallye Club (Damaged Thruxton 16.10.87: on rebuild 1992: wrecked fuselage 5.99 & cancelled as WFU 16.10.99)	1328		25. 3.69	J.E.Compton	Kemble	24. 7.87
G-AXCX	Beagle B.121 Pup 2	B121-046	G-35-046	31. 3.69	L.A.Pink	Farley Farm, Winchester	10. 7.94
G-AXCY	SAN Jodel D.117A	499	F-BHXB	31. 3.69	R.D.P.Cadle	Long Marston	8. 5.00P
G-AXDC	PA-23-250 Aztec D	27-4169	N6829Y	8. 4.69	N.J.Lilley	Bodmin	24. 8.98T
G-AXDI	Reims Cessna F.172H	0574		14. 4.69	M.F. & J.R.Leusby t/a Jeanair	Wellesbourne Mountford	25.11.99
G-AXDK	CEA DR.315 Petit Prince	378		16. 4.69	M.R.Weatherhead & T.J.Thomas t/a Delta Kilo Flying Group	Sywell	6. 5.02
G-AXDM	HS.125 Srs.400B	25194		17. 4.69	GEC - Marconi Avionics (Holdings) Ltd	Edinburgh	7. 6.00
G-AXDN*	BAC/Aerospatiale Concorde	13522 & 01		16. 4.69	Duxford Aviation Society	Duxford	30. 9.77
G-AXDV	Beagle B.121 Pup 1	B121-049		18. 4.69	T.A.White	Bagby	7. 4.01
G-AXDW	Beagle B.121 Pup 1	B121-053		18. 4.69	I.Beaty, P.J.Abbott & J.R.A.Stevens t/a Cranfield Delta Whiskey Group	Cranfield	28. 1.02
G-AXDY*	Falconar F-11 (Incorporated redundant parts from Jodel D.112 G-AYBR; fuselage stored 9.91)	PFA/906		21. 4.69	R.A.Yates	Sibsey	
G-AXED	PA-25-235 Pawnee B	25-3586	OH-PIM	24. 4.69	Wolds Gliding Club Ltd	Pocklington	11. 3.00
G-AXEH*	Beagle B.125 Bulldog 1	B.125-001		25. 4.69	The Museum of Flight/Royal Museum of Scotland	East Fortune	15. 1.77
G-AXEI*	Ward P.45 Gnome	P.45		25. 4.69	A.J.E.Smith & N.H.Ponsford	Breighton	
G-AXEO	Scheibe SF-25B Falke	4645	D-KEBC	1. 5.69	The Borders (Milfield) GC Ltd	Millfield	19. 3.01
G-AXEV	Beagle B.121 Pup 2	B121-070		6. 5.69	D.S.Russell & J.Powell-Tuck	Gloucestershire	21. 5.00
G-AXFG	Cessna 337D Super Skymaster	337-1070	(EI-) G-AXFG/OY-BVP/G-AXFG/N86081	14. 5.69	Helitechnique Ltd	Cumbernauld	5. 11.01T
G-AXFM*	Cierva Rotorcraft CR.LTH.1 Grasshopper III	GB.2		19. 5.69	The Helicopter Museum Weston-super-Mare (Completed as ground-running rig; stored 3.96)		
G-AXFN	Jodel D.119	980	F-PHBU	19. 5.69	D.M.Jackson & P.A.Munster t/a Fox November Group	(Belper)	2. 3.00P

52

Regn	Type	C/n	P/I	Date	Owner/operator	Probable Base	CA Expy
G-AXGA*	PA-18-95 Super Cub	18-2047	PH-NLE	22. 5.69	R.A.Yates	Sibsey	1. 8.89
	(L-18C-PI) (Frame No.18-2059)		(PH-CUB)/R.Neth.AF R-51/8A-51/52-2447				
					(Damaged Felthorpe 26.12.86; stored 8.90)		
G-AXGC	Socata MS.880B Rallye Club	1349		23. 5.69	P.A.Crawford & M.C.Bennett		
					(Stored Elstree 9.95)	(Saltash/Redruth)	12. 5.88
G-AXGE	Socata MS.880B Rallye Club	1353		23. 5.69	R.P.Loxton	(Bridport)	25. 5.01
G-AXGG	Reims Cessna F.150J	0440		28. 5.69	U.Schluter	(Ely)	17. 7.00
G-AXGP	Piper J3C-90 Cub (L-4J-PI)	12544	F-BGPS	2. 6.69	W.K.Butler	Whittles Farm, Mapledurham	5. 5.94P
	(Frame No.12374) (Quoted as c/n 9542 ex 43-28251) F-BDTM/44-80248						
G-AXGR	Phoenix Luton LA-4A Minor	PAL/1125		2. 6.69	Barbara A.Schlussler	(Bourne)	10. 4.91P
	(JAP J.99)				(Stored Eshott 4.94)		
G-AXGS	Rollason-Druine D.62B Condor	RAE/638		3. 6.69	L.D.Johnston	Cumbernauld	21. 6.99P
G-AXGU*	Rollason-Druine D.62B Condor	RAE/640		3. 6.69	Not known	Eshott	22. 5.76
					(Crashed nr Godalming, Surrey 31.3.75; stored 9.94)		
G-AXGV	Rollason-Druine D.62B Condor	RAE/641		3. 6.69	S.B.Robson	Watchford Farm, Yarcombe	18. 4.00P
G-AXGZ	Rollason-Druine D.62B Condor	RAE/643		3. 6.69	J.Evans	Griffins Farm, Temple Bruer	19. 5.99P
G-AXHA	Cessna 337A Super Skymaster	337-0484	(EI-ATH) N5384S	5. 6.69	G.R.E.Evans	Little Staughton	30. 8.02
G-AXHC	SNCAN Stampe SV-4C	293	F-BCFU	6. 6.69	D.L.Webley	Cranwell	16. 4.99T
G-AXHE*	BN-2A Islander	86	4X-AYV G-AXHE	6. 6.69	Not known	Cumbernauld	14. 4.94
					(Crashed Cark 5.2.94: rear fuselage at Strathallan 8.98)		
G-AXHG*	Socata MS.880B Rallye Club	1371		6. 6.69	A.Smails	Ketton, Darlington	26. 5.85
					(Spares use 4.95)		
G-AXHO	Beagle B.121 Pup 2	B121-077		9. 6.69	L.H.Grundy	Thurrock	6. 5.01
G-AXHP	Piper J3C-65 Cub (L-4J-PI)	12932	F-BETT NC74121/44-80636	9. 6.69	Witham (Specialist) Vehicles Ltd	(Grantham)	11.10.99P
	(Frame No.12762)						
	(Regd with c/n "AF36506" which is a USAAC contract number; as "480636 A-58" in US Army c/s)						
G-AXHR	Piper J3C-65 Cub (L-4H-PI)	10892	F-BETI 43-29601	9. 6.69	K.B.Raven & E.Cundy	Bagby	6. 6.00P
					t/a G-AXHR Cub Group (As "329601/D-44" in US Army c/s)		
G-AXHS	Socata MS.880B Rallye Club	1357		9. 6.69	B. & A. Swales	Bagby	1. 7.99
G-AXHT	Socata MS.880B Rallye Club	1358		9. 6.69	D.E.Guck	Wellesbourne Mountford	25. 2.01
G-AXHV	SAN Jodel D.117A	695	F-BIDF	9. 6.69	J.S.Ponsford	Hucknall	29. 3.00P
					t/a Derwent Flying Group		
G-AXIA	Beagle B.121 Pup 1	B121-078		17. 6.69	M.R.J.Hill & S.W.Goodswen	Old Sarum	1. 4.01T
G-AXIE	Beagle B.121 Pup 2	B121-087		17. 6.69	G.A.Ponsford	Goodwood	28. 4.01
G-AXIF	Beagle B.121 Pup 2	B121-088	(SE-FGV)	17. 6.69	J.A.Holmes & S.A.Self	Dunkeswell	16. 9.02
					"Susie II"		
G-AXIG	Scottish Avn Bulldog Srs.100/104	BH120-002		24. 6.69	A.A.Douglas-Hamilton	Cumbernauld	25. 4.02
G-AXIO	PA-28-140 Cherokee B	28-25764		26. 6.69	White Waltham Airfield Ltd	White Waltham	18. 1.02T
					(Op West London Aero Services)		
G-AXIR	PA-28-140 Cherokee B	28-25795		26. 6.69	A.G.Birch	Weston Zoyland	13. 5.00
G-AXIT	Socata MS.893A Rallye Commodore 180	11430		27. 6.69	T.J.Price	Bidford	22. 9.99
					(Op Avon Soaring Centre) (Damaged at Seighford 7.11.98)		
G-AXIW	Scheibe SF-25B Falke	4657	(D-KABJ)	3. 7.69	M.B.Hill	Nympsfield	20. 9.02
G-AXIX	AESL Airtourer T4 (150)	A.527		3. 7.69	J.C.Wood	Oaksey Park	16.12.00
G-AXIY*	Bird Gyrocopter	GB.001		3. 7.69	R Light & T Smith	Stockport	
					(Complete - awaiting restoration 2.99)		
G-AXJB	Omega 84 HAFB	04		9. 7.69	Semajan Ltd	Romsey, Wilts	20. 8.73S
	(Initially flown as G-AXDT)				t/a Southern Balloon Group "Jester"		
G-AXJH	Beagle B.121 Pup 2	B121-089		11. 7.69	NK	NK	28. 1.01
G-AXJI	Beagle B.121 Pup 2	B121-090		11. 7.69	D.R.Vale	Egginton	12. 8.02
G-AXJJ	Beagle B.121 Pup 2	B121-091		11. 7.69	M.L.,T.M.,D.A.& P.M.Jones	Egginton	17. 7.00
	(Reported as on long term rebuild 8.99: at odds with CofA or did it have an accident ?)						
G-AXJO	Beagle B.121 Pup 2	B121-094		11. 7.69	J.A.D.Bradshaw Three Mile Cross, Reading		7. 8.00
					"Joey"		
G-AXJR	Scheibe SF-25B Falke	4652	D-KICD	14. 7.69	R.I.Hey	Nympsfield	14. 4.00
					t/a The Falke Syndicate		
G-AXJV	PA-28-140 Cherokee B	28-25572	N11C	14. 7.69	N.J.Atherton	Blackbushe	8. 6.01
G-AXJX	PA-28-140 Cherokee B	28-25990		14. 7.69	Patrolwatch Ltd	Barton	24. 8.01
G-AXKH	Phoenix Luton LA-4A Minor	PAL/1316 & PFA/823		21. 7.69	M.E.Vaisey	(Hemel Hempstead)	18. 4.84P
	(VW1600)				(Status uncertain)		
G-AXKJ	Jodel D.9 Bebe	SAS/002, PFA/928B & PFA/941		22. 7.69	C.C.Gordon & N.Mowbray "Le Bebe"		
	(VW1600)				Eastbach Farm, English Bicknor		11.12.97P
G-AXKN*	Westland Bell 47G-4A	WA/719	EC-EDF	22. 7.69	Nash Group Ltd	(Warwick)	
				(D-H...)/G-AXKN/G-17-4 (Cancelled by CAA 9.2.99)			
G-AXKO	Westland-Bell 47G-4A	WA/720	G-17-5	22. 7.69	G.P.Hinkley	Channons Hall, Tibenham	27. 8.99
G-AXKS*	Westland-Bell 47G-4A	WA/723	G-17-8	22. 7.69	Museum of Army Flying	AAC Middle Wallop	21. 9.82
G-AXKW	Westland-Bell 47G-4A	WA/727	G-17-12	22. 7.69	Eyre Spier Associates Ltd		
					(See G-AYOE)	Richmond, N.Yorks	8. 8.02T

Regn	Type	C/n	P/I	Date	Owner/operator	Probable Base	CA Expy
G-AXKX	Westland-Bell 47G-4A	WA/728	G-17-13	22. 7.69	Copley Farms Ltd		
						Copley Hill Farm, Babraham	18. 5.01
G-AXKY	Westland-Bell 47G-4A	WA/729	G-17-14	22. 7.69	G.A.Knight & G.M.Vowles	Gamston	1. 8.02
G-AXLG	Cessna 310K	310K-0204	N3804X	25. 7.69	Smiths (Harlow) Aerospace Ltd	Willingale	17. 7.00
G-AXLI	Slingsby Nipper T.66 RA.45 Srs.3	S.131/1707		25. 7.69	K.R.H.Wingate	Dunkeswell	8.12.99P
G-AXLL	BAC One-Eleven 523FJ	BAC.193	OB-R1173	29. 7.69	European Aviation Air Charter Ltd		
			OB-R1137/PP-SDT/G-AXLL/G-16-8			Bournemouth	20. 7.01T
G-AXLS	SAN Jodel DR.105A Ambassadeur	86	F-BIVR	31. 7.69	J.C.M.Robb	Popham	15. 3.01
					t/a Axle Flying Club		
					(Damaged Manor Farm, Wilts 10.7.99: dismantled Chilbolton 8.99)		
G-AXLZ	PA-18-95 Super Cub (L-18C-PI) 18-2052		PH-NLB	31. 7.69	R.J.Quantrell	Low Farm, South Walsham	23. 4.00
	(Frame No.18-2065)		R.Neth.AF R-45/8A-45/52-2452 (Damaged Low Farm 14.8.97)				
G-AXMA	PA-24-180 Comanche	24-3467	N8214P	5. 8.69	J.D.Bingham	Gamston	11. 6.01
G-AXMB*	Slingsby T.7 Motor Cadet Mk.2		BGA805	5. 8.69	Not known	(Sussex)	9. 7.82P
	(Triumph T.100)		VM590		(On rebuild 1992)		
G-AXMD*	Omega O-20 HAFB	06		7. 8.69	British Balloon Museum	Newbury	
	(Has second envelope c/n 07 but not known which BBM holds) "Nimble"						
G-AXMN	Auster J/5B Autocar	2962	F-BGPN	14. 8.69	A.Phillips	Haverfordwest	30. 7.01
G-AXMP	PA-28-180 Cherokee D	28-5436		19. 8.69	B.Stewart	Stapleford	23. 1.00
					(Destroyed in arson attack Stapleford overnight 12.9.99)		
G-AXMT	Dornier Bucker Bu.133C Jungmeister	46	N133SJ	19. 8.69	W.R.M.Beesley	Breighton	14. 9.00P
			G-AXMT/HB-MIY/U-99				
G-AXMW	Beagle B.121 Pup 1	B121-101		19. 8.69	DJP Engineering (Knebworth) Ltd		
						Cambridge	22. 1.01
G-AXMX	Beagle B.121 Pup 2	B121-103	VH-UPT	19. 8.69	Susan A.Jones	Cannes, France	5.10.00
			G-AXMX/G-35-103				
G-AXNJ	Jodel Wassmer D.120 Paris-Nice	52	F-BHYO	29. 8.69	D.R.Groom & Ptnrs	Sleap	30. 9.00P
					t/a Clive Flying Group		
G-AXNL	Beagle B.121 Pup 1	B121-113		3. 9.69	J.Coleman	Sywell	7. 4.01T
G-AXNM	Beagle B.121 Pup 1	B121-114		3. 9.69	F.E.Green "Bertie"		
						Bourne Park, Hurstbourne Tarrant	17.10.02
G-AXNN	Beagle B.121 Pup 2	B121-104		3. 9.69	Gabrielle Aviation Ltd	Shoreham	29. 7.00
					"Gabrielle"		
G-AXNP	Beagle B.121 Pup 2	B121-106		3. 9.69	J.W.Ellis	Ashcroft Farm, Winsford	1. 7.02
G-AXNR	Beagle B.121 Pup 2	B121-108		3. 9.69	M.H.Wood Brookfield Farm, Great Stukeley		17. 2.02
					t/a November Romeo Group		
G-AXNS	Beagle B.121 Pup 2	B121-110		3. 9.69	M.J.D.Probert & A.J.Stone	Gamston	8. 7.01
					t/a Derwent Aero Group		
G-AXNW	SNCAN Stampe SV-4C	381	F-BFZX Fr.Mil	11. 9.69	Carolyn S.Grace		
						Blooms Farm, Sible Hedingham	4. 5.02
G-AXNX	Cessna 182M	182-59322	N70606	16. 9.69	D.B.Harper	Biggin Hill	15. 7.02T
G-AXNZ	Pitts S-1C Special EB.1 & PFA/1383			16. 9.69	W.A.Jordan	Little Gransden	30. 8.91P
	(Lycoming IO-360) (Quoted c/n EB.2)				(Stored 3.97)		
G-AXOG	PA-E23-250 Aztec D	27-4330	N6965Y	17. 9.69	G.H.Nolan	Biggin Hill	19.10.00
G-AXOH	Socata MS.894A Rallye Minerva 220	11062	D-EAGU	17. 9.69	Bristol Cars Ltd	White Waltham	18. 5.00
G-AXOJ	Beagle B.121 Pup 2	B121-109	G-35-109	24. 9.69	T.J.Martin	Rochester	28. 8.00
					t/a Pup Flying Group		
G-AXOM*	Penn-Smith Gyroplane DJPS.1			26. 9.69	Stondon Transport Museum & Garden Centre		
	(VW1600)					Lower Stondon, Beds	24.2.71P*
G-AXOR	PA-28-180 Cherokee D	28-5453		30. 9.69	Oscar Romeo Aviation Ltd	Redhill	1. 4.02
G-AXOS	Socata MS.894A Rallye Minerva 220	11079		3.10.69	P.Mather	Audley End	20. 5.00
G-AXOT	Socata MS.893A Rallye Commodore 180	11433		3.10.69	P.Evans & J.C.Graves	Doncaster	26. 3.00
G-AXOZ	Beagle B.121 Pup 1	B121-115	N70290	7.10.69	R.J.Ogborn	Chester	11.12.00
			G-AXOZ/G-35-115				
G-AXPA	Beagle B.121 Pup 1	B121-116	D-EATL	7.10.69	D.G.Lewendon	Gloucestershire	4.11.87
			G-AXPA/G-35-116				
G-AXPB	Beagle B.121 Pup 1	B121-117	G-35-117	7.10.69	M.J.K.Seary & R.T.Austin	Leicester	11.11.01
G-AXPC	Beagle B.121 Pup 1	B121-119	PH-VRS G-AXPC	7.10.69	T.A.White	Bagby	12. 8.00
G-AXPF	Reims Cessna F.150K	0543		14.10.69	D.R.Marks	Hinton-in-The-Hedges	22. 4.02
G-AXPG	Mignet HM.293	PFA/1333		14.10.69	W.H.Cole	Spilsted Farm, Sedlescombe	20. 1.77P
	(VW1300)				(Stored 3.97)		
G-AXPM	Beagle B.121 Pup 1	B121-122	G-35-122	20.10.69	R.G.Hayes	North Weald	20. 4.02T
G-AXPN	Beagle B.121 Pup 2	B121-123	G-35-123	20.10.69	D.M.Bell	Top Farm, Royston	12. 2.02
					t/a The Pup Club		
G-AXPZ	Campbell Cricket	CA/320		3.11.69	W.R.Partridge	St.Merryn	27. 4.99P
	(Rotax 582)						

Regn	Type	C/n	P/I	Date	Owner/operator	Probable Base	CA Expy
G-AXRC	Campbell Cricket (VW1600)	CA/323		3.11.69	E.N.Simmons	(Boston)	18. 5.78S
	(Damaged Wittering 22.10.77; stored Tattershall Thorpe 7.91)						
G-AXRK*	Practavia Pilot Sprite 115	15 & PFA/1381		4.11.69	M.Oliver	Crowborough	
	(Under construction 7.95)						
G-AXRO	PA-30-160 Twin Comanche C	30-1978	N8820Y	5.11.69	Comanche Hire Ltd	Gloucestershire	3. 3.01T
G-BXRP	SNCAN Stampe SV.4A	554	F-BDCZ	7.11.69	T Moore t/a Skysport Engineering (Sandy)		5. 6.76S
	(Originally registered 7.11.69 as SV.4C G-AXRP {554} ex F-BDCZ): damaged Gransden 19.10.74; restored 2.85 as SV.4A G-BLOL with c/n SS-SV-R1: NTU and restored in 9.94 as G-AXRP: stored Rotary Farm, Hatch 7.95)							
G-AXRR	Auster AOP.9	AUS.178 & B5/10/178	XR241 G-AXRR/XR241	7.11.69	R.J.Burgess	Redhill	21. 9.99P
	(Damaged 1.2.99: as "XR241" in Army yellow c/s)						
G-AXRT	Reims Cessna FA.150K Aerobat (Tail-wheel conversion)	0018		12.11.69	C.C.Walley	Elstree	24. 1.00T
G-AXRU*	Reims Cessna FA.150K Aerobat	0020		12.11.69	Arrival Enterprises Ltd	Kemble	10.12.87
	(Stored 6.97: cancelled by CAA 2.3.99)						
G-AXSC	Beagle B.121 Pup 1	B121-138	G-35-138	13.11.69	R.J.MacCarthy	Denham	3. 2.01
G-AXSD	Beagle B.121 Pup 1	B121-139	G-35-139	13.11.69	A.C.Townend	Bagby	2. 9.01
G-AXSF	Nash Petrel	PFA/1516 & P.003		17.11.69	Nash Aircraft Ltd	Lasham	.4.94P*
	(Lycoming O-360) (Second allocation of this PFA c/n has no connection with G-BACA: stored 10.95)						
G-AXSG	PA-28-180 Cherokee E	28-5605		17.11.69	Admiral Property Ltd	NK	21. 2.02
G-AXSI	Reims Cessna F.172H	0687	G-SNIP G-AXSI	19.11.69	A.J.G.Davis St.Marys, Isles of Scilly t/a St.Mary's Flying Club		23. 7.01
G-AXSM	CEA Jodel DR.1051 Sicile	512	F-BLRH	20.11.69	K.D.Doyle	Maypole Farm, Chislet	3.10.98
G-AXSR	Brantly B.2B	474	G-ROOF G-AXSR/N2237U	24.11.69	A.Murzyn	West End Farm, Stevington, Bedford	6. 7.01
G-AXSW	Reims Cessna FA.150K Aerobat	0003		25.11.69	R.Mitchell	(Chalfont St.Giles)	2. 3.01
G-AXSZ	PA-28-140 Cherokee B	28-26188		26.11.69	R.Gibson & B.Collins White Waltham t/a The White Wings Flying Group		24. 4.00
G-AXTA	PA-28-140 Cherokee B	28-26301		26.11.69	P.J.Farrell Shoreham t/a G-AXTA Aircraft Group		25. 5.01
G-AXTC	PA-28-140 Cherokee B	28-26265		26.11.69	B.Mellor & W.J.Knott t/a G-AXTC Group Beeches Farm, South Scarle		8. 4.02
G-AXTJ	PA-28-140 Cherokee B	28-26241		26.11.69	K.Patel	Elstree	1. 2.01T
G-AXTL	PA-28-140 Cherokee B	28-26247		26.11.69	Pegasus Aviation (Midlands) Ltd	Halfpenny Green	14.10.01
G-AXTO	PA-24-260 Comanche C	24-4900	N9449P	28.11.69	Jean L.Richardson Turweston "Betsy Baby"		21. 7.00
G-AXTP	PA-28-180 Cherokee C	28-3791	OH-PID	1.12.69	C.W.R.Moore	Elstree	26.11.00
G-AXTX	Wassmer Jodel D.112	1077	F-BKCA	3.12.69	C.Sawford	Swansea	14. 9.00P
G-AXTZ*	Beagle B.121 Pup 1	B121-148	G-35-148	4.12.69	R.S. & A.D.Kent	Shoreham	14. 2.76
	(Crashed Andrewsfield 30.3.75; on rebuild 10.96 for Shoreham Aviation Heritage Trust- cancelled by CAA 2.3.99)							
G-AXUA	Beagle B.121 Pup 1	B121-150	G-35-150	4.12.69	D.S. Sweet	Wedmore	28. 4.00
G-AXUB	BN-2A Islander	121	5N-AIJ G-AXUB/N859JA/G-51-47	4.12.69	Headcorn Parachute Club Ltd	Headcorn	25. 4.00
G-AXUC	PA-12 Super Cruiser	12-621	5Y-KFR VP-KFR/ZS-BIN	5.12.69	J.J.Bunton	Maypole Farm, Chislet	28.10.01
G-AXUF	Reims Cessna FA.150K Aerobat	0043		9.12.69	A.D.McLeod	Blackpool	23. 7.99T
G-AXUK	SAN Jodel DR.1050 Ambassadeur	292	F-BJYU	11.12.69	C.J.Dark Enstone t/a The Ambassadeurs Flying Group		2. 9.00
G-AXUM*	HP.137 Jetstream 1	245		12.12.69	(Sodeteg Formation) Toussous-le-Noble, France		11.12.99A
	(Cancelled as WFU 20.1.99: instructional airframe 6.99)							
G-AXUY*	SAN Jodel DR.100A Ambassadeur	51	F-BIZI	18.12.69	J.J.Mott/1 Sqdn ATC	Stockport	3.11.78
	(Crashed Ash House Farm, Winsford 3.9.78; instructional airframe 1.96)							
G-AXVB	Reims Cessna F.172H	0703		22.12.69	R.& J.Turner Charlton Park, Malmesbury		26. 5.01
G-AXVK*	Campbell Cricket	CA/327		1. 1.70	R Light & T Smith	Stockport	
	(Under restoration 2.99)							
G-AXVL*	Campbell Cricket	CA/328		1. 1.70	Syrian Military Museum Tekkiye Mosque, Damascus		
G-AXVM	Campbell Cricket (VW1834)	CA/329		1. 1.70	D.M.Organ Stoke Orchard, Cheltenham		6. 5.00P
G-AXVN	McCandless M.4 (Modified) (VW1700)	M4/6		5. 1.70	W.R.Partridge	St.Merryn	
G-AXVU*	Omega 84 HAFB	09		7. 1.70	British Balloon Museum Newbury "Henry VIII"		28. 4.77S
G-AXVV*	Piper J3C-65 Cub (L-4H-PI)	10863	F-BBQB 43-29572	7. 1.70	J.D.MacCarthy Rathcoole, Ireland		16. 6.73
	(Stored 4.96: cancelled by CAA 12.4.99)							
G-AXWA	Auster AOP.9	B5/10/133	XN437	13. 1.70	M.L. & C.M.Edwards North Weald		
	(Noted 1.99)							
G-AXWF*	Reims Cessna F.172H	0697		16. 1.70	Not known		
	(Damaged Clacton 26/27.11.83; stored 7.95) Starling Green, Clavering, Essex							22. 5.85T

Regn	Type	C/n	P/I	Date	Owner/operator	Probable Base	CA Expy
G-AXWT	Jodel D.11 (Continental C90)	PFA/911		26. 1.70	R.C.Owen	Danehill	2. 6.00P
G-AXWV	CEA DR.253 Regent	104	F-OCKL	2. 2.70	J.R.D.Bygraves	Little Gransden	14. 7.00
G-AXWZ	PA-28R-200 Cherokee Arrow	28R-35605		3. 2.70	P.Walkley	(Insch)	15. 9.02
G-AXXC	Rousseau Piel CP.301B Emeraude	117	F-BJAT	4. 2.70	J.A.Sykes	Stretton	10.11.00P
G-AXXP*	Bradshaw HAB-76 (Ax7) HAFB	RB.001		20. 2.70	British Balloon Museum & Library Newbury "Ignis Volens" (Stored)		
G-AXXU*	HP.137 Jetstream T.2	262	XX480 G-AXXU	23. 2.70	Ministry of Defence (As "565")	RAF Shawbury	
G-AXXV	DH.82A Tiger Moth	85852	F-BGJI Fr.AF/DE992	24. 2.70	C.N.Wookey (As "DE992")	France Farm, Upavon	28. 4.01
G-AXXW	SAN Jodel D.117	632	F-BIBN	26. 2.70	M.Ward	Sturgate	18. 6.00P
G-AXYK	Taylor JT.1 Monoplane (VW1500)	PFA/1409		2. 3.70	D.J.Hulks & R.W.Davies	Headcorn	9. 9.00P
G-AXYU	Jodel D.9 Bebe (VW1600)	547	EI-BVE G-AXYU	5. 3.70	D.J.Laughlin	Eglinton	4. 9.99P
G-AXYX*	WHE Airbuggy (VW1600)	1003		10. 3.70	W.B.Lumb (Moston, Manchester) (Damaged Melbourne, York 30.7.83 - on rebuild/spares for G-AXYZ 7.94)		15. 4.84S
G-AXYZ	WHE Airbuggy (VW1600)	1005		10. 3.70	B.Gunn, (North Ferriby) 22.12.92P		
G-AXZA	WHE Airbuggy (VW1700)	1006		10. 3.70	Not known (Hoofdoorp, The Netherlands)		15. 8.96P
G-AXZB*	WHE Airbuggy (VW1834)	1007		10. 3.70	Not known (Temp unregd 19.2.97)	Caersws, Powys	18.11.86P
G-AXZD	PA-28-180 Cherokee E	28-5609		12. 3.70	G.M.Whitmore	High Cross, Ware	6. 9.01T
G-AXZF	PA-28-180 Cherokee E	28-5688		12. 3.70	E.P.C. & W.R.Rabson	Eastleigh	23. 7.01T
G-AXZK	BN-2A-26 Islander	153	V2-LAD VP-LAD/G-AXZK/G-51-153	12. 3.70	Headcorn Parachute Club Ltd	Peterlee	27. 1.00
G-AXZM	Slingsby Nipper T.66 RA.45 Srs.3A (VW1600) (Slingsby kit c/n S.133/1709)	PFA/1378		16. 3.70	G.R.Harlow (Damaged nr Eshott 21.8.89; possible rebuild 5.90)	Newcastle	24. 8.89P
G-AXZO	Cessna 180	31137	N3639C	17. 3.70	Golf Centres Group Ltd	Bridport	8.12.99
G-AXZP	PA-E23-250 Aztec D	27-4464	N13819	17. 3.70	I.P.McEvoy t/a Aztec Flying Group	(Sherborne)	9. 7.01T
G-AXZT	SAN Jodel D.117A	607	F-BIBD	17. 3.70	N.Batty	Bagby	31.10.00P
G-AXZU	Cessna 182N Skylane	182-60104	N92233	19. 3.70	Susan E.Bradney	Goodwood	31. 3.02

G-AYAA – G-AYZZ

Regn	Type	C/n	P/I	Date	Owner/operator	Probable Base	CA Expy
G-AYAA	PA-28-180 Cherokee E	28-5799		24. 3.70	Alpha-Alpha Ltd	Liverpool	27. 9.98T
G-AYAB	PA-28-180 Cherokee E	28-5804		24. 3.70	Films Ltd	Fairoaks	18. 7.00
G-AYAC	PA-28R-200 Cherokee Arrow	28R-35606		24. 3.70	G.A.J.Smith-Bosanquet t/a The Fersfield Flying Group	Knettishall	23. 4.01
G-AYAF*	PA-30-160 Twin Comanche	30-2000	N8842Y	26. 3.70	Arrow Air Centre Ltd (Stored 9.95)	Shipdham	8. 5.77
G-AYAJ*	Cameron O-84 HAFB	11		31. 3.70	British Balloon Museum & Library Newbury "Flaming Pearl"		
G-AYAL*	Omega 56 HAFB	10		2. 4.70	British Balloon Museum "Nimble II"	Newbury	25. 8.76
G-AYAN	Slingsby Cadet III (VW1600)	003 & PFA/1385	BGA1224 RAFGSA 223	6. 4.70	N.C.Stone "Thermal Hopper" (Converted from T.31B Frame No.SSK/FF776; stored 5.97)	Brunton	26. 2.93P
G-AYAR	PA-28-180 Cherokee E	28-5797		8. 4.70	Seawing Flying Club	Southend	28. 1 02T
G-AYAT	PA-28-180 Cherokee E	28-5801		8. 4.70	A.J.Foyster & D.F.Sargant t/a AYAT Flying Group	Ludham	7. 3.01T
G-AYAW	PA-28-180 Cherokee E	28-5805		14. 4.70	R.C.Pendle & M.J.Rose	Blackbushe	5. 5.02T
G-AYBD	Reims Cessna F.150K	0583		7. 4.70	S.S.Delwarte t/a Evendy Holdings	Shoreham	26. 5.01T
G-AYBG	Scheibe SF-25B Falke	4696	(D-KECJ)	13. 4.70	D.J.Rickman (Stored 5.98)	Gallows Hill	4. 4.97
G-AYBO	PA-23-250 Aztec D	27-4510	N13874	15. 4.70	Twinguard Aviation Ltd	Denham	28. 3.00
G-AYBP	Jodel D.112	1131	F-PMEK	16. 4.70	G.J.Langston	Bidford	24. 8.00P
G-AYBR	Wassmer Jodel D.112	1259	F-BMIG	16. 4.70	R.T.Mosforth	Netherthorpe	10. 8.00P
G-AYBV*	Chasle YC-12 Tourbillon	MA.001W & PFA/1335		20. 4.70	B.A.Mills (Not completed; stored 10.91)	Great Eversden	
G-AYBW*	Reims Cessna FA.150K Aerobat	0044		22. 4.70	Not known (Crashed nr Perth 8.10.72; stored 5.97)	Linley Hill, Leven	16. 6.73
G-AYCC	Campbell Cricket (Rotax 582)	CA/336		20. 4.70	D.J.M.Charity	Cranfield	10.12.00P
G-AYCE	Scintex CP.301C1 Emeraude	530	F-BJFH	20. 4.70	S.D.Glover	Plymouth	1. 8.00P
G-AYCF	Reims Cessna FA.150K Aerobat	0055		22. 4.70	E.J.Atkins	Thruxton	3. 6.00

Regn	Type	C/n	P/I	Date	Owner/operator	Probable Base	CA Expy
G-AYCG	SNCAN Stampe SV-4C	59	F-BOHF F-BBAE/Fr.Mil	24. 4.70	Nancy Bignall	White Waltham	6. 7.01
G-AYCJ	Cessna TP206D Turbo Super Skylane	P206-0552	N8752Z	27. 4.70	White Knuckle Airways Ltd	Leeds-Bradford	30. 4.00
G-AYCK	AIA Stampe SV-4C (Gipsy Major)	1139	G-BUNT G-AYCK/F-BANE	28. 4.70	J.F.Graham	Jersey	3. 9.01
G-AYCN	Piper J3C-65 Cub	"13365"	F-BCPO	28. 4.70	W.R. & B.M.Young Furze Hill Farm, Rosemarket, Milford Haven		27. 1.89P

(The c/n quoted became PH-UCM in 11.46 & p/i is doubtful; stored 4.91)

Regn	Type	C/n	P/I	Date	Owner/operator	Probable Base	CA Expy
G-AYCO	CEA DR.360 Chevalier	362	F-BRFI	29. 4.70	B.N.Stevens	St Just	6. 7.00
G-AYCP	Jodel D.112	67	F-BGKO	30. 4.70	D.J.Nunn	St.Just	24. 6.00P
G-AYCT	Reims Cessna F.172H	0724		1. 5.70	Haimoss Ltd & D.C.Scouller (Op Old Sarum Flying Club)	Old Sarum	8.12.01T
G-AYDG	Socata MS.894A Rallye Minerva 220	11620		7. 5.70	Hunt and Partners Ltd	White Waltham	18. 5.00
G-AYDI	DH.82A Tiger Moth	85910	F-BDOE Fr.AF/DF174	7. 5.70	R.B. & E.W.Woods & J.D.M.Barr	Hampstead Norreys	28. 4.98

(Dismantled with Hampshire Light Aircraft Services Chilbolton 8.99)

Regn	Type	C/n	P/I	Date	Owner/operator	Probable Base	CA Expy
G-AYDR	SNCAN Stampe SV-4C	307	F-BCLG	13. 5.70	A.J.McLuskie		27. 3.75

(Damaged 16.6.73: on rebuild 8.93) Bishopstrow Farm, Warminster

Regn	Type	C/n	P/I	Date	Owner/operator	Probable Base	CA Expy
G-AYDW*	Beagle A.61 Terrier 2 (Conversion of Auster 6 c/n 1936)	B.646	G-ARLM(1) TW568	20. 5.70	Stick & Rudder Associates (On rebuild Kings Lynn 12.95)	St.Neots	1. 7.73
G-AYDX*	Beagle A.61 Terrier 2	B.647	VX121	20. 5.70	R.A.Kirby (Cancelled by CAA 24.8.99)	Spanhoe	12. 1.00
G-AYDY	Phoenix Luton LA-4A Minor (VW1600)	PAL/1302 & PFA/817		21. 5.70	T.Littlefair & N.Clark	Lymington, Hants	15. 8.97P
G-AYDZ	CEA Jodel DR.200 (Lycoming O-235)	01	F-BLKV F-WLKV	21. 5.70	L.J.Cudd & C.A.Bailey	Dunkeswell	29. 3.02
G-AYEB	Wassmer Jodel D.112	586	F-BIQR	26. 5.70	C.H.G.Baulf	RAF Wattisham	24. 7.00P
G-AYEC	Menavia Piel CP.301A Emeraude	249	F-BIMV	26. 5.70	J.J.Shepherd "Antoinette" t/a Red Wing Flying Group	Netherthorpe	17. 3.00P
G-AYED	PA-24-260 Comanche C	24-4923	N9417P	28. 5.70	J.V.Hutchinson	(Frangy, France)	7.11.02
G-AYEE	PA-28-180 Cherokee E	28-5813		28. 5.70	Rankart Ltd	, Hinton-in-The-Hedges	16. 6.02
G-AYEF	PA-28-180 Cherokee E	28-5815		28. 5.70	J.C.Rideout & A.L.Beaumont t/a G-AYEF Group	Barton	1.12.01
G-AYEG	Falconar F-9 (VW1600)	PFA/1321		29. 5.70	T.J.Wilkinson Sackville Farm, Riseley		6. 7.00P
G-AYEH	SAN Jodel DR.1050 Ambassadeur	455	F-BLJB	8. 6.70	J.W.Scott Wellesbourne Mountford t/a John Scott Jodel Group "Jemima"		18. 8.02
G-AYEI*	PA-31 Turbo Navajo	31-631	N6730L	29. 5.70	Not known (Hubbardair titles) (Crash rescue training 1.00)	Southend	11. 5.89
G-AYEJ	SAN Jodel DR.1050 Ambassadeur	253	F-BJYG	1. 6.70	J.M.Newbold	Enstone	20. 7.00
G-AYEN	Piper J3C-65 Cub (L-4H-PI)	12184	F-BGQD (F-BGQA)/Fr.AF/44-79888	4. 6.70	P.J.Warde & C.F.Morris Grove Farm, Raveningham		27. 6.00P

(Frame No.12012; official identity is c/n 9696/43-835 but fuselages probably exchanged with F-BGQA on conversion in 1952/53)

Regn	Type	C/n	P/I	Date	Owner/operator	Probable Base	CA Expy
G-AYET*	GEMS MS.892A Rallye Commodore 150	10565	F-BNBR	8. 6.70	Not known (Stored 3.97)	Spanhoe	15. 9.96

(Originally in unknown circumstances Cranfield 1986 the remains arrived at Ipswich 6.8.86 as spares for G-BKGA. They were restored to the register 11.89 but cancelled by the CAA 10.96, it would seem reasonable to assume a rebuild was contemplated but not completed)

Regn	Type	C/n	P/I	Date	Owner/operator	Probable Base	CA Expy
G-AYEV	SAN Jodel DR.1050 Ambassadeur	179	F-BERH F-OBTH/F-OBRH	10. 6.70	L.G.Evans	Redhill	15.10.99
G-AYEW	CEA Jodel DR.1050 Sicile	443	F-BLMJ	11. 6.70	A.W.Woodcock t/a The Taildragger Group	Long Marston	13. 8.00
G-AYEY*	Reims Cessna F.150K	0553		15. 6.70	W.J.Moyse	Bournemouth	15.10.99T

(Damaged nr Exbury 24.6.88; stored 8.95; cancelled by CAA 2.3.99)

Regn	Type	C/n	P/I	Date	Owner/operator	Probable Base	CA Expy
G-AYFC	Rollason-Druine D.62B Condor	RAE/644		19. 6.70	A.G.Stevens Little Battleflats Farm, Ellistown, Coalville		4.12.98P
G-AYFD	Rollason-Druine D.62B Condor	RAE/645		19. 6.70	B.G.Manning Little Down Farm, Milson		13. 5.01
G-AYFE	Rollason-Druine D.62C Condor	RAE/646		19. 6.70	D.I.H.Johnstone & W.T.Barnard	Cumbernauld	6.12.01
G-AYFF	Rollason-Druine D.62B Condor	RAE/647		19. 6.70	D.Ellis t/a Condor Syndicate	Eaton Bray	23. 6.00P
G-AYFG	Rollason-Druine D.62C Condor	RAE/648		19. 6.70	C Jobling & A J Mackay	(Grantham)	28.10 02
G-AYFJ	SEEMS MS.880B Rallye Club	333	F-BKZR	19. 6.70	D.G.Tucker t/a Rallye FJ Group (Stored 6.94)	West Thurrock	18. 5.92
G-AYFO*	Dornier Bucker Bu.133 Jungmeister				See N40BJ in SECTION 6		
G-AYFP	SAN Jodel D.140 Mousquetaire	18	F-BMSI F-OBLH/F-WNDO	24. 6.70	F.L.Rivett	Redhill	23. 5.02
G-AYFV	Crosby Andreasson Super BA.4B (Lycoming IO-320) 002 & PFA/1359			26. 6.70	A.R.C.Mathie	RAF Coltishall	5. 7.95P

Regn	Type	C/n	P/I	Date	Owner/operator	Probable Base	CA Expy
G-AYFX*	American AA-1 Yankee Clipper	AA1-0318	N6118L	26. 6.70	Not known (On rebuild 12.95)	Sherburn in Elmet	8. 7.84
G-AYFY*	EAA Biplane	PFA/1319		26. 6.70	Not known	Not known	
	(Stored, unfinished Tattershall Thorpe 7.91; since sold to unknown Public House for display)						
G-AYGA	SAN Jodel D.117	436	F-BHNU	30. 6.70	R.L.E.Horrell	Oxenhope	30. 3.00P
G-AYGB*	Cessna 310Q	310Q-0111	N7611Q	2. 7.70	Perth College (Instructional airframe 10.97)	Perth	23.10.87T
G-AYGC	Reims Cessna F.150K	0556		2. 7.70	I.R.Jones t/a Alpha Aviation Group	Barton	21. 5.01
G-AYGD	CEA Jodel DR.1050 Sicile	515	F-BLRE	3. 7.70	D.Street t/a G-AYGD Flying Group (Damaged Grove Farm, Retford 24.6.99)	Netherthorpe	4.11.01
G-AYGE	SNCAN Stampe SV-4C	242	F-BCGM	6. 7.70	I.,L.J. & S.Proudfoot (Stored 1.99)	Duxford	8. 5.97
G-AYGG	Jodel Wassmer D.120 Paris-Nice	184	F-BJPH	10. 7.70	J.M.Dean Stoneacre Farm, Farthing Corner		5. 4.00P
G-AYGX	Reims Cessna FR.172G Rocket	0208		15. 7.70	C.Taylor t/a Reims Rocket Group	Barton	8. 7.00
G-AYHA	American AA-1 Yankee Clipper	AA1-0396	N6196L	21. 7.70	K.& A.D.Ambrose-Hunt	Elstree	4. 3.02
G-AYHI*	Campbell Cricket (VW1600)	CA/341		21. 7.70	J.F.MacKay North Kessock, Inverness (Cancelled by CAA 2.3.99)		19. 8.86P
G-AYHX	SAN Jodel D.117A	903	F-BIVE	23. 7.70	L.J.E.Goldfinch	Old Sarum	28. 4.00P
G-AYHY	Sportavia Fournier RF4D	4156		24. 7.70	P.J. & S.M.Wells	Booker	23. 6.00
G-AYIA	Hughes 369HS (500)	99-0120S		29. 7.70	G.D.E.Bilton (Damaged S.France 1.6.88; stored for spares 8.97)	Sywell	16. 7.88
G-AYIF	PA-28-140 Cherokee C	28-26877		31. 7.70	R.Jackson-Moore & P.R.Wright t/a The Hare Flying Group	Enstone	30. 6.01
G-AYIG	PA-28-140 Cherokee C	28-26878		31. 7.70	Biggles Ltd	Booker	26.11.02T
G-AYII	PA-28R-200 Cherokee Arrow	28R-35736		4. 8.70	P.W.J. & P.A.S.Gove	Exeter	13. 3.00
G-AYIJ	SNCAN Stampe SV-4B	376	F-BCOM	4. 8.70	E.A.Stevenson-Rouse & T.C.Beadle	Headcorn	16. 6.00
G-AYIM	HS.748 Srs.2A/270	1687	G-11-687 CS-TAG/G-AYIM/G-11-5	11. 8.70	Emerald Airways Ltd	Liverpool	21.12.01T
G-AYIT	DH.82A Tiger Moth	86343	F-BGEZ Fr.AF/NL896	20. 8.70	S.R.Pollitt & H.M.Eassie t/a Ulster Tiger Group	Newtownards	29. 7.01
G-AYJA	SAN Jodel DR.1050 Ambassadeur	150	F-BJJJ	8. 9.70	G.Connell	Navan, Co.Meath	2. 6.02
G-AYJB	SNCAN Stampe SV-4C	560	F-BDDF	8. 9.70	F.J.M. & J.P.Esson "Odette"	Bere Farm, Warnford	26. 5.01
G-AYJD	Alpavia Fournier RF3	11	F-BLXA	8. 9.70	E.Shouler (Stored 9.97)	Beeches Farm, South Scarle	19. 5.95P
G-AYJP	PA-28-140 Cherokee C	28-26403		15. 9.70	RAF Brize Norton Flying Club Ltd (Crashed landing Bembridge 22.5.99)	RAF Brize Norton	20. 4.01T
G-AYJR	PA-28-140 Cherokee C	28-26694		15. 9.70	RAF Brize Norton Flying Club Ltd	RAF Brize Norton	30.11.00T
G-AYJW	Reims Cessna FR.172G Rocket	0225		17. 9.70	J.D.Kelsall, R.J.Catley & P.Marsden	Netherthorpe	30. 6.00T
G-AYJY	Isaacs Fury II (Continental C90)	PFA/1373		23. 9.70	M.G.Jefferies	Little Gransden	17. 6.00P
G-AYKA*	Beechcraft 95-B55A Baron	TC-523	HB-GEW G-AYKA/D-IKUN/N8683M	30. 9.70	Northbrook College (Damaged Elstree 18. 6.89; instructional airframe 8.99)	Shoreham	15. 9.91
G-AYKD	SAN Jodel DR.1050 Ambassadeur	351	F-BKHR	30. 9.70	S.D.Morris	Deanland, Hailsham	20. 6.00
G-AYKJ	SAN Jodel D.117A	730	F-BIDX	6.10.70	J.M.Alexander	Lichfield	15. 6.00P
G-AYKK	SAN Jodel D.117	378	F-BHGM	6.10.70	D.M.Whitham (On rebuild 1995)	Crosland Moor	22. 5.85S
G-AYKL	Reims Cessna F.150L	0676		6.10.70	M.A.Judge t/a Aero Group 78	Netherthorpe	19.11.99T
G-AYKS	Leopoldoff L.7 Colibri (Continental A65)	125	F-PCZX F-APZQ	8.10.70	W.B.Cooper	Walkeridge Farm, Overton	18.10.00P
G-AYKT	SAN Jodel D.117	507	F-BGYY F-OAYY	9.10.70	D.I.Walker & S.A.Chambers	Scotland Farm, Hook	27. 6.00P
G-AYKW	PA-28-140 Cherokee C	28-26931		12.10.70	B.A.Mills	Bourn	18.11.02T
G-AYKX	PA-28-140 Cherokee C	28-26933		12.10.70	B.Malpas t/a Robin Flying Group	Woodford	9.11.00
G-AYKZ	SAI KZ-VIII (Gipsy Major 7)	202	HB-EPB OY-ACB	13.10.70	R.E.Mitchell (Stored 3.95)	RAF Cosford	17. 7.81P
G-AYLA	AESL Airtourer T2 (115)	524		12.10.70	D.S.P.Disney	Cardiff	2. 7.01
G-AYLB	PA-39-160 Twin Comanche C/R	39-63	N8908Y	12.10.70	G.N.Snell	Biggin Hill	15. 6.01
G-AYLC	CEA Jodel DR.1051 Sicile (Lycoming O-235)	536	F-BLZG	12.10.70	E.W.B.Trollope	Wing Farm, Longbridge Deverill	3. 8.00P
G-AYLF	CEA Jodel DR.1051 Sicile	547	F-BLZQ	14.10.70	A.Haigh & A.C.Frost t/a Sicile Group	Rectory Farm, Abbotsley	16. 6.00
G-AYLL	CEA Jodel DR.1050 Ambassadeur	11	F-BJHK	27.10.70	C.Joly	Lee-on-Solent	18. 5.01

Regn	Type	C/n	P/I	Date	Owner/operator	Probable Base	CA Expy
G-AYLP	American AA-1 Yankee	AA1-0445	EI-AVV G-AYLP	21.10.70	D.Nairn & E.Y.Hawkins	Henstridge	10. 2.02
G-AYLV	Jodel Wassmer D.120 Paris-Nice	300	F-BNCG	27.10.70	M.R.Henham (Status uncertain)	(London N2)	13. 9.83P
G-AYLZ	SPP CZL Super Aero 45 Srs.04	06-014	9M-AOF F-BILP	2.11.70	M.Emery (Damaged Andrewsfield 2.1.76: stored 1997)	(Gatwick)	11. 6.76
G-AYME	Sportavia Fournier RF5	5089		6.11.70	R.D.Goodger	Laddingford	26. 8.00P
G-AYMF*	AESL Airtourer T6/24	B.557		10.11.70	Not known (Crashed nr St.Just 9.6.72: wreck stored 4.96)	St.Just	20. 1.73
G-AYMK	PA-28-140 Cherokee C	28-26772	(PT-DPU)	17.11.70	M.Wright t/a The Piper Flying Group	Newcastle	29. 9.01
G-AYMN*	PA-28-140 Cherokee C	28-26754	(PT-DPT)	18.11.70	S.Boylan (Damaged Isle of Wight 18.9.88: stored 3.95)	(Shipdham)	4. 9.89
G-AYMO	PA-23-250 Aztec C	27-2995	5Y-ACX N5845Y	18.11.70	R.W.Hinton	Stapleford	17. 2.01
G-AYMP	Phoenix Currie Wot Special (Walter Mikron 3)	PFA/3014		18.11.70	H.F.Moffatt	Woodlow Farm, Bosbury	4.10.94P
G-AYMR	Lederlin 380L Ladybug (Continental C90) EAA/55189 & PFA/1513			19.11.70	J.S.Brayshaw (Under construction 1992)	(Harrogate)	
G-AYMU	Wassmer Jodel D.112	1015	F-BJPB	23.11.70	M.R.Baker Bradleys Lawn, Heathfield (Damaged Hailsham, E.Sussex 7.1.92: on rebuild Eastbourne 7.92)		5. 6.92P
G-AYMV	Western 20 HAFB	002		23.11.70	G.F.Turnbull "Tinkerbelle"	Clyro, Hereford	
G-AYMW	Bell 206B JetRanger	587	EI-BJR G-AYMW	25.11.70	PLM Dollar Group Ltd	Cumbernauld	21. 4.01T
G-AYNA	Phoenix Currie Wot (Continental A65)	PFA/3016		25.11.70	J.Evans Griffins Farm, Temple Bruer		12. 5.00P
G-AYND	Cessna 310Q	310Q-0110	N7610Q	2.12.70	Source Ltd	Bournemouth	17. 6.01T
G-AYNF	PA-28-140 Cherokee C	28-26778	(PT-DPV)	3.12.70	W.S.Bath, M.H.Jones & G.H.Round t/a BW Aviation	Coventry	15. 6.00T
G-AYNJ	PA-28-140 Cherokee C	28-26810		3.12.70	R.H.Ribbons	Swansea	3. 5.00T
G-AYNN	Cessna 185B Skywagon	0518	8R-GCC VP-GCC/N2518Z	11.12.70	Bencray Ltd t/a Blackpool & Fylde Aero Club	Blackpool	28. 9.00T
G-AYNP*	Westland WS.55 Whirlwind Srs.3	WA/71	ZS-HCY G-AYNP/XG576	14.12.70	The Helicopter Museum Berlin, Germany (to Aero Park Brandenburg collection 5.98)		27.10.85T
G-AYOE*	Bell 47G	1515	F-OCBF F-BKQZ/D-HEBO	21.12.70	Grenville Helicopters Boship Barn Farm Hotel, Hailsham (Crashed Exmouth 16.7.77: composite static rebuild as "G-AXKW" and used as heliport marker 3.97)		5. 5.79
G-AYOP	BAC One-Eleven 530FX	BAC.233		4. 1.71	European Aviation Ltd	Bournemouth	8. 5.01T
G-AYOW	Cessna 182N Skylane	182-60481	N8941G	6. 1.71	D.W.Parfrey	Coventry	29. 4.01
G-AYOY	Sikorsky S-61N	61-476		7. 1.71	Brintel Helicopters Ltd t/a British International Helicopters	Inverness	21. 4.00T
G-AYOZ	Reims Cessna FA.150L Aerobat	0085		7. 1.71	I.J.Black	(Belfast)	12.10.00
G-AYPE	MBB Bo.209 Monsun 160RV	123	D-EFJA	11. 1.71	Papa Echo Ltd "Buswells Spirit"	Biggin Hill	23. 9.00
G-AYPG	Reims Cessna F.177RG Cardinal (Wichita c/n 00102)	0007		11. 1.71	D.P.McDermott	Haverfordwest	20.12.01
G-AYPH	Reims Cessna F.177RG Cardinal (Wichita c/n 00146)	0018		11. 1.71	M.R. & K.E.Slack	Cambridge	15. 4.01
G-AYPI	Reims Cessna F.177RG Cardinal (Wichita c/n 00177)	0025		11. 1.71	Cardinal Aviation Ltd	Guernsey	20. 4.00
G-AYPJ	PA-28-180 Cherokee E	28-5821		12. 1.71	Mona Aviation Ltd (Op Mona Flying Club)	RAF Mona	27. 9.01T
G-AYPM	PA-18-95 Super Cub (L-18C-PI)18-1373 (Frame No.18-1282)		ALAT 18-1373/51-15373	13. 1.71	R.Horner	Dunkeswell	28. 6.00P
G-AYPO	PA-18-95 Super Cub (L-18C-PI)18-1615 (Continental O-200-A) (Rebuilt 1984 using OO-TSJ c/n 18-1398 (Frame No.18-1325) & ex (LN-TSJ)/OO-HMH/51-15398)		ALAT 18-1615/51-15615	13. 1.71	A.W.Knowles	Bodmin	19. 6.00
G-AYPP*	PA-18-95 Super Cub (L-18C-PI)18-1626		ALAT 18-1626/51-15626	13. 1.71	R.W.Sage Priory Farm, Tibenham t/a Blackbarn Aviation (Crashed Stoke St.Mary, Norfolk 29.12.83: stored 8.97)		31. 8.85
G-AYPR	PA-18-95 Super Cub (L-18C-PI)18-1631		ALAT 18-1631/51-15631	13. 1.71	D.G.Holman & J.E.Burrell	Leicester	14. 9.00T
G-AYPS	PA-18-95 Super Cub (L-18C-PI)18-2092		ALAT 18-2092/52-2492	13. 1.71	R.J.Hamlett, L.G & D.C.Callow	(Harlow)	25. 2.00P
G-AYPT	PA-18-95 Super Cub (L-18C-PI)18-1533 (Frame No.18-1508)		(D-EALX) ALAT 18-1533/51-15533	13. 1.71	B.L.Proctor & T.F.Lyddon	Dunkeswell	11. 5.02
G-AYPU	PA-28R-200 Cherokee Arrow	28R-7135005		13. 1.71	Alpine Ltd	Jersey	14. 3.02
G-AYPV	PA-28-140 Cherokee D	28-7125039		13. 1.71	Ashley Gardner Flying Club Ltd	Ronaldsway	6. 9.01T

Regn	Type	C/n	P/I	Date	Owner/operator	Probable Base	CA Expy
G-AYPZ	Campbell Cricket (VW1600)	CA/343		13. 1.71	A.Melody	Uxbridge	20. 8.87P
G-AYRA	Campbell Cricket (VW1600)	CA/344		13. 1.71	R.C.Thomas Deopham Green, Wymondham		31. 8.83P
					(Damaged nr Great Billingham School, Norfolk 28.3.98)		
G-AYRC*	Campbell Cricket	CA/346		13. 1.71	Not known	Wroughton	17. 8.77S
					(Stored 1.96)		
G-AYRF	Reims Cessna F.150L	0665		14. 1.71	D.T.A.Rees	Haverfordwest	25.11.00T
					(Crashed Upper Welson Farm, Haverfordwest 13.3.99)		
G-AYRG	Reims Cessna F.172K	0761		14. 1.71	Comed Aviation Ltd	Blackpool	26. 7.00T
G-AYRH	GEMS MS.892A Rallye Commodore 150	10558	F-BNBX	14. 1.71	J.D.Watt Damyns Hall, Upminster		28. 9.95
G-AYRI	PA-28R-200 Cherokee Arrow	28R-7135004		15. 1.71	A.E.Thompson White Waltham & Delta Motor Co (Windsor) Sales Ltd		25. 7.02
G-AYRM	PA-28-140 Cherokee D	28-7125049		19. 1.71	M.J. Saggers	Biggin Hill	7. 8.00T
G-AYRO	Reims Cessna FA.150L Aerobat	0102		21. 1.71	J.J.Woodhouse Hinton-in-The-Hedges t/a Flying Services (Op Fat Boys Flying Club)		21. 5.01T
G-AYRS	Jodel Wassmer D.120A Paris-Nice	255	F-BMAV	22. 1.71	L.R.H.D'Eath	(Diss)	4. 5.00P
G-AYRT	Reims Cessna F.172K	0777		22. 1.71	P.E.Crees	Shobdon	16. 3.01
G-AYRU	BN-2A-6 Islander	181	G-51-181 OH-BNA/G-51-181	22. 1.71	Joint Services Parachute Centre	AAC Netheravon	10. 3.00
G-AYSA	PA-23-250 Aztec C	27-3799	N6509Y	1. 2.71	N.Parkinson & W.Smith	Coventry	14. 5.99T
G-AYSB	PA-30-160 Twin Comanche C	30-1916	N8760Y	1. 2.71	C.P.Heptonstall	Sturgate	26. 2.00
G-AYSD	Slingsby T.61A Falke	1726		4. 2.71	P.W.Hextall (Stored 1.95)	Tatenhill	29. 4.94
G-AYSH	Taylor JT.1 Monoplane (VW1600)	PFA/1413		10. 2.71	C.J.Lodge Hill Farm, Nayland		5. 5.99P
G-AYSJ	Dornier Bucker Bu.133C Jungmeister	38	D-EHVP G-AYSJ HB-MIW/Swiss AF U-91	12. 2.71	Patina Ltd Duxford (Op The Fighter Collection: as "LG+01" in Luftwaffe c/s)		1.12.99P
G-AYSK	Phoenix Luton LA-4A Minor (Continental A65)	PFA/832		17. 2.71	S.R.Smith t/a Luton Minor Group	Barton	27.10.99P
G-AYSX	Reims Cessna F.177RG Cardinal (Wichita c/n 00175)	0024		17. 2.71	C.P.Heptonstall	Sandtoft	16. 5.02
G-AYSY	Reims Cessna F.177RG Cardinal (Wichita c/n 00180)	0026		17. 2.71	Horizon Flyers Ltd	Denham	6. 6.00
G-AYTA*	Socata MS.880B Rallye Club	1789		19. 2.71	The Aeroplane Collection Manchester (On loan to Manchester Museum of Science & Industry)		7.11.88
G-AYTR	Menavia Piel CP.301A Emeraude	229	F-BIMD	3. 3.71	G.N.Hopcraft Croft Farm, Defford		11. 6.00P
G-AYTT	Phoenix PM-3 Duet (Continental C90) (Regd as Luton Minor III)	PFA/841		4. 3.71	H.E.Jenner	Rochester	31. 8.00P
G-AYTV	Jurca MJ.2D Tempete (Continental C90)	PFA/2002		10. 3.71	A.R.Clark t/a Shoestring Flying Group	Shoreham	22.11.00P
G-AYUA	Auster AOP.9	B5/10-119	7855M XK416	12. 3.71	P.T.Bolton South Lodge Farm, Widmerpool (As "XK416")		
G-AYUB	CEA Jodel DR.253B Regent	185		15. 3.71	D.J.Brook	Deanland, Hailsham	14. 9.02
G-AYUH	PA-28-180 Cherokee F	28-7105042		17. 3.71	C.S.Sidle	Sherburn in Elmet	21. 3.02
G-AYUI*	PA-28-180 Cherokee F	28-7105043	N8557 G-AYUI	17. 3.71	Ansair Aviation Ltd Andrewsfield (Semi-derelict in open storage 3.99)		5.11.93T
G-AYUJ	Evans VP-1 (VW1776)	PFA/1538		17. 3.71	T.N.Howard Woodvale "Unforgettable Juliet" (Damaged Ainsdale Beach, Southport 16.6.96)		28. 2.97P
G-AYUM	Slingsby T.61A Falke	1730		19. 3.71	R.Sharman t/a Hereward Flying Group	Crowland	10. 6.02
G-AYUN	Slingsby T.61A Falke	1731		19. 3.71	C.W.Vigar & R.J.Watts	Rattlesden	20. 5.99
G-AYUP	Slingsby T.61A Falke	1735	XW983 G-AYUP	19. 3.71	P.R.Williams RAF Bicester (Stored 2.97)		15. 7.96
G-AYUR	Slingsby T.61A Falke	1736		19. 3.71	R.Hannigan & R.Lingard	Strubby	4.11.01
G-AYUS	Taylor JT.1 Monoplane (VW1600)	PFA/1412		19. 3.71	R.R.McKinnon Old Sarum (Damaged Coombe Down, Salisbury 3.11.92)		8.10.93P
G-AYUT	SAN Jodel DR.1050 Ambassadeur	479	F-BLJZ	22. 3.71	R.Norris	Wigtown	29. 9.01
G-AYUV	Reims Cessna F.172H	0752		26. 3.71	Justgold Ltd	Blackpool	11. 3.00T
G-AYVA*	Cameron O-84 HAFB	17		30. 3.71	A.Kirk "April Fool" Lancing (Balloon Preservation Group 7.98)		6. 9.76S
G-AYVO	Wallis WA-120 Srs.1 (RR Continental O-240-B)	K/602/X		6. 4.71	K.H.Wallis Reymerston Hall (Stored 5.99)		31.12.75P
G-AYVP	Aerosport Woody Pusher	181 & PFA/1344		6. 4.71	J.R.Wraight Chatham (Stored incomplete)		
G-AYVT*	Brochet MB.84	9	F-BGLI	13. 4.71	R.A.Yates Sibsey (Damaged 28.6.77; stored 8.90)		20. 7.77
G-AYWA*	Avro 19 Srs.2	1361	OO-VIT OO-DFA/OO-CFA	14. 4.71	N.K.Geddes Lochwinnoch (Stored 5.95)		
G-AYWD	Cessna 182N Skylane	182-60468	N8928G	15. 4.71	S.I.Zorb t/a Wild Dreams Group	Leicester	4.11.02T

Regn	Type	C/n	P/I	Date	Owner/operator	Probable Base	CA Expy
G-AYWE	PA-28-140 Cherokee C	28-26826	N5910U	16. 4.71	N.Roberson	Fenland	31. 3.02
					t/a Whiskey Echo Group		
G-AYWH	SAN Jodel D.117A	844	F-BIVO	16. 4.71	D.Kynaston & J.Deakin		22.12.00P
						Cold Harbour Farm, Willingham	
G-AYWM	AESL Airtourer T5 (Super 150)	A.534		16. 4.71	H.E.Collett	Gloucestershire	4. 5.00
					t/a The Star Flying Group		
G-AYWT	AIA Stampe SV-4C	1111	F-BLEY	21. 4.71	B.K.Lecomber	RAF Halton	22. 5.99T
	(Gipsy Major 10)		F-BAGL				
G-AYWY*	PA-23-250 Aztec D	27-4069	EI-ATI	22. 4.71	Dublin College of Technology	Dublin	21. 5.77
			N6735Y (Crashed Castlebridge, Wexford 15.10.75; instructional airframe 5.92)					
G-AYXO*	Phoenix Luton LA-5A Major	PFA/1211		27. 4.71	C.H.Bestwick	Brenchley, Kent	
	(Walter Minor 65hp)				(Flown in 1971 but not certified; stored 1.96)		
G-AYXP	SAN Jodel D.117A	693	F-BIDD	27. 4.71	G.N.Davies	Vowchurch, Hereford	29. 2.00P
G-AYXS	SIAI-Marchetti S.205-18R	4-165	OY-DNG	28. 4.71	M.D.Friend	Denham	25. 6.01
G-AYXT	Westland WS-55 Whirlwind HAS.7 (Srs.2)	XK940 WA/167		28. 4.71	G.P.Hinkley	Channons Hall, Tibenham	4. 2.99P
					(As "XK940"; on rebuild 3.97)		
G-AYXU	Champion 7KCAB Citabria	232-70	N7587F	28. 4.71	Norfolk Gliding Club Ltd	Nayland	21. 5.01
G-AYXW	Evans VP-1	PFA/1544		30. 4.71	M.Howe	North Coates	27. 7.00P
	(Ardem 4C02)						
G-AYYF*	Reims Cessna F.150L	0716		10. 5.71	D.T.A.Rees		20. 2.92T
			(Destroyed Aber Farm, Talybont-on-Usk 27.11.90: cancelled 18.5.99 as destroyed)					
G-AYYK	Slingsby T.61A Falke	1737		10. 5.71	Cornish Gliding & Flying Club Ltd		
						Perranporth	11. 4.97
G-AYYL	Slingsby T.61A Falke	1738		10. 5.71	C.Wood	Challock	2. 6.83
					(Gale damage Manston 15.12.82; on rebuild 7.90)		
G-AYYO	CEA Jodel DR.1050/M1 Sicile Record	622	EI-BAI G-AYYO/F-BMPZ	11. 5.71	D.J.M.White	DRA Boscombe Down	6. 5.02
					t/a Bustard Jodel Group		
G-AYYT	CEA Jodel DR.1050/M1 Sicile Record	587	F-BMGU	13. 5.71	C.J.Turner & S.D.Kent t/a Echo November Flight		
						Garston Farm, Marshfield	22. 6.02
G-AYYU	Beechcraft C23 Musketeer Custom	M-1353		14. 5.71	P.W.Johnson & A.G.Payne	Sturgate	28. 4.01
					t/a Sundowner Aviation		
G-AYYW	BN-2A-2 Islander	277	D-IOLA	17. 5.71	A T Usher "Iron Horse"	Dunkeswell	2. 4.99
			G-AYYW/G-51-277 t/a Royal Navy & Royal Marines Sport Parachute Asstn					
G-AYYX	Socata MS.880B Rallye Club	1812		18. 5.71	J.G.MacDonald	Morganstield, Fishburn	23. 1.02
G-AYZE	PA-39-160 Twin Comanche C/R	39-92	N8934Y	20. 5.71	J.E.Balmer	Gloucestershire	13. 8.00
G-AYZH*	Taylor JT.2 Titch	PFA/1316		21. 5.71	P.J.G.Goddard	(Stratford-upon-Avon)	
			(Cancelled by CAA 23.2.99; no Permit issued & probably not completed)					
G-AYZI	SNCAN Stampe SV-4C	15	(EI-)	24. 5.71	W.H.Smout	Spanhoe	28. 7.95
			G-AYZI/F-BBAA/Fr mil (On rebuld 6.98)					
G-AYZJ*	Westland WS-55 Whirlwind HAS.7	XM685 WA/263		24. 5.71	Newark Air Museum	Winthorpe	
					(As "XM685/PO-513")		
G-AYZK	CEA Jodel DR.1050/M1 Sicile Record	590	F-BMGY	24. 5.71	R.L.Sambell & D.G.Hesketh	Stoke Golding	10. 7.00
G-AYZS	Rollason-Druine D.62B Condor	RAE/650		4. 6.71	P.E.J.Huntley & M.N.Thrush		
						Manor Farm, Inglesham	25. 9.00P
G-AYZU	Slingsby T.61A Falke	1740		4. 6.71	R.G.Garner	Coventry	4. 6.01
					t/a The Falcon Gliding Group		
G-AYZW	Slingsby T.61A Falke	1743		4. 6.71	V.D.Blaxill & R.J.Jones	Portmoak	10. 4.01
					t/a Portmoak Falke Syndicate		

G-AZAA – G-AZZZ

Regn	Type	C/n	P/I	Date	Owner/operator	Probable Base	CA Expy
G-AZAB	PA-30-160 Twin Comanche B	30-1475	5H-MNM 5Y-AGB	8. 6.71	Bickertons Aerodromes Ltd	Denham	19. 8.01
G-AZAD*	CEA Jodel DR.1050 Sicile	501	F-BLMX	10. 6.71	J.A.D.Reedie & G.W. Mair	Inverness	18. 4.00
					t/a Cawdor Flying Group		
			(Crashed Rosemarkie Mast 9.5.99: cancelled as destroyed 10.12.99)					
G-AZAJ	PA-28R-200 Cherokee Arrow	28R-7135116		18. 6.71	J.C.McHugh & P.Woulfe	Stapleford	10. 6.00
G-AZAU*	Cierva Rotorcraft Grasshopper III	GB.3		21. 6.71	The Helicopter Museum	Weston-super-Mare	
			(Incomplete - only floor pan, panel, power and lift group; stored 3.96)					
G-AZAW	Gardan GY-80-160 Horizon	104	F-BMUL	24. 6.71	T.Brown	Maypole Farm, Chislet	11. 2.02
G-AZAZ*	Bensen B-8M	RNEC.1		2. 7.71	Fleet Air Arm Museum	Wroughton	
					(Stored 3.96)		
G-AZBA	Tipsy T.66 Nipper Srs.3B	PFA/1390		30. 6.71	L.A. Brown	Swansea	10.12.99P
	(VW1834) (Slingsby-built kit)						
G-AZBB	MBB Bo 209 Monsun 160FV	137	D-EFJO	1. 7.71	G.N.Richardson t/a GN Richardson Motors		
						Shelsley Beauchamp, Worcester	14.11.99
G-AZBC	PA-39-160 Twin Comanche C/R	39-111	N8951Y	1. 7.71	R.G.James & P.E.Mitchell	Cambridge	2. 2.01

Regn	Type	C/n	P/I	Date	Owner/operator	Probable Base	CA Expy
G-AZBE	AESL Airtourer T5 (Super 150)	A.535		5. 7.71	R.G.Vincent t/a BE Flying Group	Gloucestershire	15.12.02
G-AZBH*	Cameron O-84 HAFB	23		8. 7.71	British Balloon Museum & Library "Serendipity"	Newbury	10. 5.81
G-AZBI	SAN Jodel 150 Mascaret	43	F-BMFB	12. 7.71	F.M.Ward	RAF Dishforth	8. 2.00P
G-AZBL	Jodel D.9 Bebe (VW1500)	PFA/938		12. 7.71	J.Hill (Status uncertain - on rebuild 1993 ?)	(Dudley)	15.10.85P
G-AZBN	Noorduyn AT-16-ND Harvard IIB	14A-1431	PH-HON R.Neth.AF B-97/FT391/43-13132	13. 7.71	Swaygate Ltd (As "FT391")	Shoreham	18. 6.99P
G-AZBT*	Western O-65 HAFB	005		15. 7.71	D Harries "Hermes" (Stored 7.98)	Brighton	9. 4.76S
G-AZBU	Auster AOP.9	AUS.183	7862M XR246	15. 7.71	E.Wright South Lodge Farm, Widmerpool t/a Auster Nine Group (As "XR246" in RAE c/s)		13. 5.00P
G-AZBY*	Westland Wessex 60 Srs.1 (Possibly former G-AWOX)	WA/740	G-17-5 G-AZBY/5N-ALR/G-AZBY	21. 7.71	Not known Honey Crook Farm, Redhill (As "EM-16" in USMC c/s; on rebuild 8.98)		14.12.82
G-AZCB	SNCAN Stampe SV-4C (Gipsy Major 1C)	140	F-BBCR	21. 7.71	M.L.Martin	Redhill	30. 4.96
G-AZCE	Pitts S.1C Special (Lycoming O-235)	373.H & PFA/1527		26. 7.71	Not known (Crashed Eastbach Farm 2.9.75 - on rebuild)		18. 6.76S
G-AZCI*	Cessna 320A Skyknight	320A-0021	CF-PKY N3021R	29. 7.71	Not known (Stored in wrecked condition 7.91)	Kano, Nigeria	29. 6.83A
G-AZCK	Beagle B.121 Pup 2	B121-153		30. 7.71	D.R.Newell	Newtownards	10. 6.00
G-AZCL	Beagle B.121 Pup 2	B121-154		30. 7.71	J.J.Watts & D.Fletcher	Old Sarum	8. 7.01T
G-AZCN	Beagle B.121 Pup 2	B121-156	HB-NAY G-AZCN	30. 7.71	R.C.Antonini	Biggin Hill	15. 6.01
G-AZCP	Beagle B.121 Pup 1	B121-158	(D-EKWA) G-AZCP	30. 7.71	T.J.Watson	Elstree	18. 7.01
G-AZCT	Beagle B.121 Pup 1	B121-161		30. 7.71	J.Coleman	Sywell	28. 7.02T
G-AZCU	Beagle B.121 Pup 1	B121-162		30. 7.71	A.A.Harris	Shobdon	5. 8.01
G-AZCV	Beagle B.121 Pup 2	B121-163	HB-NAR G-AZCV	30. 7.71	N.R.W.Long	Compton Abbas	5. 7.99
G-AZCY	Beagle B.121 Pup 2	B121-166	HB-NAW G-AZCY	30. 7.71	D.J. Deas (Carries Swiss Cross on fin)	Bentwaters	15.11.01T
G-AZCZ	Beagle B.121 Pup 2	B121-167		30. 7.71	L. & J.M.Northover	Cardiff	22. 5.01T
G-AZDA	Beagle B.121 Pup 1	B121-168		30. 7.71	B.D.Deubelbeiss	Elstree	23.12.99
G-AZDD	MBB Bo.209 Monsun 150FF	143	D-EBJC	3. 8.71	J D Hall & D Lawrence t/a Double Delta Flying Group	Biggin Hill	11. 4.01
G-AZDE	PA-28R-200 Cherokee Arrow	28R-7135141		3. 8.71	Paul James Knitwear Ltd	Leicester	15. 9.02
G-AZDG	Beagle B.121 Pup 2	B121-145	(G-BLYM) HB-NAM/(VH-EPT)/G-35-145	17. 6.85	J.R.Heaps (DHL c/s)	Elstree	25. 2.01
G-AZDJ	PA-32-300 Cherokee Six D	32-7140068	OY-AJK G-AZDJ/N5273S	23. 8.71	K.J.Mansbridge & D.C.Gibbs	Cardiff	3. 4.00T
G-AZDK	Beechcraft 95-B55 Baron	TC-1406		23. 8.71	C.C.Forrester	Denham	23. 2.01
G-AZDX	PA-28-180 Cherokee F	28-7105186		25. 8.71	M.Cowan	Hundon, Suffolk	4. 2.02
G-AZDY	DH.82A Tiger Moth	86559	F-BGDJ Fr.AF/PG650	25. 8.71	J.B.Mills	Willingham	18. 8.97
G-AZDZ*	Cessna 172K Skyhawk	172-58501	5N-AIH N1647C/N84508	25. 8.71	The Fire Service College (Damaged Delapre GC, Northants 19.9.81 & used for fire training 8.98)	Moreton-in-Marsh	25. 2.83
G-AZEE	Morane MS.880B Rallye Club	74	F-BKKA	1. 9.71	J.Shelton (Composite incl fuselage of G-AZNJ c/n 5375 in 1980; original fuselage stored in rafters South Scarle 9.94)	North Coates	27. 9.98
G-AZEF	Jodel Wassmer D.120 Paris-Nice	321	F-BNZS	1. 9.71	J.R.Legge	Lumb-in-Rossendale	21. 7.00P
G-AZEG	PA-28-140 Cherokee D	28-7125530		1. 9.71	The Ashley Gardner Flying Club Ltd	Ronaldsway	3. 7.01T
G-AZER*	Cameron O-42 HAFB	26		9. 9.71	Not known "Shy-Tot"		15. 5.81A
G-AZEU	Beagle B.121 Pup 2	B121-130	VH-EPL G-35-130	15. 9.71	G.M.Moir	Egginton	13. 2.00
G-AZEV	Beagle B.121 Pup 2	B121-131	VH-EPM G-35-131	15. 9.71	G.P.Martin	Goodwood	23. 8.02
G-AZEW	Beagle B.121 Pup 2	B121-132	VH-EPN G-35-132	15. 9.71	K.Cameron	Headcorn	12. 5.00
G-AZEY	Beagle B.121 Pup 2	B121-136	HB-NAK G-AZEY/VH-EPP/G-35-136	15. 9.71	M.E.Reynolds	Goodwood	26. 6.00
G-AZFA	Beagle B.121 Pup 2	B121-143	VH-EPR G-35-143	15. 9.71	K.F.Plummer Buttermilk Hall Farm, Blisworth		22. 7.01
G-AZFC	PA-28-140 Cherokee D	28-7125486		16. 9.71	M.L.Hannah	Blackbushe	27. 7.02
G-AZFF	Wassmer Jodel D.112	1175	F-BLFI	17. 9.71	R.Pidcock	Fenland	19. 5.00P
G-AZFI	PA-28R-200 Cherokee Arrow	28R-7135160		21. 9.71	GAZFI Ltd	Sherburn in Elmet	6. 4.01

Regn	Type	C/n	P/I	Date	Owner/operator	Probable Base	CA Expy
G-AZFM	PA-28R-200 Cherokee Arrow	28R-7135218		24. 9.71	T.N.Jenness	Biggin Hill	5. 2 01
G-AZFR	Cessna 401B	401B-0121	N7981Q	30. 9.71	Westair Flying Services Ltd	Blackpool	7. 9.02T
G-AZGA	Jodel Wassmer D.120 Paris-Nice	144	F-BIXV	30. 9.71	A.F.Vizoso	RAF Halton	5. 1.00P
G-AZGC	SNCAN Stampe SV-4C	120	F-BCGE	4.10.71	V.Lindsay	Kidmore End, Reading	22. 2.91
	(As "No.120" in French A/F c/s) (Damaged Folly Farm, Hungerford 28.5.90; stored 5.93)						
G-AZGE	SNCAN Stampe SV-4C	576	F-BDDV	6.10.71	M.R.L.Astor	East Hatley, Tadlow	15. 8.94
	(Stored 3.97)						
G-AZGF	Beagle B.121 Pup 2	B121-076	PH-KUF G-35-076	6.10.71	K.Singh	Barton	2. 5.98
G-AZGI	Socata MS.880B Rallye Club	1896		7.10.71	B.McIntyre	Movenis, Co.Londonderry	12.11.01
G-AZGL	Socata MS.894A Rallye Minerva 220	11929		7.10.71	The Cambridge Aero Club Ltd	Cambridge	7. 9.02T
G-AZGY	Rousseau CP.301B Emeraude	122	F-BRAA	12.10.71	C.J.R.Gray	(Wrexham)	24. 4.00P
G-AZGZ	DH.82A Tiger Moth	86489	F-BGCF Fr.AF/NM181	13.10.71	R.J.King	Rush Green	16. 3.02
	(As "NM181")						
G-AZHB	Robin HR.100/200B Royal	118		14.10.71	C. & P.P.Scarlett	Lydd	6. 8.00
G-AZHC	Wassmer Jodel D.112	585	F-BIQQ	18.10.71	D.H.Wilson	Netherthorpe	17. 5.00P
	t/a Aerodel Flying Group						
G-AZHD	Slingsby T.61A Falke	1753		18.10.71	Nicola J.Orchard-Armitage	(Deal)	2. 6.00
G-AZHE*	Slingsby T.61B Falke	1755	N61TB G-AZHE	18.10.71	M.R.Shelton	Tatenhill	AC
	(Damaged 17.6.88 & on rebuild - cancelled by CAA 14.3.99)						
G-AZHH	K & S SA.102.5 Cavalier (Lycoming O-290)	PFA/1393		20.10.71	D.W.Buckle	Morton Carr Farm, Nunthorpe	20. 1.00P
G-AZHI	AESL Airtourer T5 (Super 150)	A.540		20.10.71	H.J.Douglas	Lydd	27. 3.99T
	t/a Airtourer Squadron						
G-AZHJ*	Scottish Avn Twin Pioneer 3	577	G-31-16 XP295	20.10.71	Air Atlantique Ltd	Coventry	23. 8.90S
	(Stored 7.97)						
G-AZHK	Robin HR.100/200B Royal	113	G-ILEG G-AZHK	22.10.71	A.Bendkowski & T.A.Houghton	Rochester	19. 5.02
G-AZHR	Piccard Ax6 HAFB	617	N17US	27.10.71	C.Fisher	Sheffield	AC
	t/a Halcyon Balloon Group "Happiness"						
G-AZHT	AESL Airtourer T3	525		29.10.71	Aviation West Ltd	(Glasgow)	29. 1.89T
	(Damaged Glenforsa, Mull 29.4.88; stored 6.95)						
G-AZHU	Phoenix Luton LA-4A Minor (VW1834)	PFA/839		1.11.71	W.Cawrey	Netherthorpe	13. 7.00P
G-AZIB	Socata ST-10 Diplomate	141		4.11.71	W.B.Bateson	Blackpool	6. 2.00
G-AZID	Reims Cessna FA.150L Aerobat	0083	N9447	8.11.71	Aerobat Ltd	Halfpenny Green	3.11.99T
G-AZII	SAN Jodel D.117A	848	F-BNDO F-OBFO	12.11.71	P J Brayshaw	Haddock Stone Farm, Markington	3.12.99P
G-AZIJ	Robin DR.360 Chevalier	634		15.11.71	K.J.Fleming & T.W.Conlan	Caernarfon	4. 6.00
G-AZIK	PA-34-200-2 Seneca	34-7250018	N2392T	15.11.71	Walkbury Aviation Ltd	Sibson	19. 3.99T
G-AZIL	Slingsby T.61A Falke	1756		16.11.71	D.W.Savage	Portmoak	19.11.99
G-AZIP	Cameron O-65 HAFB	29		24.11.71	P.G.Dunnington "Dante"	Hungerford	5. 5.81A
	t/a Dante Balloon Group (Non-airworthy - stored 2.97)						
G-AZJC	Sportavia Fournier RF5	5108		30.11.71	W.S.V.Stoney	(Arezzo, Italy)	14.10.00
G-AZJE	Barritault JB.01 Minicab (Continental C90)	JBE.1 & PFA/1806		1.12.71	J.B.Evans (Stored 12.95)	Ventnor, IOW	7. 7.82P
G-AZJI*	Western O-65 HAFB	007		2.12.71	British Balloon Museum "Peek-A-Boo"	Newbury	NE(A)
G-AZJN	Robin DR.300/140 Major	642		6.12.71	Wright Farm Eggs Ltd	Cherry Tree Farm, Monewden	3. 8.02T
G-AZJV	Reims Cessna F.172L	0810		8.12.71	J.A. & A.J.Boyd	Cardiff	11. 2.00
G-AZJY	Reims Cessna FRA.150L Aerobat	0126		8.12.71	R.P.Smith	Barton	21. 5.01
G-AZKC	Socata MS.880B Rallye Club	1914		8.12.71	L.J.Martin	Sandown	2. 7.00
G-AZKE	Socata MS.880B Rallye Club	1950		8.12.71	B.S.Rowden & W.L.Rogers	Hemborough Farm, Capton, Dartmouth	6.10.99
G-AZKK	Cameron O-56 HAFB	32		13.12.71	P.J.Green & C.Bosley	Newbury	NE(A)
	t/a Gemini Balloon Group "Gemini"						
G-AZKO	Reims Cessna F.337F Super Skymaster (Wichita c/n 01380)	0041		20.12.71	P.W. Crispe "Bird Dog"	Wellesbourne Mountford	25. 7.99
G-AZKP	SAN Jodel D.117	419	F-BHND	20.12.71	J.Lowe	Griffins Farm, Temple Bruer	4. 6.99P
G-AZKR	PA-24-180 Comanche	24-2192	N7044P	23.12.71	T.E.Groves	Rochester	15. 7.00
G-AZKS	American AA-1A Trainer	0334	N6134L	23.12.71	M.D.Henson	Coventry	3. 6.00
G-AZKV	Reims Cessna FRA.150L Aerobat	0127		23.12.71	B.Flay & T.C.Hocking	Bodmin	31.10.93T
	t/a The Penguin Flight						
	(Damaged Redlake, Lostwithiel 15.9.91; status uncertain - only small parts and wings stored 8.96)						
G-AZKW	Reims Cessna F.172L	0836		23.12.71	J.C.C.Wright	Hinton-in-The-Hedges	21. 6.02T
G-AZKZ	Reims Cessna F.172L	0814		23.12.71	R.D. & E.Forster	Beccles	20. 7.01T
	(Op Norfolk Flying Club)						

63

Regn	Type	C/n	P/I	Date	Owner/operator	Probable Base	CA Expy
G-AZLE	Boeing-Stearman E75 (N2S-5) Kaydet (Continental W670)	75-8543	CF-XRD N5619N/Bu43449	29.12.71	A.E.Poulsom Manor Farm, Tongham t/a Air Farm Flyers (As "2"in US Army c/s)	23. 3.01	
G-AZLF	Jodel Wassmer D.120 Paris-Nice	230	F-BLFL	30.12.71	M.S.C.Ball Garston Farm, Marshfield	16.11.00P	
G-AZLH	Reims Cessna F.150L	0757		31.12.71	Coulson Flying Services Ltd North Coates	20.11.00T	
G-AZLJ	BN-2A mk.III-1 Trislander	319	G-OREG SX-CBN/G-OREG/G-OAVW/G-AZLJ/G-51-319	31.12.71	Hebridean Air Services Ltd Cumbernauld	2. 2.00T	
G-AZLM*	Reims Cessna F.172L	0842		31.12.71	Norfolk & Suffolk Aviation Musm Flixton (Crashed Badminton 23.3.91; fuselage stored 9.97)	16. 7.93T	
G-AZLN	PA-28-180 Cherokee F	28-7105210		3. 1.72	Liteflite Ltd Oxford	19. 2.01	
G-AZLO*	Reims Cessna F.337F Super Skymaster (Wichita c/n 01347)	0029		4. 1.72	Not known Bourn (Rear-fuselage stored 5.97)	22. 4.82	
G-AZLP*	Vickers 813 Viscount	346	(ZS-SBT) ZS-CDT	4. 1.72	Teeside Airport Fire Services Teeside	3. 4.82T	
G-AZLS*	Vickers 813 Viscount	348	(ZS-SBV) ZS-CDV	4. 1.72	CAA International Fire Training Centre Teeside	9. 6.83T	
G-AZLV	Cessna 172K	172-57908	4X-ALM N79138	10. 1.72	B.L.F.Karthaus Newcastle	18. 1.01	
G-AZLY	Reims Cessna F.150L	0771		10. 1.72	Cleveland Flying School Ltd Teeside	5.12.02T	
G-AZLZ	Reims Cessna F.150L	0772		10. 1.72	A.G.Martlew Haverfordwest	16. 7.00	
G-AZMC	Slingsby T.61A Falke	1757		12. 1.72	Essex Gliding Club Ltd Challock (Sold - stored 8.90)	22. 9.86	
G-AZMD	Slingsby T.61C Falke	1758		12. 1.72	R.A.Rice Wellesbourne Mountford	1. 6.01	
G-AZMF	BAC One-Eleven 530FX	BAC.240	7Q-YKJ	14. 1.72	European Aviation Ltd Bournemouth	22. 1.01T	
			G-AZMF/PT-TYY/G-AZMF (Op European VIP First) "The European Express"				
G-AZMJ	American AA-5 Traveler	0019		27. 1.72	R.T.Love St.Merryn	25. 2.01	
G-AZMN*	AESL Airtourer T5 (Super 150)	A.550		28. 1.72	Not known Kemble (Damaged Glasgow 23.6.87; stored 6.97)	7. 5.89	
G-AZMX*	PA-28-140 Cherokee	28-24777	SE-FLL LN-LMK	7. 2.72	North East Wales Institute of Higher Education (Instructional airframe 3.96) Connah's Quay	9. 1.82	
G-AZMZ	Socata MS.893A Rallye Commodore 180	11927		8. 2.72	Patricia J.Wilcox Lyveden	31. 1.97	
G-AZNA*	Vickers 813 Viscount	350	(ZS-SBX) ZS-CDX	8. 2.72	Not known Zomergem, Belgium (Displayed in car park 7.97)	24. 8.90T	
G-AZNC*	Vickers 813 Viscount	352	(ZS-SBZ) ZS-CDZ	8. 2.72	CAA International Fire Training Centre Teeside (Green/unmarked & used for non-destructive training 5.97)	18. 5.83T	
G-AZNK	SNCAN Stampe SV-4A (Gipsy Major 10)	290	F-BKXF F-BCGZ	15. 2.72	P.D.Jackson & R.A.G.Lucas Redhill "Globird"	11. 8.00	
G-AZNL	PA-28R-200 Cherokee Arrow II	28R-7235006		16. 2.72	B.P.Liversidge Framlingham	8. 8.02T	
G-AZNO	Cessna 182P Skylane	182-61005	N7365Q	18. 2.72	T & K.Andrewes Brunton	10. 4.00	
G-AZNT	Cameron O-84 HAFB	34		21. 2.72	N.Tasker "Oberon" Bristol	5. 6.85	
G-AZOA	MBB Bo.209 Monsun 150FF	183	D-EAAY	21. 2.72	M.W.Hurst Seighford	13. 5.01	
G-AZOB	MBB Bo.209 Monsun 150FF	184	D-EAAZ	21. 2.72	G.N.Richardson		
			(Crashed Droitwich 21.8.83; stored 8.92) Shelsley Beauchamp, Worcester				9. 7.84
G-AZOE	AESL Airtourer T2 (115)	528		21. 2.72	B.J.Edmondson & J.K.Smithson Newcastle t/a G-AZOE 607 Group	30. 6.00	
G-AZOF	AESL Airtourer T5 (Super 150)	A.549		21. 2.72	R.J.W.Bayliff & A.C.Hart Booker t/a Cirrus Flying Group	17. 2.01	
G-AZOG	PA-28R-200 Cherokee Arrow II	28R-7235009		21. 2.72	J.G.Collins Little Gransden	23. 7.01	
G-AZOL	PA-34-200-2 Seneca	34-7250075	N4348T	28. 2.72	D.I.Barnes (White Waltham)	30. 1.00	
G-AZOO	Western O-65 HAFB	015		1. 3.72	Semajan Ltd Romsey t/a Southern Balloon Group "Carousel"	6. 6.77S	
G-AZOR	MBB Bo.105DB	S.20	EC-DOE G-AZOR/D-HDAC	1. 3.72	Bond Air Services Boreham (Op Essex Air Ambulance)	31. 5.02T	
G-AZOS	Jurca MJ.5-H1 Sirocco 001 & PFA/2206 (Lycoming O-320)			1. 3.72	M.K.Field Sleap	14. 6.99P	
G-AZOT	PA-34-200 Seneca	34-7250073	N4340T	3. 3.72	MK Aero Support Ltd Andrewsfield (Wings only 1.99)	4. 3.98T	
G-AZOU	SAN Jodel DR.1050 Sicile	354	F-BJYX	7. 3.72	D.Elliott & D.Holl t/a Horsham Flying Group Wellcross Grange, Slinfold	1. 6.02	
G-AZOZ	Reims Cessna FRA.150L Aerobat	0136		7. 3.72	Seawing Flying Club Ltd Southend "The Wizard of Oz"	14. 7.02T	
G-AZPA	PA-25-235 Pawnee C	25-5223	N8797L	7. 3.72	Black Mountains Gliding Club Ltd Talgarth	1. 5.01	
G-AZPC	Slingsby T.61C Falke	1767		7. 3.72	Ann-Marie Parker Feshiebridge	31. 7.01	
G-AZPF	Sportavia Fournier RF5	5001	D-KOLT	10. 3.72	R.Pye Blackpool	29. 1.00P	
G-AZPH*	Craft-Pitts S.1S Special (Lycoming IO-360)	S1S-001-C	N11CB	13. 3.72	The Science Museum (Flight Gallery) South Kensington, London	4. 9.91P	

Regn	Type	C/n	P/I	Date	Owner/operator	Probable Base	CA Expy
G-AZPV	Phoenix-Luton LA-4A Minor (Lycoming O-145)	PFA/833		14. 3.72	J.R.Faulkner (Stored 6.99)	RAF Bicester	18. 9.97P
G-AZPX	Western O-31 HAFB	011		20. 3.72	B.L.King t/a Eugena Rex Balloon Group "Eugena Rex"	Coulsdon	
G-AZRA	MBB Bo.209 Monsun 150FF	192	D-EAIH	21. 3.72	Alpha Flying Ltd	Booker	4. 9.00
G-AZRD	Cessna 401B	401B-0218	N7999Q	22. 3.72	G.Hatton t/a Romeo Delta Group	Blackpool	13. 3.00T
G-AZRG*	PA-23-250 Aztec D	27-4386	N6536Y	23. 3.72	Woodgate Aviation (IOM) Ltd (On fire dump 4.97)	Ronaldsway	8. 7.93T
G-AZRH	PA-28-140 Cherokee D	28-7125585		23. 3.72	H.B.Carter t/a Trust Flying Group Jersey		24. 2.00
G-AZRI	Payne HAFB (56,500 cu.ft)	GFP.1		21. 3.72	C.A.Butter & J.J.T.Cooke "Shoestring" t/a Aardvark Balloon Co Newbury/Southall		
G-AZRK	Sportavia Fournier RF5	5112		23. 3.72	P.M.Brockington & J.F.Rogers Shennington		22. 6.00P
G-AZRL	PA-18-95 Super Cub (L-18C-PI) (Frame No.18-1213)	18-1331	OO-SBR OO-HML/ALAT 18-1331/51-15331	23. 3.72	M.G.Fountain	Leicester	20. 8.01
G-AZRM	Sportavia Fournier RF5 (VW 1834)	5111		24. 3.72	A.R.Dearden & R.Speer	Kitson Field	24. 2.00P
G-AZRN	Cameron O-84 HAFB	28		28. 3.72	C.A.Butter & J.J.T.Cooke "Old Money"	Newbury	4. 7.81A
G-AZRP	AESL Airtourer T2 (115)	529		28. 3.72	B.F.Strawford	Shobdon	21. 3.01
G-AZRR	Cessna 310Q	310Q-0490	N9923F	28. 3.72	Routarrow Ltd	Seething	23. 4.01
G-AZRS	PA-22-150 Tri-Pacer	22-5141	XT-AAH F-OCGZ/ALAT 22-5141/"FMKAC"	28. 3.72	J.B.Nicholson Watchford Farm, Yarcombe t/a Sandpiper Group "Sandpiper"		3. 4.00
G-AZRV	PA-28R-200 Cherokee Arrow	28R-7135191	N2309T	4. 4.72	General Airline Ltd	Blackbushe	28. 5.02T
G-AZRW*	Cessna T337C Turbo Super Skymaster	337-0914	9XR-DB N2614S	4. 4.72	Not known Standalone Farm, Meppershall (Stored 7.94)		7. 6.82
G-AZRX*	Gardan GY-80-160 Horizon	14	F-BLIJ	4. 4.72	Adventure Island Pleasure Ground Marine Parade, Southend-on-Sea (Damaged Sandtoft 14.8.91; on display in Crazy Golf Course, Sea-front 1.00)		20.2.92
G-AZRZ	Cessna U206F Stationair	U206-01803	N9603G	4. 4.72	M.R.Browne & R.G.Wood t/a Hinton Skydiving Centre Hinton-in-The-Hedges		26. 5.00
G-AZSA	Stampe et Renard SV-4B (Registered in error as c/n "64")	1203	V-61 Belgian AF	5. 4.72	J.K.Faulkner	Biggin Hill	30. 4.98
G-AZSC	Noorduyn AT-16-ND Harvard IIB	14A-1363	PH-SKK R.Neth AF B-19/FT323/43-13064 (As "43/SC" in USAAF c/s)	7. 4.72	Machine Music Ltd (Gary Numan)	Duxford	28. 6.00P
G-AZSD	Slingsby T.29B Motor Tutor (Rebuild of Slingsby c/n 561) RGB 01/72 & PFA/1574			7. 4.72	R.G.Boyton Halstead, Essex t/a Essex Aviation		
G-AZSF	PA-28R-200 Cherokee Arrow II	28R-7235048		10. 4.72	W.T.Northorpe t/a Flight Simulation Air Park	Coventry	5. 8.02
G-AZSP*	Cameron O-84 HAFB	43		18. 4.72	British Balloon Museum "Esso"	Newbury	22. 3.82
G-AZSW	Beagle B.121 Pup 1	B121-140	PH-VRT G-35-140	24. 4.72	I.T.Dall	Sywell	4.11.02
G-AZSZ	PA-23-250 Aztec D	27-4194	N6851Y	25. 4.72	Industrial Cladding Systems Ltd	Kemble	2. 6.01T
G-AZTA	MBB Bo.209 Monsun 150FF	190	D-EAIF	25. 4.72	A.I.D.Rich	Elstree	7. 9.01
G-AZTD	PA-32-300 Cherokee Six D	32-7140001	N8611N	26. 4.72	Presshouse Publications Ltd	Enstone	16. 8.98T
G-AZTF	Reims Cessna F.177RG Cardinal	0054		28. 4.72	D.A.Wiggins	Booker	13. 8.01
G-AZTK	Reims Cessna F.172F	0116	PH-CON OO-SIR	27. 4.72	Vascas Ltd	Weston, Ireland	20.10.00
G-AZTN*	AESL Airtourer T2 (115)	A.531		28. 4.72	Not known St.Just (Crashed Puriton, Somerset 27.6.77; wreck stored 9.95)		24. 6.78
G-AZTR	SNCAN Stampe SV-4C	596	F-BDEQ	28. 4.72	P.G.Palumbo (Stored in Blue Max Movie Acft Museum 3.96)	Booker	15. 7.94
G-AZTS	Reims Cessna F.172L	0866		28. 4.72	C.E.Stringer	Bagby	16. 1.00T
G-AZTV	Stolp SA.500 Starlet (Continental C90) SSM.2 & PFA/1584			19. 5.72	G.G.Rowland (Christchurch) (Damaged Manor Farm, Grateley, Hants 4.7.92; status uncertain)		19.11.92
G-AZTW	Reims Cessna F.177RG Cardinal	0043		28. 4.72	R.M.Clarke	Leicester	15. 5.00
G-AZUM	Reims Cessna F.172L	0863		11. 5.72	L.R.Sullivan t/a Fowlmere Flyers	Fowlmere	16.11.00
G-AZUP	Cameron O-65 HAFB	36		11. 5.72	R.S.Bailey & A.B.Simpson "Eight of Hearts" Aylesbury/Hemel Hempstead		23.10.77S
G-AZUT	Socata MS.893A Rallye Commodore 180	10963	VH-TCH	12. 5.72	J.Palethorpe Blakedown, Kidderminster t/a Rallye Flying Group		9.11.02
G-AZUV*	Cameron O-65 HAFB	41		12. 5.72	British Balloon Museum "Icarus" (Stored - no longer airworthy)	Newbury	23. 6.83
G-AZUX	Western O-56 HAFB	017		15. 5.72	D.M.Sandford "Slow Djinn"	Knutsford	
G-AZUY	Cessna 310L	310L-0012	SE-FEC LN-LMH/N2212F	15. 5.72	George Moss & Sons Ltd (Damaged Liverpool 3.7.98; on repair 8.98)	Liverpool	1.12.99
G-AZUZ	Reims Cessna FRA.150L Aerobat	0146		16. 5.72	D.J.Parker	Netherthorpe	12. 1.00
G-AZVA	MBB Bo.209 Monsun 150FF	177	(D-EAAQ)	16. 5.72	J.Nivison	Thruxton	8. 9.00
G-AZVB	MBB Bo.209 Monsun 150FF	178	(D-EAAS)	16. 5.72	P.C.Logsdon	Dunkeswell	6. 5.00

Regn	Type	C/n	P/I	Date	Owner/operator	Probable Base	CA Expy
G-AZVF	Socata MS.894A Rallye Minerva 220	11999	(F-OCSR)	16. 5.72	F.A.Cavacuiti & G.Hammond (Usk) t/a Minerva Flying Group		9. 3.02
G-AZVG	American AA-5 Traveler	AA5-0075		16. 5.72	R.P.Watkins Newtownards t/a Grumair Flying Group		25. 6.02
G-AZVH	Socata MS.894A Rallye Minerva 220	12017		16. 5.72	P.L.Jubb Poplar Hall Farm, Elmsett		17. 6.01
G-AZVI	Socata MS.892A Rallye Commodore 150	12039		16. 5.72	H.R.Dyas & V.S.Bryan Shobdon t/a Shobdon Flying Group		5. 2.01
G-AZVJ	PA-34-200-2 Seneca	34-7250125	N4529T	16. 5.72	Skyfotos Ltd (Op Foto Flite) Headcorn		21. 8.00A
G-AZVL	Jodel D.119 (Built Ets Valladeau)	794	F-BILB	19. 5.72	P.T.East Stapleford t/a Forest Flying Group		26. 8.00P
G-AZVM	Hughes 369HS (500C)	61-0326S	N9091F	19. 5.72	Diagnostic Reagents Ltd Thame		7. 8.00
G-AZVP	Reims Cessna F.177RG Cardinal	0057		22. 5.72	Cardinal Flyers Ltd Elstree		25. 6.01
G-AZWB	PA-28-140 Cherokee E	28-7225244		5. 6.72	B.N.Rides & L.Connor Hinton-in-The-Hedges		11.12.00
G-AZWD	PA-28-140 Cherokee E	28-7225298		6. 6.72	C.B.Mellor Southampton t/a BM Aviation (Damaged Cardiff 15.11.98)		6. 5.02T
G-AZWE	PA-28-140 Cherokee E	28-7225303		6. 6.72	P.M.Tucker Dunkeswell t/a G-AZWE Flying Group		18. 3.02T
G-AZWF	SAN Jodel DR.1050 Ambassadeur	130	F-BJJT	7. 6.72	R.J.M.Clement Portmoak		27. 8.01
	(Composite including fuselage of DR.1050M F-BLJX c/n 492)				t/a G-AZWF Jodel Syndicate		
G-AZWS	PA-28R-180 Cherokee Arrow	28R-30749	N4993J	8. 6.72	G.S.Blair & I.Parkinson Newcastle t/a Arrow 88 Flying Group		24. 4.00
G-AZWT	Westland Lysander IIIA	Y1536	RCAF 1582 V9552	9. 6.72	The Shuttleworth Trust Old Warden (As "V9441/AR-A" in 309 Sqn c/s)		28. 5.99P
G-AZWY	PA-24-260 Comanche C	24-4806	N9310P	16. 6.72	Keymer, Son & Co Ltd Biggin Hill		15. 4.00
G-AZXA	Beechcraft 95-C55 Baron	TE-72	SE-EKZ	19. 6.72	Cobham Leasing Ltd Bournemouth		5. 5.02A
G-AZXB	Cameron O-65 HAFB	48		20. 6.72	R.J.Mitchener & P.F.Smart t/a Balloon Collection "London Pride II"		6. 5.81A
G-AZXC	Reims Cessna F.150L	0793		20. 6.72	D.C.Bonsall Netherthorpe		28. 4.00T
G-AZXD	Reims Cessna F.172L	0878		20. 6.72	Birdlake Ltd Birmingham (Op Birdlake Aviation)		29. 5.00T
G-AZXG*	PA-23-250 Aztec D	27-4328	N6963Y	23. 6.72	Cranfield University Cranfield		18. 9.94
	(Crashed Little Snoring 25.10.91; instructional airframe 7.99)						
G-AZYA	Gardan GY-80-160 Horizon	57	F-BLPT	7. 7.72	T.Twelvetree & M.L.Moore (Holyhead)		20. 3.00
G-AZYB*	Bell 47H-1	1538	LN-OQG SE-HBE/OO-SHW	4. 7.72	E.D.Ap Rees Weston-super-Mare t/a The Helicopter Museum (On rebuild 5.97)		8. 9.84
G-AZYD	GEMS MS.893A Rallye Commodore 180	10645	F-BNSE	30. 6.72	P.Storey Husbands Bosworth t/a Storey Aviation Services		8. 8.02
G-AZYM	Cessna 310Q	310Q-0507	N4592L	6. 7.72	Offshore Marine Consultants Ltd Gamston		17.10.99
G-AZYS	Scintex CP.301C-1 Emeraude	568	F-BJAY	7. 7.72	F.P.L.Clauson Draycott Farm, Chiseldon		5. 5.00P
G-AZYU	PA-23-250 Aztec E	27-4601	N13983	13. 7.72	L.J.Martin Redhill/Sandown		2.11.98
G-AZYY	Slingsby T.61A Falke	1770		12. 7.72	J.A.Towers Yearby		22. 3.02
G-AZYZ	Wassmer WA.51A Pacific	30	F-OCSE	14. 7.72	J.Ward Norwich		11. 8.00
G-AZZG	Cessna 188 Agwagon 230	188-0279	OY-AHT N8029V	12. 7.72	N.C.Kensington Lairg (On rebuild 5.92)		1. 5.81A
G-AZZH	Practavia Pilot Sprite 115	PFA/1532		13. 7.72	A.Moore (Brentwood) (Stored in back garden Dagenham 1992)		
G-AZZO	PA-28-140 Cherokee	28-22887	N4471J	18. 7.72	R.J.Hind Stapleford		24. 8.97
G-AZZR	Reims Cessna F.150L	0690	LN-LJX	24. 7.72	M.W.Smith t/a G-AZZR Flying Group Exeter		20. 7.01
G-AZZV	Reims Cessna F.172L	0883		18. 7.72	D.J.Hockings Rochester		6. 6.99T
G-AZZX	Reims Cessna FRA.150L Aerobat	0152		27. 7.72	Mary Hewison (Luton)		16. 8.88
	(Damaged Newtownards 28.2.87; on rebuild Maypole Farm, Chislet 12.93)						
G-AZZZ	DH.82A Tiger Moth	86311	F-BGJE Fr.AF/NL864	27. 7.72	S.W.McKay Blue Tile Farm, Langham		21.12.01

G-BAAA – G-BAZZ

Regn	Type	C/n	P/I	Date	Owner/operator	Probable Base	CA Expy
G-BAAD	Evans Super VP-1 (VW1600)	PFA/1540		27. 7.72	K.McNaughton	Breighton	13.10.00P
G-BAAF	Manning-Flanders MF.1 rep (Continental C75)	PPS/REP/8		27. 7.72	Bianchi Aviation Film Services Ltd (Op Blue Max Movie A/c Museum;: no external marks)	Booker	6. 8.96P
G-BAAI	Socata MS.893A Rallye Commodore 180	10705	F-BOVG	31. 7.72	R.D.Taylor	Thruxton	11. 9.00
G-BAAL	Cessna 172A	47678	PH-KAP D-ELGU/N9878T	31. 7.72	Rochester Aviation Ltd (Flying Club ceased trading & for sale 9.99)	Rochester	10. 3.01T
G-BAAT	Cessna 182P Skylane	182-60835	N399JF G-BAAT/N9295G	8.72	Melrose Pigs Ltd Melrose Farm, Melbourne		30. 4.00
G-BAAU	Enstrom F-28A-UK	092		10. 8.72	G.Firbank	(Macclesfield)	6. 5.02T
G-BAAW	Jodel D.119 (Continental O-200-A) (Built Ets Valladeau)	366	F-BHMY	11. 8.72	P J Newson Cherry Tree Farm, Monewden t/a Alpha Whiskey Flying Group (Damaged Monewden 25.8.98)		13. 5.00P
G-BAAZ	PA-28R-200 Cherokee Arrow	28R-7135146	N2388T (XB-VOC)	15. 8.72	A.W.Rix	Guernsey	9. 3.00
G-BABB	Reims Cessna F.150L	0830		15. 8.72	Seawing Flying Club Ltd	Southend	2. 7.00T
G-BABC	Reims Cessna F.150L	0831		15. 8.72	Fordaire Aviation Ltd	Sywell	1. 9.00T
G-BABD	Reims Cessna FRA.150L Aerobat	0153		3. 8.72	R.C.Boyall	(Harleston)	11. 2.01T
G-BABE	Taylor JT.2 Titch (Continental O-200-A)	PEB/01 & PFA/1394		3. 8.72	P.D.G.Grist	Sibson	7. 5.98P
G-BABG	PA-28-180 Cherokee C	28-2031	PH-APU N7978W	15. 8.72	C.E.Dodge t/a Mendip Flying Group	Bristol	11.11.00
G-BABH	Reims Cessna F.150L	0820	EI-CCZ G-BABH	15. 8.72	Sherburn Aero Club Ltd Sherburn in Elmet		1. 4.01T
G-BABK	PA-34-200-2 Seneca	34-7250219	PH-DMN G-BABK/N5203T	18. 8.72	D.F.J.Flashman	Biggin Hill	24. 9.01
G-BACB	PA-34-200-2 Seneca	34-7250251	N5354T	25. 8.72	Rankart Ltd	Hinton-in-The-Hedges	24. 6.02T
G-BACC	Reims Cessna FRA.150L Aerobat	0157		16. 8.72	C.M. & J.H.Cooper	Cranfield	13.12.01
G-BACE	Sportavia Fournier RF5	5102	(PT-DVZ) D-KCID	25. 8.72	R.W.K.Stead Perranporth t/a Clockwork Mouse Flying Group "The Clockwork Mouse"		17. 8.01
G-BACJ	Jodel Wassmer D.120 Paris-Nice	315	F-BNZC	1. 9.72	J.M.Allan t/a Wearside Flying Association	Newcastle	15. 3.00P
G-BACL	SAN Jodel 150 Mascaret	31	F-BSTY CN-TYY	4. 9.72	G.R.French	Bensons Farm, Laindon	8. 9.01
G-BACN	Reims Cessna FRA.150L Aerobat	0161		4. 9.72	Cornwall Flying Club Ltd	Bodmin	27. 5.00T
G-BACO	Reims Cessna FRA.150L Aerobat	0163		4. 9.72	M.M.Pepper	Sibson	14. 5.01
G-BACP	Reims Cessna F.150L Aerobat (Converted from FRA.150L standard)	0164		4. 9.72	Vectair Aviation 1995 Ltd	Goodwood	28. 2.01T
G-BADC	Rollason Beta B.2A (Continental C90)	JJF.1 & PFA/1384		7. 9.72	J.C.Mead (On overhaul Barton 5.95)	(Wrexham)	31. 1.85P
G-BADH	Slingsby T.61A Falke	1774		6. 9.72	D.W.Smart t/a Falke Flying Group	Gallows Hill	31. 3.02
G-BADI	PA-23-250 Aztec D	27-4235	N6885Y	5. 9.72	West London Aero Services Ltd	North Weald	29.10.92T
	(Open storage 5.97: as "G-BABF" 1999 for TV episode of "The Bill" to portray crashed a/c)						
G-BADJ	PA-E23-250 Aztec E	27-4841	N14279	11. 9.72	C.Papadakis	Oxford	21.12.01T
G-BADM	Rollason-Druine D.62B Condor	RAE/653 & PFA/49-11442		8. 9.72	M.Harris & J.StJ.Mehta	Yeldon Farm, Nutley	16. 6.00P
G-BADO	PA-32-300 Cherokee Six E	32-7240011	N8664N	15. 9.72	G-BADO Ltd	Gloucestershire	15.10.01
G-BADU*	Cameron O-56 HAFB	47		18. 4.72	J.Philp t/a Serendipity Balloon Group "Dream Machine"	Pinner	29. 3.78S
G-BADV*	Brochet MB.50 Pipistrelle (Salmson AD9B)	78	F-PBRJ	13. 9.72	H.F.Moffatt (On rebuild)	Woodlow Farm, Bosbury	9. 5.79P
G-BADW	Aerotek Pitts S-2A Special	2035		21. 9.72	R.E.Mitchell	RAF Cosford	16. 9.95T
G-BADZ	Aerotek Pitts S-2A Special	2038		21. 9.72	A.F.D.Kingdon	Blackpool	5. 6.00T
G-BAEB	Robin DR.400/160 Knight	733		19. 9.72	P.D.W.King	Lydd	3. 2.01T
G-BAEC	Robin HR.100/210 Royal	145	EI-BDG G-BAEC	15. 9.72	Designways (Intr Design) Ltd, J.Marriner & L.Stevens t/a Robin Travel	Elstree	24. 3.00
G-BAED	PA-23-250 Aztec C	27-3864	N6567Y	18. 9.72	K.G.Manktelow & N.Brewitt (Manx Airlines c/s)	Ronaldsway	10. 6.01T
G-BAEE	CEA Jodel DR.1050/M1 Sicile Record	579	F-BMGN	29. 9.72	R.Little	Shoreham	12. 6.00
G-BAEM	Robin DR.400/125 Petit Prince	728		25. 9.72	M.A.Webb	Denham	31. 5.00
G-BAEN	Robin DR.400/180 Regent	736		25. 9.72	European Soaring Club Ltd	Le Blanc, France	4.12.99
G-BAEO	Reims Cessna F.172M	0911		14. 9.72	L.W.Scattergood Sherburn-in-Elmet (Re-built with original fuselage and remains of G-YTWO)		AC

Regn	Type	C/n	P/I	Date	Owner/operator	Probable Base	CA Expy
G-BAEP	Reims Cessna FRA.150L Aerobat (Converted to F150L standard)	0170		14. 9.72	A.M.Lynn t/a Busy Bee	Fenland	4. 5.01T
G-BAER	LeVier Cosmic Wind 106 & PFA/1571 (Continental O-200-A)			14. 9.72	R.S.Voice "Filly"	Rushett Farm, Chessington	21.11.01P
G-BAET	Piper J3C-65 Cub (L-4H-PI) (Frame No.11430)	11605	OO-AJI 43-30314	26. 9.72	C.J.Rees	Valley Farm, Winwick	30. 4.00P
G-BAEU	Reims Cessna F.150L	0873		26. 9.72	L.W.Scattergood	Sherburn-in-Elmet	19. 1.01T
G-BAEV	Reims Cessna FRA.150L Aerobat	0173		27. 9.72	Susan C.Griffin	Sibson	28. 2.01
G-BAEW*	Reims Cessna F.172M	0914	N12798	27. 9.72	Westley Aircraft (Damaged nr Sywell 12.11.93; stored 7.97)	Cranfield	9. 4.94T
G-BAEY	Reims Cessna F.172M	0915		28. 9.72	R.Fursman	Plymouth	25. 7.99
G-BAEZ	Reims Cessna FRA.150L Aerobat	0169		28. 9.72	Donair Flying Club Ltd	East Midlands	16. 5.99T
G-BAFA	American AA-5 Traveler	AA5-0201	N6136A	6.10.72	C.F.Mackley	Sleap	31. 8.01
G-BAFG	DH.82A Tiger Moth	85995	F-BGEL Fr.AF/EM778	13.10.72	J.E. & P.E.Shaw	Nottingham	18. 8.02
G-BAFH	Evans VP-1	PFA/1579		5.10.72	Not known (Permit expired 14.7.87 & cancelled 4.12.96; possibly open stored Thruxton 8.99)		
G-BAFL	Cessna 182P Skylane	182-61469	N21180	15. 8.72	Farm Aviation Services Ltd "Honey Lingers"	Cranfield	23. 7.01
G-BAFP	Robin DR.400/160 Knight	735		19.10.72	T.A.Pugh t/a Breidden Flying Group	Pool Quay, Breidden	22. 2.01
G-BAFS	PA-18-150 Super Cub	18-5338	ALAT 18-5338	3. 8.72	N.K.Watts t/a G-BAFS Group	Bembridge	31. 3.02
G-BAFT	PA-18-150 Super Cub	18-5340	ALAT 18-5340	3. 8.72	T.J.Wilkinson	Sackville Farm, Riseley	2. 5.00
G-BAFU	PA-28-140 Cherokee	28-20759	PH-NLS	11.10.72	M.Kostiuk	Beeches Farm, South Scarle	10. 4.00
G-BAFV	PA-18-95 Super Cub (L-18C-PI) (Frame No.18-2055)	18-2045	PH-WJK R.Neth AF R-40/8A-40/52-2445	24.10.72	T.F. & S.J.Thorpe	Coldharbour Farm, Willingham	16. 9.01
G-BAFX	Robin DR.400/140 Earl	739		30.10.72	K.R.Gough	Clutton Hill Farm, High Littleton	4. 5.01
G-BAGB	SIAI-Marchetti SF.260	1-07	LN-BIV	20.10.72	British Midland Airways Ltd	East Midlands	16. 6.00
G-BAGC	Robin DR.400/140 Earl	737		13.10.72	W.P.Nutt	(Scarborough)	15. 6.02
G-BAGF	Jodel D.92 Bebe	59	F-PHFC	13.11.72	E.Evans (Wings stored 7.99)	NK	
G-BAGG(2)	PA-32-300 Cherokee Six	32-7340186		7.12.73	D.Anthill	Guernsey	16. 2.01
G-BAGI	Cameron O-31 HAFB	56		25.10.72	D.C.Boxall t/a Red Section Balloon Group "Vital Spark"	Bristol	19. 9.76S
G-BAGL	Westland SA.341G Gazelle 1	1067		26.10.72	Triangle Computer Services Ltd (Op Bournemouth Helicopters) Bournemouth		11. 3.00T
G-BAGN	Reims Cessna F.177RG Cardinal	0068		24.10.72	R.W.J.Andrews	Halfpenny Green	26. 3.01
G-BAGO	Cessna 421B Golden Eagle	421B-0356	N7613Q	24.10.72	M.S.Choksey	(Coventry)	6. 7.00T
G-BAGR	Robin DR.400/140 Petit Prince	753		30.10.72	F.C.Aris & J.D.Last	Caernarfon	8. 4.01
G-BAGS	Robin DR.400/100 2+2	760		30.10.72	J.J.Woodhouse t/a Flying Services	Thruxton	18. 1.03T
G-BAGT	Helio H.295 Super Courier	1288	CR-LJG	31.10.72	B.J.C.Woodall Ltd	Rushett Farm, Chessington	24. 6.01
G-BAGV	Cessna U206F Stationair	U206-01867	N9667G	31.10.72	K.Brady t/a The Scottish Parachute Club	Strathallan	14. 5.01
G-BAGX	PA-28-140 Cherokee	28-23633	N3574K	30.10.72	K.F.Harris t/a Golf X-Ray Group	Conington	20.10.02
G-BAGY	Cameron O-84 HAFB	54		17.10.72	P.G.Dunnington "Beatrice" (Stored 2.97)	Hungerford	16. 6.81A
G-BAHD	Cessna 182P Skylane	182-61501	N21228	25.10.72	G.G.Ferriman t/a Lambley Flying Group	Jericho Farm, Lambley	22.12.00
G-BAHE	PA-28-140 Cherokee C	28-26494	N5696U	30.10.72	A.H.Evans & A.O.Jones (Stored 5.96)	Pool Quay, Breidden	8. 6.95
G-BAHF	PA-28-140 Fliteliner	28-7125215	N431FL	30.10.72	BJ Services (Midlands) Ltd	Coventry	14. 5.01T
G-BAHG	PA-24-260 Comanche B	24-4306	5Y-AFX N8831P	2.11.72	B.Walker & Co (Dursley) Ltd	Gloucestershire	21. 7.00
G-BAHH	Wallis WA-121/Mc (McCulloch)	K/701/X		7.11.72	K.H.Wallis (Noted 5.99)	Reymerston Hall	27. 5.98P
G-BAHI	Reims Cessna F.150H	0330	PH-EHA	6.11.72	P.Wagstaff	Elstree	19.11.01
G-BAHJ	PA-24-250 Comanche	24-1863	PH-RED N6735P	6.11.72	K.Cooper	Halfpenny Green	21. 5.01
G-BAHL	Robin DR.400/160 Knight	704	F-OCSR	8.11.72	M.D.Hinge & L.A.Maynard	Old Sarum	24. 3.00
G-BAHO	Beechcraft C23 Sundowner	M-1456		7.11.72	P.H.White & J.A.L.Staig	Bournemouth	22.11.02
G-BAHP	Volmer VJ.22 Sportsman (Continental C90)	PFA/1313		9.11.72	G.K.Holloway t/a Seaplane Group (Stored 8.98)	Aboyne	18.10.93P
G-BAHS	PA-28R-200 Cherokee Arrow II	28R-7335017	N15147	9.11.72	A.R.N.Morris	(Bishops Castle)	29. 5.00
G-BAHX	Cessna 182P Skylane	182-61588	N21363	16.11.72	A.D.Carr t/a PP Dupost Group	Blackpool	17. 7.00

Regn	Type	C/n	P/I	Date	Owner/operator	Probable Base	CA Expy
G-BAIG	PA-34-200-2 Seneca	34-7250243	OY-BSU G-BAIG/N5257T	21.11.72	Mid-Anglia Flying Centre Ltd Cambridge t/a Mid-Anglia School of Flying		6. 8.00T
G-BAIH	PA-28R-200 Cherokee Arrow II	28R-7335011		21.11.72	M.G.West Kings Farm, Thurrock		9. 2.01
G-BAII	Reims Cessna FRA.150L Aerobat	0178		22.11.72	Cornwall Flying Club Ltd	Bodmin	27. 5.00T
G-BAIK	Reims Cessna F.150L	0903		22.11.72	Wickenby Aviation Ltd (Op Lincoln Flight Centre)	Wickenby	9. 4.00T
G-BAIL*	Reims Cessna FR.172J Rocket	0370		22.11.72	R.H.Blair Gloucestershire t/a Gloucestershire Flying Club		7. 7.00
	(Damaged Farley Farm, Winchester 6.3.99: wreck acquired by Bournemouth College: cancelled by CAA 6.7.99)						
G-BAIN	Reims Cessna FRA.150L Aerobat	0177		23.11.72	Cornwall Flying Club Ltd	Bodmin	3.11.00T
G-BAIP	Reims Cessna F.150L	0898		13.11.72	G. & S.A.Jones Linley Hill, Leven (Damaged Linley Hill 30.5.95)		28. 9.97T
G-BAIR*	Thunder Ax7-77 HAFB	003		27.11.72	S.Faithfull "Jumping Jack"	Not known	NE(A)
G-BAIS	Reims Cessna F.177RG Cardinal	0069		13.11.72	R.M.Graham & E.P.Howard Seething t/a Cardinal Syndicate		22. 8.02
G-BAIW	Reims Cessna F.172M	0928		14.11.72	W.J.Greenfield	Humberside	4.12.00T
G-BAIX	Reims Cessna F.172M	0931		14.11.72	R.A.Nichols	Elstree	19.12.99
G-BAIZ	Slingsby T.61A Falke	1776		27.11.72	G.C.Rumsey & R.G.Sangster t/a Falke Syndicate Hinton-in-The-Hedges		7. 7.00
G-BAJA	Reims Cessna F.177RG Cardinal	0078		29.11.72	Don Ward Productions Ltd	Rochester	15.10.99
G-BAJB	Reims Cessna F.177RG Cardinal	0080		29.11.72	C.M.Bain	Inverness	5. 8.00
G-BAJC	Evans VP-1 Srs.2 (VW1834)	PFA/1548		30.11.72	S.J.Greer Romney Street Farm, Sevenoaks (Damaged landing Bovingdon 4.3.99)		22. 3.99P
G-BAJE	Cessna 177 Cardinal	177-00812	N29322	30.11.72	H.Snelson	Nottingham	20. 5.00
G-BAJN	American AA-5 Traveler	AA5-0259		29.11.72	K.Bell & J.C.Robinson Sherburn in Elmet t/a Janacrew Flying Group		24. 3.00
G-BAJO	American AA-5 Traveler	AA5-0260		29.11.72	P.J.Kelsall t/a G-BAJO Flying Group	Blackpool	19. 1.01
G-BAJR	PA-28-180 Challenger	28-7305008		1.12.72	D.P.Bannister & D.T.Given Newtownards t/a Chosen Flew Flying Group		26. 3.00
G-BAJY	Robin DR.400/180 Regent	758		4.12.72	J.H.Fenwick Wickenby t/a Rolincs Aviation		6. 7.01
G-BAJZ	Robin DR.400/125 Petit Prince	759		4.12.72	Weald Air Services Ltd	Headcorn	24. 6.00T
G-BAKD	PA-34-200-2 Seneca	34-7350013	N1378T	28.11.72	Andrews Professional Colour Laboratories Ltd (Op Foto Flite)	Lydd	17.12.00A
G-BAKH	PA-28-140 Cherokee F	28-7325014		12.12.72	Marnham Investments Ltd Newtownards (Op Ulster Flying Club)		16. 3.00T
G-BAKJ	PA-30-160 Twin Comanche B	30-1232	TJ-AAI TJ-ADH/N8122Y	13.12.72	G.D.Colover, M.F.Fisher, W.R.Lawes & ITS Trading Systems Ltd Elstree		2. 7.00
G-BAKM	Robin DR.400/140 Earl	755		15.12.72	D.V.Pieri	Kirkbride	2.10.00
G-BAKN	SNCAN Stampe SV-4C	348	F-BCOY	15.12.72	M.Holloway Roughay Farm, Bishops Waltham		13. 6.02
G-BAKO*	Cameron O-84 HAFB	57		18.12.72	A D Kent "Pied Piper" Lancing (Balloon Preservation Group 7.98)		12. 7.76S
G-BAKR	SAN Jodel D.117	814	F-BIOV	27.12.72	R.W.Brown Stoneacre Farm, Farthing Corner		4. 7.00P
G-BAKS	Agusta-Bell 206B JetRanger II	8339		28.12.72	Stephenson Marine Co Ltd Goodwood (Crashed Cocking, West Sussex 14.11.97)		26. 6.00T
G-BAKV	PA-18-150 Super Cub	18-8993		22.12.72	A.J.B.Shaw, Western Air (Thruxton) Ltd & F.Taylor Thruxton		6. 8.01
G-BAKW	Beagle B.121 Pup 2	B121-175		15.12.72	H.Beavan	White Waltham	26. 5.00
G-BAKY	Slingsby T.61C Falke	1777		20.12.72	T.J.Wiltshire	Spilsby	7. 8.98
G-BALD	Cameron O-84 HAFB	58		2. 1.73	C.A.Gould Ipswich t/a Inter-Varsity Balloon Club "Puffin"		2. 7.78S
	(Wfu after severe damage 25.6.78; basket to G-PUFF)						
G-BALF	Robin DR.400/140 Earl	772		5. 1.73	N.A.Smith	Barton	15. 5.00
G-BALG	Robin DR.400/180 Regent	771		5. 1.73	R.Jones t/a Southern Sailplanes	Membury	5. 8.01
G-BALH	Robin DR.400/140B Earl	766		5. 1.73	C.Johnson Fenland t/a G-BALH Flying Group		21. 6.01
G-BALI	Robin DR.400 2 + 2	764		5. 1.73	A.Brinkley	(Shefford)	3. 9.88
G-BALJ	Robin DR.400/180 Regent	767		5. 1.73	D.A.Batt & D. de Lacey-Rowe Fridd Farm, Bethersden, Kent		31. 5.00
G-BALK*	SNCAN Stampe SV-4C	387	F-BBAN Fr.Mil	3. 1.73	J.Thorogood (Noted 5.98) Insch		
G-BALN	Cessna T310Q	310Q-0684	N7980Q	8. 1.73	O'Brien Properties Ltd	Shoreham	1. 5.00T
G-BALY	Practavia Pilot Sprite 150	PFA/05-10009		10. 1.73	A.L.Young t/a Aly Aviation (Henstridge) (Project part completed and stored 8.95)		
G-BALZ	Bell 212	30542	EC-GCR	10. 1.73	Bristow Helicopters Ltd	Redhill	5.10.00T
	EC-931/G-BALZ/9Y-TIL/G-BALZ/VR-BIB/N8069A/G-BALZ/N99040/G-BALZ/EI-AWK/G-BALZ/VR-BEK/N2961W						
G-BAMB	Slingsby T.61C Falke	1778		9. 1.73	A.E.T.Nye Kingston Deverill t/a G-BAMB Syndicate		18. 5.00
G-BAMC	Reims Cessna F.150L	0892		12. 1.73	Billy Pickles Ltd	(Haywards Heath)	18. 7.02T

Regn	Type	C/n	P/I	Date	Owner/operator	Probable Base	CA Expy
G-BAMF	MBB Bo.105DB	S.36	D-HDAM	10. 1.73	Bond Air Services (Pollution Patrol)	Sullom Voe	20. 6.00T
G-BAMG*	Avions Lobet Ganagobie	PFA/1336		11. 1.73	Not known (Complete 4.97 but unflown)	Yearby	
G-BAMJ	Cessna 182P	182-61650	N21469	10. 1.73	A.E.Kedros	Thruxton	29. 5.00
G-BAMK	Cameron D-96 Hot-Air Airship	72		11. 1.73	D.W.Liddiard "Isibidbi" (To British Balloon Museum)	Newbury	24. 4.90A
G-BAML	Bell 206B JetRanger	36	N7844S	5. 1.73	Heliscott Ltd Walton Wood, Pontefract		1. 6.00T
G-BAMM	PA-28-235 Cherokee	28-10642	SE-EOA	16. 1.73	T.R.Astell	Lydd	9. 8.01
G-BAMR	PA-16 Clipper (Lycoming O-290)	16-392	F-BFMS CU-P339	12. 1.73	H.Royce Bradleys Lawn, Heathfield		10. 5.01
G-BAMS	Robin DR.400/160 Knight	774		15. 1.73	G-BAMS Ltd	Biggin Hill	29. 5.00T
G-BAMT*	Robin DR.400/160 Knight	775		15. 1.73	Southern Sailplanes (Crashed Cudham 8.1.78; wreck stored 1.92)	Membury	15. 5.79
G-BAMU	Robin DR.400/160 Knight	778		15. 1.73	J.W.L.Otty t/a The Alternative Flying Group	Sywell	15. 6.00
G-BAMV	Robin DR.400/180 Regent	777		15. 1.73	K.Jones & E.A.Anderson	Booker	3. 5.00
G-BAMY	PA-28R-200 Cherokee Arrow II 28R-7335015			9. 1.73	G.R.Gilbert t/a G-BAMY Group	Birmingham	29. 3.01
G-BANA	CEA Jodel DR.221 Dauphin	73	F-BOZR	22. 1.73	G.T.Pryor	Seething	21.10.02
G-BANB	Robin DR.400/180 Regent	776		22. 1.73	D.R.L.Jones	(Malmesbury)	27. 1.00
G-BANC	Gardan GY-201 Minicab (Continental C90)	A.203	F-PCZV F-BCZV	22. 1.73	J.T.S.Lewis & J.E.Williams Brickhouse Farm, Frogland Cross		17. 8.00P
G-BANF	Phoenix Luton LA-4A Minor (Continental A65)	PFA/838		22. 1.73	W.J.McCollum		5. 6.92P
	(Damaged Mullaghmore 27.6.92; status uncertain) (Magherafelt, Co.Londonderry)						
G-BANK*	PA-34-200-2 Seneca	34-7350081	N15636	23. 1.73	Sue Eastwood	Blackbushe	16. 7.01T
	(Cancelled as wfu 31.7.99: apparently broken up & sold as spares)						
G-BANU	Jodel Wassmer D.120 Paris-Nice	247	F-BLNZ	31. 1.73	W.M. & C.H.Kilner	(Stamford)	19. 7.00P
G-BANV	Phoenix Currie Wot (Lycoming O-290)	PFA/3010		25. 1.73	K.Knight (Damaged nr Leek, Staffs 15.9.83; status uncertain)	(Malvern)	26. 6.84P
G-BANW	CAARP CP.1330 Super Emeraude (Lycoming O-235-C1)	941	PH-VRF	30. 1.73	P.S.Milner Scotland Farm, Hook (Damaged nr Scotland Farm 20.6.98)		14. 6.00P
G-BANX	Reims Cessna F.172M	0941		31. 1.73	Oakfleet Ltd	(Oxted)	6. 8.00T
G-BANY*	Glos-Air Airtourer 115	A533		31. 1.73	Not known (Crashed nr Wick 10.8.75; fuselage stored 8.96)	St.Just	25. 3.77
G-BAOB	Reims Cessna F.172M	0949		2. 2.73	Rentair Ltd, M.Nicoll & D.Williams-Gardner Earls Colne		21.12.01T
G-BAOG	Socata MS.880B Rallye Club	2249		6. 2.73	J.Luck	Rochester	16. 1.00
G-BAOH	Socata MS.880B Rallye Club	2250		6. 2.73	M.Lally	(Bracknell)	28. 7.01
G-BAOJ	Socata MS.880B Rallye Club	2252		6. 2.73	R.E.Jones Emlyns Field, Rhuallt		13. 8.01
G-BAOM	Socata MS.880B Rallye Club	2255		6. 2.73	D.H.Tonkin	Bodmin	13. 4.00
G-BAOP	Reims Cessna FRA.150L Aerobat	0190		5. 2.73	M.P.Gucklan,	(Sligo, Ireland)	11. 4.02
G-BAOS	Reims Cessna F.172M	0946		6. 2.73	Wingtask 1995 Ltd	Seething	14. 8.00T
G-BAOU	Grumman-American AA-5 Traveler AA5-0298			8. 2.73	R.C.Mark	(Ludlow)	23. 3.01
G-BAOW	Cameron O-65 HAFB	59		6. 2.73	D P Bushby "Winslow Boy" (Balloon Preservation Group 7.98: tethered 5.99)	Lancing	9. 5.74S
G-BAPB	DHC.1 Chipmunk 22A	C1/0001	WB549	26. 2.73	G.V.Bunyan	Bidford	31. 5.98
G-BAPF*	Vickers 814 Viscount	338	SE-FOY	12. 2.73	The Fire Servive College		13. 6.90T
			G-BAPF/D-ANUN (Instructional airframe 8.98) Moreton-in-Marsh				
G-BAPH*	Reims Cessna FRA.150L Aerobat	0194		8. 2.73	South Yorkshire Aviation Museum		26. 7.82
	(Damaged Bodmin 12.7.81; fuselage on display 5.97) Home Farm, Firbeck						
G-BAPI	Reims Cessna FRA.150L Aerobat	0195		8. 2.73	Industrial Supplies (Peterborough) Ltd Sibson		15. 1.01
G-BAPJ	Reims Cessna FRA.150L Aerobat	0196		8. 2.73	M.D.Page	Manston	10. 6.02
G-BAPL	PA-23-250 Turbo Aztec E	27-7304966	N14377	12. 2.73	Donington Aviation Ltd East Midlands		27. 8.01T
G-BAPM*	Fuji FA.200-160 Aero Subaru FA-200-172			13. 2.73	Not known Farley Farm, Winchester (Cancelled by CAA 6.11.98: wreck noted 6.99)		
G-BAPP	Evans VP-1 Coupe (VW1834)	PFA/1580		13. 2.73	V.Mitchell	Eglinton	27. 5.98P
G-BAPR	Jodel D.11 (Continental PC60)	5295 & PFA/914		14. 2.73	J.P.Liber & J.F.M.Bartlett	Kemble	15. 4.00P
G-BAPS*	Campbell Cougar Gyroplane (Continental O-240-A)	CA/6000		14. 2.73	A.M.W.Curzon-Howe-Herrick (On loan to The Helicopter Museum) Weston-super-Mare		20. 5.74S
G-BAPV	Robin DR.400/160 Knight	742	F-OCSR	19. 2.73	J.D. & M.Millne (Stored 9.97)	Newcastle	16.12.96
G-BAPW	PA-28R-180 Cherokee Arrow	28R-30697	5Y-AIR N4951J	21. 2.73	P.S.Farren & I.W.Lindsey t/a Papa Whisky Flying Group	Denham	3.12.00
G-BAPX	Robin DR.400/160 Knight	789		21. 2.73	M.A.Musselwhite	Sywell	11. 6.00
G-BAPY	Robin HR.100/210 Royal	153		21. 2.73	D.M.Hansell	Old Buckenham	7. 7.01

Regn	Type	C/n	P/I	Date	Owner/operator	Probable Base	CA Expy
G-BARC	Reims Cessna FR.172J Rocket	0356	(D-EEDK)	5. 3.73	C.H.Porter Croft Farm, Defford		6. 4.01
					t/a Severn Valley Aviation Group		
G-BARD*	Cessna 337C Super Skymaster	337-0857	SE-FBU	1. 3.73	Not known	North Coates	9. 1.97
			N2557S		(Damaged North Coates 12.6.94; stored 12.95)		
G-BARF	Wassmer Jodel D.112	1019	F-BJPF	5. 3.73	J.J.Penney	Neath	2.12.99P
G-BARG	Cessna E310Q	310Q-0712	N8237Q	2. 3.73	Tibus Aviation Ltd	(Newbury)	8.12.02
G-BARH	Beechcraft C23 Sundowner	M-1473		2. 3.73	J.R.Pybus	Sherburn in Elmet	4. 2.01
G-BARI*	Beechcraft C23 Sundowner	M-1475		2. 3.73	Not known	Bushey	15. 7.75
					(Crashed nr Coventry 23.4.75; wreck displayed in car-breaker's yard 5.95)		
G-BARN	Taylor JT.2 Titch	PFA/60-11136		5. 3.73	R.G.W.Newton (On rebuild)	(Seaford)	2.10.92P
	(Continental C90)						
G-BARP	Bell 206B JetRanger II	967	N18092	5. 3.73	South Western Electricity plc	Bristol	9. 5.00T
G-BARS	DHC.1 Chipmunk 22	C1/0557	WK520	26. 2.73	J.Beattie	RNAS Yeovilton	3. 8.02
					(As "1377" in Portuguese AF c/s)		
G-BARV	Cessna 310Q	310Q-0774		7. 3.73	Old England Watches Ltd	Elstree	13. 7.01
G-BARZ	Scheibe SF-28A Tandem Falke	5724	(D-KAUK)	8. 3.73	K.Kiely	RAF Dishforth	2.12.02
G-BASG	Grumman-American AA-5 Traveler	AA5-0320	N5420L	12. 3.73	D.Cunningham & D.Barr	Glenrothes	20. 1.00
					t/a ASG Aviation Group		
G-BASH	Grumman-American AA-5 Traveler	AA5-0319	EI-AWV G-BASH/N5419L	12. 3.73	G.Jenkins	Popham	9. 9.02T
					t/a BASH Flying Group		
G-BASJ	PA-28-180 Cherokee Challenger	28-7305136		13. 3.73	T.J.McElwee	Bristol	4.11.00T
					t/a Challenger Flying Group		
G-BASL	PA-28-140 Cherokee F	28-7325195		13. 3.73	Air Navigation & Trading Co Ltd	Blackpool	16. 6.01T
G-BASM	PA-34-200-2 Seneca	34-7350120	N16272	13. 3.73	M.Gipps & J.R.Whetlor	Denham	14.10.01
G-BASN	Beechcraft C23 Sundowner	M-1476		13. 3.73	M.F.Fisher	Seighford	10. 8.98
G-BASO	Lake LA-4-180 Amphibian	358	N2025L	16. 3.73	C.J.A.Macaulay	Popham	24. 6.02
G-BASP	Beagle B.121 Pup 1	B121-149	SE-FOC G-35-149	14. 3.73	B.J.Coutts	Sywell	23. 6.01
G-BAST*	Cameron O-84 HAFB	70		15. 3.73	A D Kent Longleat House, Warminster		2. 5.84A
					(Balloon Preservation Group & displayed 7.98) "Honey"		
G-BASU*	PA-31-350 Navajo Chieftain	31-7305023	N7693L	15. 3.73	Not known	Exeter	3.11.87T
					(Damaged Dounreay 12.5.87; fuselage on fire dump 11.93)		
G-BASX	PA-34-200-2 Seneca	34-7350123	N15781	16. 3.73	London Executive Aviation Ltd	Sheffield-City	22. 9.02T
G-BATC	MBB Bo.105DB	S.45	D-HDAW	9. 3.73	Bond Air Services	Exeter	22. 6.02T
					(Op Devon Ambulance Service)		
	(Rebuilt using new MBB pod 1989; original pod to Offshore Petroleum Industry Training Board, Montrose 10.90)						
G-BATD*	Cessna U206F Stationair	U206-02014	N60204	12. 3.73	British Parachute School	Langar	
					(Crashed Shobdon 5.4.80; for para-trainer use 6.97)		
G-BATJ	Jodel D.119	287	F-PIIQ	21. 3.73	D.J. & K.S.Thomas	Fenland	27. 6.00P
	(Continental C90) (Built Ecole Technique Aeronautique)						
G-BATN	PA-23-250 Aztec E	27-7304987	N14391	26. 3.73	Marshall of Cambridge Aerospace Ltd	Cambridge	21.11.99T
G-BATR	PA-34-200-2 Seneca	34-7250290	9H-ABH G-BATR/LN-BDT	23. 3.73	A.S.Bamrah	Biggin Hill	30. 3.02T
					t/a Falcon Flying Services		
G-BATT	Hughes 269C (300)	122-0175		26. 3.73	Calderbrook Estates Ltd (Sowerby Bridge)		6. 9.00T
G-BATV	PA-28-180 Cherokee F	28-7105022	N5168S	26. 3.73	J.N.Rudsdale	Sherburn in Elmet	8.11.02
					t/a The Scoreby Flying Group		
G-BATW	PA-28-140 Cherokee Fliteliner	28-7225587	N742FL	26. 3.73	N.C.Spooner & M.Butterworth	Earls Colne	10.12.02
					t/a Tango Whiskey Flying Partnership		
G-BATX	PA-23-250 Aztec E	27-4832	N14271	27. 3.73	Aviation Services (Southern) Ltd	Shoreham	28. 5.01T
G-BAUA	PA-23-250 Aztec D	27-4048	N6718Y	26. 3.73	David Parr & Associates Ltd	Aberporth	27. 7.92
					(Open store 8.96)		
G-BAUC	PA-25-235 Pawnee C	25-5243	N8761L	26. 3.73	Southdown Gliding Club Ltd	Parham Park	20. 4.00
G-BAUH	Dormois Jodel D.112	870	F-BILO	29. 3.73	G.A. & D.Shepherd	Seething	28. 6.00P
					t/a G-BAUH Flying Group		
G-BAUI*	PA-23-250 Aztec D	27-4335	LN-RTS	29. 3.73	Brunel Technical College	Bristol	5.12.88T
					(Stored 12.98)		
G-BAUJ	PA-23-250 Aztec E	27-7304986	N14390	29. 3.73	S.J. & C.J.Westley	Cranfield	25. 7.94T
G-BAUN	Bell 206B JetRanger II	464	5N-BAY G-BAUN/5N-AOU/VR-BIA/G-BAUN/N2261W	2. 4.73	Bristow Helicopters Ltd	Redhill	26. 1.02T
					"Captain Freeson"		
G-BAUR*	Fokker F-27 Friendship 200	10225	PH-FEP 9V-BAP/9M-AMI/(VR-RCZJ)/PH-FEP	5. 4.73	Jersey European Airways (UK) Ltd Exeter		5. 4.96T
					(Stored 2.96; fuselage only by 10.99)		
G-BAUW	PA-23-250 Aztec E	27-4814	N14253	9. 4.73	R.E.Myson	Jersey/Hardings Farm, Ingatestone	22. 7.00
G-BAUY	Reims Cessna FRA.150L Aerobat	0167	N10633	5. 4.73	P.A.Layzell	Old Buckenham	7. 3.02
G-BAVB	Reims Cessna F.172M	0965		10. 4.73	C.P.Course, Church Farm, Wellingborough		27. 2.02
G-BAVH	DHC.1 Chipmunk 22	C1/0841	WP975	10. 4.73	Portsmouth Naval Gliding Club	Lee-on-Solent	24. 3.96
	(On conversion to Lycoming 350hp 4.99)						

Regn	Type	C/n	P/I	Date	Owner/operator	Probable Base	CA Expy
G-BAVL	PA-23-250 Aztec E	27-4671	N14063	10. 4.73	S.P. & A.V.Chilcott	Teesside	8. 6.01T
G-BAVO	Boeing-Stearman A75N-1 Kaydet	-	4X-AIH	13. 4.73	Vallingstone Aviation Ltd (Martin Shaw)		
	(Continental W670)				(As "26" in US Army c/s)	Old Buckenham	28. 6.01
	(Regd with c/n "3250-1405" which is a part number; original identity unknown)						
G-BAVR	Grumman-American AA-5 Traveler			12. 4.73	G.E.Murray	Haverfordwest	20. 7.01
		AA5-0348					
G-BAVS*	Grumman-American AA-5 Traveler			12. 4.73	Not known	Bournemouth	8.11.94
		AA5-0349			(Stored 7.93)		
G-BAVU	Cameron A-105 HAFB	66		11. 4.73	Not known	Oxford	5.10.84A
G-BAVZ	PA-23-250 Aztec E	27-7305045	N40241	18. 4.73	Cheshire Flying Services Ltd	Liverpool	17. 2.01T
					t/a Ravenair		
G-BAWG	PA-28R-200 Cherokee Arrow II			18. 4.73	Solent Air Ltd	Goodwood	3. 2.01
		28R-7335133					
G-BAWI*	Enstrom F-28A-UK	120		9. 4.73	Lodge Road Flying Services		
						Tattershall Thorpe	10. 4.94T
					(Crashed Bosworth Hall 26.6.92; stored 10.92)		
G-BAWK	PA-28-140 Cherokee Cruiser			24. 4.73	Newcastle-upon-Tyne Aero Club Ltd		
		28-7325243			(Stored 4.97)	Newcastle	3. 8.01T
G-BAWR	Robin HR.100/210 Royal	156		27. 4.73	T.Taylor	Thruxton	8. 6.00
G-BAWU	PA-30-160 Twin Comanche B	30-1477	(G-BAWV)	30. 4.73	Syndicate Clerical Services Ltd	Exeter	2. 5.99T
			9J-RFW/ZS-FAM/N8332Y				
G-BAWW*	Thunder Ax7-77 HAFB	004	(PH-AWW)	30. 4.73	S.Faithfull	NK	11. 5.84A
			G-BAWW		"Taurus"		
G-BAXE	Hughes 269A-1	113-0313	N8931F	2. 5.73	Reeve Newfields Ltd	Sywell	21.12.93S
G-BAXF*	Cameron O-77 HAFB	74		3. 5.73	British Balloon Museum & Library		
					"Granna"	Newbury	NE(A)
G-BAXJ	PA-32-300 Cherokee Six B	32-40763	N1362Z	8. 5.73	A.G.Knight	Thornhill, Stirling	11. 6.00
			G-BAXJ/4X-ANY/N5224S		t/a Airlaunch (Op Stirling Parachute Centre)		
G-BAXK	Thunder Ax7-77 HAFB	005		9. 5.73	A.R.Snook "Jack O'Newbury"	Newbury	2. 7.91A
G-BAXP	PA-23-250 Aztec E	27-4608	N13990	11. 5.73	Amersham Est Ltd	Shoreham	5. 3.92T
					(On fire dump 10.97)		
G-BAXS	Bell 47G-5	7908	5B-CFB	11. 5.73	R.M.Kemp t/a RK Helicopters	Fairoaks	2.12.00T
			G-BAXS/N4098G				
G-BAXU	Reims Cessna F.150L	0959		14. 5.73	M.A.Wilson	RAF Mona	22. 3.01
G-BAXV	Reims Cessna F.150L	0966		14. 5.73	G. & S.A.Jones	(Hull)	14. 5.01T
G-BAXY	Reims Cessna F.172M	0905	N10636	15. 5.73	R.J.W.Wood	Gregory Farm, Mirfield	16. 7.01T
G-BAXZ	PA-28-140 Cherokee C	28-26760	PH-NLX	15. 5.73	D.Norris & H.Martin	Turweston	1. 1.01T
					t/a G-BAXZ Syndicate		
G-BAYL*	SNCAN Nord 1203 Norecrin VI	161	F-BEQV	18. 5.73	J.E.Pierce	Ley Farm, Chirk	
					(Fuselage only stored outside 9.99)		
G-BAYO	Cessna 150L	150-74435	N19471	18. 5.73	W.J.Barnes & A.J.Fisher	(Durham)	8. 6.01T
G-BAYP	Cessna 150L	150-74017	N18651	18. 5.73	D.I.Thomas	Denham	6. 4.02T
					t/a Yankee Papa Flying Group		
G-BAYR	Robin HR.100/210 Royal	164		18. 5.73	Linda A.Christie	Stapleford	23. 5.00
G-BAYV*	SNCAN 1101 Noralpha	193	F-BLTN	22. 5.73	P.Smith	Barton	2. 8.75
			Fr.AF		(Crashed Longbridge Deverill 23.2.74: loaned to		
	Macclesfield Historical Aviation Society & displayed as "3" in Luftwaffe c/s; see G-ATDB)						
G-BAYZ	Bellanca 7GCBC Citabria	461-73	-	23. 5.73	Rodger Aircraft Ltd	Old Sarum	14. 8.00T
G-BAZC	Robin DR.400-160 Knight	824		29. 5.73	R.Jones	Membury	24. 6.88
	(Damaged in crash Crosland Moor 21.5.88; stored 9.89)				t/a Southern Sailplanes		
G-BAZJ*	HPR.7 Dart Herald 209	183	4X-AHR	30. 5.73	Guernsey Airport Fire Service	Guernsey	24.11.84T
			G-8-1		(Open storage 6.97)		
G-BAZM	Jodel D.11	PAL/1416 & PFA/915		31. 5.73	A.F.Simpson	Leeds-Bradford	4. 7.00P
	(Continental O-200-A) (Identified as "D.113")				"L'Oiseau Jaime"		
G-BAZS	Reims Cessna F.150L	0954		1. 6.73	L.W.Scattergood	Sherburn in Elmet	25.10.01T
G-BAZT	Reims Cessna F.172M	0996		1. 6.73	Exeter Flying Club Ltd	Exeter	22. 5.00
G-BAZU	PA-28R-200 Cherokee Arrow		EI-AVH	6. 6.73	S.C.Simmons	White Waltham	11.11.01
		28R-7135151					

G-BBAA – G-BBZZ

Regn	Type	C/n	P/I	Date	Owner/operator	Probable Base	CA Expy
G-BBAE	Lockheed L.1011-385-1-14 TriStar 100	193N-1083	C-FCXB	6. 6.73	Caledonian Airways Ltd	Gatwick	11. 5.00T
			G-BBAE/C-FCXB/G-BBAE/N64854 "Loch Earn"				
G-BBAF	Lockheed L.1011-385-1-14 TriStar 100	193N-1093		6. 6.73	Caledonian Airways Ltd	Gatwick	9. 1.00T
					"Loch Fyne"		
G-BBAH	Lockheed L.1011-385-1-14 TriStar 100	193N-1101		6. 6.73	Caledonian Airways Ltd	Gatwick	8. 2.00T
					"Loch Avon"		
G-BBAI	Lockheed L.1011-385-1-14 TriStar 100	193N-1102	C-FCXJ	6. 6.73	Caledonian Airways Ltd	Gatwick	4. 5.02T
			G-BBAI/C-FCXJ/G-BBAI "Loch Inver"				

Regn	Type	C/n	P/I	Date	Owner/operator	Probable Base	CA Expy
G-BBAJ	Lockheed L.1011-385-1-14 TriStar 100	193N-1106		6. 6.73	Caledonian Airways Ltd "Loch Rannoch"	Gatwick	29. 3.02T
G-BBAK	Socata MS.894A Rallye Minerva 220	12080	(D-ENMK)	6. 6.73	R.B.Hemsworth & C.L.Hill		8. 8.98
						Belle Vue Farm, Yarnscombe	
G-BBAW	Robin HR.100/210 Royal	167		12. 6.73	J.R.Williams	Goodwood	12. 6.00
G-BBAX	Robin DR.400/140 Earl	835		12. 6.73	G.J.Bissex & P.H.Garbutt		11. 5.00
						New Farm, Felton	
G-BBAY	Robin DR.400/140 Earl	841		12. 6.73	D.S.Brown & V.H.R. Gray t/a Rothwell Group		
						Rothwell Lodge Farm, Kettering	31. 1.02
G-BBAZ*	Hiller UH-12E	2165	EC-DOR	13. 6.73	Not known	Gamlingay	23. 5.91
	G-BBAZ/N31707/CAF112276/RCAF10276						
					(Cancelled by CAA 29.5.96: stored for restoration 4.99)		
G-BBBB	Taylor JT.1 Monoplane			4. 6.73	S.A.MacConnacher	(Northampton)	
	(VW1600)	SAM/01 & PFA/1422					
G-BBBC	Reims Cessna F.150L	0864	N10635	14. 6.73	A.A.Gardner	(Port St. Mary, IOM)	15.12.01T
G-BBBI	Grumman-American AA-5 Traveler			15. 6.73	M.E.J.Smith & S.A.James	Elstree	20.12.02
		AA5-0392					
G-BBBK	PA-28-140 Cherokee	28-22572	SE-EYF	18. 6.73	Bencray Ltd	Blackpool	19. 4.01
G-BBBL*	Cessna 337B Super Skymaster	337-0555	EI-AVF	19. 6.73	P.R.Moss	Farley Farm, Winchester	12. 2.77
			5H-MNL/N5455S		(Stored 3.92)		
G-BBBN	PA-28-180 Cherokee Challenger			20. 6.73	Estuary Aviation Ltd	Southend	13. 1.00T
		28-7305365					
G-BBBO	SIPA 903	67	F-BGBQ	16. 1.74	G.K.Brothwood & P.R.Tonks	Liverpool	5. 5.98P
					t/a Mersey SIPA Group		

(This was roaded-in to Liverpool during May/June 1999 and is worked on by Keenair. The a/c came from storage in a double-garage in the Wirral and which also houses SIPA 903 c/n 63 (ex F-BGBM) also registered to the Mersey SIPA Group. The original plan had been to make one airworthy a/c from these two but this has now changed. Once G-BBBO has flown this will be sold and c/n 63 will undergo restoration by Keenair and be locally based)

Regn	Type	C/n	P/I	Date	Owner/operator	Probable Base	CA Expy
G-BBBW	Clutton FRED Srs.2 DLW.1 & PFA/1551			26. 6.73	M.Palfreman	Bagby	1.12.99P
	(VW1834)						
G-BBBX	Cessna 310L	310L-0134	OY-EGW	28. 6.73	Atlantic Air Transport Ltd		
			N3284X			Jersey/Coventry	23.10.02
G-BBBY	PA-28-140 Cherokee Cruiser			28. 6.73	J.M.Scott	Luqa, Malta	5. 5.00
		28-7325533					
G-BBCA	Bell 206B JetRanger II	1101	N18091	29. 6.73	Stonewell Services Ltd	Blackpool	8.10.01T
G-BBCB	Western O-65 HAFB	018		29. 6.73	G.M.Bulmer "Cee Bee"	Hereford	19. 5.76S
G-BBCC	PA-23-250 Aztec D	27-4317	N6953Y	29. 6.73	Richard Nash Cars Ltd	Norwich	1. 4.01T
G-BBCF*	Reims Cessna FRA.150L Aerobat	0209		3. 7.73	Air Service Training Ltd	Perth	6. 3.86T
					(Damaged nr Harrogate 8.9.84 & dumped 6.98)		
G-BBCH	Robin DR.400 2 + 2	850		4. 7.73	A.J.& S.P.Smith	(Oxford)	19. 2.01T
G-BBCI	Cessna 150H	150-69282	N50409	4. 7.73	Domeastral Ltd	Elstree	22. 5.00T
G-BBCK	Cameron O-77 HAFB	76		4. 7.73	W R Teasdale	Maidenhead	
G-BBCN	Robin HR.100/210 Royal	168		11. 7.73	S.J.Goodburn	Gloucestershire	17. 4.00
					t/a Gloucestershire Flying Club		
G-BBCP	Thunder Ax6-56 HAFB	007		11. 7.73	J.M.Robinson	Milton-under-Wychwood	10. 7.81A
					"Jack Frost"		
G-BBCS	Robin DR.400/140B Earl	851		12. 7.73	J.C.Harvey	Spilsted Farm, Sedlescombe	12. 5.01
					t/a Westfield Flying Group		
G-BBCW	PA-23-250 Aztec E	27-4806	N14251	17. 7.73	Jack Tighe Holdings Ltd	Sturgate	20.10.00T
					(Op Eastern Air Executive)		
G-BBCY	Phoenix Luton LA-4A Minor	PFA/825		17. 7.73	T.G. Solomon		
	(VW1600)				Kitty Hawk Farm, nr Deanland, E Sussex	1. 8.00P
G-BBCZ	Grumman-American AA-5 Traveler			18. 7.73	Golf Charlie Zulu Ltd	Shoreham	13. 8.01T
		AA5-0382					
G-BBDB*	PA-28-180 Cherokee Challenger			18. 7.73	Not known	Newtownards	7. 6.85
		28-7305361			(Wreck stored 4.96)		
G-BBDC	PA-28-140 Cherokee Cruiser			18. 7.73	P.Doggett & P.A.Gray	Andrewsfield	18. 3.01
		28-7325437					
G-BBDE	PA-28R-200 Cherokee Arrow II			18. 7.73	R.L.Coleman & A.E.Stevens	Panshanger	9. 9.02
		28R-7335250					
G-BBDG*	BAC/Aerospatiale Concorde 100			7. 8.73	British Airways plc	Filton	1.3.82P*
		100-002 & 13523			(Stored for spares 2.96)		
G-BBDH	Reims Cessna F.172M	0990		19. 7.73	J.C.Holland	(Hungerford)	18. 5.02
G-BBDJ*	Thunder Ax6-56 HAFB	006		20. 7.73	D P Bushby "Jack Tar"	Lancing	
					(Balloon Preservation Group 7.98)		
G-BBDL	Grumman-American AA-5 Traveler			18. 7.73	R.J.Baker & W.Woods	Coventry	4. 2.02
		AA5-0406			t/a Delta Lima Flying Group		
G-BBDM	Grumman-American AA-5 Traveler			18. 7.73	P.J.Marchant	Rush Green	28. 9.01
		AA5-0407					

Regn	Type	C/n	P/I	Date	Owner/operator	Probable Base	CA Expy
G-BBDN*	Taylor JT.1 Monoplane	PFA/1437		24. 7.73	T.Barnes	Ely	
	(VW1600)				(Under construction 10.90)		
G-BBDO	PA-23-250 Turbo Aztec E	27-7305120	N40361	24. 7.73	J W Anstee	Bristol	1. 5.00T
G-BBDP	Robin DR.400/160 Knight	853		25. 7.73	Robin Lance Aviation Associates Ltd		
						Rochester	14. 7.01T
G-BBDT	Cessna 150H	150-68839	N23272	26. 7.73	J.S.Firth	Sherburn in Elmet	19. 3.00
					t/a Delta Tango Group		
G-BBDV	SIPA 903	7/21	F-BEYY	30. 7.73	W.McAndrew	Cardington	11. 6.00P
	(Continental C90) (Originally ex F-BEYJ c/n 7 but rebuilt in 1978 from F-BEYY c/n 21)						
G-BBEA	Phoenix Luton LA-4A Minor	PFA/843		30. 7.73	P.A.Kirkham	(Guildford)	2.11.99P
	(VW1600)				t/a Luton Minor Group		
G-BBEB	PA-28R-200 Cherokee Arrow II			31. 7.73	R.D.W.Rippingale Anvil Farm, Hungerford		22. 2.01
G-BBEC	PA-28-180 Cherokee Challenger			30. 7.73	J.B.Conway	Blackpool	31. 5.01
		28-7305478					
G-BBED	Socata MS.894A Rallye Minerva 220			30. 7.73	C.A.Shelley	Alcester	13. 9.87T
		12097			t/a Vista Products (Stored 9.95)		
G-BBEF	PA-28-140 Cherokee Cruiser	28-7325527		31. 7.73	Comed Aviation Ltd	Blackpool	20.10.01T
					(Rebuilt using parts of G-AVWG by 4.99)		
G-BBEL	PA-28R-180 Cherokee Arrow	28R-30877	SE-FDX	6. 8.73	J.Paulson	Liverpool	26. 4.01
					(Op Merseyside Aviation)		
G-BBEN	Bellanca 7GCBC Citabria	496-73	(D-EAUT)	7. 8.73	C.A.G.Schofield		
			N36416		Harpsden Court, Henley-on-Thames		10. 5.02
G-BBEO	Reims Cessna FRA.150L Aerobat	0205		3. 8.73	Moray Flying Club (1990) Ltd	Inverness	7. 6.01T
G-BBEV	PA-28-140 Cherokee D	28-7125340	LN-MTM	8. 8.73	Comed Aviation Ltd	Blackpool	9. 9.01T
G-BBEW*	PA-23-250 Aztec E	27-7305075	EI-BYK	9. 8.73	Mano et Mano Ltd	(New Malden)	3. 9.01T
			G-BBEW/N40262				
	(Damaged landing Phoenix Farm, Lower Upham 20.4.99: cancelled by CAA 16.8.99)						
G-BBEX	Cessna 185A Skywagon	185-0491	EI-CMC	7. 8.73	V.M.McCarthy	Weston, N Ireland	2.11.02T
			G-BBEX/4X-ALD/N99992/N1691Z				
G-BBEY	PA-23-250 Aztec E	27-7305160	LN-FOE	8. 8.73	M.Hall	Cumbernauld	29. 1.01
			G-BBEY/N40396				
G-BBFC*	Grumman-American AA-1B Trainer		(N9945L)	14. 8.73	Not known	Enstone	25.12.96
		AA1B-0245			(Damaged Perranporth 9.6.96; temp unregd 14.10.96)		
G-BBFD	PA-28R-200 Cherokee Arrow II			8. 8.73	CR Aviation Ltd	White Waltham	5. 1.01T
		28R-7335342					
G-BBFL	SRCM Gardan GY-201 Minicab	21	F-BHCQ	17. 8.73	D.Silsbury	Dunkeswell	21. 9.93P
	(Continental A65)				(Damaged Bere Alston, Devon 9.6.93; on rebuild 12.95)		
G-BBFS*	Van Den Bemden K-460 (Gas) Free Balloon						
		VDB-16	OO-BGX	10. 8.73	British Balloon Museum	Newbury	
					"Le Tomate" (Stored 12.94)		
G-BBFV	PA-32-260 Cherokee Six	32-778	5Y-ADF	13. 8.73	A.G.Knight t/a Airlaunch Old Buckenham		26. 2.00
G-BBGB	PA-E23-250 Aztec E	27-7305004	N40206	16. 8.73	Cheshire Flying Services Ltd Liverpool		28. 1.00T
					t/a Ravenair		
G-BBGC	Socata MS.893E Rallye 180GT	12215	F-BUCV	16. 8.73	C.Squibb	RNAS Culdrose	15. 2.01
					t/a Seahawk Gliding Club		
G-BBGE*	PA-23-250 Aztec D	27-4373	N6137Y	20. 8.73	Not known (Stored 9.96)	Bournemouth	17. 8.92T
G-BBGI	Fuji FA.200-160 Aero Subaru	228		21. 8.73	G.C.B.Weir	Hill Farm, Nayland	17. 9.98
G-BBGL	Oldfield Baby Lakes			22. 8.73	F.Ball	Jubilee Farm, Wisbech St.Mary	16.12.99P
	(Continental C90) 7223-B412-B & PFA/1593						
G-BBGR	Cameron O-65 HAFB	85		20. 8.73	M.L. & L.P.Willoughby	Reading	26. 5.81A
					"Jabberwock"		
G-BBGX	Cessna 182P Skylane	182-62350	N58861	30. 8.73	A.C.Pearson t/a GX Group	Denham	1. 4.01T
G-BBGZ	Cambridge Hot-Air Ballooning Assocn			31. 8.73	R.A. & G.Laslett & J.L.Hinton Newbury		
	HAFB (42,000 cu.ft)	CHABA 42			"Phlogiston"(Basket only to British Balloon Museum)		
G-BBHF	PA-23-250 Aztec E	27-7305166	N40453	5. 9.73	G.J.Williams	Sherburn in Elmet	25. 5.02T
G-BBHG*	Cessna 310Q	310Q-0806	N69591	6. 9.73	G.P.Williams	Bournemouth	16. 7.95
					(Damaged Manston 19.7.93; on rebuild 10.95)		
G-BBHI	Cessna 177RG Cardinal RG	177RG-0225	5Y-ANX	7. 9.73	T.G.W.Bunce	Newtownards	6. 8.00
			N1825Q				
G-BBHJ	Piper J3C-85 Cub	16378	OO-GEC	7. 9.73	J.Stanbridge & R.V.Miller t/a Wellcross Flying Group		
	(Frame No.16037)				Wellcross Grange, Slinfold		19. 5.99P
G-BBHK	Noorduyn AT-16-ND Harvard IIB	14-787	PH-PPS	7. 9.73	R.F.Warner	(Malvern)	7. 5.86
			(PH-HTC)/R.Neth AF B-158/FH153/42-12540 t/a Bob Warner Aviation				
					(As "FH153": status uncertain)		
G-BBHL	Sikorsky S-61N Mk.II	61-712	N4032S	7. 9.73	Bristow Helicopters Ltd	Portland	4.12.01T
					(Op H.M. Coastguard) "Glamis"		
G-BBHM	Sikorsky S-61N Mk.II	61-713	8Q-HUM	7. 9.73	Bristow Helicopters Ltd	Aberdeen	1.11.01T
			G-BBHM/N4033S		"Braemar"		
G-BBHX*	Socata MS.893E Rallye 180GT	12211		7. 9.73	Not known	Bidford	7. 4.96
					(Wreck in open store 5.96)		

Regn	Type	C/n	P/I	Date	Owner/operator	Probable Base	CA Expy
G-BBHY	PA-28-180 Cherokee Challenger	28-7305474	EI-BBS G-BBHY/N9508N	7. 9.73	Air Operations Ltd	Guernsey	8. 6.02
G-BBIA	PA-28R-200 Cherokee Arrow II	28R-7335287		7. 9.73	G.H.Kilby	Stapleford	14.12.00
G-BBIF	PA-23-250 Aztec E	27-7305234		10. 9.73	Home Doors (GB) Ltd "Flying Miss Daisie"	Tatenhill	28. 7.01T
G-BBIH	Enstrom F-28A-UK	026	N4875	12. 9.73	Stephenson Marine Co Ltd	Goodwood	28. 6.02T
G-BBII	Fiat G.46-3B	44	I-AEHU MM52801	13. 9.73	Bianchi Aviation Film Services Ltd (As "14+" in Luftwaffe c/s)	Booker	19. 7.89P
G-BBIL	PA-28-140 Cherokee	28-22567	SE-FAR N4219J	13. 9.73	M.C.Addison & R.Brierley t/a India Lima Flying Group	Andrewsfield	23. 4.01
G-BBIN*	Enstrom F-28A	157		13. 9.73	Southernair Ltd (Stored 10.96)	Shoreham	26. 9.94T
G-BBIO	Robin HR.100/210 Royal	178		14. 9.73	R.A.King	Headcorn	29.10.00
G-BBIX	PA-28-140 Cherokee E	28-7225442	LN-AEN	17. 9.73	Sterling Aviation Ltd	Elstree	28. 1.02T
G-BBJD*	Cessna 172M	172-61374	N20537	17. 9.73	Not known (Crashed Sywell 30.6.78; fuselage as para-trainer 9.95)	Oaksey Park	18. 1.80
G-BBJI	Isaacs Spitfire 2 & PFA/27-10055 (Continental O-200-A)			18. 9.73	T.E.W.Terrell (As "RN218/N")	(Atherstone)	27. 7.00P
G-BBJU	Robin DR.400/140 Earl	874		19. 9.73	J.C.Lister t/a Victor Sierra Aero Club	Valley Farm, Winwick	25. 5.01
G-BBJV	Reims Cessna F.177RG Cardinal	0098		20. 9.73	Pilot Publishing Co Ltd t/a Pilot Magazine	Biggin Hill	6. 3.00
G-BBJX	Reims Cessna F.150L Commuter	1017		20. 9.73	Yorkshire Flying Services Ltd	Leeds-Bradford	5. 8.02T
G-BBJY	Reims Cessna F.172M Skyhawk II	1075		20. 9.73	J.Lucketti	Gamston	17. 6.02
G-BBJZ	Reims Cessna F.172M Skyhawk II	1035		20. 9.73	J.K.Green t/a Burks Green & Ptnrs	Gamston	28. 2.01T
G-BBKA	Reims Cessna F.150L Commuter	1029		20. 9.73	R.Hall	Full Sutton	1. 5.00T
G-BBKB	Reims Cessna F.150L	1030		20. 9.73	Justgold Ltd t/a Blackpool Air Centre	Blackpool	21. 7.96T
G-BBKE	Reims Cessna F.150L Commuter	1026		20. 9.73	J.D.Woodward	Bristol	2. 7.01T
G-BBKF	Reims Cessna FRA.150L Aerobat	0222		20. 9.73	D.W.Mickleburgh (Stored Compton Abbas 6.95)	(Leicester)	13. 6.91T
G-BBKG	Reims Cessna FR.172J Rocket	0465		20. 9.73	R.Wright Twycross	Burton-on-Trent/Coventry	22. 2.01
G-BBKI	Reims Cessna F.172M Skyhawk II	1069		20. 9.73	C.W. & S.A.Burman	East Winch	16. 9.01
G-BBKL	Menavia Piel CP.301A Emeraude	237	F-BIMK	21. 9.73	P.J.Griggs (Damaged Ketton 14.7.91; on rebuild East Fortune 7.99)	(Huntingdon)	21. 1.92P
G-BBKR	Scheibe SF-24A Motorspatz	4018	D-KECA	24. 9.73	P.I.Morgans (Stored 5.95) Furze Hill Farm, Rosemarket, Milford Haven		30. 3.79S
G-BBKU	Reims Cessna FRA.150L Aerobat	0214		26. 9.73	T.Hartley & R.J.Stainer t/a Penguin Group	Bodmin	4. 6.01T
G-BBKX	PA-28-180 Cherokee Challenger	28-7305581		26. 9.73	RAE Aero Club Ltd	Farnborough	22. 7.01T
G-BBKY	Reims Cessna F.150L	0991		26. 9.73	Telesonic Ltd	Barton	24.11.00T
G-BBKZ	Cessna 172M	172-61495	N20694	27. 9.73	R.S.Thomson t/a KZ Flying Group (Damaged landing Thruxton 22.6.99)	Exeter	23. 3.00T
G-BBLH	Piper J3C-65 Cub (L-4B-PI) (Frame No.9838) (Regd with c/n 10549)	10006	F-BFQY Fr.Mil/43-1145	24. 9.73	Shipping & Airlines Ltd (As "31145/26/G" in 183rd Field Battalion US Army c/s)	Biggin Hill	4. 2.02T
G-BBLL*	Cameron O-84 HAFB	84		2.10.73	British Balloon Museum "Boadicea"	Newbury	25. 5.81A
G-BBLM	Socata Rallye 100S	2392		3.10.73	Skillcomps Ltd	Halfpenny Green	1.10.01
G-BBLS	Grumman-American AA-5 Traveler	AA5-0440	EI-AYM G-BBLS	8.10.73	A.D.Grant	Perth	28. 3.02
G-BBLU	PA-34-200-2 Seneca	34-7350271	N55984	8.10.73	A.S.Bamrah t/a Falcon Flying Services	Biggin Hill	3. 4.00T
G-BBMB	Robin DR.400/180 Regent	848	5Y-ASB	27. 9.73	D.S.Seex t/a Regent Flying Group	Thurrock	5. 4.01
G-BBMH	EAA Sport Biplane Model P.1 PFA/1348 (Continental C90)			11.10.73	K.Dawson (Status uncertain)	(Billericay)	29. 6.87P
G-BBMJ	PA-23-250 Aztec E	27-7305150	N40387	12.10.73	Tindon Ltd	Little Snoring	21. 9.02T
G-BBMN	DHC.1 Chipmunk 22	C1/0300	WD359	12.10.73	R.Steiner	White Waltham	20.10.00
G-BBMO	DHC.1 Chipmunk 22	C1/0550	WK514	12.10.73	D.M.Squires	Wellesbourne Mountford	23. 2.01
G-BBMR	DHC.1 Chipmunk 22	C1/0213	WB763	12.10.73	A.J.Parkhouse (As "WB763/14") (Stored 12.93)	Camberley	
G-BBMT	DHC.1 Chipmunk 22	C1/0712	WP831	12.10.73	J.Evans & D.Withers	Graveley	17. 8.00
G-BBMV	DHC.1 Chipmunk 22	C1/0432	WG348	12.10.73	P.J.Morgan (Aviation) Ltd (As "WG348") Top Farm, Royston		28. 3.97
G-BBMW	DHC.1 Chipmunk 22	C1/0641	WK628	12.10.73	J.A.Challen & B.J.Pook t/a Mike Whiskey Group (As "WK628")	Shoreham	13. 6.02

Regn	Type	C/n	P/I	Date	Owner/operator	Probable Base	CA Expy
G-BBMX	DHC.1 Chipmunk 22	C1/0800	WP924	12.10.73	B.R.Schudel Epse, The Netherlands		12. 5.02
					t/a Chipmunk 4 Ever Foundation		
G-BBMZ	DHC.1 Chipmunk 22	C1/0563	WK548	12.10.73	P.C.G.Wyld Booker		1. 9.00
					t/a The Wycombe Gliding School Syndicate		
G-BBNA	DHC.1 Chipmunk 22	C1/0491	WG417	12.10.73	Coventry Gliding Club Ltd		
	(Lycoming O-360)				"Carrie" Husbands Bosworth		22. 6.00
G-BBNC*	DHC.1 Chipmunk T.10	C1/0682	WP790	12.10.73	de Havilland Aircraft Museum		
					(As "WP790/T") Salisbury Hall, London Colney		
G-BBND	DHC.1 Chipmunk 22	C1/0225	WD286	12.10.73	J.W.Bissett & W.Norton Top Farm, Royston		17. 8.00
					t/a Chipmunk G-BCIW Syndicate 1984 (As "WD286/J")		
G-BBNG	Bell 206B JetRanger	134	VH-BHX	16.10.73	MB Air Ltd (Op Eagle Helicopters)		
		G-BBNG/VR-BEY/G-BBNG/PK-HBO/N6268N			Winchester Farm, Ouston/Newcastle		9. 5.02T
G-BBNH	PA-34-200-2 Seneca	34-7350339	N56492	16.10.73	M.G.D.Baverstock Bournemouth		8. 8.01
G-BBNI	PA-34-200-2 Seneca	34-7350312	N56286	16.10.73	Channel Aviation Holdings Ltd Guernsey		26. 3.01T
G-BBNJ	Reims Cessna F.150L Commuter	1038		16.10.73	Sherburn Aero Club Ltd Sherburn in Elmet		27.10.02T
G-BBNO	PA-23-250 Aztec E	27-4656	N964PA	22.10.73	A.S.Bamrah Biggin Hill		18. 1.92
					t/a Falcon Flying Services (Stored 8.97)		
G-BBNV	Fuji FA.200-160 Aero Subaru	232		23.10.73	Caseright Ltd Hinton-in-The-Hedges		25. 4.99
G-BBNX	Reims Cessna FRA.150L Aerobat	0219		23.10.73	General Airline Ltd Blackbushe		8. 4.01T
	(Continental O-200-A)				t/a European Flyers		
G-BBNY*	Reims Cessna FRA.150L Aerobat	0223		23.10.73	Air Tows Ltd White Waltham		2. 8.87T
					(Damaged Blackbushe 8.6.86; wreck in open storage 5.96)		
G-BBNZ	Reims Cessna F.172M Skyhawk II	1054		23.10.73	R.E.Nunn Maypole Farm, Chislet		18. 4.00
G-BBOA	Reims Cessna F.172M Skyhawk II	1066		23.10.73	J.D.& A.M.Black, (Colchester)		15. 6.02
G-BBOC	Cameron O-77 HAFB	86		24.10.73	J.A.B.Gray Cirencester		6. 1.90A
					t/a Bacchus Balloons "Bacchus"		
G-BBOD	Thunder O.5 HAFB	013		24.10.73	B.R. & M.Boyle "Little Titch" Newbury		
					(On loan to British Balloon Museum 12.93)		
G-BBOE	Robin HR.200/100	26		24.10.73	T.D.Saveker Bodmin		7. 7.02
G-BBOH	AJEP Pitts S-1S Special			25.10.73	Venom Jet Promotions Ltd (P.Meeson)		
	(Lycoming IO-360) AJEP-PS1-S-1 & PFA/1570				Oaklands Farm, East Tytherley/Popham		8. 9.97P
G-BBOL	PA-18-150 Super Cub	18-7561	D-EMFE	26.10.73	Lakes Gliding Club Ltd Walney Island		11. 9.96
			N3821Z				
G-BBOO	Thunder Ax6-56 HAFB	012		24.10.73	K.Meehan Much Wenlock, Shropshire		22. 9.96A
					"Tiger Jack"		
G-BBOR	Bell 206B JetRanger II	1197	(SE-)	30.10.73	M.J.Easey Town Farm, Hoxne, Eye		8. 7.99T
			G-BBOR				
G-BBOX	Thunder Ax7-77 HAFB	011		24.10.73	R.C.Weyda "Rocinante" Newbury		NE(A)
					(To British Balloon Museum & Library 1999)		
G-BBPK	Evans VP-1	PFA/7013		30.10.73	G.D.E.MacDonald Lasham		8. 6.90P
	(VW1600)				(Stored 10.95)		
G-BBPM	Enstrom F-28A-UK	165	PH-DMH	30.10.73	R.Brennan, M.G.Redford & D.M. Arends		
			G-BBPM		Damaged 9.98) Chester		3. 7.98
G-BBPN	Enstrom F-28A-UK	166		30.10.73	J.R.Jeffers Coventry		17. 7.00T
G-BBPO	Enstrom F-28A	176		30.10.73	Southern Air Ltd & Jewelhaven Ltd		
					Shoreham		1. 5.00T
G-BBPS	SAN Jodel D.117	597	F-BHXS	30.10.73	A.Appleby Burtenshaw Farm, Barcombe		20. 5.00P
G-BBPW	Robin HR.100/210 Royal	176		7.11.73	S.D.Cole Kemble		13. 4.97
					(Damaged Kemble 24.8.98: airframe present 9.99)		
G-BBPX	PA-34-200-2 Seneca	34-7250262	N1202T	7.11.73	Richel Investments Ltd Guernsey		15. 9.01
G-BBPY	PA-28-180 Challenger	28-7305590		8.11.73	Sunsaver Ltd Barton		29. 7.02
G-BBRA	PA-23-250 Aztec E	27-7305197	N40479	12.11.73	F.Kratky t/a F.K.Global Aviation Denham		7. 5.00
G-BBRB	DH.82A Tiger Moth	85934	OO-EVB	21.11.73	R.Barham (Biggin Hill)		
			Belgian AF T-8/ETA-8/DF198				
					(Damaged Biggin Hill 16.1.87: sold for long-term rebuild - status uncertain)		
G-BBRC	Fuji FA.200-180 Aero Subaru	235		8.11.73	G-BBRC Ltd Blackbushe		31. 7.02T
G-BBRI	Bell 47G-5A	25158	N18092	8.11.73	Alan Mann Helicopters Ltd Fairoaks		28. 7.02T
	(Composite following several major rebuilds)						
G-BBRJ	PA-E23-250 Turbo Aztec E	27-7305223	EI-BOK	12.11.73	Millennium Air Ltd		
			G-BBRJ/N40493		Farley Farm, Winchester		22. 2.99T
G-BBRN	Mitchell-Procter Kittiwake I	XW784		20.11.73	R.D.Dobree-Carey Henstridge		9. 6.00P
	(Continental O-200-A) 02 & PFA/1352				(As "XW784/VL")		
G-BBRV	DHC.1 Chipmunk 22	C1/0284	WD347	13.11.73	ABC Advertising Ltd Biggin Hill		28. 4.99T
G-BBRX	SIAI-Marchetti S.205-18F	342	LN-VYH	13.11.73	R.C. & A.K.West Goodwood		21.12.01
			OO-HAQ				
G-BBRY*	Cessna 210 Centurion	57091	5Y-KRZ	15.11.73	Not known Enstone		13. 4.79
			VP-KRZ/N7391E		(Crashed Chessington 2.4.78; derelict 4.99)		
G-BBRZ	Grumman-American AA-5 Traveler		(EI-AYV)	15.11.73	C.P.Osborne Mullaghmore		30. 4.99
		AA5-0471	G-BBRZ				
G-BBSA	Grumman-American AA-5 Traveler			15.11.73	Usworth 84 Flying Associates Ltd		
		AA5-0472			Newcastle		31. 1.02

Regn	Type	C/n	P/I	Date	Owner/operator	Probable Base	CA Expy
G-BBSB	Beechcraft C23 Sundowner 180	M-1516		15.11.73	Amalmay Ltd	Woodford	31. 7.02
					t/a Sundowner Group		
G-BBSC	Beechcraft B24R Sierra 200	MC-217		15.11.73	I.Millar & G.H.Emerson	Newtownards	3. 6.99
					t/a The Beechcombers Flying Group		
G-BBSM	PA-32-300 Cherokee Six	32-7440005	N11C	14.11.73	MT Management Ltd	Ronaldsway	11. 7.00T
G-BBSS	DHC.1 Chipmunk 22	C1/0520	WG470	21.11.73	Coventry Gliding Club Ltd		
						Husbands Bosworth	1. 4.01
G-BBSW	Pietenpol Air Camper	PFA/1506		21.11.73	J.K.S.Wills	(London SE3)	
G-BBTB	Reims Cessna FRA.150L Aerobat	0224		26.11.73	Griffin Marston Ltd	Compton Abbas	2.11.02T
					(Op Abbas Air)		
G-BBTG	Reims Cessna F.172M Skyhawk II	1097		26.11.73	R.W. & V.P.J.Simpson	Redhill	15. 5.02
					t/a Tango Golf Flying Group		
G-BBTH	Reims Cessna F.172M Skyhawk II	1089		26.11.73	K.Kwok-Kin Lee.	(Bangor, NI)	3. 8.02
G-BBTJ	PA-23-250 Aztec E	27-7305131	N40369	27.11.73	Cooper Aerial Surveys Ltd	Sandtoft	28. 3.01T
G-BBTK	Reims Cessna FRA.150L Aerobat	0230		27.11.73	Cleveland Flying School Ltd	Teesside	17.10.99T
G-BBTL	PA-23-250 Aztec C	27-3816	N6525Y	29.11.73	Air Navigation & Trading Co Ltd		
					(Stored 9.99)	Blackpool	14. 8.89T
G-BBTS	Beechcraft V35B Bonanza	D-9551	N3051W	29.11.73	Sarah Wenham	Cannes-Mandelieu	2. 1.00
					t/a Eastern Air		
G-BBTT*	Reims Cessna F.150L Commuter	1055		30.11.73	Not known	Newtownards	12. 3.76
					(Crashed Newtownards 9.3.75; stored 4.96)		
G-BBTU*	Socata ST-10 Diplomate	140	F-BTIO	18.12.73	Not known (Wreck stored 3.94)	Coventry	14. 4.88
G-BBTX	Beechcraft C23 Sundowner 180	M-1524	5N-AGJ G-BBTX	29.11.73	K.Harding t/a Sundowner Group	Blackbushe	8. 6.01
G-BBTY	Beechcraft C23 Sundowner 180	M-1525		29.11.73	A.W.Roderick & W.Price	Cardiff	23. 2.01
G-BBTZ	Reims Cessna F.150L	1063		30.11.73	Marnham Investments Ltd	Perth	16. 1.00T
					(Op Tayside Aviation)		
G-BBUE	Grumman-American AA-5 Traveler	0479		6.12.73	Hebog (Mon) Cyf	Caernarfon	10. 3.00
G-BBUF	Grumman-American AA-5 Traveler	0480		6.12.73	W.McLaren	Dundee	31.10.99T
G-BBUG	PA-16-150 Clipper	16-29	F-BFMC	6.12.73	J.Dolan	Enniskillen	15.11.98
G-BBUJ	Cessna 421B Golden Eagle	421B-0335	OY-RYD	7.12.73	Coolflourish Ltd.	(Mansfield)	17. 9.02
G-BBUL*	Mitchell-Procter Kittiwake 1	RB.1		7.12.73	R.C.Bull	(Yorkshire)	
	(No Permit issued & probably not completed: cancelled by CAA 22.2.99)						
G-BBUT	Western O-65 HAFB	020		11.12.73	G.F.Turnbull	Clyro, Hereford	23. 4.97A
					"Christabelle II"		
G-BBUU	Piper J3C-75 Cub (L-4A-PI)	10529	F-BBSQ	14. 1.74	O.J.J.Rogers Hulcote Farm, Salford, Beds		3. 8.00P
	(Frame No.10354)		F-OAEZ/Fr.AF/43-29238				
G-BBVA	Sikorsky S-61N Mk.II	61-718		12. 2.74	Bristow Helicopters Ltd	Lee-on-Solent	24. 2.00T
					"Vega"		
G-BBVF*	Scottish Avn Twin Pioneer Srs.3	558	7978M XM961	17.12.73	Museum of Flight/Royal Museum of Scotland	East Fortune	14. 5.82
G-BBVG*	PA-23-250 Aztec C	27-2610	ET-AEB 5Y-AAT	20.12.73	Colton Aviation Ltd	Little Staughton	10. 9.88T
					(Stored 9.96)		
G-BBVJ	Beechcraft B24R Sierra 200	MC-230		21.12.73	T.Keely	Gamston	26. 3.00
G-BBVO	Isaacs Fury II	PFA/11-10091		20.12.73	C.M.Barnes & D.A.Wirdnam		
	(Lycoming O-320)					Garden Piece, Basingstoke	20. 9.99P
	(As Hawker Nimrod "S1579/571" of 408 Flt FAA, HMS Glorious)						
G-BBVP*	Westland-Bell 47G-3B1	WA/580	S.Yemen AF 401/XT401	3. 1.74	Not known (Stored 5.93)	Barton	3. 6.93T
	(Line No.WAS/177)						
G-BBWZ	Grumman-American AA-1B Tr 2	AA1B-0334		14. 1.74	D.K.Barrett, G.Moorby, M.Kelly	Sherburn in Elmet	24. 7.00T
G-BBXB	Reims Cessna FRA.150L Aerobat	0236		16. 1.74	D.M.Fenton	Breighton	12. 7.98T
G-BBXH	Reims Cessna FR.172F Rocket	0113	SE-FKG	21. 1.74	D.Ridley	Chester-le-Street	7. 8.00
G-BBXJ*	HPR.7 Herald 203	196	I-TIVI	18. 1.74	Jersey Airport Fire Service	Jersey	30. 5.75T
					(Crashed Jersey 24.12.74)		
G-BBXK	PA-34-200-2 Seneca I	34-7450056	N54366	21. 1.74	J.A.Rees	Haverfordwest	15. 3.02T
					t/a Poyston Aviation		
G-BBXL	Cessna 310Q II	310Q-1076	EI-CLX G-BBXL/(N1223G)	21. 1.74	Thornhill Aviation Ltd	(London N1)	22. 1.01T
G-BBXO	Enstrom F-28A-UK	181		29. 1.74	Stephenson Marine Co Ltd	Goodwood	29. 9.01T
G-BBXS	Piper J3C-90 Cub (L-4H-PI)	12214	N9865K G-ALMA/44-79918	25. 1.74	M.J.Butler Ranksborough Farm, Langham		12. 6.99P
	(Regd as c/n "9865"; Frame No. 12042)						
G-BBXU*	Beechcraft B24R Sierra 200	MC-238		30. 1.74	J.Coggins (Stored 11.95)	Coventry	18.11.93T
G-BBXY	Bellanca 7GCBC Citabria	614-74	N57639	1. 2.74	R.R.L.Windus		
						Truleigh Manor Farm, Edburton	12. 6.99
G-BBXZ	Evans VP-1	PFA/1562		31. 1.74	R.W.Burrows	Swanton Morley	8. 3.96P
	(VW1600)				(Stored 5.99)		
G-BBYB	PA-18-95 Super Cub (L-18C-PI)	18-1627	PH-TMA (D-ENCH)/ALAT 18-1627/51-15627	4. 2.74	The Tiger Club (1990) Ltd	Headcorn	15. 6.01T
	(Frame No. 18-1628)						
G-BBYH	Cessna 182P	182-62814	N52744	6. 2.74	Croftmarsh Ltd		
						Poplar Farm, Croft, Skegness	1.12.02

Regn	Type	C/n	P/I	Date	Owner/operator	Probable Base	CA Expy
G-BBYL*	Cameron O-77 HAFB	89		8. 2.74	R.Warner "Phoenix"		19. 6.77S
					(Cancelled by CAA 19.5.93: noted 2.97)		
G-BBYM	HP.137 Jetstream 200	243	G-AYWR G-8-13	13. 2.74	British Aerospace (Operations) Ltd	Dunsfold	20. 9.98A
G-BBYO*	BN-2A Mk.III-1 Trislander	362	ZS-KMH G-BBYO/G-BBWR	27. 2.74	Aurigny Air Services Ltd	Guernsey	1. 5.92T
					(WFU 2.92; stored 6.97; to be rebuilt using fuselage of c/n 1072/N3267J)		
G-BBYP	PA-28-140 Cherokee F	28-7425158		19. 2.74	Jersey Aircraft Maintenance Ltd	Jersey	17. 8.98T
					(Dismantled 12.98)		
G-BBYR*	Cameron O-65 HAFB	97		14. 2.74	I M Martin "Phoenix"	Lancing	
					(Balloon Preservation Group 7.98)		
G-BBYS	Cessna 182P Skylane	182-61520	5Y-ATE N21256	14. 2.74	I.M.Jones	Gamston	1. 5.00
G-BBYU*	Cameron O-56 HAFB	96		19. 2.74	British Balloon Museum & Library "Chieftain"	Newbury	28. 2.82A
G-BBZF	PA-28-140 Cherokee F	28-7425195		19. 2.74	Winchester Associates (95) Ltd	Popham	23. 6.00
G-BBZH	PA-28R-200 Cherokee Arrow II	28R-7435102		22. 2.74	M.J.Sandry t/a Zulu Hotel Club	Exeter	4. 6.01
G-BBZJ	PA-34-200-2 Seneca	34-7450088	N40880	26. 2.74	Eurofly Share Ltd	Blackbushe	11. 8.00T
					(Op European Flyers)		
G-BBZN	Fuji FA.200-180 Aero Subaru	230		26. 2.74	J.Westwood & P.D.Wedd	Cambridge	10. 4.00T
G-BBZO	Fuji FA.200-160 Aero Subaru	238		26. 2.74	L.A.N.King & M.J.Herlihy t/a G-BBZO Group	Redhill	1. 7.02
G-BBZS*	Enstrom F-28A-UK	192		27. 2.74	Not known	Goodwood	30. 9.89T
					(Damaged nr Tyldesley 29.4.89; stored 6.93)		
G-BBZV	PA-28R-200 Cherokee Arrow II			11. 3.74	P.B.Mellor	Top Farm, Royston	2. 9.02T

G-BCAA – G-BCZZ

Regn	Type	C/n	P/I	Date	Owner/operator	Probable Base	CA Expy
G-BCAC*	Socata MS.894A Rallye Minerva 220	12099		4. 3.74	Not known Clarence Way, Westpoint Enterprise Park, Trafford Park		7.12.90
					(Damaged Sandown 6.5.90; on display 1994 by Kamikazee Ken's Kitchens)		
G-BCAH	DHC.1 Chipmunk 22	C1/0372	WG316	6. 5.74	Southern Air Ltd (As "WG316")	Shoreham	7. 6.02T
G-BCAN	Thunder Ax7-77 HAFB	015		5. 3.74	D.D.Owen "Beacon"	Wotton-under-Edge	7. 8.88A
G-BCAP*	Cameron O-56 HAFB	92		5. 3.74	K.Tanner "Honey Child"	Lancing	NE(A)
					(Balloon Preservation Group 12.98)		
G-BCAR*	Thunder Ax7-77 HAFB	019		5. 3.74	British Balloon Museum "Marie Antoinette"	Newbury	NE(A)
G-BCAS	Thunder Ax7-77 HAFB	018		5. 3.74	D.P.Busby "Drifter"	Lancing	9. 4.91A
					(Balloon Preservation Group 7.98)		
G-BCAZ	PA-12 Super Cruiser	12-2312	5Y-KGK VP-KGK/ZS-BYJ/ZS-BPH	12. 3.74	A.D.Williams	Rhos-Y-Gilwen Farm, Rhos Hill	10. 8.01
G-BCBG	PA-23-250 Aztec E	27-7305224	VP-BBN VR-BBN/G-BCBG/N40494	13. 3.74	M.J.L Batt	Booker	29.10.01
G-BCBH	Fairchild 24R-46A Argus III (UC-61K-FA)	975	(VH-AAQ) G-BCBH/ZS-AXH/HB737/43-15011	13. 3.74	Ebork Ltd	Biggin Hill	20. 3.00
G-BCBJ	PA-25-235 Pawnee C	25-2380/R		18. 3.74	Deeside Gliding Club (Aberdeenshire) Ltd	Aboyne	2. 9.01
	(Rebuild of c/n 25-2380/G-ASLA/N6802Z,				quoting c/n 25-5544 the new fuselage of G-ASLA !)		
G-BCBL	Fairchild 24R-46A Argus III (UC-61K-FA)	989	OO-EKE D-EKEQ/HB-AEC/HB751/43-15025	19. 3.74	F.J.Cox (As "HB751")	Eaglescott	31. 3.96
G-BCBM	PA-23-250 Aztec C	27-3006	N5854Y	19. 3.74	Hatton & Westerman Trawlers	(Douglas, IoM)	12. 5.01
G-BCBR	AJEP/Wittman W.8 Tailwind (Continental O-200-A)	TW3-380		20. 3.74	R.J.Willies	Honeydon Farm, Colmworth, Bedford	25. 5.00P
G-BCBX	Reims Cessna F.150L	1001	F-BUEO	25. 3.74	J.Kelly (Stored 6.97)	Aldergrove	19. 2.95T
G-BCBZ	Cessna 337C Super Skymaster (Robertson STOL conversion)	337-0942	SE-FKB N2642S	28. 3.74	J.J.Zwetsloot	Bourn	18. 2.02
G-BCCB*	Robin HR.200/100 Club	29		2. 4.74	M.J.Ellis	(Devizes)	12. 6.89
					(Last known stored at Old Sarum 8.90 after damage by gales 25.01.90: cancelled by CAA 2.3.99)		
G-BCCC	Reims Cessna F.150L Commuter	1041		8. 4.74	Airtime Maintenance Ltd (Op Airbourne School of Flying)	Bournemouth	15. 2.01T
G-BCCD	Reims Cessna F.172M Skyhawk II	1144		8. 4.74	R.M.Austin t/a Austin Aviation	Biggin Hill	23. 1.01T
G-BCCE	PA-23-250 Aztec E	27-7405282	N40544	3. 4.74	A.S.Bamrah t/a Falcon Flying Services	Lydd	5. 7.99T
G-BCCF	PA-28-180 Cherokee Archer	28-7405069		3. 4.74	Topcat Aviation Ltd	Liverpool	13. 6.00
G-BCCG	Thunder Ax7-65 HAFB	020		4. 4.74	N.H.Ponsford t/a Rango Balloon & Kite Co "Zephyr" (Active 1999)	Leeds	NE(A)
G-BCCH*	Thunder Ax6-56A HAFB	024		4. 4.74	A D Kent "Wrangler"	Lancing	
					(Balloon Preservation Group 7.98)		

Regn	Type	C/n	P/I	Date	Owner/operator	Probable Base	CA Expy
G-BCCJ	Grumman-American AA-5 Traveler	AA5-0546		8. 4.74	T.Needham	Woodford	21. 4.00
G-BCCK	Grumman-American AA-5 Traveler	AA5-0547		8. 4.74	Prospect Air Ltd	Manchester	14. 9.02
G-BCCR	Piel CP.301A Emeraude (Continental O-200-A)	PFA/712		8. 4.74	J.H. & C.J.Waterman Armshold Farm, Kingston, Cambs		22. 2.00P
G-BCCU	BN-2A mk.III-1 Trislander	366	4X-CCK	17. 4.74	Hebridean Air Services Ltd	Cumbernauld	26. 1.99TC
			G-BCCU/9L-LAR/G-BCCU/(LN-VIV)				
G-BCCX	DHC.1 Chipmunk 22 (Lycoming O-360)	C1/0531	WG481	17. 4.74	T.Holloway t/a RAFGSA (Op Clevelands Gliding Club)	RAF Dishforth	28. 3.00
G-BCCY	Robin HR.200/100 Club	37		18. 4.74	Charlie Yankee Ltd	Filton	30. 6.02
G-BCDB	PA-34-200-2 Seneca	34-7450110	N41346	22. 4.74	P A S Dyke	Elstree	30. 7.01T
G-BCDJ	PA-28-140 Cherokee	28-24276	PH-NLV N1841J	29. 4.74	B.F.Graham t/a Bristol Aero Club	Filton	26. 5.01T
G-BCDK(2)	Partenavia P.68B	32	A6-ALN G-BCDK	4. 7.75	Flyteam Aviation Ltd	Elstree	26. 4.02
G-BCDL	Cameron O-42 HAFB	115		24. 4.74	D.P. & Mrs B.O.Turner "Chums" (Balloon Preservation Group 12.98)	Bath	NE(A)
G-BCDN*	Fokker F-27 Friendship 200	10201	PH-OGA	29. 4.74	Air UK Ltd	Norwich	19. 7.96T
			JA8615/(LV-PMR)/PH-FDP (Used as apprentice trainer 5.99)				
G-BCDO*	Fokker F-27 Friendship 200	10234	PH-OGB	29. 4.74	Air UK Ltd	Norwich	20. 6.91T
			JA8621/PH-FEZ		"Friendship Lord Butler"		
			(Damaged Amsterdam 19.7.90; Technical College airframe 10.96)				
G-BCDY	Reims Cessna FRA.150L Aerobat	0237		7. 5.74	Mid-Anglia Flying School Ltd	Cambridge	17. 6.00T
G-BCEA	Sikorsky S-61N Mk.II	61-721		7. 6.74	Brintel Helicopters Ltd t/a British International Helicopters	Sumburgh	13. 7.00T
G-BCEB	Sikorsky S-61N Mk.II	61-454	N4023S	2.10.74	Brintel Helicopters Ltd t/a British Intl Helicopters "The Isles of Scilly"	Penzance	16.12.02T
G-BCEC	Reims Cessna F.172M Skyhawk II	1082		7. 5.74	A.R. & S.D.Bamber	Barton	18. 5.00
G-BCEE	Grumman-American AA-5 Traveler	AA5-0571		7. 5.74	Echo Echo Ltd	Bournemouth	15. 5.00
G-BCEF	Grumman-American AA-5 Traveler	AA5-0572		7. 5.74	K.W.Longden	Popham	1. 7.00T
G-BCEN	BN-2A-26 Islander	403	4X-AYG	6. 5.74	Atlantic Air Transport Ltd	Lydd/Coventry	7.11.00A
			SX-BFB/4X-AYG/N90JA/G-BCEN (Coastguard c/s)				
G-BCEO	Grumman-American AA-5 Traveler	AA5-0575		7. 5.74	D.M.Jenden t/a Echo Oscar Flying Group	Teesside	20.11.02
G-BCEP	Grumman-American AA-5 Traveler	AA5-0576		7. 5.74	C.H.Mitchell & G.Pontin t/a Golf Echo Papa Flying Group	(Hastings)	7. 5.00
G-BCER	CAB GY-201 Minicab	8	F-BGJP	8. 5.74	D.Beaumont	Sherburn in Elmet	24. 3.00P
G-BCEU	Cameron O-42 HAFB	111		9. 5.74	Not known "Harlequin" (Cancelled by CAA 19.5.93: noted Ashton Court 8.99)	NK	
G-BCEX	PA-23-250 Aztec E	27-7305024	N40225	13. 5.74	Western Air (Thruxton) Ltd	Thruxton	23. 6.02T
G-BCEY	DHC.1 Chipmunk 22	C1/0515	WG465	14. 5.74	T.C.B.Dehn & C.A.Robey t/a Gopher Flying Group (As "WG465" in RAF c/s)	White Waltham	14. 1.02
G-BCEZ	Cameron O-84 HAFB	107		13. 5.74	P.F.Smart & R.J.Mitchener t/a Balloon Collection "Stars & Bars"	Romsey/Andover	20. 7.82A
G-BCFC	Cameron O-65 HAFB	116		15. 5.74	B.H.Mead "Candy Twist"	Bude	20. 3.88A
G-BCFD*	West Ax3-15 HAFB	JW.1		16. 5.74	British Balloon Museum "Hellfire" (Stored)	Newbury	
G-BCFF	Fuji FA.200-160 Aero Subaru	237		21. 5.74	G.W.Brown & M.R.Gibbons	Popham	2.12.00
G-BCFN	Cameron O-65 HAFB	109		23. 5.74	W.G.Johnston & H.M.Savage "Fireball"	Edinburgh	15. 5.77S
G-BCFO	PA-18-150 Super Cub	18-5335	(D-EIOZ) ALAT 18-5335	29. 5.74	Portsmouth Naval Gliding Club	Lee-on-Solent	13. 4.00
G-BCFR	Reims Cessna FRA.150L Aerobat	0244		30. 5.74	Rentair Ltd (Op Essex Flying School)	Earls Colne	13.12.02T
G-BCFU*	Thunder Ax-6-56 HAFB	027	EI-BAF G-BCFU	17. 5.74	British Balloon Museum "Smithwicks"	Newbury	31. 7.86
			(Cancelled 7.74: flew Warren Farm, Savernake 9.1.00 as "G-BCFU")				
G-BCFW	SAAB 91D Safir	91-437	PH-RLZ	29. 5.74	D.R.Williams	Peplow	22. 7.00
G-BCFY	Phoenix Luton LA-4A Minor (Ardem Mk.6)	PAL/1301 & PFA/824		29. 5.74	G.Capes (Stored Sywell 8.92)	(Brough)	17. 1.92P
G-BCGA*	PA-34-200-2 Seneca	34-7450166	N41975	4. 6.74	Not known (Crashed Waddington 18.12.77; wreck stored 4.91)	Ronaldsway	15. 7.78
G-BCGB	Bensen B.8 (Rotax 503)	PCL.14		3. 6.74	J.W.Birkett	Bursledon, Southampton	23. 6.99P
G-BCGC*	DHC.1 Chipmunk 22	C1/0776	WP903	13. 3.74	Transport Command Ltd (As "WP903" in Queen's Flt c/s) (Cancelled by CAA 16.10.99)	Shoreham	16. 7.99T
G-BCGG(2)	CEA Jodel DR.250/160	87	G-ATZL	3.11.81	C.G.Gray	Mere House, Stow, Lincs	25. 5.00

Regn	Type	C/n	P/I	Date	Owner/operator	Probable Base	CA Expy
G-BCGH	SNCAN NC.854S	122	F-BAFG	10. 6.74	T.J.N.H.Palmer Hill Farm, Nayland		28. 5.00P
					t/a Nord Flying Group		
G-BCGI	PA-28-140 Cherokee Cruiser		N9573N	10. 6.74	A.Dodd	Panshanger	8. 6.00T
		28-7425283					
G-BCGJ	PA-28-140 Cherokee Cruiser		N9574N	10. 6.74	BCT Aircraft Leasing Ltd	Bristol	11. 2.00T
		28-7425286					
G-BCGM	Jodel Wassmer D.120 Paris-Nice	50	F-BHQM	15. 7.74	M.H.D.Soltau		
			F-BHYM		Clench Farm, Bury St.Edmonds		20.12.00P
G-BCGN	PA-28-140 Cherokee F	28-7425323	N9595N	10. 6.74	Golf November Ltd	Oxford	4. 8.02
G-BCGP*	Gazebo Ax6-65 HAFB	1		13. 6.74	British Balloon Museum & Library		
					"Aries"	(Newbury)	
G-BCGS	PA-28R-200 Cherokee Arrow II		N4893T	13. 6.74	S.Rayne Top Farm, Royston		26.10.00
		28R-7235133			t/a Arrow Aviation Group		
G-BCGT	PA-28-140 Cherokee	28-24504	N6779J	17. 6.74	M.Fryer	Earls Colne	18. 2.00T
					t/a EFS Flying Group (Op Essex School of Flying)		
G-BCGW	Chittenden-Jodel D.11			14. 6.74	G.H. & M.D.Chittenden	Highwood Hall	30. 1.85P
	(Lycoming O-290) CC.001 & EAA/61554 & PFA/912				(Stored)		
G-BCHK	Reims Cessna F.172H	0716	9H-AAD	19. 6.74	E.C. & A.K.Shimmin	Bagby	29.10.00
G-BCHL	DHC.1 Chipmunk 22A	C1/0680	WP788	20. 6.74	Shropshire Soaring Ltd	Sleap	18.10.01
					(As "WP788")		
G-BCHM	Westland SA.341G Gazelle 1	WA/1168	G-17-20	14. 6.74	The Auster Aircraft Co Ltd		
					(Damaged Springfield Farm, Melton Mowbray 5.7.97) Melton Mowbray		23. 8.99
G-BCHP	Scintex CP.1310-C3 Super Emeraude		G-JOSI	24. 6.74	G.Hughes & A.G.Just	Earls Colne	21. 6.00P
		902	G-BCHP/F-BJVQ				
G-BCHT	Schleicher ASK 16	16021	(BGA1996)	25. 6.74	D.E.Cadisch & K.A.Lilleywhite	Dunstable	13. 5.01
			D-KAMY		t/a Dunstable K16 Group		
G-BCHV*	DHC.1 Chipmunk 22	C1/0703	WP807	27. 6.74	N.F.Charles Old Manor Farm, Anwick		20. 6.98
					(Cancelled by CAA 29.6.99)		
G-BCHX	Scheibe SF-23A Sperling	2013	D-EGIZ	28. 6.74	R.L.McLean	Rufforth	29. 6.83P
					t/a DG Powered Sailplanes (Damaged 7.8.82; frame stored 9.99)		
G-BCID	PA-34-200-2 Seneca	34-7250303	N1381T	3. 7.74	C.J.Freeman	Headcorn	27. 7.01T
G-BCIH	DHC.1 Chipmunk 22	C1/0304	WD363	3. 7.74	J.M.Hosey (As "WD363")	Andrewsfield	19. 6.99
G-BCIJ	Grumman-American AA-5 Traveler		N6143A	3. 7.74	R.J.Warne	White Waltham	27. 5.00
		AA5-0603					
G-BCIK	Grumman-American AA-5 Traveler		N6144A	3. 7.74	Trent Aviation Ltd	Tatenhill	5. 6.00
		AA5-0604					
G-BCIL*	Grumman-American AA-1B Trainer	0378	N6168A	5. 7.74	M.Hobson Cruden Bay, Grampian		2.10.88
		AA1B-0378			(Crashed Auchnagatt, Aberdeen 14.6.86; stored 2.96)		
G-BCIN	Thunder Ax7-77 HAFB	030		5. 7.74	R.A. & P G.Vale	Kidderminster	5. 5.84A
					t/a Isambard Kingdom Brunel Balloon Group		
G-BCIR	PA-28-151 Cherokee Warrior		N9587N	9. 7.74	P.J.Brennan	Southend	12. 6.00
		28-7415401					
G-BCIW*	DHC.1 Chipmunk 22	C1/0899	WZ868	8. 7.74	M.L.Biggs Fownhope, Hereford		11. 7.94
					(Damaged Hulcote Farm, Beds 26.11.91; fuselage stored 9.98)		
	(As "WZ868/H" in Cambridge UAS c/s; the replacment a/c, G-ARMF, also carries WZ868/H")						
G-BCJH	Mooney M.20F Executive 21	670126	N9549M	11. 7.74	P.J.Bossard (Open store 4.99)	Bourn	30. 6.93
G-BCJM	PA-28-140 Cherokee F	28-7425321		17. 7.74	Topcat Aviation Ltd	Manchester	10.11.02T
					(Op Manchester School of Flying)		
G-BCJN	PA-28-140 Cherokee Cruiser		N9618N	17. 7.74	Topcat Aviation Ltd	Barton	15. 8.02
		28-7425350					
G-BCJO	PA-28R-200 Cherokee Arrow II			17. 7.74	R.Ross	Oaksey Park	11. 6.00
		28R-7435272					
G-BCJP	PA-28-140 Cherokee	28-24187	N1766J	15. 8.74	D.J. & D.Pitman	Bournemouth	30. 3.01
					t/a Omletair Flying Group		
G-BCKN	DHC.1 Chipmunk 22	C1/0707	WP811	5. 8.74	T.Holloway	RAF Cranwell	16. 2.01
	(Lycoming O-360)				t/a RAFGSA (Op Cranwell Gliding Club)		
G-BCKP	Phoenix Luton LA-5A Major	PFA/1213		6. 8.74	D. & W.H.Gough	Popham	10. 6.98P
	(Continental C90)						
G-BCKS	Fuji FA.200-180AO Aero Subaru			2. 8.74	Kestrel Aviation Ltd	Thruxton	30. 4.01T
		FA200-250					
G-BCKT	Fuji FA.200-180 Aero Subaru			2. 8.74	M.A.Petrie	Shoreham	20. 5.02
		FA200-251			t/a G-BCKT Group		
G-BCKU	Reims Cessna FRA.150L Aerobat	0256		1. 8.74	Stapleford Flying Club Ltd	Stapleford	18.10.01T
G-BCKV	Reims Cessna FRA.150L Aerobat	0251		1. 8.74	Cleveland Flying School Ltd	Teesside	19.12.99T
G-BCLC	Sikorsky S-61N Mk.II	61-737		9. 1.75	Bristow Helicopters Ltd "Craigievar"		
					Mount Pleasant, Falkland Islands		12. 1.003
G-BCLD	Sikorsky S-61N Mk.II	61-739		4. 2.75	Bristow Helicopters Ltd	Sumburgh	2. 2.00T
					(Op HM Coast Guard) "Slains"		
G-BCLI	Grumman-American AA-5 Traveler			12. 8.74	Pioneer Aviation Ltd	Cranfield	8. 5.00T
		AA5-0643					

Regn	Type	C/n	P/I	Date	Owner/operator	Probable Base	CA Expy
G-BCLJ*	Grumman-American AA-5 Traveler			12. 8.74	Effie A.A.Andree-Wiltens		
		AA5-0644				Rotterdam, The Netherlands	7.11.99
					(Cancelled by CAA 24.9.99).		
G-BCLL	PA-28-180 Cherokee C	28-2400	SE-EON	13. 8.74	S.R.& J.Nash	Blackbushe	5.10.01
G-BCLS*	Cessna 170B	20946	N8094A	23. 8.74	Teesside Flt Centre Ltd	Teesside	27. 1.83
G-BCLT	Socata MS.894A Rallye Minerva 220	EI-BBW	1. 8.74	K.M.Hood		Bristol	3. 6.02
		12003	G-BCLT/F-BTRL		t/a Rallye Group		
G-BCLU	SAN Jodel D.117	506	F-BHXG	28. 8.74	N.A.Wallace	Knettishall	22. 9.00P
G-BCLW	Grumman-American AA-1B Tr2 AA1B-0463			29. 8.74	A.E.Duncan & B.Hepburn	Dundee	27. 7.02
G-BCMD	PA-18-95 Super Cub	18-2055	OO-SPF	4. 9.74	J.G.Brooks	Exeter	4. 2.02
	(L-18C-PI) (Frame No. 18-2071)		R.Neth AF R-70/52-2455				
G-BCMF*	Levi Go-Plane RL.6 Srs.1	EAA.3678		5. 9.74	R.Levi	Newport, IoW	
					(Damaged Bembridge 16.11.74: stored 12.95)		
G-BCMJ*	K & S SA.102.5 Cavalier MJ.1 & PFA/1546			9. 9.74	R.G.Sykes	Cranfield	8. 8.85P
	(Continental O-200-A) (Tail-wheel conversion)				(Last known on rebuild 7.94: cancelled by CAA 2.3.99)		
G-BCMT	Isaacs Fury II	PFA/1522		9. 9.74	M.H.Turner	(Brixham)	
	(Continental O-200-A)						
G-BCNC	Gardan GY-201 Minicab	A.202	F-BICF	9. 9.74	J.R.Wraight	(Chatham)	
G-BCNP	Cameron O-77 HAFB	117		16. 9.74	P.Spellward "Blue Fret"	Bristol	28. 7.00A
G-BCNR*	Thunder Ax7-77A HAFB	028		13. 9.74	R.Warner "Howdy"	Cranfield	15. 5.81A
G-BCNX	Piper J3C-65 Cub (L-4H-PI)	"11831"	F-BEGM	17. 9.74	K.J.Lord	Cherry Tree Farm, Monewden	28. 3.00P
					t/a The Grasshopper Flying Group (As "540" in USAF c/s)		
	(Previous French identity of c/n 11831 and p/i 43-30540 are quoted although rebuilt in 1960/61 with c/n 10993:						
	true origin is thought to be Frame No.10993 with c/n 11168 and ex Fr.AF/43-29877)						
G-BCNZ	Fuji FA-200-160 Aero Subaru	257		16. 9.74	J.Bruton & A.Lincoln	Barton	8. 2.99
G-BCOB	Piper J3C-65 Cub (L-4H-PI)	10696	F-BCPV	19. 9.74	R.W. & Mrs.J.Marjoram		
	(Frame No.10521)		43-29405			Low Farm, South Walsham	10. 5.00P
					(As "329405/A/23" in USAAC c/s)		
G-BCOI	DHC.1 Chipmunk 22	C1/0759	WP870	24. 9.74	D.S.McGregor	Rayne Hall Farm, Rayne	14. 4.01
G-BCOJ	Cameron O-56 HAFB	124		25. 9.74	T.J.Knott & M.J.Webber	Rickmansworth	12. 7.87A
					t/a Phoenix Balloon Group "Red Squirrel"		
G-BCOL	Reims Cessna F.172M Skyhawk II	1233		25. 9.74	A.H.Creaser	Old Manor Farm, Anwick	8. 4.00T
G-BCOM	Piper J3C-90 Cub (L-4A-PI)	10478	F-BDTP	27. 9.74	Penelope A.Kidd & D.E.S.Clarke	Shoreham	26. 5.00P
			F-BFQP/OO-ADI/43-29187 t/a Dougal Flying Group "Dougal"				
	(Frame No.10303 - officially regd as c/n 12040 which is correct identity of G-BGROUPD: fuselages probably						
	exchanged in France)						
G-BCOO	DHC.1 Chipmunk 22	C1/0209	WB760	10.10.74	T.G.Fielding & M.S.Morton	Blackpool	10.11.00
G-BCOP	PA-28R-200 Cherokee Arrow II			8.10.74	Oscar Papa Ltd	Halfpenny Green	26. 2.01
		28R-7435296					
G-BCOR	Socata Rallye 100ST	2544	F-OCZK	7. 1.75	P.R.W.Goslin, P.Nichamin	Henstridge	27. 9.01
					& I.M.Speight		
G-BCOU	DHC.1 Chipmunk 22	C1/0559	WK522	10.10.74	P.J.Loweth "Thunderbird 5"	High Easter	30. 3.95
					(As "WK522" in RAF c/s) (Stored 4.95)		
G-BCOX	Bede BD-5A	HJC.4523		10.10.74	H.J.Cox & B.L.Robinson	Chivenor	27.11.95P*
					(To Mid-West for new engine fitment: noted 7.99)		
G-BCOY	DHC.1 Chipmunk 22	C1/0212	WB762	10.10.74	Coventry Gliding Club Ltd		
	(Lycoming O-360)					Husbands Bosworth	23. 1.00
G-BCPD	CAB GY-201 Minicab	18	F-BGKN	24.10.74	A.H.K.Denniss	Leicester	1. 4.98P
G-BCPG	PA-28R-200 Cherokee Arrow	28R-35705	N4985S	16.10.74	A.G.Antoniades	Barton	21. 5.01
					t/a Roses Flying Group		
G-BCPH	Piper J3C-65 Cub (L-4H-PI)	11225	F-BCZA	13.12.74	M.J.Janaway	Thatcham	24. 3.00P
	(Frame No.11050)		Fr.AF/43-29934 (As "329934/B/72" in 25th AOP French Armoured Divn of US 3rd Army c/s)				
G-BCPJ	Piper J3C-65 Cub (L-4J-PI)	13206	F-BDTJ	5.11.74	S.Hollingsworth	Popham	27.10.00P
	(Frame No.13036)		45-4466		t/a Piper Cub Group		
G-BCPK	Reims Cessna F.172M Skyhawk II	1194	(D-ELOB)	21.10.74	Tilbrook Industries Ltd	Coventry	12. 1.01T
G-BCPN	Grumman-American AA-5 Traveler		N6155A	21.10.74	A.Butterfield	Melrose Farm, Melbourne	11. 9.00
		AA5-0665					
G-BCPO	Partenavia P.68B	27		18.10.74	J.Bowles, J.M.Smith & P.J.Wardle	Sywell	29. 6.01
G-BCPU	DHC.1 Chipmunk 22	C1/0839	WP973	24.10.74	P.Waller	Booker	3. 3.02
G-BCPX	Szep HFC.125	PFA/12-10019		24.10.74	A.Szep	Netherthorpe	20. 9.97P
	(Lycoming O-290)						
G-BCRB	Reims Cessna F.172M Skyhawk II	1259		29.10.74	D.E.Lamb	Fenland	4. 5.01
G-BCRE*	Cameron O-77 HAFB	128		30.10.74	K Tanner "Snapdragon"	Lancing	6.10.83A
					(Balloon Preservation Group 7.98)		
G-BCRH*	Alaparma 75 Baldo	41	I-DONP	5.11.74	Not known	(Wiltshire)	
			MM53647		(Stored w/o engine 1997)		
G-BCRI	Cameron O-65 HAFB	135		5.11.74	V.J.Thorne "Joseph"	Bristol	26. 8.81A
G-BCRK	K & S SA.102.5 Cavalier PFA/01-10049			5.11.74	M.F.Newman	Swanton Morley	14. 7.00P
	(Lycoming O-235)						
G-BCRL	PA-28-151 Cherokee Warrior			5.11.74	BCRL Ltd	(Brough)	18. 6.00
		28-7415689					

Regn	Type	C/n	P/I	Date	Owner/operator	Probable Base	CA Expy
G-BCRP	PA-E23-250 Aztec E	27-7305082	N40269	7.11.74	Airlong Charter Ltd	Norwich	25. 9.00T
G-BCRR	Grumman-American AA-5B Tiger			7.11.74	N.A.Whatling	(Stamford)	13.11.00
		AA5B-0006					
G-BCRT	Reims Cessna F.150M Commuter	1164		18.11.74	G.Matthews	Coventry	24. 3.01T
					t/a Blue Max Flying Group		
G-BCRX	DHC.1 Chipmunk 22	C1/0232	WD292	22.11.74	Tuplin Ltd	White Waltham	1. 8.00
					(As "WD292" in RAF c/s)		
G-BCSA	DHC.1 Chipmunk 22	C1/0691	WP799	25.11.74	T.Holloway	RAF Bicester	3. 4.00
	(Lycoming O-360)				t/a RAFGSA		
G-BCSB	DHC.1 Chipmunk 22	C1/0770	WP899	25.11.74	T.Holloway	RAF Bicester	5. 6.00
	(Lycoming O-360)				t/a RAFGSA		
G-BCSL	DHC.1 Chipmunk 22	C1/0524	WG474	26.11.74	Jalawain Ltd	Barton	30. 3.01
					t/a Barton Chipmunk Flyers		
G-BCSM	Bellanca 8GCBC Scout	108-74		14. 7.99	York Gliding Centre Ltd	Rufforth	
G-BCST	Socata MS.893A Rallye Commodore 180		F-BPQD	18.11.74	Patricia J.Wilcox	Cranfield	8. 4.00
		10748					
G-BCSX	Thunder Ax7-77 HAFB	031		2.12.74	C.Wolstenholme	Macclesfield	5. 7.86A
					"Woophski"		
G-BCSY	Taylor JT.2 Titch	PFA/1504		5.12.74	I.L.Harding	Sackville Farm, Riseley	
	(VW 1600)				(Construction abandoned at advanced state; stored 3.97)		
G-BCTF	PA-28-151 Cherokee Warrior			11.12.74	E.Reed	Teesside	2. 9.02T
		28-7515033			t/a The St.George Flying Club		
	(Rebuilt 1989/90 using major components from G-BFXZ)						
G-BCTI	Schleicher ASK 16	16029	D-KIWA	23.12.74	A.J.Southard	Hinton-in-The-Hedges	19. 7.01
					t/a Tango India Syndicate		
G-BCTJ	Cessna 310Q II	310Q-1072	N1219G	23.12.74	D.Pearce & P.Golding	Biggin Hill	14. 7.02T
					t/a TJ Flying Group		
G-BCTK	Reims Cessna FR.172J Rocket	0546		23.12.74	R.T.Love	Bodmin	11.12.99
G-BCTT	Evans VP-1	PFA/1543		24.12.74	B.J.Boughton	Knettishall	25. 6.99P
	(VW1600)				t/a The Fersfield Flying Group		
G-BCTU	Reims Cessna FRA.150M Aerobat	0268		30.12.74	J.A.Rees	Haverfordwest	24. 3.02T
					t/a Haverfordwest School of Flying		
G-BCTW*	Reims Cessna F.150M	1170		2. 1.75	Wickenby Aviation Ltd	Wickenby	20.12.91T
	(Damaged Strangford Lough, NI 12.4.89 & flooding Newtownards 13.12.91; stored 2.93)						
G-BCUB	Piper J3C-65 Cub (L-4J-PI)	13186	F-BCPC	13.12.74	A.L.Brown & G.Attwell	Bourn	23. 6.00P
	(Lippert Reed conversion)		45-4446				
	(Identity incorrect & may be c/n 13370 (ex F-BFBU/45-4630) which is G-BDOL; possibly frames exchanged)						
G-BCUF	Reims Cessna F.172M Skyhawk II	1279		3. 1.75	John L.R.James & Co Ltd		
						Clough Farm, Croft, Skegness	5. 5.00
G-BCUH	Reims Cessna F.150M Commuter	1195		7. 1.75	M.G.Montgomerie	Elstree	18.11.00T
					t/a G-BCUH Group		
G-BCUJ	Reims Cessna F.150M Commuter	1176		9. 1.75	N.E.Binner	(Malton)	13.12.01T
G-BCUL	Socata Rallye 100ST	2545	F-OCZL	27. 1.75	C.A.Ussher & Fountain Estates Ltd		
						New Laithe Farm, Harewood, Leeds	8. 5.00
G-BCUO	Scottish Avn Bulldog 120/122		G-107	9. 1.75	Cranfield University	Cranfield	16.10.00T
		BH120-371	Ghana AF/G-BCUO				
G-BCUS	Scottish Avn Bulldog 120/122		G-109	9. 1.75	S.J. & J.J.Ollier	Tatenhill	29. 4.02
		BH120-373	Ghana AF/G-BCUS				
G-BCUV	Scottish Avn Bulldog 120/122		G-112	9. 1.75	Dolphin Property (Management) Ltd		
		BH120-376	Ghana AF/G-BCUV			Hurstbourne Tarrent, Hants	13. 4.00T
					(As "CB733" in RAF c/s)		
G-BCUW	Reims Cessna F.177RG Cardinal	0119	SE-GKL	10. 1.75	S.J.Westley (Westley Acft)	Cranfield	12. 5.00T
G-BCUY	Reims Cessna FRA.150M Aerobat	0269		14. 1.75	J.C.Carpenter	Clipgate	4. 2.01
G-BCVB	PA-17 Vagabond	17-190	F-BFMT	22. 1.75	A.T.Nowak	Popham	17. 6.00P
	(Continental A65)		N4890H				
G-BCVC	Socata Rallye 100ST	2548	F-OCZO	16. 1.75	N.R Vine	Old Sarum	25. 1.02
G-BCVE*	Evans VP-2	V2-1015 & PFA/7210		16. 1.75	North Western PFA Strut	Barton	
					(Under construction 12.97)		
G-BCVF	Practavia Pilot Sprite 115			27. 1.75	D.G.Hammersley	Tatenhill	16. 6.00P
	(Continental C125) GBC.1 & PFA/1362						
G-BCVG	Reims Cessna FRA.150L Aerobat	0245	(I-AFAD)	16. 1.75	I.G.Cooper	Compton Abbas	23.11.00
					t/a G-BCVG Flying Group		
G-BCVH	Reims Cessna FRA.150L Aerobat	0258		16. 1.75	Yorkshire Light Acft Ltd	Leeds-Bradford	20.10.02T
G-BCVJ	Reims Cessna F.172M Skyhawk II	1305		16. 1.75	Rothland Ltd	Blackpool	23.10.00
G-BCVW	Socata GY-80-180 Horizon	145	D-EHST	23. 1.75	P.M.A.Parrett	High Ham, Somerset	19. 3.99
					(Front fuselage stored Haverfordwest 7.99)		
G-BCVY	PA-34-200T Seneca II	34-7570022	N32447	28. 1.75	Oxford Aviation Services Ltd	Oxford	9. 6.00T
G-BCWB	Cessna 182P Skylane II	182-63566	N5848J	29. 1.75	Whisky Bravo Ltd	(Chippenham)	17.12.01T
G-BCWH	Practavia Pilot Sprite 115	PFA/1366		3. 2.75	R.Tasker	Blackpool	14. 6.00P
	(Continental O-240-A)						
G-BCWK	Alpavia Fournier RF3	24	F-BMDD	7. 2.75	T.J.Hartwell & D.R.Wilkinson	Thurleigh	22. 6.00P

Regn	Type	C/n	P/I	Date	Owner/operator	Probable Base	CA Expy
G-BCXB	Socata Rallye 100ST	2546	F-OCZM	7. 2.75	A.Smails	Fishburn	17. 2.01
G-BCXE	Robin DR.400 2 + 2	1015		19. 2.75	C.J.Freeman	Headcorn	3. 8.02T
G-BCXJ	Piper J3C-65 Cub (L-4J-PI)	13048	F-BFFH	21. 2.75	W.F.Stockdale	Old Sarum	17. 5.00P
	(Frame No.12878)		OO-SWA/44-80752		(As "480752/E/39" in USAAC c/s)		
G-BCXN	DHC.1 Chipmunk 22	C1/0692	WP800	7. 3.75	G.M.Turner	RAF Halton	26. 3.00
					(As "WP800/2" in Southampton UAS c/s)		
G-BCXO*	MBB Bo.105D	S.80	D-HDCE	27. 2.75	Lands End Theme Park	Lands End	23. 5.94T
	(Original pod replaced 1992 and rebuilt as a display piece: as "G-CDBS")						
G-BCXZ*	Cameron O-56 HAFB	154		4. 3.75	Not known "Olive"	NK	NE(A)
G-BCYH	DAW Privateer Mk.3 Motor Glider	BGA.1158	10. 3.75	D.B.Limbert	Crosland Moor	15. 8.00P
	(VW1600)	2 & PFA/1568	RAFGSA.264/XA297				
	(Regd as Cadet III and is a converted Slingsby T.31B c/n 839: marked incorrectly as "RAFGSA.246")						
G-BCYJ	DHC.1 Chipmunk 22	C1/0360	WG307	12. 3.75	R.A.L.Falconer	Shempston Farm, Elgin	19.12.02
					(As "WG307")		
G-BCYK*	Avro (Canada) CF-100	-	RCAF/18393	18. 3.75	Imperial War Museum	Duxford	
	Canuck Mk.IV				(As "18393" in RCAF c/s)		
G-BCYM	DHC.1 Chipmunk 22	C1/0598	WK577	13. 3.75	C.H.Nicholls	Oaksey Park	13. 7.00
					t/a G-BCYM Group		
G-BCYR	Reims Cessna F.172M Skyhawk II	1288		20. 3.75	J. & L.Donne	Edinburgh	30. 7.01T
					t/a Donne Enterprise (Op Edinburgh Flying Club)		
G-BCZH	DHC.1 Chipmunk 22	C1/0635	WK622	19. 3.75	A.C.Byrne Botany Bay, Horsford, Norwich	31. 7.87
			(As "WK622" in RAF c/s) (Crashed Pentney, Norfolk 6.9.87: stored 8.93)				
G-BCZI	Thunder Ax7-77 HAFB	037		24. 3.75	R.G.Griffin & R.Blackwell	Newbury	16. 3.86A
					t/a North Hampshire Balloon Group "Motorway"		
G-BCZM	Reims Cessna F.172M Skyhawk II	1350		3. 4.75	Cornwall Flying Club Ltd	Bodmin	20.10.00T
G-BCZN	Reims Cessna F.150M	1149		27. 3.75	Mona Aviation Ltd	RAF Mona	10.12.00T
G-BCZO	Cameron O-77 HAFB	158		27. 3.75	W.O.T.Holmes "Leo"	Shrewsbury	11.10.86A

G-BDAA – G-BDZZ

Regn	Type	C/n	P/I	Date	Owner/operator	Probable Base	CA Expy
G-BDAC*	Cameron O-77 HAFB	146		2. 4.75	Not known "Chocolate Ripple"	NK	NE(A)
G-BDAD	Taylor JT.1 Monoplane	PFA/1453		2. 4.75	J.Gunson t/a G-BDAD Group	(Preston)	3. 4.92P
	(VW1700)				(Damaged Blackpool 21.7.91: status uncertain)		
G-BDAG	Taylor JT.1 Monoplane	PFA/1430		1. 4.75	T.K.Gough	(Worcester)	20. 5.00P
	(VW1600)				"Biggles Too"		
G-BDAH	Evans VP-1	PFA/7007		2. 4.75	G.H.J.Geurts	Cranfield	26. 5.99
	(VW1600)						
G-BDAI	Reims Cessna FRA.150M Aerobat	0266		21. 4.75	A.Sharma	Popham	10. 5.01T
G-BDAK	Rockwell Commander 112A	252	N1252J	10. 4.75	R.W.Fairless	Thruxton	28. 8.00
G-BDAL	Rockwell 500S Shrike Commander	3226	N57134	25. 4.75	Quantel Ltd	Biggin Hill	17. 7.00
G-BDAM	Noorduyn AT-16-ND Harvard IIB	14-726	LN-MAA	10. 4.75	K.D.English & N.A.Lees	Duxford	1. 8.00P
			Fv16047/FE992/42-12479 (As "FE992/K-T" in 5(P)AFU c/s)				
G-BDAO	SIPA 91	2	F-BEPT	10. 4.75	J.E.Mead	(Cowbridge)	1. 8.00P
	(Continental C85)						
G-BDAP	AJEP/Wittman TW.8 Tailwind			9. 4.75	J.Whiting	Bagby	21. 4.00P
	(Continental O-200-A) 0387 & PFA/3507						
G-BDAR	Evans VP-1 Srs.2			10. 4.75	R.B.Valler	Hill Farm, Durley	20. 7.84P
	(VW1600)	PFA/1537 & PFA/62-10461					
G-BDAX*	PA-23-250 Aztec C	27-3494	5B-CAO	15. 4.75	Barry Technical College (Stored 11.95)		
			N6399Y			Cardiff Airport Industrial Park	12.11.93
G-BDAY	Thunder Ax5-42A HAFB	042		8. 4.75	T.M.Donnelly "Meconium"	Doncaster	16. 1.93A
G-BDBD	Wittman W.8 Tailwind	133	N1198S	25. 4.75	S.D.Arnold & T.Douglas		
	(Continental O-200-A)			t/a Tailwind Taildragger Group Wellesbourne Mountford	21. 4.00P
G-BDBF	Clutton FRED Srs.II	PFA/1528		15. 4.75	J.M.Brightwell & A.J.Wright	(Derby)	18. 3.98P
	(VW 1600)						
G-BDBH	Bellanca 7GCBC Citabria	758-74	OE-AOL	15. 4.75	R.Dixon	(Leatherhead)	16. 6.99
G-BDBI	Cameron O-77 HAFB	162		15. 4.75	C.A.Butter & J.J.Cooke	Marsh Benham	11. 7.87A
					"Funny Money"		
G-BDBJ	Cessna 182P Skylane II	182-63646	N4644K	18. 4.75	H.C.Wilson	Great Ashfield, Suffolk	18.12.99
G-BDBP	DHC.1 Chipmunk 22	C1/0727	WP843	23. 4.75	F.A.De Munck (Op Pionier Hangaar Collection)		
					(As "WP843/F" in RAF c/s) Lelystad, The Netherlands	1. 7.99
G-BDBS*	Short SD.3-30	SH.1935 & SH.3001 G-14-3001	21. 4.75	Ulster Aviation Society (Stored 4.96)		
					Langford Lodge, Belfast	28. 9.92S
G-BDBU	Reims Cessna F.150M	1174		30. 4.75	R.Edgar	(Ayr)	27. 6.00
G-BDBV	Aero Jodel D.11A	V.3	D-EGIB	23. 4.75	G.G.Long	Seething	31.10.00P
	(Continental C90)				t/a Seething Jodel Group		
G-BDBZ*	Westland WS.55 Whirlwind 2 (HAR.10)	XJ398	23. 4.75	Yorkshire Air Museum	Elvington	
	(Regd with c/n WA.386)	WA/62	(XD768)		(To Museum 1999)		
G-BDCC	DHC.1 Chipmunk 22	C1/0258	WD321	25. 4.75	Coventry Gliding Club Ltd		
	(Lycoming O-360)					Husbands Bosworth	24. 3.02

Regn	Type	C/n	P/I	Date	Owner/operator	Probable Base	CA Expy
G-BDCD	Piper J3C-90 Cub (L-4J-PI) (Frame No.12257)	12429	OO-AVS 44-80133	28. 4.75	Suzanne C.Brook Wellcross Grange, Slinfold (As "480133/B/44" in US Army c/s)		22. 7.00P
G-BDCE	Reims Cessna F.172H	0704	PH-EHB	5. 5.75	Copperplane Ltd Bournemouth (Damaged in gales Bournemouth 3.1.99: dumped 8.99)		26. 4.01T
G-BDCI	Scanor Piel CP.301C Emeraude	503	F-BIRC	25. 4.75	D.L.Sentance Rothwell Lodge Farm, Kettering		22.11.00P
G-BDCL	Grumman-American AA-5 Traveler	AA5-0773	EI-CCI	5. 5.75	J.Crowe Coventry G-BDCL/EI-BGV/G-BDCL/N1373R (Stored 11.95)		29.11.93T
G-BDCO	Beagle B.121 Pup 1	B121-171		6. 5.75	J.K.Healey Old Buckenham t/a Shipdham Aviators Flying Group		28. 7.97
G-BDCS	Cessna 421B Golden Eagle	421B-0832	N1931G	13. 5.75	British Aerospace (Operations) Ltd Warton		9.10.00T
G-BDDD	DHC.1 Chipmunk 22	C1/0326	WD387	16. 5.75	RAE Aero Club Ltd Farnborough		16. 8.02T
G-BDDF	Jodel Wassmer D.120 Paris-Nice	97	F-BIKZ	20. 5.75	H.E.G.Luxton & R.P.Peach Sywell t/a The Sywell Skyriders Flying Group		17. 8.00P
G-BDDG	Dormois Jodel D.112	855	F-BILM	20. 5.75	D.G.Palmer & S.Robinson Sturgate t/a Wandering Imp Group		13.10.00P
G-BDDS	PA-25-260 Pawnee C	25-4757	CS-AIU	22. 5.75	T.J.Price Rhigos t/a Vale of Neath Gliding Club		21. 4.02
G-BDDT	PA-25-235 Pawnee C	25-5324	CS-AIX N8820L	22. 5.75	W.J.& A.E.Taylor Wyberton t/a Pawneee Aviation		8. 7.99A
G-BDDX*	Whittaker MW.2B Excalibur (VW 1500)	001 & PFA/41-10106		28. 5.75	Flambards Village Theme Park Helston		
G-BDDZ	Menavia Piel CP.301A Emeraude	253	F-BIMZ	30. 5.75	V.W.Smith & E.C.Mort (Warrington) (Damaged Cranwell North 3.6.84; on rebuild)		20. 6.84P
G-BDEC	Socata Rallye 100ST	2552	F-OCZS	28. 5.75	M.Mulhall (Kilkenny, Ireland)		27. 2.00
G-BDEF	PA-34-200T Seneca II	34-7570150	N33695	2. 6.75	L.R.Chiswell Alderney		24. 5.02T
G-BDEH	Jodel Wassmer D.120A Paris-Nice	239	F-BLNE	2. 6.75	E.R.O'Hara Oaksey Park t/a EH Flying Group		28. 6.02P
G-BDEI	Jodel D.9 Bebe (VW1600)	585 & PFA/936		2. 6.75	R.Q.T.Newns White Waltham t/a The Noddy Group "Noddy"		22. 9.00P
G-BDET	DHC.1 Chipmunk 22	C1/0736	(PH-RTH) G-BDET/WP851	17. 6.75	C.Zoeteman Lelystad, The Netherlands (Op Pionier Hangaar Collection) (As "WP851 in RAF c/s)		13. 4.00
G-BDEU	DHC.1 Chipmunk 22	C1/0704	WP808	17. 6.75	A.Taylor Manor Farm, Binham (As "WP808")		28. 1.02
G-BDEX	Reims Cessna FRA.150M Aerobat	0279		12. 6.75	Griffin Marston Ltd Compton Abbas (Op Abbas Air)		30.10.99T
G-BDEY	Piper J3C-65 Cub (L-4J-PI) (Frame No.12366)	12538	OO-AAT OO-GAC/44-80242	17. 6.75	W.J. & Mrs.J.Morecraft t/a Ducksworth Flying Club Highfield Farm, Empingham		13.12.00P
G-BDEZ	Piper J3C-65 Cub (L-4J-PI) (Frame No.12211)	12383	OO-SOC OO-EPI/44-80087	17. 6.75	R.J.M.Turnbull Rydinghurst Farm, Cranleigh		25. 5.00P
G-BDFB	Phoenix Currie Wot (Walter Mikron III)	PFA/3008		20. 6.75	J.Jennings Fenland		9. 6.00P
G-BDFC	Rockwell Commander 112A	273	N1273J	17. 6.75	R.Fletcher Halfpenny Green		25. 9.97
G-BDFG	Cameron O-65 HAFB	179		24. 6.75	N.A.Robertson Combe Hay Manor, Bath "Golly II"		16. 4.88A
G-BDFH	Auster AOP.9 (Frame No.AUS 177 FM)	B5/10/176	XR240	24. 6.75	R.O.Holden Booker (As "XR240")		2. 6.99P
G-BDFJ	Reims Cessna F.150M	1182		25. 6.75	Cassandra J.Hopewell (Huntingdon)		13. 7.02T
G-BDFR	Fuji FA.200-160 Aero Subaru	FA200-262		7. 7.75	A.G.Brindle & A.Houghton Blackpool t/a G-BDFR Group		18. 8.01
G-BDFS	Fuji FA.200-160 Aero Subaru	FA200-263		7. 7.75	B.Lawrence Goodwood		24. 9.00T
G-BDFU*	Dragonfly MPA Mk.1	01		14. 7.75	R.J.Hardy & R.Churcher East Fortune (On loan to Museum of Flight/Royal Museum of Scotland)		
G-BDFW	Rockwell Commander 112A	308	N1308J	18. 6.75	M.E.& E.G.Reynolds Blackbushe		3. 9.01T
G-BDFX	Taylorcraft J Auster 5	2060	F-BGXG TW517	9. 7.75	J.Eagles Kemble (Damaged Oaksey Park 10.10.93; on rebuild 9.99)		3. 6.94T
G-BDFY	Grumman-American AA-5 Traveler	AA5-0806		10. 7.75	R.L.Bagnall & J.Wishart Edinburgh t/a Grumman Group (Op Edinburgh Flying Club)		5. 3.00
G-BDFZ	Reims Cessna F.150M	1184	(D-EIWB) (F-BXIH)	14. 7.75	L.W.Scattergood Sherburn in Elmet		28. 4.00T
G-BDGB	Barritault JB-01 Minicab (Continental PC-60)	PFA/1819		23. 6.75	D.G.Burden Armshold Farm, Kingston, Cambs		23. 8.99P
G-BDGH	Thunder Ax7-77 HAFB	049		16. 7.75	R.J.Mitchener & P.F.Smart Andover t/a Balloon Collection "London Pride III"		NE(A)
G-BDGM	PA-28-151 Cherokee Warrior	28-7415165	N41307	30. 7.75	B.Whiting Blackpool (Op Comed Aviation)		26. 5.00T
G-BDGO	Thunder Ax7-77 HAFB	048		16. 7.75	Justerini & Brooks Ltd "J & B" Latimer		2. 2.82A

Regn	Type	C/n	P/I	Date	Owner/operator	Probable Base	CA Expy
G-BDGP	Cameron V-65 HAFB	658	(N.....)	2. 9.80	A.Mayes & V.Lawton	Leamington Spa	17.11.96A
			G-BDGP		t/a Warwick Balloons "Ladbroke Motor Group"		
G-BDGY	PA-28-140 Cherokee	28-23613	N3536K	5. 8.75	S.J.Willcox	Bristol	2. 9.02T
G-BDHJ	Pazmany PL-1 Laminar	PFA/3604		5. 8.75	L.J.Greenhough	Bodmin	5.11.97P
	(Franklin Sport 4B)				(Wings only 7.98)		
G-BDHK	Piper J3C-65 Cub (L-4A-PI)	8969	F-PHFZ	24. 7.75	A.Liddiard	Eastbach Farm, Coleford	23. 8.00P
	(Frame No.9068)		42-38400		(As "329417" in USAAC c/s)		
	(Official c/n quoted as "261" with p/i 42-36414 but this corresponds to c/n 8538/N75366)						
G-BDIE	Rockwell Commander 112A	342	N1342J	14. 8.75	R.J.Adams	RAF Brize Norton	13. 5.01
G-BDIG	Cessna 182P Skylane II	182-63938	N9877E	26. 8.75	P.B.Barrett & P.Brause	Gamston	13. 7.02
	(Reims-assembled with c/n 0020)				t/a Air Group 6		
G-BDIH	SAN Jodel D.117	812	F-BIOT	22. 8.75	N.D.H.Stokes	(Bath)	4. 7.85P
	(Regd with incorrect c/n 817)				(Damaged Rydinghurst Farm, Cranleigh 9.12.84; on rebuild)		
G-BDIJ	Sikorsky S-61N Mk.II	61-751	9M-AYF	3.10.75	Bristow Helicopters Ltd	Lee-on-Solent	31. 5.01T
	(SAR conversion)		G-BDIJ		(Op for HM Coastguard) "Crathes"		
G-BDIW*	DH.106 Comet 4C	6470	XR398	1. 9.75	Flugausstellung L & P Junior Museum		
						Hermeskeil, Germany	8. 6.81T
G-BDIX*	DH.106 Comet 4C	6471	XR399	1. 9.75	Royal Museum of Scotland, Museum of Flight		
					(Dan-Air c/s)	East Fortune	11.10.81T
G-BDJB*	Taylor JT.1 Monoplane Srs.2			2. 9.75	J.F.Barber	Benfleet	19. 1.79S
	JB.JT.1 001 & PFA/1428						
	(Last known on rebuild with VW1835 engine after accident at Andrewsfield 25.5.78: cancelled by CAA 2.3.99)						
G-BDJC	AJEP/Wittman W.8 Tailwind			29. 8.75	J.H.Medforth		
	(Continental O-200-A) 387AW & PFA/3508				Willy Howe Farm, Wold Newton, Driffield		13. 6.00P
G-BDJD	Jodel D.112	PFA/910		3. 9.75	J.E.Preston	(Hull)	9.11.00P
	(Continental A65)				"Marianne"		
G-BDJF	Bensen B.8MV	RPW.1 & PFA G/01-1075		4. 9.75	R.P.White	(Haslemere)	
G-BDJG	Phoenix Luton LA-4A Minor	PFA/828		3. 9.75	S.C.Barry	White Waltham	26. 5.00P
	(VW1835)				t/a Very Slow Flying Club		
G-BDJN	Robin HR.200/100 Club	76		22. 9.75	E.C.Huggett	(Wokingham)	29. 4.01
G-BDJP	Piper J3C-90 Cub	22992	OO-SKZ	11.12.75	Holdcroft Aviation Services Ltd		
	(Frame No.21017)		PH-NCV/NC3908K			Hinton-in-The-Hedges	19.11.99T
G-BDJR	SNCAN NC.858S	2	F-BFIY	30. 9.75	R.F.M.Marson & P.M.Harmer (On rebuild 10.97)		
						(Farnborough, Hants)	23. 5.92P
G-BDKB*	Socata Rallye 150ST	2631		30. 9.75	N.C.Anderson		
						West Galdenoch Farm, Stranraer	4. 6.82
	(Last known on rebuild 6.90 after accident at Coleraine, NI 5.7.81: cancelled by CAA 18.2.99)						
G-BDKC	Cessna A185F Skywagon	185-02569	N1854R	30. 9.75	Bridge of Tilt Co Ltd	Blair Atholl	23. 4.01
G-BDKD	Enstrom F-28A	319		30. 9.75	Normans (Burton-on-Trent) Ltd		
						Burton-on-Trent	16.12.01
G-BDKH	Menavia Piel CP.301A Emeraude	241	F-BIMN	15.10.75	P.N.Marshall	Insch	30. 9.98P
G-BDKJ	K & S SA.102.5 Cavalier			14.10.75	D.A.Garner	(Swansea)	5. 6.95P
	(Continental O-240-A) 72207 & PFA/1589				(Damaged Gloucestershire 14.9.97)		
G-BDKM	SIPA 903	98	F-BGHX	17.11.75	S.W.Markham	Valentine Farm, Odiham	17. 6.00P
G-BDKU	Taylor JT.1 Monoplane	PFA/1456		22.10.75	B.N.Stevens & A.J.L.Eves.		
	(VW1500) (Possibly incorporates PFA/55-10301)					St Mary's, Scilly Isles	22. 2.00P
G-BDKW	Rockwell Commander 112	106	N1277J	3.11.75	R.W.Denny	Poplar Hall Farm, Elmsett	15. 7.00T
			ZS-MIB/N1106J				
G-BDLO	Grumman-American AA-5A Cheetah		N6154A	3.11.75	S. & J.Dolan	Elstree	25. 6.01T
		AA5A-0026					
G-BDLR	Grumman-American AA-5B Tiger			3.11.75	Magec Aviation Ltd	Luton	22. 7.01T
		AA5B-0128					
	(Caught by strong crosswind landing Luton 18.9.99 & collided with parked Short SD.3-30, G-SSWU.						
	The AA-5B was destroyed and removed to AAIB Farnborough)						
G-BDLS	Grumman-American AA-1B Tr.2		N6153A	3.11.75	A.L.Hall-Carpenter	Brimpton	28.10.01
		AA1B-0564					
G-BDLT	Rockwell Commander 112A	363	N1363J	4.11.75	D.L.Churchward	Exeter	18. 5.02
G-BDLY	K & S SA.102.5 Cavalier			14.11.75	P.R.Stevens	Thruxton	27. 7.99P
	(Lycoming O-290)	PFA/01-10011					
G-BDMM*	Jodel D.11	PFA/901		5.11.75	P.N.Marshall	Aboyne	
					(Stored unfinished 6.98)		
G-BDMO	Thunder Ax7-77	053	(EC-)	25.11.75	Balloon Preservation Group	Lancing	
			G-BDMO		"Flash Harry" (Noted 12.98)		
G-BDMS	Piper J3C-65 Cub (L-4J-PI)	13049	F-BEGZ	4.11.75	A.T.H.Martin	Old Sarum	10. 5.00P
			44-80753		(As "FR886" in RAF c/s)		
G-BDMW	SAN Jodel DR.100A Ambassadeur	79	F-BIVM	2.12.75	R.O.F.Harper	Yew Tree Farm, Lymm Dam	12. 8.02
					t/a G-BDMW Flying Group		
G-BDNC	Taylor JT.1 Monoplane	PFA/1454		8.12.75	A.W.Wright & P.Gaskell	Barton	25. 2.00P
	(Walter Mikron III)						
G-BDNG	Taylor JT.1 Monoplane	PFA/1405		12.12.75	S.B.Churchill	Eastbach Farm, Coleford	31. 3.00P
	(VW 1834)				"The Red Sparrow"		

Regn	Type	C/n	P/I	Date	Owner/operator	Probable Base	CA Expy
G-BDNO	Taylor JT.1 Monoplane (VW1600)	PFA/1431		15.12.75	S.D.Glover	(Gunnislake)	2. 5.96P
G-BDNR*	Reims Cessna FRA.150M Aerobat	0284		18.12.75	Busy Bee Aviation Ltd (Damaged Liverpool 22.1.92; stored 9.99)	Sibson	26. 7.92T
G-BDNT	Jodel D.92 (VW1600)	397	F-PINL	2. 1.76	R.F.Morton	Manor Farm, Inglesham	7. 7.99P
G-BDNU	Reims Cessna F.172M Skyhawk II	1405		2. 1.76	J. & K.G.McVicar	Elstree	31. 3.00T
G-BDNW	Grumman-American AA-1B Trainer	AA1B-0588		8. 1.76	P.Mitchell	Humberside	5. 3.00
G-BDNX	Grumman-American AA-1B Trainer	AA1B-0590		8. 1.76	R.M.North	Kimbolton	25. 5.01
G-BDNZ*	Cameron O-77 HAFB	203		8. 1.76	I.L.McHale "Winston Churchill"	Sutton, Surrey	28. 7.81A
G-BDOC	Sikorsky S-61N Mk.II (SAR conversion)	61-765		20. 3.76	Bristow Helicopters Ltd "Tolquhoun"	Sumburgh	28.12.01T
G-BDOD	Reims Cessna F.150M Commuter	1266		20. 1.76	D.M.Moreau	(Wickham)	2. 7.00
G-BDOE	Reims Cessna FR.172J Rocket	0559		20. 1.76	D. & P.A.Sansome	Little Chase Farm, Honiley	9.10.99
G-BDOG	Scottish Avn Bulldog Srs.200	200/381		18.12.75	D.C.Bonsall (Phoenix Flying Group c/s)	Netherthorpe	12. 5.00P
G-BDOL	Piper J3C-65 Cub (L-4J-PI)	13186	F-BCPC 45-4446	18.12.75	L.R.Balthazor	Lee-on-Solent	23.11.00P
	(Frame No.13016 - see comments for G-BCUB; officially has c/n 13370 but has genuine c/n and USAAC plates relating to c/n 13370/ex 45-4630)						
G-BDON	Thunder Ax7-77A HAFB	063		17.12.75	M.J.Smith "Fred"	York	24. 6.94A
G-BDOT	BN-2A mk.III-2 Trislander	1025	ZK-SFF N900TA/N903GD/N3850K/VH-BPB/G-BDOT (Op Sky Trek Airways)	21. 1.76	Atlantic Bridge Aviation Ltd	Lydd	3.12.00T
G-BDOW	Reims Cessna FRA.150M Aerobat	0296		26. 1.76	A.Brinkley (Euroair)	NK	26. 3.01T
G-BDPA	PA-28-151 Cherokee Warrior	28-7615033		26. 1.76	D.R.Allard t/a G-BDPA Flying Group	Gloucestershire	6.11.00
G-BDPJ	PA-25-235 Pawnee B	25-3665	PH-VBF SE-EPZ	2. 2.76	W.J.Taylor (On rebuild 1.00)	Oxford	AC
G-BDPK	Cameron O-56 HAFB	191		4. 2.76	N.H.Ponsford & A.M.Lindsay t/a Rango Balloon & Kite Co	Leeds	29.12.88A
G-BDRD	Reims Cessna FRA.150M Aerobat	0289		9. 2.76	I.P.Diment	Edinburgh	6. 5.00T
G-BDRG	Taylor JT.2 Titch	PFA/60-10295		19.12.78	D.R.Gray	(Wilmslow)	
G-BDRJ	DHC.1 Chipmunk 22	C1/0742	WP857	19. 2.76	J.C.Schooling (As "WP857/24")	Elstree	4. 7.02
G-BDRK	Cameron O-65 HAFB	205		12. 2.76	D.L.Smith "Smirk"	Eling Hill, Newbury	20. 6.86A
G-BDRL	Stits SA-3A Playboy (Continental C85)	P-689	N730GF	12. 2.76	O.C.Bradley	Mullaghmore	17. 6.98P
G-BDSA	Clutton Fred Srs.II (VW 1600)	LAS.1803 & PFA/29-10141	EI-BFS G-BDSA	23. 2.76	W.D.M.Turtle	(Ballymena)	5. 7.79P
G-BDSB	PA-28-181 Cherokee Archer II	28-7690107	N8221C	23. 2.76	Testfair Ltd	Fairoaks	20. 7.01
G-BDSE	Cameron O-77 HAFB	210		27. 2.76	British Airways plc "Concorde"	Worplesdon	31. 3.90A
G-BDSF	Cameron O-56 HAFB	209		1. 3.76	J.H.Greensides "Itzuma"	Hull	24. 5.93A
G-BDSH	PA-28-140 Cherokee Cruiser	28-7625063		1. 3.76	D.Jones t/a The Wright Brothers Flying Group	Nottingham	26. 8.02
G-BDSK	Cameron O-65 HAFB	166		3. 3.76	Semajan Ltd t/a Southern Balloon Group "Carousel II"	Romsey	3. 7.00A
G-BDSL	Reims Cessna F.150M Commuter	1306		5. 3.76	D.C.Bonsall	Gamston	24. 6.01T
G-BDSM	Slingsby T.31 Motor Cadet III			5. 3.76	N.F.James	Husbands Bosworth	22. 7.98P
G-BDSO*	Cameron O-31 HAFB	207		10. 3.76	Not known "Baby Budget"	Bristol	24. 6.81A
G-BDTB	Evans VP-1 Srs.2 (VW1834)	PFA/7009		15. 3.76	T.F.Crossman	(Loddon, Norwich)	26.11.96P
G-BDTL	Evans VP-1 (VW1600)	PFA/7012		17. 3.76	A.K.Lang (Stoke-sub-Hamdon, Somerset) (Stored 5.98)		5. 9.85P
G-BDTN	BN-2A Mk III-2 Trislander	1026	S7-AAN VQ-SAN/G-BDTN	16. 3.76	Aurigny Air Services Ltd (Stored 1.99)	Guernsey	10. 6.98T
G-BDTO	BN-2A Mk.III-2 Trislander	1027	G-RBSI G-OTSB/G-BDTO/8P-ASC/G-BDTO/(C-GYOX)/G-BDTO "Nessie" (Mercury Asset Management c/s)	16. 3.76	Aurigny Air Services Ltd	Guernsey	31. 3.02T
G-BDTT*	Bede BD-5	3795 & PFA/14-10084		17. 3.76	Martini's Night-Club	Barrow-in-Furness	
G-BDTU	Van Den Bemden Omega III (Gas) Free Balloon (20,000 cu.ft)	VDB-35 & AFB.4		16. 3.76	R.G.Turnbull "Omega III"	Clyro, Hereford	4. 8.99A
G-BDTV	Mooney M.20F Executive	22-1307	N6934V	16. 3.76	S.Redfearn	Gamston	21. 4.00
G-BDTW	Cassutt Racer IIIM (Continental C90)	PFA/34-10102		18. 3.76	R.Mohlenkamp "The Thunder Box"	Damme, Germany	1.11.99P

Regn	Type	C/n	P/I	Date	Owner/operator	Probable Base	CA Expy
G-BDTX	Reims Cessna F.150M Commuter	1275		19. 3.76	S.L.Lefley & F.W.Ellis Water Leisure Park, Skegness		6. 4.00T
G-BDUI	Cameron V-56 HAFB	218		19. 3.76	D.C.Johnson "True Brit"	Farnham	6. 7.91A
G-BDUL	Evans VP-1 (VW1834)	PFA/1557		25. 3.76	C.K.Brown	(Helston)	25. 3.00P
G-BDUM	Reims Cessna F.150M Commuter	1301	F-BXZB	29. 3.76	Techair Aviation Ltd	Norwich	16. 1.97T
G-BDUN	PA-34-200T Seneca II	34-7570163	(EI-BLR) G-BDUN/SE-GIA	29. 3.76	Air Medical Ltd	Oxford	27. 2.01T
G-BDUO	Reims Cessna F.150M Commuter	1304		29. 3.76	C.B.Mellor t/a BM Aviation	(Winchester)	8. 2.01T
G-BDUY	Robin DR.400/140B Major	1120		5. 4.76	J.G.Anderson	Gamston	20. 1.00
G-BDUZ	Cameron V-56 HAFB	213		30. 3.76	P.J.Bish t/a Zebedee Balloon Service "Hot Lips"	Hungerford	19. 2.00A
G-BDVA	PA-17 Vagabond (Continental C90)	17-206	CN-TVY F-BFFE	23. 4.76	I.M.Callier	Liss	24. 7.00P
G-BDVB	PA-15 Vagabond (Continental C90)	15-229	F-BHHE SL-AAY/F-BETG	23. 4.76	B.P.Gardner Whittles Farm, Mapledurham		5. 6.00P
G-BDVC	PA-17 Vagabond (Continental C90)	17-140	F-BFBL	29. 9.76	A.R.Caveen Sandford Hall, Knockin		13. 8.98P
G-BDVG*	Thunder Ax6-56A HAFB	067		2. 4.76	D.Body "Argonaut"	Not Known	NE(A)
G-BDVU	Mooney M.20F Executive	22-1380		23. 4.76	D.H.G.Penney	Biggin Hill	22. 7.01
G-BDWA	Socata Rallye 150ST	2695		20. 4.76	J.T.Wilson Bann Foot, Lough Neagh (Stored 6.97)		7. 6.01
G-BDWE	Flaglor Sky Scooter (VW1600) KF-S-66 & DWE-01 & PFA/1332			12. 4.76	B.A.Schlussler Blackspring Farm t/a Flagor Fliers		8. 4.00P
G-BDWH	Socata Rallye 150ST	2697		20. 4.76	M.A.Jones Upper Harford Farm, Bourton-on-the-Water		29. 6.01
G-BDWJ	Replica Plans SE-5A PFA/20-10034 (Continental C90)		"C1904" "F8010"	27. 4.76	D.W.Linney (Langport) (As "F8010/Z" in RFC c/s)		18.11.00P
G-BDWL	PA-25-235 Pawnee B	25-3575	PH-IPO N7531Z	4. 5.76	R.Sharman Crowland t/a Peterborough & Spalding Gliding Club		31. 7.00
G-BDWM	Bonsall DB-1 Mustang PFA/73-10200 (Lycoming IO-360)			3. 5.76	D.C.Bonsall Netherthorpe (As "FB226/MT-A" in RAF c/s)		15. 6.98P
G-BDWO	Howes Ax6 HAFB RBH.2 (Complete and extant 11.88 but never certified)			5. 5.76	R.B. & Mrs C.Howes Keysoe, Bedford "Griffin"		
G-BDWP	PA-32R-300 Cherokee Lance	32R-7680176	N8784E	7. 5.76	W.M.Brown & B.J.Wood	Coventry	12.10.00
G-BDWV	BN-2A Mk.III-2 Trislander	1035	8P-ASF G-BDWV	11. 5.76	Aurigny Air Services Ltd	Guernsey	15. 4.02T
G-BDWX	Jodel Wassmer D.120A Paris-Nice	311	F-BNHT	13. 5.76	R.P.Rochester	Wombleton	6.10.98P
G-BDWY	PA-28-140 Cherokee E	28-7225378	PH-NSC	14. 5.76	Comed Aviation Ltd	Blackpool	27. 2.00
G-BDXA	Boeing 747-236B	21238	N1790B	18. 3.77	British Airways plc	Heathrow	26. 7.02T
G-BDXB	Boeing 747-236B	21239	N8280V	13. 1.77	British Airways plc (Nigerian Airways c/s)	Heathrow	15. 6.92T
G-BDXC	Boeing 747-236B	21240		18. 3.77	British Airways plc	Heathrow	21. 6.02T
G-BDXE	Boeing 747-236B	21350		23. 2.78	British Airways plc	Gatwick	4. 4.00T
G-BDXF	Boeing 747-236B	21351		23. 3.78	British Airways plc	Gatwick	30. 4.00T
G-BDXG	Boeing 747-236B	21536		16. 6.78	British Airways plc (Blomsterang t/s)	Gatwick	30. 6.00T
G-BDXH	Boeing 747-236B	21635		23. 2.79	British Airways plc	Gatwick	2. 5.01T
G-BDXI	Boeing 747-236B	21830		21. 2.80	British Airways plc	Heathrow	13. 3.01T
G-BDXJ	Boeing 747-236B	21831	N1792B	2. 5.80	British Airways plc	Heathrow	7. 5.01T
G-BDXK	Boeing 747-236B	22303		29. 4.83	British Airways plc (Chelsea Rose t/s)	Gatwick	13. 6.00T
G-BDXL	Boeing 747-236B	22305	N8280V	9. 1.84	British Airways plc	Gatwick	18. 3.01T
G-BDXM	Boeing 747-236M	23711	N6055X	25. 2.87	British Airways plc	Heathrow	27. 3.00T
G-BDXN	Boeing 747-236M	23735	N6046P	17. 3.87	British Airways plc	Heathrow	12. 4.00T
G-BDXO	Boeing 747-236B	23799	N6055X	22. 4.87	British Airways plc (Paithani t/s)	Heathrow	14. 5.00T
G-BDXP	Boeing 747-236M	24088	N6009F	24. 2.88	British Airways plc (Nigerian Airways c/s)	Heathrow	20. 3.01T
G-BDXX	SNCAN NC.858S	110	F-BEZQ	17. 5.76	M.Gaffney & K.Davis	(Waltham Cross)	3. 7.96P
G-BDYD	Rockwell Commander 114	14014	N1914J	21. 5.76	L.A. & A.A.Buckley	Chester	3. 8.00
G-BDYF	Cessna 421C Golden Eagle II	421C-0055	N98468	24. 5.76	Widehawk Aviation t/a Hawkair	Cambridge	24. 6.00T
G-BDYG*	Percival P.56 Provost T.1 PAC/F/056		7696M WV493	25. 5.76	Royal Museum of Scotland/Museum of Flight (As "WV493/29/A-P")	East Fortune	28.11.80P
G-BDYH	Cameron V-56 HAFB	233		24. 5.76	B.J.Godding "Novocastrian"	Didcot	25.11.90A
G-BDYM*	Skysales S-31 HAFB	1		27. 5.76	Not known "Cheeky Devil"	Bristol	NE(A)
G-BDZA	Scheibe SF-25E Super Falke	4320	(D-KECW)	1. 6.76	Norfolk Gliding Club Ltd	Tibenham	21. 9.01
G-BDZC	Reims Cessna F.150M Commuter	1316		1. 6.76	A.M.Lynn	Norwich	21. 7.02T

Regn	Type	C/n	P/I	Date	Owner/operator	Probable Base	CA Expy
G-BDZD	Reims Cessna F.172M Skyhawk II	1478		1. 6.76	Northamptonshire School of Flying Ltd		
						Sywell	11. 9.00T
G-BDZU	Cessna 421C Golden Eagle II		N98791	14. 6.76	R.Richardson	East Midlands	28. 3.00T
		421C-0094			t/a Eagle Flying Group		
G-BDZY*	Phoenix Luton LA-4A Minor	PFA/842		15. 6.76	P.J.Dalby	(Ventnor, IoW)	
	(Under construction 11.92: not completed & no permit issued: cancelled as WFU 26.2.99)						

G-BEAA – G-BEZZ

Regn	Type	C/n	P/I	Date	Owner/operator	Probable Base	CA Expy
G-BEAB	CEA Jodel DR.1051 Sicile	228	F-BKGH	18. 8.76	R.C.Hibberd Draycott Farm, Chiseldon		10.12.99
G-BEAC	PA-28-140 Cherokee	28-21963	4X-AND	4. 6.76	C.E.Stringer	Elstree	18. 5.00T
					t/a Clipwing Flying Group		
G-BEAD*	Westland WG.13 Lynx	WA.00.001	XW835	15. 6.76	Army Air Corps, 9 Regiment RAF Dishforth		
					(Stored 8.93)		
G-BEAG	PA-34-200T Seneca II	34-7670204	N9395K	18. 6.76	Oxford Aviation Services Ltd	Oxford	22.10.00T
G-BEAH	Auster 5 J/2 Arrow	2366	F-BFUV	28. 6.76	J.G.Parish t/a Bedwell Hey Flying Group		
	(Continental C85)		F-BFVV/OO-ABS		Bedwell Hey Farm, Little Thetford, Ely		13.12.99P
G-BEBC*	Westland WS-55 Whirlwind HAR.10	8463M	25. 6.76	City of Norwich Aviation Museum Norwich			
	(Line No. WAJ/30)	WA/371	XP355		(As "XP355/A")		
G-BEBE	Grumman-American AA-5A Cheetah			28. 6.76	Bills Aviation Ltd	Biggin Hill	26.10.02T
		AA5A-0154					
G-BEBG	WSK-PZL SZD-45A Ogar	B-655		29. 6.76	D.W.Coultrip Hinton-in-The-Hedges		23. 9.02
					t/a The Ogar Syndicate		
G-BEBI	Reims Cessna F.172M Skyhawk II	1461		28. 6.76	R.G.A.Willoughby	Elstree	22.12.99T
					t/a Hatfield Flying Club (Damaged Elstree 8.4.99)		
G-BEBL	McDonnell Douglas DC-10-30	46949	N54643	31. 1.77	British Airways plc		13. 4.01T
	(With FLS, Manchester 9.99 awaiting delivery to Aeronavali for cargo conversion).						
G-BEBN	Cessna 177B Cardinal	177-01631	4X-CEW	1. 7.76	A.J.Franchi & D.J.French	Earls Colne	6.12.96
			N34031				
G-BEBO	Turner Special TSW.2	PFA/46-10127		30. 6.76	E.Newsham & P.Moffatt	Breighton	19. 3.99P
	(Lycoming O-290)				t/a The Turner Special Flying Group		
G-BEBS	Andreasson BA-4B HA/01 & PFA/38-10157			7. 7.76	N.J.W.Reid	Lee-on-Solent	4. 5.00P
	(Continental O-200-A)						
G-BEBT	Andreasson BA-4B HA/02 & PFA/38-10158			7. 7.76	A.Horsfall	Breighton	10. 9.97P
	(Lycoming O-235)						
G-BEBU	Rockwell Commander 112A	272	N1272J	8. 7.76	R.Hodgkinson	Cardiff	11.11.00
G-BEBZ	PA-28-151 Cherokee Warrior		N6193J	14. 7.76	Goodwood Road Racing Co Ltd	Goodwood	2. 4.00T
		28-7615328					
G-BECA	Socata Rallye 100ST	2751		14. 7.76	M.A.Neale & P.A.Brain		
					t/a Bredon Flying Group Croft Farm, Defford		30. 6.00
G-BECB	Socata Rallye 100ST	2783		14. 7.76	A.J.Trible Henscott Farm, Holsworthy		12. 2.01
G-BECC	Socata Rallye 150ST	2748		14. 7.76	D.T.Price	Cardiff	15. 5.00
G-BECE*	Aerospace Developments	1214/1		14. 7.76	Friends of Cardington Airship Station		
	AD500 Airship					Cardington	1. 4.79P
	(Damaged Cardington 9.3.79: parts stored for future museum 9.94)						
G-BECF	Scheibe SF-25A Motorfalke	4555	OO-WIZ	14. 7.76	North County Ltd	(Middleton)	1.3.94P*
			(D-KARA)				
G-BECK	Cameron V-56 HAFB	136		27. 7.76	H. & D.J.Farrar	Seacroft, Leeds	21. 2.00A
					"Joyride"		
G-BECN	Piper J3C-65 Cub (L-4J-PI)	12776	F-BCPS	27. 7.76	R.C.Partridge & M.Oliver		
			44-80480		Sampsons Hall, Kersey, Suffolk		30. 8.02
	(As "80480/44/E" in US Army c/s)						
G-BECT	CASA I-131E Jungmann	"3974"	E3B-338	3. 8.76	G.M.S.Scott t (London SW18)		14. 1.00P
					t/a Alpha 57 Group (As "A-57" in Swiss AF c/s)		
G-BECW	CASA I-131E Jungmann	2037	E3B-423	3. 8.76	R.G.Meredith	Headcorn	21. 9.00P
	(Incorporating parts of G-BECY ex E3B-459)				(As "A-10" in Swiss AF c/s)		
G-BECZ	Mudry/CAARP CAP.10B	68	F-BXHK	26. 7.76	Avia Special Ltd	White Waltham	17. 3.01T
G-BEDA	CASA I-131E Jungmann	2099	E3B-504	3. 8.76	M.G.Kates & D.J.Berry t/a DA Group		
					Sheffield Park, Haywards Heath		2. 4.00P
G-BEDB*	SNCAN 1203 Norecrin II	117	F-BEOB	5. 8.76	J.E.Pierce	Ley Farm, Chirk	11. 6.80PF
					(On rebuild 3.98)		
G-BEDD	SAN Jodel D.117A	915	F-BITY	3. 8.76	P.B.Duhig	(Chippenham)	29. 9.00P
G-BEDF	Boeing B-17G-105-VE Flying Fortress	N17TE	5. 8.76	B-17 Preservation Ltd	Duxford	5. 5.99P	
		8693	F-BGSR/44-85784 (As "124485/DF-A" in USAAC c/s) "Sally B/Memphis Belle"				
G-BEDG	Rockwell Commander 112A	482	N1219J	5. 8.76	P.J.Lawton	Blackbushe	13. 2.02
G-BEDJ	Piper J3C-65 Cub (L-4J-PI)	12890	F-BDTC	5. 8.76	R.Earl	White Waltham	8.10.96P
	(Frame No.12720)		44-80594		(As "44-805942 in USAAC c/s)		
G-BEDK*	Hiller UH-12E	2300	XS706	5. 8.76	Alpha Aerotech Ltd	Chilbolton	14. 6.85T
	(Pod in open store 1.96: cancelled by CAA 6.3.99)						

Regn	Type	C/n	P/I	Date	Owner/operator	Probable Base	CA Expy
G-BEDP	BN-2A mk.III-2 Trislander	1039	ZK-SFG	17. 8.76	Atlantic Bridge Aviation Ltd	Lydd	12.10.00T
			N902TA/N1FY/N401JA/G-BEDP (Op Sky Trek Airways)				
G-BEDV*	V.668 Varsity T.1	-	WJ945	26. 7.76	Duxford Aviation Society	Duxford	15.10.87P
					(As "WJ945/21")		
G-BEEE*	Thunder Ax6-56A HAFB	070		20. 8.76	British Balloon Museum & Library	Newbury	11. 5.84A
					"Avia"		
G-BEEG	BN-2A-26 Islander	550	(C-GYUH)	25. 8.76	North West Parachute Centre Ltd	Cark	30. 3.01T
			G-BEEG				
G-BEEH	Cameron V-56 HAFB	250		24. 8.76	Sade Balloons Ltd	Coulsdon, Surrey	28. 5.00A
					"Tywi"		
G-BEEP	Thunder Ax5-42 HAFB	086		20. 8.76	Mrs B.C.Faithfull "Also Kenneth"		
						Wagenberg, The Netherlands	11.5.84A
G-BEER	Isaacs Fury II	PFA/1588		31. 8.76	N.Davis	Headcorn	5. 5.00
	(Lycoming O-235)				(As "K2075" in RAF c/s)		
G-BEEU	PA-28-140 Cherokee F	28-7325247	PH-NSE	9. 9.76	J.Maffia & H.Merkado	Panshanger	28. 2.00
G-BEEV*	PA-28-140 Cherokee F	28-7325229	PH-NSG	29. 9.76	Not known	Panshanger	28. 3.93
					(Damaged Rayne 16.4.91; stored 5.97)		
G-BEEW	Taylor JT.1 Monoplane	PFA/55-10189		3. 9.76	P.A.Boyden	(Godalming)	
	(VW1600) (Modified to resemble Boeing P-26A Peashooter)				(As "5" in 34th Pursuit Sqdn, US Army c/s)		
					(Damaged early 1989)		
G-BEFA	PA-28-151 Cherokee Warrior		N6978J	8. 9.76	M.A.Verran	(Wallingford)	31. 3.00
		28-7615416			t/a Verran Freight		
G-BEFF	PA-28-140 Cherokee F	28-7325228	PH-NSF	27. 9.76	H.Howard	Panshanger	19. 5.00
			N33696				
G-BEFO	BN-2A mk.III-2 Trislander	1041	5H-AZP	27. 9.76	Keen Leasing Ltd	Aldergrove	28.11.02T
			G-BEFO/G-SARN/F-BYCJ/V2-LMB/VP-LMB/G-BEFO (Op Woodgate Executive Air Services)				
G-BEFV*	Evans VP-2 V2-2390, YA-3 & PFA/63-10203			5.10.76	Not known	Mickleton, Long Marston	
	(Continental A65)				(Stored incomplete 8.93)		
G-BEGA	Westland-Bell 47G-3B1	WA/705	XW185	19.10.76	Reel-Time Entertainments Ltd	Bracknell	23. 7.01
	(Regd with Line No. WAT/227)						
G-BEGG	Scheibe SF-25E Super Falke	4326	(D-KDFB)	15.10.76	R.Culley & A.Collett		
					t/a G-BEGG Flying Group	Hall Farm, Turweston	29. 4.00
G-BEHH	PA-32R-300 Cherokee Lance		N6172J	29.10.76	SMK Engineers Ltd	Sherburn in Elmet	7. 8.00
		32R-7680323					
G-BEHJ*	Evans VP-1	PFA/1545		26.10.76	C.Bestwick (Stored 1992)	(Beeston)	
G-BEHM*	Taylor JT.1 Monoplane	PFA/1420		29.10.76	Not known	(Bedfordshire)	
	(VW1700) (Modified as Wildfire PDH.001; complete 1990 but C of A problems; on rebuild 11.95)						
G-BEHS	PA-25-260 Pawnee C	25-5207	OE-AFX	2.11.76	Southern Sailplanes Ltd	Membury	25. 6.93A
			N8755L		(On overhaul 2.95)		
G-BEHU	PA-34-200T Seneca II	34-7670265	N6175J	3.11.76	Pirin Aeronautical Ltd	Stapleford	4. 3.02T
G-BEHV	Reims Cessna F.172N Skyhawk II	1541		3.11.76	Fraggle Leasing Ltd	Edinburgh	13. 4.01T
					(Op Edinburgh Air Centre)		
G-BEHX	Evans VP-2 V2-2338 & PFA/7222			8.11.76	G.S.Adams "Ulster Flyer"	Coalisland	22. 1.90P
	(VW1834)				(Stored 6.97)		
G-BEIA	Reims Cessna FRA.150M Aerobat	0317		8.11.76	Rankart Ltd	Hinton-in-The-Hedges	27.10.00T
G-BEIC	Sikorsky S-61N mk.II	61-222	N307Y	28.12.76	Brintel Helicopters Ltd	Sumburgh	8. 2.00T
					t/a British International Helicopters		
G-BEIF	Cameron O-65 HAFB	259		17.11.76	R S Kent "Solitaire"	Lancing	25. 3.90A
					(Balloon Preservation Group 7.98)		
G-BEIG	Reims Cessna F.150M Commuter	1361		18.11.76	D.A.Hardiman	Shobdon	14. 1.02T
G-BEII	PA-25-235 Pawnee D	25-7656059	N54918	16.11.76	Burn Gliding Club Ltd	Burn	7. 4.99
G-BEIL	Socata Rallye 150T	2653	F-BXDL	1.12.76	J.I.Oakes & R.A.Harris t/a The Rallye Flying Group		
						Hill Farm, Nayland	6. 1.00
G-BEIP	PA-28-181 Cherokee Archer II		N6628F	22.11.76	S.W.& J.K.Stevens		
		28-7790158			Lower Wasing Farm, Brimpton	16. 8.01
G-BEIS	Evans VP-1	PFA/7029		25.11.76	P.J.Hunt	Thruxton	16. 7.90P
	(VW1600)				(Stored 2.99)		
G-BEJB	Thunder Ax6-56A HAFB	096		31.12.76	Justerini & Brooks Ltd	Latimer	21. 5.87A
	(Flies with second canopy; first one destroyed by fire at Latimer 4.9.77) "Baby J & B"						
G-BEJD	Avro 748 Srs.1/105	1543	LV-HHE	17.12.76	Emerald Airways Ltd	Liverpool	29. 3.00T
			LV-PUF		(Reed Aviation c/s) "Sisyphus"		
G-BEJK	Cameron S-31 HAFB	256		1.12.76	N.H.Ponsford & A.Lindsay	Leeds	16. 2.92A
					t/a Rango Balloon & Kite Co "L'Essence" (or "Esso")		
G-BEJL	Sikorsky S-61N mk.II	61-224	EI-BPK	30.12.76	Brintel Helicopters Ltd	Aberdeen	30. 9.98T
			G-BEJL/N4606G		t/a British International Helicopters		
G-BEJV	PA-34-200T Seneca II	34-7770062	N7657F	31.12.76	Oxford Aviation Services Ltd	Oxford	8. 6.00T
G-BEKL	Bede BD-4E-150	151 & BD4E/2	(G-AYKB)	11. 1.77	A.J.Harpley	(Hawes, N.Yorks)	14.10.80PF
	(Lycoming O-320)				(On rebuild Bladon-on-Tyne 5.93)		
G-BEKM	Evans VP-1	PFA/7025		12. 1.77	G.J.McDill	Park Farm, Eaton Bray	23. 3.95P
	(VW 1834)						

Regn	Type	C/n	P/I	Date	Owner/operator	Probable Base	CA Expy
G-BEKN	Reims Cessna FRA.150M Aerobat	0318		12. 1.77	RFC (Bourn) Ltd	Bourn	8.10.89T
	(Open store 4.99 w/o engines)						
G-BEKO	Reims Cessna F.182Q Skylane	0037		12. 1.77	G.J. & F.J.Leese	Sherburn in Elmet	11. 6.00
G-BEKR	Rand Robinson KR-2 EAA/102591 & PFA/129-11046			14. 1.77	A.N.Purchase (Status uncertain)		
	(VW1834)				(Woodlands Park, Maidenhead)		20. 8.88P
G-BELF	IRMA BN-2A-26 Islander	823	D-IBRA	13. 1.77	The Black Knights Parachute Centre Ltd		
			G-BELF			Cark	12. 3.01
G-BELP	PA-28-151 Cherokee Warrior	N9543N		18. 1.77	R.J.Doughton	Dunkeswell	2. 8.01T
		28-7715219					
G-BELT	Reims Cessna F.150J	0409X		26. 1.77	Yorkshire Light Acft Ltd	Leeds-Bradford	5. 2.01T
	(Mainly rebuild of G-AWUV and parts of G-ATND)						
G-BELX	Cameron V-56 HAFB	261		31. 1.77	V. & A.M.Dyer "Topsy Taffy"	Launceston	15. 8.93A
G-BEMB	Reims Cessna F.172M Skyhawk II	1487		27. 1.77	Stocklaunch Ltd	Goodwood	6. 4.01
G-BEMM	Slingsby Cadet III	1247	BGA942	27. 1.77	J.Beirne	Kilrush, Co.Kildare, Ireland	27.10.99P
	(VW1600) (Converted from T.31B)		RAFGSA 289/BGA942				
G-BEMU	Thunder Ax5-42 HAFB	097		9. 2.77	I.J.Liddiard	Newbury	16. 1.99A
					"Chrysophylax"		
G-BEMW	PA-28-181 Cherokee Archer II	N9566N		9. 2.77	Touch & Go Ltd	White Waltham	24. 5.00
		28-7790243					
G-BEMY	Reims Cessna FRA.150M Aerobat	0315		9. 2.77	Euroair Flying Club Ltd	Cranfield	4.11.01T
G-BEND	Cameron V-56 HAFB	260		14. 2.77	P.J.Bish	Hungerford	1. 1.94A
					t/a Dante Balloon Group "Le Billet"		
G-BENF*	Cessna T210L Turbo Centurion II		N732AE	17. 2.77	Not known	Cherry Tree Farm, Monewden	24. 5.82
		210-61356	D-EIPY/N732AE		(Crashed Ipswich 29.5.81; wreck in open storage 8.97)		
G-BENJ	Rockwell Commander 112B	522	N1391J	7. 3.77	E.J.Percival	Blackbushe	26. 7.00
G-BENK	Reims Cessna F.172M Skyhawk II	1509		2. 3.77	Graham Churchill Plant Ltd	Turweston	27. 5.00
G-BENL*	PA-25-235 Pawnee D	25-7656038	N54893	1. 3.77	W.J. & A.E.Taylor	RAF West Raynham	14.11.85
					(Crashed Sutton Bank 10.7.85; stored 2.96)		
G-BENN	Cameron V-56 HAFB	278		4. 3.77	S.H.Budd "English Rose"	Pewsey	15. 3.87A
G-BEOD*	Cessna 180	32092	OO-SPZ	14. 3.77	I.Addy	(Ivychurch, Kent)	6. 9.91
			D-EDAH/SL-AAT/N3294D		(Damaged Errol, Perthshire 29.6.89; stored 3.97)		
G-BEOE	Reims Cessna FRA.150M Aerobat	0322		21. 3.77	W.J.Henderson t/a Air Images	Carlisle	11. 7.00T
G-BEOH	PA-28R-201T Turbo Arrow III	N1905H		11. 3.77	J.J.Evendon	Blackbushe	6. 7.01
		28R-7703038			t/a G-BEOH Group		
G-BEOI	PA-18-180 Super Cub	18-7709028	N54976	11. 3.77	Southdown Gliding Club Ltd	Parham Park	2.11.01
					(On overhaul 10.97)		
G-BEOK	Reims Cessna F.150M Commuter	1366		14. 3.77	D.C.Bonsall	Netherthorpe	11. 5.00T
G-BEOX*	Lockheed 414 Hudson IIIA	414-6464	VH-AGJ	25. 3.77	RAF Museum	Hendon	
	(A-29A-LO)		VH-SMM/A16-199/FH174/41-36975		(As "A16-199/SF-R")		
G-BEOY	Reims Cessna FRA.150L Aerobat	0150	F-BTFS	30. 3.77	R.W.Denny	Crowfield	23. 2.02T
					(Op Crowfield Flying Club)		
G-BEOZ*	AW.650 Argosy 101	6660	N895U	28. 3.77	East Midlands Aeropark	East Midlands	28. 5.86T
			N6502R/G-1-7		(Elan c/s) "Fat Albert" (Noted 6.99)		
G-BEPC	SNCAN Stampe SV-4C	64	F-BFUM	17.10.77	Dawn Patrol Flight Training Ltd		
			F-BFZM/Fr.Mil			Dunkeswell	24. 3.01T
G-BEPF	SNCAN Stampe SV-4C	424	F-BCVD	30. 3.77	L.J.Rice (On rebuild 1.97)	Chilbolton	
G-BEPH	BN-2A Mk.III-2 Trislander	1052	S7-AAG	4. 4.77	Aurigny Air Services Ltd	Guernsey	14. 6.01T
			G-BEPH		(Steeple Finance c/s) "Jack"		
G-BEPI	BN-2A Mk.III-2 Trislander	1053		4. 4.77	Aurigny Air Services Ltd	Guernsey	18.12.02T
					(Hambros Bank c/s)		
G-BEPN*	PA-25-235 Pawnee D	25-7656022	N54877	7. 4.77	Not known	(Shobdon)	6. 4.79
					(Crashed nr Cirencester 11.2.78; frame in store 3.96)		
G-BEPS	Short SC.5 Belfast C.1	SH.1822	G-52-13	6. 4.77	Heavylift Aviation Holdings Ltd Stansted		31. 8.02T
			XR368		(Op Heavylift Cargo Airlines)		
G-BEPV	Fokker S.11.1 Instructor	6274	PH-ANK	13. 4.77	L.C.MacKnight	Elstree	15. 4.93P
			Dutch Navy 174/Dutch AF E-31		(Frame stored 4.95)		
G-BEPY	Rockwell Commander 112B	524	N1399J	20. 4.77	K.M.Coke t/a G-BEPY Group	Blackbushe	28. 6.01
G-BERA	Socata Rallye 150ST	2821	F-ODEX	13. 4.77	C.S.Randall	Earls Colne	26. 1.00T
G-BERC	Socata Rallye 150ST	2858		13. 4.77	R S Jones	Welshpool	14. 3.02
					t/a The Severn Valley Aero Group		
G-BERD	Thunder Ax6-56A HAFB	106		25. 4.77	P.M.Gaines	Stockton-on-Tees	15. 5.99A
					"Goldfinger"		
G-BERI	Rockwell Commander 114	14234	N4909W	6. 5.77	K.B.Harper	Blackbushe	12. 5.00
G-BERN	Saffery S.330 HAFB (Model)	4		19. 4.77	B.Martin "Beeze I"	Somersham, Cambs	
G-BERT	Cameron V-56 HAFB	273		19. 4.77	Semajan Ltd	Romsey	28. 8.00A
					t/a Southern Balloon Group "Bert"		
G-BERW	Rockwell Commander 114	14214	N4884W	6. 5.77	Malvern Holdings Ltd	Conington	5. 5.01
G-BERY	Grumman-American AA-1B Trainer	0193	N9693L	27.10.77	R.H.J.Levi	Stapleford	11. 5.01
G-BETD	Robin HR.200/100 Club	20	PH-SRL	28. 4.77	W.A.Stewart	(Dunoon)	18. 2.02
G-BETE	Rollason Beta B.2A	PFA/02-10169		26. 4.77	T.M.Jones	Egginton, Derby	
					(Incorporates parts from PFA/1304; under construction 8.99)		

Regn	Type	C/n	P/I	Date	Owner/operator	Probable Base	CA Expy
G-BETF*	Cameron Champion 35SS HAFB (Champion Spark Plug shape)	280		17. 5.77	British Balloon Museum "Champion"	Newbury	6. 4.84A
G-BETG	Cessna 180K Skywagon	180-52873	N64146	17. 5.77	A.J.Norman t/a Norman Aeroplane Trust	Rendcomb	27. 4.00
G-BETH*	Thunder Ax6-56A HAFB	113		27. 5.77	British Balloon Museum	Newbury	31. 5.78S
G-BETI	Pitts S-1D Special (Lycoming O-320)	7-0314 & PFA/09-10156		28. 4.77	P.Metcalfe	Morgansfield, Fishburn	15. 4.02P
G-BETL	PA-25-235 Pawnee D	25-7656016	N54874	27. 5.77	Cambridge Gliding Club Ltd	Gransden Lodge	15. 9.00
G-BETM	PA-25-235 Pawnee D	25-7656066	N54927	5. 5.77	Yorkshire Gliding Club (Pty) Ltd	Sutton Bank	8. 4.01
G-BETO	MS.885 Super Rallye	34	F-BKED	18. 5.77	A.J. & A.Hawley Farley Farm, Winchester t/a G-BETO Group		31. 3.01
G-BETP	Cameron O-65 HAFB	286		3. 5.77	J.R.Rix & Sons Ltd "Rix"	Hull	12. 6.88A
G-BETT	PA-34-200-2 Seneca	34-7250011	EI-BCD PH-AVM/N1978T	20. 6.77	D.F.J.Flashman	Biggin Hill	28. 7.99A
G-BEUA	PA-18-180 Super Cub	18-8212	D-ECSY N4146Z	21. 6.77	London Gliding Club Pty Ltd	Dunstable	30. 5.00
G-BEUD	Robin HR.100/285 Tiara	534	F-BXRC	8. 6.77	E.A. & L.M.C.Payton	Cranfield	11. 7.02
G-BEUI	Piper J3C-65 Cub (L-4H-PI) (Frame No.12002 - regd as c/n 10536 ex 45-29245)	12174	F-BFEC F-OAJF/Fr.AF/44-79878	19. 5.77	C.P.L.Jenkins	(Great Yarmouth)	9. 9.00P
G-BEUK	Fuji FA.200-160 Aero Subaru	284		24. 5.77	C.B.Mellor t/a BM Aviation (Damaged Glebe Farm, Stockton, Wilts 8.1.99)	Southampton	2.11.00T
G-BEUM	Taylor JT.1 Monoplane (VW1700)	PFA/1438		8. 6.77	J.M.Burgess	(Helston)	3. 8.00P
G-BEUN	Cassutt Racer IIIM (Continental C90)	PFA/34-10241		20. 2.78	R.McNulty	Breighton	7. 7.97P
G-BEUP	Robin DR.400/180 Regent	1228		19. 5.77	A.V.Pound & Co Ltd	Biggin Hill	19. 2.01
G-BEUU	PA-18-95 Super Cub (L-18C-PI) (Frame No.should be 18-1523)	18-1551	F-BOUU ALAT 18-1551/51-15551	27. 6.77	F.Sharples	Sandown	3. 7.00P
G-BEUX	Reims Cessna F.172N Skyhawk II	1596		30. 5.77	Multiflight Ltd	Leeds-Bradford	18.10.00T
G-BEUY	Cameron N-31 HAFB	283		31. 5.77	A.C.Beaumont "Little Red"	Henley-on-Thames	17.10.90A
G-BEVB	Socata Rallye 150ST	2860		2. 6.77	N.R.Haines	RAF Hullavington	22. 7.01
G-BEVC	Socata Rallye 150ST	2861		2. 6.77	B.W.Walpole Old Hall Farm, St.Nicholas, South Elmham, Harleston		3. 4.00
G-BEVG	PA-34-200T Seneca II	34-7570060	VQ-SAM N32854	31. 5.77	C.Deith	(Harrogate)	22. 6.02T
G-BEVI*	Thunder Ax7-77A HAFB	125		30. 5.77	British Balloon Museum & Library Newbury "Prime Bang"		NE(A)
G-BEVO	Sportavia Fournier RF5	5107	5N-AIX D-KAAZ	27. 6.77	T.Barlow (Stored 12.97)	Barton	20. 8.96P
G-BEVP*	Evans VP-2 (VW2074)	ISW/7207/1 & PFA/7207		9. 6.77	G.Moscrop & R.C.Crowley (Damaged Truleigh Manor Farm, Edburton 13.6.92; on rebuild 10.95)	Netherthorpe	22.9.80P*
G-BEVR	BN-2A Mk.III-2 Trislander	1056	6Y-JQE	10. 6.77	Cormack (Aircraft Services) Cumbernauld G-BEVR/XA-THE(2)/G-BEVR (Stored as "6Y-JQE" 5.99)		6. 7.82S
G-BEVS	Taylor JT.1 Monoplane (VW1835)	PFA/1429		8. 6.77	D.Hunter	Kemble	27. 5.00P
G-BEVT	BN-2A Mk.III-2 Trislander	1057		10. 6.77	Aurigny Air Services Ltd (Islands Insurance c/s) "Polly"	Guernsey	15.11.00T
G-BEVV	BN-2A Mk.111-2 Trislander	1059	6Y-JQK G-BNZD/G-BEVV	10. 6.77	Cormack (Aero Club Services) Ltd Cumbernauld (Stored dismantled as "6Y-JQK" 5.99)		
G-BEVW	Socata Rallye 150ST	2928		2. 6.77	P.C.Goodwin	RAF Keevil	23. 3.00
G-BEWN	DH.82A Tiger Moth (Built Australia - DHA rebuild c/n T305) RAAF A17-529	952	VH-WAL	16. 6.77	H.D.Labouchere Blue Tile Farm, Langham		14. 7.00
G-BEWO	Moravan Zlin Z.326 Trener Master	915	CS-ALU	23.11.77	Nimrod Group Ltd	Gloucestershire	10. 4.00
G-BEWP*	Reims Cessna F.150M	1426		13. 6.77	Perth College (Crashed Aboyne 4.10.83; instructional airframe 10.97)	Perth	12. 8.85
G-BEWR	Reims Cessna F.172N Skyhawk II	1613		13. 6.77	Cheshire Air Training Services Ltd	Liverpool	7. 4.01T
G-BEWX	PA-28R-201 Cherokee Arrow III	28R-7737070	N5723V	23. 6.77	A.Vickers	North Weald	23. 5.00
G-BEWY	Bell 206B JetRanger	348	G-CULL EI-BXQ/G-BEWY/9Y-TDF	27. 6.77	PLM Dollar Group Ltd	Cumbernauld	4. 5.01T
G-BEXK	PA-25-235 Pawnee D	25-7756004	(N82424)	14. 7.77	Eastern Stearman Ltd (Crashed 3/4.10.92; stored for spares 9.97)	East Winch	3. 6.93A
G-BEXN	Grumman-American AA-1C Lynx	AA1C-0045	N6147A	7. 9.77	C.J.Morgan t/a Lynx Flying Group	Elstree	1. 4.00

Regn	Type	C/n	P/I	Date	Owner/operator	Probable Base	CA Expy
G-BEXO	PA-23-160 Apache	23-213	OO-APH N1176P	4. 7.77	G.R.Moore & A.K.Hulme Kings Farm, Thurrock		5.11.96
G-BEXW	PA-28-181 Cherokee Archer II 28-7790521		N38122	11. 7.77	T.R.Kingsley	Norwich	14.10.99
G-BEXX	Cameron V-56 HAFB	274		29. 6.77	K.A.Schlussler "Rupert of Rutland"	Bourne	2. 7.86A
G-BEXZ	Cameron N-56 HAFB	294		7. 7.77	D.C.Eager & G.C.Clark "Valor" Bracknell/Worcester		13. 4.97A
G-BEYA	Enstrom 280C Shark	1104		15. 8.77	Hovercam Ltd	Goodwood	29. 5.00T
G-BEYB*	Fairey Flycatcher rep (PW R985)	WA/3		11. 7.77	Fleet Air Arm Museum RNAS Yeovilton (As "S1287/5" in 405 Flt FAA c/s)		4. 7.96P
G-BEYF*	HPR.7 Dart Herald 401	175	FM1022	13. 7.77	Dart Group plc	Bournemouth	17. 3.00T
	(Cancelled as wfu 18.11.99: to Bournemouth Aviation Museum 1999)						
G-BEYL	PA-28-180 Cherokee Archer	28-7405098	PH-SDW	6. 9.77	J. & N.Baker t/a Yankee Lima Group	Compton Abbas	11. 3.01
G-BEYN*	Evans VP-2	V2-3167 & PFA/63-10271		1. 8.77	Not known (Incomplete airframe stored in hangar roof 9.98)	East Fortune	
G-BEYO	PA-28-140 Cherokee Cruiser 28-7725215		N9648N	14. 7.77	W.B.Bateson	Blackpool	12. 5.01
G-BEYT*	PA-28-140 Cherokee	28-20330	D-EBWO N6280W	19. 7.77	B.A.Mills (Re-built 4.99)	Bourne	AC
G-BEYV	Cessna T210M Turbo Centurion II 210-61583		N732KX	19. 7.77	P.J.W. & N.Austen t/a Austen Aviation (Damaged at Edinburgh 28.7.98)	Edinburgh	13. 4.01T
G-BEYW	Taylor JT.1 Monoplane (VW1834) RJS.100 & PFA/55-10279			22. 7.77	R.A.Abrahams "Red Hot"	Barton	15. 3.00P
G-BEYZ	CEA Jodel DR.1050/M1 Sicile Record	588	F-BMGV	22. 7.77	M.L.Balding	Biggin Hill	25. 5.00
G-BEZA	Moravan Zlin Z.226T Trener 6	370	HA-TRL G-BEZA/D-EMUD/OK-MUA	24. 1.78	L.Bezak	(Sittingbourne)	
G-BEZC	Grumman-American AA-5 Traveler AA5-0493		F-BUYN (N7193L)	29. 7.77	P.N. & S.E.Field	Elstree	24. 6.01
G-BEZE	Rutan VariEze	PFA/74-10207		26. 7.77	H.C.MacKinnon	(Alton)	2. 6.92P
	(Continental O-200-A)				(Status uncertain)		
G-BEZF	Grumman-American AA-5 Traveler AA5-0538		F-BVJP	29. 7.77	RAF College Flying Club Ltd RAF Cranwell		23.10.01T
G-BEZG	Grumman-American AA-5 Traveler AA5-0561		F-BVRJ	29. 7.77	M.D.R.Harling & T.W.Cubbin Andrewsfield		31. 5.02
G-BEZH	Grumman-American AA-5 Traveler AA5-0566		F-BVRK N9566L	29. 7.77	L. & S.M.Sims	Fenland	25. 2.01
G-BEZI	Grumman-American AA-5 Traveler AA5-0567		F-BVRL N9567L	29. 7.77	Heather Matthews t/a The BEZI Flying Group	Cranfield	6. 5.01
G-BEZK	Reims Cessna F.172H	0462	D-EBUD D-ENHC/SLN-07/N20462	17. 8.77	I.M.Halifax t/a Zulu Kilo Flying Group	Earls Colne	22. 5.99
G-BEZL	PA-31-310 Turbo Navajo C	31-7712054	SE-GPA	1. 8.77	London Flt Centre (Stansted) Ltd (Op Love Air)	Biggin Hill	25. 9.98T
G-BEZO	Reims Cessna F.172M Skyhawk II	1392		24. 8.77	Gloucestershire Flying Services Ltd Gloucestershire		28. 3.01T
G-BEZP	PA-32-300 Cherokee Six	32-7740087	N38572	19. 8.77	Falcon Styles Ltd	White Waltham	22. 1.01
G-BEZR	Reims Cessna F.172M Skyhawk II	1395		24. 8.77	Kirmington Aviation Ltd	Sandown	11. 3.01T
G-BEZS*	Reims Cessna FR.172J Rocket	0562	(I-CCAJ)	11. 8.77	Not known	Bourn	22. 9.79
	(Damaged nr Stapleford 15.6.79; front fuselage stored 4.99)						
G-BEZV	Reims Cessna F.172M Skyhawk II	1474	(I-CCAY)	24. 8.77	A.T.Wilson t/a Insch Flying Group	Insch	4. 5.98
G-BEZY	Rutan VariEze	1167 & PFA/74-10225		26. 7.77	R.J.Jones	Cranfield	18. 5.96P
	(Continental PC60)						
G-BEZZ	Jodel D.112	397	F-BHMC	12. 8.77	M.J.Coles t/a G-BEZZ Jodel Group	Barton	7. 6.00P
	(Built Passot Aviation)						

G-BFAA – G-BFZZ

Regn	Type	C/n	P/I	Date	Owner/operator	Probable Base	CA Expy
G-BFAA	Socata GY-80-160 Horizon	78	F-BLVY	20.10.77	Mary Poppins Ltd (Status uncertain)	(Stoke-on-Trent)	18.11.90
G-BFAB*	Cameron N-56 HAFB	297		15. 8.77	A.Gibson "Phonogram" (for British Balloon Museum & Library)	Stockport	NE(A)
G-BFAF	Aeronca 7BCM Champion (L-16A-AE)	7BCM-11	N797US N2552B/47-797	15. 8.77	D.C.W.Harper (As "7797" in US Army c/s)	Finmere	26. 8.00P
G-BFAH	Phoenix Currie Wot	PFA/3017		22. 8.77	R.W.Clarke	(Cheadle)	
	(Continental O-200A) (Being built as Replica SE-5A and to be in RFC c/s)						
	(Regd as c/n PFA/58-11376 but mistaken with PFA/101-11376, a Sopwith Pup rep by same owner/builder)						
G-BFAI	Rockwell Commander 114	14304	N4984W	17. 8.77	G.Gore-Brown t/a Alpha India Flying Group	Sherburn-in-Elmet	21.10.02

Regn	Type	C/n	P/I	Date	Owner/operator	Probable Base	CA Expy
G-BFAK	GEMS MS.892A Rallye Commodore 150	10595	F-BNNJ	9. 8.77	P.G.Wells　　Draycott Farm, Chiseldon t/a Draycott Rallye Group		19. 4.01
G-BFAO	PA-20-135 Pacer	20-674	ZS-CMH ZS-CAH	10.10.77	Erica A.M.Austin	Kemble	18.11.02
G-BFAP	SIAI-Marchetti S.205-20R	4-213	I-ALEN	1. 9.77	A.O'Broin 　　Brookfield Farm, Great Stukeley		22. 5.00
G-BFAS	Evans VP-1 Srs.2 (VW1834)	PFA/7033		15. 8.77	A.I.Sutherland	Fearn	11. 3.00
G-BFAW	DHC.1 Chipmunk 22 (Fuselage No. DHB/F/625)	C1/0733	8342M WP848	31. 8.77	R.V.Bowles　　Watchford Farm, Yarcombe		7.10.00
G-BFAX	DHC.1 Chipmunk 22 (Fuselage No. DHB/F/364)	C1/0496	8394M WG422	31. 8.77	A.C.Kerr (As "WG422")	Cumbernauld	28. 4.02
G-BFBA	SAN Jodel DR.100A Ambassadeur	88	F-BIVU	12. 9.77	W.H.Sherlock　　Drayton St.Leonard, Oxon		7.10.02
G-BFBB	PA-23-250 Aztec E	27-7405294	SE-GBI	1. 9.77	Air Training Services Ltd	Booker	16. 6.01T
	(An Aztec wreck was marked "G-BFBB" for film use in Halland Handling Scrapyard, Braydon, Wilts 2.96)						
G-BFBC	Taylor JT.1 Monoplane　PFA/55-10280 (VW1600)			5. 9.77	R.Trickett　　(King's Lynn) (Under construction 2.93)		
G-BFBE	Robin HR.200/100	12	PH-SRK	9. 9.77	A.C.Pearson	Denham	23. 3.02
G-BFBF	PA-28-140 Cherokee F	28-7325240	EI-BMG G-BFBF/PH-SRF	9. 9.77	Marnham Investments Ltd　　Aldergrove (Op Woodgate Executive Air Services)		30. 9.01T
G-BFBM	Saffery S.330 HAFB (Model)	7		1. 9.77	B.Martin "Beeze II"	Somersham, Cambs	
G-BFBR	PA-28-161 Cherokee Warrior II	28-7716277	N38845	15. 9.77	Lowery Holdings Ltd	Fairoaks	29. 1.01T
G-BFBU	Partenavia P.68B	24	SE-FTM	25. 1.78	Premiair Charter Ltd	Bournemouth	19. 4.00T
G-BFBY	Piper J-3C-65 Cub (L-4H-PI)	10998	F-BDTG 43-29707	29. 9.77	U.Schuhmacher	Hahn, Germany	28. 6.00P
G-BFCT	Cessna TU206F Turbo Stationair II	U206-03202	(LN-TVF) N8341Q	15. 9.77	Cecil Aviation Ltd	Cambridge	26. 1.01
G-BFCZ	Sopwith Camel F.1 rep (Clerget 9B)	WA/2		12.10.77	Brooklands Museum Trust Ltd　　Brooklands (As "B7270")		23. 2.89P
G-BFDC	DHC.1 Chipmunk 22	C1/0525	7989M WG475	15.11.77	N.F.O'Neill	Newtownards	6. 2.00
G-BFDE*	Sopwith Tabloid Scout rep (Continental PC.60) 168 & PFA/67-10186			22. 9.77	RAF Museum	Hendon	4. 6.83P
					(As "168" in RNAS c/s)		
G-BFDF	Socata Rallye 235E	12834	F-GAKT	6.10.77	D.J.Lindsay Wood	Bournemouth	21. 2.02
G-BFDI	PA-28-181 Cherokee Archer II	28-7790382	N2205Q	5.10.77	Truman Aviation Ltd	Nottingham	10. 9.01T
G-BFDK	PA-28-161 Warrior II	28-7816010	N40061	23. 9.77	R.D.H.Cole t/a Priory Garage	Enstone	8. 4.01T
G-BFDL	Piper J3C Cub (L-4J-PI) (Continental O-200-A) (Frame No.13107)	13277 45-4537	HB-OIF	30.11.77	S.Beresford & G.S.Claybourn　Walton Wood (As "454537/04-J" in US Army c/s)		28. 4.00P
G-BFDO	PA-28R-201T Turbo Cherokee Arrow III	28R-7703212	N38396	3.10.77	A.J.Gow　　Wellesbourne Mountford		22. 9.02
G-BFDZ	Taylor JT.1 Monoplane　PFA/55-10185 (VW1600)			5.10.77	G.J.Clare	(Bath)	23. 9.99P
G-BFEB	SAN Jodel 150 Mascaret	34	F-BMJR OO-LDY/F-BLDX	14.10.77	S.Russell　　Wilkieston Farm, Cupar (Damaged Marston Moor 14.4.91; on rebuild 5.98)		19. 4.91P
G-BFEF	Agusta-Bell 47G-3B1	1541	XT132	11.10.77	R.C.Hields	Sherburn-in-Elmet	17. 6.02T
G-BFEH	SAN Jodel D.117A	828	F-BITG	5.10.77	C.V. & S.J.Philpot (Dismantled 9.99)	Kemble	30. 9.94P
G-BFEK	Reims Cessna F.152 II	1442		11.10.77	Gloucestershire Flying Services Ltd 　　Gloucestershire		20. 2.01T
G-BFEO*	Boeing 707-323C	18691	5X-UWM N7557A	14.10.77	Boeing Aircraft Co/USAF 　　Davis-Monthan AFB, Arizona, USA (Stored for spares use 10.92)		30.12.85T
G-BFER	Bell 212	30835	N18099	7.11.77	Bristow Helicopters Ltd	Scatsta	27.11.02T
G-BFEV	PA-25-235 Pawnee D	25-7756060		20.10.77	Trent Valley Aerotowing Club Ltd 　　Kirton-in-Lindsey		18. 4.01
G-BFEW	PA-25-235 Pawnee D	25-7756062		20.10.77	Cornish Gliding & Flying Club Ltd 　　Perranporth		25. 3.01
G-BFFB*	Evans VP-2　V2-2289 & PFA/63-10159			27.10.77	Not known　　Park Farm, Eaton Bray (Stored 6.96)		
G-BFFC	Reims Cessna F.152 II	1451		27.10.77	Yorkshire Flying Services Ltd 　　Leeds-Bradford		11. 6.01T
G-BFFE	Reims Cessna F.152 II	1454		27.10.77	J.Easson (Dumped 3.99)	Edinburgh	19. 4.98T
G-BFFJ	Sikorsky S-61N Mk.II	61-777	N6231	17. 1.78	Brintel Helicopters Ltd	Penzance	22. 3.00T
					t/a British International Helicopters "Tresco"		
G-BFFP	PA-18-180 Super Cub (Frame No. 18-8402)	18-8187	PH-OTC	9.11.77	Booker Gliding Club Ltd	Booker	12. 4.01
G-BFFT	Cameron V-56 HAFB	360		7.11.77	R.I.McKean Kerr & D.C.Boxall　Bristol t/a The Red Section Balloon Group "Red Leader"		22. 7.00A

Regn	Type	C/n	P/I	Date	Owner/operator	Probable Base	CA Expy
G-BFFW	Reims Cessna F.152 II	1447		14.11.77	Tayside Aviation Ltd	Dundee	28. 5.01T
G-BFFY	Reims Cessna F.150M Commuter	1376		14.11.77	G. & S.A.Jones Linley Hill, Beverley		3. 3.01T
G-BFFZ	Reims Cessna FR.172K Hawk XPII	0603	F-WZDU	14.11.77	Bravo Aviation Ltd	Caernarfon	26. 4.00T
					(Op Air Caernarfon)		
G-BFGD	Reims Cessna F.172N Skyhawk II	1545	F-WZDT	14.11.77	J.T.Armstrong	Fairoaks	6. 9.01T
G-BFGF	Reims Cessna F.177RG Cardinal II			14.11.77	J.E.Searson	Spanhoe	25.11.01
		0166					
G-BFGG	Reims Cessna FRA.150M Aerobat	0321	F-WZDS	14.11.77	Cornwall Flying Club Ltd	Bodmin	3. 3.01T
G-BFGH	Reims Cessna F.337G Super Skymaster II			14.11.77	T.Perkins	Bagby	5. 7.02
	(Wichita c/n 01754)	0081					
G-BFGK	SAN Jodel D.117	644	F-BIBT	27. 6.78	B.F.J.Hope		17. 5.00P
					Stoneacre Farm, Farthing Corner		
G-BFGL	Reims Cessna FA.152 Aerobat	0339		14.11.77	Yorkshire Flying Services Ltd		
						Leeds-Bradford	5. 4.01T
G-BFGO	Fuji FA.200-160 Aero Subaru	219	PH-KDB	25.11.77	Butane Buzzard Aviation Corporation Ltd		
					(Damaged Rush Green 18.8.93; stored 7.96) Cranfield		23. 8.92
G-BFGS	Socata MS.893E Rallye 180GT	12571	F-BXYK	31. 8.76	Chiltern Flyers Ltd		
			Fr.AF 12571 FSCAZ/"41-AZ"			Park Farm, Eaton Bray	15. 9.00
G-BFGW	Reims Cessna F.150H	0370	PH-TGO	24.11.77	C.E.Stringer	Humberside	19.10.95T
G-BFGX*	Reims Cessna FRA.150M Aerobat	0328	F-BUDX	28.11.77	Perth Airport Ltd	Redhill	27. 8.01T
					(Cancelled by CAA 9.12.99)		
G-BFGZ	Reims Cessna FRA.150M Aerobat	0329		28.11.77	W J D Tollett	Oxford	10. 3.00T
G-BFHD*	CASA C.352L	146	T2B-255	23.11.77	National Air & Space Museum		
			"721-8"		Dulles Airport, Washington, USA		
					(As "D-ODLH" in Lufthansa c/s)		
G-BFHF*	CASA C.352L	166	T2B-275	23.11.77	Auto und Technik MuseumSinsheim, Germany		
			"721-15"		(As "RJ+NP" in Luftwaffe c/s)		
G-BFHH	DH.82A Tiger Moth	85933	F-BDOH	25.11.77	P.Harrison & M.J.Gambrell		
			Fr.AF/DF197		Swanborough Farm, Lewes		14. 8.00
G-BFHI	Piper J3C-65 Cub (L-4J-PI)	12532	F-BFBT	25.11.77	N Glass & A J Richardson		
			44-80236		Bann Foot, Lough Neagh		26. 1.00P
G-BFHP	Champion 7GCAA Citabria	114	HB-UAX	8.12.77	Griffin Marston Ltd	Compton Abbas	30. 9.02T
					(Op Abbas Air)		
G-BFHR	CEA Jodel DR.220 2 + 2	30	F-BOCX	1.12.77	J.E.Sweetman		
					Bourne Park, Hurstbourne Tarrant		3. 6.00
G-BFHT	Reims Cessna F.152 II	1441		7.12.77	Westward Airways (Lands End) Ltd St.Just		16. 4.01T
G-BFHU	Reims Cessna F.152 II	1461		7.12.77	Deltair Ltd	Chester	16. 2.02T
G-BFHV	Reims Cessna F.152 II	1470		21.12.77	A.S.Bamrah	Blackbushe	27. 8.01T
					t/a Falcon Flying Services (Op European Flyers)		
G-BFHX	Evans VP-1 PFA/62-10283			2.12.77	A.D.Bohanna & D.I.Trussler	(Swindon)	7. 4.99P
	(VW1600)						
G-BFIB	PA-31 Turbo Navajo	31-684	LN-NPE	21.12.77	Richard Hannon Ltd	Thruxton	13. 8.00T
			OY-DVH/LN-RTJ				
G-BFID	Taylor JT.2 Titch Mk.III			13.12.77	N.A.Scully Griffins Farm, Temple Bruer		23. 8.99P
	(Continental O-200-A) PFA/60-10311				(Damaged Breighton 31.5.99)		
G-BFIE	Reims Cessna FRA.150M Aerobat	0331		12. 1.78	Solo Services Ltd	Shoreham	13.10.00T
G-BFIG	Reims Cessna FR.172K Hawk XPII	0615		12. 1.78	Tenair Ltd	Barton	1.12.00
G-BFIJ	Grumman-American AA-5A Cheetah		N6160A	1. 3.78	T.H.& M.G.Weetman	(West Kilbride)	3.12.00
		AA5A-0486					
G-BFIN	Grumman-American AA-5A Cheetah		N6145A	22. 3.78	I.W.Lewis	Wellesbourne Mountford	21. 1.02
		AA5A-0520			t/a G-BFIN Flying Group		
G-BFIP	Wallbro Monoplane rep	WA-1		16.12.77	K.H.Wallis	Shipdham	22. 4.82P
	(McCulloch/Wallis)				(No external marks; stored 8.97)		
G-BFIU	Reims Cessna FR.172K Hawk XP	0591	N96098	12. 1.78	B.M.Jobling	Hinton-in-The-Hedges	30. 4.00
G-BFIV	Reims Cessna F.177RG Cardinal II		N96106	12. 1.78	Kingfishair Ltd	Blackbushe	27. 5.02
G-BFIX	Thunder Ax7-77A HAFB	133		9.12.77	R.Owen "Animal Magic"	Wigan	3. 5.00S
G-BFIY	Reims Cessna F.150M	1381	OE-CMT	11. 1.78	Yorkshire Light Acft Ltd Leeds-Bradford		23. 6.02T
					(Op Yorkshire Aeroplane Club)		
G-BFJJ	Evans VP-1 PFA/62-10273			30.12.77	Marion J.Collins Farley Farm, Winchester		23. 6.96P
	(VW1800)						
G-BFJK	PA-23-250 Aztec F	27-7654137	N62678	16. 1.78	H.G.Keighley	Sherburn in Elmet	24.11.01
G-BFJR	Reims Cessna F.337G Super Skymaster II	N46297	4. 1.78	Robot (UK) Ltd	East Midlands	11. 2.02
	(Wichita c/n 01761)	0082	(N53658)		t/a Mannix Aviation		
G-BFJZ	Robin DR.400/140B Major	1290		20. 1.78	Weald Air Services Ltd	Headcorn	24. 6.01T
G-BFKB	Reims Cessna F.172N Skyhawk II	1601	PH-AXO	16. 1.78	R.M.Collins	Ludham	19. 2.00T
G-BFKC	Rand Robinson KR-2			20. 1.78	L.H.S.Stephens & I.S.Hewitt		
		KKC.5 & PFA/129-10809			(Littleover, Derby)		
G-BFKF	Reims Cessna FA.152 Aerobat	0337		26. 1.78	Klingair Ltd	Conington	27. 4.01T
G-BFKG*	Reims Cessna F.152 II	1463		26. 1.78	Not known	Biggin Hill	25.11.90T
					(Damaged Luton 11.11.89; wreck stored 8.97)		

Regn	Type	C/n	P/I	Date	Owner/operator	Probable Base	CA Expy
G-BFKH	Reims Cessna F.152 II	1464		26. 1.78	TG Aviation Ltd	Manston	26. 3.01T
					(Op Thanet Flying Club)		
G-BFKL	Cameron N-56 HAFB	369		23. 1.78	Merrythought Ltd	Telford	17. 7.92A
G-BFKY	PA-34-200-2 Seneca	34-7350318	PH-NAZ	22. 2.78	SLH Construction Ltd	Biggin Hill	24. 9.01T
			N56332				
G-BFLH	PA-34-200T Seneca II	34-7870065	N2126M	16. 2.78	Air Medical Ltd	Oxford	10. 5.00T
G-BFLI	PA-28R-201T Turbo Arrow III		N2582M	16. 2.78	J.K.Chudzicki	Fairoaks	11. 6.01
		28R-7803134					
G-BFLM*	Cessna 150M Commuter	150-76352	N3017V	15. 6.78	Cornwall Flying Club Ltd	Bodmin	16.11.96T
					(Crashed nr Bodmin 14.1.97; open store 7.97)		
G-BFLP	Amethyst Ax6-56 HAFB	001		20. 2.78	K.J.Hendry	Gillingham, Kent	
					"Amethyst"		
G-BFLU	Reims Cessna F.152 II	1433		15. 2.78	Bravo Aviation Ltd	Coventry	8. 5.01T
					(Op Atlantic Flight Training)		
G-BFLX	Grumman-American AA-5A Cheetah		N6147A	14. 3.78	G-Force Aviation Ltd.	Blackbushe	23.11.01T
		AA5A-0524					
G-BFLZ	Beechcraft 95-A55 Baron	TC-220	PH-ILE	16. 3.78	K.A.Graham	Carlisle	23. 7.01
			HB-GOV		t/a Caterite Food Service		
G-BFME	Cameron V-56 HAFB	371		17. 2.78	A.Mayes & V.Lawton	Leamington Spa	29. 1.88A
					t/a Warwick Balloons "Avon Lad"		
G-BFMF*	Cassutt Racer IIIM	PFA/34-10147		17. 2.78	Not known	(Shaftesbury)	24. 5.91P
	(Continental C90)				(Stored 8.95; cancelled by CAA 27.1.99)		
G-BFMG	PA-28-161 Cherokee Warrior II		N3506Q	11. 5.78	Stardial Ltd	Fairoaks	16. 9.02T
		28-7716160					
G-BFMH	Cessna 177B Cardinal	177-02034	N34836	18. 4.78	Span Aviation Ltd	Newcastle	16. 5.02
G-BFMK	Reims Cessna FA.152 Aerobat	0344		6. 3.78	RAF Halton Aeroplane Club Ltd	RAF Halton	23. 2.02T
G-BFMM	PA-28-181 Archer II	28-7890127	N47735	28. 2.78	K.Hobbs	Belfast	26. 8.01T
					t/a Aldergrove Flight Training Centre		
G-BFMR	PA-20-125 Pacer	20-130	N7025K	20. 2.78	J.Knight	Headcorn	11. 1.00
G-BFMX	Reims Cessna F.172N Skyhawk II	1732		24. 8.78	Broomco (406) Ltd		12. 6.00
						Farley Farm, Winchester	
G-BFMY	Sikorsky S-61N mk.II	61-745	N4040S	14. 3.78	Bristow Helicopters Ltd "Diamond"		3. 2.00T
						Mount Pleasant, Falkland Islands	
G-BFMZ*	Payne Ax6-62 HAFB	GFP.2		1. 3.78	E.G.Woolnough	Halesworth, Suffolk	
G-BFNG	Wassmer Jodel D.112	1321	F-BNHI	6. 3.78	M.T.Taylor	Griffins Farm, Temple Bruer	4. 8.00P
G-BFNI	PA-28-161 Warrior II	28-7816215	N9505N	8. 3.78	P.Elliott	Biggin Hill	26. 7.02
G-BFNJ	PA-28-161 Warrior II	28-7816281	N9520N	8. 3.78	Fleetlands Flying Association Ltd		
						Lee-on-Solent	23. 5.01T
G-BFNK	PA-28-161 Warrior II	28-7816282	N9527N	8. 3.78	Oxford Aviation Services Ltd	Oxford	22.12.99T
G-BFNU*	IRMA BN-2B-21 Islander	877		16. 3.78	Isles of Scilly Skybus Ltd	St.Just	18. 8.89T
					(Fuselage stored 5.99)		
G-BFOD	Reims Cessna F.182Q Skylane II	0068		23. 3.78	G.N.Clarke	Alderney	6. 7.02
G-BFOE	Reims Cessna F.152 II	1475		23. 3.78	Redhill Air Services Ltd	Redhill	19.12.02T
G-BFOF	Reims Cessna F.152 II	1448		9. 3.78	Gloucestershire Flying Services Ltd		
						Gloucestershire	21. 6.02T
G-BFOG	Cessna 150M	150-76223	N66706	13. 3.78	Griffin Marston Ltd	Compton Abbas	20.11.00T
G-BFOJ	American AA-1 Yankee	AA1-0395	OH-AYB	4. 4.78	A.J.Morton & N.W.Thomas	Bournemouth	14.10.02
			(LN-KAJ)/(N6195L)				
G-BFOM	Piper PA-31 Turbo Navajo C		EI-DMI	17. 3.78	Deer Hill Aviation Ltd	Exeter	25. 1.01T
		31-7512017	G-BFOM/HB-LHH/N59933				
G-BFOP	Jodel Wassmer D.120 Paris-Nice	32	F-BHTX	23. 3.78	R.J.Wesley & G.D.Western "Jean"		21. 9.00P
						Sampsons Hall, Kersey	
G-BFOS	Thunder Ax6-56A HAFB	147		20. 3.78	N.T.Petty	Sudbury, Suffolk	25.11.93A
					"Milton Keynes"		
G-BFOU	Taylor JT.1 Monoplane	PFA/55-10333		17. 3.78	G.Bee	(Stockton-on-Tees)	
G-BFOV	Reims Cessna F.172N Skyhawk II	1675		18. 5.78	D.J.Walker	Shoreham	18.10.02
G-BFOZ*	Thunder Ax6-56 Plug HAFB	144		20. 3.78	British Balloon Museum & Library Newbury		
					"Motorway" (Cancelled by CAA 16.4.92)		
G-BFPA	Scheibe SF-25B Falke	46179	D-KAGM	29. 3.78	N.Meiklejohn & J.Steel	Falgunzeon	13. 9.98
G-BFPB	Grumman-American AA-5B Tiger			7. 4.78	Stesco Ltd	Guernsey	1. 9.02
		AA5B-0706					
G-BFPE*	PA-28-140 Cherokee C	28-26410	OH-PCY	22. 3.78	Not known	Framlingham	26. 5.84
					(Crashed Clacton 9.6.82; wreck stored 4.92)		
G-BFPH	Reims Cessna F.172K	0802	PH-VHN	23. 3.78	M.Pollard	Sturgate	13. 6.02
					t/a Linc-Air Flying Group		
G-BFPM	Reims Cessna F.172M Skyhawk II	1384	PH-MIO	13. 4.78	Sigma Corporation Ltd	Wickenby	22.12.02T
G-BFPO	Rockwell Commander 112B	530	N1412J	10. 5.78	J.G.Hale Ltd	Shoreham	25. 8.00
G-BFPP	Bell 47J-2 Ranger	2851	F-BJAN	23. 5.78	M.R.Masters	Lower Upham	11.11.99
			TR-LKD/F-OCBU				
G-BFPS	PA-25-235 Pawnee D	25-7856013		4. 4.78	Kent Gliding Club Ltd	Challock	19. 1.00
G-BFRA	Rockwell Commander 114	14292	N4972W	28. 3.78	Ischia Investments Ltd	Cascais, Portugal	24.10.00

Regn	Type	C/n	P/I	Date	Owner/operator	Probable Base	CA Expy
G-BFRD	Bowers FlyBaby 1A	PFA/16-10300		27. 1.78	R.A.Phillips	(Elgin)	
G-BFRF	Taylor JT.1 Monoplane (VW1500)	PFA/55-10330		7. 4.78	E.R.Bailey	(Hockley, Essex)	
G-BFRI	Sikorsky S-61N Mk.II	61-809		26. 5.78	Bristow Helicopters Ltd "Braeriach"	Unst	14. 6.01T
G-AFRL*	Reims Cessna F.152 II	1490		11. 4.78	Bristol & Wessex Flying Club Ltd		
				(Damaged 24.8.92: cancelled by CAA 14.3.97: stored 1.99)		Bristol	
G-BFRM	Cessna 550 Citation II (Unit No.027)	550-0027	N527CC N3245M	31. 1.78	Marshall of Cambridge Aerospace Ltd	Cambridge	14. 1.02T
G-BFRR	Reims Cessna FRA.150M Aerobat	0326	LN-ALO	19. 4.78	J.R.Duller	Tatenhill	6. 7.00
G-BFRS	Reims Cessna F.172N Skyhawk II	1555	LN-ALP	19. 4.78	Poplar Models Ltd	Poplar Hall Farm, Elmsett	24. 4.00T
G-BFRV	Reims Cessna FA.152 Aerobat	0345		17. 4.78	Solo Services Ltd	Shoreham	22. 9.02T
G-BFRX*	PA-25-235 Pawnee D	25-7405787	SE-GDZ	23. 5.78	Yorkshire Gliding Club (Pty) Ltd		
				(Damaged Sutton Bank 27.3.94; spares use 1.95) Sutton Bank			28. 2.96
G-BFRY	PA-25-260 Pawnee D	25-7405789	SE-GIB	23. 5.78	Yorkshire Gliding Club (Pty) Ltd	Sutton Bank	28. 5.00
G-BFSA	Reims Cessna F.182Q Skylane II	0074	F-WZDG	17. 4.78	Clark Masts Teksam Ltd	Zwartberg/Sandown	28. 9.02
G-BFSB	Reims Cessna F.152 II	1506		20. 4.78	M.R.Shelton t/a Tatenhill Aviation	Tatenhill	6. 2.00T
G-BFSC	PA-25-235 Pawnee D	25-7656068	N82302	2. 6.78	M.A.Pruden	(Bedford)	17. 6.00A
G-BFSD	PA-25-235 Pawnee D	25-7656084	N82338	2. 6.78	Deeside Gliding Club (Aberdeenshire) Ltd	Aboyne	8.11.01
G-BFSR	Reims Cessna F150J	0504	OH-CBN	7. 7.78	Sandra Jayyousi	Bourn	16. 4.01T
G-BFSS	Reims Cessna FR172G Rocket	0167	OH-CDY	7. 7.78	J.R. & S.J.Goddard & F.West t/a Minerva Services	Grateley, Andover	27. 3.00
G-BFSY	PA-28-181 Archer II	28-7890200	N9503N	19. 4.78	A.S.Domone t/a Downland Aviation	Goodwood	24. 5.02
G-BFTC	PA-28R-201T Turbo Arrow III	28R-7803197	N3868M	19. 4.78	M.J.Milns	Sherburn in Elmet	22. 6.00
G-BFTF	Grumman-American AA-5B Tiger	AA5B-0879		7. 9.78	F.C.Burrow Ltd	Sherburn in Elmet	22. 5.00
G-BFTG	Grumman-American AA-5B Tiger	AA5B-0777		15. 5.78	D.Hepburn & G.R.Montgomery	Perth	29. 9.02
G-BFTH	Reims Cessna F.172N Skyhawk II	1671		3. 5.78	J.Birkett	Wickenby	12. 9.02T
G-BFTT	Cessna 421C Golden Eagle II	421C-0462	N6789C	3. 5.78	P & B Metal Components Ltd (Op TG Aviation)	Manston	3. 5.00T
G-BFTX	Reims Cessna F.172N Skyhawk II	1715		2. 5.78	P.Howlett t/a East Kent Flying Group	Manston	28. 3.00
G-BFTZ*	Socata MS.880B Rallye Club	1269	F-BPAX	2. 6.78	The Aeroplane Collection Ltd (On loan to Newark Air Museum)	Winthorpe	19. 9.81
G-BFUB	PA-32RT-300 Lance II	32R-7885052	N9509C	18. 5.78	Jolida Holdings Ltd	Jersey	3. 4.02
G-BFUD	Scheibe SF-25E Super Falke	4313	D-KLDC	19. 5.78	P.A.Lewis t/a The Lakes Libelle Syndicate	Walney Island	21. 9.01
G-BFUF*	PA-30-160 Twin Comanche	30-363	F-OCZF 5R-MCA/N7361Y	19. 5.78	Not known (Dismantled & stored 9.92; Kenyan regn not issued)	Wilson, Nairobi	
G-BFUG	Cameron N-77 HAFB	394		15. 5.78	Cornwall Ballooning Adventures Ltd	Newquay	19. 4.99A
G-BFVF	PA-38-112 Tomahawk	38-78A0055	N9691N	1. 6.78	Goodair Leasing Ltd	Cardiff	18. 8.02T
G-BFVG	PA-28-181 Archer II	28-7890408	N31746 N9558N	1. 6.78	M.S.Cornah t/a G-BFVG Flying Group	Blackpool	22. 6.02
G-BFVH	Airco DH.2 rep (Kinner B54 125 hp)	WA/4	"5964"	1. 6.78	M.J.Kirk (Rebuilt by 1999)	Haverfordwest	23.7.86P*
G-BFVM*	Westland-Bell 47G-3B1 (Line No. WAP/96)	WA/393	XT234	14. 6.78	Not known (Stored 5.96)	Coventry	20.11.87T
G-BFVP	PA-23-250 Aztec F	27-7854096	N63966	6. 7.78	Litton Aviation Services Ltd	Sherburn in Elmet	24. 7.02
G-BFVS	Grumman-American AA-5B Tiger	0784	N28736	11. 8.78	S.W.Biroth & T.Chapman	Denham	2.10.00
G-BFVU	Cessna 150L Commuter	150-74684	N75189	10. 8.78	Deer Hill Aviation Ltd	Exeter	19. 6.00T
G-BFWB	PA-28-161 Warrior II	28-7816584	N31752	22. 6.78	Mid-Anglia Flight Centre Ltd t/a Mid-Anglia School of Flyinge	Cambridge	17. 7.02T
G-BFWD	Phoenix Currie Wot (Walter Mikron 3)	PFA/3009		22. 6.78	F.R.Donaldson	Goodwood	6.10.96P
G-BFWE	PA-23-250 Aztec E	27-4583	9M-AQT 9V-BDI/N13968	13. 7.78	Air Navigation & Trading Co Ltd	Blackpool	10. 2.00T
G-BFWL	Reims Cessna F.150L	0971	PH-KDC	4.10.78	P.Maher t/a G-BFWL Flying Group	Caernarfon	27. 3.00
G-BFXD	PA-28-161 Warrior II	28-7816583	N31750	10. 7.78	Oxford Aviation Services Ltd	Oxford	23. 5.00T
G-BFXE	PA-28-161 Warrior II	28-7816585	N31802	10. 7.78	Oxford Aviation Services Ltd	Oxford	6.10.02T
G-BFXF	Andreasson BA.4B	AAB-001 & PFA/38-10351		10. 7.78	A.Brown (Under build 9.99)	Breighton	

Regn	Type	C/n	P/I	Date	Owner/operator	Probable Base	CA Expy
G-BFXG	Druine D.31 Turbulent	PFA/1663		10. 7.78	E.J.I.Musty & M.J.Whatley	White Waltham	
G-BFXH*	Reims Cessna F.152 II	1469	(F-BXQJ)	21. 7.78	M.Entwistle	(Warwick)	1. 2.93T
					(Status unknown: cancelled by CAA 6.3.99)		
G-BFXK	PA-28-140 Cherokee F	28-7325387	PH-NSK	1. 8.78	J.T.Mirley	Halfpenny Green	16. 4.00
G-BFXL*	Albatros D.Va rep	0034	D-EGKO	24. 8.78	Fleet Air Arm Museum	RNAS Yeovilton	5.11.91P*
	(Ranger 6-440-C5) (Built Williams Flugzeugbau)				(As "D5397/17" in German c/s)		
G-BFXM*	Jurca MJ.5 Sirocco	PFA/2205		18. 7.78	R.Bradbury & A.R.Greenfield		
					(Open store incomplete 2.93)	Stansted Mountfichet	
G-BFXR	Wassmer Jodel D.112	247	F-BFTM	27. 7.78	P.M.Beresford	Crosland Moor	24.11.00P
					t/a Jodel Group		
G-BFXS	Rockwell Commander 114	14271	N4949W	3. 8.78	I.Cashmore	(Richmond, Surrey)	22. 8.02
					t/a Cashmore Associates		
G-BFXW	Gulfstream AA-5B Tiger	AA5B-0940		21. 2.79	Campsol Ltd	Leeds-Bradford	19. 6.00
G-BFXX	Gulfstream AA-5B Tiger	AA5B-0917		3.10.78	W.R.Gibson	(Woodford Green)	11.11.00
G-BFYA	MBB Bo.105DB	S.321	D-HJET	31.10.78	Sterling Helicopters Ltd	Norwich	12. 5.00T
G-BFYB	PA-28-161 Warrior II	28-7816581	N31731	27. 7.78	Oxford Aviation Services Ltd	Oxford	12. 4.00T
G-BFYC	PA-32RT-300 Lance II	32R-7885200	N36645	31. 7.78	A.A.Barnes	Biggin Hill	3. 9.00
					t/a Cyril Silver & Ptnrs		
G-BFYI	Westland-Bell 47G-3B1	WA/326	XT167	24. 1.79	B.Walker & Co (Dursley) Ltd	Nympsfield	1. 6.00
	(Line No.WAN/17)						
G-BFYK	Cameron V-77 HAFB	433	EI-BAY	16. 8.78	Louise E.Jones	Worcester	31.12.99A
			G-BFYK				
G-BFYL	Evans VP-2	PFA/63-10146		15. 8.78	W.C.Brown	(Camberley)	17.12.98P
	(VW1834)						
G-BFYM	PA-28-161 Warrior II	28-7816586	N31813	14. 8.78	Oxford Aviation Services Ltd	Oxford	6.10.02T
G-BFYO*	SPAD XIII rep	0035	D-EOWM	16.11.78	American Air Museum	Duxford	21. 6.82P
	(Lycoming AIO-360) (Built Williams Flugzeugbau)				(As "1/4513" in 3rd Escadrille French AF c/s)		
G-BFYP	Wombat Gyrocopter	AJP.1		7. 7.78	A.J.Philpotts	St.Merryn	
	(Originally regd to unbuilt Bensen B.7 - Wombat built 1995)						
G-BFYU*	Short SC.5 Belfast C.1	SH.1821	G-52-15	13.11.78	Heavylift Aviation Holdings Ltd Southend		10. 4.93T
			XR367		(Heavylift Cargo Airlines) "St.David" (Wfu 27.6.92; open store 1.00)		
G-BFZA	Alpavia Fournier RF3	5	F-BLEL	14. 9.78	T.J.Hartwell	Sackville Farm, Riseley	
G-BFZB	Piper J3C-85 Cub (L-4J-PI)	13019	D-ECEL	21. 9.78	P.F.Ansell & J.Noble t/a Zebedee Flying Group		
	(Frame No.12849)		HB-OSP/44-80723			West Chiltington, Pulborough	9. 4.88P
					(On rebuild 9.94)		
G-BFZD	Reims Cessna FR.182 Skylane RG II			9.10.78	J.McCloskey	(Coleraine, NI)	15. 1.00
		0010					
G-BFZG	PA-28-161 Warrior II	28-7816582	N31748	18. 9.78	Oxford Aviation Services Ltd	Oxford	8. 2.00T
G-BFZH	PA-28R-200 Cherokee Arrow	28R-35307	OY-BDB	25.10.78	W.E.Lowe	Shobdon	25. 9.00
G-BFZM	Rockwell Commander 112TC-A	13191	N4661W	9.10.78	R.J.Lamplough	Filton/North Weald	8. 8.97
G-BFZN	Reims Cessna FA.152 Aerobat	0348		20.10.78	A.S.Bamrah	Biggin Hill	29.11.81T
					t/a Falcon Flying Services (Crashed Narborough, Leics 4.10.80; on rebuild 2.95)		
G-BFZO	Gulfstream AA-5A Cheetah	AA5A-0697		1.11.78	P.Young	(Portstewart, Co.Londonderry)	12. 5.00
					t/a Coleraine Landscape Services		
G-BFZT	Reims Cessna FA.152 Aerobat	0356		4. 7.79	N.Grantham	Bourne	6.11.00
G-BFZU	Reims Cessna FA.152 Aerobat	0355		29. 6.79	Redhill Air Services Ltd	Redhill	10. 2.02T
G-BFZV	Reims Cessna F.172M	1093	SE-FZR	2.11.78	R.Thomas	AAC Middle Wallop	7. 3.00T

G-BGAA – G-BGZZ

Regn	Type	C/n	P/I	Date	Owner/operator	Probable Base	CA Expy
G-BGAA	Cessna 152 II	152-81894	N67529	18. 7.78	PJC (Leasing) Ltd	Stapleford	22. 6.01T
G-BGAB	Reims Cessna F.152 II	1531		13.10.78	TG Aviation Ltd	Manston	7. 4.00T
					(Op Thanet Flying Club)		
G-BGAD	Reims Cessna F.152 II	1532		13.10.78	Keen Leasing (IoM) Ltd	Ronaldsway	29.10.00T
G-BGAE	Reims Cessna F.152 II	1540		8.11.78	Klingair Ltd	Conington	30. 4.00T
G-BGAF	Reims Cessna FA.152 Aerobat	0349		13.10.78	M.F.Hatt, P.E.Preston, R.W.Harris, A.Jahanfar & D.S.Woolf		
					(Op Southend Flying Club)	Southend	1. 8.00T
G-BGAG	Reims Cessna F.172N Skyhawk II	1754	"G-KING"	13.10.78	Aerohire Ltd	Dunkeswell	11. 5.01T
					(Op Devon School of Flying)		
G-BGAH*	Clutton Fred Srs.II	PFA/29-10324		15. 2.78	Not known	Hethersett, Wymondham	
					(Under construction 8.97)		
G-BGAJ	Reims Cessna F.182Q Skylane II	0096		13.10.78	Ground Airport Services Ltd	Guernsey	4. 5.00
G-BGAU*	Rearwin 9000L Sportster	572D	N18548	23.10.78	Not known	(Ventnor,IoW)	
			NC18548		(For rebuild - status uncertain)		
G-BGAX	PA-28-140 Cherokee F	28-7325409	PH-NSH	20.10.78	C.D.Brack	Breighton	17. 6.02
G-BGAZ	Cameron V-77 HAFB	439		20.10.78	C.J.Madigan & D.H.McGibbon	Bristol	1. 8.00A
	(New envelope ?)				"Silicon Chip/Robocop"		
G-BGBA	Robin R.2100A Club	133	F-OCBJ	2. 5.78	D.Faulkner	Headcorn	24. 3.00
G-BGBE	SAN Jodel DR.1050 Ambassadeur	260	F-BJYT	29.11.78	J.A. & B.Mawby	Gravely	6. 9.01

Regn	Type	C/n	P/I	Date	Owner/operator	Probable Base	CA Expy
G-BGBF	Druine D.31A Turbulent (VW1600)	PFA/1658		24.10.78	S.M.Cryer	(Lincoln)	27. 7.00P
G-BGBG	PA-28-181 Archer II	28-7990012	N39730	2.11.78	Harlow Printing Ltd	Newcastle	27. 4.00
G-BGBI	Reims Cessna F.150L	0688	PH-LUA	28.11.78	A.S.Bamrah t/a Falcon Flying Services	Cardiff	19. 3.01T
G-BGBK*	PA-38-112 Tomahawk	38-78A0433		2.11.78	Not known (Temp unregd 30.12.96)Sandtoft		5. 9.96
G-BGBN	PA-38-112 Tomahawk	38-78A0511		29.11.78	Bonus Aviation Ltd	Cranfield	14. 7.00T
G-BGBP	Reims Cessna F.152 II	1546		8.11.78	Stapleford Flying Club Ltd (Damaged Stapleford 18.8.92; status uncertain)	Stapleford	19. 6.94T
G-BGBR	Reims Cessna F.172N Skyhawk II	1772		8.11.78	A.S.Bamrah t/a Falcon Flying Services (Op Willowair Flying Club)	Southend	16. 2.01T
G-BGBU*	Auster AOP.9	B5/10/131	XN435	8.11.78	P.Neilson (On rebuild 1992)	Egham	
G-BGBW	PA-38-112 Tomahawk	38-78A0670		8.11.78	Truman Aviation Ltd	Nottingham	19. 6.00T
G-BGBY	PA-38-112 Tomahawk	38-78A0711		8.11.78	Cheshire Flying Services Ltd	Liverpool	18. 3.00T
G-BGBZ	Rockwell Commander 114	14423	N5878N	9.10.78	R.S.Fenwick	Rochester	7. 5.01
G-BGCG*	Douglas C-47A-85DL Dakota	20002	N5595T	28.11.78	Datran Holdings Ltd Rotary Farm, Hatch G-BGCG/Sp.AF T3-27/N49V/NC50322/43-15536 (Stored 8.95)		8.8.80PF
G-BGCM	Gulfstream AA-5A Cheetah	AA5A-0835		23. 3.79	G. & S.A.Jones Linley Hill, Beverley		28.10.00T
G-BGCO	PA-44-180 Seminole	44-7995128	N2103D	20.12.78	J.R.Henderson (Op British Aerospace plc)	Dunsfold	2. 7.00
G-BGCX*	Taylor JT.2 Titch	PFA/3221		23.11.78	G.M.R.Walters (Cancelled as PWFU 27.3.99)	(Kingswinford)	
G-BGCY	Taylor JT.1 Monoplane (VW1600)	PFA/55-10370		23.11.78	M.T.Taylor	(Lincoln)	14. 3.00P
G-BGDA	Boeing 737-236ADV	21790	N1285E	4.12.81	British Airways plc (Martha Masanabo/Ndebele t/s)	Gatwick	3.12.02T
G-BGDE	Boeing 737-236ADV	21794		12. 3.80	British Airways plc (Sterntaler/Bauhaus t/s)	Gatwick	12. 3.01T
G-BGDF	Boeing 737-236ADV	21795		20. 3.80	British Airways plc (Delftblue Daybreak t/s)	Gatwick	20. 3.01T
G-BGDJ	Boeing 737-236ADV	21799		7. 5.80	British Airways plc (Waves & Cranes t/s)	Manchester	8. 5.01T
G-BGDL	Boeing 737-236ADV	21801		9. 6.80	British Airways plc (Mountain of the Birds/Benyhone Tartan t/s)	Gatwick	10. 6.01T
G-BGDO	Boeing 737-236ADV	21803		25. 7.80	British Airways plc (Whale Rider t/s)	Manchester	27. 7.01T
G-BGDR	Boeing 737-236ADV	21805	N1786B	18. 9.80	British Airways plc (Dove/Colum t/s)	Gatwick	7. 9.01T
G-BGDS	Boeing 737-236ADV	21806		18. 9.80	British Airways plc	Heathrow	28. 9.01T
G-BGDT	Boeing 737-236ADV	21807		4.11.80	British Airways plc (Animals and Trees/Kg-Oocoan-Naka-Hiian-Thee-E t/s)	Manchester	5.11.01T
G-BGEA	Reims Cessna F.150M	1396	OY-BJK	22. 3.79	Mrs C.J.Hopewell	Sibson	23. 6.00T
G-BGED	Cessna U206F Stationair	U206-02279	LN-BGQ N1911U	12.12.78	Chapman Aviation Ltd	Sibson	28. 3.00
G-BGEE	Evans VP-1 (VW1679)	PFA/62-10287		27.11.78	R.Wheeler & B.E.Holmes (Norwich/Ely) (Wings at Priory Farm, Tibenham 8.97)		16. 5.95P
G-BGEF*	Wassmer Jodel D.112	1309	F-BMYL	7.12.78	Not known North Coates (Damaged North Coates 8.10.95; stored 6.96)		12. 9.96P
G-BGEH	Monnett Sonerai II 209 & PFA/15-10254 (VW2340)			1.12.78	P.C.Dowbor	Enstone	16. 8.96P
G-BGEI	Oldfield Baby Lakes PFA/10-10016 (Continental A65) (Fuselage of PFA/1576 incorporated during construction)			1.12.78	A.R.Robinson	(Macclesfield)	12. 7.00P
G-BGEK	PA-38-112 Tomahawk	38-78A0575		13.12.78	Cheshire Flying Services Ltd t/a Ravenair	Liverpool	26. 3.00T
G-BGEP	Cameron D-38 Hot-Air Airship	442		6.12.78	Aeronord SAS	Milan, Italy	8. 6.99A
G-BGES*	Phoenix Currie Wot JR.1 & PFA/58-10291			30.11.78	H.F.Moffatt Woodlow Farm, Bosbury (Stored 1989)		
G-BGEW	SNCAN NC.854S (Continental A65)	63	F-BFSJ	13.12.78	Tavair Ltd	Holywell	11. 5.00P
G-BGEX*	Brookland Mosquito Mk.2 (VW1800)	JB.1		13.12.78	Not known Horsford, Norwich (Stored 9.97)		14. 8.81P
G-BGFC	Evans VP-2 V2-1278 & PFA/63-10441 (VW1834)			15.12.78	S.W.C.Hollins	Llandegla	29. 9.93P
G-BGFF	Clutton FRED Srs.II PFA/29-10261 (VW1834)			18.12.78	I.Daniels	Popham	24. 5.00P
G-BGFG	Gulfstream AA-5A Cheetah	AA5A-0687	N6158A	25. 1.79	Plane Talking Ltd	Elstree	22. 5.00T
G-BGFH	Reims Cessna F182Q Skylane II	0105		18. 1.79	Ray Thompson Engineering Ltd (Rebuilt with fuselage of G-EMMA 1994/95; original fuselage scrapped) Lower Wasing Field, Brimpton		13. 5.01T
G-BGFI	Gulfstream AA-5A Cheetah	AA5A-0733	N6142A	5. 3.79	I.J.Hay & A.Nayyar t/a GFI Group	Biggin Hill	21.10.00

Regn	Type	C/n	P/I	Date	Owner/operator	Probable Base	CA Expy
G-BGFJ	Jodel D.9 Bebe (VW1600)	PFA/1324		11.12.78	M.D.Mold	Watchford Farm, Yarcombe	22. 6.00P
G-BGFK*	Evans VP-1	PFA/62-10343		20.12.78	I.N.M.Cameron		
					Wathstones Farm, Newby Wiske		
					(Stored 10.97: cancelled by CAA 7.4.99)		
G-BGFT	PA-34-200T Seneca II	34-7870218	N9714C	17. 1.79	Oxford Aviation Services Ltd	Oxford	1. 9.00T
G-BGFX	Reims Cessna F.152 II	1555		28.12.78	A.S.Bamrah	Biggin Hill	23. 6.91T
					t/a Falcon Flying Services (Spares use 2.95)		
G-BGGA	Bellanca 7GCBC Citabria 150S	1104-79		5. 2.79	L.A.King	North Connel	2.11.00
G-BGGB	Bellanca 7GCBC Citabria 150S	1105-79		7. 2.79	G.H.N.Chamberlain	Rattlesden	2.12.01
G-BGGC	Bellanca 7GCBC Citabria 150S	1106-79		5. 2.79	R.P.Ashfield & J.M.Stone		
					Gorwell Farm, Littlebredy, Dorset		18. 9.00
G-BGGD	Bellanca 8GCBC Scout	284-78		5. 2.79	Bristol & Gloucestershire Gliding Club Ltd		
					Nympsfield		22. 6.01
G-BGGE	PA-38-112 Tomahawk	38-79A0161		10. 1.79	Truman Aviation Ltd	Nottingham	5. 6.00T
G-BGGF	PA-38-112 Tomahawk	38-79A0162		10. 1.79	Truman Aviation Ltd	Nottingham	15.10.94T
	(Stored 7.99)						
G-BGGG	PA-38-112 Tomahawk	38-79A0163		10. 1.79	Teesside Flt Centre Ltd	Teesside	13. 5.01T
G-BGGI	PA-38-112 Tomahawk	38-79A0165		10. 1.79	Truman Aviation Ltd	Nottingham	12. 2.01T
G-BGGL	PA-38-112 Tomahawk	38-79A0169		10. 1.79	Grunwick Processing Laboratories Ltd		
					(Op Bonus Aviation)	Cranfield	5. 6.00T
G-BGGM	PA-38-112 Tomahawk	38-79A0170		10. 1.79	Grunwick Processing Laboratories Ltd		
					(Op Bonus Aviation)	Cranfield	12. 6.00T
G-BGGN	PA-38-112 Tomahawk	38-79A0171		10. 1.79	Domeastral Ltd	Elstree	20. 7.00T
G-BGGO	Reims Cessna F.152 II	1569		8. 3.79	East Midlands Flying School Ltd		
						East Midlands	27. 6.00T
G-BGGP	Reims Cessna F.152 II	1580		8. 3.79	East Midlands Flying School Ltd		
						East Midlands	28. 9.00T
G-BGGU	Wallis WA-116/RR (Subaru EA61)	702		28.12.78	K.H.Wallis	Reymerston Hall	
					(Noted 5.99)		
G-BGGV	Wallis WA-120 Srs.2	703		28.12.78	K.H.Wallis (Not built) (Reymerston Hall)		
G-BGGW	Wallis WA-122/RR (Continental O-240-A)	704		28.12.78	K.H.Wallis	Reymerston Hall	24. 4.98P
					(Noted 5.99)		
G-BGHE	Convair L-13A-CO	-	N1132V 47-346	4. 8.80	J.M.Davis	Wichita, USA	
					(Long-term rebuild)		
G-BGHF*	Westland WG.30 Srs.100-60	WA.001.P		4. 1.79	The Helicopter Museum	Weston-super-Mare	1. 8.86S
G-BGHI	Reims Cessna F.152 II	1560		15. 1.79	Taxon Ltd	Shoreham	8. 5.00T
G-BGHM	Robin R.1180T Aiglon	227		19. 2.79	H.Price	Blackpool	23.10.00
G-BGHP	Beechcraft 76 Duchess	ME-190	N60132	16. 1.79	Magenta Ltd	Exeter	22. 4.00T
					(Op Airways Flight Training)		
G-BGHS	Cameron N-31 HAFB	501		15. 1.79	W.R.Teasdale "Blackjack"	Maidenhead	17. 1.00A
G-BGHT	Falconar F-12 (Lycoming O-290)	PFA/22-10040		17. 1.79	C.R.Coates	Sneaton Thorpe, Whitby	
G-BGHU	North American T-6G-NF Texan	182-729 Fr.AF 115042/51-15042	FAP1707	22. 1.79	C.E.Bellhouse	Headcorn	17. 5.00P
					(As "115042/TA-042" in USAF c/s) "Carly"		
G-BGHV	Cameron V-77 HAFB	483		12. 1.79	E.Davies	Penlan Farm, Llanwrda	28. 5.00A
					t/a Adeilad Claddings "Adclad"		
G-BGHY	Taylor JT.1 Monoplane (VW1600)	PFA/1455		12. 1.79	R.A.Hand	RAF Barkston Heath	21. 6.00P
					"Shy Talk"		
G-BGHZ	Clutton FRED Srs.II	PFA/29-10445		12. 1.79	A.Smith	(Swansea)	
					(Under construction Birmingham 1999)		
G-BGIB	Cessna 152 II	152-82161	N68169	3. 7.79	Redhill Air Services Ltd	Redhill	26. 4.01T
G-BGID	Westland-Bell 47G-3B1 (Line No. WAN/31)	WA/340	XT181	28. 2.79	M.J.Cuttell	Gloucestershire	10. 5.02
G-BGIG	PA-38-112 Tomahawk	38-78A0773		23. 1.79	Air Claire Ltd	Manchester	8. 4.01T
G-BGIO	Montgomerie-Bensen B.8MR (Rotax 503)	PFA G/01-1259		11. 1.79	R.M.Savage & F.G.Shepherd	Carlisle	4. 7.00P
					t/a Great Orton Group		
G-BGIP	Colt 56A HAFB	038		2. 1.79	R.D.Allen & M.Walker	Bristol	21. 6.94A
					"The Snake"		
G-BGIU	Reims Cessna F.172H	0620	PH-VIT	26. 2.79	D W Clifton & M Ruggieri		
					t/a Skyhawk F/Group	Top Farm, Royston	22. 3.01
G-BGIX	Helio H.295 Super Courier	1467	(G-BGAO) N68861	17.10.79	Caroline M.Lee		
					Fanners Farm, Great Waltham, Essex		23.11.01
G-BGIY	Reims Cessna F.172N Skyhawk II	1824		31. 1.79	S.Kerr t/a Glasgow 172 Group	Glasgow	21.12.00T
G-BGJE	Boeing 737-236ADV	22026		21. 3.80	British Airways plc	Gatwick	21. 3.01T
					(Rendezvous c/s)		
G-BGJU	Cameron V-65 HAFB	499		5. 2.79	Janet A.Folkes "Spoils"	Loughborough	4. 4.93A
G-BGKC	Socata Rallye 110ST	3262		25. 4.79	J.H.Cranmer & T.A.Timms	Bidford	8. 9.99
G-BGKD	Socata Rallye 110ST	3263		25. 4.79	P.A.Cairns	Exeter	23. 7.98T
					(Damaged Stone Hill, Exeter 27.10.97 & fuselage stored 2.99)		

Regn	Type	C/n	P/I	Date	Owner/operator	Probable Base	CA Expy
G-BGKJ*	MBB Bo.105D	S.128	D-HDDV	20. 4.79	Bond Helicopters Ltd	Bourn	19. 4.88T
	(Ditched nr Mossbank, Shetland Isles 25.4.89; used as demonstration airframe 7.93)						
G-BGKO	Gardan GY-20 Minicab	PFA/1827		14. 2.79	R.B.Webber	Hayrish Farm, Okehampton	
	(Stored incomplete 7.97)						
G-BGKS	PA-28-161 Warrior II	28-7916221	N9562N	12. 2.79	Marnham Investments Ltd	Newtownards	20. 3.00T
	(Op Woodgate Executive Air Services)						
G-BGKT	Auster AOP.9	B5/10/137	XN441	28.12.78	E.Wright	South Lodge Farm, Widmerpool	
	(c/n possibly B5/10/139 ?)				t/a Auster Nine Group (On rebuild 9.97: as "XN441")		
G-BGKU	PA-28R-201 Arrow III	28R-7837237	N31585	8. 3.79	Aerolease Ltd.	Conington	12. 1.01T
G-BGKV	PA-28R-201 Cherokee Arrow III	28R-7737156	N44985	21. 5.79	R.Haverson & R.G.Watson	Shipdham	2. 3.01
G-BGKY	PA-38-112 Tomahawk	38-78A0737		2. 3.79	Prospect Air Ltd	Manchester	7. 7.00T
	(Op Manchester School of Flying)						
G-BGKZ	Auster J/5F Aiglet Trainer	2776	F-BGKZ	15.12.78	Deborah Hatelie	(Liverpool)	25. 2.95
	(Damaged nr Nayland 30.1.93)						
G-BGLA	PA-38-112 Tomahawk	38-78A0741		9. 3.79	B.H. & P.M.Illston	Norwich	6. 8.00T
	t/a Norwich School of Flying						
G-BGLB*	Bede BD.5B (Hirth 230R)	3796 & PFA/14-10085		2. 3.79	The Science Museum	Wroughton	4. 8.81P*
G-BGLF	Evans VP-1 Srs.2 (VW1834)	PFA/62-10388		28. 2.79	J.B.McNab	(Claylands, Cowbit)	1. 8.00P
G-BGLG	Cessna 152 II	152-82092	N67909	11. 4.79	A.T. Wright	Leeds-Bradford	1. 7.01T
G-BGLK*	Monnett Sonerai IIL (VW1783)	PFA/15-10304		24. 2.78	N.M.Smorthit	RAF Linton-on-Ouse	31. 8.89P
	(Stored 10.92: cancelled by CAA 6.3.99)						
G-BGLN	Reims Cessna FA.152 Aerobat	0354		8. 3.79	Bournemouth Flying Club Ltd	Bournemouth	5. 8.00T
G-BGLO	Reims Cessna F.172N Skyhawk II	1900		8. 3.79	A.H.Slaughter	Southend	27.11.00
G-BGLS	Oldfield Super Baby Lakes (Lycoming O-235)	PFA/10-10237		11.12.78	J.F.Dowe (Status uncertain)	(Ipswich)	18. 6.88P
G-BGLW	PA-34-200-2 Seneca	34-7250132	OY-BDZ SE-FYS	2. 6.78	London Executive Aviation Ltd	Stapleford	28. 8.00T
G-BGLZ	Stits SA-3A Playboy (Continental C90)	71-100	N9996	19. 6.79	S.A.Cooke	Mitchell's Farm, Wilburton	10.11.00P
	t/a Stitts Playboy (Fenland) Flying Group						
G-BGMA	Druine D.31 Turbulent	PFA/48-10438		27.11.78	G.C.Masterton (Not built)	(Guildford)	
G-BGME	SIPA 903	96	G-BCML "G-BCHU"/F-BGHU	1. 1.81	M.Emery & C.A.Suckling	Guildford	17. 6.94P
	(Stored 1995)						
G-BGMJ	CAB GY-201 Minicab	12	F-BGMJ	19. 6.78	S.L. & A.W.Wakefield, J.F.Hawkins & N.Birchall	Conington	19. 8.99P
G-BGMN	HS.748 Srs.2A/347	1766	PK-OCH	9. 3.79	Emerald Airways Ltd	Liverpool	19.11.01T
			G-BGMN/9Y-TGH/G-BGMN/9Y-TGH				
G-BGMO	HS.748 Srs.2A/347	1767	ZK-MCB	9. 3.79	Emerald Airways Ltd	Liverpool	22. 4.02T
	(Freight conversion mid/late 1999)		G-BGMO/9Y-TGI/V2-LDB/9Y-TGI/(G-BGMO)				
G-BGMP	Reims Cessna F.172G	0240	PH-BNV	26. 3.79	R.W.Collings	Hinton-in-The-Hedges	24. 3.01
G-BGMR	Barritault JB-01 Minicab (Continental C90)	PFA/56-10153		12. 3.79	R.A.M.Smith	White Waltham	29. 9.99P
	t/a Mike Romeo Flying Group						
G-BGMS	Taylor JT.2 Titch	MS.1 & PFA/60-10400		20.10.78	M.A.J.Spice	(Middlewich, Cheshire)	
G-BGMT	Socata Rallye 235E	13126		14. 9.78	C.G.Wheeler	(Newton Aycliffe)	13.12.00
G-BGMU	Westland-Bell 47G-3B1 (Line No. WAP/83)	WA/514	XT807	14. 5.79	V.L.J. & V.English	Whittlesey, Peterborough	14. 1.95
G-BGMV	Scheibe SF-25B Falke	4648	D-KEBG	15. 5.79	P.Turner	Halesland	16.11.01
	t/a Mendip Falke Flying Group						
G-BGND	Reims Cessna F.172N Skyhawk II	1576	PH-AYI (F-GAQA)	3. 3.78	A.J.M.Freeman	Andrewsfield	19. 8.02
G-BGNH*	Short SD.3-30 Var.200	SH.3035	N331L G-BGNH	22. 3.79	Newcastle Airport Fire Service	Newcastle	22.9.79F
G-BGNS*	Reims Cessna F.172N Skyhawk II	1901		23.10.79	F & H (Acft) Ltd	Tattershall Thorpe	6. 1.89T
	(Damaged Shoreham 16.10.87; wreck stored 10.92)						
G-BGNT	Reims Cessna F.152 II	1644		23.10.79	Klingair Ltd	Conington	1. 3.01T
G-BGNV	Gulfstream GA-7 Cougar	GA7-0078	N790GA	20. 4.79	G.J.Bissex	Bristol	25.11.00T
G-BGOD	Colt 77A HAFB	040		4. 4.79	C. & M.D.Steuer "Harvey Wallbanger"	London NW1	18. 6.97A
G-BGOG	PA-28-161 Warrior II	28-7916350	N9639N	8. 6.79	W.D.Moore	Cranfield	8.10.00
G-BGOI	Cameron O-56 HAFB	526		4. 4.79	S.H.Budd "Skymaster"	Pewsey	13. 5.87A
G-BGOL	PA-28R-201T Turbo Arrow III	28R-7803335	N36705	11. 4.79	Valley Flying Co Ltd	Valley Farm, Stafford	14. 5.00
G-BGON	Gulfstream GA-7 Cougar	GA7-0095	N9527Z	24. 4.79	J.P.E.Walsh	Elstree	4. 8.00T
	t/a Walsh Aviation (Op Cabair)						
G-BGOO*	Colt Flame 56SS HAFB ("Smiling Flame" Shape)	039		27. 4.79	British Balloon Museum "Mr Gas"	Newbury	NE(A)
G-BGOP	Dassault Falcon 20F	406/557	F-WMKF	19. 4.79	Nissan UK Ltd	Heathrow	21.10.00T
	(Op by Falcon Jet Centre)						

Regn	Type	C/n	P/I	Date	Owner/operator	Probable Base	CA Expy
G-BGOR	North American AT-6D-NT Harvard III	FAP1508		28. 3.79	M.L. Sargeant	(Goudhurst)	20. 5.99P
	(Reported as c/n 88-14880)	88-14863			SAAF7504/EX935/41-33908 (As "14863/TA-863" in USAAF c/s)		
G-BGPA	Cessna 182Q Skylane II	182-66538	C-GYBW (N94935)	11. 7.79	J.J. & J.Walsh t/a Papa Alpha Group	Bodmin	22. 4.01
G-BGPB	CCF Harvard 4 (T-6J-CCF Texan)	CCF4-538	FAP1747	4. 4.79	J.Romain	Duxford	6. 6.90P
			WGAF BF+050/WGAF AA+050/53-4619 (Op The Aircraft Restoration Co)				
	(Damaged Little Gransden 15.6.89; on rebuild 11.97) (As "1747" in Portuguese AF c/s)						
G-BGPD	Piper J3C-65 Cub (L-4H-PI)	12040	F-BFQP	18. 4.79	P.D.Whiteman Marsh Hill Farm, Aylesbury		16. 3.99P
			F-BDTP/44-79744 (As "479744/49/M" in 92nd Armoured FA Btn, US 9th Army c/s)				
	(Officially regd as c/n 10478 which is ex 43-29187/00-ADI/F-BFQP; G-BGPD has Frame No.11867						
	which is ex 44-79744/F-BDTP; presumably the fuselages were exchanged in France - see G-BCOM)						
G-BGPF*	Thunder Ax6-56Z HAFB	206		13. 7.79	P.J.Bish "Pepsi"	Hungerford	27. 6.82A
G-BGPH	Gulfstream AA-5B Tiger	AA5B-1248	(G-BGRU)	14. 8.79	Shipping & Airlines Ltd	Biggin Hill	30. 9.01T
	(Damaged landing Rochester 14.3.99)						
G-BGPI	Plumb BGP.1 Biplane (Jabiru)	PFA/83-10359		26. 6.78	B.G.Plumb	Hinton-in-The-Hedges	4. 8.00P
G-BGPJ	PA-28-161 Warrior II	28-7916288	N9602N	24. 4.79	West Lancs Warrior Co Ltd	Woodvale	24. 6.00
G-BGPK	Gulfstream AA-5B Tiger	AA5B-1258	(G-BGRV)	28. 8.79	Ann Green	Elstree	4. 9.98T
G-BGPL	PA-28-161 Warrior II	28-7916289	N9603N	20. 4.79	TG Aviation Ltd (Op Thanet Flying Club)	Manston	12. 6.00T
G-BGPM	Evans VP-2 (VW2075)	PFA/63-10335		17. 4.79	M.G.Reilly (Open storage Old Sarum 9.91 - status uncertain)	(Basingstoke)	29. 4.86P
G-BGPN	PA-18-150 Super Cub	18-7909044		12. 4.79	Clacton Aero Club (1988) Ltd (Damaged Nayland 27.1.90; on rebuild 5.93)	Clacton	7. 3.92T
G-BGPU	PA-28-140 Cherokee F	28-7325282	PH-GNT	25. 4.79	Air Navigation & Trading Co Ltd	Blackpool	17. 8.00T
G-BGPZ	Morane MS.890A Rallye Commodore 145	10284	F-BLBD	3. 5.79	A.S.Cowan t/a Popham Flying Group G-BGPZ	Popham	28. 1.02
G-BGRC	PA-28-140 Cherokee B	28-26208	SE-FHF	12. 6.79	Tecair Aviation Ltd	Swanton Morley	26.10.97T
G-BGRE	Beechcraft 200 Super King Air	BB-568		8. 5.79	Martin-Baker (Engineering) Ltd	Chalgrove	23.10.02T
G-BGRG	Beechcraft 76 Duchess	ME-233		8. 5.79	Liddell Aircraft Ltd (Op Langtry Flying Group)	Bournemouth	24. 2.02T
G-BGRH	Robin DR.400 2+2	1411		21. 5.79	T.A.White t/a Bagby Aviation	Bagby	4.11.00T
G-BGRI	CEA Jodel DR.1050 Sicile	540	F-BLZJ	27. 4.79	R.T.Gunn & J.R.Redhead	Sherburn in Elmet	29. 5.00
G-BGRK	PA-38-112 Tomahawk	38-79A0983		8. 5.79	Goodwood Road Racing Co Ltd	Goodwood	14.12.99T
G-BGRL	PA-38-112 Tomahawk	38-79A0917		25. 4.79	G.G.Mepham	Goodwood	3. 5.00T
G-BGRM	PA-38-112 Tomahawk	38-79A1067		1. 8.79	Goodwood Road Racing Co Ltd	Goodwood	8. 5.00T
G-BGRN	PA-38-112 Tomahawk	38-79A0897		25. 4.79	Goodwood Road Racing Co Ltd	Goodwood	12. 2.00T
G-BGRO	Reims Cessna F.172M Skyhawk II	1129	PH-KAB	4. 5.79	Alarmond Ltd t/a Edinburgh Flying Club	Edinburgh	19.11.00T
G-BGRR	PA-38-112 Tomahawk	38-78A0336	OO-FLT	8. 5.79	Goodair Leasing Ltd	Cardiff	23. 8.02T
G-BGRS	Thunder Ax7-77Z HAFB	203		21. 5.79	P.M.Gaines & P.B.Fountain "Hassall Homes"	Stockton/Luton	19. 8.95A
G-BGRT	Steen Skybolt RCT.001 & PFA/64-10171 (Lycoming O-360)			12. 9.78	J.H.Kimber & O.Meier	Damyns Hall, Upminster	30. 9.00P
G-BGRX	PA-38-112 Tomahawk	38-79A0609		11. 5.79	Bonus Aviation Ltd	Cranfield	30.10.00T
G-BGSA	Socata MS.892E Rallye 150GT	12838	F-GAKC	29. 5.79	D.H.Tonkin	Bodmin	4. 6.01
G-BGSB*	Percival P.56 Provost T.1	PAC/F/057	7992M WV494	21. 5.79	Military Museum of Oman (As "WV494/04")	Oman	19. 7.82P
G-BGSG	PA-44-180 Seminole	44-7995004	N36538	21. 5.79	D.J.McSorley	Enniskillen	25. 8.01
G-BGSH	PA-38-112 Tomahawk	38-79A0562		11. 5.79	Scotia Safari Ltd (Op Carlisle Flt Centre)	Carlisle	1. 9.02T
G-BGSI	PA-38-112 Tomahawk	38-79A0564		18. 5.79	Cheshire Flying Services Ltd t/a Ravenair	Liverpool	14. 9.00T
G-BGSJ	Piper J3C-65 Cub (L-4A-PI) (Frame No.8917)	8781	F-BGXJ Fr.AF/42-36657	21. 5.79	A.J.Higgins	(Lanport)	20. 9.99P
G-BGST	Thunder Ax7-65 Bolt HAFB	217		14. 5.79	J.L.Bond "Black Fred"	Haywards Heath	23. 3.91A
G-BGSV	Reims Cessna F.172N Skyhawk II	1830		1. 8.79	Southwell Air Services Ltd	Linley Hill, Leven	2.12.00
G-BGSW	Beechcraft F33 Bonanza	CD-1253	OH-BDD	30. 5.79	Marketprior Ltd	Swansea	28. 4.99T
G-BGSX	Reims Cessna F.152 II	1603		29. 5.79	Denham Aircraft Maintenance Ltd	Denham	25. 5.01T
G-BGSY	Gulfstream GA-7 Cougar	GA7-0096		4. 6.79	Plane Talking Ltd	Elstree	29. 4.02T
G-BGTC	Auster AOP.9	AUS/168	XP282	12.10.79	P.T.Bolton South Lodge Farm, Widmerpool (As "XP282") (Damaged Widmerpool 2.10.96)		9. 6.97P
G-BGTF	PA-44-180 Seminole	44-7995287	N2131Y	20. 6.79	NG Trustees & Nominees Ltd	Jersey	26. 4.00
G-BGTG	PA-23-250 Aztec F	27-7954061	N2454M	23. 5.79	Keen Leasing (IOM) Ltd	(Castletown)	21.10.00T
G-BGTI	Piper J3C-65 Cub (L-4J-PI) (Rotax 582) (Frame No.12770)	12940	F-BFFL 44-80644	17. 5.79	A.P.Broad	Brandy Wharf, Waddington	1. 8.00P
G-BGTJ	PA-28-180 Cherokee Archer	28-7405083	OY-BIO SE-GAH	3. 7.79	Serendipity Aviation Ltd	Gloucestershire	8.12.00

Regn	Type	C/n	P/I	Date	Owner/operator	Probable Base	CA Expy
G-BGTP	Robin HR.100/210 Safari	188	(G-BGTN) F-BVCP	25. 6.79	J.C.Parker	Thruxton	18. 1.01
G-BGTT	Cessna 310R II	310R-1641	N1AN (N2635D)	13. 7.79	Aviation Beauport Ltd	Jersey	5. 2.01T
G-BGTX	SAN Jodel D.117	698	F-BIDI	22. 6.79	C.Adams & D.Wain t/a The Madley Flying Group	Shobdon	4. 8.00P
G-BGUB	PA-32-300 Six	32-7940252	N2387U	29.11.79	A.J.Diplock	Biggin Hill	31. 1.01
G-BGUY	Cameron V-56 HAFB	441		27. 9.78	J.L.Guy "Good Guy"	Skipton	13.10.95A
G-BGVB	CEA DR.315 Petit Prince	308	F-BPOP	20. 7.79	C.P.Jones & J.A.Alliss t/a Victor Bravo Group	Popham	25. 7.02
G-BGVE	Scintex CP.1310-C3 Super Emeraude	931	F-BMJE	8. 6.79	R.T.L.Arkell t/a Victor Echo Group "Mon Papillon" Little Battleflats Farm, Ellistown, Coalville		22. 7.00P
G-BGVH	Beechcraft 76 Duchess	ME-260		8. 6.79	W.J. & J.C.M.Golden t/a Valco Marketing Bowerchalke, Salisbury		22. 6.01
G-BGVK	PA-28-161 Warrior II	28-7816400	PH-WPT G-BGVK/N6244C	13. 6.79	D.S.Wells	Fenland	17. 5.01
G-BGVL*	PA-38-112 Tomahawk	38-78A0263	N9963T	13. 6.79	Shirley A Boyall (Shipdham) (Crashed Priory Farm, Tibenham 16.7.93; spares for G-BPHI)		5. 2.95T
G-BGVN	PA-28RT-201 Arrow IV	28R-7918168	N2846U	22. 6.79	H.S.Davies	Stapleford	10. 9.00
G-BGVS	Reims Cessna F.172M	0992	PH-HVS (PH-LUK)	3. 5.79	J.W.Tulloch t/a Kirkwall Flying Club	Kirkwall	14.12.00T
G-BGVT	Cessna R182 Skylane RGII	R182-00244	N3162C	28. 6.79	J.M.Bain t/a Bain Transport	Perth	9.11.00
G-BGVU	PA-28-180 Cherokee D	28-5359	PH-AVU	5. 7.79	P.E.Toleman (Op Ravenair) (Damaged Welshpool 14.1.97)	Manchester	2. 6.97T
G-BGVV	Gulfstream AA-5A Cheetah	AA5A-0750		27. 6.79	A.H.McVicar	Prestwick	1. 4.01T
G-BGVW	Gulfstream AA-5A Cheetah	AA5A-0774		21. 6.79	Computech Aviation Ltd	Southampton	14. 8.00T
G-BGVY	Gulfstream AA-5B Tiger	AA5B-1080	(G-BGVU) (F-GBOO)	21. 8.79	R.J.C.Neal-Smith	Shoreham	5.10.00
G-BGVZ	PA-28-181 Archer II	28-7990528	N2886A	12. 7.79	W.Walsh & S.R.Mitchell	Liverpool	3. 7.00T
G-BGWC	Robin DR.400/180 Regent	1420		26. 6.79	D.C.Shepherd	Rochester	8. 2.01T
G-BGWH	PA-18-150 Super Cub	18-7605	ST-ABR G-ARSR	18. 6.79	V.D.Speck (Damaged Clacton 7.7.92; stored 9.97)	Clacton	14. 6.93T
G-BGWJ	Sikorsky S-61N Mk.II	61-819		20. 8.79	British Executive Air Services Ltd (Op by Bristow Helicopters) "Monadh Mor" Aberdeen		12.10.00T
G-BGWK	Sikorsky S-61N Mk.II	61-820	N1346C G-BGWK	10. 9.79	British Executive Air Services Ltd (Op by Bristow Helicopters) "Dun Robin" Aberdeen		28.11.02T
G-BGWM	PA-28-181 Archer II	28-7990458	N2817Y	29. 6.79	Thames Valley Flying Club Ltd	Booker	10. 5.00T
G-BGWN	PA-38-112 Tomahawk	38-79A0918		2. 7.79	Teesside Flight Centre Ltd	Teesside	25. 3.02T
G-BGWO	Jodel D.112 (Built Ets Valladeau)	227	F-BHGQ	22. 6.79	R.C.Williams t/a G-BGWO Group	Breighton	21. 9.99P
G-BGWR	Cessna U206A Super Skywagon	U206-0653	G-DISC G-BGWR/PH-OTD/N4953F	6. 7.79	C.M.J.Parton	Tilstock	20.10.00
G-BGWS	Enstrom 280C Shark	1050		8.11.76	JHS Consultants Ltd	(London W1)	20. 5.99
G-BGWU	PA-38-112 Tomahawk	38-79A0788		2. 7.79	J.S. & L.M.Markey	Draycott Farm, Chiseldon	1.12.00
G-BGWV	Aeronca 7AC Champion	7AC-4082	OO-GRI OO-TWR	23. 8.79	J.A.Webb t/a RFC Flying Group (Alton) (Damaged Popham 8.6.86; status uncertain)		10.10.86P
G-BGWW	PA-23-250 Turbo Aztec E	27-4587	OO-ABH N13971	15. 6.79	Kathleen Hobbs t/a Aldergrove Flight Training Centre	Aldergrove	28. 9.01T
G-BGWY	Thunder Ax6-56Z HAFB	229		23. 8.79	P.J.Eley	Braintree	19. 8.95A
G-BGWZ*	Eclipse Super Eagle	ESE.007		29. 6.79	Fleet Air Arm Museum (Stored 3.96)	Wroughton	
G-BGXA	Piper J3C-65 Cub (L-4H-PI) (Frame No.10587 - regd with c/n 11170)	10762	F-BGXA Fr.AF/43-29471	1. 3.78	K.Nicholls Broadheath, Worcester (As "329471/F/44" in USAAC c/s)		16. 8.00P
G-BGXB	PA-38-112 Tomahawk	38-79A1007		2. 7.79	Signtest Ltd	Cardiff	10. 3.01T
G-BGXC	Socata TB-10 Tobago	35		19.10.79	D.H.Courtley	Alderney	23. 7.01
G-BGXD	Socata TB-10 Tobago	39		19.10.79	P.N.Atkin, T.M.Sloan, R.J.Wright & J.S.Smith	Goodwood	18. 5.01
G-BGXJ	Partenavia P.68B	189		6. 9.79	Cecil Aviation Ltd	Cambridge	3.10.02
G-BGXK	Cessna 310R II	310R-1257	N6070X	7. 8.79	Alarmond Ltd t/a Edinburgh Flying Club	Edinburgh	1.11.00T
G-BGXN	PA-38-112 Tomahawk	38-79A0898		5. 7.79	Panshanger School of Flying Ltd (Damaged 1991; stored for rebuild 6.98) Manor Farm, Glatton		24. 8.91T
G-BGXO	PA-38-112 Tomahawk	38-79A0982		5. 7.79	Goodwood Road Racing Co Ltd	Goodwood	12. 2.01T
G-BGXR	Robin HR.200/100	53	F-BVYH	1.10.79	E.G.Cleobury	Wellesbourne Mountford	27.11.01
G-BGXS	PA-28-236 Dakota	28-7911198	N2836Z	12. 7.79	Bawtry Road Service Station Ltd	Gamston	23. 3.01T
G-BGXT	Socata TB-10 Tobago	40		3.10.79	D.A.H.Morris	Halfpenny Green	18. 8.01
G-BGYG	PA-28-161 Warrior II	28-7916431	N9528N	17. 7.79	Oxford Aviation Services Ltd	Oxford	31. 8.00T
G-BGYH	PA-28-161 Warrior II	28-7916313	N9619N	17. 7.79	Oxford Aviation Services Ltd	Oxford	3. 2.01T
G-BGYN	PA-18-150 Super Cub	18-7709137	N62747	19. 7.79	B.J.Dunford	Long Wood, Morestead	26. 4.01

Regn	Type	C/n	P/I	Date	Owner/operator	Probable Base	CA Expy
G-BGYR	HS.125 Srs.F600B	256045	G-5-11 EC-CQT/G-5-18	3.12.79	British Aerospace (Operations) Ltd Warton		30. 9.00
G-BGYT	Embraer EMB-110P1 Bandeirante	110-234	N104VA G-BGYT/PT-SAA	11.10.79	Keenair Charter Ltd (Keenair c/s)	Liverpool	12. 1.00T
G-BGZF	PA-38-112 Tomahawk	38-79A1015		26. 7.79	Aerohire Ltd	Egginton	25. 5.98T
G-BGZJ*	PA-38-112 Tomahawk	38-79A0999		7. 9.79	Midland Aircraft Maintenance Ltd Bourne Park, Hurstbourne Tarrant (Damaged Cambridge 5.8.90; stored 8.99)		14. 6.92T
G-BGZL	Eiri PIK.20E	20218		21. 8.79	F.Casolari (Castellarano, Italy)		28. 7.01
G-BGZO*	SEEMS MS.880B Rallye Club	378	F-BKZO	24.10.79	Not known (Shoreham) (Damaged East Meon, Petersfield 3.5.89; stored 12.92)		9. 4.92
G-BGZW	PA-38-112 Tomahawk	38-79A1068		1. 8.79	Cheshire Flying Services Ltd Manchester t/a Ravenair		19.11.01T
G-BGZY	Jodel Wassmer D.120 Paris-Nice	118	F-BIQU	17. 8.79	M.Hale (La Trinite Sur Mer, France)		22.11.99P
G-BGZZ	Thunder Ax6-56 Bolt HAFB	220		10. 8.79	Jennifer M.Robinson Milton-under-Wychwood "Robinson's Cruiser"		16. 7.94A

G-BHAA – G-BHZZ

Regn	Type	C/n	P/I	Date	Owner/operator	Probable Base	CA Expy
G-BHAA	Cessna 152 II	152-81330	N49809	12. 2.79	Herefordshire Aero Club Ltd	Shobdon	14. 5.00T
G-BHAC	Cessna A152 Aerobat	A152-0776	N7595B	12. 2.79	Herefordshire Aero Club Ltd	Shobdon	17. 4.00T
G-BHAD	Cessna A152 Aerobat	A152-0807	N7390L	12. 2.79	Shropshire Aero Club Ltd	Sleap	11. 4.00T
G-BHAI	Reims Cessna F.152 II	1625	(D-EJAY)	14. 8.79	Fraggle Leasing Ltd	Netherthorpe	14.10.01T
G-BHAJ	Robin DR.400/160 Major 80	1430		22. 8.79	Rowantask Ltd	Rochester	5. 3.01T
G-BHAL	Rango-Saffery S.200SS HAFB (Model) (Face & pigtails shape)	NHP-2		14. 8.79	Anne.M.Lindsay Leeds t/a Rango Balloon & Kite Co "Anneky Panky"		
G-BHAM	Thunder Ax6-56 Bolt HAFB	251		28. 1.80	D.M. & K.R.Sandford "Levitation"	Knutsford	7. 4.86A
G-BHAR	Westland-Bell 47G-3B1 (Line No.WAN/44)	WA/353	XT194	7. 8.79	J.Bird & R.Cove (Buckworth)		10. 6.00
G-BHAT*	Thunder Ax7-77 Bolt HAFB	250		28. 1.80	Not known "Witter"	NK	6. 2.83A
G-BHAV	Reims Cessna F.152 II	1633		15. 8.79	T.M. & M.L.Jones t/a Derby Aero Club	Egginton	13. 8.01T
G-BHAW	Reims Cessna F.172N Skyhawk II	1858		15. 8.79	E.Alexander	(Braintree)	1. 6.01
G-BHAX	Enstrom F-28C-2-UK	486-2	N5689N	22.10.79	J.L.Ferguson	South Wirral	21. 3.02
G-BHAY	PA-28RT-201 Arrow IV	28R-7918213	N2910N	17. 8.79	Alpha Yankee Ltd	Newcastle	26. 3.01
G-BHBA	Campbell Cricket (Rotax 503)	SMI/1		15. 8.79	G.J.Layzell	Quedgeley, Glos	3. 6.97P
G-BHBB*	Colting 77A HAFB	77A-012	EI-BFG	14.9. 79	Not known NK (Cancelled by CAA 19.5.93: tethered 5.99)		
G-BHBE	Westland-Bell 47G-3B1 (Soloy conversion) (Line No.WAP/136)	WA/422	XT510	29.10.79	T.R.Smith (Agricultural Machinery) Ltd Dereham		21.12.01
G-BHBF	Sikorsky S-76A II Plus	760022	N4247S	9.11.79	Bristow Helicopters Ltd "Spirit of Paris"	North Denes	3. 1.01T
G-BHBG	PA-32R-300 Cherokee Lance	32R-7780515	N408RC	18. 9.79	L.T.Halpin	Leicester	4. 6.00T
G-BHBI	Mooney M.20J (201)	24-0842	N4764H	24. 9.79	A.M.McGlone t/a G-BHBI Group Biggin Hill		10. 4.00
G-BHBT	Marquart MA-5 Charger	PFA/68-10190		3. 9.79	R.G. & C.J.Maidment Shoreham (Re-emerged at maintentance at Goodwood 5.99)		
G-BHBZ	Partenavia P.68B	191		10. 9.79	P.C.Hamer & P.C.W.Landau	Humberside	31. 3.02
G-BHCC	Cessna 172M Skyhawk II	172-66711	(G-BGLY) N80713	26.10.79	Langtry Flying Group Ltd	Bournemouth	16. 6.02T
G-BHCE	SAN Jodel D.117A	381	F-BHME	1.10.79	D.M.Parsons (Highnam, Gloucester) t/a Parwebb Flying Group (Status uncertain)		27. 2.85P
G-BHCM	Reims Cessna F.172H	0468	SE-FBD	25. 9.79	J. Dominic	Denham	24. 4.01
G-BHCP	Reims Cessna F.152 II	1640		31.10.79	D.Copley	Sandtoft	12.10.98T
G-BHCW*	PA-22-150 Tri-Pacer	22-3006	F-BHDT	11. 2.80	Not known (Stored 10.94)	Shoreham	
G-BHCZ	PA-38-112 Tomahawk	38-78A0321	N214MD	26. 9.79	Jennifer E.Abbott	Goodwood	25. 9.00
G-BHDD	V.668 Varsity T.1	-	WL626	18.10.79	G.Vale East Midlands (As "WL626/P": to East Midlands Aeropark 6.99)		AC
G-BHDE	Socata TB-10 Tobago	58		2. 1.80	A.E.Allsop Antwerp, Belgium (Op ACS Belgium BVBA)		29. 7.01
G-BHDK*	Boeing TB-29A-45-BN Superfortress	44-61748 11225	27. 9.79		Imperial War Museum Duxford (As "461748/Y" in USAF c/s) "Hawg Wild"		
G-BHDM	Reims Cessna F.152 II	1684		15.10.79	Tayside Aviation Ltd	Aberdeen	9. 4.01T
G-BHDP	Reims Cessna F.182Q Skylane	0131		15.10.79	Zone Travel Ltd	Booker	21.12.02
G-BHDR	Reims Cessna F.152 II	1680		15.10.79	Tayside Aviation Ltd	Dundee	2. 7.01T
G-BHDS	Reims Cessna F.152 II	1682		15.10.79	Tayside Aviation Ltd	Dundee	8. 7.02T
G-BHDU	Reims Cessna F.152 II	1681		15.10.79	A.S.Bamrah t/a Falcon Flying Services	Biggin Hill	27. 5.01T

Regn	Type	C/n	P/I	Date	Owner/operator	Probable Base	CA Expy
G-BHDV	Cameron V-77 HAFB	585		1. 2.80	P.Glydon Barnt Green, Birmingham		27. 3.00A
					"Dormouse"		
G-BHDW	Reims Cessna F.152 II	1652		15.10.79	Tayside Aviation Ltd	Dundee	7. 5.01T
G-BHDX	Reims Cessna F.172N Skyhawk II	1889		5.10.79	J.Mitchell	Newtownards	4. 6.01
					t/a Skyhawk DX Group		
G-BHDZ	Reims Cessna F.172N Skyhawk II	1911		3.12.79	Arrow Flying Ltd.	Denham	15. 5.01T
G-BHEC	Reims Cessna F.152 II	1676		3.12.79	Stapleford Flying Club Ltd	Stapleford	16. 7.01T
G-BHED	Reims Cessna FA.152 Aerobat	0359		3.12.79	TG Aviation Ltd	Manston	26. 4.01T
					(Op Thanet Flying Club)		
G-BHEG	SAN Jodel 150 Mascaret	46	PH-ULS	3. 7.80	D.M.Griffiths	RAF Mona	25. 6.00P
			OO-SET				
G-BHEH	Cessna 310G	310G-0016	N1720	14. 4.80	F.J.Shevill	Shoreham	9.12.96
			N8916Z		(Dismantled & stored 5.98)		
G-BHEK	Scintex CP.1315-C3 Super Emeraude		F-BJMU	11.10.79	D.B.Winstanley	Barton	9.11.00P
		923					
G-BHEL	SAN Jodel D.117	735	F-BIOA	8.10.79	N.Wright & C.M.Kettlewell		7.11.00P
					Queach Farm, Bury St.Edmunds		
G-BHEM	Bensen B.8MV EK.14 & PFA G/01-1016			8.10.79	G.C.Kerr	Carlisle	5.10.00P
	(Rotax 503)						
G-BHEN	Reims Cessna FA.152 Aerobat	0363		3. 1.80	Leicestershire Aero Club Ltd	Leicester	3.12.01T
G-BHEO	Reims Cessna FR.182 Skylane RG II			3. 1.80	J.G.Hogg	Rochester	6. 6.01
		0049					
G-BHER	Socata TB-10 Tobago	60	4X-AKK	19.10.79	Vale Aviation Ltd	Biggin Hill	20. 7.00T
			G-BHER				
G-BHEU	Thunder Ax7-65 Srs.1 HAFB	238		16.10.79	D.G.Such "Polomoche"	Birmingham	31. 5.00A
G-BHEV	PA-28R-200 Cherokee Arrow II		PH-BOY	23.10.79	P.Hardy	Gamston	24. 3.00T
		28R-7435159	N41244		t/a 7-Up Group		
G-BHEX	Colt 56A HAFB	056		15.10.79	A.S.Dear, R.B.Green & W.S.Templeton "Superwasp"		
					t/a Hale Hot-Air Balloon Group Fordingbridge		11.11.98A
G-BHEZ	SAN Jodel 150 Mascaret	22	F-BLDO	31. 1.80	A.Shorter	Sherburn in Elmet	20. 6.00P
					t/a Air Yorkshire Group		
G-BHFC	Reims Cessna F.152 II	1436		7. 4.78	TG Aviation Ltd	Manston	1. 8.02T
					(Op Thanet Flying Club)		
G-BHFE	PA-44-180 Seminole	44-7995324	ADAF 005	22.10.79	Grunwick Ltd	Cranfield	9.12.99T
			G-BHFE/N2383U		(Op Bonus Aviation)		
G-BHFF	Dormois Jodel D.112	322	F-BEKJ	19.10.79	P.A.Dowell Watchford Farm, Yarcombe		28. 3.00P
G-BHFG	SNCAN Stampe SV-4C	45	F-BJDN	31.10.79	Stormswift Ltd	Kemble	7.10.01T
			Fr.Mil				
G-BHFH	PA-34-200T Seneca II	34-7970482	N8075Q	23.10.79	Aerohire Ltd	Halfpenny Green	22. 1.01T
G-BHFI	Reims Cessna F.152 II	1685		22.10.79	R.Bilson & D.Turner	Blackpool	8. 4.01T
					t/a BAe Warton Flying Club		
G-BHFJ	PA-28RT-201T Turbo Arrow IV		N8072R	22.10.79	T.L.P.Delaney	White Waltham	6. 8.01
		28R-7931298					
G-BHFK	PA-28-151 Cherokee Warrior		N8325C	12.12.79	Ilkeston Car Sales Ltd		
		28-7615088			Jericho Farm, Lambley		19. 3.01
G-BHFR	Eiri PIK-20E Srs.1	20228	(D-KHJR)	8.11.79	J.T.Morgan	Husbands Bosworth	5. 8.01
			G-BHFR		(As "FR")		
G-BHFS	Robin DR.400/180 Regent	1304		7. 3.78	D.S.Chandler	Shoreham	4.11.02
G-BHGA	PA-31-310 Turbo Navajo	31-7912117	N3539M	12.11.79	Heltor Ltd	Exeter	25. 3.00
G-BHGC	PA-18-150 Super Cub	18-8793	PH-NKH	3. 4.79	M.R. & P.A.Dawson	RAF Keevil	4.11.99
			N4447Z				
G-BHGF	Cameron V-56 HAFB	574		5.11.79	P.Spellward "Biggles"	Bristol	29. 8.00A
G-BHGJ	Jodel Wassmer D.120 Paris-Nice	336	F-BOYB	15. 1.80	Q.M.B.Oswell	RAF Halton	12. 4.00P
G-BHGK	Sikorsky S-76A II Plus	760049	N1545Y	27. 3.80	Bond Helicopters Ltd	Humberside	8. 5.00T
G-BHGO	PA-32-260 Cherokee Six	32-7800007	PH-BGP	16.11.79	DDCS Ltd	Newcastle	12. 4.01T
			N9656C		(Op Cherokee Six Group)		
G-BHGP	Socata TB-10 Tobago	100		17. 1.80	Inter Textiles Ltd	Stapleford	12. 5.02
G-BHGX	Colt 56B HAFB	057		22.11.79	M.N.Dixon "Prospect"	Bicester	22. 7.90A
G-BHGY	PA-28R-200-2 Cherokee Arrow II		PH-NSL	23.11.79	V.Humphries	Nottingham	28. 6.01
		28R-7435086	N57365				
G-BHHB	Cameron V-77 HAFB	170		26.11.79	R.M.Powell "Pax"	Stockbridge	8. 6.00T
G-BHHE	CEA Jodel DR.1051/M1 Sicile Record		F-BMZC	26. 4.80	P.Bridges	Headcorn	6.12.01
G-BHHG	Reims Cessna F.152 II	1725		4. 3.80	TG Aviation Ltd	Manston	17. 6.01T
					(Op Thanet Flying Club)		
G-BHHH	Thunder Ax7-65 Bolt HAFB	245		5.12.79	C.A.Hendley (Essex) Ltd	Loughton	27. 9.87A
					"Christmas"		
G-BHHK	Cameron N-77 HAFB	547		5.12.79	I.S.Bridge "Shadowfax II"	Shrewsbury	7.12.87A
G-BHHN	Cameron V-77 HAFB	549		29.11.79	P.Gooch	Alresford, Hants	23. 7.99A
					t/a The Itchen Valley Balloon Group "Valley Crusader"		
G-BHHX	Jodel D.112	223	F-BFAJ	19. 2.80	P.J.Reed & D.M.Gale	Dunkeswell	8. 9.00P
	(Built Ets Valladeau)						

Regn	Type	C/n	P/I	Date	Owner/operator	Probable Base	CA Expy
G-BHHZ	Rotorway Scorpion 133	MSI.1195		12.12.79	L.W. & O.Underwood (Stored 12.94)		
						Stoneacre Farm, Farthing Corner	23. 9.81P
G-BHIB	Reims Cessna F.182Q Skylane II	0134		18.12.79	S.N.Chater & B.Payne	Jersey	3. 4.00
G-BHIC	Reims Cessna F.182Q Skylane II	0135		18.12.79	W W, J B & D S Alton	(Wetherby)	16. 6.02
					t/a W.F.Alton & Son		
G-BHIG	Colt 31A Air Chair HAFB	060	SE-... G-BHIG	12.12.79	P.A.Lindstrand Upplands Vasby, Sweden		13. 3.00A
					(Op S.Ericsson)		
G-BHIH	Reims Cessna F.172N Skyhawk II	1945		3. 1.80	M.A.Wilkinson	Sywell	30. 7.01
G-BHII	Cameron V-77 HAFB	548		10.12.79	R.V.Brown "Tosca"	Maidenhead	2. 9.96A
G-BHIJ	Eiri PIK.20E Srs.1	20241		9. 1.80	I.W.Paterson	Portmoak	13. 4.98
G-BHIK	Adam RA.14 Loisirs	11-bis	F-PHLK	6. 2.80	L.Lewis	(Redcar)	20. 8.85P
	(Continental A65)				(Damaged nr Lancaster 17.4.85 - on rebuild)		
G-BHIN*	Reims Cessna F.152 II	1715		28. 1.80	P.Skinner	Egginton	7. 7.98T
					(Noted 6.99 wrecked: cancelled as wfu 4.11.99)		
G-BHIR	PA-28R-200 Cherokee Arrow	28R-35614	SE-FHP	21. 2.80	Factorcore Ltd	Woodford	22.10.01T
					(Op Manchester School of Flying)		
G-BHIS	Thunder Ax7-65 Bolt HAFB	254		26.11.79	J.R.Wilson	Didcot	21. 3.96A
					t/a The Hedgehoppers Balloon Group "Yo-Yo"		
G-BHIT	Socata TB-9 Tampico	63		7.12.79	ABC Advertising Ltd	Biggin Hill	31. 1.01T
G-BHIY	Reims Cessna F.150K	0627	F-BRXR	18.12.79	G.J.Ball	Old Sarum	8. 4.01
G-BHJA	Cessna A152 Aerobat	A152-0835	N4954A	11. 3.80	Cornwall Flying Club Ltd	Bodmin	9. 4.92T
					(Damaged Bodmin 21.7.90; stored 5.98)		
G-BHJB	Cessna A152 Aerobat	A152-0856	N4662A	11. 3.80	Sky Pro Ltd	Gamston	21.12.98T
G-BHJF	Socata TB-10 Tobago	83		2. 1.80	P.Crutchfield	Blackbushe	16.12.00
					t/a Flying Fox Group		
G-BHJI	Mooney M.20J (201)	24-0925	N3753H	11. 2.80	S.F.Lister	Gamston	19.12.98
G-BHJK	Maule M.5-235C Lunar Rocket	7296C	N56359	25. 2.80	T.P.Spurge	East Winch	23. 2.02
G-BHJN	Sportavia Fournier RF4D	4021	F-BORH	3. 1.80	G.E.Reeman & G.R.Beers	Enstone	8. 9.00P
					t/a RF4 Flying Group		
G-BHJO	PA-28-161 Warrior II	28-7816213	OO-FLD N9507N/N6034H	4. 1.80	J.G.Chree, K.J.Utting & A.Sangster		
					t/a The Brackla Flying Group	Inverness	12. 5.01
G-BHJS	Partenavia P.68B	172	I-KLUB	28.12.79	J.J.Watts & D.Fletcher	Bournemouth	1. 7.01T
G-BHJU	Robin DR.400 2+2	1288	D-ECDK	9. 1.80	T.J.Harlow	Frid Farm, Bethersden	29. 5.01
G-BHKA*	Evans VP-1 Srs.2	PFA/62-10496		4. 1.80	Not known Stoke Orchard, Cheltenham		8.10.90P
	(VW1834)				(Open store 7.91)		
G-BHKE	Bensen B.8MS	VW.1 & PFA G/01-1009		7. 1.80	C.Baldwin	Carlisle	
G-BHKH	Cameron O-65 HAFB	592		7. 1.80	D.G.Body	Leighton Buzzard	11. 8.96A
					t/a Mid-Bucks Farmers Balloon Group "Daisy"		
G-BHKJ	Cessna 421C Golden Eagle III		(N26596)	25. 1.80	Totaljet Ltd	Chester	10. 9.01T
	(Robertson STOL conversion)	421C-0848					
G-BHKN*	Colt 14A Cloudhopper HAFB	068		17. 1.80	British Balloon Museum	Newbury	
					"Green Ice 2"		
G-BHKR*	Colt 14A Cloudhopper HAFB	071		17. 1.80	British Balloon Museum	Newbury	
					"Green Ice 5"		
G-BHKT	Wassmer Jodel D.112	1265	F-BMIQ	10. 1.80	K.A.Stewart & G.Oldfield Croft-on-Tees		4. 8.00P
					t/a The Evans Flying Group		
G-BHKV*	Gulfstream AA-5A Cheetah	AA5A-0894	N27465	31. 1.80	Not known	Biggin Hill	24. 4.95T
					(Damaged Deanland 11.6.94; on rebuild 9.94)		
G-BHLE	Robin DR.400/180 Regent	1466		25. 1.80	B.D.Greenwood	Ronaldsway	2. 5.01
G-BHLH	Robin DR.400/180 Regent	1320	F-GBIG	11. 2.80	P.E.Davis	Netherthorpe	28. 6.01
G-BHLJ	Saffery-Rigg S.200 Skyliner HAFB (Model)	IAR/01		23. 1.80	I.A.Rigg	Manchester	
					"Skyliner"		
G-BHLT	DH.82A Tiger Moth	84997	ZS-DGA SAAF2272/T6697	9. 6.80	P.J. & A.J.Borsberry (On rebuild 8.90)		
	(Regd as c/n "911")				Kidmore End, Reading		26. 2.90
G-BHLU	Alpavia Fournier RF3	79	F-BMTN	14. 4.80	M.C.Roper	Swanton Morley	16. 6.00P
					(Op Norwich RF3 Group)		
G-BHLW	Cessna 120	10210	N73005 NC73005	24. 3.80	L.W.Scattergood	Sherburn in Elmet	9.11.00P
	(Continental C85)				"Sky Ranger"		
G-BHLX	Grumman-American AA-5B Tiger		OY-GAR	1. 2.80	C.B.Dew	Southampton	10. 6.01
		AA5B-0573					
G-BHMA	SIPA 903	61	OO-FAE F-BGBK	13. 3.80	H.J.Taggart	Ballymoney, Co.Antrim	18. 5.98P
G-BHMG	Reims Cessna FA.152 Aerobat	0368		10. 6.80	R.D.Smith	Popham	19. 4.02
G-BHMI	Reims Cessna F.172N Skyhawk II	2036	G-WADE G-BHMI	6. 8.80	GMI Aviation Ltd	Blackpool	9. 3.02T
G-BHMJ	Avenger T.200-2112 HAFB (Model)	002		29. 1.80	R.Light "Lord Anthony I"	Stockport	
G-BHMK	Avenger T.200-2112 HAFB (Model)	003		29. 1.80	P.Kinder "Lord Anthony II"	Stockport	
G-BHMR	Stinson 108-3 Station Wagon	108-4352	F-BABO F-DABO/NC6352M	12. 2.80	D.G.French	Sandown	23.11.90
					(Stored 12.95)		
G-BHMT	Evans VP-1	PFA/62-10473		18. 2.80	P.E.J.Sturgeon	Chestnut Farm, Tipps End	14. 6.00P
	(VW1834)						

Regn	Type	C/n	P/I	Date	Owner/operator	Probable Base	CA Expy
G-BHMY	Fokker F-27 Friendship 200	10196	F-GBDK	6. 5.80	KLM UK Ltd	Stansted	22. 5.99T
			(F-GBRV)/PK-PFS/JA8606/PH-FDL				
G-BHNA	Reims Cessna F.152 II	1683		12. 2.80	Sheffield Aero Club Ltd	Netherthorpe	20.10.95T
					(Damaged Netherthorpe 17.6.95; fuselage stored 5.99)		
G-BHNC	Cameron O-65 HAFB	588		7. 2.80	D. & C.Bareford	Kidderminster	5. 3.94A
					"Hot N'Cold"		
G-BHND	Cameron N-65 HAFB	582		7. 2.80	S.M.Wellband	Frome	24. 6.89A
G-BHNG*	PA-23-250 Aztec E	27-7405432	N54125	13. 5.80	Riverside Metals Ltd		
			(Crashed Shoreham 19.12.81; fuselage stored 3.97) Cradle Hill, Seaford				11. 8.83T
G-BHNK	Jodel Wassmer D.120A Paris-Nice	243	F-BLNK	26. 3.80	D.A.Bates	St.Marys, Isles of Scilly	7. 3.00P
					t/a G-BHNK Flying Group		
G-BHNL	Wassmer Jodel D.112	1206	F-BLNL	30. 1.80	J.C.Mansell	Watchford Farm, Yarcombe	15. 7.00P
G-BHNO	PA-28-181 Archer II	28-8090211	N81413	7. 2.80	Airfluid Hydraulics & Pneumatics (Wolverhampton) Ltd		1. 7.01
						Sleap	
G-BHNP	Eiri PIK-20E Srs.1	20253		29. 2.80	D.A.Sutton	Sackville Farm, Riseley	26. 5.02
					(As "NP")		
G-BHNV	Westland-Bell 47G-3B1	WA/700	F-GHNM	11. 3.80	Leyline Helicopters Ltd	(Billingham)	28. 5.89T
	(Line No.WAT/222)		G-BHNV/XW180				
G-BHNX	SAN Jodel D.117	493	F-BHNX	7. 9.78	A.J.Chalkley	(Pwllheli)	12. 1.87P
					(On rebuild 4.91)		
G-BHOA	Robin DR.400/160 Major 80	1478		27. 1.80	M.L.Sargeant	(Goudhurst)	1. 9.02
G-BHOH	Sikorsky S-61N Mk.II	61-827		25. 4.80	Bristow Helicopters Ltd	Aberdeen	20. 5.02T
					"Ben Avon"		
G-BHOJ*	Colt 14A Cloudhopper HAFB	080		27. 2.80	G.Elson "Green Ice 6"	(Spain)	
G-BHOL	CEA Jodel DR.1050 Ambassadeur	35	F-BJQL	6. 2.80	D.G.Hart	Inverness	28.10.01
					t/a Cawdor Flying Group "Nicolette"		
G-BHOM	PA-18-95 Super Cub	18-1391	OO-PIU	7. 3.80	C.H.A.Bott	Whitehall Farm, Benington	8. 3.00P
	(L-18C-PI) (Frame No.18-1272)		OO-HMT/ALAT 51-15391				
G-BHOO	Livesey-Purves Thunder Ax7-65 HAFB			26. 2.80	D.Livesey & J.M.Purves	Crayke, York	
		001			"Scraps"		
G-BHOR	PA-28-161 Warrior II	28-8016331	N82162	12. 6.80	A.J.Harewood	Biggin Hill	12. 6.01
					t/a Oscar Romeo Flying Group		
G-BHOT	Cameron V-65 HAFB	777		15. 9.81	J.A.Baker	Marsh Benham	8. 8.99A
					t/a The Dante Balloon Group "Le Billet Doux"		
G-BHOZ	Socata TB-9 Tampico	84		11. 3.80	A.N.Hendley	Blackbushe	1. 5.01
G-BHPK	Piper J3C-65 Cub (L-4A-PI)	8979	F-BEPK	26. 2.80	P.H.J.Scrase	Priory Farm, Tibenham	21. 9.00P
			Fr.Mil/42-38410		t/a L4 Group (As "236800/44/A" in USAAF c/s)		
	(Frame No.9098; official c/n is 12161/44-79865 which is F-BFYU)						
G-BHPL	CASA I-131E Jungmann	1058	E3B-350	17. 7.80	R.G.Gray	(London N1)	9. 9.00P
					(As "E3B-350/05-97" in Spanish AF c/s)		
G-BHPM	PA-18-95 Super Cub (L-18C-PI)	18-1501	F-BOUR	10. 4.80	P.I.Morgans (Stored 5.95)		
	(Frame No.18-1469)		ALAT 51-15501		Furze Hill Farm, Rosemarket, Milford Haven		
G-BHPN	Colt 14A Cloudhopper HAFB	081	(SE-)	6. 3.80	Lindstrand Balloons Ltd (Op by S.Ericsson)		
			G-BHPN			Upplands Vasby, Sweden	13. 3.00A
G-BHPS	Jodel Wassmer D.120A Paris-Nice	148	F-BIXI	11. 6.80	T.J. Price	Neath	12. 5.00P
G-BHPT	Piper J3C-65 Cub	"17792"	F-BSGQ	10. 4.80	J.R.I.Rolfe	Willington, Beds	12. 5.96P
			LX-AIH/N70688/NC70688		t/a Rolfe Air Services		
	(Frame No.17792; the quoted p/i is suspect - possibly c/n 18105 ex NC71076/N71076)						
G-BHPX	Cessna 152 II	152-82994	N46073	26. 3.80	Fraggle Leasing Ltd	Shoreham	23. 7.01T
					(Still leased to Southern Air ?)		
G-BHPY	Cessna 152 II	152-82983	N46009	26. 3.80	Rankart Ltd	Hinton-in-The-Hedges	10. 9.01T
G-BHPZ	Cessna 172N Skyhawk II	172-72017	N6411E	26. 3.80	O'Brien Properties Ltd	Shoreham	4.10.02T
G-BHRB	Reims Cessna F.152 II	1707		20. 3.80	LAC (Enterprises) Ltd	Barton	27. 1.02T
					t/a Lancashire Aero Club		
G-BHRC	PA-28-161 Warrior II	28-7916430	N9527N	3. 4.80	Sherwood Flying Club Ltd	Tatenhill	5. 1.01T
G-BHRH	Reims Cessna FA.150K Aerobat	0056	PH-ECB	24. 3.80	Merlin Flying Club Ltd	Hucknall	17. 6.02T
			D-ECBL/(D-EKKW)				
G-BHRI	Saffery S.200 Phoenix HAFB (Model)		G-BGHD(1)	12. 3.80	N.J. & H.L.Dunnington "Can-Can"	Bristol	
		20					
G-BHRM	Reims Cessna F.152 II	1718	F-GCHR	8. 4.80	Aerohire Ltd	Halfpenny Green	27. 9.02T
G-BHRN	Reims Cessna F.152 II	1728	F-GCHV	8. 4.80	Fraggle Leasing Ltd	Netherthorpe	27. 7.02T
G-BHRO	Rockwell Commander 112A	364	N1364J	20. 3.80	John Raymond Transport Ltd	Cardiff	17. 8.01
G-BHRP	PA-44-180 Seminole	44-8095021	N81602	1. 4.80	M.S.Farmers	Leicester	22.12.00T
G-BHRR	Menavia Piel CP.301A Emeraude	270	F-BISK	28. 3.80	T.W.Offen	Lake Farm, Sutton Valence	28. 5.87P
					(Status uncertain)		
G-BHRW	CEA Jodel DR.221 Dauphin	93	F-BPCP	10. 7.80	M.F.Filer & D.H.Williams	Bristol	13. 4.02
G-BHRY	Colt 56A HAFB	030		2. 4.80	A.S.Davidson	Burton-on-Trent	29. 4.95A
					"Turkish Delight"		
G-BHSA	Cessna 152 II	152-83693	(N4889B)	1. 5.80	D.Copley	Sherburn in Elmet	11. 4.98T
G-BHSB	Cessna 172N Skyhawk II	172-72977	(N1225F)	25. 6.80	ABK Aviation Services Ltd	(Pontefract)	3. 1.02
G-BHSD	Scheibe SF-25E Super Falke	4357	D-KDGG	21. 7.80	Lasham Gliding Society Ltd	Lasham	1. 2.02

Regn	Type	C/n	P/I	Date	Owner/operator	Probable Base	CA Expy
G-BHSE	Rockwell Commander 114	14161	N4831W	15. 5.80	604 Squadron Flying Group Ltd	Booker	7. 5.02
			AN-BRL/(N4831W)				
G-BHSL	CASA I-131E Jungmann	1117	E3B-236	18. 6.80	H.I.Taylor	Gloucestershire	19. 7.96P
					(As "05-97") (Damaged Cranfield 6.7.96)		
G-BHSN	Cameron N-56 HAFB	595		10. 4.80	I.Bentley	Bath	9. 5.97A
G-BHSP	Thunder Ax7-77Z HAFB	272		15. 4.80	G.A.Fisher	Guildford	23. 2.94A
	(Originally built as D-TRIER c/n 221)				t/a Out-Of-The-Blue "Chicago"		
G-BHSS	Pitts S-1C Special	C.1461M	N1704	19. 9.80	K.Lyons	Tatenhill	23. 6.00P
	(Lycoming O-320)				t/a Bottoms Up Syndicate		
G-BHSY	CEA Jodel DR.1050 Sicile	546	F-BLZO	6. 5.80	T.R.Allebone	Easton Maudit	3. 9.01
G-BHTA	PA-28-236 Dakota	28-8011102	N8197H	22. 4.80	Dakota Ltd	Jersey	3. 9.01
G-BHTC	CEA Jodel DR.1051/M1 Sicile Record	581	F-BMGR	1. 5.80	G.Clark	Garston Farm, Marshfield	7.10.01
G-BHTD	Cessna T188C AGhusky	T188-03338T	(G-BGTN)	18. 4.80	ADS (Aerial) Ltd	(Benfleet)	26. 6.83A
			N2033J		(Status uncertain - probably exported/destroyed)		
G-BHTG	Thunder Ax6-56 Bolt HAFB	273		18. 4.80	F.R. & Mrs S.H.MacDonald "Halcyon"	Newdigate, Surrey	18.12.91A
G-BHTH	North American T-6G-NT Texan	168-176	N2807G 49-3072A	20. 5.80	J.J.Woodhouse	Shoreham	11. 5.97T
					(As "2807/V-103" -US Navy/VF-111 Sqdn c/s)		
					(Damaged Bourne Park, nr Andover 13.3.95; on rebuild 8.97)		
G-BHUB*	Douglas C-47A-85DL Dakota	19975	"G-AGIV"	30. 4.80	Imperial War Museum/American Air Museum		
	Sp.AF T3-29/N51V/N9985F/SE-BBH/43-15509				(As "315509/W7-S" in USAAF c/s)	Duxford	
G-BHUE	SAN Jodel DR.1050 Ambassadeur	185	F-BERM F-OBRM	21. 4.80	M.J.Harris	(Worcester)	19.10.92
G-BHUG	Cessna 172N Skyhawk II	172-72985	N1283F	24. 6.80	F.G.Baulch	Dunkeswell	14. 9.01T
					t/a FGT Aircraft Hire		
G-BHUI	Cessna 152 II	152-83144	N46932	27. 5.80	Galair International Ltd	Wellesbourne Mountford	19.11.01T
G-BHUJ	Cessna 172N Skyhawk II	172-71932	N5752E	27. 5.80	Flightline Ltd	Southend	8. 4.02T
G-BHUM	DH.82A Tiger Moth	85453	VT-DGA	9. 6.80	S.G.Towers	Beckwithshaw, Harrogate	8. 4.02
			VT-DDN/RIAF/SAAF 4622/DE457				
G-BHUO	Evans VP-2	PFA/63-10552		12. 5.80	D.A.Wood	Yearby	21.12.94P
	(Continental A65)						
G-BHUP*	Reims Cessna F.152 II	1773		2. 5.80	Not known	Stapleford	9.10.89T
					(Damaged nr Barton 17.5.89; stored 5.98)		
G-BHUR	Thunder Ax3 Mini Sky Chariot HAFB	277		9. 5.80	B.F.G.Ribbans "Sheppard"	Lancing	31. 8.90A
					(Op Balloon Preservation Group 10.97)		
G-BHUU	PA-25-260 Pawnee D	25-8056035		28. 5.80	Booker Gliding Club Ltd	Booker	23.10.00A
G-BHVB	PA-28-161 Warrior II	28-8016260	N9638N	16. 5.80	Bobbington Air Training School Ltd	Halfpenny Green	30. 7.01T
G-BHVF	SAN Jodel 150A Mascaret	11	F-BLDF	28.10.80	J.D.Walton	Swanborough Farm, Lewes	25. 4.00P
G-BHVP	Cessna 182Q Skylane II	182-67071	N97374	15.12.80	R.J.W.Wood	Gregory Farm, Mirfield	22.10.99T
G-BHVR	Cessna 172N Skyhawk II	172-70196	N738SG	27. 5.80	M.G.Montgomerie	Elstree	15. 5.00T
					t/a G-BHVR Group		
G-BHVV	Piper J3C-65 Cub (L-4A-PI)	8953	F-BGXF 42-38384	27. 6.80	P.R.Wright	Aboyne	3. 7.85P
					(Stored 8.98)		
	(Frame No.9048; regd with c/n 10291/43-1430 which was F-BEGF; frames probably exchanged in 1953 rebuild)						
G-BHWA	Reims Cessna F.152 II	1775		28. 3.80	M.Housley & J.H.Mills	Wickenby	2. 6.01T
					t/a Lincoln Aviation		
G-BHWB	Reims Cessna F.152 II	1776	(G-BHWA)	14. 4.80	M.Housley & J.H.Mills	Wickenby	19. 7.01T
					t/a Lincoln Aviation		
G-BHWH	Weedhopper JC-24A	0074		23. 4.80	G.A.Clephane	Basingstoke	30.11.86E
	(EC-34-PM) (Modified to JC-24C)				"Dream Machine" (As "Bu.126603" in US Navy c/s)		
G-BHWK	Socata MS.880B Rallye Club	870	F-BONK	27. 8.80	L.L.Gayther	Shobdon	23. 9.01
G-BHWS	Reims Cessna F.152 II	1785	(G-BHHD)	16. 6.80	Alarmond Ltd	Perth	24. 8.95T
					t/a Edinburgh Flying Club		
					(Damaged Whalsay, Shetland Isles 15.7.94; on rebuild 12.95)		
G-BHWY	PA-28R-200-2 Cherokee Arrow II	28R-7435059	N56904	17. 6.80	P.R.Gould & R.B.Cheek	Sandown	8. 4.02
					t/a Kilo Foxtrot Flying Group		
G-BHWZ	PA-28-181 Archer II	28-7890299	N3379M	8. 4.80	I.R.McCue	Southampton	20. 5.01
G-BHXA	Scottish Avn Bulldog 120/1210	BH120-407	9. 6.80	D.A.Williams (Stored 1.97)	Chester	AC
			Botswana DF OD1/G-BHXA				
G-BHXD	Jodel Wassmer D.120 Paris-Nice	258	F-BMIA	3. 7.80	P.H.C.Hall	Manor Farm, Inglesham	9. 8.00P
G-BHXJ*	Nord 1203-2 Norecrin II	103	F-BEMX	23.10.80	Camp Hill Ltd	(Kirklington, Bedale)	
					(For rebuild 1.99)		
G-BHXK	PA-28-140 Cherokee	28-21106	VR-HGB 9V-BAJ/(9M-AOM)	14. 7.80	J.C.King Bourne Park	Hurstbourne Tarrant	1. 6.00
					t/a GXK Flying Group		
G-BHXL	Evans VP-2	PFA/63-10520		17. 6.80	R.S.Wharton	(Cardiff)	
	(VW1834)						
G-BHXN*	Van's RV-3 EAA/105098 & PFA/99-10518			9. 6.80	Not known (On rebuild 4.99)	Bourn	
G-BHXS	Jodel Wassmer D.120 Paris-Nice	133	F-BIXS	27. 8.80	I.R.Willis	Dundee	4. 8.00P

Regn	Type	C/n	P/I	Date	Owner/operator	Probable Base	CA Expy
G-BHXT*	Thunder Ax6-56Z HAFB	281		2. 7.80	Not known "Blue Eagle"	(Wigan)	NE(A)
G-BHXY	Piper J3C-65 Cub (L-4H-PI)	11905	D-EAXY	1. 7.80	F.W.Rogers	Bodmin	18. 6.99P
	(Frame No.11733)		F-BFQX/44-79609		(As "44-79609/"PR"-"L4 in USAAC c/s) "Heather"		
G-BHYA	Cessna R182 Skylane RGII	R182-00532	N1717R	10. 7.80	Card Tech Ltd	Denham	9. 3.02
G-BHYC	Cessna 172RG Cutlass II	172RG-0404	(N4868V)	24. 6.80	IB Aeroplanes Ltd.	(Coleraine, NI)	28. 3.02
G-BHYD	Cessna R172K Hawk XPII	R172-2734	N736RS	11.12.80	Sylmar Aviation & Services Ltd		
						Lower Wasing Farm, Brimpton	16. 9.02
G-BHYE	PA-34-200T Seneca II	34-8070233	N8225U	27. 6.80	Oxford Aviation Services Ltd	Oxford	10. 6.01T
G-BHYF	PA-34-200T Seneca II	34-8070234	N8225V	27. 6.80	Oxford Aviation Services Ltd	Oxford	25.11.02T
G-BHYG	PA-34-200T Seneca II	34-8070235	N8225X	30. 6.80	Oxford Aviation Services Ltd	Oxford	27. 9.01T
G-BHYI	SNCAN Stampe SV-4A	18	F-BAAF	11. 7.80	P.A.Irwin	White Waltham	21.10.99
			Fr.Mil				
G-BHYO	Cameron N-77 HAFB	659		30. 6.80	Adventure Balloon Co Ltd	(London W3)	NE
G-BHYP	Reims Cessna F.172M Skyhawk II	1108	OY-BFR	30. 6.80	Avior Ltd	Oxford	16. 6.02T
G-BHYR	Reims Cessna F.172M	0922	OY-DZH	30. 6.80	S.D.Undrill	Stapleford	23. 6.99
			SE-FZH/(OH-CFQ)		t/a G-BHYR Group		
G-BHYS*	PA-28-181 Archer II	28-8090319	N8218Y	30. 6.80	Not known	Biggin Hill	22. 8.86T
					(Damaged Biggin Hill 7.12.85; wreck in open storage 8.97)		
G-BHYV	Evans VP-1	LC.2 & PFA/1569		2. 7.80	L.Chiappi	(Blackburn)	
	(VW1600)				(Flown 5.89; stored Blackpool 8.90 - status uncertain)		
G-BHYX	Cessna 152 II	152-81832	N67434	4. 7.80	Stapleford Flying Club Ltd	Stapleford	32. 3.02T
G-BHZE	PA-28-181 Archer II	28-7890291	OO-FLR	4.11.80	Wild Blue Aviation Ltd	(Kinross)	12.12.02T
			(OO-HEM)/N3053M				
G-BHZF	Evans VP-2	PFA/63-10509		9. 7.80	W.J.Evans "Miss Louise"	RAF St.Athan	30. 3.94P
	(Continental A65)				(Damaged nr Swansea 3.7.93)		
G-BHZH	Reims Cessna F.152 II	1786		25. 7.80	Plymouth School of Flying Ltd,	Plymouth	21. 9.01T
G-BHZK	Grumman-American AA-5B Tiger	N28670		8. 9.80	R.G.Seth-Smith	Elstree	23. 5.02
		AA5B-0743			t/a Zulu Kilo Group		
G-BHZO	Gulfstream AA-5A Cheetah	AA5A-0692	N26750	21. 7.80	A.H.McVicar	Prestwick	12.11.01T
G-BHZR	Scottish Avn Bulldog 120/1210			23. 7.80	M.A.Elobeid	Henstridge	7.10.80
		BH120-410	Botswana DF OD4/G-BHZR (Flying again 10.99)				
G-BHZS	Scottish Avn Bulldog 120/1210			23. 7.80	D.A.Williams	Chester	8. 2.99T
		BH120-411	Botswana DF OD5/G-BHZS				
G-BHZT	Scottish Avn Bulldog 120/1210			23. 7.80	Jean M.Bax	Old Sarum	18. 2.02T
		BH120-412	Botswana DF OD6/G-BHZT				
G-BHZU	Piper J3C-65 Cub (L-4B-PI)	9775	F-BETO	17. 7.80	J.K.Tomkinson		
	(Continental O-200-A)		(F-BFKH)/43-914		Brook Farm, Boylestone, Derbyshire		25. 6.99P
	(Regd with Frame No.9606 which was fitted to F-BETO in 1961 rebuild replacing c/n 13164 ex 45-4424)						
G-BHZV	Jodel Wassmer D.120A Paris-Nice	278	F-BMON	23. 7.80	K.J.Scott		
					Stoneacre Farm, Farthing Corner		26. 6.00P
G-BHZX	Thunder Ax7-69A HAFB	288		25. 7.80	R.J. & H.M.Beattie	Aylesbury	2. 4.94A
					"After Eight"		

G-BIAA – G-BIZZ

Regn	Type	C/n	P/I	Date	Owner/operator	Probable Base	CA Expy
G-BIAC	Socata Rallye 235E Gabier	13323		17. 7.80	Aerobatic Displays Ltd & A.E.Kay Oakley		18. 6.02T
G-BIAH	Wassmer Jodel D.112	1218	F-BMAH	20. 8.80	D.Mitchell	Muirhouses Farm, Errol	12. 5.00P
G-BIAI	WMB.2 Windtracker HAFB (Model)	008		1. 7.80	I.Chadwick	Horsham	
					t/a Unicorn Group "Amanda I"		
G-BIAK	Socata TB-10 Tobago	150		17. 7.80	Westmead Business Group Ltd Biggin Hill		15. 1.00
G-BIAL	Rango NA.8 Super HAFB (Model)	AL.9		28. 7.80	Anne M.Lindsay	Leeds	
					t/a Rango Balloon & Kite Co "Tristophone"		
G-BIAP	PA-16-108 Clipper	16-732	F-BBGM	25. 6.80	P.J.Bish	Draycott Farm, Chiseldon	23. 2.01
			F-OAGS				
G-BIAR*	Rigg Skyliner II HAFB (Model)			9. 7.80	I.A.Rigg	Manchester	
		AKC-59 & IAR/02					
G-BIAU*	Sopwith Pup rep	EMK/002		4. 1.83	Fleet Air Arm Museum	RNAS Yeovilton	13. 9.89P
	(Le Rhone 80hp)				(As "N6452" in RNAS c/s)		
G-BIAX	Taylor JT.2 Titch	GFR-1 & PFA/3228		30. 7.80	J.T.Everest	Lasham	10.10.00P
G-BIAY	Grumman-American AA-5 Traveler	OY-GAD		26. 8.80	S.Martin	Southend	28. 7.02
		AA5-0423	N7123L				
G-BIAZ*	Cameron AT-165 (Helium/Hot-Air) Free Balloon			7. 2.78	British Balloon Museum	Newbury	31.10.78
		400			"Zanussi"		
	(Part destroyed Trubenbuch, Austria 14.1.80; inner helium cell envelope held)						
G-BIBA	Socata TB-9 Tampico	149		17. 7.80	TB Aviation Ltd	RAF Halton	14. 7.00
G-BIBB	Mooney M.20C Mark 21	2803	OH-MOD	22. 7.80	P.M.Breton	Kemble	2.12.01
G-BIBG	Sikorsky S-76A II Plus	760083		18. 8.80	Bristow Helicopters Ltd	Redhill	9. 5.01T
					"Loch Seaforth"		
G-BIBJ	Enstrom 280C-UK-2 Shark	1187		13. 8.80	Kemspray Ltd Coleraine, Co.Londonderry		30.11.01
G-BIBN	Reims Cessna FA150K Aerobat	0078	F-BSHN	29.10.80	B.V.Mayo	Maypole Farm, Chislet	22.11.01T

Regn	Type	C/n	P/I	Date	Owner/operator	Probable Base	CA Expy
G-BIBO	Cameron V-65 HAFB	667		7. 8.80	I.Harris "Diadem"	Devizes	30. 6.89A
G-BIBS	Cameron P-20 HAFB	671		14. 8.80	Cameron Balloons Ltd	Bristol	
G-BIBT	Gulfstream AA-5B Tiger	AA5B-1047	N4518V	8. 9.80	Vizor Tempered Glass Ltd	(Port Talbot)	21. 3.01
G-BIBW	Reims Cessna F.172N Skyhawk II	1756		13.10.78	O. Hill	Farley Farm, Winchester	28. 2.02
					t/a Farley Aviation		
G-BIBX	WMB.2 Windtracker HAFB (Model)	9		18. 8.80	I.A.Rigg "Bumble"	Manchester	
G-BICC	Vulture TX3 HAFB (Model)	CC.1		31. 7.80	C.P.Clitheroe (Not built)	Altrincham	
G-BICD	Taylorcraft J Auster 5	735	F-BFXH MT166	20. 8.80	R.T.Parsons	Beeches Farm, South Scarle	3. 8.00P
G-BICE	North American AT-6C-1NT Harvard IIA	FAP1545 88-9755	SAAF 7084/EX302/41-33275	3. 9.80	C.M.L.Edwards	Seething	30. 3.00P
			(As "41-33275/CE" in US Army c/s)				
G-BICG	Reims Cessna F.152 II	1796		3. 9.80	A.S.Bamrah	Biggin Hill	24. 3.02T
					t/a Falcon Flying Services		
G-BICJ	Monnett Sonerai II (VW 1834)	726 & PFA/15-10531		22. 8.80	I.Parr	(Berwick-on-Tweed)	20.10.90P
					(On rebuild 1997)		
G-BICM	Colt 56A HAFB	095		1. 9.80	W.S.Templeton & R.B.Green	Fordingbridge	6. 7.00A
					t/a The Avon Advertiser Balloon Club "Ladybird"		
G-BICN*	Sequoia Falco F.8L	PU-001-2 & PFA/100-10563		3. 9.80	R.J.Barber	(Beccles)	
					(Cancelled 12.4.99 as WFU)		
G-BICP	Robin DR.360 Chevalier	610	F-BSPH	2.10.80	Bravo India Flying Group Ltd	Woodvale	13. 5.02
G-BICR	Jodel Wassmer D.120A Paris-Nice	135	F-BIXR	5. 9.80	M.Ashfield	White Waltham	23. 5.99P
					t/a Beehive Flying Group		
G-BICS	Robin R.2100A Club	128	F-GBAC	4.12.80	I.Young	Sandown	27. 4.00
G-BICT	Evans VP-1 (VW1600)	PFA/62-10455		12. 8.80	A.C.Combe & D.L.Tribe	Long Marston	20. 2.97P
					(Damaged nr Evesham 4.8.96)		
G-BICU	Cameron V-56 HAFB	680		9. 9.80	S.D.Bather "Nobby"	Melksham	1. 5.00A
G-BICW	PA-28-161 Warrior II	28-7916309	N2091U	8.10.80	D.Gellhorn	Blackbushe	3. 2.00
G-BICX	Maule M.5-235C Lunar Rocket	7287C	G-MAUL(1) N56352	2. 2.81	A.T.Jeans & J.F.Clarkson	Compton Chamberlayne, Salisbury	1. 7.02
G-BICY	PA-23-160 Apache	23-1640	OO-AOL 5N-ACL/VR-NDF/PH-ACL/N4010P	26. 9.80	A.M.Lynn	Sibson	9. 7.01T
					(Op Busy Bee)		
G-BIDD	Evans VP-1 (VW1600)	PFA/62-10974		27.10.78	Jane Hodgkinson	Gamston	2.12.00P
			(Initially regd with c/n PFA/62-10167 and combined with both projects)				
G-BIDF	Reims Cessna F.172P Skyhawk II	2045	(PH-JPO)	18. 9.80	E.Alexander	Kings Farm, Thurrock	25. 2.00T
G-BIDG	SAN Jodel 150A Mascaret	08	F-BLDG	11. 9.80	D.R.Gray	Barton	26. 6.99P
G-BIDH	Cessna 152 II	152-80546	G-DONA G-BIDH/N25234	12. 9.80	J.A. & R.M.Nichol	Carlisle	23. 6.02T
					t/a Cumbria Aero Club		
G-BIDI	PA-28R-201 Arrow III	28R-7837135	N3759M	11.11.80	Ambrit Ltd	Elstree	9. 5.02
G-BIDJ	PA-18A-150 Super Cub (Frame No.18-6089)	18-6007	PH-MAY N7798D	22. 9.80	Flight Solutions Ltd	(Hemel Hempstead)	15. 7.00
G-BIDK	PA-18-150 Super Cub (L-21A-PI)	"18-6591"	PH-MAI R.Neth AF R-211/51-15679/N7194K	22. 9.80	J.McCullouhg t/a Kemspray	Newtownards	19. 8.01
	(This is a composite Aero Club - PH-MAI was originally c/n 18-6591 (Frame No.18-6714) ex LN-TVB/N9285D but was rebuilt in 1976 using Frame No.18-503 (c/n 18-565) and ex R.Neth AF R-211 as shown)						
G-BIDO	Piel CP.301A Emeraude	327	F-POIO	25. 3.81	A.R.Plumb	Hill Farm, Nayland	24. 6.97P
					(Stored 9.97)		
G-BIDU	Cameron V-77 HAFB	660		8. 1.81	E.Eleazor "Margaret"	London W1	26. 8.87A
G-BIDV*	Colt 17A Cloudhopper HAFB	789		29. 1.79	British Balloon Museum & Library "Smirnoff Cloudhopper"	Newbury	NE(A)
	(Second canopy - original was Colt 14A c/n 034 which may be held by the Museum)						
G-BIDW*	Sopwith "1 ½" Strutter rep (Le Clerget)	WA/5	"9382"	24. 9.80	RAF Museum	Hendon	29.12.80P*
					(As "A8226" in 45 Sqn RFC c/s)		
G-BIDX	Dormois Jodel D.112	876	F-BIQY	19. 9.80	H.N.Nuttall & P.Turton	Ash House Farm, Winsford	15.10.00P
G-BIEF	Cameron V-77 HAFB	679		25. 9.80	D.S.Bush "Daedalus"	Hertingfordbury, Herts	6. 3.94A
G-BIEJ	Sikorsky S-76A II Plus	760097		21.10.80	Bristow Helicopters Ltd "Glenlossie"	North Denes	21. 2.01T
G-BIEN	Jodel Wassmer D.120A Paris-Nice	218	F-BKNK	3. 6.81	R.J.Baker "The Lady Savage"	Stapleford	14.04.00P
G-BIEO	Wassmer Jodel D.112	1296	F-BMOK	19. 3.82	S.C.Solley	Clipgate Farm, Denton	1. 8.00P
					t/a Clipgate Flyers		
G-BIES	Maule M.5-235C Lunar Rocket	7334C	N56394	24. 7.81	W.Procter	Stowes Farm, Tillingham	26. 3.00
					t/a William Procter Farms		
G-BIET	Cameron O-77 HAFB	674		30. 9.80	G.M.Westley "Archimedes"	London SW15	5. 6.91A
G-BIEY	PA-28-151 Cherokee Warrior	28-7715213	PH-KDH OO-HCB	10.11.80	A.S.Bamrah	NK	1. 1.01T
					t/a Falcon Flying Services		
G-BIFA	Cessna 310R II	310R-1606	N36868	29. 1.81	J.S.Lee	Denham	31. 7.00
G-BIFB	PA-28-150 Cherokee C	28-1968	4X-AEC	6.10.80	N.A.Ayub	Biggin Hill	12.12.98T
G-BIFN	Bensen B.8MR	KW.1 & PFA G/01-1010		7.10.80	B.Gunn	(North Ferriby)	
G-BIFO	Evans VP-1 (VW1834)	PFA/62-10411		29. 9.80	R.Broadhead	Bagby	27. 7.00P

Regn	Type	C/n	P/I	Date	Owner/operator	Probable Base	CA Expy
G-BIFP*	Colt 56C HAFB	097		14.10.80	J.Philp	Liskeard	
					t/a The Serendipity Balloon Group "Fire Engine"		
G-BIFY	Reims Cessna F.150L	0829	PH-CEZ	9.10.80	B.W.Davis t/a Astra Associates	Elstree	21. 8.02T
G-BIFZ	Partenavia P.68C	229		24. 6.81	Jet Airmotive Ltd	Henstridge	22.12.02T
G-BIGF	Thunder Ax7-77 Bolt HAFB	295		20.10.80	M.D.Steuer & Christine A.Allen	Monmouth	6. 9.91A
					"Low Rider"		
G-BIGJ	Reims Cessna F.172M	0936	PH-SKT	2.12.80	V.D.Speck	Clacton	5. 8.02T
G-BIGK	Taylorcraft BC-12D	8302	N96002	29.10.80	N.P.St.J.Ramsay	(Woodbridge)	19. 7.99P
	(Continental A65)		NC96002				
G-BIGL	Cameron O-65 HAFB	690		22.10.80	P.L.Mossman "Biggles"	Bristol	28. 5.00A
G-BIGP	Bensen B.8M PFA G/01-1005			14.10.80	R.H.S.Cooper Cross Houses, Shrewsbury		20.10.97P
	(McCulloch)						
G-BIGR	Avenger T.200-2122 HAFB (Model)	004		6.10.80	R.Light	Stockport	
G-BIGT*	Colt 77A HAFB	078		28. 2.80	British Balloon Museum "Big T"	Newbury	20. 2.83A
					(Damaged Belton Hall nr Grantham 23.8.81; stored)		
G-BIGX	Bensen B.8M JRM.2 & PFA G/01-1033			5.11.80	W.C.Turner	Malvern	
G-BIGZ	Scheibe SF-25B Falke	46142	D-KCAI	22.12.80	R.F.Smith & C.R.Sproson	Saltby	22. 7.02
					t/a G-BIGZ Syndicate		
G-BIHD	Robin DR.400/160 Major 80	1510		29.10.80	K.B.Mainstone	Thurrock	13. 5.99
G-BIHE*	Reims Cessna FA.152 Aerobat	0373		6.11.80	Walkbury Aviation Ltd	Sibson	5. 3.99T
	(Damaged nr Sheerness 10.3.99: stored Spanhoe 4.99: cancelled as destroyed 21.7.99)						
G-BIHF	Replica Plans SE.5A PFA/20-10548			27.10.80	K.J.Garrett "Lady Di"	White Waltham	15. 6.99P
	(Continental O-200-A) (Plans No. 079275)				(As "F-943" in 92 Sqdn RFC c/s)		
G-BIHG	PA-28-140 Cherokee	28-24376	OO-JAR	25.11.80	P.W.Wilson	Framlingham	7. 6.02
			N6686J		t/a Parham Flying Group		
G-BIHI	Cessna 172M Skyhawk II	172-66854	(G-BIHA)	18.11.80	L.R.Haunch	Fenland	5. 5.02T
			N1125U		t/a Fenland Flying School		
G-BIHO	DHC.6 Twin Otter 310	738	A6-ADB	9. 1.81	Isles of Scilly Skybus Ltd	St.Just	18. 4.00T
			G-BIHO				
G-BIHP	Van Den Bemden 1000m3 Gas Free Balloon VDB-38		OO-VBA	19.12.80	J.J.Harris "Belgica"	London SW6	5. 7.99
	(C/n quoted as "18" on Belgian C of R; believed rebuilt with 600m3 balloon c/n VDB-47)						
G-BIHT	PA-17 Vagabond	17-41	N138N	9. 1.81	G.H.Cork Orchard Farm, Fradley		17. 2.00P
	(Continental A65)		N8N/N4626H/NC4626H				
G-BIHU	Saffery S.200 HAFB (Model)	25		5.11.80	B.L.King	Coulsdon	
G-BIHX	Bensen B.8MR PFA G/01-1003			12.11.80	P.P.Willmott	North Coates	8.11.00P
	(Rotax 503)						
G-BIIA	Alpavia Fournier RF3	51	F-BMTA	14.11.80	T.M.W.Webster	(Pershore)	16. 7.87P
					t/a Double M Flying Group (Status uncertain)		
G-BIIB	Reims Cessna F.172M Skyhawk II	1110	PH-GRE	18.11.80	Civil Service Flying Club (Biggin Hill) Ltd		
						Biggin Hill	24. 4.00T
G-BIID	PA-18-95 Super Cub	18-1606	OO-LPA	5. 1.81	D.A.Lacey	Cumbernauld	27. 6.00P
	(L-18C-PI) (Frame No.18-1558)		OO-HMK/ALAT 18-1606/51-15606				
G-BIIE	Reims Cessna F.172P Skyhawk II	2051		31.12.80	Sterling Helicopters Ltd	Norwich	4. 3.02T
G-BIIF*	Sportavia Fournier RF4D	4047	G-BVET	25.11.80	Not known	Biggin Hill	18. 3.93A
			F-BOXG		(Stored 8.97)		
G-BIIK	Socata MS.883 Rallye 115	1552	F-BSAP	28.11.80	H.& K.M.Bowen	Goldcliff	22.10.01
G-BIIL	Thunder Ax6-56 Bolt HAFB	306		12.11.80	G.W.Reader	Selby	1. 6.84A
G-BIIP	PBN BN-2B-27 Islander	2103	6Y-JQJ	1.12.80	Hebridean Air Services Ltd	Glasgow	AC
			6Y-JKJ/N411JA/G-BIIP				
G-BIIT	PA-28-161 Warrior II	28-8116052	N82744	1.12.80	Tayside Aviation Ltd	Glenrothes	23. 3.02T
G-BIIV	PA-28-181 Archer II	28-7990028	N20875	19.12.80	Stratton Motor Co (Norfolk) Ltd		
						Crowfield	10. 9.00T
G-BIIX	Rango NA-12 HAFB (Model)	NHP.11		1.12.80	N.H.Ponsford	Leeds	
	(Regd as c/n NHP-12)				t/a Rango Balloon & Kite Co "Lament for Jok"		
G-BIIZ	Great Lakes 2T-1A Sport Trainer	57	N603K	1. 4.81	C.D.Baird	(Farnham)	4. 2.99P
	(Warner Super Scarab 165D-5)		NC603K		(Damaged Upper Harford, Glos 8.8.98)		
G-BIJB	PA-18-150 Super Cub	18-8009001	N23923	18. 8.80	Essex Gliding Club Ltd	North Weald	31. 3.01
			(N2573H)				
G-BIJD	Bolkow Bo.208C Junior	636	PH-KAE	9.12.80	C.G.Stone	Biggin Hill	29. 7.01
			(PH-DYM)/OO-SIS/(D-EGFA)				
G-BIJE	Piper J3C-65 Cub (L-4A-PI)	8367	F-BIGN	5. 5.81	R.L.Hayward & A.G.Scott	Cardiff	
	(Frame No.8504)		Fr.AF/42-15248		(On rebuild 4.91)		
G-BIJS	Phoenix Luton LA-4A Minor			18. 5.78	I.J.Smith	Brook Farm, Boylestone	14.11.95P
	(VW 1600) PAL/1348 & PFA/835						
G-BIJU	Menavia Piel CP.301A Emeraude	221	G-BHTX	10. 6.80	A.G.Bailey	Stapleford	20. 4.00P
			F-BIJU		t/a Eastern Taildraggers Flying Group		
G-BIJV	Reims Cessna F.152 II	1813		22.12.80	A.S.Bamrah	Biggin Hill	4. 3.02T
					t/a Falcon Flying Services		
G-BIJW	Reims Cessna F.152 II	1820		22.12.80	A.S.Bamrah	Blackbushe	24. 2.02T
					t/a Falcon Flying Services (Op European Flyers)		

Regn	Type	C/n	P/I	Date	Owner/operator	Probable Base	CA Expy
G-BIJX	Reims Cessna F.152 II	1829		29.12.80	A.S.Bamrah	Lydd	3. 6.02T
					t/a Falcon Flying Services		
G-BIKA	Boeing 757-236	22172	(N757B)	28. 3.83	British Airways plc	Heathrow	28. 3.00T
					(Blue Poole t/s)		
G-BIKB	Boeing 757-236	22173		25. 1.83	British Airways plc	Heathrow	26. 1.00T
					(Chelsea Rose t/s)		
G-BIKC	Boeing 757-236	22174		31. 1.83	British Airways plc	Heathrow	9. 2.00T
					(Emmly Masanabo/Ndebele t/s)		
G-BIKD	Boeing 757-236	22175		10. 3.83	British Airways plc	Heathrow	14. 3.00T
					(Emmly Masanabo/Ndebele t/s)		
G-BIKE	PA-28R-200 Cherokee Arrow II		OY-DVT	18. 4.80	R.V.Webb Ltd	Elstree	17. 9.01
		28R-7335173	N55047				
G-BIKF	Boeing 757-236	22177	(G-BIKG)	28. 4.83	British Airways plc	Heathrow	28. 4.00T
					(Wanula Dreaming t/s)		
G-BIKG	Boeing 757-236	22178	(G-BIKH)	26. 8.83	British Airways plc	Heathrow	26. 8.00T
G-BIKH	Boeing 757-236	22179	(G-BIKI)	18.10.83	British Airways plc	Heathrow	20.10.00T
					(Golden Khokhloma t/s)		
G-BIKI	Boeing 757-236	22180	(G-BIKJ)	30.11.83	British Airways plc	Heathrow	1.12.00T
					(Rendezvous t/s)		
G-BIKJ	Boeing 757-236	22181	(G-BIKK)	9. 1.84	British Airways plc	Heathrow	11. 1.01T
					(Waves of the City t/s)		
G-BIKK	Boeing 757-236	22182	(G-BIKL)	1. 2.84	British Airways plc	Heathrow	1. 2.01T
G-BIKL	Boeing 757-236	22183	(G-BIKM)	29. 2.84	British Airways plc	Heathrow	28. 2.01T
					(Mountain of the Birds/Benyhone Tartan t/s)		
G-BIKM	Boeing 757-236	22184	N8293V	21. 3.84	British Airways plc	Heathrow	22. 3.01T
			(G-BIKN)				
G-BIKN	Boeing 757-236	22186	(G-BIKP)	23. 1.85	British Airways plc	Heathrow	24. 1.02T
					(Rendezvous t/s)		
G-BIKO	Boeing 757-236	22187	(G-BIKR)	14. 2.85	British Airways plc	Heathrow	18. 2.02T
					(Mountain of the Birds/Benyhone Tartan t/s)		
G-BIKP	Boeing 757-236	22188	(G-BIKS)	11. 3.85	British Airways plc	Heathrow	14. 3.02T
G-BIKR	Boeing 757-236	22189	(G-BIKT)	29. 3.85	British Airways plc	Heathrow	2. 4.02T
					(Union Flag c/s)		
G-BIKS	Boeing 757-236	22190	(G-BIKU)	31. 5.85	British Airways plc	Heathrow	2. 6.02T
G-BIKT	Boeing 757-236	23398		1.11.85	British Airways plc	Heathrow	3.11.02T
					(Crossing Borders t/s)		
G-BIKU	Boeing 757-236	23399		7.11.85	British Airways plc	Heathrow	7.11.02T
G-BIKV	Boeing 757-236	23400		9.12.85	British Airways plc	Heathrow	11.12.02T
					(Union Flag c/s)		
G-BIKW	Boeing 757-236	23492		7. 3.86	British Airways plc	Heathrow	9. 3.02T
					(Union Flag t/s)		
G-BIKX	Boeing 757-236	23493		14. 3.86	British Airways plc	Heathrow	16. 3.02T
					(Delftblue Daybreak t/s)		
G-BIKY	Boeing 757-236	23533		28. 3.86	British Airways plc	Heathrow	31. 3.02T
					(Primavara t/s)		
G-BIKZ	Boeing 757-236	23532		15. 5.86	British Airways plc	Heathrow	15. 5.02T
					(Union Flag t/s)		
G-BILA*	Dalotel DM-165L Viking	01	F-PPZE	5. 2.81	Not known (On rebuild 1994)	(Bristol)	14. 9.83P
G-BILB	WMB-2 Windtracker HAFB (Model)	14		22. 1.81	B.L.King	Coulsdon	
G-BILE	Scruggs BL-2B HAFB (Model)	81231		13. 3.81	P.D.Ridout	Botley	
G-BILF*	Practavia Sprite 125 PFA/05-10467			17.12.80	G.Harfield	(Derby)	
					(Cancelled by CAA 12.4.99)		
G-BILG	Scruggs BL-2B HAFB (Model)	81232		13. 3.81	P.D.Ridout	Botley	
G-BILI	Piper J3C-65 Cub (L-4J-PI)	13207	F-BDTB	14. 1.81	R.P.Grace & S.C.Wilson	White Waltham	26. 5.00P
			45-4467		t/a G-BILI Flying Group (As "454467/J/44" in US Army c/s)		
	(Original p/i is unconfirmed; a/c appears to have Frame No.15044 (c/n 15449) but current as N87791)						
G-BILJ	Reims Cessna FA.152 Aerobat	0376		31.12.80	Bournemouth Flying Club Ltd	Bournemouth	7. 6.02T
G-BILK	Reims Cessna FA.152 Aerobat	0372		9. 1.81	Exeter Flying Club Ltd	Exeter	13. 5.02T
G-BILL	PA-25-260 Pawnee D	25-7856028		3. 1.79	A E & W.J.Taylor	Wyberton	28. 5.00A
					t/a Pawnee Aviation		
G-BILR	Cessna 152 II	152-84822	N4822P	19. 3.81	Shropshire Aero Club Ltd	Sleap	8. 5.02T
G-BILS	Cessna 152 II	152-84857	N4954P	3. 6.81	Keen Leasing (IOM) Ltd.	Carlisle	5. 7.02T
G-BILU	Cessna 172RG Cutlass II	172RG-0564	N5540V	29. 1.81	R.M.English & Sons Ltd	Full Sutton	14. 6.00T
G-BILZ	Taylor JT.1 Monoplane PFA/55-10244			15.12.80	A.Petherbridge	Sibsey	29. 2.91P
	(VW1600) (Regd as c/n PFA/55-10124)				(Damaged Ingoldmells 10.6.90; stored 9.98)		
G-BIMK	Tiger T.200 Srs.1 HAFB (Model)			22.12.80	M.K.Baron	Stockport	
		7/MKB-01					
G-BIMM	PA-18-150 Super Cub	18-3868	PH-VHO	8. 1.81	Fairmont Investments Ltd	Clacton	6. 8.01T
	(L-21B-PI) (Frame No.18-3881)		R.Neth AF R-178/54-2468				
G-BIMN	Steen Skybolt PFA/64-10329			31.12.80	G.P.Gregg	Spanhoe	11. 7.00P
	(Lycoming IO-360)						

Regn	Type	C/n	P/I	Date	Owner/operator	Probable Base	CA Expy
G-BIMO	SNCAN Stampe SV-4C	394	F-BADG	5. 3.81	R.A.Robert Goodwood/Pulborough		17. 3.02
	(Gipsy Major 10)		Fr.Mil		(As "394" in French AF c/s)		
G-BIMT	Reims Cessna FA.152 Aerobat	0361	N8062L	9. 1.81	Gloucestershire Flying Services Ltd		
						Gloucestershire	26. 5.02T
G-BIMU	Sikorsky S-61N Mk II	61-752	N8511Z	9. 1.81	Bristow Helicopters Ltd Stornoway		23.10.02T
	(SAR conversion)		VH-CRU/N4042S		(Op HM Coastguard) "Stac Pollaidh"		
G-BIMX	Rutan VariEze PFA/74-10544			6. 1.81	D.G.Crew	Biggin Hill	3. 8.98P
	(Continental O-200-A)						
G-BIMZ	Beechcraft 76 Duchess	ME-169	N6021K	20. 3.81	A.J.Nurse	Gloucestershire	15.12.02
G-BINF	Saffery S.200 Heatwave HAFB (Model) 02			28. 5.81	T.C.B.Lewis	Altrincham	
G-BING	Reims Cessna F.172P Skyhawk II	2084		12. 1.81	M.P.Dolan	Eglinton	16. 4.02
G-BINL	Scruggs BL-2B HAFB (Model)	81216		5. 2.81	P.D.Ridout	Botley	
G-BINM	Scruggs BL-2B HAFB (Model)	81217		5. 2.81	P.D.Ridout	Botley	
G-BINO	Evans VP-1	PFA/1547		8. 6.78	G.Ravichandran	Chilbolton	
	(Possibly incorporates project PFA/7007)				(Under construction 1.96)		
G-BINR	Unicorn UE-1A HAFB (Model)	81004		20. 1.81	I.Chadwick	Horsham	
					t/a Unicorn Group "Lady Diana"		
G-BINS	Unicorn UE-2A HAFB (Model)	80002		22.12.80	I.Chadwick	Horsham	
					t/a Unicorn Group "Caroline"		
G-BINT	Unicorn UE-1A HAFB (Model)	80001		22.12.80	I.Chadwick	Horsham	
					t/a Unicorn Group "Belinda"		
G-BINU	Saffery S.200 Heatwave HAFB (Model)			13. 1.81	T.C.B.Lewis	Altrincham	
		TCBL/01					
G-BINX	Scruggs BL-2B HAFB (Model)	81219		5. 2.81	P.D.Ridout	Botley	
G-BINY	Oriental Air-Bag HAFB (Model) OAB-001			22. 1.81	J.L.Morton	Wokingham	
G-BIOB	Reims Cessna F.172P Skyhawk II	2042		23. 1.81	Aerofilms Ltd	Luton	16. 4.02T
G-BIOC	Reims Cessna F.150L	0848	F-BUEC	3. 2.81	D.J.Gage & G.McNaughton (Kilmarnock)		3. 8.02T
					t/a Southside Flyers,		
G-BIOI	SAN Jodel DR.1050/M Excellence	477	F-BLJQ	21. 1.81	H.F.Hambling	Fenland	30. 6.02P
G-BIOJ	Rockwell Commander 112TC-A	13192	N4662W	22. 1.82	A.T.Dalby	Sywell	13.12.02
G-BIOK	Reims Cessna F.152 II	1810		2. 2.81	Tayside Aviation Ltd Glenrothes/Aberdeen		15. 4.02T
G-BIOM	Reims Cessna F.152 II	1815		5. 2.81	A.S.Bamrah	Lydd	25. 4.02T
					t/a Falcon Flying Services		
G-BIOR	Socata MS.880B Rallye Club	1229	OO-SAF	3. 2.81	R.L. & K.P.McLean	Rufforth	26. 9.02
	(Composite rebuild with components from G-AZGJ)				t/a McLean Aviation		
G-BIOU	SAN Jodel D.117A	813	F-BIOU	9. 8.78	M.D.Howlett	Ilmer, Bucks	23. 5.00P
					t/a Dubious Group		
G-BIOW	Slingsby T.67A	1988		26. 2.81	A.B.Slinger Sherburn in Elmet		31. 3.00
					t/a Slingsby T67A Group		
G-BIPA	Grumman-American AA-5B Tiger		OY-GAM	24. 3.81	J.Campbell	Walney Island	15. 6.02
		AA5B-0200					
G-BIPH	Scruggs BL-2B HAFB (Model)	81224		10. 2.81	C.M.Dewsnap	Camberley	
G-BIPI	Everett Gyroplane	001		30. 4.81	R.Spall	Wolverhampton	29. 4.92P
	(VW1834) (Marks possibly applied to two aircraft stored at Kemble & Ipswich)						
G-BIPN	Alpavia Fournier RF3	35	F-BMDN	26. 2.81	J.C.R.Rogers & I.F.Fairhead Cranwell		17. 8.02P
G-BIPO	Mudry/CAARP CAP.20LS-200	03	F-GAUB	5. 3.81	M.C.Sandford	White Waltham	21. 2.01S
G-BIPS*	Socata Rallye 100ST	3028	F-GBCA	20. 2.81	Not known	Newcastle	27. 9.93T
					(Damaged pre 9.92; stored 5.93))		
G-BIPT	Wassmer Jodel D.112	1254	F-BMIB	11. 3.81	C.R.Davies Allensmore, Hereford		7. 9.99P
G-BIPV	Gulfstream AA-5B Tiger	AA5B-0981	N28266	10. 3.81	Airtime Aviation Ltd.	Bournemouth	13. 5.02T
G-BIPW	Avenger T200-2112 HAFB (Model)	10		24. 2.81	B.L.King	Coulsdon	
G-BIPY	Montgomerie-Bensen B.8MR			25. 2.81	C.G.Ponsford	(Maldon)	13.10.95P
	(Rotax 532) AJW.01 & PFA G/01-1007						
G-BIPZ*	McCandless M.4 Gyroplane Mk.4-4			27. 2.81	Not known Sion Mills, Strabane		
					(Stored 4.96)		
G-BIRB*	Socata MS.880B Rallye 100T	2460	F-BVAQ	30. 3.81	Hawick ATC Squadron	Carlisle	16. 6.90
					(Stored 9.97)		
G-BIRD	Pitts S-1D Special 707-H & PFA/1596			3.11.77	Sandra J.Perkins	Deenethorpe	6. 4.00P
	(Lycoming IO-360)				t/a Pitts Artists Flying Group		
G-BIRE	Colt Bottle 56SS HAFB	323		4. 3.81	K.R.Gafney "Satzenbrau"	Bracknell	NE(A)
	(Satzenbrau Bottle)						
G-BIRH	PA-18-180 Super Cub	18-3853	PH-LET	19. 3.81	Aquila Gliding Club Ltd		
	(L-21B-PI) (Frame No.18-3857)		R Neth AF R-163/54-2453		Hinton-in-The-Hedges		10. 6.02
					(As "R-163" in R.Neth AF c/s)		
G-BIRI	CASA I-131E Jungmann	1074	E3B-113	14. 4.81	M.G. & J.R.Jefferies Little Gransden		20.10.94P
					(Stored 9.96)		
G-BIRK	Avenger T200-2112 HAFB (Model)	006		10. 3.81	T.A.Smith	Cheadle, Cheshire	
G-BIRL	Avenger T200-2112 HAFB (Model)	008		10. 3.81	R.Light	Stockport	
G-BIRM	Avenger T200-2112 HAFB (Model)	007		10. 3.81	P.Higgins	Hyde	
G-BIRP	Ridout Arena Mk.17 Skyship HAFB	01		13. 3.81	Annette S.Viel	Botley	
	(Model)						

Regn	Type	C/n	P/I	Date	Owner/operator	Probable Base	CA Expy
G-BIRS	Cessna 182P Skylane	182-61436	G-BBBS N21131	10. 3.81	Air Nova plc	Chester	19. 4.01T
G-BIRT	Robin R.1180TD Aiglon	276		25. 3.81	W.D'A.Hall	White Waltham	29. 9.02
G-BIRW*	Morane-Saulnier MS.505 Criquet	695	OO-FIS F-BDQS	10. 4.81	Royal Museum of Scotland, Museum of Flight (As "F+IS" in Luftwaffe c/s)	East Fortune	3. 6.83P
G-BIRY	Cameron V-77 HAFB	715		12. 3.81	P.& H.Mann "Magic Carpet"	Luton	15. 5.99A
G-BIRZ	Zenair CH.250-100			10. 3.81	T.N.Fox & I.R.Nash	Popham	4. 8.00P
	(Lycoming O-290-G) 2-454 & PFA/24-10459						
G-BISG	Clutton FRED Srs.III			13. 3.81	R.A.Coombe (Lymington, Hants)		29.10.86P
	(VW1600) RAC 01-224 & PFA/29-10675				"Fuzz Bee" (Status uncertain)		
G-BISH	Cameron V-65 HAFB	707		16. 3.81	P.J.Bish & C.Hall	Hungerford	29. 8.99A
					t/a Zebedee Balloon Service "Tsaritsa"		
G-BISJ	Cessna 340A II	340A-0497	OO-LFK N6328X	10. 4.81	K.J. & J.G.Bill	Halfpenny Green	13. 7.02T
					t/a Billair		
G-BISL	Scruggs BL-2B HAFB (Model)	81233		13. 3.81	P.D.Ridout	Botley	
G-BISM	Scruggs BL-2B HAFB (Model)	81234		13. 3.81	P.D.Ridout	Botley	
G-BISS	Scruggs BL-2C HAFB (Model)	81235		13. 3.81	P.D.Ridout	Botley	
G-BIST	Scruggs BL-2C HAFB (Model)	81236		13. 3.81	P.D.Ridout	Botley	
G-BISW*	Cameron O-65 HAFB	713		18. 3.81	N H Ponsford	Leeds	6 .8.88
					(Cancelled by CAA 5.6.98: noted 4.99)		
G-BISX	Colt 56A HAFB	324		18. 3.81	Colt G-BISX Ltd	Pathhead, Midlothian	18. 8.99A
G-BISZ	Sikorsky S-76A II Plus	760156		19. 3.81	Bristow Helicopters Ltd	North Denes	23.10.01T
G-BITA	PA-18-150 Super Cub	18-8109037		24. 3.81	D.J.Gilmour	North Weald	7. 7.02
					t/a Intrepid Aviation Co		
G-BITE	Socata TB-10 Tobago	193		7. 5.81	M.A.Smith & R.J.Bristow	Fairoaks	4.10.02
G-BITF	Reims Cessna F.152 II	1822		27. 3.81	Tayside Aviation Ltd	Glenrothes	30. 4.00T
G-BITH	Reims Cessna F.152 II	1825		27. 3.81	Tayside Aviation Ltd	Dundee	14. 8.00T
G-BITK	Clutton FRED Srs.II	PFA/29-10369		23. 3.81	D.J.Wood	(Dover)	
	(VW1500)						
G-BITM	Reims Cessna F.172P Skyhawk II	2046		13. 4.81	D.G.Crabtree	Barton	12. 8.02T
G-BITO	Wassmer Jodel D.112D	1200	F-BIUO	20. 3.81	A.Dunbar	Barton	3. 6.00P
G-BITR	Sikorsky S-76A II Plus	760157	PT-HRW G-BITR	26. 3.81	Bristow Helicopters Ltd	North Denes	21.12.00T
					"Glenlassaugh"		
G-BITS	Drayton B-56 HAFB	MJB-01/81		16. 3.81	M.J.Betts "Hedger" Drayton, Norwich		
					t/a Eastern Region, British Balloon & Airship Club		
G-BITW*	Short SD.3-30 Var.100	SH.3070	G-EASI (G-BITW)/G-14-3070	26. 3.81	Air Cavrel Ltd		9. 6.98T
	(WFU Coventry 7.97 & stored: broken up 7.99: cancelled 20.7.99 as WFU: remains to Valley Nurseries, Alton)						
G-BITY	Bell FD.31T Flying Dodo HAFB (Model)	2604		25. 3.81	A.J.Bell	Luton	
G-BIUL*	Cameron 60 Expansion Joint SS HAFB	703		27. 3.81	(To British Balloon Museum & Library 1998)	Newbury	
G-BIUM	Reims Cessna F.152 II	1807		3. 4.81	Sheffield Aero Club Ltd	Netherthorpe	30. 1.00T
G-BIUO*	Rockwell Commander 112A	281	OY-PRH	30. 3.81	Not known	Bristol	28.10.84
					N1281J (Collided with Cirrus BGA.2138 Longdon 12.5.84: wreck dumped 10.98)		
G-BIUP	SNCAN NC.854S	54	(G-AMPE) G-BIUP/F-BFSC	4. 6.81	D.F.Hurn	Popham	6. 6.00P
					t/a BIUP Flying Group		
G-BIUV	HS.748 Srs.2A/266	1701	5W-FAN G-AYYH/G-11-8	11. 5.81	Emerald Airways Ltd	Liverpool	16. 6.02T
					"City of Liverpool"		
G-BIUW	PA-28-161 Warrior II	28-8116128	N9506N	14. 4.81	D.R.Staley	Sturgate	27. 6.02
G-BIUY	PA-28-181 Archer II	28-8190133	N8318X	3. 4.81	J.S.Devlin & Z.Islam	(East Grinstead)	27.11.01T
G-BIVA	Robin R.2112	137	F-GBAZ	6. 5.81	P.A. Richardson	Conington	4. 8.02
G-BIVB	Wassmer Jodel D.112	1009	(G-BIVC) F-BJII	18. 9.81	D.Silsbury	Dunkeswell	23. 5.00P
G-BIVC	Wassmer Jodel D.112	1219	F-BMAI	1. 6.81	M.J.Barnby		
	(Continental A65)				Brickhouse Farm, Froglan Cross		13. 7.00P
G-BIVF	Scintex CP.301C3 Emeraude	594	F-BJVN	4.11.81	R.J.Moore	Bedford	17. 6.92P
G-BIVK	Bensen B.8M	PFA G/01-1008		10. 4.81	K.Balch	Henstridge	21. 2.00P
	(VW1834)				"Skyrider"		
G-BIVL*	Bensen B.8M	PFA G/01-1011		10. 4.81	Not known	St.Merryn	29. 4.87P
	(VW1834)						
G-BIVT	Saffery S.80 HAFB (Model)	LFG-001		22. 4.81	L.F.Guyot	London SW19	
G-BIVV	Gulfstream AA-5A Cheetah	AA5A-0857	N26979	26. 5.81	Plane Talking Ltd	Blackbushe	18. 7.02T
G-BIVW	Moravan Zlin Z.326 Trener-Master	932	F-BPNQ	12. 1.82	G.C.Masterton Rushett Farm, Chessington		
	(Imported as wreck from Carcassonne for spares: frame stored in rafters 3.99 & parts present 9.99)						
G-BIWA	Stevendon Skyreacher HAFB (Model)	102		8. 6.81	S.D.Barnes	Botley	
G-BIWB	Scruggs RS.5000 HAFB (Model)	81541		8. 6.81	P.D.Ridout	Botley	
G-BIWC	Scruggs RS.5000 HAFB (Model)	81546		26. 6.81	P.D.Ridout "Waterloo"	Botley	
G-BIWD	Scruggs RS.5000 HAFB (Model)	81545		26. 6.81	D.Eaves "Spooky"	Southampton	
G-BIWF	Ridout Warren Windcatcher HAFB (Model)	WW.013		3. 7.81	P.D.Ridout	Botley	

Regn	Type	C/n	P/I	Date	Owner/operator	Probable Base	CA Expy
G-BIWG	Ridout Zelenski Mk.2 HAFB (Model)			3. 7.81	P.D.Ridout	Botley	
	(Regd with c/n 2401)	Z.401					
G-BIWH	Cremer Super Fliteliner HAFB (Model)			13. 7.81	L.Griffiths	Morecambe	
		15.700PC					
G-BIWJ	Unicorn UE-1A HAFB (Model)	81014		14. 7.81	B.L.King	Coulsdon	
G-BIWK	Cameron V-65 HAFB	719		22. 4.81	I.R.Williams & R.G.Bickerdike		
					"Double Fantasy"	Bedford/Huntingdon	30. 3.99A
G-BIWL	PA-32-301 Saratoga	32-8106056	N83684	23. 4.81	A.R.Ward	Southend	28. 6.02
G-BIWN	Wassmer Jodel D.112	1314	F-BNCN	5. 6.81	C.R.Coates	Sneaton Thorpe, Whitby	26. 4.02P
G-BIWP*	Mooney M.20J (201)	24-1094	N9923S	28. 5.81	G.Gore-Browne	Sherburn in Elmet	26.11.99
					t/a Whiskey Papa Flying Group		
	(Crashed nr Hemmingbrough, N Yorks 29.4.99, cancelled as destroyed 8.11.99)						
G-BIWR	Mooney M.20F Executive	22-1339	N6972V	1. 6.81	A.C.Brink	Bourn	7.11.99
G-BIWU	Cameron V-65 HAFB	717		15. 5.81	L.P. Hooper	Bristol	3.12.98A
					"Bumble Bee"		
G-BIWW	American AA-5 Traveler	AA5-0263	OY-AYV	2. 6.81	B.M.R. & K.R.Sheppard	Deenethorpe	8. 8.02
					t/a B & K Aviation (Op Sandra's Flying Group) "Kit-Kat"		
G-BIWY*	Westland WG-30-100	901		30. 4.81	Westland Helicopters Ltd		
					(To The Helicopter Museum 12.98)	Weston-super-Mare	30. 3.86T
G-BIXA	Socata TB-9 Tampico	205		7. 5.81	Lord de Saumarez	(Perth)	2. 9.02
G-BIXB	Socata TB-9 Tampico	208		7. 5.81	L.B.W.& F.H.Hancock	Kemble	4. 3.00T
G-BIXH	Reims Cessna F.152 II	1840		30. 4.81	The Cambridge Aero Club Ltd	Cambridge	9. 2.00T
G-BIXI	Cessna 172RG Cutlass II	172RG-0861	N7533B	7. 7.81	J.F.P.Lewis t/a X India Group	Gamston	10. 6.02
G-BIXL	North American P-51D-20NA Mustang	IDF/AF2343		3. 7.81	R.J.Lamplough "Miss L"	North Weald	8. 6.02P
		122-38675	Fv.26116/44-72216		(As "472216/"AJ-L" in 354th FG USAAC c/s)		
G-BIXN	Boeing-Stearman A75N1 (PT-17-BW) Kaydet	N51132		15. 6.81	R.R.White	Swanton Morley	3. 8.96
	(Continental W670)	75-2248	41-8689		(Damaged Frensham Pond 21.4.96; stored 10.97)		
G-BIXS	Avenger T.200-2112 HAFB (Model)	013		13. 5.81	M.Stuart	Altrincham	
G-BIXV	Bell 212	30870	N16931	27. 5.81	Bristow Helicopters Ltd		
						Safe Gothia Oil Rig	22. 7.02T
G-BIXW	Colt 56B HAFB	348		18. 5.81	N.A.P.Bates "Spam"	Tunbridge Wells	17. 8.97A
G-BIXX	Pearson Srs.II HAFB (Model)	00327		8. 5.81	D.Pearson	Solihull	
G-BIXZ	Grob G-109	6019	D-KGRO	14. 5.81	D.L.Nind & I.Allum	Booker	13. 5.01
G-BIYI	Cameron V-65 HAFB	722		21. 5.81	P.F.Smart	Basingstoke	16. 4.97A
					t/a The Sarnia Balloon Group "Penny"		
G-BIYJ	PA-18-95 Super Cub (L-18C-PI)	18-1000		5. 6.81	S.Russell	Wilkieston Farm, Cupar	21. 9.99P
			MM51-15303/I-EIST/MM51-15303/51-15303				
G-BIYK	Isaacs Fury II	PFA/11-10418		20. 5.81	D.Silsbury	Dunkeswell	19.10.99P
	(Continental C90)						
G-BIYO	PA-31-310 Turbo Navajo	31-7912022	PH-ECG	5. 6.81	Executive Jet Leasing Ltd		
			N27845			Ronaldsway/Manchester	14. 8.01T
G-BIYP	PA-20-125 Pacer	20-802	CN-TYP	25. 5.83	R.J.Whitcombe	Liss, Petersfield	8. 7.02
			F-DACJ/OO-ADP				
G-BIYR	PA-18-150 Super Cub	18-3841	(G-BIYB)	26. 5.81	B.H. & M.J.Fairclough	Dunkeswell	1. 6.01
	(L-21B-PI) (Frame No. 18-3843)		PH-GER		t/a The Delta Foxtrot Flying Group		
			R.Neth AF R-151/5G-96/54-2441 (As "R-151" in R.Neth AF c/s)				
G-BIYT	Colt 17A Cloudhopper HAFB	344		13. 7.81	J-M Francois Salles-Courbatiers, France		2.10.99A
G-BIYU	Fokker S.11-1 Instructor	6206	(PH-HOM)	13. 5.81	C.Briggs	Bagby	10.10.02P
			R.Neth AF E-15		(As "E-15" in R.Neth AF c/s)		
G-BIYW	Wassmer Jodel D.112	1209	F-BLNR	26. 5.81	K.Balaam	Elmsett, Suffolk	20.10.00P
					t/a Pollard/Balaam/Bye Flying Group		
G-BIYX	PA-28-140 Cherokee Cruiser		OY-BLD	19. 6.81	Comed Aviation Ltd	Blackpool	19.12.96T
		28-7625064			(On rebuild 9.99)		
G-BIYY	PA-18-95 Super Cub	18-1979		2. 6.81	A.E. & W.J.Taylor	Wyberton	23. 2.02T
	(L-18C-PI) (Frame No.18-1914)		MM52-2379/I-EIGA/MM52-2379/52-2379				
G-BIZB*	Agusta-Bell 206B JetRanger III	8611		10. 6.81	Not known	Fairoaks	
	(WO 28.6.89 Corfu, Greece: in use as fire training aid: in ditch on far side from Car Park by Blister Hangar)						
G-BIZE	Socata TB-9 Tampico	209	9H-ABJ	26. 7.99	C.Fordham	(Cambridge)	29. 7.02
			G-BIZE				
G-BIZF	Reims Cessna F.172P Skyhawk II	2070		16. 6.81	R.S.Bentley	Bourn	27. 1.01
G-BIZG	Reims Cessna F.152 II	1873		16. 6.81	M.A.Judge t/a Aero Group 78	Old Sarum	10. 5.00T
G-BIZI	Robin DR.400 2+2	1543		29. 5.81	BIZI Club Ltd	Booker	4. 2.00T
G-BIZK	Nord 3202B1	78	N2255E	22.11.85	A.I.Milne	Little Snoring	24.10.00P
			ALAT		(Luftwaffe c/s)		
G-BIZM	Nord 3202B	91	N2256K	22.11.85	Magnificent Obsessions Ltd	Humberside	31.10.00P
			ALAT				
G-BIZN	Slingsby T.67A	1989		16. 6.81	M.B.Smithson & A.Marsland t/a Sport to Business		
				(Damaged Leicester 23.7.97)	(Hessle/Holme-on-Spalding Moor)	24. 6.00	
G-BIZO	PA-28R-200 Cherokee Arrow II		OY-DLH	16. 6.81	Bizo Air Ltd	Clutton Hill	15. 1.00T
		28R-7535339					

Regn	Type	C/n	P/I	Date	Owner/operator	Probable Base	CA Expy
G-BIZR	Socata TB-9 Tampico	210	G-BSEC G-BIZR	15. 6.81	Rosalind C.Walker	Biggin Hill	23. 4.01
G-BIZT*	Bensen B.8M (VW1835)	PFA G/01-1015		10. 6.81	J.Ferguson (Stored 3.93)	Girvan, Ayr	12. 8.88P
G-BIZU	Thunder Ax6-56Z HAFB	358		15. 6.81	M.J.Loades "Greenall Whitley"	Southampton	4. 7.99A
G-BIZV	PA-18-95 Super Cub (L-18C-PI)	18-2001	MM52-2401 I-EIDE/MM52-2401/52-2401	12. 6.81	S.J.Pugh & R.L.Wademan (As "18-2001" in US Army c/s)	Oxenhope	27. 6.00P
G-BIZW	Champion 7GCBC Citabria	0157	D-EGROUPD	16. 7.81	J.C.Read t/a G.Read & Sons	Hall Farm, Louth	18. 8.01
G-BIZY	Wassmer Jodel D.112	1120	F-BKJL	13. 7.81	W.Tunley t/a Wayland Tunley & Associates	Hinton-in-The-Hedges	20. 5.00P

G-BJAA – G-BJZZ

Regn	Type	C/n	P/I	Date	Owner/operator	Probable Base	CA Expy
G-BJAE	Lavadoux Starck AS.80 Holiday (Continental A65)	04	F-PGGA F-WGGA	17. 6.81	D.J. & Mrs S.A.E.Phillips (Damaged Woburn 17.8.91)(Leamington Spa)		8. 8.92P
G-BJAF	Piper J3C-65 Cub (L-4A-PI) (Frame No.8540)	8437	D-EJAF HB-OAD/42-15318	23. 6.81	P.J.Cottle Craysmarsh Farm, Melksham		15. 3.00P
G-BJAG	PA-28-181 Archer II	28-7990353	PH-LDB (PH-BEG)/(OO-FLM)/N2244W	23. 6.81	J.F.Clark	(Ely)	19. 6.02
G-BJAJ	Gulfstream AA-5B Tiger	AA5B-1177	N4532V	2. 7.81	A.H.McVicar	Carlisle	20. 6.99T
G-BJAL	CASA I-131E Jungmann (Spanish AF serial no. conflicts with G-BUCC)	1028	E3B-114	11. 9.78	I.C.Underwood & S.B.J.Chandler Breighton		22. 6.00P
G-BJAN*	K & S SA.102.5 Cavalier	PFA/1554		20.12.78	J.Powlesland (Brightlingsea) (Cancelled by CAA 12.4.99)		
G-BJAO	Montgomerie-Bensen B.8MR (Rotax 582) GLS-01 & PFA G/01-1001 (Regd with c/n GL5-01)			28. 8.81	A.P.Lay	(Ilford)	10.12.98P
G-BJAP	DH.82A Tiger Moth 0482 & PFA/157-12897 (Composite rebuild)			15. 6.81	K.Knight (As "K2587" in pre-war 32 Sqn/CFS c/s)	Shobdon	6. 7.00P
G-BJAS	Rango NA-9 HAFB (Model)	TL-19		22. 6.81	A.Lindsay	Twickenham	
G-BJAV	Gardan GY-80-160 Horizon	28	OO-AJP F-BLVB	8. 9.81	A.G. Martlew	Haverfordwest	26. 1.97
G-BJAW	Cameron V-65 HAFB	745		19. 6.81	G.A.McCarthy "Breezin"	Shepton Mallet	16. 4.86A
G-BJAY	Piper J3C-65 Cub (L-4H-PI) (Frame No. 11914)	12086	F-BFBN OO-EAC/44-79790	1.11.78	K.L.Clarke	(Horncastle, Lincs)	19. 8.92P
G-BJBK	PA-18-95 Super Cub (L-18C-PI) 18-1431 (Continental O-200-A) (Frame No.18-1370)		F-BOME ALAT/51-15431	21. 8.81	M.S.Bird Pepperbox Farm, Salisbury		26. 5.00P
G-BJBM	Monnett Sonerai I (VW2074) MEA-117 & PFA/15-10022			2. 7.81	G.J.Townshend	(Kings Lynn)	9. 1.97P
G-BJBO	CEA Jodel DR.250/160 Capitaine	40	F-BNJG	24. 8.81	R.C.Thornton t/a Wiltshire Flying Group	Oaksey Park	17. 7.00
G-BJBW	PA-28-161 Warrior II	28-8116280	N2913Z	22. 7.81	J.C.Lucas	Popham	21.11.99
G-BJBX	PA-28-161 Warrior II	28-8116269	N8414H	17. 7.81	Haimoss Ltd (Op Old Sarum Flying Club)	Old Sarum	4. 3.00T
G-BJBZ*	Rotorway Exec 133	01-81		17. 7.81	P.J.D.Kerr (Bridgwater) (Cancelled by CAA 12.4.99)		
G-BJCA	PA-28-161 Warrior II	28-7916473	N2846D	30. 7.81	QBS Trading Co Ltd (Op Wellesbourne Aviation) Wellesbourne Mountford		28.11.99T
G-BJCF	Scintex CP.1310-C3 Super Emeraude	936	F-BMJH	19.11.81	K.M.Hodson & C.G.H.Gurney Manor Farm, Binham		15. 3.00P
G-BJCI	PA-18-180 Super Cub	18-6658	N9388D	10. 9.81	The Borders (Milfield) Aero-Tow Club Ltd Milfield		1. 6.00
G-BJCW	PA-32R-301 Saratoga SP	32R-8113094	N2866U	6. 8.81	G.R.Patrick & Co Ltd	Fairoaks	20. 5.02
G-BJDE	Reims Cessna F.172M	0984	OO-MSS D-EGBR	25. 8.81	H.P.K.Ferdinand	Elstree	24. 7.00
G-BJDF	Socata MS.880B Rallye 100T	3000	F-GAKP	21. 9.81	W.R.Savin Coldharbour Farm, Willingham t/a G-BJDF Group		9. 2.00
G-BJDI	Reims Cessna FR.182 Skylane RG	0046	N8062H	7. 8.81	P.R.Piggin	Leicester	3. 3.00
G-BJDJ	BAe HS.125 Srs.700B	257142	G-RCDI G-BJDJ/G-5-12	27. 7.81	Falcon Jet Centre Ltd	Fairoaks	6.10.00T
G-BJDK	Ridout European E.157 HAFB (Model)	S.2		17. 8.81	E.Osborn t/a Aeroprint Tours	Southampton	
G-BJDO	Gulfstream AA-5A Cheetah	AA5A-0823	N26936	3. 8.81	J.J.Woodhouse t/a Flying Services	(Fleet)	2. 4.00T
G-BJDT	Socata TB-9 Tampico	227		21. 8.81	A.Watson	Shoreham	25. 3.00T
G-BJDW	Reims Cessna F.172M Skyhawk II	1417	PH-JBE	10. 8.81	J.Rae Poplar Hall Farm, Elmsett (Op Suffolk Aero Club)		16.12.02T
G-BJEI	PA-18-95 Super Cub (L-18C-PI) (Frame No.18-1938)	18-1988	MM52-2388 I-EILO/MM52-2388/52-2388	27. 7.81	H.J.Cox Wendover Farm, Sheepwash		28. 9.00P

Regn	Type	C/n	P/I	Date	Owner/operator	Probable Base	CA Expy
G-BJEL	SNCAN NC.854S	113	F-BEZT	7. 8.81	N.F. & S.G.Hunter Wolvesnewton, Chepstow		3. 6.00P
G-BJEN	Scruggs RS.5000 HAFB (Model)	81548		5. 8.81	N.J.Richardson	Southampton	
G-BJEV	Aeronca 11AC Chief	11AC-270	N85897 NC85897	12. 8.81	R.F.Willcox (As "E/897" in US Navy c/s) Eastbach Farm, English Bicknor		4.12.00P
G-BJEX	Bolkow Bo.208C Junior	690	F-BRHY D-EEAM	27. 8.81	G.D.H.Crawford (Henley-on-Thames) (Status uncertain)		28. 1.88
G-BJFB	Eaves Dodo Mk.1A HAFB (Model)	DD.5		27. 8.81	S.D.Loveridge t/a Aeroprint Photographics	Southampton	
G-BJFC	Ridout European E.8 HAFB (Model)	S.1		17. 8.81	P.D.Ridout	Botley	
G-BJFE	PA-18-95 Super Cub (L-18C-PI)	18-2022	MM52-2422 I-EISU/MM52-2422/52-2422	17. 8.81	P.H.Wilmot-Allistone	Kemble	8. 3.00P
G-BJFL	Sikorsky S-76A II Plus	760056	N106BH N1546T/(G-BHRK)	28. 8.81	Bristow Helicopters Ltd "Glenmoray"	Redhill	17. 9.02T
G-BJFM	Jodel Wassmer D.120 Paris-Nice	227	F-BLFM	8.10.81	J.V.George & P.A.Smith	Popham	1. 7.00P
G-BJGE*	Thunder Ax3 Sky Chariot HAFB	367		21. 8.81	R.Warner	Cranfield	
G-BJGF	Eaves Dodo Mk.1 HAFB (Model)	DD-1		19. 8.81	D. & D.Eaves "Raphus Cacullatus"	Southampton	
G-BJGG	Eaves Dodo Mk.2 HAFB (Model)	DD-2		19. 8.81	D. & D.Eaves "Super Dodo"	Southampton	
G-BJGK	Cameron V-77 HAFB	696		3. 9.81	T.J.Orchard, N.J.Glover & S.R.Godfrey "Dollar"	Reading	15. 4.00A
G-BJGL	Cremer Cloud Challenger HAFB (Model)	15.704 PAC		24. 8.81	G.Lowther	Luton	
G-BJGM	Unicorn UE-1A HAFB (Model)	81015		21. 8.81	D.Eaves & P.D.Ridout "Capricorn"	Southampton	
G-BJGX	Sikorsky S-76A II Plus	760026	N103BH N4251S	4. 9.81	Bristow Helicopters Ltd "Glenelgin"	North Denes	8.10.00T
G-BJGY	Reims Cessna F.172P Skyhawk II	2128		13.10.81	Kit Martin (Historic Houses Rescue) Ltd Gunton Hall, Somerton, Norfolk		12. 4.00
G-BJHB	Mooney M.20J (201)	24-1190	N1145G	23.12.81	Zitair Flying Club Ltd	Booker	25. 3.99T
G-BJHK	EAA Acro-Sport 1 (Lycoming IO-360)	PFA/72-10470		20. 3.80	M.R.Holden Stoneacre Farm, Farthing Corner		17. 5.00P
G-BJHP	Osprey Lizzieliner 1C HAFB (Model)	AKC.16		9. 9.81	N.J.Richardson	Southampton	
G-BJHT	Thunder Ax7-65 Bolt HAFB	368		27. 8.81	A.H. & L.Symonds "Aura"	Chelmsford	
G-BJHV*	Voisin Scale Replica	MPS-1		1. 9.81	M.P.Sayer (On loan to Brooklands Museum)	Brooklands	
G-BJHW	Osprey Lizzieliner 1C HAFB (Model)	AKC.19		9. 9.81	N.J.Richardson	Southampton	
G-BJIA	Allport Aerostatics YUO-1A-1-DA HAFB (Model)	01		2. 9.81	D.J.Allport	Bourne, Lincs	
G-BJIC	Eaves Dodo 1A HAFB (Model)	DD.3		4. 9.81	P.D.Ridout	Botley	
G-BJID	Osprey Lizzieliner 1B HAFB (Model)	AKC.28		4. 9.81	P.D.Ridout	Botley	
G-BJIF*	Bensen B.8M (McCulloch O-90)	HR-01		7. 9.81	H.Redwin (Chiswick) (Damaged 1981/82: cancelled as wfu 25.1.99)		13.7.82P*
G-BJIG	Slingsby T.67A	1992		16. 9.81	D.Lacy t/a G-BJIG Slingsby Syndicate	Redhill	4. 3.01
G-BJIR	Cessna 550 Citation II (Unit No.326)	550-0296	N6888C	17. 9.81	Gator Aviation Ltd (Op Aviation Beauport Ltd)	Jersey	17. 1.00T
G-BJIV	PA-18-180 Super Cub	18-8262	N5972Z	17. 9.81	Yorkshire Gliding Club (Pty) Ltd	Sutton Bank	21. 7.00
G-BJJE	Eaves Dodo Mk.3 HAFB (Model)	DD.7		9. 9.81	D.Eaves	Southampton	
G-BJKF	Socata TB-9 Tampico	240		30. 9.81	P.C.Churcher t/a Venue Solutions	Denham	8. 4.01
G-BJKW	Wills Aera II	A3JKW		1. 3.78	J.K.S.Wills	(London SE3)	
G-BJKX*	Reims Cessna F.152 II	1881		22. 9.81	Not known Abbeyshrule, Ireland (Crashed nr Letterkenny 24.9.88: wreck stored 4.96)		1. 7.91T
G-BJKY	Reims Cessna F.152 II	1886		22. 9.81	Manx Aero Marine Management Ltd (Op Westair Flying Services)	Blackpool	1.10.01T
G-BJLB	SNCAN NC.854S	58	(OO-MVM) F-BFSG	5.11.81	N.F.Hunter Wolvesnewton, Chepstow (Crashed nr Newport,Gwent 29.7.84: stored 8.90)		30. 6.83P
G-BJLC	Monnett Sonerai IIL (VW 1835)	942L & PFA/15-10634		18. 9.81	A.R.Ansell "Elsie"	(Andover)	11. 5.98P
G-BJLF	Unicorn UE-1C HAFB (Model)	81018		21. 9.81	I.Chadwick t/a Unicorn Group	Horsham	
G-BJLG	Unicorn UE-1B HAFB (Model)	81017		21. 9.81	I.Chadwick t/a Unicorn Group	Horsham	
G-BJLH	PA-18-95 Super Cub (L-18C-PI) (Frame No.18-1513)	18-1541	F-BOUM ALAT 51-15541	26.10.81	Felthorpe Flying Group Ltd (As "K/33" in US Army c/s)	Felthorpe	1. 6.00P
G-BJLO	PA-31-310 Turbo Navajo	31-815	F-BTQG (F-BTDV)	23.10.81	RJ Aviation Ltd	Fairoaks	23.12.01

Regn	Type	C/n	P/I	Date	Owner/operator	Probable Base	CA Expy
G-BJLX	Cremer Cracker HAFB (Model)	15.711 PAC		24. 9.81	P.W.May	Wilmslow	
G-BJLY	Cremer Cracker HAFB (Model)	15.709 PAC		24. 9.81	P.Cannon	Luton	
G-BJMI	Eaves European E.84 HAFB (Model) S.3			9. 9.81	D.Eaves	Southampton	
G-BJML	Cessna 120 (Continental C90)	10766	N76349 NC76349	5.10.81	D.F.Lawlor	Inverness	1. 7.00P
G-BJMO	Taylor JT.1 Monoplane	PFA/55-10612		30. 9.81	R.C.Mark	(Ludlow)	
G-BJMR	Cessna 310R II	310R-1624	N2631Z	16. 7.79	J.M.Robinson	Sherburn in Elmet	18. 2.01
G-BJMW	Thunder Ax8-105 Srs.2 HAFB	369		14.10.81	G.M.Westley	London SW15	5. 1.89A
G-BJMX	Ridout Jarre JR-3 HAFB (Model)	81601		6.10.81	P.D.Ridout	Botley	
G-BJMZ	Ridout European EA-8A HAFB (Model)	S.5		6.10.81	P.D.Ridout	Botley	
G-BJNA	Ridout Arena Mk.117P HAFB (Model)	202		6.10.81	P.D.Ridout	Botley	
G-BJND	Chown Osprey Mk.1E HAFB (Model)	AKC.53		7.10.81	A.Billington & D.Whitmore	Liverpool	
G-BJNF	Reims Cessna F.152 II	1882		21.10.81	Exeter Flying Club Ltd	Exeter	28. 1.00T
G-BJNG	Slingsby T.67AM	1993		16.10.81	D.F.Hodgkinson	(Gravesend)	23. 7.01T
G-BJNH	Chown Osprey Mk.1E HAFB (Model)	AKC.57		8.10.81	D.A.Kirk	Manchester	
G-BJNN	PA-38-112 Tomahawk	38-80A0064		15.10.81	Scotia Safari Ltd	Carlisle	25. 8.00T
G-BJNP	Rango NA-32 HAFB (Model)	NHP-22		1.10.81	N.H.Ponsford t/a Rango Balloon & Kite Co	Leeds	
G-BJNX	Cameron O-65 HAFB	775		21.10.81	B.J.Petteford "Flaming Nuisance"	Bristol	12. 8.97A
G-BJNY	Aeronca 11CC Super Chief	11CC-264	CN-TYZ F-OAEE	28.10.81	P.I. & D.M.Morgans (Stored 4.91) Furze Hill Farm, Rosemarket, Milford Haven		9. 8.90P
G-BJNZ	PA-23-250 Aztec F	27-7954099	G-FANZ N6905A	5.10.81	Bonus Aviation Ltd	Cranfield	3. 8.01T
G-BJOA	PA-28-181 Archer II	28-8290048	N8453H	29.10.81	Channel Islands Aero Services Ltd Jersey (Jersey Aero Club)		21. 1.02T
G-BJOB	SAN Jodel D.140C Mousquetaire III	118	F-BMBD	2.11.81	T.W.M.Beck & M.J.Smith Monks Gate, Horsham		20. 6.00
G-BJOE	Jodel Wassmer D.120A Paris-Nice	177	F-BJIU	12.11.81	J.F.Govan t/a Forth Flying Group	East Fortune	29 6.00P
G-BJOP	PBN BN-2B-26 Islander	2132		29.10.81	Loganair Ltd (Dove/Colum t/s)	Glasgow	3. 9.00T
G-BJOT	SAN Jodel D.117	688	F-BJCO CN-TVH/F-DABU	12.11.81	R, J & Z Meares-Davies Yeatsall Farm, Abbotts Bromley		14. 9.00P
G-BJOV	Reims Cessna F.150K	0558	PH-VSD	4. 2.82	J.A.Boyd	(Maidstone)	8. 7.00
G-BJPI	Bede BD-5G 1 & PFA/14-10218 (Hirth 230R)			30.10.81	M.D.McQueen	(Beckenham, Kent)	
G-BJPL	Chown Osprey Mk.4A HAFB (Model)	AKC-39		13.10.81	M.Vincent	Jersey	
G-BJPV	Haigh Super Hi-Flyer HAFB (Model)	001		16.10.81	M.J.Haigh	Stockport	
G-BJRA	Chown Osprey Mk.4B HAFB (Model)	AKC.87		23.10.81	E.Osborn	Southampton	
G-BJRB	Eaves European E.254 HAFB (Model)	S.5		23.10.81	D.Eaves	Southampton	
G-BJRC	Eaves European E.84R HAFB (Model)	S.7		23.10.81	D.Eaves	Southampton	
G-BJRD	Eaves European E.84R HAFB (Model)	S.8		23.10.81	D.Eaves	Southampton	
G-BJRG	Chown Osprey Mk.4B HAFB (Model)	AKC.95		26.10.81	A.de Gruchy	Jersey	
G-BJRH	Rango NA-36/Ax3 HAFB (Model)	NHP-23		4.11.81	N.H.Ponsford t/a Rango Balloon & Kite Co	Leeds	
G-BJRP	Cremer Cracker HAFB (Model)	15.712 PAC		29.10.81	M.D.Williams	Dunstable	
G-BJRR	Cremer Cracker HAFB (Model)	15.715 PAC		29.10.81	M.D.Williams	Houghton Regis	
G-BJRV	Cremer Cracker HAFB (Model)	15.713 PAC		29.10.81	M.D.Williams	Dunstable	
G-BJRW	Cessna U206G Stationair 6 II	U206-05738	(N5422X)	8. 4.80	SPD Ltd	Old Sarum	23. 5.01
G-BJSA	BN-2A-26 Islander	46	HB-LIC D-IBNB/I-TRAL	15.12.81	Police Aviation Services Ltd (Stored 8.99)	Gloucestershire	25.10.95T
G-BJSC	Chown Osprey Mk.4D HAFB (Model)	AKC.84		12.11.81	N.J.Richardson	Southampton	

Regn	Type	C/n	P/I	Date	Owner/operator	Probable Base	CA Expy
G-BJSD	Chown Osprey Mk.4D HAFB (Model) AKC.83			12.11.81	N.J.Richardson	Southampton	
G-BJSF	Chown Osprey Mk.4B HAFB (Model) AKC.66			9.11.81	N.J.Richardson	Southampton	
G-BJSG	VS.361 Spitfire LF.IXc	6S/735188	Indian AF	29. 1.81	Patina Ltd	Duxford	21. 4.00P
	(C/n quoted as 6S/730116 - this is firewall no.) HS543/G-15-11/ML417 (Op The Fighter Collection)						
					(As "ML417/2I-T" in 443 (RCAF) Sqdn c/s)		
G-BJSI	Chown Osprey Mk.1E HAFB (Model) AKC.43			9.11.81	N.J.Richardson	Southampton	
G-BJSP	Guido 1A-61 HAFB (Model) GAN01/81-2609			23.11.81	G.A.Newsome	Hull	
G-BJSS	Allport YUO-1B-1-DA Neolithic Invader Superballoon Srs.2/20 HAFB (Model) 01-8101002			9.11.81	D.J.Allport	Bourne, Lincs	
G-BJST	CCF Harvard 4	CCF4-...	MM53795 SC-66	21.12.81	A.Winter	(Emmelshausen, Germany)	AC
G-BJSU*	Bensen B-8M	PFA G/01-1026		11.11.81	J.D.Newlyn	River, Dover	
	(Stored 3.97)						
G-BJSV	PA-28-161 Warrior II	28-8016229	PH-VZL (OO-HLM)/N35787	25.11.81	Airways Flight Training (Exeter) Ltd	Exeter	9. 9.00T
G-BJSW	Thunder Ax7-65Z HAFB	378		16.11.81	Sandicliffe Garage Ltd "Sandicliffe Ford"	Stapleford, Notts	7. 5.99A
G-BJSX	Unicorn UE-1C HAFB (Model)	82023		10.11.81	N.J.Richardson	Southampton	
G-BJSZ	Piper J3C-65 Cub (L-4H-PI)	12047	D-EHID (D-ECAX)/(D-EKAB)/PH-NBP/44-79751	20.11.81	H.Gilbert (Stored 6.95)	Enstone	14. 6.94P
	(Regd with Frame No.11874)						
G-BJTB	Cessna A150M Aerobat	A150-0627	(G-BIVN) N9818J	28.10.82	V.D.Speck	Clacton	21. 7.02T
G-BJTF	Skyrider Mk.1 HAFB (Model)	KSR-01		18.11.81	D.A.Kirk	Manchester	
G-BJTN	Chown Osprey Mk.4B HAFB (Model) ASC-112			23.11.81	M.Vincent	Jersey	
G-BJTO	Piper J3C-65 Cub (L-4H-PI)	11527	F-BEGK OO-AAL/43-30236	1.12.81	K.R.Nunn Fritton Decoy, Great Yarmouth		5. 3.86P
	(Frame No.11352)				(Stored 2.99)		
G-BJTP	PA-18-95 Super Cub (L-18C-PI)	18-999	MM51-15302	26.11.81	J.T.Parkins "Sittin'Duck"	Bidford	20.10.00P
			Italian AF/I-EICO/MM51-15302/51-15302				
					(As "115302/TP" in VMO-6 Sqn, US Marines c/s)		
G-BJTW	Eaves European E.107 HAFB (Model) S.10			23.11.81	C.J.Brealey	Southampton	
G-BJTY	Chown Osprey Mk.4B HAFB (Model) ASC-115			23.11.81	A.E.de Gruchy	Jersey	
G-BJUB	BVS Special 01 HAFB (Model)	VS/PW01		25.11.81	P.G.Wild	Beverley	
G-BJUC	Robinson R-22HP	0228		13. 1.82	A.J.& J.F.Thomasson t/a HeliServices	(Clitheroe)	14. 9.00T
G-BJUD	Robin DR.400/180R Remorqueur	870	PH-SRM	27.11.81	Lasham Gliding Society Ltd	Lasham	5. 1.03
	(Rebuilt using new fuselage; original scrapped Membury 11.88)						
G-BJUE	Chown Osprey Mk.4B HAFB (Model) ASC-114			23.11.81	M.Vincent	Jersey	
G-BJUI	Chown Osprey Mk.4B HAFB (Model) ASC-116			23.11.81	B.A.de Gruchy	Jersey	
G-BJUR	PA-38-112 Tomahawk	38-79A0915		5. 2.82	Truman Aviation Ltd	Nottingham	30.10.00T
					(Op Nottingham School of Flying)		
G-BJUS	PA-38-112 Tomahawk	38-80A0065		10.12.81	Panshanger School of Flying Ltd		
					(Stored 6.96)	High Cross, Ware	24. 4.94T
G-BJUU	Chown Osprey Mk.4B HAFB (Model) ASC-113			23.11.81	M.Vincent	Jersey	
G-BJUV	Cameron V-20 HAFB	792		9.12.81	P.Spellward "Busy Bee"	Bristol	
G-BJUY	Colt Ax7-77A HAFB	384	EI-BDE	15.12.81	Balloon Sports HB	Partille, Sweden	
	(Special Golf Ball shape; rebuild of Colting Ax7-77A c/n 77A-003) (Op P.Lesser)						
G-BJVB	Cremcorn Ax1-4 HAFB (Model)	82029		11.12.81	P.A.Cremer	Camberley	
G-BJVC	Evans VP-2 (VW1911)	PFA/63-10599		17. 2.82	C.J.Morris (Status uncertain)	(Andover)	19. 6.91P
G-BJVF	Thunder Ax3 Maxi Sky Chariot HAFB (C/n duplicates G-SPOP)	187		15.12.81	A.G.R.Calder	California, USA	6.10.91A
G-BJVH	Reims Cessna F.182Q Skylane	0106	D-EJMO PH-AXU(2)	21.12.81	R.J.D.Cuming	Bolt Head, Salcombe	27. 5.00
G-BJVJ	Reims Cessna F.152 II	1906		6. 1.82	The Cambridge Aero Club Ltd	Cambridge	29. 4.01T
G-BJVK	Grob G-109	6074		11. 3.82	B.A.Kimberley (Status uncertain)	(Banbury)	22. 5.92
G-BJVM	Cessna 172N Skyhawk II	172-69374	N737FA	14.12.81	I.C.Maclennan	Swanton Morley	15. 7.00T
G-BJVS	Scintex CP.1310-C3 Super Emeraude	903	F-BJVS	5. 1.79	A.E.Futter t/a The Aerofel 81 Super Emeraude Group	Felthorpe	4. 6.00P
G-BJVT	Reims Cessna F.152 II	1904		12. 1.82	The Cambridge Aero Club Ltd	Cambridge	9.10.00T

Regn	Type	C/n	P/I	Date	Owner/operator	Probable Base	CA Expy
G-BJVU	Thunder Ax6-56 Bolt HAFB	397		31.12.81	G.V.Beckwith "Cooper"	York	26. 4.91A
G-BJVV	Robin R.1180TD Aiglon	279		5.11.81	Medway Flying Group Ltd	Rochester	1. 5.00
G-BJVX	Sikorsky S-76A II Plus	760100	N108BH	15. 1.82	Bristow Helicopters Ltd	North Denes	23. 3.00T
			N1548G				
G-BJWC*	Saro Skeeter AOP.10	S2/3070	7840M	30.11.82	D.A.George	Sywell	
			XK482		(Sloane Helicopters Ltd) (Stored 5.96)		
G-BJWH	Reims Cessna F.152 II	1919		7. 5.82	Plane Talking Ltd	Biggin Hill	27. 8.00T
G-BJWI	Reims Cessna F.172P Skyhawk II	2172		14. 5.82	Bournemouth Flying Club Ltd	Bournemouth	16. 8.01T
G-BJWJ	Cameron V-65 HAFB	802		25. 1.82	R.G.Turnbull & S.G.Farse "Gawain"		
						Glasbury, Hereford	10. 9.97A
G-BJWO	BN-2A-26 Islander	334	4X-AYR	16. 2.82	Peterborough Parachute Centre Ltd Sibson		4. 2.00
			SX-BBX/4X-AYR/G-BAXC				
G-BJWT	Wittman W.10 Tailwind PFA/31-10688			5. 1.82	J.F.Bakewell	Hucknall	22. 6.00P
	(Lycoming O-290-G)				t/a Tailwind Group		
G-BJWV	Colt 17A Cloudhopper HAFB	391		22. 1.82	D.T.Meyes "Bryant Homes"	Leamington Spa	26. 3.97A
G-BJWW	Reims Cessna F.172P Skyhawk II	2148	(D-EFTV)	1. 2.82	Manx Aero Marine Management Ltd		
					(Op Westair Flying Services)	Blackpool	27. 8.00T
G-BJWX	PA-18-95 Super Cub (L-18C-PI)18-1985		MM52-2385	23. 2.82	A.White Rushett Farm, Chessington		22.11.00P
	(Continental O-200-A)		I-EIME/MM52-2385/52-2385 t/a Acebell JWX Syndicate				
G-BJWY*	Sikorsky S-55 (HRS-2) Whirlwind HAR.21	A2576		25. 1.82	D.Charles	Carlisle	
		55???	WV198/Bu.130191		(On loan to Solway Aviation Society: as "WV198/K")		
G-BJWZ	PA-18-95 Super Cub (L-18C-PI) 18-1361		OO-HMO	18. 1.82	A.J.White	Redhill	27.10.00P
	(Frame No.18-1262)		ALAT 18-1361/51-15361 t/a G-BJWZ Syndicate				
G-BJXA	Slingsby T.67A	1994		8. 2.82	Comed Aviation Ltd	Blackpool	5. 4.01T
G-BJXB	Slingsby T.67A	1995		8. 2.82	A.K.Halvorsen	Barton	5. 8.01
G-BJXK	Sportavia Fournier RF5	5054	D-KINB	3. 2.82	E.Fitzgerald & J.T.Phillips	Usk	3.12.00
					t/a G-BJXK Syndicate		
G-BJXP	Colt 56B HAFB	393		29. 3.82	H.J.Anderson	Oswestry	23. 9.99A
G-BJXR*	Auster AOP.9	184	XR267	2. 2.82	A.Southern & R.J.Rudhall	Kemble	23. 6.01
					t/a Cotswold Aircraft Restoration Group		
					(Cancelled by CAA 12.4.99)		
G-BJXX	PA-23-250 Aztec E	27-4692	F-BTCM	7. 4.82	V.Bojovic	Bournemouth	21.10.01
			N14094				
G-BJXZ	Cessna 172N Skyhawk II	172-73039	PH-CAA	24. 3.82	T.M.Jones	Egginton	21.10.01T
			N1949F		(Op Derby Aero Club)		
G-BJYD	Reims Cessna F.152 II	1915		25. 3.82	Cleveland F/School Ltd	Teesside	8. 9.00T
G-BJYF	Colt 56A HAFB	401		1. 3.82	A.van Wyk	London SE12	28. 5.00A
G-BJYG	PA-28-161 Warrior II	28-8216053	N8458B	4. 3.82	S.R.Mitchell	(Prescot)	12. 6.00T
G-BJYK	Jodel Wassmer D.120A Paris-Nice	185	(G-BJWK)	11. 5.82	T.Fox & D.A.Thorpe	Crowland	22. 5.99P
			F-BJPK				
G-BJYN	PA-38-112 Tomahawk	38-79A1076	G-BJTE	12. 3.82	Panshanger School of Flying Ltd		
						High Cross, Ware	6. 3.00T
G-BJZA	Cameron N-65 HAFB	820		4. 3.82	A.D.Pinner "Digby"	Northampton	3. 6.97A
G-BJZB	Evans VP-2 PFA/63-10633			10. 3.82	J.A.Macleod	Stornoway	6. 6.00P
	(VW 1834)						
G-BJZC*	Thunder Ax7-65Z HAFB	416		5. 3.82	K A Kent "Greenpeace Trinity"	Lancing	17. 6.94A
					(Balloon Preservation Group 7.98)		
G-BJZF	DH.82A Tiger Moth	NAS-100		8. 3.82	R.Blasi	White Waltham	1. 4.99P
	(Built Norfolk Aerial Spraying Ltd from spares)						
G-BJZN	Slingsby T.67A	1997		31. 3.82	A.R.T. Marsland	Breighton	19. 7.01
G-BJZR	Colt 42A HAFB	402		18. 3.82	A.F.Selby	Loughborough	9. 7.00A
					t/a Selfish Balloon Group "Selfish"		
G-BJZX	Grob G-109	6109	(D-KGRO)	3. 9.82	Oxfordshire Sport Flying Ltd	Enstone	4. 9.00
G-BJZY	Bensen B.8MV			18. 3.82	P.C.Dockerill	Market Harborough	
	(VW1700) DNL.21103 & PFA G/01-1012						

G-BKAA – G-BKZZ

Regn	Type	C/n	P/I	Date	Owner/operator	Probable Base	CA Expy
G-BKAB*	ICA IS-28M2A	23A		19. 3.82	T.Cust	Sandtoft	20. 5.85
					(Crashed Rattlesden 19.5.84; wreck stored 9.99)		
G-BKAE	Jodel Wassmer D.120 Paris-Nice	200	F-BKCE	5. 5.82	M.P.Wakem	Barton	20. 6.00P
G-BKAF	Clutton FRED Srs.II PFA/29-10337			23. 3.82	J.M.Robinson (Achill Island, Co.Mayo)		30. 5.97P
	(VW1835)						
G-BKAM	Slingsby T.67M Firefly 160	1999		26. 4.82	A.J.Daley Wellcross Grange, Slinfold		26. 7.02
G-BKAO	Wassmer Jodel D.112	249	F-BFTO	22. 3.82	R.Broadhead	Bagby	21.12.99P
G-BKAR	PA-38-112 Tomahawk	38-79A1091		16. 4.82	D.A.Williams (Op Deltair Ltd)	Chester	8. 7.01T
G-BKAS	PA-38-112 Tomahawk	38-79A1075		16. 4.82	D.A.Williams (Op Deltair Ltd)	Chester	27. 6.02T
G-BKAY	Rockwell Commander 114	14411	SE-GSN	28. 9.81	R.S.Morse	Dunkeswell	23. 3.01
					t/a The Rockwell Group		
G-BKAZ	Cessna 152 II	152-82832	N89705	27. 4.82	A.T.Wright	Leeds-Bradford	19. 4.00A

Regn	Type	C/n	P/I	Date	Owner/operator	Probable Base	CA Expy
G-BKBB	Hawker Fury rep (RR Kestrel 5)	WA/6	OO-HFU OO-XFU/G-BKBB	2. 4.82	R.Landuyt (Brugge, Belgium) (As "K1930" in 43 Sqn c/s)		AC
	(Damaged Keiheuval, Belgium 1.6.96; on rebuild Rotary Farm, Hatch 9.96)						
G-BKBD	Thunder Ax3 Maxi Sky Chariot HAFB	418		5. 4.82	M.J.Casson	Kendal	
G-BKBF	Socata MS.894A Rallye Minerva 220	11622	F-BSKZ	8. 9.82	J.A.Gibbs	Draycott Farm, Chisledon	16. 6.99
G-BKBH*	HS.125 Srs.600B	256052	5N-DNL	1. 4.82	Beamalong Ltd	Southampton	
	G-5-698/5N-DNL/5N-NBC/G-5-698/G-BKBH/G-5-698/TR-LAU/G-BKBH/G-BDJE/G-5-11						
	(Cancelled by CAA 15.7.99)						
G-BKBN	Socata TB-10 Tobago	287		4. 6.82	D.S.& W.A.Newby t/a David Newby Associates	(Newquay)	20. 7.01
G-BKBO	Colt 17A Cloudhopper HAFB	342		1. 9.82	J.Armstrong, M.A.Ashworth & H.Davey "Captain Courageous"	Newquay	23. 1.00A
G-BKBP	Bellanca 7GCBC Scout	465-73	N8693	1. 6.82	M.G. & J.R.Jefferies t/a H.G.Jefferies & Son (Damaged Graveley, Herts 23.5.93; stored 9.95)	Little Gransden	8. 5.95T
G-BKBR*	Cameron Chateau 84SS HAFB (Special Shape as Forbes "Chateau de Balleroy")	743		11. 5.82	Forbes Europe Inc (Stored 6.93)	Balleroy, Normandy	NE(A)
G-BKBS*	Bensen B.8MV	PFA G/01-1027		14. 4.82	Not known	(Cornwall)	
G-BKBV	Socata TB-10 Tobago	288	F-BNGO	4. 6.82	N.R.Batey	Ronaldsway	28.12.97
G-BKBW	Socata TB-10 Tobago	289		4. 6.82	P.J.Bramhall & D.F.Woodhouse t/a Merlin Aviation	Bristol	14. 4.01
G-BKCB	PA-28R-200 Cherokee Arrow II	28R-7435186	OY-POO CS-APD/N41460	21. 6.82	Western Air (Thruxton) Ltd	Thruxton	12.10.02T
G-BKCC	PA-28-180 Cherokee Archer 28-7405099		OY-BGY	13. 5.82	Archer Aviation Ltd	Gloucestershire	13. 8.01T
G-BKCE	Reims Cessna F.172P Skyhawk II 2135		N9687R	26. 4.82	Far North Flight Training	Wick	15. 5.00T
G-BKCH	Cassutt Special (Continental C90)	PFA/126-10778		21. 4.82	S.Alexander	Bidford	17. 8.00P
G-BKCI	Brugger MB.2 Colibri (VW1600)	PFA/43-10692		22. 4.82	E.R.Newall "Bugsy"	Breighton	
G-BKCJ	Oldfield Baby Lakes (Continental O-200-A)	PFA/10-10714		12. 5.82	S.V.Roberts	Sleap	26. 1.99P
G-BKCL	PA-30-160 Twin Comanche C 30-1982		G-AXSP N8824Y	12. 1.81	Yorkair Ltd	Full Sutton	26. 1.00T
G-BKCN	Phoenix Currie Wot (Continental A65)	PFA/3018		27. 4.82	N.A.A.Pogmore	Benson's Farm, Laindon	15. 6.00P
G-BKCR	Socata TB-9 Tampico	297		6. 5.82	A.Whitehouse (Fuselage noted 3.99)	Haverfordwest	3. 8.98T
G-BKCT	Cameron V-77 HAFB	837		10. 5.82	Quality Products General Engineering (Wickwar) Ltd "Quality Products" Bristol		7. 5.93A
G-BKCV	EAA Acro Sport II 430 & PFA/72A-10776 (Lycoming O-360)			5. 5.82	T.N.Jinks	Charity Farm, Baxterley	13. 9.00P
G-BKCW	Jodel Wassmer D.120A Paris-Nice 285		(G-BKCP) F-BMYF	1. 6.82	A.Greene & G.Kerr t/a The Dundee Flying Group (Damaged Dundee 13.4.97)	Dundee	21.12.99P
G-BKCX	Mudry/CAARP CAP-10B	149		28. 7.82	Mahon & Associates	Popham	8. 6.01
G-BKCY	PA-38-112 Tomahawk II 38-81A0027		OO-XKU	22. 5.82	Wellesbourne Aviation Ltd (Stored 12.97)	Welshpool	7.11.94T
G-BKCZ	Jodel Wassmer D.120A Paris-Nice 207		F-BKCZ	23. 4.82	M.R.Baker (On rebuild 6.92)	Lewes	AC
G-BKDC	Monnett Sonerai IIL (VW 1834)	876 & PFA/15-10597		2. 7.82	K.J.Towell (Guildford) (Damaged Breighton 7.8.90; status uncertain)		18. 6.90P
G-BKDH	Robin DR.400/120 Dauphin 80	1582	PH-CAB	25. 5.82	Airbase Aircraft Ltd	Shoreham	6.12.01T
G-BKDI	Robin DR.400/120 Dauphin 80	1583	PH-CAD	25. 5.82	The Cotswold Aero Club Ltd	Shoreham	9.10.00T
G-BKDJ	Robin DR.400/120 Dauphin 80	1584	PH-CAC	25. 5.82	M.D.Joyce & R.R.Wills	Sherburn in Elmet	28. 4.01
G-BKDK	Thunder Ax7-77Z HAFB	428		21. 6.82	A.J.Byrne "Cider Riser"	Thatcham	17. 9.95A
G-BKDP	Clutton FRED Srs.III	PFA/29-10650		24. 5.82	M.Whittaker	(Wolverhampton)	
G-BKDR	Pitts S-1S Special (Lycoming IO-360)	PFA/09-10654		14. 6.82	T.J.Reeve	(Bury St. Edmunds)	31. 5.00P
G-BKDT*	RAF SE.5A rep 278 & PFA/80-10325			26. 5.82	Yorkshire Air Museum (As "F943")	Elvington	
G-BKDX	SAN Jodel DR.1050 Ambassadeur	55	F-BITX	1. 6.82	T.V.Thorp & G.J.Slater t/a DX Group	Clench Common	10. 9.99
G-BKEK	PA-32-300 Cherokee Six 32-7540091		OY-TOP	30. 6.82	P.H.Maynard	Turweston	22. 4.01T
G-BKEP	Reims Cessna F.172M Skyhawk II 1095		OY-BFJ	8. 7.82	S.W.Watkins t/a G-BKEP Group	Trecorras Farm, Llangarron	1. 9.01
G-BKER	Replica Plans SE.5A (Continental O-200A)	PFA/20-10641		15. 6.82	N.K.Geddes (As "F5447/N")	Bridge of Weir	9. 7.98P
G-BKES*	Cameron Bottle 57 SS HAFB (Robinsons Barley Water Bottle)	846		25. 6.82	British Balloon Museum "Robinsons Barley Water" (Stored 1.90)	Newbury	NE(A)
G-BKET	PA-18-95 Super Cub (L-18C-PI)	18-1990	MM52-2390 I-EIBI/MM52-2390/52-2390	17. 6.82	H.M.MacKenzie	Inverness	22.11.00P

Regn	Type	C/n	P/I	Date	Owner/operator	Probable Base	CA Expy
G-BKEU	Taylor JT.1 Monoplane (VW 1600)	PFA/55-10553		18. 6.82	R.J.Whybrow & J.M.Springham	Knettishall	20. 7.95P
G-BKEV	Reims Cessna F.172M Skyhawk	1443	PH-WLH OO-CNE	8. 7.82	J.W.Finlayson	(St. Andrews)	19.11.00T
G-BKEW	Bell 206B JetRanger III	3010	D-HDAD	8. 7.82	N.R.Foster t/a Foster Associates	Denham	17. 7.00
G-BKEX	Rich Prototype Glider	1		24. 6.82	D.B.Rich	(Callington, Cornwall)	
G-BKEY	Clutton FRED Srs.III (VW1600)	PFA/29-10208		27. 5.82	G.S.Taylor	(Bewdley,Worcs)	
G-BKFA*	Monnett Sonerai IIL	PFA/15-10524		21. 6.82	R.F.Bridge Bursledon, Southampton (Cancelled by CAA 12.4.99)		
G-BKFC	Reims Cessna F.152 II	1443	OO-AWB	1. 9.82	Sulby Aerial Surveys Ltd Sibbertoft, Husbands Bosworth		5.10.01T
G-BKFI	Evans VP-1 Srs.2 (VW1834)	PFA/62-10491		24. 6.82	A.M.Witt	Barton	11. 3.00P
G-BKFK	Isaacs Fury II (Lycoming O-290-D)	PFA/11-10038		25. 6.82	G.C.Jones Waits Farm, Belchamp Walter (Persian AF c/s) "Cia Cia San"		6. 9.95P
G-BKFL	Aerosport Scamp	PFA/117-10814		17. 8.82	J.Sherwood	Breighton	
G-BKFM	QAC Quickie 1 (Rotax 503)	PFA/94-10570		28. 6.82	F.Rothera Pent Farm, Postling, Kent (Damaged on take off Cranfield 4.7.98)		29. 6.98P
G-BKFN	Bell 214ST Super Transport	28109	LZ-CAW	16. 8.82	Bristow Helicopters Ltd	Aberdeen	24.10.01T
			G-BKFN/VH-BEE/VH-LHT/G-BKFN "Loch Broome"				
G-BKFP	Bell 214ST Super Transport	28110		16. 8.82	Caledonian Helicopters Ltd Aberdeen (Op Bristow Helicopters) "Loch Roag"		27.10.00T
G-BKFR	Scintex CP.301C Emeraude	519	F-BUUR F-BJFF	30. 6.82	C.R.Beard Grove Moor Farm, Grassthorpe		15. 7.00P
G-BKFW	Percival P.56 Provost T.1	PAC/F/303	XF597	21. 9.82	Sylmar Aviation & Services Ltd (Alan House) Lower Wasing Farm, Brimpton (As "XF597/AH" in RAF College c/s)		24. 6.00P
G-BKFZ	PA-28R-200 Cherokee Arrow II	28R-7635127	OY-BLE	17. 8.82	R.S.Watt Shacklewell Lodge, Empingham t/a Shacklewell Flying Group		28.10.00
G-BKGA	Socata MS.892E Rallye 150GT	13287	F-GBXJ	15. 7.82	J.H.A.Clarke t/a BJJ Aviation Wadswick Manor Farm, Corsham		19. 3.00
G-BKGB	Jodel Wassmer D.120 Paris-Nice	267	F-BMOB	21. 6.82	B.A. Ridgway	Haverfordwest	16.11.00P
G-BKGC	Maule M.6-235C Super Rocket	7413C	N56465	23. 7.82	M.C.Woodhouse	Oaksey Park	4. 8.00
G-BKGD*	Westland WG.30 Srs.100	002	(G-BKBJ)	15. 7.82	Westland Helicopters Ltd Yeovil (Stored 3.93)		6. 7.93T
G-BKGL	Beechcraft D18S (3TM) (Beech c/n A-764)	CA-164	CF-QPD RCAF 5193/1564	14. 7.82	Propshop Ltd & T.Darrah Duxford (As "1164" in 1942 US Army c/s)		31. 5.00
G-BKGM	Beechcraft 3NM (D18S) (Beech c/n A-853)	CA-203	N5063N	14. 7.82	A.E.Hutton North Weald		21. 5.00
			G-BKGM/CF-SUQ/RCAF 2324 (Op Harvard Formation Team: as "HB275" in RAF/SEAC c/s)				
G-BKGR	Cameron O-65 HAFB	864		6. 8.82	K.Kidner & L.E.More	Newton Abbot	8. 5.93P
G-BKGT	Socata Rallye 110ST Galopin	3361		23. 7.82	A.G.Morgan Wellesbourne Mountford t/a Long Marston Flying Group		28.10.00
G-BKGW	Reims Cessna F.152 II	1878	N9071N	11. 8.82	Leicestershire Aero Club Ltd	Leicester	18. 6.01T
G-BKHA*	Westland WS-55 Whirlwind HAR.10	WA/109	XJ763	25. 8.82	C.J.Evans Thornicombe (As "XJ763/P" in 103 Sqdn c/s; believed stored)		3. 5.92P
G-BKHD	Oldfield Baby Lakes (Continental O-200-A)	8133-F-802B & PFA/10-10718		25. 8.82	P.J.Tanulak Sleap (Damaged Shrewsbury 22.10.95; on rebuild)		11. 4.96P
G-BKHG	Piper J3C-65 Cub (L-4H-PI)	12062	F-BCPT NC79820/44-79766	13. 9.82	K.G.Wakefield "Puddle Jumper" Brickhouse Farm, Frogland Cross (As "479766/D-63" in HQ 9th Army, USAAC c/s)		18. 3.00P
G-BKHJ	Cessna 182P Skylane II (Reims c/n 0040)	182-64129	PH-CAT D-EATV/N6223F	25. 8.82	Augur Films Ltd	Swanton Morley	14. 7.02
G-BKHR	Luton LA-4A Minor (VW1834)	PFA/51-10228		24. 8.82	C.B.Buscombe & R.Goldsworthy	Bodmin	10.10.00P
G-BKHW	Stoddard-Hamilton Glasair IIRG (Lycoming O-320)	357 & PFA/149-11312		27.8.82	G.R.W.Monksfield, D.Callabritto & S.T.Ballard (Woodford Green)		4. 5.00P
G-BKHY	Taylor JT.1 Monoplane (VW 1600)	PFA/1416		8. 9.82	B.C.J.O'Neill Damyns Hall, Upminster		26. 5.00P
G-BKHZ	Reims Cessna F.172P Skyhawk II	2169	D-EJOK	15.10.82	L.R.Leader	Clacton	1. 9.01
G-BKIA	Socata TB-10 Tobago	322		25. 8.82	M.F.McGinn	Cumbernauld	24. 8.01T
G-BKIB	Socata TB-9 Tampico	323		25. 8.82	G.A.Vickers	Chester	22.10.01T
G-BKIC	Cameron V-77 HAFB	859		12. 8.82	C.A.Butter "Passing Wind"	Marsh Benham	7. 6.92A
G-BKIE*	Short SD.3-30 Var.100	SH.3005	G-SLUG	15. 9.82	CAA Fire Training Centre	Teesside	22. 8.93T
			G-METP/G-METO/G-BKIE/C-GTAS/G-14-3005 (Cancelled as WFU 16.9.97)				
G-BKIF	Fournier RF6B-100	3	F-GADR	8.10.82	G.G.Milton	Kimbolton	3. 9.00
G-BKII	Reims Cessna F.172M Skyhawk II	1370	PH-PLO (D-EGIA)	8.10.82	M.S.Knight Goodwood t/a Sealand Aerial Photography		17. 2.01T
G-BKIJ	Reims Cessna F.172M	0920	PH-TGZ	15.10.82	V.D.Speck	Clacton/Duxford	2. 9.00T
G-BKIK	Cameron DG-19 Helium Airship	776		23. 8.82	Balloon Preservation Group Farnborough (On loan to Farnborough Air Sciences Trust 7.98)		4. 9.88A

Regn	Type	C/n	P/I	Date	Owner/operator	Probable Base	CA Expy
G-BKIN	Alon A-2A Aircoupe	B-253	N5453F	24. 9.82	D.W.Vernon	Blackpool	8.10.00
G-BKIR	SAN Jodel D.117	737	F-BIOC	30. 9.82	R.Shaw & D.M.Hardaker (On rebuild 3.96)		
						Birds Edge, Penistone	28. 8.92P
G-BKIS	Socata TB-10 Tobago	329		22. 9.82	R.A.Irwin	Thruxton	9. 6.02
					t/a Wessex Flyers Group		
G-BKIT	Socata TB-9 Tampico	330		22. 9.82	D.N.Garlick, P.D.Foreman, R.M.Pannell & P.Johnson		
						Southend	26. 5.01
G-BKIU*	Colt 17A Cloudhopper HAFB	420		29. 9.92	Not known "Just One"	NK	
					(Cancelled by CAA 15.5.98: noted 1999)		
G-BKIV*	Colt 21A Cloudhopper HAFB	447		29. 9.82	Not known	NK	NE(A)
G-BKIX*	Cameron V-31 Air Chair HAFB	863	(G-BKGJ)	23. 9.82	Not known "Every Penny"	NK	21. 9.95
					(Cancelled by CAA 4.8.98: noted 1999)		
G-BKIY	Thunder Ax3 Sky Chariot HAFB	464		7.10.82	Mr Martin "Michaelangelo"	Lancing	
					(Balloon Preservation Group 7.98)		
G-BKIZ	Cameron V-31 Air Chair HAFB	842		1. 2.83	A.P.S.Cox "Camberley/Kiss"	Camberley	
G-BKJB	PA-18-135 Super Cub	18-574	PH-GAI	1. 8.83	Haimoss Ltd	Old Sarum	20.12.96T
	(L-21A-PI) (Frame No.18-522)				R.Neth AF R-204/51-15657/N1003A		
					(Damaged Kingsmuir House, Anstruther, Fife 4.8.96; stored 1.97)		
G-BKJF	Socata MS.880B Rallye 100T	2300	F-BULF	16.12.82	Journeyman Aviation Ltd	Sywell	13. 5.01
G-BKJS	Jodel Wassmer D.120A Paris-Nice	191	F-BJPS	4.10.82	J.H.Leigh	Clipgate, Kent	20. 7.00P
					t/a Clipgate Flying Group		
G-BKJW	PA-23-250 Aztec E	27-4716	N14153	3.11.78	Alan Williams Entertainments Ltd		
						Southend	25. 5.02
G-BKKI*	Westland WG.30 Srs.100	003		1.11.82	Westland Helicopters Ltd	Yeovil	28. 6.85P
					(Stored 6.91)		
G-BKKN	Cessna 182R Skylane II	182-67801	N6218N	30.11.82	R.A.Marven	Coleman Green, Herts	30. 4.01
					t/a Marvagraphic		
G-BKKO	Cessna 182R Skylane II	182-67852	N4907H	30.11.82	B & G Jebson Ltd	Crosland Moor	21. 3.02
G-BKKS*	Mercury Dart Srs.1	MA 001		4.11.82	B.A.Mills	Great Eversden	
					(Stored 4.95 - construction abandoned)		
G-BKKZ	Pitts S-1S Special	PFA/09-10525	(G-BIVW)	10.11.82	J.A.Coutts	(Woodbridge)	
					(Under construction 5.99)		
G-BKLC	Cameron V-56 HAFB	879		29.11.82	M.A. & J.R.H.Ashworth "Bubbles" Newquay		6. 5.91A
G-BKLJ*	Westland Scout Srs.1	F.9618	5X-UUX	6. 7.83	R.Dagless	East Dereham	
					(Stored as "5X-UUX" 6.93 in poor condition)		
G-BKLO	Reims Cessna F.172M Skyhawk II	1380	PH-BET	22. 3.83	Stapleford Flying Club Ltd	Stapleford	11. 6.01T
				D-EFMS			
G-BKLP	Reims Cessna F.172N Skyhawk II	1809	PH-BYL	22. 3.83	Euroair Flying Club Ltd	Cranfield	11. 6.01T
G-BKLS*	Aerospatiale SA.341G Gazelle 1	1455	G-TURP	11. 1.83	Apollo Helicopters Ltd	Halstead, Essex	2.12.91T
			G-BKLS/N17MT/N14MT/N49549				
	(Damaged Stanford-le-Hope 9.9.91; on rebuild using fuselage ex N341BB [1421]; orig. fuselage to Redhill 9.93)						
G-BKLZ*	Vinten Wallis WA-116MC	UMA-01		8.12.82	Wehrtechnische Studiensammlung		
	(Aka "VJ-22 Autogyro")				(As "G-55-2")	Hermeskeil, Germany	16.12.83P
					(On loan to Flugausstellung L & P Junior Museum)		
G-BKMA	Mooney M.20J (201)	24-1316	N1170N	13.12.82	A.C.South	Cambridge	8. 4.01
					t/a Foxtrot Whisky Aviation		
G-BKMB	Mooney M.20J (201)	24-1307	N1168P	15.12.82	W.A.Cook, B.Pearson & P.Turnbull		
						Sherburn in Elmet	24.11.01
G-BKMD	Short SC.7 Skyvan 3 Var.100	SH.1907	EI-BUB	20.12.82	R.M.Burnett t/a Army Parachute Association		
			G-BKMD/A40-SK/G-BAHK/G-14-79			AAC Netheravon	30. 5.00A
G-BKMG	Handley Page 0/400 rep	TPG-1		8.12.82	M.G.King	(Wroxham, Norwich)	
	(Some components under construction 1993)				t/a The Paralyser Group		
G-BKMI	VS.359 Spitfire HF.VIIIc	6S/583793	A58-671	23.12.82	The Aerial Museum (North Weald) Ltd		
			MV154		(As "MT928/ZX-M" in 145 Sqn c/s)	Filton	4. 7.00P
G-BKMT	PA-32R-301 Saratoga SP	32R-8213013	N8005Z	4. 2.83	P.R. & B.N.Lewis	Welshpool	31. 3.01
					t/a Severn Valley Aviation Group		
G-BKMX	Short SD.3-60 Var.100	SH.3608	G-14-3608	13.12.82	Jersey European Airways (UK) Ltd Exeter		15. 3.00T
G-BKNA	Cessna 421 Golden Eagle	421-0097	F-BUYB	28. 1.83	Launchapart Ltd	Barton	13. 8.97
			HB-LDZ/N4097L		(Damaged Penbridge, Hereford 3.8.97)		
G-BKNB	Cameron V-42 HAFB	887		10. 1.83	D.N.Close	Andover	17. 7.97A
G-BKNI	Gardan GY-80-160D Horizon	249	F-BRJN	28. 1.83	A.Hartigan	Bourn	13. 5.02
					t/a Blue Horizon Flying Group "Blue Lady"		
G-BKNL	Cameron D-96 Hot-Air Airship	805	(I-)	25. 1.83	Sport Promotion SRL	Belbo, Italy	13. 2.97A
	(Rebuilt with new envelope c/n 3192/G-BVHH 1994) G-BKNL/N17830/G-BKNL						
G-BKNO	Monnett Sonerai IIL 792 & PFA/15-10528			11. 3.83	M.D.Hughes	Pauncefoot, Romsey	15. 6.99P
	(VW1834)						
G-BKNP	Cameron V-77 HAFB	874		22.12.82	I.Lilja	Kvanum, Sweden	5. 7.00A
					"Winnie The Pooh"		
G-BKNY*	Bensen B.8M-P-VW	PFA G/01-1030		1. 3.83	D.A.C.MacCormack	Ashford, Kent	
					(Cancelled by CAA 26.2.99; no Permit issued & probably not completed)		

Regn	Type	C/n	P/I	Date	Owner/operator	Probable Base	CA Expy
G-BKNZ	Menavia Piel CP.301A Emeraude	296	F-BISZ	21. 1.83	R.N.Crosland & P.R.Teager		
						Deanland, Hailsham	16.12.00P
G-BKOA	Socata MS.893E Rallye 180GT	12432	F-BOFB	2. 3.83	N.F.Nowell	St Just	31.10.02
			F-ODAT/F-BVAT				
G-BKOB	Moravan Zlin Z.326 Trener Master	757	F-BKOB	28. 9.81	W.G.V.Hall	Urchfont, Wilts	17. 5.02
G-BKOT	Wassmer WA.81 Piranha	813	F-GAIP	17. 2.87	Barbara N.Rolfe	Manor Farm, Glatton	AC
G-BKOU	Hunting P.84 Jet Provost T.3		XN637	17. 2.83	A.Haig-Thomas	North Weald	24. 6.00P
		PAC/W/13901			(As "XN637/03")		
G-BKOW*	Colt 77A HAFB	505		6. 9.84	A D Kent "Lady Di" (Elle c/s)	Lancing	14. 2.88A
					(Balloon Preservation Group 7.98)		
G-BKPA	Hoffmann H-36 Dimona	3522		16. 6.83	A.Mayhew	Longbridge Deverill	4. 6.02
G-BKPB	Aerosport Scamp	PFA/117-10736		23. 2.83	E.D.Burke	Bidford	3.11.00P
		(VW1834)					
G-BKPC	Cessna A185F AGcarryall	185-03809	N4599E	10. 7.80	The Black Knights Parachute Centre Ltd		
						Bank End Farm, Cockerham	14. 8.01
G-BKPD	Viking Dragonfly 302	PFA/139-10897		11. 3.83	E.P.Browne & G.J.Sargent	Cambridge	20. 1.00P
		(Revmaster 2100D)			(Damaged Cambridge 17.7.99)		
G-BKPE	CEA Jodel DR.250/160 Capitaine	35	F-BNJD	18. 3.83	J.S. & J.D.Lewer	Dunkeswell	17.11.01
G-BKPG*	Luscombe P3 Rattler Strike	003		7. 3.83	Not known (Stored 5.95)	Tatenhill	
G-BKPK	Everett Gyroplane	005		19. 4.83	J.C.McHugh (Stapleford Abbotts)		23. 3.93P
		(VW 1834)			(Stored Sproughton 12.95)		
G-BKPN	Cameron N-77 HAFB	923		9. 3.83	R.H.Sanderson "Do It All"	Nuneaton	21. 5.87A
G-BKPS	Grumman-American AA-5B Tiger		OO-SAS	7. 3.83	A.E.T.Clarke	Lydd	26. 8.00
		AA5B-0007	OO-HAO/(OO-WAY)/N1507R				
G-BKPX	Jodel Wassmer D.120A Paris-Nice	240	F-BLNG	19. 1.84	N.H.Martin	Skipwith, Selby	12. 2.00P
G-BKPY	SAAB 91B/2 Safir	91321	56321	23. 3.83	Newark Air Museum Ltd	Winthorpe	
			R.Nor AF "UA-B"		(As "321" in R.Nor AF c/s)		
G-BKPZ	Pitts S-1T Special	PFA/09-10852		4. 3.83	Mary A.Frost	Downland Farm, Redhill	30. 4.00P
		(Lycoming AEIO-360)					
G-BKRA	North American T-6G-NH Texan	188-90	MM53664	19. 8.83	Transport Command Ltd	Shoreham	25. 6.00T
			RM-9/51-15227		(As "51-15227/10" in US Navy c/s)		
G-BKRB*	Cessna 172N Skyhawk II	172-72969	EI-BKR	23. 3.83	Not known (Wreck stored 7.95)	Clacton	15. 5.89
			G-BHKZ/N1207F				
G-BKRD*	Cessna 320E Skyknight	320E-0101	D-IACB	24. 3.83	The Fire Service College		
			HB-LDN/N2201Q			Moreton-in-Marsh	30. 9.93
					(Crashed Lille, France 5.11.90 & for fire service use 8.98)		
G-BKRF	PA-18-95 Super Cub	18-1525	F-BOUI	7.11.83	K.M.Bishop	Croft Farm, Defford	29. 9.98P
		(L-18C-PI) (Frame No.18-1502)		ALAT/51-15525				
G-BKRG*	Beechcraft C-45G-BH	AF-222	N75WB	5. 5.83	Aces High Ltd	Bruntingthorpe	
		(Regd as C-45H)		N9072Z/51-11665		(Stored as spares source G-BKRN 1.00 qv)		
G-BKRH	Brugger MB.2 Colibri			15. 3.83	M.R.Benwell	Hinton-in-The-Hedges	22. 5.00P
		(VW1835) 142 & PFA/43-10150					
G-BKRI	Cameron V-77 HAFB	909		30. 3.83	D.W.& J.M.Westlake	Corlayl, France	24. 6.97A
					"Snapdragon II"		
G-BKRK	SNCAN Stampe SV-4C	57	Fr.Navy	30. 3.83	J.R.Bisset (Stored 8.98)	Aboyne	28. 6.98
					t/a Strathgadie Stampe Group		
G-BKRL*	Chichester-Miles Leopard	001		21. 3.83	Chichester-Miles Consultants Ltd		
		(Noel Penny 301)			(Cancelled as wfu 25.1.99: stored 9.99) Old Sarum		14.12.91P*
G-BKRN	Beechcraft D.18S	CA-75	CF-DTN	14. 4.83	A.A.Marshall & P.L.Turland		
			RCAF A675/RCAF 1500		(Stored 1.00)	Bruntingthorpe	26. 6.83PF
G-BKRS	Cameron V-56 HAFB	908		23. 3.83	D.N. & L.J.Close "Bonkers"	Andover	17. 7.97A
G-BKRU*	Ensign Crossley Racer	PFA/131-10797		30. 3.83	M.S.Crossley	Redhill	24.1.90P*
		(Continental C90)			(Stored 9.90: cancelled by CAA 2.3.99)		
G-BKRZ	Dragon 77 HAFB	001		11. 4.83	J.R.Barber "Rupert"	Newbury	5. 3.94A
					(British Balloon Museum 4.99)		
G-BKSB	Cessna T310Q II	310Q-0914	VR-CEM	22. 4.83	D.H.& P.M.Smith	(Easingwold)	1. 5.00
			G-BKSB/HB-LMO/OE-FYL/(N69680) t/a G.H.Smith & Son				
G-BKSC	Saro Skeeter AOP.12	S2/7157	XN351	23. 5.83	R.A.L.Falconer	Ipswich	8.11.84P
		(C/n officially S2/7076 but may be component no.)			(As "XN351")		
G-BKSD	Colt 56A HAFB	361		11. 4.83	M.J.Casson "Entwhistle Green"	Kendal	2. 6.96A
G-BKSE	QAC Quickie 1	PFA/94-10748		6. 4.83	M.D.Burns	Cumbernauld	8. 5.89P
		(Onan B48M) (Regd with c/n PFA/94-10784)			(Noted 8.98)		
G-BKSP	Schleicher ASK 14	14028	D-KOMO	25. 5.83	J.H.Bryson	Bellarena	28. 3.00
G-BKSS	SAN Jodel 150 Mascaret	48	F-BMFC	14. 9.83	D.H.Wilson-Spratt	(Peel, IoM)	
					(Status uncertain)		
G-BKST	Rutan VariEze	12718-001		20. 4.83	R.Towle	(Hexham)	
G-BKSX	SNCAN Stampe SV-4C	61	F-BBAF	16. 5.83	C.A.Bailey & J.A.Carr (Stored 8.90)		
			Fr.Mil			Trenchard Farm, Eggesford	15. 6.89
G-BKTA	PA-18-95 Super Cub	18-3223	OO-HBA	10. 5.83	M.J.Dyson & M.T.Clark	Fradley	19. 5.99P
		(L-18C-PI) (Frame No.18-3246)		OL-L149/53-4823				

123

Regn	Type	C/n	P/I	Date	Owner/operator	Probable Base	CA Expy
G-BKTH	Hawker Sea Hurricane IB CCF/41H/4013 (Built CCF)		Z7015	24. 5.83	The Shuttleworth Trust Duxford (As "Z7015/7-L" in 880 Sqdn, RN c/s)		31. 5.99P
G-BKTM	PZL SZD-45A Ogar	B-656		31. 5.83	Repclif Chemical Services Ltd Seighford		14.10.99
G-BKTR	Cameron V-77 HAFB	951		6. 6.83	A.Palmer Tonbridge "Diddlybopper"		29. 9.99A
G-BKTV	Reims Cessna F.152 II	1450	OY-BJB	8. 8.83	Seawing Flying Club Ltd Southend		28. 7.02T
G-BKTY	Socata TB-10 Tobago	363	F-BNGZ	7. 6.83	B.M. & G.M.McClelland Crosland Moor		26. 5.02
G-BKTZ	Slingsby T.67M Firefly	2004	G-SFTV	26. 8.83	T.D.Reid (Craigavon, NI)		16. 8.02
G-BKUE	Socata TB-9 Tampico	369	F-BNGX	31. 5.83	Pool Aviation (NW) Ltd Blackpool		15. 7.99
G-BKUJ	Thunder Ax6-56 Srs.1 HAFB	520		17. 6.83	R.J.Bent "Edward Bear" Torquay		28. 9.88A
G-BKUR	Menavia Piel CP.301A Emeraude	280	(G-BKBX) F-BMLX/F-OBLY	19.10.83	R.Wells Peterlee		21. 6.00P
G-BKUS	Bensen B.8M PFA G/01-1045			7. 7.83	A.Charles Newbury		21. 6.88P
G-BKUU	Thunder Ax7-77 Srs.1 HAFB	522		3. 8.83	D.A.Kozuba-Kozubska London WC1 "Tanglefoot"		16. 9.94A
G-BKVA	Socata Rallye 180T Galerien	3274	SE-GFS F-GBXA	30. 6.83	J.M.Airey Saltby t/a Buckminster Gliding Club Syndicate		7. 6.01T
G-BKVB	Socata Rallye 110ST Galopin	3258	OO-PIP	22. 6.83	C.Tilley (Wolverhampton)		16.12.01
G-BKVC	Socata TB-9 Tampico	372	F-BNGQ	4. 7.83	H.P.Aubin-Parvu Biggin Hill		11. 2.02
G-BKVE	Rutan VariEze PFA/74-10236 (Continental O-200-A)		G-EZLT	5. 7.83	K.Cox (Alton) (Force landed Waltham nr Canterbury 11.4.99)		3. 9.99P
G-BKVF	Clutton FRED Srs.III PFA/29-10791			29. 7.83	J.M.Brightwell & A.J.Wright (Derby)		
G-BKVG	Scheibe SF-25E Super Falke	4362	(D-KNAE)	25. 8.83	G-BKVG Ltd North Hill		4. 6.02
G-BKVK	Auster AOP.9	AUS/10/2	WZ662	8. 8.83	J.D.Butcher AAC Middle Wallop (Op Military Auster Flt) (As "WZ662" in Army c/s)		29. 9.00P
G-BKVL	Robin DR.400/160 Major	1625		26. 7.83	M.R.Shelton Tatenhill t/a Tatenhill Aviation		22. 7.02T
G-BKVM	PA-18-150 Super Cub 18-849 (L-21A-PI) (Frame No.18-824)		PH-KAZ R.Neth AF R-214/51-15684	26. 8.83	D.G.Caffrey North Reston, Louth (As "115684" in US Army c/s) "Spirit of Goxhill"		3.10.02
G-BKVO	Pietenpol Air Camper PFA/47-10799 (Continental A65)			8. 8.83	B.P.Waites Spilsted Farm, Sedlescombe "Emily"		25. 5.99P
G-BKVP	Pitts S-1D Special 002 & PFA/09-10800 (Lycoming IO-360)			19. 8.83	P.J.Leggo Leicester		27. 8.99P
G-BKVS	Campbell Cricket G/01-1047 (VW 1834)			11. 8.83	A.J.Unwin Kemble "Yorkie"		17. 2.00P
G-BKVT	PA-23-250 Aztec E	27-7754002	G-HARV N62760	6. 2.84	BKS Surveys Ltd. Belfast/Exeter		9. 4.00T
G-BKVW	Airtour AH-56 HAFB	AH.003		27. 6.84	L.D. & H.Vaughan "Lunardi" Tring		
G-BKVX	Airtour AH-56C HAFB	AH.002		27. 6.84	P.Aldridge Halesworth, Suffolk "Featherspin" or "Liebling"		
G-BKVY	Airtour B-31 HAFB	AH.001		9. 8.83	M.Davies Callington, Cornwall "Day Dream"		17. 6.97A
G-BKWD	Taylor JT.2 Titch PFA/60-10232 (Continental PC60) (Originally regd as c/n PFA/60-10143; presumed absorbed into both projects)			17. 8.83	E.H.Booker Valley Farm, Winwick		16. 6.99P
G-BKWE	Colt 17A Cloudhopper HAFB	533		1.11.83	Flying Pictures Ltd Fairoaks "Pooh Bear/DisneyChannel"		24.11.96A
G-BKWG	PZL-104 Wilga 35A	17820687	SP-WAC	10. 8.83	H & C Balfour Paul Cumbernauld		30. 9.01A
G-BKWR	Cameron V-65 HAFB	970		26. 8.83	K.J.Foster Coleshill, Birmingham "White Spirit"		9. 7.00A
G-BKWW	Cameron O-77 HAFB	984		13. 9.83	A.M.Marten "Kouros" Woking		18. 1.89A
G-BKWY	Reims Cessna F.152T	1940		22. 9.83	The Cambridge Aero Club Ltd Cambridge		5. 9.02T
G-BKXA	Robin R.2100	114	F-GAOS	24.11.83	G.G.Beal t/a G-BKXA Group Cumbernauld		22.10.99
G-BKXD	Aerospatiale SA.365N Dauphin 2	6088	F-WMHD	7. 9.83	Bond Helicopters Ltd Aberdeen		8.12.01T
G-BKXF	PA-28R-200 Cherokee Arrow II	28R-7335351	OY-DZN N56092	10.11.83	P.L.Brunton Caernarfon		22. 6.02T
G-BKXG	Cessna T303 Crusader	T303-00015	N9616C	22. 9.83	Wm Ewington & Co Ltd Woodford		1. 6.01
G-BKXM	Colt 17A Cloudhopper HAFB	531		3.10.83	R.G.Turnbull Glasbury, Hereford		26. 1.00A
G-BKXN	ICA IS-28M2A	48		24.10.83	T.J.Mills Shobdon		3. 5.00
G-BKXO	Rutan LongEz PFA/74A-10580 (Continental O-200-A)			24.10.83	D.F.P.Finan Teesside		27. 6.00P
G-BKXP	Auster AOP.6 (Frame No. TAY841BJ)	2830	Belg AF A-14/VT987	12.10.83	B.J. & W.J.Ellis Little Gransden (On rebuild 7.91)		
G-BKXR	Druine D.31A Turbulent (VW1700)	303	OY-AMW	1.11.83	M.B.Hill Draycott Farm, Chiseldon		12.11.00P
G-BKXX	Cameron V-65 HAFB	1000	(OO-) G-BKXX	1. 9.83	L.J.H.Decabooter & L.P.Neirynck "Hot Mille" St.Niklaas/Ostend, Belgium		24. 7.99A
G-BKXY*	Westland WG.30 Srs.100	013	N113WG	2.11.83	Westland Helicopters Ltd Yeovil G-BKXY/N113WG/G-BKXY (Cancelled as 11.8.88WFU; dumped 7.98)		
G-BKYA	Boeing 737-236ADV	23159		14. 9.84	British Airways plc Manchester "Ariel"		27. 9.01T
G-BKYB	Boeing 737-236ADV	23160		27. 9.84	British Airways plc Birmingham		9.10.01T

Regn	Type	C/n	P/I	Date	Owner/operator	Probable Base	CA Expy
G-BKYH	Boeing 737-236ADV	23166		13.12.84	British Airways plc	Birmingham	20.12.01T
G-BKYN	Boeing 737-236ADV	23172		21. 3.85	British Airways plc	Manchester	31. 3.02T
					(Sold to Aerolineas Argentinas 12.99)		
G-BKYP	Boeing 737-236ADV	23226		24. 4.85	British Airways plc	Manchester	1. 5.02T
					(Waves & Cranes t/s)		
G-BKZB	Cameron V-77 HAFB	995		11.11.83	G.W.G.C. Sudlow	Somerton	30. 4.95A
					"Camelot Clodhopper"		
G-BKZE	Aerospatiale AS.332L Super Puma	2102	F-WKQE	30. 9.83	Brintel Helicopters Ltd	Aberdeen	13. 3.00T
					t/a British International Helicopters		
G-BKZF	Cameron V-56 HAFB	246	F-BXUK	14.11.83	A.D.Brice "Xplorer"	Cowbridge	18. 3.97A
G-BKZG	Aerospatiale AS.332L Super Puma	2106	HB-ZBT	30. 9.83	Brintel Helicopters Ltd	Aberdeen	25. 8.02T
			G-BKZG		t/a British International Helicopters		
G-BKZH	Aerospatiale AS.332L Super Puma	2107		30. 9.83	Brintel Helicopters Ltd	Aberdeen	4. 4.00T
					t/a British International Helicopters		
G-BKZI	Bell 206A JetRanger	118	(5B-CG?)	7.12.83	Dolphin Property (Management) Ltd		
	(The P/I NTU is either 5B-CGC or CGD)		G-BKZI/N6238N			Thruxton	19. 9.01T
G-BKZM	Isaacs Fury II	PFA/11-10742		27. 9.83	B.Jones	Haverfordwest	1.10.90P
	(Continental O-200-A)				(As "K2060": stored 8.96)		
G-BKZT	Clutton FRED Srs.II	PFA/29-10715		20.10.83	D.C.Mayle & M.V.Pettifer	White Waltham	16.12.00P
	(VW1834)						
G-BKZV	Bede BD-4	380	ZS-UAB	31. 8.84	G.I.J.Thomson	Little Snoring	9. 8.00P
	(Lycoming O-320)						

G-BLAA – G-BLZZ

Regn	Type	C/n	P/I	Date	Owner/operator	Probable Base	CA Expy
G-BLAA	Sportavia Fournier RF5	5011	D-KIHI	3.10.83	A.D.Wren	Southend	11. 9.99
G-BLAC	Reims Cessna FA.152 Aerobat	0370		25. 3.80	Tilbrook Industries Ltd	Bourn	24. 3.01T
					(Op Rural Flying Corps)		
G-BLAD	Thunder Ax7-77 Srs.1 HAFB	485		7.12.83	P.J.Bish "Big Lad"	Hungerford	15.10.92A
					(Stolen from Hungerford 5.8.92)		
G-BLAF	Stolp SA.900 V-Star	PFA/106-10651		13. 9.83	P.R.Skeels	Lymm Dam	28. 9.00P
	(Continental O-200-A)						
G-BLAG	Pitts S-1D Special	PFA/09-10195		1.12.83	P.M.Ambrose	Popham	15. 4.99P
	(Lycoming AEIO-360)						
G-BLAH	Thunder Ax7-77 Srs.1 HAFB	526		3.10.83	T.M.Donnelly "Blah"	Doncaster	25. 2.00A
G-BLAI	Monnett Sonerai IIL	PFA/15-10583		6.12.83	T.Simpson	Breighton	12. 1.99P
	(Regd with c/n PFA/15-10584)				(Noted 9.98)		
G-BLAM	CEA DR.360 Chevalier	345	F-BRCM	6. 2.84	D.J.Durell	Maypole Farm, Chislet	8. 8.02
G-BLAT	SAN Jodel 150 Mascaret	56	F-BNID	30. 1.84	D.J.Dulborough & A.J.Court	Popham	11. 6.00P
G-BLAX	Reims Cessna FA.152 Aerobat	0385		11.10.83	Bournemouth Flying Club Ltd	Bournemouth	11. 5.02T
G-BLCA	Bell 206B JetRanger III	3443	N20982	1.12.83	RMH Stainless Ltd (Op Central Helicopters)		27. 5.02T
						Orgreave Gorse Farm, Lichfield	
G-BLCG	Socata TB-10 Tobago	61	G-BHES	17. 3.80	P.Hickey & M.E.Woodroffe	Shoreham	25. 6.01
					t/a Charlie Golf Flying Group		
G-BLCH	Colt 56D HAFB	392		14.11.83	Balloon Flights Club Ltd	Leicester	
					"Geronimo"		
G-BLCI	EAA AcroSport P	P-10A	N6AS	29. 2.84	M.R.Holden "Bluebottle"		16. 6.97P
			(Damaged Farthing Corner late 1996) Stoneacre Farm, Farthing Corner				
G-BLCM	Socata TB-9 Tampico	194	OO-TCT	2.12.83	Repclif Chemical Services Ltd	Liverpool	29. 5.02T
			(OO-TBC)		(Op Liverpool Flying School)		
G-BLCP	Short SD.3-30-100	SH.3672	OY-MMA	8.12.83	Comhfhorbairt Gallimn Teoranta	Dublin	
			(SE-KSU)/OY-MMA/EI-BYU/OY-MMA/G-BLCP		t/a Aer Arran		
G-BLCT	CEA Jodel DR.220 2+2	23	F-BOCQ	22.12.83	C.J.Snell	Shoreham	17. 6.00
					t/a Christopher Robin Flying Group		
G-BLCU	Scheibe SF-25B Falke	4699	D-KECC	30.12.83	C.F.Sellers	Rufforth	19. 7.02
G-BLCV	Hoffmann H-36 Dimona	36113	EI-CJO	21. 3.84	R.L.Braithwaite	Rufforth	4. 6.02
			G-BLCV				
G-BLCW	Evans VP-1	PFA/62-10835		19.12.83	K.D.Pearce	Southery	28. 6.96P
	(VW1600)				"Le Plank"		
G-BLCY	Thunder Ax7-65Z HAFB	487		13. 1.84	C.M.George	Brixton, Plymouth	26. 2.99A
G-BLDB	Taylor JT.1 Monoplane	PFA/55-10506		28.12.83	C.J.Bush	Great Oakley, Harwich	15. 5.00P
	(VW1600)						
G-BLDC*	K & S Jungster 1	PFA/44-10701		29.12.83	A.W.Brown	(Oxenhope)	
					(No permit issued: cancelled by CAA 6.3.99)		
G-BLDD*	WAG-Aero CUBy AcroTrainer			29.12.83	J.K.Davies	(Chester)	21.12.99P
	(Lycoming O-320)	PFA/108-10653			(Cancelled by CAA 17.9.99)		
G-BLDG	PA-25-260 Pawnee C	25-4501	SE-FLB	9. 1.84	Ouse Gliding Club Ltd	Rufforth	20. 6.02
			LN-VYM				
G-BLDK	Robinson R-22	0139	C-GSGU	17. 1.84	Warrenform Ltd	White Waltham	28. 6.02T

Regn	Type	C/n	P/I	Date	Owner/operator	Probable Base	CA Expy
G-BLDL*	Cameron Truck 56 SS HAFB	990		10. 1.84	I.Warrington & R.S Kent "Europa" Lancing		NE(A)
					t/a Balloon Preservation Group Balloon Team		
G-BLDV	PBN BN-2B-26 Islander	2179	D-INEY	13. 1.84	Loganair Ltd	Glasgow	10. 7.00T
			G-BLDV		(Mountain of the Birds/Benyhone Tartan t/s)		
G-BLEB	Colt 69A HAFB	537		20. 1.84	I.R.M.Jacobs "Gusto"	Reading	NE(A)
G-BLEJ	PA-28-161 Warrior II	28-7816257	N2194M	8. 2.84	Eglinton Flying Club Ltd	Eglinton	29. 3.02T
G-BLEL*	Price Ax7-77-245 HAFB	001		23. 1.84	Theresa S.Price "Butterfly"	Edgware	
G-BLEP	Cameron V-65 HAFB	1022		7. 2.84	D.Chapman	Maidstone	10. 9.96A
					t/a The Ground Hogs "Manor Marquees"		
G-BLES	Stolp SA.750 Acroduster Too			8.12.83	G.N.Davies	Vowchurch, Hereford	14. 7.00P
	(Lycoming O-360) 197 & PFA/89-10428						
G-BLET	Thunder Ax7-77 Srs.1 HAFB	539		16. 2.84	Servatruc Ltd "Servatruc"	Nottingham	15. 8.97A
G-BLEW	Reims Cessna F.182Q Skylane II	0039	F-GAQD	21. 6.78	D.J.Cross	Cumbernauld	1. 5.00
G-BLEZ	Aerospatiale SA.365N Dauphin 2	6131		24. 1.84	Bond Air Services Ltd	Liverpool	27. 8.02T
G-BLFI	PA-28-181 Archer II	28-8490034	N4333Z	22. 2.84	Bonus Aviation Ltd	Cranfield	22. 7.00T
G-BLFW	Grumman-American AA-5 Traveler		OO-GLW	22. 2.84	D.C.A.Milne Draycott Farm, Chiseldon		2. 9.02
		AA5-0786			t/a Grumman Club		
G-BLFY	Cameron V-77 HAFB	1030		16. 3.84	A.N.F.Pertwee "Groupie"	Frinton-on-Sea	5. 4.92A
G-BLFZ	PA-31-310 Turbo Navajo C	31-7912106	PH-RWS	21. 3.84	London Executive Aviation Ltd Stapleford		10. 7.02T
			N3538W				
G-BLGB*	Short SD.3-60 Var.100	SH.3641	G-14-3641	24. 2.84	British Regional Airlines Ltd	Glasgow	31. 3.98T
			(Damaged Stornaway 9.2.98 -to Exeter 1.99 & hulk remains dumped Lasham 10.99)				
G-BLGH	Robin DR.300/180R Remorqueur	570	D-EAFL	10. 4.84	Booker Gliding Club Ltd	Booker	15. 2.00
G-BLGO	Bensen B.8MV	RB-01		18. 6.84	F.Vernon	St.Merryn	15.5.87P*
	(VW 1834)				(Stored 5.98)		
G-BLGR	Bell 47G-4A	7501	N3236G	2. 5.84	H., J.R. & H.C.Wake & S.P.Broughton & Co Ltd		
			HC-ASQ/N1186W		t/a Courteenhall Farms Courteenhall, Northampton		24. 6.02
G-BLGS*	Socata Rallye 180T	3206		7. 7.78	Lasham Gliding Society Ltd	Lasham	21. 5.99
					(Cancelled by CAA 18.11.99)		
G-BLGT	PA-18-95 Super Cub (L-18C-PI)18-1445		D-EAGT	1. 6.84	T.A.Reed Watchford Farm, Yarcombe		20. 5.00P
	(Frame No.18-1399)		D-EOCC/ALAT 51-15445				
G-BLGV	Bell 206B JetRanger II	982	5B-JSB	2. 5.84	Heliflight (UK) Ltd	Halfpenny Green	29. 5.00T
			C-FDYL/CF-DYL				
G-BLGX*	Thunder Ax7-65 HAFB	551		16. 4.84	"The 45"	NK	NE(A)
					(Cancelled by CAA 19.5.93: active 9.94)		
G-BLHH	CEA DR.315 Petit Prince	324	F-BPRH	3. 7.84	Central Certification Service Ltd		
						Tower Farm	29. 5.00
G-BLHI	Colt 17A Cloudhopper HAFB	506		8. 9.86	Janet A.Folkes	Loughborough	8. 1.00A
					"Hopping Mad"		
G-BLHJ	Reims Cessna F.172P Skyhawk II	2182		26. 3.84	J.Easson	Edinburgh	8.12.02T
					(Op Edinburgh Air Centre)		
G-BLHK	Colt 105A HAFB	576		19. 6.84	A.S.Dear, R.B.Green & W.S.Templeton		
						Fordingbridge	12. 7.97A
					t/a Hale Hot-Air Balloon Group "Gloworm"		
G-BLHL*	Menavia CP.301A Emeraude	275	F-BLHL	2. 3.78	The Fire Service College		
			F-OBLM			Moreton-in-Marsh	27. 5.81P
					(Crashed Slinfold 4.8.81 & for fire service use 8.98)		
G-BLHM(2)	PA-18-95 Super Cub	18-3120	LX-AIM	23. 7.84	B.N.C.Mogg	Bibberne Farm, Stalbridge	12. 7.00P
	(L-18C-PI) (Frame No.18-3088)		D-EOAB/Belg AF OL-L46/53-4720				
G-BLHN	Robin HR.100/285 Tiara	539	F-GABF	20. 2.78	N.A.Onions	(London E6)	15. 5.00
G-BLHR	Gulfstream GA-7 Cougar	GA7-0109	OO-RTI	12. 4.84	T.E.Westley	Fowlmere	9.12.02T
			(OO-HRC)/N751G				
G-BLHS	Bellanca 7ECA Citabria 115	1342-80	OO-RTQ	12. 4.84	N.J.F.Campbell	Inverness	29. 4.02
G-BLHW	Varga 2150A Kachina	VAC161-80		17. 7.84	W.D.Garlick	Damyns Hall, Upminster	20. 1.00
					t/a Kachina Hotel Whiskey Group		
G-BLID	FFW DH.112 Venom FB.50 (FB.1)	815	J-1605	13. 7.84	P.G.Vallance Ltd	Charlwood, Surrey	AC
					(As "J-1605" in Swiss AF c/s; stored 6.97)		
G-BLIG*	Cameron V-65 HAFB	1045		24. 4.84	W.Davison "Peek-A-Boo II"	Chesterfield	3. 8.91A
					(Cancelled by CAA 4.8.98)		
G-BLIH	PA-18-135 Super Cub	18-3828	(PH-KNG)	12.11.84	I.R.F.Hammond	Stubbington	AC
	(L-21B-PI) (Frame No.18-3827)		R Neth AF R-138/54-2428				
G-BLIK	Wallis WA-116/F/S	K-218X		30. 4.84	K.H.Wallis	Reymerston Hall	24. 4.98P
	(Franklin 2A-120)				(Noted 5.99)		
G-BLIO*	Cameron R-42 Gas Free Balloon	1015		17. 4.84	British Balloon Museum & Library Newbury		17. 5.84P*
G-BLIP*	Cameron N-77 HAFB	1031		17. 4.84	Balloon Preservation Group	Lancing	26. 3.94A
					"Systems 80"		
G-BLIT	Thorp T-18CW	PFA/76-10550		24. 4.84	K.B.Hallam	Fairoaks	4.10.00P
	(Lycoming O-320)						
G-BLIW	Percival P.56 Provost T.53 PAC/F/125		IAC.177	12. 6.85	D.Mould & J.De Uphaugh	Shoreham	2. 9.00P
					t/a Provost Flying Group (As "177" in Irish Air Corps c/s)		

Regn	Type	C/n	P/I	Date	Owner/operator	Probable Base	CA Expy
G-BLIX	Saro Skeeter AOP.12	S2/5094	PH-HOF	3. 5.84	K.M.Scholes	Wilden	18. 8.99P
			(PH-SRE)/XL809		(As "XL809"in Army c/s)		
G-BLIY	Socata MS.892A Rallye Commodore 150		F-BSCX	9. 5.84	A.J.Brasher & K.R.Haynes		14. 5.00
		11639				Church Farm, North Moreton	
G-BLJD	Glaser-Dirks DG-400	4-85		15. 6.84	M.I.Gee	(London NW3)	17. 6.99
G-BLJF	Cameron O-65 HAFB	1041		14. 5.84	M.D.Mitchell "Fat Lady"	Sevenoaks	16. 8.00A
G-BLJH	Cameron N-77 HAFB	1047		14. 5.84	K A Kent "Daydream"	Lancing	27. 6.89A
					(Balloon Preservation Group 7.98)		
G-BLJM	Beechcraft 95-B55 Baron	TC-1997	SE-GRT	3. 3.78	R.A.Perrot	Guernsey	7. 8.00
G-BLJO	Reims Cessna F.152 II	1627	OY-BNB	21. 6.84	Redhill School of Flying Ltd	Redhill	17. 8.01T
					t/a Redhill Flying Club		
G-BLKA	FFW DH.112 Venom FB.54 (FB.4)	960	(G-VENM)	13. 7.84	de Havilland Aviation Ltd	Swansea	14. 7.95P
	(Regd with c/n 431)		Sw AF J-1790		(As "WR410/N" in 6 Sqdn RAF c/s) (Dismantled/stored 5.99)		
	(Note: G-DHUU also carries "WR410" & marks G-BLIE was re-registered as G-VENM 6.99)						
G-BLKJ*	Thunder Ax7-65 HAFB	580		18. 7.84	R S Kent "Up & Coming"	Lancing	3. 2.96A
					(Balloon Preservation Group 7.98)		
G-BLKK	Evans VP-1	PFA/62-10642		15. 6.84	D.J.Hunter	(Norwich)	31.10.00P
	(VW1834)						
G-BLKM	CEA Jodel DR.1051 Sicile	519	F-BLRO	26. 6.84	T.C.Humphreys	Goodwood	27. 6.00
G-BLKP	BAe Jetstream 3102	634	(G-BLEX)	9. 7.84	British Aerospace (Operations) Ltd		19. 4.01
			G-31-634			Farnborough/Warton	
G-BLKU*	Colt Flame 56SS HAFB	572		17. 7.84	British Balloon Museum & Library	Newbury	NE(A)
					"Mr.Wonderful II"		
G-BLKY	Beechcraft 58 Baron	TH-1440		22. 8.84	J.C.Hall	Guernsey	4. 3.00
G-BLKZ	Pilatus P.2-05	600-45	U-125	30. 7.84	R.W.Hinton	Duxford	21.12.99P
			A-125				
G-BLLA	Bensen B.8M	PFA G/01-1055		27. 6.84	K.T.Donaghey	Henstridge	22. 6.98P
	(VW1834)						
G-BLLB	Bensen B.8MR	PFA G/01A-1059		4. 9.84	D.H.Moss	Chilbolton	10. 3.00P
	(Rotax 532)						
G-BLLD	Cameron O-77 HAFB	1060		16. 7.84	G.Birchall	Ormskirk	4. 6.00A
G-BLLF*	Westland WG.30 Srs.100	015	N115WG	22. 4.85	Westland Helicopters Ltd	Yeovil	
			(G-BLLF)/N115WG		(Cancelled as WFU 11.8.88: dumped 7.98)		
G-BLLH	CEA Jodel DR.220A/B 2+2	131	F-BROM	17. 7.84	P.Chamberlain & D.E.Starkey		
						White Waltham	18. 6.00
G-BLLM	PA-23-250 Aztec E	27-4619	G-BBNM	18. 1.84	C & M Thomas	Cardiff	21. 8.98
			OY-POR/G-BBNM/N14001		t/a Ammanford Trade Sales		
G-BLLN	PA-18-95 Super Cub (L-18C-PI) 18-3447		D-ECLN	27. 6.84	P.A.Layzell	Old Buckenham	21.12.00T
	(Continental O-200A) (Frame No.18-3380)		96+23/PY+901/QZ+011/AC+508/AS+508/54-747				
G-BLLO	PA-18-95 Super Cub (L-18C-PI) 18-3099		D-EAUB	11. 7.84	D.G. & M.G.Margetts		
	(Frame No.18-3058)		Belg AF OL-L25/53-4699		Vaynor Farm, Llanidloes, Powys		12.10.96P
G-BLLP	Slingsby T.67B	2008		19. 7.84	Cleveland Flying School Ltd	Teesside	4.12.00T
G-BLLR	Slingsby T.67B	2011		19. 7.84	R.L.Brinklow	Bournemouth	12.10.01T
					(Op Airbourne School of Flying)		
G-BLLS	Slingsby T.67B	2013		19. 7.84	Western Air (Thruxton) Ltd	Thruxton	12.12.99T
G-BLLV	Slingsby T.67C	2015		3. 9.84	R.L.Brinklow	Turweston	10.11.00T
G-BLLW	Colt 56B HAFB	578		11. 9.84	G.Fordyce, R.Wickens & S.A.Sawyer	Olney	1. 5.00A
					"Angel Clare"		
G-BLLZ	Rutan LongEz	PFA/74A-10830		16. 7.84	R.S.Stoddart-Stones	Henstridge	22. 6.94P
	(Lycoming O-235)						
G-BLMA	Moravan Zlin Z.526A Trener Master		F-BORS	23. 7.84	G.P.Northcott	Redhill	24. 6.01
		922					
G-BLMC*	Avro 698 Vulcan B.2A	-	XM575	R	East Midlands Aeropark	East Midlands	
					(As "XM575") (Noted 6.99)		
G-BLME	Robinson R-22HP	0032	N90261	16. 4.85	Heli Air Ltd	Wellesbourne Mountford	15. 9.02T
G-BLMG	Grob G-109B	6322		27. 9.84	P.R.Holloway	Enstone	1.11.02
					t/a Mike Golf Syndicate		
G-BLMI	PA-18-95 Super Cub	18-2066	D-ENWI	5. 6.84	R.Gibson	White Waltham	31. 5.87P
	(L-18C-PI) (Frame No.18-2086)		R Neth AF R-55/52-2466		t/a G-BLMI Flying Group		
G-BLMN	Rutan LongEz	PFA/74A-10643		3. 7.84	S.E.Bowers	Thruxton	28. 9.99P
	(Lycoming O-235) (Regd as c/n PFA/74A-10648)				t/a G-BLMN Flying Group		
G-BLMP	PA-17 Vagabond	17-193	F-BFMR	15. 5.84	M.Austin	Lower Upham	29. 6.99P
	(Continental A65)		N4893H				
G-BLMR	PA-18-150 Super Cub	18-2057	PH-NLD	29. 5.84	J.J.Woodhouse	(Fleet)	9. 6.02T
	(L-18C-PI) (Frame No.18-2070)		R Neth AF R-72/52-2457		t/a Flying Services		
G-BLMT	PA-18-135 Super Cub	18-2706	D-ELGH	12. 9.84	I.S.Runnalls Church Farm, North Moreton		22. 8.02
	(Frame No.18-2724)		N8558C				
G-BLMW	Nipper T.66 RA45 Mk.IIIB			31. 8.84	S.L.Millar	Crowland	30. 6.00P
	(Ardem 10)	PFA/25-11020					
G-BLMX	Reims Cessna FR.172H Rocket	0327	PH-RPC	5. 9.84	C.J.W.Littler	Marshland, Wisbech	16.12.99
G-BLMZ	Colt 105A HAFB	404		24. 9.84	Mandy D.Dickinson "Zulu"	Bristol	28. 3.97A

Regn	Type	C/n	P/I	Date	Owner/operator	Probable Base	CA Expy
G-BLNJ	PBN BN-2B-26 Islander	2189		3. 9.84	Loganair Ltd (Martha Masanabo/Ndebele t/s)	Glasgow	3.12.00T
G-BLNO	Clutton FRED Srs.III	PFA/29-10559		17.10.84	L.W.Smith	(Sale, Cheshire)	
G-BLNW	PBN BN-2B-26 Islander	2197		3. 9.84	Loganair Ltd (Op Scottish Air Ambulance) "Sister Jean Kennedy"	Glasgow	21.12.00T
G-BLOB	Colt 31A Air Chair HAFB	599		11. 9.84	Jacques W.Soukup Enterprises Ltd	South Dakota, USA	5. 6.91A
G-BLOR	PA-30-160 Twin Comanche	30-59	HB-LAE N7097Y/N10F	19. 7.85	R.L.C.Appleton (F/f 11.2.99 Gloucestershire after rebuild)	Sheepwash	22. 4.02T
G-BLOS	Cessna 185A Skywagon (Operates on floats)	185-0359	LN-BDS N4159Y	17. 9.84	Elizabeth Brun	Great Massingham	20. 4.00
G-BLOT	Colt 56B HAFB	424		11. 9.84	H.J.Anderson "Pathfinder"	Oswestry	17. 7.96A
G-BLOU*	Rand-Robinson KR-2	PFA/129-11118		4.12.85	D.G.Cole (Cancelled by CAA 15.4.99)	(Martley, Worcs)	
G-BLOV*	Thunder Ax5-42 Srs.1 HAFB	590		11. 9.84	Not known "Puff The Magic Dragon" (Cancelled 11.2.91 as sold to USA but noted active as G-BLOV in 9.93)	(USA)	NE(A)
G-BLPA	Piper J3C-65 Cub (L-4H-PI) (Frame No.11152)	11327	OO-AJL OO-JOE/43-30036	27. 9.84	C.J.Gray	Turweston	12. 7.00P
G-BLPB	Turner TSW Hot Two Wot (Lycoming O-320-A)	PFA/46-10606		19.10.84	I.R.Hannah	Temploux, Belgium	14. 9.00P
G-BLPE	PA-18-95 Super Cub (L-18C-PI) (Continental O-200-A) (Also quoted as 18-3083)	18-3084	D-ECBE Belg Army L-10/53-4684	28. 9.84	A.A.Haig-Thomas	Clacton	6. 5.00P
G-BLPF	Reims Cessna FR.172G Rocket	0187	N4594Q D-EEFL	29. 1.85	W.A.F.Cuninghame	Prestwick	2.11.00
G-BLPG	Auster 5 J/1N Alpha	3395	G-AZIH	21. 5.82	R.Knowles (As "16693" in RCAF c/s)	(Wantage)	25. 3.00
G-BLPH	Reims Cessna FRA.150L Aerobat	0239	EI-BHH PH-ASH	19. 9.84	G.K. & T.G.Solomon t/a The New Aerobat Group Kittyhawk Farm, Deanland, E.Sussex		25. 6.00
G-BLPI	Slingsby T.67B	2016		24. 9.84	RAF Wyton Flying Club Ltd	RAF Wyton	21. 7.00T
G-BLPK*	Cameron V-65 HAFB	1069		24. 9.84	A.J. & C.P.Nicholls "Millie" t/a Bernard Hunter & Bristol Cine Sales (Cancelled by CAA 19.1.99)	Bristol	9. 8.96A
G-BLPP	Cameron V-77 HAFB	432		19. 9.78	L.P.Purfield "Merlin"	Leicester	30. 4.94A
G-BLRA	BAe 146 Srs.100	E-1017	N117TR N462AP/CP-2249/N462AP/G-BLRA/G-5-02	3.10.84	British Aerospace (Operations) Ltd	Woodford	15.10.00
G-BLRC	PA-18-135 Super Cub (L-21B-PI) (Frame No.18-3790)	18-3602	OO-DKC PH-DKC/R Neth R-112/54-2402	27.11.84	A.J.McBurnie	Seething	4.12.00
G-BLRD	MBB Bo.209 Monsun 150FV	101	D-EBOA (OE-AHM)	15.10.84	Margaret D.Ward	Kemble	23.11.00
G-BLRF	Slingsby T.67C	2014		30.11.84	Polawood Aviation Ltd	Wellesbourne Mountford	2. 1.00T
G-BLRG	Slingsby T.67B	2020		30.11.84	R.L.Brinklow	Turweston	17. 7.00T
G-BLRH*	Rutan LongEz	PFA/74A-11073		7. 2.85	G.L.Thompson (Cancelled by CAA 15.4.99)	(Kingsbridge, Devon)	
G-BLRJ	CEA Jodel DR.1051 Sicile	502	F-BLRJ	8. 2.78	M.P.Hallam	Jackrells Farm, Horsham	17. 7.00
G-BLRL	Scintex CP-301C1 Emeraude	552	(G-BLNP) F-BJFT	5.11.84	B.C.Davis	Palma/Son Bonet, Mallorca	21. 9.00P
G-BLRM	Glaser-Dirks DG-400	4-107		5. 2.85	D.J.Barke	Tatenhill	14. 4.02
G-BLRN	DH.104 Dove 8 (C.2/2)	04266	N531WB	30.10.84	C.W.Simpson Lelystad, The Netherlands G-BLRN/WB531 (To Pionier Hangaar Collection: as "WB531" in RAF c/s)		13. 3.96
G-BLRW	Cameron Elephant 77SS HAFB	1074		14.12.84	Forbes Europe Inc "Great Sky Elephant"	Balleroy, Normandy	4.11.98A
G-BLSD*	FFW DH.112 Venom FB.54	928	N203DM G-BLSD/J-1758	20. 5.85	R.J.Lamplough (As "J-1758 in Swiss AF c/s: stored 10.97)	North Weald	
G-BLSF	Gulfstream AA-5A Cheetah	AA5A-0802	G-BGCK	21. 2.83	J.P.E.Walsh t/a Walsh Aviation (Op London School of Flying)	Elstree	12. 6.00T
G-BLSH*	Cameron V-77	1085		7.12.84	A D Kent "Compass Rose" (Balloon Preservation Group 7.98)	Lancing	14. 1.95A
G-BLSK	Colt 77A HAFB	617		29.11.84	R.D.MacKenzie	Gerrards Cross	22. 5.96A
G-BLSM	BAe 125 Srs.700B	NA0346 & 257208	G-5-19 (G-BLMJ)/N710BR	18.10.84	Dravidian Air Services Ltd	Heathrow	19.11.01
G-BLST	Cessna 421C Golden Eagle III	421C-0623	N88638	29.11.78	Cecil Aviation Ltd	Cambridge	30. 8.00T
G-BLSU	Cameron A-210 HAFB	1095		31.12.84	A.C.Elson "Skysales II"	Bristol	7. 6.95T
G-BLSX	Cameron O-105 HAFB	1094		16. 1.85	B.J.Petteford "Flaming Mischief" (Petteford's Solid Fuels titles)	Bristol	20. 3.99T
G-BLTA	Colt 77A Coil HAFB	525		8. 6.84	K.A.Schlussler "James Sadler"	Bourne, Lincs	7. 8.91A
G-BLTC	Druine D.31A Turbulent (VW1600)	PFA/48-10964		18.12.84	G.P.Smith & A.W.Burton	Little Down Farm, Milson	15. 4.00P
G-BLTF	Robinson R-22 Alpha	0428	N8526A	10. 1.85	S.& J.M.Taylor t/a Stuart Taylor International	Blackpool	8. 3.01T

Regn	Type	C/n	P/I	Date	Owner/operator	Probable Base	CA Expy
G-BLTK	Rockwell Commander 112TC-A	13106	SE-GSD	11.12.84	B.Rogalewski	Denham	26. 5.00
G-BLTM	Robin HR.200/100 Club	96	F-GAEC	21.11.84	B.D.Balcanquall	Barton	19. 6.00
G-BLTN	Thunder Ax7-65 HAFB	621		4. 1.85	J.A.Liddle "Frederica"	Reading	3. 9.88A
G-BLTP	BAe 125 Srs.700B	NA0347 & 257210	G-5-18 (G-BLMK)/N710BQ	18.10.84	Dravidian Air Services Ltd	Heathrow	15. 1.02
G-BLTR	Sportavia-Putzer Scheibe SF-25B Falke	4823	D-KHEC	23. 1.85	V.Mallon	RAF Bruggen	1. 4.94
G-BLTS	Rutan LongEz	PFA/74A-10741		14. 1.85	R.W.Cutler	(Thorverton, Exeter)	
G-BLTT	Slingsby T.67B	2023		16. 1.85	S.E.Marples	Newcastle	5. 8.00T
G-BLTU	Slingsby T.67B	2024		16. 1.85	RAF Wyton Flying Club Ltd	RAF Wyton	14. 8.00T
G-BLTV	Slingsby T.67B	2025		16. 1.85	R.L.Brinklow	Turweston	9. 3.02T
G-BLTW	Slingsby T.67B	2026		16. 1.85	R.L.Brinklow	Turweston	14.10.02T
G-BLUE	Colting Ax7-77A HAFB (Regd as Colt 77A c/n 11)	77A-011		2. 5.78	D.P.Busby "Bluebird" (Balloon Preservation Group 7.98)	Lancing	20. 9.99A
G-BLUI	Thunder Ax7-65 HAFB	553		22. 2.85	Susan Johnson "Rhubarb & Custard"	Blackpool	31. 7.00A
G-BLUK	Bond Sky Dancer (Mod)	85/1		16. 1.85	J.Owen Spilsted Farm, Sedlescombe		
	(Under construction 8.93 - wings only present 8.94: cancelled by CAA 15.4.99)						
G-BLUL	CEA Jodel DR.1050/M1 Sicile Record	601	F-BMPJ	7. 3.85	J.Owen Spilsted Farm, Sedlescombe (On overhaul 4.99)		24.10.91
G-BLUM	Aerospatiale SA.365N Dauphin 2	6101		21. 1.85	Bond Helicopters Ltd	Blackpool	14. 4.02T
G-BLUN	Aerospatiale SA.365N Dauphin 2	6114	PH-SSS G-BLUN	21. 1.85	Bond Helicopters Ltd	Blackpool	5. 3.02T
G-BLUV	Grob G-109B	6336		1. 2.85	R.J.Buckels & S.K.Durso t/a The 109 Flying Group	North Weald	16. 2.02
G-BLUX	Slingsby T.67M Firefly 200	2027	G-7-145 G-BLUX/G-7-113	31. 1.85	R.L.Brinklow t/a Richard Brinklow Aviation	Turweston	22. 4.99T
G-BLUY*	Colt 69A HAFB	631		7. 3.85	Not known "Bluey"	NK	NE(A)
G-BLUZ	DH.82B Queen Bee	1435 & SAL.150	LF858	9. 4.85	C.I.Knowles & J.Flynn t/a The Bee Keepers Group (As "LF858")	RAF Henlow	16. 6.00P
G-BLVA	Airtour AH-31 HAFB	AH.004		12. 2.86	A.van Wyk	London SE12	
G-BLVB	Airtour AH-56 HAFB	AH.005		12. 2.86	T.C.Hinton "Bluejay"	Tunbridge Wells	
G-BLVI	Slingsby T.67M Firefly II	2017	(PH-KIF) G-BLVI	1. 2.85	Hunting Aviation Ltd RAF Barkston Heath (Op Hunting Acft Ltd/JEFTS)		13.12.99T
G-BLVK	Mudry/CAARP CAP-10B	141	JY-GSR	11. 3.85	E.K.Coventry	Herongate	8. 5.00
G-BLVL	PA-28-161 Warrior II	28-8416109	N43677	11. 2.85	Marair (Jersey) Ltd	Jersey	15. 5.00T
G-BLVN	Cameron N-77 HAFB	1098		4. 2.85	Servo & Electronic Sales Ltd "Connect One"	Lydd	9. 4.96A
G-BLVS	Cessna 150M Commuter	150-76869	EI-BLS N45356	19. 2.85	Tindon Ltd	Little Snoring	30. 7.00T
G-BLVW	Reims Cessna F.172H	0422	D-ENQU	16. 5.85	R & D Holloway Ltd	Stapleford	10. 7.00
G-BLWB	Thunder Ax6-56 Srs 1 HAFB	645		22. 2.85	G.J.Bell "Porky"	Wokingham	10.11.99A
G-BLWD	PA-34-200T Seneca II	34-8070334	ZS-KKV ZS-XAT/N8253E	14. 3.85	Acre 123 Ltd.	Elstree	6. 5.02T
G-BLWE	Colt 90A HAFB	648		5. 3.85	Huntair Ltd "Rair Computers"	Aachen, Germany	11. 5.00A
G-BLWF	Robin HR.100/210 Safari	183	F-BUSR	8. 3.85	Starguide Ltd	Stapleford	27. 5.00
G-BLWH	Fournier RF6B-100	7	F-GADF	3. 4.85	I.R.March	Booker	11. 8.00
G-BLWM*	Bristol M.1C rep (110 hp Gnome)	PFA/112-10892	"C4912"	12. 3.85	RAF Museum (As "C4994" in RFC c/s)	Hendon	12.8.87P*
G-BLWP	PA-38-112 Tomahawk	38-78A0367	OY-BTW	7. 6.85	A.Dodd	Panshanger	1. 3.01T
G-BLWT	Evans VP-1 Srs.2 (VW1834)	PFA/62-10639		27. 3.85	C.J.Bellworthy	Finmere	14. 4.00P
G-BLWV	Reims Cessna F.152 II	1843	EI-BIN	25. 2.85	Redhill Aviation Ltd t/a Redhill Flying Club	Redhill	19. 6.00T
G-BLWW	Aerocar Mini-Imp Model C (Continental O-200-A)	PFA/136-10880		1. 3.85	M.K.Field t/a The Brize Group (Status uncertain)	(Shrewsbury)	4. 6.87P
G-BLWX*	Cameron N-56 HAFB	1096		15. 2.85	Not Known	Not Known-	NE(A)
	(Sold as RP-C1483 9.94 but at Ashton Court, Bristol 8.95 as G-BLWX)						
G-BLWY	Robin R.2160D	176	F-GCUV SE-GXE	15. 4.85	K.D.Boardman	Popham	23.10.00
G-BLXA	Socata TB-20 Trinidad	284	SE-IMO F-ODOH	11. 4.85	Tango Bravo Aviation Ltd	Popham	14. 6.00T
G-BLXF	Cameron V-77 HAFB	1144		2. 4.85	P.Lawman "Candytwist III"	Northampton	2. 4.97A
G-BLXG	Colt 21A Cloudhopper HAFB	605		2. 5.85	A.Walker "Britannia Park"	Richmond, Surrey	6. 5.98A
G-BLXH	Alpavia Fournier RF3	39	F-BMDQ	25. 3.85	A.Rawicz-Szczerbo	Eaglescott	12.12.00P
G-BLXI	Scintex CP.1310-C3 Super Emeraude	937	F-BMJI	1. 4.85	R.Howard Grove Moor Farm, Grassthorpe		10. 4.00P
G-BLXO	SAN Jodel 150 Mascaret	10	F-BLDB	9. 5.85	P.R.Powell	Allensmore, Hereford	17. 3.00P

Regn	Type	C/n	P/I	Date	Owner/operator	Probable Base	CA Expy
G-BLXP	PA-28R-200 Cherokee Arrow II	28R-7235200	N5226T	29. 7.85	M.B.Hamlett Le Plessis-Belleville, France		20. 6.02
G-BLXR	Aerospatiale AS.332L Super Puma	2154		14. 5.85	Bristow Helicopters Ltd "Cromarty"	Aberdeen	1. 7.00T
G-BLXY	Cameron V-65 HAFB	1139		9. 4.85	Gone With The Wind Ltd Seronera, Tanzania		
G-BLYD	Socata TB-20 Trinidad	518		1. 5.85	J.M.White & R.A.Stockdale t/a Gourmet Trotters	Biggin Hill	1. 2.01
G-BLYE	Socata TB-10 Tobago	521		1. 5.85	G.Hatton	Carlisle	28. 5.01T
G-BLYK	PA-34-220T Seneca III	34-8433083	N4371J	30. 5.85	Oxford Aviation Services Ltd	Oxford	28. 9.00
G-BLYP	Robin R.3000/120	109		15. 5.85	C.J.Freeman t/a Weald Air Services	Headcorn	5. 5.01T
G-BLYT	Airtour AH-77 HAFB	AH.008		7. 7.87	I.J. & B.A.Taylor "Signal 2"	Corsham	19. 7.00A
G-BLYY*	PA-28-181 Archer II	28-7890181	OO-PAV N9792K	17. 5.85	N.J.Skinner t/a G-BLYY Group	Stapleford	20. 9.00
			(Crashed Crosland Moor 31.7.99: cancelled as wfu 26.11.99)				
G-BLZA	Scheibe SF-25B Falke	4684	D-KBAJ	22. 5.85	T.A.Lacey t/a Chiltern Gliding Club	RAF Halton	14. 9.00
G-BLZB	Cameron N-65 HAFB	1164		21. 5.85	R S Kent "Pro-Sport" (Balloon Preservation Group 7.98)	Lancing	25. 4.90A
G-BLZE	Reims Cessna F.152 II	1579	G-CSSC PH-AYF(2)	3. 5.85	Redhill Aviation Ltd t/a Redhill Flying Club	Redhill	12. 4.01T
G-BLZF	Thunder Ax7-77 HAFB	660		3. 6.85	H.M.Savage "Hector"	Edinburgh	20. 8.00A
G-BLZH	Reims Cessna F.152 II	1965		21. 6.85	Plane Talking Ltd	Biggin Hill	3. 4.01T
G-BLZM	Rutan LongEz (Lycoming O-235)	PFA/74A-10704		10. 6.85	N.J.Rushby t/a Zulu Mike Group	Shoreham	28. 8.98P
G-BLZN	Bell 206B JetRanger	314	ZS-HMV C-GWDH/N1408W	12. 7.85	Capital Helicopter Group Ltd	Biggin Hill	18. 7.00T
G-BLZP	Reims Cessna F.152 II	1959		10. 7.85	East Midlands Flying School Ltd East Midlands		7.11.00T
G-BLZS	Cameron O-77 HAFB	479		22. 5.85	M.M.Cobbold "Rainbow Brite" (Henry Africa's Hothouse Restaurant titles)	Plymouth	28. 8.00A
G-BLZT	Short SD.3-60 Var.100	SH.3676	G-14-3676	18. 6.85	Gill Aviation Ltd	Newcastle	29. 8.00T

G-BMAA – G-BMZZ

Regn	Type	C/n	P/I	Date	Owner/operator	Probable Base	CA Expy
G-BMAD	Cameron V-77 HAFB	1166		10. 6.85	M.A.Stelling "Nautilus"	Bedford	29. 9.99A
G-BMAF*	Cessna 180F	180-51219	G-BDVR ET-ABT/N2119Z	6. 3.81	P.Channon Rushett Farm, Chessington (Cancelled by CAA 2.3.99: noted 9.99)		6. 8.93T
G-BMAL	Sikorsky S-76A II Plus	760120	F-WZSA G-BMAL	27.11.80	Bond Helicopters Ltd	Humberside	9. 5.01T
G-BMAO	Taylor JT.1 Monoplane	PFA/1411		29. 7.85	V.A.Wordsworth	Hucknall	4. 7.00P
G-BMAV	Aerospatiale AS.350B Ecureuil	1089		1. 6.79	Heli-Trans Ltd.	Belfast	4. 8.00T
G-BMAX	Clutton FRED Srs.II (VW1834)	PFA/29-10322		20.12.78	D.A.Arkley	(Chelmsford)	24. 8.99P
G-BMAY	PA-18-135 Super Cub (L-21B-PI) (Frame No.18-3961)	18-3925	OO-LWB "EI-229" I-EIJZ/MM54-2525/54-2525	3. 7.85	R.W.Davies Little Robhurst Farm, Woodchurch, Kent		18.10.01T
G-BMBB	Reims Cessna F.150L	1136	OO-LWM PH-GAA	2. 8.85	A.H.Glick t/a Dacebow Aviation	Leeds-Bradford	15.11.02T
G-BMBC	PA-31-350 Chieftain	31-7952172	(ZF524) N3519C	9. 7.85	Air Navigation & Trading Co Ltd	Blackpool	12.10.02T
G-BMBE	PA-46-310P Malibu	46-8508063	N6908W	26. 7.85	The Barfax Distributing Co Ltd & Glasdon Group Ltd	Blackpool	8. 4.01T
G-BMBJ	Schempp-Hirth Janus CM	20/209	(G-BLZL)	9. 9.85	T.M.Holloway t/a RAFGSA	RAF Bicester	19. 3.01
G-BMBS	Colt 105A HAFB	704		18. 7.85	H.G.Davies	Cheltenham	27. 8.91A
G-BMBW	Bensen B.8MR MV-001 & PFA G/01-1064 (Rotax 503)			27. 8.85	M.E.Vahdat	Uxbridge	30. 6.93P
G-BMBZ	Scheibe SF-25E Super Falke	4322	D-KEFQ	17. 7.85	Cornish Gliding & Flying Club Ltd	Perranporth	18. 7.00
G-BMCC	Thunder Ax7-77 HAFB	705		12. 7.85	A.K. & C.M.Russell "Charlie Charlie"	Stafford	23. 2.99A
G-BMCD	Cameron V-65 HAFB	1234		26. 6.85	M.C.Drye "My Second Fantasy"	Winkfield	15. 8.00A
G-BMCG	Grob G-109B	6362	(EAF673)	25. 7.85	Lagerholm Finnimport Ltd	Booker	7. 7.01
G-BMCI	Reims Cessna F.172H	0683	OO-WID	19. 8.85	A.B.Davis	Aberdeen	9. 6.01T
G-BMCK	Cameron O-77 HAFB	1180		9. 7.85	D.L.Smith t/a Smith Smart Partnership "Touchy"	Newbury	20.10.92A
G-BMCN	Reims Cessna F.152 II	1471	D-ELDM	7. 8.85	Lincoln Aero Club Ltd	Sturgate	3.12.00T
G-BMCS	PA-22-135 Tri-Pacer	22-1969	5Y-KMH VP-KMH/ZS-DJI	6. 9.85	Richard Lazenby & Co Ltd & T.A.Hodges	Frinsted, Kent	15. 7.01
G-BMCV	Reims Cessna F.152 II	1963		2.10.85	Leicestershire Aero Club Ltd	Leicester	19. 3.01T

Regn	Type	C/n	P/I	Date	Owner/operator	Probable Base	CA Expy
G-BMCW	Aerospatiale AS.332L Super Puma	2161	F-WYMG	4.10.85	Bristow Helicopters Ltd "Monifieth"	(China)	7.11.02T
G-BMCX	Aerospatiale AS.332L Super Puma	2164		7.10.85	Bristow Helicopters Ltd "Lossiemouth"	Aberdeen	14.11.01T
G-BMDB	Replica Plans SE.5A (Continental O-200-A)	PFA/20-10931		12. 8.85	D.Biggs	DRA Boscombe Down	27. 5.00P
	(Damaged Lymington 2.8.92; stored 9.96: as "F235/B" in RFC c/s)						
G-BMDC	PA-32-301 Saratoga	32-8006075	OO-PAC OO-HKK/N8242A	13. 8.85	J.D.M.Tickell t/a MacLaren Aviation	Fairoaks	5.10.00T
G-BMDD	Slingsby T.29 Motor Tutor (VW1834)	PFA/42-11070		8. 8.85	A.R.Worters (Status uncertain)	(Dunoon)	7.10.88P
G-BMDE	Pietenpol Air Camper (Continental O-200-A)	PFA/47-10989		12. 8.85	P.B.Childs	New Farm, Felton	3.10.00P
G-BMDJ	Price Ax7-77S HAFB	TPB.1 & 003		1. 8.85	D.A.Kozuba-Kozubska "Wings of Phoenix"	London WC1	
G-BMDK	PA-34-220T Seneca III	34-8133155	ZS-LOS N84209	16. 9.85	Air Medical Ltd (Damaged landing Cardiff-Wales 8.9.98)	Oxford	24.11.01T
G-BMDO	ARV1 Super 2 (Hewland AE75) (Built Hornet Aviation Ltd)	K.004 & PFA/152-11127		27. 8.85	R.M.Roullier	(Newport, IoW)	12. 6.97P
G-BMDP	Partenavia P.64B Oscar 200	08	HB-EPQ	20. 8.85	B.A.Parker	Old Sarum	25. 5.01
G-BMDS	Jodel Wassmer D.120 Paris-Nice	281	F-BMOS	12. 8.85	J.V.Thompson	Lumb-in-Rossendale	29. 5.91P
G-BMEA	PA-18-95 Super Cub (L-18C-PI)	18-3204	(D-ECZF) OL-L07/L130/53-4804	27. 8.85	C.L.Towell	Ranksborough Farm, Langham	5.10.99P
	(Frame No. reported as 18-3206 (c/n 18-3194 ex OL-L20/L120/53-4794); c/n 18-3204 has Frame No.18-3216)						
G-BMEB	Rotorway Scorpion 145	2896	VR-HJB	10.12.85	L.S.Elliott	Coleraine	
G-BMEE	Cameron O-105 HAFB	1189		4. 9.85	A.G.R.Calder	Los Angeles, USA	8.10.89A
G-BMEG	Socata TB-10 Tobago	530		23.10.85	G.H.N. & R.V.Chamberlain t/a Chamberlain Leasing	Great Yeldham, Essex	17.11.01
G-BMEH	Jodel 150 Special Super Mascaret (Lycoming O-235)	PFA/151-11047		15. 8.85	W.M.Coupar	Muirhouses Farm, Errol	26. 8.00P
	(Rebuild of incomplete SAN Jodel 150 Mascaret c/n 62)						
G-BMET	Taylor JT.1 Monoplane (VW 1600)	PFA/1465		4. 9.85	M.K.A.Blyth	Little Gransden	3. 7.99P
G-BMEU	Isaacs Fury II (Salmson 90hp)	PFA/11-10179		11. 9.85	G.R.G.Smith Hints Farm, Coreley, Ludlow (90% complete 6.99)		
G-BMEV	PA-32RT-300T Turbo Lance II	32R-7887056	OO-CHB G-BMEV/ZS-KFK/N36591	30. 4.86	Arrow Aviation Ltd	Jersey	14.12.01
G-BMEW*	Lockheed 18-56 (C-60A-LO) Lodestar (Gulfstar conversion)	18-2444	OH-SIR OH-MAP/N283M/N105G/N69898/42-55983	30. 9.85	Forsvarsmuseet Flysamlingn (Norwegian AF Museum) Gardermoen, Norway		
	(Cancelled as sold abroad 15.7.86: stored as OH-SIR 5.94)						
G-BMEX	Cessna A150K Aerobat	A150-0169	N8469M	18. 9.85	N.A.M.Brain & C.Butler	Netherthorpe	21. 4.02
G-BMEZ*	Cameron DP-50 Hot-Air Airship	1130		18. 9.85	British Balloon Museum & Library Newbury		4. 5.89A
G-BMFD	PA-23-250 Aztec F	27-7954080	G-BGYY N6834A	6. 9.79	Gold Air International Ltd	Cambridge	4.12.00T
G-BMFG	Dornier Do.27A-1	27-1003-342	FAP 3460 AC+955	23. 9.85	R.F.Warner t/a Sigma Services (On rebuild 2.99)	(Broughton, Norfolk)	AC
G-BMFI	PZL SZD-45A Ogar	B-657		23. 9.85	S.L.Morrey	Andreas, IoM	25. 4.02
G-BMFL	Rand Robinson KR-2	PFA/129-11050		24. 9.85	E.W.B.Comber & M.F.Leusby	(Huntingdon)	
G-BMFN	QAC Quickie Tri-Q 200 (Continental O-200-A)	EMK-017 & PFA/94A1-11062		27. 9.85	A.H.Hartog	Thruxton	21.12.00P
G-BMFP	PA-28-161 Warrior II	28-7916243	N3032L	1.11.85	T.J.Froggatt & C.A.Lennard t/a Bravo Mike Fox Papa Group	Blackbushe	10. 5.01
G-BMFU	Cameron N-90 HAFB	628		1.10.85	J.J.Rudoni	Rugeley, Staffs	24. 6.99T
G-BMFY	Grob G-109B	6401		8.10.85	P.J.Shearer	Kirkwall	11. 6.01
G-BMFZ	Reims Cessna F.152 II	1953		3.12.85	Cornwall Flying Club Ltd	Bodmin	5. 1.01T
G-BMGB	PA-28R-200 Cherokee Arrow II	28R-7335099	N15864	8.11.85	A.L.Ings t/a Malmesbury Specialist Cars	Kemble	14. 6.01
G-BMGC*	Fairey Swordfish II (Built Blackburn Aircraft)	-	G-BMGC RCN W5856/RN W5856	23.10.85	RN Historic Flight (As "W5856/A2A" in 810 Sqn c/s) "City of Leeds"	RNAS Yeovilton	
G-BMGG	Cessna 152 II	152-79592	OO-ADB PH-ADB/D-EHUG/F-GBLM/N757AT	10.10.85	A S Bamrah t/a Falcon Flying Services	Biggin Hill	24.10.00T
G-BMGH	PA-31-325 Turbo Navajo C/R	31-7512045	ZS-LEU N8493/A2-CAT	6.12.85	Not known (Stored 1.00)	Southend	
G-BMGR	Grob G-109B	6396		27.11.85	D.S.Hawes & M.Clarke t/a BMGR Group	Lasham	9. 2.01
G-BMHA	Rutan LongEz	PFA/74A-10973		18.10.85	S.F.Elvins	(Bristol)	
G-BMHC	Cessna U206G Stationair II	U206-03427	N10TB G-BMHC/N8571Q	17.11.76	Fairmont Investments Ltd Duxford/Clacton		22. 8.97T
G-BMHJ	Thunder Ax7-65 Srs.1 HAFB	743		2. 1.86	M.G.Robinson "Kittylog"	Great Milton, Oxon	19. 5.92A
G-BMHL	Wittman W.8 Tailwind (Continental O-200-A)	PFA/31-10503		28.11.85	T.G.Hoult Octon Grange Farm, Foxholes, Driffield		28. 5.00P

Regn	Type	C/n	P/I	Date	Owner/operator	Probable Base	CA Expy
G-BMHS	Reims Cessna F.172M	0964	PH-WAB	7. 4.86	R.A.Hall Rayne Hall Farm, Rayne		21. 7.01
					t/a Tango Xray Flying Group		
G-BMHT	PA-28RT-201T Turbo Arrow IV		ZS-LCJ	18.11.85	Scalpay Ltd	Birmingham	22. 4.01
		28R-8231010	N8462Y		t/a Cartel Communications		
G-BMHZ	PA-28RT-201T Turbo Arrow IV		ZS-KII	18.11.85	B.L.Tuwie	Elstree	25. 4.00
		28R-8031001	N8096D		t/a The Arrow Association		
G-BMID	Jodel Wassmer D.120 Paris-Nice	259	F-BMID	18. 8.81	P.E.S.Latham	(Ellesmere)	27. 4.00P
					t/a G-BMID F/Group		
G-BMIG	Cessna 172N Skyhawk II	172-72376	ZS-KGI	13. 5.86	J.R.Nicholls	Sibson	15. 6.01T
			(N48630)				
G-BMIH	BAe HS.125 Srs.700B	257115	G-5-502	22. 1.86	Surewings Ltd	Luton	17. 8.00T
			5N-AMX/G-BMIH/HZ-DA3				
G-BMIM	Rutan LongEz	160	OY-CMT	12.12.85	R.M.Smith	Biggin Hill	17. 7.00P
	(Lycoming O-235)		OY-8102				
G-BMIO	Stoddard-Hamilton Glasair IIRG			25.11.85	J.W.E.de Frayssinet & J.M.Ayres	Shobdon	
		PFA/149-11016			(Nearing completion 8.99)		
G-BMIP	Wassmer Jodel D.112	1264	F-BMIP	7.12.78	M.T.Kinch Manor Farm, Inglesham		17. 9.00P
					t/a The Inglesham Flying Group		
G-BMIR*	Westland Wasp HAS.1	F.9670	XT788	24. 1.86	Park Aviation Supply (Stored as "XT788" 3.93)		
					Little Glovers Farm, Charlwood, Surrey		
G-BMIS	Monnett Sonerai II 755 & PFA/15A-10813		VR-HIS	26. 2.87	B.A.Bower	(Andover)	26.10.89P
	(Revmaster R2100DQ)				(Status uncertain)		
G-BMIV	PA-28R-201T Turbo Arrow III		ZS-JZW	7. 1.86	Maurice Mason Ltd	Swaffham	21. 4.01
		28R-7703154	N5816V				
G-BMIW	PA-28-181 Archer II	28-8190093	ZS-KTJ	6.12.85	Oldbus Ltd	Shoreham	1. 5.01T
			N8301J				
G-BMIY	Oldfield Baby Lakes PFA/10-10194		G-NOME	3.12.85	J.B.Scott	Blackpool	27. 8.87P
	(Continental O-200-A)				(Stored 6.96)		
G-BMJA	PA-32R-301 Saratoga SP	32R-8113019	ZS-KTH	23.12.85	General Airline Ltd	Blackbushe	22. 7.02
			N8309E		t/a European Flyers		
G-BMJB	Cessna 152 II	152-80030	N757VD	3. 2.86	Bobbington Air Training School Ltd		
						Halfpenny Green	21. 3.01T
G-BMJC	Cessna 152 II	152-84989	N623AP	3. 2.86	The Cambridge Aero Club Ltd	Cambridge	23. 6.01T
G-BMJD	Cessna 152 II	152-79755	N757HP	21.11.85	Donair Flying Club Ltd	Tatenhill	2. 6.01T
G-BMJG*	PA-28R-200 Cherokee Arrow	28R-35046	ZS-TNS	23.12.85	Western Air (Thruxton) Ltd	Thruxton	4. 2.99T
			ZS-FYC/N9345N				
	(Damaged Thruxton 11.10.98: cancelled by CAA 15.4.99: noted Blackpool 9.99)						
G-BMJL	Rockwell Commander 114	14006	A2-JRI	8. 1.86	Wardair Ltd.	Goodwood	12. 6.00T
			ZS-JRI/N1906J				
G-BMJM	Evans VP-1 PFA/62-10763				21.11.85	M.J.Veary	Sywell	20. 6.00P
	(VW1834)						
G-BMJN	Cameron O-65 HAFB	1212		6.12.85	P.M.Traviss "F'red"	Yarm	15. 5.00A
G-BMJO	PA-34-220T Seneca III	34-8533036	N6919K	5.12.85	Oxford Aviation Services Ltd	Oxford	14. 4.01
			N9565N				
G-BMJR	Cessna T337H Turbo Super Skymaster II		G-NOVA	10. 7.84	Eastcote Services Ltd	Sturgate	12. 7.02
		337-01895	N1259S				
G-BMJS	Thunder Ax7-77 HAFB	754		3.12.85	S.E.Burton	Northampton	7. 4.96A
G-BMJT	Beechcraft 76 Duchess	ME-376	ZS-KMI	4.12.85	Mike Osborne Properties Ltd	Ronaldsway	30. 3.01
			N3718W				
G-BMJW*	North American AT-6D-NT Harvard III	EZ259	28.11.85	B.Fenton		Wakefield	
		88-15963	SAAF7631/EZ259/42-84182				
	(Composite with rear fuselage of KF487; fuselage on rebuild 2.96)						
G-BMJX	Wallis WA-116/X Srs.1	K/219/X		31.12.85	K.H.Wallis	Reymerston Hall	1. 4.89P
	(Limbach L-2000)				(Stored 5.99)		
G-BMJY	SPP Yakovlev C.18A	NK	(France)	21. 1.86	R.J.Lamplough	North Weald	19. 1.99P
			Egypt AF 627		(As "07" in Russian AF c/s)		
G-BMJZ	Cameron N-90 HAFB	1219		16.12.85	P.Spellward "Uvistat"	Bristol	31. 3.94A
					t/a Bristol University Hot-Air Ballooning Society		
G-BMKB	PA-18-135 Super Cub	18-3817	OO-DKB	11.12.85	Cubair Flight Training Ltd	Redhill	7. 1.00T
	(L-21B-PI) (Frame No.18-3818)		PH-DKB/(PH-GROUP)/R Neth AF R-127/54-2417				
G-BMKC	Piper J3C-90 Cub (L-4H-PI)	11145	F-BFBA	2. 1.86	R.J.H.Springall	St.Just	22.11.00P
	(Frame No.10970)		43-29854		(As "329854/R/44" in USAAC 533rd BS/381st Bomb Group c/s)		
					"Little Rockette Jnr."		
G-BMKD	Beechcraft C90A King Air	LJ-1069	N223CG	30.12.85	A.E.Bristow	Godalming/Fairoaks	25. 3.00
			N67516				
G-BMKF	CEA Jodel DR.221 Dauphin	96	F-BPCS	3. 2.86	L., S.T.Gilbert & L.M.Radcliffe	Enstone	9. 6.00
G-BMKG	PA-38-112 Tomahawk II	38-82A0050	ZS-LGC	3. 2.86	APB Leasing Ltd	Welshpool	24. 8.01T
			N91544				
G-BMKI	Colt 21A Cloudhopper HAFB	753		30.12.85	A.C.Booth	Bristol	23. 6.00A
G-BMKJ	Cameron V-77 HAFB	1235		2. 1.86	R.C.Thursby	Barry	2. 5.00A

Regn	Type	C/n	P/I	Date	Owner/operator	Probable Base	CA Expy
G-BMKK	PA-28R-200 Cherokee Arrow II	28R-7535265	ZS-JNY N9537N	16. 1.86	Dawcroft Ltd t/a Colony Aviation	Blackpool	5. 1.01T
G-BMKP	Cameron V-77 HAFB	724	(G-BMFX)	10. 1.86	R.Bayly "And Baby Makes 10"	Bristol	7. 8.93A
G-BMKR	PA-28-161 Warrior II	28-7916220	G-BGKR N9561N	14. 6.84	D.R.Shrosbee t/a Field Flying Group	Goodwood	19. 6.00
G-BMKV	Thunder Ax7-77 HAFB	772		21. 1.86	A.Hornak & M.J.Nadal	London N1	8.12.93A
G-BMKW	Cameron V-77 HAFB	608		29. 1.86	A.C.Garnett "Aorangi"	Guildford	21. 9.00A
G-BMKX*	Cameron Elephant 77SS HAFB	1196		6. 2.86	A D Kent "Benjamin I" (Balloon Preservation Group 7.98)	Lancing	19. 2.89A
G-BMKY	Cameron O-65 HAFB	1246		4. 3.86	Ann R.Rich "Orion"	Hyde	8. 4.00A
G-BMLB	Jodel Wassmer D.120A Paris-Nice	295	F-BNCI	20. 1.86	W.O.Brown	Seighford	26. 8.00P
G-BMLJ	Cameron N-77 HAFB	1263		7. 3.86	C.J.Dunkley t/a Wendover Trailers "Mr Funshine"	Aylesbury	19. 3.96A
G-BMLK	Grob G-109B	6424		24. 2.86	J.J.Mawson t/a Brams Syndicate	Rufforth	15. 5.01
G-BMLL	Grob G-109B	6420		13. 3.86	P.C.Broome	Longbridge Deverill	24. 7.01
G-BMLM	Beechcraft 95-58 Baron	TH-405	N111LM G-BMLM/F-GEPV/3D-ADF/ZS-LOZ/G-BMLM/G-BBJF	2. 7.79	N.J.Webb	Cranfield	12.10.02P
G-BMLS	PA-28R-201 Cherokee Arrow III	28R-7737167	N47496	11. 2.86	R.M.Shorter	Booker	24. 4.02T
G-BMLT	Pietenpol Air Camper (Continental C90)	PFA/47-10949		28. 1.86	W.E.R.Jenkins Waits Farm, Belchamp Walter		26.10.00P
G-BMLU	Colt 90A HAFB	786		10. 4.86	L.J.Goldsmith "Firebird"	Biggin Hill	6. 3.97A
G-BMLW	Cameron O-77 HAFB	813		6. 2.86	M.L. & L.P.Willoughby "Stelrad"	Reading	7. 8.95A
G-BMLX	Reims Cessna F.150L	0700	PH-VOV	21. 3.86	C.J.Freeman (Op Weald Air Services)	Headcorn	14. 8.01T
G-BMLZ	Cessna 421C Golden Eagle II	421C-0223	G-OTAD G-BEVL/N5476G	17.12.85	Hadagain Investments Ltd (To Canada by Container 7.97)		14. 2.89T
G-BMMC	Cessna 310Q	310Q-0041	YU-BGY N7541Q	11. 2.86	Cooper Clegg Ltd	Gloucestershire	30. 3.02
G-BMMD	Rand Robinson KR-2 (VW1834 ACRO)	PFA/129-10817		7. 2.86	D.J.Howell	Halfpenny Green	14. 6.00P
G-BMMF	Clutton FRED Srs.II (VW1834)	PFA/29-10296		20. 2.86	J.M.Jones East Pennard, Shepton Mallet "Thankyou Girl"		6. 4.99P
G-BMMI	Pazmany PL-4A (Continental PC 60)	PFA/17-10149		6. 2.86	M.K.Field	Sleap	2. 9.97P
G-BMMJ	Siren PIK-30	720		13. 6.86	J.R.Greig	Feshiebridge	25. 6.01
G-BMMK	Cessna 182P Skylane II (Reims-assembled c/n 0038)	182-64117	OO-AVU N6129F	24. 3.86	G.G.Weston	(London W2)	1. 7.01T
G-BMML	PA-38-112 Tomahawk	38-80A0079	PH-TMG OO-HKD	2. 4.86	Western Air (Thruxton) Ltd	Thruxton	19. 5.01T
G-BMMM	Cessna 152 II	152-84793	N4652P	10. 9.86	A.S.Bamrah t/a Falcon Flying Services	Biggin Hill	20.10.01T
G-BMMP	Grob G-109B	6432		27. 6.86	E.W.Reynolds	Tatenhill	24. 5.02
G-BMMR	Dornier 228-202K	8063	(D-IAOT) D-CAOS	1. 4.86	Suckling Airways (Cambridge) Ltd t/a Scot Airways	Cambridge	23. 4.00T
G-BMMU	Thunder Ax7-77 HAFB	719		4. 3.86	Nicola Metcalfe "Pansy"	Didcot	11. 8.97A
G-BMMV	ICA IS-28M2A	57		10. 3.86	F.R.Temple-Brown	Henstridge	5.11.98
G-BMMW	Thunder Ax7-77 HAFB	782		10. 3.86	P.A.George "Ethos" Princes Risborough (Sports Council titles)		3. 6.96A
G-BMMY	Thunder Ax7-77 HAFB	716		11. 3.86	S.M.Wade & Sheila E.Hadley "Winco"	Salisbury	17. 7.00A
G-BMNL	PA-28R-200 Cherokee Arrow II	28R-7535040	N18MW N32280	17. 9.86	Elston Ltd t/a Arrow Flying Group	Elstree	30. 5.02
G-BMNP*	PA-38-112 Tomahawk II	38-81A0133	N23352	24. 3.86	APB Leasing Ltd (Dismantled/stored 8.99: cancelled as destroyed 19.10.99)	Welshpool	27. 6.98T
G-BMNT	PA-34-220T Seneca III	34-8133029	N8348T	19. 3.86	Channel Airways Ltd	Guernsey	1.10.01
G-BMNV	SNCAN Stampe SV-4C (Lycoming IO-360)	108	F-BBNI	14. 3.86	Wessex Aviation & Transport Ltd	Chalmington	8. 6.94P
G-BMNX	Colt 56A HAFB	790		14. 4.86	C.N.Marshall "Rosie"	Tonbridge	28. 7.00A
G-BMOE	PA-28R-200 Cherokee Arrow II	28R-7635226	PH-PCB OO-HAS/N9221K	20. 5.86	E.P.C.Rabson	Southampton	22.11.02T
G-BMOF	Cessna U206G Stationair II	U206-03658	N7427N	17. 4.86	D.M.Penny Movenis, Co.Londonderry t/a Wild Geese Skydiving Centre		11. 2.00
G-BMOG	Thunder Ax7-77 HAFB	793		2. 4.86	R.M.Boswell	Bawburgh, Norwich	28. 8.95A
G-BMOH	Cameron N-77 HAFB	1270		2. 4.86	P.J.Marshall & M.A.Clarke "Ellen Gee"	Ruislip	20. 8.91A
G-BMOI	Partenavia P.68B	103	I-EEVA	4. 4.86	Simmette Ltd	Exeter	20. 7.01
G-BMOJ	Cameron V-56 HAFB	1275		4. 4.86	S.R.Bridge	Grantham	27. 7.89A
G-BMOK	ARV1 Super 2	011		14. 4.86	J.C.F.Dalton	Bourn	17. 8.00

Regn	Type	C/n	P/I	Date	Owner/operator	Probable Base	CA Expy
G-BMOL*	PA-23-250 Aztec D	27-4394	G-BBSR N6610Y	26. 6.84	Not known (On fire dump 2.96)	Bournemouth	26. 7.87T
G-BMOM	ICA IS-28M2A	50		30. 6.86	M.K.Gill t/a Brasov Flying Group (Stored 8.96)	Rufforth	12. 7.96
G-BMOO*	Clutton FRED Srs.II (Continental A65)	PFA/29-10770		11. 4.86	N.Purllant (RAF c/s) (Last known on overhaul: cancelled by CAA 22.2.99)	(Leicester)	8. 8.91P
G-BMOP	PA-28R-201T Turbo Arrow III	28R-7703194	N38257	18. 4.86	P.Murer	Fairoaks	20. 4.98
G-BMOT	Bensen B.8M (VW 1834)	PFA G/01-1066		17. 4.86	Performance Associates Ltd	Swansea	19. 7.00P
G-BMOV	Cameron O-105 HAFB	1307		11. 4.86	Cheryl Gillott "Up & Down"	Stroud	1. 7.99A
G-BMOX*	Hovey Beta Bird	PFA/135-1097		15. 4.86	A.K.Jones (Cancelled by CAA 19.4.99)	(Stockport)	
G-BMPC	PA-28-181 Archer II	28-7790436	LN-NAT	23. 4.86	C.J. & R.J.Barnes	East Midlands	6. 2.02T
G-BMPD	Cameron V-65 HAFB	1200		4. 6.86	D.E. & J.M.Hartland "Second Dawn"	Matlock	24. 7.00A
G-BMPF*	Optica OA.7 Optica	010		14. 4.86	FLS Aerospace (Light Aircraft) Ltd (Stored 11.95)	Bournemouth	14. 1.93T
G-BMPL	Optica OA.7 Optica	016		14. 4.86	Sunhawk Ltd.	Jersey	2. 8.97T
G-BMPP	Cameron N-77 HAFB	1303		15. 4.86	I.B. & R.J.Lumsden "Tuppence"	Rickmansworth	14. 5.93A
G-BMPR	PA-28R-201 Arrow III	28R-7837175	ZS-LMF N417GH	22. 4.86	AH Flight Services Ltd Moor Farm, Humbleton, Hull		10. 5.02
G-BMPS	Strojnik S-2A	045		18. 4.86	G.J.Green	(Matlock)	
G-BMPY	DH.82A Tiger Moth	"82619"	ZS-CNR SAAF??	25. 4.86	S.M.F.Eisenstein Sandford Hall, Knocklin		16.11.01
G-BMRA	Boeing 757-236	23710		2. 3.87	British Airways plc (Paithani t/s)	Heathrow	3. 3.00T
G-BMRB	Boeing 757-236	23975		25. 9.87	British Airways plc (Union Flag t/s)	Heathrow	29. 9.00T
G-BMRC	Boeing 757-236	24072	(N) G-BMRC	2.12.87	British Airways plc (British Olympic Association t/s)	Heathrow	26. 1.01T
G-BMRD	Boeing 757-236	24073	(N) G-BMRD	2.12.87	British Airways plc (Chelsea Rose t/s)	Heathrow	3. 3.01T
G-BMRE	Boeing 757-236	24074	(N) G-BMRE	2.12.87	British Airways plc (Rendezvous t/s)	Heathrow	28. 3.01T
G-BMRF	Boeing 757-236	24101		13. 5.88	British Airways plc (Water Dreaming t/s)	Heathrow	17. 5.01T
G-BMRG	Boeing 757-236	24102		31. 5.88	British Airways plc (Rendezvous t/s)	Heathrow	2. 6.01T
G-BMRH	Boeing 757-236	24266		21. 2.89	British Airways plc (Nalanji Dreaming t/s)	Heathrow	28. 2.02T
G-BMRI	Boeing 757-236	24267		17. 2.89	British Airways plc (Blomsterang/Flower Field t/s)	Heathrow	23. 2.02T
G-BMRJ	Boeing 757-236	24268		6. 3.89	British Airways plc (Grand Union t/s)	Heathrow	13. 3.02T
G-BMSA	Stinson HW-75 Model 105 (Continental O-200-A)	7040	G-BCUM F-BGQO/NC21189	26. 3.86	M.A.Thomas t/a The Stinson Group "Iron Eagle"	Barton	8. 4.020
G-BMSB	VS.509 Spitfire XI (Regd as c/n 6S/R/749433)	CBAF.7722	G-ASOZ IAC158/G-15-171/MJ627	3. 5.78	M.S.Bayliss (As "MJ627/9G-P" in 441 Sqn c/s) (Damaged Coventry 25.4.98)	Coventry	12. 3.99P
G-BMSC	Evans VP-2 (VW1834)	V2-482MSC & PFA/63-10785		25. 8.82	J.Holme	Henstridge	8.10.99P
G-BMSD	PA-28-181 Cherokee Archer II	28-7690070	EC-CVH N9646N	2. 7.86	General Airline Ltd t/a European Flyers	Blackbushe	6. 9.01T
G-BMSE	Valentin Taifun 17E	1082	D-KHVA(17)	20. 5.86	A.J.Nurse	Gloucestershire	19. 7.02
G-BMSF	PA-38-112 Tomahawk	38-78A0524	N4277E	9. 2.79	B.Catlow	Crosland Moor	30. 6.99
G-BMSG	SAAB 32A Lansen	32028	Fv.32028	22. 7.86	J.E.Wilkie (Open storage 7.99 with no Permit or C of A issued)	Cranfield	AC
G-BMSL	Clutton FRED Srs.III (VW1834)	PFA/29-11142		19. 5.86	A.C.Coombe	Long Marston	29. 6.00P
G-BMST*	Cameron N-31 HAFB	1317		4. 6.86	I M Martin "B&Q" (Balloon Preservation Group 7.98 for restoration)	Lancing	NE(A)
G-BMSU	Cessna 152 II	152-79421	N714TN	29. 8.86	S.Waite t/a G-BMSU Group	Leeds-Bradford	27.10.02T
G-BMTA	Cessna 152 II	152-82864	N89776	27. 8.86	Alarmond Ltd t/a Edinburgh Flying Club	Edinburgh	22. 2.02T
G-BMTB	Cessna 152 II	152-80672	N25457	19. 8.86	Sky Leisure Aviation (Charters) Ltd (In damaged state 9.99)	Redhill	5.11.98T
G-BMTJ	Cessna 152 II	152-85010	N6389P	19. 6.86	The Pilot Centre Ltd	Denham	14. 6.01T
G-BMTL	Reims Cessna F.152 II	1977		11. 9.86	Bournemouth Flying Club Ltd	Bournemouth	12. 5.02T
G-BMTN	Cameron O-77 HAFB	1305		4. 6.86	Industrial Services (MH) Ltd t/a Flete Rental "Fletie"	Bristol	1. 6.97A

Regn	Type	C/n	P/I	Date	Owner/operator	Probable Base	CA Expy
G-BMTO	PA-38-112 Tomahawk II	38-81A0051	N25679	28.11.86	A.S.Bamrah Biggin Hill		10. 8.02T
					t/a Falcon Flying Services		
G-BMTP*	PA-38-112 Tomahawk	38-79A0034	N2392B	14. 8.86	Not known	Jersey	26. 4.93T
					(Damaged Alderney 1.9.92; status unknown)		
G-BMTR	PA-28-161 Warrior II	28-8116119	N83179	19. 6.86	Aeroshow Ltd	Gloucestershire	23. 9.01T
G-BMTS	Cessna 172N Skyhawk II	172-70606	N739KP	17. 7.86	A.S.Bamrah	Blackbushe	27. 7.01T
					t/a Falcon Flying Services (Op European Flyers)		
G-BMTU	Pitts S-1E Special	PFA/09-10801		4. 6.86	D.E.Hickson	Kemble	9. 9.99P
	(Lycoming 0-360)						
G-BMTX	Cameron V-77 HAFB	733		19. 6.86	J.A.Langley "Boondoggle"	Stroud	14.11.99A
					(Buses For Bristol titles)		
G-BMUD	Cessna 182P Skylane	182-61786	OY-DVS	6.11.81	Mescal E.Taylor	Netherthorpe	31. 7.00T
			N78847				
G-BMUG	Rutan LongEz	PFA/74A-10987		17. 6.86	P.Richardson & J.Shanley		
	(Lycoming 0-235)					Croft Farm,. Teesside	24. 6.00P
G-BMUJ	Colt Drachenfisch SS HAFB +	835		3. 6.86	Virgin Airship & Balloon Co Ltd Telford		27. 7.91A
					"Drachenfisch"		
G-BMUK	Colt UFO SS HAFB +	836		3. 6.86	Virgin Airship & Balloon Co Ltd Telford		26. 4.95A
					"UFO/Dream Station"		
G-BMUL	Colt Kindermond SS HAFB +	837		3. 6.86	Virgin Airship & Balloon Co Ltd Telford		26. 9.91A
	(+ Three futuristic special shapes designed by Andre Heller) "Kindermond/Childrens' Moon"						
G-BMUN	Cameron Harley 78SS HAFB	1188		10. 6.86	Forbes Europe Inc Balleroy, Normandy		23. 5.99A
	(Harley Davidson Motorcycle shape)				"Harley Davidson"		
G-BMUO	Cessna A152 Aerobat	A152-0788	4X-ALJ	4. 6.86	Sky Leisure Aviation (Charters) Ltd		
			N7328L			Shoreham	13. 8.01T
G-BMUT	PA-34-200T Seneca II	34-7570320	EC-CUH	23. 1.87	Newcastle Aeroplane Co Ltd	Newcastle	4. 7.02T
			N3935X				
G-BMUU	Thunder Ax7-77 HAFB	827		1. 8.86	G.Anorewartha "Fiesta"	Kings Lynn	29.10.98A
G-BMUZ	PA-28-161 Warrior II	28-8016329	EC-DMA	24. 7.86	Newcastle-upon-Tyne Aero Club Ltd		
			N9559N			Newcastle	14. 2.02T
G-BMVA	Scheibe SF-25B Falke	46223	RAFGGA.512	28. 7.86	M.L.Jackson	Headcorn	18. 1.02
			D-KAEN				
G-BMVB	Reims Cessna F.152 II	1974		10. 9.86	LAC (Enterprises) Ltd	Barton	10. 2.00T
					t/a Lancashire Aero Club		
G-BMVG	QAC Quickie Q-1	PFA/94-10749		11. 6.86	P.M.Wright	Coventry	22. 4.98P
	(Rotax 503)						
G-BMVI	Cameron O-105 HAFB	1326		19. 6.86	M.L.Gabb "Securicor"	Alcester	7. 7.95A
					t/a Heart of England Balloons		
G-BMVJ	Cessna 172N Skyhawk II	172-72232	N9347E	27. 6.86	Green Aviation Associates Ltd		
						Leeds-Bradford	25. 2.02T
G-BMVL	PA-38-112 Tomahawk	38-79A0033	N2391B	5. 9.86	Airways Aero Associations Ltd Booker		17.12.01T
					(Op British Airways Flying Club) (Blue Poole t/s)		
G-BMVM	PA-38-112 Tomahawk	38-79A0025	N2359B	5. 9.86	Airways Aero Associations Ltd Booker		19. 2.01T
					(Op British Airways Flying Club) (Waves of the City t/s)		
G-BMVO	Cameron N-77 HAFB	1309		23. 6.86	Warners Motors (Leasing) Ltd Gloucester		3. 5.97A
					"Warners"		
G-BMVS*	Cameron Benihana 70SS HAFB	1252		27.10.86	Shellrise Ltd "Rocky"	Miami, USA	NE(A)
	(Also described as Chef's Hat)						
G-BMVT	Thunder Ax7-77A HAFB	102	SE-ZYY	15. 7.86	M.L. & L.P.Willoughby	Reading	
					"Trygg Hansa"		
G-BMVU	Monnett Moni	PFA/142-10948		14. 8.86	J.Holme	Old Sarum	20. 9.99P
	(KEF-107)						
G-BMVW	Cameron O-65 HAFB	1331		27. 6.86	S.P.Richards "Olau Ferries"	Cranbrook	15. 8.91A
G-BMWA	Hughes 269C	14-0271	N8998F	1. 7.86	P.J.Brown	Redhill	16.11.02T
G-BMWE	ARV1 Super 2	012		1. 7.86	R.J.N.Noble	Goodwood	16. 1.00
G-BMWF	ARV1 Super 2	013		1. 7.86	N.R.Beale Deppers Bridge, Leamington Spa		2. 4.90T
	(Rotax 914 Turbo)				(Under construction 7.96)		
G-BMWM	ARV1 Super 2	020		30. 3.87	P.G.Hayward	Little Snoring	22. 4.00P
G-BMWN	Cameron Temple 80SS HAFB	1211		9. 7.86	Forbes Europe Inc Balleroy, Normandy		17. 6.96A
					"Temple"		
G-BMWR	Rockwell Commander 112A	365	N1365J	23. 9.86	M. & J.Edwards	Blackbushe	6. 5.02
G-BMWU	Cameron N-42 HAFB	1346		22.12.88	R S Kent "Baby Helix"	Lancing	
					(Balloon Preservation Group 7.98)		
G-BMWV	Putzer Elster B	024	D-EEKB	5. 8.86	E.A.J.Hibbard Hill Farm, Nayland		
			97+14/D-EBGI				
G-BMXA	Cessna 152 II	152-80125	N757ZC	14. 7.86	E.Alexander Kings Farm, Thurrock		28. 9.02T
G-BMXB	Cessna 152 II	152-80996	N48840	14. 7.86	H.Daines Electronics Ltd.	(Beccles)	21. 3.93T
G-BMXC	Cessna 152 II	152-80416	N24858	14. 7.86	General Airline Ltd	Blackbushe	7. 1.02T
					t/a European Flyers		
G-BMXD	Fokker F-27 Friendship 500	10417	TF-FLR	6.10.86	BAC Express Airlines Ltd	Gatwick	12.12.01T
			HL-5210/HL-5206/PH-FOR		"Scottish Trader"		

Regn	Type	C/n	P/I	Date	Owner/operator	Probable Base	CA Expy
G-BMXJ	Reims Cessna F.150L	0853	F-BUBA	18. 7.86	R.Harman	Tatenhill	25. 3.00
					t/a Arrow Aircraft Group		
G-BMXL	PA-38-112 Tomahawk	38-80A0018	N25060	4. 9.86	Airways Aero Associations Ltd	Booker	17. 6.02T
					(Op British Airways Flying Club) (Mountain of the Birds/Benyhone Tartan t/s)		
G-BMXX	Cessna 152 II	152-84953	N5469P	10. 9.86	Aerohire Ltd	Halfpenny Green	1. 9.02T
G-BMYA*	Colt 56A HAFB	864		13. 8.86	British Balloon Museum & Library	Newbury	2.12.92A
					"British Gas"		
G-BMYC	Socata TB-10 Tobago	696		1. 9.86	Elizabeth A. Grady	Old Buckenham	29. 4.02T
G-BMYD	Beechcraft A36 Bonanza	E-2350		28.11.86	Seabeam Partners Ltd		
						Wellesbourne Mountford	21. 3.99
G-BMYF	Bensen B.8M	PE-01		18. 8.86	G.Callaghan	Richhill, Armagh	
G-BMYG	Reims Cessna FA152 Aerobat	0365	OO-JCA	23.10.86	Edinburgh Air Centre Ltd	Edinburgh	13. 6.02T
			(OO-JCC)/PH-AXG				
G-BMYI	Grumman-American AA-5 Traveler			1. 9.86	W.C. & S.C.Westran	Shoreham	24. 5.02T
		AA5-0568	F-BVRM/N9568L				
G-BMYJ	Cameron V-65 HAFB	726		8. 9.86	A.Lutz "Skylark II"	Westbury	8. 7.00A
G-BMYN	Colt 77A HAFB	873		2. 9.86	F.R.Batersby & J.Jones	Manchester	3. 7.00A
					t/a Spectacles Balloon Group "Spectacles"		
G-BMYP	Fairey Gannet AEW.3	F.9461	8610M	16. 9.86	D.Copley	Sandtoft	29.9.89P*
			XL502		(As "XL502" in 849 Sqdn/"B" Flt RN c/s: wreck noted 9.99)		
G-BMYS	Thunder Ax7-77Z HAFB	887		3.11.86	J.E.Weidema Baambrugge, The Netherlands		2. 7.00A
					t/a Pinkel Balloons		
G-BMYU	Jodel Wassmer D.120 Paris-Nice	289	F-BMYU	23. 6.78	N.P.Chitty	(Didcot)	26. 4.00P
G-BMZA	Air Command 503 Modac	0589		11. 2.87	R.W.Husband	Sheffield	2. 6.00P
	(Rotax 503) (Probably c/n 0389)						
G-BMZB	Cameron N-77 HAFB	1370		30.10.86	D.C.Eager "Dreamland"	Bracknell	30. 4.95A
G-BMZE	Socata TB-9 Tampico	708		5.12.86	R.F.Keene	Turweston	3. 8.02T
G-BMZF*	WSK-Mielec LIM-2 (MiG-15bis)			18.12.86	Fleet Air Arm Museum	RNAS Yeovilton	
		1B-01420	Polish AF 1420		(As "01420" in North Korean c/s)		
G-BMZG	QAC Quickie Q2	PFA/94A-10919		1.10.86	R.Dann	Haverfordwest	20. 9.00P
	(Revmaster 2100D)						
G-BMZN	Everett Gyroplane 1	008		13.11.86	K.Ashford	Walsall	26. 9.00P
	(VW 1835)						
G-BMZP	Everett Gyroplane 1	010		14.11.86	M.N.Morris-Jones	Longbridge Deverill	18. 8.00P
	(VW 1835)						
G-BMZS	Everett Gyroplane 1	012		13.11.86	L.W.Cload	St.Merryn	7.11.00P
	(VW 1835)						
G-BMZW	Bensen B.8MR	PFA G/01-1021		16.10.86	P.D.Widdicombe	Huntingdon, York	25. 8.99P
	(Rotax 532)						
G-BMZX	Wolf W-11 Boredom Fighter			31.10.86	A.R.Meakin & S.W.Watkins		
	(Continental A65)	PFA/146-11042			Trecorras Farm, Llangarron	26. 5.95P
	(Represents Spad rep)				(As "146-11042/7" in AEF France 94th Aero Sqdn c/s)		
G-BMZZ	Stephens Akro Z	V.57	(HB-)	10.11.86	Flywatch (UK) Ltd	(Southend)	6. 6.00P
	(Lycoming AE10-360)		G-BMZZ/VH-AUZ				

G-BNAA – G-BNZZ

Regn	Type	C/n	P/I	Date	Owner/operator	Probable Base	CA Expy
G-BNAD	Rand Robinson KR-2	PFA/129-11077		10.11.86	P.J.Brookman	(Loughborough)	27. 2.90P
	(VW1834)				(Stored Ottringham, Hull 7.90)		
G-BNAG	Colt 105A HAFB	906		31.10.86	R.W.Batchelor	Thame	19.12.89A
G-BNAH*	Colt Paper Bag SS HAFB	865		12.11.86	Not known	(USA)	14..6.86
					(Cancelled by CAA 4..8.98: flying USA 10.98)		
G-BNAI	Wolf W-11 Boredom Fighter			31.10.86	P.J.D.Gronow	Haverfordwest	12.11.00P
	(Continental A65)	PFA/146-11083			(As "146-11083/5" in AEF France 94th Aero Sqdn c/s)		
	(Represents Spad rep)						
G-BNAJ	Cessna 152 II	152-82527	C-GZWF	3.11.86	Galair Ltd	Biggin Hill	17. 4.02T
			(N69173)		(Op Surrey & Kent Flying Club)		
G-BNAN	Cameron V-65 HAFB	1333		28.10.86	Anne M.Lindsay & N.H.Ponsford	Leeds	9. 7.00A
					t/a Rango Balloon & Kite Co "Actually"		
G-BNAO	Colt AS-105 Hot Air Airship	897		28.10.86	Heather Flight Ltd	(London SE16)	20.10.90A
G-BNAR	Taylor JT.1 Monoplane	PFA/55-10569		14.11.86	C.J.Smith	(Blackfield, Southampton)	28.12.90P
	(VW1600)				(Status uncertain)		
G-BNAU	Cameron V-65 HAFB	1395		13.11.86	Cherry L.E.Lewis	Colwyn Bay	19. 2.99A
G-BNAW	Cameron V-65 HAFB	1366		24.10.86	A. & P.A.Walker	Richmond, Surrey	25. 6.95A
					"Hippo-Thermia" (HMS Recruitment titles)		
G-BNBL	Thunder Ax7-77 HAFB	910		7. 1.87	E.Stivala	Marston Moreteyne, Bedford	21.12.99A
G-BNBP*	Colt Snowflake SS HAFB	913		21.11.86	D.Partridge/Air 2 Air Balloons Ltd		
					(Stored 8.95)	Bristol	
G-BNBR	Cameron N-90 HAFB	1412		2.12.86	Airborne Promotions Ltd "Honda"	Bath	3. 6.94T
G-BNBU	Bensen B.8MV	PFA G/01-1070		1.12.86	B.A.Lyford	Saltash	

Regn	Type	C/n	P/I	Date	Owner/operator	Probable Base	CA Expy
G-BNBV	Thunder Ax7-77 HAFB	915		2.12.86	Jennifer M.Robinson "Layla"		
						Milton-under-Wychwood	4. 9.00A
G-BNBW	Thunder Ax7-77 HAFB	914		11.12.86	I.S. & S.W.Watthews	Grange-over-Sands	9. 9.99A
					"Mutley"		
G-BNBY	Beechcraft 95-B55A Baron	TC-1347	G-AXXR	14. 2.83	Earthline Aviation Ltd		
						Draycott Farm, Chiseldon	22.10.01
G-BNBZ	LET L-200D Morava	171329	D-GGDC	16.12.86	C.A.Suckling	Rushett Farm, Chessington	15. 5.00
			EI-AOY/(D-GLIN)/EI-AOY/OK-SHB				
G-BNCB	Cameron V-77 HAFB	1401		2.12.86	G.J.Preen	Bristol	12. 5.93A
					t/a Tyred & Battered Balloon Group "Cabot Tyres"		
G-BNCC	Thunder Ax7-77 HAFB	924		11.12.86	Celia J.Burnhope "Charlie"	Leeds	9.10.99A
G-BNCE*	Grumman G.159 Gulfstream I	009	N436M	7. 4.87	Not known	Aberdeen	9. 4.92T
			N436/N436M/N43M/N709G		(For Fire Services use 6.98)		
G-BNCH	Cameron V-77 HAFB	1398		11.12.86	N.F.Mulliner	Chatham	19. 6.92A
					t/a Royal Engineers Balloon Club "Sapper II"		
G-BNCJ	Cameron V-77 HAFB	815		16.12.86	I.S.Bridge	Shrewsbury	8. 5.99A
					"Sunshine Desserts"		
G-BNCK	Cameron V-77 HAFB	1420		7. 1.87	G.Randall	Bielefeld, Germany	9.11.91A
G-BNCM	Cameron N-77 HAFB	1388		16.12.86	C.A. Stone	Bristol	3. 3.96A
G-BNCN	Glaser-Dirks DG-400	4-198		22. 1.87	M.C.Costin "421"	Husbands Bosworth	31. 3.02
G-BNCO	PA-38-112 Tomahawk	38-79A0472	N2482F	8. 1.87	Diane K.Walker	(Oakham, Leics)	12. 6.97T
G-BNCR	PA-28-161 Warrior II	28-8016111	G-PDMT	10.12.86	Airways Aero Associations Ltd	Booker	2. 5.02T
			ZS-LGW/N8103D		(Op British Airways Flying Club) (Chelsea Rose t/s)		
G-BNCS	Cessna 180	30022	OO-SPA	7. 1.87	C.Elwell Transport Ltd	Tatenhill	17. 2.95
			D-ENUX/N2822A				
G-BNCU	Thunder Ax7-77 HAFB	928		7. 1.87	P.Mann "Skylark"	Luton	14. 7.00A
G-BNCV	Bensen B.8	LWC-01		8. 1.87	J.M.Benson	St.Merryn	
	(VW1835)						
G-BNCX*	Hawker Hunter T.7	41H/695454	XL621	9. 1.87	Brooklands Museum	Brooklands	28.3.87P*
					(As "XL621")		
G-BNCZ	Rutan LongEz	PFA/74A-10723		8. 1.87	P.A.Ellway "Atlas..T"	Sherburn in Elmet	4.10.94P
	(Lycoming O-235)				(Dismantled wreck 9.99)		
G-BNDG	Wallis WA-201/R Srs.1	K/220/X		22. 1.87	K.H.Wallis	Reymerston Hall	3.3.88P*
	(2 x Rotax 64hp)				(Stored 5.99)		
G-BNDN	Cameron V-77 HAFB	1443		8. 1.87	J.A.Smith	Bristol	22.10.93A
G-BNDO	Cessna 152 II	152-84574	N5387M	11. 2.87	Simair Ltd	Andrewsfield	20. 8.02T
					(Op Essex School of Flying)		
G-BNDP	Brugger MB.2 Colibri	PFA/43-10956		8. 1.87	J.P.Kynaston	(Luton)	3. 8.00P
	(VW1834)						
G-BNDR	Socata TB-10 Tobago	740		12. 2.87	A.N.Reardon	Blackpool	8. 1.00T
G-BNDT	Brugger MB.2 Colibri	PFA/43-10981		8. 1.87	H.Haigh	Bagby	16. 7.00P
	(VW 1834)				t/a Colibri Flying Group		
G-BNDV	Cameron N-77 HAFB	1427		25. 2.87	R.E.Jones	Lytham St.Annes	9. 5.93A
					"English Lake Hotels"		
G-BNDW	DH.82A Tiger Moth	3942	N6638	10.12.86	N.D.Welch	Shobdon	
					(Components stored Shobdon Acft Maintenance 3.96)		
G-BNDY	Cessna 425 Conquest I	425-0236	N1262T	2. 6.87	Standard Aviation Ltd	Newcastle	14.10.02
G-BNED	PA-22-135 Tri Pacer	22-1640	OO-JEF	26. 1.87	P.Storey	Sywell	AC
			N3385A		(Stored 1994)		
G-BNEE	PA-28R-201 Arrow III	28R-7837084	N630DJ	28. 1.87	Britannic Management (Aviation) Ltd		
			N9518N			White Waltham	27. 6.99
G-BNEI	PA-34-200T Seneca II	34-7870429	N3058K	12. 6.87	P.J.Morrison	Stapleford	8. 4.00
			VQ-LBC/N9646N				
G-BNEK	PA-38-112 Tomahawk II	38-82A0081	N9096A	28. 1.87	APB Leasing Ltd	Welshpool	28. 5.02T
G-BNEL	PA-28-161 Warrior II	28-7916314	N2246U	27. 4.87	S.C.Westran	Shoreham	14. 9.02T
G-BNEN	PA-34-200T Seneca II	34-8070262	N8232V	18. 2.87	Warwickshire Aerocentre Ltd	Birmingham	20. 3.02T
G-BNEO	Cameron V-77 HAFB	1408		9. 2.87	J.G.O'Connell "Rowtate"	Braintree	19. 8.95
G-BNES	Cameron V-77 HAFB	1426		19. 2.87	G.Wells	Congleton	7. 1.99A
					t/a Northern Counties Photographers		
G-BNET	Cameron O-84 HAFB	1368		22. 1.87	C.& A.I.Gibson	Stockport	16.12.99A
G-BNEV	Viking Dragonfly	PFA/139-10935		28.11.86	N.W.Eyre	(Kirkbymoorside)	
	(VW 1834)				(Nearing completion 6.92)		
G-BNEX	Cameron O-120 HAFB	1414		3. 4.87	The Balloon Club Ltd	Bristol	6. 5.90A
					t/a Bristol Balloons "Sue Sheppard Employment Agency"		
G-BNFG	Cameron O-77 HAFB	1416		5. 3.87	Capital Balloon Club Ltd	London NW1	13. 1.94A
					"Dolores"		
G-BNFI	Cessna 150J	150-69417	N50588	8. 1.87	T.D.Aitken	Lower Wasing Farm, Brimpton	3. 3.00
G-BNFK	Cameron Egg 89SS HAFB	1436		20. 2.87	Forbes Europe Inc	Balleroy, Normandy	11. 7.99A
	(Faberge Rosebud Egg shape)				"Faberge Easter Egg"		
G-BNFM	Colt 21A Cloudhopper HAFB	668		5. 3.87	M.E.Dworski	Vermenton, France	7. 7.00A
G-BNFN	Cameron N-105 HAFB	1442		13. 3.87	P.Glydon	Barnt Green, Birmingham	17. 6.97T

Regn	Type	C/n	P/I	Date	Owner/operator	Probable Base	CA Expy
G-BNFO	Cameron V-77 HAFB	816		5. 3.87	D.Newton & M.Sherbourn "Funshine"	Bristol	1. 2.00A
G-BNFP	Cameron O-84 HAFB	1474		29. 4.87	B.F.G.Ribbans "Dragonfly"	Woodbridge	3. 6.99A
G-BNFR	Cessna 152 II	152-82035	N67817	8. 4.87	Eastern Executive Air Charter Ltd (Op Seawing Flying Club)	Southend	10. 3.00T
G-BNFS	Cessna 152 II	152-83899	N5545B	10. 4.87	C & S Aviation Ltd	Halfpenny Green	9. 7.02T
G-BNFV	Robin DR400/120 Dauphin 80	1767		4. 3.87	J.P.A.Freeman	Headcorn	15. 7.02T
G-BNGE	Auster AOP.6	1925	7704M TW536	18. 3.87	M.Pocock (Op by Military Auster Flight as "TW536/TS-V" in 657 AOP Sqn c/s)	(Melksham)	5. 5.00P
G-BNGJ	Cameron V-77 HAFB	1487		18. 3.87	Latham Timber Centres (Holdings) Ltd "Latham Timber"	High Wycombe	2. 9.00A
G-BNGN	Cameron N-77 HAFB	817		3. 4.87	Catherine B.Leeder "Falcon"	Diss	27. 8.00A
G-BNGO	Thunder Ax7-77 HAFB	971		26. 3.87	J.S.Finlan Hamilton, New Zealand t/a The G-BNGO Group "Thunderbird" (Philips c/s)		17. 3.00A
G-BNGP	Colt 77A HAFB	1033		30. 3.87	Cornwall Ballooning Adventures Ltd "Headland Hotel II"	Newquay	1. 8.99A
G-BNGR	PA-38-112 Tomahawk	38-79A0479	N2492F	26. 3.87	Teesside Flight Centre Ltd	Teesside	19. 3.00T
G-BNGS	PA-38-112 Tomahawk	38-78A0701	N2463A	26. 3.87	Frontline Aviation Ltd (Damaged in transit to UK 5.87; on rebuild 5.98)	Carlisle	AC
G-BNGT	PA-28-181 Archer II	28-8590036	N149AV N9559N	29. 4.87	J.H.Berry t/a Berry Air (Op Edinburgh Flying Club)	Edinburgh	18. 5.02T
G-BNGV	ARV1 Super 2	021		4. 6.87	N.A.Onions	Stapleford	21.11.99
G-BNGW	ARV1 Super 2	022		4. 6.87	Southern Gas Turbines Ltd (Stored 6.94)	Manston	8. 7.90T
G-BNGX	ARV1 Super 2	023		6. 7.87	Southern Gas Turbines Ltd (Stored 2.96)	Goodwood	7. 8.94
G-BNGY	ARV1 Super 2	019	(G-BMWL)	9. 6.87	M.T.Manwaring	RAF Wyton	25. 3.01
G-BNHB	ARV1 Super 2	026		13. 7.87	I.M.Godfrey-Davies	Thruxton	2. 2.01
G-BNHE	ARV1 Super 2	029		14. 8.87	L.J.Joyce (Wrecked 5.99)	Farley Farm, Winchester	7. 8.99
G-BNHG	PA-38-112 Tomahawk II	38-82A0030	N91435	23. 3.87	D.A.Whitmore	Turweston	14. 5.00T
G-BNHI	Cameron V-77 HAFB	1249		26. 3.87	C.J.Nicholls "Fun-Der-Bird"	Warwick	25. 3.00A
G-BNHJ	Cessna 152 II	152-81249	N49418	4. 6.87	The Pilot Centre Ltd	Denham	1. 2.02T
G-BNHK	Cessna 152 II	152-85355	N80161	30. 3.87	General Airline Ltd t/a European Flyers	Blackbushe	19.12.99T
G-BNHL*	Colt Beer Glass 90SS HAFB	1042		24 .3.87	R S Kent "Gatzweiler Alt" (Balloon Preservation Group 7.98)	Lancing	4.3.97A
G-BNHN*	Colt Ariel Bottle SS HAFB	1045		30. 3.87	British Balloon Museum "Ariel "	Newbury	NE(A)
G-BNHO	Thunder Ax7-77 HAFB	1057		30. 3.87	M.J.Forster "Bloody Mary"	Newcastle	16. 7.97A
G-BNHP	Saffery S.330 HAFB (Model)	9		21. 3.78	N.H.Ponsford t/a Rango Balloon & Kite Co "Alpha 2"	Leeds	
G-BNHT	Alpavia Fournier RF3	80	(D-KITX) D-BMTO G-BNHT/F	13. 4.87	D.G.Hey t/a G-BNHT Group	Little Gransden	20.10.00P
G-BNID	Cessna 152 II	152-84931	N5378P	24. 4.87	M.J.Ireland	Wellesbourne Mountford	5. 3.00T
G-BNIE	Cameron O-160 HAFB	1450		5. 5.87	D.K.Fish	Bedford	20. 7.95T
G-BNIF	Cameron O-56 HAFB	1464		15. 4.87	D.V.Fowler "Nifty"	Cranbrook, Kent	19. 5.00A
G-BNII	Cameron N-90 HAFB	1497		15. 4.87	S.Saunders t/a Topless Balloon Group	Petworth	14.10.99T
G-BNIJ	Socata TB-10 Tobago	758		27. 4.87	R.E.Price	(Coalville)	11. 8.01
G-BNIK	Robin HR200/120 Club	43	LX-AIK LX-PAA	15. 4.87	A.W.Eldridge	Leicester	17. 5.00
G-BNIM	PA-38-112 Tomahawk	38-78A0148	N9631T	18. 6.87	Aurs Aviation Ltd	Glasgow	10. 3.00T
G-BNIN	Cameron V-77 HAFB	1079	G-RRSG(1)	15. 4.87	M.K.Grigson t/a Cloud Nine Balloon Group "Cloud Nine"	Shoreham	16. 9.99A
G-BNIO	Luscombe 8AC Silvaire (Continental A75)	2120	N45593 NC45593	15. 4.87	G.G.Pugh	Stapleford	7.10.00P
G-BNIP	Luscombe 8A Silvaire (Continental A65)	3547	N77820 NC77820	15. 4.87	D.R.C.Hunter & S.Maric (Stored 1.99)	Cumbernauld	10. 2.93T
G-BNIU	Cameron O-77 HAFB	1499		28. 4.87	ASTP SRL	Rixensart, Belgium	3. 4.00A
G-BNIV	Cessna 152 II	152-84866	N4972P	24. 4.87	Aerohire Ltd (Op Halfpenny Green Flight Centre)	Halfpenny Green	3. 7.00T
G-BNIW	Boeing-Stearman A75N1 (PT-17) Kaydet (P&W R985)	75-1526	N49291 41-7967	22. 4.87	R.C.Goold	East Midlands	26. 3.01
G-BNIZ	Fokker F-27 Friendship 600F	10405	OY-SRA G-BNIZ/9Q-CLQ/PH-FOD	1. 6.87	Dart Group plc t/a Channel Express	Bournemouth	3.11.00T
G-BNJA	WAG-Aero Wag-a-Bond (Continental O-200-A)	PFA/137-10886		3. 4.87	B.E.Maggs	(Bristol)	12. 7.00P
G-BNJB	Cessna 152 II	152-84865	N4970P	27. 4.87	Klingair Ltd	Conington	16. 4.99T
G-BNJC	Cessna 152 II	152-83588	N4705B	27. 4.87	Stapleford Flying Club Ltd	Stapleford	26. 8.02T
G-BNJD	Cessna 152 II	152-82044	N67833	27. 4.87	Fraggle Leasing Ltd	Aberdeen	16.10.99T

138

Regn	Type	C/n	P/I	Date	Owner/operator	Probable Base	CA Expy
G-BNJF	PA-32RT-300 Lance II	32R-7885098	N31539	8. 6.78	PFB Aviation Ltd	Jersey	2.12.02T
G-BNJG	Cameron O-77 HAFB	1502		9. 5.89	A.M.Figiel "Simply Red"	High Wycombe	4. 4.97
G-BNJH	Cessna 152 II	152-85401	C-GORA (N93101)	21. 7.87	Alarmond Ltd t/a Edinburgh Flying Club	Edinburgh	10. 7.00T
G-BNJJ*	Cessna 152 II	152-83625	N4767B	22. 6.87	The Fire Service College	Moreton-in-Marsh	14. 7.90T
					(Damaged Cranfield 18.5.88 & in fire service use 8.98)		
G-BNJK*	BAe HS.748 Srs.2A	1594	C-GEPI HP-432	5. 5.87	Macavia International Ltd	Chateauroux, France	NE(X)
					(Converted to MacAvia 748 Turbine Tanker water-bomber; stored 6.95)		
G-BNJL	Bensen B.8 (VW1835)	PFA G/01-1020		30. 4.87	C.G.Ponsford	(Maldon)	
G-BNJM	PA-28-161 Warrior II	28-8216078	N8015V	27. 5.87	Teesside Flight Centre Ltd	Carlisle	4. 6.90T
					(Damaged Middleton, Cumbria 18.5.89; stored 4.97)		
G-BNJO	QAC Quickie Q2 (Revmaster 2100D)	2217	N17LM	6.10.87	J.D.McKay	Crowfield	14. 5.93P
G-BNJR	PA-28RT-201T Turbo Arrow IV	28R-8031104	N8212U	8. 5.87	Intelligent Micro Software Ltd	Blackbushe	5. 8.02
G-BNJT	PA-28-161 Warrior II	28-8116184	N8360T	11. 6.87	B.J.Newman, B.C.Williams, T.Kermode & M.Jones t/a Chester Flying Group	Chester	8.11.02T
G-BNJU	Cameron Bust 80SS HAFB	1324		13. 5.87	Ballon Team Bonn GmbH & Co. KG "Ludwig von Beethoven" Meckenheim, Germany		21. 1.00A
G-BNJV*	Cessna 152 II	152-83840	N5333B	13. 5.87	Not known	Biggin Hill	29. 6.93T
					(Crashed Stoneacre Farm, Bredhurst 8.3.92; stored 2.95)		
G-BNJX	Cameron N-90 HAFB	1480		2. 7.87	Mars UK Ltd "Maltesers"	Slough	19. 5.94A
G-BNJZ	Cassutt Racer IIIM (Continental O-200-A)	PFA/34-11228		14. 5.87	A.P.Meredith & Jill R.Burry	Hilden-le-Noble, Hants	21. 6.99P
G-BNKC	Cessna 152 II	152-81036	N48894	26. 5.87	Herefordshire Aero Club Ltd	Shobdon	31. 8.02T
G-BNKD	Cessna 172N Skyhawk II	172-72329	N4681D	19. 5.87	Bristol Flying Centre Ltd	Bristol	20. 8.99T
G-BNKE	Cessna 172N Skyhawk II	172-73886	N6534J	20. 5.87	T.Jackson t/a Kilo Echo Flying Group	Manchester	20. 8.02T
G-BNKF	Colt AS-56 Hot-Air Airship	899		20. 5.87	Formtrack Ltd	Tucson, Arizona	14. 9.88A
G-BNKH	PA-38-112 Tomahawk II	38-81A0078	N25874	14. 5.87	Goodwood Road Racing Co Ltd	Goodwood	5. 7.02T
G-BNKI	Cessna 152 II	152-81765	N67337	19. 5.87	RAF Halton Aeroplane Club Ltd	RAF Halton	6. 7.02T
G-BNKP	Cessna 152 II	152-81286	N49460	18. 5.87	Fairmont Investments Ltd	Clacton	19. 8.00T
G-BNKR	Cessna 152 II	152-81284	N49458	18. 5.87	Keen Leasing (IOM) Ltd	Ronaldsway	10. 7.02T
G-BNKS	Cessna 152 II	152-83186	N47202	18. 5.87	Shropshire Aero Club Ltd	Sleap	9. 5.02T
G-BNKT	Cameron O-77 HAFB	1356		13. 2.87	British Airways plc "Katie II"	Gatwick	5. 8.00A
G-BNKV	Cessna 152 II	152-83079	N46604	18. 5.87	Premi-Air Flying Club Ltd	Shoreham	26. 9.02T
G-BNKX*	Robinson R-22	0149	N9065L	28. 5.87	B.C.Seedle t/a Brian Seedle Helicopters (Stored 12.97)	Blackpool	16. 8.96T
G-BNLA	Boeing 747-436	23908	N60665	30. 6.89	British Airways plc (Chelsea Rose t/s)	Gatwick	29. 6.02T
G-BNLB	Boeing 747-436	23909		31. 7.89	British Airways plc (Union Flag t/s)	Gatwick	31. 7.02T
G-BNLC	Boeing 747-436	23910		21. 7.89	British Airways plc (Dove/Colum t/s)	Gatwick	26. 7.02T
G-BNLD	Boeing 747-436	23911	N6018N	5. 9.89	British Airways plc (Delftblue Daybreak t/s)	Heathrow	5. 9.02T
G-BNLE	Boeing 747-436	24047		14.11.89	British Airways plc	Heathrow	16.11.02T
G-BNLF	Boeing 747-436	24048		23. 2.90	British Airways plc (Union Flag c/s)	Heathrow	27. 2.00T
G-BNLG	Boeing 747-436	24049		23. 2.90	British Airways plc (Whale Rider t/s)	Heathrow	26. 2.00T
G-BNLH	Boeing 747-436	24050		28. 3.90	British Airways plc (Wings t/s)	Gatwick	29. 3.00T
G-BNLI	Boeing 747-436	24051		19. 4.90	British Airways plc (Mountain of the Birds/Benyhone Tartan t/s)	Heathrow	20. 4.00T
G-BNLJ	Boeing 747-436	24052	N60668	23. 5.90	British Airways plc (Martha Masanabo/Ndebele t/s)	Gatwick	24. 5.00T
G-BNLK	Boeing 747-436	24053	N6009F	25. 5.90	British Airways plc (Water Dreaming t/s)	Heathrow	28. 5.00T
G-BNLL	Boeing 747-436	24054		13. 6.90	British Airways plc (Chelsea Rose t/s)	Heathrow	13. 6.00T
G-BNLM	Boeing 747-436	24055	N6009F	28. 6.90	British Airways plc (Martha Masanabo/Ndebele t/s)	Gatwick	27. 6.00T
G-BNLN	Boeing 747-436	24056		26. 7.90	British Airways plc (Nalanji Dreaming t/s)	Heathrow	26. 7.00T
G-BNLO	Boeing 747-436	24057		25.10.90	British Airways plc (Emmly Masanabo/Ndebele t/s)	Heathrow	24.10.00T

Regn	Type	C/n	P/I	Date	Owner/operator	Probable Base	CA Expy
G-BNLP	Boeing 747-436	24058		17.12.90	British Airways plc (Union Flag t/s)	Gatwick	16.12.00T
G-BNLR	Boeing 747-436	24447	N6005C	15. 1.91	British Airways plc (Rendezvous t/s)	Heathrow	16. 1.01T
G-BNLS	Boeing 747-436	24629		13. 3.91	British Airways plc (Wanula Dreaming t/s)	Heathrow	12. 3.01T
G-BNLT	Boeing 747-436	24630		19. 3.91	British Airways plc (Cockerel of Lowicz/Koguty Lowickie t/s)	Gatwick	18. 3.01T
G-BNLU	Boeing 747-436	25406		28. 1.92	British Airways plc (Waves of the City t/s)	Heathrow	27. 1.02T
G-BNLV	Boeing 747-436	25427		20. 2.92	British Airways plc (Waves of the City t/s)	Gatwick	19. 2.02T
G-BNLW	Boeing 747-436	25432		4. 3.92	British Airways plc	Heathrow	4. 3.02T
G-BNLX	Boeing 747-436	25435		1. 4.92	British Airways plc (Waves of the City t/s)	Heathrow	2. 4.02T
G-BNLY	Boeing 747-436	27090	N60659	10. 2.93	British Airways plc "City of Swansea"	Heathrow	9. 2.00T
G-BNLZ	Boeing 747-436	27091		4. 3.93	British Airways plc (Animals and Trees/Kg-Oocoan-Naka-Hiian-Thee-E t/s)	Heathrow	3. 3.00T
G-BNMA	Cameron O-77 HAFB	830		15.12.87	A.Wilkes & N.Woodham "Finian	Bristol	12. 3.02A
G-BNMB	PA-28-151 Cherokee Warrior	28-7615369	N6826J	6.10.87	Britannia Airways Ltd (Op Britannia Airways Flying Club)	Liverpool	26. 1.00T
G-BNMC	Cessna 152 II	152-82564	N69218	29. 5.87	Margaret L.Jones (Op Derby Aero Club)	Egginton	21. 7.00T
G-BNMD	Cessna 152 II	152-83786	N5170B	28. 5.87	T.M.Jones (Op Derby Aero Club)	Egginton	28. 7.01T
G-BNME	Cessna 152 II	152-84888	N5159P	25. 9.87	Northamptonshire School of Flying Ltd	Sywell	4.12.99
G-BNMF	Cessna 152T	152-85563	N93858	21. 7.87	Aerohire Ltd (Op Midland Flight Centre)	Halfpenny Green	2. 1.00T
G-BNMG	Cameron O-77 HAFB	1500		27. 5.87	J.H.Turner	Bridgnorth	12. 5.99A
G-BNMH	Pietenpol Air Camper	NH-1-001		2. 6.87	N.M.Hitchman	(Stoke Gifford)	
G-BNMI	Colt Black Knight HAFB	1096		1. 6.87	Virgin Airship & Balloon Co.Ltd	Telford	26. 9.91A
G-BNMK	Dornier Do.27A-1	271	OE-DGO 56+04/BD+397/BA+399	14. 8.87	G.Mackie	(Lisburn, NI)	
G-BNML	Rand Robinson KR-2 (VW1834)	PFA/129-11240		23. 6.87	R.F.Cresswell	(Alfreton)	17. 8.00P
G-BNMO	Cessna R182 Skylane RG II	R182-00956	N738RK	3. 7.87	Kenrye Developments Ltd	(Dundalk, Ireland)	24. 4.00
G-BNMT	Short SD.3-60 Var.100	SH.3723	N160DD G-BNMT/G-14-3723	18. 6.87	Loganair Ltd (Cockerel of Lowicz/Koguty Lowickie t/s)	Glasgow	15.10.00T
G-BNMU	Short SD.3-60 Var.100	SH.3724	N161DD G-BNMU/G-14-3724	18. 6.87	Loganair Ltd (Dove/Colum t/s)	Glasgow	22.11.00T
G-BNMW	Short SD.3-30 Var.100	SH.3726	SE-LCC G-BNMW/EI-BTO/G-BNMW/G-14-3726	2. 7.99	Loganair Ltd (BA Express c/s)	Glasgow	8. 7.00T
G-BNMX	Thunder Ax7-77 HAFB	1003		15. 6.87	S.A.D.Beard	Cheltenham	22. 5.00A
G-BNNA	Stolp SA.300 Starduster Too (Lycoming O-360)	1462	N8SD	29. 6.87	D.F.Simpson Standalone Farm, Meppershall		11. 1.99P
G-BNNC*	Cameron N-77 HAFB	1523		16.6.87	T McCoy (Cancelled as WFU 2.6.98: stored 1999)	Bath	9.10.96
G-BNNE	Cameron N-77 HAFB	1413		15. 6.87	Balloon Flights International Ltd (Active 9.96)	Bath	
G-BNNG*	Cessna T337D Turbo Super Skymaster	337-01096	G-COLD PH-NOS/N86147	23. 6.87	Not known (Damaged Goodwood 1985; on rebuild 3.92)	Farley Farm, Winchester	15. 7.85
G-BNNI	Boeing 727-276	20950	VH-TBK	10.12.86	Swift Airways Ltd (Op Sun Country Airlines) "Lady Patricia"	(USA)	17. 3.02T
G-BNNK	Boeing 737-4Q8	24069		30.11.88	GB Airways Ltd (Waves of the City t/s)	Gatwick	7.12.01T
G-BNNL	Boeing 737-4Q8	24070		26. 1.89	GB Airways Ltd (Chelsea Rose t/s)	Gatwick	30. 1.02T
G-BNNO	PA-28-161 Warrior II	28-8116099	N8307X	15. 6.87	Tindon Ltd	Little Snoring	5. 8.02T
G-BNNR	Cessna 152 II	152-85146	N40SX N40SU/N6121Q	15. 6.87	Sussex Flying Club Ltd	Shoreham	13.10.02T
G-BNNS	PA-28-161 Warrior II	28-8116061	N8283C	26. 6.87	M.J.Allen & R.Inskip t/a Warrior Aircraft Syndicate	Fowlmere	21. 5.02
G-BNNT	PA-28-151 Cherokee Warrior	28-7615056	N7624C	12. 6.87	S.T.Gilbert & D.J.Kirkwood	Hinton-in-The-Hedges	3. 7.00T
G-BNNU	PA-38-112 Tomahawk II	38-81A0037	N25650	12. 6.87	Edinburgh Flying Club Ltd	Edinburgh	11.11.02T
G-BNNX	PA-28R-201T Turbo Arrow III	28R-7703009	N9005F	14. 7.87	P.J.Lague	Kings Farm, Thurrock	10.11.02

Regn	Type	C/n	P/I	Date	Owner/operator	Probable Base	CA Expy
G-BNNY	PA-28-161 Warrior II	28-8016084	N8092M	1. 9.87	A.S.Bamrah	Shoreham	14.12.02T
					t/a Falcon Flying Services (Op Southern Air)		
G-BNNZ	PA-28-161 Warrior II	28-8016177	N8135Y	24. 7.87	General Airline Ltd	Blackbushe	20.10.02T
					t/a European Flyers		
G-BNOB	Wittman W.8 Tailwind			13. 7.87	M.Robson-Robinson	(Abbots Bromley)	16. 5.00P
	(Continental.PC60) 258/DH1 & PFA/3502				"Imogen"		
G-BNOE	PA-28-161 Warrior II	2816013	N9121X	26. 6.87	Sherburn Aero Club Ltd Sherburn in Elmet		9. 2.01T
			N9568N				
G-BNOF	PA-28-161 Warrior II	2816014	N9122B	26. 6.87	Tayside Aviation Ltd	Dundee	31. 3.01T
G-BNOG	PA-28-161 Warrior II	2816015	N9122D	26. 6.87	British Aerospace Flight Training (UK) Ltd		
						Prestwick	5. 7.01T
G-BNOH	PA-28-161 Warrior II	2816016	N9122L	26. 6.87	Sherburn Aero Club Ltd Sherburn in Elmet		25. 1.01T
G-BNOI	PA-28-161 Warrior II	2816017	N9122N	26. 6.87	British Aerospace Flight Training (UK) Ltd		
						Prestwick	2.11.02T
G-BNOJ	PA-28-161 Warrior II	2816018	N9122R	26. 6.87	W.M.Brown & R.D.Turner	Blackpool	26. 6.00T
					t/a British Aerospace (Warton) Flying Club		
G-BNOK	PA-28-161 Warrior II	2816019	N9122U	26. 6.87	British Aerospace Flight Training (UK) Ltd		
						Prestwick	19. 5.01T
G-BNOL	PA-28-161 Warrior II	2816023		26. 6.87	British Aerospace Flight Training (UK) Ltd		
						Prestwick	17. 5.01T
G-BNOM	PA-28-161 Warrior II	2816024		26. 6.87	Sherburn Aero Club Ltd Sherburn in Elmet		4. 2.01T
G-BNON	PA-28-161 Warrior II	2816025		26. 6.87	Tayside Aviation Ltd	Dundee	22. 2.01T
G-BNOO	PA-28-161 Warrior II	2816026		26. 6.87	British Aerospace Flight Training (UK) Ltd		
						Prestwick	16. 8.02T
G-BNOP	PA-28-161 Warrior II	2816027		26. 6.87	R.D.Turner & F.J.Smith	Warton	29. 7.02T
					t/a BAe (Warton) Flying Club		
G-BNOR	PA-28-161 Warrior II	2816028		26. 6.87	British Aerospace Flight Training (UK) Ltd		
						Perth	7. 9.02T
G-BNOS	PA-28-161 Warrior II	2816029		26. 6.87	British Aerospace Flight Training (UK) Ltd		
						Prestwick	28. 3.98T
G-BNOT	PA-28-161 Warrior II	2816030		26. 6.87	British Aerospace Flight Training (UK) Ltd		
						Prestwick	24. 6.01T
G-BNOU	PA-28-161 Warrior II	2816031		26. 6.87	British Aerospace Flight Training (UK) Ltd		
						Prestwick	11.11.02T
G-BNOV	PA-28-161 Warrior II	2816032		26. 6.87	British Aerospace Flight Training (UK) Ltd		
						Prestwick	17. 6.00T
G-BNOW	PA-28-161 Warrior II	2816033		26. 6.87	British Aerospace Flight Training (UK) Ltd		
						Prestwick	30. 8.02T
G-BNOX	Cessna R182 Skylane RG II R182-01026		N756AW	24. 6.87	D.C.Sherhered	Rochester	20. 3.00
G-BNOZ	Cessna 152 II	152-81625	EI-CCP	22. 6.87	Halfpenny Green Flight Centre Ltd		
			G-BNOZ/N65570			Halfpenny Green	17. 2.02T
G-BNPE	Cameron N-77 HAFB	1519	(G-BNPX)	25. 8.87	Kent Garden Centres Ltd	Maidstone	7. 9.95A
					"Kent Garden Centres"		
G-BNPF	Slingsby T.31M Cadet III	XA284		3.11.87	S.Luck, P.Norman & D.R.Winder Audley End		10. 8.02P
	(Stark Stamo MS.1400A) 826 & PFA/42-11122				"Noddy"		
	(Contains wings from XE791 which became OO-ZDQ)						
G-BNPH	Hunting-Percival P.66 Pembroke C.1	WV740		30. 6.87	M.J.Willing	Jersey	5. 5.00P
	(Regd with c/n "PAC66/027")	P66/41			(As "WV740" in 60 Sqn RAF c/s)		
G-BNPI	Colt 21A Cloudhopper HAFB	1038		23. 6.87	Virgin Airship & Balloon Co Ltd	Telford	7. 8.95A
					"Virgin Cloudhopper"		
G-BNPL	PA-38-112 Tomahawk	38-79A0524	N2420G	28. 7.87	Modern Air (UK) Ltd	Fowlmere	30. 1.00T
G-BNPM	PA-38-112 Tomahawk	38-79A0374	N2561D	28. 7.87	Papa Mike Aviation Ltd	Cranfield	10. 5.02T
					(Op Bonus Aviation)		
G-BNPN	PA-28-181 Archer II	28-7890059	N47379	28. 7.87	Z.Mahmood	Elstree	19.12.99T
G-BNPO	PA-28-181 Archer II	28-7890123	N47720	28. 7.87	Bonus Aviation Ltd	Cranfield	29. 5.00T
G-BNPU*	Hunting-Percival P.66 Pembroke C.1	XL929		30. 6.87	Museum of D-Day Aviation	Shoreham	17.5.88P*
	(Regd with c/n "K66/089")	P66/87			(As "XL929") (Open storage 1.99)		
G-BNPV	Bowers Fly Baby 1A/1B	PFA/16-11120		2. 7.87	J.G.Day & R.Gauld-Galliers		
	(Continental C90)				Rushett Farm, Chessington		18.10.00P
G-BNPY	Cessna 152 II	152-80249	N24388	30. 6.87	J.C.Birdsall	Gamston	19.12.02T
					t/a Traffic Management Services		
G-BNPZ	Cessna 152 II	152-85134	N6109Q	30. 6.87	C & S Aviation Ltd	Halfpenny Green	17.10.02T
G-BNRA	Socata TB-10 Tobago	772		15. 7.87	D.Teece	Nottingham	8. 5.00
					t/a Double D Air Group "Triple One"		
G-BNRG	PA-28-161 Warrior II	28-8116217	N83810	7. 7.87	RAF Brize Norton Flying Club Ltd		
						RAF Brize Norton	26. 3.00T
G-BNRI	Cessna U206G Stationair II		N756ED	28. 7.87	Target Technology Ltd	Headcorn	10. 4.00
		U206-04024					
G-BNRK	Cessna 152 II	152-84659	N6297M	29. 7.87	Redhill Aviation Ltd	Redhill	26.11.99T
					t/a Redhill Flying Club		
G-BNRL	Cessna 152 II	152-84250	N5084L	13. 7.87	J.R.Nicholls	Sibson	25. 4.00T

Regn	Type	C/n	P/I	Date	Owner/operator	Probable Base	CA Expy
G-BNRP	PA-28-181 Archer II	28-7790528	N984BT	25.11.87	Bonus Aviation Ltd	Cranfield	3. 4.00T
G-BNRR	Cessna 172P Skyhawk II	172-74013	N5213K	13. 7.87	Cornwall Flying Club Ltd	Bodmin	15.12.02
G-BNRX	PA-34-200T Seneca II	34-7970336	N2898A	25.11.87	Truman Aviation Ltd.	Nottingham	9. 2.00
G-BNRY	Cessna 182Q Skylane II	182-65629	N735RR	20. 7.87	Reefly Ltd	Booker	28. 5.00T
G-BNRZ	Robinson R-22 Beta	0670		28. 7.87	R.D.Jordan	Cranfield	14. 7.02
G-BNSG	PA-28R-201 Arrow III	28R-7837205	N9516C	30. 7.87	Armada Aviation Ltd	Redhill	9.10.99
G-BNSI	Cessna 152 II	152-84853	N4945P	6. 8.87	Sky Leisure Aviation (Charters) Ltd		
						Shoreham	3.11.02T
G-BNSL	PA-38-112 Tomahawk II	38-81A0086	N25956	21. 7.87	APB Leasing Ltd	Welshpool	23. 1.00T
G-BNSM	Cessna 152 II	152-85342	N68948	23. 7.87	Cornwall Flying Club Ltd	Bodmin	29. 1.00T
G-BNSN	Cessna 152 II	152-85776	N94738	21. 7.87	M.K.Barnes & G.N.Olson	Bristol	20. 2.00T
					(Op Bristol Flying Centre)		
G-BNSO	Slingsby T.67M Firefly II	2021		20. 8.87	Hunting Aviation Ltd RAF Barkston Heath		3. 1.00T
					(Op Hunting Acft Ltd/JEFTS)		
G-BNSP	Slingsby T.67M Firefly II	2044		20. 8.87	Hunting Aviation Ltd RAF Barkston Heath		4. 2.00T
					(Op Hunting Acft Ltd/JEFTS)		
G-BNSR	Slingsby T.67M Firefly II	2047		20. 8.87	Hunting Aviation Ltd RAF Barkston Heath		7. 4.00T
					(Op Hunting Acft Ltd/JEFTS)		
G-BNST	Cessna 172N Skyhawk II	172-73661	N4670J	21. 9.87	B.& R.P.Martin	Netherthorpe	6. 3.00T
					t/a Martin Aviation		
G-BNSU	Cessna 152 II	152-81245	N49410	2.12.87	Channel Aviation Ltd	Bourn	21. 8.00T
					(Op Rural Flying Corps)		
G-BNSV	Cessna 152 II	152-84531	N5322M	4.12.87	Channel Aviation Ltd	Bourn	12. 7.97T
					(Dismantled 4.99)		
G-BNSY	PA-28-161 Warrior II	28-8016017	N4512M	18. 8.87	Carill Aviation Ltd	Southampton	12. 3.00T
G-BNSZ	PA-28-161 Warrior II	28-8116315	N8433B	20. 8.87	Carill Aviation Ltd	Southampton	2.12.02T
G-BNTC	PA-28RT-201T Turbo Arrow IV	28R-8131081	N83428	4.11.87	M.F.Lassan	(Kidderminster)	14. 6.02
G-BNTD	PA-28-161 Cherokee Warrior II	28-7716235	N38490 N9539N	5. 8.87	A.M.Alam & H.S.Patel	Elstree	28.10.02T
G-BNTE	FFA AS.202/18A4 Bravo	224		7. 8.87	British Aerospace Flight Training (UK) Ltd		
						Prestwick	11. 3.97T
G-BNTF	FFA AS.202/18A4 Bravo	225		7. 8.87	British Aerospace Flight Training (UK) Ltd		
						Blackpool	24. 8.01T
G-BNTH	FFA AS.202/18A4 Bravo	227		7. 8.87	British Aerospace Flight Training (UK) Ltd		
						Prestwick	14. 7.97T
G-BNTI	FFA AS.202/18A4 Bravo	228		7. 8.87	British Aerospace Flight Training (UK) Ltd		
						Prestwick	1. 7.01T
G-BNTJ	FFA AS.202/18A4 Bravo	229		7. 8.87	British Aerospace Flight Training (UK) Ltd		
						Prestwick	22. 8.97T
G-BNTK	FFA AS.202/18A4 Bravo	230		7. 8.87	British Aerospace Flight Training (UK) Ltd		
					(Status uncertain)	Prestwick	18. 4.91T
G-BNTL	FFA AS.202/18A4 Bravo	231		7. 8.87	British Aerospace Flight Training (UK) Ltd		
						Prestwick	8. 3.98T
G-BNTM	FFA AS.202/18A4 Bravo	232		7. 8.87	British Aerospace Flight Training (UK) Ltd		
						Prestwick	8. 3.01T
G-BNTN	FFA AS.202/18A4 Bravo	233		7. 8.87	British Aerospace Flight Training (UK) Ltd		
						Prestwick	1. 5.97T
G-BNTO	FFA AS.202/18A4 Bravo	234		7. 8.87	British Aerospace Flight Training (UK) Ltd		
						Prestwick	23. 8.96T
G-BNTP	Cessna 172N Skyhawk II	172-72030	N6531E	4. 9.87	Westnet Ltd	Barton	16.12.99T
G-BNTS	PA-28RT-201T Turbo Arrow IV	28R-8131024	N8296R	6. 8.87	Nasaire Ltd	Liverpool	11. 2.00
G-BNTT	Beechcraft 76 Duchess	ME-228	N54SB	8.10.87	Airtime Maintenance Ltd	Leicester	6. 4.97T
G-BNTW	Cameron V-77 HAFB	1574		13. 8.87	P.Goss "Cecilia"	Alton	6.11.99A
G-BNTZ	Cameron N-77 HAFB	1518		27. 8.87	P.M.Watkins	Chippenham	20. 5.00A
					t/a Balloon Team "Nationwide Anglia"		
G-BNUC	Cameron O-77 HAFB	1575		18. 8.87	T.J.Bucknall	Chester	
					"Bridges Van Hire II"		
G-BNUI	Rutan VariEze	PFA/74-10960		12. 8.87	I.T.Kennedy & K.H.McConnell	Aldergrove	8.11.00P
	(Continental O-200-A)						
G-BNUL	Cessna 152 II	152-84486	N4852M	2.10.87	Exeter Air Training School Ltd	Exeter	13. 2.00T
G-BNUN	Beechcraft 58PA Baron	TJ-256	N6732Y	19. 8.87	British Midland Airways Ltd		
						East Midlands	16. 5.02T
G-BNUO	Beechcraft 76 Duchess	ME-250	N6635Y	29. 9.87	G.A.F.Tilley	Bournemouth	27. 5.02T
					(Op Langtry Flying Group)		
G-BNUS	Cessna 152 II	152-82166	N68179	26. 8.87	Stapleford Flying Club Ltd	Stapleford	1. 7.00T
G-BNUT	Cessna 152 II	152-79458	N714VC	26. 8.87	Stapleford Flying Club Ltd	Stapleford	25. 5.00T
G-BNUV	PA-23-250 Aztec F	27-7854038	N97BB N63894	2.10.87	L.J.Martin	Sandown/Redhill	21.10.99

Regn	Type	C/n	P/I	Date	Owner/operator	Probable Base	CA Expy
G-BNUX	Hoffmann H.36 Dimona	36236		26. 8.87	G.Hill	Saltby	30. 5.00
					t/a Buckminster Dimona Syndicate		
G-BNUY	PA-38-112 Tomahawk II	38-81A0093	N26006	10. 9.87	Aerohire Ltd	Halfpenny Green	9. 3.00T
G-BNUZ	Robinson R-22 Beta	0680		28. 8.87	J.C.Reid	Stockton-on-Tees	1. 4.00
G-BNVB	Grumman-American AA-5A Cheetah	AA5A-0758	N26843	28. 8.87	A.M.Glazer	Turweston	23. 2.00
G-BNVD	PA-38-112 Tomahawk	38-79A0055	N2421B	16.11.87	Polawood Aviation Ltd	Wellesbourne Mountford	10. 4.00T
G-BNVE	PA-28-181 Archer II	28-8490046	N4338D	28. 8.87	S.Parrish	Fowlmere	24.11.02T
					t/a Steve Parrish Racing		
G-BNVT	PA-28R-201T Turbo Cherokee Arrow III	28R-7703157	N5863V	26. 1.88	T.Yeung	Glasgow	6.10.00
					t/a Victor Tango Group		
G-BNVZ	Beechcraft 95-B55 Baron	TC-2042	N17720	25. 9.87	W.J.Forrest & P.Schon	White Waltham	7. 4.01
G-BNWA	Boeing 767-336ER	24333	N6009F	19. 4.90	British Airways plc	Heathrow	24. 4.00T
					(Delftblue Daybreak t/s)		
G-BNWB	Boeing 767-336ER	24334	N6046P	2. 2.90	British Airways plc	Heathrow	12. 2.00T
					(Chelsea Rose t/s)		
G-BNWC	Boeing 767-336ER	24335		2. 2.90	British Airways plc	Heathrow	21. 2.00T
					(Rendezvous t/s)		
G-BNWD	Boeing 767-336ER	24336	N6018N	2. 2.90	British Airways plc	Heathrow	27. 2.02T
					(Emmly Masanabo t/s)		
G-BNWE	Boeing 767-336ER	24337		23. 2.90	British Airways plc	Heathrow	17. 3.00T
					(Chelsea Rose t/s)		
G-BNWF	Boeing 767-336ER	24338	N1788B	22. 6.90	British Airways plc	Heathrow	22. 6.00T
					(Mountain of the Birds/Benyhone Tartan t/s)		
G-BNWG	Boeing 767-336ER	24339		11. 7.90	British Airways plc	Cambridge	12. 7.00T
					(Stored 1.00)		
G-BNWH	Boeing 767-336ER	24340	N6005C	31.10.90	British Airways plc	Heathrow	30.10.00T
					(Union Flag t/s)		
G-BNWI	Boeing 767-336ER	24341		18.12.90	British Airways plc	Gatwick	17.12.00T
G-BNWJ	Boeing 767-336ER	24342		24. 4.91	British Airways plc	Heathrow	23. 4.01T
					(Golden Khokhloma t/s)		
G-BNWK	Boeing 767-336ER	24343		18. 4.91	British Airways plc	Heathrow	17. 4.01T
					(Dove/Colum t/s)		
G-BNWL	Boeing 767-336ER	25203		30. 4.91	British Airways plc	Heathrow	29. 4.01T
					(Union Flag t/s)		
G-BNWM	Boeing 767-336ER	25204		24. 6.91	British Airways plc	Manchester	24. 6.01T
G-BNWN	Boeing 767-336ER	25444		30.10.91	British Airways plc	Heathrow	29.10.01T
G-BNWO	Boeing 767-336ER	25442		2. 3.92	British Airways plc	Gatwick	1. 3.02T
G-BNWP	Boeing 767-336ER	25443		9. 3.92	British Airways plc	Heathrow	8. 3.02T
					(Rendezvous t/s)		
G-BNWR	Boeing 767-336ER	25732		20. 3.92	British Airways plc	Gatwick	19. 3.02T
					(Union Flag t/s)		
G-BNWS	Boeing 767-336ER	25826	N6018N	19. 2.93	British Airways plc	Heathrow	18. 2.00T
G-BNWT	Boeing 767-336ER	25828		8. 2.93	British Airways plc	Heathrow	29.11.02T
					(Mountain of the Birds/Benyhone Tartan t/s)		
G-BNWU	Boeing 767-336ER	25829		16. 3.93	British Airways plc	Gatwick	15. 3.00T
					(Blomsterang t/s)		
G-BNWV	Boeing 767-336ER	27140		29. 4.93	British Airways plc	Heathrow	28. 4.00T
					(Dove/Colum t/s)		
G-BNWW	Boeing 767-336ER	25831		3. 2.94	British Airways plc	Heathrow	2. 2.00T
G-BNWX	Boeing 767-336ER	25832		1. 3.94	British Airways plc	Heathrow	28. 2.00T
G-BNWY	Boeing 767-336ER	25834	N5005C	22. 4.96	British Airways plc	Heathrow	21. 4.02T
G-BNWZ	Boeing 767-336ER	25733		25. 2.97	British Airways plc	Heathrow	24. 2.00T
G-BNXA	BN-2A Islander	80	V2-LAC VP-LAC/N854JA/G-51-21	17. 9.87	Cormack (Aero Club Services) Ltd	Cumbernauld	12. 4.02T
G-BNXC	Cessna 152 II	152-85429	N93171	24. 9.87	R.A.Page	Coventry	30. 1.00T
					t/a Sir W.G.Armstrong-Whitworth Flying Group		
G-BNXD	Cessna 172N Skyhawk II	172-72692	N6285D	25. 9.87	A.Jahanfar	Southend	22. 4.01T
G-BNXE	PA-28-161 Warrior II	28-8116034	N8262D	24. 9.87	M.S.Brown	Coventry	23.12.02
					t/a Rugby Autobody Repairs		
G-BNXI	Robin DR.400/180R Remorqueur	1021	SE-FNI	13.10.87	London Gliding Club Pty Ltd	Dunstable	30.12.99
G-BNXK	Nott/Cameron/Airship Industries ULD/3 Explorer Rozier HAFB	7 & 1110	(G-BLJN)	23. 9.87	J.R.P.Nott	(London NW3)	
	(Hot-air envelope in Twain Harte, California, USA 12.97 - helium inner envelope stored Bristol 1995)						
G-BNXL	Glaser-Dirks DG-400	4-216		2.10.87	J.McLaughlin	Sleap	14. 4.00
					t/a G-BNXL Group		
G-BNXM	PA-18-95 Super Cub (Continental O-200-A) (L-21B-PI) (Italian Frame rebuild No.0006)	18-4019	MM54-2619 EI-276/I-EIVC/MM54-2619/54-2619	23.11.87	R.Thorp t/a G-BNXM Group	Gipsy Wood	15. 4.00P

Regn	Type	C/n	P/I	Date	Owner/operator	Probable Base	CA Expy
G-BNXR	Cameron O-84 HAFB	1515		23. 9.87	J.A.B. Gray "Bacchus II"	Bowness-on-Windermere	26. 3.00T
G-BNXT	PA-28-161 Cherokee Warrior II	28-7716168	N4047Q	23. 9.87	A.S.Bamrah t/a Falcon Flying Services (Op Euroflyers)	Blackbushe	27.10.02T
G-BNXU	PA-28-161 Warrior II	28-7916129	N2082C	23. 9.87	D.J.G.Carphin & R.E.Woolsey t/a Friendly Warrior Group	Newtownards	28.12.99
G-BNXV	PA-38-112 Tomahawk	38-79A0826	N2399N	10.12.87	E.Reed t/a The St.George Flying Club	Teesside	5.10.01T
G-BNXX	Socata TB-20 Trinidad	664	N20GZ	15. 9.87	D.M.Carr	Wellesbourne Mountford	12. 5.00
G-BNXZ	Thunder Ax7-77 HAFB	1105		13.10.87	W.S.Templeton, R.B.Green & A.S.Dear t/a Hale Hot-Air Balloon Group "Dragonfly"	Fordingbridge	6. 7.00A
G-BNYB	PA-28-201T Turbo Dakota	28-7921040	N2856A	27. 1.88	A.G.E.Camisa & C.J.Freeman	Elstree	22.10.00T
G-BNYD	Bell 206B JetRanger II	1911	N3254P C-GTWM/N49712	1.10.87	Sterling Helicopters Ltd	Norwich	31.10.02T
G-BNYI	Short SD.3-60 Var.100	SH.3731	N360CC G-BNYI/G-14-3731	12.10.87	Gill Aviation Ltd	Newcastle	10. 5.00T
G-BNYK	PA-38-112 Tomahawk II	38-82A0059	N2376V	23.10.87	APB Leasing Ltd	Welshpool	17. 5.02T
G-BNYL	Cessna 152 II	152-80671	N25454	6.10.87	APB Leasing Ltd	Headcorn	24. 9.00T
G-BNYM	Cessna 172N Skyhawk II	172-73854	N6089J	13.11.87	N.B.Lindley	Crosland Moor	20. 1.00
G-BNYN	Cessna 152 II	152-85433	N93185	2.10.87	Redhill Aviation Ltd t/a Redhill Flying Club	Redhill	6. 2.00T
G-BNYO	Beechcraft 76 Duchess	ME-78	N2010P	28.10.87	Sub Marine Services Ltd (Damaged landing St.Mawgan 18.8.99)	Bodmin	11.12.01T
G-BNYP	PA-28-181 Archer II	28-8490027	N4330K	19.10.87	R.D.Cooper (Op Sandra's Flying Group)	Cranfield	13. 3.00T
G-BNYS	Boeing 767-204ER	24013	N6009F	22. 2.88	Britannia Airways Ltd	Luton	13. 2.02T
G-BNYV	PA-38-112 Tomahawk	38-78A0073	N9364T	13.11.87	T.E.Evans (Stored for spares use 1.99)	Wellesbourne Mountford	4. 3.94T
G-BNYX	Denney Kitfox Mk.1 (Rotax 532)			28.10.87	R.W.Husband (Stored 3.96)	Birds Edge, Penistone	14. 3.95P
G-BNYZ	SNCAN Stampe SV-4E (Lycoming O-360)	200	F-BFZR Fr Mil	10.12.87	Tapestry Colour Ltd	White Waltham	2.10.00
G-BNZB	PA-28-161 Warrior II	28-7916521	N2900U	18.11.87	EFG Flying Services Ltd	, Biggin Hill	24. 1.03T
G-BNZC	DHC.1 Chipmunk 22	C1/0778	G-ROYS 7438M/WP905	11.11.87	D.A.Horsley (As "671" in RCAF c/s)	Wombleton	12. 4.00
G-BNZG	PA-28RT-201T Turbo Arrow IV	28R-8031132	N82376	23.11.87	Brightday Ltd	Sleap	18. 3.02
G-BNZJ	Colt 21A Cloudhopper HAFB	1150		27.10.87	N.Charbonnier	Aosta, Italy	31. 8.96A
G-BNZK	Thunder Ax7-77 HAFB	1104		10.11.87	T.D.Marsden "Shropshire Lass"	Grimsby	28. 5.97A
G-BNZL	Rotorway Scorpion 133	2839		2.11.87	J.R.Wraight (Complete but stored 5.95) Stoneacre Farm, Farthing Corner		
G-BNZM	Cessna T210N Turbo Centurion II	210-63640	N4828C	9.11.87	A.J.M.Freeman	Stansted	5. 2.00
G-BNZO	Rotorway Exec 90 (RW152)	3535		9.11.87	M.G.Wiltshire Albany Farm, Hullavington "Bonzo"		24. 6.99P
G-BNZR	Clutton FRED Srs.II (VW 1834)	PFA/29-10727		10.11.87	R.M.Waugh	Newtownards	25. 5.99P
G-BNZV	PA-25-235 Pawnee	25-7405649	C-GSKU N9548P	22. 2.88	Northumbria Gliding Club Ltd	Currock Hill	3. 4.00
G-BNZZ	PA-28-161 Warrior II	28-8216184	N8253Z	17.11.87	Zooom Aviation Ltd	Denham	26. 2.00T

G-BOAA – G-BOZZ

Regn	Type	C/n	P/I	Date	Owner/operator	Probable Base	CA Expy
G-BOAA	BAC-Aerospatiale Concorde 102	100-006	G-N94AA G-BOAA	3. 4.74	British Airways plc (Union Flag t/s)	Heathrow	24. 2.01T
G-BOAB	BAC-Aerospatiale Concorde 102	100-008	G-N94AB G-BOAB	3. 4.74	British Airways plc (Union Flag t/s)	Heathrow	19. 9.01T
G-BOAC	BAC-Aerospatiale Concorde 102	100-004	G-N81AC G-BOAC	3. 4.74	British Airways plc (Union Flag t/s)	Heathrow	11. 2.01T
G-BOAD	BAC-Aerospatiale Concorde 102	100-010	G-N94AD G-BOAD	9. 5.75	British Airways plc (Union Flag t/s)	Heathrow	4.11.01T
G-BOAE	BAC-Aerospatiale Concorde 102	100-012	G-N94AE G-BOAE	9. 5.75	British Airways plc (Union Flag t/s)	Heathrow	18. 7.02T
G-BOAF	BAC-Aerospatiale Concorde 102	100-016	G-N94AF G-BFKX	12. 6.80	British Airways plc (Union Flag t/s)	Heathrow	11. 6.01T
G-BOAG	BAC-Aerospatiale Concorde 102	100-014	G-BFKW	9. 2.81	British Airways plc (Union Flag t/s)	Heathrow	3. 4.02T
G-BOAH	PA-28-161 Warrior II	28-8416030	N43401	21. 1.88	Keen Leasing (IOM) Ltd.	(Castletown)	27. 2.00T

Regn	Type	C/n	P/I	Date	Owner/operator	Probable Base	CA Expy
G-BOAI	Cessna 152 II	152-79830	C-GSJH N757LS	8. 1.88	Galair Ltd	Biggin Hill	22. 5.00T
G-BOAK	PA-22-150 Tri-Pacer	22-5101	N7313D	23.11.87	Alison M.Noble	Pepperbox, Salisbury	
					(On rebuild to PA-20 configuration 6.93)		
G-BOAL	Cameron V-65 HAFB	1600		5.11.87	A.Lindsay "No Name Balloon"	Twickenham	27. 7.00A
G-BOAM	Robinson R-22 Beta	0717		10.12.87	Burman Aviation Ltd	Cranfield	21.12.99T
G-BOAO	Thunder Ax7-77 HAFB	1162		2.12.87	D.V.Fowler	Cranbrook, Kent	16. 6.97A
G-BOAS	Air Command 503 Commander	0388 & PFA G/04-1094		3.12.87	R.Robinson	(Leighton Buzzard)	
G-BOAU	Cameron V-77 HAFB	1606		10.12.87	G.T.Barstow "Flying Colours/Duster I"	Llandrindod Wells	9.12.96A
G-BOBA	PA-28R-201 Arrow III	28R-7837232	N31249	4. 1.88	A.P.Dyer t/a Small World Aviation	Gloucestershire	26. 3.00T
G-BOBB	Cameron O-120 HAFB	1609		24.11.87	S.E.& V.D.Hurst	Mansfield	3. 3.00A
G-BOBD	Cameron O-160 HAFB	1594		22.12.87	J.Spindler	Kinross	6. 9.95T
G-BOBF*	Brugger MB.2 Colibri	PFA/43-11172		10.12.87	R.Bennett	Sproughton, Ipswich	
				(Not completed & sold to a new owner in 1997: cancelled by CAA 6.3.99)			
G-BOBH	Airtour AH-77B HAFB	009		2.12.87	J. & K.Francis "Gloworm"	Southampton	12. 6.00A
G-BOBJ	PA-38-112 Tomahawk	38-80A0021	N25096 N9656N	4. 1.88	Pearl Technology Ltd	Biggin Hill	8. 5.00T
G-BOBK	PA-38-112 Tomahawk	38-79A0503	N2352G	4. 1.88	Pearl Technology Ltd	Biggin Hill	23. 3.00T
G-BOBL	PA-38-112 Tomahawk II	38-81A0140	N91335	4. 1.88	Aerohire Ltd	Cardiff	18. 8.00T
G-BOBR	Cameron N-77 HAFB	1623		10.12.87	C.Bradley & M.Morris "Loganair"	Llanymynech, Powys	4. 5.00A
G-BOBS*	QAC Quickie Q2 (Revmaster 2100)	PFA/94A-10840		27. 9.82	M.A.Hales	RAF Brize Norton	22.12.92P
				(Wreck stored 4.95 cancelled by CAA 18.3.99)			
G-BOBT	Stolp SA.300 Starduster Too (Lycoming O-360)	CJ-01	N690CM	15.12.87	S.C.Lever t/a G-BOBT Group	White Waltham	5. 5.00P
G-BOBU	Colt 90A HAFB	900		15.12.87	Prescott Hot Air Balloons Ltd	Cheltenham	3.10.99A
G-BOBV	Reims Cessna F.150M Commuter	1415	EI-BCV	14.12.87	Sheffield Aero Club Ltd	Netherthorpe	10. 3.00T
G-BOBY	Monnett Sonerai II (VW2233)	PFA/15-10223		26.10.78	R.G.Hallam	Netherthorpe	8.11.82P
				(Damaged nr Barton 31.10.82; stored 9.96)			
G-BOBZ	PA-28-181 Archer II	28-8090257	N81671	21.12.87	Trustcomms Intl Ltd	Goodwood	9. 3.98T
G-BOCB*	HS.125 Srs.1B/522	25106	G-OMCA	14. 9.87	Barry Technical College		
			G-DJMJ/G-AWUF/5N-ALY/G-AWUF/HZ-BIN		Cardiff Airport Industrial Park		16.10.90T
				(Instructional airframe 11.95)			
G-BOCC	PA-38-112 Tomahawk	38-79A0362	N2540D	14.12.87	J.M.Green	Goodwood	14.12.00T
G-BOCF	Colt 77A HAFB	1178		4. 1.88	Lindstrand Balloons Ltd	Oswestry	25. 7.94T
				(Stored 9.95)			
G-BOCG	PA-34-200T Seneca II	34-7870359	N36759	30.12.87	Oxford Aviation Services Ltd	Oxford	23.10.00T
G-BOCI	Cessna 140A (Continental C90)	15497	N5366C	17.11.87	J.B.Bonnell "Whitey"	Thruxton	30. 9.02
G-BOCK	Sopwith Triplane rep (Clerget Rotary 9B 130 hp)	153 & NAW-1		26. 1.88	The Shuttleworth Trust (As "N6290" in RNAS 8 Sqdn c/s) "Dixie II"	Old Warden	20. 7.00P
G-BOCL	Slingsby T.67C	2035		5. 1.88	Richard Brinklow Aviation Ltd	Shoreham	10. 7.00T
G-BOCM	Slingsby T.67C	2036		5. 1.88	Richard Brinklow Aviation Ltd	Hinton-in-The-Hedges	27. 4.00T
G-BOCN	Robinson R-22 Beta	0726	N... G-BOCN	8. 1.88	Sloane Helicopters Ltd	Sywell	16. 1.00T
G-BOCP	PA-34-220T Seneca III	3433089		17.12.87	British Aerospace Flight Training (UK) Ltd	Prestwick	6. 5.01T
G-BOCR	PA-34-220T Seneca III	3433111		26. 2.88	British Aerospace Flight Training (UK) Ltd	Prestwick	27. 5.01T
G-BOCS	PA-34-220T Seneca III	3433112		26. 2.88	British Aerospace Flight Training (UK) Ltd	Prestwick	24. 9.01T
G-BOCT	PA-34-220T Seneca III	3433113		26. 2.88	British Aerospace Flight Training (UK) Ltd	Prestwick	30. 3.98T
G-BOCU	PA-34-220T Seneca III	3433114		26. 2.88	British Aerospace Flight Training (UK) Ltd	Prestwick	24. 6.01T
G-BOCV	PA-34-220T Seneca III	3433115		26. 2.88	British Aerospace Flight Training (UK) Ltd	Prestwick	11. 3.02T
G-BOCW	PA-34-220T Seneca III	3433120		25. 8.88	British Aerospace Flight Training (UK) Ltd	Prestwick	30.11.01T
G-BOCX	PA-34-220T Seneca III	3433121		29. 9.88	British Aerospace Flight Training (UK) Ltd	Prestwick	31. 5.02T
G-BOCY	PA-34-220T Seneca III	3433122		29. 9.88	British Aerospace Flight Training (UK) Ltd	Prestwick	3.12.01T
G-BODA	PA-28-161 Warrior II	2816037	N9601N	19. 1.88	Oxford Aviation Services Ltd	Oxford	13. 4.00T
G-BODB	PA-28-161 Warrior II	2816042		23. 2.88	Oxford Aviation Services Ltd	Oxford	7. 9.00T
G-BODC	PA-28-161 Warrior II	2816041		23. 2.88	Oxford Aviation Services Ltd	Oxford	7. 4.00T
G-BODD	PA-28-161 Warrior II	2816040		23. 2.88	Oxford Aviation Services Ltd	Oxford	7. 8.00T

Regn	Type	C/n	P/I	Date	Owner/operator	Probable Base	CA Expy
G-BODE	PA-28-161 Warrior II	2816039	N9603N	23. 2.88	Oxford Aviation Services Ltd	Oxford	25. 5.00T
G-BODF	PA-28-161 Warrior II	2816038	N9602N	19. 1.88	Oxford Aviation Services Ltd	Oxford	20. 4.00T
G-BODG*	Slingsby Cadet III	PFA/42-11310	WT911	9. 6.88	H.P.Vox	East Fortune	
	(Conversion of T.31B c/n 706)				(Op East Fortune Flying Group)		
					(Stored incomplete 9.98: cancelled by CAA 15.4.99)		
G-BODH	Slingsby Cadet III	PFA/42-10108	BGA.474	5. 1.88	H.P.Vox	East Fortune	6. 3.00P
	(VW1834)				(Op East Fortune Flying Group) "Fochinell"		
	(If p/i is as quoted then this is a conversion from T.8 Tutor c/n MHL/RT.13 ex G-ALNK/BGA.474)						
G-BODI	Stoddard-Hamilton SH-2H Glasair III		(HB-)	14. 4.89	C.A.C.Tilney	Cranfield	7. 7.00P
		3088	G-BODI				
G-BODM	PA-28-180 Cherokee Challenger		N56016	2. 2.88	R.Emery	Clutton Hill, High Littleton	14. 9.02T
		28-7305519					
G-BODO	Cessna 152 II	152-82404	N68923	29. 1.88	Annie R.Sarson	Popham	29. 5.00
G-BODP	PA-38-112 Tomahawk II	38-81A0010	N25616	5. 1.88	D.A.Whitmore	Oxford	1.12.00T
G-BODR	PA-28-161 Warrior II	28-8116318	N8436B	5. 1.88	Airways Aero Associations Ltd	Booker	2. 9.00T
					(Op British Airways Flying Club) (Waves & Cranes t/s)		
G-BODS	PA-38-112 Tomahawk	38-79A0410	N2379F	3. 2.88	P.J.Houlton	(Telford)	8. 6.01T
G-BODT	Jodel D.18	173 & PFA/169-11290		14. 1.88	L.D.McPhillips	Portmoak	6. 5.99P
	(Rotax 912UL)				t/a Jodel G-BODT Syndicate		
G-BODU	Scheibe SF.25C-2000 Falke	44434	D-KIAA	19. 1.88	R.G.G.English	Rufforth	9. 5.00
					t/a Monica English Memorial Trust		
G-BODX	Beechcraft 76 Duchess	ME-309	N67094	26. 2.88	Liddell Aircraft Ltd	Bournemouth	30. 7.00
G-BODY	Cessna 310R II	310R-1503	N4897A	17.12.87	Atlantic Air Transport Ltd	Coventry	23. 2.00T
G-BODZ	Robinson R-22 Beta	0729		8. 1.88	Langley Construction Ltd	Nottingham	21. 4.01
G-BOEC*	PA-38-112 Tomahawk	38-78A0138	N9587C	8. 1.88	Not known (Temp unregd 8.7.97)	Jersey	22. 8.97T
G-BOEE	PA-28-181 Cherokee Archer II		N6168J	20. 1.88	T.B.Parmenter		
		28-7690359				Lodge Farm, St.Osyth, Clacton	13. 6.00
G-BOEH	Robin DR.340 Major	434	F-BRVN	4. 1.88	G.Bowles	Bradleys Lawn, Heathfield	14. 5.01
					t/a Piper Flyers Group		
G-BOEK	Cameron V-77 HAFB	1658		25. 1.88	A.J.E.Jones "Secret One"	Bristol	7. 8.97A
G-BOEM	Aerotek Pitts S-2A Special	2255	N31525	17. 2.88	Margaret Murphy	Spanhoe	21. 7.01
	(Lycoming AEIO-360)						
G-BOEN	Cessna 172M Skyhawk	172-61325	N20482	12. 2.88	H.B.Davies	Elstree	19. 6.00T
G-BOER	PA-28-161 Warrior II	28-8116094	N83030	21. 1.88	M. & W.Fraser-Urquhart	White Waltham	7. 4.00
G-BOET	PA-28RT-201 Arrow IV	28R-8018020	G-IBEC	28. 1.88	B.C.Chambers	Jersey	4. 8.00
			G-BOET/N8116V				
G-BOEW	Robinson R-22 Beta	0750		27. 1.88	Plane Talking Ltd	Elstree	14. 3.00T
G-BOEX	Robinson R-22 Beta	0751		27. 1.88	Plane Talking Ltd	Elstree	12. 2.00T
G-BOEZ	Robinson R-22 Beta	0753		27. 1.88	Plane Talking Ltd	Elstree	9. 3.97T
G-BOFC	Beechcraft 76 Duchess	ME-217	N6628M	28. 1.88	Magenta Ltd	Exeter	18. 2.00T
					(Op Airways Flight Training)		
G-BOFD	Cessna U206G Stationair II		N756LS	27. 1.88	D.M.Penny	Movenis, Co.Londonderry	24. 6.00
		U206-04181			(Op Wild Geese Parachute Centre)		
G-BOFE	PA-34-200T Seneca II	34-7870381	N39493	22. 2.88	Alstons Upholstery Ltd	(Colchester)	15. 7.00T
G-BOFF	Cameron N-77 HAFB	1666		26. 1.88	R.C.Corcoran	Bristol	13.11.98A
G-BOFL	Cessna 152 II	152-84101	N5457H	28. 1.88	Gem Rewinds Ltd	Coventry	23. 2.00T
G-BOFM	Cessna 152 II	152-84730	N6445M	28. 1.88	Gem Rewinds Ltd	Coventry	27. 5.00T
G-BOFO	Ultimate Acft 10 Dash 200	(HB-)		15. 2.88	M.Werdmuller	(Felton, Bristol)	16. 6.92P
	(Lycoming HIO-360) 10-200-004 & PFA/180-11319 G-BOFO				(Status uncertain)		
G-BOFW	Cessna A150M Aerobat	A150-0612	N9803J	15. 2.88	Vectair Aviation 1995 Ltd	Goodwood	2. 9.00T
G-BOFX	Cessna A150M Aerobat	A150-0678	N9869J	15. 2.88	K.Hobbs	Aldergrove	27.11.00T
					t/a Aldergrove Flight Training Centre		
G-BOFY	PA-28-140 Cherokee Cruiser		N43521	3. 2.88	BCT Aircraft Leasing Ltd		
		28-7425374				New Farm, Felton	10.12.00T
G-BOFZ	PA-28-161 Warrior II	28-7816255	N2189M	10. 2.88	R.W.Harris	Southend	19. 1.01T
					(Op Willowair Flying Club)		
G-BOGC	Cessna 152 II	152-84550	N5346M	8. 2.88	Keen Leasing (IOM) Ltd	(Castletown)	4. 8.01T
G-BOGG	Cessna 152 II	152-82960	N45956	15. 2.88	The Royal Artillery Aero Club Ltd		
						AAC Middle Wallop	20. 8.00T
G-BOGI	Robin DR.400/180 Regent	1821		15. 2.88	A.L.M.Shepherd	Rochester	13. 5.00T
G-BOGK	ARV Super 2	K.006 & PFA/152-11138		10. 2.88	D.R.Trouse	Cherry Tree Farm, Monewden	21.12.99P
	(Hewland AE75)				t/a Suffolk Super Two Group		
G-BOGM	PA-28RT-201T Turbo Arrow IV		N8173C	10. 2.88	R.J.Pearce	Halfpenny Green	18. 9.00
		28R-8031077			t/a RJP Aviation		
G-BOGO	PA-32R-301T Saratoga SP	32R-8029064	N8165W	6. 4.88	A.S.Doman	Denham	13. 8.00
G-BOGP	Cameron V-77 HAFB	896		30. 3.88	T.Gunn	Crowborough	10. 7.00A
					"Dire Straits"		
G-BOGR*	Colt 180A HAFB	1183		11. 5.88	British Balloon Museum & Library	Newbury	13. 3.92T
					"Britannia"		
G-BOGT*	Colt 77A HAFB	1212		21. 3.88	R S Kent "British Gas"	Lancing	2.12.94A
					(Balloon Preservation Group 7.98)		

Regn	Type	C/n	P/I	Date	Owner/operator	Probable Base	CA Expy
G-BOGV	Air Command 532 Elite			10. 3.88	G.M.Hobman	Heworth, York	10. 1.91P
	0399 & PFA G/04-1102						
G-BOGW	Air Command 532 Elite			16. 2.88	A.Gault	(Forth, Lanark)	30. 6.89P
	AC532-UK001 & 0398						
G-BOGY	Cameron V-77 HAFB	1650		15. 2.88	R.A.Preston "Bella"	Bristol	30. 1.99A
G-BOHA	PA-28-161 Warrior II	28-7816352	N3526M	16. 3.88	M.Clark	Shoreham	16. 6.00T
G-BOHD	Colt 77A HAFB	1214		4. 3.88	D.B.Court "Bluebird"	Ormskirk	12. 4.95A
G-BOHF	Thunder Ax8-84 HAFB	1197		8. 4.88	J.A.Harris	Sturminster Newton	19. 9.94A
G-BOHG	Air Command 532 Elite			10. 3.88	T.E.McDonald	Melrose Farm, Melbourne	4. 6.91P
	0402 & PFA G/04-1122						
G-BOHH	Cessna 172N Skyhawk II	172-73906	N131FR	19. 2.88	T.Scott	Gamston	27. 4.01T
			N7333J				
G-BOHI	Cessna 152 II	152-81241	N49406	29. 2.88	V.D.Speck	Clacton	7. 7.00T
G-BOHJ	Cessna 152 II	152-80558	N25259	29. 2.88	A.G.Knight t/a Airlaunch	Old Buckenham	10. 2.02T
G-BOHL	Cameron A-120 HAFB	1701		11. 3.88	T.J.Bucknall	Chester	3. 2.98
					"Son of City of Bath"		
G-BOHM	PA-28-180 Cherokee Challenger		N55000	18. 2.88	M.J.Anthony & B.Keogh		
	28-7305287					Lockmead Farm, South Marston	23. 4.00
G-BOHN*	PA-38-112 Tomahawk II	38-81A0151	N23593	19. 2.88	Not known	Cardiff	19. 6.94T
					(Crashed Cardiff 13.8.93; stored 8.94)		
G-BOHO	PA-28-161 Warrior II	28-8016196	N747RH	25. 2.88	G.J.Craig & D.L.H.Barrel	Cambridge	21. 8.00T
			N9560N		t/a Egressus Flying Group		
G-BOHR	PA-28-151 Cherokee Warrior		C-GNFE	29. 2.88	G.Cockerton	Coventry	13. 4.01
	28-7515245						
G-BOHS	PA-38-112 Tomahawk	38-79A0988	N2418P	26. 2.88	A.S.Bamrah	Biggin Hill	12. 3.01T
					t/a Falcon Flying Services		
G-BOHT	PA-38-112 Tomahawk	38-79A1079	N25304	14. 4.88	E.Reed	Teesside	26. 7.00T
			C-GAYW/N24052		t/a The St.George Flying Club		
G-BOHU	PA-38-112 Tomahawk	38-80A0031	N25093	26. 2.88	Avon Aero Club Lsg Ltd	Turweston	1. 5.00T
G-BOHV	Wittman W.8 Tailwind			3. 3.88	R.A.Povall	Yearsby	10. 9.00P
	(Continental O-200-A) 621 & PFA/31-11151						
G-BOHW	Van's RV-4	PFA/181-11309		16. 6.88	P.J.Robins	Deenethorpe	20. 8.00P
	(Lycoming O-320)						
G-BOHX	PA-44-180 Seminole	44-7995008	N36814	9. 3.88	Airpart Supply Ltd	Oxford	3. 8.00T
G-BOIA	Cessna 180K Skywagon II	180-53121	N2895K	3. 3.88	R.E., P.E.R., J.E.R. & R.J.W.Styles		
					t/a Old Warden Flying & Parachute Group	Hinton-in-The-Hedges	13.11.00
G-BOIB	Wittman W.10 Tailwind	PFA/31-10551		3. 3.88	L.Fairs	Popham	11. 7.00P
G-BOIC	PA-28R-201T Turbo Arrow III		N2336M	7. 4.88	M.J.Pearson	Stapleford	19. 6.00
	28R-7803123						
G-BOID	Bellanca 7ECA Citabria	1092-75	N8676V	3. 3.88	D.Mallinson	Birds Edge, Penistone	11.12.00
G-BOIG	PA-28-161 Warrior II	28-8516027	N4390B	1. 3.88	D.Vallance-Pell	Gamston	10. 7.00
			N9519N				
G-BOIJ	Thunder Ax7-77 Srs.1 HAFB	964		11. 3.88	R.A.Hughes "Shropshire Lad"	Oswestry	24. 7.00A
G-BOIK	Air Command 503 Commander			8. 3.88	F.G.Shepherd	Alston, Cumbria	22. 1.90P
	(Rotax 503) 0420 & PFA G/04-1087			(Erroneously regd as c/n PFA G/04-1090)			
G-BOIL	Cessna 172N Skyhawk II	172-71301	N23FL	2. 3.88	Upperstack Ltd	Barton	29. 5.00T
			N23ER/(N2494E)				
G-BOIN	Bellanca 7ECA Citabria	1190-77	N4160Y	7. 3.88	LAC (Enterprises) Ltd	Barton	22. 4.01T
					(Op Lancashire Aero Club)		
G-BOIO	Cessna 152 II	152-80260	N24445	7. 3.88	AV Aviation Ltd	Carlisle	12. 7.01T
					(Op Cumbria Aero Club)		
G-BOIP	Cessna 152 II	152-83444	N49264	7. 3.88	Stapleford Flying Club Ltd	Stapleford	26. 5.91T
					(Damaged Uckington 11.1.90; stored 5.98)		
G-BOIR	Cessna 152 II	152-83272	N48041	7. 3.88	Shropshire Aero Club Ltd	Sleap	13. 6.00T
G-BOIT	Socata TB-10 Tobago	810		10. 3.88	Buckland Newton Hire Ltd	Henstridge	27. 8.01T
G-BOIU	Socata TB-10 Tobago	811		10. 3.88	R & B Aviation Ltd	Guernsey	20. 4.01
G-BOIV	Cessna 150M Commuter	150-78620	N704HH	30. 3.88	J.B.Green	South Burlingham, Norwich	25.11.00
G-BOIW	Cessna 152 II	152-82845	N89731	6. 4.88	EFG Flying Services Ltd	Biggin Hill	15.10.00T
G-BOIX	Cessna 172N Skyhawk II	172-71206	C-GMMX	9. 3.88	JR Flying Ltd	Bournemouth	27. 1.01T
			N2253E				
G-BOIY	Cessna 172N Skyhawk II	172-67738	N73901	9. 3.88	Aviation Acess Ltd	Leeds-Bradford	1. 7.00T
G-BOIZ	PA-34-200T Seneca II	34-8070014	N81081	25. 2.88	R.W.Tebby	Bristol	29. 6.00T
					t/a S.F.Tebby & Son (Op Bristol Flying Centre)		
G-BOJB	Cameron V-77 HAFB	1615		11. 3.88	K.L.Heron & R.M.Trotter	Bristol	31. 7.00A
G-BOJD	Cameron N-77 HAFB	1653		11. 3.88	L.H.Ellis "Bluebird"	Marlow	31. 5.00
G-BOJF	Air Command 532 Elite	0425		11. 3.88	Not known	(Hoofddorp, The Netherlands)	4. 6.91P
	(Rotax 532)						
G-BOJH	PA-28R-200 Cherokee Arrow II		N2821T	6. 4.88	Piper-Air (Glasgow) Ltd	Glasgow	22.10.00T
	28R-7235139				(Op Glasgow Flying Club)		
G-BOJI	PA-28RT-201 Arrow IV	28R-7918221	N2919X	31. 3.88	B.A.Mintowt-Czyz & T.A.Stoate	Blackbushe	8. 5.00

Regn	Type	C/n	P/I	Date	Owner/operator	Probable Base	CA Expy
G-BOJK	PA-34-220T Seneca III	3433020	G-BRUF N9113D	11. 3.88	Redhill Aviation Ltd t/a Redhill Flying Club	Redhill	3. 4.00T
G-BOJL*	GEMS MS.885 Super Rallye	122	F-BKLI	21. 3.88	J.A.Rees & F.Doncaster (No C of A issued: cancelled by CAA 18.5.99)	Haverfordwest	
G-BOJM	PA-28-181 Archer II	28-8090244	N8155L	21. 3.88	Fernborough Ltd	Humberside	12. 5.00
G-BOJO*	Colt 120A HAFB	1208		7. 3.88	Not known (Temp unregd 6.8.97)	Newcastle	23. 9.97T
G-BOJR	Cessna 172P Skyhawk II	172-75574	N64539	22. 4.88	Exeter Flying Club Ltd	Exeter	30. 6.00T
G-BOJS	Cessna 172P Skyhawk II	172-74582	N52699	29. 3.88	I.S.H.Paul	Denham	25. 5.00T
G-BOJU	Cameron N-77 HAFB	1718		21. 3.88	M.A.Scholes "GB Transport"	London SE25	7. 9.97A
G-BOJW	PA-28-161 Cherokee Warrior II	28-7716038	N1668H	28. 3.88	S.C.Brown	Enstone	25. 9.00T
G-BOJZ	PA-28-161 Warrior II	28-7916223	N2113J	28. 3.88	Southern Air Ltd	Shoreham	22. 5.00T
G-BOKA	PA-28-201T Turbo Dakota	28-7921076	N2860S	15. 3.88	CBG Aviation Ltd	Fairoaks	24. 4.00
G-BOKB	PA-28-161 Warrior II	28-8216077	N8013Y	29. 3.88	Southern Air Ltd	Shoreham	1. 5.00T
G-BOKF	Air Command 532 Elite (Rotax 532)	0404 & PFA G/04-1101		28. 3.88	D.Beevers	Melrose Farm, Melbourne	22. 9.99P
G-BOKH	Whittaker MW.7 (Rotax 532)	PFA/171-11281 (Regd as PFA/171-11231)	(G-MTWT)	21. 3.88	I.D.Evans	Thame	1. 7.96P
G-BOKI	Whittaker MW.7 (Rotax 532)	PFA/171-11282	(G-MTWU)	21. 3.88	R.K.Willcox (Damaged Old Sodbury, Bristol 9.4.95)	Chipping Sodbury	28. 7.95P
G-BOKJ	Whittaker MW.7 (Rotax 532)	PFA/171-11283	(G-MTWV)	21. 3.88	M.R.Payne	(Watford)	4. 6.97P
G-BOKK*	PA-28-161 Warrior II	28-8116300	N8427L	6. 4.88	Not known (Damaged Hamgreen nr Redditch 18.5.95; on rebuild 6.96)	Blackpool	7. 6.97T
G-BOKL	PA-28-161 Warrior II	2816044		24. 3.88	British Aerospace Flight Training (UK) Ltd	Prestwick	1.12.91T
G-BOKM	PA-28-161 Warrior II	2816045		24. 3.88	British Aerospace Flight Training (UK) Ltd	Prestwick	12.11.02T
G-BOKN	PA-28-161 Warrior II	2816046		24. 3.88	British Aerospace Flight Training (UK) Ltd	Prestwick	7.11.02T
G-BOKO	PA-28-161 Warrior II	2816049		24. 3.88	British Aerospace Flight Training (UK) Ltd	Prestwick	22.11.02T
G-BOKP	PA-28-161 Warrior II	2816050		24. 3.88	British Aerospace Flight Training (UK) Ltd	Prestwick	18.12.99T
G-BOKR	PA-28-161 Warrior II	2816051		24. 3.88	British Aerospace Flight Training (UK) Ltd	Prestwick	22. 4.01T
G-BOKS	PA-28-161 Warrior II	2816052		24. 3.88	British Aerospace Flight Training (UK) Ltd	Prestwick	18. 1.92T
G-BOKT	PA-28-161 Warrior II	2816053		24. 3.88	British Aerospace Flight Training (UK) Ltd	Prestwick	30. 4.01T
G-BOKU	PA-28-161 Warrior II	2816054		24. 3.88	British Aerospace Flight Training (UK) Ltd	Prestwick	21.11.02T
G-BOKW*	Bolkow Bo.208C Junior	689	G-BITT F-BRHX/D-EEAL	6. 1.88	Not known (Temp unregd 19.7.96)	Croft Farm, Defford	3.11.95P
G-BOKX	PA-28-161 Warrior II	28-7816680	N39709	28. 3.88	C.J.Freeman (Op Weald Air Services)	Headcorn	22. 8.00T
G-BOKY	Cessna 152 II	152-85298	N67409	6. 4.88	D.F.F.Poore	Bournemouth	8. 3.01T
G-BOLB	Taylorcraft BC-12-65 (Continental A65)	3165	N36211 NC36211	17. 5.88	A.T.E.Pacewicz & R.J.Rhys-Williams "Spirit of California"	Eastbach Farm, English Bicknor	10. 7.98P
G-BOLC	Fournier RF6B-100	1	F-BVKS	28. 3.88	W.H.Hendy	Dunkeswell	27.11.00
G-BOLD	PA-38-112 Tomahawk	38-78A0180	N9740T	8. 7.88	B.R.Pearson & B.F.Fraser-Smith (Stored 5.98)	Eaglescott	21. 1.96T
G-BOLE	PA-38-112 Tomahawk	38-78A0475	N2506E	13. 7.88	M.W.Kibble & E.A.Minard	Eaglescott	27. 5.01
G-BOLF	PA-38-112 Tomahawk	38-79A0375	N583P YV-133E/YV-1696P/N9666N	13. 7.88	Teesside Flight Centre Ltd	Bagby	1. 7.01T
G-BOLG	Bellanca 7KCAB Citabria	517-75	N8706V	25.11.88	B.R.Pearson t/a Aerotug	Eaglescott	24. 5.01
G-BOLI	Cessna 172P Skyhawk II	172-75484	N63794	30. 3.88	A.A.Mackinnon t/a BOLI Flying Club	Denham	11. 7.00T
G-BOLL	Lake LA-4-200 Skimmer	295	(F-GRMX) G-BOLL/EI-ANR/N1133L	4. 5.88	S.Armstrong	St. Angelo	19. 5.00
G-BOLN	Colt 21A Cloudhopper HAFB	1226		4. 5.88	Virgin Airship & Balloon Co Ltd "Pepsi Cola 1"	Telford	7. 8.95A
G-BOLO	Bell 206B JetRanger II	1522	N59409	2.11.87	Hargreaves Construction Co Ltd (Op Blades Helicopters)	Goodwood	13. 1.00T
G-BOLP	Colt 21A Cloudhopper HAFB	1227		4. 5.88	Virgin Airship & Balloon Co Ltd "Pepsi Cola 2"	Telford	7. 8.95A
G-BOLR	Colt 21A Cloudhopper HAFB	1228		3. 5.88	Virgin Airship & Balloon Co Ltd "Pepsi Cola 3"	Telford	7. 8.95A
G-BOLS	Clutton FRED Srs.II	PFA/29-10676		6. 4.88	I.F.Vaughan "The Ruptured Uck"	(Melton Mowbray)	

Regn	Type	C/n	P/I	Date	Owner/operator	Probable Base	CA Expy
G-BOLT	Rockwell Commander 114	14428	N5883N	16.10.78	H.J.D.S.Baioes	Cranfield	30. 7.01
G-BOLU	Robin R.3000/120	106	F-GFAO SE-IMS	14. 4.88	I.W.Goodger t/a Classair	Biggin Hill	6. 7.00T
G-BOLV	Cessna 152 II	152-80492	N24983	8. 4.88	A.S.Bamrah t/a Falcon Flying Services	Biggin Hill	20.12.02T
G-BOLW	Cessna 152 II	152-80589	N25316	9. 6.88	JRB Aviation Ltd (Op Seawing Flying Club)	Southend	30. 8.00T
G-BOLX	Cessna 172N Skyhawk II	172-69099	N734TK	8. 4.88	R.J.Burrough	Lydd	12.11.00
G-BOLY	Cessna 172N Skyhawk II	172-69004	N734PJ	31. 3.88	D.A.T.Skidmore	NK	16.10.00T
G-BOLZ	Rand Robinson KR-2 (VW 1834)	PFA/129-10866		6. 4.88	B.Normington	Coventry	24. 7.00P
G-BOMB	Cassutt Racer IIIM (Continental O-200-A)	PFA/34-10386		18.12.78	S.Adams RAF Weston-on-the-Green "Blind Panic" (Damaged Weston Park nr Telford 22.6.97)		23. 5.98P
G-BOMK	BAe 146-200QT	E-2112	F-GTNU G-5-112/(EC-231)/G-BOMK	13. 4.88	GD Express Worlwide BV Amsterdam, The Netherlands		AC
G-BOML	Hispano HA-1112-MIL Buchon	151	N170BG Sp AF C4K-107	15. 4.88	Classic Aviation Ltd (Op The Old Flying Machine Co) "Red 3"	Duxford	7. 7.00P
	(C/n quoted as 170 originally but may be a corruption of Spanish AF serial)(As W/No "166238" in Luftwaffe c/s)						
	(Crashed on landing Sabadell, near Barcelona, Spain 26.9.99 & destroyed)						
G-BOMN	Cessna 150F	150-63089	N6489F	25. 4.89	D.G.Williams	Shoreham	29. 7.00T
G-BOMO	PA-38-112 Tomahawk II	38-81A0161	N91324	8. 4.88	APB Leasing Ltd (Damaged landing Welshpool 17.5.99)	Welshpool	13. 7.00T
G-BOMP	PA-28-181 Cherokee Archer II	28-7790249	N8482F	8. 4.88	SRC Contractors Ltd & D Carter	Elstree	27. 8.00T
G-BOMS	Cessna 172N Skyhawk II	172-69448	N737JG	11. 4.88	Aerohire Ltd	Stapleford	2. 7.01
G-BOMT	Cessna 172N Skyhawk II	172-70396	N739AU	12. 7.88	C.E.Derbyshire Kings Farm, Thurrock		6. 5.01T
G-BOMU	PA-28-181 Cherokee Archer II	28-7790318	N1631H	8. 4.88	J.Sawyer & P.R.Kinge t/a RJ Aviation	Blackbushe	19. 5.00T
G-BOMY	PA-28-161 Warrior II	28-8216049	N8457S	28. 6.88	Carill Aviation Ltd	Southampton	7.12.00T
G-BOMZ	PA-38-112 Tomahawk	38-78A0635	N2315A	30. 6.88	D.P.Cloet & R.A.Cook t/a BOMZ Aviation	Booker	25. 4.00T
G-BONC	PA-28RT-201 Arrow IV	28R-7918007	C-GXYX N3069K	13. 5.88	Finglow Ltd	(Hertford)	7. 7.00T
G-BOND	Sikorsky S-76A II Plus	760036	N4931Y	31. 1.80	Bond Helicopters Ltd	Aberdeen	5. 3.00T
G-BONE	Pilatus P.2-06	600-62	Sw.AF U-142/U-113	8. 7.81	R.H.Cooper & S.Swallow	(Lincoln)	23. 2.87P
G-BONG	Enstrom F-28A-UK	154	N9604	22. 4.88	M.A.Crook Appleton, Warrington t/a TR Bitz		16. 8.98T
G-BONK	Colt 180A HAFB	1167		14.12.87	Wye Valley Aviation Ltd	Ross-on-Wye	2.11.94T
G-BONO	Cessna 172N Skyhawk II	172-70299	C-GSMF N738WS	11. 5.88	Mer-Air Aviation Ltd	Welshpool	23. 9.00T
G-BONP	CFM Streak Shadow (Rotax 582) SS-01P & PFA/161A-11344			4. 5.88	T.J.Palmer	(Kilmarnock)	7. 9.00P
G-BONR	Cessna 172N Skyhawk II	172-68164	C-GYGK (N733BH)	18. 4.88	D.I.Claik	Biggin Hill	6. 8.00
G-BONS	Cessna 172N Skyhawk II	172-68345	C-GIUF	18. 4.88	M.G.Montgomerie t/a G-BONS Group	Elstree	2. 7.00
G-BONT	Slingsby T.67M Firefly II	2054		3. 5.88	Hunting Aviation Ltd RAF Barkston Heath (Op Hunting Acft Ltd/JEFTS)		7. 9.00T
G-BONU	Slingsby T.67B	2037		3. 5.88	R.L.Brinklow	Turweston	29. 6.00T
G-BONV	Colt 17A Cloudhopper HAFB	1238		3. 5.88	K A Kent "Bryant Group (Balloon Preservation Group 7.98)	Lancing	1. 4.93A
G-BONW	Cessna 152 II	152-80401	OY-CPL N24825	15. 4.88	Lincoln Aero Club Ltd	Sturgate	23. 7.00T
G-BONY	Denney Kitfox mk.1 (Rotax 532) 166 & PFA/172-11351 (Inscribed as "mk.2")			11. 5.88	M.J.Walker	Banbury	31. 5.00P
G-BONZ	Beechcraft V35B Bonanza	D-10282	N6661D	6. 4.88	P.M.Coulten	Boughton, Norfolk	22. 7.00
G-BOOB	Cameron N-65 HAFB	515		12.11.79	J.Rumming "Cracker"	Swindon	8. 4.90A
G-BOOC	PA-18-150 Super Cub	18-8279	SE-EPC	29. 4.88	R.R. & S.A.Marriott	Meon	17. 7.00
G-BOOD	Slingsby T.31M Motor Tutor (Fuji-Robin EC-44-2PM) PFA/42-11264 (Wings ex XE810 c/n 923)			4. 5.88	G.F.M.Garner	Clench Common	24.10.00
G-BOOE	Gulfstream GA-7 Cougar	GA7-0093	N718G	7. 6.88	N.Gardner	Southampton	18. 7.00T
G-BOOF	PA-28-181 Archer II	28-7890084	N47510	16. 6.88	General Airline Ltd t/a European Flyers	Blackbushe	3. 9.00T
G-BOOG	PA-28RT-201T Turbo Arrow IV	28R-8331036	N4303K	6. 5.88	Simair Ltd	Andrewsfield	14. 1.02
G-BOOH	Jodel D.112 (Built Ets Valladeau)	481	F-BHVK	16. 5.88	J.A.Crabb,	(Chard)	17. 5.00P
G-BOOI	Cessna 152 II	152-80751	N25590	22. 8.88	Stapleford Flying Club Ltd	Stapleford	23. 4.01T

Regn	Type	C/n	P/I	Date	Owner/operator	Probable Base	CA Expy
G-BOOJ	Air Command 532 Elite II			4. 5.88	Roger Savage (Gyroplanes) Ltd	Portmoak	6.12.91P
	(Rotax 532) PB206 & PFA G/04-1098						
G-BOOL	Cessna 172N Skyhawk II	172-72486	C-GJSY	27. 4.88	Surrey & Kent Flying Club Ltd		
			N5271D			Biggin Hill	16.12.00T
G-BOOV	Aerospatiale AS.355F2 Twin Squirrel			3. 5.88	Merseyside Police Authority Air Support Group		
		5374				Liverpool	2.10.00T
G-BOOW	Aerosport Scamp	PFA/117-10709		10. 5.88	I.E.Bloys	Great Yeldham, Essex	14. 6.00P
	(VW1834)						
G-BOOX	Rutan LongEz	PFA/74A-10844		3. 5.88	I.R.Wilde	Deenethorpe	9. 3.00P
	(Lycoming O-235)						
G-BOOZ	Cameron N-77 HAFB	904	(G-BKSJ)	21. 6.83	J.E.F.Kettley "Bluebell"	Chippenham	
	(New envelope c 6.98 · c/n not known)						
G-BOPA	PA-28-181 Archer II	28-8490024	N43299	28. 4.88	J H & L F Strutt	Andrewsfield	4. 8.00
G-BOPB	Boeing 767-204ER	24239	N6009F	1.11.88	Britannia Airways Ltd	Luton	21. 3.01T
					"Captain Sir Ross Smith"		
G-BOPC	PA-28-161 Warrior II	28-8216006	N2124X	6. 5.88	Channel Aviation Ltd	Guernsey	16. 6.00T
G-BOPD	Bede BD-4	632	N632DH	25. 5.88	S.T.Dauncey	Yearsby	16. 6.00P
	(Lycoming O-320)						
G-BOPG	Cessna 182Q Skylane II	182-66689	N95962	6. 5.88	G.Wimlett	Blackpool	17. 7.00T
G-BOPH	Cessna TR182 Turbo Skylane RG II		N756BJ	11. 5.88	M.K.Trautman	(London W2)	4. 5.00
		R182-01031					
G-BOPO	FLS OA.7 Optica 301	021	EC-FVM	17. 5.88	Sunhawk Ltd	Jersey	27. 5.96T
			G-BOPO				
G-BOPR	FLS OA.7 Optica 301	023		17. 5.88	Sunhawk Ltd.	Jersey	
G-BOPT	Grob G-115	8046		10. 5.88	LAC (Enterprises) Ltd	Barton	6. 8.00T
					t/a Lancashire Aero Club		
G-BOPU	Grob G-115	8059		10. 5.88	LAC (Enterprises) Ltd	Barton	8. 7.00T
					t/a Lancashire Aero Club		
G-BOPV	PA-34-200T Seneca II	34-8070265	N82323	7. 6.88	G.J.Powell	Biggin Hill	11. 7.00T
G-BOPW*	Cessna A152 Aerobat	A152-0908	N4922A	11. 5.88	Northamptonshire School of Flying Ltd		
						Sywell	20. 6.98T
	(Damaged Sywell 30.8.95: cancelled 11.6.99 as Destroyed)						
G-BOPX	Cessna A152 Aerobat	A152-0932	N761BK	11. 5.88	Aerohire Ltd		
					Bourne Park, Hurstbourne Tarrant		24. 1.98T
	(Major rebuild with AeroFab Restorations 8.99)						
G-BORA*	Colt 77A	1233		19. 5.88	Balloon Preservation Group	Lancing	24. 8.94A
					"Cala Homes"		
G-BORB	Cameron V-77 HAFB	1348		24. 8.88	M.H.Wolff	Liskeard	2. 9.92A
G-BORD	Thunder Ax7-77 HAFB	1164		26. 5.88	D.D.Owen "Marvin"	Wotton-under-Edge	11.12.99A
G-BORE	Colt 77A HAFB	642		24. 5.88	J.D.Medcalf & C.Wilson	Enfield	31. 7.00A
					t/a Little Secret Hot Air Balloon Group "My Little Secret"		
G-BORF	Colt AS-80 Mk II Hot-Air Airship	1241		22.12.88	Belton Dream Ltd	(Canada)	18. 7.91A
					(Op Sunrise Balloons) (Crashed Brooks, Alberta 9.7.91)		
G-BORG	Campbell Cricket	PFA G/03-1085		8. 6.88	N.G.Bailey	Kemble	7. 8.96P
	(Rotax 503)				(Damaged 1996)		
G-BORH	PA-34-200T Seneca II	34-8070352	N8261V	7. 6.88	Aerolease Ltd.	Conington	22.11.00T
G-BORI	Cessna 152 II	152-81672	N66936	8. 6.88	Staryear Ltd	Barton	23. 9.00T
G-BORJ	Cessna 152 II	152-82649	N89148	27. 5.88	Pool Aviation (NW) Ltd	Blackpool	13.11.00T
G-BORK	PA-28-161 Warrior II	28-8116095	N83036	8. 6.88	A.W.Collett	Turweston	13.11.00T
G-BORL	PA-28-161 Warrior II	28-7816256	N2190M	28. 9.88	Westair Flying School Ltd	Blackpool	14.12.00T
G-BORM*	HS.748 Srs.2B/217	1670	RP-C1043	29. 7.88	Exeter Fire Services	Exeter	
			V2-LAA/VP-LAA/9Y-TDH (Noted 10.99)				
G-BORN	Cameron N-77 HAFB	1777		13. 5.88	I.Chadwick	Partridge Green, W.Sussex	8. 8.00A
					"Ian"		
G-BORO	Cessna 152 II	152-83767	N5130B	27. 5.88	M.R.Shelton	Tatenhill	29. 1.01T
					t/a Tatenhill Aviation		
G-BORR	Thunder AX8-90 HAFB	1256		29. 7.99	W.J.Harris	Cheltenham	
G-BORS	PA-28-181 Archer II	28-8090156	N8127C	31. 5.88	B.K. & S.C.Ambrose	Fowlmere	11. 6.00T
					t/a Ambrose Air		
G-BORT	Colt 77A HAFB	1255		7. 6.88	Y.J.Joslyn	Wilhelmshaven, Germany	24. 7.00A
G-BORV	Bell 206B JetRanger II	2202	C-GVTY	8. 6.88	C.A.Rosenberg	Abergavenny	5. 5.02T
G-BORW	Cessna 172P Skyhawk II	172-74301	N51357	23. 8.88	Briter Aviation Ltd	Coventry	25. 6.01T
G-BORY	Cessna 150L	150-72292	N6792G	27. 5.88	Harrison Aviation Ltd	Norwich	19. 9.02T
G-BOSB	Thunder Ax7-77 HAFB	1199		7. 6.88	M.Gallagher	Consett	17. 9.99A
	(Regd as c/n 581 but built as c/n 1199)						
G-BOSD	PA-34-200T Seneca II	34-7570085	N33086	7. 6.88	Barnes Olson Aeroleasing Ltd	Bristol	11. 8.01T
					(Op Bristol Flying Centre) (Damaged landing Exeter 19.6.99)		
G-BOSE	PA-28-181 Archer II	28-8590007	N143AV	17. 5.88	C.Hudson & A.Thomas	(Wokingham)	23. 5.00
G-BOSF	Colt 69A HAFB	1271		23. 6.88	Virgin Airship & Balloon Co Ltd	Telford	28. 1.93A
					"Lloyds Bank"		

Regn	Type	C/n	P/I	Date	Owner/operator	Probable Base	CA Expy
G-BOSG	Colt 17A Cloudhopper HAFB	1272		23. 6.88	Virgin Airship & Balloon Co Ltd Telford		22. 5.89A
					"Lloyds Bank Cloudhopper"		
G-BOSJ	Nord 3400	124	N9048P	26. 5.88	A.I.Milne	Little Snoring	1.11.94P
			ALAT "MOO"		(As "124" in Fr.AF c/s)		
					(Damaged Fenland 12.6.94; stored 9.97)		
G-BOSM	CEA Jodel DR.253B Regent	168	F-BSBH	24. 5.88	S.H.Gibson	High Cross, Ware	10.12.01
					t/a Sierra Mike (Ware) Group		
G-BOSO	Cessna A152 Aerobat	A152-0975	N761PD	25. 5.88	Redhill Aviation Ltd	Redhill	20. 8.01T
					t/a Redhill Flying Club (Damaged landing Fairoaks 4.3.99)		
G-BOSP	PA-28-151 Cherokee Warrior		N1143X	26. 5.88	A.S.Bamrah	Biggin Hill	17.11.01T
		28-7515307	N9563N		t/a Falcon Flying Services (Damaged take-off Clacton 4.10.99)		
G-BOSR	PA-28-140 Cherokee	28-22092	N7464R	26. 5.88	C R.Guggenheim Farley Farm, Winchester		3. 6.00T
					t/a Sierra-Romeo Group		
G-BOSU	PA-28-140 Cherokee Cruiser		N55635	19. 7.88	R.A.Sands	Oxford	8. 6.01
		28-7325449					
G-BOSV	Cameron V-77 HAFB	1320		17. 6.88	K.H.Greenaway	Market Harborough	7. 6.97A
					"Joyride II"		
G-BOTB	Cessna 152 II	152-85733	N94571	7. 6.88	Stapleford Flying Club Ltd	Stapleford	18. 9.00T
G-BOTD	Cameron O-105 HAFB	1611		6. 6.88	P.J.Beglan	Belves, France	10. 6.00A
G-BOTE*	Thunder Ax8-90 HAFB	555		14. 6.88	I M Martin "Barge Fox"	Lancing	16. 2.95T
					(Balloon Preservation Group 7.98)		
G-BOTF	PA-28-151 Cherokee Warrior		C-GGIF	8. 6.88	D.S.Woolf	Southend	20. 8.00T
		28-7515436			t/a G-BOTF Group (Op Southend Flying Club)		
G-BOTG	Cessna 152 II	152-83035	N46343	9. 6.88	Donington Aviation Ltd	East Midlands	20. 8.00T
G-BOTH	Cessna 182Q Skylane II	182-67558	N202PS	9. 6.88	W.J.Forrest	Barton	24. 2.01
			N114SP/N5172N		t/a G-BOTH Group		
G-BOTI	PA-28-151 Cherokee Warrior		C-GNFF	9. 6.88	A.J.Bamrah	Birmingham	29. 8.00T
	(Convd to Srs.161 status)	28-7515251			t/a Falcon Flying Services		
G-BOTK	Cameron O-105 HAFB	1765		9. 6.88	F.R. & V.L.Higgins	Bath	12. 7.96T
					"Champagne Rides"		
G-BOTL*	Colt 42A SS HAFB	466		23.11.82	British Balloon Museum	Newbury	
					& Library "Bottle"		
G-BOTM	Bell 206B JetRanger III	3881	N31940	9. 6.88	David McLean Homes Ltd	Flint	31. 7.00
G-BOTN	PA-28-161 Warrior II	28-7916261	N2173N	9. 6.88	A.Watson	Shoreham	19. 1.01T
G-BOTO	Bellanca 7ECA Citabria	939-73	N57398	9. 6.88	A.K.Hulme Rayne Hall Farm, Rayne		6.11.97
					t/a G-BOTO Group		
G-BOTP	Cessna 150J	150-70736	N61017	2. 8.88	M.Colson	(Devizes)	29. 3.01
G-BOTT*	Rand-Robinson KR-2	PFA/129-11164		16. 6.88	M.D.Ott & M.R.Hutchins	(Dunmow)	
					(Project abandoned: cancelled by CAA 12.4.99		
G-BOTU	Piper J3C-75 Cub	19045	N98803	8. 7.88	T.L.Giles	Hill Farm, Nayland	29. 6.00P
			NC98803				
G-BOTV	PA-32RT-300 Lance II	32R-7885153	N36039	7. 6.88	Robin Lance Aviation Associates Ltd		
						Rochester	7. 7.02
G-BOTW	Cameron V-77 HAFB	1761		14. 6.88	M.R.Jeynes	(Worcester)	3. 9.00A
G-BOTZ	Bensen B.8MR	PFA G/01-1086		17. 6.88	C.Jones	Stonehouse, Ayr	9.12.00P
	(Rotax 532)						
G-BOUD	PA-38-112 Tomahawk II	38-82A0017	N91365	26. 7.88	A.J.Wiggins	(Longhope, Glos)	25. 3.01T
G-BOUE	Cessna 172N Skyhawk II	172-73235	N6535F	8. 8.88	Aviation Access Ltd	Leeds-Bradford	9. 2.01T
G-BOUF	Cessna 172N Skyhawk II	172-71900	N5605E	24. 8.88	M.I. & B.P.Sneap	Ripley, Derby	8. 6.01T
					t/a Amber Valley Aviation		
G-BOUJ	Cessna 150M Commuter	150-76373	N3058V	25. 8.88	R.D.Billins	Denham	23.12.99T
G-BOUK	PA-34-200T Seneca II	34-7570124	N33476	31. 8.88	C.J. & R.J.Barnes	East Midlands	28. 7.02T
G-BOUL	PA-34-200T Seneca II	34-7670157	N8936C	28. 6.88	Oxford Aviation Services Ltd	Oxford	5. 4.01T
G-BOUM	PA-34-200T Seneca II	34-7670136	N8401C	3. 8.88	Oxford Aviation Services Ltd	Oxford	5. 8.01T
G-BOUN	Rand-Robinson KR-2	PFA/129-10945		23. 6.88	W.J.Allan	Charterhall	27. 7.99P
	(VW 1834)						
G-BOUP	PA-28-161 Warrior II	2816059	N9139X	12. 7.88	Oxford Aviation Services Ltd	Oxford	21. 1.00T
G-BOUR	PA-28-161 Warrior II	2816060	N9139Z	12. 7.88	Oxford Aviation Services Ltd	Oxford	14.10.00T
G-BOUS	PA-28RT-201 Arrow IV	28R-7918109	N32WC	23. 6.88	Air Nova plc	Chester	3. 8.00T
			N9644N		(Crashed on take-off Cark 25.11.99 & destroyed)		
G-BOUT	Zenair Colomban MC-12 Cri-Cri		N120JN	14. 6.88	C.K.Farley	Southampton	
		12-0135					
G-BOUU	Everett Autogyro	015		R	A.Everett	Sproughton, Ipswich	
					(Stored 5.97)		
G-BOUV	Montgomerie-Bensen B.8MR			23. 6.88	A.J.Dickson	Carlisle	28. 7.97P
	(Rotax 532)	PFA G/01-1092					
G-BOUX	Everett Autogyro	016		R	A.Everett	Sproughton, Ipswich	
					(Stored 7.94)		
G-BOUZ	Cessna 150G	150-65606	N2606J	15. 6.88	Atlantic Bridge Aviation Ltd	Lydd	16. 3.00T
					(Op Weald Air Services)		

Regn	Type	C/n	P/I	Date	Owner/operator	Probable Base	CA Expy
G-BOVB	PA-15 Vagabond (Lycoming O-145)	15-180	N4396H NC4396H	23. 6.88	P.Laycock & J R Pike t/a Oscar Flying Group	Twineham	11. 1.00P
G-BOVG*	Reims Cessna F.172H	0627	OO-ANN D-ELTR	2. 8.88	No.1476 Squadron, ATC Rayleigh, Essex (Damaged Southend 1991; instructional airframe 1.00)		14. 9.91
G-BOVH	PA-28-161 Warrior II	28-8316091	N4311M	28. 6.88	R.W.Tebby t/a S.F.Tebby & Son Bristol (Damaged Bristol 1.4.94; status uncertain)		12. 9.94T
G-BOVK	PA-28-161 Warrior II	28-8516061	N69168	7. 9.88	Air Nova plc	Chester	14. 5.01T
G-BOVR	Robinson R-22HP	0176	N9069D	28. 6.88	P.J.Homan	Shoreham	19. 8.00T
G-BOVS	Cessna 150M Commuter	150-78663	N704KC	21. 7.88	Blue Skies Aviation Ltd	(Salcombe)	13.11.00T
G-BOVT	Cessna 150M Commuter	150-78032	N8962U	1.12.88	C.J.Hopewell	Crowfield	5. 3.01T
G-BOVU	Stoddard-Hamilton Glasair III (Lycoming IO-540)	3090		16. 9.88	B.R.Chaplin	Deenethorpe	15. 2.00P
G-BOVW	Colt 69A HAFB	1286		13. 7.88	V.Hyland "Enderby-Hyland Painting"	Nottingham	6. 4.94A
G-BOVX	Hughes 269C	38-0673	N58170	12. 7.88	Autohaus Ltd	Sywell	16. 7.01T
G-BOVY	Hughes 269C	40-0915	EI-CIL G-BOVY/N1096K	12. 7.88	P.J.Brown (Damaged landing Redhill 17.3.99)	Redhill	15. 5.99T
G-BOWB	Cameron V-77 HAFB	1767		13. 7.88	R.C.Stone "Richard's Rainbow"	Reading	1. 5.00A
G-BOWD	Reims Cessna F337G Super Skymaster (Wichita c/n 01791)	0084	N337BC G-BLSB/EI-BET/D-INAI/(N53697)	8. 7.88	Badgehurst Ltd	Southend	4. 4.01T
G-BOWE	PA-34-200T Seneca II	34-7870405	N39668	14. 7.88	Oxford Aviation Services Ltd	Oxford	29. 6.01T
G-BOWK	Cameron N-90 HAFB	1764		1. 8.88	S.R.Bridge "Burley Stables"	Grantham	
G-BOWL	Cameron V-77 HAFB	1780		26. 7.88	P.G. & G.R.Hall "Matrix"	Chard	12. 5.00A
G-BOWM	Cameron V-56 HAFB	1781		26. 7.88	C.G.Caldecott & G.Pitt	Newcastle-under-Lyme	30. 7.00A
G-BOWN	PA-12 Super Cruiser (Lycoming O-235)	12-1912	N3661N NC3661N	26. 7.88	R.W.Bucknell	Andrewsfield	26. 2.00T
G-BOWO	Cessna R182 Skylane RG II	R182-00146	(G-BOTR) N2301C	20. 7.88	D.P.Bennett	Gamston	15. 3.01
G-BOWP	Jodel Wassmer D.120A Paris-Nice (Continental O-200-A)	319	F-BNZM	26. 7.88	A.R.Gedney, G.Morris & J.M.Palmer	Cowbit, Lincs	16.12.99P
G-BOWU	Cameron O-84 HAFB	1779		1. 8.88	C.F.Pooley & D.C.Ball t/a St.Elmos Fire Syndicate "Elmo"	Gloucester	4. 8.00A
G-BOWV	Cameron V-65 HAFB	1800		24. 8.88	R.A.Harris "Sigmund"	Axminster	12. 5.00A
G-BOWY	PA-28RT-201T Turbo Arrow IV	28R-8131114	N404EL N83648	8. 8.88	A.Davies (Op Redhill Flying Club)	Redhill	27. 7.00T
G-BOWZ	Bensen B.80V (Rotax 532)	PFA G/01-1060		27. 7.88	W.M.Day	Great Orton	31. 7.98P
G-BOXA	PA-28-161 Warrior II	2816075	N9149Q	1.11.88	Channel Islands Aero Services Ltd Jersey t/a Jersey Aero Club		21.12.00T
G-BOXB	PA-28-161 Warrior II	2816064	N9142H	12. 8.88	Channel Islands Aero Services Ltd Jersey t/a Jersey Aero Club		6. 2.00T
G-BOXC	PA-28-161 Warrior II	2816063	N9142D	12. 8.88	Channel Islands Aero Services Ltd Jersey t/a Jersey Aero Club		14. 5.00T
G-BOXG	Cameron O-77 HAFB	1792		26. 8.88	R.A.Wicks	Norwich	5. 8.00A
G-BOXH	Pitts S-1S Special (Lycoming O-360)	MP4	N8LA	29. 7.88	D.Medrek & M.Turkington	Breighton	14. 4.00P
G-BOXJ	Piper J3C-90 Cub (L-4H-PI) (Frame No.12021)	12193	OO-ADJ 44-79897	1. 8.88	J.D.Tseliki	Shoreham	20. 3.91P
G-BOXR	Gulfstream GA-7 Cougar	GA7-0059	N772GA	19.10.88	Plane Talking Ltd	Cranfield	11. 9.00T
G-BOXT	Hughes 269C	104-0367	SE-HMR PH-JOH/D-HBOL	1. 8.88	Goldenfly Ltd	Denham	17. 1.99T
G-BOXU	Grumman-American AA-5B Tiger	AA5B-0026	N1526R	28. 7.88	G.C.Baker t/a Marcher Aviation Group	Welshpool	15. 5.01
G-BOXV	Pitts S-1D Special (Lycoming O-360) (Regd with c/n 7-0432)	7-0433	N27822	8. 8.88	G.R.Clark Yeatsall Farm, Abbots Bromley		24. 7.98P
G-BOXW	Cassutt Racer IIIM	PFA/34-11317		11. 8.88	D.I.Johnson	(Leigh-on-Sea)	
G-BOXX	Robinson R-22 Beta	0815	N2640D	15. 6.88	Plane Talking Ltd	Redhill	25. 7.00T
G-BOXY	PA-28-181 Archer II	28-7990175	N3073D	29. 7.88	Sheffield Aero Club Ltd	Netherthorpe	17. 3.01T
G-BOYB	Cessna A152 Aerobat	A152-0928	N761AW	29. 7.88	Northamptonshire School of Flying Ltd	Sywell	14.12.00T
G-BOYC	Robinson R-22 Beta	0837		22. 8.88	M.D.Thorpe Coney Park, Leeds t/a Yorkshire Helicopters		10. 5.01T
G-BOYF	Sikorsky S-76B	760343		15. 9.88	Darley Stud Management Co Ltd Blackbushe (Op Air Hanson)		24.11.00T
G-BOYH	PA-28-151 Cherokee Warrior (Convd to Srs.161 status)	28-7715290	N8795F	8. 8.88	Superpause Ltd White Waltham (Op West London Aero Club)		18. 3.01T
G-BOYI	PA-28-161 Warrior II	28-7816183	N9032K	8. 8.88	S.J.Harris	RAF Woodvale	24. 3.01
G-BOYL	Cessna 152 II	152-84379	N6232L	11. 8.88	Aerohire Ltd Wellesbourne Mountford		26. 2.01T
G-BOYM	Cameron O-84 HAFB	1796		25. 8.88	Frontline Distribution Ltd Basingstoke "Frontline"		

Regn	Type	C/n	P/I	Date	Owner/operator	Probable Base	CA Expy
G-BOYO	Cameron V-20 HAFB	1843		27. 9.88	J.M.Willard	Burgess Hill, W.Sussex	
G-BOYP	Cessna 172N Skyhawk II	172-70349	N738YU	22. 8.88	Guildtons Ltd	North Weald	1. 3.01
G-BOYU	Cessna A150L Aerobat	A150-0497	N8121L	31. 8.88	Upperstack Ltd	Barton	17. 9.00T
G-BOYV	PA-28RT-201T Turbo Arrow III	28R-7703014	N1143H	1. 9.88	Arrow Air Ltd	(Broadway)	14. 1.01
G-BOYX	Robinson R-22 Beta	0862	N90813	25. 8.88	R.Towle	Hexham	28. 9.91T
					(Damaged Teesside 18.7.90)		
G-BOYY	Cameron A-105 HAFB	1786		22. 8.88	Hoyers (UK) Ltd "Hoyer"	Huddersfield	20. 4.97A
G-BOZI	PA-28-161 Warrior II	28-8116120	(G-BOSZ) N8318A	14. 7.88	Klingair Ltd	Conington	25.11.00T
G-BOZK	Aerospatiale AS.332L Super Puma	2179	LN-OMQ G-BOZK/F-GINN	5. 8.88	Brintel Helicopters Ltd t/a British International Helicopters	Aberdeen	8. 7.00T
G-BOZM	PA-38-112 Tomahawk	38-78A0352	N6247A	25. 8.88	A.S.Bamrah t/a Falcon Flying Services	Biggin Hill	17. 6.01T
G-BOZN	Cameron N-77 HAFB	1807		1. 9.88	Calarel Developments Ltd "Calarel Developments"	Chipping Campden	29.10.94A
G-BOZO	Gulfstream AA-5B Tiger	AA5B-1282	N4536Q	12. 8.88	Caslon Ltd	Elstree	27.11.00T
G-BOZP	Beechcraft 76 Duchess	ME-99	N6010Z	26. 8.88	Newcastle-upon-Tyne Aero Club Ltd	Newcastle	15. 4.01T
G-BOZR	Cessna 152 II	152-84614	N6083M	7. 9.88	Gem Rewinds Ltd	Coventry	18.12.00T
G-BOZS	Pitts S-1C Special (Lycoming O-320)	221-H	N10EZ	31. 8.88	R.J. & M.B.Trickey	Perth	5. 5.98P
G-BOZU	Aero Dynamics Sparrow Hawk Mk II	PFA/184-11371		12.12.88	R.V.Phillimore	(Bexhill-on-Sea)	
G-BOZV	Robin DR.340 Major	416	F-BRTS	9. 8.88	Datamax Computer Consultants Ltd	Kemble	27. 8.00
G-BOZW	Bensen B.8MR (Rotax 532)	PFA G/01-1096		1. 9.88	M.E.Wills	Lytchett Matravers	27. 5.00P
G-BOZY	Cameron RTW-120 Airship/HAFB	1770		1. 9.88	L.V.Mastis	West Bloomfield, Mi, USA	21. 4.97A
G-BOZZ	Gulfstream AA-5B Tiger	AA5B-1155	N4530N	22. 8.88	A.W.Matthews t/a Solent Tiger Group	Southampton	14.10.00

G-BPAA – G-BPZZ

Regn	Type	C/n	P/I	Date	Owner/operator	Probable Base	CA Expy
G-BPAA	Acro Advanced AA-001 & PFA/200-11528 (Acro VW2100)			26. 8.88	Acro Engines & Airframes Ltd	Yearby	7. 6.99P
G-BPAB	Cessna 150M Commuter	150-77244	N63335	21. 9.88	A.N.Wicks & R.Carr-Ellison Wheeler t/a Alpha Bravo Group	(Sudbury)	18. 2.01
G-BPAC	PA-28-161 Cherokee Warrior II	28-7716112	N2567Q	21. 9.88	G.G.Pratt	High Cross	27. 2.01
G-APAD*	PA-34-200T Seneca II	34-7870431	N21208	23.8.88	The Fire Service College	Moreton-in-Marsh	9.4.95T
				(Damaged Bowland, Lancs 15.7.92 & in fire service use 8.98)			
G-BPAE*	Cameron V-77 HAFB	1798		1. 9.88	I.J.Jackson	Lytham St.Annes	1. 1.96
				(Cancelled as wfu 26.10.99)			
G-BPAF	PA-28-161 Cherokee Warrior II	28-7716142	N3199Q	6. 9.88	RAF Brize Norton Flying Club Ltd	RAF Brize Norton	7. 5.00T
G-BPAH	Colt 69A HAFB	512		2. 6.83	Justerini & Brooks Ltd "Phil"	London SW1	15. 8.88A
G-BPAI	Bell 47G-3B-1	6528	N8588F	9. 9.88	LRC Leisure Ltd (Op Manchester Helicopter Centre)	Barton	29. 3.01
G-BPAJ	DH.82A Tiger Moth (Composite with "real" G-AMNN ?)	83472	G-AOIX T7087	5.11.88	P.A.Jackson	(Huntingdon)	13. 6.00
G-BPAL	DHC.1 Chipmunk 22	C1/0437	G-BCYE WG350	29.10.86	K.F. & P.Tomsett (As "WG350")	(Leatherhead)	9. 6.00
G-BPAO*	Air Command 503 Commander 0424 & PFA G/04-1097			8. 9.88	D.J.Sagar	Upton Snodsbury, Worcester	8. 8.91P
				(Cancelled as WFU 23.2.99)			
G-BPAS	Socata TB-20 Trinidad	283	A2-ADR F-GDBO	9.11.88	Syndicate Clerical Services Ltd	(Exeter)	1. 3.01T
G-BPAU	PA-28-161 Warrior II	28-7916218	N3063H	3.11.88	Lapwing Flying Group Ltd	Denham	26. 3.01T
G-BPAV	Clutton FRED Srs.II (VW 1600)	PFA/29-10274		21.11.78	P.A.Valentine (Under construction 1990)	(Uxbridge)	
G-BPAW	Cessna 150M Commuter	150-77923	N8348U	5. 9.88	A.Phillips	Watchford Farm, Yarcombe	22. 6.01
G-BPAX	Cessna 150M Commuter	150-77401	N63571	5. 9.88	W.E.Rodwell & N.J.Smith t/a The Dirty Dozen	Shoreham	18. 5.01T
G-BPAY	PA-28-181 Archer II	28-8090191	N3568X	12. 9.88	Leicestershire Aero Club Ltd	Leicester	23.12.00T
G-BPBA*	Bensen B.80MR (Rotax 532)	PFA G/01-1036		5. 9.88	M.E.Green	Crewe	17. 9.90P
G-BPBB	Evans VP-2 (Arrow GT500)	PFA/63-11261		2. 9.88	P.J.Manifold	Priory Farm, Tibenham	9. 6.97P
G-BPBG	Cessna 152 II	152-84941	N5418P	16. 9.88	Atlantic Air Transport Ltd (Damaged Inverness 26.7.99)	Inverness	18. 6.01T
G-BPBJ	Cessna 152 II	152-83639	N4793B	9. 9.88	W.Shaw & P.G.Haines	Whaley Farm, New York, Lincs	19. 1.01
G-BPBK	Cessna 152 II	152-83417	N49095	9. 9.88	Burbage Farms Ltd	Not known	14. 1.01T
G-BPBM	PA-28-161 Warrior II	28-7916272	N3050N	12. 9.88	Halfpenny Green Flight Centre Ltd	Halfpenny Green	14.12.00T
G-BPBO	PA-28RT-201T Turbo Arrow IV	28R-8131195	N8431H	28. 9.88	S.C.May	(Rednal)	11. 5.01
G-BPBP	Brugger MB.2 Colibri mk.II (VW1600)	PFA/43-10246		6. 2.78	D.A.Preston	(Ulverston)	25. 1.99P
G-BPBR	PA-38-112 Tomahawk	38-80A0020	N25082	8. 9.88	Cardiff Wales Flying Club Ltd	Cardiff	30. 6.01T
G-BPBU	Cameron V-77 HAFB	1844		23. 9.88	M.C.Gibbons & J.E.Kite "Sky Maid" t/a G-BPBU Skymaid Balloon (Keep Music Live titles)	Bristol	5. 7.00A
G-BPBV	Cameron V-77 HAFB	1821		21. 9.88	W.E. & L.A.Newman "Sugar Plumb"	Carnforth	
G-BPBW	Cameron O-105 HAFB	1841		14.10.88	R.J.Mansfield "October Gold"	Huddersfield	15. 9.96A
G-BPBY	Cameron V-77 HAFB	1818	(G-BPCS)	9.12.88	Louise Hutley "Brewster's Toy"	Guildford	15. 8.97A
G-BPBZ	Thunder Ax7-77 HAFB	1258		10.10.88	A.W.J.Weston	Ross-on-Wye	
G-BPCA	PBN BN-2B-26 Islander	2198	G-BLNX	28. 1.88	Loganair Ltd (Op Scottish Air Ambulance) "Captain David Barclay MBE"	Glasgow	16. 2.00T
G-BPCE*	Stolp SA.300 Starduster Too (Continental O-470-M)	36	N8HM	26. 9.88	Not known (Stored 2.92)	Sabadella, Barcelona	14.2.89PF
G-BPCF	Piper J3C-65 Cub (Continental O-200-A) (Lippert Reed clipped-wing conversion - S/No.SA811SW)	4532	N140DC N28033/NC28033	12. 5.89	T.I.Williams	(Uckfield)	14. 6.00P
G-BPCG	Colt AS-80 Mk.II Hot-Air Airship	1300		14.10.88	N.Charbonnier "Greensport/Napapijri"	Aosta, Italy	10.10.96A
G-BPCI	Cessna R172K Hawk XP II	R172-2360	N9976V	3. 1.89	P.A.Warner	Lower Wasing Farm, Brimpton	24. 5.02
G-BPCJ*	Cessna 150J	150-70797	N61096	26. 9.88	Solihull College Engineering Dept	Blossomfield Rd, Solihull	3. 8.92T
				(Damaged Compton Abbas 25.1.90; instructional airframe 3.95)			

Regn	Type	C/n	P/I	Date	Owner/operator	Probable Base	CA Expy
G-BPCK	PA-28-161 Warrior II	28-8016279	N8529N C-GMEI/(N9519N)	26. 9.88	W.G.Booth	Compton Abbas	10. 8.01T
G-BPCL	Scottish Avn Bulldog Srs.120/128	BH120/393	HKG-6 G-31-19	20. 9.88	Isohigh Ltd t/a 121 Group (DHL c/s)	Elstree	2. 7.01T
G-BPCM	Rotorway Exec 152 (RW152)	E.3293	N979WP	21. 9.88	R.J.Turner Weavers Loft, Wem t/a Aircare Group (Stored 7.96)		25.11.91P*
G-BPCR	Mooney M.20K (231)	25-0532	N98433	23. 9.88	T. & R.Harris "Over The Moony"	Biggin Hill	17. 6.01
G-BPCV	Montgomerie-Bensen B-8MR (Rotax 532)	PFA G/01-1088		11.10.88	O.J.Blackbourn Tremethick Cross, Penzance		25. 7.91P
G-BPCX	PA-28-236 Dakota	28-8211004	N8441S	25.10.88	G.E.J.Spooner	Andrewsfield	11. 6.01T
G-BPDE	Colt 56A HAFB	1296		26.10.88	J.E.Weidema Baambrugge, The Netherlands t/a Pinkel Balloons		25. 6.97A
G-BPDF	Cameron V-77 HAFB	1806		6.10.88	The Ballooning Business Ltd Northampton "Burning Ambition"		31. 7.00T
G-BPDG	Cameron V-77 HAFB	1839		21.10.88	D.F.H.Smith "Pretty Damn Good"	Burnley	4. 9.00A
G-BPDJ	Chris Tena Mini Coupe (VW1835)	275	N13877	4.10.88	J.J.Morrissey (Stored 9.98)	Popham	
G-BPDK*	Sorrell SNS-7 Hyperbipe (Lycoming IO-360)	242	N85BL	6.10.88	A.J.Cable (Cancelled by CAA 17.2.99: on rebuild 4.99)	Barton	23.6.95P*
G-BPDM	CASA I-131E Jungmann	2058	E3B-369	24.10.88	J.D.Haslam (Northallerton) (As "E3B-369/781-32" in Spanish AF c/s)		22. 6.96P
G-BPDT	PA-28-161 Warrior II	28-8416004	N4317Z	22.12.88	Channel Islands Aero Services Ltd Jersey t/a Jersey Aero Club		11. 3.02T
G-BPDU	PA-28-161 Cherokee Warrior II	28-7716195	N5672V	30. 9.88	Southern Air Ltd	Shoreham	14. 7.02T
G-BPDV	Pitts S-1S Special (Lycoming O-360)	27P	N330VE	15. 9.88	J.Vize	Sywell	7. 6.99P
G-BPDY	Westland-Bell 47G-3B1 (Line No.WAN/48)	WA/356	OY-HCO SE-HIF/XT197	10.10.88	M.O.Simpson & A.C.Lindner t/a Howden Helicopters	Howden	3. 8.01T
G-BPEA	Boeing 757-236ER	24370		31. 3.89	British Airways plc (Union Flag c/s)	Gatwick	5. 6.02T
G-BPEB	Boeing 757-236ER	24371		27. 4.89	British Airways plc (Union Flag t/s)	Gatwick	1. 5.02T
G-BPEC	Boeing 757-236ER	24882		6.11.90	British Airways plc (Waves & Cranes t/s)	Gatwick	12.11.00T
G-BPED	Boeing 757-236	25059		30. 4.91	British Airways plc (Cockerel of Lowicz/Koguty Lowickie t/s)	Heathrow	29. 4.01T
G-BPEE	Boeing 757-236ER	25060		3. 5.91	British Airways plc (Union Flag c/s)	Gatwick	2. 5.01T
G-BPEF	Boeing 757-236ER	24120	G-BOHC EC-ELA/EC-516/G-BOHC/EC-ELA/EC-202/G-BOHC	18. 5.92	British Airways plc	Gatwick	17. 5.02T
G-BPEI	Boeing 757-236	25806	(G-BMRK)	9. 3.94	British Airways plc (Union Flag c/s)	Heathrow	8. 3.00T
G-BPEJ	Boeing 757-236	25807	(G-BMRL)	22. 4.94	British Airways plc (Union Flag t/s)	Heathrow	24. 4.00T
G-BPEK	Boeing 757-236	25808	(G-BMRM)	17. 3.95	British Airways plc	Heathrow	16. 3.01T
G-BPEL	PA-28-151 Cherokee Warrior	28-7415172	C-FEYM	10.10.88	R.W.Harris & A.Jahanfar (Wreck stored 1.00)	Southend	8. 2.92T
G-BPEM	Cessna 150K	150-71707	N6207G	24.10.88	R.Strong & R.G.Lindsey	Netherthorpe	17. 6.01
G-BPEO	Cessna 152 II	152-83775	C-GQVO (N5147B)	10.10.88	Seawing Flying Club Ltd & Eastern Executive Air Charter Ltd	Southend	1. 7.01T
G-BPER*	PA-38-112 Tomahawk II	38-82A0036	N91465	11.10.88	APB Leasing Ltd	Welshpool	22. 7.98T
	(Damaged Welshpool 30.8.96; dismantled 4.99: cancelled as destroyed 31.8.99)						
G-BPES	PA-38-112 Tomahawk II	38-81A0064	N25728	2.11.88	Sherwood Flying Club Ltd	Nottingham	5. 1.01T
G-BPEZ	Colt 77A HAFB	1324		14.10.88	J.E.F.Kettley & W.J.Honey	Chippenham/Bristol	21. 5.00A
G-BPFB	Colt 77A HAFB	1334		26.10.88	S.Ingram	Oldham	19. 6.95A
G-BPFC	Mooney M.20C Ranger	20-1243	N3606H	21.10.88	D.P.Tinsley	Sleap	1. 3.02
G-BPFD	Jodel D.112	312	F-PHJT	3.11.88	K.Manley Swanborough Farm, Lewes		23.12.00P
G-BPFF	Cameron DP-70 Hot-Air Airship	1831		24.10.88	E.F.H.Wothe	Bruhl, Germany	29. 4.92A
G-BPFH	PA-28-161 Warrior II	28-8116201	N83723	3.11.88	Muriel H.Kleiser (Op Edinburgh Flying Club)	Edinburgh	23.11.00T
G-BPFI	PA-28-181 Archer II	28-8090113	N8103G	5. 1.89	F.Teagle	Perranporth	12. 7.01
G-BPFJ*	Cameron Can 90SS HAFB (Budweiser Beer Can Shape)	1834		14.11.88	I M Martin "Budweiser" (Balloon Preservation Group 7.98)	Lancing	10.12.93A
G-BPFK	Montgomerie-Bensen B.8MR (Rotax 532)	SJB-1 & PFA G/01A-1116		27.10.88	J.W.Birkett (Southampton) (Destroyed Enstone 6.11.94)		9. 6.95P
G-BPFL	Davis DA-2A (Continental O-200-A)	051	N72RJ	27.10.88	B.W.Griffiths	Coventry	26. 1.99P

Regn	Type	C/n	P/I	Date	Owner/operator	Probable Base	CA Expy
G-BPFM	Aeronca 7AC Champion	7AC-4751	N1193E NC1193E	13.10.88	Linda A.Borrill	Netherthorpe	8. 4.00P
G-BPFN	Short SD.3-60 Var.100	SH.3747	N747HH	2.11.88	Loganair Ltd.	Glasgow	27. 8.00T
					N747SA/G-BPFN/G-14-3747 (Mountain of the Birds/Benyhone Tartan t/s)		
G-BPFX*	Colt 21A Cloudhopper HAFB	1348		7.11.88	Not known "Bud Hopper"		
					(Cancelled as WFU 23.12.98: stored BBAC Museum 1999)		
G-BPFZ	Cessna 152 II	152-85741	N94594	27.10.88	C.J.Ward	Wellesbourne Mountford	3. 8.01T
G-BPGB	Cessna 150J	150-69722	N51042	2.11.88	Magnificent Obsessions Ltd	(Grimsby)	1. 3.92T
					(Stored 10.92)		
G-BPGC	Air Command 532 Elite (Rotax 532) 0440 & PFA G/04-1108			11.10.88	E.C.E.Brown Goodworth Clatford, Andover		1. 8.91P
G-BPGD	Cameron V-65 HAFB	2000		9. 9.88	Gone With The Wind Ltd "Silver Lining"	Bristol	4.12.99A
G-BPGE	Cessna U206C Super Skywagon	U206-1013	N29017	7.11.88	K.Brady t/a The Scottish Parachute Club	Strathallan	14. 5.01
G-BPGF	Thunder Ax7-77 HAFB	1355		22.11.88	M.Schiavo "Dovetail"	Manchester	25. 8.95A
G-BPGH	EAA Acrosport II (Continental IO-346)	422	N12JE	14.11.88	G.M.Bradley	Crowfield	31. 8.00P
G-BPGJ*	Colt 31A Air Chair HAFB	1333		22.11.88	Airtrack Adventures	Johannesburg, SA	
G-BPGK	Aeronca 7AC Champion (Continental A65)	7AC-7187	N4409E	7. 2.89	T.M.Williams (Stored 5.99)	Haverfordwest	21. 8.91P
G-BPGM	Cessna 152 II	152-84932	N5380P	14.11.88	Fraggle Leasing Ltd	Aberdeen	18. 2.02T
G-BPGT	Colt AS-80 Mk.II HA Airship	1248	(I-) G-BPGT	14. 7.99	P.Porati	Milan, Italy	20. 7.00A
G-BPGU	PA-28-181 Archer II	28-8490025	N4330B	26.10.88	G.Underwood	Nottingham	25.11.00
G-BPGV	Robinson R-22 Beta	0887		3.11.88	Polo Aviation Ltd	Bristol	21.11.00T
G-BPGX	Socata TB-9 Tampico Club	884		4.11.88	D.A.Lee	Denham	13. 2.00T
G-BPGY	Cessna 150H	150-67325	N6525S	24. 1.89	Rita A.Watson (Op Premi-Air Flying Club)	Shoreham	2.12.02T
G-BPGZ	Cessna 150G	150-64912	N3612J	14.11.88	J.B.Scott	Blackpool	17. 5.01
G-BPHB	PA-28-161 Warrior II	2816069	N9148G	14.11.88	Channel Islands Aero Services Ltd t/a Jersey Aero Club	Jersey	3. 2.01T
G-BPHD	Cameron N-42 HAFB	1863		21. 2.89	P.J.Marshall & M.A.Clarke "Ellen Gee II"	Ruislip	19. 8.95A
G-BPHE	PA-28-161 Warrior II	28-7916536	N2911D	28.12.88	APB Leasing Ltd	Welshpool	26. 3.01T
G-BPHG	Robin DR.400/180 Regent	1887		29.11.88	K.J. & M.B.White Homefield Farm, Crowhurst, Lingfield		20. 5.01
G-BPHH	Cameron V-77 HAFB	1840		2.12.88	C.D.Aindow "Office Angels"	London SW18	2. 9.00A
G-BPHI	PA-38-112 Tomahawk	38-79A0002	N2535T	22.11.88	J.S.Devlin & Z.Islam	Redhill	4. 6.01T
G-BPHJ	Cameron V-77 HAFB	1881		23.11.88	C.W.Brown "Twiggy"	Nottingham	9. 1.00A
G-BPHL	PA-28-161 Warrior II	28-7916315	N555PY N2247U	2.12.88	Teesside Flt Centre Ltd	Teesside	2. 7.01T
G-BPHO	Taylorcraft BC-12D	8497	N96197 NC96197	10. 1.89	A.A.Alderdice "Spirit of Missouri"	(Newry, NI)	18. 8.00P
G-BPHP	Taylorcraft BC-12-65 (Continental A65)	2799	N33948 NC33948	12.12.88	D.C.Stephens "Spirit of Mississippi" (Crashed landing Wellesbourne Mountford 11.4.99)	Llangarron	2.11.99P
G-BPHR	DH 82A Tiger Moth (Australian built)	45	N48DH VH-BLX/A17-48	3. 1.89	N.Parry (As "A17-48" in RAAF c/s) Lotmead Farm, Wanborough, Swindon		11.10.01
G-BPHT	Cessna 152 II	152-82401	N961LP	5.12.88	Bobbington Air Training School Ltd	Halfpenny Green	16. 8.01T
G-BPHU	Thunder Ax7-77 HAFB	1365		19.12.88	R.P.Waite	St.Helens	15. 8.99A
G-BPHV*	Colt Montgolfiere SS HAFB	1281	F-GGFK F-GFLZ	9.12.88	Not known (Cancelled 5.10.90 sold to France: noted 8.98 as "G-BPHV" in UK)		
G-BPHW	Cessna 140 (Continental C85)	11035	N76595 NC76595	13. 1.89	M.Day	White Waltham	17. 6.02
G-BPHX	Cessna 140 (Continental C85)	12488	N2252N NC2252N	2.12.88	M.McChesney (Stored 2.93)	Enniskillen	23. 5.93
G-BPHZ	Morane-Saulnier MS.505 Criquet	53/7	F-BJQC Fr Mil	17. 4.89	G.A.Warner t/a The Aircraft Restoration Co (As "TA+RC" in I/JG54 Luftwaffe c/s)	Duxford	26. 4.99P
G-BPID	PA-28-161 Warrior II	28-7916325	N2137V	16. 3.89	K.J.Newman	North Coates	19. 5.01
G-BPIE	Bell 206B JetRanger III	2533	N327WM	22.11.88	Frey Aviation Ltd (Op Cabair)	Elstree	15. 2.01T
G-BPIF*	Bensen-Parsons Two-Place (Rotax 532)	UK-01		19.12.88	A.P.Barden (Cancelled by CAA 6.3.99)	Inverness	28. 3.96P
G-BPIH	Rand Robinson KR-2 8023 & PFA/129-11436			19.12.88	J.R.Rowley & T.E.Masters	(Birmingham)	
G-BPII	Denney Kitfox 213 & PFA/172-11496 (KFM 112)			15.12.88	G.A.Davidson	Oxenhope	5. 4.94P
G-BPIJ	Brantly B.2B	465	N2293U	23. 3.89	R.B.Payne	Willand, Cullompton	13. 7.98
G-BPIK	PA-38-112 Tomahawk II	38-82A0028	N3947M ZP-EAP/N91423	2.12.88	A.P.Daines	Earls Colne	2. 2.95T

Regn	Type	C/n	P/I	Date	Owner/operator	Probable Base	CA Expy
G-BPIL	Cessna 310B	35620	N620GS	16.11.89	A.L.Brown & R.A.Parsons	Bourn	28. 4.00T
			OO-SEF/N5420A		"Fast Lady"		
G-BPIM	Cameron N-77 HAFB	1896		6. 1.89	Thermalite Ltd	Birmingham	
G-BPIN	Glaser-Dirks DG-400	4-242		14.12.88	J.N.Stevenson	Lasham	10. 4.01
G-BPIO	Reims Cessna F.152 II	1556	PH-VSO	23. 1.89	I.D.McClelland	Biggin Hill	27. 8.01T
			PH-AXS				
G-BPIP	Slingsby T.31 Cadet III	PFA/42-10771		14.11.88	J.H.Beard	Bodmin	27. 9.96P
	(VW1600)						
G-BPIR	Scheibe SF-25E Super Falke	4332	N25SF	15.12.88	Coventry Gliding Club Ltd		
			(D-KDFX)			Husbands Bosworth	3. 4.01
G-BPIT	Robinson R-22 Beta	0907	N80011	22.12.88	NA Air Ltd	Chester	27. 6.02T
G-BPIU	PA-28-161 Warrior II	28-7916303	N3028T	28.12.88	P.G.Doble & P.G.Stewart	Fairoaks	28. 3.01
G-BPIV	Bristol 149 Blenheim IV	-	"Z5722"	15. 2.89	G.A.Warner	Duxford	7. 6.00P
	(Bolingbroke IVT)		RCAF 10201		t/a The Aircraft Restoration Co		
					(As "R3281/UX-N" "Spirit of Britain First"		
G-BPIY	Cessna 152 II	152-84073	N5249H	19.12.88	A.S.Bamrah	Biggin Hill	19.11.97T
					t/a Falcon Flying Services (Damaged Earls Colne 12.8.97)		
G-BPIZ	Gulfstream AA-5B Tiger	AA5B-1154	N4530L	14. 2.89	N.R.F.McNally	Shoreham	30. 7.01
G-BPJB	Schweizer Hughes 269C	S.1331	N75065	7.11.88	Elborne Holdings Ltd	Cascais, Portugal	24.10.02
G-BPJD	Socata Rallye 110ST	3253	OY-CAV	22.12.88	J.G.Murphy	(Nunthorpe)	14. 6.01
					t/a G-BPJD Rallye Group		
G-BPJE	Cameron A-105 HAFB	1864		8.11.88	J.S.Eckersley	Henley-on-Thames	30. 6.00A
					"Burley Stables"		
G-BPJF*	PA-38-112 Tomahawk	38-78A0021	N9312T	5. 4.89	S McNulty	Woodford	4.10.98
				(Crashed on take-off Egginton 20.6.98: wreck in undergrowth 8.99)			
G-BPJG	PA-18-150 Super Cub	18-8350	SE-EZG	4. 1.89	M.W.Stein	Oaksey Park	31. 7.01
			N4172Z				
G-BPJH	PA-18-95 Super Cub	18-1980	MM52-2380	24. 5.83	P.J.Heron	Ballymoney, Co.Antrim	5.10.00P
	(L-18C-PI)		I-EICA/MM52-2380/52-2380				
G-BPJK	Colt 77A HAFB	1362		22.12.88	Saran UK Ltd	Cheltenham	17. 9.97A
G-BPJL	Cessna 152 II	152-81296	N49473	28.12.88	Eastern Executive Air Charter Ltd		
					(Op Seawing Flying Club)	Southend	27. 5.01T
G-BPJN	Jodel D.18	254 & PFA/169-11409		19.12.88	W.J.Evans	Rhigos	28.11.96P
	(VW 1834)				(Damaged Pencefen Farm nr Aberystwyth 21.7.96)		
G-BPJO	PA-28-161 Cadet	2841014	N9153Z	15.12.88	Plane Talking Ltd	Denham	20.12.01T
G-BPJP	PA-28-161 Cadet	2841015	N9154K	22.12.88	Oxford Aviation Services Ltd	Oxford	21. 5.01T
G-BPJR	PA-28-161 Cadet	2841024	N9154X	17. 1.89	J.P.E.Walsh t/a Walsh Aviation	Turweston	22. 2.01T
G-BPJS	PA-28-161 Cadet	2841025	N9154Z	12. 1.89	Oxford Aviation Services Ltd	Oxford	26. 2.01T
					(Damaged near Chipping Norton 1.6.99)		
G-BPJT*	PA-28-161 Cadet	2841031	N9156X	6. 1.89	The Fire Service College		
						Moreton-in-Marsh	17. 2.95T
					(Crashed Oxford 12.7.92 & in fire service use 8.98)		
G-BPJU	PA-28-161 Cadet	2841032	N9156Z	11. 1.89	Oxford Aviation Services Ltd	Oxford	22. 2.01T
G-BPJV	Taylorcraft F-21	F-1005	N2004L	12. 1.89	P.Glennon t/a TC Flying Group	Rochester	17. 6.99P
G-BPJW	Cessna A150K Aerobat	A150-0127	C-FAJX	4. 1.89	G & S.A.Jones	Linley Hill, Leven	21. 5.00T
			CF-AJX/N8427M				
G-BPJZ	Cameron O-160 HAFB	1904		4. 1.89	M.L.Gabb	Alcester	3. 7.97T
G-BPKF	Grob G-115	8075		3. 1.89	R.V.Morgan & J.F.W.Steventon		
					t/a Steventon Morgan Aviation	Compton Abbas	28.12.00
G-BPKI*	EAA Acrosport I	PFA/72A-11391		15. 2.89	M.Swanborough	Breighton	31. 3.00P
	(Lycoming O-320)				(Cancelled as wfu 11.11.99)		
G-BPKK	Denney Kitfox mk.1	264 & PFA/172-11411		19.12.88	D.Moffat	Blackpool	20. 9.00P
	(Rotax 532)						
G-BPKL	Mooney M.20J (201)	24-1102	N1008K	12. 1.89	London Link Flying Ltd	Stapleford	25. 6.01
G-BPKM	PA-28-161 Warrior II	28-7916341	PH-CKO	6. 1.89	M.J.Greasby	RAF Halton	20. 6.01T
			N2140X/N9630N				
G-BPKN*	Colt AS-80 Mk.II Hot-Air Airship	1297		11. 1.89	British Balloon Museum	Newbury	14. 3.91A
					(Stored 12.94)		
G-BPKO	Cessna 140	8936	N89891	12. 1.89	G.R.Pitchfork	(Cheltenham)	18. 5.00
			NC89891				
G-BPKR	PA-28-151 Cherokee Warrior	28-7515446	N4341X	13. 3.89	Aeroshow Ltd	Gloucestershire	12. 3.01T
G-BPLF	Cameron V-77 HAFB	1903		16. 1.89	I.R.Warrington & R.A.Macmillan	Stamford	8. 6.00A
					"Star Attraction"		
G-BPLH	CEA Jodel DR.1051 Sicile	401	F-BLAE	27. 2.89	D.W.Tovey	Dunkeswell	24.11.01
	(Potez 4E20A)						
G-BPLM	AIA Stampe SV-4C	1004	F-BHET	8. 2.89	C.J.Jesson	Headcorn	19. 8.01T
			Fr.Mil/F-BDKC				
G-BPLV	Cameron V-77 HAFB	1822		23. 1.89	MC VH SA	Brussels, Belgium	1. 2.00A
G-BPLY	Christen Pitts S-2B Special	5149		25. 1.89	M.Mountstephen	Goodwood	13. 5.01
	(Lycoming AEIO-540)						

Regn	Type	C/n	P/I	Date	Owner/operator	Probable Base	CA Expy
G-BPLZ	Hughes 369HS	91-0342S	N126CM	15. 2.89	Pyramid Precision Engineering Ltd		
						Halfpenny Green	14. 6.01
G-BPMB	Maule M.5-235C Lunar Rocket	7284C	N5635T	13. 8.79	Earth Products Ltd	Sherburn-in-Elmet	16.12.00
G-BPMC*	Air Command 503 Commander			16.12.88	M.A.Cheshire	Exeter	2. 9.91P
	0403 & PFA G/04-1107				(Thought sold in France: cancelled by CAA 8.3.99)		
G-BPME	Cessna 152 II	152-85585	N94021	24. 1.89	Eastern Executive Air Charter Ltd		
					(Op Seawing Flying Club)	Southend	26. 7.01T
G-BPMF	PA-28-151 Cherokee Warrior		C-GOXL	2. 2.89	L. & A.Hill	Walney Island	2. 5.01
	28-7515050						
G-BPMH	Schempp-Hirth Nimbus 3DM	7/23		20. 3.89	R.Jones "60"	Lasham	20. 4.01
	(Regd as c/n 07)				t/a Southern Sailplanes		
G-BPML	Cessna 172M Skyhawk II	172-67102	N1435U	17.11.89	J.P.Birnie	Sandown	11. 4.00T
					(Op Birnie Air Services)		
G-BPMM	Champion 7ECA Citabria	7ECA-498	N5132T	22. 3.89	J.Murray	(Ballymoney, Co.Antrim)	25. 2.97P
G-BPMR	PA-28-161 Warrior II	28-8416119	N4373S	25. 1.89	B.McIntyre	Gloucestershire	26. 4.01T
			N9620N				
G-BPMU	Nord 3202B	70	(G-BIZJ)	26. 1.89	A.I.Milne	Little Snoring	19.10.90P*
			N22546/ALAT "AIX"		(Stored 9.97)		
G-BPMV	PA-28-161 Warrior II	28-8416127	N4374M	25. 1.89	Oxford Aviation Services Ltd	Oxford	23. 4.01T
			N9628N				
G-BPMW	QAC Quickie Q2	PFA/94A-10790	G-OICI	13. 3.89	P.M.Wright	Cambridge	17. 8.91P
	(Revmaster R2100DQ)		G-OGKN		(Damaged nr Basingstoke 16.2.91: stored 8.99)		
G-BPMX	ARV1 Super 2 K.005 & PFA/152-11128			30. 1.89	T.P.Toth	Enstone	21. 6.00P
	(Hewland AE75)						
G-BPNA	Cessna 150L Commuter	150-73042	N1742Q	10. 2.89	Griffin Marston Ltd	Compton Abbas	2. 3.00T
					(Op Abbas Air)		
G-BPNC	Rotorway Exec 152	3600		3. 2.89	S.J.Hanson	Farleton, Lancaster	30. 5.92P
	(RW152)				(Damaged Quernmore near Lancaster 16.5.92)		
G-BPND	Boeing 727-2D3	21021	OK-EGK	18.12.87	Sabre Airways Ltd "Katie"	Lasham	10. 4.01T
			N500AV/G-BPND/PH-AHZ/N500AV/HI-452/JY-ADV				
G-BPNF	Robinson R-22 Beta	0967		1. 3.89	Not known	NK	24. 4.01
G-BPNI	Robinson R-22 Beta	0948		6. 2.89	Heliflight (UK) Ltd	Halfpenny Green	8. 4.01T
G-BPNL	QAC Quickie Q2	PFA/94A-11014		6. 2.89	J.Catley	Coventry	16. 1.96P
	(Revmaster 2100D)				(Damaged Swansea 30.4.95; wreck stored Longbridge Deverill 3.99)		
G-BPNN	Montgomerie-Bensen B.8MR	MV-003		3. 2.89	M.E.Vahdat	(Uxbridge)	
G-BPNO	Moravan Zlin Z.526 Trener Master 930		F-BPNO	18. 2.86	J.A.S.Baldry & S.T.Logan	RAF Cranwell	11. 9.00
G-BPNT	BAe 146 Srs.300	E-3126		4. 1.89	Flightline Ltd	Bournemouth	31. 5.02T
					(Swissair Express c/s)		
G-BPNU	Thunder Ax7-77 HAFB	1011		9. 2.89	M.J.Barnes "Firefly"	Ivybridge	28. 8.00T
G-BPNW*	HS.748 Srs.2/217	1584	G-11-4	7. 2.89	British Aerospace plc	Irvine	
			RP-C1042/V2-LIP/VP-LIP		(Stored in Maxi-Haulage Yard 8.94)		
G-BPOA*	Gloster Meteor T.7	-	WF877	16. 3.89	Not known	Kemble	
					(As "WF877": stored 8.99)		
G-BPOB	Tallmantz Sopwith Camel F.1 rep		N8997	14. 3.89	Bianchi Aviation Film Services Ltd		
	(Warner Scarab 165)	TM-10				Booker	6. 8.97P
					(Op Blue Max Movie Acft Museum: as "B2458/R" in RFC c/s)		
G-BPOL	Pietenpol Air Camper	PFA/47-10941		16. 2.89	G.W.Postance	(Burgess Hill, Sussex)	
G-BPOM	PA-28-161 Warrior II	28-8416118	N4373Q	15. 2.89	APB Leasing Ltd	Norwich	13. 5.01T
			N9619N				
G-BPON	PA-34-200T Seneca II	34-7570040	N675ES	13. 2.89	Aeroshow Ltd	Gloucestershire	15. 6.01T
			N32644				
G-BPOO	Montgomerie-Bensen B.8MR			3. 2.89	M.E.Vahdat	(Uxbridge)	
	MV-002 & PFA G/01A-1109				(Not constructed)		
G-BPOS	Cessna 150M Commuter	150-75905	N66187	21. 2.89	K.J.Goggins	Bourn	10.10.99T
G-BPOT	PA-28-181 Cherokee Archer II		N8807K	7. 2.89	P.Fraser	Cumbernauld	14. 5.01
	28-7790267						
G-BPOU	Luscombe 8A Silvaire	4159	N1432K	14. 2.89	M.J.Negus & R.Hardley		
	(Continental A65)		NC1432K		Stoneacre Farm, Farthing Corner	23. 8.99P	
G-BPOV	Cameron Magazine 90SS HAFB	1890		10. 3.89	Forbes Europe Inc	Balleroy, Normandy	14. 7.00A
	(Forbes Magazine shape)				"Forbes Capitalist Tool"		
G-BPPA	Cameron O-65 HAFB	1930		15. 2.89	Rix Petroleum Ltd "Rix Petroleum"	Hull	5. 9.99A
G-BPPD	PA-38-112 Tomahawk	38-79A0457	N2456F	15. 2.89	S.Snodgrass & M.A.Wood	Kemble	13. 9.01T
					t/a AS Belting Products		
G-BPPE	PA-38-112 Tomahawk	38-79A0189	N2445C	15. 2.89	M.R.Tingle	Norwich	30. 5.98T
G-BPPF	PA-38-112 Tomahawk	38-79A0578	N2329K	15. 2.89	D.J.Bellamy	Bristol	13. 9.01
					t/a Bristol Strut Flying Group		
G-BPPJ	Cameron A-180 HAFB	1924		2. 3.89	Heather R.Evans	Ross-on-Wye	18. 2.98T
G-BPPK	PA-28-151 Cherokee Warrior		N7592C	10. 3.89	UK Technical Consultants Ltd		
	28-7615054					(Peterborough)	24. 6.98T

Regn	Type	C/n	P/I	Date	Owner/operator	Probable Base	CA Expy
G-BPPL	Enstrom F-28A	251	HB-XER	15. 2.89	M & P Food Products Ltd t/a Coventry Helicopters	Coventry	9. 5.98T
					(Observed transported south on M6 through Staffordshire 24.3.99)		
G-BPPM	Beechcraft B200 Super King Air	BB-1044	N7061T C-GJJT/N815CE/(N815CF)/N815CE/N62895	16. 2.89	Gama Aviation Ltd (Op Bond Air Services)	Aberdeen	24. 9.01T
G-BPPO	Luscombe 8A Silvaire (Continental A65)	2541	N3519M N71114/NC71114	15. 2.89	I.K.Ratcliffe	Popham	28. 6.00P
G-BPPP	Cameron V-77 HAFB	1700		29. 2.88	P.F.Smart t/a The Sarnia Balloon Group "Thruppence"	Basingstoke	28. 6.97A
G-BPPR*	Air Command 532 Elite	0434 & PFA G/04-1105		22. 2.89	T.D.Inch (Cancelled by CAA 10.3.99)	Banstead	14. 5.91P
G-BPPS	Mudry/CAARP CAP.21	9	F-GDTD	3. 5.85	C.Baldwin & N.B.Gray	Barton	21.10.00S
G-BPPU	Air Command 532 Elite	0438 & PFA G/04-1120		22. 2.89	J.Hough	Alresford, Hants	18.10.91P
G-BPPW	Schweizer Hughes 269C (300C)	S.1172	N3624J	22. 2.89	Browns Distribution Services Ltd	Ravensdale, Stoke-on-Trent	28. 5.01
G-BPPY	Hughes 269B (300)	20-0448	N9554F	10. 3.89	N.J.Edmonds	Wellesbourne Mountford	29.10.99
G-BPPZ	Taylorcraft BC-12D (Continental C85)	7988	N28286 NC28286	22. 3.89	J.Gordon & M.Hart t/a Zulu Warriors Flying Group	Charterhall	26. 8.00P
G-BPRA	Aeronca 11AC Chief	11AC-1344	N9702E NC9702E	22. 3.89	R.M.C.Hunter	Scotland Farm, Hook	14. 6.99P
G-BPRC	Cameron Elephant 77SS HAFB	1871		21. 2.89	G.V.Beckwith	(Germany)	30. 3.00A
G-BPRD	Pitts S-1C Special (Lycoming O-360)	ZZ.1	N10ZZ	21. 2.89	Shiela M.Trickey	Bodmin	17. 5.00P
G-BPRI	Aerospatiale AS.355F1 Twin Squirrel	5181	G-TVPA G-BPRI/N364E	22. 2.89	Skyhopper Ltd	Booker	9. 9.02T
G-BPRJ	Aerospatiale AS.355F1 Twin Squirrel	5201	N368E	22. 2.89	PLM Dollar Group Ltd	Cumbernauld	14.12.01T
G-BPRL	Aerospatiale AS.355F1 Twin Squirrel	5154	N362E	22. 2.89	Gas & Air Ltd (Op Virgin Helicopters)	Booker	24. 3.00T
G-BPRM	Reims Cessna F.172L	0825	G-AZKG	20. 4.88	D.Rychlik	(Shetland)	19. 4.01
G-BPRN	PA-28-161 Warrior II	28-8116109	N83112	6. 3.89	Air Navigation & Trading Co Ltd	Blackpool	10. 6.01T
G-BPRO	Cessna A150K Aerobat	A150-0221	N221AR VP-LAQ/8P-LAC/N5921J	1. 3.89	Armphase Ltd	Southampton	24. 3.99
G-BPRP*	Cessna 150E	150-61269	N3569J	10. 3.89	P.A.Griffin (Remains noted 8.98: cancelled as wfu 22.10.99)	Shoreham	23 5.98T
G-BPRR	Rand Robinson KR-2	PFA/129-11105		1. 3.89	R.Trickett	(King's Lynn)	
G-BPRS	Air Command 532 Elite	0432		14. 4.89	B.K.Snoxall (Believed damaged: cancelled by CAA 3.3.99)	(Whitchurch, Hants)	
G-BPRX	Aeronca 11AC Chief (Continental A75)	11AC-94	N86288 NC86288	3. 3.89	D.J.Dumolo & C.R.Barnes	Breighton	23. 8.99P
G-BPRY	PA-28-161 Warrior II	28-8416120	N4373Y N9621N	2. 3.89	R.C.White t/a White Wings Aviation	East Midlands	4. 6.01T
G-BPSB*	Air Command 532 Elite	0431		10. 3.89	D.K.Duckworth (Cancelled by CAA 3.3.99)	Northampton	
G-BPSH	Cameron V-77 HAFB	1837		21. 2.89	P.G.Hossack "Coconut Ice"	Pewsey	5. 4.97T
G-BPSI	Thunder Ax10-160 HAFB	1420		10. 3.89	Airborne Adventures Ltd "Airborne Adventures"	Skipton	19. 2.96T
G-BPSJ	Thunder Ax6-56 HAFB	1479		13. 3.89	Capricorn Balloons Ltd	Loughborough	4. 4.99A
G-BPSK	Montgomerie-Bensen B.8M	PFA G/01-1100		15. 3.89	G.C.Kerr	Carlisle	25.11.99P
G-BPSL	Cessna 177 Cardinal	177-01138	N659SR	3. 3.89	N.P.Bendle t/a G-BPSL Group	Dunkeswell	12.11.01
G-BPSO	Cameron N-90 HAFB	1959		10. 3.89	J.Oberprieler	Mauern, Germany	23. 6.00A
G-BPSP	Cameron Ship 90SS HAFB (Columbus "Santa Maria" shape)	1848		10. 3.89	Forbes Europe Inc "Santa Maria"	Balleroy, Normandy	17. 6.94
G-BPSR	Cameron V-77 HAFB	1962		10. 3.89	K.J.A.Maxwell "Norma Jean"	Haywards Heath	21. 6.00T
G-BPSS	Cameron A-120 HAFB	1947		27. 2.89	T.J.Parker t/a Anglian Countryside Balloons	Burnham-on-Crouch	3.11.99T
G-BPSZ	Cameron N-180 HAFB	1911		14. 3.89	A.Bolger "Park Furnishers II"	Salisbury	4. 1.00T
G-BPTA	Stinson 108-2 Station Wagon (Franklin 6A4)	108-3429	N429C NC429C	22. 3.89	M.L.Ryan	Garston Farm, Marshfield	30. 9.01
G-BPTB	Boeing-Stearman A75N1 (PT-17) Kaydet (Lycoming R-680)	75-442	N55581 40-1885	22. 3.89	Aero Vintage Ltd (As "FJ992" in RAF c/s)	Andrewsfield	15. 7.99
G-BPTC*	Taylorcraft BC-12D	9388	N94988 NC94988	18. 1.89	Not known (Temp unregd 28.1.97)	(London SW15)	29. 5.96P
G-BPTD	Cameron V-77 HAFB	2001		14. 3.89	J.Lippett "Visions 2001"	South Petherton, Somerset	20. 6.00A
G-BPTE	PA-28-181 Cherokee Archer II	28-7690178	N8553E	9. 3.89	I.Chaplin	Southend	9. 8.01T

Regn	Type	C/n	P/I	Date	Owner/operator	Probable Base	CA Expy
G-BPTF	Cessna 152 II	152-81979	N67715	9. 3.89	A.S.Bamrah	Shoreham	12. 8.01T
					t/a Falcon Flying Services		
G-BPTG	Rockwell Commander 112TC	13067	N4577W	31. 3.89	Marita A.Watteau	Shoreham	23. 4.01
G-BPTH*	Air Command 532 Elite	01	N532KR	25. 4.89	R.Wheeler		
					North Green Farm, Reymerston, Norwich		
					(Damaged 1991 - parts only remain 1992: cancelled by CAA 16.4.99)		
G-BPTI	Socata TB-20 Trinidad	414	N41BM	21. 4.89	N.Davis	Blackbushe	25. 5.01
G-BPTL	Cessna 172N Skyhawk II	172-68652	N733YJ	22. 3.89	Cleveland Flying School Ltd	Teesside	3.12.01T
G-BPTO	Zenair CH-200-AA	2-563	EI-BKP	22. 3.89	Barbara Philips Ledbury/Gloucestershire		8. 9.91P
	(Lycoming O-320)				(Damaged Aldersfield, Worcs 27. 5.91)		
G-BPTP	Robinson R-22	0140	N9056H	17. 3.89	Thorneygrove Ltd	Newcastle	2. 6.01T
G-BPTS	CASA I-131E Jungmann	1....	E3B-153	23. 5.89	Aerobatic Displays Ltd	Duxford	28. 9.00P
			"781-75"		(Op The Old Flying Machine Co)		
					(As "E3B-153/781-75" in Spanish AF c/s)		
G-BPTT	Robin DR400/120 Dauphin 2+2	1906		14. 3.89	The Cotswold Aero Club Ltd		
						Gloucestershire	10. 6.01T
G-BPTU	Cessna 152 II	152-82955	N45946	22. 3.89	A.M.Alam	Elstree	23. 6.02
G-BPTV	Bensen B.8	PFA G/01-1058		30. 3.89	C.Munro	(Colne)	
G-BPTX	Cameron O-120 HAFB	1972		29. 3.89	S.J.Colin & A.S.Pinder	Maidstone	14. 5.97T
					t/a Skybus Ballooning		
G-BPTZ	Robinson R-22 Beta	0958		22. 3.89	J.Lucketti	Barton	16.11.98
G-BPUA	EAA Sport Biplane	SAAC-02	EI-BBF	30. 3.89	V.Millard	Hardwick	30. 3.00P
	(Lycoming O-235)						
G-BPUB	Cameron V-31 Air Chair HAFB	1114		15. 3.89	M.T.Evans	Bath	3. 6.94A
G-BPUC	QAC Quickie Q.235	2583	N250CE	22. 3.89	S.R.Harvey	RAF Brize Norton	27.10.00P
	(Lycoming O-235)						
G-BPUE	Air Command 532 Elite			29. 3.89	A.H.Brent	Brough	11. 9.91P
		0441 & PFA G/04-1136					
G-BPUF	Thunder Ax6-56Z HAFB	270	(G-BHRL)	30. 4.80	R.C. & M.A.Trimble	Henley-on-Thames	10. 2.90A
					"Buf Puf"		
G-BPUG	Air Command 532 Elite			29. 3.89	T.A.Holmes	Melrose Farm, Melbourne	18. 4.91P
		0401 & PFA G/04-1157					
G-BPUI*	Air Command 532 Elite			31. 3.89	D.C.E.Streeter	Tatenhill	2. 5.91P
		0442 & PFA G/04-1128			(Cancelled as wfu 21.10.99)		
G-BPUJ	Cameron N-90 HAFB	1977		17. 4.89	D.Grimshaw	Preston	4. 6.00T
G-BPUL	PA-18A-150 Super Cub	18-2017	OO-LUL	12. 4.89	C.D.Duthy-James	(Presteigne)	15. 6.02
	(L-18C-PI)(Regd with Frame No.18-2517)	I-EIRU/EI-87/MM52-2417/52-2417					
G-BPUM	Cessna R182 Skylane RG II	R182-00915	N738DZ	2. 5.89	R.C.Chapman	Marley Hall,Ledbury	30. 4.01
G-BPUP	Whittaker MW.7	PFA/171-11473		2. 8.89	J.H.Beard	(Buckfastleigh, Devon)	
G-BPUR	Piper J3L-65 Cub	4708	N30228	14. 6.89	H.A.D.Monro	(Hastings)	
			NC30228				
G-BPUS	Rans S-9	PFA/196-11487		7. 4.89	T.A.Wright	Langtoft	21. 4.01P
	(Rotax 532)						
G-BPUU	Cessna 140	13722	N4251N	31. 3.89	Sherburn Aero Club Ltd Sherburn in Elmet		28.11.02T
			NC4251N				
G-BPUW	Colt 90A HAFB	1436		12. 4.89	Huntair Ltd	(London SE16)	27. 7.00A
G-BPUX	Cessna 150J Commuter	150-70619	N60851	25. 4.89	BCT Aero Club Leasing Ltd (Chesterfield)		13. 2.97
G-BPVA	Cessna 172F Skyhawk	172-52286	N8386U	13. 4.89	J.Madders & J.Pilkington	Barton	8. 7.00
					t/a South Lancashire Flyers Group		
G-BPVC	Cameron V-77 HAFB	1302		7. 4.89	J.B.R.Elliot	Great Yarmouth	18. 9.97A
G-BPVE	Bleriot XI 1909 rep	1	N1197	20. 6.89	Bianchi Aviation Film Services Ltd		
	(Built R.D.Henry, Texas 1967)				(Blue Max Movie Acft Museum: as "1197") Booker		8. 6.00P
G-BPVH	Cub J3C-85 Prospector	178C	CF-DRY	7. 4.89	D.E.Cooper-Maguire	Findon, Worthing	18. 8.00P
G-BPVI	PA-32R-301 Saratoga SP	3213021	N91685	24. 4.89	M.T.Coppen	Goodwood	16. 7.01
G-BPVJ	Cessna 152 II	152-82596	N70741	13. 4.89	Multiflight Ltd	Leeds-Bradford	14.10.02T
G-BPVK	Varga 2150A Kachina	VAC85-77	N4626V	4. 5.89	H.W.Hall	Southend	10.11.00P
G-BPVM	Cameron V-77 HAFB	1970		4. 4.89	N.F.Mulliner	Chatham	9. 9.97A
					t/a Royal Engineers Balloon Club "Viscount"		
G-BPVN	PA-32R-301T Saratoga SP	32R-8029073	N8178W	14. 4.89	Y.Leysen	Goodwood	20. 7.01T
G-BPVO	Cassutt Racer IIIM	DG.1	N19DD	13. 4.89	R.J.Adams & D.R.Puleston	Old Buckenham	22. 9.98P
	(Continental O-200-A)				"VooDoo"		
G-BPVP	Aerotek Pitts S-2B Special	5000	N5302M	13. 4.89	J.A.Harris	(Gillingham, Dorset)	17. 5.95
					(Damaged Clacton 19.6.92; on rebuild 5.93)		
G-BPVU	Thunder Ax7-77 HAFB	965		12. 4.89	B.J.Hammond	Chelmsford	18. 9.98T
G-BPVW	CASA I-131E Jungmann	2133	E3B-559	17. 5.89	C. & J.W.Labeij		
						Lelystad, The Netherlands	9. 9.97P
G-BPVX*	Cassutt Racer IIIM	99JC	N99JC	17. 4.89	D.D.Milne	(Maidstone)	19. 4.00P
	(Continental C90)				"Whitey"		
					(Crashed Bembridge 3.7.99 & destroyed: cancelled as PWFU 15.12.99)		
G-BPVY	Cessna 172D Skyhawk	172-50568	N2968U	20. 4.89	Unitek Aviation Ltd	Denham	11. 6.02

Regn	Type	C/n	P/I	Date	Owner/operator	Probable Base	CA Expy
G-BPVZ	Luscombe 8E Silvaire (Continental C85)	5565	N2838K NC2838K	9. 5.89	W.E.Gillham & P.Ryman Croft Farm, Defford		31. 5.00P
G-BPWA	PA-28-161 Warrior II	28-7816074	N47450	7. 4.89	Leisure Park Management Ltd	Goodwood	15. 5.01T
G-BPWB	Sikorsky S-61N	61822	EI-BHO G-BPWB/EI-BHO	4. 5.89	Bristow Helicopters Ltd (Op HM Coastguard) "Druminnor"	Portland	10. 7.01T
G-BPWC	Cameron V-77 HAFB	1986		12. 4.89	H.B.Roberts "Hot Flush"	Bristol	29. 4.00T
G-BPWD	Cessna 120 (Continental O-240-E)	10026	N72839 NC72839	14. 4.89	M.B.Horan & M.W.Albery t/a Peregrine Flying Group	Hucknall	29. 6.00P
G-BPWE	PA-28-161 Warrior II	28-8116143	N8330P	2. 5.89	RPR Associates Ltd	Swansea	22. 6.02T
G-BPWG	Cessna 150M Commuter	150-76707	(G-BPTK) N45029	10. 4.89	W.R.Spicer & I.D.Carling Nanbeck Farm, Wilsford, Grantham		26. 7.01T
G-BPWI	Bell 206B JetRanger III	3087	9M-BSR VH-HXZ/ZK-HXX/XC-PFH	14. 4.89	S. & J.M.Taylor	Blackpool	13. 8.01T
G-BPWK	Sportavia Fournier RF5B Sperber	51036	N56JM (D-KEAR)	17. 4.89	S.L.Reed	Usk	28. 7.00P
G-BPWL	PA-25-235 Pawnee	25-2304	N6690Z G-BPWL/N6690Z	14. 4.89	Marchington Gliding Club Ltd	Tatenhill	19. 6.99
G-BPWM	Cessna 150L	150-72820	N1520Q	17. 4.89	M.E.Creasey	Crowfield	11.11.02
G-BPWN	Cessna 150L Commuter	150-74325	N19308	17. 4.89	International Aerospace Engineering Ltd	Cranfield	12. 9.02T
G-BPWP	Rutan LongEz (Continental O-240)	PFA/74A-11132		17. 4.89	J.F.O'Hara & A.J.Voyle	Denham	29. 6.00P
G-BPWR	Cessna R172K Hawk XPII	R172-2953	N758AZ	21. 4.89	A.M.Skelton	Humberside	9. 8.01
G-BPWS	Cessna 172P Skyhawk II	172-74306	N51387	21. 4.89	Chartstone Ltd	Redhill	2. 8.01T
G-BPWT	Cameron DG-19 Helium Airship	1772		18. 4.89	Airspace Outdoor Advertising Ltd	Southampton	3. 7.90A
G-BPWW*	Focke-Wulf Piaggio FWP.149D	087	OO-FDF D-EFDF/(D-EBDF)/West German AF 90+69/SC+332/AS+496 t/a G-BPWW Group	12. 6.89	J S Holborn Standalone Farm, Meppershall (Force landed nr Lydd 17.5.98: cancelled 10.6.99: fuselage noted 7.99)		23..4.01
G-BPWY*	Isaacs Fury II	PFA/11-11437		21. 4.89	R.J.Knights (Cancelled by CAA 16.4.99)	(North Weald)	
G-BPXA	PA-28-181 Archer II	28-8390064	N4305T	12. 5.89	D.Howdle & D.L.Heighington t/a Cherokee Flying Group	Netherthorpe	4. 6.01
G-BPXB	Glaser-Dirks DG-400	4-248		2. 5.89	K.M.Fresson & G.C.Westgate	Parham Park	25. 7.02
G-BPXE	Enstrom 280C Shark	1089	N379KH C-GMLH/N660H	21. 4.89	A.Healy	Littlehampden, Bucks	4. 1.02
G-BPXF	Cameron V-65 HAFB	2003		21. 4.89	D.Pascall "Gwei-Lo"	Croydon	
G-BPXH	Colt 17A Cloudhopper HAFB	667	OO-BWG	21. 4.89	Sport Promotion SRL	Belbo, Italy	8. 9.00A
G-BPXJ	PA-28RT-201T Turbo Arrow IV	28R-8231023	N8061U	21. 4.89	K.M.Hollamby	Biggin Hill	7. 7.01
G-BPXX	PA-34-200T Seneca II	34-7970069	N923SM N9556N	21. 4.89	E.C.& S.G.D.Clark t/a Laden Project Management Services	Biggin Hill	29. 6.01T
G-BPXY	Aeronca 11AC Chief	11AC-S-50	N3842E	10. 4.89	J.H.Tetley	Sherburn-in-Elmet	20. 6.00P
G-BPYI	Cameron O-77 HAFB	1988		9. 5.89	A.J.Clarke t/a Fly By Night Balloon Group	Godalming	2. 5.00A
G-BPYJ	Wittman W.8 Tailwind (Continental PC60)	PFA/31-11028		12. 5.89	J.Dixon	Bagby	19.10.00P
G-BPYK	Thunder Ax7-77 HAFB	1166		15. 5.89	A.R.Swinnerton "Yorick"	London EC2	29. 5.93
G-BPYL	Hughes 369D	100-0796D	N65AM G-BPYL/HB-XKT	10. 5.89	Morcorp (BVI) Ltd	Halfpenny Green	7. 6.01T
G-BPYN	Piper J3C-65 Cub (L-4H-PI)	11422	F-BFYN HB-OFN/43-30131	14. 3.79	D.W.Stubbs t/a The Aquila Group	White Waltham	14. 7.00P
G-BPYO	PA-28-181 Archer II	2890114	(SE-KIH)	22. 5.89	Sherburn Aero Club Ltd Sherburn in Elmet		26. 7.01
G-BPYR	PA-31-310 Turbo Navajo	31-7812032	G-ECMA N27493	15. 5.89	Multi Ltd (Op Adam Construction)	Sturgate	12.10.00T
G-BPYS	Cameron O-77 HAFB	2008		9. 5.89	D.J.Goldsmith "Aqualisa II"	Edenbridge	14.12.99A
G-BPYT	Cameron V-77 HAFB	1984		9. 5.89	M.H.Redman	Sturminster Newton	
G-BPYV	Cameron V-77 HAFB	1992		17. 5.89	Zebedee Balloon Service Ltd	Hungerford	22. 7.00A
G-BPYW*	Air Command 532 Elite	PFA G/04-1114		2. 6.89	W.V.Tatters (Cancelled by CAA 12.4.99)	Keswick	
G-BPYY	Cameron A-180 HAFB	2013		11. 5.89	G.D.Fitzpatrick	Thame	28. 6.96T
G-BPYZ	Thunder Ax7-77 HAFB	1521		11. 5.89	J.E.Astall "Axis" (Stolen Crewkerne, Somerset 23.10.97)	Hinton St.George	7. 7.96A
G-BPZA	Luscombe 8A Silvaire (Continental A65)	4326	N1599K NC1599K	18. 4.89	T.P.W.Hyde Chestnut Farm, Tipps End		18. 5.00P
G-BPZB	Cessna 120 (Continental C90)	8898	N89853 NC89853	25. 5.89	C. & M.A.Grime	Headcorn	26. 4.00P
G-BPZC	Luscombe 8A Silvaire (Continental A65)	4322	N1595K NC1595K	6. 6.89	Not known (Damaged by gales Cranfield 25.1.90: stored 10.96)	Dinton	5. 7.90P
G-BPZD	SNCAN NC.858S	97	F-BEZD	26. 1.79	G.Richards	Headcorn	10. 1.00P

Regn	Type	C/n	P/I	Date	Owner/operator	Probable Base	CA Expy
G-BPZE	Luscombe 8E Silvaire (Continental C85)	3904	N1177K NC1177K	6. 6.89	B.A.Webster t/a WFG Luscombe Associates	Seething	27.10.00P
G-BPZI	Christen Eagle II (Lycoming IO-360)	T.0001	N48BB	22. 5.89	S.D.Quigley "Thunder Eagle"	Breighton	18. 4.00P
G-BPZK	Cameron O-120 HAFB	1982		7. 4.89	D.L.Smith "Hot Stuff"	Newbury	12. 5.97T
G-BPZM	PA-28RT-201 Arrow IV	28R-7918238	G-ROYW G-CRTI/SE-ICY	12. 5.89	Airways Flight Training (Exeter) Ltd	Exeter	22. 8.01
G-BPZO	Cameron N-90 HAFB	1998		15. 5.89	Seaward Homes (South) Ltd "Seaward Homes"	Chichester	4. 6.96A
G-BPZP	Robin DR.400/180R Remorqueur	1471	D-EFZP	4. 5.89	Lasham Gliding Society Ltd	Lasham	14. 5.01
G-BPZS	Colt 105A HAFB	1312		25. 5.89	L.V.Mastis West Bloomfield, MI, USA "Chamonix"		29. 6.97A
G-BPZU	Scheibe SF-25C-2000 Falke	44471	D-KIAV	21. 7.89	A.J.Buchanan t/a G-BPZU Group	Parham Park	12. 8.01
G-BPZY	Pitts S-1C Special (Lycoming O-320)	RN-1	N1159	15. 5.89	J.S.Mitchell	White Waltham	5. 5.00P
G-BPZZ	Thunder Ax8-105 HAFB	1441		25. 5.89	Capricorn Balloons Ltd	Loughborough	27. 3.00T

G-BRAA – G-BRZZ

Regn	Type	C/n	P/I	Date	Owner/operator	Probable Base	CA Expy
G-BRAA	Pitts S-1C Special (Lycoming O-290)	101-GM	N14T	12. 5.89	C.Davidson (Castle Donington) (Stored Blackpool 6.96)		26. 4.91P
G-BRAF	VS.394 Spitfire FR.XVIIIe	6S/663052	Indian AF HS877/SM969	29.12.78	Wizzard Investments Ltd. (As "SM969/D-A" ?)	North Weald	23. 9.93P
G-BRAJ	Cameron V-77 HAFB	1876		25. 5.89	A.W.J.& C.Weston	Ross-on-Wye	
G-BRAK	Cessna 172N Skyhawk II	172-73795	C-GBPN (N5438J)	23. 6.88	T.I.Mason & C.J.Mewis	Kemble	15. 1.01T
G-BRAM*	Mikoyan MiG-21PF	-	503/	22. 5.89	R.Parker Hungarian AF t/a Universal Aviation Group (As "503" in Russian AF c/s) (Cancelled by CAA 16.4.99: to Bournemouth Aviation Museum 1999)	Bournemouth	
G-BRAP	Thermal Aircraft 104 HAFB	001		11. 5.89	R.A.Patey t/a Thermal Acft (London SE1)		
G-BRAR	Aeronca 7AC Champion	7AC-6564	N2978E NC2978E	14. 6.89	C.D.Ward	Wombleton	20. 8.98P
G-BRAW	Pitts S-1C Special (Lycoming O-290)	52544	N24DB	24. 5.89	P.G.Bond & P.B.Hunter	Swanton Morley	31. 8.99P
G-BRAX	Payne Knight Twister 85B (Continental O-200-A)	203	N979	24. 5.89	R.Earl	White Waltham	29. 9.93P
G-BRBA	PA-28-161 Warrior II	28-7916109	N2090B	25. 5.89	Bobbington Air Training School Ltd	Halfpenny Green	22.11.01T
G-BRBB	PA-28-161 Warrior II	28-8116030	N8260W	28. 6.89	Aeroshow Ltd	Cardiff	13.10.01T
G-BRBC	North American T-6G Texan (Reported as c/n 182-155 ex 51-14469)	182-156	MM54099 RR-56/51-14470	4. 9.92	A.P.Murphy (Chigwell) (On rebuild Audley End 9.90 - status uncertain)		
G-BRBD	PA-28-151 Cherokee Warrior	28-7415315	N41702	28. 6.89	W.E.Rispin t/a Bravo Delta Group "Shaftesbury Belle"	Compton Abbas	22. 3.02
G-BRBE	PA-28-161 Warrior II	28-7916437	N2815D	13. 6.89	Solo Services Ltd (Op Sussex Flying Club)	Shoreham	17.12.01T
G-BRBF	Cessna 152 II	152-81993	N67748	8. 6.89	G.Jackson t/a Jacksons Tool & Plant Hire	Bagby	5. 7.98T
G-BRBG	PA-28-180 Cherokee Archer	28-7505248	N3927X	12. 6.89	Ken MacDonald & Co	Stornoway	19. 8.01
G-BRBH	Cessna 150H Commuter	150-69283	N50410	13. 6.89	Professional Flight Management Ltd & S.J.Reeves	Panshanger	7. 8.01T
G-BRBI	Cessna 172N Skyhawk II	172-69613	N737RJ	7. 7.89	M.D.Harcourt-Brown t/a G-BRBI Flying Group	Popham	3. 9.01
G-BRBJ	Cessna 172M Skyhawk II	172-67492	N73476	26. 5.89	L.C.Macknight	Elstree	12. 1.02
G-BRBK	Robin DR.400/180 Regent	1915		31. 5.89	R.Kemp	Thruxton	15.10.01
G-BRBL	Robin DR.400/180 Regent	1920		5. 7.89	C.A.Marren	Upavon	19. 5.01
G-BRBM	Robin DR.400/180 Regent	1921		5. 7.89	R.W.Davies Little Robhurst Farm, Woodchurch, Kent		24. 1.02
G-BRBN	Pitts S-1S Special (Lycoming O-360)	G.3	N81BG	14. 7.89	D.R.Evans	Gloucestershire	14. 6.99P
G-BRBO	Cameron V-77 HAFB	1877		30. 5.89	M B Murphy "Patches"	Cheltenham	14. 6.00A
G-BRBP	Cessna 152 II	152-84915	N5324P	14. 6.89	Staverton Flying Services Ltd	Gloucestershire	23. 7.01T
G-BRBS	Bensen B.8M (Rotax 503)	PFA G/01-1039		30. 5.89	K.T.MacFarlane	Kilmacolm, Renfrew	
G-BRBT	Trotter Ax3-20 HAFB	RMT-001		13. 6.89	R.M.Trotter	Bristol	
G-BRBU	Colt 17A Cloudhopper HAFB	1506		12. 6.89	Virgin Airship & Balloon Co Ltd "National Theatre"	Telford	29. 5.90A
G-BRBV	Piper J/4A Cub Coupe (Continental A75)	4-1080	N27860 NC27860	13. 6.89	Janette Schonburg & Miriam Yeo	Exeter	18. 4.96P

Regn	Type		C/n	P/I	Date	Owner/operator	Probable Base	CA Expy
G-BRBW	PA-28-140 Cherokee Cruiser	28-7425153		N40737	3. 7.89	R.W.Langley Shoreham t/a Cherokee Cruiser Aircraft Group		18.10.01
G-BRBX	PA-28-181 Cherokee Archer II	28-7690185		N8674E	20. 7.89	M.J.Ireland Birmingham t/a Archer Air		18. 2.02T
G-BRBY	Robinson R-22 Beta		1027		15. 6.89	Plane Talking Ltd	Blackbushe	13. 7.01T
G-BRCA	Jodel D.112 (Built Ets Valladeau)		1203	F-BLIU	11. 7.89	R.C.Jordan	Turweston	10.11.99P
G-BRCD	Cessna A152 Aerobat		A152-0796	N7377L	8. 6.89	D.E.Simmons Shoreham t/a Charlie Delta Group		12. 8.01
G-BRCE	Pitts S-1C Special (Lycoming O-290)		1001	N4611G	22. 6.89	R.D.Rogers Hulcote Farm, Salford, Beds (Op Skylark Aerobatic Co)		25.11.97P
G-BRCF	Montgomerie-Bensen B.8MR (Rotax 532)	PFA G/01A-1131			12. 6.89	J.S.Walton	Mold	30.10.91P
G-BRCG	Grob G-109		6077	N64BG	15. 6.89	Oxfordshire Sportflying Ltd	Enstone	11.11.01
G-BRCI	Pitts S-1C Special (Lycoming O-320)		4668	N351S	6. 7.89	G.L.A.Vandormael	Tatenhill	5. 1.00P
						(Damaged on take off Tatenhill 15.3.99)		
G-BRCJ	Cameron H-20 HAFB		2028		13. 6.89	P.de Cock	Waasmunster, Belgium	25. 7.99A
G-BRCM	Cessna 172L Skyhawk		172-59960	N3860Q	19. 6.89	S.G.E.Plessis & D.C.C.Handley Cranfield (Op Osprey Flying Club)		22. 7.02T
G-BRCO	Cameron H-20 HAFB		2030		19. 6.89	M.Davies Callington, Cornwall "Shell Unleaded"		17. 6.97A
G-BRCT	Denney Kitfox Mk.2		396		23. 6.89	L.A.James (Nuneaton) (Frame stored 4.94)		
G-BRCV	Aeronca 7AC Champion (Continental A65)		7AC-282	N81661 NC81661	19. 9.89	J.M.Gale Belle Vue Farm, Yarnscombe		3.12.00P
G-BRCW	Aeronca 11BC Chief (Continental C85)		11AC-366	N85954 NC85954	16.10.89	R.B.McComish Bow, Totnes		26. 4.00P
	(Registered P/i N85954 & c/n are correct but actual P/i is now known to be N85964 [11AC-386]							
G-BRDB	Zenair CH-701 STOL	PFA/187-11412			11. 7.89	D.L.Bowtell (Ware)		
G-BRDC	Thunder Ax7-77 HAFB		1547		26. 6.89	P.J.Bish & C.Kunert Hungerford t/a Zebedee Balloon Service "Purple Rising"		18. 1.00A
G-BRDD	Mudry CAP.10B		224		3. 8.88	R.D.Dickson Coal Aston/Gamston		9. 9.00
G-BRDE	Thunder Ax7-77 HAFB		1538		22. 6.89	C.C.Brash "Veronica" Maidenhead		24. 7.96A
G-BRDF	PA-28-161 Cherokee Warrior II	28-7716085		N1139Q	26. 6.89	White Waltham Airfield Ltd White Waltham (Op West London Aero Services)		19. 5.02T
G-BRDG	PA-28-161 Warrior II	28-7816047		N44934	26. 6.89	White Waltham Airfield Ltd White Waltham (Op West London Aero Services)		10.12.01T
G-BRDJ	Luscombe 8A Silvaire (Continental A65)		3411	N71984 NC71984	28. 6.89	J.D.Parker Franklyn's Field, Chewton Mendip		8. 7.00P
G-BRDM	PA-28-161 Cherokee Warrior II	28-7716004		N8464F	26. 6.89	White Waltham Airfield Ltd White Waltham (Op West London Aero Services)		12.11.01T
G-BRDN	Socata MS.880B Rallye Club		1212	OY-DTV	14. 7.89	B.J.D.Peatfield	Redhill	27. 4.02
G-BRDO	Cessna 177B Cardinal II		177-02166	N35030	13. 7.89	P.G.Wood & A.J.Renham Bagby t/a Cardinal Group		21.12.01
G-BRDP	Colt Jumbo SS HAFB		1526		3. 7.89	Virgin Airship & Balloon Co Ltd Florida, USA		3. 8.94A
G-BRDT	Cameron DP-70 Hot-Air Airship	2029			3. 7.89	M.M.Cobbold Plymouth		2. 9.96A
G-BRDV	VS Spitfire Prototype rep (Jaguar V-12 350hp) HD36/001 & PFA/130-10796				3. 7.89	Replica Spitfire Ltd RAF Keevil (As "K5054" in RAF c/s: stored 4.96)		18. 2.95P*
G-BRDW	PA-24-180 Comanche		24-1733	N6612P	12. 3.90	I.P.Gibson	Southampton	19.12.02
G-BREA	Bensen B.8MR (Rotax 503)	PFA G/01-1006			6. 7.89	T.J.Deane	Henstridge	24.10.00P
G-BREB	Piper J3C-65 Cub		7705	N41094 NC41094	3. 7.89	L.W.& O.Usherwood Rochester		22. 7.00P
G-BREE	Whittaker MW.7 (Rotax 503)	PFA/171-11497			22. 6.89	G.Hawkins Newton Peverill		20. 6.00P
G-BREH	Cameron V-65 HAFB		2049		7. 7.89	S.E. & V.D.Hurst "Promise" Mansfield		15. 5.00A
G-BREL	Cameron O-77 HAFB		386		5. 4.78	R.A.Patey London N11 "Gabrielle/Big Six"		9. 3.93A
G-BREM	Air Command 532 Elite 0614 & PFA G/04-1139				20. 7.89	T.W.Freeman Fowlmere (Stored 7.91)		25. 3.91P
G-BREP	PA-28RT-201 Arrow IV	28R-7918119		N2230Z	19. 6.90	TDR Aviation Ltd Enniskillen		22. 1.00
G-BRER	Aeronca 7AC Champion (Continental A65)		7AC-6758	N3157E NC3157E	12. 7.89	I.Sinnett (Liskeard) t/a Rabbit Flight		23. 6.00P
G-BREU	Montgomerie-Bensen B.8 (Rotax 582)	PFA G/01A-1137			20. 7.89	J.S.Firth Sherburn-in-Elmet		16. 6.99P
G-BREX	Cameron O-84 HAFB		2019		14. 7.89	Ovolo Ltd Belfast		2. 8.90A
G-BREY	Taylorcraft BC-12D		7299	N43640 NC43640	14. 7.89	R.J.Pitts Leicester t/a BREY Group		24. 3.00P
G-BRFB	Rutan LongEz (Lycoming O-290)	PFA/74A-10646			14. 7.89	R.A.Gardiner Cumbernauld		13. 6.00P

Regn	Type	C/n	P/I	Date	Owner/operator	Probable Base	CA Expy
G-BRFE	Cameron V-77 HAFB	1835		20. 7.89	D.L.C.Nelmes — Bristol		6. 8.00A
					t/a Esmerelda Balloon Syndicate "Esmerelda"		
G-BRFF	Colt 90A HAFB	1548		14. 7.89	M.I. & B.P.Sneap — Ripley, Derbyshire		17. 7.97A
					t/a Amber Valley Aviation "Zycomm"		
G-BRFH	Colt 90A HAFB	1543		14. 7.89	Polydron International Ltd — Kemble		14. 3.97A
					"Polydron"		
G-BRFI	Aeronca 7DC Champion (Continental C85)	7AC-4609	N1058E NC1058E	1. 8.89	A.C.Lines — Leicester (Damaged 1990; on rebuild 4.96)		19. 2.91P
G-BRFJ	Aeronca 11AC Chief (Continental A65)	11AC-796	N9163E NC9163E	28. 7.89	A.Gault — (Carluke)		16. 6.00P
G-BRFL	PA-38-112 Tomahawk	38-79A0431	N2416F	17. 8.89	Teesside Flight Centre Ltd — Teesside		13. 8.02T
G-BRFM	PA-28-161 Warrior II	28-7916279	N2234P	17.10.89	Air Caernarfon Ltd — Caernarfon		15.12.01T
G-BRFN	PA-38-112 Tomahawk	38-79A0397	N2326F	23.10.89	Light Aircraft Leasing (UK) Ltd — Norwich		6.11.00T
G-BRFO	Cameron V-77 HAFB	2025		6. 7.89	N.J.Bland — Oxford		31. 7.00A
					t/a Hedgehoppers Balloon Group "Lurcher"		
G-BRFP	Schweizer Hughes 269C	S.1389		14. 7.89	Heli Hopper Ltd — Yeovil		31. 3.02T
G-BRFR*	Cameron N-105 HAFB	2042		14. 7.89	I M Martin "Rover" — Lancing		6.12.93A
					(Balloon Preservation Group 7.98)		
G-BRFS*	Cameron N-90 HAFB	2041		14. 7.89	Flying Pictures Ltd "Jaguar" — Fairoaks		21.11.96A
					(Cancelled as wfu 20.1.99)		
G-BRFW	Montgomerie-Bensen B.8 Two-Seat (Rotax 582)	PFA G/01-1073		20. 7.89	J.M.Montgomerie — Crosshills, Maybole		7.10.98P
G-BRFX	Pazmany PL-4A (VW1700)	PFA/17-10079		14. 7.89	D.E.Hills — (Ipswich)		
G-BRGD	Cameron O-84 HAFB	2043		20. 7.89	J.R.H. & M.A.Ashworth — Newquay		
G-BRGE	Cameron N-90 HAFB	2047		20. 7.89	Oakfield Farm Products Ltd "Oakfield Farm Products" — Broadway, Worcester		15.12.99A
G-BRGF	Luscombe 8E Silvaire (Continental C85)	5475	N23FP N944BL/N2748K/NC2748K	20. 7.89	N.Surman — RAF Henlow t/a Luscombe Flying Group		18. 5.00P
G-BRGG	Luscombe 8A Silvaire (Continental A65)	3795	N1068K NC1068K	20. 7.89	M.A.Lamprell — (East Grinstead)		20. 8.00P
G-BRGI	PA-28-180 Cherokee E	28-5827	N77VG N11VG	24. 7.89	Golf India Aviation Ltd — Redhill		31. 3.02
G-BRGN	BAe Jetstream 3102	637	G-BLHC G-31-637	20. 3.87	British Aerospace (Operations) Ltd (Noted as G-6-367 mid 1999) — Woodford		16. 5.01
G-BRGO	Air Command 532 Elite	0615 & PFA G/04-1149		7. 8.89	A.McCredie — (Penrith)		13. 2.91P
G-BRGP*	Colt Flying Stork SS HAFB	1409		25. 7.89	Not known "Great Eggspectations" (USA)		NE(A)
G-BRGT	PA-32-260 Cherokee Six	32-658	N3744W	7.11.89	P.Cowley — East Midlands		28. 6.02
G-BRGW	Barritault JB-01 Minicab (Continental O-200-A)	PFA/1823		13.11.78	R.G.White — Hildon-le-Noble, Hants		18. 6.00P
G-BRGX	Rotorway Exec 152 (RW152D)	3597		3. 8.89	D.W.J.Lee — South Burlingham, Norwich		8. 6.00P
G-BRHA	PA-32RT-300 Lance II	32R-7985076	N2093P	27. 7.89	D.J.Chatterton & P.MacKinnon t/a Lance G-BRHA Group — Earls Colne/Southend		11.11.01
G-BRHB	Boeing-Stearman B75N1 (N2S-3) Kaydet	75-6508 AC	EC-AID N67955/Bu.05334	10. 8.89	D.Calabritto — (Billericay)		
G-BRHC	Cameron V-77 HAFB	1842		3. 8.89	Golf Centres Balloons Ltd "Green Dragon" — Gargonza, Italy		30. 8.94T
G-BRHG	Colt 90A HAFB	1568		11. 9.89	Bath University Students Union — Bath "Badgerline"		29. 8.00A
G-BRHL	Montgomerie-Bensen B.8MR (Rotax 503)	PFA G/01A-1123		7. 8.89	A.McCredie — Carlisle		19. 7.00P
G-BRHM	Bensen B.8M	PFA G/01-1144		3. 8.89	H.P.Latham — Stockbridge		
G-BRHN	Robinson R-22 Beta	1093		4. 8.89	Plane Talking Ltd — Elstree		21. 5.01T
G-BRHO	PA-34-200 Seneca	34-7350037	N15222	20. 9.89	D.A.Lewis — Luton		30. 7.01
G-BRHP	Aeronca O-58B Defender (Continental A65)	058B-8533	N58JR N46536/43-1923	2. 8.89	C.J.Willis — (Giola dell Colle, Italy) (As "3-1923" in US Army c/s)		7. 2.00P
	(If US Army serial is correct, type should be L-3C-AE Grasshopper)						
G-BRHR	PA-38-112 Tomahawk	38-79A0969	N2377P	21. 8.89	Air Nova plc — Chester		27. 9.01T
G-BRHT	PA-38-112 Tomahawk	38-79A0199	N2474C	4. 8.89	Air Nova plc — Chester		9. 8.01T
G-BRHU	Montgomerie-Bensen B.8MR (Rotax 532)	PFA G/01A-1133		4. 8.89	G.L. & S.R.Moon — Camberley		10. 1.92P
G-BRHW	DH.82A Tiger Moth	85612	7Q-YMY VP-YMY/ZS-DLB/SAAF 4606/DE671	26. 7.89	P.J. & A.J.Borsberry (On rebuild) — Kidmore End, Reading		
G-BRHX	Luscombe 8E Silvaire (Continental C90)	5114	N176M N2387K/NC2387K	8. 8.89	J.Lakin — Eaglescott		18. 5.00P
G-BRHY	Luscombe 8E Silvaire (Continental C85)	5138	N2411K NC2411K	8. 8.89	D.Lofts & A.R.W.Taylor — Sleap		19. 4.00P
G-BRHZ	Stephens Akro Z (Lycoming IO-360) (Aka "Astro 235")	A-235	N35EJ	20.12.89	T.A.Shears — White Waltham		16. 4.98P

Regn	Type	C/n	P/I	Date	Owner/operator	Probable Base	CA Expy
G-BRIA	Cessna 310L	310L-0010	N2210F	4. 8.89	B.J.Tucker & R.C.Pugsley	Kemble	15.10.01T
G-BRIB	Cameron N-77 HAFB	2065		8. 8.89	D.Stitt	Tunbridge Wells	17. 8.00A
					"American Adventures"		
G-BRID*	Cessna U206A Super Skywagon		N4874F	7. 5.87	British Skysports	Grindale	20. 5.93
		U206-0574			(Used as para-trainer 1.96)		
G-BRIE	Cameron N-77 HAFB	2076		8. 8.89	S J Bettin	Farnham	27. 3.99A
G-BRIF	Boeing 767-204ER	24736	(PH-AHM)	10. 3.90	Britannia Airways Ltd	Luton	18.11.02T
			G-BRIF		"Lord Horatio Nelson"		
G-BRIG	Boeing 767-204ER	24757	(PH-AHN)	10. 4.90	Britannia Airways Ltd	Luton	17. 4.00T
			G-BRIG		"Eglantyne Jebb"		
G-BRIH	Taylorcraft BC-12D	7421	N43762	24. 8.89	A.D.Duke	(Lichfield)	12. 5.00P
	(Continental A75)		NC43762				
G-BRII	Zenair CH-600 Zodiac	PFA/162-11392		18. 8.89	A.C.Bowdrey	(Hemel Hempstead)	
G-BRIJ	Taylorcraft F-19	F-119	N3863T	23. 8.89	K.E.Ballington		
						Yeatsall Farm, Abbots Bromley	31. 8.99P
G-BRIK	Nipper T.66S RA45 Srs.3B			26. 4.77	C.W.R.Piper	Hinton-in-The-Hedges	14. 6.00P
	(VW1834)	PFA/25-10174	(Rebuild of G-AVKH)				
G-BRIL	Piper J/5A Cub Cruiser	5-572	N35183	2. 8.89	P.L.Jobes	Spilhall Farm, Co.Durham	19.12.00P
	(Continental A75)		NC35183				
G-BRIM	Cameron O-160 HAFB	1856		10. 8.89	Golf Centres Balloons Ltd	Bridport	11. 8.93T
G-BRIO	Turner Super T-40A	PFA/104-10636		7. 8.89	R.W.L.Breckell	(Liverpool)	15. 8.00P
	(Continental O-200-A) (Regd incorrectly as PFA/104-10736)				t/a BRIO Flyers		
G-BRIR	Cameron V-56 HAFB	2056		17. 8.89	H.G.Davies & C.Dowd	Cheltenham	6. 9.97A
					"Spirit of Century" (Skyviews Windows c/s)		
G-BRIS	Steen Skybolt	01	N870MC	30. 8.89	Little Bear Ltd	Exeter	3. 1.00P
	(Lycoming IO-360)						
G-BRIV	Socata TB-9 Tampico Club	939		24. 8.89	Gowad Aviation Ltd	Blackbushe	10. 2.00T
G-BRIY	Taylorcraft DF-65	6183	N59687	1. 2.90	J.D.Tseliki	(Brighton)	10. 7.98P
	(Continental A65) (Built as TG-6 glider) NC59687/42-58678 (As "42-58678/IY" in L-2A USAAC c/s)						
G-BRIZ*	Druine D.31 Turbulent	PFA/48-11513		8. 8.89	M.C.Hunt	(Farnborough)	
					(No Permit issued: cancelled by CAA 2.3.99)		
G-BRJA	Luscombe 8A Silvaire	3744	N1017K	12. 9.89	A.D.Keen	Dunkeswell	14. 1.99P
	(Continental A65)		NC1017K				
G-BRJB	Zenair CH-600 Zodiac			2. 8.89	D.J.Hunter	Priory Farm, Tibbenham	
		6-1283 & PFA/162-11573			(Exhibited incomplete PFA Cranfield 7.95)		
G-BRJC	Cessna 120	12077	N1833N	21. 8.89	C.J.Elliott & D.J.Wheeler	Nottingham	22. 3.00P
	(Continental C85)		NC1833N		t/a One Twenty Group		
G-BRJK	Luscombe 8A Silvaire	4205	N1478K	21. 8.89	C.J.L.Peat & M.Richardson	Redhill	1. 4.00P
	(Continental A65)		NC1478K				
G-BRJL	PA-15 Vagabond	15-157	N4370H	21. 8.89	C.P.Ware & C.R.Leech		
	(Continental C85)		NC4370H			Garston Farm, Marshfield	29. 6.00P
G-BRJN	Pitts S-1C Special	1-MA	N6A	23. 8.89	W.Chapel	Sherburn-in-Elmet	20.10.00P
	(Lycoming O-320)						
G-BRJR	PA-38-112 Tomahawk	38-79A0144	N2598B	31. 8.89	Chester Aviation Ltd	Chester	31. 3.02T
G-BRJT	Cessna 150H	150-68426	N44SS	31. 8.89	J.Eagles	Kemble	2. 8.01T
			N22649				
G-BRJV	PA-28-161 Cadet	2841167	N9185G	24. 8.89	Newcastle upon Tyne Aero Club Ltd	Newcastle	4.12.01T
					(Damaged at Kirkbride 17.5.98)		
G-BRJW	Bellanca 7GCBC Citabria 150S 1200-80		OO-LPG	7. 4.82	F.A.L.Castleden & A.J.Sillis	Henstridge	4. 8.00
G-BRJX	Rand Robinson KR-2	PFA/129-11386		22. 8.89	D.H.Evans	Cardiff	15. 4.97P
	(Revmaster 2100D)						
G-BRJY	Rand Robinson KR-2	PFA/129-11308		22. 8.89	R.E.Taylor	Inverness	23. 5.96P
	(Revmaster 2100D)						
G-BRKA*	Luscombe 8F Silvaire	5084	N2357K	13. 3.89	H.Savage-Jones	(Cheltenham)	1. 8.99P
	(Continental C90)		NC2357K		(Cancelled 20.4.99 as destroyed: on rebuild Chilbolton 8.99)		
G-BRKC	Auster 5 J/1 Autocrat	2749	F-BFYT	31. 8.89	J.W.Conlon (On rebuild 5.97) High Easter		
G-BRKD*	Piaggio P.149D	306	D-EAMS	15. 9.89	P.E.H.Scott Standalone Farm, Meppershall		5.11.92
			92+10/AC+457/AS+457 (Cancelled by CAA 28.5.99)				
G-BRKH	PA-28-236 Dakota	28-7911003	N21444	30. 8.89	P.A.Wright & P.W.Lever	Newcastle	28.12.01
G-BRKL	Cameron H-34 HAFB	2075		29. 8.89	B.J.Newman	Rushden, Northampton	2. 4.00A
G-BRKN	Robinson R-22 Mariner	0578M	N2454M	5. 9.89	P.M.Webber	Koropi Heliport, Greece	9. 6.99
G-BRKO*	Oldfield Baby Lakes	1	N8GL	18. 1.90	C.Wren	Stapleford	
					(Cancelled by CAA 18.3.99 but Cf/f 19.10.99)		
G-BRKP*	Colt 31A HAFB	1590		30. 8.89	Bavarian Balloon Co Ltd	(Germany)	
					(Cancelled as PWFU 22.3.99)		
G-BRKR	Cessna 182R Skylane II	182-68468	N9896E	2. 6.89	A.R.D.Brooker		
						Springfield Farm, Ettington	27. 1.02
G-BRKS*	Air Command 532 Elite			1. 9.89	G.Sandercock	Reigate	11. 3.91P
		GS-01 & PFA G/04-1146			(Cancelled by CAA 10.3.99)		
G-BRKW	Cameron V-77 HAFB	2093		1. 9.89	T.J.Parker	Burnham-on-Crouch	3.11.98

Regn	Type	C/n	P/I	Date	Owner/operator	Probable Base	CA Expy
G-BRKX	Air Command 532 Elite			8. 9.89	K.Davis	Alfreton, Derbyshire	10.12.90P
	(Rotax 532) 0619 & PFA G/04-1150						
G-BRKY	Viking Dragonfly mk II PFA/139-11117			7. 9.89	G.D.Price	Deanland,.Hailsham	8. 6.94P
	(VW 2180)				(Stored 3.97)		
G-BRLB	Air Command 532 Elite	0622		4. 9.89	F.G.Shepherd	Great Orton	
G-BRLD*	Robinson R-22 Beta	1099		4. 9.89	R.Everett	Sproughton, Ipswich	25.10.95
				(Damaged Rayleigh 28.3.93: stored 12.95 - pod at Redhill 12.96)			
G-BRLF	Campbell Cricket	PFA G/03-1077		6. 9.89	D.Wood	Holbeach	1.12.00P
	(Rotax 503)						
G-BRLG	PA-28RT-201T Turbo Arrow IV		N4379P	12. 9.89	C.G.Westwood	Welshpool	11. 1.02
		28R-8431027	N9600N				
G-BRLH*	Air Command 532 Elite			12. 9.89	Childs Garages (Sherborne) Ltd (Stored 4.96)		
		0623 & PFA G/04-1148			(Cancelled by CAA 26.1.99)	Henstridge	28.12.90P
G-BRLI	Piper J/5A Cub Cruiser	5-822	N35951	23. 8.89	Little Bear Ltd	Exeter	16. 6.00P
	(Lycoming O-290)		NC35951				
G-BRLK*	Air Command 532 Elite			7. 9.89	G.L.Hunt	Ripley, Derbyshire	1. 1.91P
		0618 & PFA G/04-1155			(Used for spares 1998: cancelled by CAA 10.3.99)		
G-BRLL	Cameron A-105 HAFB	2032		7. 9.89	Adventure Flights Ltd	London W7	23.10.99T
					"Chris Evan Ltd"		
G-BRLO	PA-38-112 Tomahawk	38-78A0621	N2397K	26.10.89	Scotia Safari Ltd	Carlisle	1. 7.99T
			N9680N				
G-BRLP	PA-38-112 Tomahawk	38-78A0011	N9301T	4.10.89	D.A.Whitmore	Cardiff	19. 3.01T
G-BRLR	Cessna 150G	150-64822	N4772X	4.10.89	D.C.Maxwell	Morgansfield, Fishburn	17. 5.98
G-BRLS	Thunder Ax7-77 HAFB	1603		29. 9.89	Elizabeth C.Meek	Oswestry	15. 7.99A
G-BRLT	Colt 77A HAFB	1588		12. 9.89	D.Bareford "Pro-Sport"	Kidderminster	23. 4.00A
G-BRLU*	Cameron H-24 HAFB	2082		8. 9.89	Not known (Temp unregd 21.5.97)	Bedford	10. 1.97A
G-BRLV	CCF Harvard 4	CCF4-194	N90448	14. 9.89	B.C.Abela	North Weald	6. 7.00P
			RCAF 20403		(Op Bar-Belle Aviation) "Texan Belle"		
					(As "93542/LTA-542" in 6148th TCS USAF c/s)		
G-BRLX	Cameron N-77 HAFB	2095		13. 9.89	National Power plc	Swindon	1. 6.96A
					"National Power"		
G-BRLY	BAe ATP	2025	TC-THP	22. 9.89	Trident Aviation Leasing Services (Jersey) Ltd.,		
			G-BRLY			Woodford	29.10.99T
G-BRMA*	Westland WS-51 Dragonfly HR.5		WG719	15. 6.78	E.D. Ap Rees	Weston-super-Mare	
		WA/H/50			t/a The Helicopter Museum (As "WG719/705")		
G-BRMB*	Bristol 192 Belvedere HC.1	13347	7997M	15. 6.78	E.D. Ap Rees	Weston-super-Mare	
			XG452		t/a The Helicopter Museum (As "XG452")		
G-BRME	PA-28-181 Cherokee Archer II		OY-BTA	14. 9.89	Keen Leasing Ltd	(Castletown, IoM)	21. 4.02T
		28-7790105					
G-BRMG	VS.384 Seafire F.XVII	FLWA.25488	A2055	19. 9.89	P.J.Woods	Twyford, Bucks	AC
			SX336		(On rebuild 3.96: as "SX336"		
G-BRMI	Cameron V-65 HAFB	2104		14. 9.89	M.Davies	Callington, Cornwall	17. 6.97A
					"Sapphire"		
G-BRMJ	PA-38-112 Tomahawk	38-79A0784	N2316N	15. 9.89	Aerohire Ltd	Wellesbourne Mountford	25. 4.96T
					(Op Wellesbourne Aviation)		
G-BRML	PA-38-112 Tomahawk	38-79A1017	N2510P	3.10.89	P.H.Rogers	Halfpenny Green	3. 2.02T
G-BRMM*	Air Command 532 Elite			15. 9.89	R. de Serville	(London SW7)	
		0624 & PFA G/04-1159			(Cancelled by CAA 16.4.99)		
G-BRMS	PA-28RT-201 Arrow IV	28R-8118004	N82708	25. 9.89	Fleetbridge Ltd	White Waltham	22. 6.02
G-BRMT	Cameron V-31 Air Chair HAFB	2038		31. 8.89	T.C.Hinton	Tunbridge Wells	
G-BRMU	Cameron V-77 HAFB	2109		19. 9.89	K.J. & G.R Ibbotson	Gloucester	
G-BRMV	Cameron O-77 HAFB	2103		25. 9.89	P.D.Griffiths "Viscount"	Southampton	6. 7.00A
G-BRMW	Whittaker MW.7	PFA/171-11395		25. 9.89	N.Crisp	Sittles Farm, Alrewas	6. 9.00P
	(Rotax 532)						
G-BRNC	Cessna 150M Commuter	150-78833	N704SG	29. 9.89	D.C.Bonsall	Netherthorpe	9. 9.02T
G-BRND	Cessna 152 II	152-83776	N5148B	7.11.89	T.M. & M.L.Jones	Egginton	28. 3.02T
					(Op Derby Aero Club)		
G-BRNE	Cessna 152 II	152-84248	N5082L	4.10.89	Aerohire Ltd	Hinton-in-The-Hedges	21. 2.99T
G-BRNJ	PA-38-112 Tomahawk	38-79A0415	N2395F	22. 9.89	Aerohire Ltd	Wellesbourne Mountford	4.11.02T
G-BRNK	Cessna 152 II	152-80479	N24969	22. 9.89	Sheffield Aero Club Ltd	Netherthorpe	18. 2.02T
G-BRNM	Chichester-Miles Leopard	002		17.10.89	Chichester-Miles Consultants Ltd		
						Bournemouth	AC
G-BRNN	Cessna 152 II	152-84735	N6452M	22. 9.89	Sheffield Aero Club Ltd	Netherthorpe	23.12.01T
G-BRNP	Rotorway Exec 152	3578		22. 9.89	R.Turner	(Bristol)	AC
G-BRNT	Robin DR.400/180 Regent	1935		3.10.89	M.J.Cowham	Little Gransden	20.12.01
G-BRNU	Robin DR.400/180 Regent	1937		31.10.89	November Uniform Travel Syndicate Ltd		
						White Waltham	19. 5.02
G-BRNV	PA-28-181 Cherokee Archer II		N2537Q	7.12.89	B.S.Hobbs	Goodwood	10. 3.02
		28-7790402					
G-BRNW	Cameron V-77 HAFB	2138		2.10.89	N.Robertson & G.Smith	Truro/Bristol	5. 8.00A
					"Mr Blue Sky"		

Regn	Type	C/n	P/I	Date	Owner/operator	Probable Base	CA Expy
G-BRNX	PA-22-150 Tri-Pacer	22-2945	N2610P	3.10.89	R.S.Tomlinson & B.Yager	Elstree	19.12.02
G-BRNZ	PA-32-300 Cherokee Six B	32-40594	N4229R	7. 2.90	IML Aviation Ltd	Elstree	4. 6.02T
G-BROB	Cameron V-77 HAFB	2073		29. 8.89	R.W.Richardson	Cardiff	26. 3.00a
G-BROE	Cameron N-65 HAFB	2098		5.10.89	R.H.Sanderson "Lancia Dedra"	Nuneaton	3. 8.97A
G-BROF*	Air Command 532 Elite 0625 & PFA G/04-1154			5.10.89	M.J.Hoskins	Banbury	
					(Thought sold in Spain 1994: cancelled by CAA 12.4.99)		
G-BROG	Cameron V-65 HAFB	2121		6. 9.89	R.Kunert "The Dodger"	Wokingham	15. 8.00A
G-BROH	Cameron O-90 HAFB	2120		6.10.89	Patricia A.Wenlock "Linde"	Stretton, Staffs	1. 8.99T
G-BROI	CFM Streak Shadow (Rotax 532) K.115-SA & PFA/161-11586			16.11.89	G.W.Rowbotham	Wymeswold	18. 7.00P
G-BROJ	Colt 31A HAFB	1468		6.10.89	Virgin Airship & Balloon Co Ltd "Fly Virgin"	Telford	23. 9.92A
G-BROL	Colt AS-80 Mk.II Hot-Air Airship	1578		6.10.89	G.Gratius "Hansa-Dental"	Stretten, Germany	14. 3.00A
G-BROM*	ICA IS-28M2A	04A		5.12.77	Not known (Open storage/derelict 4.95)	Cuatro Vientos, Spain	18. 8.87
G-BROP	Van's RV-4 (Lycoming O-360)	3	N19AT	25.10.89	K.E.Armstrong	Armshold Farm, Kingston, Cambs	1. 8.00P
G-BROR	Piper J3C-65 Cub (L-4H-PI)	10885	F-BHMQ 43-29594	7.12.89	J.H.Bailey & A.P.J.Wiseman t/a White Hart Flying Group	Sturgate	16. 6.00P
G-BROX	Robinson R-22 Beta	1127	N8061V	13.10.89	Defence Products Ltd	Blackbushe	9.11.01T
G-BROY	Cameron O-90 HAFB	2173		6. 9.89	T.G.S.Dixon "Dixon Furnace Division"	Bromsgrove	17. 6.00A
G-BROZ	PA-18-150 Super Cub	18-6754	HB-ORC N9572D	20. 9.89	P.G.Kynsey	Rushett Farm, Chessington	7. 3.02T
G-BRPE	Cessna 120 (Continental C85)	13326	N3068N NC3068N	11.10.89	J.M.Fowler	Nottingham	4. 8.00P
G-BRPF	Cessna 120 (Continental C85)	9902	N72723 NC72723	11.10.89	D.Sharp	Breighton	9. 6.00P
G-BRPG	Cessna 120 (Continental C85)	9882	N72703 NC72703	11.10.89	I.C.Lomax	Ottringham	29. 8.94P
G-BRPH	Cessna 120 (Continental C85)	12137	N1893N NC1893N	11.10.89	J.A.Cook	Pent Farm, Postling, Kent	4. 7.00P
G-BRPJ	Cameron N-90 HAFB	2071		11. 9.89	Paul Johnson t/a Cloud Nine Balloon Co "Presto"	Consett	10. 3.99T
G-BRPK	PA-28-140 Cherokee Cruiser	28-7325070	N15449	17.11.89	J.P.A.Gomes	Cascais, Portugal	17. 6.02
G-BRPL	PA-28-140 Cherokee Cruiser	28-7325160	N15771	13.10.89	Comed Aviation Ltd	Blackpool	10. 8.02T
G-BRPM	Nipper T.66 Srs.3B	PFA/25-11038		4. 3.85	T.C.Horner (Under construction 1995)	(Glasgow)	
G-BRPO	Enstrom 280C Shark	1092	N636H	13.10.89	C.M.Evans & J.W.Blaylock	(Boston)	24. 5.02
G-BRPP	Brookland Hornet (VW1776)	DC-1		16.10.89	B.J.L.P.& W.J.A.L.de Saar	(Aberdeen)	19. 8.93P
G-BRPR	Aeronca L-3C Defender (Continental A65)	058B-8823	N49880 43-1952	17.10.89	C.S.Tolchard (As "31952" in US Army c/s)	Earls Colne	14. 2.00P
G-BRPS	Cessna 177B Cardinal	177-02101	N34935	23.10.89	R.C.Tebbett	(Tenbury Wells)	12. 1.02
G-BRPT	Rans S-10 Sakota (Rotax 532)	PFA/194-11554		18.10.89	B.G.Morris	Dunkeswell	17. 6.00P
G-BRPU	Beechcraft 76 Duchess	ME-140	N6007Z	17.10.89	Air Nova plc	Chester	4.10.01T
G-BRPV	Cessna 152 II	152-85228	N6311Q	6.11.89	GEM Rewinds Ltd	Coventry	7. 2.00T
G-BRPX	Taylorcraft BC-12D (Continental A65)	6462	N39208 NC39208	12.12.89	M.J.Brett	Little Gransden	27. 7.00P
G-BRPY	PA-15 Vagabond (Continental C85)	15-141	N4356H NC4356H	23.10.89	Joanne P.Esson	Fareham	18. 5.00P
G-BRPZ	Luscombe 8A Silvaire (Continental A65)	911	N22089 NC22089	13.12.89	S.L. & J.P.Waring	Shacklewell Lodge, Empingham	9. 5.00P
G-BRRA	VS.361 Spitfire LF.IXc (Regd with c/n CBAF.8185)	CBAF.IX.1875		10.10.89	Historic Flying Ltd R.Belg AF SM.29/R.Neth AF H.59/H.119/Fokker B-1/MK912 (On rebuild 12.99 as "MK912/HN-P")	Audley End	
G-BRRB	Luscombe 8E Silvaire (Continental C85)	2611	N71184 NC71184	23.10.89	C.G.Ferguson & D.W.Gladwin	RAF Newton	14. 5.00P
G-BRRD	Scheibe SF-25B Falke	4811	D-KBAT	30.10.89	Richard Collings Ltd	Hinton-in-The-Hedges	12. 1.01
G-BRRF	Cameron O-77 HAFB	2101		24.10.89	D.G.Body t/a Mid-Bucks Farmers Balloon Group "Daisy Chain"	Leighton Buzzard	25. 3.00T
G-BRRG	Glaser-Dirks DG-500M	5E7-M5		7.11.89	D.C.Chaplin "492" t/a Glider Syndicate	Sutton Bank	6.10.00
G-BRRJ	PA-28RT-201T Turbo Arrow IV	28R-8431021	N4353T	27.11.89	M.Stower	Elstree	6. 7.02

Regn	Type	C/n	P/I	Date	Owner/operator	Probable Base	CA Expy
G-BRRK	Cessna 182Q Skylane II	182-66160	N759PW	30.10.89	M.G.Mitchell	Elstree	7. 5.02
G-BRRL	PA-18-95 Super Cub	18-2050	D-EMKE	17. 9.90	A.J.White	Redhill	
	(L-18C-PI)				R Neth AF R-44/52-2450 t/a Acebell G-BRRL Syndicate		
	(Believed to comprise Frame No.18-1602/G-AYPO [18-1615])				(On rebuild Whitehall Farm, Benington 4.93)		
G-BRRM	PA-28-161 Cadet	2841260	N9194B	25.10.89	R.H.Sellier	Biggin Hill	7.12.01T
G-BRRN	PA-28-161 Warrior II	28-8216043	N84533	30.10.89	Spinseal Ltd	Cranfield	22. 1.02T
G-BRRO	Cameron N-77 HAFB	2142		30.10.89	P.W.Limpus & I.J.Liddiard	Newbury	19. 3.00A
					"Newbury Building Society II"		
G-BRRR	Cameron V-77 HAFB	2070		13.10.89	L.M.Heal & A.P.Wilcox	Chippenham	19. 8.00A
					"Breezy"		
G-BRRS	Pitts S-1S Special	TM-1	N18TM	1.11.89	R.C.Atkinson Ransborough Farm, Langham		25. 6.93P
	(Lycoming O-360)				(Stored 5.95)		
G-BRRU	Colt 90A HAFB	1591		1.11.89	Reach For The Sky Ltd	Guildford	5. 8.00T
G-BRRW	Cameron O-77 HAFB	2125		7.11.89	D.V.Fowler "Mobiloon"	Cranbrook	3. 7.00T
G-BRRY	Robinson R-22 Beta	1193		14.11.89	P.W.Vellacott	Thruxton	11.12.01T
G-BRSA	Cameron N-56 HAFB	2113		8.11.89	C.Wilkinson	Newcastle	17.10.92A
G-BRSC	Rans S-10 Sakota	0589-051		8.11.89	M.A.C.Stephenson	Blackpool	12. 8.97P
	(Rotax 532)						
G-BRSD	Cameron V-77 HAFB	2174		8.11.89	T.J.Porter & J.E.Kelly	Belper, Derby	3. 2.94A
G-BRSE	PA-28-161 Warrior II	28-8016276	N8163R	5.12.89	Startown Ltd	Edinburgh	24. 2.02T
					(Op Edinburgh Flying Club)		
G-BRSF*	VS.361 Spitfire HF.IXc		SAAF 5632	22.11.89	J.Peace	Lancing	
		-	RR232		(As "RR232": stored 3.96)		
	(Composite incl tail/parts ex Mk.VIII/JF629 from W.Australia & wings ex Mk.XIV/R.Thai AF U14-6/93/RAF RM873)						
G-BRSG	PA-28-161 Cadet	2841285	N92011	23.11.89	J.Appleton	Denham	4. 1.02T
					t/a Holmes Rentals (Op Cabair)		
G-BRSH	CASA I-131E Jungmann	2156	E3B-540	29.11.89	L.Ness	(Nannestad, Norway)	22. 4.00P
	(Spanish AF serial conflicts with F-AZGG)				(As "781-25" in Spanish AF c/s)		
G-BRSJ	PA-38-112 Tomahawk II	38-81A0044	N25664	29.12.89	APB Leasing Ltd	Welshpool	25. 3.02T
G-BRSK	Boeing-Stearman B75N1 (N2S-3) Kaydet	N5565N		15.11.89	C.R.Lawrence	Priory Farm, Tibenham	20. 1.97
	(Continental W670)	75-1180	Bu.3403		t/a Wymondham Engineering (Stored 8.97: as "1180" in USN c/s)		
G-BRSL	Cameron N-56 HAFB	468		21.12.78	S.H.Budd "Boris"	Pewsey	28. 5.87A
G-BRSN	Rand Robinson KR-2	PFA/129-11178		10.11.89	K.W.Darby	(Teignmouth)	
	(VW1834)						
G-BRSO	CFM Streak Shadow			16.11.89	D.J.Smith	Old Sarum	10.10.00P
	(Rotax 532) K.133-SA & PFA/161A-11601						
G-BRSP	Air Command 532 Elite			13.11.89	G.M. Hobman	(York)	10. 1.92P
	0626 & PFA G/04-1158						
G-BRSW	Luscombe 8AC Silvaire	3249	N71822	15.11.89	P.J.Allitt & M.A.Harris	Fenland	25. 6.00P
	(Continental A75)		NC71822		t/a Bloody Mary Aviation "Bloody Mary"		
G-BRSX	PA-15 Vagabond	15-117	N4334H	27.10.89	C.Milne-Fowler Craysmarsh Farm, Melksham		6. 6.00P
	(Continental A65)		NC4334H				
G-BRSY	Hatz CB-1	6	N2257J	15.11.89	J.P.Barrett	Breighton	10. 7.98P
	(Lycoming O-290-D)				t/a G.A.Barrett & Son		
G-BRTA	PA-38-112 Tomahawk	38-79A0047	N2407B	27.11.89	Cardiff-Wales Flying Club Ltd	Cardiff	5. 6.00T
G-BRTD	Cessna 152 II	152-80023	N757UW	11. 1.90	T.G.Phillips, C.Greenland & J.Page		
					t/a 152 Group	Booker	21. 6.02
G-BRTH	Cameron A-180 HAFB	2016		21.11.89	The Ballooning Business Ltd	Northampton	2. 5.00T
	(Replacement envelope c/n 3199 fitted 1994)				"Burning Ambition II"		
G-BRTI	Robinson R-22 Beta	1130	EI-CDW	23. 2.90	A.J.& P.D.Morgan	Cardiff	25. 3.00T
			(EI-CFJ)/G-BRTI/N8044U t/a Morhire				
G-BRTJ	Cessna 150F	150-61749	N8149S	22.11.89	Avon Aviation Ltd	Bristol	16. 1.00T
G-BRTK	Boeing-Stearman E75 (PT-13D) Kaydet	N16716		29.11.89	Eastern Stearman Ltd	Swanton Morley	24. 4.93
	(Continental W670)	75-5949	42-17786/Bu.38728		(As "FJ777" in RCAF c/s) (On re-build 5.99)		
G-BRTL	MDH Hughes 369E	0356E	(F-GHLF)	5. 1.90	Crewhall Ltd	Leatherhead	31. 3.02
G-BRTM	PA-28-161 Warrior II	28-8416083	N4334L	12.12.89	Oxford Aviation Services Ltd	Oxford	15. 2.02T
G-BRTN	Beechcraft 58 Baron	TH-1400	N58VF	29.11.89	Colneway Ltd	Guernsey	28. 1.02
			N6763U				
G-BRTP	Cessna 152 II	152-81275	N49448	28.11.89	M.R.Shelton	Tatenhill	29. 7.02T
					t/a Tatenhill Aviation		
G-BRTT	Schweizer Hughes 269C	S.1411		29.11.89	Technical Exponents Ltd	Redhill	27. 5.02T
G-BRTV	Cameron O-77 HAFB	2182		1.12.89	Carole Vening	Littlehampton	11. 6.97A
					"Solitaire II"		
G-BRTW	Glaser-Dirks DG-400	4-259		22.12.89	I.J.Carruthers	Great Orton	4. 2.02
G-BRTX	PA-28-151 Cherokee Warrior	N8307C	27.12.89	J.Phelan & D.G.Scott	Aldergrove	9. 4.01T
		28-7615085			t/a Spectrum Flying Group		
G-BRTZ	Slingsby Cadet III	PFA/42-10545		24. 1.90	R.R.Walters	Haamstede, Belgium	14. 3.97P
	(VW1600)						
G-BRUA	Cessna 152 II	152-81212	N49267	11. 1.90	Griffin Marston Ltd	Compton Abbas	12. 9.02T
					(Op Abbas Air)		
G-BRUB	PA-28-161 Warrior II	28-8116177	N8351Y	27.12.89	Flytrek Ltd	Compton Abbas	7.11.99

Regn	Type	C/n	P/I	Date	Owner/operator	Probable Base	CA Expy
G-BRUD	PA-28-181 Archer II	28-8390010	N8300S	9. 2.90	Wilkins & Wilkins Special Auctions Ltd		
						RAF Henlow	18. 3.02T
G-BRUE	Cameron V-77 HAFB	2183		15.12.89	B.J.Newman & P.L.Harrison	Kettering	26. 7.99A
					"Bruer"		
G-BRUG	Luscombe 8E Silvaire	4462	N1735K	15.12.89	P.A.Cain & N.W.Barratt	Compton Abbas	12. 5.00P
	(Continental C85)		NC1735K				
G-BRUH	Colt 105A HAFB	1650		15.12.89	D.C.Chipping	Evora, Portugal	29. 7.93T
G-BRUI	PA-44-180 Seminole	44-7995150	N2230E	15.12.89	M.R.Shelton	Tatenhill	28. 8.02T
			G-BRUI/N2230E		t/a Tatenhill Aviation		
G-BRUJ	Boeing-Stearman A75N1 (PT-17) Kaydet	N55557	6. 4.90	M.Walker	Liverpool	16. 7.01T
	(Continental R670)	75-4299	42-16136		(As "16136/205" in USN c/s)		
G-BRUM	Cessna A152 Aerobat	A152-0870	N4693A	12. 3.86	Aerohire Ltd	Halfpenny Green	2. 9.01T
G-BRUN	Cessna 120	9294	G-BRDH	29. 8.89	O.C.Brun	Great Massingham	12. 1.01P
	(Continental C85)		N72127/NC72127				
G-BRUO	Taylor JT.1 Monoplane	PFA/55-10859		15.12.89	G.Verity	Crosland Moor	10. 8.02P
	(VW1600)						
G-BRUT	Thunder Ax8-90 HAFB	1392		30. 3.89	Moet and Chandon (London) Ltd London SW1		6.12.93A
					"L'Esprit D'Aventure II/Mercier II"		
G-BRUU	EAA Biplane Model P1	1	N41MW	22.12.89	R.D.Harper	High Ham, Langport	17. 6.98P
	(Lycoming O-360)		N4775G				
G-BRUV	Cameron V-77 HAFB	2100		16. 8.89	T.W. & R.F.Benbrook	Romford	23. 9.00A
					"BiGBRUVver"		
G-BRUX	PA-44-180 Seminole	44-7995151	N2245E	8. 3.79	Hambrair Ltd	Tatenhill	27.11.00
G-BRUZ*	MFM Raven-Europe FS-57A HAFB	E-066	F-GMFM	1.12.89	R.H.Etherington Rapollano Terme, Italy		15. 4.93A
			HB-BKB		(Cancelled by CAA 13.4.99)		
G-BRVB	Stolp SA.300 Starduster Too	409	N33MH	21.12.89	M.N.Petchey & S.Turner	Andrewsfield	10. 5.00P
	(Lycoming O-360)						
G-BRVC	Cameron N-180 HAFB	2180		15.12.89	A.J.Street	Whimple, Exeter	24. 3.00T
G-BRVE	Beechcraft D17S Traveller (UC-43-BH)	N1193V	12. 3.90	D.J.Gilmour	North Weald	25. 3.02
		6701	NC1193V/Bu.32874/FT475/44-67724/(Bu.23689) t/a Intrepid Aviation Co				
G-BRVF	Colt 77A HAFB	1651		19.12.89	The Ballooning Business Ltd	Northampton	25. 8.00T
G-BRVG	North American SNJ-7C Texan	88-17676	N830X	24. 1.90	D.J.Gilmour	North Weald	6. 6.02
		N4134A/Bu.90678/(42-85895) t/a Intrepid Aviation Co					
					(As "27" in VS-932 Sqn, USN c/s)		

(This A/c was built in 1944 by North American, Dallas -Texas originally as a SNJ-5 Bu No.90678, and saw service in
W.W.II as a USN advanced fighter trainer at Pearl Harbour & Guam. It was fitted later with an arrestor hook &
redesignated as a SNJ-5C and served on US escort carrier "USS Point Cruze" and, later, with a Hawaiian based night
fighter squadron. It returned to mainland USA in 1950 and was fitted with improved radios, larger fuel tanks & a
Mustang tail wheel and became a SNJ-7C. This was one of only three such conversions made. The aircraft was sold
privately in the 1960s & imported into the UK in 1990 by David Gilmour taking up the present markings. It is the
only surviving SNJ-7C flying and currently in a standard tactical colour scheme representative of the Guam era)

Regn	Type	C/n	P/I	Date	Owner/operator	Probable Base	CA Expy
G-BRVH	Smyth Model S Sidewinder	PFA/92-11251		19.12.89	I.S.Bellamy	Netherthorpe	10. 5.00P
	(Lycoming O-290)						
G-BRVI	Robinson R-22 Beta	1240		27.12.89	P.M.Whitaker	Ilkley	12. 4.02T
G-BRVJ	Slingsby Cadet III 701 & PFA/42-11382 (BGA3360)	24. 1.90	B.Outhwaite	Breighton	29. 9.00P
	(VW1600) (Modified ex T.31B)		WT906				
G-BRVL	Pitts S-1C Special	559H	N2NW	10. 1.90	M.F.Pocock	RAF Linton-on-Ouse	2.11.99P
	(Lycoming IO-320)						
G-BRVN	Thunder Ax7-77 HAFB	1614		28.12.89	D.L.Beckwith	Northampton	24. 6.00A
G-BRVO	Aerospatiale AS.350B Ecureuil	2315		3. 1.90	Malcolm Wilson (Motorsport) Ltd		
						Cockermouth	24. 4.02T
G-BRVR	Barnett Rotorcraft J4B-2	216-2		20. 2.90	M.Richardson	Ilkeston	AC
					t/a Ilkeston Continentalractors		
G-BRVS	Barnett Rotorcraft J4B-2	210-2		20. 2.90	M.Richardson	Ilkeston	AC
					t/a Ilkeston Continentalractors		
G-BRVT	Christen Pitts S-2B Special	5189		6. 4.90	C J & M D Green	Bournemouth	14. 1.00T
	(Lycoming AEIO-540)				(Op SFT Aviation) "The Tart"		
G-BRVU	Colt 77A HAFB	1652		4. 1.90	J.K.Woods	Chatham	11.12.98A
					"Concorde Watches"		
G-BRVV	Colt 56B HAFB	1386		8. 1.90	S.J. & M.P.A.Hollingsworth	Matlock	28. 3.95A
					"Rosie"		
G-BRVX*	Cameron A-210 HAFB	2194		9. 1.90	Not known (Cancelled as WFU 3.6.98)	NK	
					(Noted 1999)		
G-BRVY	Thunder Ax8-90 HAFB	1676		9. 1.90	G.E. & J.V.Morris	Cheltenham	7. 4.00A
					"Golden Gem"		
G-BRVZ	SAN Jodel D.117	433	F-BHNR	22.12.89	J.G.Patton South Lodge Farm, Widmerpool		31. 5.00P
G-BRWA	Aeronca 7AC Champion	7AC-351	N81730	20. 3.90	D.D.Smith & J.R.Edwards	Hook	16. 8.00P
			NC81730				
G-BRWB	North American T-6G Texan	182-213	Fr.Mil	28. 3.90	R.Clifford	(London NW3)	29. 4.00P
			51-14526		(As "526" in USAF c/s)		
	(Reported as an original Harvard II, s/n 41-32473, rebuilt in 1951)						

Regn	Type	C/n	P/I	Date	Owner/operator	Probable Base	CA Expy
G-BRWC*	Cessna 152 II	152-81918	TF-GMT N67569	19. 1.90	T.Hayselden (Doncaster) Ltd	Sandtoft	15. 5.93T

(Damaged Sandtoft 29.8.90; old fuselage in open store Egginton 3.98; on rebuild using cockpit & front fuselage of G-BITG 6.96 which became G-ODAC; cancelled as wfu 16.2.99: cockpit Firbeck 8.99)

Regn	Type	C/n	P/I	Date	Owner/operator	Probable Base	CA Expy
G-BRWD	Robinson R-22 Beta	1231	N8064U	15. 1.90	Matrix Aviation Ltd	Fenland	12. 5.02
G-BRWF	Thunder Ax7-77 HAFB	1200		15. 1.90	Deborah J.Greaves	Tenterden, Kent	7. 8.99A
G-BRWH	Cameron N-77 HAFB	2186		15. 1.90	C.P.G.E.Rodrigues	Sint Niklaas, Belgium	19. 4.00A
G-BRWO	PA-28-140 Cherokee Cruiser	28-7325548	N55985	11. 1.90	Fergair Ltd	Bournemouth	17.11.02T
G-BRWP	CFM Streak Shadow	PFA/161A-11596		17. 1.90	M.M.Bain	(Roslin)	31. 3.00P
G-BRWR	Aeronca 11AC Chief (Continental A65)	11AC-1319	N9676E	17. 1.90	R.M.Lee	Bristol	28. 6.00P
G-BRWT	Scheibe SF-25C-2000 Falke	44480	D-KIAY	11. 1.90	Booker Gliding Club Ltd	Booker	8. 4.02
G-BRWU	Phoenix Luton LA-4A Minor	PAL/1141		18. 1.90	R.B.Webber & P.K.Pike	Trenchard Farm, Eggesford	31. 8.99P

(JAP J.99)) (Regd incorrectly as PFA/1141 but no PFA No.known)

Regn	Type	C/n	P/I	Date	Owner/operator	Probable Base	CA Expy
G-BRWV	Brugger MB.2 Colibri (VW 1834)	PFA/43-11027		18. 1.90	S.J.McCollum	Newtownards	9. 6.00P
G-BRWX	Cessna 172P Skyhawk II	172-74729	N53363	17. 1.90	D.A.Abels	Oaksey Park	26.10.02T
G-BRWY	Cameron H-34 HAFB	2214		17. 1.90	E.Krafft	Annweiler, Germany	17. 4.94A
G-BRWZ	Cameron Macaw 90SS HAFB	2206		29. 1.90	Forbes Europe Inc "Capitalist Tool"	Balleroy, Normandy	3. 9.00
G-BRXA	Cameron O-120 HAFB	2217		19. 1.90	Gone With The Wind Ltd & R.J.Mansfield	Bowness-on-Windermere/Huddersfield	26. 3.00T
G-BRXB	Thunder Ax7-77 HAFB	1631		18. 1.90	H.Peel	Worcester	23. 4.00A
G-BRXC	PA-28-161 Warrior II	28-8416043	N4339X N9563N	19. 2.90	Oxford Aviation Services Ltd	Oxford	24. 3.02T
G-BRXD	PA-28-181 Archer II	28-8290126	N9690N N8203E	19. 2.90	D.D.Stone	Wellesbourne Mountford	12. 3.00
G-BRXE	Taylorcraft BC-12D (Continental A65)	9459	N95059 NC95059	25. 1.90	Wendy J.Durrad "Flying Fishes"	Eastbach Farm, Coleford	25. 8.00P
G-BRXF	Aeronca 11AC Chief (Continental A65)	11AC-1033	N9396E NC9396E	25. 1.90	A.B.Newman	Bidford/Bickmarsh	22. 6.00P
G-BRXG	Aeronca 7AC Champion (Continental A65)	7AC-3910	N85178 NC85178	1. 3.90	J.D.Webb t/a X-Ray Golf Flying Group	Hill Farm, Nayland	17. 6.00P
G-BRXH	Cessna 120 (Continental C85)	10462	N76068 NC76068	25. 1.90	A.C.Garside t/a BRXH Group	Headcorn	10. 3.00P
G-BRXL	Aeronca 11AC Chief (Continental A65)	11AC-1629	N3254E NC3254E	31. 1.90	P.R.A.Hammond "Fat Bullet" t/a G-BRXL Group (As "42-78044" in US Army L-3F c/s)	Rush Green	22. 9.99P
G-BRXN	Montgomerie-Bensen B.8MR (Rotax 532)	PFA G/01-1160		31. 1.90	G.Robertson	Kingsmuir	13. 9.00P
G-BRXO	PA-34-200T Seneca II	34-7970149	N111ED N9618N	12. 4.90	Aviation Services Ltd	Ronaldsway	31. 7.02
G-BRXP	SNCAN Stampe SV-4C (Lycoming)	678	N33528 F-BGGU/Fr AF/(F-BDNX)	2. 2.90	P.G.Kavanagh & D.T.Kaberry (Fuselage noted 9.99)	Barton	AC
G-BRXS	Howard Special T-Minus (Lycoming O-290) (Modified Taylorcraft BC)	REC-1	N2278C	14. 2.90	A.Shuttleworth	Barton	30. 6.00P
G-BRXU	Aerospatiale AS.332L Super Puma	2092	VH-BHV G-BRXU/HC-BMZ/C-GSLO "Crail"	6. 3.90	Bristow Helicopters Ltd	Scatsta	11. 9.01T
G-BRXV	Robinson R-22 Beta	1246		7. 2.90	J.W.F. & S.M.Tuke t/a Tukair Aircraft Charter	Headcorn	31. 5.02T
G-BRXW	PA-24-260 Comanche	24-4069	N8621P	16. 2.90	P.A.Jenkins t/a Oak Group	Coventry	22.12.99
G-BRXY	Pietenpol Air Camper (Continental C90)	PFA/47-11416		7. 2.90	P.S.Ganczakowski	Great Eversden	19. 6.97P
G-BRYA	DHC.7-110 Dash Seven	062		17.11.81	Brymon Airways Ltd (Op Brymon Offshore)	Eindhoven/Aberdeen	19.10.02T
G-BRYD	DHC.7-110 Dash Seven	109	C-GEWQ	24.12.87	Brymon Airways Ltd (Op Brymon Offshore)	Eindhoven/Aberdeen	18. 1.00T
G-BRYI	DHC.8-311A Dash Eight	256	C-GEOA	26. 3.91	Brymon Airways Ltd (Chelsea Rose t/s)	Bristol	27. 3.00T
G-BRYJ	DHC.8-311A Dash Eight	319	C-GEOA	27. 3.92	Brymon Airways Ltd (Grand Union t/s)	Bristol	2. 4.00T
G-BRYM	DHC.8-311A Dash Eight	305	N433AW C-GDFT	25. 3.96	Brymon Airways Ltd	Bristol	24. 3.02T
G-BRYN	Socata TB-20 Trinidad	959		22. 3.89	Anglo American Airmotive Ltd	Bournemouth	13. 5.02
G-BRYO	DHC.8-311A Dash Eight	311	N434AW C-GEVP	26. 4.96	Brymon Airways Ltd	Bristol	25. 4.02T
G-BRYP	DHC.8-311A Dash Eight	315	N435AW C-GFCF	22. 4.96	Brymon Airways Ltd	Bristol	26. 5.02T
G-BRYR	DHC.8-311A Dash Eight	336	N436AW C-GFRP	20. 5.96	Brymon Airways Ltd	Bristol	19. 5.02T

Regn	Type	C/n	P/I	Date	Owner/operator	Probable Base	CA Expy
G-BRYS	DHC.8-311A Dash Eight	296	PH-SDG D-BKIS/C-GFQL	23. 4.97	Brymon Airways Ltd (Waves of the City t/s)	Bristol	4. 5.00T
G-BRYT	DHC.8-311A Dash Eight	334	D-BKIR C-GFEN	11. 3.97	Brymon Airways Ltd (Colour Down the Side t/s)	Bristol	25. 3.00T
G-BRYU	DHC.8-311A Dash Eight	458	(9M-PGA) C-GFEN	4. 4.98	Brymon Airways Ltd (Mountain of the Birds/Benyhone Tartan t/s)	Bristol	3. 4.00I
G-BRYV	DHC.8-311A Dash Eight	462	(9M-PGD) C-GFHZ	10. 4.98	Brymon Airways Ltd (Dove/Colum t/s)	Bristol	9. 4.01T
G-BRYW	DHC.8-311A Dash Eight	474	(9M-PG.) C-GDIU	26. 5.98	Brymon Airways Ltd (Cockerel of Lowicz/Koguty Lowickie t/s)	Bristol	24. 5.01T
G-BRYX	DHC.8-311A Dash Eight	508	C-GDOE	25. 9.98	Brymon Airways Ltd	Plymouth	27. 9.01T
G-BRYY	DHC.8-311A Dash Eight	519	C-FDHD	11.12.98	Brymon Airways Ltd. (Rendezvous t/s)	Plymouth	10.12.01T
G-BRYZ	DHC.8-311A Dash Eight	464	C-FCSG	16.10.98	Brymon Airways Ltd	Plymouth	15.10.01T
G-BRZA	Cameron O-77 HAFB	2231		7. 2.90	L. & R.J.Mold "Breezy"	High Wycombe	6. 2.00A
G-BRZB	Cameron A-105 HAFB	2212		7. 2.90	Cornwall Ballooning Adventures Ltd "Headland Hotel"	Newquay	28. 4.99A
G-BRZC*	Cameron N-90 HAFB	2227		8. 2.90	British Balloon Museum & Library "Unipart II"	Newbury	2.12.92A
G-BRZD	HAPI Cygnet SF-2A (VW2078)	PFA/182-11443		8. 2.90	L.G.Millen Stoneacre Farm, Farthing Corner		15. 3.00P
G-BRZE	Thunder Ax7-77 HAFB	1633		8. 2.90	G.V.Beckwith & F.Schoeder "Jenlain" York		31. 8.97A
G-BRZG	Enstrom F-28A	169	N9053	8. 2.90	S.M.Bell	Woodford	7. 4.00
G-BRZI	Cameron N-180 HAFB	2215		8. 2.90	C.E.Wood t/a Eastern Balloon Rides	Witham	24. 2.00T
G-BRZK	Stinson 108-2 Voyager	108-2846	N9846K NC9846K	17. 4.90	P.C.G.Wyld t/a Voyager G-BRZK Syndicate	Booker	15. 8.99
G-BRZL	Pitts S-1D Special (Lycoming O-360)	01	N899RN	26. 2.90	R.T.Cardwell (Stored 2.97) Standalone Farm, Meppershall		2. 8.96P
G-BRZO	Jodel D.18	PFA/169-11275		14. 2.90	J.D.Anson (Liskeard)		
G-BRZP	PA-28-161 Warrior II	28-8616013	N9140Y	17. 4.90	Keen Leasing (IOM) Ltd.	Ronaldsway	15. 6.02T
G-BRZS	Cessna 172P Skyhawk II	172-75004	N54585	2.10.90	H.Hargreaves & P.F.Hughes t/a G-BHYP Flying Group	Blackpool	20.11.99
G-BRZT	Cameron V-77 HAFB	2241		21. 2.90	Beverley Drawbridge "Hoopla"	Cranbrook, Kent	1. 3.00A
G-BRZU	Colt Flying Cheese SS HAFB	1544		26. 2.90	N.Charbonnier "Grana Padano"	Aosta, Italy	25. 9.97A
G-BRZV	Colt Flying Apple SS HAFB	1662		26. 2.90	Obst Vom Bodensee Marketing Gbr (Tettnang-Siggenweiler, Germany)		14. 9.97A
G-BRZW	Rans S-10 Sakota (Rotax 532) 0789-058 & PFA/194-11932			21. 2.90	D.L.Davies Emlyns Field, Rhuallt		6. 8.98P
G-BRZX	Pitts S-1S Special (Lycoming O-320)	711-H	N272H	22. 2.90	J.H.Milne & T.H.Bishop	Felthorpe	21. 4.00P
G-BRZZ	CFM Streak Shadow (Rotax 532) (C/n duplicates Renegade Spirit G-MWDM)	PFA/161A-11628		22. 2.90	T.Mooney t/a Shetland Flying Group	Kirkwall	16. 8.00P

G-BSAA – G-BSZZ

Regn	Type	C/n	P/I	Date	Owner/operator	Probable Base	CA Expy
G-BSAI	Stoddard-Hamilton Glasair III	3102		31. 1.90	K.J. & P.J.Whitehead	Booker	19. 9.00P
G-BSAJ	CASA I-131E Jungmann	2209	E3B-209	23. 1.90	P.G.Kynsey	Headcorn	15. 6.00P
G-BSAK	Colt 21A Sky Chariot HAFB	1696		26. 2.90	K.Meehan t/a Northern Flights	Much Wenlock	24. 7.99A
G-BSAR*	Air Command 532 Elite	0443		20. 4.89	T.A.Holmes (Leeds) (Cancelled as wfu 4.11.99 - no Permit to Fly issued)		
G-BSAS	Cameron V-65 HAFB	2191		27. 2.90	J.R.Barber	Kings Lynn	9. 7.00A
G-BSAV	Thunder Ax7-77 HAFB	1555		26. 2.90	E.A. & H.A.Evans, I.G. & C.A.Lloyd "Burnt Savings"	Chesterfield	8. 4.00A
G-BSAW	PA-28-161 Warrior II	28-8216152	N8203C	27. 2.90	Carill Aviation Ltd	Southampton	12. 7.02T
G-BSAX	Piper J3C-65 Cub	18432	N98260 NC98260	17. 1.91	K.& J.I.Harness (Louth, Lincs)		
G-BSAZ	Denney Kitfox mk.2 (Rotax 582) 602 & PFA/172-11664		(G-BRVW)	5. 3.90	A.J.Lloyd, D.M.Garrett & J.T.Lane (Bromyard)		26. 6.97P
G-BSBA	PA-28-161 Warrior II	28-8016041	N2574U	1. 3.90	R.J.Doughton t/a Doughton Aviation Services	Dunkeswell	28. 4.00T
G-BSBG	CCF Harvard 4 (T-6J-CCF Texan) 1753 CCF4-483		Moz.PLAF 5. 3.90 FAP 1753/BF+053/AA+053/52-8562		A.P.St.John (As "20310/310" in RCAF c/s)	Liverpool	17. 5.00P
G-BSBH*	Short SD.3-30	SH.3000		6. 6.74	Belfast Harbour Fire Service Belfast Harbour		13. 4.81S
G-BSBI	Cameron O-77 HAFB	2245		6. 3.90	D.M.Billing "Calibre"	Uckfield	12. 6.00A

Regn	Type	C/n	P/I	Date	Owner/operator	Probable Base	CA Expy
G-BSBK	Colt 105A HAFB	1319		6. 3.90	Zebra Ballooning Ltd	Maidstone	12. 6.97T
G-BSBM	Cameron N-77	2229		8. 3.90	R S Kent "Nuclear Electric 1" (Balloon Preservation Group 7.98)	Lancing	21.11.96A
G-BSBN	Thunder Ax7-77 HAFB	1531		6. 3.90	B.Pawson "Venus"	Cambridge	9.12.93A
G-BSBP	Jodel D.18 (Revmaster R2100)	PFA/169-11613		15. 1.90	R.T.Pratt	(Crickhowell)	
G-BSBR	Cameron V-77 HAFB	2247		26. 2.90	R.P.Wade "Honey"	Wigan	10.10.99A
G-BSBT	Piper J3C-65 Cub	17712	N70694 NC70694	9. 3.90	R.W.H.Watson	Grimmet Farm, Maybole	14. 2.00P
G-BSBV	Rans S-10 Sakota (Rotax 532) 1089-064 & PFA/194-11769			9. 3.90	R.G.Cameron	Errol	20. 7.00P
G-BSBW	Bell 206B JetRanger III	3664	N43EA 9Y-THC	12. 3.90	D.T.Sharpe	Sherburn in Elmet	8. 7.02T
G-BSBX	Montgomerie-Bensen B.8MR (Rotax 503) PFA G/01A-1135			12. 3.90	R.J.Roan	(Peterborough)	26. 5.93P
G-BSBZ	Cessna 150M Commuter	150-77093	N63086	29. 3.90	D.T.Given t/a DTG Aviation	Newtownards	13. 6.99T
G-BSCA	Cameron N-90 HAFB	2237		12. 3.90	P.J.Marshall & M.A.Clarke "The Graduate"	Ruislip	12. 2.00A
G-BSCB	Air Command 532 Elite 0627 & PFA G/04-1172			16. 3.90	P.H.Smith	Nottingham	18. 9.97P
G-BSCC	Colt 105A HAFB	1006		15. 3.90	Capricorn Balloons Ltd	Loughborough	5. 4.99T
G-BSCE	Robinson R-22 Beta	1245		15. 3.90	H.Sugden	(Leeds)	14. 3.02T
G-BSCF	Thunder Ax7-77 HAFB	1537		14. 3.90	V.P.Gardiner "Charlie Farley"	Stoke-on-Trent	15. 8.00A
G-BSCG	Denney Kitfox mk.2 (Rotax 582)	PFA/172-11620		23. 4.90	N.L.Beever	Breighton	15. 8.00P
G-BSCH	Denney Kitfox mk.2 (Rotax 582) 510 & PFA/172-11621			16. 3.90	M.P.M.Read	Carlisle	4. 1.99P
G-BSCI	Colt 77A HAFB	1683		16. 3.90	J.L. & S.Wrigglesworth "Brody"	Ilminster	12. 6.00A
G-BSCK	Cameron H-24 HAFB	2263		16. 3.90	J.D.Shapland "Monacle"	Wadebridge	11. 6.95A
G-BSCL	Robinson R-22 Beta	1249		28. 3.90	Skyhopper Ltd	Booker	16. 6.99T
G-BSCM	Denney Kitfox mk.2 (Rotax 582) 638 & PFA/172-11745			28. 3.90	S.A.Hewitt	Sheepcote Farm	11. 8.02P
G-BSCN	Socata TB-20 Trinidad	1070	D-EGTC G-BSCN	27. 3.90	B.W.Dye	Biggin Hill	1. 6.02
G-BSCO	Thunder Ax7-77 HAFB	1635		6. 3.90	F.J.Whalley "Bluebell"	Cleish, Kinross	27. 8.00A
G-BSCP	Cessna 152 II	152-83289	N48135	20. 3.90	Moray Flying Club (1990) Ltd	RAF Kinloss	13.10.02T
G-BSCS	PA-28-181 Archer II	28-7890064	N47392	3. 4.90	Wingtask Ltd	Seething	30. 5.02T
G-BSCV	PA-28-161 Warrior II	28-7816135	C-GQXW	22. 3.90	S.E.Burton t/a Southwood Flying Group	Earls Colne	18.10.02
G-BSCW	Taylorcraft BC-65	1798	N24461 NC24461	22. 3.90	S.Leach	Plymouth	30. 6.00P
G-BSCX	Thunder Ax8-105 HAFB	1748		21. 3.90	Balloon Flights Club Ltd "Balloon Flights"	Leicester	14. 7.99T
G-BSCY	PA-28-151 Cherokee Warrior (Convd to Srs.161 status)	28-7515046	C-GOBE	22. 3.90	A.S.Bamrah t/a Falcon Flying Services	Oxford	1. 8.02T
G-BSCZ	Cessna 152 II	152-82199	N68226	22. 3.90	Eastern Executive Air Charter Ltd	Southend	3. 6.00T
G-BSDA	Taylorcraft BC-12D (Continental A75)	7316	N43657 NC43657	15.11.90	D.G.Edwards	Shoreham	22. 9.00P
G-BSDB	Pitts S-1C Special (Lycoming O-320)	01	(N1867) N77R	22. 3.90	S.Adams	Yeatsall Farm, Abbots Bromley	31. 5.99P
G-BSDD	Denney Kitfox mk.2 (Rotax 582) 639 & PFA/172-11797			28. 3.90	J.Windmill	Priory Farm, Tibenham	21. 6.96P
G-BSDG	Robin DR.400/180 Regent	1974		29. 3.90	P.A.Stephens	Manor Farm, Heslerton	23. 5.02
G-BSDH	Robin DR.400/180 Regent	1980		18. 4.90	R.L.Brucciani	Leicester	16. 5.02
G-BSDI	Corben Junior Ace Model E (Continental A75)	3961	N91706	28. 3.90	T.K.Pullen & A.J.Staplehurst	Eaglescott	3.10.98P
G-BSDJ	Piper J/4E Cub Coupe (Continental C85)	4-1456	N35975 NC35975	13. 2.91	B.M.Jackson	(Thame)	14. 6.98P
G-BSDK	Piper J/5A Cub Cruiser (Continental A75)	5-175	N30337 NC30337	28. 3.90	S.Haughton & I.S.Hodge	Field Farm, Great Missenden	8. 4.00P
G-BSDL	Socata TB-10 Tobago	156		7.10.80	P.Middleton & G.Corbin t/a Delta Lima Group	Sherburn in Elmet	1. 5.00
G-BSDN	PA-34-200T Seneca II	34-7970335	N2893A	2. 4.90	McCormick Consulting Ltd	Manchester	20. 6.02T
G-BSDO	Cessna 152 II	152-81657	N65894	23. 5.90	L.W.Scattergood	Sherburn-in-Elmet	17. 9.99T
G-BSDP	Cessna 152 II	152-80268	N24468	11. 6.90	I.S.H.Paul	Denham	10. 7.00T
G-BSDS	Boeing-Stearman E75 (PT-13A) Kaydet (Continental W670) 75-118	38-470	N57852	6. 4.90	E.Hopper (As "118" in US Army c/s)	Sherburn-in-Elmet	13. 5.00
G-BSDU	Bell 206B JetRanger III	4097	C-FHZV	5. 6.90	Eaglecray Ltd	Cannock	29. 7.02

Regn	Type	C/n	P/I	Date	Owner/operator	Probable Base	CA Expy
G-BSDV	Colt 31A HAFB	1722		30. 3.90	Virgin Airship & Balloon Co Ltd Telford		27. 6.96A
					"Baby Carrots"		
G-BSDW	Cessna 182P Skylane II	182-64688	N9125M	9. 4.90	Delta Whisky Ltd	Old Buckenham	4. 7.01
G-BSDX	Cameron V-77 HAFB	2050		30. 3.90	D.K.Fish	Bedford	
	(Canopy fitted to G-SNOW and rebuilt with G-SNOW's original canopy)						
G-BSDZ	Enstrom 280FX	2051	OO-MHV	3. 4.90	Avalon Group Ltd	Chester	3. 1.02
			(OO-JMH)/G-ODSC/G-BSDZ				
G-BSED	PA-22-160 Tri-Pacer	22-6377	N9404D	7. 6.90	M.Henderson	Stonehaven	15. 6.00
	(Tail-wheel conversion)						
G-BSEE	Rans S-9	PFA/196-11635		2. 3.90	P.M.Semler		
	(Rotax 532)					Buttermilk Farm, Easton Maudit	30. 6.00P
G-BSEF	PA-28-180 Cherokee C	28-1846	N7831W	18. 4.90	B.Mills	Sandtoft	4.11.02
G-BSEG	Ken Brock KB-2	PFA G/01-1106		3. 4.90	S.J.M.Ledingham	Boulmer	25. 6.99P
	(Rotax 582) (C/n possibly PFA G/06-1106)						
G-BSEJ	Cessna 150M Commuter	150-76261	N66767	4. 5.90	Halfpenny Green Flight Centre Ltd		
						Halfpenny Green	15. 9.02T
G-BSEK	Robinson R-22	0027	N45AD	10. 4.90	Heli Air Ltd	Panshanger	28. 4.02T
			N90193				
G-BSEL	Slingsby T.61G Super Falke	1986		31. 3.80	T.Holloway	Keevil	11. 1.01
					t/a RAFGSA (Op Bannerdown Gliding Club)		
G-BSEP	Cessna 172	46555	N6455E	12. 4.90	A.P Wall, R.J.Tyson & R.J Watts Redhill		19. 8.02
G-BSER	PA-28-160 Cherokee B	28-790	N5665W	19. 4.90	Yorkair Ltd	Sandtoft	15. 8.99T
G-BSES*	Denney Kitfox	PFA/172-11587		17. 4.90	M.Albert-Brecht & J.J.M.Donnelly Aboyne		5. 2.93P
	(Rotax 532)		(Destroyed by fire Aboyne 1992/93; parts only stored 3.94; cancelled by CAA 6.3.99)					
G-BSET	Beagle B.206 Basset CC.1	B.006	XS765	3.12.86	Lawgra (No.386) Ltd	Cranfield	28. 7.02
					t/a International Aerospace Engineering		
					(As "XS765" in RAF Transport Command c/s)		
G-BSEU	PA-28-181 Archer II	28-7890108	N47639	1. 5.90	Euro Aviation 91 Ltd	Blackbushe	12. 5.00
G-BSEV	Cameron O-77 HAFB	2271		20. 4.90	The Ballooning Business Ltd Northampton		
G-BSEX	Cameron A-180 HAFB	2254		18. 4.90	M.L.Gabb	Alcester	3. 7.97T
					t/a Heart of England Balloons		
G-BSEY	Beechcraft A36 Bonanza	E-1873	N1809F	17. 5.90	K.Phillips Ltd	Coventry	24. 8.02
G-BSEZ*	Air Command 532 Elite			18. 4.90	D.S.Robinson	(Swansea)	14. 6.91P
		0629 & PFA G/04-1165			(Used for spares 1998; cancelled as wfu 29.1.99)		
G-BSFA	Aero Designs Pulsar 176 & PFA/202-11754			18. 4.90	S.A.Gill	White Waltham	21. 6.00P
	(Rotax 582) (Tri-cycle u/c)						
G-BSFB	CASA I-131E Jungmann	2053	E3B-449	27. 4.90	C.D.Beal	Watchford Farm, Yarcombe	20.10.00P
					(As "S5+B06" in Luftwaffe c/s)		
G-BSFD	Piper J3C-65 Cub	16037	N88419	25. 5.90	E.G. & N.S.C.English	North Weald	20. 5.00P
	(Frame No.15443)		NC88419				
G-BSFE	PA-38-112 Tomahawk II	38-82A0033	N91452	26. 4.90	Chubbs Aviation Services (UK) Ltd		21.10.99T
					(Op Glasgow Flying Club)	Glasgow	
G-BSFF	Robin DR.400/180R Remorqueur	1295	D-ELMM	20. 4.90	Lasham Gliding Society Ltd	Lasham	11. 7.02
G-BSFJ	Thunder Ax8-105 HAFB	1762		20. 4.90	C.Gibson, L.Kirby & J.Russon Stockport		16. 7.00
G-BSFK	PA-28-161 Warrior II	28-8516062	N6918D	1. 5.90	Oxford Aviation Services Ltd	Oxford	16. 6.02T
G-BSFN	Sud SE.313B Alouette II	1500	XP967	30. 5.90	A.C.Watson	(Barnsley)	2.10.00
G-BSFP	Cessna 152T	152-85548	N93764	9. 5.90	J.R.Nicholls	Sibson	5. 8.02T
G-BSFR	Cessna 152 II	152-82268	N68341	9. 5.90	Galair Ltd	Biggin Hill	10. 7.02T
G-BSFS	Sud SE.313B Alouette II	1582	XR378	30. 5.90	S.Lee	Wilden, Bedford	15. 7.00T
			F-WIFM		(Possibly ex F-WIEM)		
G-BSFU*	Sud SE.313B Alouette II	1645	XR385	30. 5.90	Not known (Stored 7.97)	Coventry	
G-BSFV	Woods Woody Pusher	201	N16WP	30. 4.90	M.J.Wells	Watchford Farm, Yarcombe	26. 3.00P
	(Continental C85)				"Woody's Pusher"		
G-BSFW	PA-15 Vagabond	15-273	N4484H	26. 4.90	J.R.Kimberley	Bounds Farm, Ardleigh	28.11.00P
	(Continental A65)		NC4484H				
G-BSFX	Denney Kitfox Mk.2			23. 4.90	T.A.Crone	Turweston	3. 8.99P
	(Rotax 582)	506 & PFA/172-11723					
G-BSFY	Denney Kitfox Mk.2	PFA/172-11632		16. 3.90	A.R.Hawes	Crowfield	9.11.99P
	(Rotax 582)						
G-BSGB	Gaertner Ax4 Skyranger HAFB	SR.0001		30. 3.90	B.Gaertner	Oxford	
G-BSGC*	PA-18-95 Super Cub	18-3227	OO-HBC	22. 3.90	G.Churchill	(Towcester)	
	(L-18C-PI)		OL-L53/L-153/53-4827				
			(On overhaul Norfolk 1996 but no Permit or CofA issued & cancelled 15.5.99 as WFU)					
G-BSGD	PA-28-180 Cherokee E	28-5691	N3463R	4. 5.90	R.J.Cleverley	Draycott Farm, Chiseldon	6. 5.00
G-BSGF	Robinson R-22 Beta	1383		1. 5.90	Direct Helicopters (Southend) Ltd		
						Southend	24. 6.02T
G-BSGG	Denney Kitfox mk.2	PFA/172-11666		1. 5.90	C.G.Richardson	Fulbeck, Lincs	7. 3.00P
	(Jabiru 2200A)						
G-BSGH	Airtour AH-56B HAFB	014		1. 5.90	G.Luck	Habrough, Lincolnshire	
					"Battle of Britain"		

Regn	Type	C/n	P/I	Date	Owner/operator	Probable Base	CA Expy
G-BSGJ	Monnett Sonerai II (VW1835)	300	N34WH	1. 5.90	G.A.Brady	(Burford, Oxon)	6. 9.91P
G-BSGK	PA-34-200T Seneca II	34-7870331	N36450	22. 5.90	R.Hope, M.J.Martin & B.W.Powell t/a GK Aviation	Manston	17.11.02
G-BSGL	PA-28-161 Warrior II	28-8116041	N82690	10. 5.90	Keywest Air Charter Ltd (Op Liverpool Flying School) "Liverbird V"	Liverpool	8. 8.02T
G-BSGP	Cameron N-65 HAFB	2293		1. 5.90	M.D.Hammond t/a Mid Sussex Flying School	Burgess Hill	
G-BSGR*	Boeing-Stearman E75 (PT-17) Kaydet	75-4721	N75864 EC-ATY/N55050/42-16558	19. 6.90	A.G.Dunkerley (Cancelled by CAA 10.3.99: noted 9.99)	Kemble	
	(Reported as c/n 75-6714 ex N66870/Bu.07110)						
G-BSGS	Rans S-10 Sakota (Rotax 532) 1289-076 & PFA/194-11724			9. 5.90	M.R.Parr (Damaged Coventry late 1.93; status uncertain)	(Holmbrook, Cumbria)	4. 3.93P
G-BSGT	Cessna T210N Turbo Centurion II (Reims-assembled c/n 0020) 210-63361		LX-ATL D-EOGB/N5308A	21. 5.90	B.J.Sharpe	Booker	17. 3.00
G-BSGV*	Rotorway Exec (RW 152)	3823		8. 5.90	Not known (Stored 5.95)	Elstree	14. 7.92P*
G-BSGY	Thunder Ax7-77 HAFB (Envelope ex G-BROA c/n 1535)	1760		18. 7.90	P.B.Kenington "Bugsy"	Winterbourne, Bristol	15. 5.00A
G-BSHA	PA-34-200T Seneca II	34-7670216	N9707K	2. 5.90	Justgold Ltd	Blackpool	24. 7.99T
G-BSHC	Colt 69A HAFB	1668		8. 5.90	L.V.Mastis	West Bloomfield. Mi, USA	12.10.98A
G-BSHD	Colt 69A HAFB	1736		8. 5.90	D.B.Court "Jester"	Ormskirk	18. 8.00A
G-BSHE	Cessna 152 II	152-81302	N49483	17. 3.89	J.A.Pothecary t/a Air South (Damaged Shoreham 6.11.92; stored for spares 9.93)	Shoreham	28. 1.93
G-BSHH	Luscombe 8E Silvaire (Continental C85)	3981	N1254K NC1254K	11. 5.90	G.M.Wightman	(Leamington Spa)	28.10.99P
G-BSHI	Luscombe 8DF Silvaire Trainer (Continental C90)	1821	N39060 NC39060	11. 5.90	D.J.Dimmer & B.Robins t/a G-BSHI Group	Weston Zoyland	12. 5.00P
G-BSHK	Denney Kitfox mk.2 (Rotax 532) 449 & PFA/172-11752			11. 5.90	D.Doyle & C.Aherne	Kilrush, Dublin	4. 7.00P
G-BSHO	Cameron V-77 HAFB	2313		16. 5.90	D J Duckworth & C Stewart "Peugeot/Talbot"	Chesham	2. 5.00A
G-BSHP	PA-28-161 Warrior II	28-8616002	N9107Y	31. 5.90	Keen Leasing (IoM) Ltd	Liverpool	12. 9.02T
G-BSHR	Reims Cessna F.172N Skyhawk II	1616	G-BFGE	23.10.84	A.Simmers Ltd	Kemble	22. 5.00
G-BSHS	Colt 105A HAFB	1674	(D-OCAT) G-BSHS	16. 5.90	I.Novosad	Planegg, Germany	11. 8.99A
G-BSHT	Cameron V-77 HAFB	2321		30. 5.90	E.C.Moore "Buckshot II"	Great Missenden	13. 5.00T
G-BSHV	PA-18-135 Super Cub (L-18C-PI)	18-3123	OO-GDG Belgian Army L49/53-4723	5. 7.90	A.Furness t/a Fen Tigers Flying Group	Mitchell's Farm, Wilburton	5. 4.01
G-BSHW	Hawker Tempest II (Built Bristol Aircraft)	12177	IAF HA564 MW376	21. 3.91	P.Y.C.Denis (Stored North Weald 5.96; to be "MW800/HF-V" in 54 Sqn c/s)	(Romans, France)	
G-BSHX	Enstrom F-28A	155	N9605	16. 5.90	Stephenson Aviation Ltd (Stored 4.96)	Goodwood	AC
G-BSHY	EAA Acrosport 1 PFA/72-10928 (Lycoming 0-290)			17. 4.90	R.J.Hodder	Eastfield Farm, Manby	14. 6.00P
G-BSHZ	Enstrom F-28F	427	N51702	16. 5.90	S.G.Oliphant-Hope	Shoreham	25. 3.00
G-BSIB*	PA-28-161 Warrior II	28-8016304	N8182C	13. 6.90	Bobbington Air Training School Ltd (Op Dee Training) (Cancelled as wfu 22.11.99)	Halfpenny Green	5. 7.99T
G-BSIC	Cameron V-77 HAFB	2322		17. 5.90	C.Wilcock	Rickmansworth	11. 7.91A
G-BSIE	Enstrom 280FX	2052	HA-MIN G-BSIE	17. 5.90	S.G.Oliphant-Hope	(Worthing)	18. 1.01T
G-BSIF	Denney Kitfox mk.2 (Rotax 582) 563 & PFA/172-11889			5. 7.90	J.C.W. & J.Smith	Hungerford	1. 2.00P
G-BSIG	Colt 21A Cloudhopper HAFB	1322		18. 5.90	E.C. & A.J.Moore	Great Missenden	4. 8.00A
G-BSIH	Rutan LongEz 1200-1 & PFA/74A-11492			31. 5.90	W.S.Allen	(Cheltenham)	
G-BSII	PA-34-200T Seneca II	34-8070336	N8253N	16. 5.90	N.H.N.Gardner	Manston	4. 8.02
G-BSIJ	Cameron V-77 HAFB	2164		23. 5.90	A.S.Jones	Wolverhampton	20. 9.99A
G-BSIK	Denney Kitfox Mk.1	51		5. 6.90	G.J.Sargent	Cambridge	31. 1.00P
G-BSIM	PA-28-181 Archer II	28-8690017	N9092Y	22. 5.90	East Midlands Aircraft Hire Ltd	East Midlands	25. 8.02T
G-BSIN	Robinson R-22 Beta	1379	N4015H	25. 5.90	P.D.Mardell t/a PDM Aviation	Pulloxhill, Bedford	6.10.02T
G-BSIO	Cameron Furness House 56SS HAFB	2310		25. 5.90	R.E.Jones "Pinkie"	Lytham St.Annes	6. 2.00A
G-BSIT*	Robinson R-22 Beta	0762		9. 3.88	Helicentre Ltd (Damaged Ashcroft, Cheshire 20.4.97: cancelled by CAA 16.11.99)	Blackpool	26. 5.97T
G-BSIU	Colt 90A HAFB	1774		25. 5.90	S.Travaglia	Firenze, Italy	23.11.99A
G-BSIY	Schleicher ASK14	14005	5Y-AID D-KOIC	4. 6.90	E.V.Goodwin t/a Winwick Flying Group	(Huntingdon)	20.10.96
G-BSIZ	PA-28-181 Archer II	28-7990377	N2162Y	25. 5.90	A.M.L.Maxwell	Alderney	20. 6.02
G-BSJB	Bensen B.8	PFA G/01-1080		5. 6.90	J.W.Limbrick	(Bewdley)	

Regn	Type	C/n	P/I	Date	Owner/operator	Probable Base	CA Expy
G-BSJU	Cessna 150M Commuter	150-76430	N3230V	14. 6.90	A.C.Williamson (Op Crowfield Flying Club)	Crowfield	26. 2.01T
G-BSJW	Everett Gyroplane Srs.2 (Rotax 532)	020		6. 6.90	R.Sarwan	(Beccles)	25.10.91P
G-BSJX	PA-28-161 Warrior II	28-8216084	N8036N	30. 5.90	D.A.Shields & L.C.Brekkeflat	Elstree	22. 7.02T
G-BSJZ	Cessna 150J	150-70485	N60661	7. 5.91	BCT Aircraft Leasing Ltd	Bristol	1. 3.01T
G-BSKA	Cessna 150M Commuter	150-76137	N66588	31. 7.90	P.R.Edwards	Andrewsfield	13. 3.00T
G-BSKC	PA-38-112 Tomahawk	38-79A0748	OY-PJB N748RM/C-GRQI	27. 7.90	J.Marioni (Damaged nr Tewin 2.6.96; stored 9.97)	Panshanger	24. 1.97T
G-BSKD	Cameron V-77 HAFB	2336		4. 6.90	M.J.Gunston "Skulduggery"	Camberley	6. 7.00A
G-BSKE	Cameron O-84 HAFB	1604	ZS-HYD G-BSKE	4. 6.90	B.W.Smith Wisborough Green, W.Sussex t/a The Blunt Arrows Balloon Team		12. 7.00A
G-BSKG	Maule MX-7-180 Star Rocket	11072C		7. 6.90	J.R.Surbey Blockmoor Farm, Barway, Ely		5. 2.00
G-BSKI	Thunder Ax8-90 HAFB	1623		18. 5.90	P.G.Ward t/a G-BSKI Balloon Group "Ski Maiden"	Camberley	12.11.02A
G-BSKK	PA-38-112 Tomahawk	38-79A0671	N2525K	11. 6.90	A.S.Bamrah t/a Falcon Flying Services	Biggin Hill	20.11.02T
G-BSKL	PA-38-112 Tomahawk	38-78A0509	N4252E	11. 6.90	A.S.Bamrah t/a Falcon Flying Services (Op Warwickshire Aero Centre)	Birmingham	20.11.02T
G-BSKO	Maule MXT-7-180 Star Rocket	14008C		7. 6.90	M.A.Ashmole	Perth	12. 5.00
G-BSKP	VS.379 Spitfire F.XIVe	6S/663417	RBAF SG-31/RN201	27. 6.90	Historic Flying Ltd (On rebuild 3.96)	Audley End	AC
G-BSKS*	Nieuport 28C-1 (Gnome Monosoupape 160hp) (Identity obscure - ex Tallmantz but not ex N4123A)	6531	"N5246" US Navy	27. 6.90	US Army Aviation Museum Fort Rucker, Alabama, USA (As "6531/5" in 94th Aero Sqn AEF c/s)		13. 5.93P
G-BSKT	Maule MX-7-180 Star Rocket	11070C		7. 6.90	B.P.Young t/a Maule Flying Group	Dunkeswell	17.11.02
G-BSKU	Cameron O-84 HAFB	2330		8. 6.90	Alfred Bagnall & Sons (West) Ltd "Bagnalls II"	Bristol	27. 7.00A
G-BSKW	PA-28-181 Archer II	2890138	N91940	1. 6.90	Shropshire Aero Club Ltd	Sleap	9. 4.00T
G-BSLA	Robin DR.400/180 Regent	1997		22. 6.90	A.B.McCoig t/a Robin Lima Alpha Group	Biggin Hill	24. 6.02
G-BSLD	PA-28RT-201 Arrow IV	28R-7918231	N2943D	22. 6.90	E.Gawronek	Barton	20.11.99
G-BSLE	PA-28-161 Warrior II	28-8116028	N8260L	25. 6.90	Oxford Aviation Services Ltd	Oxford	6. 9.02T
G-BSLG	Cameron A-180 HAFB	2332		15. 6.90	B.J.Newman "Spot"	Rushden	2. 4.00T
G-BSLH	CASA I-131E Jungmann	2222	E3B-622	27. 7.90	P.Warden	Brive, France	11. 8.00P
G-BSLI	Cameron V-77 HAFB	2115		15. 6.90	J.D.C. & F.E.Bevan "Blackbird"	Market Drayton	30. 7.00T
G-BSLJ*	Denney Kitfox mk.2 (Rotax 532)	364 & PFA/172-11589		15. 6.90	A.F.Reid	Comber, NI	14. 4.93P
	(Damaged Bundoran Beach, Co.Donegal 28.5.92; stored 6.97; cancelled by CAA 10.3.99)						
G-BSLK	PA-28-161 Warrior II	28-7916018	N20849	15. 6.90	R.A.Rose Wellesbourne Mountford		3. 2.00T
G-BSLM	PA-28-160 Cherokee	28-308	N5262W	22. 6.90	C.W.Barker & A.J.Pollinger Old Sarum t/a Old Sarum Cherokee Group		19. 2.00
G-BSLT	PA-28-161 Warrior II	28-8016303	N81817	19. 6.90	APB Leasing Ltd	Welshpool	18. 1.00T
G-BSLU	PA-28-140 Cherokee	28-24733	OY-PJL OH-PJL/SE-FFA	19. 6.90	D.J.Budden	Shobdon	22. 9.02
G-BSLV	Enstrom 280FX	2054	D-HHAS G-BSLV	26. 6.90	Beaufort Securities Ltd Kings Somborne, Stockbridge		10. 7.00T
G-BSLW	Bellanca 7ECA Citabria	431-66	N9696S	16. 7.90	D.W.Mann t/a Shoreham Citabria Group	Shoreham	28. 4.00
G-BSLX	WAR Focke-Wulf 190 rep	24	N698WW	19. 6.90	E.C.Murgatroyd Sackville Farm, Riseley (As "1+4" in Luftwaffe c/s)		29. 2.00P
G-BSMB	Cessna U206E Super Skywagon	U206-01659	N9459G C-GUUW/N9459G	25. 6.90	R.M.Burnett AAC Netheravon t/a Army Parachute Association		18. 2.00
G-BSMD	SNCAN 1101 Noralpha	139	F-GDPQ F-YEEE/F-YCZK/CAN-11/Fr.Mil	26. 6.90	R.J.Lamplough North Weald (Stored 3.97: as "+114" in Luftwaffe c/s)		4. 5.96P
G-BSME	Bolkow Bo.208C Junior	596	D-ECGA	25. 6.90	D.J.Hampson	Fenland	11. 2.00
G-BSMF	Avro 652A Anson C.19	-	TX183	5. 9.90	G.M.K.Fraser Friockheim, Arbroath (As "TX183"; on rebuild 12.93)		AC
G-BSMG	Montgomerie-Bensen B.8M (Rotax 532)	PFA G/01-1170		22. 6.90	A.C.Timperley	Great Orton	16. 7.97P
G-BSMK	Cameron O-84 HAFB	2328		26. 6.90	D.F.Maine & D.M.Newton t/a G-BSMK Shareholders	Redditch	25. 5.00A
G-BSML	Schweizer Hughes 269C (300C)	S.1462	PH-HUH N134DM	10.10.90	K.P.Foster & B.I.Winsor	Bodmin	17. 3.00
G-BSMM	Colt 31A Sky Chariot HAFB	1779		27. 6.90	D.V.Fowler	Cranbrook, Kent	8. 6.00A
G-BSMN	CFM Streak Shadow (Rotax 582) K.137-SA & PFA/161A-11656			26. 6.90	D.K.Daniels	Swansea	18. 5.00P
G-BSMO	Denney Kitfox (Rotax 582)	PFA/172-11773		16. 7.90	R.H.Taylor t/a Kitfox Group	Seething	27. 6.00P

Regn	Type	C/n	P/I	Date	Owner/operator	Probable Base	CA Expy
G-BSMS	Cameron V-77 HAFB	2356		26. 6.90	Sade Balloons Ltd "Sadie" Coulsdon		4. 8.99A
G-BSMT	Rans S-10 Sakota			29. 6.90	I.M.Ashpole & Wye Valley Aviation Ltd		
	(Rotax 532) 1289-077 & PFA/194-11793					(Ross-on-Wye)	19.10.99P
G-BSMU	Rans S-6 Coyote II		G-MWJE	27. 6.90	J.S.M.Cattle	Eshott	16.10.00P
	1089-090 & PFA/204-11732						
G-BSMV	PA-17 Vagabond	17-94	N4696H	29. 6.90	A.Cheriton Wellesbourne Mountford		11. 1.00P
	(Continental C85)		NC4696H		"Sophie"		
G-BSMX	Bensen B.8MR	PFA G/01-1171		3. 7.90	J.S.E.R.McGregor	(Birmingham)	
G-BSND	Air Command 532 Elite	PFA G/04-1180		16. 7.90	K.Brogden & W.B.Lumb		
						(Heywood, Manchester)	
G-BSNE	Luscombe 8E Silvaire	5757	N1130B	2.11.90	S.C.Weston Long Marston		1. 6.00P
	(Continental C85)		NC1130B		t/a Aerolite Luscombe Group "B's Neez"		
G-BSNF	Piper J3C-65 Cub	3070	N23317	17. 8.90	D.A.Hammant		
	(Continental O-200-A) (Frame No.3070)		NC23317		Bere Farm, Warnford, Southampton		17. 9.00P
	(Lippert Reed conversion)						
G-BSNG	Cessna 172N Skyhawk II	172-70192	N738SB	19. 7.90	A.J. & P.C.MacDonald	Edinburgh	12.10.02T
					(Op Edinburgh Flying Club)		
G-BSNI*	Bensen B.8V	PFA G/01-1161		18. 7.90	Not known	(Cumbria)	
					(Cancelled by CAA 16.4.99)		
G-BSNJ	Cameron N-90 HAFB	2335		6. 7.90	D.P.H.Smith	(France)	29. 3.00A
G-BSNL	Bensen B.8MR	PFA G/01-1181		16. 7.90	A.C.Breane	Popham	20. 7.97P
	(Rotax 532)						
G-BSNN	Rans S-10 Sakota	PFA/194-11846		31. 7.90	O. & S.D.Barnard Packington, Coalville		27. 6.00P
	(Rotax 532)						
G-BSNP	PA-28R-201T Turbo Arrow III		N38537	18. 7.90	D.F.K.Singleton	(Teck, Germany)	14. 9.02
	28R-7703236						
G-BSNR	BAe 146 Srs.300	E-3165	EC-FGT	13. 7.90	KLM UK Ltd	Stansted	20.11.00T
	EC-807/G-6-165/G-BSNR/N886DV/G-BSNR/(N886DV)/G-6-165						
G-BSNS	BAe 146 Srs.300	E-3169	EC-FHU	13. 7.90	KLM UK Ltd	Stansted	18.10.00T
	EC-839/G-6-169/G-BSNS/N887DV/G-BSNS/(N887DV)/G-6-169						
	(Reserved as EI-CTN for delivery 5.00 - see SECTION 2)						
G-BSNT	Luscombe 8A Master	1679	N37018	16. 7.90	A.L.Nightingale	RAF Mona	14. 5.00P
	(Continental A65)		NC37018		"Beryl"		
G-BSNU	Colt 105A HAFB	1811		23. 7.90	Sun Life Assurance Society plc	Bristol	2. 2.97A
					"Sun Life"		
G-BSNV	Boeing 737-4Q8	25168		5. 2.92	British Airways (European Operations at Gatwick) Ltd		
						Gatwick	18. 2.02T
G-BSNW	Boeing 737-4Q8	25169		12. 3.92	British Airways (European Operations at Gatwick) Ltd		
					(Union Flag t/s)	Gatwick	19. 3.02T
G-BSNX	PA-28-181 Archer II	28-7990311	N3028S	19. 7.90	CAVOK Aviation Ltd	Barton	19. 8.02T
G-BSNY	Bensen B.8M	PFA G/01-1176		16. 7.90	H.McCartney	Newtownards, NI	3.12.99P
	(Arrow GT500R)						
G-BSNZ	Cameron O-105 HAFB	2364		16. 7.90	W.O.Hawkins	(London N11)	14. 2.02A
G-BSOE*	Luscombe 8A Silvaire	4331	N1604K	22. 8.90	S.B.Marsden	Sturgate	
			NC1604K		(Stored dismantled as "N1604K" 8.98: cancelled by CAA 16.4.99)		
G-BSOF	Colt 25A Sky Chariot Mk.II HAFB	1820		27. 7.90	H.C.J.Williams	Bristol	22. 7.00A
G-BSOG	Cessna 172M Skyhawk II	172-63636	N1508V	16. 7.90	B.Chapman & A.R.Budden	Goodwood	12.12.99
G-BSOI	Aerospatiale AS.332L Super Puma	2063	C-GSLE	21. 9.90	Brintel Helicopters Ltd	Aberdeen	12.12.02T
			G-BSOI/C-GSLE		t/a British International Helicopters		
G-BSOJ	Thunder Ax7-77 HAFB	1818	JA-	31. 7.90	R.J.S.Jones	Stourbridge	20.12.99A
			G-BSOJ				
G-BSOK	PA-28-161 Warrior II	28-7816191	N9749K	19. 7.90	Archer Aviation Ltd Gloucestershire		12. 1.00T
G-BSOM	Glaser-Dirks DG-400	4-126	LN-GMC	12. 7.90	M.J.Watson	Winthorpe	7. 3.00
			D-KGDG		t/a G-BSOM Group "403"		
G-BSON	Green S-25 HAFB	001		7. 6.90	J.J.Green	Newbury	
G-BSOO	Cessna 172F	172-52431	N8531U	19. 7.90	P.W.Lawrence	Old Buckenham	28.10.02
					t/a Double Oscar Flying Group		
G-BSOR	CFM Streak Shadow			23.10.89	J.P.Sorenson	Cranfield	21. 1.01P
	(Rotax 532) K.131-SA & PFA/161A-11602						
G-BSOT	PA-38-112 Tomahawk II	38-81A0053	N25682	23. 7.90	APB Leasing Ltd	Welshpool	25.11.00T
G-BSOU	PA-38-112 Tomahawk II	38-81A0130	N23373	23. 7.90	Chubbs Aviation Services (UK) Ltd		
					(Op Glasgow Flying Club)	Cumbernauld	10. 9.00T
G-BSOV	PA-38-112 Tomahawk II	38-81A0031	N25637	20. 8.90	A.Dodd	Cranfield	1. 3.98T
					(Damaged Panshanger 7.10.95; dismantled 7.99)		
G-BSOX	Luscombe 8AE Silvaire	2318	N45791	7. 8.90	D.Gill Maypole Farm, Chislet		5. 6.00P
	(Continental C85)		NC45791		"Bobby Sox"		
G-BSOY	PA-34-220T Seneca III	3433155	OY-CEU	1. 8.90	British Aerospace Flight Training (UK) Ltd		
						Prestwick	27.11.00T
G-BSOZ	PA-28-161 Warrior II	28-7916080	N30220	14. 8.90	P.S.Lanary	Compton Abbas	19.12.99T
G-BSPA	QAC Quickie Q.2	2227	N227T	16. 8.90	G.V.Mckirdy & B.K.Glover	Enstone	13. 7.00P
	(Revmaster R2100DQ)						

Regn	Type	C/n	P/I	Date	Owner/operator	Probable Base	CA Expy
G-BSPB	Thunder Ax8-84 HAFB	1803		24. 7.90	Nigs Pertwee Ltd	Frinton-on-Sea	19. 7.93T
G-BSPC*	SAN Jodel D.140C Mousquetaire III	150	F-BMFN	2.11.81	Not known	Headcorn	31.10.85
					(Derelict remains noted 10.99)		
G-BSPE	Reims Cessna F.172P Skyhawk II	2073		31.12.80	A.M.J.Clark	(Northallerton)	8. 6.02
G-BSPF*	Cessna T.303 Crusader	T303-00100	OY-SVH	31. 7.90	K P Gibben	Blackpool	
			N3116C		t/a G-BSPF Crusader Group		
					(Cancelled as WFU 25.8.98: noted 9.99)		
G-BSPG	PA-34-200T Seneca II	34-8070168	N8176S	8. 8.90	D.P.Hughes	Elstree	4.11.02
G-BSPI	PA-28-161 Warrior II	28-8116025	N8258V	26. 7.90	Oxford Aviation Services Ltd	Oxford	28. 1.01T
G-BSPJ	Bensen B.8	PFA G/01-1061		3. 8.90	C.M.Jones	(Stowmarket)	
G-BSPK	Cessna 195A	7691	N1079D	14. 8.90	A.G. & D.L.Bompas	Biggin Hill	25. 4.00
	(Jacobs R-755-9)				(Damaged landing Conington 24.4.99)		
G-BSPL	CFM Streak Shadow	K.140-SA		26. 7.90	MEL (Aviation Oxygen) Ltd	Northrepps	1. 9.00P
	(Rotax 582)						
G-BSPM	PA-28-161 Warrior II	28-8116046	N82679	27. 7.90	White Waltham Airfield Ltd	White Waltham	13. 8.00T
					(Op West London Aero Services)		
G-BSPN	PA-28R-201T Turbo Arrow III	28R-7703171	N5965V	31. 7.90	R.G. & W.Allison	Sandtoft	21.12.99
					t/a G-BSPN Flying Group		
G-BSPW	Light Aero Avid Speed Wing	PFA/189-11840		17. 7.90	M.J.Sewell	(Windermere)	27. 5.94P
	(Rotax 582)						
G-BSPX	Neico Lancair 320	521-320-259FB & PFA/191-11865		31. 7.90	C.H.Skelt	(Reigate)	
G-BSPY	BN-2A Islander	156	G-AXYM 5N-AIQ/G-AXYM/G-51-156	1. 6.90	G-WATS Aviation Ltd	Bagby	16. 7.00
G-BSRH	Pitts S-1C Special	LS-2	N4111	7. 8.90	M.R.Janney	Redhill	10. 8.00P
	(Lycoming O-360)						
G-BSRI	Neico Lancair 235	PFA/191-11467		9. 8.90	G.Lewis	Liverpool	14. 6.00P
	(Lycoming O-235) (Tri-cycle u/c)						
G-BSRJ*	Colt AA-1050 Gas FB	1782		20. 8.90	Trezpark Ltd	(Colorado, USA)	31. 8.98A
					(Cancelled by CAA 10.3.95: noted USA 1999)		
G-BSRK	ARV1 Super 2	K.007	ZK-FSQ	8. 8.90	D.M.Blair	(Holywell)	1. 6.00P
	(Hewland AE75)						
G-BSRL	Everett Gyroplane Srs.2	022		8. 8.90	R.F.E.Burley	Sproughton	
					(Noted 12.95)		
G-BSRP	Rotorway Exec	3824		15. 8.90	R.J.Baker	Bromsgrove	24. 9.92P
	(RW152) (Originally quoted c/n 3647)						
G-BSRR	Cessna 182Q Skylane II	182-66915	N96961	25. 7.90	Select Management Services Ltd		
						Egelsbach, Germany	22. 5.00
G-BSRT	Denney Kitfox mk.2	742 & PFA/172-11873		9. 8.90	A.J.Lloyd	Little Down Farm, Milson	1. 6.00P
	(Rotax 582)						
G-BSRX	CFM Streak Shadow			15. 8.90	P.Williams	Netherthorpe	6. 5.00P
	(Rotax 618) K.148-SA & PFA/206-11870						
G-BSRZ	Air Command 532 Elite Two-Seat	PFA G/05-1188		15. 8.90	A.S.G.Crabb	(Beverley)	
G-BSSA	Luscombe 8E Silvaire	4176	N1449K NC1449K	15. 8.90	Luscombe Aircraft Ltd	White Waltham	26. 3.00P
	(Continental C85)						
G-BSSB	Cessna 150L Commuter	150-74147	N19076	15. 8.90	D.T.A.Rees	Haverfordwest	29. 4.00T
G-BSSC	PA-28-161 Warrior II	28-8216176	N81993 N9529N/N8234B	15. 8.90	Oxford Aviation Services Ltd	Oxford	17. 1.00T
G-BSSE	PA-28-140 Cherokee	28-7525192	N33440	22.10.90	Comed Aviation Ltd	Blackpool	27. 5.02T
G-BSSF	Denney Kitfox mk.2	738 & PFA/172-11796		15. 8.90	S.G.Moores	Denthorpe	20.10.00P
	(Rotax 582)						
G-BSSI	Rans S-6 Coyote II	0190-112 & PFA/204-11782	(G-MWJA)	17. 8.90	R.W.Skelton	(Craigavon, Co.Armagh)	16.11.99P
	(Rotax 582)						
G-BSSJ	Clutton FRED Srs.2	PFA/29-10753		23. 8.90	R.F.Jopling	Bagby	27. 6.00P
	(VW 1834)						
G-BSSK	QAC Quickie Q.200	PFA/94A-11354		5. 9.90	D.G.Greatrex	Enstone	23. 9.99P
	(Continental O-200-A)						
G-BSSN*	Air Command 532 Elite Two-Seat	0631		21. 8.90	R.C.Bettany	(Swansea)	
	(Possibly c/n PFA G/05-1187)				(No permit issued: cancelled by CAA 10.3.99)		
G-BSSO	Cameron O-90 HAFB	2255		23. 7.90	R.R. & J.E.Hatton "Just So"	Warminster	21. 5.00A
G-BSSP	Robin DR.400/180R Remorqueur	2015		24. 9.90	Soaring (Oxford) Ltd	RAF Syerston	8. 1.00
					(Op Air Cadets Gliding School)		
G-BSSR	PA-28-151 Cherokee Warrior	28-7615001	N1190X	29. 8.90	Flying Pig Aviation Ltd	Biggin Hill	19. 2.00
G-BSST*	BAC-Sud Concorde SST	002 & 13520		6. 5.68	The Science Museum	RNAS Yeovilton	31.10.74P*
G-BSSV	CFM Streak Shadow K.129-SA & PFA/206-11657			21. 8.90	R.W.Payne	Langtoft	5. 5.98P
	(Rotax 532)						
G-BSSW	PA-28-161 Warrior II	28-7816143	N47850	29. 8.90	R.L.Hayward	Filton	8. 7.02T
					(Op Bristol Flying Club)		

Regn	Type	C/n	P/I	Date	Owner/operator	Probable Base	CA Expy
G-BSSX	PA-28-161 Warrior II	2816056	N9141H	11. 9.90	Airways Aero Associations Ltd Booker	11.11.02T
					(Op British Airways Flying Club) (Martha Masanabo/Ndebele t/s)	
G-BSTC	Aeronca 11AC Chief	11AC-1660	N3289E	15.10.90	B.Bridgman & N.J.Mortimore	
	(Continental A65)		NC3289E			Watchford Farm, Yarcombe	26. 6.93P
					(Damaged Henstridge 18.4.93; on rebuild 12.95)	
G-BSTE	Aerospatiale AS.355F2 Twin Squirrel			29. 8.90	Hygrade Foods Ltd	Biggin Hill	1. 8.00
		5453					
G-BSTH	PA-25-235 Pawnee C	25-5009	N8599L	25. 9.90	Scottish Gliding Union Ltd	Portmoak	17. 3.00
G-BSTI	Piper J3C-85 Cub	19144	N6007H	31. 8.90	I.Fraser & G.L.Nunn	Knettishall	28. 3.99P
			NC6007H				
G-BSTK	Thunder Ax8-90 HAFB	1838		17. 9.90	M.Williams	Wadhurst, E.Sussex	4. 5.95A
G-BSTL	Rand Robinson KR-2	PFA/129-11863		6. 9.90	C.S.Hales	(Walsall)	
G-BSTM	Cessna 172L Skyhawk	172-60143	N4243Q	25. 9.90	A.H.Windle t/a G-BSTM Group	Cambridge	27. 2.00
G-BSTO	Cessna 152 II	152-82133	N68005	4. 9.90	Plymouth School of Flying Ltd	Plymouth	15.11.02T
G-BSTP	Cessna 152 II	152-82925	N89953	4. 9.90	Cobham Leasing Ltd	Bournemouth	4.11.02T
G-BSTR	Grumman-American AA-5 Traveler		OO-ALR	8.10.90	James Allan (Aviation & Engineering) Ltd	
		AA5-0688	OO-HAN/(OO-WAZ)			Glenrothes	4.12.02
G-BSTT	Rans S-6 Coyote II			5. 9.90	D.G.Palmer	(Peterhead)	16. 6.00P
	(Rotax 582) 0190-115 & PFA/204-11880						
G-BSTV	PA-32-300 Cherokee Six	32-40378	N4069R	13. 9.90	B.C.Hudson (Open store 5.99)	Popham	AC
G-BSTX	Luscombe 8A Silvaire	3301	EI-CDZ	10. 9.90	A.A.Alderdice	Kilkeel, Co.Down	18. 6.00P
			G-BSTX/N71874/NC71874				
G-BSTY	Thunder Ax8-90 HAFB	394		12. 9.90	J.W.Cato	Leicester	15. 6.97A
G-BSTZ	PA-28-140 Cherokee Cruiser		N1674H	10.10.90	Air Navigation & Trading Co Ltd	
		28-7725153				Blackpool	18.11.02T
G-BSUA	Rans S-6 Coyote II	PFA/204-11910		29.10.90	A.J.Todd	
	(Rotax 582)				Abbey Warren Farm, Bucknall, Lincoln	1.12.00P
G-BSUB	Colt 77A HAFB	1801		30.10.90	R.R.J.Wilson & M.P.Hill	Bristol	19. 3.00A
G-BSUD	Luscombe 8A Master	1745	N37084	14. 9.90	I.G.Harrison	Egginton	1.12.00P
	(Continental A65)		NC37084				
G-BSUE	Cessna U206G Stationair II		N756TB	6. 9.90	R.A.Robinson	Little Gransden	7.12.00
		U206-04334					
G-BSUF	PA-32RT-300 Lance II	32R-7885240	N32PL	17. 9.90	M.J.Parker	Elstree	2. 6.00
			ZP-PJQ/N9641N				
G-BSUH*	Cessna 140	8092	N89088	15.10.90	Not known	Abbeyshrule, Ireland	2. 5.94
	(Continental C85)		NC89088		(Damaged Gowran Grange 6.93; airframe stored 9.99)	
G-BSUJ	Brugger MB.2 Colibri	PFA/43-10726		17. 9.90	M.A.Farrelly	(Liverpool)	
G-BSUK	Colt 77A HAFB	1374		21. 9.90	A.J.Moore	Northwood, Middlesex	2. 8.94A
G-BSUM*	Scheibe SF.27MB	6303	D-KIBE	31.10.90	M.J.Davies t/a M Syndicate	Winthorpe	
					(Cancelled as wfu 21.01.99 - no UK CofA issued)	
G-BSUO	Scheibe SF-25C-2000 Falke	44501	D-KIOK	6.12.90	British Gliding Association Ltd	
					RAF Bicester	26. 2.00
G-BSUR	Rotorway Exec 90	5003		21. 9.90	Psion Manufacturing Ltd	
	(RW 162)				(Mullingar, Ireland)	1.12.93P
G-BSUT	Rans S-6-ESA Coyote II			2.10.90	J.Bell	Barton	1.12.00P
	(Rotax 582) 0990-138 & PFA/204-11897						
G-BSUU	Colt 180A HAFB	1851		17. 9.90	Balloon School (International) Ltd Bath	26.11.99T
					t/a British School of Ballooning	
					(Op Heritage Balloons) (VW/Audi titles)	
G-BSUV	Cameron O-77 HAFB	2407		26. 9.90	R.Moss	Banchory	24. 9.00A
G-BSUW	PA-34-200T Seneca II	34-7870081	N2360M	26. 9.90	TG Aviation Ltd	Manston	20.12.02T
					(Op Thanet Flying Club)	
G-BSUX	Carlson Sparrow II	PFA/209-11794		5.10.90	J.Stephenson	Bagby	10. 1.00P
	(Rotax 532)				(Stored 4.97)	
G-BSUZ	Denney Kitfox mk.3			10. 9.90	M.J.Clark	Sedgwick	17. 5.00P
	(Rotax 582) 745 & PFA/172-11875						
G-BSVB	PA-28-181 Archer II	2890098	N9155S	10. 9.90	B.R.Janman & PEPS Intl Ltd	Sywell	30.12.99T
G-BSVE	Binder CP.301S Smaragd	113	HB-SED	27. 9.90	R.E.Perry	Jersey	2. 9.00P
					t/a Smaragd Flying Group	
G-BSVF	PA-28-161 Warrior II	28-8416047	C-GVSJ	2.10.90	Airways Aero Associations Ltd	Booker	29.11.99T
			N9575N		(Op British Airways Flying Club) (Wings t/s)	
G-BSVG	PA-28-161 Warrior II	28-8516013	C-GZAV	2.10.90	Airways Aero Associations Ltd	Booker	22.12.99T
					(Op British Airways Flying Club) (Dove/Colum t/s)	
G-BSVH	Piper J3C-75 Cub	15360	N87702	2.10.90	A.R.Meakin	Eastbach Farm, Coleford	9. 8.00P
			NC87702				
G-BSVI	PA-16 Clipper	16-186	N5379H	7.11.90	I.R.Blakemore	Old Sarum	30. 6.01
					"Spirit of St.Petersburg"	
G-BSVJ	Piper J3C-65 Cub	17521	N2MD R	V.S.E.Norman	Rendcomb	
			N70515/NC70515				
G-BSVK	Denney Kitfox mk.2	PFA/172-11731		2.10.90	C.M.Looney	(Leatherhead)	5. 4.94P
	(Rotax 582)						

Regn	Type	C/n	P/I	Date	Owner/operator	Probable Base	CA Expy
G-BSVM	PA-28-161 Warrior II	28-8116173	N8351N	7.11.90	EFG Flying Services Ltd	Biggin Hill	23. 1.00T
G-BSVN	Thorp T-18 (Lycoming O-290)	107	N4881	17. 9.90	J.H.Kirkham	Barton	6. 6.00P
G-BSVP	PA-23-250 Aztec F	27-7754115	N63787	9. 2.78	Time Electronics Ltd	Lydd	24. 6.02
G-BSVR	Schweizer Hughes 269C (300C)	S.1236	OO-JWW D-HLEB	14.11.90	Martinair Ltd	Sherburn in Elmet	1.12.00
G-BSVS	Robin DR.400/100 Cadet	2017		22.10.90	D.M.Chalmers	Upper Harford	22. 3.00
G-BSVV	PA-38-112 Tomahawk	38-79A0723	N2492L	3.10.90	J.Maffia & H.Merkado	Panshanger	10. 6.00T
G-BSVW	PA-38-112 Tomahawk	38-79A0149	N2606B	9.11.90	EFG Flying Services Ltd	Cardiff	27. 7.00T
G-BSVX	PA-38-112 Tomahawk	38-79A0950	N2336P	10. 1.91	Cristal Air Ltd.	(Heathfield)	13. 4.00T
G-BSVY	PA-38-112 Tomahawk	38-79A0038	N2396B	10. 1.91	Cardiff-Wales Flying Club Ltd	Cardiff	23. 7.00T
G-BSVZ	Pietenpol Air Camper (Regd as a Pietenpol/Challis Chaffinch)	1008	N3265	6.11.90	G.F.M.Garner (Stored 5.98)	Clench Common	6. 9.93P*
G-BSWB	Rans S-10 Sakota (Rotax 532) 0489-046 & PFA/194-11560			8.10.90	F.A.Hewitt	Garston Farm, Marshfield	5. 3.00P
G-BSWC	Boeing-Stearman E75 (PT-13D) Kaydet (Lycoming R-680)	75-5560	N17112 N5021V/42-17397	16.11.90	R.R.White (As "112" in US Army c/s)	Old Sarum	31. 8.00T
G-BSWF	PA-16 Clipper (Lycoming O-320)	16-475	N5865H	12.10.90	T.M.Storey (Active 9.99)	Bolney	4. 2.02
G-BSWG	PA-15 Vagabond (Continental A65)	15-99	N4316H NC4316H	8.10.90	P.E.J.Sturgeon	Priory Farm, Tibenham	31. 8.97P
G-BSWH	Cessna 152 II	152-81365	N49861	15.10.90	Airspeed Aviation Ltd	Swansea	14. 3.02T
G-BSWI	Rans S-10 Sakota (Rotax 532)	PFA/194-11872		16.10.90	J.M.Mooney (Shotts, Lanark) (Damaged Braehead 26.10.93)		11. 6.94P
G-BSWJ	Cameron O-77 HAFB	2433		17.10.90	G.A.Board, Tonbridge 4. 6.99A		
G-BSWL	Slingsby T.61F Venture T.2	1974	EI-CCQ G-BSWL/ZA655	15.10.90	K.Richards	(Bridgend)	17. 2.01
G-BSWM	Slingsby T.61F Venture T.2	1965	ZA629	12.10.90	L.J.McKelvie	Bellarena	26. 3.00
G-BSWR	PBN BN-2T Turbine Islander	2245		22.10.90	Police Authority for Northern Ireland	Aldergrove	2. 3.01T
G-BSWV	Cameron N-77 HAFB	2369		22.10.90	Leicester Mercury Ltd "Leicester Mercury"	Leicester	23. 3.00A
G-BSWX	Cameron V-90 HAFB	2401		22.10.90	B.J.Burrows "Beeswax"	Bristol	29. 6.00A
G-BSWY	Cameron N-77 HAFB	2428		12.10.90	M.R.Nanda t/a Nottingham Balloon Club	Nottingham	12. 8.98A
G-BSWZ	Cameron A-180 HAFB	2419	C-FGWZ G-BSWZ	22.10.90	G.C.Ludlow	Hythe	19. 7.99T
G-BSXA	PA-28-161 Warrior II	28-8416121	N4373Z N9622N	11.12.90	A.S.Bamrah t/a Falcon Flying Services	Biggin Hill	31. 7.00T
G-BSXB	PA-28-161 Warrior II	28-8416125	N4374D N9626N	4.12.90	Aeroshow Ltd	Gloucestershire	24. 3.00T
G-BSXC	PA-28-161 Warrior II	28-8416126	N4374F N9627N	4.12.90	L.T.Halpin Clutton Hill Farm, High Littleton		25. 6.00T
G-BSXD	Soko P-2 Kraguj	030	30146 Yugoslav Army	22.10.90	L.C.MacKnight (As "30146" in Yugoslav Army c/s)	Elstree	22. 4.99P
G-BSXI	Mooney M.20E Chapparal	700056	N6766V	31.10.90	A.N.Pain	(Chelmsford)	4. 5.00
G-BSXM	Cameron V-77 HAFB	2446		5.11.90	C.A.Oxby "Oxby"	Doncaster	16. 7.00A
G-BSXN	Robinson R-22 Beta	1611		14.11.90	J.G.Gray	Berwick-upon-Tweed	23. 1.00
G-BSXP	Air Command 532 Elite	0633 & PFA G/04-1195		5.11.90	B.J.West	(Sevenoaks)	
G-BSXS	PA-28-181 Archer II	28-7990151	N3055C	26.11.90	Pipe-Air Ltd	Shoreham	9.12.02
G-BSXT	Piper J/5A Cub Cruiser (Continental C85)	5-498	N33409 NC33409	8.11.90	M.G. & K.J.Thompson Belle Vue Farm, Yarnscombe		14.10.00P
G-BSXX	Whittaker MW7	PFA/171-11469		16.10.90	H.J.Stanley	(Abingdon)	
G-BSXY*	Oldfield Baby Lakes	PFA/10-10094	(G-JENY)	15.10.90	B.Freeman-Jones (Alford, Aberdeen) (Cancelled by CAA 16.4.99)		
G-BSYA	Jodel D.18 (VW1834)	PFA/169-11316		7.11.90	S.Harrison	Eshott	2. 6.00P
G-BSYB	Cameron N-120 HAFB	2406		7.11.90	M.Buono	Siena, Italy	21. 6.00A
G-BSYC	PA-32R-300 Cherokee Lance	32R-7780159	N7745T N1435H	2. 4.91	M.N.Pinches	Halfpenny Green	4. 4.00
G-BSYD	Cameron A-180 HAFB	2426		18.10.90	A.A.Brown t/a Balloon Company "Discovery"	Guildford	31.10.98T
G-BSYF	Luscombe 8A Silvaire	3455	N72028 NC72028	12.11.90	Atlantic Connexions Ltd (Stored 7.95) t/a Atlantic Aviation Manor Farm, Glatton		
G-BSYG	PA-12 Super Cruiser (Lycoming O-235)	12-2106	N3228M NC3228M	12.11.90	E.R.Newall t/a Fat Cub Group	Breighton	15. 7.00P
G-BSYH	Luscombe 8A Silvaire (Continental A65)	2842	N71415 NC71415	13.11.90	N.R.Osborne	Insch	29.11.00P
G-BSYI	Aerospatiale AS.355F1 Twin Squirrel	5197	M-MJI	14.11.90	Lynton Aviation Ltd (Op European Helicopters Ltd)	Denham	28.11.02T

Regn	Type	C/n	P/I	Date	Owner/operator	Probable Base	CA Expy
G-BSYJ	Cameron N-77 HAFB	2441		13.11.90	Chubb Fire Ltd "Chubb Fire II"	Sunbury-on-Thames	16.12.99A
G-BSYK*	PA-38-112 Tomahawk II	38-81A0143	N23449	30. 1.91	Flychoice Ltd	Halfpenny Green	
	(No C of A issued: cancelled by CAA 10.3.99)						
G-BSYL*	PA-38-112 Tomahawk II	38-81A0172	N91333	23. 1.91	Flychoice Ltd	Halfpenny Green	
	(Stored 9.97; no C of A issued: cancelled by CAA 10.3.99)						
G-BSYM	PA-38-112 Tomahawk II	38-82A0072	N2507V	30. 1.91	Flychoice Ltd	Wellesbourne Mountford	4. 9.94T
	(Damaged 27.7.94; open store 5.98)						
G-BSYO	Piper J3C-90 Cub (L-4B-PI)	12809	(G-BSMJ)	19. 2.91	C.R.Reynolds & J.D.Fuller		
	(Continental O-200-A) (Frame No.12639)		(G-BRHE)/EC-AIY/HB-ODO/44-80513		Pent Farm, Postling, Kent		12. 7.00P
	(Officially regd as c/n 10244 ex 43-1383/F-BFYF which is HB-OVG)						
G-BSYP	Bensen B.8MR (Rotax 503)	PFA G/01-1186		16.11.90	C.R.Gordon	Carlisle	3. 6.98P
G-BSYU	Robin DR.400/180 Regent	2027		26.11.90	K.J.J.Jarman & P.D.Smoothy	Hinton-in-The-Hedges	27. 2.00
G-BSYV	Cessna 150M Commuter	150-78371	N9423U	16.11.90	L.R.Haunch t/a Fenland Flying School	Fenland	28. 2.00T
G-BSYW	Cessna 150M Commuter	150-78446	N9498U	16.11.90	J Cropper	Barton	25. 3.00
G-BSYY	PA-28-161 Warrior II	2816009	N9100X	26.11.90	Oxford Aviation Services Ltd	Oxford	1. 2.00T
G-BSYZ	PA-28-161 Warrior II	28-8516051	N6908H	22.11.90	Piper Air (Glasgow) Ltd	Glasgow	8. 9.00T
G-BSZB	Stolp SA.300 Starduster Too (Lycoming O-360)	545	N5495M	3.12.90	D.T.Gethin	Haverfordwest	26. 4.00P
G-BSZC	Beechcraft C-45H-BH Expeditor AF-258		N9541Z 51-11701	14.12.90	A.A.Hodgson "Southern Comfort" (As "AF258/51-11701A" in USAF c/s)	Bryngwyn Bach	29. 5.00
	(Originally built as AT-7 42-2490 c/n 4166; re-manufactured 4.52)						
G-BSZD	Robin DR.400/180 Regent	2029		21.11.90	R.J.Hitchman & P.J.Rowland & Sons (Farmers) Ltd	Draycott Farm, Chiseldon	17. 3.00
G-BSZF	CEA Jodel DR.250/160 Capitaine	32	F-BNJB	29.11.90	J.B.Randle	Piltdown, E.Sussex	24. 4.00
G-BSZG	Stolp SA.100 Starduster (Lycoming O-320)	101	N70P	27.11.90	S.W.Watkins & D.F.Chapman	Trecorras Farm, Llangarron	4. 7.00P
G-BSZH	Thunder Ax7-77 HAFB	1848		27.11.90	K.E.Viney & L.J.Weston "Her Outdoors"	Olney	30.11.99T
G-BSZI	Cessna 152 II	152-85856	N95139	17.12.90	Eglinton Flying Club Ltd	Eglinton	9. 2.00T
G-BSZJ	PA-28-181 Archer II	28-8190216	N8373Z	6.12.90	R.D.Fuller & M.L.A.Pudney	St Lawrence, Bradwell-on-Sea	3. 5.00
G-BSZL	Colt 77A HAFB	1883		28.11.90	Staedtler Mars GmbH "Staedtler"	Nurnberg, Germany	12.12.97A
G-BSZM	Montgomerie-Bensen B.8MR (Rotax 582)	PFA G/01-1193		30.11.90	A.McCredie	(Penrith)	1. 6.00P
G-BSZN	Bucker Bu.133D-1 Jungmeister (Siemens Bramo SH14A) (Built Bitz)	2002	N8103 D-ECAY	30.11.90	A.J.Norman t/a Norman Aeroplane Trust	Rendcomb	13. 9.00P
G-BSZO	Cessna 152 II	152-80221	N24334	30.11.90	Aerohire Ltd	Halfpenny Green	19.10.01T
G-BSZS	Robinson R-22 Beta	1235	N8058J	13.12.90	A.Liddiard t/a Bladerunner Helicopters	Bristol	16. 3.00
G-BSZT	PA-28-161 Warrior II	28-8116027	N8260D	31.12.90	Airbase Aircraft Ltd	Shoreham	8. 4.00T
G-BSZU	Cessna 150F	150-63481	N6881F	3.12.90	M.J.Tarrant	Old Sarum	19.12.00T
G-BSZV	Cessna 150F	150-62304	N3504L	3.12.90	Kirmington Aviation Ltd (Bembridge, IOW)		17. 7.00T
G-BSZW	Cessna 152 II	152-81072	N48958	3.12.90	Haimoss Ltd	Old Sarum	6.10.00T
G-BSZY	Cameron A-180 HAFB	2479		3. 1.91	K.H.Benning	Telgte, Germany	2. 1.96A

G-BTAA – G-BTZZ

Regn	Type	C/n	P/I	Date	Owner/operator	Probable Base	CA Expy
G-BTAB	BAe 125 Srs.800B	258088	G-5-563	12. 7.88	Dean Finance Co Ltd	Heathrow	6. 5.00T
			G-BOOA/(ZK-RHP)/G-5-563		(Op by Aravco)		
G-BTAD*	Macair Merlin	PFA/208-11661		6.11.90	A.T. & M.R.Dowie	Scotland Farm, Hook	
					(Under construction 5.95: cancelled by CAA 16.4.99)		
G-BTAG	Cameron O-77 HAFB	2454		12.11.90	R.A.Shapland "Tag-Along"	Petworth	21. 9.99A
G-BTAH	Bensen B.8M (Arrow GT500R)	PFA G/07-1196		13.12.90	T.B.Johnson	St.Merryn	31. 8.98P
G-BTAK	EAA Acrosport 2 (Lycoming O-320)	1-468	N440X	27.12.90	P.G.Harrison "The Duck"	Sywell	2. 3.00P
G-BTAL	Reims Cessna F.152 II	1444		7. 4.78	TG Aviation Ltd (Op Thanet Flying Club)	Manston	14. 3.00T
G-BTAM	PA-28-181 Archer II	2890093	N9153D	10. 1.91	Tri-Star Farms Ltd	Ronaldsway	24. 4.00T
G-BTAN	Thunder Ax7-65Z HAFB	517		4. 5.83	A.S.Newnham	Southampton	2. 8.00A
G-BTAP	PA-38-112 Tomahawk	38-78A0141	N9603T	8. 1.91	Western Air (Thruxton) Ltd	Thruxton	20. 7.00T
G-BTAR	PA-38-112 Tomahawk	38-79A0383	N2584D	13. 2.91	Aerohire Ltd	Blackpool	12. 3.00T
					(Damaged Liverpool 19.6.98: on rebuild 2.99)		
G-BTAS	PA-38-112 Tomahawk	38-79A0545	F-GTAS G-BTAS/N2492G	21. 2.91	W.Brooks	Cardiff	17. 3.00T

Regn	Type	C/n	P/I	Date	Owner/operator	Probable Base	CA Expy
G-BTAT	Denney Kitfox mk.2			6.11.90	O.W.Owen & M.D.Harris	Kemble	13. 5.00P
	(Rotax 582)	689 & PFA/172-11832					
G-BTAU	Thunder Ax7-77 HAFB	1429		13.12.90	S.& G.Gebauer	Lippstadt, Germany	13.12.91A
G-BTAV	Colt 105A HAFB	1858		13.12.90	D.C.Chipping	Evora, Portugal	20.12.93A
G-BTAW	PA-28-161 Warrior II	28-8616031	N9259T	14.12.90	A.J.Wiggins	Gloucestershire	30. 4.00T
					(Op Gloucester & Cheltenham Flying School)		
G-BTAX*	PA-31-350 Navajo Chieftain		N63721	3. 9.87	Meggair Ltd		6.12.91T
		31-7752036			(To Canada by Container 7.97)		
G-BTAZ	Evans VP-2	PFA/63-11474		13.12.90	G.S.Poulter	Norwich	
					(Complete 8.99)		
G-BTBA	Robinson R-22 Beta	1717		18. 3.91	Heliflight (UK) Ltd	Halfpenny Green	30. 4.00
G-BTBB	Thunder Ax8-105 Srs.2 HAFB	1871		23.11.90	W.J.Brogan	(London SW6)	3. 3.98T
G-BTBC	PA-28-161 Warrior II	28-7916414	N28755	19.12.90	M.J.L.MacDonald	Wellesbourne Mountford	21. 4.00T
					(Op Wellesbourne Aviation)		
G-BTBF	Fisher FP.202 Super Koala	(G-MWOZ)	24.12.90	E.A.Taylor	(Southend)	
		SK.067 & PFA/158-11954			(Under construction off airfield 1.00)		
G-BTBG	Denney Kitfox	PFA/172-11845		18.12.90	J.Catley	(Bristol)	
G-BTBH	Ryan ST3KR (PT-22-RY)	2063	N854	18. 2.91	A.T.Hooper & C.C.Silk t/a Ryan Group		
	(Kinner R56)		N50993/41-20854		Bericote Farm, Blackdown, Leamington Spa	17. 1.99P
					(As "854" in US Army c/s)		
G-BTBI	WAR P-47 Thunderbolt rep	0054	N47DL	8. 1.91	E.C.Murgatroyd	Sackville Farm, Riseley	8. 9.98P
	(Continental O-200-A) (Marked as "Project No.52685A")			(As "85" in USAF c/s) "Lil Jug"		
					(Crashed on take off Carlisle 26.4.99)		
G-BTBJ	Cessna 195B	16046	N4461C	2.10.91	J.Griffin	Popham	20. 5.00
G-BTBL	Montgomerie-Bensen B.8MR Merlin			21.12.90	R.D.H.Dobree-Carey		
	(Rotax 532)	PFA G/01A-1183				Blandford Forum/Kemble	2. 9.00P
G-BTBN	Denney Kitfox mk.2			31.12.90	R.C.Bowley	Croft Farm, Defford	8. 4.00P
	(Rotax 582)	686 & PFA/172-11859					
G-BTBP	Cameron N-90 HAFB	2464		21.12.90	Julia B.Turnau	Pianella, Italy	21. 6.00A
					t/a Chianti Balloon Club		
G-BTBR	Cameron DP-80 Hot-Air Airship	2344		21.12.90	Cameron Balloons Ltd	Bristol	3.12.97A
					"Cameron Skyship"		
G-BTBS*	Cameron N-180 HAFB	2440		21.12.90	Balloon Preservation Group	Lancing	27. 6.97T
					"The Big Sod"		
G-BTBU	PA-18-150 Super Cub	18-7509010	N9665P	3. 1.91	A.J.White t/a G-BTBU Syndicate	Denham	9. 7.00
G-BTBV	Cessna 140	12727	N2474N	2. 4.91	M.S.Johnson	Enstone	11. 6.00
	(Continental C85)		NC2474N				
G-BTBW	Cessna 120	14220	N2009V	24. 1.91	Melanie J.Willies		
	(Continental C90)		NC2009V			Standalone Farm, Meppershall	13. 7.01
G-BTBX	Piper J3C-65 Cub	6334	N35367	29. 1.91	J.B.Hargrave & D.T.C.Collins	RAF Henlow	18. 9.00
			NC35367		t/a Henlow Taildraggers		
G-BTBY	PA-17 Vagabond	17-195	N4894H	4. 1.91	G.J.Smith	Clipgate Farm, Denton	1. 5.00P
	(Continental C85)						
G-BTCA	PA-32R-300 Cherokee Lance		N5941V	10. 1.91	P.Taylor	Halfpenny Green	26. 5.00
		32R-7780381			t/a Lance Group		
G-BTCB	Air Command 582 Sport			9. 1.91	G.Scurrah	Millom	
		0634 & PFA G/04-1198			(Nearing completion 5.95)		
G-BTCC	Grumman F6F-5K Hellcat	A-11286	(N10CN)	31.12.90	Patina Ltd	Duxford	18. 8.99P
			N100T/FN80142/Bu.80141 (Op The Fighter Collection)			
	(Composite with centre section from F6F-3 Bu.08831 c/n A-218) (As "Bu.40467/19" in VF-6 Sqn US Navy c/s)						
G-BTCD	North American P-51D-25NA Mustang	N51JJ	11. 1.91	Pelham Ltd	Duxford	28. 4.00P
		122-39608	N6340T/RCAF 9568/44-73149 (Op The Fighter Collection) "Candyman"/"Moose"			
				(As "463221/G4-S" in 362nd FS/357th FG USAAF c/s)		
G-BTCE	Cessna 152 II	152-81376	N49876	10. 1.91	S.T.Gilbert	Enstone	13. 8.00T
	(Tail-wheel conversion)						
G-BTCH	Luscombe 8E Silvaire	6403	N1976B	11. 2.91	J.Grewcock & R.C.Carroll	Popham	9. 9.99P
	(Continental C85)		NC1976B				
G-BTCI	PA-17 Vagabond	17-136	N4839H	11. 1.91	T.R.Whittome	Inverness	5. 7.00P
	(Continental A65)		NC4839H				
G-BTCJ	Luscombe 8AE Silvaire	1869	N41908	16. 1.91	Mrs J.M.Lovell	Chilbolton	20. 6.00P
	(Continental O-200A)		NC41908				
G-BTCK	Cameron A-210 HAFB	2451		8. 1.91	M.W.A.Shemilt	Henley-on-Thames	9. 5.00T
					t/a H-O-T Air Balloons		
G-BTCM	Cameron N-90 HAFB	1306	(G-BMPW)	8. 5.86	J.D. & K.Griffiths "TCM"	Newark	10.10.00A
G-BTCO	Clutton FRED Srs.II	PFA/29-10558		11. 1.91	I.P.Manley	(Yeovil)	
G-BTCR	Rans S-10 Sakota	PFA/194-11877		11. 1.91	B.J.Hewitt	(Dromore, NI)	20.10.00P
	(Rotax 532)						
G-BTCS	Colt 90A HAFB	1895		11. 1.91	R.C.Stone	Reading	2. 5.00A
					"Rosie Rags" (Variety Club of GB c/s)		
G-BTCT	Aerospatiale AS.332L Super Puma	2129	FAP 1012	14. 1.91	Bristow Helicopters Ltd	Aberdeen	31. 3.01T
					"Anstruther"		

Regn	Type	C/n	P/I	Date	Owner/operator	Probable Base	CA Expy
G-BTCW	Cameron A-180 HAFB	2458		17. 1.91	P.Clark t/a Bristol Balloons	Bristol	21. 7.00T
G-BTCZ	Cameron Chateau 84SS HAFB	2246		18. 1.91	Forbes Europe Inc "Chateau II"	Balleroy, Normandy	18. 6.00
G-BTDA	Slingsby T-61F Venture T.2	1870	XZ550	17. 4.91	T.Holloway t/a RAFGSA (Op Anglia Gliding Club)	RAF Wattisham	16. 3.00
G-BTDC	Denney Kitfox mk.2 405 & PFA/172-11483			11. 1.91	O.Smith	(Crook)	
G-BTDD	CFM Streak Shadow K.127-SA & PFA/161A-11622 (Rotax 582)			14. 1.91	R.D.Davidson	Perth	1. 9.00P
G-BTDE	Cessna C-165 Airmaster	551	N21911 NC21911	18. 1.91	G.S.Moss	Popham	3. 9.00
G-BTDF	Luscombe 8AF Silvaire (Continental C90)	2205	N45678 NC45678	17. 4.91	R.Harrison t/a Delta Foxtrot Group	(Sunderland)	19. 8.93P
G-BTDH	Hunting-Percival P.56 Provost T.1	PAC/F/183	N2416R 7925M/WV666	25. 1.91	J.J.Woodhouse t/a Flying Services (As "WV666/O-D" in 6 FTS c/s)	Thruxton	25. 9.98P
G-BTDI	Robinson R-22 Beta	1670		29. 1.91	Heli Air Ltd	Wellesbourne Mountford	15. 5.00
G-BTDN	Denney Kitfox mk.2 688 & PFA/172-11826			22. 1.91	S.D.Arnold t/a Foxy Flyers Group	(Coventry)	
G-BTDP	Grumman TBM-3R Avenger	3381	N3966A Bu.53319	5. 2.91	A.Haig-Thomas (As "53319/RB-319" in USN c/s)	North Weald	13. 5.00P
G-BTDR	Aero Designs Pulsar PFA/202-11962 (Rotax 582)			24. 1.91	M.Jordan	North Weald	14. 6.00P
G-BTDS	Colt 77A HAFB	1897		29. 1.91	CP Witter Ltd "Witters II"	Chester	16. 7.00A
G-BTDT	CASA I-131E Jungmann	2131	E3B-505	5. 2.91	T.A.Reed (Noted 8.99)	Watchford Farm, Yarcombe	8. 6.94P
G-BTDV	PA-28-161 Warrior II	28-7816355	N3548M	25. 2.91	R.E.Thorne	Alderney	17. 5.01
G-BTDW	Cessna 152 II	152-79864	N757NC	25. 2.91	J.A.Blenkharn	Carlisle	27. 8.00T
G-BTDX	PA-18-150 Super Cub	18-7809098	N62595	28. 1.91	A.D. Hammond Waits Farm, Belchamp Walter t/a Hammond Aviation (On rebuild 7.99)		25. 5.00T
G-BTDY	PA-18-150 Super Cub	18-8109007	N24570	28. 1.91	Rodger Aviation Ltd (Op Medway Flt Training) Stoneacre Farm, Farthing Corner (DBF Stoneacre Farm 1993 and used in rebuild of G-HAHA)		23. 7.94T
G-BTDZ	CASA I-131E Jungmann	2104	E3B-524	5. 2.91	R.J.Pickin & I.M.White	Redhill	29. 5.00P
G-BTEA	Cameron N-105 HAFB	284		31. 5.77	M.W.A.Shemilt t/a H-O-T Air Balloons "Big Red"	Henley-on-Thames	8. 5.99A
G-BTEE	Cameron O-120 HAFB	2499		24. 1.91	W.H. & J.P.Morgan "Y Ddraig Goch/The Red Dragon"	Swansea	21. 3.99T
G-BTEF	Pitts S-1 Special (Lycoming IO-360)	515H	N88PR	19. 2.91	C.Davidson t/a Northwest Aerobatics	Blackpool	28.10.97P
G-BTEI	Everett Campbell Cricket (Arrow GT500R)	023		31. 1.91	R.A.Jarvis	Kingsmuir	21.12.98P
G-BTEK	Socata TB-20 Trinidad	1240		4. 2.91	D.F.Fagan Vendee Air Park, Talmont, St.Hilaire, France		19. 8.02
G-BTEL	CFM Streak Shadow (Rotax 532) K.125-SA & PFA/206-11667			31. 1.91	J.E.Eatwell	Boscombe Down	26. 8.00P
G-BTES	Cessna 150H	150-68371	N22575	29. 4.91	R.A.Forward	(Crowborough)	20. 8.00
G-BTET	Piper J3C-65 Cub	18296	N98141 NC98141	5. 2.91	R.M.Jones	Blackpool	7.10.00P
G-BTEU	Aerospatiale SA.365N2 Dauphin 2	6392		11. 2.91	Bond Helicopters Ltd	Humberside	1. 4.01T
G-BTEV	PA-38-112 Tomahawk	38-78A0025	N9315T	13. 2.91	T.R.Blockley	Cardiff	15. 4.00T
G-BTEW	Cessna 120 (Continental C90)	10238	CF-ELE	29. 4.91	Kay F.Mason	Little Snoring	21. 6.01
G-BTEX	PA-28-140 Cherokee	28-23773	CF-XXL N3907X	24. 4.91	McAully Flying Group Ltd	Little Snoring	11. 4.01T
G-BTFA	Denney Kitfox mk.2 (Rotax 503) 566 & PFA/172-11520			13. 2.91	K.R.Peek Church Farm, North Moreton (Damaged North Moreton 18.6.97)		6.10.94P
G-BTFB	Cameron DG-14 Gas Airship	2527		9. 7.99	Cameron Balloons Ltd	Bristol	20. 7.00
G-BTFC	Reims Cessna F.152 II	1668		23. 5.79	Tayside Aviation Ltd	Aberdeen	8. 1.01T
G-BTFD	Colt AS-105 mk.II Hot-Air Airship	1856		13. 2.91	Media Fantasy Aviation UK Ltd	(London SE16)	AC
G-BTFE	Parsons Gyroplane Model 1 (Rotax 582) (Tandem Trainer)	38		13. 2.91	N.C.White	Kingsmuir	22.11.00P
G-BTFF	Cessna T310R II	310R-0718	N1363G	25. 2.91	United Sales Equipment Dealers Ltd Sandford Hall, Knockin		29. 5.00
G-BTFG	Boeing-Stearman A75N1 (N2S-4) Kaydet (Continental W670) 75-3441		N4467N Bu.30010	20. 2.91	D.W.N.Johnson Bunns Bank, Norfolk (As "441" in USN c/s)		6. 4.02
G-BTFJ	PA-15 Vagabond (Lycoming O-145)	15-159	N4373H NC4373H	13. 2.91	C.W.Thirtle & R.J.Court t/a Vagabond FJ Flying Group	Old Sarum	20. 6.00P
G-BTFK	Taylorcraft BC-12D (Continental A65)	10540	N599SB N5240M	13. 2.91	J.J.Sheeran	(Newry, NI)	16. 2.00P
G-BTFL	Aeronca 11AC Chief	11AC-1727	N3403E NC3403E	18. 2.91	J.G.Vaughan Eastbach Farm, Coleford t/a BTFL Group		15.11.00P

Regn	Type	C/n	P/I	Date	Owner/operator	Probable Base	CA Expy
G-BTFM	Cameron O-105 HAFB	2623		12. 8.91	P.Forster & J.Trehern	Edinburgh	18. 8.99A
					t/a Edinburgh University Hot-Air Balloon Club		
G-BTFO	PA-28-161 Warrior II	28-7816580	N31728	12. 3.91	Flyfar Ltd	Blackpool	5. 5.00
G-BTFP	PA-38-112 Tomahawk	38-78A0340	N6201A	17. 4.91	Teesside Flight Centre Ltd	Teesside	6. 8.00T
G-BTFS	Cessna A150M Aerobat	A150-0719	N20331	20. 2.91	K.Ford	Rochester	1. 5.00T
G-BTFT	Beechcraft 58 Baron	TH-979	N2036W	14. 3.91	Fastwing Air Charter Ltd	Thruxton	18. 3.01T
G-BTFU	Cameron N-90 HAFB	2391		28. 2.91	J.J.Rudoni & A.C.K.Rawson	Stafford	26. 7.00A
					t/a Wickers World Hot Air Balloon Co "Maltesers II"		
G-BTFV	Whittaker MW7	PFA/171-11722		8. 2.91	S.J.Luck	Tower Farm, Wollaston	31.10.00P
	(Rotax 532)						
G-BTFW	Montgomerie-Bensen B.8MR			20. 2.91	A.Mansfield	Crowland	9. 8.96P
	(Rotax 532)	PFA G/01A-1141					
G-BTFX	Bell 206B JetRanger II	1648	N400MH	20. 2.91	J.Selwyn Smith (Shepley) Ltd		
			N90219			Shepley, Huddersfield	28. 3.00T
G-BTGA	Boeing-Stearman A75N1 (PT-17) Kaydet	N65501		21. 2.91	D.J.Morris	(Royston)	6. 7.01
	(P+W R985)	75-3132	41-25625				
G-BTGD	Rand-Robinson KR-2	PFA/129-11150		22. 2.91	J.N.Kerr	(Buckley)	7.10.00P
	(VW1915)						
G-BTGG	Rans S-10 Sakota	PFA/194-11944		20. 2.91	A.R.Cameron	Oaksey Park	22. 6.96P
	(Rotax 582)						
G-BTGH	Cessna 152 II	152-81048	N48919	2. 4.91	C & S Aviation Ltd	Halfpenny Green	7. 4.01T
G-BTGI	Rearwin 175 Skyranger	1517	N32308	26. 2.91	A.H.Hunt		
	(Continental A75)		NC32308		Lower Botrea Farm, Newbridge, Penzance		18. 5.00P
G-BTGJ	Smith DSA-1 Miniplane	NM.II	N1471	25. 3.91	G.J.Knowles	(Hayling Island)	20. 5.94P
	(Continental C90)				(Status uncertain)		
G-BTGL	Light Aero Avid Speed Wing			27. 2.91	A.F.Vizoso	RAF Halton	17. 6.00P
		PFA/189-11885					
G-BTGM	Aeronca 7AC Champion	7AC-3665	N84943	11. 3.91	J.R.L.White	(Neuilly, France)	11. 2.00P
	(Continental A65)		NC84943				
G-BTGN*	Cessna 310R II	310R-1541	N5331C	3. 4.91	Perth Airport Ltd	Redhill	27. 1.01T
					(Cancelled by CAA 9.12.99)		
G-BTGO	PA-28-140 Cherokee D	28-7125613	N1998T	20. 2.91	Rankart Ltd	Oxford	3. 7.00T
G-BTGP	Cessna 150M Commuter	150-78921	N704WA	28. 2.91	Billins Air Services Ltd	White Waltham	24. 4.00T
					(Op City Air)		
G-BTGR	Cessna 152 II	152-84447	N6581L	28. 2.91	A.J.Gomes	Shoreham	25. 7.00T
					(Op Sky Leisure Aviation) (Force-landed nr Shoreham 10.99)		
G-BTGS(2)	Stolp SA.300 Starduster Too	G-AYMA		30. 9.87	A.E.Bailey	(Cranleigh)	6. 6.00P
	(Lycoming O-320) EAA/50553 & PFA/35-10076				t/a A.E.Bailey & Partners		
G-BTGT	CFM Streak Shadow	(G-MWPY)		1. 3.91	G.Arscott	(Fleet)	20. 6.99P
	(Rotax 582) K164-SA & PFA/206-11964						
G-BTGU	PA-34-220T Seneca III	34-8233106	N999PW	1. 3.91	Carill Aviation Ltd	Southampton	30. 5.00T
			N8160V				
G-BTGV	PA-34-200T Seneca II	34-7970077	N3004H	26. 3.91	MS 124 Ltd	Shobdon	23. 6.00
G-BTGW	Cessna 152 II	152-79812	N757KY	5. 3.91	Stapleford Flying Club Ltd	Stapleford	31. 7.00T
G-BTGX	Cessna 152 II	152-84950	N5462P	5. 3.91	Stapleford Flying Club Ltd	Stapleford	20. 8.00T
G-BTGY	PA-28-161 Warrior II	28-8216199	N209FT	5. 3.91	Stapleford Flying Club Ltd	Stapleford	23. 6.00T
			N9574N				
G-BTGZ	PA-28-181 Archer II	28-7890160	N47956	8. 4.91	Allzones Travel Ltd	Biggin Hill	17. 8.00T
G-BTHA	Cessna 182P	182-63420	N2932P	22. 3.91	T.P.Hall	Liverpool	5. 8.00
					t/a Hotel Alpha Flying Group		
G-BTHD	Yakovlev Yak-3U	170101	(France)	7. 3.91	Patina Ltd	Duxford	AC
	(Conversion of LET Yak C.11)		EAF.533		(Op The Fighter Collection: rebuilt Russia 1996/99)		
G-BTHE	Cessna 150L	150-75340	N11348	7. 3.91	J.H.Loose & F.P.White	Burn	26. 5.00T
					t/a Humberside Police Flying Club		
G-BTHF	Cameron V-90 HAFB	2543		7. 3.91	N.J. & S.J.Langley	Bristol	17. 5.00T
G-BTHH	CEA Jodel DR.100A Ambassadeur	5	F-BJCH	28. 2.91	H.R.Leefe	Bourg-en-Bresse, France	1. 9.02
G-BTHI	Robinson R-22 Beta	1732		26. 3.91	G.R.Day	Liverpool	19. 6.00
G-BTHJ	Evans VP-2	PFA/63-10901		14. 3.91	C.J.Moseley	Bournemouth	
					(Under construction 8.92)		
G-BTHK	Thunder Ax7-77 HAFB	1906		11. 3.91	M.J.Chandler	Cranbrook	29. 8.99A
G-BTHM	Thunder Ax8-105 HAFB	1925		11. 3.91	Anglia Balloon School Ltd	Norwich	13. 4.96T
					t/a Anglia Balloons		
G-BTHN	Murphy Renegade 912			12. 3.91	F.A.Purvis	Eshott	19. 4.00P
	(Rotax 912) 384 & PFA/188-12005				"Spirit of England II"		
G-BTHP	Thorp T.211	101		13. 6.91	M.J.Newton	Barton	5.10.01T
G-BTHR	Socata TB-10 Tobago	1296		13. 3.91	Computer 100 Ltd	White Waltham	25. 3.02
G-BTHU	Light Aero Avid Flyer	PFA/189-11427		14. 3.91	R.C.Bowley	(Earls Croome, Worcester)	
	(Rotax 532)				(Damaged Field Head Farm, Denholme, Bradford 7.6.92; on rebuild 5.95)		
G-BTHV	MBB Bo.105DBS-4	S.855	D-HMBV	20. 3.91	Bond Air Services Ltd	Aberdeen	12. 5.00T
			G-BTHV/D-HFHM				

Regn	Type	C/n	P/I	Date	Owner/operator	Probable Base	CA Expy
G-BTHW	Beechcraft F33C Bonanza	CJ-130	PH-BNA N23787	18. 3.91	Robin Lance Aviation Associates Ltd Rochester		20. 8.00
G-BTHX	Colt 105A HAFB	1939		18. 3.91	R.Ollier	Northwich, Cheshire	19. 3.92A
G-BTHY	Bell 206B JetRanger III	2290	N6606M VH-BIQ/ZK-HBQ/DQ-FEN/ZK-HLU	20. 3.91	Sterling Helicopters Ltd	Norwich	19. 5.00T
G-BTHZ	Cameron V-56 HAFB	486	OO-BBC	20. 3.91	C.N.Marshall Nairobi, Kenya (Noted as OO-BBC 9.95)		
G-BTIC	PA-22-150 Tri-Pacer	22-6780	N9988D (N702DE)/N9988D	25. 3.91	T.Richards & G.C.Winters (Colne/Bradford) (Damaged Newhouse Farm, Birds Edge, Huddersfield 24.4.93)		24. 6.94
G-BTID	PA-28-161 Warrior II	28-8116036	N82647	25. 6.91	Plymouth School of Flying Ltd	Plymouth	22. 5.00T
G-BTIE	Socata TB-10 Tobago	187		30. 3.81	JGH Computer Services Ltd	Cardiff	7. 9.99T
G-BTIF	Denney Kitfox mk.3 (Rotax 582)	684 & PFA/172-11862		27. 2.91	D.A.Murchie	(Brodick)	26.10.98P
G-BTIG	Montgomerie-Bensen B.8MR (Rotax 532)	PFA G/01-1093		21. 3.91	K.Jarvis	(Sheffield)	4. 1.99P
G-BTIH	PA-28-151 Cherokee Warrior	28-7615315	N6158J	20. 3.91	J.S.Edmunds-Jones & M.Stedman Blackbushe t/a MPM Aviation (Crashed on take-off from a strip near Torrington, Devon 14.11.99 & extensively damaged)		26. 5.00
G-BTII	Gulfstream AA-5B Tiger	AA5B-1256	N4560S	5. 6.91	B.D.Greenwood	Ronaldsway	13. 5.02
G-BTIJ	Luscombe 8E Silvaire (Continental C85)	5194	N2467K NC2467K	3. 4.91	S.J.Hornsby	Lee-on-Solent	12. 9.00P
G-BTIK	Cessna 152 II	152-82993	N46068	26. 3.91	P.R.Edwards & E.Alexander	Andrewsfield	25. 5.02T
G-BTIL	PA-38-112 Tomahawk	38-80A0004	N24730	26. 3.91	B.J.Pearson	Eaglescott	AC
G-BTIM	PA-28-161 Cadet	2841159	(SE-KIO) N9185D	24. 8.89	Mid Sussex Timber Co Ltd	Biggin Hill	25.10.01T
G-BTIN	Cessna 150C	150-59905	N7805Z	26. 3.91	Cormack (Aircraft Services) Ltd Cumbernauld		6.10.01T
G-BTIO	SNCAN Stampe SV-4C	303	N73NS F-BCLC	28. 3.91	M.D. & C.F.Garratt	(Bushey, Watford)	11. 5.02
G-BTIP*	Denney Kitfox mk.3 (Rotax 582)	850 & PFA/172-11973		5. 3.91	P.A.Hardy Wadswick Manor Farm, Corsham (Damaged Wadswick Manor Farm, 31.5.92: cancelled by CAA 16.4.99)		
G-BTIR	Denney Kitfox mk.2 (Hewland AE75)	PFA/172-11952		26. 3.91	R.B.Wilson	(Kendal)	9.10.00P
G-BTIS	Aerospatiale AS.355F1 Twin Squirrel	5261	G-TALI	10. 4.91	J.P.E.Walsh Elstree t/a Walsh Aviation (Op Cabair Helicopters)		9. 6.01T
G-BTIU	Socata MS.892A Rallye Commodore 150	10914	F-BPQS	7. 5.91	W.H.Cole Spilsted Farm, Sedlescombe		30. 6.01
G-BTIV	PA-28-161 Warrior II	28-8116044	N82697	10. 5.91	B.R.Pearson Eaglescott t/a Warrior Group		3. 7.00T
G-BTIW*	CEA Jodel DR.1050/M1 Sicile Record	618	F-BMPV	28. 6.91	Not known Crosland Moor (Damaged Westbury-sub-Mendip 1.7.94: stored 9.96)		4. 7.94
G-BTIX	Cameron V-77 HAFB	2087		27. 3.91	D.J.Cook "Sky's The Limit"	Norwich	23. 9.99T
G-BTIZ	Cameron A-105 HAFB	2546		11. 3.91	Wendy A.Board Penshurst t/a Gleen Board Promotions		15. 2.00A
G-BTJA	Luscombe 8E Silvaire (Continental C85)	5037	N2310K NC2310K	4. 4.91	M.W.Rudkin	Woodford	3. 6.00P
G-BTJB	Luscombe 8E Silvaire (Continental C85)	6194	N1567B NC1567B	4. 4.91	M.Loxton	Leysdown-on-Sea, Sheppey	12. 7.00P
	(G-BTJA may be ex NC1567B which suggests the identities of G-BTJA/BTJB were changed on conversion)						
G-BTJC	Luscombe 8F Silvaire (Lycoming O-290)	6589	N2162B	4. 4.91	Alison M.Noble Thruxton (Damged Glebe Farm, Stockton, Warminster 31.7.99)		18.10.99P
G-BTJD	Thunder Ax8-90 Srs.2 HAFB	1865		28. 3.91	S.J.Wardle	Kettering	15. 5.99A
G-BTJF	Thunder Ax10-180 Srs.2 HAFB	1952		28. 3.91	Airborne Adventures Ltd Skipton "Yorkshire Lad"		2. 3.00T
G-BTJH	Cameron O-77 HAFB	2559		3. 4.91	H.& F.Stringer "Oriel"	Scarborough	3. 4.00T
G-BTJK	PA-38-112 Tomahawk	38-79A0838	N2427N	3. 4.91	Western Air (Thruxton) Ltd	Thruxton	4. 8.00T
G-BTJL	PA-38-112 Tomahawk	38-79A0863	N2477N	3. 4.91	J.S.Develin & Z.Islam	Redhill	23. 7.01T
G-BTJN	Montgomerie-Bensen B.8MR (Rotax 532)	PFA G/01-1194		3. 4.91	A.Hamilton	Larkhall, Lanark	9.12.00P
G-BTJO	Thunder Ax9-140 HAFB	1948		3. 4.91	G.P.Lane	Waltham Abbey	28. 4.92A
G-BTJS	Montgomerie-Bensen B.8MR (Rotax 532)	PFA G/01-1083		8. 4.91	T.C. & P.K.Jackson Melrose Farm, Melbourne		18.10.00P
G-BTJU	Cameron V-90 HAFB	2554		8. 4.91	C.W.Jones (Floorings) Ltd	Bristol	31. 7.00A
G-BTJX	Rans S-10 Sakota (Rotax 582)	PFA/194-12014		9. 4.91	W.C.Dobson Beeches Farm, South Scarle (Damaged Moseley Farm, Annesley 28.4.99)		2. 3.00P
G-BTKA	Piper J/5A Cub Cruiser	5-954	N38403 NC38403	11. 4.91	Janet M.Lister Valley Farm, Winwick (Active 10.99)		17. 6.00P
G-BTKB	Murphy Renegade 912 (Rotax 912)	376 & PFA/188-11876		11. 4.91	G.S.Blundell "Spirit of Kinross"	Perth	8. 6.00P
G-BTKD	Denney Kitfox mk.4 (Rotax 582)	853 & PFA/172-11941		15. 4.91	J.F.White Walkerburn Farm, Peebles (Denney c/n conflicts with N653CP) (Op Border Aviation Ltd)		9. 7.98P

Regn	Type	C/n	P/I	Date	Owner/operator	Probable Base	CA Expy
G-BTKG	Light Aero Avid Flyer (Rotax 582)	PFA/189-12037		16. 4.91	I.Holt	(Reading)	9. 7.00P
G-BTKI	North American T-6G-NF Texan (C/n also quoted as FO-8002-088)	197-88	Fr AF 534592"RA"/53-4592	17. 4.91	P.S. & S.M.Warner Bredon, Pershore (On rebuild 3.96)		
G-BTKL	MBB Bo.105DB-4	S.422	D-HDMU Swedish Army/D-HDMU	2. 5.91	Veritair Ltd Halfpenny Green (Op by Central Counties Police Air Operations Unit)		2. 3.00T
G-BTKP	CFM Streak Shadow (Rotax 582)	PFA/206-12036		24. 4.91	G.D.Martin	(Cambridge)	11. 5.00P
G-BTKS	Rans S-10 Sakota (Rotax 532)	PFA/194-11861		9. 7.91	J.R.I. & S.M.Rolfe, A.J. & M.L.Reed, N.Parkinson, R.Clarke & R.P.Sandford Cranfield (Damaged Insch 19.8.93; stored 7.94)		5. 7.94P
G-BTKT	PA-28-161 Warrior II	28-8216218	N429FT N9606N	9. 5.91	Eastern Executive Air Charter Ltd & E.Alexander t/a General Aero Services Thurrock (Damaged nr Shoreham 8.8.95: fuselage only Kings Farm, Thurrock 9.99)		14. 7.97T
G-BTKV	PA-22-160 Tri-Pacer	22-7157	N3216Z	25. 4.91	R.A.Moore	Newtownards	26. 6.01
G-BTKW	Cameron O-105 HAFB	2566		25. 4.91	P.Spellward	Bristol	10. 6.00A
G-BTKX	PA-28-181 Archer II	28-7890146	N47866	14. 5.91	R.M.Pannell	(Barnstaple)	30. 4.00
G-BTKZ	Cameron V-77 HAFB	2573		26. 4.91	S.P.Richards "Lancaster Jaguar"	Cranbrook	7. 6.97T
G-BTLA	Sikorsky S-76B	760367		22. 4.91	Skyhopper Ltd	Blackbushe	9. 5.00
G-BTLB	Wassmer WA.52 Europa	42	F-BTLB	17. 4.89	M.D.O'Brien Shoreham (Damaged Rufforth 29.5.99)		8. 6.01
G-BTLE	PA-31-350 Navajo Chieftain	31-7405428	D-IBPL N54288	20.10.77	Boal Air Services (UK) Ltd East Midlands		10. 9.00
G-BTLG	PA-28R-200 Cherokee Arrow	28R-35811	N5045S	29. 4.91	A.P.Reilly Blackpool (Crashed Kirkbride 10.2.99)		17. 7.00
G-BTLL*	Pilatus P.3-03	323-5	A-806	18. 4.91	Not known Headcorn (As "A-806" in Swiss AF c/s; stored 9.97)		23. 6.94P
G-BTLM	PA-22-160 Tri-Pacer (Univair Tail-wheel conversion)	22-6162	N9025D	16. 5.91	M.D.N. & A.C.Fisher	Leicester	1. 9.00
G-BTLP	Grumman-American AA-1C Lynx	AA1C-0109	N9732U	13. 5.91	Partlease Ltd	Stapleford	22.12.00
G-BTMA	Cessna 172N Skyhawk II	172-73711	N5136J	2. 5.91	East of England Flying Group Ltd North Weald		7. 8.00T
G-BTMF*	Taylorcraft BC-12D	6609	N43990 NC43990	10. 7.91	C.M.Churchill (Cambridge) (Cancelled by CAA 17.4.99)		
G-BTMH	Colt 90A HAFB	1963		14. 5.91	European Balloon Corporation Espinette, Belgium		26. 7.00A
G-BTMJ	Maule MX-7-180 Star Rocket	11073C		11. 6.91	C.M.McGill	Biggin Hill	6. 7.01
G-BTMK	Cessna R172K Hawk XPII	R172-2787	N736TZ	10. 6.91	S.P. & A.C.Barker	East Midlands	24.11.00T
G-BTML*	Cameron Rupert Bear 90SS HAFB	2533		16. 5.91	Balloon Preservation Group Lancing "Rupert The Bear" (For restoration 12.98)		31.12.94A
G-BTMN	Thunder Ax9-120	2003		17 .5.91	D J Farrer "Batman"	Leeds	8. 3.99T
G-BTMO	Colt 69A HAFB	2004		20. 5.91	Cameron Balloons Ltd t/a Thunder & Colt	Bristol	
G-BTMP	Everett Campbell Cricket (Rotax 532)	024 & PFA G/03-1226		20. 5.91	P.W.McLaughlin	Henstridge	17. 8.00P
G-BTMR	Cessna 172M Skyhawk II	172-64985	N64047	20. 5.91	J.A.Nicol t/a Cumbria Aero Club Carlisle		29. 5.00T
G-BTMS	Avid Speed Wing	PFA/189-12023	(CS-) G-BTMS	24. 4.91	D.L.Docking (Boston) (Cf/f 22.11.99)		
G-BTMT	Denney Kitfox mk.1 (Rotax 532)	66		10. 5.91	M.D.Burns t/a Skulk Flying Group	Cumbernauld	20.10.99P
G-BTMV	Everett Gyroplane Srs.2	025		21. 5.91	L.Armes	Basildon	
G-BTMW	Zenair CH-701 STOL (Rotax 582)	PFA/187-11808		21. 5.91	L.Lewis Yearby (Stored 4.97)		9. 4.96P
G-BTMX	Denney Kitfox mk.3 (Rotax 582)	916 & PFA/172-12079		13. 5.91	P.B.Lowry	Deanland	6. 9.99P
G-BTNA	Robinson R-22 Beta	1800	N40820	23. 5.91	Heli Charter Ltd	Manston	24.11.00T
G-BTNB	Robinson R-22 Beta	1802	N23006	30. 5.91	G.Kidger	Netherthorpe	24. 7.00
G-BTNC	Aerospatiale SA.365N2 Dauphin 2	6409		21. 6.91	Bond Helicopters Ltd	Strubby	9.10.01T
G-BTND	PA-38-112 Tomahawk	38-78A0155	N9671T	23. 5.91	R.B.Turner	Gloucestershire	8.12.01T
G-BTNE	PA-28-161 Warrior II	28-8116212	N8379H	22. 7.91	D.Rowe	Wellesbourne Mountford	16. 6.01T
G-BTNL	Thunder AX10-180 HAFB	2006	(OO-ntu) G-BTNL	29. 5.91	M.P.A.Sevrin Court St.Etienne, Belgium		5 .8.00T
G-BTNN	Colt 21A Cloudhopper HAFB	2018		3. 6.91	Cameron Balloons Ltd	Bristol	9. 6.92A
G-BTNO	Aeronca 7AC Champion	7AC-3132	N84441 NC84441	31. 5.91	D.B.Evans & A.McGarrell Netherthorpe t/a November Oscar Group		4. 8.99P
G-BTNP	Light Aero Avid Commuter (Rotax 582)	PFA/189-11988		31. 5.91	N.Evans Silfield, Wymondham (Damaged Swardeston, Norfolk 25.6.92; stored 8.97)		23. 6.92P*
G-BTNR	Denney Kitfox mk.3 (Rotax 582)	921 & PFA/172-12035		31. 5.91	D.E.Steade	(Worcester)	21. 6.00P

Regn	Type	C/n	P/I	Date	Owner/operator	Probable Base	CA Expy
G-BTNS	WSK PZL-104 Wilga 80	CF.20890883	N71695	22. 7.91	D.Rowland	Shoreham	26.10.00
G-BTNT	PA-28-151 Cherokee Warrior	28-7615401	N6929J	31. 5.91	Britannia Airways Ltd (Op Britannia Airways Flying Club)	Luton	24.11.00T
G-BTNV	PA-28-161 Warrior II	28-7816590	N31878	20. 6.91	D.K.Oakeley & A.M.Dawson	Oxford	6. 7.00
G-BTNW	Rans S-6-ESA Coyote II (Rotax 582) 0391-171 & PFA/204-12077			3. 6.91	A.F.Stafford	Melrose Farm, Melbourne	2. 1.00P
G-BTOA	Mong Sport MS-2 (Continental C85)	FHC-1	N1067Z	3. 6.91	G.Gilding (On rebuild 6.99)	Priory Farm, Tibenham	28. 9.94P
G-BTOC	Robinson R-22 Beta	1801	N23004	10. 6.91	N.Parkhouse	Chelwood Gate, W.Sussex	10. 7.00
G-BTOD	PA-38-112 Tomahawk	38-78A0675	N2421A	7. 6.91	S.M.P & D.A.Adams	(Doncaster)	10. 9.00T
G-BTOG	DH.82A Tiger Moth	86500	F-BGCJ Fr.AF/NM192	5. 9.91	P.T.Szluha (On overhaul 4.94)	Audley End	
G-BTOI	Cameron N-77 HAFB	2588		20. 6.91	The Nestle Co Ltd "Rowntree/Nestle"	Croydon	29. 6.95A
G-BTOL	Denney Kitfox mk.3 (Rotax 582) 919 & PFA/172-12052			26. 6.91	P.J.Gibbs	(Truro)	14. 4.00P
G-BTOM*	PA-38-112 Tomahawk	38-78A0763		15. 1.79	Lorch Airways Ltd (Crashed Alderney 26.9.92; stored 10.97)	Norwich	10. 4.94T
G-BTON	PA-28-140 Cherokee Cruiser	28-7425343	N43193	15. 7.91	S.G.Woodsford	Earls Colne	2. 7.01T
G-BTOO	Pitts S-1C Special	5215-24A	N37H	12. 6.91	G.H.Matthews (On overhaul 5.92)	Sandown	
G-BTOP	Cameron V-77 HAFB	2484		14. 6.91	J.J.Winter "Big Top"	Cardiff	
G-BTOS	Cessna 140 (Continental C85)	8353	N89325 NC89325	7. 6.91	J.L.Kaiser	Nancy-Essais, France	1. 7.99
G-BTOT	PA-15 Vagabond (Lycoming O-145)	15-60	N4176H NC4176H	22. 5.91	P.J.Rutter	East Farm, Garmondsway	17. 8.00P
G-BTOU	Cameron O-120 HAFB	2606		2. 7.91	R.St.J.Gillespie	Bath	27. 1.99T
G-BTOW	Socata Rallye 180T Galerien	3360	F-BNGZ	9.11.82	Cambridge Gliding Club Ltd	Gransden Lodge	23. 3.01
G-BTOZ	Thunder Ax9-120 Srs.2 HAFB	2008		28. 6.91	H.G.Davies	Cheltenham	8. 6.00T
G-BTPB	Cameron N-105 HAFB	1536		6. 7.87	C.N.Rawnson t/a Test Valley Balloon Group "Phone Book"	Stockbridge	21. 9.96A
G-BTPT	Cameron N-77 HAFB	2575		10. 6.91	Derbyshire Building Society	Derby	20.11.99A
G-BTPV*	Colt 90A HAFB	1956		14. 6.91	Virgin Airship & Balloon Co Ltd "Mondial Assistance" (Cancelled as PWFU 25.3.99)	Telford	1. 8.97A
G-BTPX	Thunder Ax8-90 HAFB	1873		18. 6.91	E.Cordall	Chichester	4. 3.00
G-BTPZ	Isaacs Fury II	PFA/11-11927		1. 7.91	M.A.Farrelly (As "85" in Portuguese AF c/s)	Ormskirk	
G-BTRB	Colt Mickey Mouse SS HAFB	1959		4. 7.91	Benedikt Haggeney GmbH "Mickey Mause"	Ennigerloh, Germany	20 .7.00A
G-BTRC	Light Aero Avid Speed Wing (BMW 1000cc/80bhp) 913 & PFA/189-12076			2. 7.91	Grangecote Ltd (Damaged Chichester 25.6.99)	Goodwood	8.11.00P
G-BTRE	Reims Cessna F.172H	0657	N10657	3. 7.91	M.L.J.Warwick	Stapleford	18.10.01T
G-BTRF	Aero Designs Pulsar (Rotax 582)	PFA/202-12051		4. 7.91	C.Smith	Spilsted Farm, Sedlescombe	19.10.00P
G-BTRG	Aeronca 65C Super Chief (Continental A65)	C4149	N22466 NC22466	4. 7.91	H.J.Cox	Lukes Farm, Sheepwash	8. 6.00P
G-BTRH	Aeronca 7AC Champion (Continental A65)	7AC-2895	N84204 NC84204	4. 7.91	M.A.N.Newall	Bagby	15. 5.00P
G-BTRI	Aeronca 11CC Super Chief (Continental C85)	11CC-246	N4540E NC4540E	4. 7.91	P.A.Wensak	Bounds Farm, Ardleigh	30. 6.00P
G-BTRK	PA-28-161 Warrior II	28-8216206	N297FT N9594N	8. 7.91	Stapleford Flying Club Ltd	Stapleford	22.10.00T
G-BTRL	Cameron N-105 HAFB	2622		5. 7.91	J.Lippett "Harrods"	South Petherton, Somerset	29. 7.00A
G-BTRN	Thunder AX9-120 S2 HAFB	1983		11. 7.91	P.B.D.Bird	Bristol	22.12.95T
G-BTRO	Thunder Ax8-90 HAFB	1872		11. 7.91	Capital Balloon Club Ltd	London NW1	13. 4.00A
G-BTRP	MDH Hughes 369E (500E)	0475E	N1607D	11. 7.91	P.C.Shann & P.C.Shann Management & Research Ltd	Fulford, York	15. 4.01
G-BTRR	Thunder Ax7-77 HAFB	1905		12. 7.91	Sheila M.Roberts	Skipton	26. 8.96A
G-BTRS	PA-28-161 Warrior II	28-8116004	N8248V	12. 7.91	I.C.Tyson & G.R.Berry t/a Tyberry Aviation	Barton	16.12.01
G-BTRT	PA-28R-200 Cherokee Arrow II	28R-7535270	N1189X	24. 7.91	C.E.Yates	Barton	9.12.00
G-BTRU	Robin DR.400/180 Regent	2089		12. 7.91	R & M Engineering Ltd	Inverness	24.11.00
G-BTRW	Slingsby T.61F Venture T.2	1968	ZA632	5. 7.91	B.Kerby & G.Grainger	(Rednal)	1.11.00
G-BTRX*	Cameron V-77 HAFB	1143	VH-HIH	12. 7.91	Not known (Temp unregd 2.5.97)	Horsham	16. 4.97A
G-BTRY	PA-28-161 Warrior II	28-8116190	N8363L	18. 7.91	Oxford Aviation Services Ltd	Oxford	6.12.01T
G-BTRZ	Jodel D.18 (VW1834)	148 & PFA/169-11271		16. 7.91	R.M.Johnson & R.Collin	Midlem	18. 8.00P

Regn	Type	C/n	P/I	Date	Owner/operator	Probable Base	CA Expy
G-BTSB	Corben Baby Ace D (Continental A65)	JC-1	N3599	16. 7.91	D.G.Kelly	Shempston Farm, Elgin	28. 3.00P
G-BTSC	Evans VP-2 (Arrow GT500)	PFA/63-10342		20.10.78	G.B.O'Neill (Northampton) (On overhaul Chilbolton 6.96)		13. 2.96P
G-BTSD*	Loehle 5151 Mustang	PFA/213-11867		17. 7.91	R.Fitzpatrick (Newquay) (Cancelled by CAA 20.4.99)		
G-BTSJ	PA-28-161 Warrior II	28-7816473	N9417C	23. 7.91	Plymouth School of Flying Ltd	Plymouth	18.12.00T
G-BTSL	Cameron Glass 70SS HAFB (Tennent's Lager Glass Shape)	1627		27. 1.88	M.R.Humphrey & J.R.Clifton "Tennent's Glass"	Brackley	25. 4.90A
G-BTSM	Cessna 180A	32678	P2-DEQ VH-DEQ/VH-DEC/N7781A	9. 7.91	C.Couston Church Farm, North Moreton t/a Sierra Mike Group		12. 4.02
G-BTSN	Cessna 150G	150-65106	N3806J	30. 8.91	N.A.Bilton Priory Farm, Tibenham		23. 3.02
G-BTSP	Piper J3C-65 Cub	7647	N41013 NC41013	30. 8.91	J.A.Walshe & A.Corcoran Strandhill, Sligo, Ireland		10. 1.00P
G-BTSR	Aeronca 11AC Chief (Continental A65)	11AC-785	N9152E NC9152E	30. 8.91	R.D.& E.G.N.Morris	Perth	23. 3.00P
G-BTST	Bensen B.8M	002VS		23. 7.91	V.Scott	Shipdham	
G-BTSU*	Bensen B.8MR	BTG-01		24. 7.91	B.T.Goggin (Swansea) (Cancelled by CAA 22.3.99)		
G-BTSV	Denney Kitfox mk.3 (Rotax 582)	PFA/172-11920		24. 7.91	M.G.Dovey	(Woking)	21. 6.99P
G-BTSW	Colt AS-105GD Hot-Air Airship	1999		24. 7.91	Gefa-Flug GmbH Aachen, Germany (Adler Modemarkt c/s)		14. 3.00A
G-BTSX	Thunder Ax7-77 HAFB	2027		24. 7.91	Christine Moris-Gallimore Hinton St.George, Somerset		18. 9.94
G-BTSY*	English Electric Lightning F.6	95207	XR724	25. 7.91	B.J.Pover Binbrook t/a Lightning Association (Stored 4.97: as "XR724")		
G-BTSZ	Cessna 177A Cardinal	177-01198	N30332	30. 7.91	K.D.Harvey	Cranfield	24.11.99T
G-BTTA	Hawker Iraqi Fury FB.11	37534 & ISS13	VH-HFX N28SF/Iraqi AF 243	25. 7.91	Classic Aviation Ltd Duxford (Op The Old Flying Machine Co) (As "PR772 in RAF c/s)		11. 6.99P
G-BTTB	Cameron V-90 HAFB	2624		22. 7.91	N.F.Mulliner Chatham t/a Royal Engineers Balloon Club "Sapper IV"		22. 7.00A
G-BTTD	Montgomerie-Bensen B.8MR (Rotax 582)	PFA G/01-1204		31. 7.91	K.B.Gutridge (London SE5)		20. 7.99P
G-BTTE	Cessna 150L	150-75558	N11602	31. 7.91	W.E.Rodwell	Shoreham	22. 1.99T
G-BTTK	Thunder Ax8-105 HAFB	2036		9. 8.91	Tempowish Ltd	Frinton-on-Sea	31. 3.00A
G-BTTL	Cameron V-90 HAFB	2649		12. 8.91	A.J.Baird "Hyde Farm Dairy"	Cheltenham	16. 7.96A
G-BTTO	BAe ATP	2033	EC-GJU G-BTTO/G-OEDE/G-BTTO/TC-THV/G-BTTO/S2-ACX/G-11-033	16. 8.91	British Aerospace (Operations) Ltd (Exported 1999) Woodford		8.12.97T
G-BTTP	BAe 146 Srs.300	E-3203	G-6-203	20. 8.91	KLM UK Ltd	Stansted	11.11.00T
G-BTTR	Aerotek Pitts S-2A Special (Lycoming IO-360)	2208	N38MP	16. 8.91	T.W.Cassells	Bagby	22. 3.01
G-BTTS	Colt 77A HAFB	1861		16. 8.91	J.A.Lomas Melton Mowbray t/a Rutland Balloon Club		6. 7.00A
G-BTTW	Thunder Ax7-77 HAFB	2016		27. 8.91	J.Kenny Athlone, Co.Roscommon		17. 6.00A
G-BTTY	Denney Kitfox mk.2	PFA/172-11823		29. 7.91	K.J.Fleming	(Liverpool)	
G-BTTZ	Slingsby T.61F Venture T.2	1961	ZA625	30. 7.91	G.J.Bridgewater	Bidford/Bickmarsh	4. 8.00
G-BTUA	Slingsby T.61F Venture T.2	1985	ZA666	20. 8.91	C.Edmunds Edge Hill t/a Shenington Gliding Club		29. 5.01
G-BTUB	LET Yakovlev C.11 (Identity of 039 quoted)	172623	(France) Egyptian AF 543	29. 8.91	M.G. & J.R.Jefferies White Waltham (Soviet AF c/s without serial)		20. 7.00P
G-BTUD*	CFM Image IM-01 & PFA/222-12012 (Rotax 532)		G-MWPV	21. 8.91	D.G.Cook Leiston, Suffolk (Cancelled as wfu 5.2.99)		21.1.95P*
G-BTUG	Socata Rallye 180T	3208		10. 7.78	Herefordshire Gliding Club Ltd	Shobdon	16. 4.00
G-BTUH	Cameron N-65 HAFB (Originally the "attached" balloon to G-WASH c/n 1451)	1452		28. 8.91	B.J.Godding	Didcot	
G-BTUJ	Thunder Ax9-120 HAFB	2022		30. 8.91	ECM Construction Ltd	Great Missenden	13. 5.00T
G-BTUK	Aerotek Pitts S-2A Special (Lycoming AEIO-360)	2260	N5300J	2. 9.91	S.H.Elkington	Wickenby	9.10.00T
G-BTUL	Aerotek Pitts S-2A Special (Lycoming AEIO-360)	2200	N900RS	2. 9.91	J.M.Adams	Spanhoe	27.11.00
G-BTUM	Piper J3C-85 Cub (Frame No.19536)	19516	N6335H NC6335H	6. 9.91	C.Johnstone White Waltham t/a G-BTUM Syndicate "Jingle-Belle"		27. 5.00P
G-BTUR	PA-18-95 Super Cub (L-18C-PI)	18-3205	OO-LVM OL-L08/L-131/53-4805	11. 9.91	K.E.Wilson	Bourn	25. 3.02
G-BTUS	Whittaker MW7 (Rotax 503)	PFA/171-11999		5. 9.91	J.D.Webb	(Hereford)	9. 6.98P
G-BTUU	Cameron O-120 HAFB	2669		16. 9.91	J.L.Guy	Skipton	29.10.99T
G-BTUV	Aeronca 65TAC Defender	C.1661TA	N36816 NC36816	12. 9.91	J.T.Ingrouille Guernsey (On rebuild 6.97)		

Regn	Type	C/n	P/I	Date	Owner/operator	Probable Base	CA Expy
G-BTUW	PA-28-151 Cherokee Warrior	N54458		12. 9.91	T.S.Kemp	Turweston	25. 6.01T
		28-7415066					
G-BTUX	Aerospatiale SA.365N2 Dauphin 2			12. 9.91	Bond Helicopters Ltd	Strubby	1. 2.02T
		6424					
G-BTUZ	American General AG-5B Tiger	10075	N11939	3.10.91	Grocontinental Ltd	Sleap	26. 2.00
G-BTVA	Thunder Ax7-77 HAFB	2009		16. 9.91	A.H.Symonds "Bertie Bassett"	Chelmsford	7. 5.99A
G-BTVB	Everett Gyroplane Srs.3	026		24. 9.91	J.Pumford	Epsom	16.12.99P
	(Rotax 532)						
G-BTVC	Denney Kitfox mk.2 PFA/172-11784			23. 9.91	P.Mitchell "Zebedee"	Long Marston	18. 1.00P
	(Rotax 582)						
G-BTVE	Hawker Demon I	-	2292M	18. 9.91	Demon Displays Ltd Rotary Farm, Hatch		AC
	(Kestrel V)		K8203		(As "K8203" in 64 Sqn c/s)		
	(Composite of ex Irish/front and K8203/rear)				(On rebuild by Skysport Engineering Ltd 7.99)		
G-BTVF	Rotorway Exec 90	5058		13. 9.91	E.P.Sadler	(Market Drayton)	AC
G-BTVG	Cessna 140	12350	N2114N	30. 8.91	V.C.Gover	Plockton	15. 4.99
	(Continental O-200-A)		NC2114N				
G-BTVH	Colt 77A HAFB	1027	G-ZADT	24. 9.91	D.N. & L.J.Close	Andover	19. 8.97A
			G-ZBCA				
G-BTVR	PA-28-140 Cherokee Cruiser		N4328X	16. 9.91	Full Sutton Flying Centre Ltd		
		28-7625012				Full Sutton	26. 3.01T
G-BTVU	Robinson R-22 Beta	1937		26. 9.91	B.Enzo	Bologna, Italy	17. 3.00
G-BTVV	Reims Cessna FA337G Super Skymaster	PH-RPD		25. 9.91	B.Maddock	Bournemouth	8. 9.99T
	(Wichita c/n 01476)	0058	N1876M				
G-BTVW	Cessna 152 II	152-79631	N757CK	23. 9.91	Rankart Ltd Hinton-in-The-Hedges		14. 1.01T
G-BTVX	Cessna 152 II	152-83375	N48786	23. 9.91	J.C.Birdsall	Gamston	30. 6.01T
					t/a Trafic Management Services		
G-BTWB*	Denney Kitfox mk.3	(G-BTTM)		21. 8.91	J.E.Tootell	(Aylesbury)	
		920 & PFA/172-12278			(Cancelled by CAA 14.3.99)		
G-BTWC	Slingsby T.61F Venture T.2	1975	ZA656	23. 9.91	T.M.Holloway	Upavon	4. 1.02
					t/a RAFGSA		
G-BTWD	Slingsby T.61F Venture T.2	1976	ZA657	23. 9.91	Ouse Gliding Club Ltd	Rufforth	26. 9.00
					t/a York Gliding Centre		
G-BTWE	Slingsby T.61F Venture T.2	1980	ZA661	23. 9.91	T.M.Holloway t/a RAFGSA RAF Syerston		13. 3.01
					(Op Four Counties Gliding Club)		
G-BTWF	DHC.1 Chipmunk 22	C1/0564	WK549	30. 9.91	J.A. & V.G.Simms	Rufforth	
					(As "WK549": on rebuild)		
G-BTWI	EAA Acrosport I	230	N10JW	2.10.91	C.N.Carter Charterhall, Newcastle		26. 1.99P
	(Lycoming O-290)				t/a WI Group		
G-BTWJ	Cameron V-77 HAFB	2670		3.10.91	S.J. & J.A.Bellaby	Nottingham	3. 4.00A
					"Windy Jack"		
G-BTWL	Wag-Aero CUBy Acro Sport Trainer			3.10.91	I.M.Ashpole	(Ross-on-Wye)	8. 9.00P
	(Lycoming O-235) PFA/108-10893						
G-BTWM	Cameron V-77 HAFB	2163		4.10.91	R.C.Franklin "Aerolus"	Chesham	24. 9.99A
G-BTWN	Maule MXT-7-180 Star Rocket	14025C		7.10.91	C.T.Rolls	Redhill	5. 2.01
G-BTWR	Bell P-63A-7BE Kingcobra	33-397	N52113	7.10.91	Patina Ltd	Duxford	19. 5.00P
	(C/n officially 33-37 but quoted as 296A-5-3) NX52113/42-69097 (B.J.S.Grey t/a The Fighter Collection)						
					(As "269097" in USAAF c/s) "Trust Me"		
G-BTWS*	Thunder Ax7-77 HAFB	1971		9.10.91	Bavarian Balloon Co Ltd (Frinton-on-Sea)		8. 3.96A
					(Cancelled as PWFU 22.3.99)		
G-BTWU	PA-22-135 Tri-Pacer	22-2135	N3320B	10.10.91	Prestige Air (Engineers) Ltd		
					(Noted 7.99 as "N3320B") Haverfordwest		
G-BTWV	Cameron O-90 HAFB	2675		10.10.91	S.F.Hancke	Sunbury-on-Thames	21. 5.00A
G-BTWX	Socata TB-9 Tampico Club	1401		14.10.91	D.Weston	(Bury St. Edmunds)	30. 7.00T
					t/a British Car Rentals		
G-BTWY	Aero Designs Pulsar PFA/202-12040			15.10.91	M.Stevenson Pepperbox Farm, Salisbury		14. 6.00P
	(Rotax 582) (Tail-wheel u/c)						
G-BTWZ	Rans S-10 Sakota PFA/194-12117			15.10.91	D.G.Hey	Little Gransden	
					(Under construction 3.97)		
G-BTXB	Colt 77A HAFB	2072		16.10.91	SGL Ltd	Bristol	1. 8.99T
					t/a Shellgas South West Area "Shellgas"		
G-BTXD	Rans S-6-ESA Coyote II (Tail-wheel u/c)			22.10.91	M.Isterling	Insch	6. 6.00P
	(Rotax 582) 0591-191 & PFA/204-12104						
G-BTXF	Cameron V-90 HAFB	2692		2.10.91	G.Thompson	Ambleside	24. 1.96T
G-BTXH	Colt AS-56 Hot-Air Airship	2078		23.10.91	L.Kiefer March-Flugstetten, Germany		26. 3.93A
G-BTXI	Noorduyn AT-16-ND Harvard IIB	14-429	Fv.16105	25.10.91	Patina Ltd	Duxford	5. 7.00P
			RCAF FE695/FE695/42-892		(Op The Fighter Collection) (As "FE695/94")		
G-BTXK	Thunder Ax7-65 HAFB	1910	ZS-HYP	28.10.91	T.M.Dawson	Woodford Green	5.12.96
			G-BTXK				
G-BTXM	Colt 21A Cloudhopper HAFB	2082		29.10.91	Virgin Airship & Balloon Co Ltd Telford		22. 8.97A
					"Virgin Megastore Hopper"		

Regn	Type	C/n	P/I	Date	Owner/operator	Probable Base	CA Expy
G-BTXS	Cameron O-120 HAFB	2141		16.10.91	Semajan Ltd t/a Southern Balloon Group	Romsey	1. 5.00A
G-BTXT	Maule MXT-7-180 Star Rocket	14027C		7.10.91	W.C.Evans	(Bicester)	19.12.00
G-BTXV	Cameron A-210 HAFB	2703		30.10.91	The Ballooning Business Ltd "Burning Ambition III"	Northampton	27. 3.99T
G-BTXW	Cameron V-77 HAFB	2717		31.10.91	P.C.Waterhouse "Scott's Whisky"	Wadhurst, E.Sussex	29. 8.99A
G-BTXX	Bellanca 8KCAB Decathlon	595-80	OY-CYC SE-IEP/N5063G	1.10.91	M.R.Shelton t/a Tatenhill Aviation	Tatenhill	11. 2.01T
G-BTXZ	Zenair CH.250 (Lycoming O-290)	PFA/113-12170		24.10.91	I.Parris & P.W.J.Hull	Hinton-in-The-Hedges	30.10.00P
G-BTYC	Cessna 150L	150-75767	N66002	4.11.91	Polestar Aviation Ltd	Jersey	5. 3.02T
G-BTYE	Cameron A-180 HAFB	2704		5.11.91	K.J.A.Maxwell & D.S.Messmer "Rolling Rock"	Haywards Heath	26. 3.00T
G-BTYF	Thunder Ax10-180 Srs.2 HAFB	2086		7.11.91	P.Glydon	Barnt Green, Birmingham	8. 4.00T
G-BTYH	Pottier P.80S (VW1834)	PFA/160-11121		11.11.91	R.Pickett	Tatenhill	18. 8.00P
G-BTYI	PA-28-181 Archer II	28-8190078	N8287T	15.11.91	C.E.Wright	(Wisbech)	11. 2.01T
G-BTYK	Cessna 310R II	310R-0138	N200VC N5018J	21.11.91	Revere Aviation Ltd	Jersey	24. 6.00
G-BTYT	Cessna 152 II	152-80455	N24931	25.11.91	M.J.Green	Southend	20. 3.99T
G-BTYW	Cessna 120 (Continental C85)	11725	N77283 NC77283	27.11.91	C.J.Parker Shacklewell Farm, Wittering t/a G-BTYW Group		1.10.01
G-BTYX	Cessna 140 (Continental C90)	11004	N76568 NC76568	27.11.91	A.Coulson & J.R.H.Willis t/a G-BTYX Group	Rochester	23. 2.98T
G-BTYY	Curtiss Robin C-2 (Continental W-670)	475	N348K NC348K	8.10.91	R.R.L.Windus	Truleigh Manor Farm, Edburton	1. 9.97P
G-BTYZ	Colt 210A HAFB	2083		17.10.91	T.M.Donnelly	Doncaster	16.12.99T
G-BTZA	Beechcraft F33A Bonanza	CE-957	PH-BNT	22.11.91	H.Mendelssohn t/a G-BTZA Group	Edinburgh	29. 1.01
G-BTZB	Yakovlev Yak-50	801810	DOSAAF 77	27.11.91	J.S.Allison (As "69" in Soviet AF c/s)	RAF Wyton/Duxford	22. 3.00P
G-BTZD	Yakovlev Yak.1 Srs.1 (C/n stamped on engine bearers)	8188	1342 (Soviet AF)	10.12.91	Historic Acft Collection Ltd	Audley End	AC
	(Salvaged from lake in N.Russia mid 1991 after forced landing c.1942; stored 3.96)						
G-BTZE	LET Yakovlev C.11	171312	(France)	11. 2.92	Bianchi Aviation Film Services Ltd Egypt AF/OK-JIK (Blue Max Movie Acft Museum 3.96)	Booker	
G-BTZG	BAe ATP	2046	PK-MTV (PK-MAA)	11.12.91	Trident Aviation Leasing Services Ltd	Jersey	
G-BTZJ	BAe ATP	2049	PK-MTY (PK-MAE)/G-BTZJ	11.12.91	British Aerospace (Operations) Ltd	Woodford	
G-BTZL	Oldfield Baby Lakes (Continental C85)	8506-M-28B	N2288B	12.12.91	J.M.Roach (Stored 4.99)	Little Gransden	16. 6.95P
G-BTZO	Socata TB-20 Trinidad	1409		18.12.91	M.R.Munn	(Leighton Buzzard)	19. 3.01
G-BTZP	Socata TB-9 Tampico Club	1421		18.12.91	M.R.Clark	(Sunderland)	14. 6.01T
G-BTZR	Colt 77B HAFB	2087		18.12.91	P.J.Fell "Bullet"	Maidenhead	12. 9.99A
G-BTZS	Colt 77B HAFB	2088		18.12.91	P.T.R.Ollivere "Petal"	Sutton	30. 3.00A
G-BTZU	Cameron Concept 60 HAFB	2734		20.12.91	A.C.Rackham	Keswick	28. 1.96A
G-BTZV	Cameron V-77 HAFB	2410		20.12.91	A.W.Sumner "Vulcan"	Newark	11. 9.98A
G-BTZX	Piper J3C-65 Cub	18871	N98648 NC98648	27. 2.92	D.A.Woodhams & J.T.Coulthard	Bidford	28.11.00P
G-BTZY	Colt 56A HAFB	2084		17.10.91	T.M.Donnelly	Doncaster	13.10.94A
G-BTZZ	CFM Streak Shadow	K.169-SA & PFA/206-12155		23.12.91	D.R.Stennett	Mendlesham	21. 5.00P

G-BUAA – G-BUZZ

Regn	Type	C/n	P/I	Date	Owner/operator	Probable Base	CA Expy
G-BUAA	Corben Baby Ace D (Continental A65)	561	N516DH	19.11.91	J.M.Walsh	Haverfordwest	7.10.98P
G-BUAB	Aeronca 11AC Chief (Continental A65)	11AC-1759	N3458E NC3458E	17. 1.92	J.Reed	Craysmarsh Farm, Melksham	30. 4.00P
G-BUAC	Slingsby Cadet III (VW1200)	PFA/42-12059	(ex)	17. 1.92	D.A.Wilson (Original identity unknown, possibly home-built; stored 8.99)	Brunton	4.10.94P
G-BUAF	Cameron N-77 HAFB (Rebuilt from 5N-ATT)	2746		2. 1.92	T.H.Wadden "Ariston"	Ringwood	7. 7.99
G-BUAG	Jodel D.18 (VW1834)	PFA/169-11651		3. 1.92	A.L.Silcox	Bodmin	16. 8.99P
G-BUAI	Everett Gyroplane Srs.3 (Rotax 532)	030		6. 1.92	C.J.Sullivan	Henstridge	22. 3.00P

Regn	Type	C/n	P/I	Date	Owner/operator	Probable Base	CA Expy
G-BUAJ	Cameron N-90 HAFB	2735		7. 1.92	J.R. & S.J.Huggins "Chunnel Plant Hire"	Dover	16. 6.00A
G-BUAM	Cameron V-77 HAFB	2470		10. 1.92	N.Florence "J & E Page Flowers"	London SW11	10. 6.97T
G-BUAN	Cessna 172N Skyhawk II	172-70290	N738WH	23.12.91	R.J.Cawdell	Booker	7. 7.01T
G-BUAO	Luscombe 8A Silvaire (Continental A65)	4089	N1362K NC1362K	15. 1.92	D.Gough	Popham	21. 6.00P
G-BUAR	VS.358 Seafire LF.IIIc (Built Westland)	-	PP972/Aeronavale/PP972	21. 1.92	Wizzard Investments Ltd Earls Colne (David Arnold/Flying A Services) (As "PP972")		AC
G-BUAT	Thunder Ax9-120 HAFB	2093		24. 1.92	J.Fenton "Calor"	Preston	17. 3.00T
G-BUAU	Cameron A-180 HAFB	2744		17. 1.92	C.J.Sandell t/a Out of this World Balloons	Sevenoaks	22. 3.96T
G-BUAW	Pitts S-1C Special (Lycoming O-320)	1921-77	N29DH	27. 1.92	A.J.Seymour	Swanton Morley	1.12.00P
G-BUAX	Rans S-10 Sakota (Rotax 582)	PFA/194-11848		28. 1.92	S.P.Wakeham	RAF St.Mawgan	12. 7.99P
G-BUAY	Cameron A-210 HAFB	2751		28. 1.92	Virgin Balloon Flights Ltd (London SE16)		3. 5.96T
G-BUBA	PA-18S-150 Super Cub	18-7909047	N6BL N83522	17. 1.92	Sunseeker Sales (UK) Ltd (Op Skywriters Ltd)	Bournemouth	22. 5.01T
G-BUBC	QAC Quickie Tri-Q 200 (Continental O-200-A)	PFA/94-11909		3. 2.92	D.J.Clarke	Sturgate	24. 1.00P
G-BUBL*	Thunder Ax8-105 HAFB	1147		10.12.87	British Balloon Museum & Library Newbury "Mercier/l'Espit D'Adventure" (Cancelled as WFU 16.6.98: noted 1999)		
G-BUBN	PBN BN-2B-26 Islander	2270		14. 2.92	Isles of Scilly Skybus Ltd	St.Just	18. 2.00T
G-BUBR	Cameron A-250 HAFB	2779		5. 2.92	Balloon Flights International Ltd Bath (Bath Building Society titles)"BIBS I"		13.10.99T
G-BUBS	Lindstrand LBL-77B HAFB (Possibly a new envelope c 9.95?)	144		10.10.94	Beaulah J.Bower "Bubbles Balloon" Middle Wyke Farm, St.Mary Bourne, Andover		8.10.99A
G-BUBT	Stoddard-Hamilton IIS RG Glasair (Lycoming IO-320) 2026 & PFA/149-11633			6. 2.92	M.D.Evans	Haverfordwest	5. 5.99P
G-BUBU	PA-34-220T Seneca III	34-8233060	N8043B	9. 7.87	Brinor (Holdings) Ltd Poplar Hall Farm, Elmsett		28. 4.00
G-BUBW	Robinson R-22 Beta	2048		7. 2.92	Forth Helicopter Services Ltd Edinburgh		16. 4.01T
G-BUBY	Thunder Ax8-105 Srs.2 HAFB	2115		3. 2.92	T.M.Donnelly "Jorvik Viking Centre"	Doncaster	13. 3.00T
G-BUCA	Cessna A150K Aerobat	A150-0220	N5920J	14. 6.89	T.R.Kingsley	Norwich	3. 3.02T
G-BUCB	Cameron H-34 HAFB	2777		11. 2.92	A.S.Jones	Wolverhampton	21.11.96A
G-BUCC	CASA I-131E Jungmann (Spanish AF serial conflicts with G-BJAL) G-BUCC/E3B-114	1109	G-BUEM	11. 2.92	P.L.Gaze (As "BU+CC" in Luftwaffe c/s)	(Pulborough)	11. 6.00P
G-BUCG	Schleicher ASW 20L (Konig SD430)	20396	BGA.3140 I-FEEL	19. 2.92	W.B.Andrews (As "344")	Booker	16. 6.00
G-BUCH	Stinson V-77 (AT-19) Reliant	77-381	N9570H FB531(RN)	21. 2.92	Pullmerit Ltd	White Waltham	7. 9.02
G-BUCI	Auster AOP.9	B5/10/150	XP242	10. 2.92	M.Somerton-Rayner AAC Middle Wallop t/a Historic Acft Flight Reserve Collection (As "XP242" in Army Air Corps c/s)		19. 5.00P
G-BUCJ	DHC.2 Beaver AL.1	1442	XP772	23. 3.92	Propshop Ltd & G.Warner Duxford t/a British Aerial Museum (As "XP772" in Army c/s)		
G-BUCK	CASA I-131E Jungmann Srs.1000	1113	E3B-322	11. 9.78	R.A.Cayless & J.G.Brander White Waltham t/a Jungmann Flying Group (As "BU+CK" in Luftwaffe c/s)		20. 7.99P
G-BUCM	Hawker Sea Fury FB.11	-	VX653	26. 2.92	Patina Ltd Duxford (Op The Fighter Collection) (On rebuild 1.99)		
G-BUCO	Pietenpol Air Camper (Continental C90)	PFA/47-11829		10. 2.92	A.James Siege Cross Farm, Thatcham		28. 6.00P
G-BUCS	Cessna 150F	150-62368	N3568L	25. 8.89	Atlantic Bridge Aviation Ltd	Lydd	20.10.99T
G-BUCT	Cessna 150L	150-75326	N11320	14. 6.89	JK Aviation Services Ltd	Lydd	20.10.99T
G-BUDA	Slingsby T.61F Venture T.2	1963	ZA627	18. 2.92	T.M.Holloway t/a RAFGSA	RAF Bicester	11. 9.98
G-BUDB	Slingsby T.61F Venture T.2	1964	ZA628	18. 2.92	T.M.Holloway t/a RAFGSA	RAF Bicester	8. 7.99
G-BUDC	Slingsby T.61F Venture T.2	1971	ZA652	18. 2.92	R.A.Boddy	Rufforth	30. 8.02
G-BUDE	PA-22-135 Tri-Pacer (Tail-wheel conversion)	22-980	N1144C	9. 4.92	B.A.Bower	Hong Kong	
G-BUDF	Rand Robinson KR-2 (HAPI Magnum 75)	PFA/129-11155		26. 2.92	E.C.King	Kemble	11. 3.00P
G-BUDI	Aero Designs Pulsar (Rotax 582)	PFA/202-12185		25. 2.92	R.W.L.Oliver	Popham	27. 8.99P
G-BUDK	Thunder Ax7-77 HAFB	2076		2. 3.92	W.Evans	Wrexham	22. 3.00A
G-BUDL	Taylorcraft E Auster III (Regd with Frame No.TAY 5810)	458	PH-POL 8A-2/R Neth AF R-17/NX534		M.Pocock AAC Middle Wallop (On rebuild 6.98 for Military Auster Flt as "NX534")		
G-BUDN	Cameron Shoe 90SS HAFB (Converse Allstar Trainers shape)	2761		6. 3.92	L.V.Mastis West Bloomfield, Mi. USA "Converse Allstar Boot"		1. 8.00A
G-BUDO	PZL-110 Koliber 150	03900045	(D-EIVT)	12. 3.92	A.S.Vine	Old Sarum	27. 7.02

Regn	Type	C/n	P/I	Date	Owner/operator	Probable Base	CA Expy
G-BUDR	Denney Kitfox Mk.3			16. 3.92	N.J.P.Mayled	Dunkeswell	17. 8.00P
	(Rotax 582)	1086 & PFA/172-12107					
G-BUDS	Rand Robinson KR-2	PFA/129-10937		31.12.85	D.W.Munday	(Aldershot)	
G-BUDT	Slingsby T.61F Venture T.2	1883	XZ563	30. 3.92	R.V.Andrews t/a G-BUDT Group	Eaglescott	17. 6.01
G-BUDU	Cameron V-77 HAFB	2447		16. 3.92	T.M.G.Amery Faux Court, Llandeilo, Dyfed		28. 5.00A
G-BUDW	Brugger MB.2 Colibri	PFA/43-10644	G-GODS	19. 3.92	J.M.Hoblyn Watchford Farm, Yarcombe		3.10.00P
	(VW1600)						
G-BUEA	Aerospatiale/Alenia ATR-42-300	268	F-WWEW	30. 4.92	CityFlyer Express Ltd	Gatwick	16. 5.02T
G-BUEC	Van's RV-6	21015 & PFA/181C-11884		17. 3.92	R.D.Harper High Ham, Langport		23. 7.00P
	(Lycoming O-360)						
G-BUED	Slingsby T.61F Venture T.2	1979	ZA660	12. 3.92	D.J.Wood Waldershare Park		14. 5.01
					t/a SE Kent Civil Service Flying Club		
G-BUEE	Cameron A-210 HAFB	2803		20. 3.92	The Balloon Club Ltd	Bristol	21. 7.00T
					t/a Bristol Balloons "Wookey Hole Caves"		
G-BUEF	Cessna 152 II	152-80862	N25928	17. 3.92	A.L.Brown t/a Channel Aviation	Bourn	12.11.98T
G-BUEG	Cessna 152 II	152-80347	N24736	17. 3.92	Plymouth School of Flying Ltd	Plymouth	9.11.01T
G-BUEI	Thunder Ax8-105 HAFB	2172		23. 3.92	Anglia Balloon School Ltd t/a Anglia Balloons		
						Marlingford, Norwich	29. 7.00A
G-BUEK	Slingsby T.61F Venture T.2	1879	XZ559	30. 3.92	Norfolk Gliding Club Ltd	Tibenham	7. 7.01
G-BUEN	VPM M.14 Scout	VPM14-UK101		19. 3.92	W.M.Day	Ulverston	4.12.96P
	(Arrow GT1000R)						
G-BUEO	Maule MX-7-180 Star Rocket	11082C		24. 3.92	K. & S.C.Knight	Shobdon	10. 8.98
					(Damaged in France 21.8.95)		
G-BUEP	Maule MXT-7-180 Star Rocket	14023C		24. 3.92	G.M.Bunn	Goodwood	1. 5.01
G-BUES	Cameron N-77 HAFB	2828		26. 3.92	R.J.Shortall "Bath in Bloom"	Bath	1. 5.00T
G-BUET*	Colt Flying Drinks Can SS HAFB	2162		30. 3.92	R S Kent "Bud King of Beers"	Lancing	10.12.93A
	(Budweiser Can Shape)				(Balloon Preservation Group 7.98)		
G-BUEU*	Colt 21A Cloudhopper HAFB	2163		30. 3.92	R S Kent "Bud King of Beers"	Lancing	2.12.94A
	(Budweiser Can Shape)				(Balloon Preservation Group 7.98)		
G-BUEV	Cameron O-77 HAFB	2810	EI-CFW	31. 3.92	R.R.McCormack & R.J.Mercer	Belfast	8. 7.97X
			G-BUEV		(Exported 1998)		
G-BUEX	Schweizer Hughes 269C (300C)	S.1412	G-HFLR	14. 4.92	Group 2 Aviation Ltd	(Market Rasen)	5. 6.02T
G-BUEZ	Hawker Hunter F.6A	S4U-3275	8736M	3. 4.92	The Old Flying Machine (Air Museum) Co Ltd		
	(Built AWA)		XF375		(As "XF375/05")	Duxford	
				(To acquire "Raspberry Ripple" c/s & transfer to Museum at Sola, Norway)			
G-BUFA	Cameron R-77 Gas Balloon	2712		19. 3.92	Noble Adventures Ltd (The Netherlands)		10. 6.93A
					(Stored 1996)		
G-BUFC	Cameron R-77 Gas Balloon	2823		19. 3.92	Noble Adventures Ltd (The Netherlands)		23. 6.93A
					(Stored 1996)		
G-BUFE	Cameron R-77 Gas Balloon	2825		19. 3.92	Noble Adventures Ltd (The Netherlands)		21. 6.93A
					(Stored 1996)		
G-BUFG	Slingsby T.61F Venture T.2	1977	ZA658	3. 4.92	T.W.Eagles	Hinton-in-The-Hedges	27. 7.01
G-BUFH	PA-28-161 Warrior II	28-8416076	N43520	15. 4.92	M.P.Rainford & J.E.Slee	Blackpool	1. 6.01T
					t/a The Tiger Leisure Group		
G-BUFJ	Cameron V-90 HAFB	2809		7. 4.92	S.P.Richards	Cranbrook	30. 5.00T
G-BUFK	Cassutt Racer IIIM	PFA/34-11069		7. 4.92	D.I.H.Johnstone & W.T.Barnard	Strathaven	
					(Under construction 5.95)		
G-BUFN	Slingsby T.61F Venture T.2	1967	ZA631	8. 4.92	S.C.Foggin Sandhill Farm, Shrivenham		19. 8.01
					t/a BUFN Group		
G-BUFO	Cameron UFO 70SS HAFB	1929		10. 3.89	Virgin Airship & Balloon Co Ltd	Telford	26. 4.97A
	(Flying Saucer shape)				"UFO"		
G-BUFP	Slingsby T.61F Venture T.2	1982	ZA663	8. 4.92	London Sailplanes Ltd	Dunstable	28. 4.01
					(As "ZA663")		
G-BUFR	Slingsby T.61F Venture T.2	1880	XZ560	9. 4.92	R.F.Warren & P.A.Hazell		
						Upper Broyle Farm, Ringmer	29. 4.01
G-BUFT	Cameron O-120 HAFB	2814		9. 4.92	N.D.Hicks	Alton	24. 9.01T
G-BUFV	Light Aero Avid Speed Wing mk.4			15. 4.92	S.C.Ord	Holywell	9. 5.99P
	(Rotax 582)	PFA/189-12192					
G-BUFX	Cameron N-90 HAFB	2835		22. 4.92	Kerridge Computer Co Ltd	Newbury	19. 7.00A
					"Kerridge II"		
G-BUFY	PA-28-161 Warrior II	28-8016211	N130CT	14. 4.92	Bickertons Aerodromes Ltd	Denham	30. 6.01T
			N8TS/N3571K				
G-BUGB	Stolp SA.750 Acroduster Too			22. 4.92	D.Burnham	Andrewsfield	6. 6.00P
		PFA/89-11942					
G-BUGC	Jurca MJ.5 Sirocco	PFA/2207	(G-BWDJ)	14. 4.92	A.Burani	Manor Farm, Glatton	
	(Regd as PFA/59-2207)				(Nearing completion 7.95)		
G-BUGD	Cameron V-77 HAFB	2195		23. 4.92	P.Haslett	Arcy sur Cure, France	8. 7.00A
G-BUGE	Bellanca 7GCAA Citabria	339-77	N4165Y	23. 4.92	P.White	(Fethard, Ireland)	13. 9.01T
G-BUGG	Cessna 150F	150-62479	N8379G	24. 3.92	C.P.J.Taylor & D.M.Forshaw	Panshanger	13. 5.02

Regn	Type	C/n	P/I	Date	Owner/operator	Probable Base	CA Expy
G-BUGH	Rans S-10 Sakota			24. 4.92	D.T.Smith	Bagby	31. 8.99P
	(Rotax 582) 0790-110 & PFA/194-11899						
G-BUGI	Evans VP-2	PFA/7201		16. 4.92	D.G.Gibson	(Braunton)	14. 9.00P
					(Under construction 9.95)		
G-BUGJ	Robin DR.400/180 Regent	2137		28. 4.92	Alfred Graham Ltd	Southend	23. 7.01
G-BUGL	Slingsby T.61F Venture T.2	1966	ZA630	29. 4.92	D.E.Hills & J.Edwards	Tibenham	1. 6.01
					t/a VMG Group		
G-BUGM	CFM Streak Shadow			29. 4.92	D.Penn-Smith	Sywell	29. 6.00P
	(Rotax 582) K.176-SA & PFA/206-12069				t/a The Shadow Group		
G-BUGN	Colt 210A HAFB	2193		1. 5.92	R.W.Batchelor	Thame	31. 7.99T
G-BUGO	Colt 56B HAFB	2143		18. 5.92	Escuela de Aerostacion Mica		
						Valencia, Spain	19. 7.00A
G-BUGP	Cameron V-77 HAFB	2278	OO-BEE	10. 3.92	R. Churcher	Canterbury	17. 2.00A
G-BUGS	Cameron V-77 HAFB	2482		14. 4.92	T J Orchard	Booker	19. 6.97T
					t/a A Load of Hot Air "Bugs Bunny"		
G-BUGT	Slingsby T.61F Venture T.2	1871	XZ551	22. 4.92	R.W.Hornsey	(Stanford-le-Hope)	5. 8.02
G-BUGV	Slingsby T.61F Venture T.2	1884	XZ564	28. 4.92	Oxfordshire Sportflying Ltd	Enstone	28. 6.01
G-BUGW	Slingsby T.61F Venture T.2	1962	ZA626	22. 4.92	Rankart Ltd	Hinton-in-The-Hedges	16. 8.01
G-BUGX	Socata MS.880B Rallye Club	2957	OO-FLO	24. 4.92	R.W.H.Watson	(Spalding)	9. 9.99
					(Fuselage stored 4.99)		
G-BUGY	Cameron V-90 HAFB	2800		9. 4.92	I.J.Culley	Hungerford	22. 7.00A
					t/a Dante Balloon Group "Florance"		
G-BUGZ	Slingsby T.61F Venture T.2	1981	ZA662	22. 4.92	R.W.Spiller	RAF Dishforth	24. 5.02
					t/a Dishforth Flying Group		
G-BUHA	Slingsby T.61F Venture T.2	1970	ZA634	29. 4.92	A.W.Swales (As "ZA634/C")	Rufforth	19. 7.02
G-BUHC	BAe 146 Srs 300	E-3193	G-BTMI	30. 6.92	KLM UK Ltd	Stansted	8. 7.01T
			G-6-193		(Reserved as EI-CTO for delivery 6.00 - see SECTION 2)		
G-BUHJ	Boeing 737-4Q8	25164		19. 3.93	British Airways (European Operations at Gatwick) Ltd		
						Gatwick	18. 3.00T
G-BUHK	Boeing 737-4Q8	26289		14. 6.93	British Airways (European Operations at Gatwick) Ltd		
					(Union Flag t/s)	Gatwick	13. 6.00T
G-BUHL	Boeing 737-4S3	25134	9M-MLH	22. 3.93	GB Airways Ltd	Gatwick	6. 4.00T
			N1799B/(G-BSRB)		(Wings t/s)		
G-BUHM	Cameron V-77 HAFB	2481		7. 5.92	L.A.Watts	Pangbourne, Reading	25.11.99A
					"Blue Horizon"		
G-BUHO	Cessna 140	14402	N2173V	1. 5.92	W.B.Bateson	Blackpool	27. 7.01T
	(Continental C90)						
G-BUHP	Ailes De K Flyair 1100	01219935		7. 5.92	R.White	(Henley-on-Thames)	
G-BUHR	Slingsby T.61F Venture T.2	1874	XZ554	8. 5.92	W.L.Grey	Lleweni Parc	27. 4.02
					t/a Denbeigh Falke Group		
G-BUHS	Stoddard-Hamilton Glasair I TD	149	C-GYMB	8. 5.92	E.J.Spalding	Dingwall	6. 9.00P
	(Lycoming O-360)				(Crashed on landing Lerwick 7.4.99)		
G-BUHU	Cameron N-105 HAFB	2785		13. 5.92	Unipart Group Ltd	Cowley, Oxford	21.11.96A
					t/a Unipart Balloon Club "Land Rover"		
G-BUHY	Cameron A-210 HAFB	2858		14. 5.92	Adventure Balloon Co Ltd	London W7	26. 8.00T
G-BUHZ	Cessna 120	14950	N3676V	1. 5.92	G.L.Brown	Spanhoe	
G-BUIB	MBB Bo.105DBS-4	S.138/911	G-BDYZ	21. 5.92	Bond Air Services	Inverness	24. 6.01T
			D-HDEF		(Op Scottish Air Ambulance)		
	(Original Aero Club remanufactured with new pod c/n S.911 in 1992)						
G-BUIC	Denney Kitfox mk.2	PFA/172-11802		1. 5.92	C.R.Northrop & B.M.Chilvers		
						(Huntingdon/Wisbech)	
G-BUIE	Cameron N-90 HAFB	2863		22. 5.92	Flying Pictures Ltd	Fairoaks	28. 7.00A
					"Unipart III"		
G-BUIF	PA-28-161 Warrior II	28-7916406	N28375	29. 5.92	Newcastle upon Tyne Aero Club Ltd		
						Newcastle	8. 9.01T
G-BUIG	Campbell Cricket	PFA G/03-1173		27. 5.92	T.A.Holmes	Melrose Farm, Melbourne	9. 6.97P
	(Rotax 532)						
G-BUIH	Slingsby T.61F Venture T.2	1876	XZ556	29. 5.92	Yorkshire Gliding Club (Pty) Ltd		
						Sutton Bank	8. 6.01
G-BUIJ	PA-28-161 Warrior II	28-8116210	N83784	3. 6.92	Ashurst Technologies Ltd	Blackbushe	9. 7.01
G-BUIK	PA-28-161 Warrior II	28-7916469	N2845P	2. 6.92	A.S.Bamrah	Biggin Hill	12. 8.01T
					t/a Falcon Flying Services		
G-BUIL	CFM Streak Shadow			8. 5.92	P.N.Bevan & L.M.Poor	Perth	18.10.00P
	(Rotax 582) K.182-SA & PFA/206-12121						
G-BUIN	Thunder Ax7-77 HAFB	1882		5. 6.92	J.R.Birkenhead & E.J.Case		
						Runcorn/St.Helens	30. 5.97A
					t/a Free Flight Aerostat Group (Klea 32 c/s)		
G-BUIP	Denney Kitfox mk.2			8. 6.92	Avcomm Developments Ltd	Enstone	20. 7.99P
	(Rotax 582) 710 & PFA/172-11874						
G-BUIR	Light Aero Avid Speed Wing mk.4			9. 6.92	K.N.Pollard	Sturgate	29. 4.97P
	(Rotax 582) PFA/189-12213				(Damaged nr Gainsborough 26.1.97; on rebuild 5.97)		

Regn	Type	C/n	P/I	Date	Owner/operator	Probable Base	CA Expy
G-BUIU	Cameron V-90 HAFB	2641		11. 6.92	H.Micketeit	Bielefeld, Germany	16. 2.00A
G-BUIZ	Cameron N-90 HAFB	2850		12. 6.92	Virgin Airship & Balloon Co Ltd	Telford	7. 8.95A
					(Hutchinson Telecom titles)		
G-BUJA	Slingsby T.61F Venture T.2	1972	ZA653	22. 5.92	T.M.Holloway	RAF Cosford	8. 7.01
					t/a RAFGSA (Op Wrekin Gliding Club)		
G-BUJB	Slingsby T.61F Venture T.2	1978	ZA659	21. 5.92	O.F.Vaughan & D.A.Fall	Shobdon	6. 7.01
					t/a Falke Syndicate		
G-BUJE	Cessna 177B Cardinal	177-01920	N34646	10. 6.92	J.Flux t/a FG93 Group	Old Sarum	5. 5.01
G-BUJH	Colt 77B HAFB	2207		23. 6.92	R.P.Cross & R.Stanley	Luton/Harpenden	8. 7.00A
G-BUJI	Slingsby T.61F Venture T.2	1882	XZ562	22. 5.92	R.A.Boddy	Rufforth	1. 6.01
G-BUJJ	Light Aero Avid Speed Wing	213	N614JD	20.10.92	P.A.Ellis	Popham	21. 6.00P
	(Rotax 582)						
G-BUJK	Montgomerie-Bensen B.8MR Merlin			25. 6.92	C.Moffat	Henstridge	10. 2.99P
	(Rotax 582)	PFA G/01-1211					
G-BUJL	Aero Designs Pulsar	PFA/202-11892		16. 6.92	J.J.Lynch	(Dunstable)	
G-BUJM	Cessna 120	11784	N77343	19. 6.92	B.R.Johnstone	RNAS Yeovilton	28.10.02
	(Continental C85)		NC77343		t/a Cessna 120 Flying Group		
G-BUJN	Cessna 172N Skyhawk II	172-72713	N6315D	19. 6.92	A.S.Bamrah	Biggin Hill	30.11.95T
					t/a Falcon Flying Services		
G-BUJO	PA-28-161 Cherokee Warrior II		N1014Q	19. 6.92	Channel Islands Aero Holdings (Jersey) Ltd		
		28-7716077			t/a Jersey Aero Club	Jersey	24. 3.00T
G-BUJP	PA-28-161 Warrior II	28-7916047	N21624	19. 6.92	APB Leasing Ltd	Welshpool	27. 6.02T
G-BUJR	Cameron A-180 HAFB	2821		22. 6.92	W.I.Hooker & C.Parker	Nottingham	13. 8.99T
G-BUJT*	BAe Jetstream 3100	699	N414MX	8. 7.92	British Aerospace plc	Prestwick	NE(X)
			G-31-699		(Stored as "N414MX" 11.96)		
G-BUJU	Cessna 150H	150-67285	N6485S	30. 6.92	P.J.Smith	Shoreham	9. 9.01
					t/a BUJU Flying Club & Associates (Substantial damaged by winds 24.10.99)		
G-BUJV	Light Aero Avid mk.4 Speed Wing			3. 7.92	C.Thomas	(Tamworth)	28. 7.94P
	(Rotax 582)	PFA/189-12250			(Damaged Caernarfon 13.8.93)		
G-BUJW	Thunder Ax8-90 Srs.2 HAFB	2208		6. 7.92	R.T.Fagan	Bath	6. 8.95T
G-BUJX	Slingsby T.61F Venture T.2	1873	XZ553	7. 7.92	J.R.Chichester-Constable		
						Burton Constable, Hull	19. 7.02
G-BUJY	DH.82A Tiger Moth	"OU/04/1967"	VT-DPE	1. 7.92	Aero Vintage Ltd	St.Leonards-on-Sea	
			HU-858		(On rebuild 3.94)		
G-BUJZ	Rotorway Exec 90	5119		9. 7.92	T.W.Aisthorpe & R.J.D.Crick		
	(RI 162)				(Damaged Eggesford 23.10.93) Tedburn St.Mary, Exeter		25. 5.94P
G-BUKA	Fairchild SA.227AC Metro III	AC-706B	ZK-NSQ	24. 8.88	Atlantic Air Transport Ltd	Coventry	11. 6.00T
			N27185/G-BUKA/N27185		(Atlantic Airlines c/s)		
G-BUKB	Rans S-10 Sakota	PFA/194-12078		13. 7.92	M.K.Blatch & M.P.Lee	Keevil	20. 6.00P
	(Rotax 582)						
G-BUKC*	Cameron A-180 HAFB	2870		3. 7.92	P.Johnson	Consett	2. 3.00T
					t/a Cloud Nine Balloon Co (Cancelled as wfu 11.10.99)		
G-BUKE	Boeing-Stearman A75N1 (PT-17) Kaydet		(G-BRIP)	17. 7.92	R.G.Rance	Goodwood	27. 8.01T
		75-2732	N53127/41-25243		(As "243" in USAAC c/s) "Sharkey's Machine"		
G-BUKF	Denney Kitfox mk.4	PFA/172A-12247		2. 6.92	A.G.V.McClintock	(Longniddry, NI)	12.12.00P
	(Rotax 582)				t/a Kilo Foxtrot Group		
G-BUKH	Druine D.31 Turbulent	PFA/48-11419		14. 8.92	P.M.Newman		
	(VW 1600)					Stoneacre Farm, Farthing Corner	19. 8.00P
G-BUKI	Thunder Ax7-77 HAFB	2239		8. 7.92	C.Wilkinson	Newcastle	3. 2.99T
					t/a Adventures Aloft (Sunderland 92 titles)		
G-BUKK	Dornier Bucker Bu.133D Jungmeister		N44DD	15.11.89	E.J.F.McEntee	Kirdford, Billingshurst	18. 7.00P
		27	HB-MKG/Sw AF U-80		(As "U-80" in Swiss AF c/s)		
G-BUKN	PA-15 Vagabond	15-215	N4427H	15. 7.92	M.A. & A.M.Watts	(Southampton)	
			NC4427H				
G-BUKO	Cessna 120	13089	N2828N	15. 7.92	N.G.Abbott		
	(Continental C85)		NC2828N		Manor Farm, Bishopstone, Salisbury		31. 7.98P
G-BUKP	Denney Kitfox mk.2	PFA/172-12301		22. 7.92	T.D.Reid	Newtownards	25. 2.00P
	(Rotax 582)						
G-BUKR	SOCATA MS.880B Rallye 100T	2923	LN-BIY	27. 7.92	G.R.Russell	Bridport	14.11.02
					t/a G-BUKR Flying Group		
G-BUKS	Colt 77B HAFB	2241		6. 7.92	R.& M.Bairstow	Middlewich, Cheshire	25. 6.00A
G-BUKT	Luscombe 8E Silvaire	2197	N45670	30. 7.92	M.G.Talbot & J.N.Wilshaw		
	(Continental C85)		NC45670			Sherburn in Elmet	6.10.00P
G-BUKU	Luscombe 8E Silvaire	4720	N1993K	30. 7.92	F.G.Miskelly	Thruxton	15. 8.00P
	(Continental C85)		NC1993K				
G-BUKV	Colt AS-105 Mk.II Hot-Air Airship		ZS-HYO	3. 8.92	A.Ockelmann	Buchholz, Germany	20. 7.00A
		2212	G-BUKV		t/a Ballon Reisen		
G-BUKX	PA-28-161 Warrior II	28-7816674	N231PA	5. 8.92	LNP Ltd	Exeter	28.11.01T
G-BUKY	CCF T-6J Texan	CCF4-464	FAP1766	13. 7.92	R.A.Fleming	Breighton	5.10.00P
			BF+063/AA+063/52-8543		(As "52-8543/66" in US Navy c/s)		
G-BUKZ	Evans VP-2	PFA/63-10761		5. 8.92	P.R.Farnell (Extant 5.97)	Wombleton	

Regn	Type	C/n	P/I	Date	Owner/operator	Probable Base	CA Expy
G-BULB	Thunder Ax7-77 HAFB	1968		3. 7.92	Elinore French Ltd t/a Shiltons of Rothbury	Morpeth	8. 6.00A
G-BULC	Light Aero Avid Flyer mk.4 PFA/189-12202			6. 7.92	C.Nice	Popham	19. 5.00P
G-BULD	Cameron N-105 HAFB	2136		6. 8.92	S.J.Boxall	Sheffield	14. 2.00T
G-BULE	Price TPB.2 HAFB	004		10. 8.92	A.G.R.Calder	London NW1	
G-BULF	Colt 77A HAFB	2043		10. 8.92	M.V.Farrant "Nursey II" or "Max" ?	Billingshurst	22. 5.99A
G-BULG	Van's RV-4 (Lycoming O-320)	JRV4-1	C-FELJ	28. 7.92	R.I.Warman Priory Farm, Tibenham		25. 4.00P
G-BULH	Cessna 172N Skyhawk II	172-69869	N738CJ	2. 7.92	Comed Aviation Ltd	Blackpool	9. 9.02T
G-BULJ	CFM Streak Shadow (Rotax 582) K.191-SA & PFA/206-12199			10. 8.92	C.C.Brown	Lubenham	26. 5.00P
G-BULK	Thunder Ax9-120 Srs.2 HAFB	2237		3. 7.92	S.J.Colin & A.S.Pinder t/a Skybus Ballooning	Maidstone	2. 6.00T
G-BULL	Scottish Avn Bulldog Srs.120/128 BH120/392	HKG-5 G-31-18		20. 9.88	C.D.Weiswall (As "HKG-5" in Hong Kong c/s)	Elstree	17. 6.98
G-BULM	Aero Designs Pulsar PFA/202-12010 (Rotax 582)			11. 8.92	J.Webb	Graveley	19. 4.00P
G-BULN	Colt 210A HAFB	2265		13. 8.92	H.G.Davies	Cheltenham	8. 6.00T
G-BULO	Luscombe 8A Silvaire (Continental A65)	4216	N1489K NC1489K	13. 8.92	A.F.S.Caldecourt	Popham	16. 4.99P
G-BULR	PA-28-140 Cherokee B	28-25230	HB-OHP N7320F	8. 7.92	R & H Wale (General Woodworks) Ltd "Margaret Ann" Little Gransden		15.10.01T
G-BULT	Campbell Cricket	PFA G/03-1213		20. 8.92	A.T.Pocklington (Bishops Stortford)		
G-BULY	Light Aero Avid Flyer (Rotax 582)	PFA/189-12309		12. 8.92	D.R.Piercy "Lady Irene"	Newton Peverill	6. 7.00P
G-BULZ	Denney Kitfox mk.2 (Rotax 582)	PFA/172-11546		31. 7.92	T.G.F.Trenchard	Newton Peverill	6. 6.00P
G-BUMP	PA-28-181 Cherokee Archer II	28-7790437	PH-MVA OO-HCH/N3105Q	17. 1.79	Marnham Investments Ltd Ronaldsway (Op Manx Flyers Aero Club)		23.10.00T
G-BUNB	Slingsby T.61F Venture T.2	1969	ZA633	25. 8.92	T.M.Holloway RAF Cranwell t/a RAFGSA (Op Cranwell Gliding Club)		14.12.01
G-BUNC	PZL-104 Wilga 35A	129444	SP-TWP	2. 9.92	M.Prew t/a Paravia Group	Framlingham	8. 6.02
G-BUND	PA-28RT-201T Turbo Arrow IV	28R-8031107	N8219V	18. 7.88	Jenrick Ltd & A.Somerville	Blackbushe	29. 6.01
G-BUNG	Cameron N-77 HAFB	2905		2. 9.92	A.Kaye Wellingborough t/a The Bungle Balloon Group "Bungle" (Aspen titles)		25. 9.99A
G-BUNH	PA-28RT-201T Turbo Arrow IV	28R-8031166	N8255H	26. 8.92	Jennifer A.Blenkharn Carlisle t/a JB Consultants (Aviation)		30.11.01T
G-BUNI	Cameron Bunny 90SS HAFB (Cadburys Caramel Bunny shape)	2897		23. 9.92	Virgin Airship & Balloon Co Ltd	Telford	29.10.99A
G-BUNJ	K & S SA.102-5 Cavalier PFA/01-10058			10. 9.92	J.A.Smith Great Massingham (Nearing completion 9.97)		
G-BUNM	Denney Kitfox mk.3 (Rotax 582)	PFA/172-12111		15. 9.92	P.J.Carter	Inverness	16.11.00P
G-BUNO	Neico Lancair 320	PFA/191-12332		11. 9.92	J.Softley	(Newbury)	
G-BUNS	Reims Cessna F150K	0648	F-BSIL	28. 8.92	R.W.H.Cole Spilsted Farm, Sedlescombe t/a Cole Aviation (Stored 3.97)		
G-BUNV	Thunder Ax7-77 HAFB	1967		23. 9.92	J.A.Lister "Skylark"	Aldershot	24. 7.00A
G-BUNZ	Thunder Ax10-180 Srs.2 HAFB	2271		7. 9.92	T.M.Donnelly	Doncaster	26. 4.00T
G-BUOA	Whittaker MW6S Srs.A Fatboy Flyer (Rotax 582)	PFA/164-11959		25. 9.92	D.A.Izod Gerpins Farm, Upminster		1. 8.00P
G-BUOB	CFM Streak Shadow (Rotax 582) K.186-SA & PFA/206-12156			29. 9.92	A.M.Simmons Belle Vue Farm, Yarnscombe		12. 5.00P
G-BUOC	Cameron A-210 HAFB	2924		5.10.92	C.& J.Bailey Bristol t/a Bailey Balloons		24. 3.00T
G-BUOD	Replica Plans SE.5A (Continental C90)	PFA/20-10474		5.10.92	M.D.Waldron Braschaat, Belgium (As "B595/W" in 56 Sqdn, RFC c/s)		6.10.00P
G-BUOE	Cameron V-90 HAFB	2938		6.10.92	B. & J.Smallwood Chippenham t/a Dusters & Co "Flying Colours 2"		28. 5.00A
G-BUOF	Druine D.62B Condor (Continental O-200-A)	PFA/49-11236		6.10.92	R.P.Loxton Loxton Farm, Sherbourne		8.11.00P
G-BUOI	PA-20-135 Pacer (Lycoming O-320)	20-571	OY-ALS D-EHEN/N7750K	18. 9.92	R.A.L.Hubbard Meon t/a Foley Farm Flying Group		15. 5.02
G-BUOJ	Cessna 172N Skyhawk II	172-71701	N5064E	8.10.92	EFG Flying Services Ltd	Biggin Hill	8. 7.01T
G-BUOK	Rans S-6-116 Coyote II (Rotax 912UL) 0692-314 & PFA/204A-12317			9.10.92	M.Morris Fieldhead Farm, Denholme, Bradford		22. 4.00P
G-BUOL	Denney Kitfox mk.3 (Rotax 582)	PFA/172-12142		12.10.92	J.G.D.Barbour Sheriff Hall, Balgone, Berwick		28. 4.00P

Regn	Type	C/n	P/I	Date	Owner/operator	Probable Base	CA Expy
G-BUON	Light Aero Avid Aerobat PFA/189-12160 (Rotax 582)			13.10.92	I.A.J.Lappin	Newtownards	10.10.00P
G-BUOO	QAC Quickie Tri-Q 200 (Continental O-200A)	01	N10RX	17. 5.93	J.J.Donely & A.D.P.Thompson (Damaged Cranfield 4.7.97)	Coventry	16. 6.97P
G-BUOP	Dorrington Skycycle D2 Airship	D2-218		15.10.92	G.E.Dorrington (Southampton University)		
G-BUOR	CASA I-131E Jungmann Srs.2000	2134	N89542 EC-336/E3B-508	21.10.92	M.I.M.Schermer Voest (As "781-26" in Spanish AF c/s) Lelystad, The Netherlands		13.11.95P
G-BUOS	VS.394 Spitfire FR.XVIIIe 6S/672224 (Regd with c/n 6S/676224)		HS687 (IAF)/SM845	19.10.92	Historic Flying Ltd (On rebuild 12.99 as "SM845")	Audley End	AC
G-BUOW	Aero Designs Pulsar XP PFA/202-12206 (Rotax 912)			22.10.92	T.J.Hartwell & M.J.Riley t/a RAE Bedford Flying Club	(Bedford)	8. 6.95P
G-BUOX	Cameron V-77 HAFB	2925		23.10.92	R.M.Pursey & C.M.Richardson "High Flyer"	Newbury/Oxford	14. 5.00A
G-BUPA	Rutan LongEz (Lycoming O-235)	750	N72SD	22. 9.92	G.J.Banfield	Gloucestershire	12. 8.99P
G-BUPB	Stolp SA.300 Starduster Too RH.100 (Lycoming IO-360)		N8035E	3.11.92	J.R.Edwards t/a Starduster PB Group	(Shepperton)	15. 7.00P
G-BUPC	Rollason Beta B2 PFA/02-12369 (Continental C90)			29.10.92	C.A.Rolph	Shoreham	29. 2.00P
G-BUPF	Bensen B.8MR PFA G/01-1209 (Rotax 532)			5.11.92	P.W.Hewitt-Dean	(Wootton Bassett)	11. 5.99P
G-BUPG	Cessna 180J Skywagon	180-52490	N52086	15.10.92	T.P.A.Norman	Rendcomb	17.10.02
G-BUPI	Cameron V-77 HAFB	1778	G-BOUC	28. 7.88	Sally A.Masey "Bristol United Press" (Western Daily Press/Evening Post titles)	Bristol	30. 4.00A
G-BUPJ	Sportavia Fournier RF4D	4119	N7752	10.11.92	M.R.Shelton	Tatenhill	
G-BUPM*	VPM M-16 Tandem Trainer VPM16-UK-102 (Arrow GT1000R)			16.10.92	J.G.Erskine (Cancelled by CAA 23.12.99)	Carlisle	12. 5.97P
G-BUPO	Moravan Zlin Z.526F Trener Master	1267	YR-OAZ YR-ZAO	23.11.92	P.J.Behr & F.Mendelssohn (Sarreguemines/Strasbourg, France)		31. 1.96
G-BUPP	Cameron V-42 HAFB	2789		21. 7.92	M.W.A.Shemlit	Henley-on-Thames	21.10.95A
G-BUPR	Jodel D.18 PFA/169-11289 (Limbach L2000)			23.11.92	R.W.Burrows	Priory Farm, Tibenham	12.11.99P
G-BUPS	Aerospatiale/Alenia ATR-42-300	109	DQ-FEP F-WWEF	16.12.92	Titan Airways Ltd	Stansted	5. 6.02T
G-BUPT	Cameron O-105 HAFB	2960		25.11.92	P.M.Simpson t/a Chiltern Balloons	Hemel Hempstead	13. 2.00T
G-BUPU	Thunder Ax7-77 HAFB	2305		25.11.92	R.C.Barkworth & D.G.Maguire "Puzzle"	(USA)	8. 6.99A
G-BUPV	Great Lakes 2T-1A Sport Trainer 126 (Gladden Kinner R55)		N865K NC865K	26.11.92	R.J.Fray (Damaged Sibson 29.5.99)	Sibson	28. 6.99P
G-BUPW	Denney Kitfox mk.3 PFA/172-12281 (Rotax 912)			22.10.92	G.M. Park t/a Kitfox Group	Kerse Farm, Beith	9. 7.99P
G-BURD	Reims Cessna F.172N Skyhawk II 1677		PH-AXI	26. 4.78	L.M.Bateman & Co Ltd	Tatenhill	26.11.02T
G-BURE	Jodel D.9 Bebe PFA/944			30.11.92	Lucy J.Kingsford (Under construction 12.95)	Headcorn	
G-BURF	Rand Robinson KR-2 PFA/129-11345 (VW1834)			30.11.92	P.J.H.Moorhouse & B.L.Hewart (Stockport)		
G-BURG	Colt 77A HAFB	2042		12. 1.93	S.T.Humphreys "Lily"	Great Missenden	17. 6.00A
G-BURH	Cessna 150E	150-61225	EI-A0O	2.12.92	C.A.Davis & R F H Roberst	Popham	6.11.02
			G-BURH/EI-A0O/N2125J t/a BURH Flying Group				
G-BURI	Enstrom F-28C	433	N51743	11.12.92	R.L.Heath t/a India Helicopters Group	Goodwood	31. 3.02
G-BURL	Colt 105A HAFB	2297		18.11.92	J.E.Rose	Abingdon	16. 1.00T
G-BURM	English Electric Canberra TT.18 - (Built Handley Page)		WJ680	11.12.92	Mitchell Aircraft Ltd (Op by Canberra Flight as "WJ680/CT" in 100 Sqdn c/s: to RAF Marham 1.00)	NK	18. 8.97P
G-BURN	Cameron O-120 HAFB	2793		18. 2.92	Innovation Ballooning Ltd "Innovations II"	Bath	22. 3.00T
G-BURP	Rotorway Exec 90 (RI 162)	5116		8.10.92	N.K.Newman (Stored 7.99)	Sywell	13. 9.96P
G-BURR*	Auster AOP.9 -		7851M WZ706	28. 9.92	R.P.D.Folkes (Op Military Auster Flight as "WZ706"; cancelled by CAA 18.3.99)	AAC Middle Wallop	
G-BURS	Sikorsky S-76A II Plus	760040		4. 5.89	Lynton Aviation Ltd	Denham	25.10.00T
			G-BURS/G-OHTL (Op European Helicopters Ltd)				
G-BURT	PA-28-161 Cherokee Warrior II	28-7716105	N2459Q	10. 6.81	J.D.F.Fendick	Tibenham	2. 6.02
G-BURZ	Hawker Nimrod II	41H-59890	K3661	22.12.91	Historic Aircraft Collection Ltd (On rebuild 8.95) St.Leonards-on-Sea		AC
G-BUSB	Airbus A320-111 (Originally flown as G-BRSA)	0006	(G-BRAA) F-WWDD	30. 3.88	British Airways plc (Cockerel of Lowicz/Koguty Lowickie t/s)	Heathrow	19. 4.01T

Regn	Type	C/n	P/I	Date	Owner/operator	Probable Base	CA Expy
G-BUSC	Airbus A320-111	0008	(G-BRAB) F-WWDE	26. 5.88	British Airways plc (British Olympic Association t/s)	Heathrow	1. 6.01T
G-BUSD	Airbus A320-111	0011	(G-BRAC) F-WWDF	21. 7.88	British Airways plc	Heathrow	21. 7.01T
G-BUSE	Airbus A320-111	0017	F-WWDG	1.12.88	British Airways plc (Mountain of the Birds/Benyhone Tartan t/s)	Heathrow	30.11.01T
G-BUSF	Airbus A320-111	0018	F-WWDH	26. 5.89	British Airways plc (Sterntaler/Bauhaus t/s)	Heathrow	25. 5.02T
G-BUSG	Airbus A320-211	0039	F-WWDM	30. 5.89	British Airways plc (Sterntaler/Bauhaus t/s)	Heathrow	30. 5.02T
G-BUSH	Airbus A320-211	0042	F-WWDT	19. 6.89	British Airways plc	Heathrow	18. 6.02T
G-BUSI	Airbus A320-211	0103	F-WWDB	23. 3.90	British Airways plc (Wings t/s)	Heathrow	21. 3.00T
G-BUSJ	Airbus A320-211	0109	F-WWIC	6. 8.90	British Airways plc (Water Dreaming t/s)	Heathrow	5. 8.00T
G-BUSK	Airbus A320-211	0120	F-WWIN	12.10.90	British Airways plc (Waves & Cranes t/s)	Heathrow	11.10.00T
G-BUSN	Rotorway Exec 90 (RI 162)	5141		6. 1.93	J.A.McGinley	(Dublin, Ireland)	23. 8.99P
G-BUSR	Aero Designs Pulsar (Rotax 582)	PFA/202-12356		15.12.92	S.S.Bateman & R.A.Watts	Cheddington	21. 6.00P
G-BUSS	Cameron Bus 90SS HAFB	1685		11. 3.88	L.V.Mastis West Bloomfield, MI, USA "National Express"		31. 1.96A
G-BUST	Neico Lancair IV	LIV-114A		23.10.92	C.C.Butt (Stored 2.99)	Chester	AC
G-BUSV	Colt 105A HAFB	2324		12. 1.93	M.N.J.Kirby	Northwich, Cheshire	26. 1.95
G-BUSW	Rockwell Commander 114	14079	N4749W	18. 1.93	P.A.Nesbitt	(Bohemia, NY, USA)	AC
G-BUSY	Thunder Ax6-56A HAFB	111		20. 6.77	M.E.Hooker "Busy Bodies"	Whitchurch	27. 4.86A
G-BUSZ	Light Aero Avid Speed Wing mk.4 (Rotax 582)	PFA/189-12280		20. 1.93	T.J.Allan	Drayton St.Leonard	21.12.98P
G-BUTA	CASA I-131E Jungmann Srs.2000 1101/A (Correct c/n not known)	E3B-336		20. 1.93	A.G.Dunkerley	Breighton	22. 2.00P
G-BUTB	CFM Streak Shadow (Hirth 2706 R05) K.190 & PFA/206-12243			20. 1.93	S.Vestuti	(Kidwelly)	11. 4.00P
G-BUTC	Cyclone Ax3 (Rotax 618) B.1122981 & PFA/245-12365		G-MYHO	11. 1.93	P.R.Berridge	Enniscorthy, Co.Wexford	4.11.98P
G-BUTD	Van's RV-6 (Lycoming O-320)	PFA/181-12152		21. 1.93	N.W.Beadle	Benson's Farm, Laindon	25. 6.00P
G-BUTE	Anderson EA-1 Kingfisher Amphibian (Lycoming O-235)	PFA/132-10798	G-BRCK	15. 8.91	T.Crawford	Cumbernauld	15.10.99P
G-BUTF	Aeronca 11AC Chief	11AC-1578	N3231E NC3231E	21. 1.93	N.J.Mortimore Watchford Farm, Yarcombe (Stored 1.98)		
G-BUTG	Zenair CH-601HD Zodiac (Continental C90)	PFA/162-12225		22. 1.93	J.M.Palmer Coldharbour Farm, Willingham		12. 5.00P
G-BUTH	CEA Jodel DR.220 2+2	6	F-BNVK	10. 2.93	A.A.M. & C.W.N.Huke	(Colchester)	29. 5.00
G-BUTJ	Cameron O-77 HAFB	2991		25. 1.93	A.J.A. & P.A.Bubb "Purple Haze"	Guildford	5. 4.97A
G-BUTK	Murphy Rebel (Rotax 912-UL)	PFA/232-12091		25. 1.93	A.Allen	Aberdeen	22. 3.00P
G-BUTL	PA-24-250 Comanche	24-2352	G-ARLB	4. 4.84	D.Heater	Blackbushe	28. 7.02
G-BUTM	Rans S-6-116 Coyote II (Rotax 912UL)	PFA/204A-12414		22. 1.93	N.D.White t/a G-BUTM Group	Turweston	2. 7.00P
G-BUTP*	Bede BD-5G	008801		5. 2.93	Heather Flight Ltd (Cancelled by CAA 25.3.99)	(Germany)	
G-BUTT	Reims Cessna FA.150K Aerobat	0029	G-AXSJ	18. 8.86	C.R.Guggenheim	Bournemouth	24.10.99T
	(Op Airbourne School of Flying) (Blown over in gales 1.99 & derelict 1999)						
G-BUTX	Bucker 133C Jungmeister (Warner Super Scarab) (Possibly c/n 1010 or a CASA built I-133L)	E1-4 Sp AF ES.1-4/35-4		3. 2.93	A.J.E.Smith	Breighton	
G-BUTY	Brugger MB.2 Colibri	PFA/43-12387		30.11.92	R.M.Lawday	(Milford, Derby)	
G-BUTZ	PA-28-180 Cherokee C	28-3107	G-DARL 4R-ARL/4R-ONE/SE-EYD	23. 4.93	A.J. & J.M.Davis	Cranfield	14. 5.00T
G-BUUA	Slingsby T.67M Firefly II	2111		17. 3.93	Hunting Aviation Ltd RAF Barkston Heath (Op JEFTS)		23. 8.02T
G-BUUB	Slingsby T.67M Firefly II	2112		17. 3.93	Hunting Aviation Ltd RAF Barkston Heath (Op JEFTS)		1. 6.02T
G-BUUC	Slingsby T.67M Firefly II	2113		17. 3.93	Hunting Aviation Ltd RAF Barkston Heath (Op JEFTS)		14. 8.02T
G-BUUD	Slingsby T.67M Firefly II	2114		17. 3.93	Hunting Aviation Ltd RAF Barkston Heath (Op JEFTS)		31. 8.02T

Regn	Type	C/n	P/I	Date	Owner/operator	Probable Base	CA Expy
G-BUUE	Slingsby T.67M Firefly II	2115		17. 3.93	Hunting Aviation Ltd RAF Barkston Heath (Op JEFTS)		29. 9.02T
G-BUUF	Slingsby T.67M Firefly II	2116		17. 3.93	Hunting Aviation Ltd RAF Barkston Heath (Op JEFTS)		26.10.02T
G-BUUG	Slingsby T.67M Firefly II	2117		17. 3.93	Hunting Aviation Ltd RAF Barkston Heath (Op JEFTS)		19. 7.02T
G-BUUI	Slingsby T.67M Firefly II	2119		17. 3.93	Hunting Aviation Ltd RAF Barkston Heath (Op JEFTS)		18.11.02T
G-BUUJ	Slingsby T.67M Firefly II	2120		17. 3.93	Hunting Aviation Ltd RAF Barkston Heath (Op JEFTS)		20. 8.02T
G-BUUK	Slingsby T.67M Firefly II	2121		17. 3.93	Hunting Aviation Ltd RAF Barkston Heath (Op JEFTS)		16. 1.03T
G-BUUL	Slingsby T.67M Firefly II	2122		17. 3.93	Hunting Aviation Ltd RAF Barkston Heath (Op JEFTS)		16. 1.00T
G-BUUM	PA-28RT-201 Arrow IV	28R-7918090	N2145X	14. 1.93	J.Phelan & J.M.O'Grady t/a Bluebird Flying Group	Aldergrove	3. 4.02
G-BUUN	Lindstrand LBL-105A HAFB	015		9. 2.93	Flying Pictures Ltd "British Gas"	Fairoaks	25. 5.00A
G-BUUO	Cameron N-90 HAFB	2994		9. 2.93	Bryan Brothers Ltd	Bristol	4. 7.00A
G-BUUS*	Skyraider Gyrocopter (Arrow GT500)	P.01		9. 2.93	Sycamore Aviation Ltd Healinks Farm, Clitheroe (Cancelled 13.4.99 as WFU)		11. 5.95P*
G-BUUT	Interavia 70TA HAFB	04509-92		21. 1.93	Aero Vintage Ltd	Rye	
G-BUUU	Cameron Bottle 77SS HAFB (Bells Whisky Bottle shape)	2980		11. 2.93	United Distillers UK plc "Bells Whisky"	Perth	4. 3.94A
G-BUUX	PA-28-180 Cherokee D	28-5128	OY-BCW	17. 2.93	M.A.Judge t/a Aero Group 78	Netherthorpe	22. 9.02T
G-BUVA	PA-22-135 Tri-Pacer	22-1301	N8626C	12. 2.93	K.W.Thomas t/a Oaksey VA Group	Oaksey Park	14.11.99
G-BUVB	Colt 77A HAFB	2041		22. 2.93	T.L.Regan	Newcastle	23. 3.94A
G-BUVE	Colt 77B HAFB	2376		8. 3.93	G.D.Philpot	Hemel Hempstead	2. 9.00A
G-BUVG	Cameron N-56 HAFB	3012		8. 3.93	Cameron Balloons Ltd	Bristol	10. 8.00A
G-BUVK*	Cameron A-210 HAFB	2996		8. 3.93	Balloon Preservation Group "Burgundy Blaze"	Lancing	18. 8.97T
G-BUVL	Fisher Super Koala (Jabiru 2200)	PFA/228-11399		3. 3.93	A.D.Malcolm "Spirit of Throwley" Park Farm, Throwley, Faversham		21.10.97P
G-BUVM	CEA Jodel DR.250/160 Capitaine	54	OO-NJR F-BNJR	11. 3.93	G.G.Milton	Kimbolton	AC
G-BUVN	CASA I-131E-2000 Jungmann	2092	EC-333 E3B-487	12. 3.93	W.Van Egmond Hoogeveen, The Netherlands (As "BI-005" in R.Neth AF c/s)		27. 7.00P
G-BUVO	Reims Cessna F182P Skylane II	0022	G-WTFA PH-VDH/D-EJCL	10. 3.93	D.W.Wall t/a BUVO Group	Southend	1. 6.02
G-BUVP	CASA I-131E-2000 Jungmann (Regd with c/n 2155)	2139	EC-338 E3B-539	12. 3.93	M.I.M.Schermer Voest Lelystad, The Netherlands		14. 9.98P
G-BUVR	Christen A-1 Husky	1162		12. 3.93	A.E.Poulsom Manor Farm, Tongham		26. 4.02
G-BUVS	Colt 77A HAFB	2381		12. 3.93	Supergas Ltd "Supergas I"	Birmingham	18.11.99A
G-BUVT	Colt 77A HAFB	2382		12. 3.93	Zebedee Balloon Service Ltd	Hungerford	9. 4.94A
G-BUVW	Cameron N-90 HAFB	3020		19. 3.93	Bristol Balloon Fiestas Ltd	Bristol	10. 5.00A
G-BUVX	CFM Streak Shadow (Rotax 582)	PFA/206-12410		22. 3.93	G.K.R.Linney	East Fortune	28. 7.99P
					(Crashed landing nr Sheriff Hall 6.12.98)		
G-BUVZ	Thunder Ax10-180 Srs.2 HAFB	2380		24. 3.93	Lakeside Lodge Balloon Rides (Cambridgeshire) Ltd Huntingdon		14. 4.00T
G-BUWA	VS.349 Spitfire F.Vc	WASP/20/288	C-FDUY 7555M/5378M/AR614	19. 3.93	Alpine Deer Group Ltd (Wanaka, NZ) (As "AR614/DU-Z"'in 312 Sqdn c/s)		1..7.00P
					(Destined for American Flying Heritage Collection, Seattle, Washington in 1999/2000)		
G-BUWE	Replica Plans SE.5A (Continental C90)	PFA/20-11816		25. 3.93	P.N.Davis & H.Wilebore Leicester t/a Taildragger Classics (As "C9533/M" in RFC c/s)		30. 3.00P
G-BUWF	Cameron N-105 HAFB	3036		26. 3.93	R.E.Jones	Lytham St.Annes	6. 2.00T
					"British Aerospace II"		
G-BUWH	Parsons Two-Place Gyroplane (Rotax 532)	PFA G/08-1215		1. 4.93	R.V.Brunskill Melrose Farm, Melbourne		22. 8.95P
G-BUWI	Lindstrand LBL-77A HAFB	023		5. 4.93	Capital Balloon Club Ltd "Throw Up"	London NW1	13. 4.00T
G-BUWJ	Pitts S-1C Special (Lycoming O-320)	2002	N110R	25. 3.93	P.A.Willmington	Kemble	8. 2.00P
G-BUWK	Rans S-6-116 Coyote II (Rotax 912)	PFA/204A-12448		7. 4.93	R.Warriner Bradleys Lawn, Heathfield		28. 4.00P
G-BUWL*	Piper J/4A Cub Coupe	4-1047	N27828 NC27828	8. 4.93	V.F.Kemp (Cancelled by CAA 8.5.99)	Oaksey Park	
G-BUWM	BAe ATP	2009	CS-TGB	19. 4.93	British Aerospace (Operations) Ltd		
			G-BUWM/CS-TGB/G-11-9		(Stored 8.97)	Woodford	12. 6.93X

197

Regn	Type	C/n	P/I	Date	Owner/operator	Probable Base	CA Expy
G-BUWR	CFM Streak Shadow			26. 4.93	T.Harvey Grove Farm, Raveningham		6. 5.00P
	(Rotax 582) K.177-SA & PFA/206-12068				(Damaged Little Cornard, Suffolk 4.7.99)		
G-BUWS	Denney Kitfox Mk.2	PFA/172-11831		26. 4.93	J.E.Brewis	(Castletown, IoM)	
G-BUWT	Rand Robinson KR-2	PFA/129-10952		5. 4.93	Cynthia M.Coombe	(Greenford, Middx)	
G-BUWU	Cameron V-77 HAFB	3053		27. 4.93	G.Thompson Ashford, Kent		1. 6.97A
G-BUWW	Cameron O-105 HAFB	3023		1. 4.93	M.T.Evans	Bath	20. 6.00T
G-BUWY	Cameron V-77 HAFB	2961		27. 4.93	P.A.Sachs "Pixel"	West Byfleet	30. 7.00A
G-BUWZ	Robin HR.200/120B	254		22. 4.93	A.Cox Winks Farm, Boship, Hailsham		27. 1.00
G-BUXA	Colt 210A HAFB	2400		28. 4.93	Balloon School (Intnl) Ltd	Petworth	7. 4.99T
G-BUXB	Sikorsky S-76A	760086	(F-GSJG)	11. 6.93	Lynton Aviation Ltd	Denham	16. 8.00T
			G-BUXB/VR-CCZ/N399BB/N39RP				
G-BUXC	CFM Streak Shadow			20. 4.93	J.P.Mimnagh	(Wirral)	13.12.99P
	(Rotax 582) K.188 & PFA/206-12177						
G-BUXD	Maule MXT-7-160 Star Rocket	17001C	N9231R	4. 5.93	S.Baigent	Jersey	12. 9.02
	(Tri-cycle u/c)						
G-BUXI	Steen Skybolt	PFA/64-10755		16. 3.93	M.Frankland	Caernarfon	5. 8.99P
	(Lycoming IO-360)						
G-BUXJ	Slingsby T.61F Venture T.2	1878	XZ558	6. 5.93	R.A.P.McLachlan	RAF Halton	17. 6.02
G-BUXK	Pietenpol Aircamper	PFA/47-11901		12. 5.93	G.R.G.Smith Little Down Farm, Milson		14. 7.00P
	(Continental C90)				t/a XIX Crawley Flying Club		
G-BUXL	Taylor JT.1 Monoplane	PFA/55-11819		12. 5.93	M.W.Elliott	(Derby)	
G-BUXM	QAC Quickie Tri-Q	2343	N4435Y	23. 2.93	A.J.Ross & D.Ramwell	Tatenhill	10. 8.95P
	(Revmaster 2100D)				(Stored 10.97)		
G-BUXN	Beechcraft C23 Sundowner	M-1752	N9256S	13. 5.93	J.L.Pearce	Bournemouth	16. 9.02
					t/a Private Pilots Syndicate		
G-BUXO	Pober P-9 Pixie	PFA/105-10647		17. 5.93	J.Mangiapane	(Nottingham)	
					t/a P-9 Flying Group		
G-BUXP	American Aircraft Falcon XPS			16. 3.93	J.C. & B.E.Greenslade		
		PFA/250-12439				(Ilfracombe/Ipswich)	
G-BUXR	Cameron A-250 HAFB	3056		13. 5.93	D.S.King Nottingham		14. 5.02T
					t/a Celebration Balloon Flights		
G-BUXS	MBB Bo.105DBS-4	S.41/913	G-PASA	19. 5.93	Bond Air Services "Irn Bru" Aberdeen		25. 5.02T
			G-BGWP/F-ODMZ/G-BGWP/HB-XFD/N153BB/D-HDAS				
	(Rebuilt with new pod S.913 1993/D-HIFA originally allocated 4.93)						
G-BUXT	Dornier 228-202K	8065	D-CBOL	24. 5.93	Suckling Airways (Cambridge) Ltd		
			TC-FBM/D-CBOL		t/a Scot Airways	Cambridge	26. 5.00T
G-BUXU	Beechcraft D17S (GB-2) Traveler	4823	N9113H	20. 5.93	S.J.Ellis Bryngwyn Bach		AC
			Bu 33024		(Noted 9.99)		
G-BUXV	PA-22-160 Tri-Pacer	22-6685	N9769D	20. 5.93	T.McManus & W.Connor Weston, Ireland		30. 9.00
	(Super Pacer Tail-wheel conversion)				t/a Bogavia Two		
G-BUXW	Thunder Ax8-90 Srs.2 HAFB	2405		25. 5.93	J.M.Percival Burton-on-the-Wolds		15. 7.00A
					"Silver Lady"		
G-BUXX	PA-17 Vagabond	17-28	N4611H	31. 3.93	R.H.Hunt	Old Sarum	3. 5.00P
	(Continental A75)		NC4611H				
G-BUXY	PA-25-235 Pawnee	25-2705	C-GZCR	18. 3.93	Bath, Wilts & North Dorset Gliding Club Ltd		
			N6959Z			Kingston Deverill	29.12.00
G-BUYB	Aero Designs Pulsar	PFA/202-12193		28. 5.93	A.P.Fenn	Shobdon	14. 9.00P
	(Rotax 582)						
G-BUYC	Cameron Concept 80 HAFB	3095		28. 5.93	P.J.Dorward	Witney	20. 7.94
G-BUYD	Thunder Ax8-90 HAFB	2422		28. 5.93	Anglia Balloon School Ltd Norwich		18. 3.99A
					t/a Anglia Balloons "Air UK"		
G-BUYE	Aeronca 7AC Champion	7AC-4327	N85584	30. 4.93	R.Mazey	(Bristol)	16.11.96P
	(Continental A65)		NC85584				
G-BUYF	American Aircraft Falcon XP	600179	N512AA	13. 5.93	J.C.Greenslade		
	(Rotax 503)				Belle Vue Farm, Yarnscombe		26.10.00P
G-BUYG	Colt Flying Gin Bottle 12 SS HAFB			28. 5.93	United Distillers plc (Spain)		20. 5.96
	(Gordon's Gin Bottle shape)	2331			"Gordon's Gin"		
G-BUYH	Cameron A-210 HAFB	3045		28. 5.93	A.J.Street Whimple, Exeter		11. 5.00T
					"Kennet Centre"		
G-BUYI	Thunder Ax7-77 HAFB	1266		20. 6.88	Chelmsford Management Ltd Chelmsford		18. 7.99A
					"Elevation"		
G-BUYJ	Lindstrand LBL-105A HAFB	039		1. 6.93	D.K.Fish	Bedford	8. 5.99T
G-BUYK	Denney Kitfox mk.4	PFA/172A-12214		1. 6.93	I.Burrows	(Dungannon, NI)	9. 8.00P
	(Rotax 912UL)						
G-BUYL	Rotary Air Force RAF 2000	H2-92-361	C-FPFN	2. 6.93	Newtonair Gyroplanes Ltd		
	(Subaru EJ22)				Newton Abbot/St.Merryn		25. 9.98P
G-BUYM	Thunder Ax8-105 HAFB	2419		3. 6.93	G.M.Houston Lesmahagow, Lanark		4. 3.00T
					t/a Scotair Balloons		
G-BUYN	Cameron O-84 HAFB	1214	OE-KZG	4. 6.93	J.T.L.Challenger	(Thailand)	11. 7.94A
					(Challenger Balloons)		
G-BUYO	Colt 77A HAFB	2398		4. 6.93	S.F.Burden Noordwijk, The Netherlands		23. 5.00A

Regn	Type	C/n	P/I	Date	Owner/operator	Probable Base	CA Expy
G-BUYR	Mooney M.20C Mark 21	2650	N1369W	7. 6.93	Charmaine R.Weldon	Haverfordwest	15. 9.00
G-BUYS	Robin DR.400/180 Regent	2197		21. 6.93	F.A.Spear	Nuthampstead	7. 4.02
G-BUYT	Ken Brock KB-2　PFA G/06-1214			7. 6.93	Janet E.Harris	(Ashby-De-La-Zouch)	6. 2.95P
	(Rotax 582)						
G-BUYU	Bowers Fly Baby 1A　PFA/16-12222			7. 6.93	J.A.Nugent	Haverfordwest	17. 6.00P
	(Continental A65)						
G-BUYY	PA-28-180 Cherokee B	28-1028	C-FXDP	18. 3.93	A.J.Hedges & C.E.Yates	Bristol	25. 4.02T
			CF-XDP/N7214W		t/a G-BUYY Group		
G-BUZA	Denney Kitfox mk.3			10. 6.93	R.Hill	Haverfordwest	6. 9.99P
	1178 & PFA/172-12547						
G-BUZB	Aero Designs Pulsar XP PFA/202-12312			14. 6.93	S.M.Lancashire	Lymm Dam	21. 3.00P
	(Rotax 912) (Tail-wheel u/c)						
G-BUZC	Everett Gyroplane Srs.3A	034		14. 7.93	M.P.Lhermette	(Faversham)	
					(Damaged 7.94; stored Sproughton 12.95)		
G-BUZD	Aerospatiale AS.332L Super Puma 2069		C-GSLJ	11. 2.93	Brintel Helicopters Ltd	Aberdeen	14.12.02T
			N189EH/C-GSLJ/HC-BNB/C-GSLJ/PT-HRN/C-GSLJ t/a British Intl Helicopters				
G-BUZE	Light Aero Avid Speed Wing			16. 6.93	G.J.Bridgewater	Bidford	21. 3.00P
	(Rotax 582)　　PFA/189-12047						
G-BUZF	Colt 77B HAFB	1993		16. 6.93	I.J.Jackson	Lytham St.Annes	4. 6.00A
G-BUZG	Zenair CH.601HD　PFA/162-12457			17. 6.93	N.C.White	Portmoak	10. 6.00P
	(Continental O-200-A)						
G-BUZH	Star-Lite SL-1	119	N4HC	17. 6.93	C.Moffatt	(Reading)	8. 9.00P
G-BUZK	Cameron V-77 HAFB	2962		17. 6.93	J.T.Wilkinson	Calne	1. 4.00A
G-BUZL	VPM M-16 Tandem Trainer VPM16-UK-105			18. 6.93	R.M.Savage	Orton	22. 2.00P
	(Arrow GT1000R)				t/a Roger Savage (Photography)		
G-BUZM	Light Aero Avid mk.3 Speed Wing			30. 4.93	R.McLuckie & O.G.Jones	RAF Mona	27. 7.00P
	(Jabiru 2200)　　PFA/189-12179						
G-BUZN	Cessna 172H	172-56056	N2856L	24. 6.93	H.Jones	Barton	26.10.02
G-BUZO	Pietenpol Aircamper　PFA/47-12408			28. 6.93	D.A.Jones	(Maidenhead)	
	(Salmson AD9)						
G-BUZR	Lindstrand LBL-77A HAFB	044		29. 6.93	Lindstrand Balloons Ltd	Oswestry	11. 1.00A
G-BUZS	Colt Flying Pig SS HAFB	2415		2. 7.93	Banco Bilbao Vizcaya	(Spain)	20. 5.96A
G-BUZT	Kolb Twinstar Mk.3　PFA/205-12367			1. 7.93	A.C.Goadby	(Sudbury)	
G-BUZV	Ken Brock KB-2　PFA G/06-1152			1. 7.93	K.Hughes	(Amlwch, Gwynedd)	
G-BUZY	Cameron A-250 HAFB	2936		29. 4.93	P.J.D.Kerr	Bridgwater	28. 1.00T
G-BUZZ	Agusta-Bell 206B JetRanger II	8178	F-GAMS	13. 4.78	Virgin Helicopters Ltd	Booker	19. 6.02T
			HB-XGI/OE-DXF				

G-BVAA – G-BVZZ

Regn	Type	C/n	P/I	Date	Owner/operator	Probable Base	CA Expy
G-BVAA	Light Aero Avid Speed Wing mk.4			10. 6.93	D.T.Searchfield	Popham	26. 8.00P
	(Rotax 582)　　PFA/189-12166						
G-BVAB	Zenair CH.601HDS　PFA/162-12475			26. 5.93	A.R.Bender	Deanland, Hailsham	19. 6.02T
	(Rotax 912UL)						
G-BVAC	Zenair CH.601HD　PFA/162-12504			1. 6.93	A.G.Cozens	Goodwood	6. 9.00P
	(Rotax 912UL)						
G-BVAF	Piper J3C-85 Cub	4645	OO-UBU	14. 6.93	N.M.Hitchman	Garston Farm, Marshfield	18. 6.00P
			N28199/NC28199				
G-BVAG	Lindstrand LBL-90A HAFB	022		7. 7.93	T.Moult, P.Ellis & R.Tillson	Nottingham	4.10.97A
					"Gee Tee"		
G-BVAH	Denney Kitfox mk.3　PFA/172-12031			22.10.91	V.A.Hutchinson	Market Bosworth	13.10.00P
	(Rotax 912)						
G-BVAI	PZL-110 Koliber 150	03900040	OY-CYJ	7. 7.93	N.J. & R.F.Morgan	Tatenhill	3.11.99
G-BVAM	Evans VP-1　　PFA/62-12132			7. 7.93	R.F.Selby	(Littlehampton)	
G-BVAN	SOCATA MS.892E Rallye 150GT	12376	F-BVAN	21.11.88	D.R.Stringer	Elstree	26. 4.01
G-BVAO	Colt 25A Sky Chariot HAFB	2024		9. 7.93	Janice M.Frazer	Hexham, Northumberland	26. 5.00A
G-BVAW	Staaken Z-1 Flitzer　PFA/223-12058			12. 7.93	D.J.Evans & L.R.Williams (As "D692")		29. 6.99P
	(VW1834)				Brickhouse Farm, Frogland Cross		
G-BVAX	Colt 77A HAFB	1213		30. 3.88	P.H.Porter "Vax"	Tenbury Wells	5. 8.95A
G-BVAY	Rutan VariEze	RS.8673/345	N5MS	3. 9.93	D.A.Young	(Sunderland)	
G-BVAZ*	Montgomerie-Bensen B.8MR			12. 7.93	R Patrick	Perth	
	PFA G/01-1190						
G-BVBD	Vertical Avn Technologies S-52-3		N4643S	21. 7.93	J.Windmill	Ilkeston	
		52014	Bu.125521		(Stored 10.95)		
G-BVBF*	PA-28-151 Cherokee Warrior		N31JM	22. 7.93	R.K.Spence	Cardiff	AC
		28-7515206	N32633		(Cancelled by CAA 18.3.99: noted 11.99)		
G-BVBG	PA-32R-300 Cherokee Lance		N19BP	22. 7.93	R.K.Spence	Cardiff	7. 1.01T
		32R-7680151					
G-BVBJ*	Colt Flying Coffee Jar 1 SS HAFB			27. 7.93	Balloon Preservation Group	Newbury	21.11.96A
	(Maxwell House Jar)	2427			"Maxwell House 1" (On loan to BBM & L 7.98)		

Regn	Type	C/n	P/I	Date	Owner/operator	Probable Base	CA Expy
G-BVBK*	Colt Flying Coffee Jar 2 SS HAFB			27. 7.93	A D Kent "Maxwell House 2" Lancing		14. 2.97A
	(Maxwell House Jar)	2428			(Balloon Preservation Group 7.98)		
G-BVBL	PA-38-112 Tomahawk II	38-82A0004	N91339	2. 8.93	Aerohire Ltd Wellesbourne Mountford		30. 1.00T
					(Op Wellesbourne Aviation)		
G-BVBN	Cameron A-210 HAFB	2904		2. 8.93	M.L. & S.M.Gabb	Alcester	24. 3.00T
					t/a Heart of England Balloons		
G-BVBO	Vertical Avn Technologies S-52-3	N9329R		4. 8.93	M.Richardson	Ilkeston	
		52046	Bu.128616		t/a Ilkeston Contractors (Stored 10.95)		
G-BVBP	Avro 683 Lancaster B.10	-	RCAF KB994	4. 8.93	Aces High Ltd	North Weald	
			KB994		(Open storage 5.96)		
G-BVBR	Light Aero Avid Speed Wing			3. 8.93	N.M.Robbins & A.A.Jones	(Oswestry)	11. 4.00P
	(Rotax 582)	PFA/189-12085					
G-BVBS	Cameron N-77 HAFB	3128		4. 8.93	Marley Building Materials Ltd Birmingham		14.10.99A
G-BVBT	DHC.1 Chipmunk 22	C1/0547	WK511	4. 8.93	T.J.Manna	Cranfield	13.10.97
	(Fuselage No. DHB/F/432)				(Op Kennet Aviation: as "WK511" in RN c/s)		
G-BVBU	Cameron V-77 HAFB	3076	(OO-BYS)	5. 8.93	J.Manclark	Haddington	26. 7.97A
G-BVBV	Light Aero Avid Speed Wing			4. 8.93	L.W.M.Summers	Sandown	19. 5.00P
	(Rotax 582)	PFA/189-12187					
G-BVBX*	Cameron N-90M HAFB	3102		10. 8.93	British Balloon Museum & Library Newbury		27. 9.95A
					"Mercury"		
G-BVCA	Cameron N-105 HAFB	3129		11. 8.93	Unipart Group Ltd	Cowley	25. 6.00A
					t/a Unipart Balloon Club "Unipart 4"		
G-BVCB	Rans S-10 Sakota	PFA/194-11882		11. 8.93	M.D.T.Barley	Top Farm, Royston	3. 4.00P
G-BVCC	Monnett Sonerai 2LT	PFA/15-10547		12. 8.93	J.Eggleston	(Northallerton)	
G-BVCG	Van's RV-6	PFA/181-11783		17. 8.93	C.A.Simmonds	Leicester	15. 3.00P
	(Lycoming O-320)						
G-BVCJ	Agusta A.109A II	7265	G-CLRL	23. 8.93	Castle Air Charters Ltd		5. 3.00T
			G-EJCB			Trebrown, Liskeard	
G-BVCL	Rans S-6-116 Coyote II			25. 8.93	R.A.Blackbourn & J.K.McFarlane	Perth	9. 2.00P
	(Rotax 912UL)	PFA/204A-12551					
G-BVCM	Cessna 525 Citation Jet	525-0022	N1329N	2. 5.94	Kwik Fit plc	Edinburgh	22. 5.00
G-BVCN	Colt 56A HAFB	2445		25. 8.93	N.R.Mason	Llandudno	8. 9.94A
G-BVCO	Clutton Fred Srs.2	PFA/29-10947		25. 8.93	I.W.Bremner (Dornoch, Sutherland)		23. 6.99P
G-BVCP	Piper CP.1 Metisse	PFA/253-12512		24. 6.93	C.W.R.Piper	Harpenden	
	(Revmaster)				(Cf/f 19.10.99)		
G-BVCS	Aeronca 7AC Champion	7AC-1346	N69BD	1. 9.93	P.C.Isbell Cherry Tree Farm, Monewden		20. 9.00P
	(Continental A65)		N82702/NC82702				
G-BVCT	Denney Kitfox mk.4-1200			27. 8.93	A.F.Reid	Comber, NI	19. 4.99P
	(Rotax 912UL) 1761 & PFA/172A-12456						
G-BVCY	Cameron H-24 HAFB	3136		3. 9.93	Bryant Group plc	Solihull	27. 1.99A
G-BVCZ	Colt 240A HAFB	2480		3. 9.93	Schemedraw Ltd	(USA)	21. 8.96
G-BVDB	Thunder AX7-77 HAFB	2364	G-ORDY	6. 9.93	M.J.Smith & J.Towler	York	17.10.99A
G-BVDC	Van's RV-3	PFA/99-12218		12. 7.93	D.Calabritto	Stapleford	27. 5.00P
	(Lycoming O-235)						
G-BVDD	Colt 69A HAFB	2170		6. 9.93	R.M.Cambridge & D.Harrison-Morris		
						Oswestry	1. 9.00
G-BVDE	Taylor JT-1 Monoplane	PFA/55-11278		6. 9.93	C.R.J.Norman	Headcorn	
					(F/f 12.10.99)		
G-BVDF	Cameron Doll 105SS HAFB	3112		7. 9.93	Cameron Balloons Ltd	(Germany)	3.11.94A
G-BVDH	PA-28RT-201 Arrow IV	28R-7918030	N2176L	13. 9.93	P.Heffron	Swansea	20.10.99
G-BVDI	Van's RV-4	2058	N55GJ	13. 9.93	J.P.Leigh Yeatsall Farm, Abbotts Bromley		25. 2.00P
	(Lycoming O-320)						
G-BVDJ	Campbell Cricket	PFA G/03-1189		13. 9.93	Shirley Jennings	Crowthorne	17. 5.00P
	(Rotax 582)						
G-BVDM	Cameron Concept 60 HAFB	3141		15. 9.93	M.P.Young	Dover	8. 4.00A
G-BVDN	PA-34-220T Seneca III	34-8133185	G-IGHA	16. 9.93	Convergence Aviation Ltd	Jersey	19.11.00T
			G-IPUT/N8424D				
G-BVDO	Lindstrand LBL-105A HAFB	055		16. 9.93	J.Burlinson	Aston Clinton	1. 4.00T
G-BVDP	Sequoia F8L Falco	PFA/100-10879		17. 9.93	T.G.Painter	(Felixstowe)	
G-BVDR	Cameron O-77 HAFB	2452		21. 9.93	T.Duggan	Selby	24. 5.97A
G-BVDS	Lindstrand LBL-69A HAFB	102		23. 9.93	Lindstrand Balloons Ltd	Oswestry	16. 6.00A
G-BVDT	CFM Streak Shadow			23. 9.93	H.J.Bennet	Inverness	27. 4.00P
	(Rotax 582) K.223 & PFA/206-12462						
G-BVDW	Thunder Ax8-90 HAFB	2507		30. 9.93	J.G.Wilson "Cosmic"	Thirsk	10. 7.00
G-BVDX	Cameron V-90 HAFB	3159	OO-BMY	30. 9.93	R.K.Scott	Yeovil	18. 5.99A
			G-BVDX				
G-BVDY	Cameron Concept 60 HAFB	3167		30. 9.93	K.A. & G.N.Connolly	Monmouth	23. 3.96A
G-BVDZ	Taylorcraft BC-12D	9043	N96743	21. 1.94	P.N.W.England	(Hove)	
			NC96743				
G-BVEA	Nostalgair N.3 Pup	G-MWEA		7. 6.93	N.Lynch	Breighton	25. 5.00P
	(Mosler MM-CB35) 01-GB & PFA/212-11837						

Regn	Type	C/n	P/I	Date	Owner/operator	Probable Base	CA Expy
G-BVEB	PA-32R-301 Saratoga SP	3213055	N9224X	15. 9.93	Transea Trading Co Ltd	Stapleford	26. 9.99
G-BVEC	Aerospatiale/Alenia ATR-42-300	356	F-WWEW	30. 4.93	CityFlyer Express Ltd	Gatwick	29. 4.00T
G-BVED	Aerospatiale/Alenia ATR-42-300	315	F-WWEN	4.11.93	CityFlyer Express Ltd	Gatwick	3.11.02T
G-BVEF	Aerospatiale/Alenia ATR-42-300	331	F-GKNF	24. 3.94	CityFlyer Express Ltd	Gatwick	23. 3.00T
			F-WWLP				
G-BVEH	Wassmer Jodel D.112	1294	F-BMOH	29.10.93	M.L.Copland	Breighton	4. 8.99P
G-BVEJ	Cameron V-90 HAFB	3169		5.10.93	J.D.A.Snields & A.R.Craze	Battle	9. 7.00T
G-BVEK	Cameron Concept 80 HAFB	3133		5.10.93	S.Andrews	Pewsey	30. 4.97A
G-BVEL*	Evans VP-1 Srs.2	PFA/62-11983		6.10.93	M.J. & S.J.Quinn	(Kilmacolm)	
					(Cancelled by CAA 22.3.99)		
G-BVEN	Cameron Concept 80 HAFB	3164		6.10.93	J.M.Stables	Knaresborough	11. 7.00T
					t/a Aire Valley Balloons		
G-BVEP	Luscombe 8A Master	1468	N28707	8.10.93	B.H.Austen	Oaksey Park	21.10.02
			NC28707				
G-BVER	DHC.2 Beaver 1	1648	G-BTDM	13. 8.91	A.F.Allen	(Leavesden)	23. 4.95T
			XV268		(Status uncertain) (As "XV268" in AAC c/s)		
G-BVES	Cessna 340A II	340A-0077	N1378G	8. 9.93	Firfax Systems Ltd	Gloucestershire	9.12.02T
G-BVEU	Cameron O-105 HAFB	3145		12.10.93	H.C.Wright	Kelfield, York	13.11.99T
G-BVEV	PA-34-200 Seneca	34-7250316	N1428T	8.10.93	R.W.Harris, M.F.Hatt & JRB Aviation Ltd		14. 7.00T
			HB-LLN/D-GHSG/N1428T		(Op Southend Flying Club)	Southend	
G-BVEW	Lindstrand LBL-150A HAFB	057		14.10.93	P.Trumper	Ashford	14. 7.00T
G-BVEY	Denney Kitfox mk.4/1200			14.10.93	J.H.H.Turner	Carlisle	12. 5.00P
	(Rotax 582)	PFA/172A-12527					
G-BVEZ	Hunting-Percival P.84 Jet Provost T.3A	XM479		13.10.93	Newcastle Jet Provost Co Ltd	Newcastle	26. 8.00P
		PAC/W/9287			(As "XM479/54" in RAF c/s)		
G-BVFA	Rans S-10 Sakota	PFA/194-12298		7. 9.93	M.W.Hanley	(Truro)	3. 8.00P
	(Rotax 582)						
G-BVFB	Cameron N-31 HAFB	3175		20.10.93	Bath City Council "Bath Heritage"	Bath	21. 5.00A
G-BVFF	Cameron V-77 HAFB	3161		26.10.93	R.G.Barry	Newbury	7. 4.96A
					"Roy Barry Carpets"		
G-BVFM	Rans S-6-116 Coyote II			2.11.93	P.G.Walton	Morgansfield, Fishburn	26. 6.00P
	(Rotax 912UL) 0793-522 & PFA/204A-12579						
G-BVFN	Pitts S-1E Special	JAS.7	N41JS	1.11.93	N.W.Parkinson	Little Gransden	13. 3.98P
	(Lycoming O-360)						
G-BVFO	Light Aero Avid Speed Wing			9. 9.93	P.Chisman	Enstone	20. 4.00P
	(Rotax 582)	PFA/189-12053					
G-BVFP	Cameron V-90 HAFB	3179		2.11.93	C.Duppa-Miller	Warwick	31.12.99A
G-BVFR	CFM Streak Shadow			3.11.93	R.W.Chatterton		
	(Rotax 582) K.237-SA & PFA/206-12567					Griffins Farm, Temple Bruer	26. 2.00P
G-BVFS	Slingsby T.31M Cadet III	PFA/42-11387	ex RAF?	3.11.93	V.M.Crabb	High Cross, Ware	
G-BVFT	Maule M.5-235C Lunar Rocket	7183C	N6180M	5.11.93	Pagodaplan Ltd	(Wadebridge)	1. 4.00
					t/a Avon Air Services		
G-BVFU	Cameron Sphere 105SS HAFB	3137		18.11.93	Lascar Investments Ltd		
						Junglinster, Luxembourg	22. 5.00
G-BVFX	Nanchang CJ-6A (Yak-18)	1532008	Chinese AF	9.11.93	J.Davidson	(Kirknewton)	8. 4.00P
					(As "1532008/08" in Chinese People's Liberation Army c/s)		
G-BVFZ	Maule M.5-180C Lunar Rocket	8082C	N5664D	21. 2.94	C.N.White		
						Franklyns Field, Chewton Mendip	7. 3.00
G-BVGA	Bell 206B JetRanger III	2922	N54AJ	11.11.93	J.L Leonard	Shoreham	30. 1.00T
			VH-SBC		t/a Findon Air Services		
G-BVGB	Thunder Ax8-105 Srs.2 HAFB	2408		11.11.93	Flying Pictures Ltd	Fairoaks	24. 1.00A
G-BVGC*	Cessna 411A	411A-0274	EI-BCT	16.11.93	Taylor Acft Services Ltd	Leicester	
			G-AVEK/N3274R		(Cancelled as WFU 10.2.99)		
G-BVGE	Westland WS-55 Whirlwind HAR.10	8732M		18.11.93	J.F.Kelly	(Mullingar, Ireland)	18. 3.00P
		WA/100	XJ729		(As "XJ729" in RAF Rescue c/s)		
G-BVGF	Europa Avn Europa	PFA/247-12565		18.11.93	A.Graham & G.G.Beal	Brunton	20.10.99P
	(Rotax 912UL)						
G-BVGG	Lindstrand LBL-69A HAFB	011		30.11.93	Lindstrand Balloons Ltd	Oswestry	11. 1.99A
G-BVGH	Hawker Hunter T.7	HABL 004328	XL573	26.11.93	B.J.Pover	Exeter	28. 7.99P
	(Centre fuselage no.is confirmed as HABL 003360)				(Op Lightning Flying Club: as "XL573")		
G-BVGI	Pereira Osprey 2	PFA/70-10536		29.11.93	A.A.Knight	(Isle of Mull)	25. 4.00P
	(Lycoming O-320)						
G-BVGJ	Cameron Concept 80 HAFB	3099		7.12.93	D.T.Watkins "Pizza Express"	Hexham	23. 4.00A
G-BVGO	Denney Kitfox mk.4/1200			15.11.93	A.Morgan	(Ilkeston)	8. 9.00P
	(Rotax 582)	PFA/172A-12362					
G-BVGP	Dornier Bucker Bu.133C Jungmeister	F-AZFQ		3.12.93	J.P.H.A.Delvaux	(Auflance, France)	19. 6.00P
	(Siemens-Bramo SH14A)	42	N15696/HB-MIE/D-EIII/HB-MIE/Sw AF U-95		(As "U-95" in Swiss AF c/s)		
G-BVGR	RAF BE.2E	133/A1325	R Nor AF 37	8.12.93	Aero Vintage Ltd	Rotary Farm, Hatch	
	(RAF 1e)				(On rebuild 8.95)		
G-BVGS	Robinson R-22 Beta	2389	N2363S	9.12.93	Bristol & Wessex Helicopters Ltd	Bristol	16. 1.00T

Regn	Type	C/n	P/I	Date	Owner/operator	Probable Base	CA Expy
G-BVGT	Crofton Auster 5 J/1A Special			19.11.93	P.N.Birch	(North Walsham)	8. 4.00P
	(Blackburn Cirrus 2)	PFA/00-220		(Rebuild of unregd Auster J/1 Autocrat frame used as an engine test rig)			
G-BVGW	Luscombe 8A Silvaire	4823	N2096K NC2096K	18.11.93	L.A.Groves	(Stubbington)	
G-BVGX	Thunder Ax8-90 Srs.2 HAFB	2490		16.12.93	J.S.Finlan Hamilton, New Zealand t/a G-BVGX Group		31. 3.97A
G-BVGY	Luscombe 8E Silvaire	4754	N2027K NC2027K	18.11.93	Tracey Groves	(Fareham)	
G-BVGZ	Fokker DR.1 Triplane rep			20.12.93	P.N.Davis & H.Wilebore Leicester t/a Taildragger Classics (German AF c/s)		8. 2.00P
	(Lycoming AIO-360) VHB-10 & PFA/238-12654						
G-BVHC	Grob G-115D-2 Heron	82005	D-EARG	14.12.93	Short Bros plc (Op for Royal Navy)	Plymouth	9. 3.00T
G-BVHD	Grob G-115D-2 Heron	82006	D-EARJ	14.12.93	Short Bros plc (Op for Royal Navy)	Plymouth	19. 3.00T
G-BVHE	Grob G-115D-2 Heron	82008	D-EARQ	14.12.93	Short Bros plc (Op for Royal Navy)	Plymouth	26. 3.00T
G-BVHF	Grob G-115D-2 Heron	82011	D-EARV	14.12.93	Short Bros plc (Op for Royal Navy)	Plymouth	6. 4.00T
G-BVHG	Grob G-115D-2 Heron	82012	D-EARX	14.12.93	Short Bros plc (Op for Royal Navy)	Plymouth	14. 4.00T
G-BVHI	Rans S-10 Sakota (Rotax 582)	PFA/194-12608		20.12.93	P.D.Rowley	Popham	2. 6.99P
G-BVHK	Cameron V-77 HAFB	3209		23.12.93	Ann R.Rich "Intel Inside"	Hyde	3. 7.00
G-BVHL*	Nicollier HN.700 Menestrel II	PFA/217-12614		24.12.93	I.H.R.Walker (Ashford, Kent) (Cancelled by CAA 8.5.99)		
G-BVHM	PA-38-112 Tomahawk	38-79A0313	G-DCAN N9713N	14.11.91	A.J.Gomes (Op Sky Leisure Aviation)	Shoreham	17. 7.02T
G-BVHN*	Lindstrand LBL-G144 HAFB	076		24.12.93	Lindstrand Balloons Ltd Oswestry (Cancelled 3.6.99 as WFU: no C of A issued)		
G-BVHO	Cameron V-90 HAFB	3158		29.12.93	N.W.B.Bews	Tenbury Wells	17. 7.00
G-BVHP	Colt 42A HAFB	2533		31.12.93	Danny Bertels Ballooning BVBA	Wommelgem, Belgium	30. 5.00
G-BVHR	Cameron V-90 HAFB	3174		5. 1.94	G.P.Walton	Bagshot	30. 5.00T
G-BVHS	Murphy Rebel (Lycoming O-235)	050 & PFA/232-12180		5. 1.94	J.Brown	Breighton	27. 4.00P
G-BVHT	Light Aero Avid mk.4 Speed Wing (Rotax 582)	PFA/189-12226		28.10.93	R.S.Holt	Long Marston	15. 6.00P
G-BVHU	Colt Flying Bottle 13 SS HAFB	2499		6. 1.94	Bias International Ltd "Kaiser"	Rio De Janeiro, Brazil	19. 2.95A
G-BVHV	Cameron N-105 HAFB	3215		6. 1.94	Flying Pictures Ltd "Rover" Fairoaks		14.12.98A
G-BVHX	PBN BN-2T-4R Defender 4000	4003		21. 1.94	Britten-Norman Ltd (Stored 8.99)	Bembridge	AC
G-BVHY	PBN BN-2T-4R Defender 4000	4004		21. 1.94	Britten-Norman Ltd (Stored 4.97)	Bembridge	
G-BVIA	Rand Robinson KR-2	PFA/129-11004		14. 1.94	K.Atkinson	(Ulverston)	
G-BVIC	English Electric Canberra B.2/B.6	71105	XH568	25.10.93	Classic Aviation Projects Ltd (As "XH568" in DRA c/s: stored 9.97) Bruntingthorpe		30. 1.97P
	(C/n relates to nose section only as ex WG788 from 1970 rebuild; XH568 was c/n 71399)						
G-BVID	Lindstrand LBL Lozenge SS HAFB	064		17. 1.94	Respatex International Ltd	Chesham, Bucks	4. 6.00A
G-BVIE	PA-18-95 Super Cub (L-18C-PI) 18-1549		G-CLIK	26. 1.94	J.C.Best (Bishops Stortford)		21. 4.00P
	(Continental O-200-A) (Frame No.18-1521) (G-BLMB)/D-EDRB/ALAT 51-15549/51-15549 t/a C'est La Vie Group "C'est La Vie"						
G-BVIF	Montgomerie-Bensen B.8MR (Rotax 582)	PFA G/01A-1228		26. 1.94	R.M. & D.Mann (Brodick, Isle of Arran)		21. 8.95P
G-BVIG	Cameron A-250 HAFB	3213		26. 1.94	Balloon Flights International Ltd Bath (Bath Building Society title) "BIBS II"		30. 8.00T
G-BVIH	PA-28-161 Warrior II	28-7916191	G-GFCE G-BNJP/N2212G	26.10.93	Ocean Developments Ltd	Redhill	23. 1.00T
G-BVIK	Maule MXT-7-180 Star Rocket	14056C		31. 1.94	R.D.Masters	Panshanger	30. 5.00
G-BVIL	Maule MXT-7-180 Star Rocket	14059C		31. 1.94	K. & S.C.Knight	Shobdon	21. 6.00
G-BVIM	Cameron N-77 HAFB	2222		2. 2.94	The Ballooning Business Ltd Northampton "NAPS"		14. 7.00T
G-BVIN	Rans S-6-ESA Coyote II (Rotax 503)	PFA/204-12533		25.10.93	K.J.Vincent	(Bromley)	28. 8.97P
G-BVIO	Colt Flying Drinks Can SS HAFB (Budweiser Can shape)	2538		4. 2.94	Virgin Balloon & Airship Co Ltd Telford "Budweiser"		9. 6.00A
G-BVIR	Lindstrand LBL-69A HAFB	079		2. 2.94	Aerial Promotions Ltd "Vauxhall"	Cannock	2. 3.97A
G-BVIS	Brugger MB.2 Colibri	PFA/43-10666		2. 2.94	M.J.Sharp (Under construction 5.95)	RAF Kinloss	

Regn	Type	C/n	P/I	Date	Owner/operator	Probable Base	CA Expy
G-BVIT	Campbell Cricket PFA G/03-1229 (Rotax 582)			4. 2.94	A.N.Nisbet	Kemble	24. 7.97P
G-BVIV	Light Aero Avid Speed Wing (Rotax 582) PFA/189-12034			25.10.93	M.Burton	(Malpas)	27. 1.99P
G-BVIW	PA-18-150 Super Cub	18-8277	SE-EPD	4. 2.94	Rodger Aircraft Ltd	Old Sarum	27. 5.00T
G-BVIX	Lindstrand LBL-180A HAFB	082		8. 2.94	European Balloon Display Co Ltd	Great Missenden	26. 3.00T
G-BVIZ	Europa Avn Europa 52 & PFA/247-12601 (Rotax 912UL)			24. 1.94	T.J.Punter & P.G.Jeffers	Booker	17. 3.00P
G-BVJA	Fokker F.100-650	11489	PH-EZE	22. 4.94	British Midland Airways Ltd	East Midlands	24. 4.00T
G-BVJB	Fokker F.100-650	11488	PH-EZD	7. 7.94	British Midland Airways Ltd	East Midlands	6. 7.00T
G-BVJC	Fokker F.100-650	11497	PH-EZJ	2.12.94	British Midland Airways Ltd	East Midlands	1.12.00T
G-BVJD	Fokker F.100-650	11503	PH-EZO	14.12.94	British Midland Airways Ltd	East Midlands	13.12.00T
G-BVJE	Aerospatiale AS.350B1 Ecureuil	1991	SE-HRS	3. 2.94	I.S. & G.Steel Stockholders Ltd (Op PLM Dollar Group Ltd)	Cumbernauld	24. 2.00T
G-BVJF	Montgomerie-Bensen B.8MR PFA G/01-1082			18. 2.94	D.M.F.Harvey	(Yate, Bristol)	
G-BVJG	Cyclone Ax3/K (Rotax 582) C.3123187 & PFA/245-12663	G-69-14 (G-MYOP)		15. 2.94	T.D.Reid	Tandragee, Co.Armagh	25. 2.00P
G-BVJH	Aero Designs Pulsar PFA/202-12196 (Rotax 582)			22. 2.94	J.A.C.Tweedie	(Wymondham)	26. 4.96P
G-BVJJ	Cameron DP-90 Hot-Air Airship	3216		25. 2.94	Cameron Balloons Ltd	Rio De Janeiro, Brazil	
G-BVJK	Glaser-Dirks DG-800A	8-24-A21		30. 3.94	B.A.Eastwell	Ringmer	4. 8.00
G-BVJN	Europa Avn Europa 66 & PFA/247-12666 (Rotax 912UL) (Tri-cycle u/c)			2. 3.94	A.C.Beaumont t/a JN Europa Group "Better by Redesign"	Oxford	14. 6.99P
G-BVJO	Cameron R-77 Gas Free Balloon	3228		8. 3.94	Bondbaste Ltd	Faux Court, St.Etienne, Belgium	25. 5.95A
G-BVJP	Aerospatiale/Alenia ATR-42-300	371	F-WWLN	7. 4.94	Gill Aviation Ltd "Newcastle Initiative"	Newcastle	6. 4.00T
G-BVJT	Reims Cessna F406 Caravan II	0073		2. 2.94	P Madent & M Evans t/a Nor Leasing	Fairoaks	29. 3.00
G-BVJU	Evans VP-1 PFA/62-10691			10. 3.94	Barbara A.Schlussler	(Bourne)	
G-BVJX	Marquart MA.5 Charger PFA/68-11239 (Lycoming O-360)			12. 1.94	M.L.Martin	Redhill	29. 6.00P
G-BVJZ	PA-28-161 Warrior II	28-7816248	N2088M	22. 3.94	A.R.Fowkes	Denham	16. 4.00T
G-BVKA	Boeing 737-59D	24694	SE-DNA (SE-DLA)	15. 2.94	British Midland Airways Ltd	East Midlands	28. 2.00T
G-BVKB	Boeing 737-59D	27268	SE-DNM	24. 3.94	British Midland Airways Ltd	East Midlands	11. 4.00T
G-BVKC	Boeing 737-59D	24695	SE-DNB (SE-DLB)	5. 5.94	British Midland Airways Ltd	East Midlands	15. 5.00T
G-BVKD	Boeing 737-59D	26421	SE-DNK	25.11.94	British Midland Airways Ltd	East Midlands	15.12.00T
G-BVKF	Europa Avn Europa 50 & PFA/247-12638 (Rotax 912UL)			11. 3.94	T.R.Sinclair	(Lamb Holm)	19. 6.00P
G-BVKG	Colt Flying Hot Dog SS HAFB	2571		15. 3.94	Longbreak Ltd	Greenwood, MS, USA	23. 4.00A
G-BVKH	Thunder Ax-8-90 HAFB	2574		15. 3.94	R.B.Gruzelier	Salisbury	22. 4.00
G-BVKJ	Bensen B.8M PFA G/01-1221 (Arrow GT500R)			17. 3.94	A.G.Foster	Grimsby	27. 8.99P
G-BVKK	Slingsby T.61F Venture T.2	1984	ZA665	22. 2.94	K.E.Ballington	(Burton-on-Trent)	13. 9.01
G-BVKL	Cameron A-180 HAFB	3255		17. 3.94	W.I. & C.Hooker	Nottingham	7.11.99T
G-BVKM	Rutan VariEze (Continental O-200-A)	1933	N7137G	5. 4.94	J.P.G.Lindquist (Kilchberg, Switzerland)		25. 1.00P
G-BVKR	Sikorsky S-76A	760115	RJAF 734	4. 3.94	Bristow Helicopters Ltd	Aberdeen	8.12.00T
G-BVKU	Slingsby T.61F Venture T.2	1877	XZ557	22. 3.94	S.P.Wareham t/a G-BVKU Syndicate	(Blandford Forum)	4.11.01
G-BVKV	Cameron N-90 HAFB	3236		24. 3.94	Pringle of Scotland Ltd	Hawick	3. 2.97A
G-BVKX	Colt 14A Cloudhopper HAFB	2580		28. 3.94	H.C.J.Williams	Bristol	
G-BVKZ	Thunder Ax9-120 HAFB	2547		23. 3.94	D.J.Head	Newbury	25. 7.00T
G-BVLA	NEICO Lancair 320 PFA/191-11751			29. 3.94	A.R.Welstead	(Oxford)	
G-BVLC	Cameron N-42 HAFB	3256		28. 3.94	Cameron Balloons Ltd	Bristol	15. 9.98A
G-BVLD	Campbell Cricket PFA G/01A-1163			29. 3.94	C.Berry	(Wigston, Leics)	25. 2.00P
G-BVLE	McCandless M.4 PFA G/10-1232			29. 3.94	H.Walls (Near completion 4.96)	Sion Mills, Strabane	
G-BVLF	CFM Starstreak Shadow SS-D K.250-SSD			4. 3.94	B.R.Johnson	Wokingham	

Regn	Type	C/n	P/I	Date	Owner/operator	Probable Base	CA Expy
G-BVLG	Aerospatiale AS.355F1 Twin Squirrel	N57745		31. 3.94	PLM Dollar Group Ltd	Cumbernauld	6. 4.00T
		5011					
G-BVLH	Europa Avn Europa	PFA/247-12491		30. 3.94	D.Barraclough	(Alnwick)	
G-BVLI	Cameron V-77 HAFB	5568	N9544G	30. 3.94	Janet Lewis-Richardson		
						Waiheke, New Zealand	5. 5.00A
G-BVLK	Rearwin 8125 Cloudster	803	N25403	6. 4.94	M.C.Hiscock	Titchfield, Hants	
			NC25403		(On rebuild 2.96)		
G-BVLL	Lindstrand LBL-210A HAFB	101		9. 3.94	Aerial Promotions Ltd	Cannock	11. 5.00T
G-BVLN	Aero Designs Pulsar XP	PFA/202-12530		6. 4.94	D.A.Campbell	(Leek)	
G-BVLP	PA-38-112 Tomahawk II	38-82A0002	N91355	8. 4.94	D.A.Whitmore	Turweston	29. 4.00T
G-BVLR	Van's RV-4	PFA/181-12306		13. 4.94	S.D.Arnold & S.J.Moodey	(Coventry)	
	(Avco Lycoming 0320-E2A s/n 46482-27A)				t/a RV4 Group (Fuselage exhibited PFA Cranfield 7.99)		
G-BVLS	Thunder Ax8-90 Srs.2 HAFB	2577		13. 4.94	J.R.Henderson	Stratford-upon-Avon	8. 7.00A
G-BVLT	Bellanca 7GCBC Citabria 150S 1103-79		SE-GHV	6. 4.94	M.D.Hinge	Old Sarum	26. 8.02T
G-BVLU	Druine D.31 Turbulent	PFA/1604		18. 4.94	C.D.Bancroft	Litte Down Farm, Milson	
					(Noted 6.99)		
G-BVLV	Europa Avn Europa 39 & PFA/247-12585			10. 3.94	J.T.Naylor	Bidford	9. 4.00P
	(Rotax 912UL)				t/a Euro 39 Group		
G-BVLW	Light Aero Avid Hauler mk.4			24. 3.94	D.M.Johnstone	Shobdon	28. 9.00P
	(Hirth F30)	PFA/189-12577					
G-BVLX	Slingsby T.61F Venture T.2	1973	ZA654	19. 4.94	T.M.Holloway t/a RAFGSA	RAF Bicester	22.12.00
G-BVLZ	Lindstrand LBL-120A HAFB	063		4. 3.94	Balloon Flights Club Ltd		
						Kings Norton, Leicester	21. 3.00T
G-BVMA	Beechcraft 200 Super King Air BB-797		G-VPLC	22. 7.93	Manhattan Air Ltd	Blackbushe	21.10.01T
			N84B				
G-BVMB	Hawker Hunter T.7A	41H/695347	XL613	26. 4.94	Hunter Aviation Ltd	Exeter	28.11.95P*
	(Regd with c/n 41H/695334)				(As "XL613": stored 3.96)		
G-BVMC	Robinson R-44 Astro	0060		15. 4.94	E.Wooton	Sywell	9. 7.00T
G-BVMD	Luscombe 8E Silvaire	5265	9Q-CGB	15. 4.94	G.M.Scott	Standalone Farm, Meppershall	5. 1.00P
			KAT-?/VP-YRB/ZS-BWC/NC2538K				
G-BVMF	Cameron V-77 HAFB	3195		22. 4.94	P.A.Meecham	Milton-Under-Wychwood	3. 8.00A
G-BVMG	Bensen B.80V	PFA G/01-1056		25. 4.94	D.Moffatt	(Slamannan, Falkirk)	
G-BVMH	Wag-Aero Sport Trainer PFA/108-12647			28. 4.94	D.M.Jagger	Woodhall Spa	27.10.98P
	(Continental C90)				(As "624/D-39" in US Army c/s)		
G-BVMI	PA-18-150 Super Cub	18-4649	N1136Z	6. 4.94	S.Sampson	Bagby	2. 3.01
			D-EIAC/(PH-WDP)/D-EIAC/D-EKAF/N10F				
	(Frame No.18-4613; initially and currently regd with c/n 18-8482 ex OH-PIN/N4262Z but latterly rebuilt from						
	N1136Z/D-EIAC after crash 15.8.95; original airframe now rebuilt as G-CUBP)						
G-BVMJ	Cameron Eagle 95SS HAFB	3262		28. 4.94	R.D.Sargeant	Maidenhead	17. 9.99A
G-BVML	Lindstrand LBL-210A HAFB	094		29. 4.94	Ballooning Adventures Ltd	Hexham	3. 5.00T
G-BVMM	Robin HR.200/100 Club	41	F-BVMM	18. 8.80	R.H.Ashforth	Gloucestershire	9. 7.01
G-BVMN	Ken Brock KB-2	PFA G/06-1218		29. 4.94	S.McCullagh	(London W3)	17. 6.99P
	(Rotax 582)						
G-BVMR	Cameron V-90 HAFB	3269		28. 3.94	I.R.Comley "Midnight Rainbow" Gloucester		28. 5.00A
G-BVMU	Aerostar Yakovlev Yak-52	9211809	YR-013	11. 5.94	J.E. & A.Ashby	Little Gransden	1. 7.00P
	(Official c/n is 9411809)				(As "09" in DOSAAF c/s)		
G-BVMX	Short SD.3-60 Var.100	SH.3751	G-BPFS	25.10.93	Aurigny Air Services Ltd	Guernsey	21.11.01T
			G-REGN/G-OCIA/G-BPFS				
G-BVMZ	Robin HR.100/210 Safari	198	F-BVMZ	20. 3.85	Chiltern Handbags (London) Ltd		
						Stapleford	16. 7.01
G-BVNA*	Aces High Cuby II		G-MYMA	27. 4.94	L.S.Elliott	(Coleraine, NI)	1. 2.99P
	(Rotax 503) LC2F-931052605 & PFA/257-12584				(Cancelled as destroyed 22.9.99)		
G-BVNG	DH.60GIII Moth Major	NK	EC-AFK	17. 5.94	J.A.Pothecary	Old Sarum	
			EE1-81/30-81		(On rebuild 2.96)		
G-BVNH	Agusta A.109C	7643	G-LAXO	13. 6.94	Lochbrae Ltd	(Cork, Ireland)	11. 7.00T
G-BVNI	Taylor JT.2 Titch	PFA/60-11107		20. 5.94	T.V.Adamson	Rufforth	
G-BVNL	Rockwell Commander 114	14118	I-ECCE	13. 5.94	W.J.Hemmings, R.Lockyer & S.J.Healey		
			N4789W			Birmingham	5. 7.00
G-BVNM	Boeing 737-4S3	24163	G-BPKA	31. 3.92	British Airways (European Operations at Gatwick) Ltd		
			9M-MJJ/G-BPKA		(Union Flag c/s)	Gatwick	31. 3.02T
G-BVNN	Boeing 737-4S3	24164	G-BPKB	18. 3.92	British Airways (European Operations at Gatwick) Ltd		
			9M-MLA/G-BPKB		(Union Flag t/s)	Gatwick	18. 3.02T
G-BVNO	Boeing 737-4S3	24167	G-BPKE	18. 3.92	British Airways (European Operations at Gatwick) Ltd		
			9M-MLB/G-BPKE			Gatwick	14. 4.02T
					(Mountain of the Birds/Benyhone Tartan t/s)		
G-BVNR	Cameron N-105 HAFB	3288		24. 5.94	Liquigas SpA	Milan, Italy	21. 6.00A
G-BVNS	PA-28-181 Cherokee Archer II		N6163J	13. 4.94	Scottish Airways Flyers (Prestwick) Ltd		
		28-7690358				Prestwick	11. 8.00T
G-BVNU	FLS Sprint Club	004		25. 5.94	Sunhawk Ltd	North Weald	17.10.98T
G-BVNY	Rans S-7 Courier	PFA/218-11951		24. 5.94	Sport Air UK Ltd		
	(Rotax 582)					Yeatsall Farm, Abbotts Bromley	5. 1.00P

Regn	Type	C/n	P/I	Date	Owner/operator	Probable Base	CA Expy
G-BVOA	PA-28-181 Archer II	28-7990145	N2132C	31. 5.94	M.J. & R.J.Millen t/a Millen Aviation Services	Rochester	30. 7.00T
G-BVOB	Fokker F-27 Friendship 500	10366	PH-FMN PT-LZM/F-BPNA/PH-FMN	5. 7.94	BAC Express Airlines Ltd.	NK	6.10.00T
G-BVOC	Cameron V-90 HAFB	3291		8. 6.94	Sally A.Masey "Scoop" (Evening Post/Western Daily Press titles)	Bristol	28. 7.00A
G-BVOD	Montgomerie-Parsons Two-Place Gyroplane	PFA G/08-1238		8. 6.94	J.M.Montgomerie	Maybole, Ayr	
G-BVOG	Cameron RN-9 HAFB	3285		14. 6.94	Cameron Balloons Ltd	Klaus, Austria	12.10.95A
G-BVOH	Campbell Cricket (Rotax 532)	PFA G/03-1220		14. 6.94	G.A.Speich	Beausale, Warwick	4. 2.00P
G-BVOI	Rans S-6-116 Coyote II (Rotax 582)	PFA/204A-12712		14. 6.94	A.P.Bacon	(Wick)	24. 5.00P
G-BVOK	Aerostar Yakovlev Yak-52	9111505	RA-9111505/DOSAAF55	14. 6.94	D.J.Gilmour t/a Intrepid Aviation Co (As "55" in DOSAAF c/s)	North Weald	9.12.99P
G-BVOL*	Douglas C-47B-40DL Dakota 3	9836	ZS-NJE SAAF 6867/FD938/42-23974	14. 6.94	Aviodome Schiphol, The Netherlands "Field Marshall Jan Smuts" (As "KG391/AG" in RAF c/s)		19. 9.96
G-BVON	Lindstrand LBL-105A HAFB	001	N532LB G-BVON	16. 6.94	P.A.Lindstrand "Phoenix"	Dallas, Texas, USA	20. 5.00
G-BVOO	Lindstrand LBL-105A HAFB	123		16. 6.94	T.G.Church	Blackburn	6.12.99A
G-BVOP	Cameron N-90 HAFB	3317		21. 6.94	Cambury Ltd t/a Mr.Lazenbys	Stockton-on-Tees	26. 3.00T
G-BVOR	CFM Streak Shadow (Rotax 582) K.238-SA & PFA/206-12695			31. 3.94	J.A.Lord Wickhambrook, Bury St.Edmunds		13. 5.00P
G-BVOS	Europa Avn Europa	PFA/247-12562		11. 4.94	D.A.Young t/a Durham Europa Group	Brunton	6. 1.00P
G-BVOU	HS.748 Srs.2A/270	1721	CS-TAH G-11-6	21. 6.94	Emerald Airways Ltd (Lynx titles)	Exeter	30. 7.01T
G-BVOV	BAe 748 Srs.2A/372	1777	CS-TAO G-11-4	21. 6.94	Emerald Airways Ltd	Liverpool	11. 5.01T
G-BVOW	Europa Avn Europa 84 & PFA/247-12679 (Rotax 912UL)			27. 6.94	M.W.Cater t/a Europa Syndicate	(Sulby)	25.11.99P
G-BVOX	Taylorcraft F-22	2208	N221UK	20. 5.94	Mousquetaire Ltd (Stored 8.98)	Redhill	AC
G-BVOY	Rotorway Exec 90	5238		17. 6.94	E.Drinkwater Street Farm, Takeley		AC
G-BVOZ	Colt 56A HAFB	2595		21. 6.94	Balloon School (Intl) Ltd t/a British School of Ballooning	Petworth	21. 4.00A
G-BVPA	Thunder Ax8-105 Srs.2 HAFB	2600		24. 6.94	J.Fenton t/a Firefly Balloon Promotions	Preston	17. 3.00T
G-BVPD	CASA I-131E Jungmann	2086	F-AZNG E3B-482	12. 7.94	D.Bruton	Abbeyshrule, Ireland	14.10.00P
G-BVPH	Bensen-Parsons Two-Place Gyroplane	PFA G/08-1234		30. 6.94	I.A.Leedham	(South Wirral)	
G-BVPI*	Evans VP-1 (VW1500)	PFA/1578		7.12.78	C.M.Gibson (Weston-super-Mare) (Damaged Old Sarum 17.4.88; stored 5.89; cancelled by CAA 18.3.99		12. 7.88P
G-BVPK	Cameron O-90 HAFB	3313		1. 7.94	D.V.Fowler	Cranbrook	2. 5.00T
G-BVPL	Zenair CH.601HD (Continental O-200-A)	PFA/162-12693		4. 7.94	A.D.Walker	(York)	30. 6.00P
G-BVPM	Evans VP-2 Coupe V2-1016 & PFA/7205 (Continental A65)			6.11.78	P.Marigold (Locking, Weston-super-Mare) (Stored 7.95)		31. 5.94P
G-BVPN	Piper J3C-65 Cub	6917	G-TAFY N31073/N38207/N38307/NC38307	6. 7.94	J.Esteban	(Sevilla, Spain)	4. 7.00P
	(Regd as c/n 5298 but has Frame No.7002 which was N38207; probably used in rebuild of N31073 in early 1970s)						
G-BVPP	Folland Gnat T.1	FL.536	8620M XP534	22. 4.94	T.J.Manna t/a Kennet Aviation (As "XR993" in Red Arrows c/s)	Cranfield	30.11.00P
G-BVPR	Robinson R-22 Beta	1612	G-KNIT	17. 6.94	E.Bailey	Gloucestershire	4. 2.00T
G-BVPS	Jodel D.112	PFA/917		6. 7.94	P.J.Sharp	(Harpenden)	
G-BVPU	Cameron A-140 HAFB	3296		12. 7.94	Cameron Balloons Ltd	(Canada)	22. 7.97A
G-BVPV	Lindstrand LBL-77B HAFB	119		13. 7.94	A.R.Greensides	Burton Pidsea, Hull	9. 7.00A
G-BVPW	Rans S-6-116 Coyote II (Nose-wheel u/c) (Rotax 582) 029H-587 & PFA/204A-12737			12. 7.94	J.G.Beesley	Halwell, Totnes	3.10.00P
G-BVPX*	Lovegrove Tyro Gyro mk.II PCL125 & PFA G/011-1237			13. 7.94	A.W.Harvey (Cancelled by CAA 29.7.99: noted 9.99)	Henstridge	8.11.99P
G-BVPY	CFM Streak Shadow (Rotax 582)	PFA/206-12375		14. 6.94	R.J.Mitchell	(Tingwall, Shetland)	25. 4.00P
G-BVRA	Europa Avn Europa	PFA/247-12635		25. 7.94	E.J.J. & S.W.Pels	(Mold)	
G-BVRD	VPM M-16 Tandem Trainer (Arrow GT1000)	VPM16-UK-108		27. 7.94	Whisky Mike (Aviation) Ltd Forfar (Damaged Cranfield 12.1.95: frame stored at Healinks Farm, Clitheroe)		
G-BVRE	Van's RV-6A (Lycoming O-320)	PFA/181-12677		1. 8.94	C.M.Dixon	Barton	1.11.99P
G-BVRI	Thunder Ax6-56 HAFB	2622		2. 8.94	A.Van Wyk	Caxton, Cambs	31. 5.00A
G-BVRK	Rans S-6-ESA Coyote II	1193-566	G-MYPK	14. 7.94	J.Secular	(Beckenham)	

Regn	Type	C/n	P/I	Date	Owner/operator	Probable Base	CA Expy
G-BVRL	Lindstrand LBL-21A HAFB	130		3. 8.94	Blown Away UK Ltd	Shrewsbury	22. 6.00A
G-BVRM	Cameron A-210 HAFB	3134		4. 8.94	Virgin Balloon Flights Ltd	Muscat, Oman	16.10.98T
G-BVRP	Lindstrand LBL-9A HAFB	108		9. 8.94	Lindstrand Balloons Ltd	(Austria)	1.11.95P
G-BVRR	Lindstrand LBL-77A HAFB	133		9. 8.94	G.C.Elson	(Malaga, Spain)	5. 7.00A
G-BVRS	Beechcraft B90 King Air	LJ-481	G-KJET	29.12.93	City Flight Ltd	(Banstead)	15. 3.00T
			G-AXFE				
G-BVRU	Lindstrand LBL-105A HAFB	131		15. 8.94	Flying Pictures Ltd	Fairoaks	19. 1.00A
G-BVRV	Van's RV-4	793	N144TH	23. 6.94	A.Troughton	Armagh Field, Woodview	29. 9.00P
	(Lycoming AEIO-320)						
G-BVRY	Cyclone Ax3K C3013085 & PFA/245-12471			18. 8.94	A.N.Bowerman	(Dorking)	2. 3.99P
	(Rotax 582)						
G-BVRZ	PA-18-95 Super Cub	18-3442	SE-ITP	22.11.94	R.G.Warwick	Kilrea, Co.Londonderry	25. 5.01
	(Regd with Frame No.18-3381)		LN-LJG/D-EDCM/96+19/QW+901/QZ+001/AC+507/AS+506/54-752					
			(Damaged on take off Kilrea 30.7.98)					
G-BVSB	TEAM miniMax 91A	PFA/186-12241		1. 7.94	D.G. Palmer	(Peterhead)	26. 8.00P
	(Rotax 503)						
G-BVSD	Sud SE.3130 Alouette II	1897	V-54	8. 9.94	M.J.Cuttell	Gloucestershire	12. 4.02
			Swiss AF		(As "V-54" in Swiss AF c/s)		
G-BVSF	Aero Designs Pulsar	PFA/202-12071		1. 7.94	S.N. & R.J.Freestone	Deanland	13.10.00P
	(Rotax 582) (Tri-cycle u/c)						
G-BVSJ	PBN BN-2T Turbine Islander	2286		31. 1.95	Britten-Norman Ltd	Bembridge	AC
G-BVSL	PBN BN-2B-26 Islander	2288		31. 1.95	Britten-Norman Ltd	Bembridge	AC
G-BVSM	Rotary Air Force RAF 2000	EW-42		24. 8.94	K.Quigley	(Dundalk, Co.Louth)	24. 1.97P
	(Subaru EA82)						
G-BVSN	Light Aero Avid Speed Wing			24. 8.94	D.J. & C.Park	Rush Green	2. 9.99P
	(Rotax 582)	PFA/189-12088					
G-BVSO	Cameron A-120 HAFB	3339		25. 8.94	Up and Away Ballooning Ltd	High Wycombe	2. 8.00T
G-BVSP	Hunting P.84 Jet Provost T.3A	XM370		31. 8.94	Shoal Ltd (Frank Heneghan)	Norwich	5. 8.00P
		PAC/W/6327			(As "XM370")		
G-BVSR	Colt 210A HAFB	2470		8. 9.94	Eagle Security Ltd	(London EC1)	13.10.96T
G-BVSS	Jodel 150 Mascaret			22. 8.94	A.P.Burns	Woodvale	19. 5.00P
		118 & PFA/151-11878					
G-BVST	Jodel 150 Mascaret			11. 8.94	A.Shipp	Full Sutton	26. 8.00P
	(Continental O-200-A) 130 & PFA/235-12198						
G-BVSV	Cameron C-80 HAFB	3194		5. 9.94	Cameron Balloons Ltd	Beirut, Lebanon	1. 9.95A
G-BVSW	Cameron C-80 HAFB	3210		5. 9.94	Cameron Balloons Ltd	Beirut, Lebanon	1. 9.95A
G-BVSX	TEAM miniMax 91A	PFA/186-12463		9. 9.94	G.N.Smith	Headcorn	18. 3.98P
	(Mosler MM CB-35)						
G-BVSY	Thunder Ax9-120 HAFB	2631		16. 8.94	G.R.Elson	Malaga, Spain	15. 2.00T
G-BVSZ	Pitts S-1E(S) Special	PFA/09-11235		9. 9.94	R.C.F.Bailey	(Swinmore Farm, Ledbury)	10.11.00P
	(Lycoming AEIO-360)						
G-BVTA	Tri-R Kis	PFA/239-12450		26. 8.94	P.J.Webb	Dunkeswell	
G-BVTC	BAC.145 Jet Provost T.5A	EEP/JP/997	XW333	7. 9.94	Global Aviation Ltd	Binbrook	25. 2.00P
					(As "XW333/79")		
G-BVTD	CFM Streak Shadow			14. 9.94	M.Walton	Old Sarum	10. 8.00P
	(Rotax 582) K.159-SA & PFA/206-11972						
G-BVTE	Fokker F.28-0070	11538	PH-EZX	13. 4.95	British Midland Airways Ltd		
						East Midlands	12. 4.01T
G-BVTF	Fokker F.28-0070	11539	PH-EZZ	24. 5.95	British Midland Airways Ltd		
			PH-EZA			East Midlands	23. 5.01T
G-BVTG	Fokker F.28-0070	11551	PH-EZK	1. 9.95	British Midland Airways Ltd		
						East Midlands	31. 8.01T
G-BVTJ	Aerospatiale/Alenia ATR-72-202	342	F-WWEV	7.12.94	CityFlyer Express Ltd	Gatwick	6.12.01T
			F-GKOI/F-WWLX		(Waves & Cranes t/s)		
G-BVTK	Aerospatiale/Alenia ATR-72-202	357	F-WWEW	21.10.94	CityFlyer Express Ltd	Gatwick	20.10.01T
			F-GKOJ		(Chelsea Rose t/s)		
G-BVTL	Colt 31A Air Chair HAFB	2572		5. 7.94	A.Lindsay	Twickenham	15. 5.97
G-BVTM	Reims Cessna F152 II	1827	G-WACS	31. 8.94	RAF Halton Aeroplane Club Ltd	RAF Halton	25. 8.01T
			D-EFGZ				
G-BVTN	Cameron N-90 HAFB	3361		16. 9.94	P.Zulehner	Peterskirchen, Austria	25. 9.96A
G-BVTO	PA-28-151 Cherokee Warrior		G-SEWL	19. 9.94	A.S.Bamrah	Lydd	15. 1.01T
		28-7415253	D-EDOS/N9550N		t/a Falcon Flying Services		
G-BVTV	Rotorway Exec 90	5243		16. 9.94	H.G.Orchin	Ely/Bourne	27. 6.00P
	(RI 162)						
G-BVTW	Aero Designs Pulsar	PFA/202-12172		14. 9.94	J.D.Webb	(Hereford)	
G-BVTX	DHC.1 Chipmunk 22A	C1/0705	WP809	2. 8.94	M.W.Cater	(Swadlingcote)	11.11.01
					t/a TX Flying Group (As "WP809/78" in RN c/s)		
G-BVUA	Cameron O-105 HAFB	3369		27. 9.94	D.C.Eager	Bracknell	28. 5.00A
G-BVUC	Colt 56A HAFB	2608	G-639	30. 9.94	Cameron Balloons Ltd	Bristol	28. 4.99A
					t/a Thunder & Colt		

Regn	Type	C/n	P/I	Date	Owner/operator	Probable Base	CA Expy
G-BVUD	Cameron A-250 HAFB	3370		30. 9.94	Balloon School (Intl) Ltd	Petworth	27. 9.99T
					t/a British School of Ballooning		
G-BVUE	Cameron C-80 HAFB	3374		30. 9.94	Balloon School (Intl) Ltd	Petworth	13. 9.00T
					t/a British School of Ballooning		
G-BVUF*	Thunder Ax10-180 Srs.2 HAFB	2642		3.10.94	A.J.Nunns	Harare, Zimbabwe	NE(A)
	(Cameron c/n 3508)				(Cancelled by CAA 13.12.99)		
G-BVUG	Betts TB.1			3.10.94	William Tomkins Ltd	Spanhoe	13. 9.99P
	(Modified AIA Stampe SV.4C c/n 1045 ex G-BEUS/F-BKFK/F-DAFK/Fr.Mil)						
G-BVUH	Thunder Ax6-65B HAFB	243	JA-A0075	3.10.94	N.C.A.Crawley	Great Yarmouth	
G-BVUI	Lindstrand LBL-25A Cloudhopper HAFB			5.10.94	Lindstrand Balloons Ltd	Oswestry	14. 4.00A
		148					
G-BVUJ	Ken Brock KB-2 PFA G/06-1244			10.10.94	R.J.Hutchinson	Kemble	17. 5.99P
	(Rotax 503)						
G-BVUK	Cameron V-77 HAFB	3372		11.10.94	H.G.Griffiths & W.A.Steel	Reading	19. 8.00A
G-BVUM	Rans S-6-116 Coyote II			11.10.94	M.A.Abbott	(Montrose)	7. 7.00P
	(Rotax 582) PFA/204A-12685						
G-BVUN	Van's RV-4 3363UK & PFA/181-12488			11.10.94	I.G. & M.Glenn	Kingston, Cambs	7. 6.00P
	(Lycoming O-360)						
G-BVUO	Cameron R-150 Gas Free Balloon	3365		13.10.94	M.Severin	Court St.Etienne, Belgium	21.12.95A
G-BVUP	Schleicher ASW24E	24828	D-KEWI	14.10.94	E. & C.F.Specht	Husbands Bosworth	22. 1.01P
G-BVUT	Evans VP-1 Srs.2 PFA/62-12092			24.10.94	P.J.Weston	Pepperbox Farm, Salisbury	29. 9.99
	(VW1600)				(Damaged on take off Pepperbox 13.3.99)		
G-BVUU	Cameron C-80 HAFB	3383		11.10.94	T.M.C.McCoy	Bath	9.10.96T
					(Op Ascent Balloons) "Ascent"		
G-BVUV	Europa Avn Europa			23. 9.94	R.J.Mills	Gamston	2. 6.00P
		141 & PFA/247-12762					
G-BVUZ	Cessna 120	11334	Z-YGH	20. 9.94	N.O.Anderson	(Trumpington, Cambridge)	
			VP-YGH/VP-NAM/VP-YGH				
G-BVVA	Aerostar Yakovlev Yak-52	877610	LY-ANN	24.10.94	T.W.Freeman	Fowlmere	21. 4.00P
			DOSAAF 52				
	(Has c/n plate 889109 and marked as ex LY-AMV which was based in France 1995)						
G-BVVB	Carlson Sparrow II PFA/209-11809			26. 9.94	L.M.McCullen	North Connel	12.10.99P
	(Rotax 532)						
G-BVVC	Hawker Hunter F.6A	S4/U/3362	8685M	28.10.94	P.Hellier	Exeter	27. 8.00P
	(Built Armstrong-Whitworth)		XF516		(As "XF516/F")		
G-BVVE	Wassmer Jodel D.112	1070	F-BKAJ	28.10.94	G.W.Jarvis	Halfpenny Green	2. 9.99P
G-BVVF	Nanchang CJ-6A (Yak 18)	2232028		10.10.94	R.A.Fleming & A.J.E.Smith	Breighton	1. 4.00P
			Chinese PLAF		(As "2028/69" in PRC AF c/s)		
G-BVVG	Nanchang CJ-6A (Yak 18)	2751219		10.10.94	G.Beda	(Paris, France)	20. 5.00P
			Chinese PLAF		(As "1219/57" in PRC AF c/s)		
G-BVVH	Europa Avn Europa PFA/247-12505			31.10.94	T.G.Hoult	(Driffield)	
G-BVVI	Hawker Audax I	-	2015M	3.11.94	Aero Vintage Ltd	St.Leonards-on-Sea	
	(Built Avro)		K5600		(On rebuild 8.95)		
G-BVVK	DHC.6-310 Twin Otter	666	LN-BEZ	21.12.94	Loganair Ltd	Glasgow	12. 1.00T
G-BVVL	EAA Acrosport 2 PFA/72A-10887			11.11.94	G.A.Breen	(Algarve, Portugal)	22. 6.00P
	(Lycoming O-360)						
G-BVVM	Zenair CH.601HD Zodiac			3.10.94	J.G.Small	Woodvale	9. 5.00P
	(Rotax 912UL) PFA/162-12539						
G-BVVN	Brugger MB.2 Colibri PFA/43-10979			12.10.94	N.F.Andrews	Emlyns Field, Rhuallt	18.10.00P
	(VW1834)						
G-BVVP	Europa Avn Europa 88 & PFA/247-12697			20. 9.94	W.Komm	(Munich, Germany)	13.10.00P
	(Rotax 912UL)						
G-BVVR	Stits SA-1A Playboy	P-736	N4620S	14.11.94	I.T.James	(Wallingford)	24. 2.99P
	(Continental A65)						
G-BVVS	Van's RV-4 PFA/181-12324			15.11.94	E.C. & N.S.C.English		
	(Lycoming O-320)					Blue Tile Farm, Langham	1. 3.00P
G-BVVT	Colt 240A HAFB	2682		17.11.94	R.W.Keron	Dereham	21. 6.00T
G-BVVW	IAV-Bacau Yakovlev Yak-52	844605	RA-01361	16.11.94	J.E.Blackman	(Newton Green)	2.10.00P
	(C/n plate shows c/n 833519)		DOSAAF15/DOSAAF95				
G-BVVX	Yakovlev Yak-18A	NK	307	11.11.94	J.M. & E.M.Wicks (On rebuild 10.96)		
			Russian AF		Boones Farm, High Garrett, Braintree		
G-BVVY*	Air Command 532 Elite PFA G/04-1104		G-CORK	22.11.94	T.A.Holmes	(Leeds)	AC
					(Cancelled as wfu 4.11.99 - No Permit to Fly issued)		
G-BVVZ	Corby CJ-1 Starlet PFA/134-12293			9.11.94	A.E.Morris	Fairoaks	9. 3.00P
	(VW1834)						
G-BVWA	Socata MS.880B Rallye 100T	2747	F-GACD	29.11.94	G.K.Brunwin	Kemble	14. 4.01
G-BVWB	Thunder Ax8-90 Srs.2 HAFB	3000		2.12.94	S.C.Clayton	Shrewsbury	19. 7.00
G-BVWC	English Electric Canberra B.2	71399	WK163	2.12.94	Classic Aviation Projects Ltd		
	(C/n relates to nose section originally fitted to XH568)				(As "WK163")	Bruntingthorpe	5. 6.00P
G-BVWE	Cameron C-80 HAFB	3414		6.12.94	Daicel Polymers Ltd	Milton Keynes	25. 3.00T

Regn	Type	C/n	P/I	Date	Owner/operator	Probable Base	CA Expy
G-BVWH	Cameron N-90 Lightbulb SS HAFB	3404		8.12.94	Virgin Airship & Balloon Co Ltd Telford (Phillips Energy Saving Lightbulbs titles)		2. 9.98A
G-BVWI	Cameron Light Bulb 65SS HAFB	3405		8.12.94	Virgin Airship & Balloon Co Ltd Telford		2. 6.97A
G-BVWK	Air & Space 18-A Gyroplane	18-14	SE-HID N6108S	19.12.94	Whisky Mike (Aviation) Ltd	Kinnettles, Forfar	AC
G-BVWL	Air & Space 18-A Gyroplane	18-63	SE-HIE N90588/N6152S	19.12.94	Whisky Mike (Aviation) Ltd	Kinnettles, Forfar	AC
G-BVWM	Europa Avn Europa	PFA/247-12620		14.12.94	A.Aubeelack t/a Europa Syndicate	(London W5)	
G-BVWP	DHC.1 Chipmunk 22	C1/0741	WP856	19.12.94	T.W.M.Beck Monks Gate, Horsham (As "WP856/904" in RN c/s)		26. 4.01
G-BVWW	Lindstrand LBL-90A HAFB	169		28.12.94	R.B.Naylor "Double Whiskey" Pulborough		6. 7.00A
G-BVWX	VPM M-16 Tandem Trainer (Arrow GT1000R)	VPM16-UK-111		3. 1.95	M.L.Smith	Popham	27. 6.00P
G-BVWY	Porterfield CP.65 (Continental A65)	720	N27223 NC27223	23.11.94	B.Morris	Oaksey Park	7. 7.00P
G-BVWZ	PA-32-301 Saratoga	3206055	I-TASP N9184N	3. 1.95	J.W.V.Edmonds	Malaga, Spain	16. 2.01
G-BVXA	Cameron N-105 HAFB	3441		4. 1.95	R.E.Jones	Lytham St.Annes	6. 2.00T
G-BVXB	Cameron V-77 HAFB	3442		4. 1.95	J.A.Lawton "Pat McLean"	Godalming	17. 2.00A
G-BVXC	English Electric Canberra B(I).8	6649	WT333	9. 1.95	Classic Aviation Projects Ltd (As "WT333" in DRA c/s) Bruntingthorpe		AC
G-BVXD	Cameron O-84 HAFB	3432		5. 1.95	N.J.Langley "Prudential"	Bristol	2. 2.97A
G-BVXE	Steen Skybolt (Lycoming IO-360)	PFA/64-11123	G-LISA	5. 1.95	J.Buglass	(Shrewsbury)	1. 2.00P
G-BVXF	Cameron O-120 HAFB	3400		21. 9.94	Gone With The Wind Ltd	Carryduff, Co.Down	12. 2.00T
G-BVXG	Lindstrand LBL-90A HAFB	110		5. 1.95	G.C.Elson t/a Lindstrand Balloon School	(Spain)	5. 7.00A
G-BVXI	Klemm Kl.35D (Hirth HM504)	1981	D-EFEG SE-BHT/Fv.5052	5. 1.95	J.J.Van Egmond	(Nyverdal, The Netherlands)	AC
G-BVXJ	CASA Bucker Bu.133 Jungmeister	-	E1-9 ES1-9/35-9	11. 1.95	J.D.Haslam	(Northallerton) (Cf/f 1.10.99)	
G-BVXK	Aerostar Yakovlev Yak-52	9111306	RA-44508 DOSAAF 26	12. 1.95	E.Gavazzi White Waltham (As "26" in DOSAAF c/s)		16. 4.00P
G-BVXM	Aerospatiale AS.350B Ecureuil	2013	I-AUDI I-CIOC	10. 1.95	The Berkeley Leisure Group Ltd Sparkford		5. 2.01T
G-BVXP	Cameron N-105 HAFB	1311	VH-URU	13. 1.95	P.M.Gaines "El Gas" Stockton-on-Tees		
G-BVXR	DH.104 Devon C.2	04436	XA880	13. 1.95	M.Whale & M.W.A.Lunn Kemble (As "XA880" in RAE c/s: stored 8.99)		
G-BVXS	Taylorcraft BC-12D (Continental A65)	9284	N96984 NC96984	27. 1.95	Janet M.Allison Swanton Morley "Obsession"		2. 8.00P
G-BVXW	Short SC.7 Skyvan 3A-100	SH.1889	LX-DEF Arg.Coast Guard PA-52/G-14-61	15.11.95	Hunting Aviation Ltd Weston-on-the-Green/Oxford		24.11.00T
G-BVYA	Airbus A.320-231	354	F-WQAY (N301SA)/F-WWDZ	7. 4.95	Caledonian Airways Ltd Gatwick (JMC Air c/s)		6. 4.01T
G-BVYB	Airbus A.320-231	357	F-WQAZ (N302SA)/F-WWBH	20. 4.95	Caledonian Airways Ltd Gatwick "Loch Hourn"		19. 4.01T
G-BVYC	Airbus A.320-231	411	F-WWQB (N303SA)/F-WWDX	26. 4.95	Caledonian Airways Ltd Gatwick (JMC Air c/s)		25. 4.01T
G-BVYF	PA-31-350 Navajo Chieftain	31-7952102	G-SAVE N3518T	8. 2.95	Warwickshire Aerocentre Ltd Birmingham		23. 1.00T
G-BVYG	Robin DR.300/180R	611	F-BSQB F-BSPI	9. 1.95	Ulster Gliding Club Ltd (Limavady, NI)		9. 4.02
G-BVYJ	Cameron Fire Extinguisher 90SS HAFB	3398		2. 2.95	Chubb Fire Ltd Sunbury-on-Thames		16.12.99A
G-BVYK	TEAM miniMax 91A (Rotax 447)	PFA/186-12598		13. 2.95	S.B.Churchill Eastbach Farm, Coleford		4. 8.98P
G-BVYM	Robin DR.300/180R	656	F-BTBL	9.12.94	London Gliding Club Pty Ltd Dunstable		19. 7.01
G-BVYO	Robin R.2160	288		11. 1.95	The Cotswold Aero Club Ltd Gloucestershire		15. 4.01T
G-BVYP	PA-25-235 Pawnee B	25-3481	N7475D	13. 2.95	Bidford Gliding Centre Ltd Bidford		16. 3.01
G-BVYR	Cameron A-250 HAFB	3411		2. 2.95	Voyager Balloons Ltd Cambridge		14.10.99T
G-BVYT	QAC Quickie Q-2 (Revmaster R2100D)	2443	N3797S	18. 1.95	C.A.McGee (Luton)		2. 9.00P
G-BVYU	Cameron A-140 HAFB	3544		17. 2.95	B.J.Petteford "Blue Belle" Bristol		26. 3.00T
G-BVYX	Light-Aero Avid Speed Wing mk.4 (Rotax 582)	PFA/189-12370		16. 2.95	G.J.Keen Andrewsfield		29.10.98P
G-BVYY	Pietenpol Aircamper	PFA/47-12559		20. 2.95	J.R.Orchard Halfpenny Green		28. 6.98P
G-BVYZ	Stemme S-10V	14-011	D-KGDD	6. 3.95	L.Gubbay & S.Sagar Denham		7. 7.01

Regn	Type	C/n	P/I	Date	Owner/operator	Probable Base	CA Expy
G-BVZD	Tri-R Kis (CAM.100)	PFA/239-12416		21. 2.95	R.T.Clegg	Netherthorpe	18. 6.00P
G-BVZE	Boeing 737-59D	26422	SE-DNL	7. 3.95	British Midland Airways Ltd	East Midlands	22. 3.01T
G-BVZG	Boeing 737-5Q8	25160	SE-DNF	12. 4.95	British Midland Airways Ltd	East Midlands	1. 5.01T
G-BVZH	Boeing 737-5Q8	25166	SE-DNG	25. 4.95	British Midland Airways Ltd	East Midlands	26. 5.01T
G-BVZI	Boeing 737-5Q8	25167	SE-DNH	15. 5.95	British Midland Airways Ltd	East Midlands	11. 6.01T
G-BVZJ	Rand-Robinson KR-2 (Revmaster)	PFA/129-11049		21. 2.95	J.P.McConnell-Wood Phoenix Farm, Hants (Damaged landing Phoenix Farm 15.7.98)		
G-BVZM	Cessna 210M Centurion II	210-61674	OO-CNJ N732PV	28. 2.95	R.W.Bonner-Davies	(London SW11)	25. 3.01
G-BVZN	Cameron C-80 HAFB	3546		28. 2.95	Sally J.Langley t/a Sky Fly Balloons "Taywood Homes"	Bristol	17. 5.00A
G-BVZO	Rans S-6-116 Coyote II (Rotax 582) 0494-606 & PFA/204A-12710			1. 3.95	P.Atkinson	Sandtoft	30. 3.00P
G-BVZR	Zenair CH.601HD (Rotax 912UL)	PFA/162-12417		2. 3.95	J.D.White	Nottingham	11.10.00P
G-BVZT	Lindstrand LBL-90A HAFB	183		9. 3.95	F.W.Farnsworth Ltd t/a Pork Farms Bowyers	Nottingham	9. 7.00A
G-BVZV	Rans S-6-116 Coyote II (Rotax 582)	PFA/204A-12832		16. 2.95	A.G.Cameron & W.G.Dunn	(Winkleigh)	16. 5.00P
G-BVZX	Cameron H-34 HAFB	3564		15. 3.95	Julia B.Turnau t/a Chianti Balloon Club	Siena, Italy	21. 6.96A
G-BVZZ	DHC.1 Chipmunk 22	C1/0687	WP795	5. 1.95	D.C.Murray t/a Portsmouth Naval Gliding Club (As "WP795/901" in RN c/s)	Lee-on-Solent	2. 6.01

G-BWAA – G-BWZZ

Regn	Type	C/n	P/I	Date	Owner/operator	Probable Base	CA Expy
G-BWAA	Cameron N-133 HAFB	3471		9. 3.95	C.& J.Bailey t/a Bailey Balloons	Bristol	16. 4.00T
G-BWAB	Jodel D.140 Mousquetaire	PFA/251-12469		25. 1.95	W.A.Braim	(Driffield)	29. 7.00P
G-BWAC	Waco YKS-7 (Jacobs R-755)	4693	N50RA N53361/NC50	19. 8.92	D.N.Peters	Little Gransden	29.10.01
G-BWAD	Rotary Air Force RAF 2000 (Subaru EJ22) 147 & PFA G/13-1254			27. 2.95	Newtonair Gyroplanes Ltd	Dunkeswell	26. 1.99P
G-BWAE	Rotary Air Force RAF 2000 (Subaru EA82) PFA G/13-1252			27. 2.95	B.J.Crockett Redhill, Hereford (Damaged Kemble 30.7.96)		15.11.96P
G-BWAF	Hawker Hunter F.6A (Built Armstrong-Whitworth)	S4/U/3393	8831M XG160	24. 2.95	RV Aviation Ltd (For Royal Jordanian Historic Flt: on rebuild 1.00 as "XG160/U")	Bournemouth	
G-BWAG	Cameron O-120 HAFB	3478		3. 2.95	M.F.Glue	Hertford	18. 6.00T
G-BWAH	Montgomerie-Bensen B.8MR	PFA G/01-1208		16. 3.95	S.J.O.Tinn	(Weymouth)	
G-BWAI	CFM Streak Shadow (Rotax 582)	PFA/206-12556		21. 3.95	N.J.Mines	Kemble	24.11.00P
G-BWAJ	Cameron V-77 HAFB	3579		22. 3.95	R.S. & S.H.Ham Axbridge, Somerset "Robsel"		2. 8.97A
G-BWAK	Robinson R-22 Beta	2507	N83311	22. 3.95	Caudwell Communications Ltd	Stoke-on-Trent	17. 6.01
G-BWAN	Cameron N-77 HAFB	3499		24. 3.95	Virgin Airship & Balloon Co Ltd Telford (National Power titles)		16. 8.97A
G-BWAO	Cameron C-80 HAFB	3436		24. 3.95	Virgin Airship & Balloon Co Ltd Telford "Grundfos"		20. 7.98T
G-BWAP	Clutton FRED Srs.3	PFA/29-10959		24. 3.95	R.J.Smyth	(York)	
G-BWAR	Denney Kitfox mk.3 (Rotax 582)	PFA/172-12432		16. 3.95	B.J.Finch	Long Marston	27. 8.00P
G-BWAT	Pietenpol Aircamper (Continental C90)	PFA/47-11594		15. 3.95	M.H.James	(Bath)	28. 7.00P
G-BWAU	Cameron V-90 HAFB	3569		27. 3.95	K.M. & A.M.F.Hall	London N10	10. 7.99A
G-BWAV	Schweizer Hughes 269C (300C)	S.1204	SE-JAY LN-OTS/OY-HDW/N41S	28. 2.95	B.Maggs t/a Helihire	(Guildford)	2. 7.01T
G-BWAW	Lindstrand LBL-77A HAFB	207		28. 3.95	D.Bareford	Kidderminster	23. 4.00A
G-BWBA	Cameron V-65 HAFB	3456		27. 2.95	P.G.Dunnington t/a Dante Balloon Group (British Airways titles)	Hungerford	10. 5.00A
G-BWBB	Lindstrand LBL-14A HAFB	222		3. 4.95	Oxford Promotions (UK) Ltd	(USA)	

Regn	Type	C/n	P/I	Date	Owner/operator	Probable Base	CA Expy
G-BWBC	Cameron N-90AS HAFB	3574		12. 6.95	Kurhessischer Verein Fur Luftfahrt "Zeppelin" Colbe-Schonstadt, Germany		31. 3.00A
G-BWBE	Colt Flying Ice Cream Cone SS HAFB	3560		3. 4.95	Benedikt Haggeney GmbH	Ennigerloh, Germany	16. 2.00A
G-BWBF	Colt Flying Ice Cream Cone SS HAFB	3561		3. 4.95	Benedikt Haggeney GmbH	Ennigerloh, Germany	17. 2.00A
G-BWBG	Cvjetkovic CA-65 Skyfly	PFA/1566		6. 4.95	T.White & M.C.Fawkes	Charity Farm, Baxterley	
G-BWBH	Thunder Fork Lift Truck 90SS HAFB	3472		6. 4.95	Jungheinrich AG Hamburg, Germany		18. 4.00A
G-BWBI	Taylorcraft F-22A	2207	N22UK	3. 4.95	P.J.Wallace	Eshott	10. 3.02
G-BWBJ	Colt 21A HAFB	3532		6. 4.95	U.Schneider	Giessen, Germany	8. 7.00A
G-BWBO	Lindstrand LBL-77A HAFB	157		10. 4.95	R.C.McCarthy Galena, Illinois, USA "Lost in America"		30. 5.97A
G-BWBT	Lindstrand LBL-90A HAFB	184		3. 4.95	British Telecommunications plc	Newbury	18. 3.00A
G-BWBV	Colt Piggy Bank SS HAFB	3535		19. 4.95	Iduna-Bausparkasse AG Hamburg, Germany		23. 2.00A
G-BWBY	Schleicher ASH26E	26076		30. 8.95	F.B.Jeynes	Bidford	14.11.01
G-BWBZ	ARV1 Super 2 PFA/152-12802 (Mid-West AE.100R)			10. 3.95	J.N.C.Shields & D.J.Millar	Newtownards	16. 5.00P
G-BWCA	CFM Streak Shadow PFA/206-11985 (Rotax 582)			19. 4.95	R.Thompson	(Redhill)	19. 8.00P
G-BWCC	Van Den Bemden 460m3 (Gas) Free Balloon PH-BOX "022"			5. 4.95	R.W.Batchelor "Prof A.Piccard" Thame (C/n may be a corruption of Dutch CofR 622) t/a Piccard Balloon Group		
G-BWCE	Campbell Cricket	PFA G/03-1235		24. 4.95	M.K.Hoban	(Ruislip)	
G-BWCG	Lindstrand LBL-42A HAFB	223		25. 4.95	Oxford Promotions (UK) Ltd	(USA)	10. 1.97A
G-BWCI	Light Aero Avid Hauler mk.4 (Rotax 582) PFA/189-12299			19. 8.92	M.J. Lowis t/a Avid Group (Boston) (Damaged near Fenland 16.5.98)		31. 7.98P
G-BWCK	Everett Gyroplane Srs.3 (Rotax 582)	036		26. 4.95	A.C.S.M.Hart	(Haslemere)	AC
G-BWCL	Lindstrand LBL-180A HAFB	150		27. 4.95	G.McFarland "Flames"	Towcester	1.10.99T
G-BWCO	Dornier Do.28D-2 Skyservant	4337	EI-CJU (N5TK)/5N-AOH/D-ILIF	19. 6.95	Wingglider Ltd	Hibaldstow	19. 5.99A
G-BWCS	BAC Jet Provost T.Mk.5	EEP/JP/957	XW293	7. 7.99	R.E.Todd	Sandtoft	24.10.96P
G-BWCT	Tipsy T.66 Nipper Srs.1	11	"OO-NIC" PH-MEC/D-EMEC/OO-NIC	27. 4.95	J.S.Hemmings & C.R.Steer (Rye/Bexhill-on-Sea)		
G-BWCV	Europa Avn Europa PFA/247-12591 (NSI EA-81/100)			4. 5.95	M.P.Chetwynd-Talbot Coxwold, Thirsk (Damaged Coxwold 31.10.97)		14. 4.98P
G-BWCW	Barnett Rotorcraft J4B	PFA G/14-1256		5. 5.95	S.H.Kirkby	(Southampton)	
G-BWCY	Murphy Rebel PFA/232-12135 (Lycoming O-235)			15. 5.95	A.Konieczek	St.Michaels	27. 7.00P
G-BWCZ	Revolution Helicopters Mini-500 (Rotax 582)	0010		1. 5.95	D.Nieman (Milton Common, Oxford)		AC
G-BWDA	Aerospatiale/Alenia ATR-72-202	444	F-WWEQ	29. 6.95	Gill Aviation Ltd	Newcastle	28. 6.01T
G-BWDB	Aerospatiale/Alenia ATR-72-202	449	F-WWEE	14. 6.95	Gill Aviation Ltd "City of Newcastle"	Newcastle	13. 6.01T
G-BWDE	PA-31P Pressurised Navajo	31P-7400193	G-HWKN HB-LIR/D-IAIR/N7304L	12. 5.95	Tomkat Aviation Ltd (Stored 10.97)	Shoreham	18.12.96T
G-BWDF	WSK PZL-104 Wilga 35A	21950955		17. 5.95	Shivair Ltd	White Waltham	30.11.98
G-BWDH	Cameron N-105 HAFB	3549		22. 5.95	Bridges Van Hire Ltd	Awsworth, Nottingham	12. 6.00T
G-BWDM	Lindstrand LBL-120A HAFB	263		26. 5.95	G.D. & L.Fitzpatrick	Thame	30. 6.97T
G-BWDO	Sikorsky S-76B	760356	VR-CPN N9HM	2. 6.95	Haughey Air Ltd	(Newry, NI)	8. 6.00T
G-BWDP	Europa Avn Europa 62 & (Rotax 912UL) PFA/247-12637			7. 6.95	H.Linke (Ahrensburg, Germany)		18. 4.00P
G-BWDR	Hunting-Percival P.84 Jet Provost T.3A XM376 PAC/W/6603			6. 6.95	W.O.Bayazid (As "XM376/27")	North Weald	1.11.00P
G-BWDS	Hunting P.84 Jet Provost T.Mk.3A (C/n incomplete ?) 'PAC/W/932'		XM424 N77506-ntu?	6. 6.95	J.Sinclair (As "XM424")	North Weald	4. 3.00P
G-BWDT	PA-34-220T Seneca II	34-8233045	PH-TWI G-BKHS/N8472H	21. 9.88	A.C.Morgan	Biggin Hill	30. 6.00
G-BWDU	Cameron V-90 HAFB	3143		19. 6.95	C.J.Jenkins & M.Stone Bath t/a Bath & West Security "Stella Tortoise"		21. 5.00A
G-BWDV	Schweizer Hughes 269C	S.1712	N86G	16. 6.95	Oxford Aviation Services Ltd	Oxford	26. 7.01T
G-BWDX	Europa Avn Europa PFA/247-12603 (Rotax 912UL)			13. 6.95	J.B.Crane	Fenland	22. 5.00P
G-BWDY*	Sky 65-24 HAFB	001		13. 6.95	Sky Balloons Ltd (Cancelled by CAA 26.11.99)	Wrexham	31.10.96T
G-BWDZ	Sky 105-24 HAFB	002		13. 6.95	Skyride Balloons Ltd	Kings Lynn	5.10.99T
G-BWEA	Lindstrand LBL-120A HAFB	252		14. 6.95	S.R.Seager	Aylesbury	8. 7.00T

Regn	Type	C/n	P/I	Date	Owner/operator	Probable Base	CA Expy
G-BWEB	BAC.145 Jet Provost T.5A EEP/JP/1044		XW422	19. 6.95	D.W.N.Johnson (Transair Pilot Shop titles)	North Weald	8.10.99P
G-BWEC	Cassutt-Colson Variant PFA/34-10444			20.12.78	N.R.Thomson & M.P.J.Hill (On overhaul 5.98)	Sywell	11. 9.91P
G-BWED	Thunder Ax7-77 HAFB	3575		20. 6.95	J.Tod	London WC2	20. 6.96
G-BWEE	Cameron V-42 HAFB	3480		8. 3.95	Aeromantics Ltd	Bristol	
G-BWEF	SNCAN Stampe SV-4C (Gipsy Major 10)	208	G-BOVL N20SV/F-BHES/F-BBLC	13. 5.93	A.J.White t/a Acebell BWEF Syndicate	Redhill	14.12.00
G-BWEG	Europa Avn Europa PFA/247-12600 (Rotax 912UL)			4. 4.95	B.A.Selmes & R.J.Marsh t/a Wessex Europa Group	Weston Zoyland	9. 5.00P
G-BWEH	HOAC DV-20 Katana	20123		19. 6.95	Diamond Aircraft Industries GmbH	Bristol	19. 7.01T
G-BWEL	Sky 200-24 HAFB	003		27. 6.95	M.W.A.Shemilt t/a H-O-T Air Balloons	Henley-on-Thames	9. 5.00T
G-BWEM	VS.358 Seafire L.III		IAC.157 RX168	28. 6.95	C.J.Warrilow & S.W.Atkins		

(This project starte life with the late Charles Church and Dick Melton's "resurrection-line" at Winchester
followed by a brief spell with Hull Aero in Norfolk. Chris Warrilow eventually decided to abandon the Mk Vc
in favour of a Seafire Mk III configuration. Although the fuselage is self evidently new build, the origin of
some parts (even if used only as a reference/pattern) is the last of 12 Westland built Seafires Mk Vc which was
allocated serial RX168 and on RN charge 20.1.45. This was converted by Vickers-Supermarine for the Irish Air Corps
by removal of all naval equipmentand f/f 12.9.47 as a Mk Vc. It was delivered IAC serial 157 to Baldonnel
27.9.47 & WFU 27.10.53 after which it moved to Dublin Technicial Institute, Bolton Street and was broken up in
1962/63. Presumably some parts survived as the identity was regd 28.6.95 as G-BWEM to the present owners.
Major rework is necessary to correct earlier build attempts. As at 8.99 the project was with AeroFab Restorations
Bourne Park, Hurstbourne Tarrant and comprised a partially built fuselage in a jig.)

G-BWEN	Macair Merlin GT (Subaru EA81) 050194 & PFA/208A-12859			20. 6.95	B.W.Davies Lower Mountpleasant, Chatteris		7.12.95P*
G-BWEO	Lindstrand LBL-14M HAFB	285		23. 6.95	Lindstrand Balloons Ltd	Oswestry	19. 5.00A
G-BWEP	Lindstrand LBL-77M HAFB	286		23. 6.95	Lindstrand Balloons Ltd	Oswestry	19. 5.00A
G-BWER	Lindstrand LBL-14M HAFB	287		23. 6.95	Lindstrand Balloons Ltd	Oswestry	NE(A)
G-BWEU	Reims Cessna F.152 II	1894	EI-BNC N9097Y	15. 6.95	Sky Pro Ltd	Copse Farm, Bourn	6. 8.01T
G-BWEV	Cessna 152 II	152-83182	EI-BVU N47184	28. 6.95	Haimoss Ltd (Wings only noted 8.99)	Old Sarum	23. 9.01T
G-BWEW	Cameron N-105 HAFB	3637		30. 6.95	Unipart Group Ltd t/a Unipart Balloon Club (Unipart titles)	Cowley, Oxon "Unipart 5"	17. 1.00A
G-BWEY	Bensen B.8 PFA G/01-1197			3. 7.95	F.G.Shepherd	Alston, Cumbria	
G-BWEZ	Piper J3C-85 Cub	6021	N29050 NC29050	3. 7.95	J.G.McTaggart t/a PJ L4 Group (As "436021" in US Army c/s)	Cumbernauld	15. 7.00P
G-BWFD	HOAC DV-20 Katana	20127		5. 7.95	Diamond Aircraft Industries GmbH (Weiner Neustadt, Austria)		30. 7.01T
G-BWFE	HOAC DV-20 Katana	20129		5. 7.95	Diamond Aircraft Industries GmbH	Cumbernauld	23. 7.01T
G-BWFG	Robin HR.200/120	293		20. 7.95	Air Caernarfon Ltd	Caernarfon	20. 1.02T
G-BWFH	Europa Avn Europa PFA/247-12842			14. 7.95	B.L.Wratten	Shoreham	20. 4.02T
G-BWFI	HOAC DV-20 Katana	20128		17. 7.95	Diamond Aircraft Industries GmbH	Exeter	12. 8.01T
G-BWFJ	Evans VP-1 (VW1600)	PFA/62-10349		1. 9.78	P.A.West (Stored Old Sarum 5.94)	(Stroud)	27. 1.93P
G-BWFK	Lindstrand LBL-77A HAFB	289		17. 7.95	Virgin Airship & Balloon Co Ltd "Orange"	Telford	24. 8.00A
G-BWFM	Yakovlev Yak-50	781208	NX5224R DDR-WQX/DM-WQX	19. 7.95	Classic Aviation Ltd (Op The Old Flying Machine Co)	Duxford	27. 7.00P
G-BWFN	HAPI Cygnet SF-2A PFA/182-11335			19. 7.95	T.Crawford	Cumbernauld	
G-BWFO	Colomban MC-15 Cri-Cri PFA/133-11253 (JPX PUL-212)			19. 7.95	O.G.Jones	(Llanbedr)	
G-BWFP	IAV-Bacau Yakovlev Yak-52	855503	RA-44501 DOSAAF 43	20. 7.95	M.C.Lee	Liverpool	6.12.00P

(C/n plate shows c/n 855606 ex DOSAAF 61 (blue) - possibly composite)

G-BWFR	Hawker Hunter F.58	41H-697398	J-4031	24. 7.95	The Old Flying Machine Air Museum Co Ltd (As "J-4031")	Scampton	3. 8.99P
G-BWFS	Hawker Hunter F.58	41H-697425	J-4058	24. 7.95	The Old Flying Machine Air Museum Co Ltd (As "J-4058")	Scampton	5. 7.99P
G-BWFT	Hawker Hunter T.8M	41H-695332	XL602	24. 7.95	B.R.Pearson t/a T8M Group (As "XL602")	Exeter	23. 7.99P
G-BWFV	HOAC DV-20 Katana	20132		26. 7.95	HOAC Austria Flugzeugwerk Wiener Neustadt GmbH	Cumbernauld	17. 8.01T
G-BWFX	Europa Avn Europa 38 & PFA/247-12586 (Rotax 912UL)			26. 7.95	A.D.Stewart	Rayne Hall Farm, Rayne	18. 2.00P
G-BWFY	Aerospatiale AS.350B1 Ecureuil	1963	N518R	31. 7.95	PLM Dollar Group Ltd	Inverness	21. 7.01T
G-BWFZ	Murphy Rebel PFA/232-12536 (Lycoming O-235L2C)		G-SAVS	19. 7.95	I.E.Spencer (Damaged landing St Michaels 15.6.99)	St Michaels	13. 5.00P

Regn	Type	C/n	P/I	Date	Owner/operator	Probable Base	CA Expy
G-BWGA*	Lindstrand LBL-105A HAFB	295		2. 8.95	Virgin Airship & Balloon Co Ltd Telford "Asda" (Cancelled 14.5.99 as WFU)		24. 3.97A
G-BWGF	BAC.145 Jet Provost T.5A EEP/JP/989		XW325	10. 8.95	J.W.Cullen Woodford t/a Specialscope Jet Provost Group (As "XW325/E")		20. 7.00P
G-BWGG	Max Holste MH.1521C1 Broussard 20		F-GGKG F-WGKG/Fr mil	10. 7.95	M.J.Burnett Jnr. & R.B.Maalouf Aberdeen (As "315-SQ" in ALAT c/s)		29. 7.01
G-BWGH	Europa Avn Europa PFA/247-12589 (Rotax 912-UL) (Tri-cycle u/c)			23. 8.95	M.H.B.Heathman Exeter t/a Golf Hotel Group		24. 3.00P
G-BWGJ	Chilton DW.1A PFA/225-12615 (Lycoming O-145)			11. 8.95	T.J.Harrison Goodwood (Complete 8.97)		
G-BWGK	Hawker Hunter GA.11 HABL-003032 (Centre fuselage no.confirmed as 41HR HABL 003032)		XE689	15. 8.95	B.J.Pover Exeter (As "XE689/864/VL")		28. 7.99P
G-BWGL	Hawker Hunter T.8C HABL-003086 (Regd with c/n 41H-695946)		XF357	15. 8.95	Mach 2 Enterprises Ltd Exeter		5.11.99P
G-BWGM	Hawker Hunter T.8C HABL-003008 (Regd with c/n 41H-695940)		XE665	15. 8.95	B.J.Pover Exeter (As "XE665/876/VL")		24. 6.98P
G-BWGN	Hawker Hunter T.8C 41H-670689		WT722	15. 8.95	B.J.Pearson t/a T8C Group Exeter (As "WT722/878/VL")		3. 9.97P
G-BWGO	Slingsby T.67M-200 Firefly 2048		SE-LBC	15. 8.95	R.Gray Fairoaks		31. 3.02
G-BWGP	Cameron C-80 HAFB 3631			17. 8.95	P.J. & C.M.Gentle Bristol "London Camera Exchange"		27. 9.99A
G-BWGR	North American TB-25N-NC Mitchell NL9494Z (Regd with c/n 108-30925) 108-34200 44-30925			18. 8.95	Aces High Ltd North Weald (As "151632" in USAF c/s: stored 10.97)		
G-BWGS	BAC.145 Jet Provost T.5A EEP/JP/974		XW310	18. 8.95	Katharina K.Gerstorfer North Weald (As "XW310/37")		24. 2.00P
G-BWGT	Hunting-Percival P.84 Jet Provost T.4 8991M PAC/W/21624 XR679 (Reported as c/n PAC/W/19992)			21. 8.95	R.E.Todd Sandtoft (Op The Jet Provost Club)		27. 5.00P
G-BWGU	Cessna 150F 150-62962		EI-CDU N8862G	18. 8.95	W.Davies (Stored 1.97) Cardiff		5. 4.01
G-BWGX	Cameron N-42 HAFB 3633			21. 8.95	Newbury Building Society Newbury		19. 1.00A
G-BWGY	HOAC DV-20 Katana 20134			22. 8.95	HOAC Austria Flugzeugwerk Wiener Neustadt GmbH (Op Plymouth School of Flying) Plymouth		12.10.01T
G-BWGZ	HOAC DV-20 Katana 20135			22. 8.95	HOAC Austria Flugzeugwerk Wiener Neustadt GmbH (Op Plymouth School of Flying) Plymouth		12.10.01T
G-BWHA	Hawker Hurricane IIB 41H/G5/21232 Z5053 (Regd with c/n 41H-G3121232) (Soviet AF)/Z5053			23. 8.95	Historic Flying Ltd Audley End (On rebuild 8.95 to be "Z5252/GO-B")		
G-BWHB	Cameron O-65 HAFB 2759			24. 8.95	G.Aimo Mondovi, Italy		21. 6.00A
G-BWHC	Cameron N-77 HAFB 3647			25. 8.95	R.B.Craik Northampton		30. 7.00A
G-BWHD	Lindstrand LBL-31A HAFB 292			29. 8.95	J.C.E.Price Portadown t/a Army Air Corps Balloon Club		22. 9.97A
G-BWHF	PA-31-325 Navajo C/R 31-7612076		F-GECA D-IBIS/N59862	7. 9.85	Awyr Cymru Cyf Welshpool		31.10.02T
G-BWHG	Cameron N-65 HAFB 3619			7. 9.95	Coffee Nannini SRL Siena, Italy		4.10.98A
G-BWHH	PA-18-135 (L-21B-PI) Super Cub (Frame No.18-3789) 18-3605		PH-KNA R.Neth AF R-115/54-2405	9. 8.95	J.W.McLeod Beccles (As "44" in US Army c/s)		18. 2.02
G-BWHI	DHC.1 Chipmunk 22A C1-0637		WK624	8. 9.95	N.E.M.Clare Duxford (As "WK624/M")		9. 9.01T
	(It is possible the bulk of WK624/M was used in the rebuild of G-AOSY at Duxford during 1998/99)						
G-BWHJ	CFM Starstreak Shadow SA-II (Rotax 618) K.269 & PFA/206-12907			12. 9.95	N.Irwin (Castle Martyr, Co.Cork)		28. 4.98P
G-BWHK	Rans S-6-116 Coyote II (Nose-wheel u/c) (Rotax 582) 0695-834 & PFA/204A-12908			15. 9.95	M.Knowles Lane Green Farm, Alveley, Bridgnorth (Damaged Little Green Farm 5.5.99)		1.11.99P
G-BWHM	Sky 140-24 HAFB 006			18. 9.95	C.J.S.Limon (London NW1)		13. 5.99T
G-BWHP	CASA I-131E Jungmann 2109		E3B-513	18. 8.95	J.F.Hopkins Watchford Farm, Yarcombe (As "S4+A07" in Luftwaffe c/s)		16. 7.00P
G-BWHR	Tipsy T.66 Nipper Srs.1 PFA/25-12843		(OO-KAM) OO-69	19. 9.95	L.R.Marnef (Koningshooikt, Belgium)		
	(Composite homebuild of original Fairey built c/n 29 & 71)						
G-BWHS	Rotary Air Force RAF.2000 (Sabaru EA82) PFA G/13-1253			25. 9.95	V.G.Freke Henstridge		9.11.00P
G-BWHU	Westland Scout AH.1 F.9517		XR595	27. 9.95	N.J.F.Boston Plymouth (As "XR595/M" in Army c/s)		27. 1.00P
G-BWHV	Denney Kitfox mk.2 PFA/172-11857			28. 9.95	A.C.Dove Headcorn		11.12.99P
	(Noted on trailer 10.99 on A264 near Copthorne, Crawley heading East)						
G-BWHW	Cameron A-180 HAFB 3634			29. 9.95	Societe Bombard SARL Meursanges, France		3.10.99A
G-BWHY	Robinson R-22 0098		N90366	24. 3.87	Helicentre Ltd Liverpool		9. 6.02T
G-BWIA	Rans S-10 Sakota PFA/194-12044			15. 9.95	P.A.Beck Cambridge		1. 4.99P

Regn	Type	C/n	P/I	Date	Owner/operator	Probable Base	CA Expy
G-BWIB	Scottish Avn Bulldog 120/122	G-103		10.10.95	D.J.T.John t/a Aerofab Restorations		
		BH120/227	Ghana AF		Bourne Park, Hurstbourne Tarrant		AC
	(Being prepared for US owner with RAF Bulldog c/s with pseudo-serial "514XX" 8.99)						
G-BWID	Druine D.31 Turbulent	201	F-PHFR	16.10.95	A.M.Turney	(Tring)	20.10.00P
G-BWII	Cessna 150G	150-65308	N4008J	22. 9.95	J.D.G.Hicks Beeches Farm, South Scarle		10. 2.02
			(G-BSKB)/N4008J				
G-BWIJ	Europa Avn Europa	PFA/247-12513		19.10.95	R.Lloyd	Gloucestershire	
					(Noted 9.99)		
G-BWIK	DH.82A Tiger Moth	86417	7015M	20.10.95	B.J.Ellis	Little Gransden	
			NL985		(On rebuild as "NL985")		
G-BWIL	Rans S-10 Sakota		G-WIEN	4.10.95	J.C.Longmore	Netherthorpe	24.10.00P
	(Rotax 582) 1089-065 & PFA/194-11770						
G-BWIP	Cameron N-90 HAFB	3668		20.10.95	Noble Adventures Ltd	Bristol	27.10.96A
G-BWIR	Dornier 328-100	3023	D-CDXF	18.10.95	Suckling Airways (Norwich) Ltd Cambridge		19.10.00T
			N328DA/D-CDHH		t/a Scot Airways		
G-BWIT	QAC Quickie 1	484	N4482Z	21. 9.95	D.E., M.S. & I.E.Johnson	Coventry	31.10.00P
	(Rotax 503)				(Damaged nr Coventry 12.10.97)		
G-BWIU	Hawker Hunter F.58	41H-691770	J-4021	26.10.95	Classic Aviation Ltd	Scampton	24. 2.99P
	(Reported as c/n 41H/694926)				(As "XG232" in RAF c/s)		
G-BWIV	Europa Avn Europa			27.10.95	T.G.Ledbury	White Waltham	9. 9.99P
	(Rotax 912UL) 210 & PFA/247-12871						
G-BWIW	Sky 180-24 HAFB	008		1.11.95	G.D. & L.Fitzpatrick	Thame	25. 6.00T
G-BWIX	Sky 120-24 HAFB	009		31.10.95	J.M.Percival "Mayfly III"	Loughborough	26. 5.00
G-BWIZ*	Quickie Tri-Q 200	PFA/94-12330		21. 8.95	B.J.Cain	(Stanford-le-Hope)	23. 6.98P
	(Continental O-200-A)				(Cancelled by CAA 8.5.99)		
G-BWJB	Thunder Ax8-105 HAFB	197		15. 6.79	Justerini & Brooks Ltd	London SW1	14. 1.88A
					"Whisky J & B"		
G-BWJC	Cameron N-65 HAFB	3754		3.11.95	Cameron Balloons Ltd	Bristol	8. 3.00
					"Coral Draw"		
G-BWJE*	Sky 105-24 HAFB	010		3.11.95	Sky Balloons Ltd	Wrexham	13.11.96A
					(Cancelled by CAA 26.11.99)		
G-BWJG	Mooney M.20J (201MSE)	24-3319	N1083P	7.11.95	Samic Ltd	Elstree	4. 2.02
G-BWJH	Europa Avn Europa	PFA/247-12643		10.11.95	A.R.D. & J.A.S.T.Hood	Sywell	24. 5.00P
	(Rotax 912UL)						
G-BWJI	Cameron V-90 HAFB	3727		13.11.95	Calarel Developments Ltd Chipping Camden		24. 7.00A
G-BWJK	Rotorway Executive 152	CWT.1	G-OKIT	24.10.95	B.Singh	(Huddersfield)	
	(RW152)						
G-BWJM	Bristol M.1C rep	NAW-2		23.11.95	The Shuttleworth Trust	Old Warden	AC
					(As "C4918" in 72 Sqn c/s)		
G-BWJN	Montgomerie-Bensen B.8MR			16.11.95	M.G.Mee	Carlisle	8. 9.00P
	(Rotax 582)	PFA G/01-1262					
G-BWJP	Cessna 172C	172-49424	N1824Y	21.11.95	Heron Air Services Ltd	(Bournemouth)	
G-BWJR	Sky 120-24 HAFB	007		22.11.95	W.J.Brogan	Steiermark, Austria	21.12.96
					"Filzmooser"		
G-BWJT	Yakovlev Yak-50	812003	RA-01385	23.11.95	M.G.Jefferies	Little Gransden	13. 5.00P
			DOSAAF 50		(As "01385")		
G-BWJW	Westland Scout AH.1	F.9705	XV130	29.11.95	C.L.Holdsworth	Redhill	18.11.00P
					(As "XV130/R" in 666 Sqdn c/s)		
G-BWJY	DHC.1 Chipmunk 22	C1/0519	WG469	5.12.95	K.J.Thompson (As "WG469")	Newtownards	14.10.99
G-BWJZ	DHC.1 Chipmunk 22	C1/0653	WK638	23.11.95	J.Zemlik (As "WK638/83")	Breighton	17. 1.02
G-BWKB	Hawker Hunter F.58	41H-697448	J-4081	12.10.95	Classic Aviation Ltd	Bournemouth	AC
					(As "J-4081": noted 8.99)		
G-BWKD	Cameron O-120 HAFB	3773		8.12.95	K.E. & L.J.Viney "Rainbow"	Olney, Bucks	30.11.99T
G-BWKE	Cameron AS-105GD Hot Air Airship			8.12.95	Gefa-Flug GmbH	Aachen, Germany	11. 2.00A
		3685					
G-BWKF	Cameron N-105 HAFB	3736		8.12.95	R.M.M.Botti	Grosseto, Italy	23. 1.99A
G-BWKG	Europa Avn Europa	PFA/247-12451		28.11.95	T.C.Jackson	(Sheffield)	
					(Cf/f 26.8.99)		
G-BWKJ	Rans S-7 Courier	PFA/218-12918		14.12.95	J.P.Kovacs	Insch	28. 7.00P
	(Verner SVS1400)						
G-BWKK	Auster AOP.9	AUS.166 & B5/10/165	XP279	30. 7.79	C.A.Davis & D.R.White	Popham	1. 8.96P
					(As "XP279" in Army c/s)		
G-BWKR	Sky 90-24 HAFB	014		18.12.95	Beverley Drawbridge	Cranbrook	1. 3.00T
G-BWKT	Stephens Akro Lazer	PFA/123-11421		19.12.95	P.D.Begley	Sywell	
G-BWKU	Cameron A-250 HAFB	3730		21.12.95	Balloon School (Intl) Ltd	Petworth	27. 9.99T
					t/a British School of Ballooning		
G-BWKV	Cameron V-77 HAFB	3780		27.12.95	Poppies (UK) Ltd		
						Wootton Fitzpaine, Dorset	16. 3.00A
G-BWKW	Thunder Ax8-90 HAFB	3770		28.12.95	Venice Simplon Orient Express Ltd		
					"Road to Mandalay"	Frinton-on-Sea	9. 1.97A

Regn	Type	C/n	P/I	Date	Owner/operator	Probable Base	CA Expy
G-BWKX	Cameron A-250 HAFB	3731		2. 1.96	Balloon School (International) Ltd		
					t/a Hot Airlines	Petworth	27. 9.99T
G-BWKZ	Lindstrand LBL-77A HAFB	340		21.12.95	Lambert Smith Hampton Group Ltd		
						Streatley, Berks	14. 1.00A
G-BWLA	Lindstrand LBL-69A HAFB	339		3. 1.96	Virgin Airship & Balloon Co Ltd		
						Telford	26. 4.00A
G-BWLD	Cameron O-120 HAFB	3774		16. 1.96	D. & P.Pedri & C.Nicolodi		
						Villalagarina, Italy	22. 1.00A
G-BWLE	Bell 212	31225	N4247M	5. 1.96	Bristow Helicopters Ltd		
			SU-CAA			AAC Middle Wallop	9. 9.00A
G-BWLF	Cessna 404 Titan II	404-0414	G-BNXS	26.10.94	P.Maden & M Evans	Fairoaks	19. 3.00
			HKG-4/(N8799K)		t/a Nor Leasing		
G-BWLH	Lindstrand HS-110 Hot Air Airship			10. 1.96	J.A.Cooper	Ivybridge	14. 4.98A
		331			t/a Ramdon International		
G-BWLJ	Taylorcraft DCO-65	0-4331	C-GUSA	16. 1.96	C.Evans	(Ipswich)	27. 6.00P
			(ex)				
G-BWLL	Murphy Rebel	PFA/232-12499		22. 1.96	F.W.Parker	(Richmond, N.Yorks)	16. 7.00P
	(Lycoming O-235)						
G-BWLM	Sky 65-24 HAFB	015		24. 1.96	W.J.Brogan	Steiermark, Austria	5. 2.97
					t/a Dachstein Tauern Balloons KG "Innsbruck"		
G-BWLN	Cameron O-84 HAFB	3737		24. 1.96	Reggiana Riduttori SRL		
						S.Polo d'Enza, Italy	21. 6.00A
G-BWLP	HOAC DV-20 Katana	20141	OE-UDV	6. 2.96	HOAC Austria Wiener Neustadt GmbH		
						Woodford	13. 3.99T
G-BWLR	Max Holste MH.1521C1 Broussard	185	F-GGKJ	25. 1.96	Chicory Crops Ltd	Sywell	4. 2.00
			F-WGKJ/French AF		(As "185/44-CA" in French AF c/s)		
G-BWLS	HOAC DV-20 Katana	20142	OE-UHK	6. 2.96	HOAC Austria Wiener Neustadt GmbH		
						Sandtoft	13. 3.99T
G-BWLT	HOAC DV-20 Katana	20149		6. 2.96	HOAC Austria Wiener Neustadt GmbH		
						Woodford	25. 3.99T
G-BWLV	HOAC DV-20 Katana	20151		6. 2.96	HOAC Austria Wiener Neustadt GmbH		
						Woodford	16. 6.02T
G-BWLW	Light Aero Avid Speed Wing mk.4			26. 1.96	P.C. & Susan A.Creswick	Weston Zoyland	
		PFA/189-12763					
G-BWLX	Westland Scout AH.1	F.9709	XV134	29.12.95	R.E.Dagless	Yaxham, Dereham	9.11.99P
					(As "XV134" in AAC c/s)		
G-BWLY	Rotorway Exec 90	5142		11. 1.93	P.W. & I.P.Bewley	Ley Farm, Chirk	8. 2.00P
	(RI 162)						
G-BWMA	Colt 105A HAFB	1853		31.10.90	C.C.Duppa-Miller	Warwick	5. 9.97A
G-BWMB	Jodel D.119	77-1492	F-BGMA	17. 2.78	C.Hughes	Finmere	19. 5.00P
	(Original F-BGMA c/n 77 became F-PHQH and was rebuilt as a Larrieu JL.2; this is presumed to be a rebuild						
	using some components of c/n 77 plus newly built c/n 1492)						
G-BWMC	Cessna 182P Skylane II	182-63117	N5462J	30. 1.96	P.F.N.Burrow & E.N.Skinner		
			G-BWMC/OO-RGM			Trenchard Farm, Eggesford	3. 7.00
					t/a Eggesford Eagles Flying Group		
G-BWMD	Enstrom 480	5013		5. 2.96	Southern Air Ltd	Shoreham	8. 7.02T
G-BWMF	Gloster Meteor T.7	G5/356460	7917M	15.12.95	C.C.Rhodes	Yatesbury	
			WA591		t/a Meteor Flight (Yatesbury) (On rebuild 3.96)		
G-BWMG	Aerospatiale AS.332L Super Puma	2046	OY-HMG	1. 2.96	Bristow Helicopters Ltd	Aberdeen	24. 6.00T
					"Catterline"		
G-BWMH	Lindstrand LBL-77B HAFB	152		7. 2.96	J.W.Hole	Much Wenlock	17. 7.99A
G-BWMI	PA-28RT-201T Turbo Arrow IV		F-GCTG	31. 1.96	C.E.R.Hewitt & D.H.Saunders		
		28R-8031131	N9571N			Poplar Hall Farm, Elmsett	7.11.02
G-BWMJ	Nieuport Scout 17/23 rep			8. 2.96	R.Gauld-Galliers & Lisa J.Day	Popham	22. 7.00P
	(Continental A75)	PFA/121-12351			(As "B3459/2" in RFC c/s)		
G-BWMK	DH.82A Tiger Moth	84483	T8191	9. 2.96	Schneider Trophy Ltd	Welshpool	AC
					(As "T8191")		
G-BWML	Cameron A-275 HAFB	3725		12. 2.96	A.J.Street	Exeter	24. 8.00T
					(Exeter Balloons titles)		
G-BWMN	Rans S-7 Courier	PFA/218-12446		14. 2.96	G.J.Knee & G.Keyser	Turweston	23. 3.00P
	(Rotax 912UL)				(Damaged Shobdon 24.4.99)		
G-BWMO	Oldfield Baby Lakes	JAL.3	G-CIII	14. 2.96	P.J.Tanulak	Sleap	17. 2.00P
	(Continental C85)		N11JL				
G-BWMS	DH.82A Tiger Moth	82712	OO-EVJ	14. 2.96	Foundation Early Birds		
			T-29/R4771			Lelystad, The Netherlands	
G-BWMU	Cameron Monster Truck 105SS HAFB			20. 2.96	Cameron Balloons Ltd	(Canada)	17. 5.00A
		3607			"Skycrusher"		
G-BWMV	Colt AS-105 mk.II Hot Air Airship			22. 2.96	D.Stuber	Bad Krenznach, Germany	27. 4.00A
		3775					
G-BWMX	DHC.1 Chipmunk 22	C1/0481	WG407	19. 2.96	Wendy H.Sanaghan	Spanhoe	2. 4.02
					(As "WG407/67")		

Regn	Type	C/n	P/I	Date	Owner/operator	Probable Base	CA Expy
G-BWMY	Cameron Bradford & Bingley 90SS HAFB	3808		23. 2.96	L.V.Mastis	(Berkeley)	20.4.00A
G-BWNB	Cessna 152 II	152-80051	N757WA	23. 8.96	Galair International Ltd	Wellesbourne Mountford	30. 9.02T
G-BWNC	Cessna 152 II	152-84415	N6487L	23. 8.96	Galair International Ltd	Wellesbourne Mountford	24.11.02T
G-BWND	Cessna 152 II	152-85905	N95493	23. 8.96	Galair International Ltd, M.R.Galiffe & G.Davis	Wellesbourne Mountford	21. 9.02T
G-BWNF	PBN BN-2T Turbine Islander	2296		28. 2.96	Britten-Norman Ltd	Bembridge	
G-BWNG	PBN BN-2B-20 Islander	2297		28. 2.96	Britten-Norman Ltd	Bembridge	AC
G-BWNH	Cameron A-375 HAFB	3553		28. 2.96	Noble Adventures Ltd	Bristol	12. 5.97A
G-BWNI	PA-24-180 Comanche	24-136	N5123P	15. 2.96	T.D.Cooper & D.F.Hurn	Popham	6. 7.02
G-BWNJ	Hughes 269C	86-0528	N42LW N27RD/N7458F	29. 2.96	L.R.Fenwick Long Fosse House, Beelsby, Grimsby		12. 6.02
G-BWNK	DHC.1 Chipmunk 22	C1/0317	WD390	4. 3.96	B.Whitworth (As "WD390")	Breighton	4. 3.00
G-BWNL	Europa Avn Europa	PFA/247-12675		27. 2.96	H.Smith Morgansfield, Fishburn (Damaged Fishburn 14.12.97)		
G-BWNM	PA-28R-180 Cherokee Arrow	28R-30435	N934BD	5. 3.96	D.Houghton	Croft Farm, Defford	28. 9.02
G-BWNN	Rand-Robinson KR-2	PFA/129-11342		5. 3.96	C.Clark	(Scunthorpe)	
G-BWNO	Cameron 0-90 HAFB	3716		5. 3.96	M.A.Pratt & N.I.Cakebread	Hertford	
G-BWNP	Cameron Club-90 SS HAFB (Club Orange Soft Drink Can shape)	1717	EI-BVQ	6. 3.96	C.J.Davies & P.Spellward	Hope Valley	2. 5.00
G-BWNR	PA-38-112 Tomahawk	38-78A0449	N2361E	6. 3.96	APB Leasing Ltd	Sleap	6. 5.02T
G-BWNS	Cameron 0-90 HAFB	3842		6. 3.96	Smithair Ltd. (Self Assessment Tax titles) "Hector"	Billingshurst	1. 7.00T
G-BWNT	DHC.1 Chipmunk 22	C1/0772	WP901	7. 3.96	R.A.Stafford t/a Three Point Aviation (As "WP901")	East Midlands	19.12.99T
G-BWNU	PA-38-112 Tomahawk	38-78A0334	N9294T	8. 3.96	Rosemary E.Best t/a G-BWNU Group	Kemble	9. 9.02
G-BWNV	PA-38-112 Tomahawk	38-79A1019	N2538P	8. 3.96	C.P.Ebbs t/a CEA Aircraft Leasing	(Dursley)	
G-BWNX	Thunder Ax10-180 Srs.2 HAFB	2352	G-OWBC	2. 1.96	MJN Balloon Management Ltd	Longleat	25. 4.00T
G-BWNY	Aeromot AMT-200 Super Ximango	200-055		11. 6.96	H.G.Nicklin	Woodford	31. 5.02
G-BWNZ	Agusta A.109C	7654		3. 4.96	Anglo Beef Processors Ltd	Shrewsbury	13. 4.02T
G-BWOA	Sky 105-24 HAFB	027		13. 3.96	Akhter Group Holdings plc	Harlow	16. 6.00A
G-BWOB	Luscombe 8F Silvaire	6179	N1552B NC1552B	14. 3.96	P.J.Tanulak & H.T.Law	(Shrewsbury)	
G-BWOD	IAV-Bacau Yakovlev Yak-52	833810	LY-ALY DOSAAF 139	14. 3.96	Insurefast Ltd (As "DOSAAF 139")	Sywell	30. 6.00P
G-BWOE	Yakovlev Yak-3U (Converted from LET Yak C.11)	1701231	(G-BUXZ) NX11SN/(France)/Egyptian AF	14. 3.96	R.G.Hanna (Op The Old Flying Machine Co)	Duxford	AC
G-BWOF	BAC.145 Jet Provost T.5	EEP/JP/955	XW291	18. 3.96	Techair London Ltd	Bournemouth	18. 2.00P
G-BWOH	PA-28-161 Cadet	2841061	D-ENXG N9142S	18. 3.96	Oxford Aviation Services Ltd	Oxford	31. 3.02T
G-BWOI	PA-28-161 Cadet	2841307	D-EJTM N9264N/N9208P	18. 3.96	Oxford Aviation Services Ltd	Oxford	16. 5.02T
G-BWOJ	PA-28-161 Cadet	2841331	D-ESTM N92242/(N123ND)/N92242	18. 3.96	Oxford Aviation Services Ltd	Oxford	11. 4.02T
G-BWOK	Lindstrand LBL-105G HAFB	370		19. 3.96	Lindstrand Balloons Ltd	Oswestry	1. 8.00A
G-BWOL	Hawker Sea Fury FB.11	ES.3617 & 61631	D-CACY G-9-66/WG599	18. 3.96	The Old Flying Machine (Air Museum) Co Ltd (K Weeks)	Catfield/Ludham	
G-BWOM	Cessna 550 Citation II	550-0671	N671EA 9M-TAA/(N6761L)	22. 3.96	Ferron Trading Ltd (Op Aviation Beauport Ltd)	Jersey	18. 4.00
G-BWON	Europa Avn Europa (Rotax 912UL)	PFA/247-12720		29. 1.96	G.T.Birks	White Waltham	16. 8.99P
G-BWOR	PA-18-135 Super Cub (L-18C)	18-2547	OO-WIS OO-HMF/ALAT/52-6229	21. 3.96	C.D.Baird	(Farnham)	23. 7.99
G-BWOS	Bell 212	35074	PNC-189 (Colombian Police)/C-FTIP	22. 3.96	RCR Aviation Ltd	Thruxton	
G-BWOT	Hunting P.84 Jet Provost T.3A (Reported as c/n PAC/W/949267)	PAC/W/10138	XN459	25. 3.96	Quasi Mondi Ltd (As "XN459" in all-red Red Pelicans c/s)	North Weald	14.11.00P
G-BWOU	Hawker Hunter F.58A	HABL.003067	J-4105 G-9-315/A2565/XF303	26. 3.96	The Old Flying Machine (Air Museum) Co Ltd (As "105")	Scampton	20. 1.99P
	(Regd with c/n 41H-003067 ex XF306/7776M/G-9-402 which became J-4133:- G-BWOU may be a composite)						
G-BWOV	Enstrom F-28A	222	N690BR G-BWOV/F-BVRG	26. 3.96	B.H.Austen t/a Austen Associates	Thruxton	16.12.99T
G-BWOW	Cameron N-105 HAFB	3805		31. 1.96	S.J.Colin & A.S.Pinder t/a Skybus Ballooning	Maidstone	25. 3.00T
G-BWOX	DHC.1 Chipmunk 22	C1/0728	WP844	27. 3.96	J.St Clair-Quentin (As "WP844")	Spanhoe	10. 7.00

Regn	Type	C/n	P/I	Date	Owner/operator	Probable Base	CA Expy
G-BWOY	Sky 31-24 HAFB	029		28. 3.96	Virgin Airship & Balloon Co Ltd Telford		5. 4.97A
G-BWOZ	CFM Streak Shadow SA			1. 4.96	N.P.Harding Plaistows, Hemel Hempstead		21. 7.00P
	(Rotax 582) K154SA & PFA/206-12988						
G-BWPA	Cameron A-340 HAFB	3714		29. 3.96	A.A.Brown	Guildford	1. 4.00T
G-BWPB	Cameron V-77 HAFB	3866		1. 4.96	R.H. & N.K.Calvert	Bristol	19. 5.99A
					t/a The Fair Weather Friends Ballooning Co		
G-BWPC	Cameron V-77 HAFB	3867		1. 4.96	Helen Vaughan "Olive"	Tring	20. 6.00A
G-BWPE	Murphy Renegade Spirit UK			2. 4.96	G.Wilson	(Solihull)	
	PFA/188-12791						
G-BWPF	Sky 120-24 HAFB	028		3. 4.96	Computeraid Services Ltd & H. & R.T.Revel		
					Farnborough/High Wycombe		1. 5.02T
					t/a Humbug Balloon Group "Whisper"		
G-BWPG*	Robin HR.200/120B	299		15. 4.96	Air Alba Ltd	Inverness	7. 7.99T
	(Damaged off Cromarty Gap, Nigg Bay 29.10.97 - fuselage stored 6.98)						
G-BWPH	PA-28-181 Cherokee Archer II		N1408H	4. 4.96	J.Maffia	Panshanger	1. 5.02T
	28-7790311						
G-BWPI*	Sky 120-24 HAFB	018		9. 4.96	Sky Balloons Ltd Indio, California, USA		12. 8.99
					"Thunderbird" (Cancelled by CAA 26.11.99)		
G-BWPJ	Steen Skybolt PFA/64-12854			9. 4.96	W.R.Penaluna	(Penzance)	28. 3.00P
	(Continental IO-346)						
G-BWPL	Airtour AH-56 HAFB	011	G-OAFC	19. 3.96	A.S.Newnham	Southampton	
G-BWPM	PBN BN-2T-4R Defender 4000	4007		24. 4.96	Britten-Norman Ltd	Bembridge	
G-BWPP	Sky 105-24 HAFB	031		9. 4.96	P.F.Smart	Basingstoke	17. 7.00A
					t/a The Sarnia Balloon Group "Fourpence"		
G-BWPR	PBN BN-2T-4S Defender 4000	4010		24. 4.96	Pilatus Britten-Norman Ltd	Bembridge	
G-BWPS	CFM Streak Shadow SA			9. 2.96	P.G.A.Sumner		
	(Rotax 618) K275SA & PFA/206-12954				Tower Farm, Woolaston, Wellingborough		4. 8.00P
G-BWPT	Cameron N-90 HAFB	3838		5. 3.96	Workplace Technologies Ltd Huddersfield		1. 5.00A
G-BWPU	PBN BN-2T-4S Defender 4000	4011		24. 4.96	Britten-Norman Ltd	Bembridge	AC
G-BWPV	PBN BN-2T-4S Defender 4000	4012		24. 4.96	Britten-Norman Ltd	Bembridge	AC
G-BWPW	PBN BN-2T-4S Defender 4000	4013		24. 4.96	Britten-Norman Ltd	Bembridge	
G-BWPX	PBN BN-2T-4S Defender 4000	4014		24. 4.96	Britten-Norman Ltd	Bembridge	
G-BWPY	HOAC DV-20 Katana	20158	OE-UDV	10. 6.96	Diamond Aircraft Industries GmbH		
					Weiner Neustadt, Austria		19. 6.99T
G-BWPZ	Cameron N-105 HAFB	3889		19. 4.96	Flying Pictures Ltd "Jaguar" Fairoaks		29. 2.00A
G-BWRA	Sopwith LC-1T Triplane rep		G-PENY	19. 4.96	S.M.Truscott & J.M.Hoblyn (As "N500" in RNAS c/s)		
	(Warner Scarab 165) PFA/21-10035				Watchford Farm, Yarcombe/RNAS Yeovilton		10.11.00P
G-BWRC	Light Aero Avid Hauler mk.4			22. 2.96	B.Williams Chilsfold Farm, Crawley		6. 6.00P
	(Hirth F30) PFA/189-12979						
G-BWRE*	SNCAN Stampe SV-4C	396	D-EJKA(2)	12. 4.96	J M Koch	Sandown	
			F-BDOT/Fr Mil		(As "No.73" in French AF c/s)		
	(Cancelled as WFU 16.7.98: still hangared at Museum 8.99)						
G-BWRJ*	Fokker DR.1 rep	003	D-EFTN	12. 4.96	J M Koch	Sandown	
	(Built J Koch)				(As "425/15" in German AF c/s)		
	(Cancelled as WFU 16.7.98: still hangared at Museum 8.99)						
G-BWRM	Colt 105A HAFB	3734		23. 4.96	N.Charbonnier	Aosta, Italy	25. 1.00A
G-BWRO	Europa Avn Europa PFA/247-12849			22. 4.96	J.G.M.McDiarmid	(Glasgow)	12.11.99P
	(Rotax 912UL)						
G-BWRP	Beechcraft 58 Baron	TH-1737	VR-BVB	23. 4.96	Astra Aviation Ltd	Guernsey	27. 5.02
			N3217H				
G-BWRR	Cessna 182Q Skylane II	182-66660	N95861	29. 3.94	D.O.Halle	(West Bridgford)	13. 7.00T
G-BWRS	SNCAN Stampe SV-4C	437	(N)	24. 4.96	G.P.J.M.Valvekens	(Diest, Belgium)	
			F-BCVQ				
G-BWRT*	Cameron Concept-60 HAFB	3078	EI-BYP	22.10.96	European Balloon Display Co Ltd		
					(Exported 1998)	Great Missenden	X
G-BWRU*	Lindstrand Audi Saloon Car SS HAFB			23. 4.96	Flying Pictures Ltd "Audi" Fairoaks		26. 9.97A
		369			(Cancelled 17.4.99 as WFU)		
G-BWRV	Lindstrand LBL-90A HAFB	371		23. 4.96	Flying Pictures Ltd "Audi" Fairoaks		24. 3.00A
G-BWRW	Sky 220-24 HAFB	032		23. 4.96	Sky Trek Ballooning Ltd Longfield, Kent		14. 5.00T
G-BWRY	Cameron N-105 HAFB	3817		24. 4.96	G.Aimo	Mondovi, Italy	21. 6.00a
G-BWRZ	Lindstrand LBL-105A HAFB	383		26. 4.96	Flying Pictures Ltd "Rover" Fairoaks		10. 3.00A
G-BWSB	Lindstrand LBL-105A HAFB	384		26. 4.96	Flying Pictures Ltd "MG" Fairoaks		10. 3.00A
G-BWSC	PA-38-112 Tomahawk II	38-81A0125	N23203	29. 4.96	APB Leasing Ltd	Welshpool	15. 7.02T
G-BWSD	Campbell Cricket PFA G/03-1216			3. 5.96	R.F.G.Moyle	(Falmouth)	
G-BWSF	Sky 180-24 HAFB	022		10. 5.96	A.Bolger	Salisbury	9. 7.97T
G-BWSG	BAC.145 Jet Provost T.5	EEP/JP/988	XW324	13. 5.96	Not known	North Weald	22. 9.99P
					(As "XW324" in 6FTS c/s)		
G-BWSH	Hunting P.84 Jet Provost T.3A	XN498		13. 5.96	Global Aviation Ltd	Binbrook	7. 6.00P
	PAC/W/10159						
G-BWSI	K & S SA.102.5 Cavalier PFA/01-10624			18. 4.84	B.W.Shaw Wathstow Farm, Newby Wiske		28. 4.00P
	(Lycoming O-235)						

Regn	Type	C/n	P/I	Date	Owner/operator	Probable Base	CA Expy
G-BWSJ	Denney Kitfox mk.3 (Rotax 582)	PFA/172-12204		15. 5.96	J.M.Miller	Swanton Morley	9.12.00P
G-BWSK	Enstrom 280FX	2016	ZK-HIR JA7724	16. 5.96	M.A. & M.Gradwell	Barton	2. 8.02
G-BWSL	Sky 77-24 HAFB	004		16. 5.96	The Balloon Co Ltd	Cheltenham	30. 4.00A
G-BWSN	Denney Kitfox mk.3 (Rotax 582)	PFA/172-12141		16. 5.96	W.J.Forrest	Thatcham	27. 8.00P
G-BWSO	Cameron Apple Sainsbury 90SS HAFB	3915		17. 5.96	Flying Pictures Ltd "Sainsbury's Apple"	Fairoaks	25. 7.00A
G-BWSP	Cameron Carrots Sainsbury 80SS HAFB	3914		17. 5.96	Flying Pictures Ltd "Sainsbury's Carrots"	Fairoaks	12. 7.00A
G-BWST	Sky 200-24 HAFB	036		20. 5.96	S.A.Townley t/a Sky High Leisure Wrexham		4. 8.00T
G-BWSU	Cameron N-105 HAFB	3848		20. 5.96	A.M.Marten "Wonder Bra"	London SW1	23. 9.99A
G-BWSV	IAV-Bacau Yakovlev Yak-52	877601	DOSAAF 43	20. 5.96	P.Traynor	Wellesbourne Mountford	5. 8.00P
G-BWSW*	IAV-Bacau Yakovlev Yak-52	866807	DOSAAF 88	20. 5.96	R.D.Doughton	(Wellington)	
					t/a Doughton Aviation Services (Cancelled as destroyed 26.2.99)		
G-BWSX	PA-28-236 Dakota II	28-7911130	C-FLMJ N2169V	28. 5.96	C. & C.Bowie	Dunkeswell	7. 7.02
G-BWSY	BAe 125 Srs.800B	258201	G-OCCI G-5-699	28. 5.96	British Aerospace Airbus Ltd	Filton	26. 8.00
G-BWSZ	Montgomerie-Bensen B.8MR (Rotax 582)	PFA G/01-1268		14. 5.96	D.Cawkwell	Goole	6. 1.98P
G-BWTA	HOAC DV-20 Katana	20159	OE-UDV	10. 6.96	Diamond Aircraft Industries GmbH Woodford		14.10.02T
G-BWTB	Lindstrand LBL-105A HAFB	374		29. 5.96	Servatruc Ltd	Nottingham	14. 5.00A
G-BWTC	Moravan Zlin Z.242L	0697		2. 8.96	Oxford Aviation Services Ltd	Oxford	17.11.02T
G-BWTD	Moravan Zlin Z.242L	0698		2. 8.96	Oxford Aviation Services Ltd	Oxford	18. 9.02T
G-BWTE	Cameron O-140 HAFB	3885		30. 5.96	R.J. & A.J.Mansfield	Windermere	26. 3.00T
G-BWTF	Lindstrand Bear SS HAFB	375		3. 6.96	Free Enterprise Balloons Ltd "Mr Biddle" East Leroy, MI, USA		15. 3.00A
G-BWTG	DHC.1 Chipmunk 22	C1/0119	WB671	4. 6.96	B.R.Schudel (Epse, The Netherlands)		4. 8.00
					t/a Chipmunk 4 Ever Foundation (As "WB671")		
G-BWTH	Robinson R-22 Beta	1767	HB-XYD N4052R	5. 6.96	Heli Air Ltd	Weston, NI	17. 6.02T
G-BWTJ	Cameron V-77 HAFB	3917		7. 6.96	A.J.Montgomery	Yeovil	25. 7.97A
G-BWTK	Rotary Air Force RAF 2000 GTX-SE (Subaru EJ22)	PFA G/13-1264		7. 6.96	Terrafirma Services Ltd		5. 6.00P
					(Damaged at base 12.7.99) Lamberhurst Farm, Faversham		
G-BWTL	Aerospatiale/Alenia ATR-72-202	441	F-WWLG	7.12.95	CityFlyer Express Ltd (Union Flag c/s)	Gatwick	6.12.01T
G-BWTM	Aerospatiale/Alenia ATR-72-202	470	F-WWED	8. 3.96	CityFlyer Express Ltd (Mountain of the Birds/Benyhone Tartan t/s)	Gatwick	7. 3.02T
G-BWTN	Lindstrand LBL-90A HAFB	357		12. 6.96	Clarks Drainage Ltd	Oakham	6. 7.00A
G-BWTO	DHC.1 Chipmunk 22	C1/0852	WP984	5. 6.96	Skycraft Services Ltd Little Gransden (As "WP984/H")		3. 6.01
G-BWTR	Slingsby T.61F Venture T.2	1881	XZ561	12. 6.96	P.R.Williams	(Brackley)	
G-BWTU	Lindstrand LBL-77A HAFB	376		17. 6.96	Virgin Airship & Balloon Co Ltd Telford "Land Rover"		9. 9.00A
G-BWTW	Mooney M.20C	20-1188	EI-CHI N6955V	5. 6.96	R.C.Volkers	(London SW1)	18.11.02
G-BWTY*	Air Command 532 Elite Two-Seat	PFA G/05-1274		14. 6.96	A.J.Unwin	Kemble	
				(Should be PFA G/04 series ?) (WFU 3.6.97)			
G-BWUA	Campbell Cricket	PFA G/03-1248		17. 6.96	R.T.Lancaster	Ash, Hants	
G-BWUB	PA-18S-135 Super Cub (L-21C) (Regd with c/n 18-3786)	18-3986	N786CS	13. 6.96	Caledonian Seaplanes Ltd	Cumbernauld	23. 6.01T
					G-BWUB/SX-AHB/EI-263/I-EIUO/MM54-2586/54-2586		
G-BWUC*	PA-18S-135 Super Cub (L-21C) (Regd with Frame No.18-3719	18-3569	SX-ASM		Caledonian Seaplanes Ltd	Cumbernauld	
					EI-181/I-EIYB/MM54-2369/54-2369 (Cancelled 23.5.97 to N719CS:		
	dismantled & frame, now covered and carrying registration, is strapped to hangar wall 4.99)						
G-BWUD	Lavochkin La-9	828	(Chinese AF)	14. 6.96	Classic Aviation Ltd	Duxford	
					(Op The Flying Machine Co: dismantled 7.99)		
					(For certfication in New Zealand ?)		
G-BWUE	Hispano HA-1112-M1L	223	N9938 G-AWHK/C4K-102	14. 6.96	R.A.Fleming (On rebuild 12.99)	Breighton	
	(Reported as c/n 172 as 223 became C4K-155)						
G-BWUF	WSK PZL-Mielec Lim-5 (MiG-17F)	1211 1C-1211	(Polish AF)	14. 6.96	Classic Aviation Ltd	Duxford	AC
					(Op The Flying Machine Co; as "1211" in Vietnam c/s)		
G-BWUG	Piper J/5C Cub Cruiser (AE-1)	5-1477	ZK-USN N62073/NC62073/Bu.30274	21. 6.96	W.D.Lincoln (On overhaul 8.97)	Henstridge	
G-BWUH	PA-28-181 Archer III	2843048	N9272E	30. 8.96	R.Paston	Birmingham	7.10.02
G-BWUJ	Rotorway Exec (RW.162F)	6153		2. 7.96	Southern Helicopters Ltd Street Farm, Takeley, Bishops Stortford		30. 6.00P
G-BWUK	Sky 160-24 HAFB	043		2. 7.96	Blagdon Balloons Ltd	Bristol	4. 2.00T

Regn	Type	C/n	P/I	Date	Owner/operator	Probable Base	CA Expy
G-BWUL	Noorduyn AT-16 Harvard IIB	14A-1415	N16NA FT375/43-13116	4. 7.96	Aereo Servizi Bresciana SRL (Montichiari, Italy)		13.10.97
G-BWUM	Sky 105-24 HAFB	038		5. 7.96	P.Stern & F.Kirchberger "Wanninger" Regen/Lam, Germany		16. 7.00
G-BWUN	DHC.1 Chipmunk 22	C1/0253	WD310	5. 7.96	T.Henderson Upper Broyle Farm, Ringmer (As "WD310")		5.11.99
G-BWUP	Europa Avn Europa	PFA/247-12703		3. 7.96	T.J.Harrison	Shotteswell	22.11.99
G-BWUR	Thunder Ax10-210 Srs.2 HAFB	3910		11. 7.96	T.J.Bucknall "Kinetic"	Chester	14. 7.00T
G-BWUS	Sky 65-24 HAFB	040		16. 7.96	N.A.P.Bates	Tunbridge Wells	6. 5.00A
G-BWUT	DHC.1 Chipmunk 22	C1/0918	WZ879	4. 6.96	Aero Vintage Ltd (As "WZ879/73")	Duxford	3.11.99
G-BWUU	Cameron N-90 HAFB	3954		17. 7.96	South Western Electricity plc	Bristol	16. 7.99A
G-BWUV	DHC.1 Chipmunk 22A	C1/0655	WK640	18. 7.96	P.Ray (As "WK640/C")	Bagby	27. 7.01
G-BWUW	BAC.145 Jet Provost T.5A	EEP/JP/1045	XW423	18. 7.96	Tindon Ltd (Little Snoring) (As "XW423/14")		11.11.00P
G-BWUZ	Campbell Cricket (Rotax 582)	PFA G/03-1267		24. 6.96	M.A.Concannon	Birmingham	20. 6.00P
G-BWVB	Pietenpol Aircamper (Continental O-200-A)	PFA/47-11777		24. 7.96	M.J.Whatley	White Waltham	16.11.00P
G-BWVC	Jodel D.18	PFA/169-11331		29. 7.96	R.W.J. Cripps	(Spondon, Derby)	
G-BWVE	Bell 206B JetRanger III	3394	G-BOSX N20681	1. 9.88	Elialfa SRL (Ozzano Emilia, Italy)		5. 9.00T
G-BWVF	Pietenpol Aircamper	PFA/47-11936		5. 8.96	R.M.Sharphouse	(Thirsk)	
G-BWVG	Robin HR.200/120B	308		16. 7.96	Air Caernarfon Ltd	Caernarfon	27.10.02T
G-BWVH	Robinson R-44 Astro	0072	SX-HDE (D-HBBT)	10. 9.96	Twinlite Developments Ltd	(Dublin)	30. 9.02T
G-BWVI	Stern ST.80 Balade	PFA/166-11190		7. 8.96	P.E.Barker Great Barford, Bedford		AC
G-BWVL	Cessna 150M	150-77229	N50NA N63286	13. 8.96	Dualworld Ltd	Kemble	23.10.99T
G-BWVM	Colt AA-1050 Gas Free Balloon	3806		14. 8.96	D.A.Gleed Langley, BC, Canada		23. 8.00A
G-BWVN	Whittaker MW.7	PFA/171-11839		19. 8.96	J.W.May	RAF Bicester	
G-BWVP*	Sky 160-24 HAFB	044		21. 8.96	Sky Balloons Ltd Wrexham (Cancelled by CAA 26.11.99)		NE(P)
G-BWVR	IAV-Bacau Yakovlev Yak-52	878202	LY-AKQ DOSAAF 134	27. 8.96	Thunderer Ltd (As "52")	Barton	8. 2.00P
G-BWVS	Europa Avn Europa	PFA/247-12686		28. 8.96	D.R.Bishop	Popham	31. 3.00P
G-BWVT	DHA.82A Tiger Moth	1039	N1350 VH-SNZ/A17-604/VH-AIN/A17-604	27. 8.96	R.Jewitt	(Horley)	
G-BWVU	Cameron O-90 HAFB	3204		28. 8.96	J.Atkinson	Dorchester	26. 1.99A
G-BWVV	Jodel D.18 (VW 1834)	PFA/169-12699		29. 8.96	P.Cooper	Sherburn in Elmet	22.11.00P
G-BWVX	IAV-Bacau Yakovlev Yak-52	866811	LY-AOJ DOSAAF 92	16. 9.96	C.J.M.Van Den Broek & R.V.De Vries Hoevenen, The Netherlands		24.11.00P
G-BWVY	DHC.1 Chipmunk 22A	C1/0766	WP896	3. 9.96	P.W.Portelli Audley End (As "WP896/M")		AC
G-BWVZ	DHC.1 Chipmunk 22	C1/0614	WK590	16. 7.96	D.Campion St.Ghislain, Belgium (As "WK590/69")		18.10.02
G-BWWA	Ultravia Pelican Club GS (Rotax 912UL)	PFA/165-12242		6. 9.96	T.J.Franklin & D.S.Simpson	(Hitchin)	22.12.99P
G-BWWB	Europa Avn Europa (Rotax 912UL)	PFA/247-12670		9. 9.96	M.G.Dolphin RAF Brize Norton "The Wheelbarrow"		14. 2.00P
G-BWWC	DH.104 Dove 7	04498	XM223	14. 6.96	Cormack (Aircraft Services) Ltd Coventry (For Air Atlantique 1.00 as "XM223")		AC
G-BWWE	Lindstrand LBL-90A HAFB	410		11. 9.96	B.J.Newman Rushden, Northants		NE(T)
G-BWWF	Cessna 185A Skywagon	185-0240	N4893K G-BWWF/9J-MCK/5Y-BBG/ET-ACI/N4040Y	13. 9.96	S M C Harvey	(Dulverton)	
G-BWWG	Socata Rallye 235E Gabier	13121	EI-BIF HB-EYT/N344RA	23.10.96	J.McEleney	Bumcrana, Ireland	3. 4.00
G-BWWH	Yakovlev Yak-50	853010	LY-ABL LY-XNI/DOSAAF	16. 9.96	De Cadenet Motor Racing Ltd (As "853010") Little Gransden		26. 4.00P
G-BWWI	Aerospatiale AS.332L Super Puma	2040	OY-HMF (G-TIGT)	11. 9.96	Bristow Helicopters Ltd Aberdeen "Johnshaven"		8.11.02T
G-BWWJ	Hughes 269C (300C)	113-0256	G-BMYZ N8996F	25. 2.87	Dave Nieman Toys Ltd Milton Common, Oxon		28.10.96
G-BWWK	Hawker Nimrod I (RR Kestrel)	41H-43617	S1581	13. 9.96	Historic Aircraft Collection Ltd (Jersey) (On rebuild as "S1581")		
G-BWWL	Colt Flying Egg SS HAFB	1813	JA-A0513	19. 9.96	L.V.Mastis West Bloomfield, Mi., USA		11.11.97A
G-BWWN	Isaacs Fury II	PFA/11-10957		23. 9.96	D.H.Pattison Draycott Farm, Chiseldon (As "K8303/D")		2 .6.00P
G-BWWP	Rans S-6-116 Coyote II (Rotax 582)	PFA/204A-12648		2.10.96	S.A.Beddus Cherry Tree Farm, Monewden		20. 8.99P

Regn	Type	C/n	P/I	Date	Owner/operator	Probable Base	CA Expy
G-BWWS	Rotary Air Force RAF 2000 GTX-SE PFA G/13-1277			7.10.96	G.R.Williams (Blackwood, Gwent)		
G-BWWT	Dornier 328-110	3022	D-CDXO VT-VIG/D-CDHG	12.11.96	Suckling Airways (Luton) Ltd t/a Scot Airways	Luton	12.11.00T
G-BWWU	PA-22-150 Tri-Pacer (Tail-wheel conversion with STOL turned down wing-tips)	22-5002	N7139D	9.10.96	Aerocars Ltd	Filton	26. 5.02
G-BWWW	BAe Jetstream 3102	614	G-31-614	18. 7.83	British Aerospace (Operations) Ltd	Warton	23.10.99A
G-BWWX	Yakovlev Yak-50	853003	LY-AOI DOSAAF	11.10.96	J.L.Pfundt Hilversum, The Netherlands		21.11.00P
G-BWWY	Lindstrand LBL-105A HAFB	411		14.10.96	M.J.Smith	Westow, York	2. 5.00T
G-BWWZ	Denney Kitfox mk.3 PFA/172-13054			15.10.96	K.M.Allan	Eshott	
G-BWXA	Slingsby T.67M-260 Firefly	2236		19. 3.96	Hunting Aviation Ltd	RAF Barkston Heath	27. 6.02T
G-BWXB	Slingsby T.67M-260 Firefly	2237		19. 3.96	Hunting Aviation Ltd	RAF Barkston Heath	17. 7.02T
G-BWXC	Slingsby T.67M-260 Firefly	2238		19. 3.96	Hunting Aviation Ltd	RAF Barkston Heath	1. 8.02T
G-BWXD	Slingsby T.67M-260 Firefly	2239		19. 3.96	Hunting Aviation Ltd	RAF Barkston Heath	15. 8.02T
G-BWXE	Slingsby T.67M-260 Firefly	2240		19. 3.96	Hunting Aviation Ltd	RAF Barkston Heath	28. 8.02T
G-BWXF	Slingsby T.67M-260 Firefly	2241		19. 3.96	Hunting Aviation Ltd	RAF Barkston Heath	5. 9.02T
G-BWXG	Slingsby T.67M-260 Firefly	2242		19. 3.96	Hunting Aviation Ltd	RAF Barkston Heath	23. 9.02T
G-BWXH	Slingsby T.67M-260 Firefly	2243		19. 3.96	Hunting Aviation Ltd	RAF Barkston Heath	20.10.02T
G-BWXI	Slingsby T.67M-260 Firefly	2244		19. 3.96	Hunting Aviation Ltd	RAF Barkston Heath	7.10.02T
G-BWXJ	Slingsby T.67M-260 Firefly	2245		19. 3.96	Hunting Aviation Ltd	RAF Barkston Heath	28.10.02T
G-BWXK	Slingsby T.67M-260 Firefly	2246		19. 3.96	Hunting Aviation Ltd	RAF Barkston Heath	5.11.02T
G-BWXL	Slingsby T.67M-260 Firefly	2247		19. 3.96	Hunting Aviation Ltd	RAF Barkston Heath	20.11.02T
G-BWXM	Slingsby T.67M-260 Firefly	2248		19. 3.96	Hunting Aviation Ltd	RAF Barkston Heath	26.11.02T
G-BWXN	Slingsby T.67M-260 Firefly	2249		19. 3.96	Hunting Aviation Ltd	RAF Barkston Heath	4.12.02T
G-BWXO	Slingsby T.67M-260 Firefly	2250		19. 3.96	Hunting Aviation Ltd	RAF Barkston Heath	15.12.99T
G-BWXP	Slingsby T.67M-260 Firefly	2251		19. 3.96	Hunting Aviation Ltd	RAF Barkston Heath	8. 1.00T
G-BWXR	Slingsby T.67M-260 Firefly	2252		19. 3.96	Hunting Aviation Ltd	RAF Barkston Heath	13. 1.00T
G-BWXS	Slingsby T.67M-260 Firefly	2253		19. 3.96	Hunting Aviation Ltd	RAF Barkston Heath	29. 1.03T
G-BWXT	Slingsby T.67M-260 Firefly	2254		19. 3.96	Hunting Aviation Ltd	RAF Barkston Heath	5. 2.00T
G-BWXU	Slingsby T.67M-260 Firefly	2255		19. 3.96	Hunting Aviation Ltd	RAF Barkston Heath	11. 2.00T
G-BWXV	Slingsby T.67M-260 Firefly	2256		19. 3.96	Hunting Aviation Ltd	RAF Barkston Heath	20. 2.00T
G-BWXW	Slingsby T.67M-260 Firefly	2257		19. 3.96	Hunting Aviation Ltd	RAF Barkston Heath	27. 2.00T
G-BWXX	Slingsby T.67M-260 Firefly	2258		19. 3.96	Hunting Aviation Ltd	RAF Barkston Heath	11. 3.00T
G-BWXY	Slingsby T.67M-260 Firefly	2259		19. 3.96	Hunting Aviation Ltd	RAF Barkston Heath	13. 3.00T
G-BWXZ	Slingsby T.67M-260 Firefly	2260		19. 3.96	Hunting Aviation Ltd	RAF Barkston Heath	26. 3.00T
G-BWYB	PA-28-160 Cherokee	28-263	N6374A G-BWYB/6Y-JLO/6Y-JCH/VP-JCH	16. 9.96	I.M.Latiff	Little Staughton	
G-BWYC	Cameron N-90 HAFB	3994		17.10.96	Cameron Balloons Ltd	Bristol	30. 4.00A
G-BWYD	Europa Avn Europa (Rotax 912UL)	PFA/247-12621		28. 8.96	H.J.Bendiksen	Biggin Hill	12. 7.00P
G-BWYE	Cessna 310R II	310R-1654	F-GBPE (N26369)	6. 9.96	Fraggle Leasing Ltd	Edinburgh	8.12.02T
G-BWYG	Cessna 310R II	310R-1580	F-GBMY (N1820E)	28.10.96	R.F.Jones t/a Kissair Aviation	(London SE10)	18.11.00T
G-BWYH	Cessna 310R II	310R-1640	F-GBPC N2634Y	28.10.96	Fraggle Leasing Ltd	Edinburgh	31. 3.00T
G-BWYI	Denney Kitfox Mk.3 (Rotax 912)	PFA/172-12143		30.10.96	J.Adamson Beeches Farm, South Scarle		31. 3.00P
G-BWYK	Yakovlev Yak-50	812004	RA-01386 DOSAAF 51	9. 8.96	Titan Airways Ltd	North Weald	20.12.00P
G-BWYL	Cameron A-200 HAFB	3996		30. 9.96	J.M.Stables t/a Aire Valley Balloons	Knaresborough	12. 3.00T
G-BWYM	HOAC DV-20 Katana	20067	D-EWAU	27. 1.97	Diamond Aircraft Industries GmbH	Gloucestershire	16. 2.00T
G-BWYN	Cameron O-77 HAFB	1162	G-ODER	13.11.96	W.H.Morgan "Hobo"	Swansea	21. 6.97A
G-BWYO	Sequoia Falco F.8L	PFA/100-10920		7.11.96	N.G.Abbott & J.Copeland	Flamstone Park	1. 4.00P
G-BWYP	Sky 56-24 HAFB	053		8.11.96	S.A.Townley t/a Sky High Leisure	Wrexham	18. 3.00A
G-BWYR	Rans S-6-116 Coyote II (Rotax 912-UL)	PFA/204A-13058		8.11.96	Stephen Palmer Ltd	Swinford, Rugby	3. 5.00P
G-BWYS	Cameron O-120 HAFB	3997		30. 9.96	J.M.Stables t/a Aire Valley Balloons	Knaresborough	12. 3.00T
G-BWYU	Sky 120-24 HAFB	052		13.11.96	R.J.Darkin t/a Bramley Park Garages	St.Ives, Cambs	28. 2.99A
G-BWYW	PBN BN-2B-20 Islander	2293		2.12.96	Britten-Norman Ltd (to PK-?)	Bembridge	AC
G-BWYX	PBN BN-2B-20 Islander	2298		2.12.96	Britten-Norman Ltd	Bembridge	AC
G-BWYY	PBN BN-2B-20 Islander	2299		2.12.96	Britten-Norman Ltd	Bembridge	AC
G-BWYZ	PBN BN-2B-20 Islander	2300		2.12.96	Britten-Norman Ltd	Bembridge	AC

Regn	Type	C/n	P/I	Date	Owner/operator	Probable Base	CA Expy
G-BWZA	Europa Avn Europa (Rotax 912UL)	PFA/247-12626		1.11.96	M.C.Costin	Sywell	13. 7.99P
G-BWZD	Light Aero Avid Flyer mk.4	PFA/189-12453		29.11.96	B.Moore	(Keady, Armagh)	
G-BWZE	Hunting Percival P.84 Jet Provost T.3A	XM378 PAC/W/6605		29.11.96	Lorch Airways (UK) Ltd. (As "XM378")	Norwich	1. 6.00P
G-BWZF	PBN BN-2B-20 Islander	2301		12.12.96	Britten-Norman Ltd	Bembridge	AC
G-BWZG	Robin R.2160	311	F-WZZZ	6.11.96	Sherburn Aero Club Ltd	Sherburn in Elmet	4. 3.00T
G-BWZI	Agusta A.109A II	7269	OH-HAD N109AK	29.11.96	P.W.Harris Pendley Farm, Aldbury, Tring t/a Pendley Farm		3. 2.00T
G-BWZJ	Cameron A-250 HAFB	4021		2.12.96	Balloon School (Intl) Ltd t/a Balloon Club of Great Britain	Petworth	5 5.00T
G-BWZK	Cameron A-210 HAFB	4020		2.12.96	Balloon School (Intl) Ltd t/a Balloon Club of Great Britain	Petworth	14.10.99T
G-BWZP	Cameron Home Special 105SS HAFB	4051		6.12.96	Flying Pictures Ltd "Barclays Mortgages"	Fairoaks	24. 3.00A
G-BWZT	Europa Avn Europa (Rotax 912-UL)	PFA/247-12727		9.12.96	A.M.Smyth t/a G-BWZT Group	Crowfield	16. 9.00P
G-BWZU	Lindstrand LBL-90B HAFB	418		12.12.96	K.D.Pierce	Cranbrook, Kent	4. 9.99
G-BWZW	Bell 206B Jet Ranger	12	G-CTEK N7812S	26.11.96	R & M International Engineering Ltd	Dereham	15. 6.98T
G-BWZX	Aerospatiale AS.332L Super Puma	2120	F-WQDX	12.12.96	Bristow Helicopters Ltd	Aberdeen	5. 5.01T
	G-BWZX/F-WQDX/5V-MCD/5V-TAH/LN-OLE "Muchalls"						
G-BWZY	Hughes 269A	95-0378		4.12.96	Katharine B.Elliott	Redhill	13. 5.01
	N269CH/N1336D/64-18066						
G-BWZZ	Hunting Percival P.84 Jet Provost T.3A	XM470 PAC/W/9278		5. 9.96	R.G.Schreiber & J.P.Trevor	(Altrincham/Warrington)	21. 7.00P

G-BXAA – G-BXZZ

Regn	Type	C/n	P/I	Date	Owner/operator	Probable Base	CA Expy
G-BXAB	PA-28-161 Warrior II	28-8416054	G-BTGK N4344C	7.10.96	TG Aviation Ltd	Manston	25. 4.00T
G-BXAC	Rotary Air Force RAF 2000 GTX-SE	PFA G/13-1279		21.11.96	D.C.Fairbrass	Kemble	10. 5.00P
G-BXAD	Cameron Thunder Ax11-225 Srs.2 HAFB	4052		18.12.96	C.E.Wood	Witham	24. 2.00T
G-BXAF	Pitts S-1D Special (Lycoming 0-360)	PFA/09-12258		6.12.96	F.Sharples	Sandown	25.11.99P
G-BXAH	Piel CP.301A Emeraude (Continental C90)	AB.422	D-EBAH	29.10.96	G.E.Valler	(Stafford)	15. 6.00P
G-BXAI	Cameron Colt 120A HAFB	4056		20.12.96	E.F. & R.F.Casswell	Maidstone	9. 6.00T
G-BXAJ	Lindstrand LBL-14A HAFB	425		23.12.96	Oscair Project AB	Taby, Sweden	
G-BXAK	IAV-Bacau Yakovlev Yak-52	811508	LY-ASC DOSAAF	23.12.96	S.L.Flannigan	Compton Abbas	27. 5.00P
G-BXAL	Cameron Bertie Bassett 90SS HAFB	4034		13. 1.97	Trebor Bassett Ltd "Bertie"	Howden, Yorks	15. 3.00A
G-BXAM	Cameron N-90 HAFB	4035		13. 1.97	Trebor Bassett Ltd "Bertie Junior"	Howden, Yorks	15. 3.00A
G-BXAN	Scheibe SF-25C Falke 1700	44299	D-KDGQ	13. 1.97	M.J.Davies & E.R.Boyle t/a C Falke Syndicate	Winthorpe	15.10.00
G-BXAO	Avtech Jabiru SK (Jabiru 2200A)	PFA/274-13066		14. 1.97	P.J.Thompson (Damaged Ledicot nr Shobdon 3.5.98)	(Gaerwen)	23. 4.99P
G-BXAP*	Cameron Hard Hat 90SS HAFB	4045		16. 1.97	Norwest Holst Ltd & C.S.Perceval Watford/Great Missenden (Cancelled as destroyed 26.11.99)		15. 5.99A
G-BXAR	Avro RJ100 (BAe 146 Srs.300)	E-3298	G-6-298	27. 3.97	CityFlyer Express Ltd (Delftblue Daybreak t/s)	Gatwick	29. 3.00T
G-BXAS	Avro RJ100 (BAe 146 Srs.300)	E-3301	G-6-301	23. 4.97	CityFlyer Express Ltd (Animals and Trees/Kg-Oocoan-Naka-Hiian-Thee-E t/s)	Gatwick	29. 4.00T
G-BXAU	Pitts S-1 Special (Lycoming 0-320)	GHG.9	N9GG	22. 1.97	P.Heckles	(Enfield)	17. 4.00P
G-BXAV	Aerostar Yakovlev Yak-52	9111608	RA-01325 DOSAAF 73	24. 1.97	G.M.Sharp (As "DOSAAF 72")	North Weald	25. 2.00P
G-BXAX	Cameron N-77 HAFB	2010		25. 5.89	Flying Pictures Ltd "Citroen"	Fairoaks	21.11.96A
G-BXAY	Bell 206B Jet Ranger III	3946	N85EA N521RC/N3210D	24. 1.97	Mainland Car Deliveries Ltd	Bournemouth	21. 7.00T
G-BXBA	Cameron A-210 HAFB	4072		10. 1.97	Reach For The Sky Ltd	Guildford	30. 5.00T
G-BXBB	PA-20-150 Pacer	20-959	EC-AOZ N1133C	24. 1.97	M.E.R.Coghlan Thornicombe, Dorset (On rebuild)		

Regn	Type	C/n	P/I	Date	Owner/operator	Probable Base	CA Expy
G-BXBC	Anderson EA-1 Kingfisher Amphibian			28. 1.97	S.Bisham		
		PFA/132-1130				Swanbister Farm, Orphir, Stromness	
G-BXBD	CASA I-131 Jungmann	1052	E3B-317	28. 1.97	B.Childs & B.L.Robinson		
						(Bristol/Clevedon)	
	(Identity uncertain as another Jungmann "E3B-317" is displayed in Musee de Jean Tinguely, Basel, Switzerland)						
G-BXBG	Cameron A-275 HAFB	4023		28. 1.97	M.L.Gabb	Alcester	29. 2.00T
G-BXBH	Hunting Percival P.84 Jet Provost T.3A	XM365		29. 1.97	G-BXBH Provost Ltd	(Douglas, IOM)	31. 8.00P
		PAC/W/9241			(As "XM365")		
G-BXBI	Hunting Percival P.84 Jet Provost T.3A	XN510		29. 1.97	Global Aviation Ltd	Binbrook	
		PAC/W/11799					
G-BXBK	Mudry/CAARP CAP.10B	17	N170RC	30. 1.97	S.Skipworth	White Waltham	24. 6.00
			French AF "307-SO"				
G-BXBL	Lindstrand LBL-240A HAFB	317		31. 1.97	J.Fenton	Preston	17. 3.00T
					t/a Firefly Balloon Promotions		
G-BXBM	Cameron O-105 HAFB	3990		31. 1.97	P.Spellward "Open University"		
					t/a Bristol University Hot Air Ballooning Society	Bristol	13. 3.00A
G-BXBN	Rans S-6-116 Coyote II			31. 1.97	W.S.Long	Bagby	17. 5.00P
		PFA/204A-13062					
G-BXBO*	DH.82A Tiger Moth	82360	(D-EAJO)	3. 2.97	Bavarian Balloon Co Ltd	(Germany)	AC
	(DHA rebuild c/n T289)		VH-ALC/N9259		(Cancelled by CAA 19.4.99)		
G-BXBP	Denney Kitfox mk.2	PFA/172-12149		3. 2.97	G.S.Adams	(Dungannon, Co.Tyrone)	
G-BXBR	Cameron A-120 HAFB	1983	SE-ZDY	4. 2.97	M.G.Barlow	Skipton	
G-BXBS	Cameron V-90 HAFB	4096		6. 2.97	D.C.Boxall "Warners"	Bristol	12. 6.00A
G-BXBT	Aerospatiale AS.355F1 Twin Squirrel	5262	G-TMMC	11. 2.97	McAlpine Helicopters Ltd	Oxford	28. 9.01T
			G-JLCO				
G-BXBU	Mudry/CAARP CAP.10B	103	N173RC	11. 2.97	J.F.Cosgrave & H.R.Pearson	Denham	24. 6.00
			French AF				
G-BXBV	Aerospatiale/Alenia ATR-42-300	245	TS-LBA	14. 5.97	Gill Aviation Ltd	Newcastle	21. 5.00T
			(EI-BYQ)/F-WWET				
G-BXBW	HOAC DV-20 Katana	20148	D-ESHM	25. 2.97	Diamond Aircraft Industries GmbH		
					(Op Euroflyers)	Blackbushe	31. 3.00T
G-BXBY	Cameron A-105 HAFB	4077		13. 2.97	S.P.Watkins	Bath	1. 5.00T
					(Op D littlewood) "Roman Baths"		
G-BXBZ	WSK PZL-104 Wilga 80	CF21910941	EC-GDA	13. 2.97	RCR Aviation Ltd	Thruxton	25. 6.00
	(C/n quoted officially as CF21930941)		ZK-PZQ				
G-BXCA	Hapi Cygnet SF-2A	PFA/182-12921		22. 1.97	G.E.Collard	Popham	13. 8.00P
	(Rotax 912-UL)						
G-BXCB	Agusta A.109A II	7347	F-GJSH	17. 2.97	Vulture Ventures Ltd	Southampton	28. 4.00T
			G-ISEB/G-IADT/G-HBCA				
G-BXCC	PA-28-201T Turbo Dakota	28-7921068	D-EKBM	19. 2.97	Greer Aviation Ltd	(Motherwell)	3. 4.00T
			N2855A				
G-BXCD	TEAM miniMax 91A	PFA/186-12393		18. 2.97	R.Davies	(London NW7)	13.10.00P
G-BXCG	CEA Jodel DR.250/160 Capitaine	60 & PFA/299-13146	D-EHGG	22. 5.97	J.M.Scott	Evesham	25. 8.00P
					t/a G-BXCG Group		
G-BXCH	Europa Avn Europa	PFA/247-12980		19. 2.97	D.M.Stevens	Haverfordwest	11.10.99P
	(Rotax 912UL)						
G-BXCJ	Campbell Cricket	PFA G/03-1177		24. 2.97	J.R.Cooper	Swansea	8. 7.00P
	(Rotax 532)				(Damaged nr Swansea 26.9.99)		
G-BXCK	Cameron Douglas-Lurpak Butterman 110SS HAFB	4076		25. 2.97	Flying Pictures Ltd	Fairoaks	25. 3.00A
					"Douglas-Lurpak Butter"		
G-BXCL	Montgomerie Bensen B.8MR	PFA G/01-1287		26. 2.97	A.V.Francis	Carlisle	14. 9.00P
G-BXCM	Lindstrand LBL-150A HAFB	443		26. 2.97	Blown Away (UK) Ltd	Walsall	29. 4.00T
G-BXCN	Sky 105-24 HAFB	047		27. 2.97	Capricorn Balloons Ltd	Loughborough	16. 3.98T
G-BXCO	Colt 120A HAFB	4086		3. 3.97	G.C.Ludlow	Hythe, Kent	19. 7.99T
G-BXCP	DHC.1 Chipmunk 22	C1/0744	WP859	27. 2.97	S.Conlan	(Kildare, Co.Kildare)	15. 6.01
G-BXCS	Cameron N-90 HAFB	4122		4. 3.97	Flying Pictures Ltd "Lurpak"	Fairoaks	24. 3.00A
G-BXCT	DHC.1 Chipmunk 22	C1/0145	WB697	3. 3.97	Wickenby Aviation Ltd	Wickenby	19. 5.00T
					(As "WB697")		
G-BXCU	Rans S-6-116 Coyote II			6. 3.97	M.R.McNeil	Breighton	22. 6.00P
	(Rotax 912UL)	PFA/204A-13105					
G-BXCV	DHC.1 Chipmunk 22	C1/0807	WP929	3. 3.97	Propshop Ltd (As "WP929/F")	Duxford	6.10.00T
G-BXCW	Denney Kitfox mk.3	PFA/172-12619		6. 3.97	M.J.Blanchard	(Swanage)	
G-BXCX	Robinson R-22 Beta	0885	G-MFHL	17. 1.97	Plane Talking Ltd	Blackbushe	10. 4.01T
G-BXCY	Grumman-American AA-5A Cheetah	AA5A-0646	N26686	31. 1.97	Plane Talking Ltd	Elstree	13. 2.00T
G-BXCZ	Gulfstream AA-5A Cheetah	AA5A-0876	N27152	31. 1.97	Plane Talking Ltd	Cranfield	25. 2.00T
G-BXDA	DHC.1 Chipmunk 22	C1/0747	WP860	7. 3.97	S.R.Cleary	Cumbernauld	17. 6.00
					(As "WP860/6")		
G-BXDB	Cessna U206F Stationair	U206-02233	G-BMNZ	18.12.96	Tindon Ltd	Little Snoring	4. 8.01
			F-BVJT/N1519U				

Regn	Type	C/n	P/I	Date	Owner/operator	Probable Base	CA Expy
G-BXDC	Montgomerie-Bensen B.8MR Merlin PFA G/01-1219			5. 2.97	D.L.Smerdon	Carlisle	
G-BXDD	Rotary Air Force RAF 2000 GTX-SE (Subaru EJ22) PFA G/13-1284			9. 1.97	R.M.Savage t/a Roger Savage (Photography)	Carlisle	4. 7.00P
G-BXDE	Rotary Air Force RAF 2000 GTX-SE PFA G/13-1280			14. 1.97	A.McRedie	Carlisle	
G-BXDF	Beechcraft 95-B55 Baron	TC-2011	SE-IXG OY-ASB	7. 3.97	Chesh-Air Ltd	(Lymm)	17. 1.03
G-BXDG	DHC.1 Chipmunk 22	C1/0644	WK630	7. 3.97	R.E.Dagless	Swanton Morley	15. 9.00
G-BXDH	DHC.1 Chipmunk 22	C1/0270	WD331	10. 3.97	Victory Workwear Ltd (As "WD331")	Kemble	21. 1.01P
G-BXDI	DHC.1 Chipmunk 22	C1/0312	WD373	10. 3.97	J.R.Gore (As "WD373/12" in RAF c/s)	Perth	10. 8.00
G-BXDL	Hunting Percival P.84 Jet Provost T.3A	8983M PAC/W/9286	XM478	18. 3.97	Jet Provost Promotions Ltd (As "XM478")	North Weald	24.11.00P
G-BXDM	DHC.1 Chipmunk 22	C1/0723	WP840	28. 2.97	Halton Aeroplane Club Ltd (As "WP840/0")	RAF Halton	5. 6.00T
G-BXDN	DHC.1 Chipmunk 22	C1/0618	WK609	18. 3.97	W.D.Lowe & L.A.Edwards (As "WK609")	Booker	2. 9.00
G-BXDO	Rutan Cozy (Lycoming O-235-C2C)	PFA/159-12032		21. 3.97	C.R.Blackburn (Damaged Ronaldsway 5.10.99)	(Kirk Michael, IoM)	27. 4.00P
G-BXDP	DHC.1 Chipmunk 22	C1/0659	WK642	27. 2.97	J.S.J.Valentine & J.P.Conlan	(Ballytore/Kildare, Co.Kildare)	9. 7.00
G-BXDR	Lindstrand LBL-77A HAFB	441		25. 3.97	British Telecommunications plc	(Thatcham, Berks)	18. 3.00A
G-BXDT	Robin HR.200/120B	315		25. 3.97	Multiflight Ltd	Leeds-Bradford	5. 6.00T
G-BXDU	Aero Designs Pulsar	PFA/202-11991		25. 3.97	M.P.Board	(London E4)	
G-BXDV	Sky 105-24 HAFB	049		26. 3.97	J.Skinner	Maidstone	10. 8.00
G-BXDW	Sky 120-24 HAFB	059		26. 3.97	M. & S.M.Sarti	Fowey	15. 3.00T
G-BXDX	Lindstrand LBL-77M HAFB	452		26. 3.97	Lindstrand Balloons Ltd	(Oswestry)	19. 5.00A
G-BXDY	Europa Avn Europa (Rotax 912UL)	PFA/247-12914		27. 3.97	D.G. & S.Watts "The Rocketeer"	Rochester	23.11.99P
G-BXDZ	Lindstrand LBL-105A HAFB	437		4. 4.97	M.A.Webb	Yarcombe, Honiton	14. 4.99A
G-BXEA	Rotary Air Force RAF 2000 GTX-SE (Subaru EJ22) PFA G/13-1270			2. 4.97	R.Firth	Netherthorpe	10.12.99P
G-BXEB	Rotary Air Force RAF 2000 GTX-SE (Subaru EJ22) PFA G/13-1285			2. 4.97	Penny Hydraulics Ltd	Netherthorpe	22.12.99P
G-BXEC	DHC.1 Chipmunk 22	C1/0647	WK633	3. 4.97	M.F.Watts t/a M.A.D. Flying Group (As "WK633/B")	Gamston	27. 4.00
G-BXEE	Enstrom 280C Shark	1117	OH-HAN N336AT	9. 4.97	S.T.Raby	Grange Farm, Woodwalton	7. 7.00
G-BXEF	Europa Avn Europa	PFA/247-12790		7. 4.97	C. & W.P.Busuttil-Reynaud	(Emsworth, Hants)	
G-BXEG	Aerospatiale/Alenia ATR-42-320	329	ZS-NKY F-WQAB/F-GKNE/F-WWLO	12. 4.95	CityFlyer Express Ltd	Gatwick	11. 4.02T
G-BXEJ	VPM M16 Tandem Trainer (Arrow GT 1000)	D-9302	D-MIFF	8. 4.97	N.H.Collins t/a AES Radionic Surveillance Systems	Cork Farm, Streethay	26. 9.00P
G-BXEM	Campbell Cricket Mk.4 PFA G/03-1282 (Built PC Lovegrove)		(EI-) G-BXEM	11. 4.97	D.M.Bracken	(Port Laoise, Ireland)	1.11.00
G-BXEN	Cameron N-105 HAFB	4090		11. 4.97	G.Aimo	Mondovi, Italy	21. 6.00A
G-BXEP	Lindstrand LBL-14M HAFB	460		14. 4.97	Lindstrand Balloons Ltd	Oswestry	19. 5.00A
G-BXER	PA-46-350P Malibu Mirage	4636110		21. 7.97	Sunseeker Sales (UK) Ltd	Bournemouth	6. 8.00
G-BXES	Hunting Percival P.66 Pembroke C.1 (Regd with c/n PAC/W/3032)	P66/101	N4234C 9042M/XL954	14. 4.97	Atlantic Air Transport Ltd (As "XL954")	Coventry	6. 4.00P
G-BXET	PA-38-112 Tomahawk	38-80A0028	N25089	14. 4.97	APB Leasing Ltd	Welshpool	AC
G-BXEX	PA-28-181 Cherokee Archer II	28-7790463	N3562Q	16. 4.97	Tunjet Ltd	Denham	12. 5.00T
G-BXEY	Colt AS-105GD Hot-Air Airship	3936		15. 4.97	D.Mayer	Neidenstein, Germany	17. 5.00A
G-BXEZ	Cessna 182P Skylane II (Reims assembled with c/n 0054)	182-64344	OH-CHJ N1479M	16. 4.97	Ray Thompson Engineering Ltd	Octon	25. 8.00T
G-BXFB	Pitts S-1 Special	9543	N77ZZ	16. 4.97	D.Dobson	Deenethorpe	3. 1.00P
G-BXFC	Jodel D.18	PFA/169-11322		17. 4.97	B.S.Godbold	(Sandy)	
G-BXFD	Enstrom 280C Shark	1084	N88MD N632H	18. 4.97	A.Smithson	Weymouth	24. 7.00
G-BXFE	Mudry/CAARP CAP.10B	135	N175RC French AF	18. 4.97	R.W.H.Cole t/a Cole Aviation	Spilsted Farm, Sedlescombe	14. 5.01
G-BXFG	Europa Avn Europa	PFA/247-12500		21. 4.97	A.Rawicz-Szczerbo (Cf/f 21.10.99)	Kemble	
G-BXFI	Hawker Hunter T.7	41H-670815	WV372	24. 4.97	Fox-One Ltd (As "WV372/R" in RAF c/s)	Kemble	13. 9.00P
G-BXFK	CFM Streak Shadow (Rotax 582) (Four-bladed propellor).	PFA/206-12329		24. 4.97	D.Adcock	Old Buckenham	6. 6.00P

Regn	Type	C/n	P/I	Date	Owner/operator	Probable Base	CA Expy
G-BXFN	Cameron Colt 77A HAFB	4145		25. 4.97	Cameron Balloons Ltd	Bristol	10. 8.00A
G-BXFP	BAC.167 Strikemaster mk.87	PS.71	OJ5	29. 4.97	C.J.& S.M.Thompson	North Weald	6. 5.00P
	Kenyan AF 602/G-27-192 (As "NZ6361" in RNZAF c/s)						
G-BXFS	BAC.167 Strikemaster mk.87	PS.74	OJ10	29. 4.97	R.J.Everett	North Weald	AC
	Kenyan AF 605/G-27-195						
G-BXFU	BAC.167 Strikemaster mk.83	PS.158	OJ1	29. 4.97	Global Aviation Ltd	Binbrook	24.11.00P
	(Regd as c/n "805")				ZG805/Kuwait AF 110/G-27-151		
G-BXFV	BAC.167 Strikemaster mk.83	PS.162	OJ7	29. 4.97	Global Aviation Ltd	Binbrook	6. 4.00P
	(Regd as c/n "806")				ZG809/Kuwait AF 114/G-27-155		
G-BXFX	BAC.167 Strikemaster mk.83	PS.167	OJ8	29. 4.97	Global Aviation Ltd	Binbrook	29.12.00P
	(Regd as c/n "809")				ZG811/Kuwait AF 119/G-27-188		
G-BXFY	Cameron Bierkrug 90SS HAFB	4133		29. 4.97	Cameron Balloons Ltd	Bristol	13. 2.00A
					(D-OIBP reserved 1999)		
G-BXFZ	Sky 65-24 HAFB	065		22. 4.97	Aerial Promotions Ltd	Cannock	14. 5.99A
G-BXGA	Eurocopter AS.350B2 Ecureuil	2493	OO-RCH	30. 4.97	PLM Dollar Group Ltd.	Inverness	27. 8.00T
			OO-XCH/F-WZFX				
G-BXGC	Cameron N-105 HAFB	4137		6. 5.97	Cliveden Ltd	Bath	23. 5.00T
					"The Royal Crescent Hotel" (Op Ascent Balloons)		
G-BXGD	Sky 90-24 HAFB	067		6. 5.97	Servo & Electronic Sales Ltd	Lydd	1. 6.00A
G-BXGE	Cessna 152 II	152-82700	N89283	8. 5.97	APB Leasing Ltd	Tatenhill	16. 7.00T
G-BXGG	Europa Avn Europa	PFA/247-12803		29. 4.97	B.W.Faulkner	(Godalming)	6. 9.00P
G-BXGH	Diamond DA-20-A1 Katana	10151		20. 5.97	Diamond Aircraft Industries GmbH Norwich	11. 6.00T
G-BXGI	Diamond HK-36TTC Super Dimona	36543	OE-UHK	7. 5.97	T.Miller t/a Enstone Flying Club Enstone	18. 6.00T
G-BXGK	Lindstrand LBL-203M HAFB	468		12. 5.97	Lindstrand Balloons Ltd	Oswestry	
G-BXGL	DHC.1 Chipmunk 22	C1/0924	WZ884	12. 5.97	Airways Aero Associations Ltd	Booker	11. 9.00T
					(Op British Airways Flying Club)		
G-BXGM	DHC.1 Chipmunk 22	C1/0806	WP928	9. 5.97	M.A.Petrie (As "WP928")	(Uckfield)	28.10.00
G-BXGO	DHC.1 Chipmunk 22	C1/0097	WB654	13. 5.97	A.Judd t/a Trees Group	Booker	18. 9.00
					(As "WB654")		
G-BXGP	DHC.1 Chipmunk 22	C1/0927	WZ882	12. 5.97	J.Pote	Eaglescott	18. 6.01T
					t/a Eaglescott Chipmunk Group (As "WZ882/K")		
G-BXGS	Rotary Air Force RAF 2000 GTX-SE			14. 5.97	C.R.Gordon	(Cupar)	5.10.00P
	(Subaru EJ22)	PFA G/13-1290					
G-BXGT	III Sky Arrow 650T	PFA/298-13085		7. 5.97	Sky Arrow (Kits) UK Ltd	Old Sarum	29. 6.99P
	(Rotax 912-UL)						
G-BXGV	Cessna 172R Skyhawk II	172-80240	N9300F	7. 1.98	Grandfort Properties Ltd	Booker	1. 2.01T
G-BXGW	Robin HR.200/120B	317		16. 5.97	Multiflight Ltd	Leeds-Bradford	2.10.00T
					(Op Multiflight Flying Club)		
G-BXGX	DHC.1 Chipmunk 22	C1/0609	WK586	19. 5.97	Interflight (Air Charter) Ltd Blackbushe	3. 9.00
G-BXGY	Cameron V-65 HAFB	4125		18. 4.97	Gone With The Wind Ltd	Hungerford	8. 8.99A
G-BXGZ	Stemme S-10V	14-023	D-KSTE	18. 8.97	D.B.Smith	Aboyne	25. 8.00
			EC-GGD/D-KGDF				
G-BXHA	DHC.1 Chipmunk 22	C1/0801	WP925	20. 5.97	A.J.Keeling	Booker	16. 9.00
					(As "WP925/C" in Army c/s)		
G-BXHD	Beechcraft 76 Duchess	ME-284	OY-ARM	22. 5.97	Liddell Aircraft Ltd	Bournemouth	24. 7.00T
			N223JC				
G-BXHE	Lindstrand LBL-105A HAFB	459		23. 5.97	Independent Insurance Co Ltd		
						(London EC3)	13. 3.00T
G-BXHF	DHC.1 Chipmunk 22	C1/0808	WP930	28. 5.97	R.Beresford	Redhill	28. 1.01
G-BXHH	Grumman-American AA-5A Cheetah		N9705U	3. 6.97	M.G.Greenslade	Biggin Hill	5. 6.00T
		AA5A-0105			t/a Oaklands Flying		
G-BXHI	Hughes 269C	77-0616	G-GBHH	18. 6.97	Dragon Helicopter Services Ltd	Redhill	13.10.02T
			TF-HRH/TF-HHO/N45CD/N9250F/(N51CC)		t/a Redhill Helicopter Centre		
G-BXHJ	Hapi Cygnet SF-2A	PFA/182-12159		29. 5.97	I.J.Smith Brook Farm, Boylestone, Derby	
	(VW1835)						
G-BXHL	Sky 77-24 HAFB	055		29. 5.97	R.A.Messenger "Harlequin"	Melksham	29. 7.99
G-BXHM	Lindstrand LBL-25A Cloudhopper HAFB			30. 5.97	Virgin Balloon & Airship Co Ltd	Telford	7. 5.00A
		466			"Bud Light"		
G-BXHN	Lindstrand Budweiser Can SS HAFB 465			30. 5.97	Virgin Balloon & Airship Co Ltd	Telford	7. 4.00A
					"Budweiser"		
G-BXHO	Lindstrand Telewest Sphere SS HAFB			30. 5.97	Flying Pictures Ltd	Fairoaks	15. 2.00A
		474			"Telewest"		
G-BXHP	Lindstrand LBL-105A HAFB	458		30. 5.97	Flying Pictures Ltd	Fairoaks	25. 6.99A
					"Britannia"		
G-BXHR	Stemme S-10V	14-030		23. 7.97	J.H.Rutherford	Teesside	12. 8.00
G-BXHT	Bushby-Long Midget Mustang			3. 6.97	P.P.Chapman	(Sevenoaks)	
		PFA/168-13077					
G-BXHU	Campbell Cricket mk.6	PFA G/16-1292		3. 6.97	P.C.Lovegrove	Didcot	18.11.00P
	(Rotax 503) (Official regd with c/n PFA G/16-1293 @ 13.12.99)						
G-BXHY	Europa Avn Europa	PFA/247-12514		6. 6.97	A.L.Thorne & B.Lewis	White Waltham	17. 2.99P
					t/a Jupiter Flying Group		

Regn	Type	C/n	P/I	Date	Owner/operator	Probable Base	CA Expy
G-BXHZ	VS 361 Spitfire HF.IX	CBAF.10164	SAAF SM520	9. 6.97	A.G.Dunkerley (Bury) (On rebuild in Oxfordshire 6.97)		
G-BXIA	DHC.1 Chipmunk 22	C1/0056	WB615	9. 6.97	W.Askew, G.Bullock Blackpool & C.Duckett t/a Dales Aviation (As "WB615/E")		16. 3.01T
G-BXIB	Bell 206L-3 Long Ranger	51300	EC-EQQ	9. 6.97	Kelwaiver Ltd (Ipswich)		2. 7.00T
G-BXIC	Cameron A-275 HAFB	4162		9. 6.97	A.J.Street Exeter		14. 6.00T
G-BXID	IAV-Bacau Yakovlev Yak-52	888802	LY-ALG DOSAAF 74	10. 6.97	L.F.Clayton Wellesbourne Mountford (As "DOSAAF 74")		13. 1.00P
G-BXIE	Cameron Colt 77B HAFB	4181		11. 6.97	The Aerial Display Co Ltd Looe		19. 5.00A
G-BXIF	PA-28-181 Cherokee Archer II	28-7690404	PH-SWM OO-HAY/N6827J	12. 6.97	Piper Flight Ltd RAF Brize Norton		9. 7.00T
G-BXIG	Zenair CH-701 STOL	PFA/187-12065		16. 6.97	A.J.Perry GoodwooD		6. 9.00P
G-BXIH	Sky 200-24 HAFB	076		16. 6.97	G.C.Ludlow Hythe		16. 6.00T
G-BXII	Europa Avn Europa	PFA/247-12812		30. 4.97	D.A.McFadyean (Alvechurch, Birmingham)		
G-BXIJ	Europa Avn Europa (Rotax 912UL)	PFA/247-12698		16. 6.97	D.G. & E.A.Bligh Inverness "Bligh's Ballistic" (Damaged Inverness 28.6.99)		13. 5.00P
G-BXIM	DHC.1 Chipmunk 22	C1/0548	WK512	13. 5.97	P.R.Joshua & A.B.Ascroft (As "WK512/A" "ARMY") RAF Brize Norton		1. 7.00
G-BXIO	SAN Jodel DR.1050M Excellance	493	F-BNIO	16. 5.97	D.N.K. & M.A.Symon Cumbernauld		1. 7.01
G-BXIT	Zebedee V-31 HAFB	Z1/3999		8. 5.97	P.J.Bish Hungerford t/a Zebedee Balloon Service		
G-BXIV	Agusta A.109A	7135	F-GERU HB-XOK/D-HFZF	13. 6.97	Castle Air Charters Ltd Trebrown, Liskeard		22.10.01T
G-BXIW	Sky 105-24 HAFB	073		24. 6.97	L.A.Watts Pangbourne, Reading		10. 4.00
G-BXIX	VPM M-16 Tandem Trainer	PFA G/12-1292		13. 6.97	D.Beevers Pocklington		12. 7.00P
G-BXIY	Blake Bluetit (Gnat 32hp)	01	BAPC37	26. 6.97	The Shuttleworth Trust Old Warden (Pre-war composite from Spartans G-AAGN/G-AAJB & Avro 504K; on rebuild 3.96)		
G-BXIZ	Lindstrand LBL-31A HAFB	476		3. 7.97	Hyundai Car (UK) Ltd High Wycombe		24. 7.00A
G-BXJA	Cessna 402B	402B-0356	N5753M XA-RFK/N5753M	17. 7.97	Fraggle Leasing Ltd Edinburgh		24. 8.00T
G-BXJB	IAV-Bacau Yakovlev Yak-52	877403	LY-ABR DOSAAF 15	30. 6.97	D.J.Young & H.Wheldon Elmsett t/a Aero Anglia "15"		15. 4.00P
G-BXJC	Cameron A-210 HAFB	4191		2. 7.97	Balloon School (Intl) Ltd Petworth t/a British School of Ballooning		21. 7.00T
G-BXJD	PA-28-180 Cherokee C	28-4215	OY-BBZ	27. 6.97	BCT Aircraft Leasing Ltd Liverpool (Operated by Air 2000 Flying Club)		31. 7.00T
G-BXJG	Lindstrand LBL-105B HAFB	478		11. 7.97	C.E.Wood Witham		15. 7.00T
G-BXJH	Cameron N-42 HAFB	4194		15. 7.97	Flying Pictures Ltd Fairoaks "Unipart"		31. 7.00A
G-BXJI	Tri-R Kis	PFA/239-12573		2. 7.97	R.M.Wakeford (Glasgow) (Nearing completion at Cumbernauld mid 1999)		
G-BXJJ	PA-28-161 Cadet	2841200	G-GFCC N9189N	26. 6.97	J.P.E.Walsh (Wootton-under-Edge) t/a Walsh Aviation		7.12.01T
G-BXJK	Aerospatiale SA.341G Gazelle 1	1417	F-GEHC N341AT/N49536	30. 6.97	R.A.Kingston Sandling, Hythe		11. 8.00
G-BXJL	Cameron Real Fruit 90SS HAFB	4172		15. 7.97	Cameron Balloons Ltd (Canada)		24. 8.99A
G-BXJM	Cessna 152 II	152-82380	OO-HOQ F-GHOQ/N68797	15. 7.97	E.Alexander Redhill (Damaged landing Redhill 19.3.99)		30. 7.00T
G-BXJO	Cameron O-90 HAFB	4190		16. 7.97	W.I. & C.Hooker Nottingham		17. 7.00T
G-BXJP	Cameron C-80 HAFB	4171		17. 7.97	AR Cobaleno Pasta Fresca SRL Perugia, Italy		16. 7.00A
G-BXJS	Schempp-Hirth Janus CM	35/265	OH-819	7. 7.97	R.A.Hall t/a Janus Syndicate Enstone		17. 8.00
G-BXJT	Sky 90-24 HAFB	072		18. 7.97	Sky Operations Ltd Oswestry (Goodyear titles)		24. 7.98A
G-BXJU	Sky 90-24 HAFB	077		18. 7.97	Sky Operations Ltd (Thailand) (Castrol titles)		24. 7.98A
G-BXJV	Dimona DA-20-A1 Katana	10152		23. 7.97	Tayside Aviation Ltd Perth		29. 7.00T
G-BXJW	Dimona DA-20-A1 Katana	10211	(OE-) N811CH	23. 7.97	Tayside Aviation Ltd Perth		29. 7.00T
G-BXJY	Van's RV-6	PFA/181-12447		23. 7.97	D.J.Sharland Popham		5. 5.00P
G-BXJZ	Cameron C-60 HAFB	4168		23. 7.97	R.S.Mohr Chippenham		15. 2.00A
G-BXKA	Airbus A.320-214	0714	N714AW F-WWIX	24.11.97	Flying Colours Airlines Ltd Manchester (Apple Vacations titles)		23.11.02T
G-BXKB	Airbus A.320-214	0716	N716AW F-WWIZ	10.12.97	Flying Colours Airlines Ltd Manchester (JMC c/s)		5. 5.02T
G-BXKC	Airbus A.320-214	730	F-WWBQ	15.12.97	Flying Colours Airlines Ltd Manchester (JMC Air c/s)		14.12.00T
G-BXKD	Airbus A.320-214	735	F-WWBV	17.12.97	Flying Colours Airlines Ltd Manchester (JMC Air c/s		16.12.00T

Regn	Type	C/n	P/I	Date	Owner/operator	Probable Base	CA Expy
G-BXKF	Hawker Hunter T.7 HABL-003314	8676M		28. 7.97	R.F.Harvey	Kemble	
	(Regd with c/n 41H-003315)	XL577			(As "XL577")		
G-BXKH	Cameron Colt Sparkasse Box 90SS HAFB			4. 8.97	Westfalisch-Lippischer Sparkassen und Giroverband		
		4161				Münster, Germany	11. 8.00A
G-BXKI	Robinson R-44 Astro	0220	OY-HEK	15. 8.97	A.D.Russell	Bourn	25. 8 00
G-BXKJ	Cameron A-275 HAFB	4215		4. 8.97	The Balloon Club Ltd	Bristol	20. 8.00T
G-BXKK	Cameron Golf Ball 90SS HAFB	4054		4. 8.97	Longbreak Ltd Greenwood, Mi., USA		30. 9.99A
G-BXKL	Bell 206B Jet Ranger III	3006	N5735Y	8.10.97	Swattons Aviation Ltd	Thruxton	18.11.00T
G-BXKM	Rotary Air Force RAF 2000 GTX-SE			5. 8.97	J.R.Huggins Lamberhurst Farm, Faversham		20. 5.99P
	PFA G/13-1291						
G-BXKO	Sky 65-24 HAFB	083		11. 8.97	P.J.Beglan Orliac, Belves, France		1. 8.99
G-BXKU	Cameron Colt AS-120 mk.II Hot Air Airship			15. 8.97	D.C.Chipping Evora, Portugal		26.11.99A
		4165					
G-BXKW	Slingsby T.67M Firefly 200	2061	VR-HZS	15. 8.97	W.R.Tandy	Dunstable	23.10.00T
			HKG-13/G-7-129				
G-BXKX	Taylorcraft J Auster 5	803	D-EMXA	19. 8.97	A.L.Jubb	Rochester	19. 4.01
			HB-EOK/MS938				
G-BXKY	Cameron DP-90 Hot Air Airship	4198		19. 8.97	Cameron Balloons Ltd "Oceania"		
					(Op Bruno Schwartz) Rio de Janeiro, Brazil		
G-BXLA	Robinson R-22 Beta	1368	SE-HVX	12. 8.97	Fast Helicopters Ltd	Thruxton	18. 9.00T
			N4014G				
G-BXLC	Sky 120-24 HAFB	085		20. 8.97	Sky Balloons Ltd	Wrexham	5.10.99A
G-BXLF	Lindstrand LBL-90A HAFB	487		3. 9.97	R. & J.Moffatt	Towcester	18.10.99A
					t/a Variohm Components		
G-BXLG	Cameron C-80 HAFB	4250		5. 3.98	D. & L.S.Litchfield	Reading	7. 6.00A
G-BXLI	Bell 206B Jet Ranger III	4041	N206JR	8. 9.97	Williams Grand Prix Engineering Ltd		
			G-JODY			Wantage	28.10.00T
G-BXLJ*	Cessna 172M Skyhawk	172-67065	N1394U	8. 9.97	APB Leasing Ltd	Welshpool	17. 6.01T
				(Crashed into Berwyn Mts, Mid-Wales 12.2.99; cancelled as destroyed 26.2.99)			
G-BXLK	Europa Avn Europa PFA/247-12613			11. 9.97	R.G.Fairall	Redhill	10. 3.00P
G-BXLN	Sportavia Fournier RF4D	4022	F-BORK	15. 9.97	E.H.Booker	(Peterborough)	AC
G-BXLO	Hunting Percival P.84 Jet Provost T.4	9032M		14. 8.97	HCR Aviation Ltd	North Weald	AC
	PAC/W/19986	XR673					
G-BXLP	Sky 90-24 HAFB	084		18. 9.97	Sky Balloons Ltd	Wrexham	23.11.98A
G-BXLR	PZL-110 Koliber 160A	04980077	SP-WGF(2)	10. 6.98	PZL Intnl Aviation Marketing & Sales plc		
	(Regd with c/n 04970077)					(London EC2)	23. 9.01T
G-BXLS	PZL-110 Koliber 160A	04980078	SP-WGG	23. 6.98	P.A.Rickells	(Retford)	15. 9.01T
	(Regd with c/n 04970078)						
G-BXLT	Socata TB-200 Tobago XL	1457	F-GRBB	28. 4.97	R.M.Shears	Blackbushe	29. 4.00
			EC-FNX/EC-234/F-GLFP				
G-BXLV	Enstrom F-28F	733	1711	11. 9.97	Solent Projects Ltd	Southampton	16. 2.01T
			Thai Government/KASET				
G-BXLW	Enstrom F-28F	734	1712	11. 9.97	M & P Food Products Ltd	Coventry	
			Thai Government/KASET				
G-BXLX	Enstrom F-28F	735	1713	11. 9.97	Dixon Development Corporation Ltd		
			Thai Government/KASET			(Hockley Heath)	
G-BXLY	PA-28-151 Cherokee Warrior		G-WATZ	19. 9.97	Air Nova plc	Chester	16. 7.01T
		28-7715220	N7641F				
G-BXLZ	Europa Avn Europa PFA/247-12815			24. 6.97	A.R.Round	Kemble	1. 6.00P
G-BXMA	Beechcraft 200 Super King Air BB-726		N622JA	31. 7.97	Manhattan Air Ltd	Blackbushe	7. 8.00T
			N522JA/N222JD				
G-BXMF	Cassutt Racer IIIM PFA/34-13003			19. 9.97	J.F.Bakewell	(Hucknall)	
G-BXMG	Rotary Air Force RAF 2000 GTX		PH-TEN	18. 8.97	B.D.Jones	Solihull	
	H2-92-3-59						
G-BXMH	Beechcraft 76 Duchess	ME-168	F-GDMO	19. 9.97	R.Clarke	Halfpenny Green	22. 1.01T
			N6021Y				
G-BXML	Mooney M.20A	1594	OY-AIZ	26. 9.97	G.Kay	Crosland Moor	25. 1.02
G-BXMM	Cameron A-180 HAFB	4252		28.10.97	Flying Pictures Ltd	Fairoaks	18.10.99A
					"Unipart"		
G-BXMN*	DH.82A Tiger Moth	86243	N82RD	2.10.97	Linda V.Handley (As "NL772")		
			N8353/ZS-IGJ/CR-AGL/FAP/NL772 Higher Barn Farm, Roach Bridge, Houghton				26.11.01
			(Badly damaged in an accident nr. Blackburn 25.5.99: cancelled as destroyed 13.11.99)				
G-BXMU	WSK PZL-104 Wilga 80	CF20890880	EC-GMH	9.10.97	RCR Aviation Ltd	Thruxton	AC
			ZK-PZP/SP-FWP				
G-BXMV	Scheibe SF-25C Falke 1700	44223	D-KDFV	7. 8.97	J.B.Marett Sandhill Farm, Shrivenham		6.11.00
					t/a Falcon Flying Group		
G-BXMW	Cameron A-275 HAFB	4247		19. 2.98	Balloon Flights International Ltd Bath		30. 7.00T
					(Bath Building Society titles) "BIBS III"		
G-BXMX	Phoenix Currie Wot PFA/58-13055			23. 9.97	M.J.Hayman	(Totnes)	
G-BXMY	Hughes 269C	74-0328	N9599F	20.10.97	P.J.Brown	Redhill	7.12.00T
G-BXMZ	Diamond DA-20-A1 Katana	10236		4.12.97	Tayside Aviation Ltd	Dundee	6. 1.01T

Regn	Type	C/n	P/I	Date	Owner/operator	Probable Base	CA Expy
G-BXNA	Light Aero Avid Flyer	118	N5531J	10.10.97	Isobel Brooks	(Cublington)	
G-BXNC	Europa Avn Europa	PFA/247-12970		13.10.97	J.K.Cantwell	(Ashton-under-Lyne)	
					"The Magic Leprechaun"		
G-BXND	Cameron Thomas The Tank Engine 110SS HAFB	4254		2. 2.98	Flying Pictures Ltd	Fairoaks	3. 2.00A
G-BXNG	Beechcraft 58 Baron	TH-874	N18747	13.10.97	Bonanza Flying Club Ltd	Booker	23.10.00
G-BXNH	PA-28-161 Warrior II	28-7816314	N2828M	22.10.97	CC Management Associates Ltd	Redhill	30.11.00T
G-BXNL	Cameron A-120 HAFB	4241		3. 3.98	R.G.Griffin "Kenett Centre"	Newbury	1. 3.00T
					t/a Newbury Balloons & Land Securities Properties Ltd		
G-BXNM	Cameron A-210 HAFB	4245		12.12.97	N.D.Hicks t/a Horizon Ballooning	Alton	10.12.99T
G-BXNN	DHC.1 Chipmunk 22	C1/0849	WP983	4. 8.97	J.N.Robinson	Old Sarum	18. 6.01
					(As "WP983/B" in RAF c/s)		
G-BXNO	Yakovlev Yak-50	822305	LY-ASD DOSAAF 82	13.10.97	N.J.Radford	Denham	12.11.99P
G-BXNS	Bell 206B Jet Ranger III	2385	N16822	3.11.97	Sterling Helicopters Ltd	Norwich	3.12.00T
G-BXNT	Bell 206B Jet Ranger III	2398	N94CA N123AL	11.11.97	Sterling Helicopters Ltd	Norwich	3.12.00T
G-BXNU	Avtech Jabiru SK	PFA/274-13218		31.10.97	J.Smith	(Downham Market)	14. 7.00P
G-BXNV	Cameron Colt AS-105 GD Hot-Air Airship	4231		19. 2.98	The Sleeping Society	Edegem, Belgium	23. 3.00A
G-BXNX	Lindstrand LBL-210A HAFB	318		3.11.97	Jane H.Cuthbert	Sevenoaks	11. 2.00T
					t/a Spirit of Adventure		
G-BXNZ	Hawker Hunter F.58	41H-697433	J-4066	7.11.97	Classic Aviation Ltd	RAF Scampton	AC
	(Regd with c/n 41H-28364)				(Stored 1999)		
G-BXOA	Robinson R-22 Beta	1614	N41132 JA7832	10.11.97	MG Group Ltd	Sywell	4. 1.01
G-BXOB	Europa Avn Europa	PFA/247-12892		6.11.97	S.J.Willett	(Maidstone)	
G-BXOC	Evans VP-2	PFA/63-10305		29. 9.97	H.J. & E.M.Cox	(Bideford)	
G-BXOF	Diamond DA-20-A1 Katana	10256		4.12.97	Tayside Aviation Ltd	Norwich	6. 1.01T
G-BXOI	Cessna 172R Skyhawk II	172-80145	N9990F	17.11.97	Anglo American Airmotive Ltd	Bournemouth	2. 2.01T
G-BXOJ	PA-28-161 Warrior III	2842010	N9265G	15.12.97	Bournemouth Flying Club Ltd	Bournemouth	15.12.00T
G-BXOM	Isaacs Spitfire	PFA/27-12768		25.11.97	J.H.Betton	(Ammanford)	
G-BXON	Auster AOP.9	AUS/10/60	WZ729	1.12.97	C.J. & D.J.Baker	Carr Farm, Newark	
					(On rebuild 4.98)		
G-BXOO	Grumman-American AA-5A Cheetah	AA5A-0674	N26721	10.12.97	Blackbushe School of Flying Ltd	Blackbushe	15.12.00T
G-BXOR	Robin HR.200/120B	321		1.12.97	Multiflight Ltd	Leeds-Bradford	19. 2.01T
G-BXOS	Cameron A-200 HAFB	4286		19. 2.98	Airbourne Balloon Mangmnt Ltd	Longleat	30. 3.00T
G-BXOT	Cameron C-70 HAFB	4200		21.10.97	Gone With The Wind Ltd	Bristol	28.10.99A
					(Op Dante Balloon Group)		
G-BXOU	CEA Jodel DR.360 Chevalier	312	F-BPOU	6.10.97	S.H. & J.A.Williams	Blackpool	15.12.00
G-BXOV	Cameron Colt 105A HAFB	4227		12.12.97	The Aerial Display Co Ltd	Looe	30.12.99A
G-BXOW	Cameron Colt 105A HAFB	4228		9. 1.98	The Aerial Display Co Ltd	Looe	11. 1.00A
G-BXOX	Grumman American AA-5A Cheetah	AA5A-0694	F-GBDS	27. 2.98	Plane Talking Ltd	Elstree	2. 3.01T
G-BXOY	QAC Quickie Q.200	PFA/94-12183		17.11.97	C.C.Clapham	North Weald	
					(Cf/f 6.9.99)		
G-BXOZ	PA-28-181 Cherokee Archer II	28-7790173	N6927F	14.10.97	Spritetone Ltd	White Waltham	8. 1.01T
G-BXPB	Diamond DA-20-A1 Katana	10257		4.12.97	Tayside Aviation Ltd	Glenrothes	8. 1.01T
G-BXPC	Diamond DA-20-A1 Katana	10258		4.12.97	Cubair Flight Training Ltd	Redhill	8. 1.01T
G-BXPD	Diamond DA-20-A1 Katana	10259		4.12.97	Tayside Aviation Ltd	Redhill	5. 3.01T
					(Op Cubair)		
G-BXPE	Diamond DA-20-A1 Katana	10263		4.12.97	Tayside Aviation Ltd	Dundee	5. 3.01T
G-BXPF	Venture Thorp T.211	105	N6524Y	8.12.97	AM Aerospace Ltd	Carlisle	29. 3.01T
G-BXPH	Sky 220-24 HAFB	096		4.12.97	J.Nolte	Aachen, Germany	1. 4.00
G-BXPI	Van's RV-4	PFA/181-12426		2. 1.98	Cavendish Aviation Ltd	Gamston	31. 8.00P
G-BXPK	Cameron A-250 HAFB	4226		2. 2.98	Broadland Balloons Ltd	Norwich	3. 8.00T
G-BXPL	PA-28-140 Cherokee	28-24560	N7224J	10.12.97	M.Jones	Bournemouth	3. 2.01T
					(Force landed in field short of runway Bournemouth 22.7.99: on repair 8.99)		
G-BXPM	Beechcraft 58 Baron	TH-1677	N207ZM	10.10.97	Foyle Flyers Ltd	Eglinton	5.11.00
G-BXPO	Venture Thorp T.211	104	N6524Q	10.12.97	DM Aerospace Ltd	White Waltham	29. 3.01T
G-BXPP	Sky 90-24 HAFB	092		17.12.97	Adam Associates Ltd	Thatcham, Berks	14. 5.00A
					"Niceday"		
G-BXPR	Cameron Colt Can 110SS HAFB	4218		2. 2.98	FRB Fleischwarenfabrik Rostock-Bramow	Rostock, Germany	16. 2.00A
G-BXPS	PA-23-250 Aztec C	27-3498	G-AYLY N6258Y	10.12.90	Wendy A.Moore	Redhill	16.10.97T
G-BXPT	Ultramagic H-77 HADB	77-140		22.12.97	G.D.O.Bartram	Ordino, Andorra	16. 6.99A
G-BXPV	PA-34-220T Seneca IV	3448035	A7-FCH N9198X	24.12.97	Oxford Aviation Services Ltd	Oxford	13. 1.01T

226

Regn	Type	C/n	P/I	Date	Owner/operator	Probable Base	CA Expy
G-BXPW	PA-34-220T Seneca IV	3448034	A7-FCG N9171R	9. 2.98	Oxford Aviation Services Ltd	Oxford	12. 2.01T
G-BXPY	Robinson R-44 Astro	0154	OY-HFV	22.12.97	O.Desmet & B.Mornie	Maarkedal, Belgium	23.12.00
G-BXPZ	DHC.8-311A Dash Eight	422	N377DC OE-LTE/C-GLOT	6. 3.98	Brymon Airways Ltd	Bristol	15. 3.01T
G-BXRA	Mudry/CAARP CAP.10B	03	FrAF 03 F-TFVR	12.12.97	P.A.Soper	(Ipswich)	17. 8.01
G-BXRB	Mudry/CAARP CAP.10B	100	FrAF 100	12.12.97	T.T.Duhig	(London WC1)	5. 7.01
G-BXRC	Mudry/CAARP CAP.10B	134	FrAF 134	12.12.97	I.F.Scott t/a Group Alpha	Sibson	9. 2.02
G-BXRD	Enstrom 280FX	2012	PH-JVM N213M	22.12.97	G.Firbank	Eastwood End Farm, Macclesfield	28. 1.01
G-BXRE	Fokker F.28 Mk.4000	11187	N102EW 9G-ADA/PH-EXW	5. 1.98	Aero Engine Support Ltd	(London W6)	
G-BXRF	Scintex CP.1310-C3 Super Emeraude	935	OO-NSF F-BMJG	9. 1.98	D.T.Gethin	(Swansea)	AC
G-BXRG	PA-28-181 Archer II	28-7990036	PH-LEC N21173	29. 1.98	Alderney Flying Training Ltd	Alderney	1. 3.01T
G-BXRH	Cessna 185A Skywagon	185-0413	HB-CRX N1613Z	10.12.97	R.E.M.Holmes	Ronaldsway	4. 6.01
G-BXRI	Cessna T303 Crusader	T303-00133	HB-LNI (N5143C)	27. 1.98	I.F.Vaughan	Guernsey	4. 3.01
G-BXRK	Robinson R-22 Beta	1341	N341MB	20. 1.98	Moy Motorsport Ltd	Sywell	5. 2.01T
G-BXRL*	Westland Scout AH.Mk.1	F.9639	XT630	20. 1.98	Raffia Enterprises Ltd	Charity Farm, Baxterley	14. 6.00P
	(Offical c/n quoted as FB-4347)						
	(Force landed in Gee's Quarry, Hartshill, Nuneaton 16.10.99: cancelled by CAA 19.11.98)						
G-BXRM	Cameron A-210 HAFB	4237		23. 4.98	W. & C.Hooker	(Nottingham)	29. 4.00T
G-BXRN	Reims Cessna F.152 II	1440	G-RICH OO-FTC	27. 1.98	Aerohire Ltd	Halfpenny Green	21. 9.01T
G-BXRO	Cessna U.206G Stationair II	U206-04217	OH-ULK N756NE	9. 2.98	M.Penny	(Coleraine, NI)	24. 3.01
G-BXRP	Schweizer Hughes 269C	S.1334	OH-HSP	27. 1.98	AH Helicopter Services Ltd	Lustleigh	18. 3.01
G-BXRR	Westland Scout AH.1	F.9740	XW612	28. 1.98	R.P.Coplestone	Thruxton	7. 2.00P
G-BXRS	Westland Scout AH.1	F.9741	XW613 (As "XV613")	28. 1.98	R.P.Coplestone	Thruxton	AC
G-BXRT	Robin DR.400/180	2382		23. 2.98	Mistral Aviation Ltd	Goodwood	2. 4.01
G-BXRV	Van's RV-4	PFA/181-12482		12. 1.98	B.J.Oke	(Wotton-under-Edge)	
G-BXRX	Airbus A.320-231	314	EC-GLT R N314RX/LZ-ABD/F-WWDO		Airworld Aviation Ltd	Manchester	
G-BXRY	Bell 206B JetRanger	208	N4054G	19. 3.98	R & M International Ltd	Dereham	27. 5.01T
G-BXRZ	Rans S-6-116 Coyote II	PFA/204A-13195		3. 2.98	C.M.White	(Dunblane)	
G-BXSA	Cameron PM-80 HAFB (Coca Cola bottle)	4297		11. 3.98	Flying Pictures Ltd	(Dubai)	2. 6.00A
G-BXSB	Cameron PM-80 HAFB (Coca Cola bottle)	4298		11. 3.98	Flying Pictures Ltd	(Dubai)	7.12.99A
G-BXSC	Cameron C-80 HAFB	4251		12.12.97	S.J.Coates "Keepsake"	Barton-le-Clay, Bedford	31.10.99A
G-BXSD	Cessna 172R Skyhawk II	172-80310	N431ES	12. 3.98	K.J.Freeman & J.A.Barlow t/a Sierra Delta Group	(Launceston)	26. 3.01
G-BXSE	Cessna 172R Skyhawk II	172-80352	N9321F	19. 5.98	MK Aero Support Ltd	Andrewsfield	26. 5.01
G-BXSG	Robinson R-22 Beta-II	2789		3. 2.98	R.M.Goodenough	Wotton-under-Edge	26. 2.01T
G-BXSH	Glaser-Dirks DG-800B	8-121-B50		5. 2.98	D.S.MaKay	Hinton-in-The-Hedges	4. 6.01
G-BXSI	Avtech Jabiru SK	PFA/274-13204		5. 2.98	V.R.Leggott	Coldharbour Farm, Willingham	5. 5.00P
G-BXSJ	Cameron C-80 HAFB	4330		24. 3.98	Balloon School (Intl) Ltd t/a British School of Ballooning	Petworth	17. 2.00T
G-BXSK	Beechcraft 76 Duchess	ME-192	EI-CMX N60450	12. 2.98	Aradian Aviation Ltd	Wellesbourne Mountford	11. 3.01T
G-BXSL	Westland Scout AH.1	F.9762	XW799	17. 2.98	M.G.Wiltshire Albany Farm, Hullavington t/a Airpro Engineering		2. 8.00P
G-BXSM	Cessna 172R Skyhawk II	172-80320	N432ES	10. 3.98	East Midlands Flying School Ltd	East Midlands	19. 3.01T
G-BXSN	Sikorsky S-61N	61761	EI-BLY C-GROUPOH/VH-IMQ/VH-PTF/N611EH	17. 2.98	Bristow Helicopters Ltd	Aberdeen	AC
G-BXSO	Lindstrand LBL-105A HAFB	114	HB-BBJ	18. 2.98	Lindstrand Balloons Ltd	Oswestry	31. 3.00A
G-BXSP	Grob G-109B	6335	D-KNEA	25. 3.98	I.M.Donnelly	Aboyne	7. 4.01
G-BXSR	Reims Cessna F.172N	2003	PH-SPY D-EITH	6. 2.98	J.A.Havers	Kings Farm, Thurrock	21. 4.01
G-BXST	PA-25-235 Pawnee C	25-4952	PH-BAT N8532L	9. 2.98	P.Channon	Lands End	AC
G-BXSU*	TEAM miniMax 91A (Rotax 503)	PFA/186-12357	G-MYGL	20. 2.98	A.R.Carr (Cancelled by CAA 17.12.99)	Breighton	28. 9.99P

Regn	Type	C/n	P/I	Date	Owner/operator	Probable Base	CA Expy
G-BXSW	Cameron Mountie 120SS HAFB	4299		20. 2.98	Cameron Balloons Ltd	(Canada)	28. 6.00A
G-BXSX	Cameron V-77 HAFB	4329		6. 4.98	D.R.Medcalf	(Bromsgrove)	25. 5.00A
G-BXSY	Robinson R-22 Beta-II	2778		27. 1.98	N.M.G.Pearson	Bristol	5. 2.01T
G-BXTB	Cessna 152 II	152-82516	OH-CMS	25. 2.98	Haimoss Ltd	Old Sarum	1. 4.01T
			N69151				
G-BXTC	Taylor JT.1 Monoplane	PFA/55-13142		25. 2.98	R.Holden-Rushworth	(Devizes)	
G-BXTD	Europa Avn Europa	PFA/247-12772		26. 2.98	P.R.Anderson	(Southwell)	
					(f/f 23.1.00)		
G-BXTE	Cameron A-275 HAFB	4028		30. 3.98	Adventure Balloon Co Ltd	Hook	29. 3.00T
G-BXTF	Cameron N-105SS HAFB	4304		2. 4.98	Flying Pictures Ltd	Fairoaks	24. 3.00A
					"Sainsbury's Strawberry"		
G-BXTG	Cameron N-42 HAFB	4305		2. 4.98	Flying Pictures Ltd	Fairoaks	3. 3.00A
					"Sainsbury"		
G-BXTH	Westland Gazelle HT.3	WA.1120	XW866	13. 3.98	Flightline Ltd	Southend	AC
					(As "E" in RAF c/s: stored 5.99)		
G-BXTI	Pitts S-1S Special	NP-1	ZS-VZX	9. 3.98	A.B.Treherne-Pollock	Kemble	30. 6.99P
			N96MM				
G-BXTJ	Cameron N-77 HAFB	4332		6. 4.98	Chubb Fire Ltd	Ampney St Peter, Glos	16.12.99A
					(Chubb titles)		
G-BXTK	Dornier Do.28D-2	4080	D-IDBB	15. 5.98	R.Ebke	(Porta Westfalica, Germany)	
			German AF 58+05				
G-BXTL	Schweizer 269C-1	0075		13. 3.98	Oxford Aviation Services Ltd	Oxford	2. 4.01T
G-BXTM*	Schweizer 269C-1	0076		13. 3.98	Oxford Aviation Services Ltd	Oxford	2. 4.01T
					(Damaged Oxford 4.1.99: cancelled as wfu 27.9.99)		
G-BXTN	Aerospatiale/Alenia ATR-72-202	483	F-WWEV	24.10.97	CityFlyer Express Ltd	Gatwick	23.10.00T
					(Whale Rider t/s)		
G-BXTO	Hindustan HAL-26 Pushpak	PK-128	9V-BAI	12. 2.98	A.A.Marshall (Cf/f 21.10.99)		
			VT-DWM		Yeatsall Farm, Abbotts Bromley		
G-BXTP	Diamond DA-20-A1 Katana	10306	N636DA	10. 3.98	Solent Flight Aircraft Ltd	Gamston	23. 4.01T
G-BXTR	Diamond DA-20-A1 Katana	10307	N607DA	10. 3.98	Solent Flight Aircraft Ltd	Southampton	23. 4.01T
G-BXTS	Diamond DA-20-A1 Katana	10308	N638DA	10. 3.98	Solent Flight Aircraft Ltd	Southampton	23. 4.01T
G-BXTT	Grumman-American AA-5B Cheetah	AA5B-0749	F-GBDH	27. 2.98	P.Curley & R.Bailes-Brown	Gamston	2. 3.01
					t/a G-BXTT Group		
G-BXTU	Robinson R-22 Beta-II	2790		3. 3.98	TDR Aviation Ltd	(Craigavon, NI)	7. 4.01T
G-BXTV	Bug	BUG.2		12. 3.98	B.R.Cope	(Bewdley)	
G-BXTW	PA-28-181 Archer III	2843137	N41279	26. 2.98	J.N.Davison	(Wolverhampton)	25. 5.01
					t/a Davison Plant Hire		
G-BXTY	PA-28-161 Cadet	2841179	PH-LED	11. 3.98	Plane Talking Ltd	Bournemouth	7. 6.01T
					(Op Bournemouth Flying Club)		
G-BXTZ	PA-28-161 Cadet	2841181	PH-LEE	11. 3.98	Plane Talking Ltd	Bournemouth	12. 3.01T
					(Op Bournemouth Flying Club)		
G-BXUA	Campbell Cricket Mk.5	PFA G/03-1272		12. 3.98	P.C.Lovegrove	(Didcot)	
G-BXUB	Lindstrand Syrup Bottle SS HAFB	508		30. 4.98	Free Enterprise Balloons Ltd		
						(London SE16)	15. 3.00A
G-BXUC	Robinson R-22 Beta	0908	OY-HFB	17. 3.98	C.W.B.Wrightson	Sherburn-in-Elmet	29. 3.01T
G-BXUE	Sky 240-24 HAFB	098		30. 4.98	G.M.Houston	Lesmahagow	4. 3.00T
					t/a Scotair Balloons		
G-BXUF	Agusta-Bell 206B JetRanger II	8633	EC-DUS	12. 5.98	SJ Contracting Services Ltd	Oxford	7. 7.01T
			OE-DXE				
G-BXUG	Lindstrand Baby Bel SS HAFB	512		14. 5.98	Virgin Airship & Balloon Co Ltd	Telford	13. 4.00A
					"Mr Cool"		
G-BXUH	Lindstrand LBL-31A HAFB	513		2. 6.98	Virgin Airship & Balloon Co Ltd	Telford	13. 4.00A
					"Baby-Bel"		
G-BXUI	Glaser-Dirks DG-800B	8-105-B39	BGA.4382	12. 5.98	J.Le Coyte	(Swindon)	25. 5.01P
			D-KKLC				
G-BXUK	Robinson R-44 Astro	0093	D-HIFF	19. 6.95	Speed Service plc	Cambridge	19. 6.01T
G-BXUL	Vought (Goodyear) FG-1D Corsair	3205	N55JP	25. 3.98	The Old Flying Machine (Air Museum) Co Ltd		
	(Officially regd as c/n P32823)		"NZ5611"/NZ5648/Bu.88391			Duxford	14. 7.00P
	(P/i of Bu.88439 quoted)				(As "NZ5648/648" in RNZAF c/s)		
G-BXUM	Europa Avn Europa	PFA/247-12611		19. 3.98	D.Bosomworth	Popham	2. 6.00P
G-BXUO	Lindstrand LBL-105A HAFB	520		27. 3.98	Lindstrand Balloons Ltd	Oswestry	3. 5.00A
G-BXUP	Schweizer Hughes 269C	S.1317	SE-HTB	30. 3.98	D.R.Kenyon	Biggin Hill	6. 4.01T
					t/a Aviation Bureau		
G-BXUS	Sky 65-24 HAFB	111		6. 4.98	Sky Balloons Ltd	Wrexham	14. 7.00A
G-BXUT	PA-34-200 Seneca	34-7250315	N1427T	11. 5.98	H.Merkado	Panshanger	25. 5.01T
			HB-LMK/N1427T				
G-BXUU	Cameron V-65 HAFB	4362		23. 4.98	D.I.Gray-Fisk "Aeolus"	Burnham	11. 6.00A
G-BXUW*	Cameron Colt 90A HAFB	4317		23. 4.98	Zycomm Electronics Ltd	Derby	30. 4.00A
					(Cancelled by CAA 30.11.99)		
G-BXUX	Fountain MF Cherry BX-2	PFA/179-12571		14. 4.98	M.F.Fountain	Lydd	26.9.00P

Regn	Type	C/n	P/I	Date	Owner/operator	Probable Base	CA Expy
G-BXUY	Cessna 310Q	310Q-0231	N137SA D-IHMT/N7731Q	16. 4.98	D.A.De Horne Rowntree	London NW3	23. 4.01
G-BXUZ	Cessna 152 II	152-82810	N89638	14. 4.98	Stapleford Flying Club Ltd	Stapleford	AC
G-BXVA	Socata TB-200 Tobago XL	1325	F-GJXL F-WJXL	15. 4.98	AMC Ltd	(Thornton-Cleveleys)	18. 5.01
G-BXVB	Cessna 152 II	152-82584	N69250	15. 4.98	PJC (Leasing) Ltd	Stapleford	14. 9.01T
G-BXVC	PA-28RT-201T Turbo Arrow IV	28R-7931113	D-ELIV N2152V	20. 4.98	J.S.Develin & I.Zahurul (Damaged nr Rye 22.8.98)	Redhill	28. 6.01T
G-BXVD	CFM Streak Shadow SA (Rotax 912) K301SA & PFA/206-13304			1. 4.98	Rotech Frabrication Ltd	(Aberdeen)	19. 5.00P
G-BXVE	Lindstrand LBL-330A HAFB	492		6. 5.98	Adventure Balloon Co Ltd	London W7	26. 5.00T
G-BXVF	Thunder Ax11-250 Srs.2 HAFB	4371		22. 5.98	T.J.Parker t/a Anglian Countryside Balloons	Burnham-on-Crouch	13. 5.00T
G-BXVG	Sky 77-24 HAFB	99		28. 5.98	M.Wolf	Wallingford	1. 5.00
G-BXVH	Sky 25-16 HAFB	120		23. 4.98	Flying Pictures Ltd "Encyclopedia Britannica"	Fairoaks	14. 3.00A
G-BXVI	VS 361 Spitfire LF.XVIe CBAF.IX.4644	6944M "RF114"/RW386		27.12.84	Wizzard Investments Ltd (On rebuild 4.89)	North Weald	AC
G-BXVJ	Cameron O-120 HAFB	2201	PH-VVJ G-IMAX	12. 3.98	Gone with the Wind Ltd	Clonskeagh, Co.Dublin	19. 7.00T
G-BXVK	Robin HR.200/120B	326		1. 7.98	Northamptonshire School of Flying Ltd	Sywell	23. 6.01T
G-BXVL	Sky 180-24 HAFB	113		16. 6.98	S.Stanley t/a Purple Balloons	Sudbury	9. 6.00T
G-BXVM	Van's RV-6A	PFA/181-13103		26. 2.98	J.G.Small	(Southport)	
G-BXVN	Sky 105-24 HAFB	115		17. 9.98	L.V.D. Avyle, t/a Skydance	Wachtebetie, Belgium	
G-BXVO	Van's RV-6A	PFA/181-12575		28. 4.98	P.J.Hynes & M.E.Holden	(Shrewsbury)	
G-BXVP	Sky 31-24 HAFB	056		28. 4.98	Sky Balloons Ltd	Wrexham	4. 5.99A
G-BXVR	Sky 90-24 HAFB	061		20. 7.98	P.Hegarty	Magherafelt, NI	25. 6.00
G-BXVS	Brugger Colibri MB.2	PFA/43-11948		5. 5.98	G.T.Snoddon	(Belfast)	21. 2.00
G-BXVT	Cameron O-77 HAFB	1444	PH-MKB	30. 7.98	R.P.Wade	Wigan	
G-BXVU	PA-28-161 Warrior II	28-7816063	N47372	5. 5.98	Atlantic Bridge Aviation Ltd	Lydd	7. 7.01T
G-BXVV	Cameron V-90 HAFB	4369		5. 5.98	Floating Sensations Ltd	Thatcham	5. 5.00A
G-BXVW	Colt Piggy Bank SS HAFB	4366		2. 7.98	G.Binder	Sonnerbuhl, Germany	8. 6.00A
G-BXVX	Rutan Cozy	PFA/159-12680		6. 5.98	G.E.Murray	(Swansea)	18. 7.00P
G-BXVY	Cessna 152	152-79808	N757KU	11. 5.98	Stapleford Flying Club Ltd	Stapleford	9.11.01T
G-BXVZ	WSK-PZL Mielec TS-11 Iskra	3H-1625	SP-DOF Polish AF?/SP-DOF	27. 3.98	J.Ziubrzynski	(Duxford)	AC
G-BXWA	Beechcraft 76 Duchess	ME-232	OY-CYM (SE-IUY)/D-GBTD	8. 4.98	Plymouth School of Flying Ltd	Plymouth	23. 6.01T
G-BXWB	Pierre Robin HR.100/200B Royale	08	HB-EMT	29. 4.98	W.A.Brunwin	Kemble	24. 6.01T
G-BXWC	Cessna 152	152-83640	N4794B	11. 5.98	PJC (Leasing) Ltd	Rochester	8. 7.01T
G-BXWD	Agusta A.109A-II	7266	N565RJ I-URIA/D-HEMZ/N109BD	14. 5.98	Castle Air Charters Ltd	Trebrown, Liskeard	AC
G-BXWE	Fokker F.100-650	11327	PH-CFE F-GJAO/PH-CFE/PH-EZL/(G-FIOX)/PH-EZL	6. 7.98	British Midland Airways Ltd	East Midlands	30. 8.01T
G-BXWF	Fokker F.100-650	11328	PH-CFF F-GKLX/PH-CFF/PH-EZM/(G-FIOY)/PH-EZM	13. 7.98	British Midland Airways Ltd	East Midlands	31. 8.01T
G-BXWG	Sky 120-24 HAFB	114		28. 5.98	Airbourne Adventures Ltd	Skipton	25. 5.00T
G-BXWH	Denney Kitfox 4-1200 Sportster	PFA/172A-12343		4. 3.98	R.Horton	(Harrogate)	
G-BXWI(2)	Cameron N-120 HAFB (Rebuild 1999)	4395		12. 6.98	Flying Pictures Ltd (Energis titles)	Fairoaks	17. 5.00A
G-BXWJ	Robinson R-22 Beta	1685	N4060W	19. 5.98	M.Horrell	Sywell	4. 6.01T
G-BXWK	Rans S-6-ESA Coyote II (Nose-wheel u/c) (Rotax 582) 0298-1020 & PFA/204-13317			19. 5.98	C.Churchyard	(Harrogate)	12. 9.00P
G-BXWL	Sky 90-24 HAFB	117		20. 7.98	I.S.Bridge t/a The Shropshire Hills Balloon Company	Shrewsbury	5. 6.00A
G-BXWO	PA-28-181 Archer II	28-8190311	D-ENHA(2) N8431C	22. 5.98	J.S.Develin & Z.Islam	(East Grinstead)	30. 6.01T
G-BXWP	PA-32-300 Cherokee Six	32-7340088	(N8143D) OE-DRR/N16452	26. 5.98	J.B.Tucker & D.J.Royle t/a Alliance Aviation	Barton	15. 7.01
	(Note: This entry should have been included in SECTION 1 of the 1999 UK Register rather last year's SECTION 6. The a/c remained on the register throughout - despite reference in 1998's Air-Britain News @ SEP.1121)						
G-BXWR	CFM Streak Shadow (Rotax 912) K289-SA & PFA/206-13205		G-MZMI	22. 5.98	M.A.Hayward	Bodmin	7. 1.00P
G-BXWS	Scheibe SF-25E Super Falke	4304	F-CHCG D-KEYB	26. 5.98	M.M.Martin	Leicester	
G-BXWT	Van's RV-6	PFA/181-12639		19. 7.96	R.C.Owen	(Haywards Heath)	
G-BXWU	Sprint 160	003	G-70-503	5. 6.98	Sunhawk Ltd	North Weald	
G-BXWV	Sprint 160	005	G-70-505	5. 6.98	Sunhawk Ltd	North Weald	

Regn	Type	C/n	P/I	Date	Owner/operator	Probable Base	CA Expy
G-BXWX	Sky 25-16 HAFB	082		29. 5.98	Sky Balloons Ltd	Wrexham	14. 3.00A
G-BXWY	Cameron A-105 HAFB	4410		12. 6.98	Richard Nash Cars Ltd	Norwich	9. 4.00A
G-BXWZ	Cameron A-210 HAFB	4083		9. 6.98	G.C.Ludlow	(Canterbury)	16. 6.99T
					t/a Kent & Canterbury Ballooning		
G-BXXA	Aerospatiale/Alenia ATR-72-202	301	F-WQGJ	27. 4.98	Gill Aviation Ltd	Newcastle	15. 6.01T
			F-OHAG/F-WWLY				
G-BXXC	Scheibe SF-25C Falke 1700	44151	D-KEFA(2)	3. 6.98	K.E.Ballington	(Burton-on-Trent)	24. 5.02
G-BXXD	Cessna 172R Skyhawk	172-80068	N9739F	15. 6.98	R.MacAire	Crowfield	30. 6.01T
					t/a Denston Hall Estate		
G-BXXE	Rand KR-2S	PFA/129-10927		8. 6.98	N.Rawlinson	(Leek)	
					(Under construction 5.99)		
G-BXXF	Cameron A-210 HAFB	4300		2. 4.98	Gone With The Wind Ltd	Windermere	26. 3.00T
G-BXXG	Cameron N-105 HAFB	3662		19. 6.98	Allen Owen Ltd	Wotton-under-Edge	24. 6.99A
G-BXXH	Hatz CB-1	PFA/143-12445		9. 6.98	R.D.Shingler	Forest Farm, Welshpool	
G-BXXI	Grob G-109B	6400	F-CAQR	9. 6.98	M.N.Martin	Leicester	13. 7.01
			F-WAQR				
G-BXXJ	Colt Flying Yacht SS HAFB	1797	JA-A015	10. 6.98	L.V.Mastis	West Bloomfield, Mi., USA	
G-BXXK	Reims Cessna F.172N	1806	D-EOPP	15. 6.98	E.Alexander	Andrewsfield	29. 7.01T
G-BXXL	Cameron N-105 HAFB	4408		16. 7.98	Flying Pictures Ltd	Fairoaks	1. 7.00A
					(Blue Peter titles)		
G-BXXN	Robinson R-22 Beta	0720	N720HH	16. 6.98	Sloane Helicopters Ltd	Sywell	2. 7.01T
G-BXXO	Lindstrand LBL-90B HAFB	534		6. 7.98	Lindstrand Balloons Ltd	Oswestry	7. 9.00A
G-BXXP	Sky 77-24 HAFB	124		20. 7.98	L.van den Avyle	Wachebetie, Belgium	6. 7.00A
G-BXXR	AV-8 Gyroplane	PFA G/15-1263		29. 6.98	P.C.Lovegrove	Didcot	
G-BXXS	Sky 105-24 HAFB	116		30. 7.98	Flying Pictures Ltd	Fairoaks	3. 8.00A
					(Eyewitness Guides titles)		
G-BXXT	Beechcraft 76 Duchess	ME-212	(N212BE)	17. 7.98	Solent Flight Aircraft Ltd	Southampton	21. 7.01T
			F-GBOZ				
G-BXXU	Colt 31A HAFB	4427		21. 8.98	Sade Balloons Ltd	Coulsdon	28. 5.00
G-BXXV	Eurocopter EC-135T-1	0049		2. 7.98	Acorn Mobility Services Ltd	(Shipley)	6. 8.01
G-BXXY	PA-34-220T Seneca III	34-8333061	PH-TLN	3. 7.98	Air Medical Ltd	Oxford	15. 7.01T
			N4295X				
G-BXXZ	CFM Starstreak Shadow SA-II			19. 5.98	A.V. & B.T.Orchard	RAF MOna	13.10.00P
		PFA/206-13171					
G-BXYC	Schweizer 269C	S.1716	D-HFDZ	8. 7.98	L.Williamson & A.Hamilton	(Rotherham)	6. 8.01T
G-BXYD	Eurocopter EC-120B	1006		7. 7.98	Finlay Block Making Equipment Ltd		
						(Dungannon, NI)	13.12.01
G-BXYE	Scintex CP.301-C1 Emeraude	559	F-BTEO	8. 7.98	D.T.Gethin	Swansea	
			F-PTEO/F-WTEO/F-BJFV				
G-BXYF	Colt AS-105 GD Airship	4433		7. 8.98	J.Schneider	Speicher, Germany	31. 8.00A
G-BXYG	Cessna 310D	310-39089	HB-LSF	14. 8.98	Equitus SARL	(Bailleul, France)	7.12.01T
			F-GEJT/3A-MCA/F-BBOT/F-OBOT/(N6789T)				
G-BXYH	Cameron N-105 HAFB	4441		7. 8.98	Virgin Airship & Balloon Co Ltd	Telford	29. 7.00A
					(Fairy titles)		
G-BXYI	Cameron H-34 HAFB	4442		7. 8.98	Virgin Airship & Balloon Co.Ltd	Telford	4. 8.00A
					"Fairy Liquid"		
G-BXYJ	SAN Jodel DR.1050 Ambassadeur	143	F-BJNA	28. 7.98	R.Manning	Netherthorpe	21.10.01
G-BXYK	Robinson R-22 Beta	1579	N4037B	27. 7.98	R.C.Hields	Sherburn in Elmet	19. 8.01T
					t/a Hields Aviation		
G-BXYL	Cameron A-275 HAFB	4450		22. 7.98	The Balloon Club Ltd	Bristol	19. 8.01T
					t/a Bristol Balloons		
G-BXYM	PA-28-235 Cherokee B	28-10858	SE-FAM	18. 8.98	E.Francis	Compton Abbas	21. 7.01T
G-BXYN	Van's RV-6	PFA/181-13265		29. 7.98	J.A.Tooley & R.M.Austin	(Thatcham)	
G-BXYO	PA-28RT-201 Arrow IV	28R-8018046	PH-SDD	18. 8.98	Oxford Aviation Services Ltd	Oxford	1.12.01T
			N8164M				
G-BXYP	PA-28RT-201 Arrow IV	28R-8018050	PH-SBO	18. 8.98	Oxford Aviation Services Ltd	Oxford	1.12.01T
			N8168H				
G-BXYR	PA-28RT-201 Arrow IV	28R-8018101	PH-SDA	3. 8.98	Oxford Aviation Services Ltd	Oxford	11.11.01T
			N8251B				
G-BXYS	PA-28RT-201 Arrow IV	28R-7918145	PH-SBS	3. 8.98	Oxford Aviation Services Ltd	Oxford	8.10.01T
			N29561				
G-BXYT	PA-28RT-201 Arrow IV	28R-7918198	PH-SBN	3. 8.98	Oxford Aviation Services Ltd	Oxford	9. 9.01T
			(PH-SBM)/OO-HLA/N2878W				
G-BXYV	ATR 72-202	322	B-22708	12.10.98	Gill Aviation Ltd.	Newcastle	15.10.01T
			F-WWEQ				
G-BXYX	Van's RV-6	22293	N2399C	31. 7.98	D.Coles	Popham	16.11.00P
	(Built M.T.Hathaway)						
G-BXYY	Reims Cessna FR.172E	0016	OY-AHO	20. 4.98	Haimoss Ltd	Old Sarum	19. 5.01T
			F-WLIP				
G-BXZA	PA-38-112 Tomahawk	38-79A0864	N2480N	6. 8.98	D.A.Whitmore	Cardiff	1. 9.01T

Regn	Type	C/n	P/I	Date	Owner/operator	Probable Base	CA Expy
G-BXZB	Nanchang CJ-6A	2632019	Chinese	18. 9.98	Wingglider Ltd (As 2632019")	Hibaldstow	5. 8.00P
G-BXZD	Westland Gazelle HT.2	WA/1174	XW895	25. 8.98	K.W.Brigden t/a KB Aviation Services	Culdrose	AC
G-BXZE	Westland Gazelle HT.3	WA/1228	XW910	25. 8.98	K.W.Brigden t/a KB Aviation Services	(Truro)	AC
G-BXZF	Lindstrand LBL-90A HAFB	575		8. 1.99	L.Van Den Avyle	Cascais, Portugal	7. 1.00A
G-BXZG	Cameron A-210 HAFB	4424		21. 8.98	Societe Bombard SARL	Beaume, France	13. 8.99A
G-BXZH	Cameron A-210 HAFB	4423		21. 8.98	Societe Bombard SARL	Beaume, France	13. 8.99A
G-BXZI	Lindstrand LBL-90A HAFB	543		14. 8.98	S.Stanley t/a Purple Balloons	Sudbury	13. 8.99A
G-BXZK	MDH MD.900 Explorer	900-00057	N9238T	27. 8.98	Dorset Police Air Support Unit	Dorchester	1. 2.02T
G-BXZM	Cessna 182S	182-80310	N2683L	8.10.98	Rankart Ltd	Hinton-in-The-Hedges	8.10.01T
G-BXZN	Advanced Technologies CH1 ATI	00002	N8186E	25. 8.98	Intora-Firebird plc (Active 10.99)	Southend	
G-BXZO	Pietenpol Air Camper	PFA/47-12818		10. 7.98	P.J.Cooke	(Uckfield)	
G-BXZS	Sikorsky S-76A II Plus	760287	N190AL N190AE/N153AE/N7265A	14. 9.98	Bristow Helicopters Ltd.	Redhill	3. 5.02T
G-BXZT	MS.880B Rallye Club	1733	OO-EDG D-EBDG/F-BSVL	2.9.98	K.P. Snipe	Draycott Farm, Chiseldon	8.12.01
G-BXZU	Bantam B22 S	98-015	ZK-JJL	21. 9.98	M.R.M.Welch	(Lewes)	4.12.00P
G-BXZV	CFM Streak Shadow SA	K293SA & PFA/206-13357		18. 9.98	CFM Aircraft Ltd.	Framlingham	
G-BXZX	Bell 206B Jet Ranger III	2288	N27EA N286CA/N93AT/N16873	28. 8.98	Titan Airways Ltd	Stansted	15.10.01T
G-BXZY	CFM Streak Shadow Srs.DD	296-DD		21. 9.98	Cloudbase Aviation Services Ltd	Redhill	16.12.99P
G-BXZZ	Sky 160-24 HAFB	109		14. 7.98	S.J.Colin & A.S.Pinder t/a Skybus Ballooning	Maidstone	14. 7.00T

G-BYAA – G-BYZZ

Regn	Type	C/n	P/I	Date	Owner/operator	Probable Base	CA Expy
G-BYAA	Boeing 767-204ER	25058	PH-AHM G-BYAA/N60659	23. 4.91	Britannia Airways Ltd	Luton	13.11.02T
G-BYAB	Boeing 767-204ER	25139	(PH-AHN) G-BYAB	11. 6.91	Britannia Airways Ltd "Brian Johnston"	Luton	26. 3.02T
G-BYAD	Boeing 757-204ER	26963		6. 5.92	Britannia Airways Ltd	Luton	22. 2.02T
G-BYAE	Boeing 757-204ER	26964		12. 5.92	Britannia Airways Ltd	Luton	26. 4.01T
G-BYAF	Boeing 757-204ER	26266		13. 1.93	Britannia Airways Ltd	Luton	19. 1.00T
G-BYAH	Boeing 757-204ER	26966		5. 2.93	Britannia Airways Ltd	Luton	10. 2.00T
G-BYAI	Boeing 757-204	26967		1. 3.93	Britannia Airways Ltd	Luton	4. 3.00T
G-BYAJ	Boeing 757-204	25623		4. 3.93	Britannia Airways Ltd	Luton	23. 1.02T
G-BYAK	Boeing 757-204	26267		6. 4.93	Britannia Airways Ltd	Luton	13. 4.00T
G-BYAL	Boeing 757-204	25626		13. 5.93	Britannia Airways Ltd	Luton	18. 5.00T
G-BYAN	Boeing 757-204	27219		26. 1.94	Britannia Airways Ltd	Luton	14. 2.01T
G-BYAO	Boeing 757-204	27235		3. 2.94	Britannia Airways Ltd	Luton	2. 2.00T
G-BYAP	Boeing 757-204	27236		15. 2.94	Britannia Airways Ltd	Luton	14. 2.00T
G-BYAR	Boeing 757-204	27237		1. 3.94	Britannia Airways Ltd	Luton	28. 2.00T
G-BYAS	Boeing 757-204	27238		9. 3.94	Britannia Airways Ltd	Luton	31. 1.02T
G-BYAT	Boeing 757-204	27208		21. 3.94	Britannia Airways Ltd	Luton	24. 3.01T
G-BYAU	Boeing 757-204	27220		18. 5.94	Britannia Airways Ltd	Luton	17. 5.00T
G-BYAV	Taylor JT.1 Monoplane	PFA/055-11010		27. 8.98	C.D.Pidler (Noted 3.99)	Dunkeswell	18. 8.00P
G-BYAW	Boeing 757-204	27234		3. 4.95	Britannia Airways Ltd "Eric Morecambe OBE"	Luton	2. 4.01T
G-BYAX	Boeing 757-204	28834		24. 2.99	Britannia Airways Ltd	Luton	28. 2.02T
G-BYAY	Boeing 757-204	28836		13. 4.99	Britannia Airways Ltd	Luton	12. 4.02T
G-BYAZ	CFM Streak Shadow	PFA/206-12656		1. 9.98	A.G.Wright	(Camberley)	22.11.99P
G-BYBA	Agusta-Bell 206B JetRanger III	8596	G-BHXV G-OWJM/G-BHXV	31. 3.98	R.Forests Ltd	White Waltham	8. 8.02T
G-BYBC	Agusta-Bell 206B JetRanger II	8567	G-BTWW EI-BJV/G-BTWW	31. 3.98	RCR Aviation Ltd	Thruxton	5. 6.00T
G-BYBD	Reims Cessna F.172H	0487	G-OBHX G-AWMU	6. 7.98	Skytrax Aviation Ltd	RAF Halton	23. 6.02T
G-BYBE	Wassmer Jodel D.120A Paris-Nice	269	OO-FDP	24. 7.98	R.J.Page	Swanton Morley	27. 1.02
G-BYBF	Robin R.2160i	329		1.10.98	D.J.R.Lloyd-Evans	Compton Abbas	10. 3.02T
G-BYBI	Bell 206B Jet Ranger III	3668	ZS-RGP N5757M	19.10.98	R & M Engineering Ltd	Dereham	19. 7.02T
G-BYBJ	Hybred 44XLR	MR156/135		22. 1.99	M Gardner	Rochester	29. 1.00P
G-BYBK	Murphy Rebel	260R	N95LD	19. 8.98	D.Webb	Shobdon	8.11.99P
G-BYBL	Gardan GY-80 Horizon 160D	127	F-BMUY	25. 9.98	P.T.Harmsworth	Exeter	AC

Regn	Type	C/n	P/I	Date	Owner/operator	Probable Base	CA Expy
G-BYBM	Avtech Jabiru SK	PFA/274-13377		18. 9.98	M.Rudd	Dorchester	16. 8.00P
G-BYBN	Cameron N-77 HAFB	3082		30. 9.98	M.G.& R.D.Howard	Bristol	29. 3.00A
G-BYBO	Hybred 44XLR Eclipser	155134		14. 9.98	R.Skene	Dartford	29. 1.00P
G-BYBP	Cessna A185F	185-03804	OO-DCD	15.10.98	J.M.Thorpe	Llangarron	4. 2 02
			F-GDCD/F-ODIA/N4593E				
G-BYBR	Rans S-6-116 Coyote II	PFA/204A-13081		10. 7.98	J.B.Robinson	Blackpool	2. 8.00P
G-BYBS	Sky 80-16 HAFB	136		27.10.98	G.W.G.C. Sudlow	Somerton	11.10.99
G-BYBU	Renegade Spirit UK	PFA/188-13229		12.10.98	K.R.Anderson	Shobdon	30. 3.00P
G-BYBV	Rapier	1183-1198-7-W986		20.10.98	M.W.Robson	York	31. 3.00P
G-BYBW	TEAM miniMax	PFA/186-12120		19.10.98	N.E.Johnson	Kettering	22.11.00P
G-BYBX	Slingsby T.67M-260 Firefly	2261		21.10.98	Slingsby Aviation Ltd	York	
G-BYBY	Thorp T-18C Tiger	492	N77KK	17. 7.98	L.J.Joyce	Liverpool	
			(Cf/f 20.8.99)				
G-BYBZ	Avtech Jabiru SK	PFA/274-13290		7. 9.98	A.W.Harris	(Birmingham)	25. 6.00P
G-BYCA	PA-28-140 Cherokee D	28-7125223	PH-VRZ	24. 9.98	R.A.Wakefield	Guernsey	16.11.01T
G-BYCB	Sky 21-16 HAFB	142		28.10.98	Sky Balloons Ltd.	Wrexham	
G-BYCC	Avtech Jabiru SK	PFA/274-13225		24. 7.98	A.R.Silvester	Sackville Farm, Riseley	2. 9.00P
G-BYCD	Cessna 140	13744	N4273N	28. 9.98	G.P.James	Bourn	7. 4.02
			NC4273N				
G-BYCE	Robinson R-44 Astro	0520		12.10.98	Walters Plant Hire Ltd	(Aberdare)	15.10.01T
G-BYCF	Robinson R-22 Beta-II	2866		12.10.98	Stableauto Ltd t/a Lisair	Liverpool	19.10.01T
G-BYCG*	Agusta-Bell 47G-3B1	1513	EC-EGO	12.10.98	Nash Group Ltd	(Warwick)	
			Spanish AF 751-12/HE7B-22/Z7B-22 (Cancelled by CAA 9.2.99)				
G-BYCH*	Agusta-Bell 47G-4A	2519	EC-BMB	12.10.98	Nash Group Ltd	(Warwick)	
			Italian AF MM80504 (Cancelled by CAA 9.2.99)				
G-BYCI*	Agusta-Bell 47G-4A	2530	EC-BSC	12.10.98	Nash Group Ltd	(Warwick)	
			(Cancelled by CAA 9.2.99)				
G-BYCJ	CFM Shadow Series DD			14.10.98	J.W.E.Pearson	St Albans	1. 9.00P
		K294-DD & PFA/161-13258					
G-BYCL	Raj Hamsa X'Air 582(1)	BMAA/HB/088		15.10.98	M.J.Sullivan	(Luton)	28. 6.00P
			(First 450kg microlight to be granted Permit)				
G-BYCM	Rans S6-ES Coyote II	PFA/204-13315		15. 9.98	E.W.McMullan	(Ballyclare, NI)	7.11.00P
G-BYCN	Rans S6-ES Coyote I	PFA/204-13314		15. 9.98	J.K.& R.L.Dunseath		
			(F/f 17.7.99)			(Lisburn/Londonderry, NI)	12. 9.00P
G-BYCO	Rans S6-ES Coyote II	PFA/204-13318		17. 9.98	T.J.Croskery	(Coleraine, NI)	
			(Cf/f 5.10.99)				
G-BYCP	Beechcraft B200 Super King Air		F-GDCS	15.10.98	Comex Services Ltd	Ronaldsway	17.11.01
		BB-966					
G-BYCS	CEA Jodel DR.1051 Sicile	201	F-BJUJ	28.10.98	R.A.Bragger	(Ringwood)	13. 2.02
G-BYCT	Aero L-29A Delfin	395142	ES-YLH	29.10.98	M.Beesley	(Nottingham)	15. 2.00P
			Estonian AF/Soviet AF				
G-BYCU	Robinson R-22 Beta	1094	G-OCGJ	3.11.98	K.S.& S.A.Faria	Redhill	15. 9.01T
G-BYCV	Murphy Maverick	PFA/259-12925		24. 9.98	P.C.Vallence	Arclid, Sandbach	1. 1.00P
G-BYCW	Mainair Blade 912	1185-1198-7-W988		5.11.98	P.Hacking	Ince Blundell	22. 3.00P
G-BYCX	Westland Wasp HAS.Mk.1		ZK-HOX	9.11.98	B.H.Austen	Thruxton	AC
		F.9754 & WA-B-Z3	SA Navy 92		t/a Austen Associates (as"92")		
G-BYCY	III Sky Arrow 650T	PFA/298-13332		10.11.98	A.S.Sprigings	Cambridge	20. 9.00P
G-BYCZ	Avtech Jabiru SK	PFA/274-13388		16.10.98	Business Operational Services Ltd		
						Carlisle	21. 2.00P
G-BYDA	Mc Donnell Douglas DC-10-30	46990	OY-CNO	25. 3.99	Airtours Intnl Airways Ltd	Manchester	29. 3.02T
			XA-SYE/F-GGMZ/C-GFHX/9V-SDA				
G-BYDB	Grob G-115B	8025	VH-JVL	26 3.99	A F Jones	Tatenhill	12. 4.02
			D-EFCG				
G-BYDD	Mooney M.20J	24-0847	D-EIWM	19.10.98	J.Akin	(Billingham)	22. 2.02
G-BYDE	VS.361 Spitfire IX	-	Sov AF	11.11.98	A.H.Soper	(Romford)	
			PT879				
G-BYDF	Sikorsky S-76A	760364	JA6615	9. 1.98	Brecqhou Development Ltd	Guernsey	8. 7.01T
G-BYDG	Beechcraft C24R Sierra	MC-627	OY-AZL	9.11.98	Liddell Aircraft Ltd.	Bournemouth	19. 4.02T
G-BYDH	Airbus A.300B4-203	210	F-OHPO	14. 1.99	TNT Express Worldwide (UK) Ltd	Filton	
			F-WHPK/SX-BAZ/N213PA/F-WZMK (Apollo c/s)				
G-BYDI	Cameron A-210 HAFB	4495		4. 2.99	N.J.Appleton	Bristol	31. 1.00T
					t/a First Flight (Park Furnishers titles)		
G-BYDJ	Colt 120A HAFB	3527		17.11.98	D.K.Hempleman-Adams	Box, Wilts	14. 5.00A
		(Used in successful trans North polar crossing with Phil Dunnington mid 1999)					
G-BYDK	Stampe SV-4C	55	F-BCXY	20.11.98	Bianchi Aviation Film Services Ltd		
		(P/i quoted officially as F-BCXV which was c/n 298)				Booker	
G-BYDL	Hawker Hurricane IIB	-	Sov AF	27.11.98	R.A.Roberts	(Billingshurst)	
			Z5207				
G-BYDM	Cyclone Pegasus Quantum 15	7488		18.11.98	B.J.Fallows	(Ammanford)	19.11.00P
G-BYDN	Fokker F.100-650	11329	N130ML	4. 6.99	Gill Aviation Ltd	Newcastle	3. 6.02T
			SE-DUF/PH-CFG/PH-EZV/(G-FIOZ)/PH-EZV				

Regn	Type	C/n	P/I	Date	Owner/operator	Probable Base	CA Expy
G-BYDO	Fokker F.100-650	11323	N131ML	17. 3.99	Gill Aviation Ltd	Newcastle	25. 3.02T
			SE-DUB/PH-CFA/(PH-LNP)/PH-EZC/(G-FIOT)/PH-EZC				
G-BYDP	Fokker F.100-650	11321	F-WQJA	18. 2.99	Gill Aviation Ltd	Newcastle	10. 3.02T
			N132ML/SE-DUA/PH-RRC/G-FIOS/PH-EZA				
G-BYDR	North American B-25D-30NC Mitchell II	N88972	22. 3.99	Patina Ltd	Duxford	29. 4.00P
	(C/n 100-23644 reported) 100-20644		CF-OGQ		(B J S Grey/The Fighter Collection)		
			RCAF KL161/43-3318 (As "VO-B" in 98 Sqdn RAF c/s) "Grumpy"				
G-BYDS	Messerschmitt Bf109E-3	1342	Luft'ffe	24.11.98	Alpine Deer Group Ltd	Not known	AC
	(On rebuild 11.99 for American Flying Heritage Collection, Seattle, Washington)						
G-BYDT	Cameron N-90 HAFB	4499		28. 1.99	Virgin Airship & Balloon Co Ltd	Telford	28. 1.00A
					(Tesco titles)		
G-BYDU	Cameron Cart SS HAFB	4500		28. 1.99	Virgin Airship & Balloon Co Ltd	Telford	28. 1.00A
					(Tesco titles)		
G-BYDV	Van's RV-6	PFA/181-13264		3.12.98	B.F.Hill	Shenstone	8. 6.00P
G-BYDW	Rotary Air Force RAF 2000 GTX-SE			4.12.98	M.T.Byrne	(London E5)	21. 9.00P
	PFA G/13-1302						
G-BYDX	American General AG-5B Tiger	10051	N374SA	25. 3.99	A.J.Watson	Southampton	19. 4.02
			G-BYDX/F-GKBH/N1191Y t/a Bibit Group				
G-BYDY	Beech 58 Baron	TH-1852	C-GBWF	10.11.98	J.F.Britten	Fairoaks	19.11.01
G-BYDZ	Cyclone Pegasus Quantum 15	7493		22.12.98	W.McCormack	(West Calder)	16.12.99
G-BYEA	Cessna 172P	172-75464	PH-ILL	7.10.98	London Aviation Ltd	Redhill	19.10.01T
			N63661				
G-BYEB	Cessna 172P	172-74634	PH-ILM	7.10.98	London Aviation Ltd	Redhill	18.10.01T
			N52917				
G-BYEC	Glaser-Dirks DG-800B	8-102-B36	D-KSDG	13.11.98	R.L.Mclean	Rufforth	23.11.01
G-BYED	BAC.145 Jet Provost T.MK.5A	N166A	23.11.98	R.E.Todd	North Weald	AC
	EEP/JP/966		XW302				
G-BYEE	Mooney M.20K (231)	25-0282	N231JZ	20. 7.88	R.J.Baker & W.Woods	Coventry	26. 3.01
					t/a Double Echo Flying Group		
G-BYEF	Lockheed L.188CF Electra	2006	EI-CHX	14.12.98	Dart Group plc	Bournemouth	
			SE-IVR/N853U/PH-LLC (Stored in Hunting Cargo c/s as "EI-CHX" 1.00)				
G-BYEG	Cessna 182S Skylane	182-80404	N23697	3. 3.99	High Flying Aviation Ltd	Jersey	4. 3.02
G-BYEH	CEA DR.250/160 Capitaine	15	OO-SOL	6.10.98	E.J.Horsfall	Blackpool	25. 8.02
			F-BMZL				
G-BYEI	Cameron 90SS Chick	4519		1. 4.99	Virgin Airship & Balloon Co Ltd	Telford	11. 4.00A
					(Bic SoftFeel titles)		
G-BYEJ	Scheibe SF-28A Tandem Falke	5713	OE-9070	18.12.98	Total Support Inc (UK) Ltd	(Barnstaple)	14. 3.02
			(D-KDAM)				
G-BYEK	Stoddard-Hamilton Glastar			14. 9.98	G.M.New	(York)	
	PFA/295-13087						
G-BYEL	Van's RV-6	PFA/181-12560		7. 1.99	D.T.Smith	(Stockton-on-Tees)	
G-BYEM	Cessna R182 Skylane RG II	R182-00822	N494	8. 1.99	Swiftair Ltd	Booker	28. 1.02
			D-ELVI/N737FT				
G-BYEN	Cessna 172P	172-74163	PH-ILU	6.10.98	Transcraft Ltd	Elstree	12.11.01T
			N97003				
G-BYEO	Zenair CH.601HDS	PFA/162-13345		11. 1.99	M.J.Diggins	White Waltham	27. 6.00P
	(Tail-wheel u/c)				t/a Cloudbase Flying Group		
G-BYEP	Lindstrand LBL 90B HAFB	560		20.11.98	D.G Macguire	Pulborough	2.12.99A
G-BYER	Cameron C-80 HAFB	4513		19.11.98	Cameron Balloons Ltd	Bristol	7. 1.00A
G-BYES	Cessna 172P	172-74514	PH-ILN	7.10.98	London Aviation Ltd	White Waltham	15.10.01T
			N172TP/N52424				
G-BYET	Cessna 172P	172-75122	PH-ILP	7.10.98	London Aviation Ltd	Redhill	15.10.01T
			N55158				
G-BYEU	Cyclone Pegasus Quantum 15	7495		28. 1.99	T.C.Brown	Roddige, Fradley	9. 2.00P
G-BYEW	Cyclone Pegasus Quantum 15	7499		15. 1.99	D McCormack	(West Calder)	13. 1.00P
G-BYEX	Sky 120-24 HAFB	135		21. 1.99	Ballongflyg Upp and Ner AB		11. 1.00A
						Stockholm, Sweden	
G-BYEY	Lindstrand LBL-21 Silver Dream	577		15. 1.99	Oscair Project Ltd	Taby, Sweden	11. 1.00A
G-BYEZ	Dyn'Aero MCR-01 Ban-bi			25.11.98	J.P.Davies	Old Sarum	28. 6.00P
	(Rotax 912) 47 & PFA 301-13185						
G-BYFA	Reims Cessna F.152 II	1968	G-WACA	19.11.98	A.J.Gomes	Biggin Hill	5. 5.96
G-BYFB	Cameron N-105 HAFB	4532		15. 1.99	Cameron Balloons Ltd	Bristol	11. 2.00A
G-BYFC	Avtech Jabiru SK	PFA/274-13344		5. 2.99	A.C.N.Freeman	Booker	1. 6.00P
	(Crashed 30.5.99 (or prior) & returned to owner's home for repair)						
G-BYFD	Grob G-115A	8100	EI-CCN	15. 1.99	R Jones	Membury	17. 7.93T
	(C/n 8110 officially corrected 7.4.99)		G-BSGE		t/a Southern Sailplanes		
G-BYFE	Cyclone Pegasus Quantum 15	7496		21.6.99	N.C.Hurry Knapthorpe Lodge, Caunton		26. 1.00P
					t/a G-BYPE Flying Group		
G-BYFF	Cyclone Pegasus Quantum 15	7500		1. 2.99	D.Young	Kemble	31. 1.00P
					t/a Kemble Flying Club		
G-BYFG	Europa Avn Europa XS	PFA/247-13407		22. 1.99	P R Brodie	(Guildford)	

Regn	Type	C/n	P/I	Date	Owner/operator	Probable Base	CA Expy
G-BYFH	Bede BD-5B	665		22. 1.99	G M J Monaghan	(Bury St Edmunds)	AC
G-BYFI	CFM Starstreak Shadow SA			11. 2.99	D.G.Cook	Leiston	
		PFA/206-13300					
G-BYFJ	Cameron N-105 HAFB	4545		4. 3.99	R.R.McCormack	Carryduff, Belfast	14. 3.00A
G-BYFK	Cameron Printer-105 SS HAFB	4522		4. 3.99	Flying Pictures Ltd	Fairoaks	18. 3.00A
					(Samsung Printers titles)		
G-BYFL	Diamond HK 36 TTS	36623		5. 2.99	C.N.J.Squibb	RNAS Culdrose	14. 6.02
					t/a Seahawk Gliding Club		
G-BYFM	Jodel DR.1050-MI Sicile Record			26. 2.99	P.M.Standen & A.J.Roxburgh	(Bolton)	
		PFA/304-13237					
G-BYFN	Thruster T600N	9029-T600N-030		8. 2.99	Thruster Air Services Ltd	Wantage	12. 2.00P
G-BYFP	PA-28-181 Archer II	2843238	N4137N	5. 7.99	B.Badley	(Dunmow)	5. 7.02T
			G-BYFP/N41270				
G-BYFR	PA-32R-301 Saratoga IIHP	3246133		13. 4.99	Harpin Ltd	(Nottingham)	12. 5.02T
G-BYFT	Pietenpol Aircamper	PFA/47-13057		22.12.98	M W Elliott	(Tamworth)	
G-BYFU	Lindstrand LBL-105B HAFB	594		9. 3.99	Balloons Lindstrand France		
					Curcay Sur Dive, France		5. 3.00
G-BYFV	TEAM miniMax 91	PFA/186-13431		5. 2.99	W.E.Gillham	(County Durham)	
G-BYFX	Colt 77A HAFB	4547		4. 3.99	Flying Pictures Ltd	Fairoaks	17. 2.00A
					(Agfa titles)		
G-BYFY	Avions Mudry CAP.10B	263	F-GKKD	9. 3.99	R.W.H.Cole	Spilsted Farm, Sedlescombe	
					t/a Cole Aviation		
G-BYGA	Boeing 747-436	28855		15.12.98	British Airways plc	Heathrow	13.12.01T
					(Chelsea Rose t/s)		
G-BYGB	Boeing 747-436	28856		17. 1.99	British Airways plc	Heathrow	16. 1.02T
					(Dove/Colum t/s)		
G-BYGC	Boeing 747-436	25823		19. 1.99	British Airways plc	Heathrow	18. 1.02T
					(Chelsea Rose t/s)		
G-BYGD	Boeing 747-436	28857		26. 1.99	British Airways plc	Heathrow	25. 1.02T
					(Rendezvous t/s)		
G-BYGE	Boeing 747-436	28858		5. 2.99	British Airways plc	Heathrow	4. 2.02T
					(Rendezvous t/s)		
G-BYGF	Boeing 747-436	25824		17. 2.99	British Airways plc	Heathrow	16. 2.02T
					(Chelsea Rose t/s)		
G-BYGG	Boeing 747-436	28859		29. 4.99	British Airways plc	Heathrow	28. 4.02T
					(Rendezvous t/s))		
G-BYGH	Boeing 747-436	25825		.00R	British Airways plc	Heathrow	
					(For delivery 2000)		
G-BYGI	Boeing 747-436	27480		.00R	British Airways plc	Heathrow	
					(For delivery 2000)		
G-BYGJ	Boeing 747-436	27481		.00R	British Airways plc	Heathrow	
					(For delivery 2000)		
G-BYGK	Boeing 747-436	28860		.00R	British Airways plc	Heathrow	
					(For delivery 2000)		
G-BYHC	Cameron Z-90 HAFB	4555		16. 3.99	N.Appleton & R.Waycott	Bristol	28.3.00T
					t/a The Balloon Co & Darlows Ltd (Darlows titles)		
G-BYHD	Robinson R-22 Beta	1455	N900AB	22. 3.99	A S Owen	Newhouse, Lanarks	17. 3.02T
G-BYHE	Robinson R-22 Beta	2023	N82128	14. 1.99	L Smith	Booker	7. 2.02T
			LV-VAB		t/a Helicopter Services		
G-BYHG	Dornier Do.328-100	3098	D-CDAE	7. 4.99	Suckling Aviation (Cambridge) Ltd		
					t/a Scot Airways	Cambridge	6. 4.00T
G-BYHH	PA-28-161 Warrior II	2842050	N4126Z	15. 6.99	Stapleford Flying Club Ltd	Stapleford	17. 6.02T
G-BYHI	PA-28-161 Warrior II	28-8116084	SE-IDP	4. 1.99	Haimoss Ltd	Old Sarum	10. 2.02T
G-BYHK	PA-28-181 Archer II	2843240	N4128V	20. 5.99	Southnet Ltd	(Douglas, IOM)	20. 5.02T
			(G-BYHK)/N9519N				
G-BYHL	DHC-1 Chipmunk 22	C1/0361	WG308	15. 3.99	W.F, M.R.& I.D.Higgins	Gamston	AC
	(Fuselage No.DHBF260 quoted as c/n)						
G-BYHM	BAe 125-800B	258233	VP-BTM	12. 2.99	Corporate Aircraft Leasing Ltd	Jersey	23. 2.00
			VR-BTM/(VR-BQH)/F-WQCD/D-CAVW/G-5-770				
G-BYHN	Mainair Blade 912	1191-0399-7-W994		9. 4.99	R.Stone	(Stoke-on-Trent)	22. 6.00P
G-BYHO	Mainair Blade 912	1197-0599-7-W1000		16. 3.99	P.J.Morton	St.Michaels)	22. 3.00P
G-BYHP	CEA DR.253B Regent	161	OO-CSK	29. 3.99	D.A.Hood	(Malta)	25. 8.02P
G-BYHR	Cyclone Pegasus Quantum 15	7518		6. 4.99	T.Lee	(Luton)	6. 4.00P
G-BYHS	Mainair Blade 912	1187-0299-7-W990		11. 3.99	D.A.Bolton	(Rochdale)	26. 4.00P
G-BYHT	Robin DR.400-180R Remorqueur	811	HB-EUU	9. 4.99	M.Recht	Aberdeen	5. 7.02
G-BYHU	Cameron N-105 HAFB	4567		30. 4.99	Freeup Ltd	Bristol	11. 4.00A
					(Iveco Ford Truck titles)		
G-BYHV	Raj Hamsa X'Air 582	BMAA/HB/090		25. 3.99	S.N.J.Huxtable	(Highbridge)	3.10.00P
	(Rotax 582)						
G-BYHW	Cameron A-160	2848	D-OWEH	25. 3.99	R H Etherington	Siena, Italy	29. 3.00A
G-BYHX	Cameron AS-250 HAFB	4565		16. 4.99	Global Ballooning Ltd	Uckfield	11. 4.00T

Regn	Type	C/n	P/I	Date	Owner/operator	Probable Base	CA Expy
G-BYHY	Cameron V-77	4493		22. 3.99	P Spellward	Bristol	21. 3.00A
G-BYHZ	Sky 160-24	140		13. 5.99	Skyride Balloons Ltd	Kings Lynn	14. 7.00T
G-BYIA	Avtech Jabiru SK	PFA/274-13436		10. 2.99	G.M.Geary	(Durham)	27. 4.00P
G-BYIB	Rans S6-ES	PFA/204-13387		26. 3.99	G A Clayton	(Chesterfield)	15. 9.00P
G-BYIC	Cessna U.206G Turbo Stationair	U206-05476	OY-NUA N113RS/N3RS/N6398U	27. 4.99	D.M.Penney t/a Wild Geese Parachute Club	(Coleraine, NI)	29. 7.02
G-BYID	Rans S6-ES Coyote II	PFA/204-13348		11. 5.99	D.J.Brotherhood	Tollerton	12. 9.00P
G-BYIE	Robinson R-22 Beta-II	2933		22. 4.99	P.Durkin t/a Moorland Windows	Blackpool	27. 4.02T
G-BYIF	Avtech Jabiru XL (Jabiru 2200A/J)	PFA/274A-13364		26. 3.99	D Cassidy	(Canterbury)	21. 6.00P
	(Struck trees landing Stowting, Ashford, Kent 24.7.99 & extensively damaged)						
G-BYIG	Murphy Renegade Spirit	PFA/188-12519		26. 2.99	J.Hatswell	(Menton, France)	15. 9.00P
G-BYII	TEAM miniMax	PFA/186-11820		22. 1.99	J S R Moodie	(Rogart)	
G-BYIJ	CASA I-131E Jungmann	2110	E3B-514	16. 7.90	P.R.Teager & R.N.Crosland	Deanland	17. 4.00P
G-BYIK	Europa Avn Europa	PFA/247-12771		2. 2.99	P. M.Davis	(Abingdon)	25. 8.00P
G-BYIL	Cameron N-105 HAFB	4591		29. 4.99	Oakfield Farm Products Ltd	Broadway	25. 4.00A
G-BYIM	Avtech Jabiru UL	PFA/274A-13397		22.12.98	W J Dale	Nottingham	21. 3.00P
G-BYIN	RAF 2000	PFA G/13-1305		19. 1.99	J.R.Legge	(Rossendale)	
G-BYIO	Colt 105A HAFB	4601		30. 4.99	N.Charbonnier	Aosta, Italy	25. 4.00A
G-BYIP	Aerotek Pitts S-2A	2244	N109WA TC-ECN	23. 2.99	Hampshire Aeroplane Co.Ltd	St.Just	14. 9.02
G-BYIR	Aerotek Pitts S-1S Special	1-0063	N103WA TC-ECP	23. 2.99	Hampshire Aeroplane Co.Ltd	St.Just	14. 9.02
G-BYIS	Cyclone Pegasus Quantum 15	7508		25. 2.99	A.J.Ridell Knapthorpe Lodge, Caunton		22. 2.00P
G-BYIT	Robin DR.400/500	0010		27. 1.99	P.R.Liddle	Rochester	23. 5.02
G-BYIU	Cameron V-90 HAFB	4552		6. 4.99	H.Micketeit	Bielefeld, Germany	31. 3.00A
G-BYIV	Cameron PM-80 HAFB	4595		14. 5.99	Flying Pictures Ltd	(Germany)	17. 5.00A
G-BYIW	Cameron PM-80 HAFB	4596		14. 5.99	Flying Pictures Ltd	(Germany)	17. 5.00A
G-BYIX	Cameron PM-80 HAFB	4597		14. 5.99	Flying Pictures Ltd	(Germany)	8. 9.00A
G-BYIY	Lindstrand LBL-105B	601		26. 3.99	J.H.Dobson	Reading	6. 6.00A
G-BYIZ	Cyclone Pegasus Quantum 15	7504		8. 2.99	J.D.Gray	Eshott	24. 1.00P
G-BYJA	RAF 2000 GTX-SE	PFA G/13-1297		6. 4.99	B.Errington-Weddle	(North Shields)	18. 7.00P
G-BYJB	Mainair Blade 912	1192-0499-7-W995		6. 4.99	J.H.Bradbury Arclid Green, Sandbach		11. 4.00P
G-BYJC	Cameron N-90 HAFB	4562		30. 4.99	D.E.Bentley Ltd	Sheffield	25. 4.00A
G-BYJD	Avtech Jabiru UL	PFA/274-13376		16. 4.99	M.W.Knights	(Dereham)	20. 5.00P
G-BYJE	TEAM miniMax 91	PFA/186-12327		6. 4.99	A.W.Austin	(Cheltenham)	
G-BYJF	Thorp T.211	107	N2545C	20. 5.99	AD Aerospace Ltd	Barton	25. 7.02
G-BYJG	Lindstrand LBL 77A HAFB	600		16. 4.99	Lindstrand Balloons Ltd	Oswestry	9. 5.00A
G-BYJH	Grob G.109B	6512	D-KFRI	19. 5.99	J.D.Scott	Cambridge	20. 5.02
G-BYJI	Europa Avn Europa (Rotax 912UL) 004 & PFA/247-13010		G-ODTI	19. 4.99	A.F.D.Kingdon	(Thirsk)	20. 4.00P
G-BYJJ	Cameron C-80 HAFB	4436	SX-MAX	20. 4.99	Proxim Franchising SRL	Milan, Italy	27. 4.00A
G-BYJK	Cyclone Pegasus Quantum 15	7524		7. 5.99	K.M.MacRae	East Fortune	16. 5.00P
G-BYJL	Aero Designs Pulsar	PFA/202-13311		20. 4.99	F.A.H.Ashmead (Cf/f 20.8.99)	(Lymington)	
G-BYJM	Cyclone AX2000	7523		25. 5.99	A.R.Hood Knapthorpe Lodge, Caunton t/a Caunton Ax2000 Syndicate		20. 5.00P
G-BYJN	Lindstrand LBL-105A HAFB	605		30. 4.99	B.Meeson	Pwllheli	29. 4.00A
G-BYJO	Rans S6-ES Coyoye II (Tail-wheel u/c)	PFA/204-13338		4. 3.99	G.Ferguson	(Kings Lynn)	5.10.00P
G-BYJP	Aerotek Pitts S-1S Special	1-0064	N105WA TC-ECR	16. 3.99	T.Riddle (Rickmansworth) t/a Eaglescott Pitts Group		14. 9.02
G-BYJR	Lindstrand LBL-77B HAFB	608		30. 4.99	C.D.Duthy-James	Presteigne	29. 4.00A
G-BYJS	Socata TB-20 Trinidad	1875	F-OIGE	15. 1.99	J K Sharkey	(London NW5)	25. 1.02
G-BYJT	Zenair CH.601HD	PFA/162-13130		4. 5.99	J.D.T.Tannock	Nottingham	
G-BYJU	Raj Hamsa X'Air 582	396		6. 5.99	C.W.Payne	(Worcester)	
G-BYJV	Cameron A-210 HAFB	4612		4. 6.99	Societe Bombard SRL	Beaune, France	
G-BYJW	Cameron Sphere 105SS HAFB	4585		15. 6.99	Forbes Europe Inc	Far Hills, NJ, USA	19. 5.00A
G-BYJX	Cameron C-70 HAFB	4580		30. 4.99	B.Perona	Torino, Italy	25. 4.00A
G-BYJY	Lindstrand LBL Pharmacist SS	581		19. 4.99	D.E.Wells	(Canada)	24. 5.00A
G-BYJZ	Lindstrand LBL 105A HAFB	609		27. 5.99	Virgin Airship & Balloon Co Ltd	Telford	1. 6.00A
G-BYKA	Lindstrand LBL-69A	612		7. 5.99	Aerial Promotions Ltd	Cannock	9. 5.00A
G-BYKB	Rockwell Commander 114	14121	SE-GSM N4801W	18. 5.99	Gwent Timber Products Ltd	(Newport)	27. 5.00P
G-BYKC	Mainair Blade 912	1196-0599-7-W999		7. 5.99	D.Gabott	(Preston)	24. 5.00P
G-BYKD	Mainair Blade 912	1198-0599-7-W1001		7. 5.99	D.C.Boyle	(Chorley)	3. 6.00P
G-BYKE	Rans S6-ESA	PFA/204-13327		22. 1.99	C.Townsend	(Malmesbury)	
G-BYKF	Enstrom F-28F	725	JA7684	19. 5.99	S.G.Oliphant-Hope	Shoreham	AC
G-BYKG	Pietenpol Aircamper	PFA/47-12827		17. 3.99	K.B.Hodge	(Mold)	
G-BYKI	Cameron N-105 HAFB	4635		4. 6.99	Flying Pictures Ltd	Navan, Ireland	1. 6.00A
G-BYKJ	Westland Scout AH.Mk.1 (Pod build no. F8-6043)	F.9696	XV121	6. 8.99	B.H.Austen t/a Austen Associates	Thruxton	1. 9.00P

235

Regn	Type	C/n	P/I	Date	Owner/operator	Probable Base	CA Expy
G-BYKK	Robinson R-44 Astro	0572		4. 3.99	Transrent plc	Halfpenny Green	18. 3.02T
G-BYKL	PA-28-181 Archer II	28-8090162	HB-PFB N8129Y	15. 7.99	Oxford Aviation Services Ltd	Oxford	18. 7.02T
G-BYKM	PA-34-220T Seneca III	34-8133177	HB-LMV	22. 6.99	Oxford Aviation Services Ltd	Oxford	21.10.02T
G-BYKN	PA-28-161 Warrior II	28-7916307	HB-PDO N2838C/N9613N	22. 6.99	Oxford Aviation Services Ltd	Oxford	1. 8.02T
G-BYKO	PA-28-161 Warrior II	28-8516063	HB-PDO F-GECN/N6920C	22. 6.99	Oxford Aviation Services Ltd	Oxford	1. 8.02T
G-BYKP	PA-28R-201T Turbo Arrow IV 28R-7931029		HB-PDB N3010G	22. 6.99	Oxford Aviation Services Ltd	Oxford	24.11.02T
G-BYKR	PA-28-161 Warrior II	2816061	HB-PLM	22. 6.99	Oxford Aviation Services Ltd	Oxford	25. 7.02T
G-BYKS	Leopoldoff L.6 Colibri	129	N10LC F-BGIT/F-WGIT	19. 4.99	I.M.Callier (On rebuild 9.96)	(Windsor)	
G-BYKT	Cyclone Pegasus Quantum 15	7529		28. 5.99	A.R.Lloyd	Hannington, Northants	26. 5.00P
G-BYKU	Quad City Challenger II PFA/177A-13252			25. 5.99	K.W.Seedhouse	Walsall	
G-BYKV	Avro 504K rep	0015		27. 5.99	Hawker Restorations Ltd	Milden	
G-BYKW	Lindstrand LBL 77B HAFB	620		22. 6.99	Ballons Lindstrand France Curcay sur Dive, France		14. 6.00A
G-BYKX	Cameron N-90 HAFB	4657		10. 8.99	G.Davis "Knowledgepool"	Reading	24. 7.00A
G-BYKY	Avtech Jabiru SK	PFA/274-13385		6. 5.99	N.J.Bond	(Lancing)	30. 8.00P
G-BYKZ	Sky 140-24 HAFB	147		25. 2.99	D.J.Head	Newbury	2. 2.00T
G-BYLA	Clutton-Tabenor FRED Srs 3 PFA/29-10775			11. 5.99	R.Holden-Rushworth	(Devizes)	
G-BYLB	DH.82A Tiger Moth	83286	T5595	24. 5.99	R.Trickett	(King's Lynn)	
G-BYLC	Cyclone Pegasus Quantum 15	7528		25. 6.99	T.Marriott	Derby	24. 6.00P
G-BYLD	Pietenpol Aircamper	PFA/47-13392		27. 4.99	S.Bryan	(Banbury)	
G-BYLE	PA-38-112 Tomahawk II	38-82A0031	N91437	18. 6.99	Surrey & Kent Flying Club Ltd Biggin Hill		AC
G-BYLF	Zenair CH.601HDS	PFA 162-13179		3. 6.99	M.Thomas	(Cowbridge)	
G-BYLG	Robin HR.200/120B	336		20. 7.99	The Cotswold Aero Club Ltd Gloucestershire		1. 8.02T
G-BYLH	Robin HR.200/120B	335		9. 7.99	Mistral Aviation Ltd (Multiflight c/s)	Leeds-Bradford	19. 7.02T
G-BYLI	NOVA Vertex 22	14319		9. 4.99	M.N.Maclean	(Dundee)	
G-BYLJ	LETOV LK-2M Sluka	PFA/263-13464		9. 6.99	N.E.Stokes	(Ellesmere)	
G-BYLK	Mainair Blade	1201-0699-7-W1004		9. 6.99	Hummingbird Microlight Flight Training Ltd (Norwich)		4. 7.00P
G-BYLL	Sequoia Falco F.8L (Lycoming O-320)	PFA/100-10843		6.12.85	N.J.Langrick	Breighton	4. 3.00P
G-BYLM	PA-46-350P Malibu Mirage	4636217		30. 7.99	Palace Aviation Ltd	Blackbushe	5. 8.02T
G-BYLN	Raj Hamsa X'Air 532 (1)	BMAA/HB/096		7. 7.99	R.Gillespie & S.P.McGirr (Killygordon, Ireland)		
G-BYLO	Tipsy Nipper T.66 Srs 1	04	OO-NIA	27. 4.99	M.J.A.Trudgill	RAF Linton-on-Ouse	
G-BYLP	Rand KR-2	PFA/129-11431		19. 4.99	C.S.Hales	(Walsall)	
G-BYLR	Cessna 404 Titan	404-0046	OH-CDC SE-GZH/N5428G	14. 6.99	Edinburgh Air Charter Ltd	Edinburgh	AC
G-BYLS	Bede BD-4 (Lycoming O-320)	PFA/37-11288		13.12.90	G.H.Bayliss	Shobdon	17. 6.00P
G-BYLT	Raj Hamsa X'Air	BMAA/HB/005		8. 6.99	R.J.Turner	(North Tawton)	
G-BYLU	Cameron A-140 HAFB	4566		22. 6.99	Cameron Balloons Ltd	Bristol	20. 6.00A
G-BYLV	Thunder Ax8-105 S2 HAFB	4061		6. 7.99	Wind Line SRL	Iesolo, Italy	20. 6.00A
G-BYLW	Lindstrand LBL 77A HAFB	615		11. 6.99	Associazione Gran Premio Italiano Perugia, Italy		10. 6.00A
G-BYLX	Lindstrand LBL 105A HAFB	614		11. 6.99	Italiana Aeronavi	Cervignano, Italy	30. 6.00A
G-BYLY	Cameron V-77 HAFB	3375	G-ULIA(2)	16.7.97	R.Bayly (See G-ULIA)	Bristol	23. 7.00A
G-BYLZ	Rutan Cozy	PFA/159-12464		21. 5.99	E.R.Allen	(Billingshurst)	
G-BYMA	BAe Jetstream 3202	840	(G-OESU) OH-JAE/N840JX/C-GSCS/G-31-840/N332QK/G-31-840	28. 7.99	Air Kilroe Ltd	Manchester	1. 9.00T
G-BYMB	Diamond Katana DA.20-C1	C0051		9. 7.99	Diamond Aircraft Industries GmbH Weiner Neustadt, Austria		AC
G-BYMC	PA-38-112 Tomahawk II	38-82A0034	N91457	18. 6.99	Surrey & Kent Flying Club Ltd Biggin Hill		AC
G-BYMD	PA-38-112 Tomahawk II	38-82A0009	N91342	18. 6.99	Surrey & Kent Flying Club Ltd (Op Willowair Flying Club)	Southend	19. 8.92T
G-BYME	Gardan GY-80 Horizon 180	207	F-BPAA	24. 5.99	G.C.J.Glenn	(St Mary's)	9. 9.02
G-BYMF	Cyclone Pegasus Quantum 15	7540		9. 7.99	G.R.Stockdale	Rufforth	13. 7.00P
G-BYMG	Cameron A-210 HAFB	4631		17. 9.99	P.Johnson t/a Cloud Nine Balloon Co	Consett	30. 8.00T
G-BYMH	Cessna 152	15284980	N6127P	15. 7.99	PJC (Leasing) Ltd	Stapleford	20. 7.02T

Regn	Type	C/n	P/I	Date	Owner/operator	Probable Base	CA Expy
G-BYMI	Cyclone Pegasus Quantum 15	7533		9. 7.99	N.C.Grayson	(West Bridgford)	13. 7.00P
G-BYMJ	Cessna 152	15285564	N93865	16. 7.99	PJC (Leasing) Ltd	Stapleford	15.11.02T
G-BYMK	Dornier Do.328-100	3062	LN-ASK D-CDXE	9. 6.99	Suckling Aviation (Cambridge) Ltd t/a Scot Airways	Cambridge	8. 6.00T
G-BYML	Dornier Do.328-100	3069	D-CDUL LN-ASL/D-CDXT(2)	27. 7.99	Suckling Aviation (Cambridge) Ltd t/a Scot Airways	Cambridge	27. 7.00T
G-BYMM	Raj Hamsa X'Air 582 (1) (Rotax 582 s/n 4013575) 417 & BMAA/HB/093			29. 4.99	J.R.Pearce	Chilbolton	11. 8.00P
G-BYMN	Rans S6-ESA Coyote II	PFA/204-13477		16. 6.99	H.Smith (Cf/f 26.8.99)	(Bishop Auckland)	5.10.00P
G-BYMO	Campbell Cricket	PFA G/03-1266		16. 7.99	D.G.Hill	(Stockton-on-Tees)	
G-BYMP	Campbell Cricket Mk 1	PFA/G/03-1265		16. 6.99	J.J.Fitzgerald	(Newtownards, NI)	
G-BYMR	Raj Hamsa X'Air 582 (1)	BMAA/HB/094		18. 6.99	W.M/McMinn	(Craigavon, NI)	2.11.00P
G-BYMT	Cyclone Pegasus Quantum 15	7549		16. 7.99	S.A.Owen	(Penicuik)	18. 7.00P
G-BYMU	Rans S6-ES Coyote II	PFA/204-13424		25. 6.99	I.R.Russell & G.Frogley	(Northampton)	
G-BYMV	Rans S6-ES Coyote II	PFA/204-13444		25. 6.99	G.A.Squires	(Wakefield)	
G-BYMW	Boland 52-12 HAFB	001		25. 6.99	C.Jones	(Reading)	
G-BYMX	Cameron A-105 HAFB	4629		16. 7.99	H.Reis	Aachen, Germany	20. 7.00A
G-BYMY	Cameron N-90 HAFB	4653		19. 7.99	Cameron Balloons Ltd	Bristol	18. 8.00A
G-BYMZ	Robin R.2160 Alpha Sport	300	F-GOVZ F-WZZX	15.11.99	Mistral Aviation Ltd	Goodwood	AC
G-BYNA	Reims Cessna F.172H	0626	OO-VDW PH-VDW/(G-AWTH)/F-WLIT	15. 1.99	Heliview Ltd	Blackbushe	4. 3.02T
G-BYND	Cyclone Pegasus Quantum 15	7546		16. 7.99	Jeff Howarth Ltd	(Mansfield)	5. 8.00P
G-BYNE	Pilatus PC-6/B2-H4 Turbo Porter	631	HB-FLW C-FRAV/N631SA/N62148/HS-.../N62148/XW-PFC/XW-PDK/HB-FCR	10. 8.99	D.M. Penny	(Coleraine, NI)	1.10.02
G-BYNF	North American NA-64 Yale I	64-2171	N55904 RCAF 3349	10. 1.00	R.S.Van Dijk	Duxford	
G-BYNH	Rotorway Executive 162F	6323		5. 7.99	R.C.Mackenzie	(Saffron Walden)	7. 7.00P
G-BYNI	Rotorway Executive 90	5216		16. 7.99	M.Bunn	(Norwich)	AC
G-BYNJ	Cameron N-77 HAFB	4661		26. 7.99	A. Giovanni	Mondovi, Italy	24. 7.00A
G-BYNK	Robin HR.200-160	338		28. 7.99	Mistral Aviation Ltd.	Goodwood	30. 9.02T
G-BYNL	Avtech Jabiru SK	PFA/274-13328		20. 7.99	R.C. Daykin	(Newcastle)	7.11.00P
G-BYNM	Mainair Blade 912	1204-0799-7-W1007		20. 7.99	M.W.Holmes	(Ilkeston)	27. 7.00P
G-BYNN	Cameron V-90 HAFB	4643		16. 7.99	M.K.Grigson	(Shoreham)	27. 6.00
G-BYNO	Cyclone Pegasus Quantum 15	7556		5. 8.99	R.J.Newsham	(Fordingbridge)	4. 8.00P
G-BYNP	Rans S6-ES Coyote II	PFA/204-13414		22. 7.99	R.J. Lines	(Scunthorpe)	
G-BYNR	Avtech Jabiru UL	0129	EI-MAT	23. 7.99	A.Parker	(Bingley)	30. 8.00P
G-BYNS	Avtech Jabiru SK	PFA/274-13235		23. 7.99	D.K.Lawry	(Diss)	
G-BYNT	Raj Hamsa X'Air 582 (1)	BMAA/HB/107		20. 7.99	G.R.Wallis	(March)	
G-BYNU	Cameron Thunder AX7-77 HAFB	3520		29. 7.99	Aerial Promotions Ltd	Cannock	1. 8.00A
G-BYNV	Sky 105-24 HAFB	165		11. 8.99	Par Rovelli Construzioni SRL	Mazzini, Italy	26. 7.00
G-BYNW	Cameron H-34 HAFB	4666		27. 7.99	Flying Pictures Ltd (Energis titles)	Fairoaks	24. 7.00A
G-BYNX	Cameron RX-105 HAFB	4656		26. 7.99	Cameron Balloons Ltd	London	1.11.00A
G-BYNY	Beechcraft 76 Duchess	ME-247	N247ME OE-FES/N6635H	4. 8.99	Magenta Ltd	(Cumnor, Oxon)	13. 9.02T
G-BYNZ	Westland Scout AH.Mk.1 (Pod build no. F8-9047)	F.9736	XW281	6. 8.99	Military Helicopters Ltd (As "XW281/U")	Thruxton	23.11.00P
G-BYOA	Slingsby T.67M-200	2262		8. 6.99	Hunting Aviation Ltd	RAF Barkston Heath	23. 9.02T
G-BYOB	Slingsby T.67M-200	2263		8. 6.99	Hunting Aviation Ltd	RAF Barkston Heath	6.10.02T
G-BYOF	Robin R.2160I	337		29. 7.99	Mistral Aviation Ltd.	Shoreham	12.10.02T
G-BYOG	Cyclone Pegasus Quantum 15	7555		15. 9.99	A.Foote & M.Fizelle	(Slough)	14. 9.00P
G-BYOH	Raj Hamsa X'Air 582 (1)	BMAA/HB/101		23. 7.99	G.A.J.Salter	(Taunton)	3.11.00P
G-BYOI	Sky 80-16 HAFB	163		5. 8.99	I.S.& S.W.Watthews	Cark-in-Cartmel	4. 8.00
G-BYOJ	Raj Hamsa X'Air 582 (1)	BMAA/HB/108		23. 7.99	R.R.Hadley	(Budleigh Salterton)	
G-BYOK	Cameron V-90 HAFB	3726		9. 8.99	D.S.Wilson	Norwich	8..8.00A
G-BYOM	Sikorsky S-76C	760464	G-IJCB	25. 8.99	Skyhopper Ltd	Blackbushe	25. 3.00T
G-BYON	Mainair Blade	1199-0599-7-W1002		4. 8.99	S.Mills & G.M.Hobman	(North Ferriby)	31. 8.00P
G-BYOO	CFM Streak Shadow	PFA/206-12806		6. 8.99	C.I.Chegwen	(Telford)	20.10.00P
G-BYOP	Robinson R-22 Beta	1682	N4072S	17. 8.99	Sloane Helicopters Ltd	Sywell	2. 9.02T
G-BYOR	Raj Hamsa X'Air 582 (1)	BMAA/HB/117		11. 8.99	A.R.Walker	(Doncaster)	
G-BYOS	Mainair Blade 912	1209-0899-7-W1012		6. 8.99	D.Smith t/a Baxby Airsports Club	(Husthwaite)	25. 8.00P
G-BYOT	Rans S6-ES Coyote II	PFA/204-13363		29. 7.99	H.F.Blakeman	(Crewe)	
G-BYOU	Rans S6-ES Coyote II	PFA/204-13460		1. 6.99	R.Germany Knapthorpe Lodge, Caunton		12. 9.00P
G-BYOV	Cyclone Pegasus Quantum 15	7554		17. 8.99	K.W.A.Ballinger	(Wokingham)	12. 8.00P
G-BYOW	Mainair Blade	1207-0899-7-W1010		9. 8.99	N.Forster	(Glasgow)	15. 9.00P
G-BYOX	Cameron Z-90 HAFB	4672		31. 8.99	Virgin Airship & Balloon Co.Ltd	Telford	18. 8.00A

Regn	Type	C/n	P/I	Date	Owner/operator	Probable Base	CA Expy
G-BYOY	Canadair T-33AN Silver Star 3 T33-231		N36TH N333DV/N134AT/N10018/N134AT/RCAF 21231	8. 2.00	K.K.Gerstorfer	North Weald	
G-BYOZ	Mainair Rapier 1208-0899-7-W1011			12. 8.99	M.Morgan	Arclid Green, Sandbach	6. 9.00P
G-BYPA	Aerospatiale AS.355F2 Twin Squirrel 5348		G-NWPI F-GMAO	20. 8.99	Aeromega Aviation Ltd	(Ipswich)	28. 3.00T
G-BYPB	Cyclone Pegasus Quantum 15	7566		3. 9.99	G.J.Slater	Clench Common	1.9.00P
G-BYPC	Lindstrand LBL AS2 HAFB	634		17. 8.99	Lindstrand Balloons Ltd	Oswestry	
G-BYPD	Cameron A-105 HAFB	4680		6. 1.00	Headland Hotel Co Ltd	Newquay	
G-BYPE	Gardan GY-80 Horizon 160	180	F-BNYD	10. 8.99	H.I.Smith & P.R.Hendry-Smith	Swanton Morley	4.11.02
G-BYPF	Thruster T600N 9089-T600N-034 (Rotax 582UL)			17. 8.99	S.Reid	Ley Farm, Chirk	1. 9.00P
G-BYPG	Thruster T600N 9089-T600N-035			17. 8.99	Thruster Air Services Ltd	Wantage	23.11.00p
G-BYPH	Thruster T600N 9089-T600N-036			17. 8.99	Thruster Air Services Ltd	Wantage	23.11.00p
G-BYPJ	Cyclone Pegasus Quantum 15	7565		17. 9.99	P.J.Manders	(Colchester)	15. 9.00p
G-BYPK	Europa Avn Europa PFA/247-13502			20. 8.99	N.J.France (Cf/f 6.12.99)	(Heanor)	
G-BYPL	Cyclone Pegasus Quantum 15	7558		9. 9.99	C.I.D.H.Garrison	Sutton Meadows	9. 9.00p
G-BYPM	Europa Avn Europa XS PFA/247-13418			16.12.98	P.Mileham	(Saffron Walden)	
G-BYPN	SOCATA MS.880B Rallye Club	2043	F-BTPN	23. 7.99	R.& T.C.Edwards	Gamston	AC
G-BYPO	Raj Hamsa X'Air 582 (1) BMAA/HB/111			25. 8.99	N.G.Woodall & A.S.Leach	(Warrington)	
G-BYPP	Medway Rebel SS 168/146			25.10.99	J.L.Gowens	(Maidstone)	
G-BYPR	Zenair CH.601HD PFA/162-12816			25. 8.99	D.Clark	(Stonehaven)	
G-BYPT	Rans S6-ES Coyote II PFA/204-13508 (Jabiru 2200)			27. 8.99	G.R & J.A.Pritchard	Newhouse Farm, Hardwicke	8.11.00P
G-BYPU	PA-32R-301 Saratoga II HP 3246150		N4160K	2.12.99	Plane Talking Ltd	Elstree	1.12.02T
G-BYPV	Cameron Colt 120A HAFB	4628		31. 8.99	Cameron Balloons Ltd.	Bristol	15. 9.00A
G-BYPW	Raj Hamsa X'Air 582 (3) BMAA/HB/113			1. 9.99	P.A.Mercer	(Ashton-on-Ribble)	
G-BYPY	Ryan ST3-KR	1001	F-AZEV N18926	5.10.99	P.B.Rice	Breighton	
G-BYPZ	Rans S6-116 Coyote II PFA/204A-13448			14. 7.99	P.G.Hayward	(North Walsham)	
G-BYRA	BAe Jetstream 3202	845	OH-JAG N845JX/N845AE/G-31-845	26.10.99	Eastern Airways Ltd	Manchester	21.11.00T
G-BYRC	Westland Wessex HC.Mk.2 WA671		XT671	23. 9.99	D.Brem-Wilson Honey Crock Farm, Redhill		AC
G-BYRE*	Rans S10 Sakota PFA/194-11729			23. 7.91	R.J. & M.B.Trickey (Cancelled by CAA 8.5.99)	(Ellon, Aberdeen)	
G-BYRF	Cameron N-77 HAFB	4692		20. 9.99	AAA Entertainments Ltd Richmond, Surrey		15 .9.00A
G-BYRG	Rans S6-ES Coyote II PFA/204-13518			9. 9.99	Sport Air UK Ltd (Cf/f 29.9.99)	Felixkirk	
G-BYRH	Medway HybredR 44XLR MR165/143			25.10.99	D.J.Stock	(Bantry, Co.Cork)	13.11.00P
G-BYRJ	Cyclone Pegasus Quantum 15	7548		24. 9.99	V.Causey & F.G.Green	(Chesterfield)	27 .9.00P
G-BYRK	Cameron V-42 HAFB	4662		14. 7.99	Gone With The Wind Ltd	Twain-Harte, Ca, USA	22..8.00A
G-BYRL	Diamond HK36 TTC Super Dimona 36.654			6.10.99	Diamond Aircraft UK Ltd	Gamston	15.12.02T
G-BYRM	BAe Jetstream 3202	847	OH-JAF N847JX/N847AE/N332QN/G-31-847	16.12.99	Air Kilroe Ltd	Manchester	AC
G-BYRO	Mainair Blade 1210-0899-7-W1013			20. 8.99	G.P.Jones	(Stoke-on-Trent)	6 9.00P
G-BYRP	Mainair Blade 912 1075-1295-7-W877			15. 9.99	B.J.Bowditch	(Bristol)	14.10.00P
G-BYRR	Mainair Blade 912 1211-0999-7-W1015			17. 8.99	G.R.Sharples	(Harrow)	16 .9.00P
G-BYRS	Rans S6-ES Coyote II PFA 204-13425			17. 9.99	R.Beniston	(Knaresborough)	
G-BYRT	Beechcraft F33A Bonanza CE-971		ZS-LFB N18384	1. 9.99	ILS Air Ltd	Cambridge	14.10.02T
G-BYRU	Cyclone Pegasus Quantum 15	7574		24. 9.99	M.A.McClelland t/a Sarum QTM912 Group	Old Sarum	27 .9.000
G-BYRV	Raj Hamsa X'Air 582 (1) BMAA/HB/106			10. 9.99	A.Hipkin	(Stourbridge)	
G-BYRX	Westland Scout AH.Mk.1 F.9640		XT634	5.10.99	Miltary Helicopters Ltd	Thruxton	AC
G-BYRY	Slingsby T.67M-200	2042	B-HZQ VR-HZQ	28. 9.99	D.S.Balman & W.R.Tandy	(Hong Kong, PRC)	AC
G-BYRZ	Lindstrand LBL 77M HAFB	643		28. 9.99	Lindstrand Balloons Ltd	Oswestry	5.12.00A
G-BYSA	Europa Avn Europa XS PFA/247-13199			23. 8.99	B.Allsop (Cf/f 17.11.99)	(Chesterfield)	
G-BYSE	Agusta-Bell 206B JetRanger II	8553	G-BFND	3.11.81	Bewise Ltd (Op PLM Dollar Group)	Inverness/Coventry	14. 7.02T
G-BYSF	Avtech Jabiru UL PFA/274A-13356			5.10.99	M.I.M.Smith	(Kelso)	7.11.00P
G-BYSG	Robin HR.200/120B	339		22.11.99	Mistral Aviation Ltd	Goodwood	9.12.02T
G-BYSI	WSK PZL Koliber 160A 04990081		SP-WGI	21. 1.00	PZL International Aviation Marketing & Sales plc	North Weald	
G-BYSJ	DHC-1 Chipmunk 22 C1/0021		SE-BON WB569	12.10.99	Propshop Ltd	Duxford	AC
G-BYSL	Cameron O-56 HAFB	1269		10. 4.86	S.M.M.Askey	Tring	22. 8.96A

Regn	Type	C/n	P/I	Date	Owner/operator	Probable Base	CA Expy
G-BYSN	Rans S6-ES Coyote II	PFA/204-13459		19.10.99	A.L.& A.R.Roberts (Coningsby) (Cf/f 19.11.99)		
G-BYSO	PA-46-350P Malibu Mirage	4636249		5. 1.00	Anglo American Airmotive Ltd Bournemouth		AC
G-BYSP	PA-28-181 Archer II	28-8590047	D-EAUL N6909D	12.10.99	Bobbington Air Training School Ltd Halfpenny Green		16.11.02T
G-BYSS	Medway Rebel SS	167/145		25.10.99	C.R.Stevens (Ashford)		
G-BYST	Cameron Home Special-105 SS HAFB	4691		15.10.99	Cameron Balloons Ltd (Australia)		2.12.00A
G-BYSU	Cameron Freddo-105 SS HAFB	4701		15.10.99	Cameron Balloons Ltd Melbourne, Australia		20.12.00A
G-BYSV	Cameron N-120 HAFB	4704		15.10.99	Cameron Balloons Ltd Bristol		22.11.00T
G-BYSX	Cyclone Pegasus Quantum 15	7586		23.11.99	R.H.Braithwaite RAF Cosford t/a RAF Microlight Flying Association		14.11.00O
G-BYSY	Raj Hamsa X'Air 582 (1)	BMAA/HB/109		21.10.99	J.M.Davidson (Tewkesbury)		
G-BYTA	Kolb Twinstar Mk.3	PFA/205-13240		2. 9.99	R.E.Gray (Oxted)		
G-BYTC	Cyclone Pegasus Quantum Q2 Sport 15	7571		25.10.99	J.Hood (Morpeth)		25.10.00P
G-BYTD	Robinson R-22 Beta-II	3003		25.10.99	Ace Air Flights Ltd (Blackrock, Co. Dublin)		4.11.02T
G-BYTE	Robinson R-22 Beta	1250		18. 4.90	J.W.Lanchbury Shobdon (Crashed on Brecon Beacons 7.11.99)		17. 6.02T
G-BYTG	Glaser-Dirks DG-400	4-211	D-KBBP	18.11.99	P.R.Williams & B.Sebestik (Brackley)		
G-BYTH	Airbus A.320-231	0429	EI-TLE D-AORX/N429RX/F-WWIZ	21. 1.00	Airtours International Airways Ltd Manchester		
G-BYTI	PA-24-250 Comanche	24-3489	D-ELOP N8297P/N10F	9.11.99	B.Richardson Slinfold		AC
G-BYTJ	Cameron Concept-80 HAFB	4703		19.11.99	M.White Cirencester		16.11.00A
G-BYTK	Avtech Jabiru UL	PFA/274A-13465		8.11.99	K.A.Fagan & S.R.Pike (High Wycombe)		
G-BYTL	Mainair Blade 912	1224-0999-7-W1017		19.10.99	A.J.Sharp Leicester		17.10.00P
G-BYTM	Dyn'Aero MCR-01 Ban-bi	PFA/301-13440		1.10.99	I.Lang (Shrewley, Warwick)		
G-BYTN	DH.82A Tiger Moth	3993	7014M N6720	18.11.99	B.D.Hughes (Kempston)		
G-BYTO	Aerospatiale/Alenia ATR-72-212	472	G-OILA F-WWEJ	17.11.99	British World Airlines Ltd Gatwick (Leased to CityFlyer Express)		27. 3.02T
G-BYTP	Aerospatiale/Alenia ATR-72-212	473	G-OILB F-WWEG	30. 4.99	CityFlyer Express Ltd Gatwick		29. 5.02T
G-BYTR	Raj Hamsa X'Air 582 (1)	BMAA/HB/105		5.10.99	A.P.Roberts & R.Dunn (Weymouth)		
G-BYTS	Montgomerie Bensen B.8MR	MGM-2		22. 9.99	M.G.Mee (South Shields)		AC
G-BYTT	Raj Hamsa X'Air 582 (1)	BMAA/HB/100		22. 9.99	R.P.& C.E.Reeves (Newton Abbot)		
G-BYTU	Mainair Blade 912	1225-1099-7-W1018		26.11.99	L.Chesworth (Malpas)		20.12.00P
G-BYTV	Avtech Jabiru UL	PFA/274A-13454		3.11.99	E.Bentley (Stockton-on-Tees)		
G-BYTX	Whittaker MW.6S Fat Boy Flyer	PFA/164-12819		2.12.99	J.K.Ewing (Poole)		
G-BYTY	Dornier Do.328-100	3104	D-CDXJ 5N-BRI	2.12.99	Sucking Airways (Cambridge) Ltd t/a Scot Airways Cambridge		8.12.02T
G-BYTZ	Raj Hamsa X'Air 582 (1)	BMAA/HB/120		26.10.99	A.B.Wilson & K.C.Millar (Dromore, NI)		
G-BYUA	Grob G.115E Tutor	82086E	D-EUKB	22. 7.99	Bombardier Services (UK) Ltd RAF Cranwell		5. 8.02T
G-BYUB	Grob G.115E Tutor	82087E		22. 7.99	Bombardier Services (UK) Ltd RAF Cranwell		5. 8.02T
G-BYUC	Grob G.115E Tutor	82088E		22. 7.99	Bombardier Services (UK) Ltd RAF Wyton		5. 8.02T
G-BYUD	Grob G.115E Tutor	82089E		22. 7.99	Bombardier Services (UK) Ltd RAF Wyton		5. 8.02T
G-BYUE	Grob G.115E Tutor	82090E		12. 8.99	Bombardier Services (UK) Ltd RAF Cranwell		30. 8.02T
G-BYUF	Grob G.115E Tutor	82091E		12. 8.99	Bombardier Services (UK) Ltd RAF Wyton		30..8.02T
G-BYUG	Grob G.115E Tutor	82092E		22. 9.99	Bombardier Services (UK) Ltd RAF Cranwell		27 .9.02T
G-BYUH	Grob G.115E Tutor	82093E		22. 9.99	Bombardier Services (UK) Ltd RAF Cranwell		27 .9.02T
G-BYUI	Grob G.115E Tutor	82094E		24. 9.99	Bombardier Services (UK) Ltd RAF Wyton		27 .9.02T
G-BYUJ	Grob G.115E Tutor	82095E		24. 9.99	Bombardier Services (UK) Ltd RAF Wyton		27 .9.02T
G-BYUK	Grob G.115E Tutor	82096E		18.10.99	Bombardier Services (UK) Ltd RAF Cranwell		28.10.02T
G-BYUL	Grob G.115E Tutor	82097E		18.10.99	Bombardier Services (UK) Ltd RAF Cranwell		28.10.02T
G-BYUM	Grob G.115E Tutor	82098E		18.10.99	Bombardier Services (UK) Ltd RAF Cranwell		28.10.02T
G-BYUN	Grob G.115E Tutor	82099E		18.10.99	Bombardier Services (UK) Ltd RAF Cranwell		28.10.02T
G-BYUO	Grob G.115E Tutor	82100E		19.11.99	Bombardier Services (UK) Ltd RAF Cranwell		28.11.02T
G-BYUP	Grob G.115E Tutor	82101E		19.11.99	Bombardier Services (UK) Ltd RAF Cranwell		28.11.02T
G-BYUR	Grob G.115E Tutor	82102E		19.11.99	Bombardier Services (UK) Ltd RAF Cranwell		28.11.02T
G-BYUS	Grob G.115E Tutor	82103E		19.11.99	Bombardier Services (UK) Ltd RAF Cranwell		28.11.02T
G-BYUT	Grob G.115E Tutor	82104E		7.12.99	Bombardier Services (UK) Ltd RAF Cranwell		14.12.02T
G-BYUU	Grob G.115E Tutor	82105E		7.12.99	Bombardier Services (UK) Ltd RAF Cranwell		AC
G-BYUV	Grob G.115E Tutor	82106E		7.12.99	Bombardier Services (UK) Ltd RAF Cranwell		14.12.02T
G-BYUW	Grob G.115E Tutor	82107E		7.12.99	Bombardier Services (UK) Ltd RAF Cranwell		AC
G-BYUX	Grob G.115E Tutor	82108E		18. 1.00	Bombardier Services (UK) Ltd RAF Cranwell		
G-BYUY	Grob G.115E Tutor	82109E		18. 1.00	Bombardier Services (UK) Ltd RAF Cranwell		
G-BYUZ	Grob G.115E Tutor	82110E		18. 1.00	Bombardier Services (UK) Ltd RAF Cranwell		

Regn	Type	C/n	P/I	Date	Owner/operator	Probable Base	CA Expy
G-BYVA	Grob G.115E Tutor	82111E		18. 1.00	Bombardier Services (UK) Ltd RAF Cranwell		
G-BYVB	Grob G.115E Tutor	82112E		R	Bombardier Services (UK) Ltd RAF Cranwell		
G-BYVC	Grob G.115E Tutor	82113E		R	Bombardier Services (UK) Ltd RAF Cranwell		
G-BYVD	Grob G.115E Tutor	82114E		R	Bombardier Services (UK) Ltd RAF Cranwell		
G-BYVE	Grob G.115E Tutor	82115E		R	Bombardier Services (UK) Ltd RAF Cranwell		
G-BYVF	Grob G.115E Tutor	82116E		R	Bombardier Services (UK) Ltd RAF Cranwell		
G-BYVG	Grob G.115E Tutor	82117E		R	Bombardier Services (UK) Ltd RAF Cranwell		
G-BYVH	Grob G.115E Tutor	82118E		R	Bombardier Services (UK) Ltd RAF Cranwell		
G-BYVI	Grob G.115E Tutor	82119E		R	Bombardier Services (UK) Ltd RAF Cranwell		
G-BYVJ	Grob G.115E Tutor	82120E		R	Bombardier Services (UK) Ltd RAF Cranwell		
G-BYVK	Grob G.115E Tutor	82121E		R	Bombardier Services (UK) Ltd RAF Cranwell		
G-BYVL	Grob G.115E Tutor	82122E		R	Bombardier Services (UK) Ltd RAF Cranwell		
G-BYVM	Grob G.115E Tutor	82123E		R	Bombardier Services (UK) Ltd RAF Cranwell		
G-BYVN	Grob G.115E Tutor	82124E		R	Bombardier Services (UK) Ltd RAF Cranwell		
G-BYVO	Grob G.115E Tutor	82125E		R	Bombardier Services (UK) Ltd RAF Cranwell		
G-BYVP	Grob G.115E Tutor	82126E		R	Bombardier Services (UK) Ltd RAF Cranwell		
G-BYVR	Grob G.115E Tutor	82127E		R	Bombardier Services (UK) Ltd RAF Cranwell		
G-BYVS	Grob G.115E Tutor	82128E		R	Bombardier Services (UK) Ltd RAF Cranwell		
G-BYVT	Grob G.115E Tutor	82129E		R	Bombardier Services (UK) Ltd RAF Cranwell		
G-BYVU	Grob G.115E Tutor	82130E		R	Bombardier Services (UK) Ltd RAF Cranwell		
G-BYVV	Grob G.115E Tutor	82131E		R	Bombardier Services (UK) Ltd RAF Cranwell		
G-BYVW	Grob G.115E Tutor	82132E		R	Bombardier Services (UK) Ltd RAF Cranwell		
G-BYVX	Grob G.115E Tutor	82133E		R	Bombardier Services (UK) Ltd RAF Cranwell		
G-BYVY	Grob G.115E Tutor	82134E		R	Bombardier Services (UK) Ltd RAF Cranwell		
G-BYVZ	Grob G.115E Tutor	82135E		R	Bombardier Services (UK) Ltd RAF Cranwell		
G-BYWA	Grob G.115E Tutor	82136E		R	Bombardier Services (UK) Ltd RAF Cranwell		
G-BYWB	Grob G.115E Tutor	82137E		R	Bombardier Services (UK) Ltd RAF Cranwell		
G-BYWC	Grob G.115E Tutor	82138E		R	Bombardier Services (UK) Ltd RAF Cranwell		
G-BYWD	Grob G.115E Tutor	82139E		R	Bombardier Services (UK) Ltd RAF Cranwell		
G-BYWE	Grob G.115E Tutor	82140E		R	Bombardier Services (UK) Ltd RAF Cranwell		
G-BYWF	Grob G.115E Tutor	82141E		R	Bombardier Services (UK) Ltd RAF Cranwell		
G-BYWG	Grob G.115E Tutor	82142E		R	Bombardier Services (UK) Ltd RAF Cranwell		
G-BYWH	Grob G.115E Tutor	82143E		R	Bombardier Services (UK) Ltd RAF Cranwell		
G-BYWI	Grob G.115E Tutor	82144E		R	Bombardier Services (UK) Ltd RAF Cranwell		
G-BYWJ	Grob G.115E Tutor	82145E		R	Bombardier Services (UK) Ltd RAF Cranwell		
G-BYWK	Grob G.115E Tutor	82146E		R	Bombardier Services (UK) Ltd RAF Cranwell		
G-BYWL	Grob G.115E Tutor	82147E		R	Bombardier Services (UK) Ltd RAF Cranwell		
G-BYWM	Grob G.115E Tutor	82148E		R	Bombardier Services (UK) Ltd RAF Cranwell		
G-BYWN	Grob G.115E Tutor	82149E		R	Bombardier Services (UK) Ltd RAF Cranwell		
G-BYWO	Grob G.115E Tutor	82150E		R	Bombardier Services (UK) Ltd RAF Cranwell		
G-BYWP	Grob G.115E Tutor	82151E		R	Bombardier Services (UK) Ltd RAF Cranwell		
G-BYWR	Grob G.115E Tutor	82152E		R	Bombardier Services (UK) Ltd RAF Cranwell		
G-BYWS	Grob G.115E Tutor	82153E		R	Bombardier Services (UK) Ltd RAF Cranwell		
G-BYWT	Grob G.115E Tutor	82154E		R	Bombardier Services (UK) Ltd RAF Cranwell		
G-BYWU	Grob G.115E Tutor	82155E		R	Bombardier Services (UK) Ltd RAF Cranwell		
G-BYWV	Grob G.115E Tutor	82156E		R	Bombardier Services (UK) Ltd RAF Cranwell		
G-BYWW	Grob G.115E Tutor	82157E		R	Bombardier Services (UK) Ltd RAF Cranwell		
G-BYWX	Grob G.115E Tutor	82158E		R	Bombardier Services (UK) Ltd RAF Cranwell		
G-BYWY	Grob G.115E Tutor	82159E		R	Bombardier Services (UK) Ltd RAF Cranwell		
G-BYWZ	Grob G.115E Tutor	82160E		R	Bombardier Services (UK) Ltd RAF Cranwell		
G-BYXA	Grob G.115E Tutor	82161E		R	Bombardier Services (UK) Ltd RAF Cranwell		
G-BYXB	Grob G.115E Tutor	82162E		R	Bombardier Services (UK) Ltd RAF Cranwell		
G-BYXC	Grob G.115E Tutor	82163E		R	Bombardier Services (UK) Ltd RAF Cranwell		
G-BYXD	Grob G.115E Tutor	82164E		R	Bombardier Services (UK) Ltd RAF Cranwell		
G-BYXE	Grob G.115E Tutor	82165E		R	Bombardier Services (UK) Ltd RAF Cranwell		
G-BYXF	Grob G.115E Tutor	82166E		R	Bombardier Services (UK) Ltd RAF Cranwell		
G-BYXG	Grob G.115E Tutor	82167E		R	Bombardier Services (UK) Ltd RAF Cranwell		
G-BYXH	Grob G.115E Tutor	82168E		R	Bombardier Services (UK) Ltd RAF Cranwell		
G-BYXI	Grob G.115E Tutor	82169E		R	Bombardier Services (UK) Ltd RAF Cranwell		
G-BYXJ	Grob G.115E Tutor	82170E		R	Bombardier Services (UK) Ltd RAF Cranwell		
G-BYXK	Grob G.115E Tutor	82171E		R	Bombardier Services (UK) Ltd RAF Cranwell		
G-BYXL	Grob G.115E Tutor	82172E		R	Bombardier Services (UK) Ltd RAF Cranwell		
G-BYXM	Grob G.115E Tutor	82173E		R	Bombardier Services (UK) Ltd RAF Cranwell		
G-BYXN	Grob G.115E Tutor	82174E		R	Bombardier Services (UK) Ltd RAF Cranwell		
G-BYXO	Grob G.115E Tutor	82175E		R	Bombardier Services (UK) Ltd RAF Cranwell		
G-BYXP	Grob G.115E Tutor	82176E		R	Bombardier Services (UK) Ltd RAF Cranwell		
G-BYXR	Grob G.115E Tutor	82177E		R	Bombardier Services (UK) Ltd RAF Cranwell		
G-BYXS	Grob G.115E Tutor	82178E		R	Bombardier Services (UK) Ltd RAF Cranwell		
G-BYXT	Grob G.115E Tutor	82179E		R	Bombardier Services (UK) Ltd RAF Cranwell		
G-BYXU	PA-28-161 Cherokee Warrior II	28-7716097	EI-BXU G-BNUP/N2282Q	8. 1.99	W T King	Brittas Bay	11. 3.02

Regn	Type	C/n	P/I	Date	Owner/operator	Probable Base	CA Expy
G-BYXV	Medway EclipseR (Jabiru)	162/140		25.10.99	K.Swann	(Rochester)	
G-BYXW	Medway EclipseR (Jabiru)	166/144		25.10.99	J.Swann	(Rochester)	
G-BYXX	Grob G.115E Tutor	82180E		R	Bombardier Services (UK) Ltd	RAF Cranwell	
G-BYXY	Grob G.115E Tutor	82181E		R	Bombardier Services (UK) Ltd	RAF Cranwell	
G-BYXZ	Grob G.115E Tutor	82182E		R	Bombardier Services (UK) Ltd	RAF Cranwell	
G-BYYA	Grob G.115E Tutor	82183E		R	Bombardier Services (UK) Ltd	RAF Cranwell	
G-BYYB	Grob G.115E Tutor	82184E		R	Bombardier Services (UK) Ltd	RAF Cranwell	
G-BYYC	Hapi Cygnet SF-2A	PFA/182-12311		25.11.99	C.D.Hughes & G.H.Smith	(Birmingham)	
G-BYYF	Boeing 737-229C	21738	OO-SDR	11. 1.00	European Aviation Air Charter Ltd	Bournemouth	
G-BYYE	Lindstrand LBL 77A HAFB	151		25.11.99	D.J.Cook	Norwich	5.12.00A
G-BYYG	Slingsby T.67C	2101	PH-SGI	30.11.99	B.Dixon (Exported 1999)	Newcastle	
G-BYYH	Aerospatiale AS.350B Ecureuil	1594	SE-JDU LN-OTO	8. 2.00	RCR Aviation Ltd	Thruxton	
G-BYYJ	Lindstrand LBL 25A Cloudhopper HAFB	651		10.12.99	A.M.Barton	Coulsdon	11.12.00A
G-BYYK	Boeing 737-229C	20916	OO-SDK	11. 1.00	European Aviation Air Charter Ltd	Bournemouth	
G-BYYL	Avtech Jabiru UL	PFA/274A-13480		10.12.99	C.Jackson	(Ormskirk)	
G-BYYM	Raj Hamsa X'Air 582 (1)	BMAA/HB/119		21.10.99	J.J.Cozens t/a G-BYYM Group	(Hermitage)	
G-BYYN	Cyclone Pegasus Quantum 15	7601		6. 1.00	E.Clarke	(Oswaldtwistle)	
G-BYYO	PA-28R-201 Arrow	28-37061	N9249C	11. 2.00	Stapleford Flying Club Ltd	Stapleford	
G-BYYP	Cyclone Pegasus Quantum 15	7603		11. 2.00	R.R. Nichol	(Carlisle)	
G-BYYR	Raj Hamsa X'Air 582 (1)	BMAA/HB/115		23.12.99	T D Bawden	(Bridgwater)	
G-BYYS	Airbus A.300B4-103	069	N471AS RP-C3002/F-WZEB	4. 1.00	SARL Hamloc	(Laval, France)	
G-BYYT	Avtech Jabiru UL	PFA/274A-13452		18.11.99	T.D.Saveker	(Truro)	
G-BYYY	Cyclone Pegasus Quantum 15	7564		8.12.99	Light Flight Ltd	(Newark)	19.12.00p
G-BYYX	TEAM miniMax 91	PFA/186-13410		6. 1.00	P.L.Turner	(Darlington)	
G-BYYZ	Staaken Z-21A Flitzer	PFA/223-13324		12.11.99	A.E.Morris	(Bagshot)	
G-BYZA	Aerospatiale AS.355F2 Twin Squirrel	5518	JA6784 F-OHNK	20.12.99	Aeromega Aviation Ltd	(Ipswich)	AC
G-BYZB	Mainair Blade	1229-1299-7-W1022		14. 1.00	O.Grati	(Annesley, Notts)	
G-BYZD	Kis Cruiser	PFA/302-13156		22.11.99	R.T.Clegg	(Worksop)	
G-BYZE	Aerospatiale AS.350B2 Ecureuil	2773	F-OGVR	8. 2.00	V.H.L.Ellis	(Arlesley)	
G-BYZF	Raj Hamsa X'Air 582 (1)	BMAA/HB/110		7. 1.00	S.W.Grainger	(Wirral)	
G-BYZJ	Boeing 737-3Q8	24962	G-COLE PP-VOX	11. 1.00	British Midland Airways Ltd	East Midlands	20.11.01T
G-BYZM	PA-28-161 Warrior II	28-8116317	HB-PNK N8436A	4. 2.00	Small World Aviation Ltd	Earls Colne	
G-BYZN	Boeing 737-229C	21139	OO-SDP	2. 2.00	European Aviation Air Charter Ltd	Bournemouth	
G-BYZO	Rans S6-ES Coyote II	PFA/204-13560		14. 1.00	S.C.Jackson	(York)	AC
G-BYZP	Robinson R-22 Beta-II	3018		9.12.99	Helicopter Training and Hire Ltd	Belfast	AC
G-BYZR	III Sky Arrow 650TC	C001	D-ENGF	24. 1.00	G.H.Jackson & R.Moncrieff	(Nottingham)	
G-BYZS	Avtech Jabiru UL	PFA/274A-13489		25. 1.00	N.Fielding	(Ormskirk)	
G-BYZT	Nova Vertex 26	13345		21. 1.00	M.N.Maclean	(Dundee)	
G-BYZW	Raj Hamsa X'Air 582 (2)	BMAA/HB/119		19. 1.00	P.A.Gilford	(Penrith)	
G-BYZY	Pietenpol Aircamper	PFA/047-12190		2.12.99	D.N.Hanchet	(Reading)	
G-BYZZ	Robinson R-22 Beta-II	3000		1.12.99	Sloane Helicopters Ltd.	Sywell	

G-BZAA – G-BZZZ

Regn	Type	C/n	P/I	Date	Owner/operator	Probable Base	CA Expy
G-BZAA	Mainair Blade 912	1142-0198-7-W945		22.11.99	C.Bodill & R.Locke	(Nottingham)	22.11.00P
G-BZAB	Mainair Rapier	1228-1299-7-W1021		23.12.99	S T Morris	(Wilmslow)	
G-BZAF	Raj Hamsa X'Air 582 (1)	BMAA/HB/130		18. 1.00	P.Hassett	(Wigan)	
G-BZAI	Cyclone Pegasus Quantum 15	7614		9. 2.00	D.Paget	(Wedmore)	
G-BZAJ	WSK PZL Koliber 160A	04990082	SP-WGK	10. 2.00	PZL International Aviation Marketing & Sales plc	North Weald	
G-BZAK	Raj Hamsa X'Air 582 (1)	BMAA/HB/114		20. 1.00	B.W.Austin	(Cheltenham)	
G-BZAL	Mainair Blade 912	1205-0799-7-W1008		27. 1.00	K.Worthington	(Chorley)	
G-BZAM	Europa Avn Europa	PFA/247-12969		6.12.99	D.Corbett	(Shobdon)	
G-BZAO	Rans S-12XL	PFA/307-13394		1. 2.00	M.L.Robinson	(Wigton)	
G-BZAP	Avtech Jabiru UL	PFA/274A-13479		13.12.99	S.Derwin	(Yarm)	
G-BZAS	Isaacs Fury II	PFA/011-10837		10. 2.00	H.A.Brunt & H.Frick	(Pulborough)	
G-BZAT	Avro RJ100 (BAe 146 Srs.300)	E-3320	G-6-320	18.11.97	CityFlyer Express Ltd (Waves of the City t/s)	Gatwick	8. 1.01T

Regn	Type	C/n	P/I	Date	Owner/operator	Probable Base	CA Expy
G-BZAU	Avro RJ100 (BAe 146 Srs.300)	E-3328		25. 4.98	CityFlyer Express Ltd (Dove/Colum t/s)	Gatwick	11. 6.01T
G-BZAV	Avro RJ100 (BAe 146 Srs 300)	E-3331		19. 5.98	CityFlyer Express Ltd (Chelsea Rose t/s)	Gatwick	23. 7.01T
G-BZAW	Avro RJ100 (BAe 146 Srs.300)	E-3354		11. 6.99	CityFlyer Express Ltd (Union Flag t/s)	Gatwick	15. 7.02T
G-BZAX	Avro RJ100 (BAe 146 Srs.300)	E-3356		9. 7.99	CityFlyer Express Ltd (Union Flag t/s)	Gatwick	16. 8.02T
G-BZBA	Avro RJ100 (BAe 146 Srs.300)	E-2028	G-DEBA N171US/N351PS	19. 1.00	British Aerospace (Operations) Ltd	Woodford	30. 4.02T
G-BZBB	Avro RJ1000 (BAe 146 Srs.200)	E-2034	G-DEBD N174US/N354PS	19. 1.00	British Aerospace (Operations) Ltd	Woodford	18. 6.02T
G-BZBC	Rans S6-ES Coyote II	PFA/204-13525		2. 2.00	A.J.Baldwin	(Ripley)	
G-BZBF	Cessna 172M Skyhawk	172-62258	9H- ACV	20.12.99	M.D.N.Fisher t//a F & H (Aircraft) Ltd	(Peterborough)	AC
G-BZBG	Thruster T.600N	0100-T600N-040		26. 1.00	Thruster Air Services Ltd	(Wantage)	
G-BZBH	Thunder Ax7-65 Bolt HAFB	173		28.11.78	R.B. & G.Craik "Serendipity II"	Northampton	24. 4.00A
G-BZBX	Rans S6-ES Coyote II	PFA/204-13501		26. 1.00	R.Johnstone	(Stone, Staffs)	
G-BZGC	Aerospatiale AS.355F1 Twin Squirrel	5077	G-CCAO G-SETA/G-NEAS/G-CMMM/G-BNBJ/C-GLKH	26. 3.99	McAlpine Helicopters Ltd	Oxford	21.11.02T
G-BZDD	Mainair Blade 912	1238-0200-7-W1031		21. 1.00	T.Williams t/a Barton Blade Group	Barton	
G-BZEC	Cessna 152	15284475	N4655M	21. 1.00	Sky Leisure Aviation (Charters) Ltd	Redhill	
G-BZGE	Medway EclipseR (Jabiru 2200A)	159/139		6. 5.99	J.A.McGill	(Westerham)	3. 5.00P
G-BZGH	Reims Cessna F.172H Skyhawk II	1789	EI-BGH	1.12.98	D.Behan t/a Golf Hotel Group	(Dublin)	11. 3.02
G-BZHA	Boeing 767-336ER	29230	N60668	22. 5.98	British Airways plc (Wings of the City t/s)	Heathrow	21. 5.01T
G-BZHB	Boeing 767-336ER	29231		30. 5.98	British Airways plc (Delftblue Daybreak t/s)	Heathrow	29. 5.01T
G-BZHC	Boeing 767-336ER	29232		29. 6.98	British Airways plc (Waves & Cranes t/s)	Heathrow	28. 6.01T
G-BZHI	Enstrom F-28A-UK	281	G-BPOZ N246Q	14.12.99	Tindon Ltd	Litle Snoring	20. 6.02
G-BZKK	Cameron V-56 HAFB	396		2. 8.78	P.J.Green & C.Bosley t/a Gemini Balloon Group "Gemini II"	Newbury	13. 8.96A
G-BZZA	Boeing 737-3L9	26441	D-ADBA OY-MAL	17.11.99	Camalac Ltd. (Op Buzz Ltd)	Stansted	
G-BZZB	Boeing 737-3L9	25125	D-ADBG OY-MMW/PP-SOR/OY-MMW	17.11.99	Shananda Ltd (Op Buzz Ltd)	Stansted	
G-BZZD	Reims Cessna F.172M Skyhawk II	1436	G-BDPF	14. 4.98	S.& C.Barry	Shoreham	5. 8.02T

G-CAAA – G-CZZZ

Regn	Type	C/n	P/I	Date	Owner/operator	Probable Base	CA Expy
G-CAHA	PA-34-200T Seneca II	34-7770010	N23PL SE-GPY/(D-IICC)/SE-GPY	7. 7.98	H & R.Marshall	Sandtoft	30. 7.01T
G-CAIN	CFM Shadow Srs.CD (Rotax 503)	062	G-MTKU	26. 1.99	A.J.Cain	(Corby)	28.11.00P
G-CALL	PA-23-250 Aztec F	27-7754061	N62826	21.12.77	Woodgate Aviation (IOM) Ltd	Aldergrove/Ronaldsway	29. 5.01T
G-CAMB	Aerospatiale AS.355F2 Twin Squirrel	5416	N813LP	17.12.96	Cambridge & Essex Air Support Consortium	Huntingdon	16. 4.00T
G-CAMM	Hawker Cygnet rep (Mosler MM-CB35)	PFA/77-10245	(G-ERDB)	30. 5.91	D.M.Cashmore (On loan to The Shuttleworth Collection)	Old Warden	18. 7.00P
G-CAMP	Cameron N-105	4546		24. 3.99	R D Parry t/a Hong Kong Balloon & Airship Club	Hong Kong	14. 3.00A
G-CAMR	Quad City Challenger II	PFA/177-12569		26. 3.99	P R A Walker	Ringwood	
G-CAPI	Mudry/CAARP CAP.10B	76	G-BEXR	16. 3.99	I.Valentine	(Dungannon)	28. 7.00
G-CAPX	Avions Mudry CAP.10B	280		21. 9.98	R.W.H.Cole Spilsted Farm, Sedlescombe t/a Cole Aviation		21.12.01T
G-CBAC	Short SD.3-60 Var.200	SH.3675	B-3608 G-BLYH/G-14-3675	20.10.95	BAC Leasing Ltd (Stored Baiyun, Guangzhou, China 2.97)	Exeter	19.11.95F
G-CBAL	PA-28-161 Warrior II	28-8116087	LN-MAD N83007	25. 3.94	Britannia Airways Ltd	Filton	13. 4.00T
G-CBCL	Stoddard-Hamilton Glastar	PFA/295-13089		5. 9.97	C.F.M.Norman	(Somerton)	
G-CBIL	Cessna 182K Skylane	182-57804	(G-BFZZ) D-ENGO/N2604Q	9.10.78	E Bannister & J R C Spooner	East Midlands	2. 9.99
G-CBKT	Cameron O-77 HAFB	1754		7. 6.88	Caledonian Airways Ltd "Caledonian"	Gatwick	22. 6.99A
G-CBNB	Eurocopter EC.120B	1040		8. 6.99	Sea & Air Charter Ltd	(London W1)	
G-CBOR	Reims Cessna F172N Skyhawk II	1656	PH-BOR PH-AXG(1)	28. 5.87	Pauline Seville	Barton	8. 5.00T
G-CCAR	Cameron N-77 HAFB	464		5.12.78	D.P.Turner "Mitsubishi Cars"	Bath	27. 7.00A
	(Rebuilt 8.1980 with envelope c/n 670; in 1989 with c/n 2108 & again in 1992 with c/n 2658)						
G-CCAT	Gulfstream AA-5A Cheetah	AA5A-0893	G-OAJH G-KILT/G-BJFA/N27169	16. 1.92	Plane Talking Ltd	Elstree	30.10.02T
G-CCAU	Eurocopter EC.135T-1	0040	G-79-01	30. 6.98	West Mercia Constabulary	Halfpenny Green	21. 7.01T
G-CCCC	Cessna 172H	172-55822	SE-ELU N2622L	9. 2.79	K.E.Wilson	Bourn	16.11.01
G-CCCP	IAV-Bacau Yakovlev Yak-52	899404	LY-AKV DOSAAF16 (Yellow)	30.11.93	R.J.N.Howarth	North Weald	15. 2.00P
G-CCIX*	VS.361 Spitfire LF.IXe (C/n is Firewall No.)	CBAF.IX.558	G-BIXP IDF/AF2046/Czech AF/TE517 (Stored pending rebuild 3.96 as "TE517")	9. 4.85	K.Weeks	Booker	
G-CCLY	Bell 206B JetRanger III	3594	G-TILT G-BRJO/N2295Z	26. 4.95	Ciceley Ltd	Samlesbury	16.10.01
G-CCOA	Scottish Avn Bulldog 120/122	BH120-375	G-111 Ghana AF/G-BCUU	4. 9.96	Cranfield University	Cranfield	23. 2.00T
G-CCOL	Gulfstream AA-5A Cheetah	AA5A-0772	G-BIVU N26859	24. 4.92	Lowlog Ltd (Op Cabair)	Elstree	1. 7.02T
G-CCOZ	Monnett Sonerai II (VW1900)	0197 & PFA/15-10107		31. 5.78	P.R.Cozens	Hinton-in-The-Hedges	21. 6.00P
G-CCSC	Cameron N-77 HAFB	4282		16. 1.98	C.J.Royden "Coherent"	Stroud	7. 1.99A
G-CCUB	Piper J3C-65 Cub	2362A	N33528 NC33528	2. 4.81	Cormack (Aircraft Services) Ltd (On rebuild 8.94)	Cumbernauld	
G-CCVV*	VS.379 Spitfire FR.XIVe	6S/649186	IAF"42" MV262	18. 5.88	K.Weeks (On rebuild 3.96 to be "MV262")	Booker	
G-CDAV	PA-34-220T Seneca V	3449033	N9284Q	27.11.97	Neric Ltd	(Guernsey)	26.11.00T
G-CDBS	MBB Bo.105DBS-4 (See G-BCXO)	S.738	D-HDRZ VH-MBK/N970MB/D-HDRZ (Op Cornwall Ambulance Service)	29. 9.89	Bond Air Services	St.Mawgan	7.11.01T
G-CDET	Culver LCA Cadet (Continental O-200-A)	129	N29261 NC29261	10.11.86	H.B.Fox (As "29261" in USAAF c/s)	Booker	31. 7.00P
G-CDGA	Taylor JT.1 Monoplane	6020/1 & PFA/55-10382		28.12.78	R.M.Larimore	(Spondon, Derby)	
G-CDON	PA-28-161 Warrior II	28-8216185	N8254D	24. 5.88	East Midlands Flying School Ltd	East Midlands	30. 6.00T
G-CDRU	CASA I-131E Jungmann	2321	EC-DRU E3B-530	19. 1.90	P.Cunniff "Yen a Bon"	White Waltham	30. 6.00P
G-CEAA	Airbus A.300B2-1C	062	F-WQGQ F-BUAI	2. 7.98	European Aviation Ltd (Open store 1.00)	Bournemouth	AC
G-CEAB	Airbus A.300B2-1C	027	F-WQGS F-BUAH/F-WLGC/F-WLGB (Open store 1.00)	15.11.99	European Aviation Air Charter Ltd	Bournemouth	

Regn	Type	C/n	P/I	Date	Owner/operator	Probable Base	CA Expy
G-CEAC	Boeing 737-229	20911	OO-SDE	11. 6.99	European Aviation Air Charter Ltd		
					C-GNDX/OO-SDE/C-GNDX/OO-SDE (Op Palmair European)		
						Bournemouth	25. 8.02T
G-CEAD	Boeing 737-229	21137	OO-SDM	11.10.99	European Aviation Air Charter Ltd		16.11.02T
						Bournemouth	
G-CEAE	Boeing 737-229	20912	OO-SDF	25. 1.00	European Aviation Air Charter Ltd		
						Bournemouth	
G-CEAF	Boeing 737-229	20910	G-BYRI	13. 1.00	European Aviation Air Charter Ltd		
					OO-SDD/EC-EEG/OO-SDD	Bournemouth	
G-CEA	Boeing 737-229C	21738	OO-SDR	11.98R	European Aviation Air Charter Ltd		
G-CEA	Boeing 737-229	20907	OO-SDA	11.98R	European Aviation Air Charter Ltd		
			LX-LGN/OO-SDA				
G-CEA	Boeing 737-229C	20915	OO-SDJ	11.98R	European Aviation Air Charter Ltd		
G-CEA	Boeing 737-229C	20916	OO-SDK	11.98R	European Aviation Air Charter Ltd		
G-CEA	Boeing 737-229	21135	OO-SDG	11.98R	European Aviation Air Charter Ltd		
G-CEAL	Short SD.3-60 Var.100	SH.3761	N161CN	11. 9.95	BAC Express Airlines Ltd	Exeter	12. 1.00T
			N161SB/G-BPXO				
G-CEAS*	HPR.7 Dart Herald 214	186	G-BEBB	31. 1.86	Dart Group plc	Bournemouth	4. 6.99T
			PP-SDH		t/a Channel Express (Stored 7.97)		
G-CEGA	PA-34-200T Seneca II	34-8070367	N8272B	20.11.80	Oxford Aviation Services Ltd	Oxford	22 .8.02T
G-CEGR	Beechcraft 200 Super King Air	BB-351	N68CP	23. 7.97	Caga Aviation Ltd	Goodwood	18. 8.00T
			N351FW/N6666C/N6666K				
G-CEJA	Cameron V-77 HAFB	2469	G-BTOF	17. 6.91	L. & C.Gray	Farnborough	19. 5.00A
G-CERT	Mooney M.20K (252TSE)	25-1134		5.10.87	K.A.Hemming	Fowlmere	5. 2.00
G-CEXA	Fokker F-27 Friendship 500RF	10503	N703A	19. 1.96	Dart Group plc	Bournemouth	24. 3.02TC
			PH-EXK		t/a Channel Express		
G-CEXB	Fokker F-27 Friendship 500RF	10550	N743A	15.11.95	Dart Group plc	Coventry/Bournemouth	30. 1.02TC
			PH-EXF		t/a Channel Express (Parcel Force titles)		
G-CEXC	Airbus A.300B4-103F	124	N407U	18. 7.97	Dart Group plc	Stansted	17. 7.00T
			N407UA/N220EA/F-GBNO		t/a Channel Express		
G-CEXD	Fokker F-27 Friendship 600	10351	PH-KFE	18. 2.97	Dart Group plc	Bournemouth	18. 2.00TC
			HB-AAX/PH-FLX				
G-CEXE	Fokker F-27 Friendship 500	10654	SU-GAF	2. 4.97	Dart Group plc	Bournemouth	14. 5.00TC
			PH-EXJ		t/a Channel Express		
G-CEXF	Fokker F-27 Friendship 500	10660	SU-GAE	2. 4.97	Dart Group plc	Bournemouth	30. 6.00TC
			PH-EXC		t/a Channel Express		
G-CEXH	Airbus A.300B4-203F	117	D-ASAZ	30. 3.98	Dart Group plc	Liege	1. 4.01T
			N14966/N966C/F-OGTB/9V-STA/F-WZER		t/a Channel Express		
G-CEXI	Airbus A.300B4-203	121	D-ASAA	3. 9.98	Dart Group plc (Op TNT)	Liege	3. 9.01T
			N15967/N967C/F-OGTC/9V-STB/F-WZEK				
G-CEXP*	HPR.7 Dart Herald 209	195	I-ZERC	29.10.87	BAA plc	Gatwick	7.11.96T
			G-BFRJ/4X-AHO		(Dsplayed South Terminal)		
G-CEXS	Lockheed L.188CF Electra	1091	N5539	14. 4.92	Dart Group plc	Bournemouth	15. 4.02T
			N171PS/N971HA/N171PS		t/a Channel Express		
G-CFBI	Colt 56A HAFB	570		11. 7.84	G.A.Fisher	Guildford	24. 7.91A
					t/a Out-of-the-Blue "Air O"		
G-CFLY*	Cessna 172F	172-52635	PH-SNO	25. 8.78	Not known	Blackpool	13. 7.95
			N8731U		(Stored 6.96)		
G-CFME	Socata TB.10 Tobago	1795	F-GNHU	15. 4.98	Charles Funke Associates Ltd	Goodwood	4. 5.01T
G-CGHM	PA-28-140 Cruiser	28-7425143	PH-NSM	25. 4.79	C.M.Jones	Shoreham	8.10.00T
G-CGOD	Cameron N-77 HAFB	2647		5. 9.91	G.P.Lane	Waltham Abbey	13. 6.96A
					"Neptune"		
G-CHAA	Cameron O-90 HAFB	2471		24.10.91	P.Farmer	Wadhurst	23. 8.00T
G-CHAM	Cameron Pot 90SS HAFB	2912		29. 9.92	B.J.Reeves & C.Walker	Brighouse	3. 7.00A
	(Chambourcy Pot shape)				t/a High Exposure Balloons "Yogpot"		
G-CHAP	Robinson R-44 Astro	0326		9. 4.97	Brierley Lifting Tackle Co Ltd		
						Halfpenny Green	30. 4.00T
G-CHAR	Grob G-109B	6435		21. 5.86	T.Holloway t/a RAFGSA	RAF Bicester	11. 5.02
G-CHAS	PA-28-181 Archer II	28-8090325	N82228	18. 3.91	C.H.Elliott	Stapleford	7. 5.00
G-CHAV	Europa Avn Europa	PFA/247-12769		28.12.94	M.B.Stoner	Kemble	
					t/a Chavenage Flying Group		
G-CHAZ	Rans S-6-ESA Coyote II	1291-250		7.10.93	C.H.Middleton	(Borrowash, Derby)	
G-CHCC	Aerospatiale AS.332L-1	2087	N25AN	27. 8.98	Brintel Helicopters Ltd	Aberdeen	AC
	Super Puma		N77GY/N58023		t/a British International Helicopters		
G-CHCD	Sikorsky S-76A II Plus	760101	G-CBJB	16. 1.98	Brintel Helicopters Ltd	Aberdeen	18. 2.01T
			N288SP/C-GIMN/YV-326C		t/a British International Helicopters		
G-CHEB	Europa Avn Europa	PFA/247-12967		16. 9.96	C.H.P.Bell	Eddsfield	16. 6.98P
	(NSI EA-81/100)						
G-CHEM	PA-34-200T Seneca II	34-8170032	N8292Y	26. 8.87	London Executive Aviation Ltd		
						London City	28. 1.00T

Regn	Type	C/n	P/I	Date	Owner/operator	Probable Base	CA Expy
G-CHES	BN-2A-26 Islander	2011	G-PASY	19. 4.94	The Cheshire Constabulary	Chester	2. 6.00T
			G-BPCB/G-BEXA/G-MALI/(ZB503)/G-DIVE/G-BEXA				
G-CHET	Europa Avn Europa (Tri-cycle u/c)			12. 2.98	H.P.Chetwynd-Talbot	Wombleton	
	(Rotax 914)	376 & PFA/247-13277			(F/f 17.1.00)		
G-CHGL	Bell 206B JetRanger II	1669	G-BPNG	29. 4.98	Capital Helicopter Group Ltd	Biggin Hill	3. 3.00T
			G-ORTC/G-BPNG/N20EA/C-GHVB				
G-CHIK	Reims Cessna F.152 II	1628	G-BHAZ	19.10.81	Stapleford Flying Club Ltd	Stapleford	3.11.00T
			(D-EHLE)				
G-CHIP	PA-28-181 Archer II	28-8290095	N81337	22. 2.82	C.M.Hough	Fairoaks	21. 4.00
G-CHIS	Robinson R-22 Beta	1740		5. 4.91	I.R.Chisholm Costock, Loughborough		30. 7.00T
					t/a Bradmore Helicopter Leasing		
G-CHKL	Cameron Kookaburra 120SS HAFB	3733		8.11.95	Eagle Ltd	Canowindra, Australia	13. 4.00A
G-CHLT	Stemme S-10	10-30	D-KGCD	3. 7.91	J.Abbess	Tibenham	24.11.00
G-CHMP	Bellanca 7ACA Champ	62-72	N68556	21.12.92	I.J.Langley	Bidford	
					(Stored 10.92)		
G-CHNX	Lockheed L.188AF Electra	1068	EI-CHO	1.11.94	Dart Group plc	Bournemouth	31.10.01T
			(G-CHNX)/N5535		(Operated Channel Express)		
G-CHOK	Cameron V-77 HAFB	1752		25. 5.88	Amanda J.Moore Great Missenden		28. 5.00A
					"S'il Vous Plais"		
G-CHOP	Westland-Bell 47G-3B1	WA/380	XT221	19.12.78	Dolphin Property (Management) Ltd		
	(Line No.WAN/79)					Old Sarum	28. 8.99T
G-CHPY	DHC.1 Chipmunk 22	C1/0093	WB652	7. 3.97	JGH Computer Services Ltd	(Cardiff)	15.10.01T
G-CHSU	Eurocopter EC.135 T1	0079		4. 2.99	Thames Valley Police Authority/		
					Chiltern Air Support Unit	RAF Benson	12..4.02T
G-CHTA	Grumman-American AA-5A Cheetah		G-BFRC	3. 3.86	Quickspin Ltd	Biggin Hill	12. 1.00T
		AA5A-0631			(Op Biggin Hill School of Flying)		
G-CHTG	Rotorway Exec 90	5118	G-BVAJ	19.11.99	G.Cooper Street Farm, Takeley		AC
	(RI 162)						
G-CHTT*	Varga 2150A Kachina	VAC162-80		7. 9.84	H.W.Hall	Southend	6. 9.87
			(Damaged nr Hatherleigh, Devon 27.4.86; fuselage Southend 9.99))				
G-CHUB	Colt Cylinder Two N-51 HAFB	1720		11. 4.90	Chubb Fire Ltd	Newbury	19.12.95A
	(Fire Extinguisher shape)				"Chubb Fire Extinguisher" (To British Balloon Museum 2.97)		
G-CHUG	Europa Avn Europa	PFA/247-12960		29. 7.96	C.M.Washington	(Stoke-on-Trent)	
G-CHUK	Cameron O-77 HAFB	2773		6. 3.92	L.C.Taylor	Burton-on-Trent	5. 4.93A
G-CHYL	Robinson R-22 Beta	1197		28.11.89	Caroline M.Gough-Cooper	Bournemouth	10. 1.02
G-CHZN	Robinson R-22 Beta	0884	G-GHZM	9.4.99	Cloudbase Ltd	Shobdon	4..3.02T
			G-FENI				
G-CIAO	III Sky Arrow 1450L	PFA/298-13095		23. 7.97	J.Hosier	Kemble	20. 5.00P
G-CIAS	PBN BN-2B-21 Islander	2162	HC-BNS	1. 5.91	Channel Island Air Search Ltd	Guernsey	11. 3.00
			G-BKJM				
G-CICI	Cameron R-15 Gas/HAFB	673	(N)	11.11.80	Ballooning Endeavours Ltd	Bristol	5.6.91P*
			G-CICI/(G-BIHP)				
G-CIFR	PA-28-181 Cherokee Archer II		PH-MIT	18. 6.97	Aeroshow Ltd	Cardiff	9. 7.00T
		28-7790208	OO-HBB/N7654F				
G-CIGY	Westland-Bell 47G-3B1	WA/350	G-BGXP	26.10.98	R.A. Perrot	Guernsey	13. 2.00
			XT191				
G-CIPI	AJEP Wittman W.8 Tailwind		G-AYDU	22. 7.87	N.R.Hurley (Roquefort Les Pins, France)		15. 6.99P
	(Continental O-200-A)	AJEP/2 & PFA/1363					
G-CITA*	Bellanca 7KCAB Citabria	543-75	N14091	2. 2.96	J.R.K.Pardoe	Hove	21. 3.99T
			G-CITA/N53785/SE-KUI/N53785 (Cancelled by CAA 24.8.99)				
G-CITI	Cessna 501 Citation	501-0084	VP-CDM	21. 9.87	Euro Executive Jet Ltd	Southampton	19. 9.00T
			VR-CDM/G-CITI/(N11JC)/(N463CJ)/N3160M				
G-CITY	PA-31-350 Navajo Chieftain		N27741	12. 9.78	Woodgate Aviation (IOM) Ltd		
		31-7852136				Ronaldsway/Aldergrove	5.11.00T
G-CITZ	Bell 206B Jet Ranger II	1997	G-BRTB	19. 2.99	Euro Executive Jet Ltd	Thruxton	11. 4.02T
			N9936K				
G-CIVA	Boeing 747-436	27092		19. 3.93	British Airways plc	Heathrow	18. 3.00T
					(Chelsea Rose t/s)		
G-CIVB	Boeing 747-436	25811	(G-BNLY)	15. 2.94	British Airways plc	Heathrow	14. 2.01T
					(Chelsea Rose t/s)		
G-CIVC	Boeing 747-436	25812	(G-BNLZ)	26. 2.94	British Airways plc	Heathrow	25. 2.00T
					(Delftblue Daybreak t/s)		
G-CIVD	Boeing 747-436	27349		14.12.94	British Airways plc	Gatwick	13.12.00T
					(Waves of the City t/s)		
G-CIVE	Boeing 747-436	27350		20.12.94	British Airways plc	Heathrow	19.12.00T
					(Union Flag t/s)		
G-CIVF	Boeing 747-436	25434	(G-BNLY)	29. 3.95	British Airways plc	Gatwick	28. 3.01T
G-CIVG	Boeing 747-436	25813	N6009F	20. 4.95	British Airways plc	Heathrow	18. 4.01T
G-CIVH	Boeing 747-436	25809		23. 4.96	British Airways plc	Gatwick	22. 4.02T
G-CIVI	Boeing 747-436	25814		2. 5.96	British Airways plc	Gatwick	1. 5.02T
G-CIVJ	Boeing 747-436	25817		11. 2.97	British Airways plc	Heathrow	10. 2.00T

Regn	Type	C/n	P/I	Date	Owner/operator	Probable Base	CA Expy
G-CIVK	Boeing 747-436	25818		28. 2.97	British Airways plc	Heathrow	27. 2.00T
					(Op British Asia Airways)		
G-CIVL	Boeing 747-436	27478		28. 3.97	British Airways plc	Heathrow	27. 3.00T
G-CIVM	Boeing 747-436	28700		5. 6.97	British Airways plc	Heathrow	4. 6.00T
					(Waves & Cranes t/s)		
G-CIVN	Boeing 747-436	28848		29. 9.97	British Airways plc	Gatwick	28. 9.00T
					(Delftblue Daybreak t/s)		
G-CIVO	Boeing 747-436	28849	N6046P	5.12.97	British Airways plc	Heathrow	4.12.00T
					(Mountain of the Birds/Benthone Tartan t/s)		
G-CIVP	Boeing 747-436	25850		17. 2.98	British Airways plc	Heathrow	16. 2.01T
					(Dove/Colum t/s)		
G-CIVR	Boeing 747-436	25820		2. 3.98	British Airways plc	Gatwick	1. 3.01T
					(Waves & Cranes t/s)		
G-CIVS	Boeing 747-436	28851		13. 3.98	British Airways plc	Heathrow	12. 3.01T
					(Whale Rider t/s)		
G-CIVT	Boeing 747-436	25821	(G-CIVN)	20. 3.98	British Airways plc	Heathrow	19. 3.01T
					(Delftblue Daybreak t/s)		
G-CIVU	Boeing 747-436	25810	(G-CIVO)	24. 4.98	British Airways plc	Heathrow	23. 4.01T
					(Wings t/s)		
G-CIVV	Boeing 747-436	25819	N6009F	23. 5.98	British Airways plc	Heathrow	21. 5.01T
			(G-CIVP)		(Rendezvous t/s)		
G-CIVW	Boeing 747-436	25822	(G-CIVR)	15. 5.98	British Airways plc	Heathrow	14. 5.01T
					(Mountain of the Birds/Benyhone Tartan t/s)		
G-CIVX	Boeing 747-436	28852		3. 9.98	British Airways plc	Heathrow	2. 9.01T
					(Union Flag c/s)		
G-CIVY	Boeing 747-436	28853		29. 9.98	British Airways plc	Heathrow	28. 9.01T
					(Whale Rider t/s)		
G-CIVZ	Boeing 747-436	28854		31.10.98	British Airways plc	Heathrow	30.10.01T
					(Mountain of the Birds/Benyhone Tartan t/s)		
G-CJBC	PA-28-180 Cherokee D	28-5470	OY-BDE	28.11.80	J.B.Cave	Halfpenny Green	5. 8.02
G-CJCI	Pilatus P.2-06	600-63	U-143	30. 7.84	J.Briscoe & P.G.Bond	Norwich	27. 9.99P
					t/a Pilatus P2 Flying Group		
					(As "CC+43"" in Luftwaffe c/s in Arado Ar.96B guise)		
G-CJIM*	Taylor JT.1 Monoplane	PFA/1419		28.12.78	J.Crawford	Farnborough	
					(Under construction 7.95: cancelled by CAA 24.3.99)		
G-CJUD	Denney Kitfox mk.3			17. 1.91	D.M.Garrett	(Defford)	25.11.99P
	(Rotax 582)	847 & PFA/172-11939			"Dougal"		
G-CKCK	Enstrom 280FX Shark	2071	OO-PVL	5. 5.95	Farmax Ltd	(Maidstone)	14. 5.98T
G-CLAC	PA-28-161 Warrior II	28-8116241	N8369U	18. 5.87	M.J.Steadman	Blackbushe	3.11.02
G-CLAG	Lindstrand LBL-90A HAFB	582		26. 1.99	Cargolifter AG	Wiesbaden, Germany	2 .2.00A
G-CLAS	Short SD.3-60 Var.200	SH.3635	EI-BEK	28. 7.93	BAC Express Airlines Ltd	Exeter	20. 7.00T
			G-BLED/G-14-3635		(Op Jersey European Airways Ltd) "City of Cardiff"		
G-CLAX	Jurca MJ.5 Sirocco	PFA/2204	G-AWKB	22.4.99	G.D.Claxton	(Pontyclun)	
G-CLEA	PA-28-161 Warrior II	28-7916081	N30296	28. 8.80	R.J.Harrison & A.R.Carpenter	Oaksey Park	30.11.01
G-CLEM	Bolkow Bo.208A-2 Junior	561	G-ASWE	22. 9.81	J.J.Donely & A.D.P.Thompson	Coventry	8.12.99P
			D-EFHE		t/a Bolkow Group		
G-CLEO	Zenair CH.601HD	PFA/162-13500		9. 8.99	H.& K.M.Bowen	Goldcliff	
G-CLIC	Cameron A-105 HAFB	2557		18. 4.91	R.S.Mohr	Corsham	14. 2.00A
	(New envelope c/n 3395 4.95)				"Clic Trust"		
G-CLIP	Eurocopter AS.355N Twin Squirrel	5580		25.11.94	Quantel Ltd	Thruxton	11. 4.01T
G-CLKE	Robinson R-44 Astro	0185	G-HREH	22. 9.98	J.Clarke	(Burnley)	10. 9.00T
			D-HREH		t/a Clarke Business		
G-CLOE	Sky 90-24 HAFB	019		11. 3.96	C.J.Sandell "Headfirst"	Sevenoaks	29. 4.00T
G-CLOS	PA-34-200T Seneca II	34-7870361	HB-LKE	17. 6.86	P.S.Kirby	Coventry	12. 9.01T
			N36783				
G-CLOW	Beechcraft 200 Super King Air	BB-821	N821RC	2.11.99	Clowes Estates Ltd	(Ashbourne)	7.12.02T
			TC-DBY/N144TM/F-GDCB				
G-CLRK	Sky 77-24 HAFB	101		3. 3.98	William Clark & Son (Parkgate) Ltd		
						Dumfries	2.12.99A
G-CLUB	Reims Cessna FRA.150M Aerobat	0347	OO-AWZ	10. 2.83	D.C.C.Handley	Cranfield	13. 5.02T
			F-WZAZ/(F-WZDZ)				
G-CLUE	PA-34-200T Seneca II	34-7970502	N8089Z	15. 9.92	Bristol Office Machines Ltd	Bristol	25. 1.02T
G-CLUX	Reims Cessna F.172N Skyhawk II	1996	PH-AYG(3)	1. 5.80	J.G.Jackman & K.M.Drewitt	Chester	20. 8.01T
					t/a J & K Aviation		
G-CMGC	PA-25-235 Pawnee D	25-7756042	G-BFEX	19.11.91	Midland Gliding Club Ltd	Long Mynd	19. 4.01
			N82525				
G-CNDY	Robinson R-22 Beta-II	2677	G-BXEW	15. 5.97	Testgate Ltd	Goodwood	27. 5.00T
G-COAI	Cranfield A.1-200 Eagle	001	G-BCIT	1. 6.98	Cranfield University	Cranfield	
G-COCO	Reims Cessna F.172M Skyhawk II	1373	PH-SMO	27.10.80	P.C.Sheard & R.C.Larder		
			OO-ADI			North Reston, Louth	25. 2.02

Regn	Type	C/n	P/I	Date	Owner/operator	Probable Base	CA Expy
G-CODE	Bell 206B Jet Ranger III	3850	N222DM N84TC	27. 8.96	Datel Direct Ltd	Stone	7.12.02
G-COEZ	Airbus A.320-231	179	OY-CNH F-WWIS	10. 2.97	Airtours International Airways Ltd	Manchester	11. 2.00T
G-COIN	Bell 206B JetRanger II	897	EI-AWA	11. 3.85	C.Sarno	Luton	22. 6.00
G-COLA	Beechcraft F33C Bonanza	CJ-137	G-BUAZ PH-BNH	31. 3.92	J.A.Kelman & Cola Aviation Ltd	Spilsted Farm, Sedlescombe	3. 4.01
G-COLL	Enstrom 280C-UK-2 Shark	1223		17. 8.81	SG Aviation Services Ltd	Olney	11. 1.01
G-COLR*	Colt 69A HAFB	780		8. 4.86	K.A Kent "Colourtech" (Balloon Preservation Group 7.98)	Lancing	N/E(A)
G-COMB	PA-30-160 Twin Comanche B	30-1362	G-AVBL N8236Y	14. 9.84	J.T.Bateson	Weston, Ireland	28.10.01
G-COMP	Cameron N-90 HAFB	1564		24. 9.87	Computacenter Ltd "Computacenter"	London SE1	20. 5.97A
G-CONB	Robin DR.400/180 Regent	2176	G-BUPX	14. 4.93	C.C. & C.Blakey t/a Winchcombe Farm	Redhill	24. 2.02
G-CONC	Cameron N-90 HAFB	2139		13.11.89	British Airways plc "Concorde"	Heathrow	30.10.93T
G-CONI*	Lockheed 749A-79 Constellation	2553	N7777G	12. 5.82	The Science Museum	Wroughton	
	(N173X)/N7777G/TI-1045P/PH-LDT/PH-TET (As "N7777G" in TWA c/s)						
G-CONL	Socata TB.10 Tobago	173	F-GCOR	22.12.98	J Macgilvray	(Oban)	14. 3.02
G-COOP	Cameron N-31 HAFB	382		2. 3.78	D P Bushby "Co-op" (Balloon Preservation Group 7.98)	Lancing	13. 5.87A
G-COOT	Taylor Coot A	EE-1A		16. 9.81	P.M.Napp	(Newcastle)	
G-COPS	Piper J3C-65 Cub (L-4H-PI)	11911	F-BFYC Fr.AF/44-79615	17. 7.79	R.W.Sproat & C.E.Simpson	Lennox Plunton, Borgue	18.10.00P
	(Regd as c/n 36-817 which is a USAAC Continental ract No.; Frame No.11739)						
G-COPT	Aerospatiale AS.350B Ecureuil	2168	9M-FSA 9V-BOR	25. 2.98	Owenlars Ltd	(Odiham)	6. 5.01T
G-CORB	Socata TB.20 Trinidad	1178	F-GKUX	12. 4.99	G.D.Corbin	Old Sarum	21. 4.02
G-CORC	Bell 206B JetRanger II	1129	G-CJHI G-BBFB/N18094	18.12.89	Air Corcoran Ltd	Redhill	27.10.00
G-CORD	Slingsby Nipper T.66 RA.45 Srs.3 (Rebuild from S.105/1565) S.129/1676		G-AVTB	21. 3.88	B.A.Wright & K.E.Wilson	Little Gransden	1.11.99P
G-CORN	Bell 206B JetRanger III	3035	G-BHTR N18098	4. 6.99	John A.Wells Ltd	Costock	12. 4.02T
G-CORP	BAe ATP	2037	G-BTNK N860AW/G-BTNK/G-11-037	2. 3.98	British Aerospace (Operations) Ltd	Warton	28. 3.01T
G-CORT	Agusta-Bell 206B Jet Ranger III	8739		21. 6.96	Helicopter Training & Hire Ltd	Aldergrove	28. 7.02T
G-COSY	Lindstrand LBL-56A HAFB	017		18. 2.93	D.D.Owen	Wotton-under-Edge	10.12.99A
G-COTT	Cameron Flying Cottage 60SS HAFB	687	"G-HOUS"	13. 2.81	M.R.Nanda t/a Nottingham Hot-Air Balloon Club "Cottage"	Nottingham	15.12.98A
G-COUP	Ercoupe 415C (Continental C75)	1903	N99280 NC99280	27. 5.93	S.M.Gerrard "Jenny Lin"	Goodwood	17. 7.99
G-COVE	Avtech Jabiru UL PFA/274A-13409			23. 7.99	A.A.Rowson	(Abergele)	17.10.00P
G-COWS	ARV Super 2 K.009 & PFA/152-11182 (Hewland AE75)		(G-BONB)	27. 5.88	T.C.Harrold	Felthorpe	26. 5.00P
G-COZI	Rutan Cozy III PFA/159-12162 (Lycoming O-320)			19. 7.93	D.G.Machin	Biggin Hill	14. 1.99P
G-CPCD	CEA Jodel DR-221 Dauphin	81	F-BPCD	11.12.90	P.G.Bumpus & R.Thwaites	Spilsted Farm, Sedlescombe	9. 6.01
G-CPEL	Boeing 757-236	24398	N602DF EC-EOL EC-597/G-BRJE/EC-EOL/EC-278/G-BRJE	24. 8.92	British Airways plc (Animals and Trees/Kg-Oocoan-Naka-Hiian-Thee-E t/s)	Heathrow	26.10.02T
G-CPEM	Boeing 757-236	28665		28. 3.97	British Airways plc (Blue Poole t/s)	Heathrow	27. 3.00T
G-CPEN	Boeing 757-236	28666		23. 4.97	British Airways plc (Union Flag c/s)	Heathrow	22. 4.00T
G-CPEO	Boeing 757-236	28667		11. 7.97	British Airways plc (Whale Rider t/s)	Heathrow	10. 7.00T
G-CPEP	Boeing 757-2Y0	25268	C-GTSU EI-CLP/N400KL/XA-TAE	16. 4.97	British Airways plc (Dove/Colum t/s)	Heathrow	9. 7.00T
G-CPER	Boeing 757-236	29113		29.12.97	British Airways plc (Wings t/s)	Gatwick	28.12.00T
G-CPES	Boeing 757-236	29114		17. 3.98	British Airways plc (Wings t/s)	Heathrow	16. 3.01T
G-CPET	Boeing 757-236	29115		12. 5.98	British Airways plc (Sterntaler/Bauhaus t/s)	Heathrow	11. 5.01T
G-CPEU	Boeing 757-236	29941		1. 5.99	British Airways plc (Rendezvous t/s)	Heathrow	30. 4.02T

Regn	Type	C/n	P/I	Date	Owner/operator	Probable Base	CA Expy
G-CPEV	Boeing 757-236	29943	(G-CPEW)	11. 6.99	British Airways plc	Heathrow	10 .6.02T
					(Rendezvous t/s)		
G-CPEX	Boeing 757-236		.	6.99R	British Airways plc	Heathrow	
G-CPEY	Boeing 757-236			6.99R	British Airways plc	Heathrow	
G-CPEZ	Boeing 757-236			.7.99R	British Airways plc	Heathrow	
G-CPFC	Reims Cessna F.152 II	1430		1.12.77	A.S.Bamrah	Southend	25. 6.01T
					t/a Falcon Flying Services (Op Willowair Flying Club)		
G-CPMK	DHC.1 Chipmunk 22	C1/0866	WZ847	28. 6.96	Towerdrive Ltd	Sleap	19. 9.02
					(As "WZ847")		
G-CPMS	Socata TB.20 Trinidad	1607	F-GNHA	7. 4.98	Charlotte Park Management Services Ltd		
						Goodwood	7. 4.01T
G-CPOL	Aerospatiale AS.355F1 Twin Squirrel	N5775T	30.11.95	Thames Valley Police Authority	Luton	30. 1.02T
		5007	C-GJJB/N5775T		(Op Chiltern Air Support Unit)		
G-CPSF	Cameron N-90	3747	G-OISK	21. 4.99	S.A.Simington & J.D.Rigden	Norwich	26. 2.97A
G-CPTM	PA-28-151 Cherokee Warrior		G-BTOE	9. 7.91	T.J.Mackay & C.M.Pollett	Woodford	4. 9.00T
		28-7715012	N4264F				
G-CPTS	Agusta-Bell 206B JetRanger II	8556		1. 6.78	A.R.B.Aspinall	Skipton	6. 5.00
G-CRAK	Cameron N-77 HAFB	2291		7. 6.90	Mobile Windscreens Ltd	Bristol	14. 7.97A
					"Mobile Windscreens"		
G-CRAY	Robinson R-22 Beta	0919		12. 1.89	W.H.Grimshaw	Barton	7. 4.98
G-CRES	Denney Kitfox mk.2 PFA/172-11574			7. 6.90	K.M.James Higher Barn Farm, Houghton		15. 8.00P
	(Rotax 912)						
G-CRIC	Colomban MC.15 Cri-Cri PFA/133-10915			22. 7.83	R.S.Stoddart-Stones	(Caterham)	5. 5.99P
	(JPX PUL.212)						
G-CRIL	Rockwell Commander 112B	521	N1388J	22. 6.79	J.W.Reynolds	Cardiff	21.10.00
					t/a Rockwell Aviation Group		
G-CRIS	Taylor JT.1 Monoplane PFA/55-10318			5. 6.79	C.R.Steer	(Bexhill-on-Sea)	
G-CROL	Maule MXT-7-180 Star Rocket 14032C		N9232F	24.11.93	N.G.P.Evans	(Chippenham)	17. 2.00
G-CROY	Europa Avn Europa PFA/247-12896			7. 2.97	A.Croy	(Kirkwall)	22. 6.00P
G-CRPH	Airbus A.320-231	424	F-WQBB	10. 4.95	Airtours International Airways Ltd		
			F-WWIV			Manchester	14. 4.01T
G-CRPS	Bell 206B Jet Ranger II	1967	A6-BCC	22. 9.97	Helisport Ltd	Biggin Hill	3. 9.00T
G-CRUM	Westland Scout AH.1	F.9712	XV137	17. 3.98	Crummock Development Ltd	(Bonnyrigg)	17.12.99
	(Pod No.F8-6151)						
G-CRUS	Cessna T303 Crusader	T303-00313	N6498V	27. 2.90	B.A.Groves	Guernsey	18. 4.02T
G-CRUZ	Cessna T303 Crusader	T303-00004	N9336T	7.12.90	Bank Farm Ltd Bank Farm, Benwick, Cambs		5. 3.00
G-CSBM	Reims Cessna F.150M	1359	PH-AYC	24. 5.78	Motorglider Centre Ltd		
						Hinton-in-The-Hedges	14.11.00T
G-CSCS	Reims Cessna F.172N Skyhawk II	1707	PH-MEM	28.11.86	Cheryl Sullivan	Stapleford	10. 6.02T
			(PH-WEB)/N9899A				
G-CSDJ	Avtech Jabiru UL PFA/274A-13337			23. 3.99	D W Johnston	Kemble	14. 4.00P
G-CSFC	Cessna 150L Commuter	150-75360	(G-BFLX)	21. 3.78	I.G.McDonald	(Helston)	6. 3.02
			N11370		t/a Foxtrot Charlie F/Gp		
G-CSFT*	PA-23-250 Aztec D	27-4521	G-AYKU	20. 9.84	Aces High Ltd	North Weald	3.12.94T
			N13885		(Stored 5.97)		
G-CSJS	Airbus A.330-243	309	F-WWYM	10. 2.99	Airtours Intl Airways Ltd	Manchester	9.12.00T
G-CSNA	Cessna 421C Golden Eagle III		(D-IOSS)	11. 6.79	Claessens International Ltd	Blackbushe	18. 8.00T
		421C-0677	N26522				
G-CSPJ	Hughes 369HS	55-0745S	G-BXJF	24. 7.97	W.& J.Lowry	Biggin Hill	3. 9.00T
			N99KS/N9KS		t/a JWL Services		
G-CSWL	Bell 206L-1 Long Ranger	45565	G-SIRI	6. 5.97	Helicorp Ltd	(Stone)	5. 6.00T
			G-CSWL/F-GDAD				
G-CTCL	Socata TB.10 Tobago	1107	G-BSIV	16. 7.90	Whitesands Investments Ltd	Jersey	30. 9.00
G-CTEC	Stoddard-Hamilton Glastar			9.11.99	A.J.Clarry	(Pewsey)	
		PFA/295-13260					
G-CTEL	Cameron N-90 HAFB	3933		27. 8.96	Cabletel Surrey & Hampshire Ltd		
						Farnborough	24. 8.99A
G-CTGR	Cameron N-77 HAFB	1775	G-CCDI	28. 8.97	T.G.Read	Knutsford	8. 4.97T
					(Charles Church titles)		
G-CTIX	VS.509 Spitfire T.IX		N462JC	9. 4.85	A.A.Hodgson	Brynwyn Bach	28. 3.00P
	(Major rebuild from parts pre 1994)		G-CTIX/IDFAF 2067/0607/MM4100/PT462 (As PT462/SW-A")				
G-CTKL	Noorduyn Harvard IIB	07-30	(G-BKWZ)	22.11.83	A.P.Williams	(Ware)	25. 2.00P
	(C/n quoted as "76-80")		MM54137/RCAF3064		(As "5413769" in US Navy c/s)		
G-CTOY	Denney Kitfox mk.3			14.10.91	B.McNeilly	Newtownards	10. 5.93P
	(Rotax 582) 1176 & PFA/172-12150						
G-CTPW	Bell 206B JetRanger 4	4374	(N9145B)	30.11.95	C.T.Wheatley	Newtown, Powys	19. 2.02T
G-CTWW	PA-34-200T Seneca II	34-7970191	G-ROYZ	21. 7.93	Seneca Consortium Ltd	Welshpool	16. 8.99
			G-GALE/N3052X		(Damaged Welshpool 14.5.99)		
G-CUBB	PA-18-180 Super Cub	18-3111	PH-WAM	5.12.78	Bidford Gliding Centre Ltd	Bidford	18. 4.01
	(L-18C-PI) (Frame No.18-3009)		Belgian AF OL-L37/53-4711				

Regn	Type	C/n	P/I	Date	Owner/operator	Probable Base	CA Expy
G-CUBI*	PA-18-135 Super Cub (Mod.)	18-3181	PH-GAV	26. 2.79	Teresa Watson	Clacton	4.11.94
	(L-18C-PI)		PH-VCV/R.Neth R-83/Belgian AF L-107/53-4781 (Official c/n 18-559 related to PH-GAV prior to				
	1970 rebuild when it incorporated Frame No.18-3170 from PH-VCV; cancelled by CAA 29.1.99)						
G-CUBJ	PA-18-150 Super Cub	18-2036	PH-MBF	15.12.82	R.A.Fleming	Kemble	10. 8.00
	(L-18C-PI) (Frame No.18-2035)		PH-NLF/R.Neth AF R-43/8A-43/52-2436 (As "18-5395/CDG" in French Army c/s)				
	(Regd with c/n 18-5395 following 1974 rebuild of PH-NLF which acquired data plate from, and took the						
	identity of, PH-MBF - note G-SUPA carries this c/n)						
G-CUBP	PA-18-150 Super Cub	18-8482	G-BVMI	8. 8.96	P.Grenet	Shotteswell	24. 8.02
			OH-PIN/N4262Z				
	(Frame No.18-8725; regd with c/n 18-8823 the "official" identity of N1136Z/D-EIAC. This was rebuilt 1984/85						
	with Frame No.18-4613 from D-EKAF. This latter frame was fitted to G-BVMI following an accident on 15.8.95;						
	the repaired frame of G-BVMI has become G-CUBP)						
G-CUBY	Piper J3C-65 Cub	16317	G-BTZW	2. 3.95	Claudine A.Bloom	Shoreham	31. 3.00P
	(Rebuilt with new fuselage 1996/97)		N88689/NC88689				
G-CUCU	Colt 180A HAFB	3869		22. 4.96	G.M.N. & S.Spencer	Watford	15. 5.00T
					"Commercial Union"		
G-CUPN	PA-46-350P Malibu Mirage	4636144		11. 2.98	K.Fletcher t/a Airpark	Coventry	23. 4.01
G-CURE*	Colt 77A HAFB	1424		3. 7.89	T Gunn "Alka Seltzer 3"	Lancing	21.11.96A
	(Standard shape plus Alka Seltzer tablet blisters)				(Balloon Preservation Group 7.98)		
G-CURR	Cessna 172R Skyhawk II	172-80143	G-BXOH	27. 5.98	JS Aviation Ltd	Booker	2. 3.01T
			N9989F				
G-CUTE	Dyn'Aero MCR-01 Ban-bi	PFA/301-13511		7. 9.99	E.G.Shimmin	(Bringsty, Worcs)	
G-CUTY	Europa Avn Europa	PFA/247-12910		20. 8.96	D.J. & M.Watson	(Selby)	
G-CVBF	Cameron A-210 HAFB	3588		2. 6.95	Virgin Balloon Flights Ltd	Bath	30. 8.00T
G-CVIL	Piper J3C-65 Cub (L-4H-PI)	12005	OO-VIL	23. 8.96	H.A.D.Munro	(Hastings)	
			OO-VVV/44-79709				
G-CVIX	DH.110 Sea Vixen D.3	10125	XP924	26. 2.96	De Havilland Aviation Ltd	Swansea	AC
	(Regd as FAW.2 with c/n 10132)				(As "XP924")		
G-CVPM	VPM M-16 Tandem Trainer	VPM16-UK-110		26. 3.98	C.S.Teuber	(Hannover, Germany)	24. 5.00P
G-CVYD	Airbus A.320-231	0393	B-HYO	24. 2.98	Caledonian Airways Ltd	Gatwick	16. 3.01T
			VR-HYO/F-WWIR		(JMC Air c/s)		
G-CVYE	Airbus A.320-231	0394	B-HYP	23. 3.98	Caledonian Airways Ltd	Gatwick	6. 4.01T
			VR-HYP/F-WWBB		(JMC Air c/s)		
G-CVYG	Airbus A.320-231	0443	B-HYT	10.11.98	Caledonian Airways Ltd.	Gatwick	30.11.01T
			VR-HYT/F-WWBV				
G-CWAG	Sequoia Falco F.8L	PFA/100-10895		11. 5.92	B.B.Wagner	Prestwick	19. 9.00P
	(Lycoming O-320)						
G-CWBM	Phoenix Currie Wot	PFA/3020	G-BTVP	28. 3.94	B.V.Mayo	Maypole Farm, Chislet	8. 9.00P
	(Continental C85)				(Damaged landing Headcorn 26.5.99)		
G-CWCW	Cameron R-900 HAFB	4386		9.11.98	Around The World Balloon Ltd	Glastonbury	
					(Cable & Wireless tiles) (Ditched into Pacific Ocean nr Omaezaki, Japan 7.3.99)		
G-CWFA	PA-38-112 Tomahawk	38-78A0120	G-BTGC	17. 8.99	Cardiff-Wales Flying Club Ltd.	Cardiff	28. 8.00T
			N9507T				
G-CWFB	PA-38-112 Tomahawk	38-78A0623	G-OAAL	13. 1.00	Cardiff Wales Aviation Services Ltd		
			N4471E			Cardiff	
G-CWFY	Cessna 152 II	15284639	G-OAMY	13. 1.00	Cardiff Wales Aviation Services Ltd		
			N6214M			Cardiff	
G-CWFZ	PA-28-151 Cherokee Warrior		G-CPCH	27.10.99	Cardiff Wales Flying Club Ltd	Cardiff	14. 1.00T
		28-7715131	G-BRGJ/(G-BPGP)/N5425F				
G-CWIZ	Aerospatiale AS.350B Ecureuil	1847	CS-HDF	18.10.95	Kensington Aviation Ltd	(Blairgowrie)	6. 4.02T
			G-DJEM/G-ZBAC/G-SEBI/G-BMCU				
G-CWOT	Phoenix Currie Wot	PFA/3019		31. 1.78	J.P.Conlan "Jonah"	(Kildare, Ireland)	21.12.00P
	(Walter Mikron II)						
G-CXCX	Cameron N-90 HAFB	1242		14. 3.86	Cathay Pacific Airways (London) Ltd		
	(Replacement envelope c/n 3332)				"Cathay Pacific IV"	(London SW1)	23. 2.00A
G-CYGI*	Hapi Cygnet SF-2A	PFA/182-12084		17.12.93	B.Brown	Kemble	
					(Cancelled by CAA 8.5.99: noted 9.99)		
G-CYLS	Cessna T303 Crusader	T303-00005	N20736	20.12.90	Gledhill Water Storage Ltd	Blackpool	16. 3.00
			G-BKXI/N303CC/(N9355T)				
G-CYMA	Gulfstream GA-7 Cougar	GA7-0083	G-BKOM	15. 8.83	Cyma Petroleum Ltd	Elstree	4. 6.01
			N794GA				
G-CZAG	Sky 90-24 HAFB	171		5.10.99	S.McCarthy	Rothersthorpe	
G-CZAR	Cessna 560 Citation V	560-0046	(N26656)	29.11.89	Chauffair (CI) Ltd	Farnborough	6. 3.00T
G-CZCZ	Mudry/CAARP CAP.10B	54	OE-AYY	28. 7.94	P.R.Moorhead & M.F.R.B.Collett		
			F-WZCG/HB-SAK/F-BUDT			Garston Farm, Marshfield	1. 8.00

G-DAAA – G-DZZZ

Regn	Type	C/n	P/I	Date	Owner/operator	Probable Base	CA Expy
G-DAAH	PA-28RT-201T Turbo Arrow IV		N3026U	27. 4.79	R.Peplow	Halfpenny Green	21. 5.00
		28R-7931104					
G-DAAM	Robinson R-22 Beta	2043		3. 6.92	Kenley Consultantcy Ltd	Liverpool	2. 7.01T

Regn	Type	C/n	P/I	Date	Owner/operator	Probable Base	CA Expy
G-DACA	Percival P.57 Sea Prince T.1	P57/12	WF118	6. 5.80	P.G.Vallance Ltd Charlwood, Surrey		17. 7.81P
					(Stored 6.97)		
G-DACC	Cessna 401B	401B-0112	N77GR	1. 9.86	Niglon Ltd	Coventry	9. 9.01
			N4488A/G-AYOU/N7972Q				
G-DACF	Cessna 152 II	152-81724	G-BURY	13. 6.97	T.M. & M.L.Jones	Egginton	10. 7.00T
			N67285		t/a Derby Aero Club		
G-DACS	Short SD.3-30 Var.100	SH.3089	C-GLAL	6. 7.98	Air Cavrel Ltd	Manston	21..7.00T
G-DADS	Hughes 369HS	22-0369S	N888SS	11. 6.90	Executive Aviation Services Ltd		
			N9101F			Gloucestershire	2. 8.02
G-DAFY	Beechcraft 58 Baron	TH-1591	N5684C	6.10.93	P.R.Earp	Gloucestershire	10.11.01
G-DAIR	Luscombe 8A Master	1474	G-BURK	3.10.97	D.F.Soul Standalone Farm, Meppershall		19.10.99P
	(Diesel Air 100hp)		N28713/NC28713				
G-DAJB	Boeing 757-2T7ER	23770		26. 2.87	Monarch Airlines Ltd	Luton	13. 5.02T
G-DAJC	Boeing 767-31KER	27206		15. 4.94	Airtours Intl Airways Ltd	Manchester	14. 4.00T
G-DAKK	Douglas C-47A-35DL Skytrain	9798	(G-OFON)	26. 7.94	Meridian Aircraft Ltd	Bournemouth	23. 4.00T
			F-GEOM/Fr Navy 36/OK-WZB/OK-WDU/42-23936 (Op South Coast Airways)				
G-DAKO	PA-28-236 Dakota	28-7911187	PH-ARW	29. 7.99	First European Airways Ltd	Denham	26. 8.02T
			(PH-MFB)/D-EECG/PH-ARW/OO-HCX/N29718				
G-DAMY	Europa Avn Europa	105 & PFA/247-12781		21.10.94	M.J.Ashby-Arnold	(Knaresborough)	20. 4.00P
	(Rotax 912UL)						
G-DAND	Socata TB.10 Tobago	72		5.12.79	Whitemoor Engineering Co Ltd	Coventry	21. 6.01
G-DANT	Rockwell Commander 114	14298	N4978W	9. 7.96	D.P.Tierney	Biggin Hill	17. 7.02T
G-DANZ	Eurocopter AS.355N Twin Squirrel	5658		14. 9.98	Frewton Ltd	Oxford	AC
G-DAPH	Cessna 180K Skywagon II	180-53016	N2620K	29. 1.92	M.R.L.Astor East Hatley, Tadlow		18. 2.02
G-DARA	PA-34-220T Seneca III	34-8333060	PH-TCT	8.11.88	Sys (Scaffolding Continentalractors) Ltd		
			N83JR/N4297J/N9632N			Gamston	25. 2.01
G-DASH	Rockwell Commander 112A	237	G-BDAJ	31. 3.87	Josef D.J.Jons & Co Ltd	Woodford	26. 3.00
			N1237J				
G-DASI	Short SD.3-60 Var.100	SH.3606	G-14-3606	14. 2.83	Gill Aviation Ltd	Newcastle	21. 3.00T
			G-BKKW				
G-DASU	Cameron V-77 HAFB	2300		6. 4.90	D. & L.S.Litchfield "Borne Free" Reading		11. 8.97A
G-DAVD	Reims Cessna FR172K Hawk XP	0632	D-EFJT	23.12.99	D M Driver	(Harpenden)	AC
			(PH-ADL)/PH-AXO				
G-DAVE	Jodel D.112	667	F-BICH	16. 8.78	D.A.Porter Griffins Farm, Temple Bruer		2. 3.00P
	(Built Valladeau)						
G-DAVO	Gulfstream AA-5B Tiger	AA5B-1226	G-GAGA	5. 1.96	Kadala Aviation Ltd	Elstree	19. 1.01T
			G-BGPG/(G-BGRW)				
G-DAVT	Schleicher ASH26E	26090		24. 4.96	D.A.Triplett	Sleap	10. 5.02
G-DAYI	Europa Avn Europa	PFA/247-13027		19. 8.96	A.F.Day	(West Wickham)	
G-DAYS	Europa Avn Europa	PFA/247-12810		9. 5.95	D.J.Bowie	Sleap	21. 7.00P
	(Rotax 912UL)						
G-DBAL*	HS.125 Srs.3B	25117	G-BSAA	20. 7.84	Southampton Airport Fire Services		
			5N-AKT/5N-AET			Southampton	16. 6.92
G-DBDB	VPM M16 Tandem Trainer	PFA/G/12-1239		19.10.99	D.R.Bolsover	(Scampton)	AC
G-DBHH	Agusta-Bell 206B JetRanger	8111	G-AWVO	24. 5.96	UK Helicopter Charter Ltd	Rochester	22. 6.01
			VH-BHI/PK-HCA/G-AWVO/9Y-TDN/PK-HBG/G-AWVO				
G-DBMW	Bell 206B Jet Ranger 4	4401		8. 3.96	Lind Ltd	Attlebridge, Norwich	2. 6.99T
G-DBYE	Mooney M.20M	27-0098	N91462	24. 3.98	A.J.Thomas	Cranfield	23. 3.01
G-DCAV	PA-32R-301 Saratoga IIHP	3246075	N92864	8. 5.97	Airsys Communications Technology Ltd		
						Blackbushe	7. 5.00
G-DCCH	MBB Bo.105DBS/4	S-770	D-HDYF	19. 9.86	Bond Air Services	Aberdeen	10.12.01T
G-DCDB	Bell 407	53137	C-FCDB	19.10.99	Paycourt Ltd	Belfast	19.10.02T
			N7238A				
G-DCEA	PA-34-200T Seneca II	34-8070079	N3567D	13. 2.91	Chazair Ltd	RAF Halton	14. 5.00T
G-DCIO	McDonnell Douglas DC-10-30	48277		27. 1.81	British Airways plc	Manchester	14. 4.01T
					"Epping Forest"		
G-DCKK	Reims Cessna F.172N Skyhawk II	1589	PH-GRT	19. 5.80	M.Manston	Panshanger	24. 4.01
			PH-AXA				
G-DCPA	MBB BK-117C-1C	7511	D-HECU	16.12.97	Devon & Cornwall Constabulary		
			D-HXXL/G-LFBA/D-HECU/D-HMBF			Middlemoor, Exeter	16. 6.02T
G-DCSE	Robinson R-44 Astro	0659		23. 9.99	DCS Europe plc Wellesbourne Mountford		
G-DCXL	SAN Jodel D.140C Mousquetaire III	101	F-BKSM	27. 5.88	C.F.Mugford	Little Gransden	22.12.99
					t/a X-Ray Lima Group		
G-DDAY	PA-28R-201T Turbo Arrow III	28R-7703112	G-BPDO	24.11.88	K.E.Hogg	Tatenhill	15. 4.01
			N3496Q		t/a G-DDAY Group		
G-DDMV	North American T-6G-NF Texan	168-313	N3240N	30. 4.90	E.A.Morgan Sywell/Gloucestershire		13.11.99
			Haitian AF 3209/49-3209 (As "493209" in Calif ANG c/s)				
G-DDOD	Enstrom 280FX	2086		25.11.99	Sunseeker Sales (UK) Ltd.	Bournemouth	9 .12.02
G-DEAN	Solar Wings Pegasus XL-Q	SW-TE-0117 & SW-WQ-0123	G-MVJV	30.11.98	D.C.P.Cardey & G.D.Tannahill	Hereford	7. 9.00P
	(Rotax 462)						

Regn	Type	C/n	P/I	Date	Owner/operator	Probable Base	CA Expy
G-DEBC	BAe 146 Srs.200	E-2024	N166US N348PS	23. 5.96	Debonair Airways Ltd "Team Spirit"	Luton	22. 5.02T
G-DEBE	BAe 146 Srs.200	E-2022	N163US N346PS	5. 8.96	US Airways Inc (Arlington, Vi, USA) "Bird of Paradise"		6. 8.02T
G-DEBF	BAe 146 Srs.200	E-2023	N165US N347PS	25. 9.96	Debonair Airways Ltd "Freedom of Europe"	Luton	26. 9.02T
G-DEBG	BAe 146 Srs.200	E-2040	N178US N357PS	1. 4.97	Debonair Airways Ltd "Jumbolino"	Luton	31. 3.00T
G-DEBH	BAe 146 Srs.200	E-2045	N185US N362PS	27. 8.97	Debonair Airways Ltd "Prosperity"	Luton	27. 8.00T
G-DEER	Robinson R-22 Beta-II	2827		17. 7.98	M.Taylor	Shoreham	28. 7.01T
G-DEFK	Bae 146 Srs.200	E-2012	G-DEBK C-FHAV/N601AW	22.10.99	Flightline Ltd	Southend	25. 4.02T
G-DEFL	BAe 146 Srs.200	E-2014	G-DEBL C-FHAX/N602AW	22.10.99	Flightline Ltd	Southend	28. 1.02T
G-DEFM	BAe 146 Srs.200	E-2016	G-DEBM C-FHAZ	22.10.99	Flightline Ltd	Southend	16 .3.02T
G-DEJL*	Robinson R-22 Beta	2001		31. 3.92	G.& B.Dobson Ltd The Estate, South Elkington, Louth		18. 5.01T
					(Substantially damaged on local flight 19.4.99: cancelled as wfu 22.7.99)		
G-DELF	Aero L-29A Delfin	194555	ES-YLM Soviet AF 12 (red)	28. 8.97	P.A.Greenhalgh & B.R.Green	Manston	26. 9.00P
G-DELT	Robinson R-22 Beta	0898		11.11.88	Virgin Helicopters Ltd	Booker	15. 4.02T
G-DEMH	Reims Cessna F.172M Skyhawk II	1137	G-BFLO PH-DMF/(EI-AYO)	18.11.91	M.Hammond	Crowfield/Hardwick	11. 6.01
G-DENA	Reims Cessna F.150G	0204	G-AVEO EI-BOI/G-AVEO	14.12.95	Plane Talking Ltd	Elstree	20. 1.02T
G-DENB	Reims Cessna F.150G	0136	G-ATZZ	14.12.95	Plane Talking Ltd	Elstree	11.12.98T
G-DENC	Reims Cessna F.150G	0107	G-AVAP	14.12.95	Plane Talking Ltd	Elstree	31.10.02T
G-DEND	Reims Cessna F.150M	1201	G-WAFC G-BDFI/(OH-CGD)	6. 6.97	Plane Talking Ltd	Elstree	3. 8.01T
G-DENE	PA-28-140 Cherokee	28-21710	G-ATOS	5. 2.98	Den Air Aviation Ltd t/a Aviators Flight Center	Southend	17. 6.02T
G-DENH	PA-28-161 Warrior II	28-8216202	G-BTNH N253FT/N9577N	14. 4.97	Plane Talking Ltd	Elstree	1. 3.01T
G-DENI	PA-32-300 Cherokee Six	32-7340006	G-BAIA	7.12.95	A.Bendkowski	Rochester	14. 3.01T
G-DENK	PA-28-181 Archer II	28-8290108	G-BXRJ HB-PGO	5. 2.98	Plane Talking Ltd (Swiss Cross on fin)	Elstree	10. 2.01T
G-DENN	Bell 206B Jet Ranger 4	4409	N75486	10. 6.96	Abbey Flight Ltd	Fairoaks	22. 7.02
G-DENR	Reims Cessna F.172N Skyhawk II	1839	G-BGNR	30. 4.97	Den Air Aviation Ltd t/a Aviators Flight Center	Southend	22.10.00T
G-DENS	Binder CP.301S Smaragd	121	D-ENSA	20.11.85	J.K.Davies	(Chester)	3. 9.00P
G-DENT	Cameron N-145 HAFB	4135		8. 4.97	Deproco UK Ltd	Dorking	21. 9.00A
G-DENZ	PA-44-180 Seminole	44-7995327	G-INDE G-BHNM/N8077X	3. 7.97	Den Air Aviation Ltd t/a Aviators Flight Center	Southend	31. 3.02T
G-DERB	Robinson R-22 Beta	1005	G-BPYH	28. 6.95	S Thompson	(Leamington Spa)	25. 6.01T
G-DERV	Cameron Truck 56SS HAFB	1719		21. 3.88	J.M.Percival "Shell UK Truck"	Loughborough	22. 2.00A
G-DESI	Aero Designs Pulsar XP PFA/202-12147			14.11.91	D.F.Gaughan	(Minehead)	
G-DESS	Mooney M.20J (201)	24-1272	N11598	20.10.87	W.E.Newnes	Birmingham	14. 1.00
G-DEST	Mooney M.20J	24-3429		6.11.98	Allegro Aviation Ltd	(Guernsey)	12. 1.02
G-DESY	Cessna A152 Aerobat	A152-0805	G-BNJE N7386L	20.10.97	General Airline Ltd	Blackbushe	23. 3.00T
G-DEVN*	DH.104 Devon C.2/2	04269	WB533	26.10.84	Air Classic GmbH (As "WB533") Frankfurt Rhein-Main, Germany		4. 2.85P*
G-DEVS	PA-28-180 Cherokee	28-830	G-BGVJ D-ENPI/N7066W	5. 3.85	B.J.Hoptroff & J.M.Whiteley t/a 180 Group	Blackbushe	9. 1.02
G-DEXP	ARV1 Super 2 003 & PFA/152-11154 (Hewland AE75)			24. 4.85	W.G.McKinnon	Perth	20. 4.00P
G-DEXY	Beechcraft E90 King Air	LW-136	N750DC N30CW/N84GA/N328TB/TR-LTT	6. 4.89	Specsavers Aviation Ltd	Guernsey	18. 1.00
G-DEZC	BAe HS.125 Srs.700B	257070	G-BWCR G-5-604/HB-VGG/G-5-604/HB-VGG	28. 5.96	Frewton Ltd	Jersey	17. 7.00
G-DFLY	PA-38-112 Tomahawk	38-79A0450		15. 2.79	H.M.Simmonds	(Hook)	4.12.00T
G-DGDG	Glaser-Dirks DG-400-17	4-27		25. 3.83	M.Clarke t/a DG-400 Flying Group	Lasham	2. 5.01
G-DGIV	Glaser Dirks DG-800B	8-145-B69		27.11.98	W.R.McNair	(Holywood, NI)	23.11.01
G-DGLM	Glaser Dirks DG-400	4-48		2.12.99	L J McKelvie	(Lisburn, NI)	14.12.02
G-DGWW	Rand Robinson KR-2 PFA/129-11044 (Hapi Magnum 75)			7. 3.91	W.Wilson	Liverpool	7. 7.00P

Regn	Type	C/n	P/I	Date	Owner/operator	Probable Base	CA Expy
G-DHAV	DH.115 Vampire T.11 (T.55)	15682	U-1234	13.10.95	Jacquelyn Jones (De Havilland Aviation Ltd)		
	(Regd with Nacelle No. DHP.48913)		XH308		(As "U-1234" in Swiss AF c/s)	Swansea	27. 8.99P
	(Reported as built by FFW with c/n 994)						
G-DHCB	DHC.2 Beaver 1 Floatplane	1450	G-BTDL	20. 6.91	Seaflite Ltd	Loughearnhead	16. 9.97T
			XP779				
G-DHCC	DHC.1 Chipmunk 22	C1/0393	WG321	28. 5.97	Eureka Aviation NV	Wevelgem, Belgium	3. 9.00
G-DHCI	DHC.1 Chipmunk 22	C1/0884	G-BBSE	12. 7.89	Felthorpe Flying Group Ltd	Felthorpe	14. 8.00
			WZ858				
G-DHDV	DH.104 Dove 8	04205	VP981	26.10.98	Air Atlantique Ltd	Coventry	12. 8.00
					(As "VP981" in BoBMF c/s)		
G-DHGS	Robinson R-22 Beta-II	2592		19. 4.96	Driver Hire Group Services Ltd		
						Leeds-Bradford	23. 5.02T
G-DHJH	Airbus A.321-…	1238		.00R	Airtours International Ltd		
G-DHLB	Cameron N-90 HAFB	3261		20. 4.94	DHL International (UK) Ltd	Hounslow	28.10.96A
G-DHLI*	Colt World 90SS HAFB	2603		2. 6.94	Virgin Airship & Balloon Co Ltd	Telford	17.12.98A
					(Cancelled 9.4.99 as WFU)		
G-DHLZ*	Colt 31A Air Chair HAFB	2604		2. 6.94	Virgin Airship & Balloon Co Ltd	Telford	23. 7.99A
					(Cancelled 9.4.99 as WFU)		
G-DHSS	FFW DH.112 Venom FB.50 (FB.1)	836	J-1626	26. 3.99	D J L Wood	Bournemouth	AC
G-DHTM	DH.82A Tiger Moth	PFA/157-11095		6. 1.86	E.G.Waite-Roberts	(Basingstoke)	
					(On rebuild from original unidentified components)		
G-DHTT	FFW DH.112 Venom FB.50 (FB.1)	821	(G-BMOC)	17.10.96	D.J.Lindsay Wood	Bournemouth	17. 7.99P
			J-1611		(Op Source Classic Jet Flight: as "WR421" in all-red c/s)		
G-DHUU	FFW DH.112 Venom FB.50 (FB.1)	749	(G-BMOD)	26. 2.96	D.J.Lindsay Wood	Bournemouth	17. 7.99P
			J-1539		(Op Source Classic Jet Flight: as "WR410" in 6 Sqdn RAF c/s)		
	(Note: G-BLKA marked as "WR410" dismantled at Bouremnouth 5.99)						
G-DHVV	DH.115 Vampire T.55	55092	U-1214	5. 9.91	Lindsay Wood Promotions Ltd	Bournemouth	24. 3.99P
	(Also quoted as c/n 974)				(Op Source Classic Jet Flight: as "XE897" in 54 Sqdn RAF c/s)		
G-DHWW	FFW DH.115 Vampire T.55	979	U-1219	5. 9.91	Lindsay Wood Promotions Ltd	Bournemouth	27. 1.00P
					(Op Source Classic Jet Flight: as "XG775/VL" in RN FOFT Yeovilton c/s)		
G-DHXX	FFW DH.100 Vampire FB.6	682	J-1173	5. 9.91	Lindsay Wood Promotions Ltd	Bournemouth	27. 1.00P
					(Op Source Classic Jet Flight: (As "VT871" in 54 Sqdn RAF c/s)		
G-DHYY	DH.115 Vampire T.11	15112	WZ553	17. 3.95	Lindsay Wood Promotions Ltd (As "WZ553/40")		
					(Stored 3.96)	Bruntingthorpe	
G-DHZF	DH.82A Tiger Moth	82309	G-BSTJ	7. 7.99	M.R. Parker	Sywell	14. 8.02
			OO-MEH/OO-GEB/RNeth AF A-13/PH-UFB/A-13/N9192 (As N9192 in RAF c/s)				
G-DHZZ	FFW DH.115 Vampire T.55	990	U-1230	5. 9.91	Lindsay Wood Promotions Ltd	Bournemouth	24.11.98P
					(Op Source Classic Jet Flight: as "WZ589" in 54 Sqdn RAF c/s)		
G-DIAL	Cameron N-90 HAFB	1851		7.11.88	A.J.Street "London"	Exeter	11. 5.00A
G-DIAT	PA-28-140 Cherokee Cruiser		G-BCGK	19. 7.89	The RAF Benevolent Fund Enterprises Ltd		
		28-7425322	N9594N		(Op Disabled Flyers Group/Bristol & Wessex Aeroplane Club)		
						Bristol	2. 9.00T
G-DICE	Enstrom F-28F	787	D-HANA	8.11.96	Dice Aviation Services Ltd	Goodwood	5.12.99
G-DICK	Thunder Ax6-56Z HAFB	159		6. 7.78	R.D.Sargeant "Dandag"	(Switzerland)	13. 9.99A
G-DIET	Lindstrand Drinks Can SS HAFB	220		1. 5.95	Pepsi Cola Overseas Ltd		
	(Diet Pepsi Can)					Des Moines, IA, USA	19. 4.00A
					(Cancelled by CAA 21.9.99)		
G-DIGI	PA-32-300 Cherokee Six	32-7940224	D-EIES	13.10.98	D.Stokes	Stapleford	19.11.01T
			N2947M		t/a Security UN Ltd Group		
G-DIKY	Murphy Rebel	PFA/232-13182		13. 2.98	R.J.P.Herivel	(Alderney)	
G-DIMB	Boeing 767-31KER	28865		28. 4.97	Airtours Intl Airways Ltd	Manchester	27. 4.00T
G-DIME	Rockwell Commander 114	14123	N49829	9. 3.88	H.B.Richardson	Badminton	2. 7.01
G-DINA	Gulfstream AA-5B Tiger	AA5B-1218	N4555Y	27. 2.81	J.Gosling & N.R.J.Mifflin	Kemble	6. 5.02T
					t/a Portway Aviation		
G-DING	Colt 77A HAFB	1862		28. 6.91	G.J.Bell "Dingbat"	Wokingham	10.11.99A
G-DINO	Cyclone Pegasus Quantum 15	7225	G-MGMT	15.12.98	G.D.Hall	(March)	23. 7.00P
	(Rotax 582)						
G-DINT	Bristol 156 Beaufighter IF	3858M	17. 6.91	T.E.Moore	Rotary Farm, Hatch	
		STAN B1 184604	X7688		(On rebuild from various ex Australian components 8.95)		
G-DIPI	Cameron Tub 80SS HAFB	1745		6. 5.88	D.K.Fish "KP Choc Dips Tub"	Bedford	11.12.98A
G-DIPS*	Taylor JT.1 Monoplane	PFA/55-10320		19.12.78	B.J.Halls	(Boston)	
	(VW1500)				(Project stored 1990: cancelled by CAA 31.3.99)		
G-DIRE	Robinson R-22 Beta	1663		29. 1.91	Holly Aviation Ltd	Cambridge	19. 3.00T
G-DIRK	Glaser-Dirks DG-400	4-124	D-KEKT	18. 9.86	C.J.Lowrie	Parham Park	29. 1.02
G-DISK	PA-24-250 Comanche	24-1197	G-APZG	9. 8.89	A.Johnston	Guernsey	29. 5.00
			EI-AKW				
G-DISO	SAN Jodel 150 Mascaret	24	9Q-CPK	16.12.86	P.F.Craven & J.H.Shearer	Cumbernauld	30. 5.00P
			OO-APK/F-BLDT				
G-DIVA	Cessna R172K Hawk XPII	3071	N758FX	10. 2.86	Bob Crowe Aircraft Sales Ltd	Cranfield	20. 8.01T
G-DIWY	PA-32-300 Cherokee Six	32-40731	OY-DLW	26.11.91	IFS Chemicals Ltd	East Winch	19. 5.01
			D-EHMW/N8931N				

Regn	Type	C/n	P/I	Date	Owner/operator	Probable Base	CA Expy
G-DIXY	PA-28-181 Archer III	2843195	N41284	10.12.98	S.Dixon-Smith t/a Lyons Aviation	Fowlmere	16.12.01T
G-DIZO	Jodel Wassmer D.120A Paris-Nice	326	G-EMKM F-BOBG	30. 5.91	D. & E.Aldersea	Breighton	31.10.00P
G-DIZY	PA-28R-201T Turbo Arrow III	28R-7703401	N47570	13.10.88	T.D.Melen t/a Medway Arrow Group	Rochester	9.12.00
G-DIZZ	Hughes 369HE	89-0105E	N9029F	19. 2.97	H.J.Pelham	Cleeves Farm, Salisbury	22. 4.00T
G-DJAE	Cessna 500 Citation (Unit No.339)	500-0339	G-JEAN N300EC/N707US/G-JEAN/(N5339J)	3.11.98	Source Ltd.	Bournemouth	27. 3.99T
G-DJAR	Airbus A.320-231	164	OY-CNE (D-ACSL)/OY-CNE/F-WWIE	3.11.98	Airtours Intl Airways Ltd	Manchester	17. 3.00T
G-DJCR	Varga 2150A Kachina	VAC 155-80	EI-CFK G-BLWG/OO-HTD/N8360J	11. 4.96	D.J.C.Robertson	Perth	30. 4.99
G-DJEA	Cessna 421C Golden Eagle II	421C-0654	TC-AAA N37379/(N24BS)/N37379	16. 4.98	Source Ltd	Bournemouth	11.10.01T
G-DJHB	Beechcraft A23-19 Musketeer Sport III MB-200		G-AZZE LN-TVH	6. 8.82	W.B.Murray t/a Nayland Aiglet Group	Hill Farm, Nayland	15. 7.02
G-DJIM*	DHCA.1	DHCA.1		28.12.78	J.Crawford (Cancelled by CAA 24.3.99)	(Oxford)	
G-DJJA	PA-28-181 Archer II	28-8490014	N4326D	14. 9.87	B.Cheese & S.M.Price t/a Choice Aircraft (Op Modern Air)	Fowlmere	18.12.02T
G-DJLW	HS.125 Srs.3B/RA	25140	G-AVVB G-5-17/(G-5-16)	19. 1.89	Mark IV Aviation (IOM) Ltd	(Douglas, IOM)	1. 7.00
G-DJNH	Denney Kitfox mk.3 (Rotax 582)	772 & PFA/172-11896		20. 9.90	D.J.N.Hall	Downwood, Dorset	20. 7.98P
G-DKDP	Grob G-109	6100	(G-BMBD) D-KAMS	9. 7.85	D.W. & J.E.Page	Tibenham	12. 8.00
G-DKGF	Viking Dragonfly mk.1 (VW1834)	PFA/139-10898		16.10.86	P.C.Dowbor (Stored 6.98)	Enstone	
G-DLCB	Europa Avn Europa 46 & PFA/247-12652 (Rotax 912UL)			16.11.95	D.J.Lockett & C.R.C.Bowen	Inverness	14. 5.00P
G-DLDL	Robinson R-22 Beta	1971		2. 1.92	A.J.Wagstaff (Damaged Cambridge 28.11.98)	Sywell	5. 2.01
G-DLFN	Aero L-29 Delfin	294872	ES-YLE Estonian AF/Soviet AF	28. 5.98	T.W.Freeman & N.Gooderham	North Weald	16. 9.00P
G-DLOM	Socata TB.20 Trinidad	1102	N2823Y	13.12.90	J.N.A.Adderley	Rochester	30. 9.00
G-DLTR	PA-28-180 Cherokee E	28-5803	G-AYAV	15. 3.96	BCT Aircraft Leasing Ltd	Bristol	18. 7.02T
G-DMAC	Avtech Jabiru UL	PFA/274-13321		15.10.98	C.J.Pratt	Goodwood	13. 4.00P
G-DMCA	McDonnell Douglas DC-10-30	48266	N3016Z	12. 3.96	Monarch Airlines Ltd	Luton	11. 3.02T
G-DMCD	Robinson R-22 Beta	1201	G-OOLI G-DMCD	14.11.89	R.W.Pomphrett	Thruxton	10.12.01T
G-DMCS	PA-28R-200 Cherokee Arrow II 28R-7635284		G-CPAC PH-SMW/OO-HAU/N75220	29. 5.84	W.G.Ashton & J Bingley t/a Arrow Associates	(Wokingham)	19. 4.02T
G-DMWW	CFM Shadow Srs.DD (Rotax 582)	304-DD		12.10.98	Microlight Sport Aviation Ltd	(West Wickham)	29. 3.00P
G-DNCN	Agusta-Bell 206A Jet Ranger	8185	9H-AAJ Libyan Arab Rep.AF 8185/5A-BAM	21.11.97	Heli-Tele Ltd	Thruxton	20.11.00T
G-DNCS	PA-28R-201T Turbo Arrow III 28R-7803024		N47841	3. 1.89	BC Arrow Ltd.	Barton	6. 4.01
G-DNLB	MBB Bo.105DBS-4 (Rebuilt with new pod S.850 1992)	S.60/850	G-BUDP G-BTBD/VH-LCS/VH-HRM/G-BCDH/EC-DUO/G-BCDH/D-HDBK	10. 4.92	Bond Air Services (Op for Northern Lighthouse Board)	Oban/Aberdeen	23. 4.01T
G-DNVT	Gulfstream G.1159C Gulfstream IV 1078		(G-BPJM) N17589	29. 9.89	Shell Aircraft Ltd	Heathrow	28. 9.00T
G-DOBN	Cessna 402B II	402B-1243	N24PL N4604G	25. 4.96	Fraggle Leasing Ltd	Edinburgh	27. 6.00T
G-DOCA	Boeing 737-436	25267		21.10.91	British Airways plc (Mountains of the Birds/Benyhone Tartan)	Gatwick	20.10.01T
G-DOCB	Boeing 737-436	25304		16.10.91	British Airways plc (Wings t/s)	Gatwick	16.10.01T
G-DOCC	Boeing 737-436	25305		24.10.91	British Airways plc (Blue Poole t/s)	Gatwick	24.10.01T
G-DOCD	Boeing 737-436	25349		6.11.91	British Airways plc (Animals & Trees t/s)	Gatwick	6.11.01T
G-DOCE	Boeing 737-436	25350		20.11.91	British Airways plc (Blomsterang t/s)	Gatwick	19.11.01T
G-DOCF	Boeing 737-436	25407		9.12.91	British Airways plc (Cockerel of Lowicz/Koguty Lowickie t/s)	Gatwick	9.12.01T
G-DOCG	Boeing 737-436	25408		16.12.91	British Airways plc (Chelsea Rose t/s)	Gatwick	15.12.01T

Regn	Type	C/n	P/I	Date	Owner/operator	Probable Base	CA Expy
G-DOCH	Boeing 737-436	25428		19.12.91	British Airways plc (Grand Union t/s)	Gatwick	18.12.01T
G-DOCI	Boeing 737-436	25839		8. 1.92	British Airways plc (Union Flag t/s)	Gatwick	7. 1.02T
G-DOCJ	Boeing 737-436	25840		15. 1.92	British Airways plc (Mountains of the Birds/Benyhone Tartan)	Gatwick	14. 1.02T
G-DOCK	Boeing 737-436	25841		25. 2.92	British Airways plc (Union Flag t/s)	Gatwick	24. 2.02T
G-DOCL	Boeing 737-436	25842		2. 3.92	British Airways plc (Martha Masanabo/Ndebele t/s)	Gatwick	1. 3.02T
G-DOCM	Boeing 737-436	25843		19. 3.92	British Airways plc (Rendezvous t/s)	Gatwick	18. 3.02T
G-DOCN	Boeing 737-436	25848		21.10.92	British Airways plc (Union Flag t/s)	Gatwick	20.10.02T
G-DOCO	Boeing 737-436	25849		26.10.92	British Airways plc	Gatwick	25.10.02T
G-DOCP	Boeing 737-436	25850		2.11.92	British Airways plc	Gatwick	1.11.02T
G-DOCR	Boeing 737-436	25851		6.11.92	British Airways plc (Waves of the City t/s)	Gatwick	5.11.02T
G-DOCS	Boeing 737-436	25852		1.12.92	British Airways plc (Chelsea Rose t/s)	Gatwick	30.11.02T
G-DOCT	Boeing 737-436	25853		22.12.92	British Airways plc (Crossing Borders t/s)	Gatwick	23.12.02T
G-DOCU	Boeing 737-436	25854		18. 1.93	British Airways plc (Martha Masanabo/Ndebele t/s)	Gatwick	19. 1.00T
G-DOCV	Boeing 737-436	25855		25. 1.93	British Airways plc (Mountain of the Birds/Benyhone Tartan t/s)	Gatwick	24. 1.00T
G-DOCW	Boeing 737-436	25856		2. 2.93	British Airways plc (Rendezvous t/s)	Gatwick	3. 2.00T
G-DOCX	Boeing 737-436	25857		29. 3.93	British Airways plc (Dove/Colum t/s)	Gatwick	28. 3.00T
G-DOCY	Boeing 737-436	25844	OO-LTQ G-BVBY/TC-ALS/G-BVBY/(G-DOCY)	17.10.96	British Airways plc	Gatwick	17.10.02T
G-DOCZ	Boeing 737-436	25858	EC-FXJ EC-657/G-BVBZ/(G-DOCZ)	12.12.94	British Airways plc	Gatwick	11. 1.01T
G-DODB	Robinson R-22 Beta	0911	N8005R	3. 5.96	Exmoor Helicopters Ltd Withiel Farm, Minehead		29. 7.02T
G-DODD	Reims Cessna F.172P Skyhawk II	2175		5.10.82	K.Watts	Denham	4.10.98
G-DODI	PA-46-350P Malibu Mirage	4636019		26.10.95	CAVOK SRL	(Milan)	24.11.00
G-DODR	Robinson R-22 Beta	1325	N80721	5. 6.96	Exmoor Helicopters Ltd Withiel Farm, Minehead		25. 7.02T
G-DOEA	Gulfstream AA-5A Cheetah	AA5A-0895	G-RJMI N27170	30. 4.96	Plane Talking Ltd (Op Cabair Aerospace Education Sevice) (Duke of Edinburgh Award & British Aerospace c/s)	Elstree	28. 7.00T
G-DOFY	Bell 206B JetRanger III	3637	N2283F	26. 8.87	Cinnamond Ltd (Op Cabair Helicopters)	Elstree	8. 6.02T
G-DOGZ	Horizon 1	PFA/241-13129		10. 8.98	J.E.D.Rogerson	(Ferryhill)	
G-DOLY	Cessna T303 Crusader	T303-00107	N303MK G-BJZK/(N3645C)	20. 7.94	R.M.Jones	Blackpool	12. 8.00
G-DOME	PA-28-161 Warrior III	28-42062	N4160V	12. 1.00	Plane Talking Ltd	Elstree	
G-DONG	Sky 105-24 HAFB	011	G-BWKP	5. 2.97	G.J.Bell "Ting A Ling"	Wokingham	10. 9.99A
G-DONI	Gulfstream AA-5B Tiger	AA5B-1029	G-BLLT OO-RTG/(OO-HRS)	20. 7.95	D.M.McLean	Wellesbourne Mountford	1.10.00
G-DONS	PA-28RT-201T Turbo Arrow IV	28R-8131077	N8336L	22. 4.88	D.J.Murphy t/a Arrow One Group	Blackbushe	29. 9.00
G-DONZ	Europa Avn Europa	PFA/247-12545		1. 6.94	D.J.Smith & D.McNicholl (Muir of Ord/Tain, Ross-shire)		
G-DOOZ	Aerospatiale AS.355F2 Twin Squirrel	5367	G-BNSX	13. 5.88	Lynton Aviation Ltd (Op European Helicopters Ltd)	Denham	1. 4.00T
G-DORB	Bell 206B JetRanger III	3955	SE-HTI TC-HBN	15. 8.90	Dorbcrest Homes Ltd Wrightington, Wigan		28.11.02
G-DORN	EKW C-3605	332	HB-RBJ SwissAF C-552	15. 9.98	R.G.Gray (As C-552)	(London E1)	13. 5.00P
G-DOVE	Cessna 182Q Skylane II	182-66724	N96446	26. 6.80	Carel Investments Ltd	Bournemouth	7. 7.01
G-DOWN	Colt 31A Air Chair HAFB	1570		3. 8.89	M.Williams "Up & Down"	Wadhurst, Sussex	8. 6.00A
G-DPPH	Agusta A.109E Power	11053	G-BYMS	17.11.99	Sloane Helicopters Ltd ("Heddlu Dyfed Powys Police")	Carmarthen	9.12.02T
G-DPST	Phillips ST-2 Speedtwin	PFA/207-12674		10. 5.96	S.E.Phillips Upper Cae Garw Farm, Trelleck, Monmouth		
G-DPUK	Mooney M.20K (231)	25-0631	G-BNZS N1154A	2. 4.98	K.A.Horne	Turweston	26. 3.00

Regn	Type	C/n	P/I	Date	Owner/operator	Probable Base	CA Expy
G-DRAC	Cameron Dracula Skull SS HAFB	2655		14.11.91	Shiplake Investments Ltd	(Guernsey)	10. 1.93A
G-DRAG	Cessna 152 II	152-83188	G-REME	27. 4.90	L.A.Maynard & M.E.Scouller	Old Sarum	5. 8.02T
	(Tail-wheel conversion)		G-DRAG/G-BRNF/N47217 (Op Old Sarum Flying Club)				
G-DRAM	Reims Cessna FR.172F Rocket	0102	OH-CNS	18. 9.98	A.F.Allen	(Lochearnhead)	AC
	(Floatplane)				t/a Off-Water Group		
G-DRAR	MDH Hughes 369E (500E)	0486E	N101LH	15. 9.95	Readmans Ltd	Leeds-Bradford	9.10.01T
			N1608Z				
G-DRAW	Colt 77A HAFB	1830		31. 8.90	C.Wolstenholme	Oswestry	14. 7.00A
G-DRAY	Taylor JT-1 Monoplane	PFA/1452		13. 7.78	L.J.Dray	Sidmouth	
G-DRBG	Cessna 172M Skyhawk	172-65263	G-MUIL	18. 1.95	J.W.Halfpenny	(Landbeach, Cambridge)	13. 5.01T
			N64486				
G-DREX	Cameron Saturn 110SS HAFB	4217		28.10.97	LRC Products Ltd	Broxbourne, Herts	3.11.99A
G-DREY	Cessna 172R Skyhawk	17280781	N23726	16.11.99	C.J.& J.M.Wardill	(Chellaston)	24.11.02T
G-DRGN	Cameron N-105 HAFB	2024		13. 6.91	W.I.Hooker & C.Parker	Nottingham	7. 7.99T
G-DRGS	Cessna 182S	18280375	N2389X	17.11.98	Walter Scott and Partners Ltd	Edinburgh	14.12.01
G-DRHL	Eurocopter AS.350B2 Ecureuil	3032		12. 1.98	Lytonworth Ltd.	(Solihull)	29. 4.01T
G-DRMM	Europa Avn Europa	PFA/247-13201		27. 7.98	M.W.Mason	(Nantwich)	
G-DRNT	Sikorsky S-76A II Plus	760201	N93WW	5. 4.90	Bristow Helicopters Ltd	Redhill	1. 5.00T
			N3WQ/N3WL/N3121G				
G-DROP	Cessna U206C Super Skywagon			8. 1.87	Peterborough Parachute Centre Ltd Sibson		1. 1.00
		U206-1230	G-BAMN/4X-ALL/N71943				
G-DRSV	Robin DR.315X Petit Prince	624	F-ZWRS	7. 6.90	R.S.Voice	Rushett Farm, Chessington	21.11.00P
	(Regd with c/n PFA/210-11765 following major rebuild)						
G-DRUM	Thruster TST Mk.1	8068-TST-081	G-MVBR	12. 1.99	C.C.Mercer	Saltash	31. 1.00P
	(Rotax 503)						
G-DRYI	Cameron N-77 HAFB	2046		7. 8.89	J.Barbour & Sons Ltd	Marsh Benham	4. 6.94A
					"Barbour"		
G-DRYS	Cameron N-90 HAFB	3377		1.12.95	J.Barbour & Sons Ltd	Marsh Benham	6. 7.00A
G-DRZF	CEA DR.360 Chevalier	451	F-BRZF	4. 9.91	Mavis R.Parker	Sywell	28.11.00
G-DSGC	PA-25-260 Pawnee C	25-4890	OY-BDA	3. 5.95	Devon & Somerset Gliding Club Ltd		
						North Hill	14. 8.01
G-DSID	PA-34-220T Seneca	3447001		21. 7.95	R.Howton	Biggin Hill	3. 8.01
G-DSPI	Robinson R-44 Astro	0661	G-DPSI	25.10.99	Focal Point Communications Ltd		
						(London,SW6)	4.11.02T
G-DTCP	PA-32R-300 Cherokee Lance		G-TEEM	26. 1.93	Campbell Aviation Ltd	Denham	23. 3.01
		32R-7780255	N2604Q				
G-DTOO*	PA-38-112 Tomahawk	38-79A0312		15. 2.79	Not known	Panshanger	29. 7.94T
					(Damaged Seething 9.7.94; stored 3.99)		
G-DUCK*	Grumman G.44 Widgeon	1218	N3103Q	15.11.88	Musee Historique de L'Hydraviation	Biscarosse, France	
			N58337/42-38217/NC28679	(On rebuild 10.93)			
G-DUDE	Vans RV-8	PFA/303-13246		16. 7.99	W.M.Hodgkins	(Stadhampton)	
G-DUDS	CASA I-131E Jungmann	2108	D-EHDS	27. 6.90	R.D.Loder	Lower Upham Farm,. Wilts	3. 6.00P
	(Enma Tigre G-1V-B-1)		E3B-512				
G-DUDZ	Robin DR.400/180	2367	G-BXNK	3.12.97	D.H.Pattison	Lower Upham Farm,. Wilts	22.12.00
G-DUET	Wood Duet	D.001		19.12.78	C.Wood	(Aston Clinton)	
	(Thought to be modified Brugger Colibri c/n PFA/43-10468)						
G-DUGI	Lindstrand LBL 90A HAFB	562		16. 8.99	D.J.Cook	Norwich	22. 8.00A
G-DUNG	Sky 65-24 HAFB	125		20. 7.98	G.J.Bell	Wokingham	4. 3.00A
G-DUNN	Zenair CH.200 AD-1 & PFA/24-10450			5.10.78	A.Dunn	(Lancing)	
	(Lycoming O-320)				t/a Chevalier Flying Group (Under construction 1988)		
G-DURO	Europa Avn Europa	PFA/247-12554		15.11.93	D.J.Sagar	Croft Farm, Defford	24 .2.00P
G-DURX	Colt 77A HAFB	1522		25. 5.89	V.Trimble	Henley-on-Thames	4. 5.00A
					(Durex/Avanti titles)		
G-DUSK	DH.115 Vampire T.Mk.11	15596	XE856	1. 2.99	R.M.A.Robinson & R.Horsfield	Henlow	
G-DUST	Stolp SA.300 Starduster Too	JP-2	N233JP	28. 4.88	J.V.George	Popham	22. 5.90P
	(Lycoming O-360)				(Damaged in collision with G-AKTM Badminton 16.7.89)		
G-DUVL	Reims Cessna F.172N Skyhawk II	1723	G-BFMU(1)	16. 8.78	A.J.Simpson	Sibson	11. 1.01
G-DVBF	Lindstrand LBL-210A HAFB	188		6. 3.95	Virgin Balloon Flights Ltd (London SE16)		16. 7.99T
G-DVON	DH.104 Devon C.2/2 (Dove 8)	04201	(G-BLPD)	26.10.84	C.L.Thatcher	Little Staughton	29. 5.96
			VP955		t/a The 955 Preservation Group (As "VP955": stored 4.99)		
G-DWIA	Chilton DW.1A	PFA/225-12256		25. 1.93	D.Elliott	(Horsham)	
G-DWIB	Chilton DW.1B	PFA/225-12374		22.12.93	J.Jennings	(Bedford)	
G-DWPH	UltraMagic M-77 HAFB	77/109		17. 3.95	Jennifer M.Robinson	Chipping Norton	3. 8.00
					t/a UltraMagic UK "Miguel"		
G-DYAK	LET Yakovlev C-11	170103	G-BWFU	27.10.98	M.Rusche	(Hannover, Germany)	
			OK-...		(On rebuild Little Gransden 11.96)		
G-DYNE	Cessna 414 Chancellor	414-0070	N8170Q	4. 8.87	Commair Aviation Ltd	Nottingham	3. 9.02
					t/a Commodore International		
G-DYNG	Colt 105A HAFB	1721	G-HSHS	9. 2.98	M.J.Gunston	Camberley	3. 1.00A
G-DYOU*	PA-38-112 Tomahawk	38-78A0436		19.10.78	Not known	Booker	3. 3.94T
					(Damaged Booker 23.7.92; stored 6.97)		

G-EAAA – G-EZZZ - see page 1 for details of 1919 to 1928 allocations

Regn	Type	C/n	P/I	Date	Owner/operator	Probable Base	CA Expy
G-EAGA(2)	Sopwith Dove rep	3004/1	(G-BLOO)	22.11.89	A.Wood	Old Warden	14. 8.98P
	(Le Rhone 80hp)				(On loan to The Shuttleworth Collection)		
G-EAGL(2)	Cessna 421C Golden Eagle III		(N2656G)	8. 8.79	Moseley Group (PSV) Ltd	East Midlands	31.10.00
		421C-0713			& Clowes (Estates) Ltd		
G-EBJI(2)	Hawker Cygnet rep	PFA/77-10240		9. 8.77	C.J.Essex	(Coventry)	
					(Under construction 7.99)		
G-EBZN(2)	DH.60X Moth	608	VP-NAA	28.10.88	Jane Hodgkinson	(Gravesend)	
	(Cirrus I)		VP-YAA/ZS-AAP/G-UAAP		(On rebuild from some original components)		
G-ECAB	Curtiss JN-4D	1917	N2525	28.5.99	V.S.E.Norman	Rendcomb	AC
G-ECAS	Boeing 737-36N	28554		16.12.96	British Midland Airways Ltd		
						East Midlands	19.12.02T
G-ECAW	Bell 206L-4 Long Ranger	52124	9M-BCM	20. 8.99	A.J.Walter Aviation Ltd	Goodwood	
			N8159Z				
G-ECBH	Reims Cessna F.150K	0577	D-ECBH	16. 5.85	G.Harber	Haverfordwest	26. 8.02T
					t/a ECBH Flying Group		
G-ECDX	DH.71 Tiger Moth rep	SP.7		1.11.94	M.D.Souch & N.Parkhouse Hill Farm, Durley		
	(Gipsy I)				(Nearing completion 8.97)		
G-ECGC	Reims Cessna F.172N Skyhawk II	1850		10.10.79	Euroair Flying Club Ltd	Cranfield	29. 6.01T
G-ECGO	Bolkow Bo.208C Junior	599	D-ECGO	24. 8.89	A Flight Aviation Ltd	(Clydebank)	20. 3.00
G-ECHO	Enstrom 280C-UK-2 Shark	1017	G-LONS	28. 5.82	A.L.Pattinson	Oaksey Park	7. 6.00
			G-BDIB		t/a ALP Electrical (Maidenhead)		
G-ECJM	PA-28R-201T Turbo Arrow III		G-FESL	25. 9.90	Regishire Ltd	Southampton	1. 3.01
		28R-7803178	G-BNRN/N321EC/N3561M				
G-ECKE	Avro 504K rep	0014		6.10.93	N.Wright & C.M.Kettlewell		
	(Warner Scarab SS-50) (Built AJD Engineering Ltd)				(As "D8781" in RFC c/s)	Bury St.Edmunds	2.11.00P
G-ECLI	Schweizer 269C	S 1784	N69A	16. 7.99	Eclipse (UK) Ltd	(Shepton Mallet)	22. 8.02
G-ECOS	Aerospatiale AS.355F1 Twin Squirrel		G-DOLR	24. 9.92	Multiflight Ltd	Leeds-Bradford	2.10.00T
		5300	G-BPVB/OH-HAJ/D-HEHN (Op Northern Helicopters (Leeds) Ltd)				
G-ECOX	Grega GN.1 Air Camper			5.12.78	H.C.Cox Brickhouse Farm, Frogland Cross		
		WLAW.1 & PFA/47-10356			(Under construction 12.93)		
G-ECZZ	Eurocopter EC.120B	1053		15.10.99	Faiman Aviation Ltd	(London, EC1)	21.10.02
G-EDEN	Socata TB.10 Tobago	66		8. 1.80	N.G.Pistol, J.R.Priest,	Elstree	17. 4.02
					G.W.Bevan & A.K.Hilton		
G-EDFS	Pietenpol Aircamper	PFA/47-13206		24. 3.98	D.F.Slaughter	(Redhill)	
G-EDGE	Jodel 150 Mascaret			14. 9.88	A.D.Edge	(Derby)	
	(Continental O-200-A)	111 & PFA/151-11223			(Under construction 8.99))		
G-EDGI	Piper PA-28-161 Warrior	28-7916565	D-EBGI	19. 1.99	R.A.Forster	Cardiff	14..2.02
			N2941R				
G-EDMC	Cyclone Pegasus Quantum 15	7513		11. 3.99	E.McCallum	Eshott	
G-EDNA	PA-38-112 Tomahawk	38-78A0364	OY-BRG	4. 9.84	D.J.Clucas	Woodford	15. 3.00T
G-EDRV	Vans RV-6A	PFA/181A-13451		20. 8.99	E.A.Yates	(Harlow)	
G-EDRY	Cessna T303 Crusader	T303-00280	N4817V	9. 3.87	Pat Eddery Ltd	Turweston	3. 4.02
G-EDVL	PA-28R-200 Cherokee Arrow II		G-BXIN	30. 6.97	J.S.Develin & Z.Islam	Redhill	30. 7.00T
		28R-7235245	D-EDVL/N1243T				
G-EEAC	PA-31 Turbo Navajo	31-761	G-SKKA	5. 5.94	G.James Villa Farm, Fordhall, Tern Hill		9.11.00T
			G-FOAL/G-RMAE/G-BAEG/N7239L t/a Universal Consumer Products				
G-EEGL	Christen Eagle II	AES/01/0353	5Y-EGL	14.12.90	A.J.Wilson	Deenethorpe	7. 6.00P
	(Lycoming AEIO-360)						
G-EELS	Cessna 208B Caravan I	208B-0619		3. 3.97	Glass Eels Ltd	Gloucestershire	20. 8.00T
G-EEMV	Hawker Sea Fury FB.Mk.11	41H-636335	N588	10.12.97	P.J.Morgan "Baby Gorilla"	Sywell	3. 5.00P
			VH-BOU/WH588 (RAN)/WH588 (As "WH588/NW-114" in RAN c/s)				
G-EENA	PA-32R-301 Saratoga SP	32R-8013011	C-GBBU	3.10.97	Gamit Ltd	Andrewsfield	16.10.00
G-EENI	Europa Avn Europa	PFA/247-12831		28. 7.98	M.P.Grimshaw	(London W5)	
G-EENY	Gulfstream GA-7 Cougar	GA7-0094	N721G	21. 6.79	J.P.E.Walsh	Cranfield	20. 7.00T
					t/a Walsh Aviation (Op Cabair)		
G-EESA	Europa Avn Europa	PFA/247-12535	G-HIIL	9. 4.96	C.B.Stirling	Damyns Hall	29. 3.00P
	(NSI EA-81/100)						
G-EESE*	Cessna U206G Stationair	U206-03883	OO-DMA	28. 2.85	Not known Movenis, Co.Londonderry		1. 4.91
			N7344C (Crashed Magilligan, Co.Londonderry 31.12.88; wreck stored 6.97)				
G-EEUP	SNCAN Stampe SV-4C	451	F-BCXQ	1. 9.78	A.M.Wajih	Redhill	11.10.02
G-EEZE*	Rutan LongEz	11 & PFA/74-10308		13.12.77	A.J.Nurse	(Bristol)	
	(Originally regd to VariEze c/n 1567, possibly a new kit) (Cancelled by CAA 8.5.99)						
G-EEZS	Cessna 182P Skylane	18261338	D-EEZS	8.11.99	A.P.Dyer	Earls Colne	AC
			N63054/D-EEZS/(N20981) t/a Small World Aviation				
G-EFIR	PA-28-181 Archer II	28-8090275	D-EFIR	5. 5.99	Leicestershire Aero Club Ltd	Leicester	8. 6.02T
			N8179R				
G-EFRY	Light Aero Avid Aerobat			22. 3.93	F.E.Telling	(Esher)	25.11.99P
	(Rotax 582)	PFA/189-12096					
G-EFSM	Slingsby T-67M Firefly 260	2072	G-BPLK	16. 7.92	Slingsby Aviation Ltd	Kirkbymoorside	3.11.02T

Regn	Type	C/n	P/I	Date	Owner/operator	Probable Base	CA Expy
G-EFTE	Bolkow Bo.207	218	D-EFTE	4. 1.90	L.J. & A.A.Rice		
						Bishopstrow Farm, Warminster	22. 6.02
G-EGAL	Christen Eagle II	0042-86	SE-XMU	11. 3.96	J H Penfold	(Dorking)	29. 4.00P
	(Lycoming AEIO-360)						
G-EGEE	Cessna 310Q	310Q-0040	G-AZVY	14.11.83	D.Hayes	(Rye)	30. 6.00
			SE-FKV/N7540Q				
G-EGEL	Christen Eagle II	S.308		4. 2.91	R.Kirchhofer, P.Miny & U.Fritz		
	(Lycoming AEIO-360)					(Steinen, Germany)	26. 7.00P
G-EGGS	Robin DR.400/180 Regent	1443		15.11.79	R.Foot	Henstridge	16. 7.01
G-EGHB	Ercoupe 415D	1876	N3414G	1. 9.95	J.H.Spanton	Maypole Farm, Chislet	13. 7.01
	(Continental O-200-A)		N99253/NC99253				
G-EGHH	Hawker Hunter F.58	41H-697450	J-4083	4. 7.95	G.R Lacey.	(Kemble)	27. 1.01T
					(As "J-4083")		
G-EGHR	Socata TB.20 Trinidad	795	F-GGIQ	19.12.97	B.M.Prescott	Goodwood	
G-EGJA	Socata TB.20 Trinidad	1101	N2807D	13.12.90	D.A.Williamson	Alderney	6. 1.00
G-EGLD	PA-28-161 Cadet	2841283	N92007	23.11.89	J.Appleton	Denham	6. 1.02T
					t/a Holmes Rentals (Op Denham School of Flying)		
G-EGLE	Christen Eagle II	F.0053		30. 3.81	R.L.Mitcham, P.J.Meaton, S.R.Flack & I.Dinermann		
	(Lycoming AEIO-360) (Built Airmore Aviation)					Booker	3. 8.00P
G-EGLT	Cessna 310R II	310R-1874	G-BHTV	9. 9.93	Tilling Associates Ltd	Guernsey	21.12.01T
			N1EU/(N3206M)		(Op Eagle Airways)		
G-EGNR	PA-38-112 Tomahawk	38-79A0233	OY-VIG	6.10.97	Chester Aero Services Ltd	Chester	9.10.00T
			SE-KNI/N2570C				
G-EGTR	PA-28-161 Cadet	2841281	G-BRSI	25. 4.98	Plane Talking Ltd	Elstree	17. 1.02T
			N92001				
G-EGUL	Christen Eagle II	Argence 0001	G-FRYS	19. 1.93	I.S.Smith	Coventry	31. 3.00P
	(Lycoming AEIO-360)		N66EA		t/a G-EGUL Flying Group		
G-EGUY	Sky 220-24 HAFB	103		24. 4.98	J.L.Guy	(Skipton)	6. 5.00T
					t/a Black Sheep Balloons		
G-EHBJ	CASA I-131E Jungmann 2000	2150	E3B-550	19. 7.90	E.P.Howard	Priory Farm, Tibenham	7. 6.00P
G-EHIL*	EH Industries EH-101	50003		9. 7.87	Westland Helicopters Ltd		
						Weston-super-Mare	
	(Airframe No.PP3) (To MoD as ZH647 1993: cancelled 28.4.99 as WFU: to The Helicopter Museum 11.99))						
G-EHLX	PA-28-181 Archer II	28-8090317	D-EHLX	5.11.99	I.R.Carver, R.J.Barber & B.Cook		
			N8218S		t/a Carver-Barber-Cook	(Beccles)	AC
G-EHMJ	Beechcraft S35 Bonanza	D-7879	D-EHMJ	12. 1.99	A.L.Burton & A.J.Daley	Gamston	18. 2.02
G-EHMM	Robin DR.400/180R Remorqueur	867	D-EHMM	10.12.84	Booker Gliding Club Ltd	Booker	1. 4.00
G-EHUP	Aerospatiale SA.341G Gazelle 1	1407	F-GIJR	3.10.97	MW Helicopters Ltd	(Ware)	2.12.00T
			N869GT/N869/N49523				
G-EHXP	Rockwell Commander 112	227	D-EHXP	27. 1.00	R.C.Howe	(Veldhoven, The Netherlands)	
			N1227J				
G-EIBM	Robinson R-22 Beta	1993	G-BUCL	25. 3.94	Abbey Management Ltd	Dundee	5. 3.01T
					t/a Abbey Quantity Surveyors		
G-EIIR	Cameron N-77 HAFB	358		16.11.77	D.V.Howard "Silver Jubilee"	Bath	14. 5.93A
G-EIKY	Europa Avn Europa	PFA/247-12634		27. 9.94	J.D.Milbank	Insch	1. 7.00P
	(Rotax 912UL)						
G-EIWT	Reims Cessna FR.182 Skylane RG	0052	D-EIWT	28. 1.86	P.P.D.Howard-Johnston	Edinburgh	1. 4.01
			OO-BLI		(Op Edinburgh Air Centre)		
G-EJGO	Zlin Z.226 Trener 6HE Spezial	199	D-EJGO	7. 8.85	Aerotation Ltd	Biggin Hill	15. 4.01
			OK-MHB				
G-EJMG	Reims Cessna F.150H	0301	D-EJMG	27. 4.98	T.A.White t/a Bagby Aviation	Bagby	26.10.01T
G-EJOC	Aerospatiale AS.350B Ecureuil	1465	G-GEDS	21.12.94	Elmsdale (UK) Ltd	Fairoaks	8. 7.02T
			G-HMAN/G-SKIM/G-BIVP				
G-EKKL	PA-28-161 Warrior 11	28-8416087	D-EKKL	24. 3.99	Fynair Ltd	(Hassocks)	5. 4.02T
			N43588				
G-EKOS	Reims Cessna FR.182 Skylane RG	0017	D-EKOS	15. 7.98	S.Charlton	(York)	9. 9.01
G-ELBC	PA-34-200 Seneca	34-7350021	G-BANS	4. 4.91	Stapleford Flying Club Ltd	Stapleford	23.12.00T
			N15110				
G-ELEN	Robin DR.400/180	2363		16. 9.97	N.R. & E.Foster	Biggin Hill	10.11.00
G-ELFI	Robinson R-22 Beta	1126	N80513	2.10.89	A.L.Ramsden	Shobdon	11.11.01T
G-ELIT	Bell 206L Long Ranger	45091	SE-HTK	28. 7.99	Aeroturbine Ltd	(Horsham)	25. 8.02T
			N2652				
G-ELIZ	Denney Kitfox mk.2			19. 7.90	A.J.Ellis	Sandown	5.11.93P
	(Rotax 582) 717 & PFA/172-11835				t/a Tiger Helicopters (Damaged Brightstone, IoW 10.5.93)		
G-ELKA	Christen Eagle II	0001	N121DJ	18.10.94	D.Aitken & Skydance Aviation Ltd	Perth	5. 5.00P
	(Lycoming AEIO-360)						
G-ELKS	Avid Speed Wing MK.4	PFA/189-13109		6. 1.98	H.S.Elkins	(Gloucester)	9. 7.00P
G-ELLA	PA-32R-301 Saratoga IIHP	3246050	N9279Q	13. 8.96	C.C.W.Hart	White Waltham	23.11.02T
			G-ELLA				
G-ELLE	Cameron N-90 HAFB	4498		11. 1.99	S.A.Lacey t/a L.E.Electrical	Norwich	15.12.99A
G-ELLI	Bell 206B Jet Ranger III	4231	D-HMOF	24. 6.97	RA Fleming Ltd	Brandon Hall, Leeds	3. 7.00T

Regn	Type	C/n	P/I	Date	Owner/operator	Probable Base	CA Expy
G-ELMH	North American AT-6D-NT Harvard III	FAP1662	22. 7.92	M.Hammond "Fools Rush-In"	Hardwick	26. 5.00P
		88-16336	EZ341/42-84555 (As "42-84555/EP-H" in USAAC c/s to commemorate 100th BG B-17G)			
G-ELZN	PA-28-161 Warrior II	28-8416078	D-ELZN	20. 7.99	Northamptonshire School of Flying Ltd		
			N9579N			Sywell	31. 8.02T
G-ELZY	PA-28-161 Warrior II	28-8616027	D-ELZY	13. 4.99	Goodwood Road Racing School Ltd	Goodwood	23. 5.02T
			N9095Z/(N163AV)/N9641N				
G-EMAS	Eurocopter EC.135 T1	0107		6. 7.99	East Midlands Air Support Unit	(Sulby)	7.10.02T
G-EMAK	PA-28R-201 Cherokee Arrow III		D-EMAK	30. 8.85	D. & G.Rathbone	Barton	18. 9.94
		28R-7737082	N38180		(Stored 12.97)		
G-EMAX	PA-31-350 Navajo Chieftain	31-7952029	N276CT	8.12.98	AM & T Aviation Ltd	Bristol	15.12.01T
			SE-KKP/54202 Swedish Navy/SE-KKP/LN-PAI				
G-EMAZ	PA-28-181 Archer II	28-8290088	N8073W	26. 4.90	E.J.Stanley	Blackpool	18.10.02T
G-EMBA	Embraer EMB-145EU	145-016	PT-SYM	17. 7.97	British Regional Airlines Ltd		
					(Dove/Colum t/s)	East Midlands	14. 8.00T
G-EMBB	Embraer EMB-145EU	145-021	PT-SYR	27. 8.97	British Regional Airlines Ltd		
					(Sterntaler/Bauhaus t/s)	East Midlands	1. 9.00T
G-EMBC	Embraer EMB-145EU	145-024	PT-SYU	1.10.97	British Regional Airlines Ltd		
					(Cockerel of Lowicz/Koguty Lowickie t/s)	East Midlands	8.10.00T
G-EMBD	Embraer EMB-145EU	145-039		7. 1.98	British Regional Airlines Ltd		
					(Animals and Trees/Kg-Oocoan-Naka-Hiian-Thee-E t/s)	East Midlands	11. 1.01T
G-EMBE	Embraer EMB-145EU	145-042		3. 2.98	British Regional Airlines Ltd		
					(Waves of the City t/s)	East Midlands	2. 2.01T
G-EMBF	Embraer EMB-145EU	145-088		10.11.98	British Regional Airlines Ltd	Ronaldsway	9.11.01T
					(Grand Union t/s)		
G-EMBG	Embraer EMB-145EU	145-094		18.11.98	British Regional Airlines Ltd	Ronaldsway	17.11.01T
					(Water Dreaming t/s)		
G-EMBH	Embraer EMB-145EU	145-107		20. 1.99	British Regional Airlines Ltd	Birmingham	19. 1.02T
					(Blomsterang t/s)		
G-EMBI	Embraer EMB-145EU	145-126		23. 4.99	British Regional Airlines Ltd	Manchester	22. 4.02T
					(Youm-al-Suq c/s)		
G-EMBJ	Embraer EMB-145EU	145-134		24. 5.99	British Regional Airlines Ltd	Manchester	26. 5.02T
					(Paitahni t/s)		
G-EMBK	Embraer EMB-145EU	145-167		26. 8.99	British Regional Airlines Ltd	Manchester	25. 8.02T
G-EMBL	Embraer EMB-145EU	145-177		4.10.99	British Regional Airlines Ltd	Manchester	3.10.02T
G-EMBM	Embraer EMB-145EU	145-196		22.11.99	British Regional Airlines Ltd	Manchester	21.11.02T
G-EMBN	Embraer EMB-145EU	145-201		13. 1.00	British Regional Airlines Ltd	Manchester	
G-EMBO	Embraer EMB-145EU	145-...	R		British Regional Airlines Ltd	Birmingham	
					(For delivery 3.00)		
G-EMER	PA-34-200 Seneca	34-7350002	N3081T	29. 7.91	Haimoss Ltd & R.P.Thomas	Old Sarum	26. 2.01T
					(Op Old Sarum Flying Club)		
G-EMHH	Aerospatiale AS.355F2 Twin Squirrel	G-BYKH	3. 8.99	Hancocks Holdings Ltd	East Midlands	26. 7.02
		5169	SX-HNP/VR-CCM/N57967				
G-EMIN	Europa Avn Europa	PFA/247-12673		1. 3.94	G.M.Clarke	Perth	3. 6.00P
	(Rotax 912UL)				t/a Gemini Group		
G-EMJA	CASA I-131E-2000 Jungmann		(Sp.AF)	2. 9.94	P.J.Brand	Audley End	16. 2.00P
		013 & PFA/242-12340	(Composite from Spanish spares imported in 1991)				
G-EMLY	Cyclone Pegasus Quantum 15	7531		30. 6.99	A.R.White	(Farnham)	27. 6.00P
G-EMMS	PA-38-112 Tomahawk	38-78A0526	OO-TKT	14. 9.79	Cheshire Flying Services Ltd	Liverpool	22. 9.00T
			N4414E		t/a Ravenair		
G-EMMY	Rutan VariEze	577 & PFA/74-10222		21. 8.78	M.J.Tooze	Biggin Hill	22. 3.00P
	(Lycoming O-235)						
G-EMNI	Phillips ST.1 Speedtwin Mk.2			25. 5.95	A.J.Clarry	(Pewsey, Wilts)	
		006 & PFA/207-12880					
G-EMSI	Europa Avn Europa	PFA/247-12817		24. 1.95	P.W.L.Thomas	(York)	
G-EMSY	DH.82A Tiger Moth	83666	G-ASPZ	27. 6.91	B.E.Micklewright	Chilbolton	28.10.65
			D-EDUM/T7356		(On rebuild 8.99 with parts from OO-MOT)		
G-ENCE	Partenavia P.68B	141	G-OROY	1. 6.84	Bettany Aircraft Holdings Ltd	Jersey	2. 9.00
			G-BFSU				
G-ENIE	Nipper T.66 Srs.IIIB	PFA/25-10214		17. 3.78	E.J.Clarke	Seighford	24. 8.00P
	(VW1800)						
G-ENII	Reims Cessna F.172M Skyhawk II	1352	PH-WAG	18. 1.79	J.Howley	Fenland	4.11.02T
			(D-EDQM)				
G-ENNI	Robin R.3000/180	128	F-GGJA	5.10.99	F.R.Traynor	(Birmingham)	2.11.02T
G-ENNY	Cameron V-77 HAFB	1399		1.12.86	B.G.Jones "Crocks of Frome"	Devizes	16. 5.99A
G-ENOA	Reims Cessna F.172F	0138	G-ASZW	2. 9.81	M.K.Acors	Thurrock	1. 4.00
G-ENRI	Lindstrand LBL-105A HAFB	294		4. 8.95	P.G.Hall	Chard	12. 5.00T
					(Henry Numatic Vacuum Cleaners titles)		
G-ENRY	Cameron N-105 HAFB	2096		26. 9.89	P.G. & G.R.Hall "Henry"	Chard	7. 7.94T
G-ENSI	Beechcraft F33A Bonanza	CE-699	D-ENSI	17. 3.78	J.M.Eskes	Booker	19. 5.02
G-ENTT	Reims Cessna F152 II	1750	G-BHHI	9.11.93	Bournemouth Flying Club Ltd	Bournemouth	31. 3.02T
			(PH-CBA)				

258

Regn	Type	C/n	P/I	Date	Owner/operator	Probable Base	CA Expy
G-ENTW	Reims Cessna F152 II	1479	G-BFLK	21. 1.93	Firecrest Aviation Ltd & G.Bliss Elstree		21. 7.01T
G-ENUS	Cameron N-90 HAFB	1914		18. 1.89	Wye Valley Aviation Ltd	Ross-on-Wye	9. 6.00T
					"Guinness"		
G-EOFS	Europa Avn Europa	PFA/247-13033		22. 7.98	G.T.Leedham Gunby Lea Farm, Overseal		28. 8.00P
					(F/f 15.8.99)		
G-EOFW	Cyclone Pegasus Quantum Q2 Sport 15	7582		15.10.99	G.C.Weighell	Enstone	14.10.00P
G-EOHL	Cessna 182L Skylane	182-59279	D-EOHL N70505	4. 3.99	G.B.Dale & M.C.Terris	Leeds-Bradford	24. 3.02
G-EOIN	Zenair CH.701 UL	PFA/187-13490		19.11.99	I.M.Donnelly	(Aboyne)	
G-EOMA	Airbus A.330-243	265	F-WWKU	26.4.99	Monarch Airlines Ltd	Luton	25. 4.02T
G-EORG	PA-38-112 Tomahawk	38-78A0427		18. 9.78	Airways Aero Associations Ltd	Booker	14. 7.00T
	(Rebuilt with new fuselage; old one stored 2.95)				(Op British Airways Flying Club) (Whale Rider t/s)		
G-EORJ	Europa Avn Europa	PFA/247-13139		23. 7.99	P.E.George	(Sutton Coldfield)	
G-EPAR	Robinson R-22 Beta-II	2781		26. 2.98	J.W.Ramsbottom	Blackpool	26. 2.01T
					t/a Jepar Rotorcraft		
					(Crashed on landing Blackpool 22.12.99 & severely damaged)		
G-EPDI	Cameron N-77 HAFB	370		25. 1.78	R.Moss "Pegasus"	Banchory	29. 6.91A
G-EPED	PA-31-350 Chieftain	31-8252040	G-BMCJ N121CF/N41060	22. 3.95	Pedley Furniture Intl Ltd	Duxford	1. 3.00T
G-EPFR	Airbus A.320-231	0437	C-FTDF	18.11.97	Airtours Intl Airways Ltd	Manchester	28. 4.01T
			G-BVJV/N437RX/G-BVJV/C-FWDQ/G-BVJV/N437RX/F-WWDM					
G-EPJM	PA-28-181 Archer III	2843166	N41268	10. 9.98	E.J.Moorey	Bournemouth	15. 9.01
G-EPOL	Aerospatiale AS.355F1 Twin Squirrel	5302	G-SASU	13. 1.98	Cambridge and Essex Air Support Unit		
			G-BSSM/G-BMTC/G-BKUK				Boreham	11.11.02T
G-EPOX	Aero Designs Pulsar XP	PFA/202-12355		27. 4.94	K.F.Farey	(Bourne End)	
G-EPTR	PA-28R-200 Cherokee Arrow II	28R-7235090	D-EPTR OH-PTR/(SE-KVF)/N4558T	26. 5.98	T.I.Moore	Aberdeen	28. 6.01
G-ERBL	Robinson R-22 Beta-II	2711		26. 6.97	G.V.Maloney	Biggin Hill	27. 7.00T
G-ERCO	Ercoupe 415D	3210	N2585H NC2585H	7. 4.93	A.R. & M.V.Tapp Maypole Farm, Chislet		15. 8.02
	(Continental C85)						
G-ERDS	DH.82A Tiger Moth	85028	ZS-BCU SAAF 2267/T6741	27. 7.94	W.A.Gerdes	Lee-on-Solent	21. 6.01
G-ERIC	Rockwell Commander 112TC	13010	SE-GSA	26. 9.78	Atomchoice Ltd	Cranfield	15. 4.00
G-ERIK	Cameron N-77 HAFB	1753		18. 5.88	T.M.Donnelly "Norsewind"	Doncaster	24. 2.00A
G-ERIS	Hughes 369D (500D)	11-0871D	G-PJMD G-BMJV/N1110S	1. 3.96	R.J.Howard	Leeds	12. 8.01T
	(Mod to 500E standard)						
G-ERIX	Boeing-Stearman E75 (PT-13D) Kaydet	75-5093	N5055V 42-16930	9. 3.88	Flight Incentives NV Antwerp, Belgium		3.12.00
	(P&W R985)				(As "985" in US Navy c/s)		
G-ERJA	Embraer EMB-145EU	145-229		.00R	Brymon Airways Ltd	Plymouth	
G-ERJB	Embraer EMB-145EU	145-237		.00R	Brymon Airways Ltd	Plymouth	
G-ERMO	ARV Super 2	018	G-BMWK	7. 1.87	P.R.Booth	Bagby	19. 5.02
G-ERMS	Thunder AS-33 Hot Air Airship	A.1		28.11.78	B.R. & M.Boyle	Newbury	
	(Now regd as Ax3 Sky Chariot)				"Microbe" (On loan to British Balloon Museum 12.93)		
G-ERNI	PA-28-181 Archer II	28-8090146	G-OSSY N81215	9.10.91	D.C. & M.A.Greenaway	Biggin Hill	15. 2.01
G-EROS	Cameron H-34 HAFB	2296		6. 4.90	Evening Standard Co Ltd "Eros" London W8		
G-ERRY	Grumman-American AA-5B Tiger	AA5B-0725	G-BFMJ	20. 3.84	M.D.Savage & A.F.K.Horne	Shobdon	10. 5.02
					t/a Gemini Aviation		
G-ESFT	PA-28-161 Warrior II	28-7916060	G-ENNA N22065	16. 5.97	SFT Europe Ltd	Bournemouth	21. 4.00T
G-ESKU	PA-23-250 Aztec C	27-3823	G-AWIY N6599Y	11. 4.96	Gold Air International Ltd	Cambridge	16. 7.98
G-ESKY	PA-23-250 Aztec D	27-4172	G-BBNN N6832Y	24.11.95	A.Watson	Shoreham	18. 4.00T
					(Op Premi-Air Flying Club)		
G-ESSX	PA-28-161 Warrior II	28-8016261	G-BHYY N9639N	30. 7.82	S.Harcourt	Compton Abbas	16. 1.97T
					t/a Courtenay Enterprises		
G-ESTA	Cessna 550 Citation II	550-0127	G-GAUL N550TJ/(N27TG)/N29TC/N2631N	24. 6.98	Executive Aviation Services Ltd	Gloucestershire	17. 8.00T
	(Unit No.143)						
G-ESTE	Gulfstream AA-5A Cheetah	AA5A-0780	G-GHNC N26877	28. 4.87	Plane Talking Ltd	Elstree	8.12.01T
G-ESUS	Rotorway Exec 162F	6169		7.10.96	J.Tickner	(Kings Lynn)	AC
G-ETBY	PA-32-260 Cherokee Six	32-211	G-AWCY N3365W	13. 7.89	K.Richards-Green & R.Fordham	Enstone	31. 5.02
	(Rebuilt with spare Frame No.32-858S)				t/a G-ETBY Group		
G-ETDA	PA-28-161 Warrior II	28-8116256	N84051	9. 3.88	T.Griffiths	Oaksey Park	26. 3.00
G-ETDC	Cessna 172P Skyhawk II	172-74690	N53133	4. 5.88	Osprey Air Services Ltd	Exeter	22. 6.00T
G-ETFT	Colt Financial Times SS HAFB	1792	G-BSGZ	11. 1.91	Financial Times Ltd	London SE19	25. 1.00A
					"Financial Times II"		
G-ETHY	Cessna 208 Caravan	20800293	N1295M G-ETHY	19.10.98	N.A.Moore	(Cookstown, NI)	AC
G-ETIN	Robinson R-22 Beta	0853	N9081D	7. 9.88	Forestdale Hotels Ltd	Burley	24. 9.00T

Regn	Type	C/n	P/I	Date	Owner/operator	Probable Base	CA Expy
G-EUOA	Airbus A.320-...				.00R British Airways plc		
G-EUOB	Airbus A.320-...				.00R British Airways plc		
G-EUOC	Airbus A.320-...				.00R British Airways plc		
G-EUOD	Airbus A.320-...				00R British Airways plc		
G-EUOE	Airbus A.320-...				00R British Airways plc		
G-EUOF	Airbus A.320-...				00R British Airways plc		
G-EUOG	Airbus A.320-...				00R British Airways plc		
G-EUOH	Airbus A.320-...				00R British Airways plc		
G-EUOI	Airbus A.320-...				00R British Airways plc		
G-EUOJ	Airbus A.320-...				.00R British Airways plc		
G-EUOK	Airbus A.320-...				00R British Airways plc		
G-EUOL	Airbus A.320-...				00R British Airways plc		
G-EUOM	Airbus A.320-...				00R British Airways plc		
G-EUON	Airbus A.320-...				.00R British Airways plc		
G-EUOO	Airbus A.320-...				.00R British Airways plc		
G-EUOP	Airbus A.320-...				.00R British Airways plc		
G-EUOR	Airbus A.320-...				.00R British Airways plc		
G-EUOS	Airbus A.320-...				.00R British Airways plc		
G-EUOT	Airbus A.320-...				.00R British Airways plc		
G-EUOU	Airbus A.320-...				.98R British Airways plc		
G-EUOV	Airbus A.320-...				.98R British Airways plc		
G-EUOW	Airbus A.320-...				.98R British Airways plc		
G-EUOX	Airbus A.320-...				.98R British Airways plc		
G-EUOY	Airbus A.320-...				.98R British Airways plc		
G-EUOZ	Airbus A.320-...				.98R British Airways plc		
G-EUPA	Airbus A.319-131	1082	D-AVYK	6.10.99	British Airways plc (Chelsea Rose t/s)	Birmingham	5.10.02T
G-EUPB	Airbus A.319-131	1115	D-AVYT	9.11.99	British Airways plc	Birmingham	8.11.02T
G-EUPC	Airbus A.319-131	1118	D-AVYU	12.11.99	British Airways plc	Birmingham	11.11.02T
G-EUPD	Airbus A.319-131	1142	D-AVWG	10.12.99	British Airways plc	Birmingham	9.12.02T
G-EUPE	Airbus A.319-131	1193			.00R British Airways plc		
G-EUPF	Airbus A.319-131	1197			.00R British Airways plc		
G-EUPG	Airbus A.319-131	1222			.00R British Airways plc		
G-EUPH	Airbus A.319-131	1225			.00R British Airways plc		
G-EUPI	Airbus A.319-131				.00R British Airways plc		
G-EUPJ	Airbus A.319-131	1232			.00R British Airways plc		
G-EUPK	Airbus A.319-131	1236			.00R British Airways plc		
G-EUPL	Airbus A.319-131	1239			.00R British Airways plc		
G-EUPM	Airbus A.319-131	1258			.00R British Airways plc		
G-EUPN	Airbus A.319-131	1261			.00R British Airways plc		
G-EUPO	Airbus A.319-131				.00R British Airways plc		
G-EUPP	Airbus A.319-131				.00R British Airways plc		
G-EUPR	Airbus A.319-131				.00R British Airways plc		
G-EUPS	Airbus A.319-131				00R British Airways plc		
G-EUPT	Airbus A.319-131				.00R British Airways plc		
G-EUPU	Airbus A.319-131				.00R British Airways plc		
G-EUPV	Airbus A.319-131				.00R British Airways plc		
G-EUPW	Airbus A.319-131				.00R British Airways plc		
G-EUPX	Airbus A.319-131				.00R British Airways plc		
G-EUPY	Airbus A.319-131				.00R British Airways plc		
G-EUPZ	Airbus A.319-131				.00R British Airways plc		
G-EURA	Agusta-Bell 47J-2 Ranger	2061	G-ASNV	21. 7.83	L.Goddard	Thornicombe, Dorset	23.10.00
G-EVAN*	Taylor JT.2 Titch	PFA/3231		14.12.78	E.Evans (Stanford-le-Hope) (Construction suspended- cancelled by PWFU 24.3.99)		
G-EVES	Dassault Falcon 900B	165	F-WWFD	13.11.97	Northern Executive Aviation Ltd (Op for David Crossland/Airtours) Jersey/Manchester		12.11.00T
G-EVET	Cameron Concept 80 HAFB	3703		30.10.95	K.J.Foster	Coleshill, Birmingham	9. 7.00A
G-EVNT	Lindstrand LBL-180A HAFB	071		13.12.93	Redmalt Ltd (Op Bailey Balloons) Bristol		16. 4.00T
G-EWAN	Protech PT-2C-160 Prostar	PFA/249-12425		23. 6.93	C.G.Shaw Truleigh Manor Farm, Edburton		20.10.00P
G-EWFN	Socata TB.20 Trinidad	1009	G-BRTY	22. 1.90	Trinidair Ltd	Filton	21. 4.02T
G-EWIZ	Pitts S-2SE Special (Lycoming AEIO-540)	S.18	VH-EHQ	12.11.82	S.J.Carver & D.Howdle	Netherthorpe	20.10.00P
G-EWUD*	Reims Cessna F.172F	0137	(G-ESSO)	26. 5.87	Not known	Wickenby	12.12.93
					G-EWUD/G-ATBK (Damaged in Dee Estuary nr West Kirby 14.8.92; stored 2.93)		
G-EXEA	Extra EA.300/L	082		9. 3.99	Brandish Holdings Ltd	(Jersey)	30. 3.02
G-EXEC	PA-34-200 Seneca	34-7450072	(G-EXXC) OY-BGU	11. 5.78	Sky Air Travel Ltd	Stapleford	15.12.99T
G-EXEX	Cessna 404 Titan II	404-0037	SE-GZF (N5418G)	3. 5.79	Atlantic Air Transport Ltd (Op for Dept of Transport) Inverness/Coventry		29. 7.00A

Regn	Type	C/n	P/I	Date	Owner/operator	Probable Base	CA Expy
G-EXIT	Socata MS.893E Rallye 180GT	12979	F-GARX	22. 9.78	K.J.Reynolds Stoke, Kent		12. 2.01
					t/a Medway Microlights		
G-EXPL	American Champion 7GCBC Citabria			9. 5.96	J.J.Young Church Farm, Shipmeadow		24.11.02
		1220-96					
G-EXPR	Colt 90A HAFB	1064		17. 8.87	D.P.Hopkins Pidley, Huntingdon		3. 4.99A
					t/a Lakeside Lodge Golf Centre		
G-EXPS	Short SD.3-60-100	SH.3661	TC-AOA	11. 5.99	BAC Express Airlines Ltd Southend		27 .5.00T
			G-BLRT/SE-KRV/G-BLRT/G-14-3661 "City of Exeter"				
G-EXTR	Extra EA.260	004	D-EDID	10. 8.92	Diana M.Britten Fairoaks		29. 4.00P
	(Lycoming AEIO-540)				(Morse titles)		
G-EYAS	Denney Kitfox mk.2 PFA/172-11858			3. 3.93	E.J.Young (Sheffield)		1. 9.94P
	(Rotax 582)						
G-EYCO	Robin DR.400/180 Regent	1949		12. 3.90	L.M.Gould Jersey		25. 4.02
G-EYES	Cessna 402C II	402C-0008	SE-IRU	16. 7.90	Atlantic Air Promotions Ltd Coventry		15. 8.02T
			G-BLCE/N4648N		(Op for National Rivers Authority)		
G-EYET	Robinson R-44 Astro	0052	G-JPAD	30.11.98	Warwickshire Flight Training Centre Ltd		
						Coventry	29. 4.00
G-EYNL	MBB Bo.105DBS-5	S.382	LN-OTJ	19. 8.96	Humberside Police Helicopter Support Unit		
			D-HDLR/EC-DSO/D-HDLR		Normandy Barracks, Leconfield		5.12.02T
G-EYOR	Van's RV-6	PFA/181-13259		15.10.99	S.I.Fraser (Wincanton)		
G-EYRE	Bell 206L-1 Long Ranger II	45229	G-STVI	12.11.90	Hideroute Ltd Stapleford		30. 6.00T
			N60MA/N5091K				
G-EZOS	Rutan VariEze 002 & PFA/74-10221			10. 7.78	C.Moffat (Reading)		18.10.00P
	(Continental O-200-A)						
G-EZYB	Boeing 737-3M8	24020	N797BB	17.10.96	easyJet Airline Co Ltd Luton		20.10.02T
			I-TEAA/OO-LTA/(OO-BTA)				
G-EZYC	Boeing 737-3Y0	24462	G-BWJA	28. 5.97	easyJet Airline Co Ltd Luton		4. 4.02T
			EC-FJR/EC-897/G-TEAA/EI-BZQ/(N116WA)/EI-BZQ/EC-ENS/EC-244/N5573K				
G-EZYD	Boeing 737-3M8	24022	N798BB	5. 2.97	easyJet Airline Co Ltd Luton		10. 2.00T
			I-TEAE/OO-LTC/(OO-BTC)				
G-EZYF	Boeing 737-375	23708	D-AGEX	3.11.97	easyJet Airline Co Ltd Luton		9.11.00T
			(G-EZYC)/4L-AAA/PT-TEC/(C-GZPW)				
G-EZYG .	Boeing 737-33V	29331	N1768B	19. 8.98	easyJet Airline Co Ltd Luton		18. 8.01T
G-EZYH	Boeing 737-33V	29332		17. 9.98	easyJet Airline Co Ltd Luton		17. 9.01T
G-EZYI	Boeing 737-33V	29333		24.11.98	easyJet Airline Co Ltd Luton		22.11.01T
G-EZYJ	Boeing 737-33V	29334		18.12.98	easyJet Airline Co Ltd Luton		17.12.01T
G-EZYK	Boeing 737-33V	29335		31. 1.99	easyJet Airline Co.Ltd Luton		30. 1.02T
G-EZYL	Boeing 737-33V	29336		12. 3.99	easyJet Airline Co Ltd Luton		11. 3.02T
G-EZYM	Boeing 737-33V	29337		23. 6.99	easyJet Airline Co Ltd Luton		22..6.02T
G-EZYO	Boeing 737-33V	29339		23. 8.99	easyJet Airline Co Ltd Luton		22. 8.02T
G-EZYP	Boeing 737-33V	29340		17. 9.99	easyJet Airline Co Ltd Luton		16 .9.02T
G-EZYR	Boeing 737-33V	29341	N1787B	20.10.99	easyJet Airline Co.Ltd Luton		18.10.02T
G-EZYS	Boeing 737-33V	29342		9.11.99	easyJet Airline Co.Ltd Luton		

G-FAAA – G-FZZZ

Regn	Type	C/n	P/I	Date	Owner/operator	Probable Base	CA Expy
G-FABB	Cameron V-77 HAFB	822	LX-FAB	13.12.89	P.Trumper Ashford, Kent		14. 7.00T
G-FABI	Robinson R-44 Astro	0325		25. 4.97	J.Froggatt Ltd. (Dukinfield)		24. 4.00T
G-FABM	Beechcraft 95B55A Baron	TC-2259	G-JOND	22. 2.91	F.B.Miles Gloucestershire		17. 8.01
			G-BMVC/N66456		(Damaged Guernsey 27.3.99)		
G-FABS*	Thunder Ax9-120 Srs.2 HAFB	2399		8. 6.93	Not known Felixstowe/Woodbridge		10. 5.96T
					(Temp unregd 29.5.96)		
G-FAGN	Robinson R-22 Beta	0615	(N2566W)	28.11.86	C.R.Weldon Dublin		25. 5.96
G-FALC	Aeromere F.8L Falco 3	224	G-AROT	19. 2.81	P.W.Hunter Old Sarum		28. 6.01
G-FAME	CFM Starstreak Shadow SA-II			23. 5.96	T.J.Palmer (Kilmarnock)		
	(Jabiru 2200) K.273SA & PFA/206-12973						
G-FAMH	Zenair ZH.701 Stol PFA/187-13301			26. 6.98	A.M.Harrhy Sandown		16. 8.00P
G-FAMY	Maule M.5-180C	8089C	N5668B	24. 1.91	R.J. & K.C.Grimstead Petworth		2. 7.00
G-FANC	Temco Fairchild 24R-46	R46-347	N77647	16.10.89	A.T.Fines Felthorpe		26. 5.00
			NC77647				
G-FANL	Cessna R172K Hawk XPII	R172-2873	N736XQ	7. 6.79	J.A.Rees Haverfordwest		24. 6.00T
G-FANN*	HS.125 Srs.600B	256019	HZ-AAI	13. 2.89	Not known Dunsfold		
	(Also quoted as ex HZ-AA1)		G-BARR		(On fire dump 6.96 as "HZ-AAI")		
G-FARM	Socata Rallye 235E	12832	F-GARF	10.10.78	Bristol Cars Ltd White Waltham		26.10.00
G-FARO	Star-Lite SL-1 PFA/175-11359			19. 6.89	M.K.Faro (Wimborne)		16. 4.98P
	(Rotax 447)						
G-FARR	SAN Jodel 150 Mascaret	58	F-BNIN	21. 7.81	G.H.Farr Dairy House Farm, Nantwich		19. 5.00P
G-FATB	Commander 114B	14624	N6037Y	3. 7.96	Ferrier Holdings Ltd (Guernsey)		11. 8.02
G-FAYE	Reims Cessna F.150M	1252	PH-VSK	24. 1.80	Cheshire Air Training Services Ltd		
						Liverpool	21. 6.01T

Regn	Type	C/n	P/I	Date	Owner/operator	Probable Base	CA Expy
G-FBIX	DH.100 Vampire FB.9	22100	7705M WL505	24. 7.91	D.G.Jones (Bridgend) (As "WL505": on rebuild 2.96)		
G-FBMW	Cameron N-90 HAFB	3019		23. 4.93	K-J.Schwer Erbach-Donaurieden, Germany		27. 3.00A
G-FBPI	ANEC IV Missel Thrush	PFA/312-13417		19. 1.99	R.Trickett. (Kings Lynn)		
G-FBRN	PA-28-181 Archer II	28-8290166	D-ERBN N82628	3. 8.98	Herefordshire Aero Club Ltd	Shobdon	26. 8.01T
G-FBWH	PA-28R-180 Cherokee Arrow	28R-30368	SE-FCV	23. 8.78	F.T.Short	Fenland	2. 4.01
G-FCAL	Cessna 441 Conquest II	441-0293	C-FMHD N88723	19. 3.96	Cobham Leasing Ltd (Op FR Aviation)	Bournemouth	17.10.00T
G-FCLA	Boeing 757-28A	27621	N1789B	26. 2.97	Flying Colours Airlines Ltd	Manchester	25. 2.00T
G-FCLB	Boeing 757-28A	28164	N751NA G-FCLB	25. 3.97	Flying Colours Airlines Ltd	Manchester	29. 4.01T
G-FCLC	Boeing 757-28A	28166		9. 5.97	Flying Colours Airlines Ltd	Manchester	8. 5.00T
G-FCLD	Boeing 757-25F	28718		25. 4.97	Flying Colours Airlines Ltd (JMC Air c/s)	Manchester	24. 4.00T
G-FCLE	Boeing 757-28A	28171		24. 5.98	Flying Colours Airlines Ltd (JMC Air c/s)	Manchester	23. 5.01T
G-FCLF	Boeing 757-28A	28835		24. 3.99	Flying Colours Airlines Ltd (JMC Air c/s)	Manchester	22. 3.02T
G-FCLG	Boeing 757-28A	24367	N701LF EI-CLM/N381LF/N240LA/C-GTSK/C-GNXI/G-GAWB	18.12.98	Flying Colours Airlines Ltd	Manchester	2. .4.02T
G-FCLH	Boeing 757-28A	26274	N751LF EI-CLU/N161LF	17. 2.99	Flying Colours Airlines Ltd	Manchester	12. 5.02T
G-FCLI	Boeing 757-28A	26275	N651LF EI-CLV/N151LF	17. 3.99	Flying Colours Airlines Ltd	Manchester	1. 6.02T
G-FCLJ	Boeing 757-2Y0	26160	N160GE EI-CJX/N3519M/N1786B/(B-2830)	26. 4.99	Flying Colours Airlines Ltd	Manchester	25 .4.02T
G-FCLK	Boeing 757-2Y0	26161	N161GE EI-CJY/N3521N	6. 4.99	Flying Colours Airlines Ltd	Manchester	5. 4.02T
G-FCSP	Robin DR.400/180 Regent	2022		24.10.90	F.C.Smith t/a FCS Photochemicals	Biggin Hill	23. 1.00
G-FDAV	Westland SA.341G Gazelle 1	WA/1108	G-RIFA G-ORGE/G-BBHU	17. 5.93	Federal Aviation Ltd	Denham	10. 2.02
G-FEBE	Cessna 340A II	340A-0345	N405LS (N37320)	12. 7.88	C.Dugard Ltd & E.C.Dugard	Shoreham	11. 4.01
G-FEFE	Scheibe SF-25B Falke	46126	EI-BVZ D-KADB	11. 4.94	R.Bagley t/a Aston Down Falke Syndicate	Aston Down	1.11.02
G-FELL	Europa Avn Europa	PFA/247-13208		17. 3.98	J.A.Fell	(Peterborough)	
G-FELT	Cameron N-77 HAFB	1174		19. 7.85	Allan Industries Ltd "Fuzzy Felt"	Chinnor	2. 5.00A
G-FEZZ	Agusta Bell 206B Jet Ranger II	8317	SU-YAD YU-HAT	16. 9.98	L.Smith t/a Helicopter Services	Booker	23. 9.01T
G-FFAB	Cameron N-105 HAFB	4067		20. 2.97	The Andrew Brownsword Collection	Bath	21. 5.00A
G-FFEN	Reims Cessna F.150M	1204	PH-VGL	25. 8.78	R.J.Everett	Elmsett	26. 3.00T
G-FFOR	Cessna 310R II	310R-1889	G-BMGF ZS-KU/N3276M	31. 3.87	ILS Air Ltd	Bristol	14. 5.01T
G-FFOX	Hawker Hunter T.7B	41H-670792	WV318	10. 1.96	Delta Engineering Aviation Ltd	Kemble	14. 5.00P
	(Composite, possibly including components of WV322)				(As "WV318" in all-black c/s)		
G-FFRA	Dassault Falcon 20DC	132	N902FR (N23FR)/(N149FE)/N2FE/N560L/N4348F/F-WMKG	28. 5.92	Cobham Leasing Ltd	Bournemouth	20.10.02A
G-FFRI	Aerospatiale AS.355F1 Twin Squirrel	5120	G-GLOW G-PAPA/G-CNET/G-MCAH	15. 4.93	C.B. & C.M.Smith t/a Ford Farm Racing (Op Alan Mann Helicopters)	Fairoaks	5. 5.00T
G-FFTI	Socata TB.20 Trinidad	1065		23. 2.90	Romsure Ltd	Cambridge	9. 6.02T
G-FFUN	Cyclone Pegasus Quantum 15	6655	G-MYMD	9. 6.99	P.Simpson	Potters Bar	12.12.00P
G-FFWD	Cessna 310R II	310R-0579	G-TVKE G-EURO/N87468	20. 2.90	Keef & Co Ltd	Booker	16. 2.00
G-FGID	Vought (Goodyear) FG-1D Corsair	3111	N8297 N9154Z/Bu.88297	1.11.91	Patina Ltd (B J S Grey/The Fighter Collection) (As "KD345/130" in 1850 Sqn RN c/s)	Duxford	13.10.00P
G-FHAS	Scheibe SF-25E Super Falke	4359	(D-KOOG)	14. 5.81	Burn Gliding Club Ltd	Burn	23.11.02
G-FIAT	PA-28-140 Cherokee F	28-7425162	G-BBYW N9622N	19. 7.89	The RAF Benevolent Fund Enterprises Ltd (Op Disabled Flyers Group) Hinton-in-The-Hedges		20. 7.02T
G-FIBS	Aerospatiale AS.350BA Ecureuil	2074	JA9732	14. 6.94	Groveair Freight Ltd.	(London W1)	8. 8.00T
G-FIFE	Reims Cessna FA.152 Aerobat	0351	G-BFYN	15. 2.95	Tayside Aviation Ltd	Glenrothes	23.12.99T
G-FIFI	Socata TB.20 Trinidad	688	G-BMWS	16. 1.87	OLM Aviation Ltd	Denham	15. 7.00
G-FIGA	Cessna 152 II	152-84644	N6243M	3. 6.87	Aerohire Ltd (Op Midland Flight Centre)	Halfpenny Green	22. 8.99T
G-FIGB	Cessna 152 II	152-85925	N95561	16.11.87	Aerohire Ltd	Wellesbourne Mountford	12. 2.00T
G-FIJJ	Reims Cessna F.177RG Cardinal	0031	G-AZFP	29. 4.99	Middleton Miniature Mouldings Ltd	(Barnard Castle)	19. 4.00T
	(Wichita c/n 00194)						

Regn	Type	C/n	P/I	Date	Owner/operator	Probable Base	CA Expy
G-FIJR	Lockheed L.188PF Electra	1138	(EI-HCF)	12. 9.91	Atlantic Air Transport Ltd	Coventry	12. 9.01T
			G-FIJR/C-FIJR/CF-IJR/N134US				
G-FIJV	Lockheed L.188C Electra	1129	EI-HCE	29. 8.91	Atlantic Air Transport Ltd	Coventry	27. 9.01T
			G-FIJV/C-FIJV/CF-IJV/N7143C (Atlantic Airlines titles)				
G-FILE	PA-34-200T Seneca II	34-8070108	N8140Z	23. 7.87	Barnes Olson Aeroleasing Ltd	Dunkeswell	23.11.02T
G-FILL	PA-31-310 Navajo C	31-7912069	OO-EJM	28. 6.96	P.V.Naylor-Leyland	Deenethorpe	23. 8.00
			N3521C				
G-FILO	Robin DR.400/180 Regent	2063		16. 4.91	Baron G.van der Elst	Gosselies, Belgium	19.12.02
G-FINA	Reims Cessna F150L	0826	G-BIFT	12.10.93	D.Norris	Finmere	15. 8.02T
			PH-CEW				
G-FIRS	Robinson R-22 Beta-II	2807		15. 4.98	M. & S.Chantler	(Crewe)	
G-FIRZ	Murphey Renegade Spirit UK			10.12.99	D M Wood	(Banbury)	
		PFA/188-13494					
G-FISH	Cessna 310R II	310R-1845	N2740Y	8. 5.81	Edinburgh Air Charter Ltd	Edinburgh	28.10.02T
G-FISK	Pazmany PL-4A	PFA/17-10129		14.12.88	K.S.Woodard	Little Snoring	11. 4.96P
		(VW1834)			(Stored 8.99)		
G-FIST*	Fieseler Fi 156C-3 Storch	156-5802	D-EDEC	23.11.83	Italian Air Force Museum	Vigna De Valle	6. 3.96P
	(Argus AS.10C)		I-FAGG/MM12822		(As "MM12822" in Italian AF c/s)		
G-FITZ	Cessna 335	335-0044	G-RIND	20. 4.95	D.S.Hodgetts	(Bridgnorth)	20. 1.02
			N2710L				
G-FIZU	Lockheed L.188CF Electra	2014	EI-CHY	6. 4.93	Atlantic Air Transport	Coventry	3. 1.02T
			G-FIZU/SE-IZU/(N857ST)/N857U/PH-LLG (Channel Express c/s)				
G-FIZY	Europa Avn Europa XS	PFA/247-13291	G-DDSC	16.12.99	G.Holland	(Bath)	
G-FIZZ	PA-28-161 Warrior II	28-7816301	N2721M	1.12.78	Tecair Aviation Ltd	Swanton Morley	30. 4.00T
G-FJCE	Thruster T600T	9120-T600T-032		25.11.98	F Cameron	(Craigavon, NI)	
G-FJET	Cessna 550 Citation II	550-0419		7. 7.97	London Executive Aviation Ltd		
			G-WYLX/VH-JVS/G-JETD/N1217N			London City	27.12.99T
G-FJMS	Partenavia P.68B	113	G-SVHA	7. 9.92	F.J.M.Sanders	Cranfield	13. 6.02T
			OY-AJH		(Op Bonus Aviation)		
G-FKNH	PA-15 Vagabond	15-291	CF-KNH	19. 3.97	M.J.Mothershaw	Woodford	15. 5.00
	(Continental C85)		N4517H/NC4517H				
G-FLAG	Colt 77A HAFB	2000		20. 9.90	B.A.Williams	Maidstone	10. 6.97T
G-FLAK	Beechcraft E55 Baron	TE-1128	N4771M	26. 9.89	Thunder Aviation Ltd	(De Haan, Belgium)	29. 7.02T
					"Red Baron"		
G-FLAV	PA-28-161 Warrior II	28-8016283	N8171X	7. 4.94	S.W.Parker	Nottingham	17. 5.00
					t/a The Crew Flying Group		
G-FLCA	Fleet 80 Canuck	068	CS-ACQ	18. 7.90	E.C.Taylor	(Warwick)	
			CF-DQP		(On rebuild 3.96)		
G-FLCT	Hallam Fleche	PFA/309-13389		21.10.98	R G Hallam	(Macclesfield)	
G-FLEA	Socata TB.10 Tobago	235	PH-TTP	31. 7.81	J.J.Berry	Shoreham	26. 7.02
			G-FLEA				
G-FLEW	Lindstrand LBL-90A HAFB	586		21. 1.99	Lindstrand Balloons Ltd	Oswestry	21. 8.00A
G-FLII	Grumman-American GA-7 Cougar		G-GRAC	18.12.91	Plane Talking Ltd	Elstree	23.10.01T
		GA7-0003	C-GRAC/(N1367R)/N730GA (Op as Capital Radio's "Flying Eye")				
G-FLIK	Pitts S-1S Special	PFA/09-10513		7. 1.81	R.P.Millinship	Leicester	22. 5.00P
	(Lycoming O-320)						
G-FLIP	Reims Cessna FA152 Aerobat	0375	G-BOES	29.12.80	Walkbury Aviation Ltd	Sibson	8. 5.00T
			G-FLIP				
G-FLIT	Rotorway Exec 162F	6324		22.12.98	R.F.Rhodes.	(Maldon)	AC
G-FLIZ	Staaken Z-21 Flitzer 006 & PFA/223-13115			24. 3.97	G.P.Gregg (As "D-694")	Spanhoe	
G-FLOA	Cameron O-120 HAFB	4006		4.10.96	Floating Sensations Ltd	Thatcham, Berks	5.11.99T
G-FLOR	Europa Avn Europa	PFA/247-12793		11.11.98	A.F.C.Van Eldik	(Hythe)	28. 9.00P
G-FLOX	Europa Avn Europa	PFA/247-12732		28. 6.95	P.S.Buchan	(Horsham)	25.11.99P
	(Jabiru)				t/a DPT Group		
G-FLPI	Rockwell Commander 112A	205	SE-FLP	16. 3.79	L.Freeman & Son Ltd	Newcastle	13. 3.00
			(N1205J)				
G-FLSI	FLS Sprint 160	001		20. 8.93	Sunhawk Ltd	North Weald	AC
G-FLTA	BAe 146 Srs.200	E-2048	N189US	25. 2.98	Flightline Ltd	Southend	26. 2.01T
			N365PS				
G-FLTI	Beechcraft F90 King Air	LA-59	N7P	16. 3.90	Flightline Ltd	Southend/Guernsey	19. 7.00
G-FLTY	Embraer EMB-110P1 Bandeirante		G-ZUSS	28. 8.92	Keenair Charter Ltd	Liverpool	11. 7.00T
		110-215	G-REGA/N711NH/PT-GMH				
G-FLTZ	Beechcraft 58 Baron	TH-1154	G-PSVS	21. 9.93	Stesco Ltd (Flightline Ltd)		
			N5824T/YV-266P			Southend/Guernsey	11. 5.01
G-FLUF	Lindstrand Bunny SS HAFB	002		7. 4.93	Lindstrand Balloons Ltd	(Oswestry)	
					(Not built)		
G-FLVU	Cessna 501 Citation I	501-0178	N83ND	11. 6.98	Neonopal Ltd	Liverpool	23. 6.01T
	(C/n 501-580 reported)		N4246A/LV-PML/N67749				
G-FLYA	Mooney M.20J (201SE)	24-3124		8. 6.89	BRF Aviation Ltd	Full Sutton	3.12.01
G-FLYE	Cameron A-210 HAFB	4216		12.12.97	Bakers World Travel Ltd		

Regn	Type	C/n	P/I	Date	Owner/operator	Probable Base	CA Expy
					"Bakers Dolphin 2" Langford, Somerset		4.12.99T
G-FLYI*	PA-34-200 Seneca	34-7250144	G-BHVO	1. 9.81	Routair Ltd	Southend	12. 5.92T
			SE-FYY		(Damaged Elstree 21.11.91; on rebuild 10.99)		
G-FLYP	Beagle B.206 Srs 2	B.058	N40CJ	15.10.98	Key Publishing Ltd.	Cranfield	29. 4.02T
			N97JH/G-AVHO/VQ-LAY/G-AVHO				
G-FLYS	Robinson R-44 Astro	0347		5. 6.97	N.Ferris	Cookham, Maidenhead	12. 6.00
					t/a Brilliant PR		
G-FLYT	Europa Avn Europa 57 & PFA/247-12653			15. 5.95	D.W.Adams	Kemble	6. 5.00P
	(NSI EA-81/100)						
G-FLYZ	Robinson R-44 Astro	0490		7. 7.98	P., M. & K.I.Smith (Newport Pagnell)		10. 8.01T
					t/a Rotaflite Helicopter Sales		
G-FMAM	PA-28-151 Cherokee Warrior		G-BBXV	7. 6.90	P B Anderson	Southend	25.11.02T
		28-7415056	N9603N		t/a Lima Tango Flying Group		
G-FMSG	Reims Cessna FA.150K Aerobat	0081	G-POTS	4. 1.95	G.Owen	Bagby	15.10.00T
			G-AYUY				
G-FNLD	Cessna 172N Skyhawk II	172-70596	(G-BOUG)	3. 8.88	D.Wright & R.C.Laming	Fenland	11. 1.01
			N739KD		t/a Papa Hotel Flying Group		
G-FNLY	Reims Cessna F.172M	0910	G-WACX	20. 3.89	P.M.Hopkinson	(Truro)	25. 7.00T
			G-BAEX				
G-FODI	Robinson R-44 Astro	0513		21. 9.98	Sanna Industries Ltd	Leicester	15.10.01T
G-FOGG	Cameron N-90 HAFB	1365		21.11.86	J.P.E.Money-Kyrle	Chippenham	25..9.96A
					"Phileas Fogg"		
G-FOGY	Robinson R22 Beta	1020	N62991	5. 7.99	P.Turvey	(Brackley)	12. 7.02T
			F-GGAI				
G-FOKW	Focke-Wulf Fw190A-5	0151227	"A"(white)	6. 3.96	Wizzard Investments Ltd	Earls Colne	
			DG+HO (Luftwaffe)		(David Arnold/Flying A Services)		
	(Crashed nr Leningrad 19.7.43; on rebuild 11.99 for American Flying Heritage Collection, Seattle, Washington)						
G-FOLD	Light Aero Avid Speed Wing			30.10.92	A.G.Edwards	(Wrexham)	2. 6.00P
	(Rotax 582)	PFA/189-12041					
G-FOLI	Robinson R-22 Beta-II	2813		25. 4.98	K.Duckworth	(Northampton)	17. 5.01
G-FOLY	Aerotek Pitts S-2A Special	2213	N31477	26. 7.89	A.A.Laing	Dundee	24. 2.02
	(Lycoming AEIO-360)						
G-FOPP	Neico Lancair 320	PFA/191-12319		14. 8.92	Airsport (UK) Ltd	Abbots Langley	
	(Lycoming IO-320)				(Damaged Cranfield 28.5.99)		
G-FORC	SNCAN Stampe SV-4C	665	(G-BLTJ)	6. 6.85	I.A.Marsh	(Borehamwood)	23. 4.00
			F-BDNJ				
G-FORD	SNCAN Stampe SV-4C	129	F-BBNS	7. 2.78	P.H.Meeson	Chilbolton	31. 7.98
	(Gipsy Major 10)				(Damaged East Tytherley 16.7.96: stored for re-build 6.99)		
G-FORS	Slingsby T.67C	2082	PH-SGD	17.11.99	V.R.Coultan, M.J.Golding, E.P.Dablin & M.Glazer		
			(PH-SBD)		t/a Open Skies Partnership (Chipping Norton)		1.12.02T
G-FORZ	Pitts S-1S Special	PFA 009-13393		3.11.98	N.W. Parkinson	(Bedford)	
G-FOTO	PA-E23-250 Aztec F	27-7654089	G-BJDH	27. 2.79	Aerofilms Ltd	(Borehamwood)	13. 3.00A
			G-BDXV/N62614				
G-FOWL	Colt 90A HAFB	1198		11. 3.88	N.A.Fishlock	Cheltenham	10. 7.99A
					t/a G-FOWL Ballooning Group "Chicken"		
G-FOWS	Cameron N-105 HAFB	3995		11.12.96	Fowlers of Bristol Ltd	Bristol	7. 1.00T
					"Fowlers Motorcycles"		
G-FOXA	PA-28-161 Cadet	2841240	N9192B	17.11.89	Leicestershire A/C Ltd	Leicester	13. 5.02T
G-FOXC	Denney Kitfox mk.3			8. 1.91	W.N.Clark	(West Kilbride)	10. 9.99P
	(Rotax 582)	773 & PFA/172-11900			(Damaged Elie, Fife 31.10.98)		
G-FOXD	Denney Kitfox	PFA/172-11618		22.11.89	M.Hanley	Deenethorpe	10. 8.00P
	(Rotax 582)						
G-FOXE	Denney Kitfox mk.2			1. 8.90	K.M.Pinkard "Foxe Lady"	(Chester)	31. 5.95P
	(Rotax 582)	740 & PFA/172-11994			(Damaged Stewartby Lake, Beds 3. 7.94)		
G-FOXG	Denney Kitfox mk.2			15. 8.90	S.M.Jackson t/a Kitfox Group		
	(Rotax 532)	452 & PFA/172-11886			Romney Street Farm, Sevenoaks		20. 5.00P
G-FOXI	Denney Kitfox mk.2	PFA/172-11508		21. 9.89	B.Johns	Combrook, Stratford-upon-Avon	17. 8.00P
	(Rotax 532)						
G-FOXM	Bell 206B JetRanger II	1514	G-STAK	5. 2.93	R.P.Maydon	Oxford	22.12.99T
			G-BNIS/N35HF/N135VG t/a Milton Keynes City Air				
					(Op by CSE Helicopters for Fox FM Radio)		
G-FOXS	Denney Kitfox mk.2			15. 8.90	S.P.Watkins & C.C.Rea	(Worcester)	9.11.00P
	(Rotax 582)	465 & PFA/172-11571					
G-FOXX*	Denney Kitfox	PFA/172-11509		1.11.89	R.O.F.Harper	(Lymm)	
					(Cancelled by CAA 8.5.99)		
G-FOXZ	Denney Kitfox	PFA/172-11834		4.12.90	S.C.Goozee	(Wimborne)	19.10.98
G-FPLA	Beechcraft B200 Super King Air		N31WL	3.12.97	FR Aviation Ltd	Teesside	9. 3.01T
		BB-944	HB-GHZ/HL5260/N1824V (Op Flight Precision)				
G-FPLB	Beechcraft B200 Super King Air		N739MG	3.12.97	FR Aviation Ltd	Teesside	11. 1.01T
		BB-1048	N223MD/9Y-TGY		(Op Flight Precision)		
G-FPLC	Cessna 441 Conquest II	441-0207	G-FRAX	14. 1.98	FR Aviation Ltd	Teesside	29. 3.00T

Regn	Type	C/n	P/I	Date	Owner/operator	Probable Base	CA Expy
			G-BMTZ/N27280		(Op Flight Precision)		
G-FRAD	Dassault Falcon 20E	304/511	G-BCYF	26.11.86	Cobham Leasing Ltd	Bournemouth	2. 9.00A
			F-WRQP		(Op FR Aviation)		
G-FRAE	Dassault Falcon 20E	280/503	N910FR	23. 9.87	Cobham Leasing Ltd	Bournemouth	19. 1.00A
			I-EDIS/F-WPXK		(Op FR Aviation)		
G-FRAF	Dassault Falcon 20E	295/500	N911FR	1. 9.87	Cobham Leasing Ltd	Bournemouth	18.10.02A
			I-EDIM/F-WRQQ		(Op FR Aviation)		
G-FRAG	PA-32-300 Six	32-7940284	N3566L	21. 1.80	A.M.Sierant	Sherburn-in-Elmet	21. 5.01
					t/a G-FRAG Group		
G-FRAH	Dassault Falcon 20DC	223	G-60-01	31. 5.90	Cobham Leasing Ltd	Teesside	7.10.02A
			N900FR/(N904FR)/N22FE/N4407F/F-WPUX (Op FR Aviation)				
G-FRAI	Dassault Falcon 20E	270	N901FR	17.10.90	Cobham Leasing Ltd	Teesside	18. 4.00A
			N37FE/N4435F/F-WPUZ (Op FR Aviation)				
G-FRAJ	Dassault Falcon 20DC	20	N903FR	30. 4.91	Cobham Leasing Ltd	Bournemouth	12.12.02A
			(N25FR)/N5FE/(N146FE)/N5FE/N367GA/N367/N842F/F-WMKJ (Op FR Aviation)				
G-FRAK	Dassault Falcon 20DC	213	N905FR	9.10.91	Cobham Leasing Ltd	Bournemouth	13. 4.00A
			N32FE/N4390F/F-WJMM (Op FR Aviation)				
					(Reported 2.99 to be going to USA and marks only taped-on).		
G-FRAL	Dassault Falcon 20DC	151	N904FR	17. 3.93	Cobham Leasing Ltd	Teesside	22.12.02A
			(N24FR)/N3FE/(N148FE)/N3FE/N810PA/N810F/N4360F/F-WMKI (Op FR Aviation)				
G-FRAM	Dassault Falcon 20DC	224	N907FR	13. 5.93	Cobham Leasing Ltd	Bournemouth	26. 5.02A
			N23FE/N4408F/F-WPUY (Op FR Aviation)				
G-FRAN	Piper J3C-90 Cub (L-4J-PI)	12617	G-BIXY	14. 7.86	I.Dole	Rayne Hall Farm, Rayne	19. 4.00P
	(Frame No.12447)		F-BDTZ/44-80321		t/a Essex L-4 Group (As "480321/44/H" in USAAC c/s)		
G-FRAO	Dassault Falcon 20DC	214	N906FR	23.10.92	Cobham Leasing Ltd	Bournemouth	28. 1.00A
			N33FE/N4400F/F-WNGO (Op FR Aviation)				
G-FRAP	Dassault Falcon 20DC	207	N908FR	12. 7.93	Cobham Leasing Ltd	Bournemouth	19.10.02A
			N27FE/N4395F/F-WMKF (Op FR Aviation)				
G-FRAR	Dassault Falcon 20DC	209	N909FR	2.12.93	Cobham Leasing Ltd	Bournemouth	15. 2.00A
			N28FE/N4396F/F-WLCX (Op FR Aviation)				
G-FRAS	Dassault Falcon 20C	82/418	CAF 117501	31. 7.90	Cobham Leasing Ltd	Bournemouth	1.12.02A
			20501/F-WJMM		(Op FR Aviation)		
G-FRAT	Dassault Falcon 20C	87/424	CAF 117502	31. 7.90	Cobham Leasing Ltd	Teesside	21. 2.00A
			20502/F-WJMJ		(Op FR Aviation)		
G-FRAU	Dassault Falcon 20C	97/422	CAF 117504	31. 7.90	Cobham Leasing Ltd	Teesside	15.12.02A
			20504/F-WJMJ		(Op FR Aviation)		
G-FRAW	Dassault Falcon 20C	114/420	CAF 117507	31. 7.90	Cobham Leasing Ltd	Bournemouth	9. 4.02A
			20507/F-WJMM		(Op FR Aviation)		
G-FRAY	Cassutt Racer IIIM	PFA/34-11211		24.10.90	C.I.Fray	(Macclesfield)	
G-FRAZ	Cessna 441 Conquest II	441-0035	SE-GYC	14. 9.87	Cobham Leasing Ltd	Bournemouth	24. 9.02A
			(N36965)		(Op FR Aviation)		
G-FRBA	Dassault Falcon 20C	178/459	OH-FFA	16. 7.96	FR Finances Ltd	Bournemouth	AC
			F-WPXF		(Op FR Aviation)		
G-FRBY	Beechcraft E55 Baron	TE-868	N78PS	23. 9.94	FR Finances Ltd	Bournemouth	16.11.00A
			N77PS		(Op FR Aviation)		
G-FRCE	Folland Gnat T.1	FL.598	8604M	28.11.89	Butane Buzzard Aviation Corporation Ltd		
			XS104		(Op Kennet Aviation: stored 3.96) Cranfield		17. 4.95P
G-FRED*	Clutton Fred Srs.II	PFA/29-10339		18. 5.78	Not known	Priory Farm, Tibenham	
					(Incomplete and stored 4.96)		
G-FRGN	PA-28-236 Dakota	2811046	N9244N	8. 2.96	Fregon Aviation Ltd	Enstone	5. 3.02T
G-FRJB*	Britten SA-1 Sheriff	0001		18. 5.81	East Midlands Aeropark	East Midlands	
	(Not completed)						
G-FRST	PA-44-180T Turbo Seminole	44-8207020	N8236B	5.11.82	TDR Aviation Ltd	Enniskillen	28. 5.01
			N9615N				
G-FRYI	Beechcraft 200 Super King Air	BB-210	G-OAVX	15. 3.96	London Executive Aviation Ltd	Stapleford	26. 3.01T
			G-IBCA/G-BMCA/N5657N				
G-FSFT	PA-44-180 Seminole	44-7995190	EI-CCO	12.10.98	M.J.Love	Bournemouth	12.10.01T
			N2135G		(Op SFT Europe)		
G-FSHA	Denney Kitfox Mk.2	PFA/172-11906		20. 9.99	S.J.Alston	(Wendover)	
G-FSII*	Gregory Free Spirit mk.II	004		26. 2.91	M.J.Gregory & R.P.Hallam		
					(Cancelled by CAA 27.3.99) (Huntingdon/Aldershot)		AC
G-FTAX	Cessna 421C Golden Eagle II		N8363G	23. 8.84	C.R.Venner	Cambridge	4. 5.00T
		421C-0308	G-BFFM/N8363G		t/a CRV Leasing (Op Hawkair)		
G-FTFT*	Colt Financial Times 90SS HAFB	1163		14. 1.88	Financial Times Ltd	Newbury	5. 6.95A
					"Financial Times" (To British Balloon Museum 2.97)		
G-FTIL	Robin DR.400/180 Regent	1825		10. 3.88	RAF Wyton Flying Club Ltd.	RAF Wyton	25. 9.00T
G-FTIM	Robin DR.400/100 Cadet	1829		6. 5.88	Bird Investment Properties Ltd	Kemble	28. 4.01
G-FTIN	Robin DR.400/100 Cadet	1830		6. 5.88	G.D.Clark & M.J.D.Theobald	Blackpool	17. 8.00
					t/a YP Flying Group		
G-FTUO	Van's RV-4	926	C-FTUQ	23.12.97	Euroclip 2000 Ltd	Hinton-in-The-Hedges	7. 3.00P
	(Tail-wheel u/c)				"Raven"		

Regn	Type	C/n	P/I	Date	Owner/operator	Probable Base	CA Expy
G-FTWO	Aerospatiale AS.355F2 Twin Squirrel	5347	G-OJOR G-FTWO/G-BMUS	27. 1.87	McAlpine Helicopters Ltd	Oxford	18. 2.02T
G-FUEL	Robin DR.400/180 Regent	1537		15. 5.81	R.Darch	East Chinnock, Yeovil	27. 5.00
G-FUJI*	Fuji FA.200-180 Aero Subaru	156	D-EMMI	14. 9.79	Not known	(Redhill)	29. 6.92
					(Damaged Newton, Powys 5. 5.92; sold & stored 7.95 for re-build)		
G-FULL	PA-28R-200 Cherokee Arrow II	28R-7435248	G-HWAY G-JULI/(G-BKDC)/OY-POV/N43128	26.11.84	Stapleford Flying Club Ltd	Stapleford	13.12.02T
G-FUND	Thunder Ax7-65Z HAFB	376		3.11.81	Soft Sell Ltd "Paddy Wagon"	Wallingford	6.12.92A
G-FUNK	Yakovlev Yak-50	852908	RA-852908	27. 3.98	D.J.Gilmour t/a Intrepid Aviation Co	North Weald	14. 6.00P
G-FUNN	Plumb BGP-1 Biplane	PFA/83-12744		16.10.95	J.D.Anson	(Liskeard)	
G-FUSI	Robinson R-22 Beta	2506	N83306	16. 3.95	F.M.Usher-Smith	Saffron Walden	14. 6.00
G-FUZY	Cameron N-77 HAFB	1751		6. 5.88	Allan Industries Ltd "Fuzzy Felt II"	Chinnor	5.11.96A
G-FUZZ	PA-18-95 Super Cub (L-18C-PI) (Frame No.18-1086)	18-1016	OO-HMY ALAT-FMBIT/51-15319	11. 9.80	G.W.Cline	(Gipsy Wood)	8. 4.00P
G-FVBF	Lindstrand LBL-210A HAFB	311		6.12.95	Virgin Balloon Flights Ltd "Red November"	(London SE16)	17.12.99T
G-FWPW	PA-28-236 Dakota	2811018	N9145L	10.10.88	P.A. & F.C.Winters	Oxford	22.10.00
G-FWRP	Cessna 421C Golden Eagle III	421C-0418	N3919C	9.12.82	Services plc	(London W1)	17.10.02
G-FXII	VS.366 Spitfire F.XII	6S/197707	EN224	4.12.89	P.R.Arnold t/a Peter R.Arnold Collection (On rebuild from components 3.96 as "EN224")	(Newport Pagnell)	
G-FXIV*	VS.379 Spitfire FR.XIV	T44	HS_...(Indian AF)/MV370	11. 4.80	Luftfahrtmuseum Laatzen-Hannover (As "MV370/EB-Q" in 41 Sqdn c/s)	Laatzen-Hannover, Germany	
G-FYAN	Williams Westwind HAFB (Model) MDW-1			6. 1.82	M.D.Williams	Dunstable	
G-FYAO	Williams Westwind HAFB (Model)	MDW-001		6. 1.82	M.D.Williams	Dunstable	
G-FYAU	Williams Westwind Two HAFB (Model)	MDW-002		6. 1.82	M.D.Williams	Dunstable	
G-FYAV	Osprey Mk.4E2 HAFB (Model)	ASC-247		12. 1.82	C.D.Egan & C.Stiles	Hounslow	
G-FYBD	Osprey Mk.1E HAFB (Model)	ASC-136		20. 1.82	M.Vincent	Jersey	
G-FYBE	Osprey Mk.4D HAFB (Model)	ASC-128		20. 1.82	M.Vincent	Jersey	
G-FYBF	Osprey Mk.5 HAFB (Model)	ASC-218		20. 1.82	M.Vincent	Jersey	
G-FYBG	Osprey Mk.4G2 HAFB (Model)	ASC-204		20. 1.82	M.Vincent	Jersey	
G-FYBH	Osprey Mk.4G HAFB (Model)	ASC-214		20. 1.82	M.Vincent	Jersey	
G-FYBI	Osprey Mk.4H HAFB (Model)	ASC-234		20. 1.82	M.Vincent	Jersey	
G-FYBP	European E.84PW HAFB (Model)	S.20		29. 1.82	D.Eaves	Southampton	
G-FYBR	Osprey Mk.4G2 HAFB (Model)	ASC-203		29. 1.82	A.J.Pugh	Lakenheath	
G-FYCL	Osprey Mk.4G HAFB (Model)	ASC-213		9. 2.82	P.J.Rogers	Banbury	
G-FYCV	Osprey Mk.4D HAFB (Model)	ASK-276		19. 2.82	M.Thomson	London SW11	
G-FYCZ	Osprey Mk.4D2 HAFB (Model)	ASC-244		24. 2.82	P.Middleton	Colchester	
G-FYDC	European EDH.1 HAFB (Model)	S.24		17. 3.82	D.Eaves & H.W.Goddard	Southampton	
G-FYDF	Osprey Mk.4D HAFB (Model)	ASK-278		22. 3.82	K.A.Jones	Thornton Heath	
G-FYDI	Williams Westwind Two HAFB (Model)	MDW-005		29. 3.82	M.D.Williams	Dunstable	
G-FYDN	European 8C HAFB (Model)	DD34/S.22		5. 4.82	P.D.Ridout	Botley	
G-FYDO	Osprey Mk.4D HAFB (Model)	ASK-262		15. 4.82	N.L.Scallan	Hayes	
G-FYDP	Williams Westwind Three HAFB (Model)	MDW-006		29. 3.82	M.D.Williams	Dunstable	
G-FYDS	Osprey Mk.4D HAFB (Model)	ASK-261		15. 4.82	M.E.Scallan	Hayes	
G-FYDW	Osprey Mk.4B HAFB (Model)	ASK-282		27. 4.82	R.A.Balfre	Hayes	
G-FYEB	Rango Rega Srs.II (Gas Airship) (Model)	NHP-31		18. 5.82	N.H.Ponsford t/a Rango Balloon & Kite Co "Maegaera"	Leeds	
G-FYEJ	Rango NA-24 (Gas FB) (Model) (1/4 Chartres Balloon rep)	NHP-30		27. 5.82	N.H.Ponsford t/a Rango Balloon & Kite Co	Leeds	
G-FYEK	Unicorn UE-1C HAFB (Model)	82024		2. 7.82	D. & D.Eaves	Southampton	
G-FYEL	European E.84Z HAFB (Model)	S.25		24. 6.82	D.Eaves	Southampton	
G-FYEM	Rango NA-8 HAFB (Model)	RGS-32		2. 8.82	R.G.Strathdee	Aylesbury	
G-FYEO	Scallan Eagle Mk.1A HAFB (Model)	001		20. 7.82	M.E.Scallan	Hayes	
G-FYEV	Osprey Mk.1C HAFB (Model)	ASK-294		10. 8.82	M.E.Scallan	Hayes	
G-FYEZ	Scallan Firefly Mk.1 HAFB (Model)	MNS-748		22. 9.82	M.E. & N.L.Scallan	Hayes	
G-FYFA	European E.84LD HAFB (Model)	S.26		12.10.82	D.Goddard & D.Eaves	Southampton	
G-FYFG	European E.84DE HAFB (Model)	S.28		26.11.82	D.Eaves	Southampton	
G-FYFH	European E.84DS HAFB (Model)	S.30		26.11.82	D.Eaves	Southampton	
G-FYFI	European E.84PS HAFB (Model)	S.29		1.12.82	M.A.Stelling	Barton-le-Clay	
G-FYFJ	Williams Westwind Two HAFB (Model)			14.12.82	M.D.Williams	Dunstable	

Regn	Type	C/n	P/I	Date	Owner/operator	Probable Base	CA Expy
		MDW-010					
G-FYFN	Osprey Saturn 2 DC3 HAFB (Model)			17. 2.83	J.Woods & M.Woods	Bracknell	
		ATC-250/MJS-11					
G-FYFT	Rango NA-32BC HAFB (Model)	NHP-37		12. 3.84	N.H.Ponsford & A.M.Lindsay	Leeds	
					t/a Rango Kite & Balloon Co "Bear Chair"		
G-FYFW	Rango NA-55 (Radio Continentalrolled Balloon) (Model)				N.H.Ponsford & A.M.Lindsay	Leeds	
		NHP-40		8.10.84	t/a Rango Kite & Balloon Co "Vaughan Williams"		
G-FYFY	Rango NA-55RC (Radio Controlled Balloon) (Model)						
		AL-43		28. 2.85	A.M.Lindsay "Fifi"	Leeds	
G-FYGA	Rango NA-50RC (Radio Controlled Balloon) HAFB (Model)				N.H.Ponsford & A.M.Lindsay	Leeds	
		NHP-47		7. 1.86	t/a Rango Kite & Balloon Co "Tallis"		
G-FYGB	Rango NA-105RC (Radio Controlled Balloon) Gas Airship (Model)				N.H.Ponsford & A.M.Lindsay	Leeds	
		NHP-45		7. 1.86	t/a Rango Kite & Balloon Co		
G-FYGF	Busby Buz-B20 HAFB (Model)	DSD-001		8. 7.87	D.P. & D.S.Busby	Southampton	
G-FYGI	Rango NA-55RC(Radio Controlled Balloon) HAFB (Model)				D.K.Fish	Bedford	
		NHP-54		26. 6.90			
G-FYGJ	Airspeed-300 HAFB (Model)	001		8.10.91	N.Wells	Tunbridge Wells	
G-FYGK	Rango NA-42 POC HAFB (Model)	NHP-55		31.10.91	N.H.Ponsford & A.M.Lindsay	Leeds	
					t/a Rango Kite & Balloon Co		
G-FYGM	Saffery/Smith Princess HAFB (Model)			24.11.97	A. & N.Smith	Goole	
		551					
G-FZZA	General Avia F22-A	018		13. 8.98	APB Leasing Ltd	Welshpool	15.10.01T
G-FZZI	Cameron H-34 HAFB	2105		30.10.89	L.V.Mastis West Bloomfield, Mi, USA		30. 7.96A
					"Andrews" ??		
G-FZZY*	Colt 69A HAFB	779		19. 2.86	T Gunn "Alka-Seltzer 2"	Lancing	16. 2.90A
					(Balloon Preservation Group 7.98)		

G-GAAA – G-GZZZ

Regn	Type	C/n	P/I	Date	Owner/operator	Probable Base	CA Expy
G-GABD	Gulfstream GA-7 Cougar	GA7-0043	D-GABD	13. 4.82	Scotia Safari Ltd	Prestwick	5.12.02T
G-GACA	Hunting Percival P.57 Sea Prince T.1	WP308		2. 9.80	P.G.Vallance Ltd	Charlwood	4.11.80P*
		P57/58			(Stored 6.97: as "CU/572")		
G-GAFA	PA-34-200T Seneca II	34-7970218	D-GAFA	12.10.99	SRC Contractors Ltd	Luton	6.12.02T
			N2247Z				
G-GAFX	Boeing 747-245F	20827	N641FE	28. 8.99	Airfreight Express Ltd	Heathrow	9..9.02T
			VP-BXP/N641FE/(N632FE)/N812FT/N702SW				
G-GAII	Hawker Hunter GA.11	HABL-003028	XE685	7.12.94	B.J.Pover	Exeter	24. 6.98P
	(Officially regd with c/n 41H-004038)				(As "XE685/861/VL" in RN c/s)		
G-GAIW	Cameron A-140 HAFB	4131		21. 5.97	Cameron Balloons Ltd	Bristol	15. 7.00A
G-GAJB	Gulfstream AA-5B Tiger	AA5B-1179	G-BHZN	6. 4.87	G.A.J.Bowles	Elstree	7. 1.02T
			N37519				
G-GALA	PA-28-180 Cherokee E	28-5794	G-AYAP	31. 7.89	E.Alexander	Biggin Hill	10. 5.02T
					(Op Alouette Flying Club)		
G-GAME	Cessna T303 Crusader	T303-00098	(F-GDFN)	25. 2.83	Tracs Ltd	Swansea	14. 6.01
			N2693C				
G-GAND	Agusta-Bell 206B Jet Ranger	8073	G-AWMK	11. 1.00	M.D.Souster "Liberty Bell"	Redhill	5. 6.00T
			9Y-TFC/G-AWMK/(VR-BCV)/G-AWMK				
G-GANE	Sequoia F.8L Falco			25. 9.85	S.J.Gane	Kemble	13. 6.01P
	(Lycoming IO-320) 906 & PFA/100-11100						
G-GANJ	Fournier RF6B-100	38	F-GANJ	16. 8.84	Soaring Equipment Ltd (Stored 5.95)		
					Shacklewell Lodge, Empingham		31. 7.94
G-GASC	Hughes 369HS (500)	110-0270S	G-WELD	11. 7.85	Crewhall Ltd	Effingham	21. 6.02
			G-FRO/OO-KAR				
G-GASP	PA-28-181 Cherokee Archer II		N4328F	15.10.90	D.J.Turner	Fairoaks	21.11.99
		28-7790013			t/a G-GASP Flying Group		
G-GASS	Thunder Ax7-77 HAFB	1746		19. 4.90	M.W.Axon	London E9	2. 6.02A
					t/a Servowarm Balloon Syndicate "Travel Gas III"		
G-GAWA	Cessna 140	9619	G-BRSM	17. 9.91	E.C.Murgatroyd	RAF Henlow	30. 5.02
	(Continental C85)		N72454/NC72454				
G-GAZA	Aerospatiale SA.341G Gazelle 1	1187	G-RALE	19. 6.92	The Auster Aircraft Co Ltd		
			G-SFT/N87712			Waltham, Leics	23. 7.01
G-GAZI	Aerospatiale SA.341G Gazelle 1	1136	G-BKLU	29. 6.90	Stratton Motor Co (Norfolk) Ltd & UCC Intl Group Ltd		
			N32PA/N341VH/N90957			(Op Cheqair) Long Stratton	28. 6.00T
G-GAZZ	Aerospatiale SA.341G Gazelle 1	1271	F-GFHD	14. 3.90	Stratton Motor Co (Norfolk) Ltd & UCC Intl Group Ltd		
			YV-242CP/HB-XGA/F-WMHC			(Op Cheqair) Long Stratton	22. 6.02T
G-GBAO	Robin R.1180TD Aiglon	277	F-GBAO	9. 9.81	J.Kay-Movat	Slinfold	13. 9.01
	(Rebuild of R.1180 prototype F-WVKU c/n 01)						
G-GBFF	Reims Cessna F.172N	1565	F-GBFF	16. 6.99	J.S.Malcolm	(Wolverhampton)	17 .6.02T
G-GBHI	Socata TB.10 Tobago	19	F-GBHI	12.11.97	A.B.S.Garden	Stapleford	27.11.00
G-GBLP	Reims Cessna F.172M Skyhawk II	1042	G-GWEN	9.11.84	Fraggle Leasing Ltd	Edinburgh	9. 7.00T
			G-GBLP/N14496				

Regn	Type	C/n	P/I	Date	Owner/operator	Probable Base	CA Expy
G-GBLR	Reims Cessna F.150L	1109	N961L (D-EDJE)	30. 4.85	G.Matthews t/a Blue Max Flying Group	Coventry	7. 6.02T
G-GBSL	Beechcraft 76 Duchess	ME-265	G-BGVG	27. 3.81	M.H.Cundey	Redhill	12. 5.02
G-GBTA	Boeing 737-436	25859	G-BVHA (G-GBTA)	7. 2.94	British Airways plc (Youm-al-Souq t/s)	Gatwick	31.10.02T
G-GBTB	Boeing 737-436	25860	OO-LTS G-BVHB/OO-LTS/G-BVHB/(G-GBTB)	23.10.96	British Airways plc	Gatwick	28.10.02T
G-GBUE	Robin DR.400/120A Petit Prince	1354	G-BPXD F-GBUE	11. 5.89	M Winter t/a G-GBUE Group	Bagby	2. 6.01
G-GBXS	Europa Avn Europa XS	0005	"G-2000" G-GBXS	1. 4.98	Europa Aircraft Co Ltd	Wombleton	5. 6.00P
G-GCAT	PA-28-140 Cherokee B	28-26032	G-BFRH OH-PCA	22.10.81	H.Skelton t/a Group CAT	Humberside	18. 8.02
G-GCCL	Beechcraft 76 Duchess	ME-322	(G-BNRF) N6714U	5. 8.87	Aerolease Ltd	(Huntingdon)	21.11.02
G-GCJL	BAe Jetstream 4100	41001		5. 2.91	British Aerospace (Operations) Ltd	Prestwick	29. 4.95S
G-GCKI	Mooney M.20K (231)	25-0401	N4062H	15. 8.80	B.Barr	(Norwich)	6. 8.01
G-GCUB	PA-18-150 Super Cub	18-7922	SE-GCO Swedish Army 51249	11. 2.99	N.J.Morgan	Tatenhill	9 .6.02
G-GDAM*	PA-18-135 Super Cub (L-21B-PI) (Frame No.18-3648)	18-3535	PH-PVW (PH-DKE)/R-107/54-2335 (Stored 1996: cancelled by CAA 18.3.99)	30. 6.81	A.D.Martin	Reading	11. 8.91
G-GDAY*	Robinson R-22 Beta	0676	(Damaged Blackpool 24.4.99: re-regd 12.5.99 to named owner - for personal marks ?: cancelled by CAA 28.9.99)	10. 8.87	G.R.Day	(Boston)	10.12.99
G-GDER	Robin R.1180TD	280	F-GDER	15. 5.97	Berkshire Aviation Services Ltd	Fairoaks	15. 5.00
G-GDEZ	BAe 125 Srs.1000B	259026	N9026 G-5-743/ZS-ACT/ZS-CCT/G-5-743	30.10.95	Frewton Ltd	Jersey	9.11.00
G-GDGR	Socata TB.20 Trinidad	378	F-GDGR	23. 7.97	Willwright Aviation Ltd	(Oldham)	3. 8.00T
G-GDOG	PA-28R-200 Cherokee Arrow II	28R-7635227	G-BDXW N9235K	17. 4.89	R.K.& S.Perry	Thruxton	5. 8.02
G-GDTU	Avions Mudry CAP.10B	193	F-GDTU (N....)/F-GDTK/F-WZCI	27. 5.99	Sherburn Aero Club Ltd	Sherburn-in-Elmet	26 .5.02T
G-GDXK	Cameron A-140 HAFB	4467		22. 9.98	Cameron Balloons Ltd	Bristol	22. 9.99A
G-GEAR	Reims Cessna FR.182 Skylane RG	0004		21. 6.78	Wycombe Air Centre Ltd	Booker	11. 6.00T
G-GEDI	Dassault Falcon 2000	49	VP-BEF F-WWMD	23. 7.98	Victoria Aviation Ltd	(Guernsey)	22. 7.00
G-GEEE	Hughes 369HS	45-0738S	G-BDOY	2. 3.90	B.P.Stein	Denham	7. 9.01
G-GEEP	Robin R.1180TD Aiglon	266		9. 4.80	Organic Concentrates Ltd	Booker	7. 8.01
G-GEES	Cameron N-77 HAFB	357		8.11.77	N.A.Carr "Gee-Gees"	Leicester	31. 5.00A
G-GEEZ	Cameron N-77 HAFB	1159		3. 5.85	Charnwood Forest Turf Accountants Ltd "Tic Tac"	Leicester	7. 4.96A
G-GEGE	Robinson R-22 Beta-II	2994		19.10.99	S.K.Miles t/a Heli-Hire	(Nottingham)	28.10.02T
G-GEHP	PA-28RT-201 Arrow IV	28R-8218014	F-GEHP N82023	24. 4.98	Aeroshow Ltd	Gloucestershire	2. 7.01T
G-GEMS	Thunder Ax8-90 Srs.2 HAFB	2287	G-BUNP	6.11.92	B.Sevenich, B.& S.Harren & W.Christoph	Aachen, Germany	17. 1.00T
G-GENN	Gulfstream GA-7 Cougar	GA7-0114	G-BNAB G-BGYP	2.12.94	Chalrey Ltd (Op Cabair)	Cranfield	15. 1.01T
G-GEOF	Pereira Osprey 2	PFA/70-10384		7. 9.78	G.Crossley	(Blackpool)	
G-GEUP	Cameron N-77 HAFB	880		8.12.82	G Everett "Gee-Up"	Dartford	19. 7.96A
G-GFAB	Cameron N-105 HAFB	2048		4. 8.89	The Andrew Brownsword Collection Ltd	Bath	1..4.00A
G-GFCA	PA-28-161 Cadet	2841100	N9174X	24. 4.89	Aeroshow Ltd.	Rendcomb	4.10.01T
G-GFCB	PA-28-161 Cadet	2841101	N9175F	24. 4.89	AM & TAviation Ltd	Bristol	11. 7.01T
G-GFCD	PA-34-220T Seneca III	34-8133073	G-KIDS N83745	31. 5.90	Stonehurst Aviation Ltd	Coventry	18.11.02T
G-GFCF	PA-28-161 Cadet	2841259	G-RHBH N9193Z	28. 6.90	Aerohire Ltd	Halfpenny Green	27. 1.02T
G-GFEY	PA-34-200T Seneca II	34-7870343	D-GFEY D-IFEY/N36599	13. 5.98	Topa Panama Inc	Guernsey	28. 5.01
G-GFFA	Boeing 737-59D	25038	G-BVZF SE-DND/(SE-DNC)	10. 2.00	British Airways plc (For delivery 4.00)	Manchester	2. 5.01T
G-GFFB	Boeing 737-505	25789	LN-BRT	.00R	British Airways plc (For delivery 5.00)	Manchester	
G-GFFC	Boeing 737-5..			.00R	British Airways plc (For delivery 6.00)	Manchester	
G-GFFD	Boeing 737-5..			.00R	British Airways plc (For delivery 7.00)	Manchester	
G-GFFE	Boeing 737-5..			.00R	British Airways plc (For delivery 8.00)	Manchester	

Regn	Type	C/n	P/I	Date	Owner/operator	Probable Base	CA Expy
G-GFFF	Boeing 737-5..			.00R	British Airways plc (For delivery 9.00)	Manchester	
G-GFFG	Boeing 737-5..			.00R	British Airways plc (For delivery 9.00)	Manchester	
G-GFFH	Boeing 737-5..			.00R	British Airways plc (For delivery 10.00)	Manchester	
G-GFFI	Boeing 737-5..			.00R	British Airways plc (For delivery 10.00)	Manchester	
G-GFFJ	Boeing 737-5..			.00R	British Airways plc (For delivery 11.00)	Manchester	
G-GFKY	Zenair CH.250 (Lycoming O-235)	34	C-GFKY	23. 4.93	D.M.Edes	(Dingwall)	6. 6.00P
G-GFLY	Reims Cessna F.150L	0822	PH-CES	28. 8.80	Tindon Ltd	Little Snoring	1.12.01T
G-GFTA	PA-28-161 Warrior III	2842047	N4132L	1. 4.99	One Zero Three Ltd	Guernsey	31. 3.02T
G-GFTB	PA-28-161 Warrior II	2842048	N4120V	7. 5.99	One Zero Three Ltd	Guernsey	6..5.02T
G-GGGG	Thunder Ax7-77 HAFB	162		2. 8.78	T.A.Gilmour t/a Flying G Group "Flying G"	Stockbridge	17. 8.99A
G-GGLE	PA-22-108 Colt (Tail-wheel conversion incorporating parts from G-AROM c/n 22-8805)	22-8914	N5234Z	13. 5.93	S.C.Hobden	(Hungerford)	25. 7.02T
G-GGOW	Colt 77A HAFB	1542		19. 6.89	G.Everett "Charles Rennie Mackintosh"	Dartford	17. 2.00A
G-GGTT	Agusta-Bell 47G-4A	2538	F-GGTT I-ANDO	21. 8.97	Thorneygrove Ltd	Newcastle	16. 2.01
G-GHCL	Bell 206B JetRanger II	925	G-SHVV N72GM/N83106	8. 7.92	Scotia Helicopters Ltd	Cumbernauld	3. 6.02T
G-GHIA	Cameron N-120 HAFB	2442		13.11.90	J.A.Marshall	Billingshurst	13. 2.97T
G-GHIN	Thunder Ax7-77 HAFB	1802		16. 7.90	N.T.Parry "Pegasus"	Binfield	17. 8.99A
G-GHKX	PA-28-161 Warrior II	28-8416005	F-GHKX N4318X	10. 6.99	Oxford Aviation Services Ltd	Oxford	
G-GHRW	PA-28RT-201 Arrow IV	28R-7918140	G-ONAB G-BHAK/N29555	8.12.83	Bonus Aviation Ltd	Cranfield	22.12.00T
G-GHSI	PA-44-180T Turbo Seminole	44-8107026	SX-ATA N8278Z	2.12.94	M.G.Roberts (Damaged late 1994; on rebuild 8.95)	Bournemouth	1.12.97
G-GHZJ	Socata TB.9 Tampico	941	F-GHZJ	4. 3.98	M.Haller	Little Snoring	30. 4.01
G-GIGI	Socata MS.893A Rallye Commodore 180	11637	G-AYVX F-BSFJ	28. 9.81	D.J.Moore Sandhill Farm, Shrivenham		13. 4.00
G-GILT	Cessna 421C Golden Eagle III	421C-0515	G-BMZC N555WV/N555WW/N885WW/N885EC/N88541	3. 7.97	Air Nova plc	Chester	25. 9.00T
G-GIRO	Schweizer Hughes 269C	S.1328	N41S	16. 9.88	D.E.McDowell	Wantage	8.10.01
G-GIRY	American General AG-5B Tiger	10146	F-GIRY	5. 2.99	M.J.Sparshatt-Worley	Southampton	7..4.02T
G-GJCD	Robinson R-22 Beta	0966		22. 2.89	J.C.Lane Green Crize, Hereford		21. 5.01T
G-GJET	Gates Learjet 35A	35A-365	G-CJET G-SEBE/G-ZIPS/(N4564S)/G-ZONE	9. 3.95	DPS Aviation Ltd	Fairoaks/Heathrow	10. 2.00T
G-GJKK	Mooney M.20K (252TSE)	25-1227	F-GJKK	26.11.93	C.J.Davey & S.C.Shaw	Biggin Hill	11. 3.00
G-GKAT	Enstrom 280C Shark	1200	F-GKAT N5694Y	26. 8.97	Cheshire Aviators Ltd	(Warrington)	29. 1.01
G-GKFC	Tiger Cub RL5A LW Sherwood Ranger	PFA/237-12947	G-MYZI	24.11.98	K.F.Crumplin Franklyn's Field, Chewton Mendip		18.10.00P
G-GLAD	Gloster Gladiator II	-	"N2276" N5903	5. 1.95	Patina Ltd (Op The Fighter Collection: on rebuild 1.99)	Duxford	
G-GLAW	Cameron N-90 HAFB	1808		10.10.88	George Law Plant Ltd "Law Civil Engineers"	Kidderminster	17. 8.99A
G-GLBL	Lindstrand AM.32000 HAFB	444		3.10.96	Lindstrand Balloons Ltd (ICO Global Challenger) (Ditched off Hawaii, Pacific 25.12.98)	Oswestry	
G-GLED	Cessna 150M Commuter	150-76673	C-GLED	6. 1.89	Firecrest Aviation Ltd (Collided with G-GCNZ Elstree 8.4.99)	Elstree	22.10.01T
G-GLTT	PA-31-350 Chieftain	31-8452004	N27JV N606SM	19. 9.97	J.A.Robson (Op Capital Trading Aviation)	Filton	16. 3.01T
G-GLUC	Van's RV-6	20153	C-GLUC	15.10.99	K.D.Pearce	(Downham Market)	
G-GLUE	Cameron N-65 HAFB	390		17. 3.81	L.J.M.Muir & G.D.Hallett East Molesey "Tacky Jack/Jack of Hearts" (Mobile Windscreens titles)		17. 7.90A
G-GLUG	PA-31-350 Chieftain	31-8052077	N2287J G-BLOE/G-NITE/N3559A	1. 9.94	Champagne-Air Ltd	Newcastle	23.11.02T
G-GMAX	SNCAN Stampe SV-4C	141	G-BXNW F-BBPB	19. 6.87	Glidegold Ltd (Damaged in crash Booker 3.6.91; on rebuild 5.96)	Booker	29. 8.93T
G-GMPA	Aerospatiale AS.355F2 Twin Squirrel	5409	G-BPOI	26. 9.89	Greater Manchester Police Authority	Barton	9.11.01T
G-GMSI	Socata TB.9 Tampico	145		18. 9.80	M.L.Rhodes	Halfpenny Green	28. 5.00T
G-GNAT	Folland Gnat T.1	FL.595	8638M XS101	14. 4.82	Brutus Holdings Ltd (As "XS101" in Red Arrows c/s)	Cranfield	9. 9.00P

Regn	Type	C/n	P/I	Date	Owner/operator	Probable Base	CA Expy
G-GNSY*	HPR.7 Dart Herald 209	197	I-ZERD G-BFRK/4X-AHN	30. 6.87	Channel Express Group plc (Broken up 1.97)	Bournemouth	1. 8.99T
G-GNTA	Saab-Scania SF.340A	340A-049	HB-AHK SE-E49	5. 4.91	Business Air Ltd	Aberdeen	11. 4.99T
G-GNTB	Saab-Scania SF.340A	340A-082	HB-AHL SE-E82	30. 9.91	Business Air Ltd	Aberdeen	10.10.00T
G-GNTC	Saab-Fairchild SF.340A	340A-020	HB-AHE SE-E20	25. 9.92	Aurigny Air Services Ltd	Guernsey	24. 9.00T
G-GNTD	Saab-Scania SF.340A	340A-100	SE-ISK SE-E01	30.12.92	Business Air Ltd	Aberdeen	3. 1.01T
G-GNTE	Saab-Scania SF.340A	340A-133	SE-ISM SE-F33	22. 1.93	Business Air Ltd (Mountain of the Birds/Benyhone Tartan t/s)	Aberdeen	21. 1.01T
G-GNTF	Saab-Scania SF.340A	340A-113	HB-AHO SE-F13	27.10.94	Business Air Ltd	Aberdeen	27.10.00T
G-GNTG	Saab-Scania SF.340A	340A-126	HB-AHR SE-F26	18.11.94	Business Air Ltd	Aberdeen	18.11.00T
G-GNTH	Saab-Scania SF.340B	340B-169	N588MA SE-F69	23. 1.97	Business Air Ltd	Aberdeen	4. 2.00T
G-GNTI	Saab-Scania SF.340B	340B-172	N589MA SE-F72	30. 1.97	Business Air Ltd	Aberdeen	5. 2.00T
G-GNTJ	Saab-Scania SF.340B	340B-192	N591MA SE-F92	26. 2.97	Business Air Ltd	Aberdeen	4. 3.00T
G-GNTZ	BAe 146 Srs.200	E-2036	HB-IXB N175US/N355PS	26.11.94	British Regional Airlines Ltd (Mountain of the Birds/Benyhone Tartan t/s)	Manchester	25.11.00T
G-GOBT	Colt 77A HAFB	1815		13. 2.91	British Telecommunications plc "Sky Piper"	Thatcham	18. 3.00A
G-GOCC	Gulfstream AA-5A Cheetah	AA5A-0811	G-BPIX N26916	2. 9.92	Lowlog Ltd (Op Cabair)	Elstree	17. 3.01T
G-GOCX	Cameron N-90 HAFB	2619		7. 8.91	R.D.Parry	Hong Kong, PRC	9. 1.00A
G-GOGW	Cameron N-90 HAFB	3304		31. 8.94	Great Western Trains Co Ltd	Swindon	1. 5.00A
G-GOKT	McDonnell Douglas DC-10-30	47838	RP-C2114 (RP-C2004)	1. 5.96	Caledonian Airways Ltd (JMC Air c/s)	Gatwick	2. 5.02T
G-GOLF	Socata TB.10 Tobago	250		21.12.81	E.H. & A.C.Scammell, G.J.Powell & B.Bain	Biggin Hill	2. 5.00
G-GOMM	PA-32R-300 Cherokee Lance	32R-7780030	N6571F	16. 5.80	L.Major	Bournemouth	24..6.98
G-GONE	FFW DH.112 Venom FB.50 (FB.1)	752	J-1542	17. 9.84	D.G.Jones (On overhaul Bournemouth 1.00)	Swansea	7.11.95P
G-GOOD	Socata TB.20 Trinidad	1657	F-GNHJ	4.11.94	N.J.Vetch	Goodwood	25.11.00T
G-GORE	CFM Streak Shadow (Rotax 532) K.138-SA & PFA/206-11646			12. 4.90	M.S.Clinton (PFA c/n duplicates miniMax G-MWFD)	(Farnborough)	22.11.00P
G-GORF	Robin HR.200/120B	291	F-GORF	14. 1.00	J.A.Ingram	Nottingham	
G-GOSS	CEA Jodel DR-221 Dauphin	125	F-BPRA	4.12.80	M.J.Milner t/a Avon Flying Group	Bidford	12. 5.00
G-GOTC	Gulfstream GA-7 Cougar	GA7-0074	G-BMDY OO-LCR/OO-HRA	25. 6.97	Cambridge Aircraft Ltd	(Saffron Walden)	9. 1.02T
G-GOTO	PA-32R-301T Saratoga II TC	3257026	N92965	8. 1.98	J.A.Varndell	Blackbushe	7. 1.01
G-GOZO	Cessna R182 Skylane RG II	R182-01883	G-BJZO (G-BJYE)/N5521T	9. 1.85	Transmatic Fyllan Ltd	Little Staughton	11. 2.01
G-GPMW	PA-28R-201T Turbo Arrow IV	28R-8031041	N3576V	3. 7.89	M.Worrall, J.Riley & I.R.Court	Coventry	23. 7.01T
G-GPST	Phillips ST.1 Speedtwin (Continental O-200-A) 1 & PFA/207-11645			21. 6.90	Susan E.Phillips (PFA c/n duplicates Kolb Twinstar G-MWWM)	Old Sarum	26. 8.00P
G-GPWH	Dassault Falcon 900EX	48	F-WWFP	23.11.99	Lynton Corporate Jet Ltd & P.B.W. Hamlyn t/a Aviation Partnership	Luton	23.11.02T
G-GRAY	Cessna 172N Skyhawk II	172-72375	N4859D	3.12.79	Truman Aviation Ltd (Damaged in Firth of Forth, nr Mussleburgh 2.4.93; stored 4.97)	Nottingham	13. 2.95T
G-GREN	Cessna T310R II	310R-1282	N426CB N6015X	24. 7.90	B.J.Berry	(Dublin, Ireland)	1. 1.03
G-GRID	Aerospatiale AS.355F1 Twin Squirrel	5012	TG-BOS	28. 3.89	National Grid Co plc	Oxford	18. 6.01T
G-GRIF	Rockwell Commander 112TC-A	13258	G-BHXC N1005C	2.10.81	N.G.W.Cragg, E.T.N.Sutherland & C.Walker t/a Nicol Aviation	(Rotherham)	26. 3.01
G-GRIN	Van's RV-6 (Tail-wheel)	PFA/181-12409		8. 1.98	A.Phillips	Boarhunt Farm	
G-GRIP	Colt Bibendum 110SS HAFB	4224		5. 1.98	The Aerial Display Co Ltd (Michelin titles)	Looe	19.11.99A
G-GROL	Maule MXT-7-180 Star Rocket	14091C		16. 6.98	D.C., C.& C.Croll	Southend	16. 6.01
G-GRRC	PA-28-161 Warrior II	2816076	G-BXJX HB-POM/D-EJTB/N9149X	9. 3.98	Goodwood Road Racing Co Ltd	Goodwood	8.10.00T

Regn	Type	C/n	P/I	Date	Owner/operator	Probable Base	CA Expy
G-GRRR	Scotish Avn Bulldog 120/122 BH120/229		G-BXGU Ghana AF G-105	19.10.98	L Bax	Old Sarum	25. 5.02T
G-GRYZ	Beechcraft F33A Bonanza	CE-1668	F-GRYZ D-ESNE/N80011/(OY-GEN)/N80011	4.10.99	V.G.Negre	Blackbushe	19.10.02
G-GSFC	Robinson R-22 Beta	0569	N2425J	3. 7.86	London Helicopter Centre Ltd	Redhill	4.10.01T
G-GSFT	PA-44-180 Seminole	44-7995202	EI-BYZ N2193K	12.10.98	SFT Europe Ltd	Bournemouth	28.10.01T
G-GTAX	PA-31-350 Navajo Chieftain 31-7405442		G-OIAS OY-CBF/D-IGSA/N54322	11. 3.88	Hadagain Investments Ltd	NK	4. 4.98T
G-GTHM	PA-38-112 Tomahawk II	38-81A0171	C-GTHM	17.11.86	D.A.Whitmore	Booker	19.10.01T
G-GTPL	Mooney M.20K (231)	25-0301	G-BHOS N231LQ	15. 7.80	W.R.Emberton Cuidad Quesada, Alicante, Spain		27. 6.01
G-GUAY	Enstrom 480	5036		1.12.98	Testactual Ltd t/a Heliway Aviation	(Fareham)	30.12.01T
G-GUCK	Beechcraft C23 Sundowner 180	M-2221	G-BPYG N6638R	9. 4.92	S.Imber	Stapleford	9. 1.01
G-GUFO	Cameron Saucer 80SS HAFB	1641	C-GUFO G-BOUB	10. 6.98	L.V.Mastis West Bloomfield, Mi., USA		23. 6.89A
G-GUGI	Eurocopter EC.135T 1	0065		9.10.98	Sepvim SA	Geneva	AC
G-GULF	Lindstrand LBL-105A HAFB	320		3.11.95	Virgin Balloon Flights Ltd Muscat, Oman (Gulf Air titles)		13. 4.00A
G-GULL	SMAN Petrel Amphibian PFA/269-12833 (Rotax 912UL)	29-DX/ F-JBS/G-GULL		6. 3.95	Amphibians UK Ltd Dunkeswell/Salcombe		9.10.95P
G-GUNS	Cameron V-77 HAFB	2221		9. 5.90	Royal School of Artillery Hot Air Balloon Club "Guns"	Larkhill	19. 3.00A
G-GURL*	Cameron A-210 HAFB	2387		3. 9.90	R S Kent "Hot Airlines" (Balloon Preservation Group)	Lancing	29. 8.96T
G-GUSS	PA-28-151 Cherokee Warrior 28-7415497		G-BJRY N43453	16. 8.95	A.M.B.Dudley (Op Flywatch UK Ltd)	Southend	6. 6.00T
G-GUST	Agusta-Bell 206B Jet Ranger	8192	G-CBHH F-GALU/G-AYBE	30. 8.96	Gatehouse Estates Ltd	Sywell	25. 4.99T
G-GUYS	PA-34-200T Seneca II	34-7870283	G-BMWT N31984	14. 7.87	R.J.& J.M.Z.Keel	(Lincoln)	9. 5.02
G-GVBF	Lindstrand LBL-180A HAFB	250	PH-VBF G-GVBF	19. 5.95	Virgin Balloon Flights Ltd (London SE16)		2. 4.00T
G-GVIP	Agusta A.109E Power	11024		1. 7.98	Sloane Helicopters Ltd	Sywell	26. 8.01T
	(Was temporarily marked "G-TVAA" in early February 99 for AA's promotional literature)						
G-GWIZ	Colt Clown SS HAFB	1369	(G-BPWU)	25. 4.89	L.V.Mastis	(Berkeley)	13. 4.99A
G-GWYN	Reims Cessna F.172M Skyhawk II	1217	PH-TWN	5. 3.81	C.Bosher & D.J.Bruford t/a Gwyn Aviation	Exeter	27. 4.02
G-GYAV	Cessna 172N Skyhawk II	172-71362	C-GYAV	26. 8.87	Southport & Merseyside Aero Club (1979) Ltd	Liverpool	8. 3.00T
G-GYBO	Gardan GY-80-180 Horizon	228	OY-DTN SE-FGL/OY-DTN	4. 8.98	M.J.Strother	Blackpool	AC
G-GYMM	PA-28R-200 Cherokee Arrow 28R-7135049		G-AYWW	22. 2.90	J.B.A.Ainsworth t/a Gymm Group	Leicester	5. 2.01
G-GYRO	Campbell Cricket PFA G/03-1046			26. 2.82	J.W.Pavitt	St.Merryn	26. 4.99P
	(Rotax 532) (This is the airframe at Bournemouth in the 1980s & owned by Nigel Pitcher. Originally registered as a Bensen B.8 Gyrocopter (c/n 01 & PFA/G-01-1046) it was sold but converted by previous owner)						
G-GZDO	Cessna 172N Skyhawk II	172-71826	C-GZDO (N5299E)	11.10.88	G.Cambridge & G.W.J.Hall t/a Cambridge Hall Aviation (Op Firecrest Aviation)	Elstree	31. 3.01T

G-HAAA– G-HZZZ

Regn	Type	C/n	P/I	Date	Owner/operator	Probable Base	CA Expy
G-HACK	PA-18-150 Super Cub	18-7168	SE-CSA	20.11.97	S.J.Harris	North Weald	2.12.00
G-HADA	Enstrom 480	5017		17. 9.96	W.B.Steele	Whitchurch, Shropshire	24. 9.02
G-HAEC	Commonwealth CAC-18 Mustang 22 CACM-192-1517		VR-HIU (RP-C651)/PI-C651/VH-FCB/A68-192 (Op The Old Flying Machine Ltd)	1. 5.85	R.W.Davies "Big Beautiful Doll"	Duxford	30. 5.00P
	(Composite rebuilt 1974-76 using major components from Philippine AF P-51D 44-72917) (As "472218/WZ-I" in 78th FG USAAF c/s)						
G-HAIG	Rutan LongEz 1983-L & PFA/74A-11149 (Lycoming O-235)			20. 5.86	R.Casey & D.W.Parfrey	Coventry	27. 7.00P
G-HAJJ	Glaser-Dirks DG-400	4-225		15. 2.88	P.W.Endean	Perranporth	21. 4.00
G-HALC	PA-28R-200 Cherokee Arrow II 28R-7335042		N91253 C-FFQO/CF-FQO	26.11.90	Halcyon Aviation Ltd	Barton	28. 5.00
G-HALE	Robinson R-44 Astro	0492		6. 8.98	Barhale Surveying Ltd	Elstree	19. 8.01T
G-HALJ	Cessna 140 (Continental C85)	8336	N89308 NC89308	30. 4.96	H.A.Lloyd-Jennings	Haverfordwest	24. 8.02
G-HALL	PA-22-160 Tri-Pacer	22-7423	G-ARAH	8.11.79	F.P.Hall	Maypole Farm, Chislet	29. 6.00
G-HALO	Elisport CH-7 Angel	A.031	I-2858	12.11.93	Taylor Woolhouse Ltd	Not known	30. 7.94P

Regn	Type	C/n	P/I	Date	Owner/operator	Probable Base	CA Expy
G-HALP	Socata TB.10 Tobago	192	G-BITD	19. 8.81	Delia H.Halpern	Booker	30. 5.97
G-HAMA	Beechcraft 200 Super King Air	BB-30	N244JB	16.11.84	Gama Aviation Ltd	Heathrow/Fairoaks	19.11.99T
			N211JB/N3090C/N3030C/N200CA				
	(Upgraded in 1999 to B200 status & with four blade propellers - all Gama a/c are now externally identical)						
G-HAMI	Fuji FA.200-180 Aero Subaru		G-OISF	31. 1.92	S.A.R.Rose & K.G.Cameron	Biggin Hill	31. 3.02
		FA200-188	G-BAPT				
G-HAMP	Bellanca 7ACA Champ	30-72	N9173L	8. 8.88	K.Macdonald	(Clapham, Bedford)	21.11.00P
G-HAND	Cameron Startac 105SS HAFB	3895		19. 8.96	Redmalt Ltd	Witham, Essex	6. 5.00A
G-HANS	Robin DR.400 2 + 2	1384		2. 3.79	T.A.White t/a Bagby Aviation	Bagby	20. 6.00T
G-HAPR	Bristol 171 Sycamore HC.14	13387	8010M	15. 6.78	E.D. Ap Rees	Weston-super-Mare	
			XG547		t/a The Helicopter Museum	(As "XG547/T-S" in CFS c/s)	
G-HAPY	DHC.1 Chipmunk 22	C1/0697	WP803	3. 7.96	G-HAPY Ltd (As "WP803")	Booker	16. 9.02
G-HARE	Cameron N-77 HAFB	1467		12. 3.87	C.E. & J.Falkingham	Stevenage	18. 6.02A
G-HARF	Gulfstream Aerospace Gulfstream IV	1117	N1761J	9.10.91	Fayair (Jersey) Co Ltd	Stansted/Jersey	20.12.02T
					(Op Harrods)		
G-HARH	Sikorsky S-76B	760391	N7600U	30. 9.91	Air Harrods Ltd	Stansted	17. 1.02T
G-HARI	Raj Hamsa X'Air 582	BMAA/HB/099		11. 6.99	D.Mahajan Lower Mountpleasant, Chatteris		
G-HARO	Aerospatiale AS.355F2 Twin Squirrel	5364	G-DAFT	21. 8.96	Air Harrods Ltd	Denham	16. 1.00T
			G-BNNN				
G-HART	Cessna 152 II	152-79734	(G-BPBF)	2. 2.89	Atlantic Air Transport Ltd	Coventry	25. 6.01T
	(Tail-wheel conversion)		N757GS				
G-HARY	Alon A-2 Aircoupe	A.188	G-ATWP	15. 3.93	M.C.Clark	Newcastle	22. 4.01
G-HASI	Cessna 421B Golden Eagle	421B-0654	G-BTDK	17. 2.98	Hawarden Air Services Ltd	Chester	7. 3.02
			OY-BFA/N1558G				
G-HATZ	Hatz CB-1	17	N54623	11. 5.89	S.P.Rollason	Charity Farm, Baxterley	9. 9.00P
	(Lycoming O-320)						
G-HAUL*	Westland WG.30-300	020	G-17-22	3. 7.86	The Helicopter Museum	Weston-super-Mare	27.10.86P
G-HAUS	Hughes 369HM (500M)	52-0214M	G-KBOT	20. 7.99	J Pulford	(Towcester)	14.10.02
			G-RAMM/EI-AVN/N9037F		t/a Pulford Aviation		
G-HAZE	Thunder Ax8-90 HAFB	989		3. 8.88	T.G.Church	Blackburn	23. 6.97T
G-HBBC	DH.104 Dove 8	04211	G-ALFM	24. 1.96	BBC Air Ltd	Filton	25. 6.01
			VP961/G-ALFM/VP961				
G-HBMW	Robinson R-22	0170	G-BOFA	7. 7.94	J.Anderson	Edinburgh	26. 9.00T
			N9068D				
G-HBUG	Cameron N-90 HAFB	1991	G-BRCN	21. 6.89	R.T. & H.Revel "Humbug"	High Wycombe	25. 5.00T
G-HCFR	BAe 125 Srs.800B	258240	HB-VLT	23. 7.98	Chauffair (CI) Ltd	Farnborough	26. 7.00T
			G-SHEA/G-BUWC/G-5-772				
G-HCSL	PA-34-220T Seneca III	34-8133237	N84375	9. 5.91	Dawcroft Ltd	Blackpool	31. 8.00T
					t/a Colony Aviation		
G-HDEW	PA-32R-301 Saratoga SP	3213026	G-BRGZ	4.12.89	Lord Howard de Walden	(Hungerford)	11. 3.01
			N91787				
G-HDIX	Enstrom 280FX	2076	N506DH	19. 2.98	J.Poupard	(Kings Lynn)	12. 3.01T
			D-HDIX				
G-HDPP	Eurocopter EC-135T-1	0055	G-HDDP	3. 7.98	McAlpine Helicopters Ltd	Oxford	
G-HEAD	Colt 56SS Flying Head HAFB	304	SE-ZHE	18. 8.81	E.K.Nyberg	Stockholm, Sweden	24. 4.97A
	(Compac Computerised Head shape)		G-HEAD				
G-HEBE	Bell 206B Jet Ranger III	3745	CS-HDN	5. 2.97	MGGR (UK) Ltd	White Waltham	9. 3.00T
			N3179A				
G-HELE	Bell 206B Jet Ranger III	3789	G-OJFR	21. 2.91	B E E Smith	White Waltham	12. 5.00T
			N18095				
G-HELI*	Saro Skeeter AOP.12	S2/5110		15. 6.78	Luftwaffen Museum	Uetersen, Hamburg	
	(Composite of 7870M/XM556 cabin & 7979M/XM529 boom)				(In German Army c/s)		
G-HELN	PA-18-95 Super Cub	18-3365	G-BKDG	10. 1.86	J.J.Anziani	Booker	12. 4.00P
	(L-21B-PI) (Frame No.18-3400)		MM52-2392/EI-69/EI-141/I-EIWB/MM53-7765/53-7765				
	(Regd as c/n 18-1992 but frame exchanged in Italian AF service; c/n 18-3365 was officially regd as N9837Q)						
G-HELP*	Colt 17A Cloudhopper HAFB	902		16. 2.87	Virgin Airship & Balloon Co Ltd	Telford	7. 8.95A
					"Mondial Cloudhopper" (Cancelled as PWFU 27.3.99)		
G-HELV	FFW DH.115 Vampire T.55	975	U-1215	17. 9.91	Hunter Wing Ltd	Bournemouth	13. 5.00P
					(As "XJ771" in RAF c/s)		
G-HEMS	Aerospatiale SA.365N Dauphin 2	6009	F-WYMJ	22. 8.88	Virgin Executive Aviation Ltd		
			G-HEMS/N365AM/N365AH		The Royal London Hospital, Whitechapel/Denham		21.12.00T
					(Op for London Hospitals Emergency Medical Service)		
G-HENS*	Cameron N-65 HAFB	740		8. 7.81	Balloon Preservation Group	Lancing	N/E(A)
					"Free Range" (Noted 12.98)		
G-HENY	Cameron V-77 HAFB	2486		9. 1.91	R.S.D'Alton "Henny"	Newbury	29. 7.00A
G-HEPY	Robinson R-44 Astro	0695		11. 1.00	T.Everett	(Stockbridge)	
G-HERA*	Robinson R-22 Beta	1426		26. 6.90	G.R.Day	(Boston)	21. 8.99T
	(Crashed on landing Blackpool 24.2.99 & cancelled same date as Destroyed -see G-GDAY for prospects !!)						
G-HERB	PA-28R-201 Arrow III	28R-7837118	ZS-LAG	5. 6.86	Appleton Aviation Ltd	(York)	14.10.01
			N3504M				
G-HERO	PA-32RT-300 Lance II	32R-7885086	G-BOGN	26. 4.88	Air Alize Communication	Stapleford	9. 7.97

Regn	Type	C/n	P/I	Date	Owner/operator	Probable Base	CA Expy
			N33LV/N30573				
G-HERS	Cessna 750 Citation X	750-0075	N5196U	1. 7.99	Red Aviation Services Ltd Leeds-Bradford		2 .7.02T
	(Note: Jodel D.18 fuselage, c/n 255 & PFA/169-11410, c/w engine displayed PFA Cranfield 7.89 & carried						
	"G-HERS" as reserved for Angela Usherwood, Ammanford: appears not to have taken up any other UK marks as yet)						
G-HEWI	Piper J3C-90 Cub (L-4J-PI)	12566	G-BLEN	20. 7.84	R.Preston	Denham	3.10.99
	(Frame No.12396)		D-EBEN/HB-OFZ/44-80270		t/a Denham Grasshopper Flying Group		
G-HEYY	Cameron Bear 72SS HAFB	1244		21. 1.86	L.V.Mastis West Bloomfield, Mi., USA		30.11.98A
	(Hofmeister Lager Bear)				"George"		
G-HFBM	Curtiss Robin C-2	352	LV-FBM	24. 4.90	D.M.Forshaw	Panshanger	1. 8.00P
	(Continental W-670)		NC9279				
G-HFCA	Cessna A150L Aerobat	A150-0381	N6081J	30. 8.91	Horizon Flying Club Ltd	Earls Colne	3. 9.01T
	(Texas Tail-wheel conversion)						
G-HFCB	Reims Cessna F.150L	0798	G-AZVR	10. 2.87	Horizon Flying Club Ltd	Earls Colne	11. 2.00T
G-HFCI	Reims Cessna F.150L	0823	PH-CET	11. 9.80	Horizon Flying Club Ltd	Earls Colne	27. 1.02T
G-HFCL	Reims Cessna F.152 II	1663	G-BGLR	11.10.88	Horizon Flying Club Ltd	Earls Colne	23. 4.00T
G-HFCT	Reims Cessna F.152 II	1861		27. 1.81	Stapleford Flying Club Ltd	Stapleford	17. 6.02T
G-HFIX	VS.361 Spitfire HF.IXe	CBAF.7243	G-BLAS	22. 8.89	D.W.Pennell	Gloucestershire	14. 9.00P
	(C/n quoted also as CBAF.78883) IDF/AF 2066/06-06/MM4094/MJ730 (As "MJ730/GZ-?" in 32 Sqn c/s)						
G-HFLA	Schweizer Hughes 269C (300C)	S.1428		8.12.89	Sterling Helicopters Ltd	Norwich	4. 2.02T
G-HFTG	PA-23-250 Aztec E	27-7405378	G-BSOB	30. 4.87	Widehawk Aviation Ltd	Cambridge	6. 4.02T
			G-BCJR/N54040		t/a Hawkair ("Ordnance Survey" titles)		
G-HGAS	Cameron N-77 HAFB	1969		4. 5.89	N.J.Tovey	Bristol	13. 5.97A
G-HGPI	Socata TB.20 Trinidad	851		4. 8.88	M.J.Jackson	Bournemouth	21.12.00
G-HIAH*	Revolution Helicopters Mini-500	0052		4. 3.96	H.I.A.Hopkinson	(Huddersfield)	
					(No Permit issued: cancelled by CAA 10.3.99)		
G-HIBM	Cameron N-145 HAFB	3197		8. 2.94	L.& R.J.Mold	High Wycombe	15. 5.00T
					t/a Dragonfly Balloons		
G-HIEL	Robinson R-22 Beta	1120		28. 9.89	R.C.Hields	Sherburn-in-Elmet	16.11.98
					t/a Hields Aviation		
G-HIII	Extra EA.300	057	D-ETYD	10. 1.95	Firebird Aerobatics Ltd	RAF Halton	29. 1.01T
					(Rover titles)		
G-HILO	Commander 114	14224	N4894W	6. 2.98	F.H.Parkes	(Chelmsford)	7. 4.01
G-HILS	Reims Cessna F.172H	0522	G-AWCH	20.12.88	B.F.W.Lowdon	Blackbushe	12. 1.01
					t/a Lowdon Aviation Group		
G-HILT	Socata TB.10 Tobago	298	(G-BMYB)	13. 5.82	Insight Marketing & Communications Ltd		
			EI-BOF/G-HILT			Woodford	7. 7.02T
G-HIND	Maule MT-7-235 Star Rocket	18037C		26. 3.98	R.G.Humphries	(Hook)	29. 4.01T
G-HIPE	Sorrell SNS-7 Hyperbipe	209	N18RS	6. 4.93	T.A.S.Rayner	Glenrothes	30. 6.00P
	(Lycoming IO-360)						
G-HIPO	Robinson R-22 Beta	1719	G-BTGB	11. 9.92	Fleet Street Travel Ltd	(Chertsey)	19. 5.00T
G-HIRE	Gulfstream GA-7 Cougar	GA7-0091	10.12.81		London Aerial Tours Ltd	Rochester	28. 5.00T
			N704G				
G-HISS	Aerotek Pitts S-2A Special	2137	G-BLVU	17. 3.92	L.V.Adams & J.Maffia	Panshanger	24. 8.02T
	(Lycoming AEIO-360)		SE-GTX		"Always Dangerous" (Stored 11.97)		
G-HIUP	Cameron A-250 HAFB	4464		16. 4.99	Bridges Van Hire Ltd	Nottingham	11. 4.00T
G-HIVA	Cessna 337A Super Skymaster	337-0429	G-BAES	28. 3.88	G.J.Banfield	Gloucestershire	9. 7.00
			SE-CWW/N5329S				
G-HIVE	Reims Cessna F.150M	1186	G-BCXT	19. 4.85	M.P.Lynn	Norwich	30. 4.01
G-HJSS	AIA Stampe SV-4C	1101	G-AZNF	7. 9.92	H.J.Smith	Shoreham	16. 6.02
			F-BGJM/Fr mil				
G-HKHM	Hughes 369D	711019D	B-HHM	8. 4.99	Heli Air Ltd	Denham	25 .5.02
			VR-HHM/N50605				
G-HKIT	BAC One Eleven 521FH	BAC.196	VP-BEC	17. 6.97	European Aviation Ltd	Bournemouth	
			VR-BEC/LV-JNT/G-16-10 (Austral c/s) (Stored 11.99)				
G-HLAA	Airbus A.300B4-203	047	EI-TLN	6.10.97	Heavylift Cargo Airlines Ltd	Stansted	7. 7.01T
			G-HLAA/N740SC/F-BVGJ/F-WUAX				
G-HLAB	Airbus A.300B4-203F	045	N743SC	20. 2.98	Heavylift Cargo Airlines Ltd	Stansted	26. 2.01T
			F-BVGI/F-WNDA				
G-HLAC	Airbus A.300B4-203	074	N829SC	23.11.98	Heavylift Cargo Airlines Ltd	Stansted	3.12.01T
			F-BVGL				
G-HLCF	CFM Starstreak Shadow SA-II			10. 5.96	S.M.E.Solomon	North Weald	15. 3.00P
	(Rotax 618)	PFA/206-12796					
G-HLEN	Aerospatiale AS.350B Ecureuil	1836	G-LOLY	22. 4.93	N.Edmonds	Jacobstowe	15.10.01T
			JA9897/N5805T/HP-…/N5805T				
G-HLFT	Short SC.5 Belfast C.1	SH.1819	XR365	11. 9.81	Heavylift Aviation Holdings Ltd Stansted		20. 6.02T
	(Modified to Mk.2)				t/a Heavylift Cargo Airlines "St.George"		
G-HLIX*	Cameron Helix Oilcan 61SS HAFB	1192		20. 9.85	R S Kent "Helix Oil Can"	Lancing	25. 4.90A
					(Balloon Preservation Group 7.98 for restoration)		
G-HMBJ	Commander 114B	14636	N6036F	30. 6.97	B.A.Groves	Guernsey	24. 7.00
G-HMED	PA-28-161 Warrior III	2842020	LX-III	21. 7.97	H.Faizal	Denham	31. 7.00
G-HMES	PA-28-161 Warrior II	28-8216070	OY-CSN	21. 4.89	Cleveland Flying School Ltd	Bagby	20. 8.01T

Regn	Type	C/n	P/I	Date	Owner/operator	Probable Base	CA Expy
			N8471N		(Op Teesside A/C)		
G-HMJB	PA-34-220T Seneca III	34-8133040	N8356R	12. 7.89	Cross Atlantic Ventures Ltd		
						(Douglas, IOM)	1. 9.01
G-HMPH	Bell 206B JetRanger II	1232	G-BBUY	20. 6.88	Sturmer Ltd	(Tring)	31. 3.02T
			N18090				
G-HMPT	Agusta-Bell 206B JetRanger II	8168		7.11.91	S.& M.L.Lee	(Wilden)	26. 1.01T
G-HNRY	Cessna 650 Citation VI	650-0219	N219CC	23.10.92	Quantel Ltd	Farnborough	12. 1.03
G-HNTR*	Hawker Hunter T.7	HABL-003311	8834M	7. 7.89	Yorkshire Air Museum	Elvington	
			XL572		(As "XL572/83")		
G-HOBO	Denney Kitfox Mk.4	PFA/172A-12140		10. 9.92	P.Caton	(Bucknell)	15. 7.00P
	(Rotax 582)				"Navy Baby"		
G-HOCK	PA-28-180 Cherokee D	28-4395	G-AVSH	15. 5.86	Arabact Ltd	Goodwood	12. 8.01T
G-HOFC	Europa Avn Europa			25. 9.95	J.W.Lang	Hilton of Carslogie, Fife	26. 6.99P
	(Rotax 912UL)	119 & PFA/247-12736					
G-HOFM	Cameron N-56 HAFB	1245		21. 1.86	L.V.Mastis	West Bloomfield, Mi., USA	30.11.98A
G-HOGS	Cameron Pig 90SS HAFB	4121		7. 4.97	Flying Pictures Ltd	Fairoaks	1. 7.99A
					"Britannia Piggy Bank"		
G-HOHO	Colt Santa Claus SS HAFB	1671		21.12.89	Oxford Promotions (UK) Ltd	Kentucky, USA	14. 4.99A
G-HOLY	Socata ST.10 Diplomate	108	F-BSCZ	31. 1.90	M.K.Barsham	Booker	14. 4.02
G-HOME	Colt 77A HAFB	032		26. 2.79	Anglia Balloon School Ltd	Newbury	27. 5.86A
					"Tardis" (To British Balloon Museum & Library)		
G-HONG	Slingsby T-67M Firefly 200	2060	VR-HZR	24. 3.94	Hunting Aviation Ltd	RAF Barkston Heath	26. 6.00T
			HKG-12/G-7-128		(Op JEFTS)		
G-HONI	Robinson R-22 Beta	0871	G-SEGO	27. 1.00	Burman Aviation Ltd	Cranfield	
			N9081M				
G-HONK	Cameron O-105 HAFB	1813		30. 9.88	T.F.W.Dixon & Son Ltd	Bromsgrove	14. 9.97A
					"Dixons"		
G-HONY	Lilliput Type 1 Srs.A HAFB	L-01		31. 7.98	A.E. & D.E.Thomas	Honiton	
G-HOOV	Cameron N-56 HAFB	388		2. 3.78	Heather R.Evans "Hoover"	Ross-on-Wye	26. 5.89A
G-HOPE	Beechcraft F33A Bonanza	CE-805	N2024Z	27. 2.79	Hurn Aviation Ltd	Bournemouth	12. 3.01
G-HOPI	Cameron N-42 HAFB	2724		5.12.91	Ballonverbung Hamburg GmbH	Kiel Germany	29. 4.97A
G-HOPS	Thunder Ax8-90 Srs.1 HAFB	1220		11. 3.88	A.C. & B.Munn	Hastings	20. 5.96T
G-HOPY	Van's RV-6A	PFA/181-12742		4.12.95	R.C.Hopkinson	Booker	28. 1.99P
	(Lycoming O-320-B2B)				(Damaged Dunkeswell 4.9.99)		
G-HORN	Cameron V-77 HAFB	570		29.11.79	S.Herd	Mold	11.12.98A
G-HOST	Cameron N-77 HAFB	434		4. 9.78	D.Grimshaw "Suzanna"	Preston	18. 5.93A
G-HOTI	Colt 77A HAFB	750		13. 7.87	R.Ollier	Northwich, Cheshire	30. 9.90A
					"Horace Hot One"		
G-HOTT	Cameron O-120 HAFB	2581		30. 4.91	D.L.Smith "Floating Sensations"	Newbury	17. 5.97T
G-HOTZ	Colt 77B HAFB	2218		16. 6.92	C.J. & S.M.Davies	Castleton, Sheffield	10. 9.99A
G-HOUS	Colt 31A Air Chair HAFB	099		7.10.80	Anglia Balloon School Ltd "K9"	Newbury	3. 5.90A
					t/a Anglia Balloons (Barratts titles)		
					(To British Balloon Museum & Library)		
G-HOWE	Thunder Ax7-77 HAFB	1340		10. 4.89	M.F.Howe "Howie/Howzat"	Beverley	15. 8.95A
G-HPAA	PBN BN-2B-20 Islander	2244	G-BSWP	14. 8.91	Hampshire Police Authority Air Support Unit		
						Lee-on-Solent	22.12.00T
G-HPSE	Commander 114B	14638	N6038V	26. 8.97	Al Nisr Ltd	(Jersey)	16. 9.00A
G-HPSM	Commander Acft Commander 114TC	20022	N926GW	23.11.99	Fifth Floor Aviation Services Europe Ltd		
						Guernsey	AC
G-HPUX	Hawker Hunter T.Mk.7	41H-693455	8807M	12. 3.99	Classic Aviation Ltd	Duxford	
			XL587				
G-HPWH	Agusta A.109E	11051	G-HWPH	9. 8.99	Lynton Corporate Jet Ltd & P.B.W.Hamlyn		
					t/a Aviation Partnership	Denham	23. 6.02T
G-HRHE	Robinson R-22 Beta	1950	G-BTWP	24. 1.97	R.H.Everett		
						Upton Lovell, Warminster/Thruxton	11.12.00
G-HRHI	Beagle B.206 Basset Srs.1	B.014	XS770	6. 7.89	Lawgra (No.386) Ltd	Cranfield	15. 4.00
					t/a International Aerospace Engineering (As "XS770" in Queens Flight c/s)		
G-HRHS	Robinson R-44 Astro	0323		15. 4.97	Stratus Aviation Ltd	(Hong Kong, PRC)	16. 4.00
G-HRIO	Robin HR.100/210 Safari	149	F-BTZR	22. 1.87	T.W.Evans	Southampton	17.12.01
G-HRLK	Saab 91D/2 Safir	91376	G-BRZY	6. 3.90	Sylmar Aviation & Services Ltd		
			PH-RLK			Lower Wasing Farm, Brimpton	12. 5.01
G-HRLM	Brugger MB.2 Colibri	PFA/43-10118		28.12.78	S.J.Perkins & D.Dobson	Chilbolton	21.10.00P
	(VW1834)				"Titch"		
G-HRNT	Cessna 182S Skylane	18280395	N2369H	29.1.99	Dingle Star Ltd	Denham	9. 2.02
G-HROI	Rockwell Commander 112A	326	N1326J	19. 6.89	Intereuropean Aviation Ltd	Jersey	28. 4.01
G-HRON	DH.114 Heron 2B	14102	XR442	4. 4.91	M.E.R.Coghlan	Gloucestershire	AC
			G-AORH		(Unmarked 6.98)		
G-HRVD	CCF Harvard 4	CCF4-548	G-BSBC	8.12.92	J.K.Avis	Swanton Morley	
	(T-6J-CCF Texan)		Moz PLAF	1741/FAP 1741/BF+055/AA+055/53-4629			
	(Possibly a composite with rear fuselage of Moz PLAF/FAP 1780/AA+614/53-4622: on rebuild 1999)						
G-HRZN	Colt 77A HAFB	536		14.12.83	A.J.Spindler "Tequila Sunrise"	Kinross	4. 5.88A

Regn	Type	C/n	P/I	Date	Owner/operator	Probable Base	CA Expy
G-HSDW	Bell 206B JetRanger II	1789	ZS-HFC	16.12.85	Winfield Shoe Co Ltd & Stott Demolition Ltd Rossendale		2. 2.02
G-HSFT	PA-44-180 Seminole	44-7995179	EI-CCB N2093K	24. 9.99	Magenta Ltd (Op SFT Europe)	Bournemouth	27.10.02T
G-HSOO	Hughes 369HE	109-0208E	G-BFYJ F-BRSY	3.11.93	Edwards Aviation Ltd	(Wilmslow)	27. 9.99T
G-HSTH	Lindstrand HS-110 Hot-Air Airship	546		20. 8.98	Ballonsport Helmet Seitz Kisslegg, Germany		17.12.00A
G-HTAX	PA-31-350 Navajo Chieftain	31-7405435	N54305	7. 6.88	Hadagain Investments Ltd	NK	AC
G-HTPS	Aerospatiale SA.341G Gazelle 1	1301	G-BRNI YU-HBI	16.11.89	J.Malcolm	Wolverhampton	24. 7.00
G-HTVI	Cameron N-90 HAFB	1375	G-PRIT	29.10.96	HTV Group plc	Cardiff	6.10.97T
G-HUBB	Partenavia P.68B	194	OY-BJH SE-GXL	27. 5.83	G-HUBB Ltd	Denham	29. 7.01
G-HUCH	Cameron Carrots 80SS HAFB	2258	G-BYPS	13. 3.91	L.V.Mastis West Bloomfield, Mi., USA "Magic Carrots"		18. 6.00A
G-HUEY	Bell UH-1H-BF Iroquois	13560	AE-413 73-22077	23. 7.85	Butane Buzzard Aviation Corporation Ltd Bournemouth (To Bournemouth Aviation Museum 1.00)		12. 4.00P
G-HUFF	Cessna 182P Skylane II (Reims-assembled with c/n 0033)	182-64076	PH-CAS N6059F	31.10.78	A.E.G.Cousins (Op Seawing Flying Club)	Southend	8. 5.00T
G-HUGG	Gates Learjet 35A	35A-432	VR-CAD N330BC/N4445Y/F-GDCN	9. 4.96	1427 Ltd (A & D Crosland/Airtours plc) Manchester/Jersey		11. 4.00T
G-HUGO	Colt 260A HAFB	2559		20. 1.94	P.G.Hall t/a Adventure Ballooning	Chard	12. 5.00T
G-HULL	Reims Cessna F.150M	1255	PH-TGR	19. 1.79	A.D.McLeod	Linley Hill, Leven	21. 4.01T
G-HUMF	Robinson R-22 Beta	0534	N23743	18. 2.86	Plane Talking Ltd (Op Cabair)	Elstree	25. 6.01T
G-HUNI	Bellanca 7GCBC Scout	541-73	OO-IME D-EIME	21.10.96	T.I.M.Paul	Denham	16.12.99T
G-HUNK	Lindstrand LBL 77A HAFB	551		9. 9.98	Lindstrand Balloons Ltd	Oswestry	23. 9.00A
G-HUNY	Reims Cessna F.150G	0157	G-AVGL	27. 6.83	M.P.Lynn	Sibson	18. 4.88T
					(Damaged in storms Denham 16.10.87; stored 5.98)		
G-HURI	Hawker (CCF) Hurricane XIIA (IIB)	72036	RCAF 5711	9. 6.83	Patina Ltd (Op The Fighter Collection: as "Z???1/XR-T" in 71 Sqn RAF c/s)	Duxford	6. 5.00P
	(Composite - probably includes parts from c/n 44019/RCAF 5424, RCAF 5625 and RCAF 5547)						
G-HURN	Robinson R-22 Beta	1441		18. 7.90	Coventry Helicopter Centre Ltd	Coventry	5. 9.99T
G-HURR	Hawker Hurricane XII (IIB) (Built CCF)	52024	RCAF5589	30. 7.90	R.A.Fleming (As "AL-K")	Breighton	6. 4.00P
G-HURY	Hawker Hurricane IV	-	(Israel) Yugoslav AF/KZ321	31. 3.89	Patina Ltd (B J S Grey/The Fighter Collection)	Duxford	AC
	(RAF p/i unlikely as KZ321 was written off 23.5.43; frame off-site - unmarked wings only 1.99)						
G-HUTT	Denney Kitfox mk.2 (Rotax 582)	509 & PFA/172-11634		24. 1.90	P.A. Banks	(Milton Keynes)	30. 7.98P
G-HVAN	Tiger Cub RL5A LW Sherwood Ranger	PFA/237-13074		10.12.98	H.T.H.Van Neck	(Wirral)	
G-HVBF	Lindstrand LBL-210A HAFB	372		23. 5.96	Virgin Balloon Flights Ltd	(London SE16)	21. 4.00T
G-HVDM	VS.361 Spitfire LF.IXc	CBAF.IX.1732	8633M	18. 1.91	H.Wade & P.R.Monk & J.J.Van Egmond R.Neth AF 3W-17/H-25/MK732 Biggin Hill/Lelystad, The Netherlands t/a Nostalgic Flying "Baby Bea V" (Op Dutch Spitfire Flt as "MK732/OU-U" in 485 Sqn c/s)		2. 3.00P
G-HVIP	Hawker Hunter T.68	HABL-003215 G-9-415/Fv.34080/G-9-56	J-4208	7. 7.95	Golden Europe Jet De Luxe Club Ltd (Op Dr.Karl Theurer)	Bournemouth	4. 5.00P
G-HVRD	PA-31-350 Navajo Chieftain	31-7305052	G-BEZU SE-GDP	11. 6.87	London Flt Centre (Stansted) Ltd t/a Love Air	Biggin Hill	13.11.97T
G-HVRS*	Robinson R-22 Beta	1225		22.12.89	M.D.Thorpe t/a Yorkshire Helicopters	Coney Park, Leeds	29.10.99T
					(Damaged at RAF Church Fenton 19.7.98: cancelled as destroyed 23.11.99)		
G-HWKR	Colt 90A HAFB	1610		4.12.89	P.A.Henderson "Hawker Siddeley"	Stratford-upon-Avon	18. 4.99T
G-HYHY	PA-46-350P Malibu Mirage	4636131		13. 8.97	Longslow Dairy Ltd	Seething	21. 1.01
G-HYLT	PA-32R-301 Saratoga SP	32R-8213001	N84588	23. 4.86	H.Young Transport Ltd	Old Sarum	31. 1.02
G-HYST	Enstrom 280FX Shark	2082		9. 7.98	Ocean Shields Ltd	(Newton Abbot)	16. 8.01

G-IAAA – G-IZZZ

Regn	Type	C/n	P/I	Date	Owner/operator	Probable Base	CA Expy
G-IAFT	Cessna 152 II	152-85123	EI-BVW N6093Q	20. 6.95	Marnham Investments Ltd (Op Woodgate Executive Air Services)	Aldergrove	22. 7.01T
G-IAGD	Robinson R-22 Beta	0918	N2018Y G-DRAI/N8808V	16.11.99	Ramsgill Aviation Ltd	(Pudsey)	
G-IAMP	Cameron H-34 HAFB	2541		11. 3.91	Virgin Airship & Balloon Co Ltd	Telford	14. 6.97A

Regn	Type	C/n	P/I	Date	Owner/operator	Probable Base	CA Expy
					"National Power"		
G-IANG	Bell 206L Long Ranger	45132	SE-HSV	22. 1.98	Lothian Helicopters Ltd	East Fortune	29.1.01T
			PH-HMH/N16845				
G-IANJ	Reims Cessna F.150K	0548	G-AXVW	19. 5.98	B.Murelli	Thurrock	31. 7.01T
G-IARC	Stoddard-Hamilton Glastar			9.11.99	A.A.Craig	(Kilwinning)	
		PFA/295-13261					
G-IASL	Beechcraft 60 Duke	P-21	G-SING	18. 4.97	Applied Sweepers Ltd	Perth	13. 4.01
			D-IDTA/SE-EXT				
G-IBBC	Cameron Sphere 105SS HAFB	4082		2. 4.97	Virgin Airship & Balloon Co Ltd	Telford	29. 7.00A
G-IBBO	PA-28-181 Archer II	28-7790107	D-EPCA	17.12.98	M.Gibbon	Elstree	6. 1.02
			N5389F				
G-IBBS	Europa Avn Europa	PFA/247-12745		8. 9.94	R.H.Gibbs	Popham	14. 4.00P
G-IBED	Robinson R-22 Alpha	0500	G-BMHN	7. 9.93	B.C.Seedle	Blackpool	30. 9.94
			N50022		t/a Brian Seedle Helicopters		
G-IBET	Cameron Can 70SS HAFB	1625		25. 1.88	M.R.Humphrey & J.R.Clifton	Brackley	15. 8.97A
					"Carling Black Label"		
G-IBFC	Quad City Challenger II			9.11.98	K.N.Dickinson	(Lytham St. Annes)	
		PFA/177B-13369					
G-IBFW	PA-28R-201 Arrow III	28R-7837235	N31534	22. 1.79	A.W.Collett	Turweston	25. 8.00T
G-IBHH	Hughes 269C	74-0327	G-BSCD	20. 8.99	The Hughes Helicopter Co Ltd	Biggin Hill	29. 5.00T
			PH-HSH/SE-HFG		t/a Biggin Hill Helicopters		
G-IBRO	Reims Cessna F.152 II	1957	EI-BRO	11.10.95	Leicestershire Aero Club Ltd	Leicester	4. 3.02T
G-IBZS	Cessna 182S Skylane	18280529	N7269A	11.12.99	Oxford Aviation Services Ltd	Oxford	9.12.02T
G-ICAB	Robinson R-44 Astro	0086		28.11.94	JR Clark Ltd	Culverthorpe, Grantham	14.12.00
G-ICAS	Aviat Pitts S-2B Special	5344	N511P	19. 6.97	J.C.Smith	Sherburn-in-Elmet	10. 7.00T
G-ICCL	Robinson R-22 Beta	1608	G-ORZZ	25.11.93	G.Kidger	Gamstom	6. 2.00T
G-ICES	Thunder Ax6-56 SP.1 HAFB	283		3. 7.80	British Balloon Museum & Library Ltd		
	(Ice Cream special shape)					Newbury	3. 6.94A
G-ICEY	Lindstrand LBL-77A HAFB	043		11. 8.93	G.C.Elson	(Malaga, Spain)	9. 7.00A
G-ICFR	BAe 125 Srs.800B	258050	N9LR	23.11.94	Chauffair (CI) Ltd	Heathrow/Farnborough	1.12.00T
			G-5-503/I-OSLO/G-5-503/G-BUCR/HZ-OFC/G-5-503				
G-ICKY	Lindstrand LBL-77A HAFB	029		19. 5.93	Blown Away UK Ltd	Shrewsbury	3. 5.00A
G-ICOI	Lindstrand LBL-105A HAFB	564		3.11.98	Virgin Airship & Balloon Co Ltd	Telford	12.11.99A
					(ICO titles)		
G-ICOM	Reims Cessna F172M Skyhawk II	1212	G-BFXI	25. 4.94	C G Elesmore	(Folkestone)	23. 6.00
			PH-ABA/D-EEVC				
G-ICOZ	Lindstrand LBL-105A HAFB	565		3.11.98	Virgin Airship & Balloon Co Ltd	Telford	12.11.99A
					(ICO titles)		
G-ICSG	Aerospatiale AS.355F1 Twin Squirrel	5104	G-PAMI	6. 4.93	MW Helicopters Ltd	Ware	2. 5.00T
			G-BUSA				
G-IDAY	Skyfox CA-25N Gazelle	CA25N-028	VH-RCR	29. 4.96	The Anglo-Pacific Aircraft Co (UK) Ltd & G.Horne		
	(Rotax 912)					Glenrothes	23. 5.99T
G-IDDI	Cameron N-77 HAFB	2383		21. 8.90	Allen & Harris Ltd	Newbury	
					"Allen & Harris II"		
G-IDEA	Gulfstream AA-5A Cheetah	AA5A-0871	G-BGNO	7. 2.84	Lowlog Ltd (Op Cabair)	Elstree	16. 3.01T
G-IDII	DR.107 One Design	PFA 264/12953		16. 6.99	C.Darlow	(Stamford)	
G-IDUP	Enstrom 280C Shark	1163	G-BRZF	11. 5.92	Antique Buildings Ltd		
			N5687D			Hunterswood Farm, Dunsfold	31. 5.01
G-IDWR	Hughes 369HS	69-0101S	G-AXEJ	26. 5.81	Ainderfield Ltd	Tadcaster	25.12.00
					t/a Copley Electrical Continentalractors		
G-IEJH	SAN Jodel 150A Mascaret	02	G-BPAM	28. 2.95	E.J.Horsfall	Blackpool	26. 3.00P
			F-BLDA/F-WLDA				
G-IEYE	Robin DR.400/180 Regent	2123		29. 1.92	E.Hopper	Sherburn-in-Elmet	28. 6.01
G-IFAB	Reims Cessna F.182Q Skylane	0127	OO-ELM	6. 1.98	Chatham Glyn Fabrics Ltd	Southend	25. 5.01
			(OO-HNU)				
G-IFFR	PA-32-300 Cherokee Six	32-7340123	G-BWVO	1. 4.97	D.J.D. & G.D.Ritchie & J.C.Gilbert		
			OO-JPC/N55520			RAF Henlow	20. 3.00
G-IFIT	PA-31-350 Navajo Chieftain		G-NABI	31.12.85	Dart Group plc	Bournemouth	4.12.02T
		31-8052078	G-MARG/N3580C		(Op Channel Express)		
G-IFLI	Gulfstream AA-5A Cheetah	AA5A-0831	N26948	7. 7.82	ABC Aviation Ltd	Biggin Hill	17. 7.00T
G-IFDM	Robinson R-44 Astro	0707		24. 1.00	Bedgbury Aviation Ltd	(Maidstone)	
G-IFLP	PA-34-200T Seneca II	34-8070029	N81WS	4. 1.88	AD Aviation Ltd	Barton	19. 6.00T
			N81149				
G-IFTC	HS.125 Srs F3B/RA	25171	G-OPOL	21. 7.94	Albion Aviation Management Ltd	Gatwick	28. 7.01T
			G-BXPU/(N171AV)/G-BXPU/G-AXPU/G-IBIS/G-AXPU/HB-VBT/G-5-19				
G-IFTE	BAe HS.125 Srs.700B	257037	G-BFVI	16. 5.96	Albion Aviation Management Ltd	Gatwick	17. 8.02T
			G-5-18				
G-IFTS	Robinson R-44 Astro	0366		16. 9.97	Dawcroft Ltd	Blackpool	24. 9.00T
					t/a Colony Aviation		
G-IGEL	Cameron N-90 HAFB	2726		7. 4.92	Computacenter Ltd	London SE1	12. 5.97A
					"Computacenter II"		

Regn	Type	C/n	P/I	Date	Owner/operator	Probable Base	CA Expy
G-IGGL	Socata TB.10 Tobago	146	G-BYDC F-GCOL	26. 3.99	M & J S Perkin	White Waltham	2.12.01
G-IGHH	Enstrom 480	5034		1.12.98	G.H.Harding	(Whitchurch)	17.12.01T
G-IGLA	Colt 240A HAFB	2228		3. 7.92	M.L. & S.M.Gabb	Alcester	31. 3.97T
					t/a Heart of England Balloons (Barclaycard titles)		
G-IGLE	Cameron V-90 HAFB	2609		11. 6.91	A.A.Laing	Aberdeen	27. 6.00A
G-IGOA	Boeing 737-3Y0	24678	EI-BZK	16. 7.98	Orix Aviation Systems	Stansted	19. 7.01T
					(Leased Go Fly Ltd) (Torquoise c/s) "Go again/let's Go"		
G-IGOB	Boeing 737-3..	2.__..		. .98R	Go Fly Ltd	Stansted	
G-IGOC	Boeing 737-3Y0	24546	EI-BZH	1. 5.98	Orix Aviation Systems	Stansted	7. 5.01T
					(Leased Go Fly Ltd) (Purple c/s) "Go today/just Go"		
G-IGOD	Boeing 737-3..	2.........		. .98R	Go Fly Ltd	Stansted	
G-IGOE	Boeing 737-3Y0	24547	EI-BZI	19. 5.98	Orix Aviation Systems	Stansted	20. 5.01T
					(Leased Go Fly Ltd) (Pink c/s) "Go together/ready to Go"		
G-IGOF	Boeing 737-3Q8	24698	PK-GWF	2. 4.98	Go Fly Ltd	Stansted	3. 6.01T
					(Aqua Green c/s) "Go now/all Go"		
G-IGOG	Boeing 737-3Y0	23927	F-GLLE PT-TEK	3. 9.98	Go Fly Ltd	Stansted	3. 9.01T
					(Red c/s) "Go often/come and Go"		
G-IGOH	Boeing 737-3Y0	23926	F-GLLD PT-TEJ	6.11.98	Go Fly Ltd	Stansted	12.12.01T
					(Olive Green c/s) "Go for it/don't wait Go"		
G-IGOI	Boeing 737-33A	24092	G-OBMD	30.12.98	Go Fly Ltd	Stansted	13. 2.02T
					(Yellow Green c/s) "Go enjoy/away we Go"		
G-IGOJ	Boeing 737-36N	28872	N1795B	11.11.98	Go Fly Ltd	Stansted	20.11.01T
					(Medium Blue c/s) "Go anytime/free to Go"		
G-IGOK	Boeing 737-36N	28594		24. 4.99	Go Fly Ltd	Stansted	23. 4.02T
					(Purple Blue c/s) "Go as you are/get set Go"		
G-IGOL	Boeing 737-36N	28596	N1015X	26. 6.99	Go Fly Ltd	Stansted	25. 6.02T
					(Terracota c/s) "Go exploring/love to Go")		
G-IGOM	Boeing 737-36N	28599		13. 7.99	Go Fly Ltd	Stansted	12. 7.02T
					(Purple c/s) "Go for a break/off we Go"		
G-IGOP	Boeing 737-36N	28602		12. 8.99	Go Fly Ltd	Stansted	11. 8.02T
					(Pink c/s) "Go ahead/away we Go"		
G-IGOR	Boeing 737-36N	28606		22.10.99	Go Fly Ltd	Stansted	20.10.02T
					"Go to work/off you Go"		
G-IGPW	Eurocopter EC.120B	1027	G-CBRI	31. 7.99	Helihopper Ltd	Oxford	25. 5.02T
G-IHSB	Robinson R-22 Beta	0982		16. 3.89	M.Walker	Kington, Hereford	1. 2.01T
G-IIAC	Aeronca 11AC Chief (Continental A65)	11AC-169	(G-BTPY) N86359/NC86359	2. 7.91	P.K.Sheppard, E.C.Gale & N.E.Langford	Askerwell, Dorset	15. 3.00P
G-IIAN	Aero Designs Pulsar	PFA/202-12123		10. 9.91	I.G.Harrison	(Derby)	
G-IICM	Extra EA.300/L	100		19.11.99	Phonetiques Ltd	(Warrington)	24.11.02T
G-IIFR	Robinson R-22 Beta-II	2841		2. 9.98	R C Hields	Sherburn-in-Elmet	1.10.01T
					t/a Hields Aviation		
G-IIIG	Boeing-Stearman A75N1 (PT-17) Kaydet (Continental W670)	75-4354	G-BSDR N61827/42-16191	25. 3.91	Flight Incentives NV (Crunchie titles) "Annie"	Antwerp, Belgium	11. 5.00T
G-IIIH	BAC One Eleven 518FG	BAC.200	VP-BED VR-BED/LV-MEX/(G-AXMF)/PT-TYV/G-AXMF	17. 6.97	European Aviation Ltd	Bournemouth	4. 1.75
G-IIII	Pitts S-2B Special (Lycoming AEIO-540)	5010	N5330G	6. 1.89	B.K.Lecomber (Microlease titles)	Denham	20. 6.01T
G-IIIL	Pitts S-1T Special (Lycoming AEIO-360)	008	OH-XPT G-IIIL/N15JE	15. 2.89	The Sywell Boys Toy Box Ltd	Sywell	16. 8.00P
G-IIIR	Pitts S-1S Special (Lycoming IO-360)	604	N27M	21. 1.93	R.O.Rogers Hulcote Farm, Salford, Bucks		15. 9.99P
G-IIIT	Aerotek Pitts S-2A Special (Lycoming AEIO-360)	2222	N7YT	16. 1.89	Aerobatic Displays Ltd (Toyota titles)	Shoreham	13. 8.01A
G-IIIV	Pitts Super Stinker 11-260	PFA/273-13005		4. 2.97	G G Ferriman	(Nottingham)	
G-IIIX	Pitts S-1S Special (Lycoming O-360)	AJT	G-LBAT G-UCCI/G-BIYN/N455T	22. 5.89	G.C.J.Cooper (Damaged landing Egginton 7.5.99)	(Doncaster)	17. 3.00P
G-IIPM	Aerospatiale AS.350B Ecureuil	1790	G-GWIL	18.12.96	Fly West Aviation Ltd	(Clitheroe)	26.10.02T
G-IIRG	Stoddard-Hamilton Glasair IIS RG (Lycoming IO-360)	PFA/149-11937		29. 6.93	D.S.Watson	Fairoaks	27. 4.00P
G-IITI	Extra EA.300 (Lycoming O-360)	018	D-EFRR	12. 5.92	Aerobatic Displays Ltd (Nigel Lamb) (Lexus titles)	Booker	13. 8.01A
G-IIXX	Montgomerie-Parsons Two Place (Rotax 912)	PFA G/08-1225		13.10.93	J.M.Montgomerie (Unmarked 2.98)	(Maybole)	14. 6.94*
G-IIZI	Extra EA.300 (Rebuild Southern Sailplanes Ltd)	037	JY-RNB D-ETXA	12.12.96	P.J.Pengilly & S.G.Jones t/a 11-21 Flying Group (Fleet/Hungerford)		11. 2.01T
G-IJAC	Light Aero Avid mk.4 Speed Wing	PFA/189-12095		31.12.92	I.J.A.Charlton	(Petworth)	
G-IJBB	Enstrom 480	5010	G-LIVA	17. 9.99	J.B.Booth	Barton	2. 9.01

Regn	Type	C/n	P/I	Date	Owner/operator	Probable Base	CA Expy
			N900SA/G-PBTT/JA6169				
G-IJMC	VPM M-16 Tandem Trainer		G-POSA	10. 6.98	I.J.McTear	Carlisle	24. 2.00P
		VPM16-UK-106	G-BVJM				
G-IJOE	PA-28RT-201T Turbo Arrow IV		N8265X	14. 8.90	R.P.Wilson	Gamston	6. 7.02
		28R-8031178	N9599N				
G-IJYS	BAe Jetstream 3102	715	G-BTZT	5.10.92	Air Kilroe Ltd	Manchester	18.11.00T
			N416MX/G-31-715		"Flying Scotsman"		
G-IKAP	Cessna T303 Crusader	T303-00182	N63SA	4. 3.99	T.M.Beresford	Tibbenham	29..4.02T
			D-IKAP/N9518C				
G-IKBP	PA-28-161 Warrior II	28-8216132	N81762	16. 7.90	K.B.Page	Shoreham	25. 8.02
G-IKIS	Cessna 210M Centurion II	210-61754	N732TD	15. 5.78	A.C.Davison (Tzaneen, South Africa)		25.12.01
	(Reims-assembled with c/n 0002)						
G-IKPS	PA-31-310 Navajo C	31-7912098	D-IKPS	9. 8.96	Channel Aviation Ltd	Biggin Hill	24. 9.00T
			(N444BK)/D-IKPS/N3539G				
G-ILEA	PA-31-310 Navajo C	31-7812117	D-ILEA	7. 7.97	K.Payne	Sibson	13. 7.00
			N27775				
G-ILEE	Colt 56A Duo Chariot HAFB	2624		29. 7.94	G.I.Lindsay "Gillie"	Pulborough	6. 6.02A
G-ILES	Cameron O-90 HAFB	2360		29. 6.90	G.N.Lantos	Craven Arms	
					(Not built)		
G-ILGW	Cessna 404 Titan II	404-0690	D-ILGW	21. 1.98	Fraggle Leasing Ltd	Edinburgh	1. 2.01T
			N404MW/N25DC/N616R/(N6763Y)				
	(Crashed Linwood, west of Glasgow 3.9.99 shortly after take-off: burned out & destroyed)						
G-ILLE	Boeing-Stearman E75 (PT-13D) Kaydet		N68979	7. 3.90	J.Griffin	Compton Abbas	7. 6.02T
	(Continental W670)	75-5028	42-16865/Bu.60906 (As "379" in USAAC c/s)				
G-ILLY	PA-28-181 Archer II	28-7690193	SE-GND	21. 2.80	A.G. & K.M.Spiers Ltd		
						Hinton-in-The-Hedges	19.12.93
G-ILSE	Corby CJ-1 Starlet	PFA/134-10818		9. 1.84	S.Stride	Halfpenny Green	17.10.00P
	(HAPI Magnum 1915cc)				(F/f 13.9.99)		
G-ILTS	PA-32-300 Six	32-7940217	G-CVOK	28. 3.90	P.G.Teasdale	Boonhill, Fadmoor	6.10.01T
			OE-DOH/N2941C				
G-ILYS	Robinson R-22 Beta	1142		5.10.89	London Helicopter Centre Ltd	Redhill	24.11.01T
G-IMAG	Colt 77A HAFB	1718		9. 3.90	Flying Pictures Ltd "Agfa"	Fairoaks	19. 1.00A
	(Second envelope c/n 2254 as c/n 1718 dbf 6.92)						
G-IMAN	Colt 31A Sky Chariot HAFB	2605		23. 6.94	Benedikt Haggeney GmbH		
						Ennigerloh, Germany	16. 2.00A
G-IMAX	Cameron O-120	2201	PH-VVJ	?. 5.98	Not known	NK	
G-IMBY	Pietenpol Air Camper	PFA/47-12402		22.12.93	P.F.Bockh	(Horsham)	
G-IMGL	Beechcraft B200 Super King Air		VP-CMA	9. 8.99	IM Aviation Ltd.	Coventry	16. 8.00T
		BB-1564	N205JT				
G-IMLI	Cessna 310Q	310Q-0491	G-AZYK	3. 4.86	M.V.Rijkse & N.M.R.Richards	Oxford	30. 4.00T
			N4182Q				
G-IMOK	Hoffmann HK-36R Super Dimona	36317	I-NELI	31. 7.97	A.L.Garfield	Dunstable	3. 8.00
			OE-9352				
G-IMPX	Rockwell Commander 112B	512	N1304J	25.10.90	T.L. & S.Hull	Aberdeen	10. 4.00
G-IMPY	Light Aero Avid Flyer C			10. 4.89	T.R.C.Griffin	Haverfordwest	3. 8.99P
	(Rotax 532)	PFA/189-11439					
G-IMVA	PA-28-181 Archer III	2843222	SE-KIH	17. 9.99	IMVA Holdings Ltd	(Brough)	27. 9.02T
			N9524N/N4166F				
G-INAV	Aviation Composites Europa	AC.001		23. 2.87	I.Shaw	(York)	AC
G-INCA	Glaser-Dirks DG-400	4-199		22. 1.87	J.S.Wand "CA"	Gloucestershire	31. 3.02
G-INCH	Montgomerie-Bensen B.8MR		G-BRES	20. 8.91	I.H.C.Branson	Great Orton	17. 8.95P
	(Rotax 532)	PFA G/01A-1117					
G-INDC	Cessna T303 Crusader	T303-00122	G-BKFH	28. 6.83	Godolphin Management Co Ltd	Newmarket	19. 5.01
			N4766C				
G-INDY	Robinson R-44 Astro	0071		11. 7.94	Reynard Racing Cars Ltd	Sywell	19.10.00
G-INGA	Thunder Ax8-84 HAFB	2149		16. 6.92	M.L.J.Ritchie	Weybridge	14. 9.94A
G-INGE	Thruster T600N	9039-T600N-033		23. 2.99	Thruster Air Services Ltd	(Wantage)	8. 9.00P
G-INGR	Reims Cessna F.150J	0492	G-AWXU	1. 8.96	R.M.Hughes & A.M.Duffill	North Weald	12. 8.02T
G-INKS	Robinson R-22 Beta	2357	N64038	25.11.99	The Ink Shop Printing & Colour Copy Centre Ltd		
			OO-CMQ/N8020Q			Glasgow	16.12.02
G-INNI	Wassmer Jodel D.112	540	F-BHPU	30. 8.94	R.G.Andrews	Damyns Hall, Upminster	15. 8.00P
G-INNY	Replica Plans SE.5A	PFA/20-10439		18.12.78	K.S.Matcham	Goodwood	14. 5.00P
	(Continental C90)				(As "F5459/Y" in RFC c/s)		
G-INOW	ARV Monnett Moni 223 &	PFA/142-10953		30. 3.84	W.C.Brown	Fairoaks	20. 8.88P
	(KFM 107)				(Stored 8.97)		
G-INSR	Cameron N-90 HAFB	4320		23. 4.98	M.J.Betts & The Smith & Pinching Group Ltd		
						(Norwich)	20. 4.99
G-INVU	Agusta-Bell 206B JetRanger II	8530	G-XXII	1. 3.95	Burman Aviation Ltd	Cranfield	28. 3.00T
			G-GGCC/G-BEHG				
G-IOCO	Beechcraft 58 Baron	TH-1783		6. 6.96	Sea & Air Charter Ltd	Blackbushe	20. 6.02
G-IOCS	Short SD.3-30 Var.100	SH.3057	G-BIFH	25. 7.96	Air Tabernacle Ltd	Southend	10.10.98T

Regn	Type	C/n	P/I	Date	Owner/operator	Probable Base	CA Expy
			N488NS/LV-OJH/G-BIFH (To Fire dump & burnt by 5.99)				
G-IOIO	Bell 206B Jet Ranger III	4359	N47EA	11. 4.96	Lynton Air Ltd	Denham	13. 5.02T
G-IOOI	Robin DR.400/160 Major 80	1700		31. 5.85	N.B.Mason & S.J.O'Rourke	Rendcomb	11.11.01
G-IOPT	Cessna 182P Skylane	182-61731	N182EE	9. 6.98	M.J.Valentine & P.R.Davis	Biggin Hill	7. 7.01
			D-ECVM/N21585				
G-IORG	Robinson R-22 Beta	1679	OH-HRU	28. 1.00	G.M.Richardson	(Market Deeping)	
			G-ZAND		t/a Commission-Air		
G-IOSI	CEA Jodel DR.1050 Sicile	526	F-BLRS	6.10.80	G.A.Saxby	Bidford	25. 6.02
					t/a Sicile Flying Group		
G-IOWE	Europa Avn Europa XS	PFA/247-13303		30. 7.99	P.A.Lowe	(Wolverhampton)	
G-IPSI(2)	Grob G-109B	6425	G-BMLO	29. 5.86	G-IPSI Ltd	Woodford	31. 3.02
G-IPSY	Rutan VariEze 1512 & PFA/74-10284		(G-IPSI)	19. 6.78	R.A.Fairclough	Biggin Hill	5. 7.00P
	(Continental PC60)						
G-IPUP	Beagle B.121 Pup 2	B121-036	HB-NAC	17. 7.95	M.Sowerby	Elstree	15.10.01T
			G-35-036				
G-IRAF	Rotary Air Force RAF 2000 GTX-SE			17. 6.96	M.S.R.Allen	(Oakham)	20. 4.00P
	(Subaru EJ22) PFA G/13-1278						
G-IRAN	Cessna 152 II	152-83907	OH-CKM	19. 8.97	E.Alexander	Andrewsfield	29. 1.01T
			C-GBJY/(N6150B)				
G-IRIS	Gulfstream AA-5B Tiger	AA5B-1184	G-BIXU	14.12.87	A.H.McVicar	Carlisle	22. 4.00T
			N4533N		(Op Carlisle Flight Centre)		
G-IRLY	Colt 90A HAFB	1620		28.12.89	S.A.Burnett & L.P.Purfield	Leicester	6. 8.94A
					"Air Canada Cargo II"		
G-IROY	Rotorway Exec 152	3525		24. 2.98	R.R.Orr	(Dromore, NI)	
	(RW-152)						
G-IRPC	Cessna 182Q Skylane II	182-66039	G-BSKM	15. 5.91	C.A.Morris	Top Farm, Royston	19. 7.02T
			N559CT/N759JV		t/a Barmoor Aviation		
G-ISCA	PA-28RT-201 Arrow IV	28R-8118012	N8288Y	12. 2.91	D.J. & P.Pay	Exeter	15. 4.00
			N9608N				
G-ISDB	PA-28-161 Cherokee Warrior II		G-BWET	19. 2.96	Action Air Services Ltd	White Waltham	22. 3.01T
		28-7716074	SX-ALX/D-EFFQ/N9612N				
G-ISDN	Boeing-Stearman A75N1 (N2S-3) Kaydet		N4197X	6. 2.95	D.R.L.Jones	Kemble	12. 3.02
		75-1263	XB-WOV/Bu.3486		(As "14" in US Army c/s)		
G-ISEH	Cessna 182R Skylane II	182-67843	G-BIWS	9.11.90	Hadsley Ltd	Thurrock	8. 5.00
			N6601N				
G-ISFC	PA-31-310 Turbo Navajo B	31-7300970	G-BNEF	23. 3.94	SFC (Air Taxis) Ltd	Stapleford	21. 9.00T
			N7574L				
G-ISIS	DH.82A Tiger Moth	86251	G-AODR	20.12.83	D.R. & M.Wood	Tunbridge Wells	29. 3.62
			NL779		(Crashed Nympsfield 18.9.61; on rebuild)		
G-ISKY	Bell 206B JetRanger III	3654	G-PSCI	5. 4.95	Kwik-Fit (GB) Ltd	Edinburgh	13. 4.00T
			G-BOKD/N3171A				
G-ISLA	BN-2A-26 Islander	206	PH-PAR	7. 5.97	Hoe Leasing Ltd	Cranfield	12. 6.00T
			G-BNEA/SE-FTA/G-51-206				
G-ISMO	Robinson R-22 Beta	0870	OH-HOR	14.10.88	R.C.Hields	Sherburn-in-Elmet	15. 7.02T
			G-ISMO/N8214T		t/a Hields Aviation		
G-ISTT	Thunder Ax8-84 HAFB	1787		12. 6.90	RAF Halton Hot Air Balloon Club		
					"RAF Halton"	RAF Halton	23. 6.00A
G-ITII	Aerotek Pitts S-2A Special	2223	I-VLAT	5. 7.95	Aerobatic Displays Ltd	Booker	13. 8.01A
	(Lycoming AEIO-360)						
G-ITOI	Cameron N-90 HAFB	4785		14. 1.00	Cameron Balloons Ltd	Bristol	
G-ITON	Maule MX-7-235 Star Rocket	10050C	N5670R	11. 9.96	J.R.S.Heaton Hawksbridge Farm, Oxenhope		19.12.02
G-IUAN	Cessna 525 CitationJet	525-0324	(N428PC)	30. 6.99	RF Celada SPA	(Milan, Italy)	7. 7.00
G-IVAC	Airtour AH-77B HAFB	012		28.11.89	T.D.Gibbs	Billingshurst	6. 7.00A
G-IVAN	Shaw Twin-Eze 39 & PFA/74-10502			11. 9.78	A.M.Aldridge	Norwich	5.10.90P
	(2 x Norton NR642)				"Mistress" (Stored 2.99)		
G-IVAR	Yakovlev Yak-50	791504	D-EIVI	24. 2.89	R.A.L.Hubbard & S.Whitcombe	(West Meon)	26. 5.00P
			(N5219K)/DDR-WQT/DM-WQT t/a Foley Farm Flying Group				
G-IVEL	Sportavia Fournier RF4D	4029	G-AVNY	29. 6.95	V.S.E.Norman	Rendcomb	14. 4.01A
					("St.Ivel/Utterly Butterly" titles)		
G-IVET	Europa Avn Europa	PFA/247-12511		23. 5.97	K.J.Fraser	(Abingdon)	
G-IVIV	Robinson R-44 Astro	0016	(N803EH)	2. 8.93	Rahtol Ltd	Sywell	16.10.02
G-IVOR	Aeronca 11AC Chief	11AC-1035	EI-BKB	18. 6.82	P.R.White & C.P.Matthews	Bodmin	10. 3.00P
			G-IVOR/EI-BKB/N9397E t/a South Western Aeronca Group				
G-IVYS	Parsons Two Place Gyroplane			11. 1.00	R.M.Harris	(Nottingham)	
		PFA G/08-1275					
G-IWON	Cameron V-90 HAFB	2504	G-BTCV	17. 2.92	D.P.P.Jenkinson "Twenty One"	Tring	21. 7.00A
G-IXCC	VS.361 Spitfire LF.IXe	-	(Fokker)	18. 5.88	Personal Plane Services Ltd	Booker	9.12.93P
			PL344 (Blue Max Movie Acft Museum as "PL344/Y2-B" in 442 Sqn RAF c/s)				
G-IYAK	SPP Yakovlev Yak.C11	171103	OK-JIM	12. 1.94	E.K.Coventry	Earls Colne	AC
			(Ex Jean Salis, France and Egyptian AF)				

Regn	Type	C/n	P/I	Date	Owner/operator	Probable Base	CA Expy
G-IZIT	Rans S-6-116 Coyote II (Rotax 912UL) PFA/204A-12965			7. 3.96	C.Wren	Larkins Farm, Laindon	12. 5.00P
G-IZZS	Cessna 172S Skyhawk	172S8152	N952SP	1. 7.99	Rankart Ltd	Hinton-in-The-Hedges	1. 7.02T
G-IZZY	Cessna 172R Skyhawk II	17280419	G-BXSF N9967F	7. 9.99	T.J.& P.S.Nicholson	Manston	28. 5.01T

G-JAAA – G-JZZZ

Regn	Type	C/n	P/I	Date	Owner/operator	Probable Base	CA Expy
G-JABA	Avtech Jabiru UL PFA/274-13297			14.12.99	A P Gornall	(Wokingham)	
G-JACK	Cessna 421C Golden Eagle III	421C-1411	N421GQ N125RS/N12028	29. 4.97	JCT 600 Ltd (Jack Tordoff)	Leeds-Bradford	28. 4.01
G-JACO	Avtech Jabiru UL PFA/274A-13371			14. 4.99	S.Jackson	Eshott	6. 9.00P
G-JACS	PA-28-181 Archer III	2843078	N9278J	15. 4.97	Vector Air Ltd	Fowlmere	1. 5.00T
G-JADJ	PA-28-181 Archer II (Originally built as c/n 2890240)	2843009	N49TP N92552	27. 7.99	D.J.Cooke	Old Sarum	28 .7.02T
G-JAHL	Bell 206B Jet Ranger III	3565	N666ST	2. 1.98	D.T.Gittins & J.A.Ruck t/a Jet Air Helicopters	Shobdon	22. 2.01T
G-JAJK	PA-31-350 Navajo Chieftain	31-8152014	G-OLDB OY-SKY/G-DIXI/N40717	16.12.99	Keen Leasing (IOM) Ltd	(IOM)	24. 7.00T
G-JAKE	DHC.1 Chipmunk 22	C1/0584	G-BBMY WK565	21. 1.80	K.Ritter	(Bangor)	11.12.01
G-JAKI	Mooney M.20R Ovation	29-0030		7. 2.95	A.Pound	(Leighton Buzzard)	31. 3.01
G-JAKS	PA-28-160 Cherokee	28-339	G-ARVS	2. 7.99	M & K Harper	Stapleford	7. 9.00
G-JALC	Boeing 757-225	22194		6. 3.95	Airtours Intl Airways Ltd	Manchester	22. 4.01T
G-JAMP	PA-28-151 Cherokee Warrior	28-7515026	G-BRJU N44762	3. 4.95	ANP Ltd (Op West London Aero Club)	White Waltham	19. 5.01T
G-JANA	PA-28-181 Archer II	28-7990483	N2838X	12. 2.87	C.Dashfield t/a Croaker Aviation	Stapleford	3. 6.02
G-JANB	Colt Flying Bottle SS HAFB (J & B Whisky Bottle shape)	1643		16. 2.90	Justerini & Brooks Ltd "Whisky Too"	London SW1	30. 9.96A
G-JANI	Robinson R-44 Astro	0110	D-HIMM	21. 7.95	Myraluck Transport Ltd	(Thurles, Ireland)	10.12.01T
G-JANK	PA-E23-250 Aztec C	27-2754	EI-BOO G-ATCY/N5640Y	24. 4.95	Liverpool Flying School Ltd (Keenair c/s)	Southend	30. 9.02T
G-JANN	PA-34-220T Seneca III	3433133	N9154W	23. 6.89	MBC Aviation Ltd	(Pluckley)	5. 8.01T
G-JANO	PA-28RT-201T Arrow IV	28R-7918091	SE-IZR N2146X	14. 5.98	Abertawe Aviation Ltd	Swansea	17. 6.01T
G-JANS	Reims Cessna FR.172J Rocket	0414	PH-GJO D-EGJO	11. 8.78	I.G.Aizlewood	Rush Green	6. 9.01
G-JANT	PA-28-181 Archer II (Originally built as c/n 28-8290117/N81992/YV-2234P; not delivered and re-manufactured as c/n 28-8390075)	28-8390075	N4297J	23. 2.87	Janair Aviation Ltd	Denham	17. 3.02T
G-JARA	Robinson R-22 Beta	1837		11. 6.91	J.A.R.Allwright	Clacton-on-Sea	18. 7.00
G-JASE	PA-28-161 Warrior II	28-8216056	N8461R	13. 2.91	Mid-Anglia Flight Centre Ltd t/a Mid-Anglia School of Flying, Cambridge	Cambridge	2. 7.01T
G-JAVO	PA-28-161 Warrior II	28-8016130	G-BSXW N8119S	17. 9.97	I.N.T.Thornhill	Wellesbourne Mountford	11. 6.00T
G-JAWZ	Pitts S-1S Special PFA/09-12846 (Lycoming AEIO-360)			6.11.95	A.R.Harding	(Ipswich)	18.10.00P
G-JAXS	Avtech Jabiru UL PFA/274A-13548			10.12.99	C A Palmer	(Marlborough)	
G-JAYI	Auster 5 J/1 Autocrat	2030	OY-ALU D-EGYK/OO-ABF	5. 2.93	Bravo Aviation Ltd (Op Air Atlantique)	Coventry	12. 8.02
G-JAZZ	Gulfstream AA-5A Cheetah	AA5A-0819	N26932	30. 3.82	R.W.Taylor t/a Jazz Club	Kings Farm, Thurrock	28. 9.02
G-JBDB	Agusta-Bell 206B Jet Ranger	8238	G-OOPS G-BNRD/Oman AF 602	11. 4.96	Brad Helicopters Ltd	Denham	21.12.-2T
G-JBDH	Robin DR.400/180 Regent	1901		17. 3.89	W.A.Clark	Rochester	23. 5.01
G-JBJB	Colt 69A HAFB	1274		26. 7.88	Justerini & Brooks Ltd "J & B Jeremy"	London SW1	27. 8.00A
G-JBPR	Wittman W.10 Tailwind PFA/31-11490			25. 5.89	P.A.Rose & J.P.Broadhurst	Walney Island	
G-JBRN	Cessna 182S Skylane	18280029	N432V G-RITZ/N9872F	11. 6.99	J.Byrne	(Reading)	9. 3.01
G-JBSP	Avtech Jabiru SP PFA/274B-13486			12.10.99	C.R.James	(Bacton, Norwich)	
G-JCAR	PA-46-350P Malibu	4636223	N4148N	17.12.99	Anglo American Airmotive Ltd	Bournemouth	21.12.02T
G-JCAS	PA-28-181 Archer II	28-8690036	N9093N (N170AV)/N9648N	12. 6.89	Charlie Alpha Ltd	Jersey	19. 6.01T
G-JCBA	Sikorsky S-76B	760352	N95UT N95LT/N120PP/N120PM	25.11.99	J.C.Bamford Excavators Ltd	East Midlands	AC
G-JCBG	Dassault Falcon 900EX	044	F-WWFG G-JCBG/F-WWFG	23. 7.99	J.C Bamford Excavators Ltd	East Midlands	22. 7.02

Regn	Type	C/n	P/I	Date	Owner/operator	Probable Base	CA Expy
G-JCBI	Dassault Falcon 2000	27	F-WWMM	13.11.96	JC Bamford Excavators Ltd	East Midlands	17.11.00
G-JCBJ	Sikorsky S-76C	760502		9. 7.99	JC Bamford Excavators Ltd	East Midlands	21. 7.00T
G-JCFR	Cessna 550 Citation II (Unit No.315)	550-0282	G-JETC N68644	14. 7.95	Chauffair Ltd	Farnborough	28. 2.00T
G-JCKT	Stemme S-10VT	11-004		8. 4.98	J.C.Taylor	(Castletown/IoM)	13. 5.01
G-JCUB	PA-18-135 Super Cub (L-21B-PI)(Frame No.18-3630)	18-3531	PH-VCH R.Neth AF R-103/54-2331	21. 1.82	Piper Cub Consortium (Jersey) Ltd	Jersey	21. 7.02
G-JCMW	Rand KR-2	PFA/129-11064		3. 2.99	M.Wildish & J.Cook	(Gainsborough)	
G-JDEE	Socata TB.20 Trinidad	333	G-BKLA F-BNGX	1. 5.84	A W Eldridge & J A Heard	Leicester	7. 9.02
G-JDEL	Jodel 150 Mascaret	112 & PFA/151-11276	G-JDLI	19. 9.95	K.F. & R.Richardson	(Solihull)	
G-JDIX	Mooney M.20B Mark 21	1866	G-ARTB	28.11.85	ADH Ltd	Tibenham	16. 1.00
G-JDTI	Cessna 421C Golden Eagle III	421C-1226	N42E	11. 8.87	MCP Aviation (Charter) Ltd (Op Hawkair)	Cambridge	23.12.99T
G-JEAD	Fokker F-27 Friendship 500	10627	VH-EWU PH-EXL	14.11.90	Jersey European Airways Ltd (Op BAC Express) "Midland Trader"	Jersey	21.11.02T
G-JEAE	Fokker F-27 Friendship 500	10633	VH-EWV PH-FSO	2. 1.91	BAC Leasing Ltd	(Horley)	15. 1.03T
G-JEAF	Fokker F-27 Friendship 500	10637	OY-SRD	2. 1.91	BAC Leasing Ltd	(Horley)	16. 9.02T
			G-JEAF/VH-EWW/PH-EXE (Dry leased to Eureca as I-JEAF by 10.99)				
G-JEAH	Fokker F-27 Friendship 500	10669	VH-EWY PH-EXL	21. 1.91	Jersey European Airways Ltd	Jersey	14. 2.00T
G-JEAI	Fokker F-27 Friendship 500	10672	VH-EWZ PH-EXS	18.12.90	Jersey European Airways Ltd	Jersey	16.12.02T
G-JEAJ	BAe 146 Srs.200	E-2099	G-OLCA G-5-099	20. 9.93	Jersey European Airways (UK) Ltd "Pride of Guernsey"	Exeter	17. 7.02T
G-JEAK	BAe 146 Srs.200	E-2103	G-OLCB G-5-103	18. 3.93	Jersey European Airways (UK) Ltd "Pride of Birmingham"	Exeter	20. 6.02T
G-JEAM	BAe 146 Srs.300	E-3128	G-BTJT	24. 5.93	Jersey European Airways (UK) Ltd	Exeter	23. 5.00T
			HS-TBK/G-11-128 "Pride of Jersey" (Mountain of the Birds/Benyhone Tartan t/s)				
G-JEAO	BAe 146 Srs.100	E-1010	G-UKPC	19. 9.94	Jersey European Airways (UK) Ltd		29. 4.02T
			C-GNVX/N802RW/G-5-512/PT-LEP/G-BKXZ/PT-LEP (Op Air France Express) Heathrow				
G-JEAP	Fokker F-27 Friendship 500	10459	9Q-CBI	13. 4.95	Jersey European Airways Ltd	Bournemouth	15. 6.01T
			OY-APF/9Q-CBI/PH-RUA/VH-EWR/F-BYAH/OY-APF/PH-EXD (Op Channel Express)				
G-JEAR	BAe 146 Srs.200	E-2018	G-HWPB	14.11.95	Jersey European Airways (UK) Ltd	Exeter	7. 4.01T
			G-6-018/G-BSRU/G-OSKI/N603AW (Air France c/s)				
G-JEAS	BAe 146 Srs.200	E-2020	G-OLHB	13. 2.96	Jersey European Airways (UK) Ltd	Exeter	13. 7.00T
			G-BSRV/G-OSUN/C-FEXN/N604AW (Air France c/s)				
G-JEAT	BAe 146 Srs.100	E-1071	N171TR	11.10.96	Jersey European Airways (UK) Ltd		23.10.02T
			J8-VBB/G-BVUY/B-2706/G-5-071 (Op Air France Express) Heathrow				
G-JEAU	BAe 146 Srs.100	E-1035	N135TR	30.12.96	Jersey European Airways (UK) Ltd	Exeter	24. 1.00T
			J8-VBC/G-BVUW/B-584L/B-2704/G-5-035				
G-JEAV	BAe 146 Srs.200	E-2064	N764BA	17. 6.97	Jersey European Airways (UK) Ltd	Exeter	19. 6.00T
			CC-CEN/N414XV/G-5-064/N404XV				
G-JEAW	BAe 146 Srs.200	E-2059	(N759BA)	21. 7.97	Jersey European Airways (UK) Ltd	Exeter	21. 8.00T
			CC-CEJ/N401XV/G-5-059/N401XV/G-5-059				
G-JEAX	BAe 146 Srs.200	E-2136	N136JV	16. 2.98	Jersey European Airways (UK) Ltd	Exeter	19. 2.01T
			C-FHAP/N136TR/N882DV/(N719TA)/N882DV/G-5-136				
G-JEBA	BAe 146 Srs.300	E-3181	HS-TBL	16. 6.98	Jersey European Airways (UK) Ltd	Exeter	27. 7.01T
			G-6-181/G-BSYR/G-6-181				
G-JEBB	BAe 146 Srs.300	E-3185	HS-TBK	26. 6.98	Jersey European Airways (UK) Ltd	Exeter	1.11.01T
			G-6-185				
G-JEBC	BAe 146 Srs.300	E-3189	HS-TBO	4. 6.98	Jersey European Airways (UK) Ltd	Exeter	1. 7.01T
			G-6-189				
G-JEBD	BAe 146 Srs.300	E-3191	HS-TBJ	14. 7.98	Jersey European Airways (UK) Ltd	Exeter	17. 9.01T
			G-6-191				
G-JEBE	BAe 146 Srs.300	E-3206	HS-TBM	28. 5.98	Jersey European Airways (UK) Ltd	Exeter	25. 6.01T
			G-6-206				
G-JECA	Canadair RJ100 (CL.600-2B19)	7345		29.10.99	Jersey European Airways (UK) Ltd	Exeter	28.10.02T
G-JECB	Canadair RJ100 (CL.600-2B19)	7393		.00R	Jersey European Airways (UK) Ltd	Exeter	
G-JEDA	DHC-8-311 Dash Eight	309	N394DC OE-LLW/C-GFHZ	23. 6.99	Jersey European Airways (UK) Ltd	Exeter	24. 6.02T
G-JEDB	DHC-8-311 Dash Eight	323	N395DC OE-LLX/C-GFEN	29. 7.99	Jersey European Airways (UK) Ltd	Exeter	28. 7.02T
G-JEDC	DHC-8-311 Dash Eight	532	C-GEOA	1.10.99	Jersey European Airways (UK) Ltd	Exeter	30. 9.02T
G-JEDD	DHC-8-311 Dash Eight	533		21.10.99	Jersey European Airways (UK) Ltd	Exeter	25.10.02T
G-JEDE	DHC-8-311 Dash Eight	534	C-GERL	25.11.99	Jersey European Airways (UK) Ltd	Exeter	2.12.02T
G-JEDH	Robin DR.400/180	2343		3. 2.97	J.B.Hoolahan	Lasham	14. 5.00
G-JEDX	DHC-8-200 Dash Eight	541		.00R	Jersey European Airways (UK) Ltd	Exeter	
G-JEDY	DHC-8-200 Dash Eight	542		.00R	Jersey European Airways (UK) Ltd	Exeter	

Regn	Type	C/n	P/I	Date	Owner/operator	Probable Base	CA Expy
G-JEET	Reims Cessna FA.152 Aerobat	0369	G-BHMF	10.12.87	A.S.Bamrah	Southend	18.10.01T
					t/a Falcon Flying Services (Op Willowair Flying Club)		
G-JEFF	PA-38-112 Tomahawk	38-79A0763		8. 3.79	T.E.Evans	Wellesbourne Mountford	15.10.95T
					(Stored 1.99)		
G-JEFS	PA-28R-201T Turbo Arrow III	28R-7703365	G-BFDG N47381	14. 4.97	Barneyline Ltd	Booker	23. 8.01
G-JEKP	Agusta-Bell 206B Jet Ranger III	8598	D-HMSF G-ESAL/G-BHXW	13. 2.97	K.Payne	Maxey, Peterborough	1. 4.00
G-JENA	Mooney M.20J (201)	24-1304	N1168D	5. 7.82	P.Leverkuehn	Antwerp-Deurne, Belgium	12.11.00
					t/a Mooney Partnership (To Mr.Allgeier)		
G-JENI	Cessna R182 Skylane RG II	R182-00267	N3284C	17. 9.87	R.A.Bentley	Stapleford	23. 4.00
G-JENN	Gulfstream AA-5B Tiger	AA5B-1187	N4533T	7.12.81	M.Reed t/a Shadow Aviation	(Boston)	21. 2.00T
G-JERS	Robinson R-22 Beta	1610		21.12.90	Preveda Ltd	Bristol	30. 4.00T
G-JESS	PA-28R-201T Turbo Arrow III	28R-7803334	G-REIS N36689	18. 9.95	N.E. & M.A.Bedggood	White Waltham	11. 5.00
G-JETG	Gates Lear Jet 35A	35A-324	G-JETN G-JJSG	5. 3.98	Gama Aviation Ltd	Fairoaks	28. 7.01T
G-JETH	Armstrong-Whitworth Sea Hawk FGA.6 (Composite with WM983/A2511)		"XE364" XE489	10. 8.83	P.G.Vallance Ltd	Charlwood	
G-JETI	BAe 125 Srs.800B	258056	G-5-509	9. 7.86	Ford Motor Co Ltd	Stansted	19.10.02T
G-JETJ	Cessna 550 Citation II (Unit No.171)	550-0154	G-EJET G-DJBE/(N8887N)	9. 2.93	Widehawk Aviation Ltd	Cambridge	15. 8.00T
G-JETM	Gloster Meteor T.7	-	VZ638	10. 8.83	P.G.Vallance Ltd	Charlwood, Surrey	
					(As "VZ638/HF" in RN/FRU c/s)		
G-JETP*	Hunting P.84 Jet Provost T.52A (T.4) (Possibly ex 105 not 107)	PAC/W/17635	Sing AF 355 S.Yemen AF 107 G-27-92 or 94/XP666	13.12.83	Shadow Valley Investments Ltd (S.Constantinides) (Cancelled by CAA 18.3.99)	Paphos, Cyprus	10.12.93P
G-JETU	Aerospatiale AS.355F2 Twin Squirrel	5450	VR-CET JA6623	18. 4.96	Helimand Ltd.	(London SE1)	22. 5.02T
G-JETX	Bell 206B JetRanger III	3208	N3898L	9. 2.88	Heli Charter Ltd	Manston	3. 3.00T
G-JETZ	MDH Hughes 369E (500E)	0450E	VR-HJI	26. 3.97	John Matchett Ltd	Oxford	5. 6.00
G-JFWI	Reims Cessna F.172N Skyhawk II	1622	PH-DPA PH-AXY	1. 9.80	Staryear Ltd	Barton	16.12.99T
G-JGMN	CASA I-131E Jungmann (Carries c/n plate 2104 in rear cockpit)	2011	E3B-407	17. 4.91	P.D.Scandrett	Rendcomb	16. 5.00P
G-JGSI	Cyclone Pegasus Quantum 15	7615		19. 4.99	J.G.Spinks	Swinford	18. 4.00P
G-JHAS	Schweizer Hughes 269C (300C)	S.1493		14. 9.90	Barton & Co (Farmers) Ltd		
						Hall Farm, Saundby, Retford	9. 1.03
G-JHEW	Robinson R-22 Beta	0672	N23677	20. 7.87	Burbage Farms Ltd	Hinckley	2.11.02
G-JIII	Stolp SA.300 Starduster Too (Lycoming IO-360)	2-3-12	N9043	27. 5.93	J.G.McTaggart	Cumbernauld	29. 4.00P
					t/a VTIO Company		
G-JILL	Rockwell Alpine Commander 112TC-A	13304	(OO-HPB) G-JILL/N8070R/HB-NCW	25. 7.80	P M & P A O'Hare	(Beverley)	6. 1.02
G-JIMB	Beagle B.121 Pup 1	B121-033	G-AWWF	7. 4.94	K.D.H.Gray & P.G.Fowler	Turweston	21. 9.01
G-JIMW	Agusta-Bell 206B JetRanger II	8440	G-UNIK G-TPPH/G-BCYP	4. 1.96	R.J.Watt (To Van Cauwelaert)	St.Pieters Leeuw, Belgium	4. 4.01T
G-JJAN	PA-28-181 Archer II	2890007	N9105Z	28. 3.88	Redhill Aviation Ltd	Redhill	1. 5.00T
					t/a Redhill Flying Club		
G-JLCA	PA-34-200T Seneca II	34-7870428	G-BOKE N21030	3. 9.97	C.A.S.Atha	(Saltburn-by-the-Sea)	29.10.00T
G-JLEE	Agusta-Bell 206B JetRanger III	8588	G-JOKE G-CSKY/G-TALY	10. 2.88	Lee Aviation Ltd	Booker	25. 6.00
G-JLHS	Beechcraft A36 Bonanza	E-2571	N8046U	30.11.90	I.G.Meredith	Lydd	16. 1.00
G-JLMW	Cameron V-77 HAFB	1768		23. 6.88	J.L.M.Watkins	Ivybridge	26. 2.99T
G-JLRW	Beechcraft 76 Duchess	ME-165	N60206	4.11.87	Moorfield Developments Ltd	Elstree	6. 1.00
G-JMAC	BAe Jetstream 4100	41004	G-JAMD G-JXLI	12. 6.92	British Aerospace (Operations) Ltd (Stored 7.97)	Prestwick	6.10.97A
G-JMDI	Schweizer Hughes 269C (300C)	S.1398	G-FLAT	24. 9.91	J.J.Potter	Sherburn-in-Elmet	2.12.01
G-JMTS	Robin DR.400/180 Regent	2045		29.11.90	J.R.Whiting	Exeter	7. 5.00
G-JMTT	PA-28R-201T Turbo Arrow III	28R-7803190	G-BMHM N3735M	8. 7.86	C.E.Passmore	Southend	25. 3.02
G-JNEE	Cameron R-420 Gas Balloon	4232		21.10.97	Bondbaste Ltd "J Renee" ?	Chicago, USA	
					(Damaged Rockford, Illinois, USA 31.12.97 on RTW attempt)		
G-JNNB	Colt 90A HAFB	2063		20.12.91	Justerini & Brooks Ltd "J&B"	London SW1	27. 7.00A
G-JODL	SAN Jodel DR.1050/M Excellence	99	F-BJJC	28. 4.86	P.A.Marsh	Old Sarum	26.11.99
					(Damaged Wharf Farm, Market Bosworth 10.10.98)		
G-JOEL	Bensen B.8M	PFA G/03-1300		6. 7.99	G.C.Young	Swansea	
	(C/n possibly incorrect as Bensen PFA series is "G/11")						
G-JOEY	BN-2A Mk.III-2 Trislander	1016	G-BDGG C-GSAA/G-BDGG	27.11.81	Aurigny Air Services Ltd "Joey"	Guernsey	26. 8.01T

Regn	Type	C/n	P/I	Date	Owner/operator	Probable Base	CA Expy
G-JOIN	Cameron V-65 HAFB	1257		8. 5.86	Derbyshire Building Society "Derbyshire Building Society"	Derby	31. 7.93A
G-JOJO	Cameron A-210 HAFB	2674		20. 9.91	Joanna Barber t/a Worcester Balloons	Ledbury	21. 3.00T
G-JOLY	Cessna 120 (Continental C85)	13872	OO-ACE	3. 9.81	B.V.Meade Garston Farm, Marshfield		16. 6.00P
G-JONB	Robinson R-22 Beta-II	2593		29. 4.96	J.Bignall Mistletoe Farm, Pinner/Denham		27. 5.02
G-JONE	Cessna 172M Skyhawk II	172-64490	N9724V	2.12.80	A.Pierce	Stapleford	13. 5.00
G-JONH	Robinson R-22 Beta	2170		3. 6.93	Scotia Helicopters Ltd	Cumbernauld	22. 6.02T
G-JONI	Reims Cessna FA.152 Aerobat	0346	G-BFTU	6. 7.84	Euroair Flying Club Ltd	Cranfield	15. 5.00T
G-JONO	Colt 77A HAFB	1086		22. 6.87	The Sandcliffe Motor Group Ltd "Sandcliffe Ford"	Stapleford, Notts	17. 9.95A
G-JONY	Cyclone AX2000 HKS	7503		12. 3.99	A.Parker	Rufforth	
G-JONZ	Cessna 172P Skyhawk II	172-76233	N97835	28. 9.89	Truman Aviation Ltd	Nottingham	26. 5.02T
G-JOON	Cessna 182D	182-53067	(N) G-JOON/OO-ACD/N9967T	9. 6.81	G.Jackson	Sibson	15. 7.01T
G-JOSS	Aerospatiale AS.350B Ecureuil	1205	F-WQJY 3A-…OG-WILX/G-RAHM/G-UNIC/G-COLN/G-BHIV	31. 8.99	M.Burby	(Jersey)	26. 9.02T
G-JOST	Europa Avn Europa	PFA/247-12916		17. 6.98	J.A.Austin	(Bangor)	
G-JOYS	Beechcraft 58 Baron	TH-1556	N1556U	4. 8.94	Dunmhor Transport Ltd (Crashed 1 nm SE Kulusuk airport, Greenland 26.7.99 & destroyed)	Cumbernauld	21.10.00
G-JOYT	PA-28-181 Archer II	28-7990132	G-BOVO N2239B	13. 2.90	John K.Cathcart Ltd	St. Angelo	30. 3.00T
G-JOYZ	PA-28-181 Archer III	2843018	N9262R	19. 1.96	S.W. & Joy E.Taylor	Biggin Hill	23. 1.02
G-JPMA	Avtech Jabiru UL	PFA/274A-13399		24. 5.99	J.P.Metcalfe	Lydd	7.11.00P
G-JPOT	PA-32-301 Saratoga SP	32R-8113065	G-BIYM N8385X	1. 8.94	S.W.Turley	Wickenby	22. 7.02T
G-JPRO	BAC.145 Jet Provost T.5A EEP/JP/1055	XW433		10. 8.95	Edwalton Aviation Ltd (As "XW433 in CFS c/s)	Humberside	15. 2.00P
G-JPTV	BAC.145 Jet Provost T.5A EEP/JP/1005	XW355		2. 5.96	M P Grimshaw	North Weald	26. 1.00P
G-JPVA	BAC.145 Jet Provost T.5A EEP/JP/953	G-BVXT XW289		22. 2.95	T.J.Manna t/a Kennet Aviation (As "XW289/73" in 1FTS c/s)	Cranfield	13. 5.00P
G-JRBH	Robinson R-22 Beta-II	2852		11. 8.98	B.C.Hunter & C.S.N.Eaton Trustees of Bernard Hunter	Edinburgh	7. 9.01T
G-JRSL	Agusta A.109E	11036		9.11.98	Perment Ltd	(Clitheroe)	22.12.01T
G-JSAK	Robinson R-22 Beta-II	2959		30. 6.99	S.M.& J.W.F.Tuke t/a Tukair Aircraft Charter)	Headcorn	12. 7.02T
G-JSAT	PBN BN-2T Turbine Islander	2277	G-BVFK	5. 2.98	A.Wright t/a Rhine Army Parachute Centre	Weston-on-the-Green	5. 3.01A
G-JSCL*	Rans S-10 Sakota 1289-075 & PFA/194-11781 (Rotax 532)			12. 4.90	Not known Emlyns Field, Rhuallt (Damaged Emlyns Field, Rhuallt 16.7.91; stored 9.96)		16. 5.92P
G-JSJX	Airbus A.321-213	0808	(EC-) D-AVZP	3. 4.98	Airtours International Ltd	Manchester	27. 4.01T
G-JSON	Cameron N-105 HAFB	2933		21. 5.92	Up & Away Ballooning Ltd High Wycombe "Jason"		1. 7.00T
G-JSPC	PBN BN-2T Turbine Islander	2264	G-BUBG	21.12.94	A.Wright t/a Rhine Army Parachute Centre	Sennelager, Germany	16. 1.00A
G-JSSD*	HP.137 Jetstream 3001	227	N510F N510E/N12227/G-AXJZ	14. 6.79	Museum of Flight	East Fortune	9.10.90S
G-JTCA	PA-23-250 Aztec E	27-7305112	G-BBCU N40297	29.12.80	J.D.Tighe t/a Eastern Air Executive	Norwich	2. 9.00T
G-JTPC	Aeromot AMT-200 Super Ximango	200-067		28. 5.97	J.T.Potter & P.G.Cowling t/a G-JTPC Falcon 3 Group	Dishforth	11. 6.00
G-JTWO	Piper J/2 Cub (Continental A65) (f/f 12.8.37)	1754	G-BPZR N19554/NC19554	23.10.89	A.T.Hooper & C.C.Silk Bericote Farm, Blackdown, Leamington Spa		3.10.00P
G-JTYE	Aeronca 7BM Champion (Continental C85) (Modified from 7AS standard)	7AC-4185	N85445 NC85445	26. 9.91	G.D.Horn Old Sarum (Damaged Longwood Farm, Southampton 2.8.98)		17. 6.99P
G-JUDE	Robin DR.400/180 Regent	1869		14.10.88	R.G.Carrell	Goodwood	7.12.00
G-JUDI	North American AT-6D-NT Harvard III (Regd with c/n "EX915-326165")	88-14722	FAP 1502 SAAF7439/EX915/41-33888	17.11.78	A.A.Hodgson (As "FX301/FD-NQ")	Bryngwyn Bach	13.12.00P
G-JUDY	Grumman-American AA-5A Cheetah	AA5A-0620	(G-BFWM) N26480	31. 8.78	Plane Talking Ltd	Biggin Hill	22.11.02T
G-JUIN	Cessna T303 Crusader	T303-00014	OO-PEN N9401T	29. 2.88	M.J.Newman	Denham	8. 5.00
G-JULS	Stemme S-10V	14-028	D-KGDC	12. 6.97	J.P.C.Fuchs	Rufforth	18. 6.00
G-JULU	Cameron V-90 HAFB	3611		7. 7.95	Datacentre Ltd	Bristol	2. 8.97A
G-JULZ	Europa Avn Europa	PFA/247-13045		8.10.96	M.Parkin	(Doncaster)	
G-JUNG	CASA I-131E Jungmann	1121	E3B-143	23.11.88	K.H.Wilson (As "E3B-143" in Spanish AF c/s)	White Waltham	10. 3.99P
G-JURE	Socata TB.10 Tobago	597	N106U	6.11.92	P.M.Ireland South Lodge Farm, Widmerpool		14. 1.01

Regn	Type	C/n	P/I	Date	Owner/operator	Probable Base	CA Expy
G-JURG	Rockwell Commander 114A GT (Laid-down as c/n 14449)	14516	N4752W	19. 9.79	R.D., S.R. & N.Spencer Fenland t/a Blue Line Trailers (To P J Taylor)		6. 4.01
G-JVBF	Lindstrand LBL-210A HAFB	265		5. 6.95	Virgin Balloon Flights Ltd (London SE16)		24. 3.00T
G-JVMD	Cessna 172N Skyhawk II	172-67794	G-BNTV N75539	7. 2.92	C.A.Morris Top Farm, Royston		30.11.02T
G-JWBB	CEA Jodel DR.1050 Sicile	534	G-LAKI F-BLZD	17. 8.92	B.F.Baldock Maypole Farm, Chislet		30. 6.02
G-JWBI	Agusta-Bell 206B Jet Ranger II	8435	G-RODS G-NOEL/G-BCWN	3. 4.96	J.W.Bonser (Walsall) Ltd Walsall		13. 4.02T
G-JWCM	Scottish Avn Bulldog 120/1210	BH120-408	G-BHXB Botswana DF OD2/G-BHXB	19.10.99	M.L.J.Goff (Norwich)		23. 4.98T
G-JWDG	Grumman-American AA-5A Cheetah	AA5A-0662	G-OCML G-JAVA/N26705	9.10.91	Lowlog Ltd Thruxton		20.11.00T
G-JWDS	Reims Cessna F.150G	0216	G-AVNB	15.12.88	C.R. & S.A.Hardiman Shobdon		29. 9.94T
G-JWFT	Robinson R-22 Beta	0989		16. 3.89	R.C.Kelly (Withernsea) t/a Giles Bros		10. 5.01
G-JWIV	CEA Jodel DR.1051 Sicile	431	F-BLMD	6. 9.78	C.M.Fitton (Stoke Fleming) (Damaged Hobbynoor Cross, Coldridge, Devon 23.9.95)		22.10.95
G-JWLS	Bell 206B JetRanger	1114	G-BSXE N40EA/C-GMVM/N83150	8. 1.99	W.Lowry t/a J.W.L.Services (Bromley)		29.12.99T

G-KAAA – G-KZZZ

Regn	Type	C/n	P/I	Date	Owner/operator	Probable Base	CA Expy
G-KADY	Rutan LongEz	PFA/74A-11094		3. 9.85	M.W.Caddy (Mansfield)		
G-KAFC*	Cessna 152 II	152-84394	N6443L	24. 8.81	Not known Biggin Hill (Damaged Biggin Hill 16.10.87; spares use 12.95)		15. 4.90T
G-KAFE	Cameron N-65 HAFB	1505		18. 5.87	M.Sarti Fowey		11. 3.00A
G-KAIR	PA-28-181 Archer II	28-7990176	N3075D	28.12.78	Belfast Flying Club Ltd Belfast		3. 9.00
G-KAMM	Hawker CCF Hurricane XIIA CCF/R32007		BW881	23. 2.95	Alpine Deer Group Ltd Wananka, NZ (On rebuild 11.99 for American Flying Heritage Collection, Seattle, Washington)		
G-KAMP	PA-18-135 Super Cub (L-18C)	18-3451	D-EDPM 96+27/NL+104/AC+502/AS+501/54-751	9. 5.97	P.R.Edwards & E.Alexander Kings Farm, Thurrock		30. 7.00T
G-KAOM	Scheibe SF.25C Falke	4417	D-KAOM	3. 2.98	E.Baker (Cambridge)		18. 2.02
G-KAPW	Percival P.56 Provost T.1 PAC/F/311		XF603	22. 9.97	T.J.Manna Cranfield (Op Kennet Aviation) (As "XF603/H")		17. 3.00P
G-KARA	Brugger MB.2 Colibri PFA/43-10980 (VW1834)		G-BMUI	1. 6.95	Cara L.Reddish Netherthorpe		17. 6.00P
G-KARI	Fuji FA.200-160 Aero Subaru	236	G-BBRE	19.12.84	I.Mansfield & F.M.Fiore Old Sarum		2. 4.00
G-KART	PA-28-161 Warrior II	28-8016088	N8097B	10. 7.91	Newcastle-upon-Tyne A/C Ltd Newcastle		12.11.00T
G-KARY	Fuji FA.200-180AO Aero Subaru	285	G-BEYP	28. 3.89	J A Davi s Old Buckenham t/a Kary-On Flying Group		11. 6.01
G-KATA	HOAC DV-20 Katana	20021	OE-CDV(1)	4. 2.94	Total Support Inc (UK) Ltd Belle Vue Farm, Yarnscombe		12. 1.00
G-KATE*	Westland WG.30 Srs.100	010		7. 7.83	Westland Helicopters Ltd Yeovil (Dumped 10.93)		16. 9.88T
G-KATI	Rans S-7 Courier PFA/218-12917 (Rotax 582)			5. 3.96	S.M. & K.E.Hall Netherthorpe		7.12.99P
G-KATS	PA-28-140 Cherokee Cruiser 28-7325022		G-BIRC OY-BGE	26. 8.83	A.G.Knight Old Buckenham t/a Airlaunch		17.11.02T
G-KATT	Cessna 152 II	152-85661	G-BMTK N94387	10. 6.93	Aerohire Ltd Halfpenny Green		1. 7.02T
G-KAUR	Colt 315A HAFB	2536		1. 3.94	Balloon School (Intl) Ltd Petworth t/a Balloon Safaris		7. 4.00T
G-KAWA	Denney Kitfox mk.2 PFA/172-11822 (Rotax 582)			11. 3.91	T.W.Maton Enstone (Damaged Wavendon, Bucks 30. 6.95)		5. 7.95P
G-KAWW	Westland Wasp HAS Mk.1	F9663	NZ3907 XT781	29. 3.99	T.J.Manna Cranfield t/a Kennet Aviation (Active 12.99)		27. .7.00P
G-KAXF	Hawker Hunter F.6A S4/U/3361 (Built AWA)		8830M XF515	20.12.95	T.J.Manna Cranfield t/a Kennet Aviation (As "XF515/R": stored 7.96)		21. 8.00P
G-KAXL	Westland Scout AH.1	F.9715	XV140	16.11.95	T.J.Manna Cranfield t/a Kennet Aviation (As "XV140")		12. 7.02P
G-KBAC	Short SD.3-60 Var.100	SH.3758	VH-MJH G-BPXL	2. 1.98	BAC Leasing Ltd Newcastle (Op Gill Airways)		21. 1.00T
G-KBKB	Thunder Ax8-90 Srs.2 HAFB	2089		30.10.91	G.Boulden "KB Cars" Aldershot		6. 9.00A
G-KBPI	PA-28-161 Warrior II	28-7816468	G-BFSZ N9556N	21. 5.81	Goodwood Road Racing Co Ltd Goodwood		1. 9.02T
G-KCIG	Sportavia Fournier RF5B Sperber 51005		D-KCIG	19. 6.80	J.R.Bisset Aboyne t/a Deeside Fournier Group		30. 3.00P
G-KDET	PA-28-161 Cadet	2841158	(SE-KIR) N91842	8. 8.89	Rapidspin Ltd Biggin Hill (Op Biggin Hill School of Flying)		22.11.01T

Regn	Type	C/n	P/I	Date	Owner/operator	Probable Base	CA Expy
G-KDEY	Scheibe SF-25E Super Falke	4325	D-KDEY	8. 1.99	J.French t/a Falke Syndicate	Aston Down	1. 3.02
G-KDFF	Scheibe SF-25E Super Falke	4330	D-KDFF	25. 4.83	K. & S.C.A.Dudley	Rufforth	25. 6.01
G-KDIX	Jodel D.9 (VW1600)	PFA/54-10293		23.11.78	D.J.Wells	Fenland	1. 6.00P
G-KDLN	LET Zlin Z.37A-2 Cmelak	19-05	OK-DLN	14. 8.95	J.Richards	Henstridge	27.10.02
G-KEAB*	Beechcraft 65-B80 Queen Air	LD-344	G-BSSL	3. 8.88	Northbrook College	Shoreham	27. 9.87T
	G-BFEP/F-BRNR/OO-VDE (Instructional airframe 8.97)						
G-KEAC	Beechcraft 65-A80 Queen Air	LD-176	G-REXY	3. 8.88	E.A.Prentice	Little Gransden	18. 9.89T
			G-AVN/D-ILBO		t/a G-KEAC Flying Group (Stored 11.96)		
G-KEEN	Stolp SA.300 Starduster Too (Lycoming IO-540)	800	PH-HAB (PH-PET)/G-KEEN/N800RE	19. 7.78	H.Sharp t/a Sharp Aerobatics	Eglinton	14. 9.00P
G-KEES	PA-28-180 Cherokee Archer	28-7505025	OO-AJV OO-HAC/N32102	29. 5.97	C.N.Ellerbrook	(Wymondham)	27. 8.00
G-KELC	PA-28-140 Cherokee	28-23328	G-AVLT N11C	27.10.99	P.J.Kelsey & H.Koffman	(London SE22)	16.11.00
G-KELL	Van's RV-6	PFA/181-12845		16. 5.95	J.D.Kelsall	Netherthorpe	14. 6.99P
G-KEMC	Grob G-109	6024	D-KEMC	19.10.84	D.L.H.Person, G.H.N.Chamberlain & R.S.Kiddy t/a Eye-Fly	Rattlesden	25. 2.00
G-KEMI	PA-28-181 Archer III	28-43180	N41493	28.10.98	R.B. Kempster	Fowlmere	
G-KENB	Air Command 503 Commander	PFA G/04-1153		7.11.89	K.Brogden	Heywood, Lancs	24. 9.93P*
G-KENI	Rotorway Exec 152 (RW 152)	3599		14. 3.89	A.J.Wheatley	Street Farm, Takeley	18 11 00P
G-KENM	Luscombe 8EF Silvaire (Continental C90)	2908	N21NK N71481/NC71481	9. 1.91	M.G.Waters	Compton Abbas	29. 9.00P
G-KENN*	Robinson R-22 Beta	0715		10.12.87	The Hangar Nightclub	Stamford, Lincs	1. 1.97T
				(Damaged Sandtoft 31.10.94; rebuilt to static condition)			
G-KERY	PA-28-180 Cherokee C	28-3049	G-ATWO N9021J	5.10.83	Seawing Flying Club Ltd & E.Alexander t/a General Aero Services	Southend	13. 4.01T
G-KEST	Steen Skybolt (Lycoming IO-360)	1	G-BNKG G-RATS/G-RHFI/N443AT	11. 6.91	B.Tempest t/a G-KEST Syndicate	Leicester	16.10.00P
G-KEVB	PA-28-181 Archer III	2843098	N9289E	29. 8.97	Palmair Ltd	Elstree	3. 9.00
G-KEVN	Robinson R-22 Beta	0781	G-BONX	5. 6.91	Helicopter Training & Hire Ltd	Belfast	22. 4.00T
G-KEYS	PA-23-250 Aztec F	27-7854052	N63909	6.10.78	T.M.Tuke & W.T.McCarter	Eglinton	4. 6.00T
G-KEYY	Cameron N-77 HAFB	1748	G-BORZ	14. 6.88	B.N.Trowbridge	Derby	4. 9.00A
G-KFAN	Scheibe SF-25B Falke	46301	D-KFAN	14. 5.96	R.G & J.A.Boyes	Eaglescott	29. 5.99
G-KFOX	Denney Kitfox mk.2 (Rotax 582)	298 & PFA/172-11447		11.10.88	I.R.Lawrence	Exeter	16.12.99P
G-KFRA	PA-32-300 Six	32-7840182	G-BGII N20879	9. 9.97	M.Drake & W.Rankin t/a West India Flying Group	Weston, Ireland	10.11.00
G-KFZI	Williams KFZ-1 Tigerfalck			2. 2.89	L.R.Williams	(Aberdare)	
	(Continental C90) PFA/153-11054 (Originally laid-down as Kestrel Sport c/n PFA/1530)						
G-KGAO	Scheibe SF-25C Falke 1700	44386	D-KGAG	30. 7.99	C.R.Ellis t/a Falke 2000 Group	(Bishops Castle)	8..8.02
G-KGMT	Aerospatiale AS.355F1 Twin Squirrel	5042	G-PASE N57818	7. 8.98	Police Aviation Services Ltd	Rochester	18. 7.02T
G-KHOM	Aeromot AMT-200 Super Ximango	200-091		5. 5.98	O.C.Masters & K.M.Haslett	Rufforth	4. 5.01
G-KHRE	Socata Rallye 150SV Garnement	2931	F-GAYR	25. 3.82	D.M.Gale & K.F.Crumplin	Dunkeswell	19.10.00
G-KIMB	Robin DR.300/140 Major	470	F-BPXX F-WPXX	23. 3.90	R.M.Kimbell	Sywell	8. 5.00
G-KIMM	Europa Avn Europa XS	PFA/247-13404		20. 7.99	P.A.D.Clarke	(Bradford-on-Avon)	
G-KINE	Gulfstream AA-5A Cheetah	AA5A-0896	N27173	20. 7.82	J.P.E.Walsh t/a Walsh Aviation (Op London School of Flying)	Biggin Hill	24. 7.00T
G-KIRK	Piper J3C-65 Cub (Frame No.12490)	10536	F-BBQC F-OAJF/Fr AF/43-29245	28. 2.79	M.J.Kirk	St.Donats	15. 9.99P
G-KISS	Rand Robinson KR.2 (VW1835)	PFA/129-10899		2. 8.83	E.A.Rooney	(Whitstable)	
G-KITE	PA-28-181 Archer II	28-8490053	N4338X	12. 4.88	L.G.Kennedy	Bournemouth	13. 4.98T
G-KITF	Denney Kitfox mk.1 (Rotax 532)	156	N156BH	10. 5.89	R.Burgun	Melbourne, Derby	10. 2.00P
G-KITI	Pitts S-2E Special (Lycoming IO-360)	002	N36BM	21. 6.90	B.R.Cornes "Super Turkey II"	RAF Colerne	15. 4.99P
G-KITS	Europa Avn Europa Tri-gear (Midwest AE100R)	003 & PFA/247-12844		13. 6.94	Europa Aviation Ltd	Wombleton	3.12.00P
G-KITT	Curtiss TP-40M Kittyhawk (Officially c/n quoted as "31423")	27490	F-AZPJ N1009N/N1233N/RCAF 840/43-5802	4. 3.98	Patina Ltd (Op The Fighter Collection)	Duxford	4. 7.00P
	(C/n 31423 was P-40N 43-23484/RCAF 877/N1009N(1) which was scrapped in 1965 when identity adopted by RCAF 840)						
	(As "49/Bengal Tiger" in US Army c/s)						

Regn	Type	C/n	P/I	Date	Owner/operator	Probable Base	CA Expy
G-KITY	Denney Kitfox mk.2 456 & PFA/172-11565			18. 8.89	T.Ringshaw	Nottingham	13.12.00P
					t/a Kitfox KFM Group		
G-KIWI	Cessna 404 Titan Courier II 404-0644		G-BHNI	25. 1.90	Aviation Beauport Ltd	Jersey	5. 2.00T
			LN-LGM/SE-IFV/G-BHNI/(N5302J)				
G-KKDL	Socata TB.20 Trinidad	1096	G-BSHU	3.12.90	M.S.Thompson	Old Buckenham	15. 8.02
G-KKER	Avtech Jabiru UL	PFA/274A-13474		1.10.99	K.Kerr	(Wirral)	
					(Cf/f 20.12.99)		
G-KKES	Socata TB.20 Trinidad	1316	G-BTLH	2. 3.92	Polestar Holdings Ltd	Alderney	15. 4.01T
G-KLEE	Bell 206B JetRanger III	3370	G-SIZL	11.10.95	L.D.Taylor-Ryan	White Waltham	1. 4.01T
			G-BOSW/N2063T		t/a Taylor-Ryan Aviation		
G-KLIK*	Air Command 532 Elite PFA G/04-1113			21. 4.89	R.M.Savage	Penrith	6. 8.99P
	(Arrow GT500)				t/a Roger Savage (Photography)		
					(Cancelled by CAA 13.7.99 with curent Permit)		
G-KNAP	PA-28-161 Warrior II	28-8116129	G-BIUX	15. 2.90	Newland Aeroleasing Ltd	Humberside	28. 4.02T
			N9507N		(Damaged Stevensons Field, Letterkenny Co Donegal 13.7.99)		
G-KNOB	Lindstrand LBL-180A HAFB	065		20.12.93	Wye Valley Aviation Ltd	Ross-on-Wye	10. 2.00T
G-KNOT	Hunting Percival P.84 Jet Provost T.Mk.3A			9. 6.99	R.S.Partridge-Hicks	North Weald	24. 8.00P
		PAC/W/13893	G-BVEG/XN629		(As "XN629/49" in RAF c/s)		
G-KNOW	PA-32-300 Six	32-7840111	N9694C	21. 9.88	Hi Fly Ltd	(London W1)	15. 3.01
G-KODA	Cameron O-77 HAFB	1448		26. 3.87	N.J.Milton	Bristol	
					"Kodasnap"		
G-KOFM	Glaser-Dirks DG-600/18M	6-66M16	D-KOFM	13. 7.99	A.Mossman	(Kingussie)	
G-KOKL	Hoffmann H-36 Dimona	36276	D-KOKL	4. 3.98	R.Smith & R.Stembrowicz	Rufforth	30. 3.01
G-KOLB	Kolb Twinstar mk.3A	PFA/205-12228		30. 6.93	T.R.Sinclair	Insch	4. 8.99P
	(Rotax 912UL)						
G-KOLI	PZL-110 Koliber 150	03900038		23. 7.90	D.Sadler	Insch	17.10.99
G-KONE	Rotorway Exec 162F	6432		15.10.99	G.Kresfelder	(Horsham)	
G-KONG	Slingsby T-67M Firefly 200	2041	VR-HZP	24. 3.94	Hunting Aviation Ltd RAF Barkston Heath		3. 8.00T
			HKG-10/G-7-119				
G-KOOL*	DH.104 Devon C.2/2	04220	VP967	12. 1.82	East Surrey College		
					(Instructional airframe 4.93) Gatton Point, Redhill		
G-KORN	Cameron Berentzen Bottle70SS HAFB			10. 5.88	R.S.Kent, I M Martin & I Chadwick		
		1655			t/a Balloon Preservation Flying Group "Berentzen" Lancing		23. 6.00A
G-KOTA	PA-28-236 Dakota	28-8011044	N8130R	23.12.88	D.J.Fravigar t/a JF Packaging		
					Clough Farm, Croft, Skegness		18. 8.01
G-KPAO	Robinson R-44 Astro	0382	G-SSSS	19.11.98	Avonline Ltd	Bristol	20.11.00T
G-KRAY	Robinson R-22HP	0266	EI-CEF	25. 5.95	Direct Helicopters (Southend) Ltd		
			G-BOBO/N712BH/N100GV/N90763			Southend	11. 6.01T
G-KRES	Stoddard-Hamilton Glasair IIS RG			12. 6.96	G.Kresfelder	(London SW11)	
		PFA/149-12984					
G-KRII	Rand-Robinson KR-2	PFA/129-10934		4. 8.89	M.R.Cleveley	(Halesworth, Suffolk)	
G-KRIS	Maule M.5-235C Lunar Rocket	7357C	N56420	21. 4.81	Maggie Penny	Movenis, Co.Londonderry	26. 3.99
G-KSFT	PA-23-250 Aztec F	27-7854137	G-BLXX	10.11.99	SFT Europe Ltd	Bournemouth	18. 9.99T
			(G-BLVM)/G-PIED/N6534A				
G-KSIR	Stoddard-Hamilton Glasair IIS RG			15. 4.94	The Hon R.Cayzer	Oxford	1. 6.00P
	(Lycoming IO-360) 2151 & PFA/149-12137						
G-KSKY	Sky 77-24 HAFB	170		15.10.99	C.R.Kirby	Oswestry	16.11.00A
G-KSVB	PA-24-260 Comanche B	24-4657	G-ENIU	8.11.91	Janice R.Pettit	Stapleford	28. 5.01
			G-AVJU/N9199P				
G-KTEE	Cameron V-77 HAFB	2177		28.12.89	D.C. & N.P.Bull "Katie"	Aylesbury	28. 5.00A
G-KTKT	Sky 260-24 HAFB	110		19. 5.98	T.M.Donnelly	Doncaster	28. 4.00T
G-KUTU	QAC Quickie Q.2	PFA/94A-10758		8. 3.82	J.Parkinson & R.Nash	Booker	29. 4.86P
	(Limbach L2000)				(Damaged Cranfield 18.5.85; stored 6.98)		
G-KVBF	Cameron A-340HL HAFB	4313		6. 4.98	Virgin Balloon Flights Ltd	London SE16	17. 6.00T
G-KWAX	Cessna 182E Skylane	182-53808	N9902	18. 5.78	J.E. & V.T.Brewis	Swanton Morley	7. 4.03
			YV-T-PTS/N2808Y				
G-KWIK	Partenavia P.68B	152		27. 9.78	ACD Cidra NV	Wevelgem, Belgium	3. 6.00T
G-KWIP	Europa Avn Europa 27 & PFA/247-12557			26. 9.95	D.Elliott Holly Meadow Farm, Bradley		4. 7.00P
	(Rotax 912UL)						
G-KWKI	QAC Quickie Q.200	PFA/94-12158		22.10.91	B.M.Jackson	Enstone	17. 9.00P
	(Continental O-200-A)						
G-KWLI	Cessna 421C Golden Eagle II		G-DARR	13.11.98	Golden Eagle Haulage Ltd	Full Sutton	12.11.00
		421C-0168	G-BNEZ/N87386				
G-KYAK	SPP Yakovlev YAK C-11	171101	F-AZQI	21.12.78	M.Gainza	(London SW3)	3. 8.00P
			G-KYAK/F-AZHQ/G-KYAK/Israeli DFAF/Egyptian AF 590/Czech AF				
G-KYDD	Robinson R-44 Astro	0106	N2123E	16. 9.99	EK Aviation Ltd	(Bury St. Edmunds)	19. 9.02T
			D-HDLW				
G-KYNG	Aviamilano F.8L Falco 1	105	I-KYNG	6. 8.97	A E Hutton	North Weald	11. 2.01
			HB-UOH/I-STRI				

G-LAAA – G-LZZZ

Regn	Type	C/n	P/I	Date	Owner/operator	Probable Base	CA Expy
G-LABS	Europa Avn Europa	PFA/247-12595		1. 3.94	C.T.H.Pattinson	(Bicester)	
G-LACA	PA-28-161 Warrior II	28-7816036	N44883	22. 6.90	LAC (Enterprises) Ltd t/a Lancashire A/C	Barton	21. 2.02T
G-LACB	PA-28-161 Warrior II	28-8216035	N8450A	12. 6.90	LAC (Enterprises) Ltd t/a Lancashire A/C	Barton	29. 7.02T
G-LACD	PA-28-181 Archer III	28-43157	G-BYBG N47BK	11.11.98	A.W.Brown t/a Cavok Aviation	Barton	28. 9.01T
G-LACE	Europa Avn Europa	PFA/247-12962		15. 4.96	J.H.Phillingham	(Wallingford)	
G-LACR	Denney Kitfox	PFA/172-11945		4.12.90	C.M.Rose	(Edinburgh)	
G-LADE	PA-32-300 Six	32-7940030	N3008L	21.11.80	Telefax 2000 Ltd "Harry O"	Blackbushe	19. 2.99
G-LADD	Enstrom 480	5037		20. 5.99	Eastern Atlantic Helicopters	Shoreham	
G-LADI	PA-30-160 Twin Comanche	30-334	G-ASOO	8. 4.94	S.H.Eastwood	(Farnborough)	7. 9.02T
G-LADS	Rockwell Commander 114	14314	N4994W (N114XT)/N4994W	6.12.90	D.F.Soul	Emberton, Olney	5. 1.00
G-LAGR	Cameron N-90 HAFB	1628		25. 1.88	J.R.Clifton	Brackley	11. 9.00A
G-LAIN	Robinson R-22 Beta	1992		7. 2.92	Deadline Programming Ltd	(London SW6)	23. 4.01T
G-LAIR	Stoddard-Hamilton Glasair IIS	2106		12. 9.91	D.L.Swallow	(Norwich)	
G-LAKE	Lake LA-250 Renegade	70	(EI-PJM) G-LAKE/N8415B	12. 7.88	Stanford Ltd Lough Derg Marina, Killaloe (Op P.J.McGoldrick)		31. 8.01
G-LAMA	Aerospatiale SA.315B Lama	2348	SE-HET	17. 3.98	PLM Dollar Group Ltd	Cumbernauld	19. 3.01T
G-LAMM	Europa Avn Europa	PFA/247-12941		20.11.95	S.A.Lamb	(Paddock Wood)	
G-LAMS	Reims Cessna F.152 II	1431	N54558	23. 6.88	Rentair Ltd (Op Essex Flying School)	Earls Colne	2.10.00T
G-LANC*	Avro 683 Lancaster B.X	-	RCAF KB889	31. 1.85	Imperial War Museum (As "KB889/NA-I" in 428 Sqn c/s)	Duxford	
G-LAND	Robinson R-22 Beta	0639		28. 4.87	Helicopter Training & Hire Ltd	Aldergrove	29. 3.02T
G-LANE	Reims Cessna F.172N Skyhawk II	1853		27. 6.79	G.C.Bantin	Sproatley	26. 5.00
G-LAOL	PA-28RT-201 Cherokee Arrow IV	28R-7918211	D-EAOL N2903Y	6.10.99	Phoenix House Developments Ltd (Reading) t/a Aviation 2000		
G-LAPN	Light Aero Avid Aerobat (Rotax 582)	PFA/189-12146		4. 3.93	R.M. & A.P.Shorter	White Waltham	26.10.98P
G-LARA	Robin DR.400/180 Regent	2050		14. 2.91	K.D. & C.A.Brackwell	Goodwood	23. 4.00
G-LARE	PA-39 Twin Comanche C/R	39-16	N8861Y	20. 2.91	Glareways (Neasden) Ltd	Biggin Hill	12. 6.00
G-LARK	Helton Lark 95	9517	N5017J	3.12.85	J.Fox	Booker	26. 3.00P
G-LASR	Stoddard-Hamilton Glasair II	2027		8. 1.90	G.Lewis	(Wirral)	
G-LASS	Rutan VariEze (Continental O-200-A)	PFA/74-10209		20. 9.78	S.Roberts	Enstone	27.10.00P
G-LAST	Cessna 340 II	340-0305	G-UNDY G-BBNR/N69452	2. 9.96	Last Engineering Ltd	Cambridge	30. 4.00
G-LATK	Robinson R-44 Astro	0064	G-BVMK	18. 7.94	Holly Aviation Ltd	Cambridge	27. 8.00T
G-LAVE	Cessna 172R Skyhawk	172-80663	G-BYEV N2377J/N41297	10. 3.99	R.W.& A.M.Glaves	(Chesterfield)	31. 3.02
G-LAWS	Sikorsky S-61N Mk.II	61-824	G-BHOF LN-ONK/G-BHOF/LN-ONK/G-BHOF	7. 7.99	Laws Helicopter Ltd	Biggin Hill	9. 7.01T
G-LAXY	Everett Gyroplane Srs.3	035 & PFA G/03-1233		17. 2.94	G.D.Western	(Ipswich)	
G-LAZA	Lazer Z.200 (Lycoming AEIO-360)	PFA/123-12682		15. 6.95	M.Hammond	Hardwick	15. 9.00P
G-LAZL	PA-28-161 Warrior II	28-8116216	D-EAZL N9536N	9. 6.99	S.Bagley & K.J.Amies t/a Hawk Aero Leasing	Cranfield	19. 7.02T
G-LAZR	Cameron O-77 HAFB	2240		6. 3.90	Laser Civil Engineering Ltd "Laser Engineering"	Pershore	10. 6.97A
G-LAZY	Lindstrand LBL Armchair SS HAFB	129		18. 9.94	The Air Chair Co Ltd "The Chair" Westville, Indiana, USA		9. 3.00A
G-LAZZ	Stoddard-Hamilton Glastar	PFA/295-13059		31.10.96	A.P.Hinchcliffe	(Kemble)	
G-LBCS	Colt 31A HAFB	1891		10. 1.91	Virgin Airship & Balloon Co Ltd "Lloyds Bank I"	Telford	13. 1.96A
G-LBLI	Lindstrand LBL-69A HAFB	010		4.11.92	N.M.Gabriel	Kimberley, Notts	22.10.99A
G-LBMM	PA-28-161 Warrior II	28-7816440	N6940C	28.11.89	Flexi-Soft Ltd	Hinton-in The-Hedges	25. 4.02
G-LBNK	Cameron N-105 HAFB	3559		20. 3.95	Virgin Airship & Balloon Co Ltd "Lloyds Bank"	Telford	25. 3.99A
G-LBRC	PA-28RT-201 Arrow IV	28R-7918051	N2245P	20. 7.88	D.J.V.Morgan	Halfpenny Green	3.12.00
G-LCGL	Comper CLA.7 Swift rep (Pobjoy Niagara 1A)	PFA/103-11089		1.7.92	J.M.Greenland	Blackacre Farm, Holt, Wilts	15.11.00P
G-LCIO*	Colt 240A HAFB	1381		23. 1.89	British Balloon Museum (Stored 12.94)	Newbury	

Regn	Type	C/n	P/I	Date	Owner/operator	Probable Base	CA Expy
G-LCON	Eurocopter AS.355N Twin Squirrel	5572		28. 6.94	Lancashire Constabulary Warton (Op Lancashire Air Support Unit)		19.10.00T
G-LCRC	Boeing 757-23A	24636	G-IEAB	27.10.93	Airtours Intl Airways Ltd Manchester		9. 5.02T
G-LDYS	Thunder Ax6-56Z HAFB (Regd as Colt 56A)	347		18. 5.81	P.Glydon & M.J.Myddelton "Gladys" Birmingham/Keynsham		27. 3.00A
G-LEAF	Reims Cessna F.406 Caravan II	0018	EI-CKY PH-ALN/OO-TIW/F-WZDX (Atlantic Airlines c/s)	7. 3.96	Atlantic Air Transport Ltd Southend		20. 5.00T
G-LEAM	PA-28-236 Dakota	28-8011061	G-BHLS N35650	1. 7.80	C.S.Doherty Gamston		8. 7.01
G-LEAP	PBN BN-2T Turbine Islander	2183	G-BLND	19. 8.87	G Burton AAC Netheravon t/a Army Parachute Association		17. 4.00A
G-LEAR	Gates Learjet 35A	35A-265	G-ZEST N1462B	20. 8.79	Northern Executive Aviation Ltd Manchester		10. 1.01T
G-LEAS	Sky 90-24	158		4. 5.99	Leasing Group plc Reading		
G-LEAU	Cameron N-31 HAFB	761		5. 8.81	P.L.Mossman "Perrier" Bristol		27. 4.00A
G-LECA	Aerospatiale AS.355F1 Twin Squirrel	5043	G-BNBK C-GBKH	6. 2.87	South Western Electricity plc Bristol		3. 6.02T
G-LEDA	Robinson R22 Beta	1938	G-IFOX	12.11.98	E.D.Obeng t/a Pentacle Denham		13.11.00T
G-LEDN	Short SD.3-30 Var.100	SH.3064	5N-AOX G-BIOF/G-14-3064/EI-BNM/G-BIOF/N280VY/N4270A/G-BIOF	12. 1.89	Streamline Aviation (SW) Ltd Luton		5. 4.00TC
G-LEED	Denney Kitfox Mk.2 (Rotax 582) 450 & PFA/172-11577			24. 4.91	G.T.Leedham Gunby Lea Farm, Overseal		25. 2.01P
G-LEEE	Avtech Jabiru UL PFA/274A-13516			18. 1.00	L.E.G.Fekete (Ellesmere Port)		
G-LEEM*	PA-28R-200 Cherokee Arrow II	28R-7435289	G-BJXW OY-CB/SE-GID/OO-HJN/N43700	28. 5.85	Not known Aldergrove (Damaged nr Newtownards 14.5.91; wreck stored 1.93)		30. 6.91
G-LEES	Glaser-Dirks DG-400	4-238		4.10.88	J Bradley (Pewsey)		25. 2.01
G-LEEZ	Bell 206L-1 LongRanger II	45761	G-BPCT D-HDBB/N3175G	22. 1.92	Pennine Helicopters Ltd Oldham		13.11.00T
G-LEGG	Reims Cessna F.182Q Skylane II	0145	G-GOOS	26. 6.96	P.J.Clegg Barton		19.12.02
G-LEGO	Cameron O-77 HAFB	1975		14. 4.89	C.H.Pearce Construction plc Bristol "Jigsaw II"		10. 8.96A
G-LEGS	Short SD.3-60 Var.100	SH.3637	G-BLEF G-14-3637	7. 3.84	Loganair Ltd Exeter (Stored 10.99)		8. 3.00T
G-LEIC	Reims Cessna FA.152 Aerobat	0416		16. 9.86	Leicestershire Aero Club Ltd Leicester		17. 6.02T
G-LEMJ	Hughes 269C	14-0272	G-BMYW N8999F	27. 8.98	L.J.J.Leeman (Buggen Hout, Belgium)		26. 3.00T
G-LEND	Cameron N-77 HAFB	2012		25. 5.89	Southern Flight Co Ltd Southampton "Southern Finance Co/Glenda"		12. 9.96T
G-LENI	Aerospatiale AS.355F1 Twin Squirrel	5311	G-ZFDB G-BLEV	9. 8.95	Grid Aviation Ltd Denham		21. 4.00T
G-LENN	Cameron V-56 HAFB	1833		29. 9.88	M.D.H.Jenkins Bradford-on-Avon		6. 5.91A
G-LENS*	Thunder Ax7-77Z HAFB	168		3.11.78	Not known (Noted 2.97) NK		N/E(A)
G-LEOS	Robin DR.400/120 Dauphin 2+2	1884		29.11.88	P.G.Newens Fairoaks		7. 4.01
G-LEPF	Fairchild F.24R-46A Argus III	952	HB-EPF N1041/NC74129/HB714/43-14988	31. 7.87	J.M.Greenland Blackacre Farm, Holt, Wilts		25.11.99
G-LESJ	Denney Kitfox mk.3 PFA/172-12001 (Rotax 582)			4.10.94	J.H.Mawson Kirkbride t/a G-LESJ Flying Group		21. 3.00P
G-LEVI	Aeronca 7AC Champion	7AC-4001	N85266 NC85266	17. 4.90	Jean P.A.Pumphrey White Waltham t/a G-LEVI Group		9. 7.00P
G-LEXI	Cameron N-77 HAFB	438		26.10.78	D.I.Shuffleton Saxmundham t/a Sedgemoor 500 Balloon Group		7. 3.93A
G-LEZE	Rutan LongEz PFA/74A-10702 (Continental O-200-A)			31. 3.82	K.G.M.Loyal, A.J.Draper, Fairoaks J.R.J.Giesler & C.McGeachy		15. 8.00P
G-LEZJ	Denney Kitfox 4-1200 Speedster (Rotax 912UL) PFA/172B-12529			7. 3.96	C.E.Brookes Egginton		19. 5.00P
G-LEZZ	Stoddard-Hamilton Glastar (Tri-cycle u/c) PFA/295-13241		G-BYCR	4.11.98	L.A.James Wharf Farm, Market Bosworth		17. 6.00P
G-LFIX	VS.509 Spitfire Trainer 9 CBAF.8463 (C/n is Firewall plate no.)		IAC162 G-15-175/ML407	1. 2.80	Carolyn S.Grace Duxford "Nicholson Leslie" (As "ML407/OU-V" (stbd) in 485 Sqn c/s & "ML407/"NL-D" (port) in 341 Sqn c/s)		8. 5.99P
G-LFJB	Boeing 737-81Q	29051		6. 2.00	Sabre Airways Ltd Gatwick		
G-LFSA	PA-38-112 Tomahawk	38-78A0430	G-BSFC	22.10.90	Liverpool Flying School Ltd Liverpool		15. 1.00T
G-LFSB	PA-38-112 Tomahawk	38-78A0072	G-BLYC D-ELID	20.10.94	Liverpool Flying School Ltd Liverpool		7.10.00T
G-LFSC	PA-28-140 Cherokee Cruiser	28-7425005	G-BGTR OY-BGO	4. 9.95	Liverpool Flying School Ltd Liverpool "Liverbird I"		27.10.01T
G-LFSD	PA-38-112 Tomahawk II	38-82A0046	G-BNPT N91522	21.10.96	Liverpool Flying School Ltd Liverpool		22.12.99T
G-LFSE	PA-28R-200 Cherokee Arrow II	28R-7335157	G-BAXT	9. 6.97	Liverpool Flying School Ltd Liverpool		7. 4.02T

Regn	Type	C/n	P/I	Date	Owner/operator	Probable Base	CA Expy
G-LFSF	Cessna 150M Commuter	150-77651	G-BSRC N6337K	9. 7.99	Liverpool Flying School Ltd	Liverpool	27. 5.00
G-LFSI	PA-28-140 Cherokee C	28-26850	G-AYKV	14. 7.89	J.Vickers	Humberside	15.11.01T
G-LFVB	VS.349 Spitfire LF.VB	CBAF.2403 5377M/EP120	8070M	9. 5.94	Patina Ltd (Op The Fighter Collection) "City of Winnipeg" (As "EP120/AE-A" in 402 Sqn c/s)	Duxford	31. 8.00P
G-LFVC	VS.349 Spitfire LF.Vc	-	ZK-MKV A58-178/JG891	28. 9.99	Historic Flying Ltd	Audley End	
G-LGNA	SAAB-Scania SF.340B	340B-199	N592MA SE-F99	11. 6.99	Loganair Ltd	Glasgow	13. 6.00T
G-LGNB	SAAB-Scania SF.340B	340B-216	N595MA SE-G16	8. 7.99	Loganair Ltd	Glasgow	8. 7.00T
G-LGRM	Bell 206B JetRanger II	1376	G-OBRU	7. 1.99	Aeromega Ltd	Stapleford	3. 12.00T
G-LHPL	Aerospatiale AS.350 Ecureuil	2189	N612LH 9M-BAZ/ZK-HJW/JA9808	11. 5.99	London Helicopter Centre Ltd	Redhill	31. 5.02
G-LIBB	Cameron V-77 HAFB	2463		21. 6.91	R.R.McCormick & R.J.Mercer	Belfast	16. 6.00A
G-LIBS	Hughes 369HS (500C)	43-0469S	N9147F	20. 8.85	A.Harvey & R.White	Whimple, Exeter	14. 5.01T
G-LIDA	Hoffman HK.36R Super Dimona	36355		15. 4.92	W.D.Inglis	Bidford/Bickmarsh	23. 7.01
G-LIDE	PA-31-350 Navajo Chieftain	31-7852156	N27800	26.10.78	Keen Leasing Ltd (Op Woodgate Executive Air Services)	Aldergrove	11.10.00T
G-LIDR	Hoffmann H-36 Dimona	36208	G-BMSK	1. 4.96	J.MacGilvray	North Connel	16. 9.01
G-LIDS	Robinson R-22 Beta-II	2808		21. 4.98	A.Wall t/a Direct	Blackpool	7. 5.01
G-LIFE	Thunder Ax6-56Z HAFB	135		11. 1.78	D.P.Hopkins "Golden Delicious" t/a Lakeside Lodge Golf Centre	Pidley	13. 4.00A
G-LILY	Bell 206B JetRanger III	4107	G-NTBI C-FIJD	14. 3.95	T.S.Brown	Goodwood	11. 4.02T
G-LIMA	Rockwell Commander 114	14415	N5870N	17.10.78	Tricolore Aeroclub Ltd	Biggin Hill	1. 7.01T
G-LINA	Stemme S-10	10-049	D-KFDF	3.11.99	J.D.Bally	(Builth Wells)	AC
G-LINC	Hughes 369HS	43-0467S	C-FDUZ CF-DUZ	14. 5.87	Sleekform Ltd	(Sowerby Bridge)	21.11.99T
G-LINE	Eurocopter AS.355N Twin Squirrel	5566		22. 3.94	National Grid Co plc	Oxford	12. 5.00T
G-LIOA	Lockheed 10A Electra	1037	N5171N NC243/NC14959	6. 5.83	The Science Museum (As "NC5171N")	Wroughton	
	(This aircraft was with Skysport Engineering, Rotary Farm, Hatch 11.99 and was being prepared for display at The Science Museum South Kensington, London where it will be suspended from the ceiling)						
G-LION	PA-18-135 Super Cub (L-21B-PI) (Frame No.18-3841)	18-3857	PH-KLB (PH-DKG) R.Neth AF R-167/54-2457	29. 9.80	C.Moore (As "R-167" in R.Neth AF c/s) "Grin 'n Bare It"	Kemble	18.11.02
G-LIOT	Cameron O-77 HAFB	2378		7. 8.90	D.Eliot	Aberdeen	31. 7.00A
G-LIPE	Robinson R-22 Beta	1882	G-BTXJ	23. 1.92	F.C.Owen	Burnley	4. 2.01T
G-LISE	Robin DR.500/200i President	0001		27. 7.98	J.Marks	Goodwood	24. 8.01
G-LITE	Rockwell Commander 112A	291	OY-RPP	13. 6.80	J.E.Dixon	Norwich	21. 8.00
G-LITZ	Pitts S-1E Special (Lycoming IO-360)	PFA/09-11131		3. 3.92	Jennifer A.Hughes "Glitz"	Leicester	15.10.99P
G-LIVH	Piper J3C-65 Cub (L-4H-PI) (Frame No.11354)	11529	OO-JAN OO-AAT/OO-PAX/43-30238	31. 3.94	M.D.Cowburn (As "330238/A-24" in US Army c/s)	Barton	1. 5.00
G-LIVR	Enstrom 480	5038		14. 7.99	Soil Tech BV (Tilburg, The Netherlands)		22. 7.02T
G-LIZA	Cessna 340A II	340A-1021	G-BMDM ZS-KRH/N4620N	15. 2.90	J.H.Fry & J.C.Merkens	Perth	17. 2.02
G-LIZI	PA-28-160 Cherokee	28-52	G-ARPP	26. 1.89	R.J.Walker & J.R.Lawson	Cranwell	19. 6.02
G-LIZY*	Westland Lysander III (C/n also quoted as "Y1351")	"504/39"	RCAF 1558 V9300	20. 6.86	Imperial War Museum (As "V9673/MA-J" in 161 Sqn c/s)	Duxford	
G-LIZZ	PA-E23-250 Aztec E	27-7405268	G-BBWM N40532	26. 7.93	T.D.Nathan, M.J.Barge & G.Walker	Fairoaks	28. 1.00
G-LJCC	Murphy Rebel	PFA/232-13355		8. 7.98	J.H.A.Clarke	(Chippenham)	
G-LJET	Gates Learjet 35A	35A-643	(N35NK) G-LJET/N39418	2.12.88	Gama Aviation Ltd	Heathrow	23. 5.01T
G-LLTT	PA-32R-301 Saratoga IIHP	3246060	N9283P	31. 1.97	Jardine Holdings	Jersey	30. 1.00
G-LLYD	Cameron N-31 HAFB	3558		20. 3.95	Virgin Airship & Balloon Co Ltd (Lloyds Bank titles)	Telford	17. 7.97A
G-LLYY	PA-32R-301T Saratoga IITC	3257120	N4165C	10. 1.00	M.J.Start	Guernsey	
G-LMLV	Dyn'Aero MCR-01 Ban-bi	PFA/301A-13524		25.10.99	L.& M.La Vecchia	(London NW6)	
G-LNYS	Reims Cessna F177RG Cardinal	0120	G-BDCM OY-BIP	30.11.92	J.W.Clarke	Egginton	19.12.99
G-LOAG*	Cameron N-77 HAFB	359		10.11.77	British Balloon Museum "Famous Grouse" (Stored 12.94)	Newbury	6. 4.84A
G-LOAN	Cameron N-77 HAFB	1434		9. 1.87	P.Lawman "Newbury Building Society"	Northampton	16. 1.99A

Regn	Type	C/n	P/I	Date	Owner/operator	Probable Base	CA Expy
G-LOAT	Rutan Cozy	PFA/159-13213		28. 5.98	P.S. & N.G.Pritchard	(Usk)	
G-LOBO	Cameron O-120 HAFB	3389		3. 1.95	C.A.Butter t/a Solo Aerostatics	Newbury	1. 8.99A
G-LOCH	Piper J3C-90 Cub (L-4J-PI) (Frame No.12517)	12687	HB-OCH 44-80391	10.12.84	J.M.Greenland	Blackacre Farm, Holt, Wilts	5.11.00P
G-LOFA*	Lockheed L.188CF Electra	2002	N359Q	10. 2.94	Atlantic Air Transport Ltd	Coventry	9. 2.00T
			F-OGST/N359AC/TI-LRM/N359AC/HC-AVX/N359AC/VH-ECA					
			(WFU for spares 7.98: noted 6.99)					
G-LOFB	Lockheed L.188CF Electra	1131	N667F	28. 6.94	Atlantic Air Transport Ltd	Coventry	28. 6.00T
			N133AJ/CF-IJW/N131US					
G-LOFC	Lockheed L.188CF Electra	1100	N665F	15. 6.95	Atlantic Air Transport Ltd	Coventry	15. 6.01T
			N289AC/N6123A					
G-LOFD	Lockheed L-188CF Electra	1143	LN-FOG	12. 6.97	Atlantic Air Transport Ltd	Coventry	15. 6.00TC
			LN-MOD/N9745C/(CF-IJC)/N9745C					
G-LOFE	Lockheed L-188CF Electra	1144	EI-CET	5. 1.99	Atlantic Air Transport Ltd	Coventry	10..3.02T
			(G-FIGF)/N668Q/N688F/N24AF/N138US (Atlantic Airlines c/s)					
G-LOFM	Maule MX-7-180A Star Rocket	20027C	N31110	19. 7.95	Atlantic Air Transport Ltd	Coventry	10. 9.01T
G-LOFT	Cessna 500 Citation I (Unit No.331)	500-0331	LN-NAT	12. 1.95	Atlantic Air Transport Ltd	Coventry	25. 3.00T
			EC-FUM/EC-500/LN-NAT/N40AC/N96RE/N86RE/N331CC/(N5331J)					
			(Atlantic Executive Aviation c/s)					
G-LOGO	MDH Hughes 369E (500E)	0454E	G-BWLC	4.10.96	R.M.Briggs	Brough	10. 3.02T
			HB-XIJ/SE-JAM					
G-LOKM	WSK-PZL Koliber 160A	04990080	G-BYSH	26.11.99	PZL International Aviation Marketing & Sales plc		
			SP-WGH				North Weald	
G-LOLL	Cameron V-77 HAFB	2964		4.12.92	C.N.Rawnson	Stockbridge	3. 5.99A
					t/a Test Valley Balloon Group		
G-LOOP	Pitts S-1C Special (Lycoming O-320)	850	5Y-AOX	11. 5.78	M.Persaud	White Waltham	26. 5.00P
					t/a G-LOOP Flying Group		
G-LOOK*	Reims Cessna 172M Skyhawk	1234	PH-MIG	4. 5.79	Not known	Fenland	
			(Damaged Laarbruch 11.8.85; mainplanes stored 8.98)					
G-LOOT*	Embraer EMB-110P1 Bandeirante	110-223	G-BNOC PT-GMP	17. 1.91	Not known	Southend	5.10.90T
			(Open store 11.99)					
G-LORA	Cameron A-250 HAFB	3828		22. 2.96	Global Ballooning Ltd	Uckfield	19. 3.00T
G-LORC	PA-28-161 Cadet	2841339	D-ESTC	12. 1.99	Tindon Ltd	Little Snoring	25. 2.02T
			N9184W/(SE-KMP)/(N620FT)					
G-LORD	PA-34-200T Seneca II	34-7970347	N2908W	6. 5.88	Aerohire Ltd	Manchester	23. 4.00T
G-LORI*	HS.125 Srs.403B	25246	G-AYOJ	19. 7.83	Not known	Lagos, Nigeria	26. 8.84
			9Q-COH/G-AYOJ/(G-5-16) (Open storage 3.95)					
G-LORN	Avions Mudry CAP.10B	282		4. 3.99	AWE Aeronautics Ltd	Oban	10. 5.02
G-LORR	PA-28-181 Archer III	2843037		19. 4.96	B.Galt	Edinburgh	20. 5.02
G-LORT	Light Aero Avid mk.4 Speed Wing (Rotax 582)	1124 & PFA/189-12219		12. 2.92	G.E.Laucht	Long Marston	2. 6.00P
G-LORY	Thunder Ax4-31Z HAFB	171		28.11.78	A.J.Moore "Glory"	Northwood, Middx	
G-LOSM	Armstrong-Whitworth Meteor NF.11	S4/U/2342	WM167	8. 6.84	Hunter Wing Ltd	Bournemouth	18. 5.00P
			(Op Jet Heritage Ltd: as "WM167" in 141 Sqdn c/s)					
G-LOSS	Cameron N-77 HAFB	1369		23. 9.86	D.K.Fish	Bedford	10. 1.97A
			"Crown" (Crown Paints titles)					
G-LOST	Denney Kitfox mk.3 Floatplane (Rotax 618)	PFA/172-12055		10. 8.95	P.N.& S.E.Akass	Beauly, Inverness	21. 7.00P
G-LOTI	Bleriot Type XI rep (ABC Scorpion II)	PFA/88-10410		21.12.78	Brooklands Museum Trust Ltd	Brooklands	19. 7.82P
G-LOTO	BN-2A-26 Islander	530	G-BDWG	27. 7.95	Scottish Parachute Club (Islander) Ltd		
			(N90255)/(C-GYUF)/G-BDWG				Strathallan	2. 8.00A
G-LOUN	Eurocopter AS.355N Twin Squirrel	5627		24. 1.97	Loune Ltd	Oxford	12. 6.00T
G-LOVB	BAe Jetstream 3102	622	VH-HSW	12. 8.99	London Flight Centre (Stansted) Ltd		
			G-31-622/G-BLCB/G-31-622				Stansted	5.10.00T
G-LOWA	Colt 77A HAFB	1451		14. 4.89	K.D.Peirce	Cranbrook	7. 6.97A
G-LOWS	Sky 77-24 HAFB	025		19. 3.96	A.J.Byrne & D.J.Bellinger	Thatcham	23. 7.00
					"Dawn Treader"		
G-LOYA	Reims Cessna FR.172J Rocket	0352	G-BLVT	4. 8.89	T.R.Scorer		
			PH-EDI/D-EEDI			Boones Farm, High Garrett, Braintree	31. 5.00
G-LOYD	Aerospatiale SA.341G Gazelle Srs.1	1289	G-SFTC N47298	19. 6.85	Apollo Manufacturing (Derby) Ltd	Ripley, Derbys	13. 3.00
		(Rebuilt 1990 using major components of N6957 c/n 1060)					
G-LPAD	Lindstrand LBL 105A HAFB	632		5. 8.99	Line Packaging & Display Ltd	Gillingham	23. 8.00A
G-LPGI	Cameron A-210 HAFB	4196		13. 8.97	A.Derbyshire	Stretton	29.10.99T
G-LSFI	Gulfstream AA-5A Cheetah	AA5A-0770	G-BGSK	13. 2.84	T.G.Dughan	Mount Airey, Hull	12. 6.00
G-LSFT	PA-28-161 Warrior II	28-8516008	G-BXTX	10.11.99	SFT Europe Ltd	Bournemouth	2. 4.01T
			PH-LEH/N130AV/N43682					
G-LSHI	Colt 77A HAFB	1264		20. 7.88	Lambert Smith Hampton Group Ltd		
					"Lambert Smith Hampton" Streatley, Berks	12. 7.95A

Regn	Type	C/n	P/I	Date	Owner/operator	Probable Base	CA Expy
G-LSMI	Reims Cessna F.152 II	1710		1. 2.80	A.S.Bamrah	Blackbushe	20. 3.02T
					t/a Falcon Flying Services (Op European Flyers)		
G-LSTR	Stoddard-Hamilton GlaStar			20. 4.98	R.Y.Kendal	Brunton	17. 6.00P
	(Tail-wheel u/c)	PFA/295-13093					
G-LTFB	PA-28-140 Cherokee	28-23343	G-AVLU	28. 2.97	London Transport Flying Club Ltd		2. 4.01T
						Fairoaks	
G-LTFC	PA-28-140 Cherokee B	28-26259	G-AXTI	8. 6.94	London Transport Flying Club Ltd		1. 9.00T
						Fairoaks	
G-LTRF	Sportavia Fournier RF7	7001	G-EHAP	10.12.97	L.J.Trute		16. 4.98P
			(G-BGVC)/D-EHAP/F-WPXV			Belle Vue Farm, Yarnscombe	
G-LTSB	Cameron LTSB-90SS HAFB	4483		15. 1.99	Virgin Airship & Balloon Co Ltd	Telford	12. 1.00
					(Lloyds TSB titles)		
G-LUBE	Cameron N-77 HAFB	1127		25. 2.85	A.C.Rawson "Lubey Loo"	Stafford	6. 8.99A
G-LUCK	Reims Cessna F.150M	1238	PH-LEO	13.12.79	Taylor Aviation Ltd	Sywell	5. 3.01T
			D-EHRA				
G-LUED	Aero Designs Pulsar	PFA/202-12122		9. 3.92	J.C.Anderson	Sturgate	4. 2.99P
	(Rotax 582)						
G-LUFF	Rotorway Exec 90	6191		24. 4.97	D.C.Luffingham	Dymock, Glos	
G-LUFT	Putzer Elster C	011	G-BOPY	31. 3.92	Bath Stone Co Ltd	North Coates	
			D-EDEZ		(Stored as "D-EDEZ" 9.96)		
G-LUKE	Rutan LongEz	PFA/74A-10978		4. 7.84	S.G.Busby	Booker	8. 4.00P
	(Lycoming O-235)						
G-LUKY	Robinson R-44 Astro	0357		10. 7.97	English Braids Ltd	Gloucestershire	7. 8.00
G-LULU	Grob G-109	6137		6. 9.82	A.P.Bowden	Enstone	15. 5.01
G-LUMA	Avtech Jabiru SP-430	PFA/274-13458		11. 5.99	B.Luyckx	(Mol, Belgium)	25. 8.00P
G-LUNA	PA-32RT-300T Turbo Lance II		N2246Q	19. 3.79	D.C.Settrington	(Beverley)	16. 3.00T
		32R-7987108					
G-LUSC	Luscombe 8E Silvaire	3975	D-EFYR	1.11.84	M.Fowler	Bruntingthorpe	
			LN-PAT/(NC1248K)		(On rebuild 9.97)		
G-LUSI	Temco Luscombe 8F Silvaire	6770	N838B	3.10.89	J.P.Hunt & D.M.Robinson		
	(Continental C85)					Hurstbourne Tarrant, Hants	26. 5.00P
G-LUST	Luscombe 8E Silvaire	6492	N2065B	9.11.89	M.Griffiths	Gloucestershire	9. 7.98P
	(Continental C85)		NC2065B				
G-LUXE	BAe 146 Srs.300	E-3001	G-5-300	9. 4.87	British Aerospace (Operations) Ltd		
			G-SSSH/(G-BIAD)			Woodford	8. 5.98S
G-LYDA	Hoffmann H-36 Dimona	3515	OE-9213	5. 4.94	M.A.Holmes & M.J.Philpott	Booker	18. 9.00
					t/a G-LYDA Flying Group		
G-LYDD*	PA-31 Turbo Navajo	31-537	G-BBDU	8. 5.89	Not known	Blackpool	12. 5.89T
			N6796L		(Damaged Lydd 17.7.91; fuselage stored 6.96)		
G-LYND	PA-25-235 Pawnee	25-6309	SE-IXU	8. 9.93	Lleweni Parc Ltd	Lleweni Parc	23. 9.02
	(Rebuild of G-BSFZ c/n 25-2246 with new frame)		G-BSFZ/G-ASFZ/N6672Z				
G-LYNE	North American P-51D-20NA Mustang	IDF/AF 41	5.12.95	E.N.Robinson & M.C.B.Anderson	Darlington	
		122-31887	N22B/44-72028		t/a P-51D Restoration Group (On rebuild 12.95)		
G-LYNK	CFM Shadow Srs.DD	303-DD		12.10.98	G.Linskey	(Douglas, IOM)	9. 2.00P
G-LYNX*	Westland WG.13 Lynx 800	WA/102	(ZA500)	6.11.78	Westland Helicopters Ltd		
			G-LYNX		(As "ZB500" in Army c/s)		
					(To The Helicopter Museum 8.98)	Weston-super-Mare	13.12.83PF
G-LYON	McDonnell Douglas DC-10-30	47818	N537MD	11. 3.98	Caledonian Airways Ltd	Gatwick	17. 3.01T
			S2-ADB/N115WA/N519MD/PP-VMS/9V-SDG				
G-LYPG	Avtech Jabiru UL-450	PFA/274A-13466		6. 7.99	P.G.Gale	Kemble	14.11.00P
	(Jabiru 2200A)						
G-LYTE	Thunder Ax7-77 HAFB	1113		29. 9.87	G.M.Bulmer "Crispen"	Hereford	19. 5.91A

G-MAAA – G-MZZZ

Regn	Type	C/n	P/I	Date	Owner/operator	Probable Base	CA Expy
G-MAAC	Advanced Airship Corpn ANR-1	01		16. 1.89	Advanced Airship Corpn Ltd	Oswestry	
					(Sold incomplete 12.93)		
G-MABE	Reims Cessna F.150L Commuter	1119	G-BLJP	20. 6.97	Herefordshire Aero Club Ltd	Shobdon	4. 6.00T
			N962L				
G-MABR	BAe 146 Srs.100	E-1015	G-DEBN	13. 1.00	British Regional Airlines Ltd	Aberdeen	22.12.01T
			EC-GEP/EC-971/N568BA/XA-RST/N461AP/G-5-01 (Union Flag t/s)				
G-MACH	SIAI-Marchetti SF.260	1-14	F-BUVY	29.10.80	Cheyne Motors Ltd	Old Sarum	19. 5.02
			OO-AHR/OO-HAZ/(OO-RAB)				
G-MACK	PA-28R-200 Cherokee Arrow II		N5213F	18. 8.78	Haimoss Ltd	Old Sarum	8.12.01T
		28R-7635449					
G-MAFA	Reims Cessna F.406 Caravan II	0036	G-DFLT	2. 6.98	Directflight Ltd	Exeter	6. 6.01T
			F-WZDZ				
G-MAFB	Reims Cessna F.406 Caravan II	0080	F-WWSR	27. 5.98	Directflight Ltd	Prestwick	28. 9.01T
G-MAFE	Dornier 228-202K	8009	G-OALF	21.12.92	FR Aviation Ltd	Bournemouth	4.11.02T
			G-MLDO/PH-SDO/D-IDON (Op on behalf of Ministry of Agriculture, Fisheries and Food)				

Regn	Type	C/n	P/I	Date	Owner/operator	Probable Base	CA Expy
G-MAFF	PBN BN-2T Turbine Islander	2119	G-BJED	20. 4.82	Cobham Leasing Ltd Teesside/Bournemouth		25. 9.02T
					(Op on behalf of Ministry of Agriculture, Fisheries & Food)		
G-MAFI	Dornier 228-200	8115	D-CAAE	16. 2.87	Cobham Leasing Ltd	Bournemouth	15. 7.02T
					(Op on behalf of Ministry of Agriculture, Fisheries & Food)		
G-MAGC	Cameron Grand Illusion SS HAFB	4000		19. 1.95	L.V.Mastis	West Bloomfield, Mi., USA	30. 5.99A
G-MAGG	Pitts S-1SE Special	PFA/09-10873		17. 3.83	C.A.Boardman	Little Gransden	1. 4.00P
	(Lycoming O-360)						
G-MAGL	Sky 77-24 HAFB	164		14. 7.99	RCM SARL	Stuppicht, Luxembourg	
G-MAIK	PA-34-220T Seneca IV	3448078	N73BS	17.11.97	TEL (IOM) Ltd	Ronaldsway	26.11.00
G-MAIN	Mainair Blade 912 1202-0689-7 & W1005			16. 6.99	Mainair Sports Ltd	Barton	4. 7.00P
G-MAIR	PA-34-200T Seneca II	34-7970140	N3029R	15. 2.89	Barnes Olson Aeroleasing Ltd	Bristol	9. 4.01T
					(Op Bristol Flying Centre)		
G-MAJA	BAe Jetstream 4100	41032	G-4-032	22. 4.94	British Regional Airlines Ltd Ronaldsway		24. 5.02T
G-MAJB	BAe Jetstream 4100	41018	G-BVKT	1. 6.94	British Regional Airlines Ltd Ronaldsway		8. 6.00T
			N140MA/G-4-018		(Martha Masanabo/Ndebele t/s)		
G-MAJC	BAe Jetstream 4100	41005	G-LOGJ	12. 9.94	British Regional Airlines Ltd Ronaldsway		20.12.00T
					(BAC Express c/s)		
G-MAJD	BAe Jetstream 4100	41006	G-WAWR	27. 3.95	British Regional Airlines Ltd Ronaldsway		2. 3.01T
G-MAJE	BAe Jetstream 4100	41007	G-LOGK	12. 9.94	British Regional Airlines Ltd Ronaldsway		24. 2.00T
					(BAC Express c/s)		
G-MAJF	BAe Jetstream 4100	41008	G-WAWL	6. 2.95	British Regional Airlines Ltd Ronaldsway		18. 3.02T
					(BAC Express c/s)		
G-MAJG	BAe Jetstream 4100	41009	G-LOGL	16. 8.94	British Regional Airlines Ltd Ronaldsway		30. 3.02T
G-MAJH	BAe Jetstream 4100	41010	G-WAYR	4. 4.95	British Regional Airlines Ltd Ronaldsway		13. 4.00T
					(BAC Express c/s)		
G-MAJI	BAe Jetstream 4100	41011	G-WAND	20. 3.95	British Regional Airlines Ltd Ronaldsway		27. 4.01T
G-MAJJ	BAe Jetstream 4100	41024	G-WAFT	27. 2.95	British Regional Airlines Ltd Ronaldsway		28.10.02T
			G-4-024				
G-MAJK	BAe Jetstream 4100	41070	G-4-070	27. 7.95	British Regional Airlines Ltd Ronaldsway		2. 9.00T
					(Wings t/s)		
G-MAJL	BAe Jetstream 4100	41087	G-4-087	1. 4.96	British Regional Airlines Ltd Ronaldsway		16. 5.00T
G-MAJM	BAe Jetstream 4100	41096	G-4-096	23. 9.96	British Regional Airlines Ltd Ronaldsway		29.10.02T
					(BAC Express c/s)		
G-MAJR	DHC.1 Chipmunk 22	C1/0699	WP805	25. 9.96	C.Adams	(Gosport)	
					t/a Chipmunk Shareholders		
G-MAJS	Airbus A.300B4-605R	604	F-WWAX	26. 4.91	Monarch Airlines Ltd	Luton	25. 4.02T
G-MALA	PA-28-181 Archer II	28-8190055	G-BIIU	6. 3.81	D.C. & M.E.Dowell	Kemble	16. 4.02T
			N82748		t/a M & D Aviation		
G-MALC	Grumman-American AA-5 Traveler		G-BCPM	19.11.79	B.P.Hogan	Sywell	27. 5.00
		AA5-0664	N6170A				
G-MALS	Mooney M.20K (231)	25-0573	N1061T	16. 8.84	J.Houlberg t/a G-MALS Group	Blackbushe	25. 4.02
G-MALT	Colt Flying Hop SS HAFB	1447		14. 4.89	P.J.Stapley "Hoppie"	Redcar	11. 9.97A
G-MAMC	Rotorway Exec 90	5057		24. 5.94	J.R.Carmichael	Cumbernauld	19. 2.99P
	(RI 162)				(Damaged Cumbernauld 22.9.98)		
G-MAMD	Beechcraft B200 Super King Air		N1069S	16. 7.99	Gamston Aviation Ltd	Gamston	15. 7.00T
		BB-1549					
G-MAMO	Cameron V-77 HAFB	1616		17.11.87	The Marble Mosaic Co Ltd	Portishead	6. 6.00A
					"Osprey"		
G-MANA	BAe ATP	2056	G-LOGH	21. 2.94	British Regional Airlines Ltd Ronaldsway		21. 3.01T
			G-11-056				
G-MANB	BAe ATP	2055	G-LOGG	14. 9.94	British Regional Airlines Ltd Ronaldsway		26. 9.02T
			G-JATP/G-11-055				
G-MANC	BAe ATP	2054	G-LOGF	7.11.94	British Regional Airlines Ltd Ronaldsway		20.10.00T
			G-11-054				
G-MAND	PA-28-161 Warrior II	28-8116284	G-BRKT	8. 3.93	Halfpenny Green Flight Centre Ltd		
			N8082Z			Halfpenny Green	3.12.01T
G-MANE	BAe ATP	2045	G-LOGB	7. 6.94	British Regional Airlines Ltd Ronaldsway		26. 2.01T
			G-11-045				
G-MANF	BAe ATP	2040	G-LOGA	19. 9.94	British Regional Airlines Ltd Ronaldsway		5.11.01T
					(BAC Express c/s)		
G-MANG	BAe ATP	2018	G-LOGD	22. 8.94	British Regional Airlines Ltd Ronaldsway		28. 9.01T
			G-OLCD		(BAC Express c/s)(Damaged on landing Manchester 18.3.98)		
G-MANH	BAe ATP	2017	G-LOGC	16.11.94	British Regional Airlines Ltd Ronaldsway		14. 8.01T
			G-OLCC		(BAC Express c/s)		
G-MANI	Cameron V-90 HAFB	3038		8. 3.93	M.P.G.Papworth	Ilkley	4. 9.00T
G-MANJ	BAe ATP	2004	G-LOGE	6. 9.94	British Regional Airlines Ltd Ronaldsway		14. 4.01T
			G-BMYL		(BAC Express c/s)		
G-MANL	BAe ATP	2003	G-ERIN	3.10.94	British Regional Airlines Ltd		
			G-BMYK		(Op British Midland Airways Ltd) East Midlands		25. 5.02T
G-MANM	BAe ATP	2005	G-OATP	17.10.94	British Regional Airlines Ltd		
			G-BZWW/(N375AE)/G-BZWW "Elaine Griffiths"			Ronaldsway	20. 3.02T

Regn	Type	C/n	P/I	Date	Owner/operator	Probable Base	CA Expy
G-MANN	Aerospatiale SA.341G Gazelle 1	1295	G-BKLW	14. 4.86	First City Air plc	Thruxton	11. 7.01T
	N4DQ/N4QQ/N444JJ/N47316/F-WKQH						
G-MANO	BAe ATP	2006	OK-TFN	28.11.94	Manx Airlines Ltd	Ronaldsway	18. 1.02T
	G-MANO/G-UIET/G-11-5/(N376AE) (Rendezvous t/s)						
G-MANP	BAe ATP	2023	OK-VFO	28.10.94	Manx Airlines Ltd	Ronaldsway	25.10.00T
	G-MANP/G-PEEL						
G-MANS	BAe 146 Srs.200	E-2088	G-CHSR	5. 5.94	British Regional Airlines Ltd	Manchester	25. 4.00T
			G-5-088				
G-MANT*	Cessna 210L Centurion II	210-60970	G-MAXY	22. 5.85	Not known	Great Yarmouth	2.10.94
	N550SV (Damaged nr Kidlington 16.2.92; displayed Sea-front Crazy Golf course 2.99)						
G-MANU	BAe ATP	2008	G-BUUP	20. 8.97	British Regional Airlines Ltd	Ronaldsway	24. 3.00T
	CS-TGA/G-11-8/(N378AE) (BAC Express c/s)						
G-MANW	Tri-R Kis	PFA/239-12628		12. 9.96	M.T.Manwaring	(Barking)	
G-MANX	Clutton FRED Srs.II			31. 5.78	S.Styles	(Birmingham)	17. 8.82P
	(Ardem 4C02)	PW.2 & PFA/29-10327	(Crashed nr Ronaldsway 30.10.81; on rebuild Wellesbourne Mountford 7.90)					
G-MAPP	Cessna 402B	402B-0583	D-INRH	16. 4.99	Simmons Mapping (UK) Ltd	(Axbridge)	5.10.02T
			N1445G				
G-MAPR	Beechcraft A36 Bonanza	E-2713	N55916	17. 9.92	Openair Ltd	Blackbushe	2. 9.01
G-MAPS	Sky Flying Map SS HAFB	105		20. 7.98	Virgin Airship & Balloon Co Ltd	Telford	10. 6.00A
					(Ordnance Survey titles)		
G-MARA	Airbus A.321-231	0983	D-AVZB	31.3.99	Monarch Airlines Ltd	Luton	30. 3.02T
G-MARE	Schweizer Hughes 269C	S-1320		12. 8.88	The Earl of Caledon		
						Caledon Castle, Co.Tyrone	9.10.00
G-MARY*	Cassutt Racer	2		14. 3.80	Not known	Standalone Farm, Meppershall	
					(Under construction 4.91 but see G-TRUC)		
G-MASC	SAN Jodel 150A Mascaret	37	F-BLDZ	1. 2.91	K.F. & R.Richardson		
						Wellesbourne Mountford	12. 5.00P
G-MASF	PA-28-181 Cherokee Archer II		OY-EPT	24. 6.97	Mid-Anglia Flight Centre Ltd	Cambridge	21. 7.00T
		28-7790191	LN-NAP		t/a Mid-Anglia School of Flying, Cambridge		
G-MASH	Westland-Bell 47G-4A	WA/725	G-AXKU	3.11.89	Defence Products Ltd	Redhill	4. 2.02
			G-17-10		(US Army c/s)		
G-MASS	Cessna 152 II	152-81605	G-BSHN	6. 3.95	MK Aero Support Ltd	Denham	23. 7.02T
			N65541				
G-MASX	Masquito Masquito M.80	03		19. 6.98	Masquito Aircraft NV (Roosdaal, Belgium)		
G-MASY	Masquito Masquito M.80	02		19. 6.98	Masquito Aircraft NV (Roosdaal, Belgium)		
G-MASZ	Masquito Masquito M.58	01		29. 4.97	Masquito Aircraft NV (Roosdaal, Belgium)		AC

(Masquito's website (http://www.masquito.be) states that the company took the prototype M80, ie c/n 02 G-MASY,
to PFA 1998. The part-built aircraft present at PFA 1999 was marked on a cowling panel as "G-MASZ" and was
also noted in a complete state in 1997 and painted yellow. The website observes this first flew in November
1998. According to literature within the 1999 machine the prototype M80 is currently flying and the
registration details were contained within the cockpit and under a photograph of a yellow example in the air.
The literature also states that the first pre-production example is currently being finished. One conclusion
is that Masquito could have been using the same registration (G-MASZ) on each airframe to date !
It is reported further that the PFA 1999 example was the pre-production prototype and not yet registered.
This may emerge as either G-MASX, G-MASY or another registration. The completed first prototype G-MASZ
Was in Belgium under test during mid 1999).

Regn	Type	C/n	P/I	Date	Owner/operator	Probable Base	CA Expy
G-MATE	Moravan Zlin Z.50LX	0068		26.10.90	J.H.Askew	Breighton	21. 4.01
G-MATT	Robin R.2160	97	G-BKRC	7. 5.85	D.J.Nicholson	East Midlands	15.10.99
			F-BZAC/F-WZAC				
G-MATZ	PA-28-140 Cherokee Cruiser		G-BASI	11.12.90	R.B.Walker	Coventry	13.10.00T
		28-7325200			t/a Midland Air Training School		
G-MAUD	BAe ATP	2002	(G-MANK)	14.12.93	British Regional Airlines Ltd		
			G-MAUD/G-BMYM		(Blue Poole t/s)	East Midlands	13. 6.01T
G-MAUK	Colt 77A HAFB	901		16. 2.87	B.Meeson "Mondial Assistance"	Walsall	4. 6.92A
G-MAVI	Robinson R-22 Beta	0960		7. 2.89	R.M.Weyman	Coventry	26. 4.01T
G-MAWL	Maule M.4-210C Rocket	1065C	D-EEAO	29. 5.81	D.Wallace	Aboyne	3. 4.00
			N2011U				
G-MAXI	PA-34-200T Seneca II	34-7670150	N8658C	11. 2.81	Draycott Seneca Syndicate Ltd	Fairoaks	8. 4.00
G-MAXV	Van's RV-4	PFA/181-13266		20. 1.00	T.P.Jenkinson	(Radlett)	
G-MAXX	Lindstrand LBL Battery SS HAFB	621		16. 7.99	M.E.White	Dublin, Ireland	31. 7.00A
					(Panasonic titles)		
G-MAYA	Aero L-29 Delfin	394912	ES-YLO	16. 6.98	Red 64 Ltd.	Biggin Hill	25.10.99
			Estonian AF 64/Soviet AF 64 (red)				
G-MAYO	PA-28-161 Warrior II	28-7716278	G-BFBG	20. 2.81	M.P.Catto	Fairoaks	17. 3.01T
			N38846		t/a Jermyk Engineering		
G-MBAA	Hiway Skytrike Mk.II/Excalibur	01		23. 4.81	M.J.Aubrey	Kington, Hereford	
G-MBAB	Hovey WD-II Whing Ding II			26. 5.81	M.J.Aubrey	Kington, Hereford	1. 2.98P
	(Konig SC430) MA-59 & PFA/116-10706						
G-MBAD	Weedhopper JC-24A	0382		3. 6.81	M.Stott	Prudhoe	
G-MBAL	Ultrasports Tripacer/Hiway Demon			29. 6.81	I.M.Munster	Nottingham	24.10.91E
	(Fuji-Robin EC-25-PS)	HD.51					

Regn	Type	C/n	P/I	Date	Owner/operator	Probable Base	CA Expy
G-MBAP*	Rotec Rally 2B	PL-1		16. 7.81	P.D.Lucas (Stored 1.91)	Needham	
G-MBAR	Wheeler Scout	389W		8. 7.81	L.Chiappi	Blackburn	
G-MBAW	Pterodactyl Ptraveler	017		14. 7.81	J.C.K.Scardifield	Lymington	31. 8.86E
G-MBBB	Wheeler Scout II	0388W		3. 8.81	A.J. & B.Chalkley	Pwllheli	
G-MBBM	Eipper Quicksilver MX	10960		11. 9.81	J.Brown	Markfield, Leics	
G-MBBY	Ultrasports Tripacer/Flexiform Solo Sealander (Fuji-Robin EC-34-PM)	JEH-1		22. 9.81	R.A.Martin	Rotherham	9. 2.94P
G-MBBZ*	Volmer VJ-24W (Yamaha KT100)	7		23. 9.81	Not known (Stored 10.97)	Old Sarum	23. 9.93E
G-MBCI	Hiway Skytrike II/Solar Wings Typhoon	T481-119P		30. 9.81	P.A.Kilburn	Urmston, Manchester	3. 9.93P
G-MBCJ	Mainair Tri-Flyer/Solar Wings Typhoon S	JRN-1		30. 9.81	R.A.Smith	Doncaster	30. 4.86E
G-MBCK	Eipper Quicksilver MX (Rotax 377)	GWR-10962		30. 9.81	P.Rowbotham	Loughborough	N/E
G-MBCL	Hiway Skytrike 160/Solar Wings Typhoon	2332 & T1181-07	(C/n probably T1181-307)	30. 9.81	P.J.Callis	Kibworth, Leicester	N/E
G-MBCU	American Aerolights Eagle Amphibian (Rotax 377)	3181		5.10.81	J.L.May	Portsmouth	22. 4.98P
G-MBCX	Hornet 250/Airwave Nimrod 165	H090 & 0090 LJH		12.10.81	M.Maylor	Louth	31.12.87E
G-MBDD*	Hiway Skytrike/Demon 175 (Fuji-Robin EC-34-PM) (Regd as MM175D & reported as Mainair Tri-Flyer)	MM17D	(Temp unregd 6.10.97)	14.10.81	Not known	Newbury	9. 7.98P
G-MBDE	Sharp & Sons Tartan/Flexiform Solo Striker (Fuji-Robin EC-34-PM) (Regd as Ultrasports Tripacer)	FS-1		15.10.81	A.R.Cantrill	Kirkmichael, IoM	3. 9.96P
G-MBDG	Eurowing Goldwing (Konig SC430)	E.20		19.10.81	B.Fussell	Llanelli	14.12.94P
G-MBDI*	Flexiform Sealander	KB-1		2.11.81	K.Bryan Sutton-in-Ashfield, Notts (Cancelled by CAA 17.2.99)		
G-MBDJ	Mainair Tri-Flyer/Flexiform Sealander (Fuji-Robin EC-25-PS)	LHP-1		19.10.81	J.W.F.Hargrave	High Wycombe	10. 2.92E
G-MBDL*	Striplin (AES) Lone Ranger	109		21.10.81	North East Acft Museum (Stored in poor condition 4.96)	Usworth	
G-MBDM	Southdown Sigma (Fuji-Robin EC-25-PS)	SST/001		26.10.81	A.R.Prentice	Dartford	N/E
G-MBEP*	American Aerolights Eagle 215B (Cuyuna 215)	2877		9.11.81	Caernarfon Air Museum	Caernarfon	N/E
G-MBET	MEA Mistral Trainer (Fuji-Robin EC-44-PM)	MEA.103		10.11.81	B.H.Stephens	Southampton	27. 9.98P
G-MBEU	Chargus T.250/Hiway Demon	T.250/06		10.11.81	R.C.Smith	Clacton	31. 5.86E
G-MBEV	Chargus Titan 38 (Fuji-Robin EC-44-PM)	LUFC-01		11.11.81	N.Hooper Lower Mountpleasent Farm, Wiblington		6. 2.94E
G-MBFK	Hiway Skytrike/Demon 175 (Fuji-Robin EC-25-PS)	LR17D		16.11.81	D.W.Stamp	Kidderminster	N/E
G-MBFO	Eipper Quicksilver MX (Cuyuna 430R)	MLD-01		17.11.81	J.C.Larkin	Maryport, Cumbria	20. 8.93P
G-MBFU*	Ultrasports Tripacer/Hiway Demon (Fuji-Robin EC-25-PS)	THJP-01		23.11.81	Not known (Temp unregd 30.1.96)	Lyndhurst	16.10.95P
G-MBFZ	MSS Eurowing Goldwing (Fuji-Robin EC-34-PM)	MSS-01		25.11.81	P.C.Piggott	Lutterworth	5. 9.00P
G-MBGA	Mainair Tri-Flyer/Flexiform Solo Sealander (Fuji-Robin EC-34-PM)	001		25.11.81	C.Murphy	Ince Blundell	14. 9.97P
G-MBGB*	American Aerolights Eagle	JCM-01		25.11.81	J.C.Miles (Cancelled as WFU 2.3.99)	Blackburn	
G-MBGF	Twamley Trike/Birdman Cherokee	RWT-01		26.11.81	T.B.Woolley	Leicester	
G-MBGP	Hiway Skytrike/Solar Wings Typhoon (Fuji-Robin EC-34-PM)	T481-141L		1.12.81	W.Niblett	Frome	9. 1.99P
G-MBGS	Rotec Rally 2B	PCB-1		2.12.81	P.C.Bell	Yalding, Kent	
G-MBGW*	Hiway Skytrike/Super Scorpion	GWRC-1 & 23		3.12.81	Not known (Stored 10.95)	Davidstow Moor	26. 9.91E
G-MBGX	Southdown Lightning DS (Fuji-Robin EC-44-PM)	RBDB-1		7.12.81	T.Knight	Newton Abbot	7. 3.92E
G-MBHE	American Aerolights Eagle (Cuyuna 430R)	4210		18.12.81	R.J.Osborne	Long Marston	12.10.96P
G-MBHJ*	Hornet 250/Skyhook Cutlass B	GH-1		30.12.81	Not known (Stored 12.97) Guy Lane Farm, Waverton, Chester		
G-MBHK	Mainair Tri-Flyer 250/Flexiform Solo Striker (Fuji-Robin EC-34-PM)	EB-1 & 036-241181		30.12.81	K.T.Vinning	Stratford-upon-Avon	11. 8.98P
G-MBHZ	Pterodactyl Ptraveler	TD-01		6. 1.82	J.C.K.Scardifield	Lymington	28. 2.86E

Regn	Type	C/n	P/I	Date	Owner/operator	Probable Base	CA Expy
G-MBIA	Hiway Skytrike/Flexiform Sealander			6. 1.82	I.P.Cook	Oldham	N/E
	(Fuji-Robin EC-34-PM)	6172349/336					
G-MBIO	American Aerolights Eagle 215B			12. 1.82	B.J.C.Hill	Bridgnorth	N/E
	(Zenoah G25B1)	E.4007-Z					
G-MBIT	Hiway Skytrike/Demon	2501		18. 1.82	Kverneland (UK) Ltd	Yarm, Cleveland	N/E
	(Fuji-Robin EC-25-PS)						
G-MBIY	Ultrasports Tripacer/Lightning Phase II			19. 1.82	D.Hamilton-Brown	Crawley	18. 4.99P
		330					
G-MBIZ	Mainair Tri-Flyer/Hiway Vulcan			20. 1.82	E.F.Clapham, W.B.S.Dobi, S.P.Slade & D.M.A.Templeman		
		039-251181 & SD9V				Bristol	
G-MBJA	Eurowing Goldwing	EW-34		20. 1.82	R.McBlain	Maybole, Ayr	29. 8.96P
	(Fuji-Robin EC-34-PM)						
G-MBJD	American Aerolights Eagle 215B	4169		21. 1.82	R.W.F.Boarder	Tring	N/E
	(Zenoah G25B1)						
G-MBJF	Hiway Skytrike Mk.II/Vulcan 80-00099			22. 1.82	C.H.Bestwick	Nottingham	31. 1.87E
	(Fuji-Robin EC-25-PS) (C/n is engine no)						
G-MBJG	Chargus T.250/Airwave Nimrod UP			25. 1.82	D.H.George	Sandown	20.11.00P
	(Fuji-Robin EC-25-PS)	CMT165045					
G-MBJK	American Aerolights Eagle	2742		16. 1.82	B.W.Olley	Ely	
G-MBJL	Hornet/Airwave Nimrod	JSRM-01		26. 1.82	A.G.Lowe	Dyce	20.10.96P
	(Fuji-Robin EC-25-PS)						
G-MBJM	Striplin Lone Ranger	LR-81-00138		26. 1.82	C.K.Brown	Loughborough	
G-MBJN	American Aerolights Eagle 215B			26. 1.82	Mary M.Wallace	Jurby, IoM	29. 6.97P
	(Fuji-Robin EC-25-PS)	MEC-01					
G-MBJO*	Birdman Cherokee mk.I	CHL-5100680		28. 1.82	C.A.James & T.T.Parr	Bristol	
					(Cancelled by CAA 15.3.99)		
G-MBJS*	Hiway Skytrike/Solar Wings Typhoon S2			28. 1.82	Not known	Mill Farm, Hughley	
	(Fuji-Robin EC-34-PM) 26X7 & T383-731L				(Rebuild with Trike from G-MWXE)		
G-MBKB*	Pterodactyl Ptraveler	47		3. 2.82	Not known	Long Acres Farm, Sandy	
					(Stored 8.92)		
G-MBKC*	Southdown Lightning Phase I 250			3. 2.82	R.I.Deakin	Rugby	
		DAI-01			(Cancelled by CAA 23.3.99)		
G-MBKW*	MEA Pterodactyl Ptraveler	PT-105		10. 2.82	M.L.Smith	Sudbury	N/E
	(Fuji-Robin EC-34-PM)				(Cancelled by CAA 14.5.98)		
G-MBKY	American Aerolights Eagle 215B			12. 2.82	M.J.Aubrey	Kington, Hereford	
		ZFE-15288 (C/n is probably engine no.)					
G-MBKZ	Hiway Skytrike/Super Scorpion			12. 2.82	S.I.Harding	Camberley	
	(Fuji-Robin EC-25-PS)	EC25P8-04 (C/n is corruption of engine type)					
G-MBLM	Hiway Skytrike 250/Southdown Sigma			18. 2.82	D.E.Peace	Leeds	
		25R7					
G-MBLN	MEA Pterodactyl Ptraveler 430D			19. 2.82	F.D.C.Luddington	Bledsoe, Bedford	2. 4.94P
	(Fuji-Robin EC-34-PM)	HCM-01					
G-MBLO*	Mainair Tri-Flyer/Flexiform Sealander 160			22. 2.82	M.W.Olliver	Ringwood	
		10676			(Cancelled by CAA 10.2.99)		
G-MBLU	Ultrasports Tripacer/Southdown Lightning L195			26. 2.82	C.R.Franklin	Barnstaple	N/E
	(Fuji-Robin EC-25-PS)	L195/191					
G-MBMG	Rotec Rally 2B	RJP-01		3. 3.82	J.R.Pyper	Craigavon, Co.Armagh	
G-MBMT	Mainair Tri-Flyer/Southdown Lightning 195			8. 3.82	D.Hamilton-Brown	Pevensey Bay	N/E
	(Fuji-Robin EC-25-PS)	TRY-01					
G-MBNH*	Southern Aerosports Scorpion	4		23. 3.82	Not known (Stored 7.92)	Branscombe	
G-MBNK	American Aerolights Eagle	E.2398MJ		17. 3.82	R.Moss	Manchester	
G-MBNT	American Aerolights Eagle	MDO-01		24. 3.82	M.P.Harper	Priory Farm, Tibenham	10. 4.95P
	(Fuji-Robin EC-25-PS)				(Stored 9.95)		
G-MBNV	Sheffield Trident	816		24. 3.82	F.Elmore	Sheffield	
G-MBNY*	Steer Terror/Manta Pfledge II	MJS-2		24. 3.82	M.J.Steer	East Molesey	
					(Cancelled as wfu 06.10.99)		
G-MBOD*	American Aerolights Eagle	3082		26. 3.82	M.A.Ford, A.F.Little & D.Young		
					(Cancelled by CAA 27.1.98)	Maidenhead/Kemble	
G-MBOF	Pakes Jackdaw	LGP-01		26. 3.82	L.G.Pakes	Ryde, IoW	
G-MBOH	MEA Mistral Trainer	008		29. 3.82	N.A.Bell	Fordingbridge	N/E
	(Fuji-Robin EC-44-PM)						
G-MBOK	Brooks Pulsar/Solar Wings Typhoon S4			1. 4.82	P.Huddleston	Marlborough	9. 5.93E
	(Sachs Dolmar 153)	153/042/6					
G-MBON	Eurowing Goldwing	EW-33 & SWA-02		1. 4.82	A.H.Dunlop	Devizes	30. 6.86E
	(Fuji-Robin EC-34-PM)						
G-MBOU*	Wheeler Scout Mk III/3/R	432R/3		2. 4.82	J.S.Millard	Newport, Gwent	
	(Regd as c/n 43ZR3)				(Cancelled as WFU 10.3.99)		
G-MBPG	Mainair Tri-Flyer/Solar Wings Typhoon			13. 4.82	S.D.Thorpe	Otherton, Cannock	19. 3.00P
	(Fuji-Robin EC-25-PS) 189-1983 & T381-105						
G-MBPJ	Centrair Moto-Delta G.11	001		14. 5.82	J.B.Jackson	Chester	

Regn	Type	C/n	P/I	Date	Owner/operator	Probable Base	CA Expy
G-MBPM	Eurowing Goldwing (Fuji-Robin EC-34-PM)	EW-21		14. 4.82	A.Gibson Wishaw, Strathclyde t/a Gartmore Flying Group		21. 8.98P
G-MBPU*	Hiway Skytrike/Demon (Fuji-Ronin EC-25-PS)	DSS-01		21. 4.82	B.Curtis Harlow (Cancelled by CAA 5.7.99 with current Permit)		30. 4.00P
G-MBPW*	Weedhopper JC-24	1306		8. 2.82	D.H.Whisker Sheriff Hutton, York (Cancelled by CAA 24.3.99)		
G-MBPX	Eurowing Goldwing SP (Konig SC430)	EW-42		21. 4.82	A.R.Channon Sawston, Cambridge		6.11.96P
G-MBPY	Ultrasports Tripacer 330/Wasp Gryphon (Fuji-Robin EC-34-PM)	RKP-01		21. 4.82	J.L.Thomas Bristol		14. 5.00P
G-MBPZ*	Mainair Tri-Flyer 250/Flexiform Striker	CRH-01 & 047-241281		23. 8.82	C.R.Harris NK		N/E
G-MBRB	Electraflyer Eagle Mk.I	E.2229		9.12.81	R.C.Bott Tywyn		
G-MBRD	American Aerolights Eagle 215B	E.2635		20. 4.82	R.J.Osborne Tiverton		31. 8.85E
G-MBRE	Wheeler Scout	73962		21. 4.82	C.A.Foster Leicester		
G-MBRH	Ultraflight Mirage Mk.II (Rotax 447)	83-009 & RALH-01		20. 4.82	R.W.F.Boarder Oakley		13. 6.99P
G-MBRS	American Aerolights Eagle 215B RWC.1			23. 4.82	W.J.Phillips (Stored 6.90) Haverfordwest		31. 8.85E
G-MBSF*	Ultraflight Mirage Mk.II	234		19. 4.82	A.J.Horne Saffron Walden (Cancelled as wfu 16.2.99)		
G-MBSG*	Ultraflight Mirage Mk.II	235		19. 4.82	P.E.Owen Dorchester (Cancelled by CAA 12.2.99)		
G-MBST	Mainair Gemini/Southdown Sprint (Fuji-Robin EC-44-PM)	141-29383	(Trike from G-MJXA ?)	10. 4.84	G.J.Bowen Llanelli		30. 7.00P
G-MBSX	Ultraflight Mirage II (Cuyuna 428)	240		14. 6.82	P.J.Careless & P.Samal Sandy		20. 9.98P
G-MBTC	Weedhopper JC-24B	ANM-01		11. 5.82	C.A.Reed (Stored 8.97) Long Marston		
G-MBTE	Hiway Skytrike/Demon (Hiro 125) (Regd with former Hornet Trike c/n)	H050		26. 4.82	K.A.Armstrong Brough (Damaged mid 1994)		1. 5.95P
G-MBTF	Mainair Gemini/Southdown Sprint (Fuji-Robin EC-44-PM)	168-30683		26. 4.82	J.R.Pyper Craigavon, Co.Armagh		11.10.98P
G-MBTG	Mainair Gemini/Southdown Sprint (Fuji-Robin EC-44-PM)	064-19482 & P.431		26. 4.82	D.M.Pearson Wallingford		15.10.94P
G-MBTH	Whittaker MW-4 (Fuji-Robin EC-34-PM)	001	(G-MBPB)	6. 4.82	L.Greenfield & M.Whittaker (Stored 8.97) t/a The MW4 F/Gtp Otherton, Cannock		1.12.91E
G-MBTJ	Ultrasports Tripacer/Solar Wings Typhoon (Fuji-Robin EC-25-PS)	CSRS-01		2. 4.82	H.A.Comber Poole		13. 9.93P
G-MBTS*	Hovey WD-II Whing-Ding (C/n is probably owner's PFA membership no)	PFA 8484/7		4. 2.82	T.G.Solomon Shoreham (Stored in North hangar 10.96)		
G-MBTW	Aerodyne Vector 600	1188		10. 5.82	W.I.Fuller Cambridge		N/E
G-MBTY*	American Aerolights Eagle	3207		11. 5.82	P.Raymond (Stored 2.96) Camberley		
G-MBUA	Hiway Demon	RJN-01		30. 4.82	R.J.Nicholson Lightwater		
G-MBUE*	MBA Tiger Cub 440 (Fuji-Robin EC-44-PM)	MBA-001		29. 4.82	Newark Air Museum Winthorpe "The Dormouse Zeitgeist"		
G-MBUK*	Mainair Tri-Flyer/Solar Wings Tyhpoon (Fuji-Robin EC-34-PM)	063-31382 & T582-473		30. 4.82	M.J.Curley London W3 (Cancelled by CAA 26.6.98)		20. 7.95P
G-MBUZ	Wheeler (Skycraft) Scout II	0366		4. 5.82	A.C.Thorne Yelverton		
G-MBVS	Hiway Skytrike 250/Super Scorpion	25T3		14. 5.82	M.A.Brown Hinckley		
G-MBVV	Hiway Skytrike Mk II/Demon 175 IS-01 (Fuji-Robin EC-34-PM)			14. 5.82	G.Hayton Skipton		27. 1.95P
G-MBVW	Skyhook TR2/Cutlass	TR2/23		14. 5.82	M.Jobling Harrogate		28. 5.87E
G-MBWE*	American Aerolights Eagle	2937		18. 5.82	A.M.Blackmun Melton Constable (Cancelled by CAA 24.3.99)		
G-MBWF	Mainair Tri-Flyer/Flexiform Solo Striker (Fuji-Robin EC-34-PM)	GAA-01 & 682-01		19. 5.82	J.B.Brierley Tarn Farm, Cockerham		29. 6.95P
G-MBWG	Huntair Pathfinder 1 (Fuji-Robin EC-34-PM)	006		19. 5.82	R.D.Groves Magherafelt, Co.Londonderry		14. 7.99P
G-MBWH	Jordan Duet 1	D82001		20. 5.82	Designability Ltd St.Leonards-on-Sea (To Jordan Aviation Ltd)		
G-MBWI*	Lafayette Hi-Nuski mk.1	30680		8. 6.82	N.H.Ponsford (Stored 3.96) Leeds		
G-MBWY*	American Aerolights Eagle	CCCW-1		24. 5.82	J.P.Donovan Milton Keynes (Cancelled by CAA 15.3.99)		
G-MBXJ*	Hiway Skytrike 250/Demon 175	DM17D		25. 5.82	S.Ward East Kilbride (Cancelled by CAA 24.3.99)		
G-MBXX	Ultraflight Mirage II	111		21. 1.82	E.J.Girling St.Just (Stored 5.94)		N/E
G-MBYD	American Aerolights Eagle 215B (Fuji-Robin EC-25-PS)	3510		3. 6.82	J.A.Hambleton Market Drayton		30. 1.92E

Regn	Type	C/n	P/I	Date	Owner/operator	Probable Base	CA Expy
G-MBYI	Ultraflight Lazair IIIE A464/001			4. 6.82	M.Sumner	Market Drayton	5. 3.99P
	(Rotax 185) (Previously quoted c/n A522)						
G-MBYK	Huntair Pathfinder 1	012		4. 6.82	R.C.Barnett	Billericay	17. 6.97P
	(Fuji-Robin EC-44-2PM)						
G-MBYL*	Huntair Pathfinder 1	009		4. 6.82	J.Morton	Mullaghmore	31. 3.00P
	(Fuji-Robin EC-44-PM)				t/a Crazy Capers (Cancelled by CAA 30.11.99)		
G-MBYM	Eipper Quicksilver MX	JW-01		4. 6.82	M.P.Harper & L.L.Perry		
	(Cuyuna 430R)				Priory Farm, Tibenham		21. 9.96P
G-MBYO*	American Aerolights Eagle	4467		8. 6.82	B.J.& M.G.Ferguson	Crawley	
					(Cancelled by CAA 24.3.99)		
G-MBYR*	American Aerolights Eagle	3310		25. 6.82	G.Walker	Burnley	
					(Cancelled by CAA 24.3.99)		
G-MBYT*	Ultraflight Mirage Mk.II	98		14. 6.82	Not known	Letterkenny, Ireland	26. 9.93E
	(Kawasaki TA440)				(Stored 8.95)		
G-MBYX*	American Aerolights Eagle	E 2904		9. 6.82	N.P.Austen	Liskeard	
					(Cancelled by CAA 24.3.99)		
G-MBZA*	Ultrasports Tripacer/Hiway Demon 175			10. 6.82	Not known	Chandlers Ford	8. 1.95P
	(Fuji-Robin EC-25-PS) MAR-01 & 100873 (Regd as Mainair Tri-Flyer 330) (Cancelled by CAA 29.6.95)						
G-MBZH	Eurowing Goldwing	EW-50		14. 6.82	J.Spavins	Long Acres Farm, Sandy	31. 3.00P
	(Fuji-Robin EC-34-PM)						
G-MBZJ	Southdown Puma (Lightning) L170-415			14. 6.82	A.K.Webster	Wallingford	1. 8.98P
	(Fuji-Robin EC-34-PM)				(Stolen mid 1998 ?)		
G-MBZK	Ultrasports Tripacer 250/Solar Wings Typhoon			14. 6.82	J A Crofts	Carmarthen	14. 2.00P
		AAL-01					
G-MBZN	Southdown Puma (Lightning DS)			14. 6.82	A.Brown	Ely	N/E
	(Fuji-Robin EC-44-PM) 80-00131 & DJC-01						
G-MBZO	Mainair Tri-Flyer/Flexiform Medium Striker			15. 6.82	A.N.Burrows	Kirk Michael, IOM	15. 4.98P
	(Fuji-Robin EC-34-PM) GRH-01 & 021-101081						
G-MCAR	PA-32-300 Cherokee Six D 32-7140008	G-LADA		11.11.83	Erintech Ltd	(Walkern)	9. 8.02T
		G-AYWK/N8616N					
G-MCEA	Boeing 757-225	22200	N510EA	6. 2.95	Airtours Intl Airways Ltd	Manchester	23. 3.01T
G-MCJL	Cyclone Pegasus Quantum 15	7497		16. 3.99	M.C.J.Ludlow	(Ashford)	15. 3.00P
	(Rotax 912)						
G-MCMS	Aero Designs Pulsar PFA/202-11982			3. 2.93	M.C.Manning	Spanhoe	1. 6.00P
	(Rotax 582)						
G-MCOX	Fuji FA.200-180AO Aero Subaru	296	(G-BIMS)	29.12.81	West Surrey Engineering Ltd	Fairoaks	30. 4.00
G-MCPI	Bell 206B JetRanger III	3191	G-ONTB	4. 4.90	D.A.C.Pipe	Westbury-sub-Mendip	9. 3.00T
			N3896C				
G-MDAC	PA-28-181 Archer II	28-8290154	N8242T	6.11.87	B.R.McKay	Jersey/Compton Abbas	17. 4.00
					t/a Alpha Charlie Flying Club		
G-MDBD	Airbus A.330-243	266	F-WWKG	24. 6.99	Airtours Intl Airways Ltd	Manchester	24..6.02T
G-MDEW*	Lindstrand LBL Drinks Can SS HAFB			4. 3.94	Pepsi Cola Overseas Ltd		
	(Mountain Dew Can Shape)	099			"Mountain Dew Supercan" Des Moines, IA, USA		19. 4.00A
					(Cancelled by CAA 21.9.99)		
G-MDKD	Robinson R-22 Beta	1247		18. 4.90	B.C.Seedle	Blackpool	20. 5.02T
					t/a Brian Seedle Helicopters		
G-MEAH	PA-28R-200 Cherokee Arrow II		G-BSNM	14. 6.91	Stapleford Flying Club Ltd	Stapleford	26. 3.00T
		28R-7435104	N46PR/G-BSNM/N46PR/N54439				
G-MEDA	Airbus A.320-231	480	N480RX	12.10.94	British Mediterranean Airways Ltd		
			F-WWDU		(Whale Rider t/s)	Heathrow	11.10.00T
G-MEDB	Airbus A.320-231	376	3B-RGY	19. 3.97	British Mediterranean Airways Ltd		
			F-OHMB/(XA-SGB)/F-WWIK (Rendezvous t/s)			Heathrow	7. 4.00T
G-MEDD	Airbus A.320-231	386	3B-RGZ	19. 3.97	British Mediterranean Airways Ltd		
			F-OHMC/(XA-SGC)/F-WWBI (Crossing Borders t/s)			Heathrow	1. 4.00T
G-MEGA	PA-28R-201T Turbo Arrow III		N999JG	13. 2.86	Multi Ltd	Breighton	14. 6.01T
		28R-7803303					
G-MELD	Gulfstream AA-5A Cheetah AA5A-0863	G-BHCB		18. 2.85	Plane Talking Ltd	Elstree	15. 1.01T
G-MELT	Reims Cessna F.172H	0580	G-AWTI	23. 9.83	Vectair Aviation 1995 Ltd	Goodwood	27. 2.00T
G-MELV	Socata Rallye 235E Gabier	13328	G-BIND	21. 5.86	Wallis & Son Ltd	Little Staughton	24.10.99
G-MEME	PA-28R-201 Arrow III	2837051	N9219N	17. 8.90	Henry J.Clare Ltd	Bodmin	4. 9.99
G-MEOW	CFM Streak Shadow			23. 4.93	G.J.Moor	RAF Shawbury	11. 1.98P
	(Rotax 582) K.172 & PFA/206-12025						
G-MERC	Colt 56A HAFB	842		11. 6.86	A.F. & C.D.Selby	Loughborough	16. 6.00A
G-MERE	Lindstrand LBL-77A HAFB	092		7. 4.94	G.T.Restell	Folkestone	9. 5.96A
G-MERF	Grob G-115A	8091	EI-CAB	24. 7.95	G.Wylie t/a G-MERF Gp	White Waltham	15. 4.02
G-MERI	PA-28-181 Archer II	28-8090267	N8175J	17. 7.80	Scotia Safari Ltd	Carlisle	30. 3.02T
					(Op Carlisle Flt Centre)		
G-MERL	PA-28RT-201 Arrow IV	28R-7918036	N2116N	27. 6.86	M.Giles	Cardiff	20. 7.01
G-METE	Gloster Meteor F.8	G5/361641	VZ467	5.11.91	Sark International Airways Ltd	Kemble	29. 6.00P
			(A.Gjertsen/Classic Jets Aircraft) (As "VZ467/A" in 601 Sqn)			"Winston"	
G-MEUP	Cameron A-120 HAFB	2117		5.10.89	Innovation Ballooning Ltd	Bath	11. 8.00A

Regn	Type	C/n	P/I	Date	Owner/operator	Probable Base	CA Expy
G-MEYO	Enstrom 280FX	2059	SX-HCN	13. 1.95	L.G.King	Shoreham	16. 3.01
G-MFHI	Europa Avn Europa PFA/247-12841			14.11.97	M.F.Howe	(Beverley)	3.11.99P
G-MFHT	Robinson R-22 Beta-II	2601	N8334H	20. 6.96	MFH Helicopters Ltd	(London W1)	19. 6.02T
G-MFLI	Cameron V-90 HAFB	2650		14. 8.91	J.M.Percival "Mayfly" (Mouldform titles)	Loughborough	3. 9.99A
G-MFMF	Bell 206B JetRanger III	3569	G-BJNJ	4. 6.84	South Western Electricity plc	Bristol	4.11.00T
G-MFMM	Scheibe SF-25C Falke	4412	(G-MBMM) D-KAEU	20. 4.82	J.A.Rees	Haverfordwest	2. 8.99
G-MGAA	Quad City Challenger II (Rotax 582) CH2-??97-1568 & PFA/177A-13124			18. 8.97	P.Gibbs Plaistows, Hemel Hempstead		22.12.00P
G-MGAG	Aviasud Mistral 870545 & BMAA/HB/009 (Rotax 532)			20. 6.89	M.Raj	Otherton, Cannock	27. 6.00P
G-MGAN	Robinson R-44 Astro	0588		10. 5.99	Meegan Motors Ltd (Castleblayney, Ireland)		9. 5.02T
G-MGCA	Avtech Jabiru UL PFA/274-13228			8. 5.98	Cloudbase Aviation Services Ltd	Redhill	10. 3.00P
G-MGCB	Cyclone Pegasus XL-Q (Rotax 462) SW-TE-0344 & 7267 (Trike ex G-MWUT)			16.10.96	C.W.Barnes & M.G.Gomez	Roddige, Fradley	25. 3.00P
G-MGCK	Whittaker MW-6 Merlin PFA/164-11262			30. 3.93	M.H.Arrowsmith	Lincoln	
G-MGDL	Cyclone Pegasus Quantum 15 (Rotax 582)	7400		17. 2.98	G.D.Lusk	Wellingborough	15. 2.99P
G-MGDM	Cyclone Pegasus Quantum 15	7406		19. 3.98	R.Jeffes	London SW13	18. 4.00P
G-MGEC	Rans S-6-ESD Coyote II XL PFA/204-13209			13.10.97	C.Slater	Dronfield	28. 1.00P
G-MGEF	Cyclone Pegasus Quantum 15	7261		18. 9.96	G.D.Castell	Sandy	26.11.00P
G-MGFK	Cyclone Pegasus Quantum 15	7396		2. 2.98	F.A.A.Kay	Chorleywood	3. 3.00P
G-MGFO*	Cyclone Pegasus Quantum 15	7410		24. 3.98	A.Gulliver (Cancelled by CAA 10.5.99)	Harrogate	19. 3.99P
G-MGGG	Cyclone Pegasus Quantum 15	7377		3.11.97	R.A.Beauchamp	Shenstone	10. 3.00P
G-MGGT	CFM Streak Shadow Srs.SA (Rotax 618) K.252 & PFA/206-12723			3. 6.94	R.K.& J.Hyatt	Newquay	23.11.99P
G-MGGV	Cyclone Pegasus Quantum 15	7484		12.10.98	R.W.Krake	Andover	20.11.00P
G-MGMC	Cyclone Pegasus Quantum 15	7430		28. 4.98	M.Clare	Gayton, Northampton	9. 6.00P
G-MGND	Rans S-6-ESD Coyote II XL (Rotax 503) PFA/204-13152			27. 6.97	N.N.Ducker	Ashbourne,Derbyshire	14. 9.00P
G-MGOD	Medway Raven X (Rotax 447)	MRB110/106		6. 7.93	P.C.Collins	Bath	1. 5.00P
G-MGOM	Medway Hybred 44XLR (Rotax 503)	MR125/103		22.11.91	B.A.Showell	Whitstable	24. 9.99P
G-MGOO	Murphy Renegade Spirit UK (Rotax 582) 301 & PFA/188-11580			14.11.89	A.R.Max	White Waltham	12.11.99P
G-MGPD	Solar Wings Pegasus XL-R (Rotax 462)	6905		9. 1.95	P.C.Davis	Weston Zoyland	22. 2.00P
G-MGPH	CFM Streak Shadow SA-M PFA/206-13166 (Rotax 582)		G-RSPH	27.11.97	R.S.Partridge-Hicks	Bury St. Edmunds	29. 7.00P
G-MGRH	Quad City Challenger II (Hirth 2705.R06) CH2-1189-0482			20. 2.90	R.A. & B.M.Roberts Griffins Farm, Temple Bruer		16. 2.00P
G-MGRW	Cyclone AX3/S BMAA/HB/024 (Rotax 503) (Originally regd with c/n C.3093155/S)			8.11.93	K.G.W.Hicks	(Bembridge)	29. 4.00P
G-MGTG	Cyclone Pegasus Quantum 15	7369	G-MZIO	19.12.97	R.B.Milton	(London E2)	6.11.99P
G-MGTR	Hunt Wing/Experience	BMAA/HB/067		24. 7.97	A.C.Ryall	Cardiff	
G-MGTW	CFM Shadow Srs.DD	287-DD		23. 1.98	G.T.Webster	Helensburgh	11. 4.00P
G-MGUN	Cyclone AX2000 (Rotax 582/48)	7284		18.12.96	B E N Sutcliffe	Tarn Farm, Cockerham	19. 3.00P
G-MGUX	Hunt Wing/Experience	BMAA/HB/064		24. 7.97	B.D.Attwell	Caerphilly	
G-MGUY	CFM Shadow Srs.CD (Rotax 447)	078		23.11.87	F.J.Luckhurst & R.G.M.Proost t/a The Shadow Flt Centre	Old Sarum	16. 8.91P
G-MGWH	Thruster T300 (Rotax 582)	9013-T300-507		8.12.92	W.Corps & A.Bass	Eastbourne	9.10.00P
G-MHCA	Enstrom F-28C	348	G-SHWW G-SMUJ/G-BHTF	10. 5.90	A.G.Forshaw	Barton	20. 6.02
G-MHCB	Enstrom 280C Shark	1031	N892PT	11.10.95	J.W.Beswick	(Bury)	14.10.02T
G-MHCD	Enstrom 280C-UK Shark	1112	G-SHGG	12. 7.96	S.J.Ellis	Bryngwyn Bach	24. 8.01T
G-MHCE	Enstrom F-28A	150	G-BBHD	22. 8.96	K.Bickley	Chester	3. 4.02T
G-MHCF	Enstrom 280C-UK Shark	1149	G-GSML G-BNNV/SE-HIY	19. 9.96	K., H.K. & D.Collier t/a HKC Helicopter Services	Barton	3. 6.01T
G-MHCG	Enstrom 280C-UK Shark	1155	G-HAYN G-BPOX/N51776	7. 3.97	D & E Motor Factors Ltd	(Barton)	27. 1.00T
G-MHCH	Enstrom 280C Shark	1043	N557H	19. 5.97	J.& S.Lewis Ltd	(Barton)	29. 7.00T
G-MHCI	Enstrom 280C Shark	1152	N100WZ	20. 5.97	B & B Helicopters Ltd	(Barton)	27. 7.00T
G-MHCJ	Enstrom F-28C-UK	453	G-CTRN	30. 3.98	C. & N.C.Bailey t/a Manchester Helicopter Centre	Barton	21. 5.01T

298

Regn	Type	C/n	P/I	Date	Owner/operator	Probable Base	CA Expy
G-MHCK	Enstrom 280FX	2006	G-BXXB ZK-HHN/JA7702	5. 6.98	N., C. & N.C. Bailey t/a Manchester Helicopter Centre	Barton	23. 6.01T
G-MHCL	Enstrom 280C Shark	1144	N51740	30. 6.98	Altolink Ltd	(Northwich)	24.11.01T
G-MICH	Robinson R-22 Beta	0647	G-BNKY	3. 9.87	A.L.Ramsden t/a Tiger Helicopters	Shobdon	4.10.02T
G-MICK	Reims Cessna F.172N Skyhawk II	1592	PH-JRA PH-AXB	9. 1.80	S.J.Gronow t/a G-MICK Flying Group	Blackpool	7. 8.01
G-MICY	Everett Gyroplane Srs.1 (VW1835)	018	(G-BOVF)	26. 2.90	D.M.Hughes	St.Merryn	2. 5.92P
G-MICZ	PA-46-310P Malibu	46-8508096	N2494X	3. 7.95	Michell Instruments Ltd	Fowlmere	25. 8.01T
G-MIDA	Airbus A.321-231	806	D-AVZQ	31. 3.98	British Midland Airways Ltd	East Midlands	30. 3.01T
G-MIDC	Airbus A.321-231	835	D-AVZZ	12. 6.98	British Midland Airways Ltd	East Midlands	11. 6.01T
G-MIDD	PA-28-140 Cherokee Cruiser	28-7325444	G-BBDD N55687	20. 1.97	R.B.Walker t/a Midland Air Training School	Coventry	25. 5.01T
G-MIDE	Airbus A.321-231	864	D-AVZB	14. 8.98	British Midland Airways Ltd	East Midlands	13. 8.01T
G-MIDF	Airbus A.321-231	810	D-AVZS	24. 4.98	British Midland Airways Ltd	East Midlands	23. 4.01T
G-MIDG	Bushby-Long MM-1 Midget Mustang (Lycoming O-320)	385	N11DE	14. 3.90	C.E.Bellhouse	Headcorn	27.10.00P
G-MIDH	Airbus A.321-231	968	D-AVXZ	22. 3.99	British Midland Airways Ltd	East Midlands	21. 1.02T
G-MIDI	Airbus A.321-231	974	D-AVZA	26. 3.99	British Midland Airways Ltd	East Midlands	25. 3.02T
G-MIDJ	Airbus A.321-231	1045	D-AVZO	16. 7.99	British Midland Airways Ltd	East Midlands	15. 7.02T
G-MIDK	Airbus A.321-231	1153	D-AVZF	12. 1.00	British Midland Airways Ltd	East Midlands	
G-MIDL	Airbus A.321-231	1174	D-AV..	.00R	British Midland Airways Ltd (For delivery 2000)	East Midlands	
G-MIDM	Airbus A.320-232	1207		R	British Midland Airways Ltd (For delivery 2000)	East Midlands	
G-MIDN	Airbus A.321-231			R	British Midland Airways Ltd (For delivery 2000)	East Midlands	
G-MIDO	Airbus A.321-231			R	British Midland Airways Ltd (For delivery 2000)	East Midlands	
G-MIDP	Airbus A.320-232			R	British Midland Airways Ltd (For delivery 2000)	East Midlands	
G-MIDR	Airbus A.320-232			R	British Midland Airways Ltd (For delivery 2000)	East Midlands	
G-MIDS	Airbus A.320-232			R	British Midland Airways Ltd (For delivery 2000)	East Midlands	
G-MIDT	Airbus A.321-231			R	British Midland Airways Ltd (For delivery 2000)	East Midlands	
G-MIDU	Airbus A.321-231			R	British Midland Airways Ltd (For delivery 2001)	East Midlands	
G-MIDV	Airbus A.320-232			R	British Midland Airways Ltd (For delivery 2001)	East Midlands	
G-MIDW	Airbus A.320-232	1177		R	British Midland Airways Ltd (For delivery 2001)	East Midlands	
G-MIDX	Airbus A.320-232	1183		R	British Midland Airways Ltd (For delivery 2001)	East Midlands	
G-MIDY	Airbus A.320-232	1014	F-WWDQ	28. 6.99	British Midland Airways Ltd	East Midlands	27. 6.02T
G-MIDZ	Airbus A.320-232	934	F-WWII	19. 1.99	British Midland Airways Ltd	East Midlands	18.1.02T
G-MIFF	Robin DR.400/180 Regent	2076		31. 5.91	G.E.Snushall	Leicester	6. 8.00
G-MIII	Extra EA.300/L (Lycoming AEIO-540)	013	D-EXFI	5. 9.95	Firebird Aerobatics Ltd (Microlease titles)	Denham	21. 9.01T
G-MIKE	Brookland Hornet (VW1830)	MG.1		15. 5.78	M.H.J.Goldring	St.Merryn	25. 9.92P
G-MIKI	Rans S-6-ESA Coyote II (Rotax 912UL)	PFA/204-13094		28. 2.97	S.P.Slade	Kemble	16. 6.00P
G-MILA	Reims Cessna F.172N Skyhawk II	1686	D-EGHC(2) PH-AYJ	9. 6.98	P.J.Miller	Cuckoo Tye Farm, Sudbury	29. 7.01A
G-MILE	Cameron N-77 HAFB	2411		26. 9.90	Miles Air Ltd "Miles Architectural"	Bristol	20. 7.00A
G-MILI	Bell 206B JetRanger III	2275	C-GGAR 5H-MPV	5.10.94	Sirius Aviation Ltd	(Northwich)	15. 9.01

Regn	Type	C/n	P/I	Date	Owner/operator	Probable Base	CA Expy
G-MILN	Cessna 182Q Skylane	18265770	N735XQ	9. 7.99	Meon Hill Farms (Stockbridge) Ltd		
						Bournemouth	8. 7.02T
G-MILY	Grumman American AA-5A Cheetah		G-BFXY	2. 9.96	Plane Talking Ltd	Elstree	11.10.02T
		AA5A-0672					
G-MIMA	BAe 146 Srs.200	E-2079	G-CNMF	3. 3.93	Manx Airlines Ltd	Ronaldsway	25.11.01T
			G-5-079		(Manxman t/s)		
G-MIME	Europa Avn Europa	PFA/247-12850		26. 9.97	N.W.Charles	(Devizes)	
G-MIND	Cessna 404 Titan II	404-0004	G-SKKC	27. 4.93	Atlantic Air Transport Ltd	Coventry	13. 2.00T
			G-OHUB/SE-GMX/(N3932C)				
G-MINI*	Phoenix Currie Wot	PFA/58-10294		4. 8.78	D.Collinson	(Durham)	
					(Cancelled as wfu 6.8.99 - no UK permit issued)		
G-MINS	Nicollier HN.700 Menestrel II			23.10.92	R.Fenion	Kirkbride	19..5.01P
		PFA/217-12354					
G-MINT	Pitts S-1S Special	PFA/09-10292		7. 2.83	T.G.Sanderson	Leicester	22.11.99P
	(Lycoming AEIO-360)						
G-MINX	Bell 47G-4A	7604	N6242N	16. 3.90	R.F.Warner	Elstree	22. 5.93T
			G-FOOR/N6242N				
G-MIOO	Miles M.100 Student 2	100/1008	G-APLK	26.10.84	Aces High Ltd	Woodley	6. 5.86P
			G-MIOO/G-APLK/XS941/G-APLK/G-35-4				
	(Damaged Duxford 24.8.85; to Museum of Berkshire Aviation Trust 4.97 and stored for rebuild)						
G-MISH	Cessna 182R Skylane II	182-67888	G-RFAB	16. 6.95	M.Konstantinovic	Southend	1. 4.00
			G-BIXT/N6397H				
G-MISS	Taylor JT.2 Titch	PFA/3234		18.12.78	Pamela L.Brenen	(Abingdon)	
G-MITS	Cameron N-77 HAFB	1115		20. 2.85	The Colt Car Co Ltd	Cirencester	25. 7.99T
	(Rebuilt with new envelope c/n 3217 1994)				"Mitsubishi Motors"		
G-MITZ	Cameron N-77 HAFB	1638		17. 3.88	The Colt Car Co Ltd	Cirencester	10. 8.90A
					"Mitsubishi Motors II"		
G-MIWS	Cessna 310R II	310R-1585	G-ODNP	1. 2.96	R.W.F. & R.B.Warner	Hawarden	9. 9.02P
			N19TP/N2DD/N1836E		t/a Bob Warner Aviation		
G-MJAE	American Aerolights Eagle	1021		12. 7.82	T.B.Woolley	Leicester	
	(C/n is probably engine no.)						
G-MJAF*	Southdown Puma (Lightning DS) BHA-01			17. 6.82	S.I.Robertson	Glasgow	20. 9.93E
	(Fuji-Robin EC-44-PM)				(Cancelled by CAA 16.4.98)		
G-MJAJ	Eurowing Goldwing	EW-36		18. 6.82	J.S.R.Moodie	Rogart, Sutherland	18. 4.00P
	(Fuji-Robin EC-44-PM)						
G-MJAL	Wheeler Scout Mk.III/3/R	0433 R/3		18. 6.82	G.W.Wickington	Hamble	
	(Fuji-Robin EC-25-PS)						
G-MJAM	Eipper Quicksilver MX	JCL-01		18. 6.82	J.C.Larkin	Maryport, Cumbria	20. 8.93P
	(Cuyuna 430)						
G-MJAN	Hiway Skytrike/Flexiform Hilander			21. 6.82	G.M.Sutcliffe	Stockport	4. 3.92E
	(Valmet)	RPFD-01 & 21U9					
G-MJAP	Hiway Skytrike/Vulcan 160	21W3		22. 6.82	A.L.Flude	Baldock	N/E
G-MJAV	Hiway Skytrike/Demon 175	817003		23. 6.82	J.N.J.Roberts Long Acres Farm, Sandy		N/E
	(Fuji-Robin EC-25-PS)				(Stored 7.96)		
G-MJAY	Eurowing Goldwing	EW-58		23. 6.82	M.Anthony	Alfreton	N/E
	(Fuji-Robin EC-34-PM)						
G-MJAZ	Aerodyne Vector 610	1251	PH-1J1	23. 6.82	B.Fussell	Swansea	23. 9.93E
	(Konig SC430)		G-MJAZ		(Stored 1.97)		
G-MJBI	Eipper Quicksilver MX	3075		24. 6.82	E.J.H.Blackbourn	Louth	1. 3.94P
	(Cuyuna 430R)						
G-MJBL	American Aerolights Eagle	2892		25. 6.82	B.W.Olley	Ely	
G-MJBN*	American Aerolights Rainbow Eagle			28. 6.82	Not known Manor Farm, Glatton		
		3132			(Open store 7.95)		
G-MJBS	UAS Storm Buggy	JL814S		29. 6.82	G.I.Sargeant	Bridgwater	
G-MJBT*	Eipper Quicksilver MX II			30. 6.82	Not known Letterkenny, Ireland		N/E
	(Cuyuna 430R)	DJ/NBII & 3662			(Stored 8.95)		
G-MJBV	American Aerolights Eagle 215B			1. 7.82	B.H.Stephens	Southampton	11. 8.96P
	(Fuji-Robin EC-25-PS)		RSP-001				
G-MJBX*	Pterodactyl Ptraveler	BJE-01		1. 7.82	R.E.Hawkes	Wellingborough	
					(Cancelled by CAA 24.3.99)		
G-MJBZ	Huntair Pathfinder 1	PK-17		2. 7.82	J.C.Rose Eastbach Farm, English Bicknor		28.12.93P
	(Fuji-Robin EC-34-PM)						
G-MJCE	Southdown Panther Sprint X	RGC-01		5. 7.82	L.I.Bateup & N.D.Dykes	Swinford	1.12.99P
	(Fuji-Robin EC-44-PM)						
G-MJCL	Eipper Quicksilver MX II	RFW-01		5. 7.82	K.J.Bunn	East Kirkby	21. 1.95P
	(Cuyuna 430R)						
G-MJCN	Southern Flyer Mk.1	005		5. 7.82	C.W.Merriam	Billingshurst	11. 6.99P
	(Fuji-Robin EC-44-PM)						
G-MJCU	Tarjani/Solar Wings Typhoon	SCG-01		7. 7.82	J.K.Ewing	Old Sarum	1. 9.94P
	(Fuji-Robin EC-25-PS)						
G-MJCW	Hiway Skytrike/Super Scorpion MGS-01			7. 7.82	M.G.Sheppard	Bournemouth	

Regn	Type	C/n	P/I	Date	Owner/operator	Probable Base	CA Expy
G-MJCX	American Aerolights Eagle 215B (Chrysler 820)	2759		7. 7.82	J.Channer	Nottingham	11. 8.94P
G-MJDA*	Hornet Executive 330/Skyhook Sabre C	H340		12. 7.82	J.Hainsworth (Cancelled as wfu 13.8.99)	Pudsey	28. 2.87E
G-MJDE	Huntair Pathfinder 1 (Fuji-Robin EC-34-PM)	020		9. 7.82	P.Rayson	Swadlincote	17.10.99P
G-MJDH	Huntair Pathfinder 1 (Fuji-Robin EC-34-PM)	015		9. 7.82	T.Mahmood	Insch	3. 7.00P
G-MJDJ	Hiway Skytrike/Demon	VW17D		9. 7.82	A.J.Cowan	Billingham	
G-MJDP	Eurowing Goldwing (Fuji-Robin EC-34-PM)	GW-001		12. 7.82	J.R.Ledbrook & F.C.James	Camberley	15.11.92P
G-MJDR	Hiway Skytrike/Demon	PJB-01		14. 7.82	D.R.Redmile	Leicester	
G-MJDU	Eipper Quicksilver MXII (Rotax 503)	14002		15. 7.82	J.Brown	Markfield, Leics	N/E
G-MJDW	Eipper Quicksilver MXII (Cuyuna 430)	RI-01		15. 7.82	T.Scarborough	Boston	3. 4.00P
G-MJEB	Southdown Puma Sprint (Rotax 447)	1231/0041		18. 4.85	R.J.Shelswell	Warwick	2. 5.96P
G-MJEE	Mainair Tri-Flyer 250/Solar Wings Typhoon (Fuji-Robin EC-25-PS)	038-251181		20. 7.82	M.F.Eddington	Wincanton	11.11.00P
G-MJEG	Eurowing Goldwing (Fuji-Robin EC-34-PM)	GJS-01		20. 7.82	G.J.Stamper	Penrith	N/E
G-MJEH*	Rotec Rally 2B	018T		20. 7.82	E.L.G.Brocklehurst (Cancelled by CAA 17.3.99)	Manningtree	
G-MJEO	American Aerolights Eagle 215B (Zenoah G25B1)	4562		26. 7.82	A.M.Shaw	Stoke-on-Trent	25. 6.93E
G-MJER	Ultrasports Tripacer/Flexiform Solo Striker (Rotax 447)	DSD-01		23. 7.82	D.S.Simpson	Radwell, Letchworth	21.11.98P
G-MJEY	Mainair Tri-Flyer/Southdown Lightning DS (Fuji-Robin EC-44-PM)	PMC-01		27. 7.82	M.McKenzie	Insch	7. 6.96P
G-MJFB	Ultrasports Tripacer/Flexiform Solo Striker (Fuji-Robin EC-34-PM)	AJK-01		27. 7.82	B.Tetley	Cowes	2. 5.00P
G-MJFH*	Eipper Quicksilver MX (Cuyuna 430R)	3077		28. 7.82	C.T.Lamb Road End Farm, Great Casterton (Stored 1.94)		N/E
G-MJFK	Mainair Tri-Flyer/Flexiform Dual Sealander	JH-01		28. 7.82	J.J.Woollen	Huby, York	N/E
G-MJFM	Huntair Pathfinder 1 (Fuji-Robin EC-34-PM)	ML-01		2. 9.82	R.Gillespie & S.P.Girr	Mullaghmore	23. 7.99P
G-MJFP	American Aerolights Eagle 215B (Cuyuna 215R)	5010		2. 8.82	R.C.Colbeck	Henley-on-Thames	N/E
G-MJFX	Skyhook TR1/Sabre	TR1/38		2. 8.82	M.R.Dean	Hebden Bridge	28. 2.87E
G-MJGO	Barnes Avon/Wasp Gryphon (Fuji-Robin EC-34-PM)	2510		5. 8.82	B.R.Barnes	Bristol	31.12.87E
G-MJHB*	AES Sky Ranger	SR.100		9. 8.82	Not known (Fuselage stored 3.97)	Enstone	
G-MJHC	Ultrasports Tripacer 330/Southdown Lightning Mk II	82-00044		9. 8.82	E.J.Allen	Cambridge	N/E
G-MJHM	Ultrasports Tripacer/Hiway Demon 175 (Regd with c/n ME-170)	ME17D		11. 8.82	D.B.Markham	Lincoln	
G-MJHR	Mainair Dual Tri-Flyer/Lightning	GNS-01		12. 8.82	B.R.Barnes	Bristol	
G-MJHU	Eipper Quicksilver MX (Cuyuna 430R)	10692		13. 8.82	P.J.Hawcock, J.W.Lupton & R.F.Hinton (Stored 9.96) Hougham, Lincs		N/E
G-MJHV	Hiway Skytrike 250/Demon	AG-17		13. 8.82	A.G.Griffiths Avenchurch, Birmingham		
G-MJHX	Eipper Quicksilver MXII (Rotax 503)	1033		13. 8.82	P.D.Lucas Needham, Harleston (Stored 9.97)		14. 5.95P
G-MJHZ	Ultrasports Tripacer/Southdown Lightning 170 (Puma DS) (Fuji-Robin EC-34-PM)	L170/267		13. 8.82	M.J.Luton	Farnborough	8.11.98P
G-MJIA	Ultrasports Tripacer/Flexiform Solo Striker (Rotax 377)	SE-007		13. 8.82	D.G.Ellis	Tamworth	20. 9.96P
G-MJIB*	Hornet 250/Skyhook Sabre	H.350		13. 8.82	S.H.Williams St Yon, France (Cancelled by CAA 25.3.99)		
G-MJIC	Ultrasports Tripacer/Flexiform Solo Striker (Fuji-Robin EC-34-PM)	82-00043		13. 8.82	J.Curran	Newry, Co.Down	15.10.94P
G-MJIF	Mainair Tri-Flyer/Flexiform Striker (Fuji-Robin EC-34-PL) "E-1 EC25PS-04" (C/n was original engine type)			16. 8.82	R.J.Payne	Newmarket	31.10.91E
G-MJIO*	American Aerolights Eagle	2625		18. 8.82	R.Apps & J.Marshall (Cancelled as PWFU 25.3.99)	Tetbury	
G-MJIR	Eipper Quicksilver MXII (Rotax 503)	1392		18. 8.82	H.Feeney (Stored 8.96)	Long Marston	26. 1.95P

Regn	Type	C/n	P/I	Date	Owner/operator	Probable Base	CA Expy
G-MJIY	Flexiform Striker/Solar Wings Panther			23. 8.82	M.I.McClelland	Old Sarum	10. 7.00P
	002 CSRS				t/a McClelland Aviation		
	(Originally regd as Ultrasports Tripacer/Flexiform Striker)						
G-MJIZ	Ultrasports Tripacer/Southdown Lightning			23. 8.82	Jacqueline J.Crudington	Hockley, Essex	
	JS-189						
G-MJJA	Huntair Pathfinder 1	031		23. 8.82	R.D.Bateman & J.M.Watkins	Fareham	N/E
G-MJJB	Eipper Quicksilver MX	3526		23. 8.82	S.A.P.Rowberry	Wallingford	31. 7.00P
	(Cuyuna 430R)						
G-MJJF	Ultrasports Tripacer/Solar Wings Medium Typhoon			25. 8.82	G.Ravichandran	London N13	21. 6.96P
	(Fuji-Robin EC-34-PM) JGS-01 & 116-108						
G-MJJK	Eipper Quicksilver MXII	3397		25. 8.82	M.J.O'Malley	Northolt	8. 7.96P
	(Rotax 503)						
G-MJJO	Mainair Tri-Flyer/Flexiform Dual Striker			26. 8.82	T.R.Marsh	Frome	5.11.96P
	(Fuji-Robin EC-44-PS) JDH-01 (Mainair c/n probably 073-31582)						
G-MJKB	Striplin Sky Ranger	ST 161		2. 9.82	A.P.Booth	Newbury	
	(Also quoted as c/n SRI-6-I)						
G-MJKF	Hiway Demon	WGR-01		2. 9.82	S.D.Hill	Henley-on-Thames	
G-MJKH	Eipper Quicksilver MXII	1020		28. 1.83	D.O'Neill	Long Marston	23. 8.96P
	(Rotax 503)				(Stored 1.98)		
G-MJKO	Farnell Trike/Goldmarque Gyr 188			7. 9.82	M.J.Barry	Bridgwater	18.11.91E
	(Fuji-Robin EC-25-PS)	90030P					
G-MJKX	Skyrider Airsports Phantom	PH.82005		14. 9.82	W.E.Willets	Bewdley	1. 8.98P
	(Fuji-Robin EC-48)						
G-MJLK*	Dragonfly 250-II	D.105		10. 9.82	Not known	Breighton	
					(Stored completely dismantled 6.96)		
G-MJLY*	American Aerolights Eagle	AMR-01		30. 9.82	A.M.Read	Plymouth	
					(Cancelled by CAA 15.3.99)		
G-MJMA	Hiway Skytrike/Demon	JCC-01		22. 9.82	R.V.Parks & S.C.Hewett		
	(Fuji-Robin EC-25-PS)					Faversham/Herne Bay	N/E
G-MJMD	Hiway Skytrike/Demon 175	0E17D		27. 9.82	T.A.N.Brierley	Baxby Manor, Husthwaite	1. 8.97P
	(Fuji-Robin EC-34-PM)						
G-MJMI*	Skyhook Sabre	260A-138824		27. 9.82	Not known	Long Acres Farm, Sandy	
					(Stored 8.92)		
G-MJMN	Mainair Tri-Flyer/Flexiform Striker			29. 9.82	E.D.Locke	Barton	24. 6.97P
	(Fuji-Robin EC-34-PM)	087-04882			(Stored 12.97)		
G-MJMR	Mainair Tri-Flyer 250/Solar Wings Typhoon			30. 9.82	J.C.S.Jones	Rhuallt	
	DR-01 & 048-5182				(Stored 12.97)		
G-MJMS	Hiway Skytrike/Demon 175	EEW-01		30. 9.82	D.E.Peace	Rawdon, Leeds	
G-MJMT	Hiway Skytrike/Demon 175	RL17D		30. 9.82	K.H.Roberts	Eshott	9.10.93P
	(Fuji-Robin EC-25-PS)						
G-MJMU	Hiway Skytrike 250/Demon	817003		1.10.82	P.Hunt	Bishop Auckland	
	(C/n duplicates that of both PH-1B2 & G-MJOI)						
G-MJMX	Mainair Tri-Flyer/Flexiform Dual Striker			4.10.82	N.Cockburn	Swanley, Kent	18. 6.97P
	(Fuji-Robin EC-44-PM) 179-5883 & RM-01						
G-MJNH*	Skyhook Cutlass	260A 156824		13.10.82	M.E.James	Telford	
					(Cancelled by CAA 25.3.99)		
G-MJNK	Hiway Skytrike/Demon 175	EA17D		14.10.82	E.W.Barker	Baxby Manor, Husthwaite	28.10.96P
	(Fuji-Robin EC-34-PM)						
G-MJNM	American Aerolights Double Eagle 430B			25.11.82	B.H.Stephens	Southampton	19. 9.93P
	(Cuyuna 430R)	702					
G-MJNO	American Aerolights Double Eagle Amphibian			24.11.82	R.S.Martin	Gosport	13. 3.00P
	(Rotax 447)	703					
G-MJNS	Swallow AeroPlane Swallow B 782039-2			9. 7.86	F.J.Marton	Dunkeswell	9. 2.93E
	(Cuyuna 430R)				(Stored 7.93)		
G-MJNT	Hiway Skytrike/Demon 175	RO17D		18.10.82	F.Tyreman	Whitby	N/E
	(Fuji-Robin EC-25-PS)						
G-MJNU	Skyhook TR1/Cutlass	TR1/17		19.10.82	R.W.Taylor	Sheffield	
G-MJNV*	Eipper Quicksilver MX	10537		19.10.82	W.Toulmin	Peterborough	
					(Cancelled as destroyed 25.3.99)		
G-MJNY	Skyhook TR1/Sabre	TR1/35		3.11.82	P.Ratcliffe	Sheffield	
G-MJOC	Huntair Pathfinder	048		25.10.82	A.J.Glynn	Southend	31. 7.99P
	(Fuji-Robin EC-34-PM)						
G-MJOD*	Rotec Rally 2B	AK-01		28.10.82	E.L.G.Brocklehurst & A.S.L.Root		
					(Cancelled by CAA 17.3.99)	Manningtree	
G-MJOE	Eurowing Goldwing	EW-55		29.10.82	R.J.Osborne	Tiverton	N/E
	(Rotax 377)						
G-MJOU	Hiway Skytrike II/Demon 175	HP-01		8.11.82	R.J.Thompson (Stored 9.96)	Milson	31. 5.86E
	(Fuji-Robin EC-34-PM) (Probably shares trike with G-MMBS)						
G-MJPA	Rotec Rally 2B	AT-01		5. 1.83	R.Boyd	Armagh	
G-MJPB*	Manuel Ladybird	WLM-14		9.11.82	Estate of W.L.Manuel	Brooklands	
					(On loan to Brooklands Museum)		

Regn	Type	C/n P/I	Date	Owner/operator	Probable Base	CA Expy
G-MJPC*	American Aerolights Double Eagle 430B PHH-01		9.11.82	D.M.Jackson (Stored 9.96; cancelled as WFU 17.2.99)	Hougham, Lincs	
G-MJPE	Hiway Skytrike/Demon 175 OG17D (Fuji-Robin EC-34-PM) (Reported as Mainair Tri-Flyer)		10.11.82	E.G.Astin	Whitby	7. 8.96P
G-MJPO	Eurowing Goldwing 018		16.12.82	M.E.Merryman	Dronfield	
G-MJPP	Hiway Skytrike/Solar Wings Typhoon (Hiro 125) KLM-01		28.11.82	A.B.Greenbank	Bradford	16. 9.97P
G-MJPU	Solar Wings Panther XL (Fuji-Robin EC-44-PM) KND-01 & T1283-948X (Regd with wing later fitted to G-MMHZ)		8. 2.83	M.B.Saunders	Poole	2.12.93P
G-MJPV	Eipper Quicksilver MX JBW-01 (Cuyuna 430R)		30.11.82	F.W.Ellis Water Leisure Park, Skegness		1. 2.95P
G-MJRL	Eurowing Goldwing EW-79 & SWA-5K (Rotax 377)		30.12.82	V.J.Morris	Truro	15. 6.00P
G-MJRO	Eurowing Goldwing EW-77 & SWA-04 (Rotax 447)		31.12.82	H.P.Welch	Taunton	22. 9.99P
G-MJRP	Mainair Tri-Flyer/Hiway Demon 175 (Fuji-Robin EC-34-PM) 118-161282 & OF17D		4. 1.83	W.H.Newton	Wombleton	9.11.97P
G-MJRR	Reece SkyRanger Srs.1 JR-3		26. 4.82	J.R.Reece	Formby	
G-MJRS	Eurowing Goldwing EW-80 & SWA-6K (Rotax 377)		5. 1.83	G.B.Gratton & J.L.Macfarlane Chilbolton		30. 3.97P
G-MJRT	Southdown Puma (Lightning DS) TJF-01 (Fuji-Robin EC-44-PM)		5. 1.83	B.D.Ronaghan	Northampton	16. 7.97P
G-MJRU	MBA Tiger Cub 440 SO.86		6. 1.83	D.J.Short	Nailsea, Bristol	31. 1.86E
G-MJRV*	Eurowing Goldwing EW-69 & BMAA/HB/084		7. 1.83	N.W.Beadle (W/O second flight; cancelled as WFU 16.9.83; sold for spares?)	Billericay	
G-MJSE	Skyrider Airsports Phantom SF-101 (Fuji-Robin EC-40-PL)		24. 1.83	C.L.Betts	Hove	21. 1.00P
G-MJSF	Skyrider Airsports Phantom SF-105	SE- G-MJSF	24. 1.83	B.J.Towers	Pershore	
G-MJSL	Dragon 200 0018 (Rotax 503)		24. 2.83	G.Kingston & N.J.Warner	Long Marston	22. 9.99P
G-MJSO	Hiway Skytrike II/Demon 175 SA17D (Hiro 22)		1. 2.83	D.C.Read	Ledbury	N/E
G-MJSP	Romain MBA Super Tiger Cub Special 440 (Tri-cycle u/c) SO.54		7. 2.83	A P Chapman	Grimsby	31. 1.86E
G-MJST	MEA Pterodactyl Ptraveler GCS-01 (Fuji-Robin EC-34-PM)		2.12.81	C.H.J.Goodwin	Bedford	7. 5.99P
G-MJSU*	MBA Tiger Cub 440 SO.75/1 (Regd with c/n SO.175)		2. 2.83	Not known (Stored in roof 5.99)	Swanton Morley	31. 1.86E
G-MJSV*	MBA Tiger Cub 440 SO.87/2		2. 2.83	Not known (Stored 5.95)	RAF Kinloss	31. 1.86E
G-MJSY	Eurowing Goldwing EW-63 (Rotax 377)		8. 2.83	A.J.Rex	Wrexham	N/E
G-MJSZ	Harker DH Wasp HA.5 (Rotax 447)		10. 2.83	J.J.Hill	Middlesbrough	28. 7.98P
G-MJTD	Gardner T-M Scout 83/001 (Thomas-Morse S4 Scout 2/3rd scale replica; as "41386" in US Army Signal Corps c/s) (Possibly c/n PFA/111-10664)		14. 2.83	D.Gardner	Rugby	AC
G-MJTE	Skyrider Airsports Phantom SF-106 (Fuji-Robin EC-44-PM)		15. 2.83	C.J.Tomlin	Little Down Farm, Milson	1. 7.98P
G-MJTM	Aerostructure Pipistrelle P2B (KFM-107ER) 019 & SAL/P2B/002		21. 2.83	K.S.Matcham	Soberton, Southampton	6.11.00P
G-MJTO	Jordan Duet Srs.1 D 101 (Rotax 503)		19. 7.83	M.E.Bates	Chesterfield	6. 3.94E
G-MJTP	Mainair Tri-Flyer/Flexiform Dual Sealander (Fuji-Robin EC-44-PM) AJDH-01 & 139-7383 (Possibly Dual Striker)		25. 2.83	P.Milton	Bedford	22. 8.00P
G-MJTR	Southdown Puma DS Mk.1 H362 (Fuji-Robin EC-44-PM)		9. 3.83	D.W.Palmer	Bexhill-on-Sea	15. 7.96P
G-MJTX	Skyrider Airsports Phantom SF-110 (Fuji-Robin EC-44-PM)		1. 3.83	G.C.Thomas	Long Marston	22. 4.96P
G-MJTZ	Skyrider Airsports Phantom MBS-01 (Fuji-Robin EC-44-PM) (Eng No.82-00119)		29. 4.83	B.J.Towers	Pershore	N/E
G-MJUC	MBA Tiger Cub 440 RRH-01 & PFA/140-10908 (Fuji-Robin EC-44-PM)		7. 3.83	J.A.Harker (Stored Kirkbride 5.96)	Southampton	20. 1.92E
G-MJUE	Southdown Puma 82-00435 & P.109 (Southdown Wildcat II Trike with Lightning II wing)		8. 3.83	J.Rae	Largs	N/E
G-MJUF*	MBA Super Tiger Cub 400 MCT-01		8. 3.83	Not known (Stored 6.96)	Full Sutton	
G-MJUJ	Eipper Quicksilver MXII 1025 (Rotax 503)		10. 3.83	J.F.A.Cooke	Llanbedr	27. 6.92E
G-MJUM	Hiway Skytrike/Flexiform Striker (Fuji-Robin EC-25-PS) 82-00493 (C/n is Engine No.)		28. 3.83	M.J.W.Holding	Stafford	N/E

Regn	Type	C/n	P/I	Date	Owner/operator	Probable Base	CA Expy
G-MJUO*	Eipper Quicksilver MXII (Cuyana 430R)	1043		22. 3.83	Not known (Noted 8.99)	Strathaven	
G-MJUR	Skyrider Airsports Phantom (Fuji-Robin EC-44-PM)	SF-108		5. 4.83	A.L.Lewis	Milson	20. 9.98P
G-MJUT	Eurowing Goldwing	DLE-01		23. 3.83	D.L.Eite	Newark	
G-MJUU	Eurowing Goldwing (Fuji-Robin EC-344-PM)	EW-70		28. 3.83	E.F.Clapham	Oldbury-on-Severn	3. 5.97P
G-MJUV	Huntair Pathfinder mk.1 (Fuji-Robin EC-44-PM)	045		18. 5.83	S.J.Overton	(Colchester)	31. 3.99P
G-MJUW	MBA Tiger Cub 440 (Fuji-Robin EC-44-PM)	SO.69		29. 3.83	D.G.Palmer	Mintlaw	25. 7.00P
G-MJUX	Skyrider Airsports Phantom (Fuji-Robin EC-44-PM)	RFF-01		29. 2.84	C.A.Crick	Desborough	6. 8.97P
G-MJUY*	Eurowing Goldwing	EW-82		6. 4.83	Not known (Stored complete 9.96)	Hougham, Lincs	N/E
G-MJUZ	Dragon 150 (Robin EC-57)	015		30. 3.83	G.S.Richardson (Stored 9.96)	North Coates	28. 2.87E
G-MJVE	Medway Hybred 44XL/Solar Wings Typhoon XLII (Fuji-Robin EC-44-PM)		4483/1	19. 4.83	T.A.Clark	Manningtree	5. 6.00P
G-MJVF	CFM Shadow Srs.CD (Rotax 503)	002		12. 4.83	J.A.Cook	Thorpeness	16.12.99P
G-MJVN	Southdown Puma/Flexiform Striker (Fuji-Robin EC-44-PM)	82-00030-PR1		18. 4.83	R.McGookin (WFU and engine to G-MJRP)	West Kilbride	5.10.93P
G-MJVP	Eipper Quicksilver MXII	1149		19. 4.83	G.J.Ward	Dorchester	10. 7.96P
G-MJVT	Eipper Quicksilver MX (Cuyuna 430R)	10961		20. 4.83	L.Swift	Skegness	4. 5.94P
G-MJVU	Eipper Quicksilver MXII (Rotax 503)	1118		3. 4.84	F.J.Griffith	Denbigh	16. 6009P
G-MJVX	Skyrider Airsports Phantom (Fuji-Robin EC-44-PM)	JAG-01 & SF-102		27. 4.83	J.R.Harris	Bewdley, Worcs	16. 4.00P
G-MJVY	Dragon 150 (Rotax 503)	D.150/013		4. 5.83	J.C.Craddock	Freshwater, IoW	6. 8.00P
G-MJWB	Eurowing Goldwing (Rotax 447)	EW-59		24. 5.83	F.C.Claydon	Newmarket	25. 8.93P
G-MJWF	MBA Tiger Cub 440	BRH-001		4. 5.83	D.M.Stewart	Kilmacolm	
G-MJWG	MBA Tiger Cub 440 (Fuji-Robin EC-44-PM)	DHC-001, PFA/140-10961 & BMAA/HB/001		4. 5.83	W.K.Evans	Llanelli	18.10.98P
G-MJWH*	Chargus Vortex 120	R			Midland Air Museum	Coventry	
	(Regn reserved in 1983 for a Chargus T.250 plus engine for F.Embleton but fitted to a 1974 Vortex hang glider; this was abandoned and only the wing is on display)						
G-MJWI*	Twamley Trike/Flexiform Striker	RWT-01		8. 7.83	M.P.Challis (Cancelled by CAA 27.3.99)	Northampton	
G-MJWJ	MBA Tiger Cub 440 (Fuji-Robin EC-44-PM)	013/191		9. 5.83	G.Whitaker	Pontypridd	18. 3.96P
G-MJWK	Huntair Pathfinder 1 (Rotax 447)	JWK-01		1.10.82	R.J.F.Coates	Kemble	23. 5.99P
G-MJWN	Hornet/Flexiform Solo Striker (Fuji-Robin EC-34-PM)	H430		10. 5.83	G.de Clara	Stoke-on-Trent	26. 7.91E
G-MJWS*	Eurowing Goldwing	EW-22		16. 5.83	Not known (Stored 4.94)	Newtownards	N/E
G-MJWW	MBA Super Tiger Cub 440 (Fuji-Robin EC-44-PM) (Possibly c/n PFA/140-10904)	MU-001		11. 5.83	R.J.Tobin	Sudbrook, Lincoln	23. 5.98P
G-MJWZ	Solar Wings Panther XL-S (Fuji-Robin EC-44-2PM)	T583-781XL		9. 9.85	C.P.Hughes	Rhuallt	27.10.99P
G-MJXD	MBA Tiger Cub 440	011/061		16. 5.83	W.L.Rogers	Totnes	
G-MJXE	Mainair Tri-Flyer/Hiway Demon 175 (Fuji-Robin EC-34-PM)	102-131082 & HS-001		17. 5.83	H.Sykes	Manchester	21. 3.95P
G-MJXJ*	MBA Tiger Cub 440	SO.100		20. 5.83	P.J.Wright (Cancelled as WFU 6.3.99)	Whitstable	
G-MJXS	Huntair Pathfinder II	134		25. 5.83	A.E.Sawyer (Stored 4.99)	Melrose Farm, Melbourne	
G-MJXX	Lancashire Micro-Trike/Flexiform Dual Striker (Fuji-Robin EC-44-2PM)	AAL-01		16. 6.83	H.A.Ward (Possibly now a Mainair Tri-Flyer)	Popham	24. 2.92E
G-MJXY	Hiway Demon/Skytrike 330 (Fuji-Robin EC-34-PM)	KQ17D		31. 5.83	H.C.Lowther	(Penrith)	25. 7.00P
G-MJYC	Solar Wings Panther XL (Fuji-Robin EC-44-PM)	JM-01		1.10.85	D J Stock	Bantry, Co.Cork	21. 4.98P
G-MJYF	Mainair Gemini/Flash 305-585-3 & W45 (Fuji-Robin EC-44-PM)			18. 4.85	W.D.Crooks	Richhill, Armagh	5. 5.97P
G-MJYP	Mainair Gemini/Flexiform Dual Striker (Fuji-Robin EC-44-PM)	167-13683		7. 6.83	R.Taylor & M.V.Rainford	Ormskirk	1.12.98P

304

Regn	Type	C/n	P/I	Date	Owner/operator	Probable Base	CA Expy
G-MJYV	Mainair/Flexiform Rapier 1 + 1			23.11.83	L.H.Phillips	Solihull	1.11.00P
	(Fuji-Robin EC-34-PM)	175-19783					
G-MJYW	Lancashire Micro-Trike Dual 330/Wasp Gryphon III			28. 6.83	P.D.Lawrence	Munlochy, Ross-shire	
	2/330PM/PGK/6.83/K						
G-MJYX	Mainair Tri-Flyer/Hiway Demon			9. 6.83	I.Dzialowski	Grimsby	27. 6.94P
	(Fji-Robin EC-33-PM)	108-251182					
G-MJYY	Hiway Skytrike/Demon 175	ZD17D		9. 6.83	N.Smith	Brunton	N/E
	(Fuji-Robin EC-34-PM)						
G-MJZC	MBA Tiger Cub 440	SO.169		14. 6.83	R.D.Slegg	Haywards Heath	17. 1.94P
	(Fuji-Robin EC-44-PM)						
G-MJZD	Mainair Gemini/Flash			18. 4.85	A.R.Gaivoto	Popham	10. 4.00P
	(Fuji-Robin EC-44-PM)	311-585-3 & W50					
G-MJZE	MBA Tiger Cub 440	SO.168		14. 6.83	J.E.D.Rogerson	Ferryhill	31. 1.86E
					t/a Fishburn Flying Tigers		
G-MJZH	Mainair Tri-Flyer/Southdown Lightning 195			27. 6.83	A.G.Thelwall	Bedford	N/E
	(Fuji-Robin EC-25-PS) BFC-01 & 002-781 (Trike unit from G-MBCC)						
G-MJZK(2)	Southdown Puma Sprint	1111/0081		3. 3.86	R.J.Osborne	Tiverton	18.10.91P*
	(Fuji-Robin EC-44-PM)						
G-MJZL	Eipper Quicksilver MXII	EEW-01		15. 6.83	A.P.Kenning	Boston	7. 7.98P
	(Rotax 503)						
G-MJZO	Lancashire Micro-Trike/Flexiform Solo Striker			24. 6.83	J.W.Coventry	Davidstow Moor	2.11.00P
	(Fuji-Robin EC-34-PM) 1/330PM/LM/683/2						
G-MJZU	Mainair Tri-Flyer/Flexiform Dual Striker			21. 6.83	P.D.Mickleburgh	Fleckney, Leicester	3. 6.99P
	(Fuji-Robin EC-44-PM)	JDR-02					
G-MJZX	Maxair Hummer TX	TX/16		21. 6.83	R.J.Folwell	London W.6	
G-MKAK	Colt 77A HAFB	2039		15. 8.91	Virgin Airship & Balloon Co Ltd	Telford	13. 6.97A
G-MKAS	PA-28-140 Cherokee Cruiser		G-BKVR	30. 4.98	MK Aero Support Ltd	Norwich	8. 7.01T
		28-7425338	OY-BGV				
G-MKIV*	Bristol 149 Bolingbroke IVT	-	(G-BLHM)	26. 3.82	G.A.Warner	Duxford	28. 5.88P
			RCAF 10038		(As "V6028/GB-D" in 105 Sqdn c/s)		
					(Damaged Denham 21.6.87; on rebuild 1999 for static exhibition)		
G-MKIX	VS.361 Spitfire IXe	CBAF.IX.2200	N238V	12.12.83	D.W.Arnold	(Bournemouth)	22. 5.93P
	(Firewall No.CBAF.8563)		OO-ARE/Belg.AF SM-36/Fokker B-8/R.Neth AF H-60/H-103/NH238				
					t/a Warbirds of GB (As "NH238/D-A": stored 1996)		
G-MKPU	Europa Avn Europa	PFA/247-12569	G-DZEL	22.12.97	M.K.Papworth	(Upwood, Cambs)	
					(Cf/f 16.11.99)		
G-MKVB	VS.349 Spitfire LF.Vb	CBAF.2461	5718M	2. 5.89	Historic Acft Collection Ltd	Duxford	25. 3.00P
			BM597		(As "BM597/JH-C" in 317 Sqdn c/s)		
G-MKVI	FFW DH.100 Vampire FB.6	676	J-1167	2. 6.92	T.C.Topen	Swansea	14. 9.95P
					(To De Havilland Aviation Ltd)		
					(As "WL505" in 614 Sqn c/s: stored 3.97)		
G-MKXI	VS.365 Spitfire PR.XII	6S/504719	R Neth AF	13.11.89	R.A.Fleming & A.J.E.Smith	Breighton	11. 6.99P
	(Packard Merlin 266)		PL965		(Op Real Aeroplane Co) (As "PL965/R" in 16 Sqn RAF c/s)		
G-MLAS*	Cessna 182E	182-53826	OO-HPE	2. 5.79	Not known	St.Merryn	2.10.82
			D-EGPE/N2826Y		(Crashed 14.12.80; cabin used as para-trainer 5.94)		
G-MLFF	PA-23-250 Aztec E	27-7305194	G-WEBB	31. 1.90	Channel Islands Aero Services Ltd Jersey		28.11.02T
			G-BJBU/N40476		t/a Jersey Aero Club		
G-MLJL	Airbus A.330-243	254	F-WWKT	15. 6.99	Airtours International Airways Ltd		14 .5.02T
					"Ben Crosland"	Manchester	
G-MLTI	Dassault Falcon 900B	164	F-WWFC	13. 6.97	Multiflight Ltd	Leeds-Bradford	12. 6.99T
G-MLTY	Aerospatiale AS.365N2 Dauphin	6431	N365EL	4. 6.99	Multiflight Ltd	Leeds-Bradford	3..6.00
			JA6673				
G-MLWI	Thunder Ax7-77 HAFB	1000		3. 9.86	M.L. & L.P.Willoughby	Reading	7. 6.00A
					"Mr Blue Sky"		
G-MMAC	Dragon Srs.200	003	OY-...	14. 7.82	J.F.Ashton & J.Kirwan	Ince Blundell	N/E
	(Fuji-Robin EC-44-PM)		G-MMAC				
G-MMAE	Dragon Srs 200	005		7. 9.82	B.P.Walmbley	Davidstow Moor	29. 7.96P
	(Fuji-Robin EC-44-PM)						
G-MMAG	MBA Tiger Cub 440	SO.47		22. 6.83	M.J.Aubrey	Kington, Hereford	14. 9.93P
	(Fuji-Robin EC-44-PM)						
G-MMAI	Dragon Srs.150	0032		1. 7.83	G.S.Richardson	North Coates	13. 7.97P
	(Fuji-Robin EC-44-PM)						
G-MMAJ	Mainair Gemini/Southdown Sprint X			12.10.83	D.M.Pearson	Chiltern Park, Wallingford	19. 3.98P
	(Fuji-Robin EC-44-PM) MLS.01 & 193-14983						
G-MMAK	MBA Tiger Cub 440	SO.155		20. 9.83	G.E.Heritage	Corley, Coventry	
G-MMAL	Mainair Tri-Flyer/Flexiform Dual Striker			20. 9.83	Tina E.Simpson	Bewdley, Worcs	1. 4.94P
	(Fuji-Robin EC-44-PM)	DHM-01			(On rebuild 10.97)		
G-MMAM	MBA Tiger Cub 440	SO.197		23. 9.83	M.G.Reilly	Old Sarum	14. 6.96P
	(Fuji-Robin EC-44-PM)						
G-MMAN	Mainair Tri-Flyer 330/Flexiform Solo Striker			27. 9.83	K.F.Gittins	Rufforth	23. 3.00P
		192-6983					

Regn	Type	C/n	P/I	Date	Owner/operator	Probable Base	CA Expy
G-MMAO	Southdown Puma Sprint X (Fuji-Robin EC-44-PM)	HS.549		28.12.83	P.A.Kershaw	Tarn Farm, Cockerham	14. 3.99P
G-MMAP	Maxair Hummer TX (Zenoah 250)	250TX-17		29. 9.83	P Williams	Leicester	5. 9.93E
G-MMAR	Mainair Gemini/Southdown Puma Sprint MS (Fuji-Robin EC-44-PM)	195-11083-2		23. 9.83	A.R. & J.Fawkes	Newbury	17. 9.98P
G-MMAW	Mainair/Flexiform Rapier 1+1 (Solo Striker) (Fuji-Robin EC-34-PM)	131-10283		18. 7.83	G.B.Hutchison	Bury St.Edmunds	29. 7.96P
G-MMAX	Hiway Skytrike/Flexiform Dual Striker	0011		5. 8.93	D A Hopewell & M T Wells	Newcastle	N/E
G-MMAZ	Southdown Puma Sprint X (Fuji-Robin EC-44-PM)	MAPB-01		5. 8.83	A.R.Smith	Chelmsford	22. 7.96P
G-MMBJ	Hiway Skytrike/Solar Wings Medium Typhoon (Fuji-Robin EC-34-PM)	RFB-01		5. 7.83	W.Wells	Belvedere, Kent	11. 6.96P
G-MMBL	Southdown Puma DS (Fuji-Robin EC-44-PM)	80-00083		4. 7.83	B.J.Farrell	Preston, Lancs	7. 3.92E
G-MMBN	Eurowing Goldwing (Rotax 447)	EW-89		28. 6.83	W.G.Reynolds (Stored 8.93)	Overstrand, Cromer	27. 8.92E
G-MMBS	Hiway Skytrike/Flexiform Striker (Fuji-Robin EC-34-PM)	JTRC-01 (Possibly shares trike with G-MJOU)		6. 7.83	R.J.Thompson (Stored 9.96)	Milson	5. 3.94E
G-MMBT	MBA Tiger Cub 440 (Probably either c/n PFA/140-10924 or 10990)	SO.131 & TA.01		19. 7.83	F.F.Chamberlain (Stored 1.91)	Ipswich	31. 1.86E
G-MMBU	Eipper Quicksilver MXII (Rotax 503)	CAL-222		8. 7.83	G.Lockwood	Bridlington	11. 5.00P
G-MMBV	Huntair Pathfinder (Fuji-Robin EC-34-PM) (New sailwing 1999)	044		8. 7.83	P.J.Bishop	Tarn Farm, Cockerham	17. 5.97P
G-MMBY	Solar Wings Panther XL (Fuji-Robin EC-44-PM)	T483-759XL		20. 7.83	R.M.Sheppard & P.Huddleston	Wantage/Marlborough	29. 7.00P
G-MMBZ	Solar Wings Typhoon P (Fuji-Robin EC-34-PM)	T981-5217 (C/n probably T981-217)		20. 7.83	T.J.Birkbeck	Rufforth	28. 4.96P
G-MMCB*	Huntair Pathfinder II	136		13. 7.83	The Science Museum (On display 7.92)	Wroughton	
G-MMCG*	Eipper Quicksilver MX I (Cuyuna 430R)	10990		14. 7.83	D.Pick (Cancelled by CAA 23.7.99)	Boston	7. 7.98P
G-MMCI	Southdown Puma Sprint X (Fuji-Robin EC-44-PM)	DMP-01 & P.421		28. 9.83	R.J.Webb	Long Marston	22. 7.00P
G-MMCJ	Flexiform Dual Striker	JJ-165		13. 2.87	L.G.Martindale	Liverpool	N/E
G-MMCM	Mainair Tri-Flyer/Southdown Puma Sprint (Fuji-Robin EC-44-PM)	CM-2		28. 6.83	J.McAvoy	Bishopton, Renfrew	17. 7.98P
G-MMCV	Hiway Skytrike II/Solar Wings Typhoon (Fuji-Robin EC-34-PM)	T583-783		27. 7.83	G.Addison	Kinross	8. 6.97P
G-MMCW	Southdown Puma Sprint 572 & 1121/0124 (Fuji-Robin EC-44-PM)			16. 9.83	J.Brandrick	Cwmdwyfran Farm, Carmarthen	6. 8.97P
G-MMCX	MBA Super Tiger Cub 440	MU.002		8. 8.83	D.Harkin	Johnstone, Renfrew	
G-MMCZ	Mainair Tri-Flyer/Flexiform Dual Striker (Fuji-Robin EC-44-PM)	TE-01 (Mainair Trike c/n 180-...)		10. 8.83	T.D.Adamson	Morgansfield, Fishburn	12.12.99P
G-MMDF	Southdown Wild Cat Mk.II/Lightning Phase II (Fuji-Robin EC-34-PM)	007		24. 8.83	J.C.Haigh	Tonbridge	27. 1.99P
G-MMDK	Mainair Tri-Flyer/Flexiform Striker (Fuji-Robin EC-34-PM)	181-16883		7. 9.83	P.E.Blyth	Rotherham	30. 5.99P
G-MMDN	Mainair Tri-Flyer/Flexiform Dual Striker	RPO.12 (Initially had Hornet Invader trike and still regd with Hornet c/n)		30. 9.83	M.G.Griffiths	Monmouth	N/E
G-MMDP	Mainair Gemini/Southdown Sprint X (Fuji-Robin EC-44-PM)	183-22883 (C/n duplicates G-MMPD; probably fitted with new Gemini trike)		20. 9.83	J.D.Bridgewater & C.H.Prince	Kirkmichael, IoM	25. 1.95P
G-MMDR	Huntair Pathfinder II	137		30. 8.83	C.Dolling	Swindon	
G-MMDS	Solar Wings Panther XL-S (Fuji-Robin EC-34-PM)	KND-02		13. 7.84	C.C.Exton	London E15	10. 1.94P
G-MMDT*	Mainair Tri-Flyer/Flexiform Striker (Fuji-Robin EC-44-PM)	178-20583		1. 9.83	Not known (Stored 8.95)	Long Marston	N/E
G-MMDU*	MBA Tiger Cub 440 (Fuji-Robin EC-44-PM)	SO.49		5. 9.83	Not known (Stored dismantled 3.98)	Chirk	N/E
G-MMDX	Lloyd Trident/Solar Wings Typhoon	EJL-01		7. 9.83	E.J.Lloyd (Status uncertain)	Caterham, Surrey	
G-MMDY	Southdown Puma Sprint X (Fuji-Robin EC-44-PM)	S.064		7. 9.83	C.Duffin	Portlaoise, Co.Laois	N/E
G-MMEF	Hiway Skytrike/Super Scorpion	SM160B 10664		13. 9.83	R.H.Evans	Bury St.Edmunds	
G-MMEG*	Eipper Quicksilver MX	DJND-02		14. 9.83	Not known (Stored 1994)	Rayne Hall Farm, Rayne	N/E

Regn	Type	C/n P/I	Date	Owner/operator	Probable Base	CA Expy
G-MMEI	Hiway Skytrike/Demon	3644C	21. 9.83	W.H.Shakeshaft	Chelmsford	30.11.94P
	(Fuji-Robin EC-34-PM)					
G-MMEJ	Mainair Tri-Flyer/Flexiform Striker		15. 9.83	R.B.Tweedie	Stoke-on-Trent	9.11.97P
	(Fuji-Robin EC-34-PM) 215-41183 & FF/LAI/83/JDR/03					
G-MMEK	Medway Hybred 44XL/Solar Wings Typhoon XL2		16. 9.83	M.G.J.Bridges	Exeter	28..8.00P
	(Fuji-Robin EC-44-PM)	12983/6				
G-MMEO	Ultrasports Tripacer/Southdown Lightning Phase II		21. 9.83	G.C.Rogers	Dartford	4. 1.95P
		135				
G-MMES*	Southdown Puma Sprint	SS.582	21.12.83	S.E.Balley	Newbury	11. 8.98P
	(Fuji-Robin EC-44-PM)			t/a Balleys Forecourt Sves (Cancelled by CAA 27.3.99)		
G-MMEY*	MBA Tiger Cub 440	SO.206	21.10.83	G.N.Harris	Grantham	26. 5.95P
	(Fuji-Robin EC-44-PM)			(Cancelled as PWFU 29.12.99)		
G-MMFC*	Mainair Gemini/Flexiform Dual Striker		20. 9.83	L.R.Orriss	Rotherham	29.12.94P
	(Fuji-Robin EC-44-PM) KR235-484-2 & FF/LAI/83/JDR/11			(Cancelled by CAA 25.8.98)		
G-MMFD	Mainair Tri-Flyer/Flexiform Dual Striker		20. 9.83	M.E. & W.L.Chapman	Oldham	6.12.93P
	(Fuji-Robin EC-44-PM) 210-31083-2 & FF/LAI/83/JDR/12					
G-MMFE	Mainair Tri-Flyer/Flexiform Striker		20. 9.83	W.Camm	Barnsley	16. 6.94P
	(Fuji-Robin EC-44-PM) FF/LAI/83/JDR/13					
G-MMFG	Lancashire Micro-Trike/Flexiform Dual Striker		20. 9.83	M.G.Dean & M.J.Hadland		
	(Fuji-Robin EC-44-PM) FF/LAI/83/JDR/15				Tarn Farm, Cockerham	18. 3.93E
G-MMFK	Mainair Tri-Flyer/Flexiform Dual Striker		20. 9.83	M.J.Robbins	Tunbridge Wells	19. 7.96P
	(Rotax 447) 234-284-2 & FF/LAI/83/JDR/19					
G-MMFL	Ultrasports Tripacer/Flexiform Solo Sealander		25.10.83	T.C.Bradley	Gloucester	N/E
	(Fuji-Robin EC-34-PM)	JGM-01				
G-MMFN	MBA Tiger Cub 440	SO.113	31.10.83	J.S.Skipp	Bromyard, Hereford	30.11.95P
	(Fuji-Robin EC-44-PM)					
G-MMFS	MBA Tiger Cub 440	SO.64	1.11.83	G.S.Taylor	Shrewsbury	3. 5.00P
	(Fuji-Robin EC-44-PM)					
G-MMFT	MBA Tiger Cub 440	SO.56	2.11.83	E.N.Simmons	Wyberton	23. 1.95P
	(Fuji-Robin EC-34-PM)					
G-MMFV	Mainair Tri-Flyer/Flexiform Dual Striker		8.12.83	R.A.Walton	Basingstoke	26. 4.97P
	(Fuji-Robin EC-44-PM)	212-271083				
G-MMFZ	Striplin Sky Ranger	HAW-01	18.11.83	H.A.Ward	Winchester	
G-MMGF	MBA Tiger Cub 440	SO.124	18.11.83	A.P.Chapman	Grimsby	30. 7.00P
G-MMGL	MBA Tiger Cub 440 SO.148 & BMAA/HB/050		23.11.83	H.E.Dunning	Knaresborough	10.11.00P
	(Fuji-Robin EC-44-PM)					
G-MMGP	Southdown Puma Sprint X	RGC-01	24.11.83	J.Garcia	Kilmarnock	5. 2.92E
	(Fuji-Robin EC-44-PM)					
G-MMGS	Solar Wings Panther XL		28.12.83	D.W.Bock	Saltash	12. 8.98P
	(Fuji-Robin EC-44-PM)	T1283-939XL				
G-MMGT	Hunt Avon Skytrike/Hunt Wing	JAH-7	28.11.83	J.A.Hunt	Hereford	17. 4.00P
	(Exhibited at PFA Cranfield 7.99 as "Huntwing R100RS" with BMW engine)					
G-MMGU	SMD Gazelle/Flexiform Sealander		1.12.83	A.D.Cranfield	Wincanton	19. 9.93E
	(Fuji-Robin EC-44-PM)	30-4883				
G-MMGV	Microknight Whittaker MW-5 Sorcerer Srs.A		2.12.83	G.N.Haffey & M.W.J.Whittaker		
		001			Chatham/Doncaster	6. 5.89P
G-MMHE*	Mainair Gemini/Southdown Sprint MS		8.12.83	L.Fekete & J.Sharp	Rhuallt	27. 5.98P
	(Fuji-Robin EC-44-PM)	229-184-2		(Cancelled by CAA 30.10.98)		
G-MMHF	Southdown Puma Sprint	EBDA-01	8.12.83	B.R.Claughton	Whitstable	2.10.99P
	(Fuji-Robin EC-44-PM)					
G-MMHK	Hiway Skytrike/Super Scorpion KSC.83		19.12.83	C.N.Bradley	Darlington	N/E
	(Fuji-Robin EC-25-PS)					
G-MMHL	Hiway Skytrike/Super Scorpion KSC.84		19.12.83	E.J.Blyth	Pickering	N/E
G-MMHN	MBA Tiger Cub 440	SO.136	19.12.83	M.J.Aubrey	Kington, Hereford	
G-MMHP	Hiway Hiro Skytrike/Demon 175		19.12.83	P.A.Bedford	Tewkesbury	N/E
	PCC-01 & OL17D	(Regd with c/n OL175)				
G-MMHR	Mainair Gemini/Southdown Sprint		29.12.83	C.A.Eagles	Basingstoke	2. 9.90P
	(Fuji-Robin EC-44-PM) 213-271083-2 & P.427					
G-MMHS	SMD Gazelle/Flexiform Dual Striker	-	21.12.83	C.J.Meadows	Shepton Mallet	
		104-11283				
G-MMHY	Hornet Invader 440/Flexiform Dual Striker		21.12.83	W.Finlay	Leeds	
		RPO.17				
G-MMHZ	Solar Wings Panther XL-S		3. 1.84	S.J.Pain	Hulcote Farm, Nottingham	28. 7.00P
	(Fuji-Robin EC-44-PM) TP2-0001 & T1283-948XL (Wing ex G-MJPU)					
G-MMIE	MBA Tiger Cub 440	G7-7	3. 1.84	B.W.Olliver	Telford	31. 1.86E
G-MMIH	MBA Tiger Cub 440	SO.130	25. 4.84	R.A.Davis	Gloucester	19. 8.93P
	(Fuji-Robin EC-44-PM)					
G-MMII	Southdown Puma Sprint	P.500	26. 1.84	P.J.Daulton	Billingshurst	24. 6.96P
	(Fuji-Robin EC-44-PM)					
G-MMIJ	Ultrasports Tripacer/Airwave Nimrod 165		1.11.83	R.J.Wheeler	Haverfordwest	9.12.96P
	(Fuji-Robin EC-34-PM)	ZX-00165				

Regn	Type	C/n	P/I	Date	Owner/operator	Probable Base	CA Expy
G-MMIL	Eipper Quicksilver MXII (Rotax 503) (C/n duplicates G-MMNA)	1046		6. 1.84	C.K.Brown	Loughborough	24. 3.94P
G-MMIM	MBA Tiger Cub 440 SO.28 & BMAA/HB/060 (Fuji-Robin EC-44-PM)			11. 1.84	T.J.Bidwell	Newtown, Powys	26. 3.00P
G-MMIO*	Huntair Pathfinder II	159		16. 1.84	Not known (Stored 6.96)	Melrose Farm, Melbourne	
G-MMIR	Mainair Gemini/Southdown Sprint (Fuji-Robin EC-44-PM) 051-20182 (Regd with original Trike c/n ex G-MBKX then G-MJDO; now rebuilt with Trike 314-585-3 ex G-MMZK; wing ex G-MMTI)			25. 1.84	J.P.Wilson (Stored 1.98)	Long Marston	15. 8.97P
G-MMIV*	Mainair Gemini/Southdown Sprint (Fuji-Robin EC-44-PM)	231-184-2		3. 2.84	W.Anderson (Cancelled by CAA 21.1.98)	Linlithgow	30. 4.98P
G-MMIW	Southdown Puma Sprint (Fuji-Robin EC-44-PM)	590		9. 2.84	F.H.Cook	Whitchurch	3. 9.99P
G-MMIX	MBA Tiger Cub 440 (Fuji-Robin EC-44-PM)	MBCB-01		14. 2.84	J.S.Morgan	Long Marston	N/E
G-MMJB*	American Aerolights Eagle	JB-01		21. 3.83	Not known	Long Marston	31. 8.85E
G-MMJD	Southdown Puma Sprint (Fuji-Robin EC-44-PM)	SP/1001		28. 6.83	A.C.Snowling	Dereham	1. 8.00P
G-MMJF	Solar Wings Panther Dual XL-S (Fuji-Robin EC-44-PM) T284-988XL			27. 2.84	D.J. & M.E.Walcroft	Great Missenden	20. 4.00P
G-MMJG	Mainair Tri-Flyer/Flexiform Dual Striker (Fuji-Robin EC-44-PM) 185-1983			31. 9.83	A.D.Stewart	Dollar, Clackmannan	1. 7.99P
G-MMJM	Southdown Puma Sprint (Fuji-Robin EC-44-PM) PD.500 & 1111/0001			27. 2.84	R.J.Sanger	Wickford	31. 5.97P
G-MMJS*	MBA Tiger Cub 440	WAM.1		8. 1.87	J.M.Robinson (Stored 1.93)	Bann Foot, Lough Neagh	
G-MMJT	Mainair Gemini/Southdown Sprint X (Fuji-Robin EC-44-PM) JBT-01			20.12.83	W.F.Murray	Swinford, Rugby	27. 7.00P
G-MMJV	MBA Tiger Cub 440 SO.195 & PFA/140-1090 (Fuji-Robin EC-44-PM)			25. 3.84	D.G.Palmer	Mintlaw, Peterhead	9. 5.93P
G-MMJX	Teman Mono-Fly (Rotax 377)	01		6. 3.84	M.Ingleton	Sheerness	27. 5.00P
G-MMKA	Solar Wings Panther Dual XL (Fuji-Robin EC-44-PM) T284-986XL			8. 3.84	R.S.Wood	Wallacestone, Falkirk	30. 4.86E
G-MMKD	Southdown Puma Sprint (Fuji-Robin EC-44-PM)	P.514		27. 2.84	G.G.Stokes	Stourport-on-Severn	11. 6.95P
G-MMKE	Birdman WT-11 Chinook	01817		2. 4.84	D.M.Jackson	Belper	31.12.87E
G-MMKG	Medway Hybred 44XL/Solar Wings Typhoon XL2 (Fuji-Robin EC-44-PM) 22284/7 (Reported with wing marked G-MNYX 8.96)			9. 3.84	G.P.Lane	Bristol	18. 7.97P
G-MMKH	Medway Hybred 44XL/Solar Wings Typhoon XL (Fuji-Robin EC-44-PM) 22284/8			9. 3.84	K.W.E.Brunnenkant	Lincoln	16.10.00P
G-MMKL	Mainair Gemini/Flash 238-384-2 & W11 (Fuji-Robin EC-44-PM)			12. 3.84	D.W.Cox	Coventry	29. 9.93P
G-MMKM	Mainair Gemini/Flexiform Dual Striker (Fuji-Robin EC-44-PM) 221-184-2 (Regd/stamped with c/n 221-0184-0002) Baxby Manor, Husthwaite			12. 3.84	N.J.Raeside & M.Grundmann		11. 6.99P
G-MMKP	MBA Tiger Cub 440	SO.203		13. 3.84	J.W.Beaty	Kettering	
G-MMKR	Mainair Tri-Flyer/Southdown Lightning DS (Fuji-Robin EC-44-PM) 209-171083			14. 3.84	C.R.Madden	Great Orton	24. 6.00P
G-MMKU	Mainair Gemini/Southdown Sprint MS (Fuji-Robin EC-44-PM) 232-284-2 & P.519			19. 3.84	T.J.Ford & R.D.McManus	Stone	2.10.94P
G-MMKV	Southdown Puma Sprint (Fuji-Robin EC-44-PM)	P.521		24. 4.84	A.Turnbull	Clitheroe	24. 7.99P
G-MMKX	Skyrider Airsports Phantom 330 (Fuji-Robin EC-34-PL-02)	PH-107R		18. 3.85	D.B.White	Little Gransden	15. 5.00P
G-MMLB	MBA Super Tiger Cub 440	SO.57		19. 3.84	A.Newton	Hull	
G-MMLE	Eurowing Goldwing SP	EW-81		21. 3.84	D.Lamberty	Linlithgow	
G-MMLF	MBA Tiger Cub 440 (Fuji-Robin EC-44-PM)	SO.115		23. 3.84	W.M.Wilson	Doncaster	31.12.91E
G-MMLH	Hiway Skytrike Mk.II 330/Demon PMH-01 & DJL-01			28. 3.84	P.M.Hendry & D.J.Lukey	Folkestone	
G-MMLM	MBA Tiger Cub 440	SO.172		26. 3.84	J.Scholefield	Glasgow	N/E
G-MMLP	Mainair Gemini/Southdown Sprint (Fuji-Robin EC-44-PM) 242-484-2			3. 4.84	K.D.Parnell	Eaglescott	13. 9.00P
G-MMLV	Southdown Puma 330 (Lightning) (Fuji-Robin EC-34-PM) P3-84-4-164 (C/n quoted as P3-84-164)			29.11.84	C.L.Newcombe	Ashford, Kent	31. 5.97P
G-MMLX	Solar Wings Panther XL-S (Fuji-Robin EC-44-PM) T584-1063XL			3. 7.84	M.J.Curnow	Marazon	7. 8.99P
G-MMMB	Mainair Tri-Flyer/Southdown Sprint (Fuji-Robin EC-44-PM) CR-01/170 & 170-16583 (Trike unit ex G-MJYU)			5. 4.84	K.Birkett	Southampton	18. 8.99P
G-MMMD	Mainair Gemini/Southdown Sprint (Fuji-Robin EC-44-PM) 224-184-2 & P.504			30.12.83	R.J.Newsham	Clench Common	14. 8.97P

Regn	Type	C/n	P/I	Date	Owner/operator	Probable Base	CA Expy
G-MMMG	Eipper Quicksilver MXL (Rotax 377)	1383		5. 6.84	J.J.James	Spilsby, Lincs	29. 6.00P
G-MMMH	Hadland Willow/Flexiform Striker (BMW R80/7)	MJH 383		9.12.83	M.J.Hadland	Wigan	3. 5.00P
G-MMMI	Ultrasports Tripacer/Southdown Lightning DS Phase II (Fuji-Robin EC-34-PM)	SW-01		30. 3.84	S.Moore Lower Mountpleasant, Chatteris		8. 7.96P
G-MMML	Dragon Srs.150 (Fuji-Robin EC-44-PM)	D150/002	OY-... G-MMML	28. 6.83	R.G.Huntley	Bradford-on-Avon	6. 9.00P
G-MMMN	Solar Wings Panther Dual XL-S (Fuji-Robin EC-44-2PM)	PXL 843-150		4. 4.84	C.Downton	Newton Abbot	5.12.99P
G-MMMR	Ultrasports Tripacer/Flexiform Striker (Fuji-Robin EC-34-PM)	MAR-01		14. 3.84	H.A.Lloyd-Jennings	London SW6	31. 3.00P
G-MMMW	Hornet Invader/Flexiform Dual Striker (Fuji-Robin EC-44-2PM)	KMS-01 & RPO.18		29. 3.84	A.Worthington	Chorley	19.11.97P
G-MMNA*	Eipper Quicksilver MXII (C/n duplicates G-MMIL)	1046		30. 3.84	K.R.Daly St.Marys, Isles of Scilly (Cancelled by CAA 28.1.99)		2.11.93P
G-MMNB	Eipper Quicksilver MX (Cuyuna 430R)	4286		30. 3.84	J.T.Lindop	Long Marston	12.10.97P
G-MMNC	Eipper Quicksilver MX (Cuyuna 430R)	4276		30. 3.84	K.R.Daly St.Marys, Isles of Scilly		31. 5.96P
G-MMND	Eipper Quicksilver MXII Q2 (Rotax 503)	1038		30. 3.84	G.B.Burby Tarn Farm, Cockerham (Status uncertain)		13.11.94P
G-MMNH	Dragon Srs.150 (Fuji-Robin EC-44-PM)	D150/42		27. 7.83	T.J.Barlow	Dromore	30. 3.93E
G-MMNM	Hornet 330/Skyhook Sabre	H310		9. 4.84	T.Pearson	Huddersfield	
G-MMNN	Sherry Buzzard	1		6. 4.84	E.W.Sherry	Stoke-on-Trent	
G-MMNS	Mitchell Super Wing U-2	PFA/114-10690		11. 4.84	C.Baldwin & J.C.Lister	Valley Farm, Winwick	
G-MMNT	Flexiform Solo Striker (Rotax 277)	SSL-1		16. 4.84	C.R.Thorne	Lyndhurst, Hants	N/E
G-MMNW	Mainair Tri-Flyer/Hiway Demon 175 (Fuji-Robin EC-34-PM)	TJ-01		2. 8.84	T.Cottrell	Douglas, IoM	29. 6.97P
G-MMNX	Solar Wings Panther XL	PXL 844-153		8. 5.84	B.Montsern	Lenham Heath, Maidstone	AC
G-MMOB	Mainair Gemini/Southdown Sprint (Fuji-Robin EC-44-PM)	244-584-2		11. 5.84	D.Woolcock	Preston	3. 9.99P
G-MMOF	MBA Tiger Cub 440 (Fuji-Robin EC-44-PM)	SO.76		14. 6.83	D.Gee	Barnsley	30.11.92E
G-MMOH	Solar Wings Pegasus XL-R	SW-TB-1450 & T484-1054XL		4. 5.84	T.H.Scott Rayne Hall Farm, Rayne (New Trike fitted replacing one formerly on G-MBTT)		
G-MMOK	Solar Wings Panther XL-S (Fuji-Robin EC-44-PM)	T584-1066XL		9. 5.84	R.F. & A.J.Foster	Woodbridge	1. 7.00P
G-MMOW	Mainair Gemini/Flash (Fuji-Robin EC-44-PM)	246-684-3		21. 5.84	J.Wakelin	Boscastle	20. 4.00P
G-MMPG	Southdown Puma Sprint (Fuji-Robin EC-34-PM)	NEA-01 (Tripacer/Lightning II)		8. 6.84	W.Parsons	Royston	14. 2.98P
G-MMPH	Southdown Puma Sprint (Fuji-Robin EC-44-PM)	P.545		20. 6.84	J.E.Mills	Shifnal	5.11.98P
G-MMPL	Lancashire Micro-Trike 440/Flexiform Dual Striker (Fuji-Robin EC-44-PM)	PDL-02 & 2/330PM/PGK/683/K		5.12.83	P.D.Lawrence	Munlochy, Ross-shire	28. 8.99P
G-MMPO	Mainair Gemini/Flash (Fuji-Robin EC-44-PM)	325-785-3 & W65		18. 4.85	H.B.Baker	Chilbolton	16. 6.00P
G-MMPR*	Dragon Srs.150	0011		18. 4.83	Not known	Letterkenny, Ireland	28. 2.87E
G-MMPT	SMD Gazelle/Flexiform Dual Striker	ECP-01		5. 6.84	A.K.Buttle	Sherborne	N/E
G-MMPU	Ultrasports Tripacer/Solar Wings Typhoon S4 (Fuji-Robin EC-34-PM)	RJH-01		5. 6.84	J.T.Halford	Holt, Norfolk	22. 5.96P
G-MMPZ	Teman Mono-Fly (Rotax 447)	JWH-01		2. 7.84	P.B.Kylo	Consett	6.11.99P
G-MMRH	Hiway Skytrike/Demon	JSM-01 & 25R1		20. 6.84	J.S.McCaig	North Berwick	
G-MMRJ*	Solar Wings Panther XL-S (Fuji-Robin EC-44-PM)	PXL846-167 & T684-1098XL		21. 6.84	Not known Hatherton, Cannock (Stored 5.93)		18. 4.90P
G-MMRK	Solar Wings Panther XL-S (Fuji-Robin EC-44-PM)	PXL846-175 & T684-1107XL		9. 7.84	L.S.Broom	London W12	28. 9.95P
G-MMRL	Solar Wings Panther XL-S (Fuji-Robin EC-44-PM)	PXL846-174 & T684-1102XL		17. 7.84	A.B.Cameron	Preston	7. 1.00P
G-MMRN	Southdown Puma Sprint (Fuji-Robin EC-44-PM)	P.544		16. 7.84	T.F.R.Calladine	Selston, Nottingham	26. 3.00P
G-MMRO	Mainair Gemini/Southdown Sprint (Fuji-Robin EC-44-PM)	258-784-2 & P.557		17.10.84	M.A.Sims (Stored 8.97)	Old Sarum	7. 4.96P
G-MMRP	Mainair Gemini/Southdown Sprint (Fuji-Robin EC-44-PM)	259-884-2 & P.561		7. 2.85	J.C.S.Jones	Rhuallt	20. 8.99P

Regn	Type	C/n	P/I	Date	Owner/operator	Probable Base	CA Expy
G-MMRT	Southdown Raven X	2232/0175		11. 7.84	V.A.Brierley (Damaged mid.1996)	Dover	11. 8.99P
	(Rotax 447) (Originally regd to Puma Sprint (Fuji-Robin EC-44-PM) c/n T.513 & P.532; amended 8.1986 but						
	possibly reverted in 1987)						
G-MMRW	Mainair Gemini 440/Flexiform Dual Striker			5. 1.84	M.D.Hinge	Salisbury	N/E
	LAI/DS/25 & 216-71283-2						
G-MMRY	Chargus T.250/Hiway Vulcan	EDG-01		17. 7.84	D.L.Edwards, I.R.Davis & R.J.Grantham		
						Weston-super-Mare/Bath	
G-MMRZ	Solar Wings Panther XL-S			16. 7.84	A.L.Lyall	East Fortune	20. 6.00P
	(Fuji-Robin EC-44-PM) PXL847-168 & T684-1099XL						
G-MMSA	Solar Wings Panther XL-S			9. 8.84	A.Draper, G.Jones & D.A.Breeze		
	(Fuji-Robin EC-44-2PM) PXL847-189 & T184-1142XL					Newtown, Powys	27. 5.98P
	(C/n probably T784-1142XL)						
G-MMSE	Eipper Quicksilver MX	10021		23. 7.84	P.Rowbotham	Loughborough	31.10.85E
G-MMSG	Solar Wings Panther XL-S			6. 9.85	R.W.McKee	Deeside	4. 6.00P
	(Fuji-Robin EC-44-2PM) T884-1165XL (Regd with c/n 8841/65XC; c/n duplicates G-MMTT)						
G-MMSH	Solar Wings Panther XL-S			28. 5.85	I.J.Drake	Billericay	7. 5.90P
	(Fuji-Robin EC-44-PM) PXL984-192 & T184-1163XL						
G-MMSO	Mainair Gemini/Southdown Sprint			14. 1.86	K.A.Maughan	Sandtoft	26. 7.99P
	(Fuji-Robin EC-44-PM) 255-784-2 & P.539						
G-MMSP	Mainair Gemini/Flash	265-984-2		17. 8.84	R.I.Henderson	Lanark	24. 4.00P
	(Fuji-Robin EC-44-PM)						
G-MMSS*	Ultrasports Tri-Pacer/Southdown Lightning			27. 3.84	G.Norn	East Kirkby	7. 7.98P
	(Fuji-Robin EC-34-PM) SRS/HJ2426				(Cancelled by CAA 11.12.98)		
G-MMST	Southdown Puma Sprint	1221/0003		7. 1.85	A.G.Cooper	Chesterfield	14. 9.97P
	(Fuji-Robin EC-44-PM)						
G-MMSV	Southdown Puma Sprint	1221/0004		21. 5.86	J.Ridgewell	Long Marston	25. 5.92P
	(Fuji-Robin EC-44-PM)						
G-MMSW	MBA Tiger Cub 440	SO.68		8. 8.84	D.R.Hemmings	Ringwood	
G-MMSZ	Medway Half Pint/Aerial Arts 130SX			27. 3.85	Lancaster Partners (Holdings) Ltd		
	(JPL PUL425) 2/21385					Ash Croft Farm, Winsford	N/E
G-MMTA	Solar Wings Panther XL-S			25.10.84	P.A.McMahon	Dun Laoghaire, Ireland	11. 6.00P
	(Fuji-Robin EC-44-PM) PXL884-194 & T884-1164XL						
G-MMTB*	Mainair Gemini/Southdown Sprint		R		Not known	Lagos, Algarve, Portugal	
G-MMTC	Solar Wings Pegasus XL-R T684-1101XL			28. 9.84	P.J.Sheehy	Warsash, Southampton	22. 3.00P
	(Rotax 447)						
G-MMTD	Mainair Tri-Flyer/Hiway Demon 175			16. 8.84	W.E.Teare	Ramsey, IoM	2. 9.99P
	(Fuji-Robin EC-34-PM) EIA-01						
G-MMTG	Mainair Gemini/Southdown Sprint			21. 8.84	H.A.Rose	Durham	13. 8.94P
	(Fuji-Robin EC-44-PM) 267-984-2 & P.577						
G-MMTH	Southdown Puma Sprint	P.538		4. 9.84	R.G.Tomlinson	Yeovil	8.12.92P
	(Fuji-Robin EC-44-PM)						
G-MMTI	Southdown Puma Sprint	1221/0005		13. 9.84	P.A.C.Bailey	Tonbridge	16. 6.00P
	(Fuji-Robin EC-44-PM) (C/n duplicates ZS-VLZ) (See G-MMIR - possibly fitted with new wing)						
G-MMTJ	Southdown Puma Sprint	1221/0006		17. 1.85	P J Kirwan Geashill, Co.Offaly, Ireland		16.4.00P
	(Fuji-Robin EC-44-PM)						
G-MMTK	Medway Hybred 44XL/Solar Wings Typhoon			30. 8.84	J.F.Nicholls	Rochester	9.10.95P
	(Fuji-Robin EC-44-PM) 12784/9						
G-MMTL	Mainair Gemini/Southdown Sprint			3.10.84	T.W.Faragher	Jurby, IoM	6. 7.00P
	(Fuji-Robin EC-44-PM) 268-1084-2 & P.576						
G-MMTM	Mainair Gemini/Southdown Sprint			12. 7.85	D.H.George	Sandown	25. 3.90P*
	(Fuji-Robin EC-44-PM) 141-29383 & P.575 (Initially regd with Trike 269-1084-27)						
G-MMTO	Mainair Tri-Flyer/Southdown Sprint			6. 9.84	R.W.Kelly	New Ross, Co.Wexford	7. 8.98P
	(Fuji-Robin EC-44-PM) 236-384-2 & P.498						
G-MMTR	Solar Wings Pegasus XL-R			27. 9.84	P.M.Kelsey	Rufforth	15. 7.00P
	(Rotax 447) KND-03						
G-MMTS	Solar Wings Panther XL			18. 9.84	A.S.Wason	Wootton Bassett	9. 4.00P
	(Fuji-Robin EC-44-PM) T784-1157XL						
G-MMTT	Ultrasports/Solar Wings Panther XL-S			12.12.84	C.T.H.Tenison	Abergavenny	7.11.97P
	(Fuji-Robin EC-44-PM) T684-1165XL (C/n possibly T884-1165XL but duplicates G-MMSG)						
G-MMTV	American Aerolights Eagle 215B Seaplane			25. 5.84	P.J.Scott	Seaview, IoW	21.11.96P
	(Fuji-Robin EC-25-PS) SGP-1						
G-MMTX	Mainair Gemini/Southdown Sprint			25. 3.85	P.C.Askew	Lancaster	6.11.00P
	(Fuji-Robin EC-44-PM) 275-1284-2 & P.590						
G-MMTY	Fisher FP202U	2140		28. 9.84	B.E.Maggs Brickhouse Farm, Frogland Cross		
					(Stored 4.96)		
G-MMTZ	Eurowing Goldwing	EW-60 & SWA-7		28. 9.84	R.B.D.Baker	Torquay	11. 7.00P
	(Rotax 447)						
G-MMUA	Southdown Puma Sprint	1221/0007		21.12.84	C.R.Gale	Kirk Michael, IoM	21. 8.00P
	(Fuji-Robin EC-44-PM)						
G-MMUE	Mainair Gemini/Flash			16.10.84	B.P.Hately	Ashton-in-Makerfield	29. 3.97P
	(Fuji-Robin EC-44-PM) 273-1284-2 & W10						

Regn	Type	C/n	P/I	Date	Owner/operator	Probable Base	CA Expy
G-MMUG*	Mainair Tri-Flyer 250/Solar Wings Typhoon S4			6. 9.82	Not known	Tonbridge	26. 5.97P
	(Fuji-Robin EC-34-PM) 032-221181 & T884-1178S			(Wing confirmed as ex G-MJKY: temp unregd 21.10.96)			
G-MMUH	Mainair Tri-Flyer/Southdown Sprint			8.11.84	J.P.Nicklin	Hayling Island	22. 7.99P
	(Fuji-Robin EC-44-PM) 270-1084-2 & P.579						
G-MMUJ*	Southdown Puma Sprint/Cougar			6.12.84	C.C.Muir	Bristol	18. 7.97P
	(Fuji-Robin EC-44-PM)	1121/0009		(Cancelled as WFU 6.3.99)			
G-MMUK	Ultrasports Tripacer II/Solar Wings Typhoon S4			15.10.84	K.T.Scholz	Little Down Farm, Milson	18. 9.99P
	(Rotax 447)	BRK-01 & T782-532					
G-MMUM	MBA Tiger Cub 440	SO.019		8. 3.83	Coulson Flying Services Ltd	Skegness	
G-MMUN	Solar Wings Panther Dual XL			23.10.84	P.J.Kirwan	Geashill, Ireland	
		T1084-1231XL					
G-MMUO	Mainair Gemini/Flash			29.10.84	B.D.Bastin & D.R.Howells	Long Marston	30. 1.00P
	(Fuji-Robin EC-44-PM) 272-1084-2 & W08						
G-MMUR	Hiway Skytrike 250/Solar Wings Storm			28.12.84	R.J.Ripley	Oakley, Bedford	
		SL.180180					
G-MMUS	Mainair Gemini/Flash 284-185-3 & W24			29. 1.85	R.L.Feechan	St.Michaels	1. 3.97P
	(Fuji-Robin EC-44-PM)						
G-MMUT	Mainair Gemini/Flash 262-884-2 & W04			5.10.84	L.R.Orriss	Rotherham	5. 7.00P
	(Fuji-Robin EC-44-PM) (Restored 29.6.98 with c/n 235-484-2-W04)						
G-MMUV	Southdown Puma Sprint	1121/0010		7.11.84	D.C.Read	Ledbury	2.11.89P*
	(Fuji-Robin EC-44-PM)						
G-MMUW	Mainair Gemini/Flash 260-784-2 & W13			17. 1.85	J.C.K.Scardifield	Lymington	23. 3.87P
	(Fuji-Robin EC-44-PM)						
G-MMUX	Mainair Gemini/Southdown Sprint			28.12.84	D.Uff	Hatfield	7. 7.95P
	(Fuji-Robin EC-44-PM) 285-185-3 & P.587						
G-MMVA	Southdown Puma Sprint			7.11.84	C.H.Tomkins	Kettering	26. 3.92P
	(Fuji-Robin EC-44-PM) 1121/0011 & P.588						
G-MMVC	Solar Wings Panther XL-S T684-1106XL			13.11.84	E.R.Holton	Lichfield	18.1.90P*
	(Fuji-Robin EC-44-PM)						
G-MMVG*	MBA Tiger Cub 440	SO.139		14.11.84	C.W.Grant	Salisbury	
				(Cancelled by CAA 15.3.99)			
G-MMVH	Southdown Raven X	2122/0015		10. 1.85	G.W. & K.M.Carwardine	Isle of Grain	16.11.99P
	(Mosler MM-CB)						
G-MMVI	Southdown Puma Sprint	1121/0012		28.11.84	G.R.Williams	Haverfordwest	2.11.97P
	(Fuji-Robin EC-44-PM)						
G-MMVO	Southdown Puma Sprint	1232/0017		20. 3.85	N.F.Thomas	Newton Abbot	7.10.98P
	(Rotax 447)						
G-MMVP	Mainair Gemini/Flash 276-1284-2 & W12			17.12.84	S.C.McGowan	Rufforth	16.10.99P
	(Fuji-Robin EC-44-PM)						
G-MMVS	Skyhook Pixie/Zeus (Solo 210) TR1/52			28. 2.85	B.W.Olley	Ely	18.11.91E
G-MMVX	Southdown Puma Sprint	41183 & P.452		29.11.83	R.J.Wheeler	Haverfordwest	10. 9.99P
	(Fuji-Robin EC-44-PM) (Possibly Mainair Gemini Trike)						
G-MMVZ	Southdown Puma Sprint	1121/0016		15. 1.85	M.J.Devane	Killarney, Ireland	2. 8.00P
	(Fuji-Robin EC-44-PM)						
G-MMWA	Mainair Gemini/Flash 271-1184-1 & W07			22.11.84	D.Muir	Lancaster	9. 6.00P
	(Fuji-Robin EC-44-PM)						
G-MMWB*	Huntair Pathfinder II	LWB.3		28. 6.84	Bryant Aircraft Ltd	Bishop Auckland	
				(Cancelled by CAA 27.3.99)			
G-MMWC	Eipper Quicksilver MXII	1041		22.10.84	G.N.Harris	Billingshurst	14. 1.97P
	(Rotax 503)						
G-MMWG	Mainair Tri-Flyer/Flexiform Solo Striker			17.12.84	C.R.Green	Redruth	26. 6.99P
	(Rotax 377)	FF/LAI/83/JDR/11					
G-MMWH	Southdown Puma Sprint	P.548		21. 6.84	S.Giles	Oxford	21. 5.93P
	(Fuji-Robin EC-44-PM)						
G-MMWI	Southdown Puma (Lightning 190)			3. 1.85	A.W.Cove	Wellingborough	5. 9.93E
	(Fuji-Robin EC-34-PM)	CAC-01					
G-MMWJ	Pterodactyl Ptraveler	WFX-33		5. 3.85	G.A.Harman	Sandy	9.11.97P
	(Fuji-Robin EC-34-PM)						
G-MMWL	Eurowing Goldwing	SWA-09 & EW-91		9. 4.85	P.J.Brookman	Lymeswold	18. 4.00P
	(Rotax 447)						
G-MMWN	Mainair Tri-Flyer/Flexiform Striker			21.11.84	D.H.George	Sandown	30. 3.97P
	(Rotax 377)	1283.NH (Possibly Ultrasports Tripacer)					
G-MMWO	Solar Wings Panther XL-S			22. 1.85	M.J.Chance	Rainham	8.12.93P
	(Fuji-Robin EC-44-PM)	T1184-1281XL					
G-MMWS	Ultrasports Tripacer/Flexiform Solo Striker			21.11.84	P.H.Risdale	Woolaston	28.11.99P
	(Rotax 377)	983.SH					
G-MMWT	CFM Shadow Srs C	B.009		27. 3.85	Skyview Systems Ltd	Sudbury	3. 6.00P
	(Rotax 503)						
G-MMWX	Southdown Puma Sprint	1121/0047		10. 4.85	S.J.Ball	Roddige, Fradley	24.11.99P
	(Fuji-Robin EC-44-PM)						

Regn	Type	C/n	P/I	Date	Owner/operator	Probable Base	CA Expy
G-MMWZ	Southdown Puma Sprint 1121/0030 (Fuji-Robin EC-44-PM)			19. 2.85	D.C.Olson	Cambridge	12.11.98P
G-MMXC	Mainair Gemini/Flash (Fuji-Robin EC-44-PM) 279-1284-2 & W17 (Trike reported as c/n 292 9.96 - see G-MMXL)			28.12.84	M.P.Birks	St.Michaels	9. 6.94P
G-MMXD	Mainair Gemini/Flash 282-185-3 & W20 (Rotax 447)			28.12.84	D.Lund	Preston	13.10.00P
G-MMXG	Mainair Gemini/Flash 288-485-1 & W32 (Fuji-Robin EC-44-PM)			17. 1.85	D.J.Butler	Wantage	8. 6.00P
G-MMXH	Mainair Gemini/Flash (Fuji-Robin EC-44-PM) 210-121283-2 & W25			4. 2.85	I.C.Willetts	Barton Turf, Norwich	28. 8.95P
G-MMXJ	Mainair Gemini/Flash 289-185-3 & W22 (Rotax 447)			17. 1.85	R.Meredith-Hardy	Radwell, Letchworth	6. 8.96P
G-MMXK	Mainair Gemini/Flash 274-485-2 & W35 (Fuji-Robin EC-44-PM)			17. 1.85	G.K.Thornton	Higher Barn Farm, Houghton	12. 6.00P
G-MMXL	Mainair Gemini/Flash 292-385-3 & W36 (Fuji-Robin EC-44-PM)			17. 1.85	J.M.Marshall	Urmston	16. 5.97P
G-MMXN	Southdown Puma Sprint 1121/0021 (Fuji-Robin EC-44-PM)			24. 1.85	N.Green	Shrewsbury	31. 7.00P
G-MMXO	Southdown Puma Sprint 1121/0018 (Fuji-Robin EC-44-PM)			23. 1.85	D.J.Tasker	Swinford, Rugby	6.11.00P
G-MMXP	Southdown Puma Sprint 1121/0014 (Fuji-Robin EC-44-PM)			19. 7.85	I.J.Knott	RAF Marham	21. 4.93P
G-MMXT	Mainair Gemini/Flash 302-485-3 & W41 (Fuji-Robin EC-44-PM)			29. 1.85	L.R.Orriss	Rotherham	16. 4.00P
G-MMXU	Mainair Gemini/Flash 254-784-2 & W21 (Fuji-Robin EC-44-PM)			29. 1.85	T.J.Franklin	Graveley	18. 2.95P
G-MMXV	Mainair Gemini/Flash 298-385-3 & W37 (Fuji-Robin EC-44-PM)			29. 1.85	A.E.Ciantar	Bury St.Edmunds	12. 3.00P
G-MMXW	Mainair Gemini/Southdown Sprint (Fuji-Robin EC-44-PM) 286-185-3 & P.597			23. 1.85	A.Hodgson	Milton Keynes	3. 5.97P
G-MMYA	Solar Wings Pegasus XL-P/Se (Rotax 447) XL-P Proto & T784-1151XL			30. 1.85	M.Harris	Clench Common	14.10.99P
G-MMYF	Southdown Puma Sprint 1121/0026 (Fuji-Robin EC-44-PM)			28. 3.85	E.Smith	Swinford, Rugby	8. 6.00P
G-MMYI	Southdown Puma Sprint 1121/0036 (Fuji-Robin EC-44-PM)			6. 3.85	D.J.Brixton t/a Shropshire Tow Group	Bishops Castle	8.11.00P
G-MMYJ	Southdown Puma Sprint 1121/0031 (Fuji-Robin EC-44-PM)			18 .2.85	R.K.Seddon	Higher Barn Farm, Houghton	3. 5.97P
G-MMYL	Cyclone 70/Aerial Arts 130SX CH.01 (Rotax 277)			8. 3.85	J.T.Halford	Holt, Norfolk	26. 7.00P
G-MMYN	Solar Wings Panther XL-R T784-1158XL (Rotax 447)			27. 2.85	B.& D.Bergin	Athenry, Ireland	16. 4.00P
G-MMYO	Southdown Puma Sprint 1121/0037 (Fuji-Robin EC-44-PM) (Fitted with new rainbow Medway sailwing 1999)			11. 4.85	M.Mills	Otherton, Cannock	29. 8.00P
G-MMYR	Eipper Quicksilver MXII 3345 (Rotax 503)			27. 2.85	M.Reed	Newhouse Farm, Loughborough	3. 7.99P
G-MMYT	Southdown Puma Sprint 1121/0046 (Fuji-Robin EC-44-PM)			15. 4.85	J.K.Divall	Chichester	25. 3.94P
G-MMYU	Southdown Puma Sprint 1231/0045 (Rotax 447)			11. 6.85	S.J.Firth	Crieff	30. 4.00P
G-MMYV	Mainair Tri-Flyer/Flexiform Striker (Rotax 277) JW-2			22. 3.85	S.B.Herbert	Presteigne	20.12.95P
G-MMYY	Southdown Puma Sprint 1231/0042 (Rotax 447)			18. 7.85	D.G.Emery & M.R.Smith	Dudley/Warley, W.Midlands	27. 4.00P
G-MMYZ	Southdown Puma Sprint 1231/0034 (Rotax 447)			28. 2.85	M.Bodill (Damaged in gales Roddidge 1.98)	West Bridgeford	19. 2.99P
G-MMZA	Mainair Gemini/Flash 266-984-3 & W60 (Fuji-Robin EC-44-PM) (Wing c/n may be W06)			4. 3.85	G.T.Johnston	Craigavon, Co.Armagh	30. 6.00P
G-MMZB	Mainair Gemini/Flash 319-685-3 & W58 (Fuji-Robin EC-44-PM)			4. 3.85	M.A.Nolan	Great Orton	23. 5.00P
G-MMZD	Mainair Gemini/Flash 309-585-3 & W49 (Fuji-Robin EC-44-PM)			4. 3.85	C.S.Povey & B.Hall	Morecambe	21. 1.00P
G-MMZE	Mainair Gemini/Flash 300-485-3 & W39 (Fuji-Robin EC-44-PM)			4. 3.85	I.P.Stubbins	Sandtoft	25. 3.00P
G-MMZF	Mainair Gemini/Flash 299-485-3 & W38 (Fuji-Robin EC-44-PM)			4. 3.85	A.R.Rhodes	Great Orton	17. 6.00P
G-MMZG	Solar Wings Panther XL-S SW-WA-1022 (Fuji-Robin EC-44-PM)			12. 8.85	P.A.Jones	North Coates	26. 2.00P
G-MMZI	Medway Half Pint Srs.1/Aerial Arts 130SX (JPX PUL425) 57			6. 3.85	J.Messenger	Workington	28. 3.93E

Regn	Type	C/n	P/I	Date	Owner/operator	Probable Base	CA Expy
G-MMZJ	Mainair Gemini/Flash 312-585-3 & W51 (Fuji-Robin EC-44-PM)			18. 3.85	M.Moulai	Scunthorpe	21. 8.00P
G-MMZK	Mainair Gemini/Flash 326-785-3 & W53 (Fuji-Robin EC-44-PM) (Trike ex G-MMEZ; originally regd with trike c/n 314-585-3; to G-MMIR)			18. 3.85	G.Jones & B.Lee	Warrington	3.11.99P
G-MMZM	Mainair Gemini/Flash 304-585-3 & W44 (Fuji-Robin EC-44-PM)			18. 3.85	A.Connelly	Forfar	26. 5.00P
G-MMZN	Mainair Gemini/Flash 283-185-3 & W23 (Fuji-Robin EC-44-PM)			18. 3.85	W.K.Dalus	Nottingham	28. 9.93P
G-MMZP	Solar Wings Panther XL (Fuji-Robin EC-44-PM)	HP-01		14. 3.85	B.Richardson	Sunderland	12. 1.94P
G-MMZR	Southdown Puma Sprint (Fuji-Robin EC-44-PM)	1121/0039		4. 7.85	J.E.Hicks t/a International Animal Rescue	Dunkeswell	6.12.93P
G-MMZU*	Southdown Lightning/Puma	006		12. 4.85	E.Clark (Cancelled by CAA 17.2.99)	Oakham	
G-MMZV	Mainair Gemini/Flash 313-585-3 & W52 (Rotax 447)			18. 4.85	P.R.M.Spengler	Bracknell	18. 6.00P
G-MMZW	Southdown Puma Sprint (Fuji-Robin EC-44-PM)	1121/0043		28. 3.85	M.G.Ashbee	Cranbrook	30. 9.00P
G-MMZX	Southdown Puma Sprint (Rotax 447)	1231/0051		17. 4.85	J.V.Rozentals	Sutton-in-Ashfield	10. 4.95P
G-MMZZ	Maxair Hummer	0010		8. 4.82	P.J.Brookman	Loughborough	
G-MNAE	Mainair Gemini/Flash 343-885-3 & W77 (Fuji-Robin EC-44-PM)			18. 4.85	G.C.Luddington	Bletsoe	29. 7.00P
G-MNAF	Solar Wings Pegasus XL-S (Fuji-Robin EC-44-PM)		SW-WA-1001	24. 4.85	G.Guy	Telford	28. 8.99P
G-MNAH	Solar Wings Panther XL-S (Fuji-Robin EC-44-PM)		SW-WA-1002	24. 4.85	J.H.Button & G.A.Harman	Sandy	18. 9.99P
G-MNAI	Solar Wings Panther XL-S (Fuji-Robin EC-44-PM)		SW-WA-1003	15. 5.85	R.G.Cameron	Dundee	23. 6.98P
G-MNAJ	Solar Wings Panther XL-S (Fuji-Robin EC-44-PM) SW-TA-1004 & SW-WA-1004			17. 5.85	C.Lonsdale	Morgansfield, Fishburn	22. 1.00P
G-MNAK	Solar Wings Panther XL-S (Fuji-Robin EC-44-PM)		SW-WA-1005	15. 5.85	R.J.Porter	Insch	2. 5.00P
G-MNAM	Solar Wings Panther XL-S (Fuji-Robin EC-44-2PM)		SW-WA-1006	17. 5.85	T.M.Gilsenan & G.E.C.Burgess	Dunstable	13.10.95P
G-MNAN	Solar Wings Pegasus XL-R (Rotax 447) SW-TB-0001 & SW-WA-1007			2. 7.85	J.W.F.Hargreave	High Wycombe	30. 4.95P
G-MNAO	Solar Wings Pegasus XL-R (Rotax 447) SW-TB-0002 & SW-WA-1008			2. 6.85	R.H.Cooke	Southampton	28. 8.00P
G-MNAR	Solar Wings Pegasus XL-R (Rotax 447)	SW-WA-1011		6. 8.85	M.C.Hastings	Hemel Hempstead	12.11.00P
G-MNAU	Solar Wings Pegasus XL-R (Rotax 447)	SW-WA-1013		30. 9.85	R.J.Ridgway	High Wycombe	25. 9.93P
G-MNAV	Southdown Puma Sprint (Fuji-Robin EC-44-PM)	1121/0033		28. 2.85	A.W.Smith	Peel, IoM	22. 8.99P
G-MNAW	Solar Wings Pegasus XL-R (Rotax 447) SW-TB-1010 & SW-WA-1014 (Trike c/n believed correct but reported on LN-YCO with Flash wing W686)			16. 8.85	D.J.Harber	Henley-on-Thames	10.11.99P
G-MNAX	Solar Wings Pegasus XL-R (Rotax 447)	SW-WA-1015		16. 8.85	B.J.Phillips	Newbury	21. 7.96P
G-MNAY	Solar Wings Pegasus XL-R (Rotax 447) SW-TB-1015 & SW-WA-1016			6. 8.85	S.J.Honeybourne	Lowdham	11. 9.99P
G-MNAZ	Solar Wings Pegasus XL-R (Rotax 447) SW-TB-1016 & SW-WA-1017			6. 8.85	R.W.Houldsworth	Rochford	23. 7.00P
G-MNBA	Solar Wings Pegasus XL-R (Rotax 447) SW-TB-1024 & SW-WA-1018			6. 9.85	K.D.Baldwin "Tigerfish"	Long Acres Farm, Sandy	21. 5.00P
G-MNBB	Solar Wings Pegasus XL-R (Rotax 447) SW-TB-1020 & SW-WA-1019			20. 9.85	M.Sims	Brynmawr, Gwent	1. 7.00P
G-MNBC	Solar Wings Pegasus XL-R (Rotax 447) SW-TB-1026 & SW-WA-1020			11.10.85	W.M.Rowley	Slough	21. 2.97P
G-MNBD	Mainair Gemini/Flash 341-585-3 & W42 (Fuji-Robin EC-44-PM)			6. 1.86	G.B.Mitchell	Nottingham	21.10.96
G-MNBE	Southdown Puma Sprint (Fuji-Robin EC-44-PM)	1121/0050		17. 5.85	A.Wherrett	Bristol	5. 7.98P
G-MNBF	Mainair Gemini/Flash 306-585-3 & W46 (Fuji-Robin EC-44-PM)			2. 5.85	H.G.Denton Newhouse Farm, Loughborough		5. 5.00P
G-MNBG	Mainair Gemini/Flash 347-585-3 & W66 (Rotax 447)			9. 5.85	J.W. & C.Richardson	New Ellerby, Hull	27. 8.00P
G-MNBH	Southdown Puma Sprint (Rotax 447)	1231/0056		20. 5.85	D.W.B.Crang	RAF Wyton	1.10.97P

Regn	Type	C/n	P/I	Date	Owner/operator	Probable Base	CA Expy
G-MNBI	Solar Wings Panther XL-S			3. 5.85	G.R.Cox	Northampton	29. 4.97P
	(Fuji-Robin EC-44-PM) PXL884-178 & T884-1161XL			(C/n duplicates G-MMVF)			
G-MNBL	American Aerolights Eagle 215B			9. 1.84	T.S.Mangat	Long Marston	20. 9.97P
	(Cuyuna 215R)	BA-1001					
G-MNBM	Southdown Puma Sprint	1231/0058		25. 6.85	D.A.Hopewell	Newcastle	23. 6.97P
	(Fuji-Robin EC-44-PM)						
G-MNBN	Mainair Gemini/Flash 303-485-3 & W43			11. 6.85	D.G.Knibbs	Evesham	27. 3.00P
	(Fuji-Robin EC-44-PM)						
G-MNBP	Mainair Gemini/Flash 338-885-3 & W75			15. 5.85	A.L.Alexandrou	Camberley	18.12.93P
	(Fuji-Robin EC-44-PM)						
G-MNBR	Mainair Gemini/Flash 345-985-3 & W79			15. 5.85	N.A.P.Gregory (Stored 1.98) Long Marston		5. 2.94P
	(Rotax 447)						
G-MNBS	Mainair Gemini/Flash 308-585-3 & W48			15. 5.85	P.A.Comins	Nottingham	20. 6.94P
	(Fuji-Robin EC-44-PM)						
G-MNBT	Mainair Gemini/Flash 322-685-3 & W62			15. 5.85	C.J.R.Hardman	St.Michaels	4.11.00P
	(Fuji-Robin EC-44-PM)						
G-MNBU	Mainair Gemini/Flash 337-885-3 & W74			15. 5.85	A.S.Dalby	Thirsk	23. 7.96P
	(Rotax 447)						
G-MNBV	Mainair Gemini/Flash 333-685-3 & W70			15. 5.85	P.Lowham	Caledon, Co.Tyrone	6. 2.00P
	(Rotax 447)						
G-MNBW	Mainair Gemini/Flash 332-685-3 & W69			15. 5.85	G.A.Brown & N.S.Brotherton		
	(Rotax 447) (C/n now SW-WF-0005 & W95 ex G-MNJI)					Weston Zoyland	8. 1.00P
G-MNCA	Hunt Avon/Hiway Demon 175	DA-01		28. 5.85	C.Kett	Bridgwater	26. 3.94E
G-MNCF	Mainair Gemini/Flash 321-685-3 & W61			3. 6.85	T.C.Edwards	Ware	10.11.95P
	(Rotax 447)						
G-MNCG	Mainair Gemini/Flash 320-685-3 & W59			3. 6.85	G.Hartley	St. Michaels	28. 1.00P
	(Rotax 447)						
G-MNCI	Southdown Puma Sprint	1231/0059		7. 6.85	R.M.Wait	Stourbridge	20.11.00P
	(Rotax 447)						
G-MNCJ	Mainair Gemini/Flash 351-785-3 & W83			3. 6.85	R.S.McLeister	Accrington	16.11.93P
	(Rotax 447)						
G-MNCK	Southdown Puma Sprint	1231/0055		11. 7.85	R.A.Beauchamp	Alrewas	3. 1.98P
	(Rotax 447)				(Damaged in gales Roddidge 1.98)		
G-MNCL	Southdown Puma Sprint	1121/0060		3. 6.85	S.A.P.Rowberry	Wallingford	20. 7.98P
	(Fuji-Robin EC-44-PM)						
G-MNCM	CFM Shadow Srs C	006		31. 5.85	K.G.D.Macrae	(Edinburgh)	30. 8.00P
	(Rotax 503)						
G-MNCO	Eipper Quicksilver MX II	1045		3. 6.85	S.Lawton	Colne	
G-MNCP	Southdown Puma Sprint	1231/0071		24. 6.85	R.A.Willetts & W.Atkinson	Long Marston	10. 4.00P
	(Rotax 447)						
G-MNCS	Skyrider Airsports Phantom PH.00098			2. 1.86	C.G.Johns	Bewdley, Worcs	25. 5.00P
	(Fuji-Robin EC-44-PM)						
G-MNCU	Medway Hybred/Solar Wings Typhoon 44XL			13. 6.85	S.P.Courtney	Westwood, Notts	10. 6.00P
	(Fuji-Robin EC-44-PM)	26485/10					
G-MNCV	Medway Hybred/Solar Wings Typhoon 44XL			13. 6.85	P.D.Mickleburgh	Swinford, Rugby	6. 9.00P
	(Fuji-Robin EC-44-PM)	26485/11 (Reported as Pegasus XL-R Wing SW-WA-1030 1997)					
G-MNDC	Mainair Gemini/Flash 336-885-3 & W73			12. 6.85	C.G.Jarvis	Southampton	12. 3.00P
	(Rotax 447)						
G-MNDD	Mainair Scorcher 358-885-1 & W85			12. 6.85	W.J.Heap	Ince Blundell	23. 6.98P
	(Rotax 447)						
G-MNDE	Medway Half Pint/Aerial Arts 130SX			19. 6.85	N.J.Dea	Birmingham	7. 4.00P
	(JPL PUL425)	3/8685	(Wing ex G-MNBZ)				
G-MNDF	Mainair Gemini/Flash 327-785-3 & W67			25. 6.85	S.K.Starling	Hethersett	13. 5.00P
	(Rotax 447)						
G-MNDG	Southdown Puma Sprint	1121/0057		18. 7.85	L.Earls	Green Swords, Ireland	14. 6.99P
	(Fuji-Robin EC-44-PM)						
G-MNDM	Mainair Gemini/Flash 324-785-3 & W64			11. 7.85	A.N.McDonough	Arclid Green, Sandbach	7. 4.98P
	(Rotax 447)						
G-MNDO	Solar Wings Pegasus/Flash SW-WF-0001			2. 7.85	D.Buchanan	Southsea	16. 8.98P
	(Rotax 447)						
G-MNDP	Southdown Puma Sprint	1121/0063		28. 6.85	S.C.Davidson	Haverfordwest	26. 4.93P
	(Fuji-Robin EC-44-PM)						
G-MNDU	Midland Ultralights Sirocco 377GB			22. 7.85	D.Dugdale	Bruntingthorpe	3. 8.00P
	(Rotax 377)	MU-011					
G-MNDV	Midland Ultralights Sirocco 377GB			1. 4.86	L.J.Dutch	Wigan	13. 7.92P
	(Rotax 377)	MU-012			(Stored Tarn Farm, Cockerham 5.93)		
G-MNDW	Midland Ultralights Sirocco 377GB			30. 7.85	G.C.Reid	Deenethorpe	24. 4.00P
	(Rotax 377)	MU-014					
G-MNDY	Southdown Puma Sprint T.504 & P.536			2. 5.84	D.J.Brixton	(Montgomery)	9..9.00P
	(Fuji-Robin EC-44-PM)				t/a Shropshire Tow Group		

Regn	Type	C/n P/I	Date	Owner/operator	Probable Base	CA Expy
G-MNDZ	Southdown Puma Sprint 1121/0062 (Fuji-Robin EC-44-PM)		28. 6.85	Wendy A.Guest	Bridgnorth	29. 4.99P
G-MNEF	Mainair Gemini/Flash 344-885-3 & W78 (Rotax 447)		8. 7.85	J.P.Faver	East Fortune	19.12.98P
G-MNEG	Mainair Gemini/Flash 360-885-3 & W92 (Rotax 447)		8. 7.85	T.McDowell	Kells, Ireland	18.10.99P
G-MNEH	Mainair Gemini/Flash 361-885-3 & W90 (Rotax 503)		8. 7.85	I.Rawson	St.Michaels	5. 7.00P
G-MNEI	Medway Hybred/Solar Wings Typhoon 44XL (Fuji-Robin EC-44-PM) 8785/12 & SW-WA-1035		9. 7.85	L.G.Thompson (Stored 8.96)	Long Marston	26. 7.93P
G-MNEK	Medway Half Pint/Aerial Arts 130SX (JPX PUL425) 4/8785		12. 7.85	M.I.Dougall	Maidstone	25. 9.94P
G-MNEL	Medway Half Pint/Aerial Arts 130SX (JPX PUL425) 5/8785		12. 7.85	K.J.Hitch	Westerham	26. 9.94P
G-MNEM	Solar Wings Pegasus XL-R (Rotax 447) SW-TB-1007 & SW-WA-1034		16. 7.85	M.D.Foster	Hastings	31. 7.93P
G-MNER	CFM Shadow Srs.CD 008 (Rotax 462)		15. 7.85	F.C.Claydon	Wickham Brook, Newmarket	27. 2.00P
G-MNET	Mainair Gemini/Flash 349-885-3 & W81 (Fuji-Robin EC-44-PM)		23. 7.85	S.W.Barker	Scarborough	5. 7.00P
G-MNEV	Mainair Gemini/Flash (Rotax 447) 362-1085-3 & W108		23. 7.85	A.A.White	St.Michaels	23. 5.00P
G-MNEY	Mainair Gemini/Flash (Rotax 447) 365-1085-3 & W94		23. 7.85	A.G.Phillips	East Fortune	4. 7.00P
G-MNFA	Mainair Tri-Flyer/Solar Wings Typhoon (Fuji-Robin EC-34-PM) DRJ-01 & GWW-01		29.12.83	R.S.Lee (Trike ex G-MJFA)	Pontesbury, Shrewsbury	10.10.92P
G-MNFB	Southdown Puma Sprint 1231/0077 (Rotax 447)		22. 7.85	C.Lawrence	Tiverton	17. 7.00P
G-MNFE	Mainair Gemini/Flash 350-885-3 & W82 (Fuji-Robin EC-44-PM)		29. 7.85	D.R.Kennedy	East Fortune	15. 7.00P
G-MNFF	Mainair Gemini/Flash (Rotax 447) 371-1185-3 & W110		29. 7.85	R.P.Cook & C.H.Spencer	Manor Farm, Inskip	8. 6.94P
G-MNFG	Southdown Puma Sprint 1231/0078 (Rotax 447)		31. 7.85	A.C.Hing	Leighton Buzzard	29. 4.00P
G-MNFH	Mainair Gemini/Flash (Rotax 447) 364-1085-3 & W93		6. 8.85	P.A.Martindale (Stored 9.97)	Great Orton	30. 6.95P
G-MNFJ	Mainair Gemini/Flash 346-985-3 & W80 (Rotax 447)		20. 9.85	S.C.Marshall	Market Harborough	21. 3.90P
G-MNFK	Mainair Gemini/Flash 2 (Rotax 462) 359-885-3 & W91		12. 8.85	S.L.Larter-Whitcher & A.L.Carroll	Hertford/Harlow	6. 5.93P
G-MNFL	AMF Microflight Chevvron CH.002 (Konig SD570)		19. 8.85	P.W.Wright	Fradley, Lichfield	13.12.00P
G-MNFM	Mainair Gemini/Flash (Rotax 447) 366-1085-3 & W98		10.10.85	P.M.Fidell	Wombleton	27. 8.00P
G-MNFN	Mainair Gemini/Flash (Rotax 447) 367-1085-3 & W99		6.11.85	J.R.Martin	Bedale	30. 4.94P
G-MNFP	Mainair Gemini/Flash (Rotax 447) 368-1085-3 & W100		23.10.85	S.Farnsworth & P.Howarth	Clitheroe	17.10.00P
G-MNFR*	Mainair Tri-Flyer/Solar Wings Medium Typhoon T981-272		15. 8.85	R.L.Arscott (Cancelled by CAA 23.6.98)	Taunton	
G-MNFW	Medway Hybred 44XL 10885/13 (Fuji-Robin EC-44-PM)		15. 8.85	A.T.Palmer	Plymouth	15. 8.99P
G-MNFX	Southdown Puma Sprint 1231/0079 (Rotax 447)		14. 8.85	A.M.Shaw	Stoke-on-Trent	26. 7.00P
G-MNFZ	Southdown Puma Sprint (Rotax 447) T.597 & 1231/0080		22. 8.85	M.J.Devane	Killarney, Ireland	22. 7.99P
G-MNGB	Mainair Gemini/Flash (Fuji-Robin EC-44-PM) 218-81183-2 & W01		14.12.83	S.L.Rowlands	Wirral	19. 4.98P
G-MNGD	Ultrasports Tripacer/Solar Wings Medium Typhoon (Fuji-Robin EC-34-PM) 012 & T681-171		13. 8.85	F.H.Cook	Whitchurch	3. 9.00P
G-MNGF	Solar Wings Pegasus/Flash (Rotax 447) W-TB-1022 & SW-WF-0003		21. 8.85	S.B.Williams	Headcorn	14. 8.98P
G-MNGG	Solar Wings Pegasus XL-R T784-1159XL (Rotax 447)		21. 8.85	T.Peckham	Faversham	19. 3.00P
G-MNGH	Skyhook TR1 Pixie/Zeus TR1/61		24. 9.85	A.R.Smith	Chelmsford	
G-MNGK	Mainair Gemini/Flash (Rotax 447) 374-1085-3 & W112		5. 9.85	R.Paton	London N1	15. 8.00P
G-MNGL	Mainair Gemini/Flash (Rotax 447) 376-1085-3 & W114		5. 9.85	G.Cusden	Davidstow Moor	10.11.00P
G-MNGM	Mainair Gemini/Flash (Rotax 447) 394-1285-3 & W109		5. 9.85	J.E.Caffull & D.R.Beale	Long Marston	10. 6.00P

Regn	Type	C/n P/I	Date	Owner/operator	Probable Base	CA Expy
G-MNGN	Mainair Gemini/Flash (Rotax 447) 378-1185-3 & W115		5. 9.85	T.B.Margetts	Poole	17. 6.99P
G-MNGR	Southdown Puma Sprint 1231/0086 (Rotax 447)		18. 9.85	A.K.Webster	Wallingford	29. 8.93P
G-MNGS	Southdown Puma (Lightning 195) (Fuji-Robin EC-34-PM) GJS-02	(Tripacer trike unit from G-MJRF)	8. 5.84	C.R.Mortlock & B.P.Cooke	Newmarket	N/E
G-MNGT	Mainair Gemini/Flash (Rotax 447) 372-1085-3 & W106	(Reported 4.96 as Huntwing 462LC- not physically confirmed by 1999)	30. 9.85	M.R.Lycett	Arclid Green, Sandbach	23. 3.00P
G-MNGU	Mainair Gemini/Flash (Rotax 503) 373-1085-3 & W111		30. 9.85	P.M.Knight	Stanford-le-Hope	4. 6.00P
G-MNGW	Mainair Gemini/Flash (Rotax 447) 386-1185-3 & W121		30. 9.85	D.G.Baker	Petersfield	6.11.00P
G-MNGX	Southdown Puma Sprint 1231/0088		26. 9.85	R.J.Morris	Ely	26. 9.99P
G-MNGZ	Mainair Gemini/Flash (Rotax 447) 385-1085-3 & W120		10.10.85	G.T.Snoddon	Newtownards	4. 9.97P
G-MNHB	Solar Wings Pegasus XL-R/Se (Rotax 447) SW-WA-1045		1.11.85	A.F.J.Freiherr-Knigge	Pattensen, Germany	28. 7.98P
G-MNHC	Solar Wings Pegasus XL-R (Rotax 447) SW-TB-1032 & SW-WA-1046		31.10.85	P.Mathews	Shobdon	27. 5.99P
G-MNHD	Solar Wings Pegasus XL-R (Rotax 447) SW-TB-1033 & SW-WA-1047		5.11.85	P.D.Stiles	Ashley Down, Bristol	11. 6.00P
G-MNHE	Solar Wings Pegasus XL-R (Rotax 447) SW-TB-1036 & SW-WA-1048		11.12.85	J.R.Austin	Truro	2. 8.00P
G-MNHF	Solar Wings Pegasus XL-R (Rotax 447) SW-TB-1038 & SW-WA-1049		29.11.85	J.Cox	Hereford	22. 6.88P
G-MNHH	Solar Wings Pegasus XL-S SW-WA-1051 (Fuji-Robin EC-44-PM)		22. 1.86	F.J.Williams	Shefford, Beds	7. 8.99P
G-MNHI	Solar Wings Pegasus XL-R (Rotax 447) SW-TB-1042 & SW-WA-1052		8. 1.86	I.D.R.Hyde	Enstone	13. 7.95P
G-MNHJ	Solar Wings Pegasus XL-R SW-WA-1053 (Rotax 447)		11. 3.86	S.J.Woodd	Oxford	26. 6.93P
G-MNHK	Solar Wings Pegasus XL-R SW-WA-1054 (Rotax 462)		9. 7.86	R.D.Proctor	Stamford	13. 6.92P
G-MNHL	Solar Wings Pegasus XL-R SW-WA-1055 (Rotax 447)		9. 7.86	S B Walters	Sidcup	14. 5.99P
G-MNHM	Solar Wings Pegasus XL-R (Rotax 447) SW-TB-1078 & SW-WA-1056		11. 7.86	J.Ellis	Baxby Manor, Husthwaite	3. 6.98P
G-MNHN	Solar Wings Pegasus XL-R SW-WA-1057 (Rotax 447)		11. 8.86	N.J.Howarth	Deenethorpe	16. 6.00P
G-MNHP	Solar Wings Pegasus XL-R SW-WA-1059 (Rotax 447)	(Damaged nr Bristol 18.11.95)	11. 8.86	P.N.Bailey & D.M.Smith	Swindon	28. 9.96P
G-MNHR	Solar Wings Pegasus XL-R (Rotax 447) SW-TB-1081 & SW-WA-1060		7. 8.86	B.D.Jackson	Wincanton	11.11.00P
G-MNHS	Solar Wings Pegasus XL-R (Rotax 447) SW-TB-1082 & SW-WA-1061		21. 8.86	T.J.Gayton-Polley	Billingshurst	7. 9.00P
G-MNHT	Solar Wings Pegasus XL-R SW-WA-1062 (Rotax 447)		4. 8.86	J.W.Coventry	Plymouth	4. 9.00P
G-MNHU	Solar Wings Pegasus XL-R SW-WA-1063 (Rotax 447)		4. 8.86	B.A.Wright & D.Lyon	Dunkeswell	16. 1.99P
G-MNHV	Solar Wings Pegasus XL-R (Rotax 447) SW-TB-1095 & SW-WA-1064		18. 8.86	E.Jenkins	Crymych, Dyfed	31. 7.99P
G-MNHZ	Mainair Gemini/Flash (Fuji-Robin EC-44-PM) 310-585-3 & W118		15.10.85	M.Salvini & S.P.Rouse	Baxby Manor, Husthwaite	28. 7.00P
G-MNIA	Mainair Gemini/Flash (Rotax 447) 370-1185-3 & W105		10.10.85	A.E.Dix	Bromsgrove	10. 4.89P
G-MNID	Mainair Gemini/Flash (Rotax 447) 369-1185-3 & W104	(Stolen from Rufforth 10/11.97; Engine No.3706877)	7. 2.86	P.Fowler	Rufforth	24. 3.98P
G-MNIE	Mainair Gemini/Flash (Rotax 447) 388-1185-3 & W123		21.11.85	A.D.Partington	Long Marston	12. 2.00P
G-MNIF	Mainair Gemini/Flash (Rotax 462) 403-286-4 & W147		7. 1.86	D.Yarr	Stockport	18. 6.00P
G-MNIG	Mainair Gemini/Flash (Rotax 447) 391-1285-3 & W139		9. 1.86	I.S.Everett	Astwood	18. 5.00P
G-MNIH	Mainair Gemini/Flash (Rotax 447) 379-1185-3 & W116		10.12.85	A.R.Richardson	Barnsley	10. 8.99P
G-MNII	Mainair Gemini/Flash (Rotax 447) 390-1285-3 & W128	(Trike reported at St.Michaels 9.96)	6.11.85	R.F.Finnis	Guildford	6. 9.91P
G-MNIK	Solar Wings Pegasus Photon SW-TP-0002 & SW-WP-0002		29.10.85	R.J.Garland	Bristol	8. 4.00P
G-MNIL	Southdown Puma Sprint 1231/0094 (Rotax 447)		4.11.85	I.K.Hogg	Kirkbride	20. 7.99P

Regn	Type	C/n	P/I	Date	Owner/operator	Probable Base	CA Expy
G-MNIM	Maxair Hummer	PJB-01		29.10.85	K.Wood	Leicester	
G-MNIP	Mainair Gemini/Flash			6.11.85	G.S.Bulpitt	Chilbolton	18. 8.00P
	(Rotax 447) 393-1285-3 & W134						
G-MNIS	CFM Shadow Srs.C	014		11.11.85	R.W.Payne	Peterborough	25. 4.92P
	(Rotax 447)						
G-MNIT	Aerial Arts Alpha Mk.II/130SX			27. 2.86	M.J.Edmett	London N3	15. 8.99P
	(Rotax 227) 130SX-176						
G-MNIU	Solar Wings Pegasus Photon			27.11.85	K.Roberts	Tarn Farm, Cockerham	N/E
	(Rotax 185) SW-WP-0003				(Damaged & stored 3.90)		
G-MNIW	Mainair Tri-Flyer/Airwave Nimrod 165		EI-BOB	29.11.85	J.A.McIntosh & R.W.Mitchell	Perth	4. 9.00P
	(Fuji-Robin EC-25-PS) 050/19181						
G-MNIX	Mainair Gemini/Flash			29.11.85	S.Farnworth	Kempston, Bedford	11. 7.98P
	(Rotax 447) 395-1285-3 & W136						
G-MNIZ	Mainair Gemini/Flash			26. 2.86	B.Fletcher	St.Michaels	1. 5.00P
	(Rotax 447) 392-1285-3 & W130						
G-MNJB	Southdown Raven X	2232/0098		10.12.85	G.Elwes	Long Acres Farm, Sandy	3. 4.00P
	(Rotax 447)						
G-MNJC	MBA Tiger Cub 440	S0.215		8. 6.84	J.G.Carpenter	Romsey	N/E
G-MNJD	Mainair Tri-Flyer 440 Sprint			2. 4.84	M.E.Smith	Verwood	8. 8.00P
	(Fuji-Robin EC-44-PM) 243-10484-2 & P.537						
G-MNJF	Dragon Srs.150	0068	(OY)9-17	2. 1.86	B.W.Langley	Bradford-on-Avon	3. 7.99P
	(Fuji-Robin EC-44-PM)						
G-MNJG	Mainair Gemini/Southdown Puma Sprint MS			29. 9.83	P.Batchelor	Crawley	13. 3.00P
	(Fuji-Robin EC-44-PM) SA.2030 & 251-684-2 & P.593						
G-MNJH	Solar Wings Pegasus/Flash			22.10.85	C.P.Course	Church Farm, Wellingborough	19. 5.00P
	(Rotax 447) SW-TB-1023 & SW-WF-0004						
G-MNJJ	Solar Wings Pegasus/Flash			22.10.85	P.A.Shelley	Sutton Meadows, Ely	26.11.96P
	(Rotax 447) SW-TB-1029 & SW-WF-0006						
G-MNJK	Solar Wings Pegasus/Flash			21.10.85	A.Jones	Ley Farm, Chirk	3. 8.94P
	(Rotax 447) SW-TB-1027 & SW-WF-0007						
G-MNJL	Solar Wings Pegasus/Flash SW-WF-0008			21.10.85	S.D.Thomas	Bilston, W.Midlands	11.11.94P
	(Rotax 447)						
G-MNJN	Solar Wings Pegasus/Flash SW-WF-0010			19.11.85	D.Thorn	St. Austell	17. 7.00P
	(Rotax 447)						
G-MNJO	Solar Wings Pegasus/Flash			19.11.85	S.Clarke	Long Marston	13.11.00P
	(Rotax 447) SW-TB-1035 & SW-WF-0011						
G-MNJP*	Solar Wings Pegasus/Flash			30.12.85	K.J.Ball	Mill Farm, Hughley	2. 5.93P
	(Rotax 447) SW-TB-1040 & SW-WF-0012				(Stored 10.97; cancelled as WFU 31.7.98)		
	(Mainair wing c/n W127-1185-1)						
G-MNJR	Solar Wings Pegasus/Flash SW-WF-0013			30.12.85	D Mullineux	Bexhill	16.11.00P
	(Rotax 447) (New engine reported 1999 - same type ?)						
G-MNJS	Southdown Puma Sprint	1231/0085		18. 9.85	W.E.Pepper	Royston	12. 7.94P
	(Rotax 447)						
G-MNJT	Southdown Raven X	2232/0087		20. 9.85	R.C.Hinkins	RAF Wyton	13. 3.00P
	(Rotax 447)						
G-MNJU	Mainair Gemini/Flash			20. 9.85	E.J.Wells	Lower Wanborough, Swindon	18. 6.00P
	(Rotax 447) 384-1185-3 & W119						
G-MNJV	Medway Half Pint/Aerial Arts 130SX			10.10.85	D.J.Lewis	Cheltenham	20. 8.92E
	8/19985 (Regd as c/n 9/19985)						
G-MNJW	Mitchell Wing B-10	JDW-01		26. 1.84	J.D.Webb	Hereford	
G-MNJX	Medway Hybred 44XL	15885/14		9.12.85	H.A.Stewart	Sittingbourne	23. 7.98P
	(Fuji-Robin EC-44-PM)						
G-MNKB	Solar Wings Pegasus/Photon			14. 1.86	M.E.Gilbert	Dunfermline	29. 4.00P
	(Solo 210) SW-WP-0005						
G-MNKC	Solar Wings Pegasus/Photon			14. 1.86	A.C.Carter	Rufforth	31. 8.97P
	(Solo 210) SW-TP-0006 & SW-WP-0006						
G-MNKD	Solar Wings Pegasus/Photon			14. 1.86	F.Walton	Bishop Auckland	28. 8.92P
	(Solo 210) SW-WP-0007						
G-MNKE	Solar Wings Pegasus/Photon			14. 1.86	M.J.Olsen	Middlesbrough	8. 6.00P
	(Solo 210) SW-WP-0008						
G-MNKG	Solar Wings Pegasus/Photon			28. 1.86	T.W.Thompson	Eshott	11. 6.95P
	(Solo 210) SW-TP-0010 & SW-WP-0010				(Trike stored 9.97)		
G-MNKH	Solar Wings Pegasus/Photon (Solo 210)			28. 1.86	L.M.Ball	Maidenhead	25. 8.93P
	SW-TP-0011 & SW-WP-0011						
G-MNKI	Solar Wings Pegasus/Photon		(EI-)	28. 1.86	T.Shivner	Salthill, Galway	24. 3.00P
	(Solo 210) SW-WP-0012		G-MNKI				
G-MNKK	Solar Wings Pegasus/Photon			28. 1.86	M.E.Gilbert	Dunfermline	7. 5.95P
	(Fuji-Robin EC-44-PM) SW-WP-0014						
G-MNKL	Mainair Gemini/Flash			6. 1.86	R.Thorpe	Pontefract	21. 5.94P
	(Rotax 447) 397-1285-3 & W143						

Regn	Type	C/n	P/I	Date	Owner/operator	Probable Base	CA Expy
G-MNKM	MBA Tiger Cub 440 SO.213 (Fuji-Robin EC-44-PM)			30.12.85	M.S.Wood	Batley	23. 9.97P
G-MNKN*	Wheeler (Skycraft) Scout Mk.III/3/R 410			6. 1.86	E.A.Diamond (Cancelled as WFU 19.2.99)	Barrow-in-Furness	
G-MNKO	Solar Wings Pegasus XL-Q (Rotax 447) SW-TB-1158 & SW-WX-0001			2. 1.86	G.Sharp	Eshott	28. 8.00P
G-MNKP	Solar Wings Pegasus/Flash (Rotax 447) SW-TB-1043 & SW-WF-0014			9. 1.86	C.Hasell	Long Marston	24.10.00P
G-MNKR	Solar Wings Pegasus/Flash (Rotax 447) SW-TB-1045 & SW-WF-0015			14. 1.86	M.A. & P.A.Hornsby	Sutton Meadows, Ely	16. 6.95P
G-MNKS	Solar Wings Pegasus/Flash (Rotax 447) SW-TB-1044 & SW-WF-0016			9. 1.86	W.J.Walker	Drummiard Farm, Bonnybank	18. 4.00P
G-MNKU	Southdown Puma Sprint 1231/0100 (Rotax 447)			29. 1.86	S.P.O'Hannrachain	Naas, Co.Kildare	24. 7.00P
G-MNKV	Solar Wings Pegasus/Flash (Rotax 447) SW-TB-1047 & SW-WF-0017			15. 1.86	R.A Banks t/a G-MNKV Group	Dunkeswell	15. 4.00P
G-MNKW	Solar Wings Pegasus/Flash SW-WF-0018 (Rotax 447)			28. 1.86	S.Rumens	Etchingham, E.Sussex	11. 3.96P
G-MNKX	Solar Wings Pegasus/Flash SW-WF-0019 (Rotax 447)			28. 2.86	P.Samal	Sandy	8. 5.00P
G-MNKZ	Southdown Raven X 2232/0102 (Rotax 447)			4. 2.86	G.B.Gratton	Andover	23. 4.00P
G-MNLB	Southdown Raven X 2232/0117 (Rotax 447)			11. 4.86	D.A.Chamberlain	Long Marston	10. 6.00P
G-MNLE	Southdown Raven X 2232/0128 (Rotax 447)			30. 4.86	I.D. & P.G.Cresswell	Rochester	6.10.98P
G-MNLH	Romain Cobra Biplane 001 (Midwest AE50R)			23. 1.86	J.W.E.Romain	Welwyn	5.11.98P
G-MNLI	Mainair Gemini/Flash 2 (Rotax 503) 407-286-4 & W152			28. 1.86	C.E. & P.M.Fessi	Coventry/Bolton	6. 6.00P
G-MNLK	Southdown Raven X 2232/0108 (Rotax 447)			4. 2.86	M.J.Robbins	Tunbridge Wells	27. 7.98P
G-MNLL	Southdown Raven X 2232/0109 (Rotax 447)			4. 2.86	S.Barrass	Doncaster	15. 8.93P
G-MNLM	Southdown Raven X 2232/0110 (Rotax 447)			6. 2.86	A.P.White	Exmouth	9. 6.93P
G-MNLN	Southdown Raven X 2232/0111 (Rotax 447)			6. 2.86	A.S.Windley	Matlock	13.12.99P
G-MNLO	Southdown Raven X 2232/0112 (Rotax 447)			6. 2.86	D.Kiddy (Damaged Upottery nr Honiton 6.4.86)	Torquay	1. 6.87P
G-MNLT	Southdown Raven X 2232/0115 (Rotax 447)			6. 2.86	J.L.Stachini	Borehamwood	5. 3.98P
G-MNLU	Southdown Raven X 2232/0116 (Rotax 447)			6. 2.86	D.J.Ainsworth	Preston	24. 7.00P
G-MNLV	Southdown Raven X 2232/0118 (Rotax 447)			6. 2.86	J.Murphy	London EC1	16. 7.90P
G-MNLW	Medway Half Pint/Aerial Arts 130SX (JPX PUL 425) 10/31186			10. 2.86	M.I.Dougall	Maidstone	15. 9.93E
G-MNLX	Mainair Gemini/Flash 2 (Rotax 462) 413-386-4 & W165			6. 2.86	K.J.Jarmin	Rushden	21. 4.98P
G-MNLY	Mainair Gemini/Flash (Rotax 503) 406-386-4 & W151			14. 2.86	J.L.Finney	Ince Blundell	5. 4.99P
G-MNLZ	Southdown Raven X 2232/0123 (Rotax 447)			6. 2.86	E.L.Jenkins	Bexleyheath	31. 5.00P
G-MNMC	Mainair Gemini/Southdown Puma Sprint MS (Fuji-Robin EC-44-PM) 222-284-2 & P524			20. 3.84	J.J.Milliken	Winchester	20. 9.96P
G-MNMD	Southdown Raven X 2000/0121 (Rotax 447) (Originally regd with c/n 2232/0121)			10. 2.86	P.G.Overall	Crawley	22.11.00P
G-MNME	Hiway Skytrike/Demon (Rotax 377) WTP-01 & 3535009			12. 2.86	J.C.P.Greene	Hereford	10. 6.93E
G-MNMG	Mainair Gemini/Flash 2 (Rotax 447) 419-386-4 & W177			11. 2.86	N.A.M.Beyer-Kay	Southport	20. 8.94P
G-MNMH	Mainair Gemini/Flash 2 (Rotax 462) 417-486-4 & W168			11. 2.86	A.B.Legge	Windermere	4.10.98P
G-MNMI	Mainair Gemini/Flash 2 (Fuji-Robin EC-44-PM) 317-685-3 & W178 (Trike ex G-MMZL)			11. 2.86	S.D.Titman	RAF Wyton	8. 8.99P
G-MNMJ	Mainair Gemini/Flash 2 (Rotax 447) 387-1185-3 & W122			11. 2.86	P.K.Appleton	(Bristol)	18. 9.99P
G-MNMK	Solar Wings Pegasus XL-R SW-WA-1038 (Rotax 447)			19. 8.85	G.P.Wayne	Okehampton	2. 7.00P

Regn	Type	C/n P/I	Date	Owner/operator	Probable Base	CA Expy
G-MNML	Southdown Puma Sprint 1111/0065 (Fuji-Robin EC-44-PM)		4. 8.83	R.C.Carr	Launceston	14. 7.97P
G-MNMM	Aerotech MW-5(K) Sorcerer 5K-0001-02 (Rotax 447) (Regd with c/n SK-0001-01)		11. 2.86	G.R.Horner	York	17. 8.99P
G-MNMN	Medway Hybred 44XLR 8286/16 (Rotax 447)		7. 3.86	D.S Blofeld	Stoke, Kent	16.12.99P
G-MNMO	Mainair Gemini/Flash 2 (Rotax 447) 398-186-4 & W141		27. 2.86	P.D.Hawkesworth & G.Wigglesworth Guy Lane Farm, Waverton		28. 5.99P
G-MNMS*	Wheeler Scout 0010		25. 5.84	M.I.Smith (Cancelled by CAA 27.3.99)	Alton	
G-MNMU	Southdown Raven X 2232/0127 (Fuji-Robin EC-44-PM)		17. 2.86	M.J.Curley	London Colney	14. 5.00P
G-MNMV	Mainair Gemini/Flash (Rotax 447) 375-1085-3 & W113		3. 3.86	B.Light	Lancaster	27. 3.00P
G-MNMW	Whittaker MW-6-1-1 Merlin (Rotax 582) PFA/164-11144		16. 4.86	E.F.Clapham Otherton, Cannock t/a G-MNMW Flying Group		14. 7.00P
G-MNMY	Cyclone 70/Aerial Arts 110SX CH-02 (Rotax 277)		6. 3.86	N.R.Beale	Leamington Spa	29. 9.96P
G-MNNA	Southdown Raven X 2232/0129 (Rotax 447)		4. 3.86	D. & G.D.Palfrey	Tiverton	20. 7.88P
G-MNNB	Southdown Raven 2122/0130 (Fuji-Robin EC-44-PM)		4. 3.86	J.K.Ewing	Poole	15. 8.99P
G-MNNC	Southdown Raven X 2232/0131 (Rotax 447)		4. 3.86	S.A.Sacker	Deenethorpe	5. 8.00P
G-MNND	Solar Wings Pegasus/Flash 2 (Rotax 447) SW-WF-0100		27. 2.86	M.J.Matthews	Crewe	2. 7.94P
G-MNNE	Mainair Gemini/Flash 2 (Rotax 462) 410-386-4 & W154		27. 2.86	R.N.Watts	Wirral	1. 7.93P
G-MNNF	Mainair Gemini/Flash 2 (Rotax 447) 402-286-4 & W148		28. 2.86	W.J.Gunn (Stored 1.98)	Long Marston	8. 4.97P
G-MNNG	Squires Lightfly/Solar Wings Photon (Rotax 277) SW-WP-0019		25. 2.86	C.C.Bilham	Huntingdon	30. 1.99P
G-MNNI	Mainair Gemini/Flash 2 (Rotax 503) 427-486-4 & W170 (Wing also quoted as c/n W173)		28. 2.86	J.C.Miller	East Fortune	2. 6.98P
G-MNNJ*	Mainair Gemini/Flash 2 (Rotax 503) 405-286-4 & W150		28. 2.86	G.D.Tannahill Broadmeadow Farm, Hereford (Cancelled as destroyed 17.8.98)		12. 4.98P
G-MNNK	Mainair Gemini/Flash 2 (Rotax 503) 428-486-4 & W185		28. 2.86	M.P.Shea Newcastle, Staffs (Trike stolen from Fradley 1.1.93)		8. 4.93P
G-MNNL	Mainair Gemini/Flash 2 (Rotax 503) 429-486-4 & W186		28. 2.86	D.Wilson	Nottingham	15. 7.00P
G-MNNM /	Mainair Scorcher Solo (Rotax 447) 424-486-1 & W182		20. 3.86	D.A.Whiteside	Ulverston	8. 9.91P
G-MNNN	Southdown Raven X 2232/0132 (Rotax 447)		4. 3.86	F.Byford & S.Hooker	Dover	21. 8.90P
G-MNNO	Southdown Raven X 2232/0133 (Rotax 447)		26. 3.86	M.J.Robbins	Tunbridge Wells	15. 7.00P
G-MNNP	Mainair Gemini/Flash 2 (Rotax 462) 409-386-4 & W155		5. 3.86	P.K.Dean	Margaretting, Kent	28. 8.94P
G-MNNR	Mainair Gemini/Flash 2 (Rotax 503) 430-586-4 & W188		6. 3.86	W.A.B.Hill Davidstow Moor (Wing originally quoted as c/n W157)		8. 4.99P
G-MNNS	Eurowing Goldwing EW-74		8. 4.86	J.S.R.Moodie	Rogart	
G-MNNU	Mainair Gemini/Flash 2 (Rotax 447) 408-386-4 & W153		19. 3.86	M.Hurn (See G-MTBK)	Graveley	13. 7.97P
G-MNNV	Mainair Gemini/Flash 2 (Rotax 503) 431-586-4 & W187		10. 3.86	R.P.Wilkinson	Bath	15. 5.99P
G-MNNY	Solar Wings Pegasus/Flash (Rotax 447) SW-TB-1059 & SW-WF-0023		14. 3.86	K.B.Stokes	Davidstow Moor	30. 8.99P
G-MNNZ	Solar Wings Pegasus/Flash 2 (Rotax 447) SW-TB-1060 & SW-WF-0101		24. 4.86	R.D.A.Henderson	Exeter	1. 4.98P
G-MNPA	Solar Wings Pegasus/Flash 2 (Rotax 462) SW-WF-0102		18. 4.86	J.M.MacDonald Mill Farm, Hughley, Much Wenlock		30. 5.98P
G-MNPB	Solar Wings Pegasus/Flash 2 (Rotax 447) SW-WF-0103		18. 4.86	M.R.Truran	Old Sarum	29. 5.95P
G-MNPC	Mainair Gemini/Flash 2 (Rotax 462) 423-586-4 & W181		17. 3.86	A.Bishop	Skelmersdale	10. 6.00P
G-MNPG	Mainair Gemini/Flash 2 (Rotax 447) 437-686-4 & W204		20. 3.86	P.Kirton	Cumbernauld	14. 6.00P
G-MNPI	Southdown Pipistrelle 2C SAL-P2C-003 (JPX PUL505)		17. 3.86	R.Riley (Damaged 1994)	Ashford, Kent	25. 7.94P
G-MNPV	Mainair Scorcher Solo (Rotax 447) 432-586-1 & W189		24. 3.86	F.Colman	Eshott	17. 5.98P

Regn	Type	C/n	P/I	Date	Owner/operator	Probable Base	CA Expy
G-MNPX*	Mainair Gemini/Flash 2 (Rotax 447) 412-486-4 & W164			24. 3.86	B.R.Ginger (Cancelled by CAA 19.7.99)	Colchester	9.11.99P
G-MNPY	Mainair Scorcher Solo (Rotax 447) 452-886-1 & W229			25. 3.86	R.N.O.Kingsbury	Tunbridge Wells	15. 6.00P
G-MNPZ	Mainair Scorcher Solo 449-886-1 & W226 (Rotax 503/3-Blade Propeller Test A/c)			25. 3.86	S.Stevens	North Shields	4. 9.93P
G-MNRD	Ultraflight Lazair IIIE (Rotax 185)	81		17. 6.83	J.K.Evans	Nazeby	15. 9.99P
G-MNRE	Mainair Scorcher Solo (Rotax 447) 453-886-1 & W230			25. 3.86	G.R.Hill	Staines	30. 7.97P
G-MNRF	Mainair Scorcher Solo (Rotax 447) 461-986-1 & W238			25. 3.86	Flylight Airsports Ltd	Sywell	14. 6.00P
G-MNRG	Mainair Scorcher Solo (Rotax 447) 462-986-1 & W239			25. 3.86	C.Murphy	Ince Blundell	19.12.99P
G-MNRI	Hornet Dual Trainer/Raven (Rotax 462) HRWA 0051 & 2000/0119			26. 3.86	D.A.Robinson (Replacement Trike HRWA-0082 now fitted)	Sandtoft	5. 7.00P
G-MNRJ	Hornet Dual Trainer/Raven (Rotax 447) HRWA 0052 & 2000/0120			26. 3.86	S.R., S.M. & R.W.Morris	Coventry	10.11.90P
G-MNRK	Hornet Dual Trainer/Raven (Rotax 447) HRWA 0053 & 2000/0183			26. 3.86	R.K.Beynon	Aberdeen	30. 7.95P
G-MNRL	Hornet Dual Trainer/Raven (Rotax 462) HRWA 0054 & 2000/0184			26. 3.86	A.G.Ward	Long Acres Farm, Sandy	30. 1.00P
G-MNRM	Hornet Dual Trainer/Raven (Rotax 447) HRWA 0055 & 2000/0214			26. 3.86	R.I.Cannan	Ramsey, IoM	26.12.99P
G-MNRP	Southdown Raven X (Rotax 447)	2232/0135		7. 4.86	C.Moore	Egremont	5. 7.95P
G-MNRS	Southdown Raven X (Rotax 447)	2232/0137		7. 4.86	A.J.Denhart	Crawley	6. 7.00P
G-MNRT	Midland Ultralights Sirocco 377GB (Rotax 377) MU-016			1. 4.86	R.F.Hinton	Mansfield	7. 8.99P
G-MNRW	Mainair Gemini/Flash 2 (Rotax 462) 411-486-4 & W156			7. 4.86	L.A.Maynard	Old Sarum	1. 8.99P
G-MNRX	Mainair Gemini/Flash 2 (Rotax 503) 434-686-4 & W220			8. 4.86	S.Foster	St.Michaels	8. 5.00P
G-MNRY	Mainair Gemini/Flash 2 (Rotax 462) 418-486-4 & W169			7. 4.86	M.Carolan	Coalisland, NI	13. 8.00P
G-MNRZ	Mainair Scorcher Solo (Rotax 447) 426-586-1 & W184			4. 4.86	J.N.Wrigley	Ley Farm, Chirk	17. 5.94P
G-MNSA	Mainair Gemini/Flash 2 (Rotax 503) 442-786-4 & W219			18. 4.86	R.E.Morris	Kidwelly, Dyfed	6. 8.00P
G-MNSB	Southdown Puma Sprint (Fuji-Robin EC-44-PM) 539 & 1121/0066			15. 6.83	A.C.Cale	Long Marston	17. 7.00P
G-MNSD	Ultrasports Tripacer/Solar Wings Typhoon S4 (Hunting HS.260A) T182-341L			23. 4.86	N.D.Dykes	Marston Moreteyne, Bedford	N/E
G-MNSE	Mainair Gemini/Flash 2 (Rotax 503) 444-886-4 & W224			4. 4.86	H.T.H. van Neck	Wirral	1. 4.98P
G-MNSH	Solar Wings Pegasus Flash 2 (Rotax 447) SW-WF-0104			14. 4.86	M.J.Aubrey	Kington, Hereford	15. 6.00P
G-MNSI	Mainair Gemini/Flash 2 (Rotax 462) 445-786-4 & W213			9. 4.86	S.Wheeldon	Manchester	3. 6.98P
G-MNSJ	Mainair Gemini/Flash 2 (Rotax 503) 443-886-4 & W223			11. 4.86	G.E.Jones	Chorley	20.11.00P
G-MNSL	Southdown Raven X (Rotax 447)	2232/0145		17. 4.86	P.B.Robinson	Ely	11. 8.00P
G-MNSN	Solar Wings Pegasus Flash 2 (Rotax 447) SW-TB-1066 & SW-WF-0105			25. 4.86	F.R. & V.L.Higgins	Leigh-upon-Mendip	19. 4.97P
G-MNSR	Mainair Gemini/Flash 2 (Rotax 503) 399-486-4 & W144			17. 4.86	A.M.Bell	Rufforth	2. 5.00P
G-MNSS	American Aerolights Eagle 215B (Zenoah G25B1)	4131		24. 4.86	G.P.Jones	Caernarfon	N/E
G-MNSV	CFM Shadow Srs.B (Rotax 447)	012		24. 4.86	P.J.W.Rowell	Southport	20.11.00P
G-MNSW	Southdown Raven X (Rotax 447)	2232/0147		23. 4.86	A.H.Gray	Tonbridge	22. 7.93P
G-MNSX	Southdown Raven X (Rotax 447)	2232/0148		30. 4.86	S.F.Chave	Honiton	11. 9.98P
G-MNSY	Southdown Raven X (Rotax 447)	2232/0149		30. 4.86	J.B.Carter	Hatherton, Cannock	7. 7.99P
G-MNTC	Southdown Raven X (Rotax 447)	2232/0150		30. 4.86	J.R.Brabbs	Brandon	12.10.92P
G-MNTD	Aerial Arts Chaser/110SX (C/n duplicates G-MTSF)	110SX/255		24. 4.86	B.Richardson	Sunderland	

Regn	Type	C/n	P/I	Date	Owner/operator	Probable Base	CA Expy
G-MNTE	Southdown Raven X (Rotax 447)	2232/0151		30. 4.86	B.K.Harrison	Glasgow	13. 3.00P
G-MNTF	Southdown Raven X	2232/0152		30. 4.86	M.D.Phillips	Mayfield, E.Sussex	24. 7.94P
G-MNTG	Southdown Raven X (Rotax 447)	2232/0153		30. 4.86	D.Thorpe (Stored 5.97)	Dunkeswell	24. 7.96P
G-MNTI	Mainair Gemini/Flash 2 (Rotax 503)	447-886-4 & W231		8. 5.86	R.T.Strathie	Melrose, Roxburgh	7. 8.99P
G-MNTK	CFM Shadow Srs.CD (Rotax 503)	024		8. 5.86	T.A.R.Davies	Brixham	17. 8.00P
G-MNTM	Southdown Raven X (Rotax 447)	2232/0154		19. 5.86	D.M.Garland	Atherstone	4. 8.99P
G-MNTN	Southdown Raven X (Rotax 447)	2232/0155		2. 6.86	J.Hall	Wolverhampton	31.12.99P
G-MNTO	Southdown Raven X (Rotax 447)	2232/0156		5. 6.86	D.J.Poole	Long Acres Farm, Sandy	9. 7.98P
G-MNTP	CFM Shadow Srs.B (Rotax 447)	K.022		19. 5.86	P.K.Hope-Lang	Milton Keynes	5. 1.00P
G-MNTS	Mainair Gemini/Flash 2 (Rotax 462)	450-886-4 & W227		3. 4.86	J.A.Colley	Tuffley, Glos	2. 5.96P
G-MNTT	Medway Half Pint/Aerial Arts 130SX	12/1486		7. 4.86	Lancaster Partners (Holdings) Ltd Ashcroft Farm, Winsford		N/E
G-MNTU	Mainair Gemini/Flash 2 (Rotax 503)	460-886-4 & W233		9. 7.86	T.J.Barley	Sawbridgeworth	16. 6.00P
G-MNTV	Mainair Gemini/Flash 2 (Rotax 462)	455-886-4 & W241		9. 7.86	P.Dunstan	Redruth	10.10.00P
G-MNTW	Mainair Gemini/Flash 2 (Rotax 462)	456-886-5 & W242		11. 9.86	J.E.Robinson	Bootle	21. 9.00P
G-MNTX	Mainair Gemini/Flash 2 (Rotax 503)	415-486-4 & W166		20. 5.86	S.Isherwood	St.Michaels	4. 7.00P
G-MNTY	Southdown Raven X (Rotax 447)	2232/0157		29. 5.86	B.J.Holloway	RAF Bicester	12. 3.00P
G-MNTZ	Mainair Gemini/Flash 2 (Rotax 503)	457-886-4 & W243		3. 6.86	R.W.Trenholm	Crewe	20. 3.00P
G-MNUA	Mainair Gemini/Flash 2 (Rotax 462)	458-886-4 & W235		29. 5.86	J.McCullough	Castlewellan, Co.Down	14. 2.00P
G-MNUB	Mainair Gemini/Flash 2 (Rotax 462)	459-986-4 & W236		3. 6.86	M.J.Hammond	South Ockendon, Essex	11. 8.97P
G-MNUD	Solar Wings Pegasus Flash 2 (Rotax 462)	SW-TE-0003 & SW-WF-0110		10. 6.86	P.G.H.Milbank	Over, Cambridge	3. 8.99P
G-MNUE	Solar Wings Pegasus Flash 2 (Rotax 462)	SW-WF-0108		10. 6.86	P.M.Rogers	Rochdale	20. 6.00P
G-MNUF	Mainair Gemini/Flash 2 (Rotax 503)	472-786-4 & W252		13. 6.86	C.Hannaby (Stored 12.97)	Guy Lane Farm, Waverton	4. 2.96P
G-MNUG	Mainair Gemini/Flash 2 (Rotax 462)	465-986-4 & W245		13. 6.86	M.L.Harris	Sittles Farm, Alrewas	1.12.99P
G-MNUH	Southdown Raven X (Rotax 447)	2232/0158		17. 6.86	A.L.Flude	Newnham	3. 5.97P
G-MNUI	Mainair Tri-Flyer/Skyhook Cutlass (Fuji-Robin EC-44-PM)	MH-01		21. 5.86	M.Holling	Goole	28. 2.87E
G-MNUJ*	Solar Wings Pegasus Photon	SW-TP-0018 & SW-WP-0018		11. 6.86	W.G.Farr (Stored 9.97; cancelled by CAA 27.3.99)	Eshott	
G-MNUM	Mainair Gemini/Southdown Puma Sprint MS (Fuji-Robin EC-44-PM)	226-184-2 & P.508		12. 3.84	J.A.Sims	Farnham	31. 7.00P
G-MNUO	Mainair Gemini/Flash 2 (Rotax 462)	421-586-4 & W179		9. 7.86	C.L.G.Innocent	Worthing	8. 5.00P
G-MNUR	Mainair Gemini/Flash 2 (Rotax 503)	470-986-4 & W250		14. 8.86	J.C.Greves	Cobham	30. 3.90P
G-MNUT	Southdown Raven X (Rotax 447)	2232/0160		10. 6.86	Irene A.De Groot (Stored 7.95) Lower Mountpleasant, Chatteris		15. 7.93P
G-MNUU	Southdown Raven X (Rotax 447)	2232/0162		26. 6.86	P.N.Jackson	Launceston	7. 8.00P
G-MNUW	Southdown Raven X (Rotax 447)	2232/0163		17. 6.86	B.A.McDonald	Sutton Meadows, Ely	19.12.96P
G-MNUX	Solar Wings Pegasus XL-R (Rotax 447)	SW-WA-1076		24. 6.86	N.Smith	Hebburn	29. 9.00P
G-MNUY	Mainair Gemini/Flash 2 (Rotax 503)	422-586-4 & W180		23. 6.86	R.M.Cornwell	Kemble	20. 6.00P
G-MNVB	Solar Wings Pegasus XL-R (Rotax 447)	SW-TB-1073 & SW-WA-1077		7. 7.86	M.J.Melvin	Spalding	2. 1.99P
G-MNVC	Solar Wings Pegasus XL-R (Rotax 447)	SW-TB-1074 & SW-WA-1078		7. 7.86	M.N.C.Ward	Shobdon	11. 6.00P

Regn	Type	C/n	P/I	Date	Owner/operator	Probable Base	CA Expy
G-MNVE	Solar Wings Pegasus XL-R (Rotax 447)	SW-WA-1079		19. 6.86	M.P.Aris	Welwyn	11. 8.00P
G-MNVF*	Solar Wings Pegasus Flash 2 (Rotax 447)	SW-WF-0112		26. 6.86	A.Rooker (Damaged mid 1996; cancelled as WFU 17.6.98)	Cambridge	23. 6.97P
G-MNVG	Solar Wings Pegasus Flash 2 (Rotax 447)	SW-WF-0109		11. 6.86	D.J.Ward Low Farm, South Walsham		7. 6.00P
G-MNVH	Solar Wings Pegasus Flash 2 (Rotax 462)	SW-TE-0001 & SW-WF-0122		23. 6.86	J.A.Clarke & C.Hall	London N22/E8	9. 4.97P
G-MNVI	CFM Shadow Srs.C (Rotax 503)	026		17. 6.86	D.R.C.Pugh	Caersws, Powys	13. 9.00P
G-MNVJ	CFM Shadow Srs.CD (Rotax 447) (Originally regd as Srs.BD)	028		17. 6.86	V.C.Readhead	Saxmundham	23. 9.99P
G-MNVK	CFM Shadow Srs.CD (Rotax 503)	029		17. 6.86	K.C.Lye	Melksham	16. 8.00P
G-MNVN	Southdown Raven (Fuji-Robin EC-34-PM)	2132/0165		27. 6.86	N.Cowlen & D.J.Francis	Spalding	26. 4.97P
G-MNVO	Hovey Whing-Ding II	CW-01		14. 8.86	C.Wilson	Basildon	
G-MNVP	Southdown Raven X (Rotax 447)	2232/0166		23. 6.86	M.J.Carnell (Damaged late 1996)	Belper	15. 9.97P
G-MNVR	Mainair Gemini/Flash 2 (Rotax 503)	471-986-4 & W251		27. 6.86	A.Munro "Loopy"	Bishops Stortford	13.11.99P
G-MNVS	Mainair Gemini/Flash 2 (Rotax 503)	476-986-4 & W257		9. 7.86	J.D.Potts	Telford	29. 1.98P
G-MNVT	Mainair Gemini/Flash 2 (Rotax 503)	477-786-4 & W258		27. 6.86	A.C.Barker Hinton-in-The-Hedges t/a ACB Hydraulics (Stored 4.90)		28. 7.87P
G-MNVU	Mainair Gemini/Flash 2 (Rotax 503)	468-986-4 & W248		26. 6.86	W.R.Marsh Newhouse Farm, Hardwicke, Hereford		28. 6.99P
G-MNVV	Mainair Gemini/Flash 2 (Rotax 503)	467-986-4 & W247		26. 6.86	R.P.Hothersall	St.Michaels	30. 3.00P
G-MNVW	Mainair Gemini/Flash 2 (Rotax 503)	466-986-4 & W246		26. 6.86	J.C.Munro-Hunt Little Down Farm, Milson		20. 9.98P
G-MNVY*	Solar Wings Pegasus Photon	SW-WP-0020		27. 6.86	Not known Hughley, Much Wenlock (On rebuild 3.97)		N/E
G-MNVZ	Solar Wings Pegasus Photon (Solo 210)	SW-WP-0021		27. 6.86	J.J.Russ	Eshott	27. 6.94P
G-MNWA	Southdown Raven X (Rotax 447)	2232/0167		26. 6.86	J.B.Mayes	Sutton Meadows	12. 6.00P
G-MNWB	Thruster TST (Rotax 503)	086-118-UK-001		25. 6.86	Heather E.Hewitt Clontilew Farm, Portadown, Co.Armagh		3. 1.95P
G-MNWC*	Mainair Gemini/Flash 2 (Rotax 503)	416-486-4 & W167		27. 6.86	Not known Kilmarnock (Temp unregd 20.10.97)		8. 6.98P
G-MNWD	Mainair Gemini/Flash 2 (Rotax 462)	474-986-4 & W254		27. 6.86	M.B.Rutherford	Swinford, Rugby	16. 3.00P
G-MNWG	Southdown Raven X (Rotax 447)	2232/0170		4. 8.86	A.J.McShane & M.J.Reeve	Sywell	28. 1.00P
G-MNWI	Mainair Gemini/Flash 2 (Rotax 503)	478-986-4 & W264		9. 7.86	W.H.Gilbertson	Manchester	3.11.99P
G-MNWK	CFM Shadow Srs.C (Rotax 503)	030		9. 7.86	J.E.Hunt	Welling, Kent	19. 8.98P
G-MNWL	Arbiter Services Trike/Aerial Arts 130S	130SX/333		23. 7.86	E.H.Snook	Newport Pagnell	
G-MNWO	Mainair Gemini/Flash 2 (Rotax 503)	490-1086-4 & W287		15. 7.86	G.Neal & Y.G.G.Lewis	Ruislip	8. 8.98P
G-MNWP	Solar Wings Pegasus/Flash 2 (Rotax 447)	SW-TB-1083 & SW-WF-0113		4. 8.86	A.G. & C.Smith	Swanton Morley	3.11.00P
G-MNWR	Medway Hybred 44XLR (Rotax 447)	23686/17		4. 8.86	P.Collins	Grays	23. 7.96P
G-MNWU	Solar Wings Pegasus/Flash 2LC (Rotax 462)	SW-TE-0006 & SW-WF-0111		4. 8.86	F.J.E.Brownshill & W.Parkin	Oakley	18. 4.99P
G-MNWV	Solar Wings Pegasus/Flash 2 (Rotax 447)	SW-TB-1090 & SW-WF-0121		4. 8.86	M.N.Tope & D.J.Brenchley	Davidstow Moor	11. 3.96P
G-MNWW	Solar Wings Pegasus XL-R/Se (Rotax 462)	SW-TE-0008 & SW-WA-1085		8.10.86	N.P.Chitty Ginge, Wantage t/a Chiltern Flyers Aero Tow Group		30. 6.00P
G-MNWX	Solar Wings Pegasus XL-R (Rotax 447)	SW-TB-1093 & SW-WA-1086		4. 8.86	J.A.Crofts & G.M.Birkett	Haverfordwest	5. 5.96P
G-MNWY	CFM Shadow Srs.CD (Rotax 503)	K.021 & PFA/161-11130		28. 7.86	R.Savage Ballynahinch, Co.Down t/a Air Photographic Ireland		1. 8.98P
G-MNWZ	Mainair Gemini/Flash 2 (Rotax 503)	436-686-4 & W203		19. 8.86	W.T.Hume	Newmilns, Ayr	16. 6.98P
G-MNXA	Southdown Raven X (Rotax 447)	2232/0180		5. 8.86	P.Johnson	Desborough	27. 7.99P

Regn	Type	C/n	P/I	Date	Owner/operator	Probable Base	CA Expy
G-MNXB	Mainair Tri-Flyer/Solar Wings Photon (Fuji-Robin EC-34-PM)	SW-WP-0022		29. 7.86	G.W.Carwardine	Uckfield	16. 6.98P
G-MNXC	Aerial Arts Chaser/110SX (Rotax 377)	110SX/335		4. 8.86	J.E.Sweetingham	Basildon	27. 4.95P
G-MNXD	Southdown Raven (Fuji-Robin EC-44-PM)	2132/0173		13. 8.86	P.Jephcott	Solihull	25.10.00P
G-MNXE	Southdown Raven X (Rotax 447)	2232/0202		7. 8.86	A.E.Silvey	Wilburton, Ely	28. 8.00P
G-MNXF	Southdown Raven (Fuji-Robin EC-44-PM)	2132/0176		2. 9.86	D.E.Gwenin	Tring	13. 5.99P
G-MNXG	Southdown Raven X (Rotax 447)	2232/0181		3. 9.86	M.A. & E.M.Williams	Tonbridge	9. 4.96P
G-MNXI	Southdown Raven X (Rotax 447)	2232/0179		19. 8.86	A.M.Yates	Wisbech	13. 7.96P
G-MNXN	Medway Hybred 44XLR (Rotax 447)	28786/18		3. 9.86	E.C.D.Williams & J.Dinwoodey (Stored 7.97)	Tarn Farm, Cockerham	16. 5.95P
G-MNXO	Medway Hybred 44XLR (Rotax 447)	29786/19		3. 9.86	D.L.Turner	Chatham	6. 7.00P
G-MNXP	Solar Wings Pegasus Flash 2 (Rotax 447)	SW-TB-1094 & SW-WF-0117		16. 9.86	D.Harrison	Bewdley	6. 8.96P
G-MNXR	Mainair Gemini/Flash 2 (Rotax 462)	479-986-4 & W265		19. 8.86	N.T.Wainwright	Bromyard	14. 6.97P
G-MNXS	Mainair Gemini/Flash 2 (Rotax 462)	480-986-4 & W267		8. 9.86	F.T.Rawlings	Hereford	16. 3.89P
G-MNXT	Mainair Gemini/Flash 2 (Rotax 503)	481-986-4 & W268		19. 8.86	B.K.Robinson	Shobdon	27. 3.96P
G-MNXU	Mainair Gemini/Flash 2 (Rotax 503)	482-1086-4 & W272		18. 8.86	J.M.Hucker	Abertillery	10. 3.98P
G-MNXX	CFM Shadow Srs.CD (Rotax 447)	K.027		13. 8.86	P.G.Gale "Shadowfax"	Old Sarum	13. 5.99P
G-MNXZ	Whittaker MW-5 Sorcerer (Fuji-Robin EC-34-PM)	PFA/163-11156		13. 8.86	P.J.Cheyney	Newhouse Farm, Loughborough	29. 5.00P
G-MNYA	Solar Wings Pegasus Flash 2 (Rotax 447)	SW-TB-1098 & SW-WF-0119		3. 9.86	D.J.Gardner	Wellingborough	6.11.00P
G-MNYB	Solar Wings Pegasus XL-R (Rotax 447)	SW-TB-1096 & SW-WA-1089		8. 9.86	P.J.Conaghy	Drogheda, Co.Louth, Ireland	3. 4.00P
G-MNYC	Solar Wings Pegasus XL-R (Rotax 447)	SW-TB-1097 & SW-WA-1090		3. 9.86	F.C.Handy	Hatherton, Cannock	20. 3.99P
G-MNYD	Aerial Arts Chaser/110SX (Rotax 377)	110SX/320		19. 8.86	B.Richardson	Sunderland	28. 6.00P
G-MNYE	Aerial Arts Chaser/110SX	110SX/321		19. 8.86	D.A.Breeze	Welshpool	18.11.99P
G-MNYF	Aerial Arts Chaser/110SX (Rotax 377)	110SX/322		19. 8.86	B.Richardson	Sunderland	4. 7.00P
G-MNYG	Southdown Raven (Fuji-Robin EC-44-PM)	2122/0172		19. 8.86	K.Clifford	Stanmore	3. 7.00P
G-MNYI	Southdown Raven X (Rotax 447)	2232/0211		3. 9.86	N.P.Lloyd	Wrexham	20. 8.00P
G-MNYJ	Mainair Gemini/Flash 2 (Rotax 462)	485-1086-4 & W275		8. 9.86	S.J.Bristow	Malvern	18. 6.99P
G-MNYK	Mainair Gemini/Flash 2 (Rotax 503)	494-1086-4 & W296		11. 9.86	D.E.Williams	Coleford, Glos	4.10.95P
G-MNYL	Southdown Raven X (Rotax 447)	2232/0195		2. 9.86	A.D.F.Clifford	Broadmeadow Farm, Hereford	9. 6.98P
G-MNYM	Southdown Raven X (Rotax 447)	2232/0196		2. 9.86	R.W.Scarr	Dunkeswell	13. 8.00P
G-MNYP	Southdown Raven X (Rotax 447)	2232/0207		3. 9.86	A.G.Davies	Bristol	11. 8.99P
G-MNYS	Southdown Raven X (Rotax 447)	2232/0208		8. 9.86	S.Connolly	Braintree	9. 1.99P
G-MNYT	Solar Wings Pegasus XL-R (Rotax 447)	SW-TB-1099 & SW-WA-1091		11. 9.86	V.Gadhia (Damaged mid 1997; stored 1.98)	Roddidge, Fradley	8. 3.98P
G-MNYU	Solar Wings Pegasus XL-R/Se (Rotax 447)	SW-TB-1100 & SW-WA-1092		16. 9.86	S.R.Wiggins	Rhuallt	1. 5.99P
G-MNYV	Solar Wings Pegasus XL-R/Se (Rotax 447)	SW-TB-1101 & SW-WA-1093		11. 9.86	B.J.Green	Marlborough	30.11.99P
G-MNYW	Solar Wings Pegasus XL-R (Rotax 447)	SW-WA-1094		11. 9.86	M.P.Waldock	Selsdon, Surrey	7. 8.98P
G-MNYX	Solar Wings Pegasus XL-R/LC (Rotax 462)	SW-TE-0009 & SW-WA-1095		19. 9.86	P.Mayes & J.P.Widdowson (See G-MMKG)	Bridgnorth	14. 6.00P
G-MNYZ	Solar Wings Pegasus Flash 2 (Rotax 462)	SW-WF-0114		11. 9.86	A.C.Bartolozzi	Ely	9. 3.00P

Regn	Type	C/n	P/I	Date	Owner/operator	Probable Base	CA Expy
G-MNZA	Solar Wings Pegasus Flash 2			3.10.86	J.M.MacDonald		
	(Rotax 462) SW-TB-1103 & SW-WF-0120				Mill Farm, Hughley, Much Wenlock		24. 8.90P
	(Mainair Alpha c/n W127-1185-1)						
G-MNZB	Mainair Gemini/Flash 2			8. 9.86	P.A.Ryder	Knebworth	11. 3.00P
	(Rotax 503) 483-1086-4 & W273						
G-MNZC	Mainair Gemini/Flash 2			6. 9.86	C.J.Whittaker	Ledbury	19. 1.89P
	(Rotax 503) 484-1086-4 & W274						
G-MNZD	Mainair Gemini/Flash 2			8. 9.86	N.D.Carter	Little Gransden	4. 4.96P
	(Rotax 503) 493-1086-4 & W295				(Stored 9.96)		
G-MNZE	Mainair Gemini/Flash 2			8. 9.86	K.J.Hughes	Wigan	6. 4.00P
	(Rotax 503) 495-1086-4 & W297 (Wing regd as W279 - see G-MTEK)						
G-MNZF	Mainair Gemini/Flash 2			8. 9.86	B.J.Marshall	Swinford, Rugby	14. 3.98P
	(Rotax 503) 496-1186-4 & W291						
G-MNZI	Prone Power Mk.2/Solar Wings Typhoon			22. 9.86	R.J.Folwell	London W6	
	PP-01						
G-MNZJ	CFM Shadow Srs.BD	033		19. 9.86	T.E.P.Eves & A.Rothery		
	(Rotax 447)					Baxby Manor, Husthwaite	26.11.99P
G-MNZK	Solar Wings Pegasus XL-R/Se			24. 9.86	J.G.Campbell & P.J.Perkins	Sandtoft	23. 7.00P
	SW-WA-1096						
G-MNZL	Solar Wings Pegasus XL-R			1.10.86	M.A.Concannon	Long Marston	27. 9.95P
	(Rotax 447) SW-TB-1106 & SW-WA-1097				(Stored 6.96)		
G-MNZO	Solar Wings Pegasus Flash 2			30. 9.86	K.B.Woods & D.Johnson	Newnham	24. 4.00P
	(Rotax 462) SW-TE-0012 & SW-WF-0125						
G-MNZP	CFM Shadow Srs.BD			19. 9.86	J.G.Wakeford	Deanland, Hailsham	25. 5.00P
	(Rotax 447) K.039 & PFA/161-11206						
G-MNZR	CFM Shadow Srs.BD	040		19. 9.86	J.S.Wilson	Swanton Morley	9. 7.00P
	(Rotax 447)						
G-MNZS	Aerial Arts Alpha/130SX	130SX/376		23. 9.86	S.B.Walters	Sidcup	1. 8.00P
	(Rotax 277)						
G-MNZU	Eurowing Goldwing	EW-88		24. 9.86	H.B.Baker	Old Sarum	19. 8.00P
	(Fuji-Robin EC-34-PM)						
G-MNZW*	Southdown Raven X	2232/0220		17.10.86	C.A.James	Filton	5. 7.98P
	(Rotax 447)				(Cancelled by CAA 15.3.99)		
G-MNZY	Mainair Tri-Flyer 330/Airwave Nimrod			17.10.86	P.W.Fieldman	Petersfield, Hants	N/E
	078-14682						
G-MNZZ	CFM Shadow Srs.CD (Rotax 503)	036		19. 9.86	P.J.Lynch	Farnborough	18. 9.99P
G-MOAC	Beechcraft F33A Bonanza	CE-1349	N1563N	25. 5.89	R.L.Camrass	La Rochelle, France	30. 5.01
G-MOAK	Schempp-Hirth Nimbus 3DM	19/46		23. 5.91	P.W.Lever	Carr Hill Farm, Corbridge	28. 5.01
						"929"	
G-MOBI	Aerospatiale AS.355F1 Twin Squirrel	G-MUFF		11.11.93	M.J.O'Brien	Redhill	3. 4.00T
	5260	G-CORR			t/a Castle Aviation (Op Gemini Redhill Ltd)		
G-MOFB	Cameron O-120 HAFB	4275		13. 1.98	D.M.Moffat	Alveston, Bristol	
G-MOFF	Cameron O-77 HAFB	2040		27. 7.89	D.M.Moffat "Moff"	Alveston, Bristol	19.12.99A
G-MOFZ	Cameron O-90 HAFB	3350		7. 9.94	D.M.Moffat	Alveston, Bristol	15. 9.96A
G-MOGI	Grumman-American AA-5A Cheetah	G-BFMU		1. 5.86	TL Aviation Ltd	Jersey	24.10.02
	AA5A-0630						
G-MOGY	Robinson R-22 Beta	0899		23.11.88	M.N.Cowley	(Towcester)	8. 6.01
					t/a Dragonfly Aviation		
G-MOHS	PA-31-350 Chieftain	31-8152115	G-BWOC	29. 4.96	Sky Air Travel Ltd	Stapleford	23. 9.00T
			N40898				
G-MOJO	Airbus A.330-243	301	F-WWYE	8.11.99	Premair A/S	(Dragoe, Denmark)	7.11 02T
G-MOKE	Cameron V-77 HAFB	3686		4.10.95	D.D.Owen	(Luxembourg)	3. 1.00A
G-MOLE	Taylor JT.2 Titch	PFA/60-10725		20. 1.87	S.R.Mowle	(Kenley)	
	(Continental O-200-A)				(Under construction 10.90)		
G-MOLI	Cameron A-250 HAFB	3429		26. 1.95	J.J.Rudoni	Rugeley	26. 1.00T
G-MOLL	PA-32-301T Turbo Saratoga		N82535	25. 3.91	M.S.Bennett	Gamston	12. 5.00
		32-8024040					
G-MOLY	PA-23-160 Apache	23-1686	EI-BAW	7. 6.79	R.R. & M.T.Thorogood	Henstridge	28. 2.02
			G-APFV/EI-ALK				
G-MONB	Boeing 757-2T7ER	22780		7. 3.83	Monarch Airlines Ltd	Luton	1. 2.00T
G-MONC	Boeing 757-2T7ER	22781	PH-AHO	15. 4.83	Monarch Airlines Ltd	Luton	29. 4.02T
			D-ABNY/G-MONC/EC-211/G-MONC				
G-MOND	Boeing 757-2T7	22960	D-ABNZ	28. 4.83	Monarch Airlines Ltd	Luton	13. 5.99T
			G-MOND				
G-MONE	Boeing 757-2T7ER	23293		27. 2.85	Monarch Airlines Ltd	Luton	25. 2.00T
					(Renaissance Cruise c/s)		
G-MONI	Monnett Moni	PFA/142-10925		12. 1.84	B.S.Carpenter	RAF Brize Norton	23.11.98P
	(KFM.107)						
G-MONJ	Boeing 757-2T7ER	24104		26. 2.88	Monarch Airlines Ltd	Luton	23. 1.00T
G-MONK	Boeing 757-2T7ER	24105		26. 2.88	Monarch Airlines Ltd	Luton	31. 5.02T

Regn	Type	C/n	P/I	Date	Owner/operator	Probable Base	CA Expy
G-MONR	Airbus A.300B4-605R	540	VH-YMJ G-MONR/F-WWAT	15. 3.90	Monarch Airlines Ltd	Luton	2. 4.02T
G-MONS	Airbus A.300B4-605R	556	VH-YMK G-MONS/F-WWAY	17. 4.90	Monarch Airlines Ltd	Luton	23. 3.00T
G-MONW	Airbus A.320-212	391	F-WWDO	24. 2.93	Monarch Airlines Ltd	Luton	7. 3.00T
G-MONX	Airbus A.320-212	392	F-WWDR	19. 3.93	Monarch Airlines Ltd	Luton	17. 3.00T
G-MOON	Mooney M.20K (252TSE)	25-1143	N252BT	22. 6.88	Moira A.Eccles	Binton, Stratford-upon-Avon	14. 8.00
G-MOOR	Socata TB-10 Tobago	82	G-MILK	23. 7.91	W.G.& R.Communications Ltd Crosland Moor		21.10.01
G-MOOS	Hunting-Percival P.56 Provost T.1	PAC/F/335	G-BGKA 8041M/XF690	5. 4.91	T.J.Manna t/a Kennet Aviation (As "XF690" in RAF c/s)	Cranfield	17. 6.99P
G-MOSI*	DH.98 Mosquito TT.35	-	N9797 G-ASKA/RS709	10.11.81	USAF Museum (As "NS519/P" in USAAF c/s) Wright Patterson AFB, Dayton, Ohio, USA		17.12.84P*
G-MOSS	Beechcraft D55 Baron	TE-548	G-AWAD	12. 6.95	S.C.Tysoe	(Desford)	17. 3.00
G-MOSY	Cameron O-84 HAFB	2315		17. 4.96	P.L.Mossman	Bristol	
G-MOTA	Bell 206B Jet Ranger III	4494	N81521	20.10.98	J W Sandle Runcton Holme, Kings Lynn		28.10.01T
G-MOTH	DH.82A Tiger Moth (Rebuilt to DH.82 standard)	85340	7035M DE306	31. 1.78	M.C.Russell (As "K2567")	Top Farm, Royston	4. 6.01
G-MOTI	Robin DR.400/500	0006		23.11.98	O.Graham-Flatebo & The Lord Saville of Newdigate t/a The Tango India Flying Group Biggin Hill		2. 2.02
G-MOTO	PA-24-180 Comanche	24-3239	G-EDHE N51867/G-ASFH/EI-AMM	24. 3.87	L.T. & S.Evans	Sandown	4.10.02
G-MOTT	Light Aero Avid Speed Wing (Rotax 582)	PFA/189-11738		29. 5.92	J.B.Ott	Cambridge	26. 2.99P
G-MOUL	Maule M.6-235C Super Rocket	7518C		1. 5.90	M.Klinge	Prestwick	10. 4.00
G-MOUR	Folland Gnat T.1	FL.596	8624M XS102	16. 5.90	D.J.Gilmour t/a Intrepid Aviation Co (As "XR991" in Yellowjacks c/s)	North Weald	29. 4.99P
G-MOVE	PA-60-601P Aerostar	61P-0593-7963263	OO-PKB G-MOVE/(N8144J)	5. 1.79	A. Kazaz & A1 Hydraulics Ltd	Leicester	8. 7.02
G-MOVI	PA-32R-301 Saratoga SP	32R-8313029	G-MARI N8248H	6. 2.89	G-BOON Ltd	(Stevenage)	24. 5.00T
G-MOZZ	Mudry CAP.10B	256		30.10.90	M.B.Smith & N.Skipworth	Booker	2. 5.00
G-MPBH	Reims Cessna FA.152 Aerobat	0374	G-FLIC G-BILV	8.12.88	S.Gwilliam & C.Hopwood Biggin Hill t/a Metropolitan Police Flying Club		18. 9.02T
G-MPBI	Cessna 310R II	310R-0584	F-GEBB HB-LMD/N87473	21. 7.97	M.P.Bolshaw & Co Ltd	Elstree	7. 8.00
G-MPCD	Airbus A.320-212	379	C-FTDU G-MPCD(x4)/F-WWDY	14. 3.94	Monarch Airlines Ltd	Luton	30. 4.01T
G-MPWH	Rotorway Exec	3579		22. 6.90	Thistle Aviation Ltd Henley-on-Thames (Stored 5.94)		AC
G-MPWI	Robin HR.100/210	163	F-GBTY F-ODFA/F-BUPD	3. 3.80	Propwash Investments Ltd	Swansea	2. 3.02
G-MPWT	PA-34-220T Seneca III (Originally built as c/n 34-8233163)	34-8333068	N4294X N9539N/N8218K	26. 9.88	Modern Air (UK) Ltd	Fowlmere	19. 5.01T
G-MRAJ	MDH Hughes 369E (500E)	0010E	N51946	19. 3.98	A.Jardine	Dundee	5. 5.01T
G-MRAM	Mignet HM-1000 Balerit	134		15.11.99	R.A.Marven	(St. Albans)	8.11.00P
G-MRED	Elmwood CA-05 Christavia mk.1	PFA/185-12935		2. 8.96	E.Hewett	(Fareham)	
G-MRKT	Lindstrand LBL-90A HAFB	037		7. 6.93	Marketplace Public Relations (London) Ltd "Kaytee" Crowthorne, Berks		30. 3.00A
G-MRLN	Sky 240-24 HAFB	161		4. 8.99	P.& J.M.Trumper Ashford t/a Merlin Balloons		
G-MRMR	PA-31-350 Chieftain	31-7952092	OH-PRE G-WROX/G-BNZI/N3517T	21. 8.97	I.D. & P.J.Margetson-Rushmore t/a MRMR Flight Services Stapleford		22.12.02T
G-MROC	Cyclone Pegasus Quantum 15	7498		22. 1.99	M.Convine	(Wellingborough)	21. 1.00P
G-MRSN	Robinson R-22 Beta	1654		21. 1.91	Leeds Lighting Ltd	(Leeds)	7. 4.00T
G-MRST	PA-28RT-201 Arrow IV	28R-7918068	9H-AAU 5B-CEC/N3019U	27.11.86	C.P.Scamp	Gloucestershire	13. 3.01
G-MRTN	Socata TB-10 Tobago	62	G-BHET	9. 7.98	Underwood Kitchens Ltd	Turweston	30. 4.01
G-MRTY	Cameron N-77 HAFB	1008		24. 4.84	P.G. & R.A.Vale "Marty"	Kidderminster	19. 5.96A
G-MSAL	Morane-Saulnier MS.733 Alcyon	143	F-BLXV Fr.Mil	16. 6.93	North Weald Flying Services Ltd North Weald (Stored 10.97: as "143" in Aeronavale c/s)		
G-MSDJ	Aerospatiale AS.350B1 Ecureuil	2174	G-BPOH	28. 3.89	Denis Ferranti Hoverknights Ltd Llanfairfechan		3. 5.01
G-MSFC	PA-38-112 Tomahawk II	38-81A0067	N25735	11. 5.90	Sherwood Flying Club Ltd	Nottingham	18. 7.02T
G-MSFT	PA-28-161 Warrior II	28-8416093	G-MUMS N118AV	2. 4.97	M.J.Love (Op SFT Aviation)	Bournemouth	3. 5.01T
G-MSIX	Glaser Dirks DG-800B	8-156-B80		21.4.99	E.Coles t/a G-MSIX Group	(Stevenage)	4. 5.02
G-MSKA	Boeing 737-5L9	24859	OY-MAC (OY-MMZ)	18.10.96	Maersk Air Ltd (Blue Poole t/s)	Birmingham	17.10.02T

Regn	Type	C/n	P/I	Date	Owner/operator	Probable Base	CA Expy
G-MSKB	Boeing 737-5L9	24928	OY-MAD (OY-MMO)	12.11.96	Maersk Air Ltd (Dove/Colum t/s)	Birmingham	11.11.02T
G-MSKC	Boeing 737-5L9	25066	OY-MAE	3.12.96	Maersk Air Ltd (Waves of the City t/s)	Birmingham	2.12.02T
G-MSKD	Boeing 737-5L9	24778	HL7230 OY-MAA/(OY-MMW)	14. 1.98	Maersk Air Ltd (Whale Rider t/s)	Birmingham	21. 1.01T
G-MSKE	Boeing 737-5L9	28084	OY-APB	4. 1.99	Maersk Air Ltd (Delftblue Daybreak t/s)	Birmingham	28. 1.02T
G-MSKK	Canadair RJ100 (CL.600-2B19)	7226	C-GCBS C-FMKZ	25. 5.98	Maersk Air Ltd (Wings t/s)	Birmingham	23. 5.01T
G-MSKL	Canadair RJ100 (CL.600-2B19)	7247		1. 7.98	Maersk Air Ltd (Martha Masanabo/Ndebele t/s)	Birmingham	30. 6.01T
G-MSKM	Canadair RJ100 (CL.600-2B19)	7248		28. 7.98	Maersk Air Ltd (Sterntaler/Bauhaus t/s)	Birmingham	29. 7.01T
G-MSKN	Canadair RJ100 (CL.600-2B19)	7283		14. 1.99	Maersk Air Ltd (Chelsea Rose t/s)	Birmingham	18. 1.02T
G-MSKO	Canadair RJ100 (CL.600-2B19)	7299	C-FMOS	19. 3.99	Maersk Air Ltd (Crossing Borders t/s)	Birmingham	23. 3.02T
G-MSKP	Canadair RJ100 (CL.600-2B19)	7329	C-FMOS	22. 7.99	Maersk Air Ltd (Grand Union t/s)	Birmingham	26. 7.02T
G-MSOO	Revolution Helicopters Mini-500	0016		16.10.95	R.H.Ryan	(Sunderland)	
G-MSMS	Eurocopter AS.350B2 Ecureuil	3119		21. 8.98	Fairview Securities (Investments) Ltd	(London SW3)	11. 1.02T
G-MSTC	Gulfstream AA-5A Cheetah	AA5A-0833	G-BIJT N26950	30. 1.95	Mid-Sussex Timber Co Ltd	Biggin Hill	4. 2.02T
G-MSTG	North American P-51D-25-NT Mustang	124-48271	NZ2427 45-11518	2. 9.97	M.Hammond	(Eye)	
G-MTAA	Solar Wings Pegasus XL-R (Rotax 447) SW-TB-1108 & SW-WA-1102			15.10.86	R.Scott	London Colney	14. 3.00P
G-MTAB	Mainair Gemini/Flash 2 (Rotax 503) 492-1086-4 & W290			8.10.86	G.S.Stokes	Kingswinford	30. 3.00P
G-MTAC	Mainair Gemini/Flash 2 (Rotax 503) 486-1086-4 & W278			15.10.86	A.Jackson	St.Michaels	1. 7.00P
G-MTAE	Mainair Gemini/Flash 2 (Rotax 503) 500-1186-4 & W302			15.10.86	S.W.Tallamy	Davidstow Moor	16. 4.00P
G-MTAF	Mainair Gemini/Flash 2 (Rotax 503) 499-1186-4 & W301			5.10.86	P.A.Long	Altrincham	30.10.99P
G-MTAG	Mainair Gemini/Flash 2 (Rotax 503) 487-1086-4 & W281			15.10.86	B.Read	Wallasey	21.10.98P
G-MTAH	Mainair Gemini/Flash 2 (Rotax 503) 488-1086-4 & W282			16.10.86	T.G.Elmhirst	St.Michaels	21. 8.00P
G-MTAI	Solar Wings Pegasus XL-R (Rotax 447) SW-TB-1109 & SW-WA-1103			14.10.86	J.Becskehazy	Oxton, Notts	4. 5.96P
G-MTAJ	Solar Wings Pegasus XL-R SW-WA-1104 (Rotax 447)			16.10.86	G.A. & S.D.Batchelor	Launceston	21. 3.00P
G-MTAL	Solar Wings Pegasus Photon SW-WP-0023 (Solo 210)			15.10.86	R.P.Wilkinson	Bath	29.10.95P
G-MTAO	Solar Wings Pegasus XL-R (Rotax 447) SW-TB-1107 & SW-WA-1107			21.10.86	S.P.Disney & R.Jones	Swinford, Rugby	17. 5.99P
G-MTAP	Southdown Raven X 2232/0225 (Rotax 447)			15.10.86	D.B.McCalvey	Hailsham	13. 6.98P
G-MTAR	Mainair Gemini Flash II (Rotax 462) 504-1286-4-W307			16.10.86	D.J.Townsend	Norwich	
G-MTAS	Whittaker MW-5C Sorcerer (Norton Rotary 50hp) PFA/163-11166			14.10.86	R.J.H.& A-M.Hayward	Hereford	19.12.00P
G-MTAT	Solar Wings Pegasus XL-R (Rotax 447) SW-TB-1113 & SW-WA-1108			28.10.86	J.Ryan	Enniscorthy, Co.Wexford	26. 3.00P
G-MTAV	Solar Wings Pegasus XL-R (Rotax 447) SW-TB-1115 & SW-WA-1110			21.10.86	Susan Fairweather & Carolyn L.Harris Nottingham/Warrington		13. 3.00P
G-MTAW	Solar Wings Pegasus XL-R SW-WA-1111 (Rotax 447)			21.10.86	J.P.Stannard	Weston Zoyland	1.10.96P
G-MTAX	Solar Wings Pegasus XL-R (Rotax 447) SW-TB-1117 & SW-WA-1112			27.10.86	G Hawes	Great Glen	7. 8.98P
G-MTAY	Solar Wings Pegasus XL-R (Rotax 447) SW-TB-1118 & SW-WA-1113			27.10.86	S.A.McLatchie	Enstone	3. 9.98P
G-MTAZ	Solar Wings Pegasus XL-R (Rotax 447) SW-TB-1119 & SW-WA-1114			28.10.86	H.W.Banham Lower Mountpleasant, Chatteris		2.10.99P
G-MTBA	Solar Wings Pegasus XL-R SW-WA-1115 (Rotax 447)			27.10.86	R.J.W.Franklin & M.C.Buffery (Stored 5.97) Redlands, Swindon		24. 6.93P
G-MTBB	Southdown Raven X 2232/0226 (Rotax 447)			16.10.86	A.Miller	Woking	2. 6.92P

Regn	Type	C/n	P/I	Date	Owner/operator	Probable Base	CA Expy
G-MTBC	Mainair Gemini/Flash 2 (Rotax 503) 501-1186-4 & W303			16.10.86	Not known (Trike stored 5.96)	Popham	11. 5.92P
G-MTBD	Mainair Gemini/Flash 2 (Rotax 503) 498-1186-4 & W299 (Wing regd as W229)			16.10.86	K.Hopkinson	West Bridgford	19. 2.00P
G-MTBE	CFM Shadow Srs.CD K.035 (Rotax 462HP)			16.10.86	S.K.Brown	Farnborough	25. 5.00P
G-MTBG	Mainair Gemini/Flash 2 (Rotax 503) 506-1286-4 & W309			27.10.86	N.Spencer-Brayn	Winchester	23. 6.90P
G-MTBH	Mainair Gemini/Flash 2 (Rotax 462) 524-187-5 & W327			28.10.86	D.E.Williams	Coleford	11. 7.00P
G-MTBI	Mainair Gemini/Flash 2 (Rotax 462) 508-1286-4 & W311			27.10.86	A.Ormson	Eshott	29. 9.00P
G-MTBJ	Mainair Gemini/Flash 2 (Rotax 503) 509-1286-4 & W312			27.10.86	R.M. & P.J.Perry Otherton, Cannock (Op Staffordshire Aero Club)		29. 5.00P
G-MTBK	Southdown Raven X 2232/0230 (Rotax 447) (Wing reported as from G-MNNU)			28.10.86	R.J.Grimwood Plaistows, Hemel Hempstead		27. 6.99P
G-MTBL	Solar Wings Pegasus XL-R (Rotax 447) SW-TB-1121 & SW-WA-1117			6.11.86	R.N.Whiting Lower Mountpleasant, Chatteris		18. 1.00P
G-MTBN	Southdown Raven X 2232/0227 (Rotax 447)			28.10.86	A.J. & S.E.Crosby-Jones Hailsham		11. 7.98P
G-MTBO	Southdown Raven X 2232/0233 (Rotax 447)			28.10.86	R.Jackson	Bristol	11. 8.99P
G-MTBP	Aerotech MW-5B Sorcerer (Rotax 447) SR102-R440B-02			28.10.86	R.Thompson (Stored 5.96)	Shobdon	21. 9.94P
G-MTBR	Aerotech MW-5B Sorcerer (Fuji-Robin EC-44-PM) SR102-R440B-03			20. 1.87	J.H.Cooling	Deenethorpe	26.10.99P
G-MTBS	Aerotech MW-5B Sorcerer (Fuji-Robin EC-44-PM) SR102-R440B-04			27.10.86	J.M.Benton	Wetheroak	30. 3.00P
G-MTBT*	Aerotech MW-5B Sorcerer (Fuji-Robin EC-44-PM) SR102-R440B-05 & BMAA/HB/027 (Wings possibly from G-MWGI: stored 7.96)			10. 4.87	N.W.Finn-Kelcey Weston Underwood, Olney		19. 5.92P
G-MTBU	Solar Wings Pegasus XL-R SW-WA-1118 (Rotax 447)			13.11.86	B J Palfreyman	Nottingham	18.10.93P
G-MTBW*	Mainair Gemini/Flash 2 (Rotax 503) 520-187-5 & W322 (Crashed Old Airfield, Aldridge 15.4.97 & cancelled by CAA 23.2.98)			6.11.86	J.Sharman Otherton, Cannock		21. 9.97P
G-MTBX	Mainair Gemini/Flash 2 (Rotax 447) 510-1286-4 & W313			6.11.86	J.E.Orbell Spean Bridge, Inverness		21. 3.00P
G-MTBY	Mainair Gemini/Flash 2 (Rotax 447) 507-1286-4 & W310			6.11.86	R.P.Wilkinson	Bath	5. 4.97P
G-MTBZ	Southdown Raven X 2232/0232 (Rotax 447)			10.11.86	C A M Anderton	Leigh	15.10.00P
G-MTCA	CFM Shadow Srs.C K.011 (Rotax 447)			6.11.86	J.R.L.Murray (Damaged mid 1997)	Edinburgh	18. 1.98P
G-MTCC	Mainair Gemini/Flash 2 (Rotax 503) 497-1186-4 & W298			13.11.86	J.Madhvani	Eshott	21.10.96P
G-MTCD*	Southdown Raven X 2232/0236			21.11.86	R.Green (Cancelled as wfu 6.4.98)	Lincoln	10. 7.96P
G-MTCE	Mainair Gemini/Flash 2 (Rotax 462) 511-1286-4 & W314			2.12.86	R.S.Acreman Hatherton, Cannock		23. 5.99P
G-MTCG	Solar Wings Pegasus XL-R/Se (Rotax 447) SW-TB-1125 & SW-WA-1123			16.12.86	R.W. & M.W.Allan (Stored 9.97)	Eshott	11. 2.95P
G-MTCH	Solar Wings Pegasus XL-R (Rotax 447) SW-TB-1126 & SW-WA-1124			28.11.86	R.E.H.Harris	Davidstow Moor	29.11.95P
G-MTCK	Solar Wings Pegasus Flash 2 (Rotax 447) SW-WF-0127			11.12.86	A.R.R.Williams St.Andrews, Bristol		11. 8.00P
G-MTCM	Southdown Raven X 2232/0239 (Rotax 447)			11.12.86	J.C & A.M.Rose	Oakley	2. 7.97P
G-MTCN	Solar Wings Pegasus XL-R SW-WA-1126 (Rotax 447)			16.12.86	T.J.Gayton-Polley	(Billingshurst)	19. 5.92P
G-MTCO	Solar Wings Pegasus XL-R (Rotax 447) SW-TB-1129 & SW-WA-1127			7. 1.87	A.J.Nesom	Husthwaite	6.11.00P
G-MTCP	Aerial Arts Chaser/110SX 110SX/476 (Rotax 377)			16.12.86	B.Richardson	Sunderland	28. 6.00P
G-MTCR	Solar Wings Pegasus XL-R SW-WA-1128 (Rotax 447)			16.12.86	J.B.Greenwood	Rufforth	17. 7.00P
G-MTCT	CFM Shadow Srs.CD 042 (Rotax 503)			16.12.86	F.W.McCann	Johnstone	4. 7.00P
G-MTCU	Mainair Gemini/Flash 2A (Rotax 503) 451-1286-4 & W228			5. 1.87	A.S.Facey	Leigh	16. 5.00P
G-MTCW	Mainair Gemini/Flash 2 (Rotax 462) 502-1186-4 & W304			5. 1.87	R.A.Watering	Bourne, Lincs	6. 5.98P

Regn	Type	C/n P/I	Date	Owner/operator	Probable Base	CA Expy
G-MTCX	Solar Wings Pegasus XL-R (Rotax 447) SW-TB-1131 & SW-WA-1129		9. 1.87	A.L.Davies	Rhuallt	30. 6.99P
G-MTDA	Hornet Dual Trainer/Southdown Raven (Rotax 462) HRWA 0060 & 2000/0245		5. 1.87	B.D.Atkinson & I.R.Buckle	Oxford	2. 9.96P
G-MTDB*	Owen Pola Mk.1	POLA/X001/001	19.12.86	P.E.Owen (Cancelled by CAA 16.2.99)	Dorchester	
G-MTDC*	Owen Pola Mk.1	POLA/X001/002	19.12.86	P.E.Owen (Cancelled by CAA 16.2.99)	Dorchester	
G-MTDD	Aerial Arts Chaser/110SX 110SX/137 (Rotax 377) (Originally regd as c/n 110SX/437)		26. 1.87	B.Richardson	Sunderland	4. 7.00P
G-MTDE	Aerial Arts Chaser/110SX 110SX/438 (Rotax 377)		5. 1.87	G.Firth	Sandtoft	27.12.98P
G-MTDF	Mainair Gemini/Flash 2 (Rotax 503) 515-287-5 & W319		5. 1.87	A.R.Haydock	St.Michaels	4. 4.00P
G-MTDG	Solar Wings Pegasus XL-R/Se (Rotax 447) SW-WA-1130		20. 1.87	E.W.Laidlaw (Stored 9.97)	Great Orton	27. 8.96P
G-MTDH	Solar Wings Pegasus XL-R (Rotax 447) SW-TB-1133 & SW-WA-1131		22. 1.87	M.Shiner	Birmingham	28. 5.00P
G-MTDI	Solar Wings Pegasus XL-R/Se (Rotax 447) SW-TB-1134 & SW-WA-1132		22. 1.87	W.Wood (Stored 9.97)	Eshott	13. 5.91P
G-MTDJ	Medway Hybred 44XL 1587/23 (Rotax 447)		20. 1.87	J.A.Slocombe & C.D.Gates	Gillingham	4. 4.96P
G-MTDK	Aerotech MW-5B Sorcerer (Fuji-Robin EC-44-PM) SR102-R440B-06		22. 1.87	R.H.Borland	Nunthorpe, Cleveland	23. 6.00P
G-MTDN	Ultraflight Lazair IIIE A465/002 (Rotax 185)		22. 1.87	B.H.Ashman	Buttermilk Hall Farm, Blisworth	27. 6.97P
G-MTDO	Eipper Quicksilver MXII 1124 (Rotax 503)		27. 2.87	D.L.Ham	Long Marston	N/E
G-MTDP	Solar Wings Pegasus XL-R (Rotax 447) SW-TB-1136 & SW-WA-1134		22. 1.87	M.J.Powell	Shobdon	29. 5.99P
G-MTDR	Mainair Gemini/Flash 2 (Rotax 503) 516-287-5 & W276		26. 1.87	J.W. & C.Richardson	Baxby Manor, Husthwaite	28. 6.00P
G-MTDS	Solar Wings Pegasus Photon (Solo 210) SW-WP-0024		29. 1.87	M.J.Wooldridge (Stored 5.97)	Clench Common	27. 4.97P
G-MTDT	Solar Wings Pegasus XL-R (Rotax 447) SW-TB-1137 & SW-WA-1135		2. 2.87	J.R.E.Gladstone t/a G-MTDT Syndicate	(Abingdon)	7. 4.00P
G-MTDU	CFM Shadow Srs.CD K.037 (Rotax 503)		26. 1.87	M.Jones	Leicester	3. 9.00P
G-MTDV	Solar Wings Pegasus XL-R SW-WA-1136 (Rotax 447)		3. 2.87	S.J.Adcock	Rufforth	28. 8.94P
G-MTDW	Mainair Gemini/Flash 2 (Rotax 503) 517-387-5 & W212		2. 2.87	S.R.Leeper	Priory Farm, Tibenham	13. 3.00P
G-MTDX	CFM Shadow Srs.CD K.043 (Rotax 503)		10. 2.87	L.Fekete	Ellesmere Port	4. 6.00P
G-MTDY	Mainair Gemini/Flash 2 (Rotax 462) 513-187-5 & W317		11. 2.87	S.Penoyre	Windlesham	13.10.00P
G-MTEB	Solar Wings Pegasus XL-R SW-WA-1139 (Rotax 447)		9. 2.87	F.Watt	Insch	10. 7.00P
G-MTEC	Solar Wings Pegasus XL-R (Rotax 447) SW-TB-1142 & SW-WA-1140		9. 2.87	R.W.Glover (Stored 6.97)	Kemble	11. 6.94P
G-MTED	Solar Wings Pegasus XL-R SW-WA-1141 (Rotax 447)		9. 2.87	D.Marsh	Charminster, Bournemouth	27. 5.95P
G-MTEE	Solar Wings Pegasus XL-R (Rotax 447) SW-TB-1144 & SW-WA-1142 (C/n plate incorrectly shows SW-WA-1144 & SW-WA-1142) (New wing ? - see G-MTLG)		13. 2.87	S.M.Dewson	Shenstone Hall Farm, Shenstone	4. 8.99P
G-MTEH	Mainair Gemini/Flash 2 (Rotax 503) 521-387-5 & W262		13. 2.87	M.P.Challis	Northampton	24. 7.97P
G-MTEJ	Mainair Gemini/Flash 2 (Rotax 462) 522-387-5 & W277		18. 2.87	D.E.Bassett	St.Michaels	5. 4.99P
G-MTEK	Mainair Gemini/Flash 2 (Rotax 503) 523-387-5 & W279		3. 3.87	M.O'Hearne & G.M.Wrigley	Rufforth	3.10.94P
G-MTEN	Mainair Gemini/Flash 2 (Rotax 503) 527-487-5 & W285		25. 2.87	B.Bennison	Brough	13.10.00P
G-MTEO*	Midlands Ultralight Sirocco 377GB (Rotax 377) MU-019		27. 2.87	Not known (Stored 8.96)	Manston	6. 3.93P
G-MTER	Solar Wings Pegasus XL-R/Se (Rotax 447) SW-TB-1146 & SW-WA-1144		19. 2.87	K.A.Wright	Grimsby	25. 3.00P
G-MTES	Solar Wings Pegasus XL-R (Rotax 447) SW-TB-1147 & SW-WA-1145		19. 2.87	K.A.Lyons	Tregavethan, Truro	22. 6.00P
G-MTET	Solar Wings Pegasus XL-R SW-WA-1146 (Rotax 447)		19. 2.87	P.A.S.Talbot	Camborne	2. 5.00P

Regn	Type	C/n	P/I	Date	Owner/operator	Probable Base	CA Expy
G-MTEU	Solar Wings Pegasus XL-R/Se (Rotax 447) SW-WA-1147			19. 2.87	B.Harris	Northwich	5. 1.00P
G-MTEV*	Solar Wings Pegasus XL-R SW-WA-1148 (Rotax 447)			19. 2.87	N.P.D.Lambert (Cancelled as destroyed 27.7.98)	London SW11	1. 5.97P
G-MTEW	Solar Wings Pegasus XL-R/Se (Rotax 447) SW-TB-1149 & SW-WA-1149			19. 2.87	R.W. & P.J.Holley	Shifnal	30.11.99P
G-MTEX	Solar Wings Pegasus XL-R (Rotax 447) SW-TB-1152 & SW-WA-1150			19. 2.87	R.J.Coppin	Hereford	11. 8.00P
G-MTEY	Mainair Gemini/Flash 2 (Rotax 503) 518-387-5 & W217			20. 2.87	A.Wells	Baxby Manor, Husthwaite	4. 6.98P
G-MTFA	Solar Wings Pegasus XL-R (Rotax 462) SW-TE-0014 & SW-WA-1156			24. 2.87	D.Baillie	Great Orton	14. 3.94P
G-MTFB	Solar Wings Pegasus XL-R SW-WA-1157 (Rotax 462)			24. 2.87	I.D.Stokes	Camelford	20. 3.00P
G-MTFC	Medway Hybred 44XLR (Rotax 447)	22087/24		23. 3.87	J.K.Masters	Chigwell	25. 7.97P
G-MTFE	Solar Wings Pegasus XL-R (Rotax 447) SW-TB-1157 & SW-WA-1155 (New sailwing fitted 1999)			6. 3.87	R.H.L.Cope-Lewis	Bath	2. 5.00P
G-MTFF	Mainair Gemini/Flash 2 (Rotax 503) 528-487-5 & W286			12. 3.87	T.N.Taylor	Sidcup	19. 4.96P
G-MTFG	AMF Chevvron 2-32C (Konig SD570)	CH.004		9. 3.87	R.Gardner	Stratford-upon-Avon	24. 7.00P
G-MTFI	Mainair Gemini/Flash 2 (Rotax 503) 531-487-5 & W289			12. 3.87	V.D.Carmichael	Carrickfergus, NI	15. 3.00P
G-MTFJ	Mainair Gemini/Flash 2 (Rotax 503) 532-487-5 & W320			12. 3.87	G.Souch & M.D.Peacock	Leatherhead/Guildford	14. 4.00P
G-MTFK*	Moult Trike/Flexiform Striker DIM-01			23. 3.87	The Norfolk & Suffolk Aviation Museum (Stored 7.97)	Flixton	
G-MTFL	Ultraflight Lazair IIIE (Rotax 185)	A466/003		12. 3.87	P.J.Turrell	Halesowen	26. 9.89P
G-MTFM	Solar Wings Pegasus XL-R SW-WA-1158 (Rotax 462)			13. 3.87	P.R.G.Morley	Sutton Meadows, Ely	9. 7.00P
G-MTFN	Whittaker MW-5 Sorcerer (Cf/f 11.10.99)	PFA/163-11207		13. 3.87	K.Southam	Newcastle	
G-MTFO	Solar Wings Pegasus XL-R/Se (Rotax 447) SW-TB-1159 & SW-WA-1159			18. 3.87	D.S.Parker & R.J.Hodgson	Great Orton	14. 3.00P
G-MTFP	Solar Wings Pegasus XL-R (Rotax 447) SW-TB-1160 & SW-WA-1160			18. 3.87	C.F.Two	Swansea	13.10.00P
G-MTFR	Solar Wings Pegasus XL-R/Se (Rotax 447) SW-TB-1161 & SW-WA-1161			18. 3.87	S.Ballantyne	Blanefield, Glasgow	19. 9.99P
G-MTFT	Solar Wings Pegasus XL-R SW-WA-1163 (Rotax 447)			18. 3.87	A.T.Smith	Hughley, Much Wenlock	30. 7.00P
G-MTFU	CFM Shadow Srs.BD (Rotax 447)	K.034		18. 3.87	G.R.Eastwood	Full Sutton	13. 8.00P
G-MTFX	Mainair Gemini/Flash 2 (Rotax 503) 534-487-5 & W321			26. 3.87	R.J.Green (Damaged nr Sandtoft 28.7.96)	Pontefract	1. 1.97P
G-MTFZ	CFM Shadow Srs.CD (Rotax 503)	053		24. 3.87	R.P.Stonor	Long Marston	22. 3.00P
G-MTGA	Mainair Gemini/Flash 2 (Rotax 503) 535-587-5 & W293			26. 3.87	B.E.Warburton	Barton	6. 7.00P
G-MTGB	Thruster TST Mk.1 (Rotax 503)	837-TST-011		10. 4.87	G.Arthur	Cheltenham	11. 9.00P
G-MTGC	Thruster TST Mk.1 (Rotax 503)	837-TST-012		10. 4.87	B.Foster & P.Smith	London E13	30. 5.00P
G-MTGD	Thruster TST Mk.1 (Rotax 503)	837-TST-013		10. 4.87	W.J.Lister	Strathaven	18. 7.00P
G-MTGE	Thruster TST Mk.1 (Rotax 503)	837-TST-014		10. 4.87	G.W.R.Swift	Hartfield	17.10.99P
G-MTGF	Thruster TST Mk.1 (Rotax 503)	837-TST-015		10. 4.87	B.Swindon	Chesham	30. 9.00P
G-MTGH	Mainair Gemini/Flash 2 (Rotax 462) 536-587-5 & W294			31. 3.87	J.R.Gillies	Waltham Cross	12. 6.00P
G-MTGJ	Solar Wings Pegasus XL-R (Rotax 447) SW-TB-1165 & SW-WA-1165			1. 4.87	M.S.Taylor	Gillingham	20.11.00P
G-MTGK	Solar Wings Pegasus XL-R SW-WA-1166 (Rotax 447)			1. 4.87	I.A.Smith	Canterbury	1. 8.91P
G-MTGL	Solar Wings Pegasus XL-R SW-WA-1167 (Rotax 447)			1. 4.87	P.J.& R.Openshaw	Warrington	7. 2.99P
G-MTGM	Solar Wings Pegasus XL-R SW-WA-1168 (Rotax 447)			1. 4.87	A.W.Rawlings & J.Smith	Roddige, Fradley	14. 5.00P

Regn	Type	C/n	P/I	Date	Owner/operator	Probable Base	CA Expy
G-MTGN	CFM Shadow Srs.BD (Rotax 447)	K.041		31. 3.87	N.G.Price	Bricket Wood, Radlett	11. 6.00P
G-MTGO	Mainair Gemini/Flash 2 (Rotax 462)	550-587-5 & W336		10. 4.87	A.W.Fish	Eshott	13. 3.00P
G-MTGP	Thruster TST Mk.1 (Rotax 503)	847-TST-016		10. 4.87	A.E.Sellers & J.H.Cooling Lower Mountpleasant, Chatteris		19.12.00P
G-MTGR	Thruster TST Mk.1 (Rotax 503)	847-TST-017		10. 4.87	M.R.Grunwell	Brentwood	26. 7.90P
G-MTGS	Thruster TST Mk.1 (Rotax 503)	847-TST-018		10. 4.87	G.J.Chadwick t/a G-MTGS Flying Group	Huddersfield	3. 5.00P
G-MTGT	Thruster TST Mk.1 (Rotax 503)	847-TST-019		10. 4.87	R.T.Manderson	Strathaven	28.11.00P
G-MTGU	Thruster TST Mk.1 (Rotax 503)	847-TST-020		10. 4.87	W Doyle	North Shields	28. 8.00P
G-MTGV	CFM Shadow Srs.CD (Rotax 503)	052		8. 4.87	V.R.Riley	Manchester	7. 5.98P
G-MTGW	CFM Shadow Srs.CD 	054	I-... G-MTGW	8. 4.87	D.Cioffi	Brighton	25. 5.00P
G-MTGX	Hornet Dual Trainer/Southdown Raven (Rotax 462) HRWA 0061 & 2000/0270			13. 4.87	S.J.M.Morling	Taunton	11. 4.97P
G-MTHB	Aerotech MW-5B Sorcerer (Fuji-Robin EC-44-PM) SR102-R440B-08			10. 4.87	J.C.P.Thornber	Peterborough	22. 4.97P
G-MTHC	Raven X (Rotax 447)	2232/0257		15. 4.87	J.Channer	Nottingham	9. 5.99P
G-MTHD	Ultrasports Tripacer/Hiway Demon 195 	JMS-01		13. 4.87	J.D.Frost	Beeston, Notts	
G-MTHG	Solar Wings Pegasus XL-R SW-WA-1171 (Rotax 447)			13. 4.87	S.T.Felton	Stockport	19. 2.99P
G-MTHH	Solar Wings Pegasus XL-R SW-WA-1172 (Rotax 447)			13. 4.87	J.Palmer	Winkleigh	28.12.98P
G-MTHI	Solar Wings Pegasus XL-R (Rotax 447 SW-TB-1172 & SW-WA-1173			13. 4.87	J.R.Bowman	Oxford	11. 9.00P
G-MTHJ	Solar Wings Pegasus XL-R (Rotax 447) SW-TB-1173 & SW-WA-1174			13. 4.87	S.A.Watson	Long Acres Farm, Sandy	4. 6.00P
G-MTHN	Solar Wings Pegasus XL-R SW-WA-1178 (Rotax 447)			13. 4.87	G.E.Murphy	Cardigan	30. 6.99P
G-MTHO	Solar Wings Pegasus XL-R SW-WA-1179 (Rotax 447)			13. 4.87	R.C.Hinds	Newnham, Gloucester	17. 8.96P
G-MTHS*	CFM Shadow Srs.CD (Rotax 503)	059		22. 4.87	A.J.McMenmamin (Cancelled by CAA 11.6.99)	Oakley	17. 5.97P
G-MTHT	CFM Shadow Srs.CD (Rotax 447)	058		22. 4.87	B.J.Topham	Long Marston	13.10.99P
G-MTHU	Hornet Dual Trainer/Raven (Rotax 462) HRWA 0062 & 2000/0269			30. 4.87	J.Barlow	Castletown, IoM	4. 9.93P
G-MTHV	CFM Shadow Srs.BD (Rotax 447)	K.049		7. 5.87	K.R.Bircher	Longhope	24. 7.00P
G-MTHW	Mainair Gemini/Flash 2 (Rotax 462)	540-587-5 & W325		14. 5.87	M.D.Kirby	Billericay	30. 3.99P
G-MTHY	Mainair Gemini/Flash 2A (Rotax 503)	543-687-5 & W331		14. 5.87	M.Stevenson	Ringwood	27. 6.94P
G-MTHZ	Mainair Gemini/Flash 2A (Rotax 503)	541-587-5 & W329		14. 5.87	B.Berry	Crosland Moor	28.10.00P
G-MTIA	Mainair Gemini/Flash 2A (Rotax 503)	544-687-5 & W332		14. 5.87	A.R.Hawkins	Farnham	27. 7.99P
G-MTIB	Mainair Gemini/Flash 2A (Rotax 503)	545-687-5 & W333		14. 5.87	P.Millership	St.Michaels	1.11.00P
G-MTIC	Mainair Gemini/Flash 2A (Rotax 462)	546-587-5 & W334		14. 5.87	B.J.Magill	Bishops Stortford	5. 8.95P
G-MTID	Raven X (Rotax 447)	2232/0276		18. 5.87	R.G.Featherby	Kings Lynn	23. 2.99P
G-MTIE	Solar Wings Pegasus XL-R SW-WA-1183 (Rotax 462)			18. 5.87	A.H.Paterson & I.M.Vass	Wick	24. 6.96P
G-MTIH	Solar Wings Pegasus XL-R SW-WA-1186 (Rotax 447)			18. 5.87	R.J.Humphries	Southampton	21. 4.98P
G-MTII	Solar Wings Pegasus XL-R SW-WA-1187 (Rotax 447)			18. 5.87	H.Greef & G.Sharp (Damaged mid 1995)	Eshott	22.10.95P
G-MTIJ	Solar Wings Pegasus XL-R/Se (Rotax 447) SW-TB-1185 & SW-WA-1188			18. 5.87	M.J.F.Gilbody	Urmston, Manchester	1. 4.98P
G-MTIK	Raven X (Rotax 447)	2232/0272		19. 5.87	J.M.Barber	Peterborough	13. 3.00P
G-MTIL	Mainair Gemini/Flash 2A (Rotax 462)	549-687-5 & W338		21. 5.87	S.Lunney	Ince Blundell	15. 8.00P

Regn	Type	C/n	P/I	Date	Owner/operator	Probable Base	CA Expy
G-MTIM	Mainair Gemini/Flash 2A (Rotax 503)	553-687-5 & W341		21. 5.87	W.M.Swan	East Fortune	17. 4.00P
G-MTIN	Mainair Gemini/Flash 2A (Rotax 503)	547-687-5 & W335		1. 6.87	D.M.Newton	Forfar	23. 5.00P
G-MTIO	Solar Wings Pegasus XL-R (Rotax 447)	SW-WA-1190		26. 5.87	M.A.Coe	Kettering	17. 6.00P
G-MTIP	Solar Wings Pegasus XL-R (Rotax 447)	SW-TB-1188 & SW-WA-1191		26. 5.87	W.B.Cooper	Sutton Meadows, Ely	3.12.99P
G-MTIR	Solar Wings Pegasus XL-R/Se (Rotax 447)	SW-WA-1192 (Original wing possibly fitted to G-MTZI in Portugal)		26. 5.87	S.J.Spearey	Bristol	19. 4.98P
G-MTIS	Solar Wings Pegasus XL-R (Rotax 447)	SW-WA-1193		26. 5.87	N.P.Power	Eastbourne	31. 8.00P
G-MTIU	Solar Wings Pegasus XL-R (Rotax 447)	SW-TB-1191 & SW-WA-1194		26. 5.87	D.Burdett	Chatteris	8. 7.00P
G-MTIV	Solar Wings Pegasus XL-R (Rotax 447)	SW-TB-1192 & SW-WA-1195		26. 5.87	P.J.Culverhouse t/a Syndicate IV	Sittles Farm, Alrewas	11.11.00P
G-MTIW	Solar Wings Pegasus XL-R (Rotax 447)	SW-TB-1193 & SW-WA-1196		26. 5.87	J.P.Byrne	Bristol	15.12.97P
G-MTIX	Solar Wings Pegasus XL-R (Rotax 447)	SW-WA-1197		26. 5.87	S.Pickering	Sutton Meadows, Ely	27. 9.98P
G-MTIY	Solar Wings Pegasus XL-R (Rotax 447)	SW-WA-1198		26. 5.87	P.C.Scott	Bristol	27. 9.99P
G-MTIZ	Solar Wings Pegasus XL-R (Rotax 447)	SW-TB-1196 & SW-WA-1199		26. 5.87	S.L.Blount	St.Ives, Huntingdon	11.10.00P
G-MTJA	Mainair Gemini/Flash 2A (Rotax 503)	551-687-5 & W339		15. 6.87	A.W.Shellis & P.Davis	Otherton, Cannock	22. 8.00P
G-MTJB	Mainair Gemini/Flash 2A (Rotax 462)	554-687-5 & W343		2. 6.87	K.Worthingon	Chorley	20. 9.99P
G-MTJC	Mainair Gemini/Flash 2A (Rotax 503)	555-687-5 & W344		1. 6.87	A.J.Fraley	Clevedon	2. 4.99P
G-MTJD	Mainair Gemini/Flash 2A (Rotax 462)	552-687-5 & W340		5. 6.87	M.Bond	Shobdon	21.11.00P
G-MTJE	Mainair Gemini/Flash 2A (Rotax 503)	556-687-5 & W345		24. 6.87	C.J.Dyke	Redlands, Swindon	28. 7.00P
G-MTJF*	Mainair Gemini/Flash 2A (Rotax 503)	557-687-5 & W346		15. 6.87	Not known (Stored 7.96)	Bruntingthorpe	13. 4.91P
G-MTJG	Medway Hybred 44XLR (Rotax 447)	22587/25		16. 6.87	Margaret A.Trodden	Tupton, Chesterfield	24. 2.99P
G-MTJH	Solar Wings Pegasus/Flash (Rotax 447)	SW-TB-1050 & W342-687-3 (Trike previously fitted to G-MMUF)		17. 6.87	C.L.Parker	Astwood	3. 7.00P
G-MTJI	Raven X (Rotax 447)	2232/0260		23. 6.87	E.J.MacPherson	Desborough	12.10.92P
G-MTJK	Mainair Gemini/Flash 2A (Rotax 503)	559-787-5 & W348		17. 6.87	R.C.White	Aldermaston	16. 6.00P
G-MTJL	Mainair Gemini/Flash 2A (Rotax 503)	548-687-5 & W337		17. 6.87	D.J.Tuplin & B.G.M.Chapman	Sandtoft	17. 7.00P
G-MTJM	Mainair Gemini/Flash 2A (Rotax 462)	560-787-5 & W349		24. 6.87	M.E.Jeffreys	Uxbridge	6. 8.00P
G-MTJN	Midland Ultralights Sirocco 377GB (Rotax 377)	MU-020		23. 6.87	R.Harris	Hailsham	19. 3.94P
G-MTJP	Medway Hybred 44XLR (Rotax 447)	25687/27		6. 7.87	P.S.Hunt t/a G-MTJP Group	Plaistows, Hemel Hempstead	25. 6.99P
G-MTJR	Solar Wings Pegasus XL-R (Rotax 462)	SW-WA-1209		15. 7.87	Ultralight Training Ltd (Damaged late 1997)	Coventry	14. 2.99P
G-MTJS	Solar Wings Pegasus XL-Q (Rotax 462)	SW-TE-0022 & SW-WX-0013		6. 7.87	A.R.Watt	Insch	9. 5.00P
G-MTJT	Mainair Gemini/Flash 2A (Rotax 462)	558-787-5 & W347		16. 7.87	D.T.A.Rees	Haverfordwest	22.12.99P
G-MTJV	Mainair Gemini/Flash 2A (Rotax 503)	562-787-5 & W351		16. 7.87	N.Charles & J.Richards	Swinford, Rugby	5. 7.99P
G-MTJW	Mainair Gemini/Flash 2A (Rotax 503)	563-787-5 & W352		16. 7.87	J.F.Ashton	Liverpool	4.10.95P
G-MTJX	Hornet Dual Trainer/Southdown Raven (Rotax 462)	HRWA 0063 & 2000/0279		5. 8.87	J.P.Kirwan	Liverpool	31. 3.99P
G-MTJY	Mainair Gemini/Flash 2A (Rotax 503)	564-887-5 & W353		15. 7.87	D.L.Silver (Damaged mid 1994; stored 9.95)	Swinford, Rugby	9.10.94P
G-MTJZ	Mainair Gemini/Flash 2A (Rotax 503)	561-787-5 & W350		16. 7.87	G.A.Murphy	Ballincollig, Ireland	17. 5.99P
G-MTKA	Thruster TST Mk.1 (Rotax 503)	867-TST-021		21. 7.87	C.W.Payne	Worcester	15. 7.00P
G-MTKB	Thruster TST Mk.1 (Rotax 503)	867-TST-022		21. 7.87	M.Hanna	Rathfriland, Co.Down	22. 3.00P

Regn	Type	C/n	P/I	Date	Owner/operator	Probable Base	CA Expy
G-MTKD	Thruster TST Mk.1	867-TST-024		21. 7.87	T.K.Duffy	Ballyclare, NI	27.10.00P
G-MTKE	Thruster TST Mk.1 (Rotax 503)	867-TST-025		21. 7.87	W.Wells & D.F.Hughes	Stoke, Kent	15. 5.00P
G-MTKG	Solar Wings Pegasus XL-R/Se (Rotax 447) SW-TB-1199 & SW-WA-1201			13. 7.87	W.J.Hodgins	Deenethorpe	4. 6.00P
G-MTKH	Solar Wings Pegasus XL-R (Rotax 447) SW-TB-1200 & SW-WA-1202			13. 7.87	N.Harford	Horley	14. 8.99P
G-MTKI	Solar Wings Pegasus XL-R (Rotax 447) SW-TB-1201 & SW-WA-1203 (Reported as c/n SW-TB-1204)			13. 7.87	I.D.A.Spanton	Malvern	24. 9.00P
G-MTKJ	Solar Wings Pegasus XL-R/Se (Rotax 447) SW-TB-1202 & SW-WA-1204			13. 7.87	P.E.Hudson	Warrington	23. 6.00P
G-MTKM	Gardner T-M Scout S2	87/003		12. 8.87	D.Gardner (As "38674" in USAS c/s)	Rugby	
G-MTKN	Mainair Gemini/Flash 2A (Rotax 503) 566-887-5 & W355			15. 7.87	A.J.Taylor	Preston	9. 6.99P
G-MTKO	Mainair Gemini/Flash 2A (Rotax 503) 567-787-5 & W356			13. 7.87	M.Leavesley	Sittles Farm, Alrewas	30.10.97P
G-MTKP	Solar Wings Pegasus XL-R SW-WA-1207 (Rotax 462)			13. 7.87	J.Chapman (Damaged mid 1995)	Tarn Farm, Cockerham	1. 5.96P
G-MTKR	CFM Shadow Srs.CD (Rotax 503)	067	9H-ABL G-MTKR	20. 7.87	Cloudbase Aviation Services Ltd	Redhill	19. 5.99P
G-MTKV	Mainair Gemini/Flash 2A (Rotax 503) 565-887-5 & W354			26. 8.87	L.A.Davidson	Sandtoft	14. 3.00P
G-MTKW	Mainair Gemini/Flash 2A (Rotax 503) 569-887-5 & W358			13. 7.87	R.T.Henry	Newtownards	3. 3.00P
G-MTKX	Mainair Gemini/Flash 2A (Rotax 503) 568-887-5 & W357			13. 7.87	A.S.Leach	Warrington	27. 8.00P
G-MTKZ	Mainair Gemini/Flash 2A (Rotax 503) 571-887-5 & W360			31. 7.87	A.Ruddy	Balerno	21. 6.98P
G-MTLB	Mainair Gemini/Flash 2A (Rotax 503) 573-887-5 & W362			31. 7.87	D.N.Bacon	Hucknall	29. 8.99P
G-MTLC	Mainair Gemini/Flash 2A (Rotax 503) 574-887-5 & W363			31. 7.87	R.J.Alston	Cromer	15. 7.99P
G-MTLD	Mainair Gemini/Flash 2A (Rotax 503) 575-887-5 & W364			31. 7.87	I.A.Forrest	East Fortune	28. 3.00P
G-MTLG	Solar Wings Pegasus XL-R (Rotax 447) SW-TB-1207 & SW-WA-1211 (Fitted with wing ex G-MTEE; thus is SW-WA-1142)			31. 7.87	D.Young t/a Kemble Flying Club	Kemble	19.10.96P
G-MTLH	Solar Wings Pegasus XL-R (Rotax 447) SW-TB-1208 & SW-WA-1212			31. 7.87	B.S.Waite (Trike stored 4.96)	Clench Common	18. 5.95P
G-MTLI	Solar Wings Pegasus XL-R SW-WA-1213 (Rotax 447)			31. 7.87	M.McKay	Robertsbridge	6. 6.97P
G-MTLJ	Solar Wings Pegasus XL-R/Se (Rotax 447) SW-TB-1210 & SW-WA-1214			31. 7.87	R.E.Pratt	Sandtoft	27. 7.99P
G-MTLL	Mainair Gemini/Flash 2A (Rotax 503) 578-987-5 & W367			14. 8.87	M.F.Shaw & M.J.Bird t/a Wrekin Communications (Stored 3.93)	Long Marston	4. 1.93P
G-MTLM	Thruster TST Mk.1 (Rotax 503)	887-TST-027		5. 8.87	E.F.Howells t/a Chloe's Flying Group "Chloe"	Manor Farm, Croughton	20. 6.00P
G-MTLN	Thruster TST Mk.1 (Rotax 503)	887-TST-028		5. 8.87	B.R.Barnes & T.A.Hinton	Bristol	11. 6.00P
G-MTLO	Thruster TST Mk.1 (Rotax 503)	887-TST-029		5. 8.87	A.Emmanuel	Haverfordwest	5. 8.96P
G-MTLR	Thruster TST Mk.1 (Rotax 503)	887-TST-031		5. 8.87	J.C.Miller	Strathaven	7.12.98P
G-MTLT	Solar Wings Pegasus XL-R SW-WA-1216 (Rotax 447)			12. 8.87	S.P.MacDonald	Stamford, Lincs	11. 2.00P
G-MTLU	Solar Wings Pegasus XL-R/Se (Rotax 447) SW-TB-1213 & SW-WA-1217			12. 8.87	B.Richardson	Eshott	12. 9.99P
G-MTLV	Solar Wings Pegasus XL-R (Rotax 447) SW-TB-1214 & SW-WA-1218			12. 8.87	D.E.Watson	Long Marston	12. 9.00P
G-MTLW	Solar Wings Pegasus XL-R (Rotax 447) SW-TB-1215 & SW-WA-1219			12. 8.87	S.R.Sutch t/a Pegasus Flt Training	Sutton Meadows, Ely	30. 8.98P
G-MTLX	Medway Hybred 44XLR (Rotax 447)	20687/26		14. 8.87	D.A.Coupland	RAF Wyton	29. 1.00P
G-MTLY	Solar Wings Pegasus XL-R SW-WA-1220 (Rotax 462)			12. 8.87	I.Johnston	Bolton	5. 7.92P
G-MTLZ	Whittaker MW-5 Sorcerer (Rotax 377) PFA/163-11241			13. 8.87	M.J.Davenport	Weymouth	20. 6.00P
G-MTMA	Mainair Gemini/Flash 2A (Rotax 503) 579-987-5 & W368			14. 8.87	D.Bussell	St.Michaels	3. 6.00P
G-MTMB*	Mainair Gemini/Flash 2A (Rotax 503) 580-987-5 & W369			14. 8.87	C.Lavender (Cancelled by CAA 1.12.98)	Kendal	1. 6.97P

Regn	Type	C/n	P/I	Date	Owner/operator	Probable Base	CA Expy
G-MTMC	Mainair Gemini/Flash 2A (Rotax 503) 581-987-5 & W370			14. 8.87	A.R.Johnson	Brenzett, Kent	11. 5.00P
G-MTMD	Whittaker MW-6 Merlin PFA/164-11225 (Rotax 503)			12. 8.87	G.C.Steele	Otherton, Cannock	1.10.97P
G-MTME	Solar Wings Pegasus XL-R SW-WA-1221 (Rotax 447)			18. 8.87	M.T.Finch	Sutton Meadows, Ely	27. 8.00P
G-MTMF	Solar Wings Pegasus XL-R SW-WA-1222 (Rotax 447)			18. 8.87	J.T.W.Smith	Mallaig, Inverness	30. 5.99P
G-MTMG	Solar Wings Pegasus XL-R SW-WA-1223 (Rotax 447)			18. 8.87	C.W. & P.E.F.Suckling	Rushden	18. 8.00P
G-MTMH	Solar Wings Pegasus XL-R SW-WA-1224 (Rotax 447)			18. 8.87	P.J.McQuie & C.N.Jones	Long Acres Farm, Sandy	21. 6.94P
G-MTMI	Solar Wings Pegasus XL-R/Se (Rotax 447) SW-TB-1220 & SW-WA-1225			18. 8.87	D.Crozier	Sunderland	26. 9.97P
G-MTMJ*	Maxair Hummer	MJM-01		18. 8.87	A.Cuthbertson (Cancelled as WFU 10.3.99)	Port Talbot	
G-MTMK	Raven X (Rotax 447)	2000/0289		2. 9.87	D.W.Thomas	Dartford	27. 7.97P
G-MTML	Mainair Gemini/Flash 2A (Rotax 462) 582-1087-5 & W371			27. 8.87	J.F.Ashton	Liverpool	30. 7.00P
G-MTMO	Raven X (Rotax 447)	2232/0278	(G-MTKL)	11. 9.87	H.Tuvey	South Ockendon	22. 5.97P
G-MTMP	Hornet Dual Trainer/Raven (Rotax 462) HRWA 0064 & 2000/0288			28. 8.87	P.G.Owen	Baxby Manor, Husthwaite	6. 8.99P
G-MTMR	Hornet Dual Trainer/Raven (Rotax 462) HRWA 0065 & 2000/0297			28. 8.87	D.J.Smith	Hucknall	10. 5.99P
G-MTMT	Mainair Gemini/Flash 2A (Rotax 462) 583-1087-5 & W372			3. 9.87	I.Howes	Penrith	31. 3.99P
G-MTMV	Mainair Gemini/Flash 2A (Rotax 503) 585-1087-5 & W374			3. 9.87	A.J.Cropper	St.Michaels	8. 4.00P
G-MTMW	Mainair Gemini/Flash 2A (Rotax 503) 587-1087-5 & W376			9. 9.87	L.Jensen-Robertson t/a G-MTMW Group	Ince Blundell	24. 9.99P
G-MTMX	CFM Shadow Srs.CD (Rotax 503)	070		4. 9.87	I.M.Cross	Long Marston	25. 8.99P
G-MTMY	CFM Shadow Srs.CD (Rotax 503)	071		4. 9.87	R.F.Learney t/a G-MTMY Syndicate	Redhill	6. 1.00P
G-MTMZ	CFM Shadow Srs.BD (Rotax 447)	074		4. 9.87	C.A.Keens	Blackbushe/Woking	29.10.97P
G-MTNB	Raven X (Rotax 447)	2232/0305		9. 9.87	R.Coar	Higher Barn Farm, Houghton	15. 9.97P
G-MTNC	Mainair Gemini/Flash 2A (Rotax 503) 588-1087-5 & W377			15. 9.87	B.Collier	Wolverhampton	17. 8.00P
G-MTNE	Medway Hybred 44XLR	7987/32		12.10.87	A.D.Chapman	Stoke, Kent	8. 9.99P
	(Rotax 447) (Presumed fitted with new trike as original was transferred to G-MVDC in 1988)						
G-MTNF	Medway Hybred 44XLR (Rotax 447)	1987/31		12.10.87	P.A.Bedford	Tewkesbury	12. 2.00P
G-MTNG	Mainair Gemini/Flash 2A (Rotax 503) 590-1087-5 & W379			21. 9.87	G.M.Yule	Shobdon	2. 6.00P
G-MTNH	Mainair Gemini/Flash 2A (Rotax 462) 589-1087-5 & W378			17. 9.87	J.R.Smart	Churchdown, Gloucester	29. 5.99P
G-MTNI	Mainair Gemini/Flash 2A (Rotax 503) 595-1187-5 & W384			18. 9.87	D.Gatland	Whitley Bay	24. 8.00P
G-MTNJ	Mainair Gemini/Flash 2A (Rotax 462) 593-1187-5 & W382			17. 9.87	R.H.Hunt	Old Sarum	17.12.99P
G-MTNK	Weedhopper JC-24B (Fuji-Robin EC-34-PM)	1936		28. 9.87	P.Scott	(Chippenham)	N/E
G-MTNL	Mainair Gemini/Flash 2A (Rotax 503) 591-1187-5 & W380			21. 9.87	A.K.Munro	Stoke-on-Trent	24. 7.00P
G-MTNM	Mainair Gemini/Flash 2A (Rotax 503) 592-1187-5 & W381			22. 9.87	C.J.Janson	Shobdon	6. 7.00P
G-MTNO	Solar Wings Pegasus XL-Q (Rotax 447) SW-TB-1252 & SW-WQ-0001			23. 9.87	A.F.Batchelor	Rayne Hall Farm, Rayne	14. 6.00P
G-MTNP	Solar Wings Pegasus XL-Q (Rotax 447) SW-TB-1253 & SW-WQ-0002			23. 9.87	G.G.Roberts	Rayne Hall Farm, Rayne	29. 6.00P
G-MTNR	Thruster TST Mk.1 (Rotax 503)	897-TST-032		1.10.87	S.J.David	Crewkerne	17. 4.00P
G-MTNS	Thruster TST Mk.1 (Rotax 503)	897-TST-033		1.10.87	S.J.Wilkinson	Tarn Farm, Cockerham	12. 6.00P
G-MTNT	Thruster TST Mk.1 (Rotax 503)	897-TST-034		1.10.87	G.Bennett	Yarmouth	8. 3.00P

Regn	Type	C/n	P/I	Date	Owner/operator	Probable Base	CA Expy
G-MTNU	Thruster TST Mk.1 (Rotax 503)	897-TST-035		1.10.87	S P Read	Langport	29. 8.00P
G-MTNV	Thruster TST Mk.1 (Rotax 503)	897-TST-036		1.10.87	J.B.Russell	Larne, Co.Antrim	11.10.88P
G-MTNW	Thruster TST Mk.1 (Rotax 503)	897-TST-037		1.10.87	S.D. & M.D.Barnard	Coalville, Leicester	17. 8.97P
G-MTNX	Mainair Gemini/Flash 2A (Rotax 503)	606-1187-5 & W393		29. 9.87	C.Evans	Grimsby	12. 6.99P
G-MTNY	Mainair Gemini/Flash 2A (Rotax 503)	594-1187-5 & W383		2.10.87	R.A.McClure & A.J.Wallace	Dunkeswell	24. 7.00P
G-MTOA	Solar Wings Pegasus XL-R (Rotax 447)	SW-TB-1221 & SW-WA-1226		15. 9.87	R.A.Bird	East Hunsbury, Northampton	17. 8.99P
G-MTOB	Solar Wings Pegasus XL-R (Rotax 447)	SW-TB-1222 & SW-WA-1227		15. 9.87	P.S.Lemm	Hatherton, Cannock	1.10.97P
G-MTOC	Solar Wings Pegasus XL-R (Rotax 447)	SW-TB-1223 & SW-WA-1228		15. 9.87	S.B.Perez	Monteleger, France	26. 5.96P
G-MTOD	Solar Wings Pegasus XL-R (Rotax 447)	SW-WA-1229		15. 9.87	T A Gordon	Liskeard	3. 9.00P
G-MTOE	Solar Wings Pegasus XL-R (Rotax 447)	SW-WA-1230		15. 9.87	A.J.Sims	Salisbury	30. 5.00P
G-MTOF	Solar Wings Pegasus XL-R/Se (Rotax 447)	SW-TB-1226 & SW-WA-1231		15. 9.87	A.B.Potts	Eshott	26. 4.99P
G-MTOG	Solar Wings Pegasus XL-R (Rotax 447)	SW-WA-1232		15. 9.87	C.R.M.Bannerman	Balfron, Glasgow	17. 4.00P
G-MTOH	Solar Wings Pegasus XL-R (Rotax 447)	SW-TB-1228 & SW-WA-1233		15. 9.87	H.Cook	Pontypool	18. 7.98P
G-MTOI	Solar Wings Pegasus XL-R (Rotax 447)	SW-TB-1229 & SW-WA-1234		15. 9.87	S.C.Key	Sutton Meadows, Ely	15. 6.00P
G-MTOJ	Solar Wings Pegasus XL-R/Se (Rotax 447)	SW-WA-1235		15. 9.87	P.G.Lloyd	Old Sarum	20. 9.00P
G-MTOK	Solar Wings Pegasus XL-R (Rotax 447)	SW-WA-1236		2.10.87	W.S. Davis	Oxton, Nottingham	14. 2.00P
G-MTOL	Solar Wings Pegasus XL-R (Rotax 447)	SW-WA-1237		2.10.87	R.D.Bertram	Gillingham	3. 6.00P
G-MTOM	Solar Wings Pegasus XL-R/Se (Rotax 447)	SW-TB-1233 & SW-WA-1238		2.10.87	D.A.Cutler	Grimsby	27. 7.00P
G-MTON	Solar Wings Pegasus XL-R (Rotax 447)	SW-TB-1234 & SW-WA-1239		2.10.87	D.J.Willett	Malpas	19. 7.00P
G-MTOO	Solar Wings Pegasus XL-R (Rotax 447)	SW-TB-1235 & SW-WA-1240		2.10.87	G.W.Bulmer	Bristol	8. 6.00P
G-MTOP	Solar Wings Pegasus XL-R/Se (Rotax 447)	SW-WA-1241		2.10.87	P.D.Larkin	Bourne End	2.10.99P
G-MTOR	Solar Wings Pegasus XL-R (Rotax 447)	SW-TB-1237 & SW-WA-1242		9.10.87	M.A.Pantling	Weston Zoyland	15. 7.98P
G-MTOS	Solar Wings Pegasus XL-R (Rotax 447)	SW-TB-1238 & SW-WA-1243		9.10.87	C.McKay	London E11	1. 9.00P
G-MTOT	Solar Wings Pegasus XL-R (Rotax 447)	SW-WA-1244		9.10.87	G.J.Howley	Coleford	10.11.00P
G-MTOU	Solar Wings Pegasus XL-R/Se (Rotax 447)	SW-TB-1240 & SW-WA-1245		9.10.87	I.E.Wallace	Eshott	18.12.99P
G-MTOW	Solar Wings Pegasus XL-R (Rotax 447)	SW-WA-1247		19.10.87	G.A.Hagger	Bristol	28. 4.94P
G-MTOX	Solar Wings Pegasus XL-R (Rotax 447)	SW-TB-1243 & SW-WA-1248		19.10.87	I.Fernihough	Roddige, Fradley	19.11.99P
G-MTOY	Solar Wings Pegasus XL-R (Rotax 447)	SW-WA-1249		19.10.87	C.M.Bradford t/a G-MTOY Group	(Marlborough)	5. 8.99P
G-MTOZ	Solar Wings Pegasus XL-R (Rotax 447)	SW-TB-1245 & SW-WA-1250		19.10.87	P.J.McCool	Enstone	12. 2.00P
G-MTPA	Mainair Gemini/Flash 2A (Rotax 462)	598-1187-5 & W394		13.10.87	K.R.Bircher	Longhope, Glos	24. 6.00P
G-MTPB	Mainair Gemini/Flash 2A (Rotax 503)	599-1187-5 & W387		15.10.87	N.Sutcliffe	Northenden, Manchester	26.10.98P
G-MTPC	Raven X (Rotax 582)	2232/0309		15.10.87	G.W.Carwardine	(Uckfield)	3.11.90P
G-MTPE	Solar Wings Pegasus XL-R (Rotax 447)	SW-TB-1258 & SW-WA-1260		21.10.87	J.Bassett	Kemble	13. 2.00P
G-MTPF	Solar Wings Pegasus XL-R (Rotax 447)	SW-TB-1259 & SW-WA-1261		21.10.87	P.J.C.Martins	Kingsbridge	4.10.00P
G-MTPG	Solar Wings Pegasus XL-R (Rotax 447)	SW-WA-1262		21.10.87	J.Sullivan	Dunkeswell	7. 7.00P

Regn	Type	C/n	P/I	Date	Owner/operator	Probable Base	CA Expy
G-MTPH	Solar Wings Pegasus XL-R (Rotax 447) SW-TB-1261 & SW-WA-1263			30.10.87	L.M.Sams	Long Marston	10. 4.00P
G-MTPI	Solar Wings Pegasus XL-R/Se (Rotax 447) SW-TB-1262 & SW-WA-1264			30.10.87	R.J.Bullock	Long Marston	1. 2.00P
G-MTPJ	Solar Wings Pegasus XL-R (Rotax 447) SW-TB-1263 & SW-WA-1265			30.10.87	D.A.Whittaker	Roddige, Fradley	31. 7.99P
G-MTPK	Solar Wings Pegasus XL-R SW-WA-1266 (Rotax 447)			30.10.87	S.H.James	Deenethorpe	21.10.00P
G-MTPL	Solar Wings Pegasus XL-R (Rotax 447) SW-TB-1265 & SW-WA-1267			30.10.87	I.R.F.King	Tunbridge Wells	2. 9.99P
G-MTPM	Solar Wings Pegasus XL-R (Rotax 447) SW-TB-1266 & SW-WA-1268			30.10.87	D.K.Seal	Roddige, Fradley	3. 8.00P
G-MTPN*	Solar Wings Pegasus XL-Q (Rotax 447) SW-TB-1267 & SW-WQ-0004			21.10.87	C.G.Johns (Cancelled by CAA 2.12.98)	Kidderminster	13. 4.94P
G-MTPO	Solar Wings Pegasus XL-Q (Rotax 462) SW-TE-0032 & SW-WQ-0005			21.10.87	P.Devlin	Hungerford	3. 8.98P
G-MTPP	Solar Wings Pegasus XL-R SW-WA-1259 (Rotax 447)			21.10.87	P Molyneux	London NW8	2.10.00P
G-MTPR	Solar Wings Pegasus XL-R SW-WA-1257 (Rotax 447)			21.10.87	W.C.Bryan	(Offaly, Ireland)	16. 6.96P
G-MTPS	Solar Wings Pegasus XL-Q SW-WX-0011 (Rotax 462)			23.10.87	K.J.Hard	Bar Hill, Cambs	18. 4.00P
G-MTPT	Thruster TST Mk.1 (Rotax 503)	8107-TST-038		23.10.87	J.T.Kendrick	Popham	3.11.96P
G-MTPU	Thruster TST Mk.1 (Rotax 503)	8107-TST-039		23.10.87	M.R.Jones "Poppy"	Compton Abbas	1. 8.00P
G-MTPV	Thruster TST Mk.1 (Rotax 503)	8107-TST-040		23.10.87	E.Bentley & A.Maxwell	Stockton-on-Tees	30. 5.00P
G-MTPW	Thruster TST Mk.1 (Rotax 503)	8107-TST-041		23.10.87	C.J.E.Nagle	Chipping Sodbury	20. 8.95P
G-MTPX	Thruster TST Mk.1 (Rotax 503)	8107-TST-042		23.10.87	T.Snook	Long Marston	2. 5.93P
G-MTPY	Thruster TST Mk.1 (Rotax 503)	8107-TST-043		23.10.87	A.N.Wicks	Sudbury	17. 7.99P
G-MTRA	Mainair Gemini/Flash 2A (Rotax 503)	605-1187-5 & W395		28.10.87	E.N.Alms	Guy Lane Farm, Waverton	2. 2.00P
G-MTRB	Mainair Gemini/Flash 2A (Rotax 503)	600-1187-5 & W388		27.10.87	N.Braude	Ely	8. 6.98P
G-MTRC	Midland Ultralights Sirocco 377GB (Rotax 377)	MU-021		2.11.87	D.Thorpe	Grantham	11. 8.99P
G-MTRE	Whittaker MW-6 Merlin PFA/164-11168 (Rotax 532)			27.10.87	M.J.Batchelor	Wickwar	19. 7.99P
G-MTRF	Mainair Gemini/Flash 2A (Rotax 503)	601-1187-5 & W389		30.10.87	J.McGaughran	Long Marston	28. 5.99P
G-MTRJ	AMF Chevvron 2-32C (Konig SD570)	CH.006		30.10.87	R.J.Wells	Chorley	25. 7.00P
G-MTRK	Hornet Dual Trainer/Raven (Rotax 462)	HRWA 0067 & 2000/0324		4.11.87	P.M.Gilfoyle	Leeds	8. 5.94P
G-MTRL	Hornet Dual Trainer/Raven (Rotax 462)	HRWA 0068 & 2000/0326		4.11.87	J.McAlpine	Largs	20. 8.00P
G-MTRM	Solar Wings Pegasus XL-R (Rotax 462) SW-TE-0030 & SW-WA-1276			10.11.87	D.B.Jones	Long Acres Farm, Sandy	5. 6.00P
G-MTRN	Solar Wings Pegasus XL-R SW-WA-1269 (Rotax 447)			2.12.87	P.Vallis	Alfreton	3. 8.00P
G-MTRO	Solar Wings Pegasus XL-R/Se (Rotax 447) SW-TB-1271 & SW-WA-1270			2.12.87	H.Lloyd-Hughes	Rhuallt	5. 9.99P
G-MTRR	Solar Wings Pegasus XL-R SW-WA-1272 (Rotax 447)			3.12.87	A.Docherty	Cleveland	26. 7.99P
G-MTRS	Solar Wings Pegasus XL-R SW-WA-1273 (Rotax 447)			2.12.87	J.J.R.Tickle	Llanerchymedd, Gwynedd	10. 6.00P
G-MTRT	Raven X (Rotax 447)	2232/0325		12.11.87	D.Hines	Fordhall Villa Farm, Ternhill	25. 6.00P
G-MTRU	Solar Wings Pegasus XL-Q SW-WQ-0009 (Rotax 447)			10.11.87	A.Barnish	Waterlooville	15.10.00P
G-MTRV	Solar Wings Pegasus XL-Q (Rotax 477) SW-TB-1276 & SW-WX-0010			10.11.87	M.J.Reed	(Luton)	5. 7.00P
G-MTRW	Raven X (Rotax 447)	2232/0328		12.11.87	S-A Wensley & T P Hale	Weston-super-Mare	1. 8.00P
G-MTRX	Whittaker MW-5 Sorcerer (Rotax 447)	PFA/163-11202		11.11.87	W.Turner (Stored 8.96)	Otherton, Cannock	13. 2.95P
G-MTRY	Noble Hardman Snowbird Mk.IV SB-005 (Rotax 532)			24.11.87	D.J.Gage & G.Simpson	Kilmarnock/Cumnock	4. 7.90P

335

Regn	Type	C/n	P/I	Date	Owner/operator	Probable Base	CA Expy
G-MTRZ	Mainair Gemini/Flash 2A (Rotax 503) 611-1287-5 & W400			17.11.87	S.J.Doyle	Ince Blundell	12. 5.00P
G-MTSB	Mainair Gemini/Flash 2A (Rotax 503) 608-1187-5 & W397			16.11.87	P.Carter, D.Gabbott & B.F.Stephenson Liverpool		22. 3.99P
G-MTSC	Mainair Gemini/Flash 2A (Rotax 503) 618-188-5 & W407			17.11.87	J.P.Lang	Chester	27. 7.99P
G-MTSD	Raven X (Rotax 447)	2232/0312		24.11.87	D.Turner	Manor Farm, Croughton	5. 3.00P
G-MTSG	CFM Shadow Srs.CD (Rotax 503)	079		24.11.87	C.A.Purvis	Plaistows, Hemel Hempstead	12. 3.00P
G-MTSH	Thruster TST Mk.1 (Rotax 503)	8117-TST-044		3.12.87	J.I.V.Hill	Newtownards	13. 3.00P
G-MTSI	Thruster TST Mk.1 (Rotax 503)	8117-TST-045		3.12.87	P.P.Trangmar	Hailsham	23. 4.00P
G-MTSJ	Thruster TST Mk.1 (Rotax 503)	8117-TST-046		3.12.87	P.J.Mogg	Sturminster Newton	8. 4.98P
G-MTSK	Thruster TST Mk.1 (Rotax 503)	8117-TST-047		3.12.87	J.S.Pyke	Westfield Farm, Hailsham	15. 5.00P
G-MTSL	Thruster TST Mk.1 (Rotax 503)	8117-TST-048		3.12.87	J.W.H.Giles & T.A.Porter Newton Abbot/Okehampton		27. 3.96P
G-MTSM	Thruster TST Mk.1 (Rotax 503)	8117-TST-049		3.12.87	Environment Agency, Thames Region Ginge, Wantage		9. 2.00P
G-MTSN	Solar Wings Pegasus XL-R (Rotax 447) SW-TB-1278 & SW-WA-1280			14.12.87	G.P.Lane (Reported as trike c/n SW-TB-1272)	Pucklechurch	9. 1.00P
G-MTSO	Solar Wings Pegasus XL-R/Se (Rotax 447) SW-WA-1281			14.12.87	I.E.Evans	Chesterfield	4. 5.97P
G-MTSP	Solar Wings Pegasus XL-R SW-WA-1282 (Rotax 447)			14.12.87	R.J.Nelson	Swinford, Rugby	14. 9.00P
G-MTSR	Solar Wings Pegasus XL-R (Rotax 447) SW-TB-1281 & SW-WA-1283			14.12.87	J.Norman	Long Acres Farm, Sandy	7. 8.99P
G-MTSS	Solar Wings Pegasus XL-R SW-WA-1284 (Rotax 462)			14.12.87	T.M.Evans	Haywards Heath	14.10.00P
G-MTST(2)	Thruster TST Mk.1 (Rotax 503)	8128-TST-111		12.12.88	D.J.Flower Baxby Manor, Husthwaite t/a Husthwaite Thruster Group		21. 5.00P
G-MTSU	Solar Wings Pegasus XL-R SW-WA-1285 (Rotax 447)			4. 1.88	J.McAldney	Ballymena, Co.Antrim	20. 3.00P
G-MTSV	Solar Wings Pegasus XL-R SW-WA-1286 (Rotax 447)			4. 1.88	R.J.Bowden	Dunkeswell	20. 8.00P
G-MTSX	Solar Wings Pegasus XL-R (Rotax 447) SW-TB-1282 & SW-WA-1288			4. 1.88	M.R.L.Smith	Lichfield	17. 3.00P
G-MTSY	Solar Wings Pegasus XL-R/Se (Rotax 447) SW-TB-1283 & SW-WA-1289			14. 1.88	N.F.Waldron	Swinford, Rugby	24. 5.99P
G-MTSZ	Solar Wings Pegasus XL-R/Se (Rotax 447) SW-TB-1284 & SW-WA-1290			14. 1.88	J.R.Appleton	Colne	17. 7.00P
G-MTTA	Solar Wings Pegasus XL-R (Rotax 462) SW-TE-0035 & SW-WA-1291			14. 1.88	J.J.McMennum	Bishop Auckland	4. 9.00P
G-MTTB	Solar Wings Pegasus XL-R SW-WA-1292 (Rotax 447)			14. 1.88	P.M.Golden	Reading	20.10.00P
G-MTTD	Solar Wings Pegasus XL-Q (Rotax 447) SW-TB-1286 & SW-WQ-0011			15. 1.88	R.S.Noremberg	Clacton-on-Sea	13. 4.00P
G-MTTE	Solar Wings Pegasus XL-Q (Rotax 447) SW-TB-1287 & SW-WQ-0012			15. 1.88	C.R.W.Masterton	Clench Common	15. 3.00P
G-MTTF	Whittaker MW-6 Merlin PFA/164-11273 (Rotax 532)			14.12.87	P.Cotton	Long Marston	29. 3.95P
G-MTTH	CFM Shadow Srs.BD (Rotax 447)	K.061		15.12.87	G.F.Hill & A.Y-T.Leung	(Birmingham)	5. 5.00P
G-MTTI	Mainair Gemini/Flash 2A (Rotax 503) 620-188-5 & W409			14.12.87	S.M.Savage	Guildford	19. 7.96P
G-MTTK	Southdown Puma (Lightning DS) (Fuji-Robin EC-44-PM) DO-8477			15.12.87	D.E.Oakley	West Bromwich	22. 8.93E
G-MTTM	Mainair Gemini/Flash 2A (Rotax 503) 609-1287-5 & W398			5. 1.88	R.K.Woods	Sheffield	20.11.00P
G-MTTN	Skyrider Airsports Phantom PH.00100			22. 1.88	H.R.Duggins	Matlock	N/E
G-MTTP	Mainair Gemini/Flash 2A (Rotax 462) 612-188-5 & W401			18. 1.88	M.J.Rawlins	Oxton, Nottingham	11. 8.98P
G-MTTR	Mainair Gemini/Flash 2A (Rotax 462) 614-188-5 & W403			27. 1.88	A.Westoby	Hucknall	22. 7.00P
G-MTTS	Mainair Gemini/Flash 2A (Rotax 503) 621-188-5 & W410			4. 1.88	J.B.Bailey	Shrewsbury	23. 4.91P
G-MTTU	Solar Wings Pegasus XL-R (Rotax 447) SW-TB-1332 & SW-WA-1294			25. 2.88	N.L.Walsh & A.T.Farmer	Shifnal	9. 7.00P

Regn	Type	C/n	P/I	Date	Owner/operator	Probable Base	CA Expy
G-MTTW	Mainair Gemini/Flash 2A (Rotax 462)	622-188-5 & W411		15. 1.88	P.J.Hughes	Chelmsford	29. 6.99P
G-MTTX	Solar Wings Pegasus XL-Q (Rotax 447)	SW-TB-1293 & SW-WQ-0013		15. 2.88	P.G.Moss	Baxby Manor, Husthwaite	1. 5.00P
G-MTTZ	Solar Wings Pegasus XL-Q (Rotax 462)	SW-WQ-0015		21. 1.88	J.Haskett	Kings Lynn	6. 9.00P
G-MTUA	Solar Wings Pegasus XL-R/Se (Rotax 447)	SW-TB-1294 & SW-WA-1295		15. 1.88	A.J.Varga	Rufforth	19. 6.00P
G-MTUB	Thruster TST Mk.1 (Rotax 503)	8018-TST-050		15. 1.88	G.Millar	Dungannon, Co.Tyrone	17. 3.00P
G-MTUC	Thruster TST Mk.1 (Rotax 503)	8018-TST-051		15. 1.88	E.J.Girling	Plymouth	5. 9.00P
G-MTUD	Thruster TST Mk.1 (Rotax 503)	8018-TST-052		15. 1.88	J.D.Smith t/a Baxby Airsports Club	Husthwaite	5.10.00P
G-MTUE	Thruster TST Mk.1 (Rotax 503)	8018-TST-053		15. 1.88	J.P.McVitty	Armagh Field, Woodview	11. 6.94P
G-MTUF	Thruster TST Mk.1 (Rotax 503)	8018-TST-054		15. 1.88	P.Stark	Strathaven	4.10.00P
G-MTUG	Thruster TST Mk.1 (Rotax 503)	8018-TST-055		15. 1.88	T.L.Davis	Popham	28. 5.94P
G-MTUI	Solar Wings Pegasus XL-R/Se (Rotax 447)	SW-WA-1296		21. 1.88	N.J.Garrett	Enstone	28. 1.00P
G-MTUJ	Solar Wings Pegasus XL-R (Rotax 447)	SW-WA-1297		21. 1.88	R.W.Pincombe	Chumleigh, Devon	31. 5.94P
G-MTUK	Solar Wings Pegasus XL-R (Rotax 447)	SW-WA-1298		21. 1.88	D.L.Pickover	Nelson, Lancs	28. 3.00P
G-MTUL	Solar Wings Pegasus XL-R/Se (Rotax 447)	SW-TB-1299 & SW-WA-1299		21. 1.88	A.G.Curtis	Deenethorpe	12. 2.00P
G-MTUN	Solar Wings Pegasus XL-Q (Rotax 447) (Fitted with Wing from G-MVUK ?)	SW-TB-1301 & SW-WQ-0016		20. 1.88	J.P.Feeney & C.G.Notarantonio (Stored 1.98)	Long Marston	6. 9.95P
G-MTUP	Solar Wings Pegasus XL-Q (Rotax 447)	SW-TB-1303 & SW-WQ-0018		20. 1.88	S.J.Allen	Blisworth, Northampton	27. 4.00P
G-MTUR	Solar Wings Pegasus XL-Q (Rotax 447)	SW-TB-1304 & SW-WQ-0019		20. 1.88	G.Ball	Tewkesbury	4. 9.00P
G-MTUS	Solar Wings Pegasus XL-Q (Rotax 447)	SW-TB-1305 & SW-WQ-0020		20. 1.88	I.Haddow	Campbeltown	29.10.00P
G-MTUT	Solar Wings Pegasus XL-Q (Rotax 462)	SW-TE-0040 & SW-WQ-0021		21. 1.88	L.F.Tanner & D.D.Lock	Sutton Meadows, Ely	28. 4.00P
G-MTUU	Mainair Gemini/Flash 2A (Rotax 503)	623-288-5 & W412		10. 2.88	M.Harris	Eshott	27. 7.00P
G-MTUV	Mainair Gemini/Flash 2A (Rotax 462)	624-288-5 & W413		28. 1.88	R.J.Griffiths	Rush Green	2. 4.99P
G-MTUX	Medway Hybred 44XLR (Rotax 503)	241287/33		2. 2.88	P.A.R.Wilson	Husthwaite	29. 8.99P
G-MTUY	Solar Wings Pegasus XL-Q (Rotax 462)	SW-TE-0041 & SW-WQ-0022		28. 1.88	H.C.Lowther	Penrith	21. 3.00P
G-MTVB	Solar Wings Pegasus XL-R (Rotax 447)	SW-TB-1307 & SW-WA-1302		28. 1.88	N.A.Martin, D.M.Roberts & T.Quantril	Clench Common	21. 3.00P
G-MTVC	Solar Wings Pegasus XL-R (Rotax 447)	SW-TB-1308 & SW-WA-1303		28. 1.88	M.R.Nurse	Milton Keynes	6. 7.97P
G-MTVG	Mainair Gemini/Flash 2A (Rotax 503)	628-388-6 & W417		12. 2.88	D.A.Whitworth	Swanton Morley	10. 3.99P
G-MTVH	Mainair Gemini/Flash 2A (Rotax 503)	626-288-6 & W415		17. 2.88	N.S.Payne	Broadmeadow Farm, Hereford	12.12.99P
G-MTVI	Mainair Gemini/Flash 2A (Rotax 503)	629-388-6 & W416		12. 2.88	R.A.McDowell	Slough	10. 5.92P
G-MTVJ	Mainair Gemini/Flash 2A (Rotax 503)	627-388-6 & W418		12. 2.88	D.M.Waller	Keighley	18. 3.00P
G-MTVK	Solar Wings Pegasus XL-R (Rotax 447)	SW-WA-1306		15. 2.88	J D MacNamara	(Crediton)	17. 3.98P
G-MTVL	Solar Wings Pegasus XL-R/Se (Rotax 447)	SW-WA-1307		15. 2.88	J.K.Pattison	Weston Zoyland	2. 8.97P
G-MTVM	Solar Wings Pegasus XL-R (Rotax 447)	SW-WA-1308		15. 2.88	C.Surman	Cranleigh	22. 5.00P
G-MTVN	Solar Wings Pegasus XL-R (Rotax 447)	SW-WA-1309		15. 2.88	A.I.Crighton	Lower Mountpleasant, Chatteris	4. 4.98P
G-MTVO	Solar Wings Pegasus XL-R (Rotax 447)	SW-TB-1315 & SW-WA-1310		15. 2.88	D A Payne	Long Marston	9. 1.00P
G-MTVP	Thruster TST Mk.1 (C/n plate marked incorrectly as 8208-TST-056)	8028-TST-056		10. 2.88	J.M.Evans	Abingdon	8. 2.00P

Regn	Type	C/n	P/I	Date	Owner/operator	Probable Base	CA Expy
G-MTVR	Thruster TST Mk.1 (Rotax 503)	8028-TST-057		10. 2.88	A.J.Wood	Baxby Manor, Husthwaite	15. 6.00P
G-MTVS	Thruster TST Mk.1 (Rotax 503)	8028-TST-058		10. 2.88	W.J.Burrell	Banbridge, Co.Down	22. 9.99P
G-MTVT	Thruster TST Mk.1 (Rotax 503)	8028-TST-059		10. 2.88	C.G.Jarvis	Chilbolton	26. 3.00P
G-MTVV	Thruster TST Mk.1 (Rotax 503)	8028-TST-061		10. 2.88	R.S.O'Carroll	Craigavon, Co.Armagh	26. 8.00P
G-MTVX	Solar Wings Pegasus XL-Q (Rotax 462HP)	SW-TE-0042 & SW-WQ-0025		3. 3.88	J.G.Spinks	Swinford, Rugby	10. 8.99P
G-MTVZ	Powerchute Raider (Rotax 447)	80104		3. 3.88	L.B.Fennelly	Melton Mowbray	25. 5.00P
G-MTWA	Solar Wings Pegasus XL-R (Rotax 447)	SW-WA-1311		25. 2.88	N.R.Henry Lower Mountpleasant, Chatteris		30.11.00P
G-MTWB	Solar Wings Pegasus XL-R (Rotax 447)	SW-TB-1342 & SW-WA-1312		25. 2.88	M.W.A.Shemilt	Henley-on-Thames	13.11.98P
G-MTWC	Solar Wings Pegasus XL-R (Rotax 447)	SW-TB-1321 & SW-WA-1313		25. 2.88	L.C.Wellington-Graham & J.P.Clements Baxby Manor, Husthwaite		17. 4.00P
G-MTWD	Solar Wings Pegasus XL-R (Rotax 447)	SW-TB-1320 & SW-WA-1314		25. 2.88	J.A.Valentine	Sutton Meadows, Ely	14. 5.00P
G-MTWE	Solar Wings Pegasus XL-R (Rotax 447)	SW-WA-1315		25. 2.88	A.Thomas	London NW10	22. 9.90P
G-MTWF	Mainair Gemini/Flash 2A (Rotax 503)	630-388-6 & W419		25. 2.88	W.Porter	Nottingham	25. 8.00P
G-MTWG	Mainair Gemini/Flash 2A (Rotax 503)	631-288-6 & W420		25. 2.88	N.Mackenzie & P.S.Bunting	Southport	28. 7.00P
G-MTWH	CFM Shadow Srs.CD (Rotax 503)	K.064		25. 2.88	V.A.Hutchinson	Nuneaton	3. 9.00P
G-MTWK	CFM Shadow Srs.CD (Rotax 503)	073		25. 2.88	R.C.Fendick	Westbury-sub-Mendip	25. 9.00P
G-MTWL	CFM Shadow Srs.BD (Rotax 447)	076		25. 2.88	M.J.Gray	Manor Farm, Croughton	31. 8.00P
G-MTWM	CFM Shadow Srs.CD (Rotax 503)	080		25. 2.88	U.A.Schliessler & R.J.Kelly "Kiwa" Plaistows, Hemel Hempstead		9.10.99P
G-MTWN	CFM Shadow Srs.CD (Rotax 503)	081		25. 2.88	P.W.Heywood	Davidstow Moor	5. 7.00P
G-MTWP*	CFM Shadow Srs.BD (Rotax 447)	K.069		29. 2.88	L.J.Chapman Alresford, Hants (See G-MZBN) (Cancelled by CAA 13.11.99)		7. 9.88P*
G-MTWR	Mainair Gemini/Flash 2A (Rotax 503)	632-388-6 & W421		3. 3.88	J.B.Hodson	Arclid Green, Sandbach	8. 4.00P
G-MTWS	Mainair Gemini/Flash 2A (Rotax 503)	633-388-6 & W422		3. 3.88	K W Roberts	Barnsley	22. 7.00P
G-MTWX	Mainair Gemini/Flash 2A (Rotax 503)	634-488-6 & W423		11. 3.88	G.A.Barrett	St.Michaels	5. 6.00P
G-MTWY	Thruster TST Mk.1 (Rotax 503)	8038-TST-062		15. 3.88	M.F.Eddington	Wincanton	10. 2.00P
G-MTWZ	Thruster TST Mk.1 (Rotax 503)	8038-TST-063		15. 3.88	A.Makepeace	Guildford	14. 5.00P
G-MTXA	Thruster TST Mk.1 (Rotax 503)	8038-TST-064		15. 3.88	S.Whittaker	Sandtoft	30. 5.00P
G-MTXB	Thruster TST Mk.1 (Rotax 503)	8038-TST-065		15. 3.88	J.J.Hill	Middlesbrough	27. 7.00P
G-MTXC	Thruster TST Mk.1 (Rotax 503)	8038-TST-066		15. 3.88	Joan A.Huntley	Bradford-on-Avon	9. 8.00P
G-MTXD	Thruster TST Mk.1 (Rotax 503)	8038-TST-067		15. 3.88	B.E.Holloway	Harrogate	18. 2.00P
G-MTXE	Hornet Dual Trainer/Raven (Rotax 462)	HRWA 0070 & 2000/0332		11. 3.88	F.J.Marton t/a Charter Systems	Long Marston	22. 5.00P
G-MTXH	Solar Wings Pegasus XL-Q (Rotax 447)	SW-WQ-0030		11. 3.88	J.Rhodes	Pontefract	21. 7.97P
G-MTXI	Solar Wings Pegasus XL-Q (Rotax 447)	SW-TB-1329 & SW-WQ-0031		11. 3.88	R.Lewis-Evans	Poole	14. 5.00P
G-MTXJ	Solar Wings Pegasus XL-Q (Rotax 447)	SW-TB-1330 & SW-WQ-0032		11. 3.88	G.C.Weighell	Enstone	25. 9.00P
G-MTXK	Solar Wings Pegasus XL-Q (Rotax 447)	SW-WQ-0033		11. 3.88	M.J.McManamon	East Fortune	2. 5.99P
G-MTXL	Noble Hardman Snowbird Mk.IV (Rotax 532)	SB-006		4. 5.88	M.Fitch & D.Connolly	Potters Bar	12. 6.00P
G-MTXM	Mainair Gemini/Flash 2A (Rotax 503)	636-488-6 & W425		10. 5.88	E.M.Escalante	Borehamwood	29. 1.00P

Regn	Type	C/n P/I	Date	Owner/operator	Probable Base	CA Expy
G-MTXO	Whittaker MW-6 Merlin PFA/164-11326 (Rotax 503)		11. 3.88	S.J.Whyatt	Brighton	4. 8.98P
G-MTXP	Mainair Gemini/Flash 2A (Rotax 503) 637-488-6 & W426		23. 3.88	M.B.Buttle	St.Michaels	12.11.00P
G-MTXR	CFM Shadow Srs.CD K.038 (Rotax 503)		23. 3.88	R.G.Q.Clarke	Chinnor	1. 8.00P
G-MTXS	Mainair Gemini/Flash 2A (Rotax 503) 638-488-6 & W427		23. 3.88	M.A.Sheehan, B.Smith, R.Harvey & T.J.Smith Roddige, Fradley		27.10.00P
G-MTXY	Hornet Dual Trainer/Raven (Rotax 462) HRWA 0073 & 2000/0354		30. 3.88	J.McAvoy	Bishopton	17. 8.00P
G-MTXZ	Mainair Gemini/Flash 2A (Rotax 503) 641-588-6 & W430		10. 5.88	S.S.Raines	Market Drayton	4. 9.00P
G-MTYA	Solar Wings Pegasus XL-Q (Rotax 462HP) SW-TE-0047 & SW-WQ-0037		29. 3.88	I.Clarkson	Long Marston	22. 9.00P
G-MTYC	Solar Wings Pegasus XL-Q SW-WQ-0039 (Rotax 462)		30. 3.88	C.I.D.H.Garrison	Huntingdon	13. 9.00P
G-MTYD	Solar Wings Pegasus XL-Q (Rotax 462) SW-TE-0050 & SW-WQ-0040		29. 3.88	Fiona E.Treveil	Liphook	4.10.00P
G-MTYE	Solar Wings Pegasus XL-Q SW-WQ-0041 (Rotax 462)		29. 3.88	K.L.Chorley & A.Cook	Enstone	8. 3.00P
G-MTYF	Solar Wings Pegasus XL-Q SW-WQ-0042 (Rotax 462)		29. 3.88	J.Hyde	Spalding	19. 9.99P
G-MTYH	Solar Wings Pegasus XL-Q (Rotax 462) SW-TE-0054 & SW-WQ-0044		30. 3.88	J.F.R.Rendell	Cheltenham	25.11.95P
G-MTYI	Solar Wings Pegasus XL-Q SW-WQ-0045 (Rotax 462)		30. 3.88	R.H.Stokes	Warboys	9. 6.00P
G-MTYL	Solar Wings Pegasus XL-Q (Rotax 462) SW-TE-0058 & SW-WQ-0048 & c/n 6412		30. 3.88	G.T.Hanson	Sywell	11. 8.99P
G-MTYM	Solar Wings Pegasus XL-Q SW-WQ-0049 (Rotax 462)		30. 3.88	Margaret E.Merrison	Chard	20. 6.98P
G-MTYN	Solar Wings Pegasus XL-Q (Rotax 462) SW-TE-0060 & SW-WQ-0050		30. 3.88	R.P.A.Turner & E.H.Jenkins (Stored 6.97) Broadmeadow Farm, Hereford		18.10.93P
G-MTYP	Solar Wings Pegasus XL-Q SW-WQ-0052 (Rotax 462)		30. 3.88	W.G.Dent (Stored 9.97)	Eshott	17. 8.00P
G-MTYR	Solar Wings Pegasus XL-Q SW-WQ-0053 (Rotax 462)		30. 3.88	C.J.Hill Broadmeadow Farm, Hereford (Stored 6.97)		30. 4.99P
G-MTYS	Solar Wings Pegasus XL-Q (Rotax 462) SW-TE-0064 & SW-WQ-0054		30. 3.88	R.G.Wall	Caerleon	4. 9.00P
G-MTYT	Solar Wings Pegasus XL-Q (Rotax 462HP) SW-TE-0065 & SW-WQ-0055		30. 3.88	M.G.Walsh	Rufforth	13. 9.99P
G-MTYU	Solar Wings Pegasus XL-Q SW-WQ-0056 (Rotax 462HP)		30. 3.88	N.I.Garland & M.Powell	Dunkeswell	6. 3.00P
G-MTYV	Raven X 2232/0341 (Rotax 447)		8. 4.88	R.E.J.Pattenden	Maidstone	26. 2.00P
G-MTYW	Raven X 2232/0344 (Rotax 447)		8. 4.88	R.Solomans	Stoke, Kent	10. 6.00P
G-MTYX	Raven X 2232/0345 (Rotax 447)		8. 4.88	J.C.Hawkins	Selsey	15. 8.00P
G-MTYY	Solar Wings Pegasus XL-R SW-WA-1326 (Rotax 447)		6. 5.88	G.J.Slater	Clench Common	13. 1.00P
G-MTZA	Thruster TST Mk.1 8048-TST-068 (Rotax 503)		13. 4.88	M.G.Davidson	Craigavon, Co.Armagh	24.11.00P
G-MTZB	Thruster TST Mk.1 8048-TST-069 (Rotax 503)		13. 4.88	S.J.O.Tinn	Weymouth	26. 2.00P
G-MTZC	Thruster TST Mk.1 8048-TST-070 (Rotax 503)		13. 4.88	R.Morton	Newtownabbey, NI	2. 5.00P
G-MTZD	Thruster TST Mk.1 8048-TST-071 (Rotax 503)		13. 4.88	M.Medlock & A.Stephenson	Popham	8.10.99P
G-MTZE	Thruster TST Mk.1 8048-TST-072 (Rotax 503)		13. 4.88	M.F.Hadley	Bourne	18. 2.00P
G-MTZF	Thruster TST Mk.1 8048-TST-073 (Rotax 503)		13. 4.88	D.Large t/a Zulu Fox Group	Long Marston	8. 9.00P
G-MTZG	Mainair Gemini/Flash 2A (Rotax 503) 642-588-6 & W431		10. 5.88	T.G.Greenhill	Leicester	31. 5.00P
G-MTZH	Mainair Gemini/Flash 2A (Rotax 462) 643-588-6 & W433		9. 6.88	D.C.Hughes	St.Michaels	27. 4.00P
G-MTZI	Solar Wings Pegasus XL-R SW-WA-1327 (Rotax 447) (Fitted with wing ex G-MTIR)		6. 5.88	E.A.S.Freitas	Lagos, Algarve	2. 6.94P
G-MTZJ	Solar Wings Pegasus XL-R (Rotax 447) SW-TB-1335 & SW-WA-1328		6. 5.88	P.D.Myer	Caldicot	19.12.99P

Regn	Type	C/n	P/I	Date	Owner/operator	Probable Base	CA Expy
G-MTZK	Solar Wings Pegasus XL-R			6. 5.88	Sara J.Singlehurst		
	(Rotax 447)	SW-TB-1336 & SW-WA-1329				Long Acres Farm, Sandy	30. 1.00P
G-MTZL	Mainair Gemini/Flash 2A			10. 5.88	N.S.Brayn	Popham	14.11.00P
	(Rotax 503)	645-588-6 & W435					
G-MTZM	Mainair Gemini/Flash 2A			3. 5.88	K.L.Smith	Leicester	15. 3.00P
	(Rotax 503)	646-588-6 & W436					
G-MTZO	Mainair Gemini/Flash 2A			6. 5.88	R.C.Hinds	Newnham, Glos	14. 6.00P
	(Rotax 462)	649-688-6 & W439					
G-MTZP	Solar Wings Pegasus XL-Q	SW-WQ-0059		6. 5.88	Island Micro Aviation Ltd	Ventnor, IoW	23. 6.00P
	(Rotax 447)						
G-MTZR	Solar Wings Pegasus XL-Q			6. 5.88	P.J.Hatchett	Rhuallt	19. 8.98P
	(Rotax 447)	SW-TB-1338 & SW-WQ-0060					
G-MTZS	Solar Wings Pegasus XL-Q	SW-WQ-0061		6. 5.88	P.A.Darling	Wilmslow	15. 7.93P
	(Rotax 447)						
G-MTZT	Solar Wings Pegasus XL-Q	SW-WQ-0062		6. 5.88	M.Y.Brown	Eshott	4. 8.00P
	(Rotax 447)						
G-MTZV	Mainair Gemini/Flash 2A			6. 5.88	G.J.Donnellon	Barton	29. 5.00P
	(Rotax 503)	650-688-6 & W440					
G-MTZW	Mainair Gemini/Flash 2A			25. 5.88	L.McIntyre	Ince Blundell	7. 4.00P
	(Rotax 503)	651-688-6 & W441					
G-MTZX	Mainair Gemini/Flash 2A			23. 6.88	J.G.Stancombe	Rufforth	27.12.98P
	(Rotax 503)	652-688-6 & W442					
G-MTZY	Mainair Gemini/Flash 2A			24. 5.88	P.K.Dale	Bagby	1. 8.99P
	(Rotax 503)	653-688-6 & W443					
G-MTZZ	Mainair Gemini/Flash 2A			14. 6.88	P.J.Litchfield	Tarn Farm, Cockerham	29. 9.99P
	(Rotax 503)	654-688-6 & W444					
G-MUFY	Robinson R-22 Beta	1248	D-HICH	13.12.96	Rotormurf Ltd	Caernarfon	22.12.02T
G-MUIR	Cameron V-65 HAFB	2037		23. 6.89	Lindsay J.M.Muir "Muriel"	East Molesey	6. 5.00A
G-MULL	McDonnell Douglas DC-10-30	47888	YA-LAS	21. 3.85	British Airways plc	Manchester	20. 5.01T
					"New Forest"		
G-MUNI	Mooney M.20J (201SE)	24-3118		12. 5.89	M.W.Fane	Fairoaks	25. 8.01
G-MURI	Gates Lear Jet 35A	35A-646	N712JB	19. 2.98	G-MURI Ltd	Edinburgh	18. 2.00T
			N717JB/N646EA/XA-UMA/N3812G (Op Northern Executive Aviation)				
G-MURR	Whittaker MW.6 Merlin	PFA/164-1250		16. 4.99	D.Murray	Bristol	
G-MURY	Robinson R-44 Astro	0201		19. 7.95	Simlot Ltd (Op Jennifer Murray)	Denham	27. 7.01T
G-MUSO	Rutan LongEz	PFA/74A-10590		11. 6.83	C.J.Tadjeran	Knivsta, Sweden	23. 6.00P
	(Lycoming O-235)						
G-MUST*	Commonwealth CA.18 Mustang 22	1524	VH-BOZ	20.12.79	Fighter World Museum		
			A68-199			RAAF Williamtown, NSW, Australia	
G-MUTE	Colt 31A Air Chair HAFB	2099		2.12.91	K.Temple	Diss	11.11.99A
G-MUVG	Cessna 421C Golden Eagle III		N421DD	13. 1.97	Air Montgomery Ltd	Leeds-Bradford	7. 2.00T
		421C-1064					
G-MUZO	Europa Avn Europa	PFA/247-12623		11. 1.94	J.T.Grant	(Norwich)	
G-MVAA	Mainair Gemini/Flash 2A			8. 6.88	T.D.Holder	Worksop	1. 7.00P
	(Rotax 503)	655-688-6 & W445					
G-MVAB	Mainair Gemini/Flash 2A			10. 5.88	W.Anderson	Linlithgow	19.11.99P
	(Rotax 503)	656-688-6 & W446					
G-MVAC	CFM Shadow Srs.CD (Rotax 503)	K.077		12. 5.88	A.C.MacDonald	Insch	21. 8.00P
G-MVAD	Mainair Gemini/Flash 2A			10. 5.88	N.G.Woodall	Warrington	9. 7.00P
	(Rotax 503)	657-688-6 & W447					
G-MVAF	Southdown Puma Sprint	P.455	G-MBAF	24. 6.87	J.F.Horn	Yelverton	23. 4.00P
	(Fuji-Robin EC-44-2PM)						
G-MVAG	Thruster TST Mk.1	8058-TST-074		18. 5.88	N.S.Brown	Higher Barn Farm, Houghton	27. 8.99P
	(Rotax 503)						
G-MVAH	Thruster TST Mk.1	8058-TST-075		18. 5.88	M.W.H.Henton "Times Four"	Popham	18. 8.00P
	(Rotax 503)						
G-MVAI	Thruster TST Mk.1	8058-TST-076		18. 5.88	G.D.Bailey	Popham	25.10.00P
	(Rotax 503)						
G-MVAJ	Thruster TST Mk.1	8058-TST-077		18. 5.88	B.W.Savory	Long Marston	6. 7.00P
	(Rotax 503)						
G-MVAK	Thruster TST Mk.1	8058-TST-078		18. 5.88	A.J.Dunlop & S.J.Pettitt		
	(Rotax 503)					Long Acres Farm, Sandy	29. 1.00P
G-MVAL	Thruster TST Mk.1	8058-TST-079		18. 5.88	G.C.Brooke	Colchester	7. 8.96P
	(Rotax 503)						
G-MVAM	CFM Shadow Srs.CD	082		18. 5.88	C.P.Barber	Preston	24. 7.00P
	(Rotax 503)						
G-MVAN	CFM Shadow Srs.CD			18. 5.88	I.Brewster	Nuthampstead	16.10.00P
	(Rotax 503)	K.048 & PFA/161-11219					
G-MVAO	Mainair Gemini/Flash 2A			24. 5.88	S.J.Robson	Preston	30. 6.00P
	(Rotax 503)	658-688-6 & W448					

Regn	Type	C/n P/I	Date	Owner/operator	Probable Base	CA Expy
G-MVAP	Mainair Gemini/Flash 2A (Rotax 503)	659-688-6 & W449	24. 5.88	R.J.Miller	Long Marston	21. 9.00P
G-MVAR	Solar Wings Pegasus XL-R SW-WA-1331 (Rotax 447)		24. 5.88	M.L.Butlin	Peterborough	26. 3.00P
G-MVAS	Solar Wings Pegasus XL-R SW-WA-1332 (Rotax 447)		24. 5.88	J.F.P.Marreiros	Lagos, Algarve	14. 4.95P
G-MVAT	Solar Wings Pegasus XL-R SW-WA-1333 (Rotax 447)		24. 5.88	S.Ward	Strathaven	28. 8.99P
G-MVAU	Solar Wings Pegasus XL-R (Rotax 447) SW-TB-1346 & SW-WA-1334		24. 5.88	B.S.Miley & J.H.M.Perry	Eshott	1. 7.98P
G-MVAV	Solar Wings Pegasus XL-R (Rotax 447) SW-TB-1347 & SW-WA-1335		24. 5.88	P.L.Alsop	Sutton Meadows, Ely	30. 8.99P
G-MVAW	Solar Wings Pegasus XL-Q (Rotax 447) SW-TB-1348 & SW-WQ-0064		24. 5.88	G.Sharman	Kettering	18. 9.00P
G-MVAX	Solar Wings Pegasus XL-Q (Rotax 447) SW-TB-1349 & SW-WQ-0065		24. 5.88	S.J.Rogers & D.W.Power	Saundersfoot	9. 6.00P
G-MVAY	Solar Wings Pegasus XL-Q SW-WQ-0066 (Rotax 447)		24. 5.88	V.O.Morris	Swansea	16. 4.97P
G-MVBB	CFM Shadow Srs.BD K.051 (Rotax 447)		24. 5.88	R.Garrod	Mendlesham	8.10.00P
G-MVBC	Mainair Tri-Flyer/Aerial Arts 130SX 130SX-616		24. 5.88	D.Beer	Ilfracombe	
G-MVBD	Mainair Gemini/Flash 2A (Rotax 462)	660-688-6 & W450	8. 6.88	D.V.Batten	Bolton	15.12.99P
G-MVBE	Mainair Scorcher (Rotax 503)	661-688-6 & W451	28. 7.88	B.L.Cook	Bradford	28. 8.99P
G-MVBF	Mainair Gemini/Flash 2A (Rotax 462)	662-688-6 & W452	14. 6.88	K.Laud	Roddige, Fradley	3. 8.00P
G-MVBG	Mainair Gemini/Flash 2A (Rotax 503)	663-688-6 & W453	25. 5.88	A.Dennison	Roddige, Fradley	6.12.99P
G-MVBH	Mainair Gemini/Flash 2A (Rotax 503)	664-688-6 & W454	25. 5.88	B.J.Egerton	Bootle	10. 7.98P
G-MVBI	Mainair Gemini/Flash 2A (Rotax 503)	665-788-6 & W455	7. 6.88	E.R.Wilson	Barrow-in-Furness	6. 9.92P
G-MVBJ	Solar Wings Pegasus XL-R SW-WA-1338 (Rotax 462)		7. 6.88	R.J.O.Page	Waddesdon	14. 4.98P
G-MVBK	Mainair Gemini/Flash 2A (Rotax 462)	666-788-6 & W456	7. 6.88	C.S.Bowen & M.D.Carruthers	Manor Farm, Inskip	8.12.99P
G-MVBL	Mainair Gemini/Flash 2A (Rotax 503)	669-788-6 & W459	7. 6.88	P.M.Wright	Higher Barn Farm, Houghton	31.10.00P
G-MVBM	Mainair Gemini/Flash 2A (Rotax 503)	667-788-6 & W457	7. 6.88	I.R.Thomas	Buntingford	2. 6.00P
G-MVBN	Mainair Gemini/Flash 2A (Rotax 503)	668-788-6 & W458	8. 6.88	M.Frankcom	Darwen	2. 6.99P
G-MVBO	Mainair Gemini/Flash 2A (Rotax 503)	671-788-6 & W461	8. 6.88	R.Brasher	Rugeley	28. 7.00P
G-MVBP	Thruster TST Mk.1 8068-TST-080 (Rotax 503)		14. 6.88	K.J.Crompton	Bangor, Co.Down	8. 3.00P
G-MVBR*	Thruster TST Mk.1 8068-TST-081 (Rotax 503)		14. 6.88	A. Stanford (Cancelled by CAA 5.11.98)	Dunkeswell	24. 9.99P
G-MVBS	Thruster TST Mk.1 8068-TST-082 (Rotax 503) (Regd as c/n 8060-TST-082)		14. 6.88	P.G.Lowrie	Tarn Farm, Cockerham	22.11.96P
G-MVBT	Thruster TST Mk.1 8068-TST-083 (BMW R100)		14. 6.88	E.L.Everitt	Ley Farm, Chirk	12.11.00P
G-MVBU	Thruster TST Mk.1 8068-TST-084 (Rotax 503)		14. 6.88	J.H.M.Weir (Stored 9.97)	Great Orton	26. 5.93P
G-MVBY	Solar Wings Pegasus XL-R SW-WA-1344 (Rotax 447)		17. 6.88	D.C.de La Haye	Newton Abbot	26. 8.99P
G-MVBZ	Solar Wings Pegasus XL-R (Rotax 447) SW-TB-1358 & SW-WA-1345		17. 6.88	A.G.Butler	Shenstone Hall Farm, Shenstone	24. 7.99P
G-MVCA	Solar Wings Pegasus XL-R SW-WA-1346 (Rotax 447)		17. 6.88	R.Walker	Sutton Meadows, Ely	6. 9.00P
G-MVCB	Solar Wings Pegasus XL-R (Rotax 447) SW-TB-1360 & SW-WA-1347		17. 6.88	G.T.Clipstone	Ipswich	18. 6.00P
G-MVCC	CFM Shadow Srs.CD (Rotax 503) K.045		17. 6.88	K.D.Mitchell	Hassocks	1. 4.00P
G-MVCD	Medway Hybred 44XLR MR001/34 (Rotax 447) (Marked as Raven)		14. 6.88	A.Cochrane	Long Acres Farm, Sandy	15. 6.00P
G-MVCE	Mainair Gemini/Flash 2A (Rotax 503)	672-788-6 & W462	23. 6.88	J.D.Berry	Ince Blundell	5. 4.99P
G-MVCF	Mainair Gemini/Flash 2A (Rotax 462)	673-788-6 & W463	14. 7.88	J.L.Hamer	Hartpury, Glos	19. 7.00P

Regn	Type	C/n	P/I	Date	Owner/operator	Probable Base	CA Expy
G-MVCI	Noble Hardman Snowbird Mk.IV SB-011 (Rotax 532)			11.10.88	W.L.Chapman	Tarn Farm, Cockerham	13. 4.95P
G-MVCJ	Noble Hardman Snowbird Mk.IV SB-012 (Rotax 532)			11.10.88	D.A. & A.H.Hopewell Newcastle, Staffs "The Strumpet"		25. 5.00P
G-MVCK	Cosmos Trike/La Mouette Profil 19 SDA-01			19. 7.88	S.D.Alsop	Bath	
G-MVCL	Solar Wings Pegasus XL-Q SW-WQ-0075 (Rotax 462HP)			27. 6.88	T.E.Robinson	Insch	22. 8.00P
G-MVCM	Solar Wings Pegasus XL-Q (Rotax 462) SW-TE-0070 & SW-WQ-0076			27. 6.88	M.M.Coggan	Sandtoft	3. 4.00P
G-MVCN	Solar Wings Pegasus XL-Q SW-WQ-0077 (Rotax 462)			27. 6.88	S.R.S.Evans	Chelmsford	11. 2.00P
G-MVCO	Solar Wings Pegasus XL-Q (Rotax 462) SW-TE-0072 & SW-WQ-0078			27. 6.88	C.F.Grainger	Fiskerton, Nottingham	8. 8.91P
G-MVCP	Solar Wings Pegasus XL-Q (Rotax 462) SW-TE-0073 & SW-WQ-0079			27. 6.88	D.Blunt & G.Handyside	Deenethorpe	9.10.96P
G-MVCR	Solar Wings Pegasus XL-Q SW-WQ-0080 (Rotax 462)			27. 6.88	G.D.Isaacs	London Colney	1. 8.99P
G-MVCS	Solar Wings Pegasus XL-Q (Rotax 462) SW-TE-0075 & SW-WQ-0081			27. 6.88	J.J.Sparrow	Sywell	14. 5.00P
G-MVCT	Solar Wings Pegasus XL-Q (Rotax 462) SW-TE-0076 & SW-WQ-0082			27. 6.88	G.J.Lampitt Pound Green, Buttonoak, Kidderminster		19. 9.99P
G-MVCV	Solar Wings Pegasus XL-Q SW-WQ-0084 (Rotax 462)			27. 6.88	D.J.Taylor & G.G.Ansell Long Acres Farm, Sandy		29. 3.99P
G-MVCW	CFM Shadow Srs.BD (Rotax 447)	084		28. 6.88	T.Green	Full Sutton	14. 7.00P
G-MVCY	Mainair Gemini/Flash 2A (Rotax 503) 674-788-6 & W464			14. 7.88	A.M.Smith	Stafford	6.11.00P
G-MVDA	Mainair Gemini/Flash 2A (Rotax 462) 676-788-6 & W466			13. 7.88	C.Tweedley	Great Orton	31. 7.00P
G-MVDB	Medway Hybred 44XLR MR005/36 (Rotax 447)			28. 7.88	G.P.Barnes & J.W.Davies	Sawbridgeworth	7.11.00P
G-MVDC	Medway Hybred 44XL MR009/37 (Rotax 447) (Fitted with trike from G-MTNE)			13. 7.88	K.B.Kealy	RAF Wyton	7. 4.98P
G-MVDD	Thruster TST Mk.1 8078-TST-086 (Rotax 503)			12. 7.88	D.J.Love	Witton, Norwich	9.11.99P
G-MVDE	Thruster TST Mk.1 8078-TST-087 (Rotax 503)			12. 7.88	R.H.Davis	Severn Beach, Bristol	26. 8.99P
G-MVDF	Thruster TST Mk.1 8078-TST-088 (Rotax 503)			12. 7.88	J.Walsh & A.R.Sunley Lower Mountpleasant, Chatteris		5. 3.00P
G-MVDG	Thruster TST Mk.1 8078-TST-089 (Rotax 503)			12. 7.88	D.G.,P.M. & A.B.Smith	Popham	26. 7.00P
G-MVDH	Thruster TST Mk.1 8078-TST-090 (Rotax 503)			12. 7.88	M.L.Roberts	St.Austell	1. 7.99P
G-MVDJ	Medway Hybred 44XLR MR010/38 (Rotax 447)			20. 7.88	W.D.Hutchings	Nottingham	1. 4.00P
G-MVDK	Aerial Arts Chaser S CH.702 (Rotax 377)			5. 8.88	S.Adams	Scraptoft, Leicester	29.11.98P
G-MVDL	Aerial Arts Chaser S CH.701 (Rotax 377)			11. 8.88	J.M.Hucker	Abertillery, Gwent	4. 7.00P
G-MVDN	Aerial Arts Chaser S CH.704 (Rotax 377)			11. 8.88	Oban Divers Ltd	North Connel	11. 2.94P
G-MVDP	Aerial Arts Chaser S CH.706 (Rotax 447)			11. 8.88	T.A.Simpson	Dunstable	16.10.00P
G-MVDR	Aerial Arts Chaser S CH.708 (Rotax 377)			11. 8.88	D.E.Wall t/a Avon Chasers Group	Long Marston	1. 8.99P
G-MVDT	Mainair Gemini/Flash 2A (Rotax 503) 670-788-6 & W460			20. 7.88	D.C.Stephens	Coleford, Glos	26. 5.00P
G-MVDU	Solar Wings Pegasus XL-R SW-WA-1348 (Rotax 447)			13. 7.88	I.K. & B.A.Marshall	Weston Zoyland	5. 4.00P
G-MVDV	Solar Wings Pegasus XL-R SW-WA-1349 (Rotax 447)			13. 7.88	E.J.Blyth & L.D.Benson	Pickering	24. 8.97P
G-MVDW	Solar Wings Pegasus XL-R SW-WA-1350 (Rotax 447)			13. 7.88	R.P.Brown	Long Acres Farm, Sandy	20. 7.97P
G-MVDX	Solar Wings Pegasus XL-R SW-WA-1351 (Rotax 447)			13. 7.88	C.Kett	Weston Zoyland	8. 8.98P
G-MVDY	Solar Wings Pegasus XL-R SW-WA-1352 (Rotax 447)			13. 7.88	C.G.Murphy	Biggin Hill	1. 6.92P
G-MVDZ	Solar Wings Pegasus XL-R SW-WA-1353 (Rotax 447)			12. 7.88	A.K.Pickering	Robertsbridge	19. 5.00P

Regn	Type	C/n	P/I	Date	Owner/operator	Probable Base	CA Expy
G-MVEA	Solar Wings Pegasus XL-R (Rotax 447) SW-TB-1367 & SW-WA-1354			20. 7.88	A.J.Jackson	Rufforth	7.12.97P
G-MVEC	Solar Wings Pegasus XL-R (Rotax 447) SW-TB-1369 & SW-WA-1356			20. 7.88	J.A.Jarvis	Bodmin	28. 1.00P
G-MVED	Solar Wings Pegasus XL-R/Se (Rotax 447) SW-TB-1370 & SW-WA-1357			20. 7.88	P.A.Sleightholme	Helmsley	16. 4.00P
G-MVEE	Medway Hybred 44XLR (Rotax 447)	MR004/35		22. 7.88	D.S.L.Evans	Gravesend	4. 9.99P
G-MVEF	Solar Wings Pegasus XL-R SW-WA-1358 (Rotax 462)			19. 7.88	N.J.Stoner	Wombleton	15.11.93P
G-MVEG	Solar Wings Pegasus XL-R (Rotax 462) SW-TE-0080 & SW-WA-1359			19. 7.88	A.W.Leadley	Strabane, NI	15. 5.99P
G-MVEH	Mainair Gemini/Flash 2A (Rotax 503) 677-788-6 & W468			26. 8.88	D.L.Morris	Dawlish	17. 7.00P
G-MVEI	CFM Shadow Srs.CD (Rotax 503)	085		26. 7.88	T.J.McKean	Castle Douglas	23. 4.99P
G-MVEJ	Mainair Gemini/Flash 2A (Rotax 462) 678-888-6 & W469			27. 7.88	M.Thornburn & S.Mair	Moffat/Lockerbie	22.11.99P
G-MVEK	Mainair Gemini/Flash 2A (Rotax 503) 679-888-6 & W470			27. 7.88	J.R.Spinks	Ludlow	20. 9.00P
G-MVEL	Mainair Gemini/Flash 2A (Rotax 503) 680-888-6 & W471			27. 7.88	M.R.Starling	Swanton Morley	3.11.99P
G-MVEN	CFM Shadow Srs.CD (Rotax 503) K.047			26. 7.88	J.A.Harker	Southampton	6.11.99P
G-MVEO	Mainair Gemini/Flash 2A (Rotax 503) 682-888-6 & W472			28. 7.88	E.J.Robson	East Fortune	30. 1.00P
G-MVER	Mainair Gemini/Flash 2A (Rotax 503) 684-888-6 & W474			28. 7.88	J.R.Davis	Cheltenham	11. 8.00P
G-MVES	Mainair Gemini/Flash 2A (Rotax 503) 685-888-6 & W475			5. 8.88	R.H.Ferguson & F.W.McLean	East Fortune	25. 3.00P
G-MVET	Mainair Gemini/Flash 2A (Rotax 503) 686-888-6 & W476			19. 8.88	T.Bailey	Otherton, Cannock	3. 2.00P
G-MVEV	Mainair Gemini/Flash 2A (Rotax 503) 687-888-6 & W477			5. 8.88	C.Allen	Alderley Edge	7. 7.00P
G-MVEW	Mainair Gemini/Flash 2A (Rotax 503) 688-988-6 & W478			16. 9.88	N.A.Dye	Swanton Morley	27. 7.98P
G-MVEX	Solar Wings Pegasus XL-Q SW-WQ-0088 (Rotax 462)			5. 8.88	R.Morelli	Malahide, Ireland	3. 4.00P
G-MVEZ	Solar Wings Pegasus XL-Q (Rotax 462) SW-TE-0084 & SW-WQ-0090			9. 8.88	P.W.Millar	Newnham	13. 6.99P
G-MVFA	Solar Wings Pegasus XL-Q (Rotax 462HP) SW-TE-0085 & SW-WQ-0091			9. 8.88	G.Frogley & P.J.Garrett	Deenethorpe	3. 6.00P
G-MVFB	Solar Wings Pegasus XL-Q SW-TE-0086 & SW-WQ-0092 (Rotax 462)			9. 8.88	M.O.Bloy	Chatteris	14. 4.99P
G-MVFC	Solar Wings Pegasus XL-Q SW-WQ-0093 (Rotax 462)			9. 8.88	D.R.Joint	Bournemouth	25. 6.95P
G-MVFD	Solar Wings Pegasus XL-Q (Rotax 462) SW-TE-0088 & SW-WQ-0094			9. 8.88	C.D.Humphries	Long Marston	21. 5.00P
G-MVFE	Solar Wings Pegasus XL-Q SW-WQ-0095 (Rotax 462)			9. 8.88	S.J.Weeks	Weston Zoyland	30. 4.00P
G-MVFF	Solar Wings Pegasus XL-Q (Rotax 462) SW-TE-0090 & SW-WQ-0096			9. 8.88	A.Makepeace	Guildford	22.11.00P
G-MVFG	Solar Wings Pegasus XL-Q (Rotax 462) SW-TE-0091 & SW-WQ-0097			9. 8.88	R.F.Cooper	Oakley	5.10.00P
G-MVFH	CFM Shadow Srs.CD (Rotax 447)	086		9. 8.88	G.R.Read	Mendlesham	8. 1.00P
G-MVFJ	Thruster TST Mk.1 (Rotax 503)	8088-TST-092		11. 8.88	B.E.Renehan t/a Kestrel Flying Group	Popham	4.12.99P
G-MVFK	Thruster TST Mk.1 (Rotax 503)	8088-TST-093		11. 8.88	E.J.Rossouw	Wetherby	10. 4.00P
G-MVFL	Thruster TST Mk.1	8088-TST-094		11. 8.88	G.Hawkins	Otherton, Cannock	14. 3.00P
G-MVFM	Thruster TST Mk.1	8088-TST-095		11. 8.88	W.J.H.Orr	Blandford Forum	17. 7.00P
G-MVFN	Thruster TST Mk.1	8088-TST-096		11. 8.88	B.Wood	Long Acres Farm, Sandy	22. 7.98P
G-MVFO	Thruster TST Mk.1	8088-TST-097		11. 8.88	A.L.Higgins & D.H.King t/a G-MVFO Group	Newport Pagnell	17.10.00P
G-MVFP	Solar Wings Pegasus XL-R (Rotax 447) SW-TB-1371 & SW-WA-1365			9. 8.88	M.F.Tobin	North Coates	27. 7.97P
G-MVFR	Solar Wings Pegasus XL-R (Rotax 447) SW-TB-1372 & SW-WA-1366			9. 8.88	P.Newton	Macclesfield	21.11.99P
G-MVFS	Solar Wings Pegasus XL-R/Se (Rotax 447) SW-TB-1373 & SW-WA-1367			9. 8.88	S.Derwin	Rufforth	3. 5.00P

Regn	Type	C/n	P/I	Date	Owner/operator	Probable Base	CA Expy
G-MVFT	Solar Wings Pegasus XL-R (Rotax 447)	SW-WA-1368		9. 8.88	J.E.Halsall	Ashby-de-la-Zouche	24.10.00P
G-MVFV	Solar Wings Pegasus XL-R (Rotax 447)	SW-WA-1370		9. 8.88	R.J.A.Warren & K.Sullivan	Peterborough/Corby	18. 5.00P
G-MVFW	Solar Wings Pegasus XL-R (Rotax 447)	SW-WA-1371		9. 8.88	S.F.Chaplin	Deenethorpe	28. 8.00P
G-MVFX	Solar Wings Pegasus XL-R (Rotax 447)	SW-WA-1372		9. 8.88	S.J.Park	Sywell	30. 6.96P
G-MVFY	Solar Wings Pegasus XL-R (Rotax 447)	SW-WA-1373		9. 8.88	D.A.Linsey-Bloom	Long Ashton, Bristol	8. 1.00P
G-MVFZ	Solar Wings Pegasus XL-R (Rotax 447)	SW-TB-1380 & SW-WA-1374		9. 8.88	R.K.Johnson	Popham	8. 5.00P
G-MVGA	Aerial Arts Chaser S (Rotax 508)	CH.707 (C/n now CH.859)		11. 8.88	I.F.Bastin	Liskeard	29. 7.99P
G-MVGB	Medway Hybred 44XLR (Rotax 447)	MR011/39		1. 9.88	R.Graham	Gravesend	19. 7.00P
G-MVGC	AMF Chevvron 2-32C (Konig SD570)	010		2. 9.88	A.E.Dobson	Broadmeadow Farm, Hereford	18.11.00P
G-MVGD	AMF Chevvron 2-32 (Konig SD570)	011		5. 9.88	Calvert Holdings Ltd	Park Farm, Eaton Bray	1. 6.98P
G-MVGE	AMF Chevvron 2-32C (Konig SD570)	012		26. 9.88	J.Lawley	Blandford Forum	15. 6.00P
G-MVGF	Aerial Arts Chaser S (Rotax 377)	CH.720		2. 9.88	R.Nicklin "The Dingbat"	Otherton, Cannock	11.11.00P
G-MVGG	Aerial Arts Chaser S (Rotax 377)	CH.721		2. 9.88	M.I.Hubbard	Horley	14. 4.00P
G-MVGH	Aerial Arts Chaser S (Rotax 447)	CH.722		2. 9.88	R.W.Cooper	Douglas, IoM	16.10.00P
G-MVGI	Aerial Arts Chaser S (Rotax 462)	CH.723		1. 9.88	J.Bagnall	Congleton	13. 7.97P
G-MVGJ	Aerial Arts Chaser S (Rotax 377)	CH.724		2. 9.88	P.J.McNamee	Rickmansworth	8.12.89P
G-MVGK	Aerial Arts Chaser S (Rotax 462)	CH.726		2. 9.88	P.S.Flynn (Stored 5.97)	Sandtoft	1. 9.99P
G-MVGL	Medway Hybred 44XLR (Rotax 447)	MR012/40		1. 9.88	S.Tensch	Chelmsford	1. 6.98P
G-MVGM	Mainair Gemini/Flash 2A (Rotax 503)	691-988-6 & W481		25. 8.88	A.R.Pitcher	Cranbrook, Kent	12. 9.00P
G-MVGN	Solar Wings Pegasus XL-R/Se (Rotax 447)	SW-TB-1381 & SW-WA-1377		23. 8.88	W.Timbrell	Martock	5. 3.00P
G-MVGO	Solar Wings Pegasus XL-R (Rotax 447)	SW-TB-1382 & SW-WA-1378		23. 8.88	J.B.Peacock	Lower Mountpleasant, Chatteris	14. 3.00P
G-MVGP	Solar Wings Pegasus XL-R (Rotax 447)	SW-WA-1379	(EC-) G-MVGP	23. 8.88	J.P.Cox	Kettering	9. 6.00P
G-MVGR	Solar Wings Pegasus XL-R/Se (Rotax 447)	SW-WA-1380		23. 8.88	G.R.Leport	Barnet, Herts	30.12.91P
G-MVGS	Solar Wings Pegasus XL-R (Rotax 447)	SW-TB-1385 & SW-WA-1381		23. 8.88	J.J.Featherstone	Long Marston	10. 3.00P
G-MVGT	Solar Wings Pegasus XL-Q (Rotax 462)	SW-TE-0092 & SW-WQ-0099		23. 8.88	R.Saunders	RAF Wyton	16. 7.00P
G-MVGU	Solar Wings Pegasus XL-Q (Rotax 462)	SW-WQ-0100		23. 8.88	T.D.Turner	Clench Common	11. 6.00P
G-MVGV	Solar Wings Pegasus XL-Q (Rotax 462)	SW-TE-0094 & SW-WQ-0101		23. 8.88	J.L.Richards	Waltham Cross	7. 3.99P
G-MVGW	Solar Wings Pegasus XL-Q (Rotax 462)	SW-WQ-0102		23. 8.88	M.J.L.de Carvalho & V.V.P.Pedro t/a G-MVGW Group	Lagos, Algarve, Portugal	8. 2.92P
G-MVGY	Medway Hybred 44XLR (Rotax 447)	MR015/41		31. 8.88	G.S.Cridland	Alton	1. 6.98P
G-MVGZ	Ultraflight Lazair IIIE (Rotax 185)	A.338	(ex?)	21.10.88	M.F.Briggs	Yateley	24. 9.98P
G-MVHA	Aerial Arts Chaser S-1000 (Mosler MM-CB)	CH.729		24. 8.88	R.Meredith-Hardy	Radwell Lodge, Baldock	27. 6.00P
G-MVHB	Powerchute Raider (Rotax 447)	80105		26. 8.88	A.E.Askew	Melton Mowbray	31. 5.00P
G-MVHC	Powerchute Raider (Rotax 447)	80106		26. 8.88	D.J.Whysall	Ripley, Derby	17.10.99P
G-MVHD	CFM Shadow Srs.CD (Rotax 503)	088		8. 9.88	Susan R Groves	Plaistows, Hemel Hempstead	16. 4.00P
G-MVHE	Mainair Gemini/Flash 2A (Rotax 503)	692-988-6 & W482		4.10.88	D.C.Brotherton	North Berwick	13.10.00P

Regn	Type	C/n	P/I	Date	Owner/operator	Probable Base	CA Expy
G-MVHF	Mainair Gemini/Flash 2A (Rotax 503)	693-988-6 & W483		4.10.88	S.B.Walsh	St.Michaels	7. 5.00P
G-MVHG	Mainair Gemini/Flash 2A (Rotax 503)	694-988-6 & W484		14.10.88	M.J.W.Brouse	Hethersett	15. 7.99P
G-MVHH	Mainair Gemini/Flash 2A (Rotax 503)	607-1187-5 & W485 (Originally Trike No.695 replaced by No.607 ex G-MTSA 1995)		24.10.88	G.Addison	Kinross	4. 9.00P
G-MVHI	Thruster TST Mk.1 (Rotax 503)	8098-TST-100		26. 9.88	C.P.Fox	Frome	16. 9.99P
G-MVHJ	Thruster TST Mk.1 (Rotax 503)	8098-TST-101		26. 9.88	A.P.Harvey & R.L.Barker	Basildon/Billericay	10. 4.00P
G-MVHK	Thruster TST Mk.1 (Rotax 503)	8098-TST-102		27. 9.88	A.L.Rowland	Davidstow Moor	30. 6.00P
G-MVHL	Thruster TST Mk.1 (Rotax 532)	8098-TST-103		27. 9.88	D.Sweeney & G.R.Thomas	Redlands, Swindon	22. 1.00P
G-MVHM	Whittaker MW-5 Sorcerer (Rotax 447)	PFA/163-11314		8. 9.88	E.M.Morris	Bexhill	4. 2.93P
G-MVHN	Aerial Arts Chaser S (Rotax 377)	CH.728		9. 9.88	M.Stoney	Chigwell	11. 8.99P
G-MVHO	Solar Wings Pegasus XL-Q (Rotax 462HP)	SW-WQ-0104		23. 9.88	S.J.Barkworth	Rufforth	29. 3.00P
G-MVHP	Solar Wings Pegasus XL-Q (Rotax 462)	SW-WQ-0105		23. 9.88	J.B.Gasson	Lower Mountpleasant, Chatteris	7. 7.00P
G-MVHR	Solar Wings Pegasus XL-Q (Rotax 462)	SW-TE-0099 & SW-WQ-0106		23. 9.88	J.M.Hucker	Full Sutton	26. 5.98P
G-MVHS	Solar Wings Pegasus XL-Q (Rotax 462)	SW-WQ-0107		23. 9.88	S.Sebastian	Long Acres Farm, Sandy	4. 6.00P
G-MVHT	Solar Wings Pegasus XL-Q (Rotax 462)	SW-WQ-0108		23. 9.88	A.M.Gould	Bristol	2.10.99P
G-MVHU	Solar Wings Pegasus XL-Q (Rotax 462HP)	SW-TE-0182 & SW-WQ-0109		23. 9.88	A.McDermid	Addlestone, Surrey	30. 7.00P
G-MVHV	Solar Wings Pegasus XL-Q (Rotax 462)	SW-WQ-0110		23. 9.88	K.J.Tomlinson	Mackworth, Derby	1. 3.93P
G-MVHW	Solar Wings Pegasus XL-Q (Rotax 462)	SW-TE-0101 & SW-WQ-0111		23. 9.88	P.E.Vincent	Roddige, Fradley	31. 8.00P
G-MVHX	Solar Wings Pegasus XL-Q (Rotax 462HP)	SW-TE-0105 & SW-WQ-0112		23. 9.88	D.F.Randall	Plaistows, Hemel Hempstead	27. 3.00P
G-MVHY	Solar Wings Pegasus XL-Q (Rotax 462HP)	SW-TE-0106 & SW-WQ-0113		23. 9.88	R.P.Paine	Mansfield	2. 5.00P
G-MVHZ	Hornet Dual Trainer/Raven (Rotax 462)	HRWA 0076 & MHR-101		26. 9.88	B.G.Colvin	Kings Lynn	10.11.98P
G-MVIA	Solar Wings Pegasus XL-R (Rotax 462)	SW-WA-1375		4.10.88	K.P.Taylor	Benington	7. 4.00P
G-MVIB	Mainair Gemini/Flash 2A (Rotax 503)	700-1088-4 & W490		14.10.88	LSA Systems Ltd	Arclid, Sandbach	30. 4.00P
G-MVIC	Mainair Gemini/Flash 2A (Rotax 503)	699-1188-4 & W489		4.10.88	G.Tomlinson	Eshott	11. 4.00P
G-MVID	Aerial Arts Chaser S (Rotax 377)	CH.731		14.10.88	M.Van Rompaey	Scunthorpe	29.10.00P
G-MVIE	Aerial Arts Chaser S (Rotax 377)	CH.732		14.10.88	T.M.Stiles	Heathfield	6. 6.97P
G-MVIF	Medway Hybred 44XLR (Rotax 447)	MR020/43		4.10.88	J.R.Harrison	Bolsover	2. 4.00P
G-MVIG	CFM Shadow Srs.B (Rotax 447)	K.044		5.10.88	M.P.& P.A.G.Harper (Damaged 1993: stored 8.93)	Priory Farm, Tibenham	20. 1.94P
G-MVIH	Mainair Gemini/Flash 2A (Rotax 503)	697-1088-6 & W487		14.10.88	M.D.Bainbridge	Dunkeswell	13. 8.00P
G-MVIL	Noble Hardman Snowbird Mk.IV (Rotax 532)	SB-014		6. 2.89	G.R.Graham	Carlisle	24.11.00P
G-MVIM	Noble Hardman Snowbird Mk.IV (Rotax 532)	SB-015		6. 2.89	R.H.Whitaker (Stored 6.96)	Wombleton	28. 6.91P
G-MVIN	Noble Hardman Snowbird Mk.IV	SB-016		6. 2.89	R.S.W.Jones	Tregaron	16. 3.00P
G-MVIO	Noble Hardman Snowbird Mk.IV (Rotax 532)	SB-017		12. 4.89	B.Mason-Baker t/a Mobility Advice Line	Selly Oak	27. 7.00P
G-MVIP	AMF Chevvron 2-32 (Konig SD570)	008		11. 5.88	C.D.Marsh t/a Chilbolton Chevvron Group	Chilbolton	21. 1.00P
G-MVIR	Thruster TST Mk.1 (Rotax 503) (C/n plate marked as 8118-TST-104)	8108-TST-104		21.10.88	E.R.Butterfield	Kingsclere, Hannington	7. 7.00P
G-MVIS	Thruster TST Mk.1 (Rotax 503)	8108-TST-105		21.10.88	J.D.Taylor t/a Taylor Project Services (Damaged mid 1995)	Warrington	21.10.95P
G-MVIU	Thruster TST Mk.1 (Rotax 503)	8108-TST-107		21.10.88	G.J.Chater	Popham	30. 1.00P

Regn	Type	C/n	P/I	Date	Owner/operator	Probable Base	CA Expy
G-MVIV	Thruster TST Mk.1 (Rotax 503)	8108-TST-108		21.10.88	P.J.Sears	Ivybridge	19. 6.99P
G-MVIW*	Thruster TST Mk.1 (Rotax 532)	8108-TST-109		21.10.88	M.P.Walsh & L.W.Stevens (Cancelled by CAA 23.3.99)	Deenethorpe	7.11.98P
G-MVIX	Mainair Gemini/Flash 2A (Rotax 503)	702-1088-6 & W492		14.10.88	T.D.Grieve (Damaged mid 1996)	Hamilton	18. 4.97P
G-MVIY	Mainair Gemini/Flash 2A (Rotax 503)	701-1088-6 & W491		14.10.88	D.H.Brown	Ince Blundell	15. 5.00P
G-MVIZ	Mainair Gemini/Flash 2A (Rotax 503)	703-1088-6 & W493		14.10.88	W.E.Richards & P.Lockey	Redlands, Swindon	8. 5.00P
G-MVJA	Mainair Gemini/Flash 2A (Rotax 503)	696-988-6 & W486		5.12.88	J.R.Harrison	Wisbech	5.10.00P
G-MVJB	Mainair Gemini/Flash 2A (Rotax 503)	704-1088-6 & W494		24.10.88	M.R.Starling	Northrepps	29. 7.97P
G-MVJC	Mainair Gemini/Flash 2A (Rotax 503)	705-1088-6 & W495		24.10.88	B.Temple	Swanton Morley	8. 7.00P
G-MVJD	Solar Wings Pegasus XL-R (Rotax 462)	SW-TE-0109 & SW-WA-1386		24.10.88	D.M.Wood	Enstone	26. 8.00P
G-MVJE	Mainair Gemini/Flash 2A (Rotax 503)	706-1188-6 & W496		21.10.88	S.J.Whistance	Bromyard	30. 4.95P
G-MVJF	Aerial Arts Chaser S (Rotax 377)	CH.743		21.11.88	N.R.Andrew	Bristol	17.10.99P
G-MVJG	Aerial Arts Chaser S (Rotax 377)	CH.749		22.11.88	J.T.Houghton	Andreas, IoM	24. 5.98P
G-MVJH	Aerial Arts Chaser S (Rotax 377)	CH.751		14.11.88	P.N.Crowther-Wilton	Enstone	8. 7.00P
G-MVJI	Aerial Arts Chaser S (Rotax 377)	CH.752		17.11.88	J.P.Kynaston	Eshott	13. 4.98P
G-MVJJ	Aerial Arts Chaser S (Rotax 508)	CH.753		14.11.88	P.Brown	Eshott	6. 5.00P
G-MVJK	Aerial Arts Chaser S (Rotax 377)	CH.754		14.11.88	T.L.Travis	Stafford	7. 4.00P
G-MVJL	Mainair Gemini/Flash 2A (Rotax 503)	698-1188-6 & W488		21.10.88	A.R.Trace & V.C.Cowles	Sittles Farm, Alrewas	20. 5.00P
G-MVJM	Microflight Spectrum (Rotax 503) 007			21.10.88	Corbett Farms Ltd	Shobdon	27. 8.96P
G-MVJN	Solar Wings Pegasus XL-Q (Rotax 462)	SW-TE-0110 & SW-WQ-0116		26.10.88	J.W.Wall (Stored 6.96)	Enstone	18. 2.96P
G-MVJO	Solar Wings Pegasus XL-Q (Rotax 462)	SW-WQ-0117		26.10.88	J.D.Hoyland	Winchester	20. 4.99P
G-MVJP	Solar Wings Pegasus XL-Q (Rotax 462)	SW-WQ-0118		26.10.88	W.G.Colyer	Paddock Wood	28. 2.00P
G-MVJR	Solar Wings Pegasus XL-Q (Rotax 462)	SW-WQ-0119		26.10.88	A.D.Woodroffe	Henley-on-Thames	30. 8.97P
G-MVJS	Solar Wings Pegasus XL-Q (Rotax 462)	SW-WQ-0120		26.10.88	S.D.Morley	Rayne Hall Farm, Rayne	12. 2.00P
G-MVJT	Solar Wings Pegasus XL-Q (Rotax 462HP)	SW-TE-0115 & SW-WQ-0121		26.10.88	R.D.McKellar & M.Howland t/a Juliet Tango Group	Ginge, Wantage	17. 4.00P
G-MVJU	Solar Wings Pegasus XL-Q (Rotax 462)	SW-TE-0116 & SW-WQ-0122		26.10.88	G.B.Hutchison	Sandtoft	27. 7.00P
G-MVJW	Solar Wings Pegasus XL-Q (Rotax 462)	SE-TE-0118 & SW-WQ-0124		26.10.88	R.Dainty & D.W.Stamp Pound Green, Buttonoak, Kidderminster		10. 8.00P
G-MVJX*	Solar Wings Pegasus XL-Q	SW-WQ-0125		26.10.88	Not known (Wing stored 9.97)Long Marston		
G-MVKB	Medway Hybred 44XLR (Rotax 447)	MR023/45		11.11.88	J.Newby	Sandtoft	11. 9.00P
G-MVKC	Mainair Gemini/Flash 2A (Rotax 503)	709-1188-6 & W499		16.11.88	J.E.Gattrell	Sittles Farm, Alrewas	28. 4.00P
G-MVKE	Solar Wings Pegasus XL-R (Rotax 447)	SW-WA-1391		14.11.88	M.R.Allan (Stored 6.96)	Wombleton	27. 3.93P
G-MVKF	Solar Wings Pegasus XL-R (Rotax 447)	SW-WA-1392		14.11.88	M.Convine	Woolaston	22. 7.00P
G-MVKG	Solar Wings Pegasus XL-R (Rotax 447)	SW-TB-1390 & SW-WA-1393		14.11.88	N.D.Meer	Sittles Farm,Alrewas	24.10.00P
G-MVKH	Solar Wings Pegasus XL-R (Rotax 447)	SW-TB-1391 & SW-WA-1394		14.11.88	K.M.Elson	Roddige, Fradley	29.10.00P
G-MVKJ	Solar Wings Pegasus XL-R (Rotax 447)	SW-TB-1393 & SW-WA-1396		14.11.88	G.V.Warner	Creighton	13. 4.00P
G-MVKK	Solar Wings Pegasus XL-R (Rotax 462)	SW-WA-1397		14.11.88	P.G.Sayers	London Colney	27. 3.00P
G-MVKL	Solar Wings Pegasus XL-R (Rotax 462)	SW-WA-1398		14.11.88	J.T.Powell-Tuck	Pontypool	6. 6.91P

Regn	Type	C/n	P/I	Date	Owner/operator	Probable Base	CA Expy
G-MVKM	Solar Wings Pegasus XL-R (Rotax 462) SW-TE-0136 & SW-WA-1399			14.11.88	D.T.Evans	Broadmeadow Farm, Hereford	19. 5.00P
G-MVKN	Solar Wings Pegasus XL-Q (Rotax 462) SW-TE-0120 & SW-WQ-0126			14.11.88	T.A.Colman	London NW8	10. 3.00P
G-MVKO	Solar Wings Pegasus XL-Q (Rotax 462HP) SW-TE-0121 & SW-WQ-0127			14.11.88	B.J.Lyford	Swanage	19. 6.00P
G-MVKP	Solar Wings Pegasus XL-Q (Rotax 462) SW-TE-0122 & SW-WQ-0128			14.11.88	J.Urwin	Eshott	4. 9.00P
G-MVKS	Solar Wings Pegasus XL-Q (Rotax 462) SW-TE-0124 & SW-WQ-0130			14.11.88	K.S.Wright (Stored 8.95)	Long Marston	13. 5.94P
G-MVKT	Solar Wings Pegasus XL-Q SW-WQ-0131 (Rotax 462)			14.11.88	N.C.Williams	Windsor	21.11.00P
G-MVKU	Solar Wings Pegasus XL-Q (Rotax 462) SW-TE-0126 & SW-WQ-0132			14.11.88	J.R.F.Shepherd	Long Acres Farm, Sandy	2. 7.00P
G-MVKV	Solar Wings Pegasus XL-Q SW-WQ-0152 (Rotax 462)			14.11.88	J.Howard	Enstone	8. 7.00P
G-MVKW	Solar Wings Pegasus XL-Q SW-WQ-0134 (Rotax 462)			14.11.88	A.T.Scott	London SW17	11. 5.99P
G-MVKX	Solar Wings Pegasus XL-Q (Rotax 462) SW-WQ-0135			14.11.88	G.R.Soper	Popham	2. 5.00P
G-MVKY	Aerial Arts Chaser S (Rotax 377)	CH.755		5.12.88	R.W.Whitehead	Swinford, Rugby	19. 2.00P
G-MVKZ	Aerial Arts Chaser S (Rotax 377)	CH.756		5.12.88	N.D.Meer	Roddige, Fradley	11. 9.00P
G-MVLA	Aerial Arts Chaser S (Rotax 377)	CH.762		12.12.88	T.Birch	Wolverhampton	23. 8.00P
G-MVLB	Aerial Arts Chaser S (Rotax 377)	CH.763		5.12.88	C.R.Read	Didcot	13. 9.97P
G-MVLC	Aerial Arts Chaser S (Rotax 377)	CH.764		22.11.88	D.C.Britton	Bristol	3. 4.00P
G-MVLD	Aerial Arts Chaser S (Rotax 377)	CH.765		22.11.88	G.F.Atkinson	Rufforth	7. 5.00P
G-MVLE	Aerial Arts Chaser S (Rotax 377)	CH.766		5.12.88	R.G.Hooker	Eshott	4. 9.00P
G-MVLF	Aerial Arts Chaser S (Rotax 377)	CH.767		11. 1.89	I.E.Bloys	Ely	28. 5.99P
G-MVLG	Aerial Arts Chaser S (Rotax 377)	CH.768		14.11.88	S.Bradie	Great Orton	25.11.96P
G-MVLH	Aerial Arts Chaser S (Rotax 377)	CH.769		22.11.88	A.W.Cove	Wellingborough	13.11.97P
	(Factory overhaul before storage: not flown for 3 years since Permit renewal)						
G-MVLJ	CFM Shadow Srs.CD (Rotax 503)	092		11.11.88	B.E.Trinder	Rushden	2.12.00P
G-MVLL	Mainair Gemini/Flash 2A (Rotax 503) 708-1188-6 & W498 (Wing c/n now W.396 ex G-MTSA)			23.11.88	J.W.Peake	Stafford	29. 9.00P
G-MVLM*	Solar Wings Pegasus Bandit SW-WX-0015			23.11.88	Solar Wings Aviation Ltd	Clench Common	
	(PWFU by CAA 29.3.94: trike stored for rebuild 4.96)						
G-MVLP	CFM Shadow Srs.B (Rotax 447)	095		22.11.88	D.Bridgland & D.T.Moran	Reading	24. 5.94P
G-MVLR	Mainair Gemini/Flash 2A (Rotax 503) 713-1288-6 & W503			30.11.88	S.R.Winter	Broxbourne, Herts	18.11.00P
G-MVLS	Aerial Arts Chaser S (Rotax 377)	CH.773		21. 2.89	E.W.P.Van Zeller	Ashford, Kent	30. 1.00P
G-MVLT	Aerial Arts Chaser S (Rotax 377)	CH.774		5.12.88	B.D.Searle	Portsmouth	22. 3.00P
G-MVLU	Aerial Arts Chaser S	CH.775		5.12.88	M.J.Aubrey	Kington, Hereford	11. 2.89P*
G-MVLW	Aerial Arts Chaser S (Rotax 377)	CH.778		28.12.88	E.W.P.van Zeller	Ashford	5. 9.99P
G-MVLX	Solar Wings Pegasus XL-Q (Rotax 462) SW-TE-0133 & SW-WQ-0114			30.11.88	D.O'Keeffe	London N3	30. 5.00P
G-MVLY	Solar Wings Pegasus XL-Q SW-WQ-0142 (Rotax 462)			5.12.88	I.Glover	Nottingham	23. 6.96P
G-MVMA	Solar Wings Pegasus XL-Q (Rotax 462) SW-TE-0139 & SW-WQ-0144			5.12.88	B.D.Clapp	Weston Zoyland	26. 4.99P
G-MVMB	Solar Wings Pegasus XL-Q SW-WQ-0145 (Rotax 462)			5.12.88	J.C.Sear	Chelmsford	23. 6.93P
G-MVMC	Solar Wings Pegasus XL-Q (Rotax 462HP) SW-TE-0141 & SW-WQ-0146			5.12.88	P.G.Becker	Washingborough, Lincoln	4. 4.00P
G-MVMD	Powerchute Raider (Rotax 447)	80924		15.12.88	A K Webster	Wallingford	13. 7.90P
G-MVME	Thruster TST Mk.1 (Rotax 503)	8128-TST-110		12.12.88	N.A.Bell & G.W.Hockey	Fordingbridge	16. 7.95P

Regn	Type	C/n P/I	Date	Owner/operator	Probable Base	CA Expy
G-MVMG	Thruster TST Mk.1 (Rotax 503)	8128-TST-112	12.12.88	B.O.McCartan	Banbridge, Co.Down	31. 8.97P
G-MVMI	Thruster TST Mk.1 (Rotax 503)	8128-TST-114	12.12.88	R E M Gibson-Bevan	Market Rasen	9.10.99P
G-MVMK	Medway Hybred 44XLR (Rotax 447)	MR022/46	12.12.88	D.J.Lewis	Damyns Hall, Upminster	5. 2.94P
G-MVML	Aerial Arts Chaser S (Rotax 377)	CH.781	28.12.88	G C Luddington	Wilden, Beds	29. 7.00P
G-MVMM	Aerial Arts Chaser S (Rotax 377)	CH.797	21. 2.89	S.C.Reeve	Slipperlow Farm, Belper	9. 1.00P
G-MVMN*	Mainair Gemini/Flash 2A (Rotax 503)	714-1288-6 & W506	18. 1.89	C.D.C.Ashdown (Cancelled as destroyed 4.8.99: noted 8.99)	Prestwick	4. 4.00P
G-MVMO	Mainair Gemini/Flash 2A (Rotax 503)	715-1288-6 & W507	12.12.88	N.Redmond	Sandtoft	20. 9.99P
G-MVMR	Mainair Gemini/Flash 2A (Rotax 503)	717-1288-6 & W509	9. 1.89	P.W.Ramage	Manor Farm, Inskip	20. 9.96P
G-MVMT	Mainair Gemini/Flash 2A (Rotax 503)	718-189-6 & W510	22.12.88	R.F.Sanders t/a Independent Financial Advisory Service	Hatherton, Cannock	25. 9.98P
G-MVMU	Mainair Gemini/Flash 2A (Rotax 503)	719-189-6 & W511	22.12.88	M.J.A.New & A.Clift "Icarus" Mill Farm, Hughley, Much Wenlock		25. 6.00P
G-MVMV	Mainair Gemini/Flash 2A (Rotax 503)	720-189-6 & W512	22.12.88	R Nicklin	Otherton, Cannock	11.11.00P
G-MVMW	Mainair Gemini/Flash 2A (Rotax 503)	710-1188-6 & W500	11.11.88	K.Downes & B.Nock	Wolverhampton	31. 7.00P
G-MVMX	Mainair Gemini/Flash 2A (Rotax 462)	721-189-6 & W513 (Trike stamped incorrectly as W512)	23.12.88	A.L.Bentham	Telford	24. 1.00P
G-MVMY	Mainair Gemini/Flash 2A (Rotax 503)	722-189-6 & W514	22.12.88	D.J.Higham	Roddige, Fradley	2. 6.00P
G-MVMZ	Mainair Gemini/Flash 2A (Rotax 503)	723-189-6 & W515	22.12.88	S A Unsworth	Otherton, Cannock	2.11.00P
G-MVNA	Powerchute Raider (Rotax 447)	81230	12. 7.89	B.Gorvett	Swansea	24. 5.93P
G-MVNB	Powerchute Raider (Rotax 447)	81231	12. 7.89	E.Nicell	Londonderry	23. 3.97P
G-MVNC	Powerchute Raider (Rotax 447)	81232	12. 7.89	W.R.Hanley	Edinburgh	25. 7.00P
G-MVNE*	Powerchute Raider (Rotax 447)	90219	12. 7.89	R.Crawley (Cancelled as wfu 21.9.99)	Hitchin	26.11.93P
G-MVNI	Powerchute Raider (Rotax 447)	90625	12. 7.89	N.J.Staib	Kemble	7. 8.98P
G-MVNK	Powerchute Raider (Rotax 447)	90623	12. 7.89	J.Cunliffe	Stoke-on-Trent	16. 7.95P
G-MVNL	Powerchute Raider (Rotax 447)	90624	12. 7.89	R.S.McFadyen t/a British Powered Paragliding Association	Burton-on-Trent	3. 6.93P
G-MVNM	Mainair Gemini/Flash 2A (Rotax 503)	725-189-6 & W517	6. 1.89	M.Castle & T.Hartwig	Shrewsbury	8. 6.00P
G-MVNN	Aerotech MW-5(K) Sorcerer (Rotax 447) 5K-0003-02 & BMAA/HB/022		28. 3.90	K.N.Dando	Shobdon	15. 5.00P
G-MVNO	Aerotech MW-5(K) Sorcerer 5K-0004-02 (Rotax 447)		4. 5.89	R.L.Wadley	Stoke, Kent	12. 2.00P
G-MVNP	Aerotech MW-5(K) Sorcerer 5K-0005-02 (Rotax 447)		13. 7.89	R.A.Davis	Leamington Spa	24. 9.96P
G-MVNR	Aerotech MW-5(K) Sorcerer 5K-0006-02 (Rotax 447)		4. 5.89	F.Jones	Ley Farm, Chirk	1. 8.00P
G-MVNS	Aerotech MW-5(K) Sorcerer 5K-0007-02 (Rotax 447)		19. 7.89	R.D.Chiles Shenstone Hall Farm, Shenstone		16. 7.00P
G-MVNT	Aerotech MW-5(K) Sorcerer 5K-0008-02 (Rotax 447)		28. 3.90	P.E.Blyth	Wombleton	21. 9.00P
G-MVNU	Aerotech MW-5(K) Sorcerer 5K-0009-02 (Rotax 447)		4. 5.89	J.C.Rose	Oakley	6. 5.00P
G-MVNW	Mainair Gemini/Flash 2A (Rotax 503)	726-189-6 & W518	25. 1.89	A.Weatherall	Preston	4. 4.00P
G-MVNX	Mainair Gemini/Flash 2A (Rotax 503)	727-289-6 & W519	10. 1.89	I.Sidebotham	Barton	16. 9.00P
G-MVNY	Mainair Gemini/Flash 2A (Rotax 462)	724-189-6 & W516	11. 1.89	M.K.Buckland	Daventry	26. 5.00P
G-MVNZ	Mainair Gemini/Flash 2A (Rotax 503)	728-289-6 & W520	11. 1.89	B.Crouch	Oxton, Notts	3. 6.99P
G-MVOA	Aerial Arts Chaser S CH.780 (Rotax 462) (Reported as Aerial Arts Alligator)		16. 1.89	A.B.Potts	Eshott	30.10.99P

Regn	Type	C/n	P/I	Date	Owner/operator	Probable Base	CA Expy
G-MVOB	Mainair Gemini/Flash 2A (Rotax 503)	729-289-6 & W521		16. 1.89	B.J.Bader	Taunton	15. 3.00P
G-MVOD	Aerial Arts Chaser/110SX (Rotax 377)	110SX/653		16. 1.89	M.A.Hodgson	Otherton, Cannock	13. 8.98P
G-MVOE	Solar Wings Pegasus XL-R (Rotax 462)	SW-WA-1401		23. 1.89	P.Ray	London N18	29. 6.94P
G-MVOF	Mainair Gemini/Flash 2A (Rotax 503)	730-289-6 & W522		31. 1.89	C.Pearce	Swanton Morley	5. 9.00P
G-MVOH	CFM Shadow Srs.CD (Rotax 447)	K.090		23. 1.89	D.I.Farmer	Dunkeswell	22. 8.00P
G-MVOI	Noble Hardman Snowbird Mk.IV (Rotax 532)	SB-018		6. 2.89	K.W. & C.A.Warn	Newbury/Uxbridge	2. 7.98P
G-MVOJ	Noble Hardman Snowbird Mk.IV (Rotax 532)	SB-019		26. 7.89	T.D.Thwaites t/a The HFC Group	Penrith	28. 7.99P
G-MVOL	Noble Hardman Snowbird Mk.IV (Rotax 532)	SB-021		29. 8.89	E.J.Lewis t/a Swansea Snowbird Fliers	Swansea	24. 9.00P
G-MVON	Mainair Gemini/Flash 2A (Rotax 503)	731-289-6 & W523		30. 1.89	J.V.Bailey	Leigh, Lancs	15. 8.98P
G-MVOO	AMF Chevvron 2- (Konig SD570)	32C 014		10. 1.89	I.R.F.Hammond	Lee-on-Solent	1. 8.00P
G-MVOP	Aerial Arts Chaser S (Rotax 377)	CH.787		21. 2.89	D.Thorpe	Grantham	28.10.96P
G-MVOR	Mainair Gemini/Flash 2A (Rotax 462)	732-289-6 & W524	(EC-) G-MVOR	6. 2.89	P.T. & R.M.Jenkins	Dunkeswell	17. 8.00P
G-MVOS	Southdown Puma/Raven (Fuji-Robin EC-44-PM)	PJB-02		6. 2.89	B.Kirkland	Tarn Farm, Cockerham	22. 8.97P
G-MVOT	Thruster TST Mk.1 (Rotax 503)	8029-TST-116		17. 2.89	H.W.Vasey	Davidstow Moor	18. 7.00P
G-MVOU	Thruster TST Mk.1 (Rotax 503)	8029-TST-117		17. 2.89	A.T.Murray	Great Orton	28. 5.98P
G-MVOV	Thruster TST Mk.1 (Rotax 503)	8029-TST-118		17. 2.89	J.N.W.Moss t/a G-MVOV Group	Old Sarum	26. 8.00P
G-MVOW	Thruster TST Mk.1 (Rotax 503)	8029-TST-119		17. 2.89	J.Short & B.J.Merret	Dunkeswell	17. 7.00P
G-MVOX	Thruster TST Mk.1 (Rotax 503)	8029-TST-120		17. 2.89	J.E.Davies	Haverfordwest	19. 2.99P
G-MVOY	Thruster TST Mk.1 (Rotax 503)	8029-TST-121		17. 2.89	G.R.Breaden	Blackpool	4. 6.00P
G-MVPA	Mainair Gemini/Flash 2A (Rotax 503)	735-289-7 & W527		29. 3.89	J.E.Milburn	Eshott	30. 8.95P
G-MVPB	Mainair Gemini/Flash 2A (Rotax 503)	736-389-7 & W528		29. 3.89	J.R.Moore	Darlington	15. 6.00P
G-MVPC	Mainair Gemini/Flash 2A (Rotax 503)	737-389-7 & W529 (Has c/n stamp 740-389-7-W532 - see G-MVPI)		7. 2.89	G.D.Scott	Ince Blundell	26. 5.98P
G-MVPD	Mainair Gemini/Flash 2A (Rotax 503)	738-389-7 & W530		7. 2.89	S.E.Blunstone	(Macclesfield)	30. 8.97P
G-MVPE	Mainair Gemini/Flash 2A (Rotax 503)	739-389-7 & W531		7. 2.89	E.A.Wrathall & H.N.Houghton	St.Michaels	10. 2.00P
G-MVPF	Medway Hybred 44XLR (Rotax 447)	MR036/52		27. 2.89	M.Sandereson	Purley	1. 7.00P
G-MVPG	Medway Hybred 44XLR (Rotax 447)	MR026/53		15. 2.89	M.A.Jones	Wigan	30.12.98P
G-MVPH	Whittaker MW-6S Fatboy Flyer (Rotax 503)	PFA/164-11404		7. 2.89	P.L.Corder & A.Rowson	Emlyns Field, Rhuallt	23. 8.99P
G-MVPI	Mainair Gemini/Flash 2A (Rotax 503)	740-389-7 & W532		9. 2.89	C.R. & P.Squibbs (See G-MVPC)	Dunkeswell	7. 4.00P
G-MVPJ	Rans S-5 Coyote (Rotax 447)	88-083 & PFA/193-11470		15. 2.89	D.Harker	Middlesbrough	2. 8.99P
G-MVPK	CFM Shadow Srs.BD K. (Rotax 447)	091		15. 2.89	G.Dalton	Davidstow Moor	25. 4.00P
G-MVPL	Medway Hybred 44XLR	MR034/50		1. 3.89	J.N.J.Roberts	Long Acres Farm, Sandy	30. 4.98P
G-MVPM	Whittaker MW-6 Merlin (Rotax 503)	PFA/164-11272		21. 2.89	P.R.A. & S.Elliston	RAF Mona	9. 8.00P
G-MVPN	Whittaker MW-6 Merlin (Rotax 503)	PFA/164-11280		21. 2.89	A.M.Field	Glastonbury	18. 5.93P
G-MVPO	Mainair Gemini/Flash 2A (Rotax 503)	741-389-7 & W533		3. 3.89	A.H. & C.I.King	Rye	9. 8.99P
G-MVPR	Solar Wings Pegasus XL-Q (Rotax 462)	SW-TE-0149 & SW-WQ-0163		14. 3.89	R.S.Swift	Milton Keynes	25. 5.00P
G-MVPS	Solar Wings Pegasus XL-Q (Rotax 462HP)	SW-WQ-0140		14. 3.89	B.R.Chamberlain	London Colney	22. 3.00P

Regn	Type	C/n	P/I	Date	Owner/operator	Probable Base	CA Expy
G-MVPU	Solar Wings Pegasus XL-Q			29. 3.89	C.W.Lark	Long Marston	2. 9.00P
	(Rotax 462) SW-TE-0150 & SW-WQ-0164						
G-MVPW	Solar Wings Pegasus XL-R SW-WA-1411			28. 3.89	C.A.Mitchell	Newport, Gwent	24.10.98P
	(Rotax 462)						
G-MVPX	Solar Wings Pegasus XL-Q SW-WQ-0158			28. 3.89	M.M.P.Evans	Romford	16. 3.00P
	(Rotax 462)						
G-MVPY	Solar Wings Pegasus XL-Q SW-WQ-0188			28. 3.89	G.H.Dawson	Swavesey, Cambridge	6. 6.99P
	(Rotax 462)						
G-MVPZ*	Rans S-4 Coyote			31. 3.89	G.A.Hagger & D.Murray	Charmy Down, Bath	11. 8.98P
	(Rotax 447) 88-084 & PFA/193-11494 (Damgd Rushmead Farm, South Wraxall, Wilts 17.8.97: cancelled CAA 2.3.98)						
G-MVRA	Mainair Gemini/Flash 2A			10. 4.89	A.J.Lowe-Jones	Dukinfield	4. 7.00P
	(Rotax 503) 743-489-7 & W535						
G-MVRB	Mainair Gemini/Flash 2A			29. 3.89	M.J.Burns & P.A.McGivern	Castlewellan	17. 4.00P
	(Rotax 503) 747-489-7 & W539						
G-MVRC	Mainair Gemini/Flash 2A			29. 3.89	M.O'Connell	Rufforth	7.11.98P
	(Rotax 503) 748-489-7 & W540						
G-MVRD	Mainair Gemini/Flash 2A			9. 5.89	J.A. & S.E.Robinson	Kendal	24. 7.00P
	(Rotax 503) 749-489-7 & W541						
G-MVRE	CFM Shadow Srs.CD	K.087		10. 4.89	G.F.Hartfield & D.A.Chamberlain		
	(Rotax 503)					Hemel Hempstead	8. 5.99P
G-MVRF	Rotec Rally 2B	AIE-01		28. 4.89	A.I.Edwards	Stafford	
G-MVRG	Aerial Arts Chaser S	CH.798		14. 4.89	J.P.Kynaston	Luton	31. 8.99P
	(Rotax 337)						
G-MVRH	Solar Wings Pegasus XL-Q			10. 4.89	K.Farr	Swinford, Rugby	4. 8.00P
	(Rotax 462) SW-TE-0160 & SW-WQ-0177						
G-MVRI	Solar Wings Pegasus XL-Q			10. 4.89	J.E.Morrison & J.D.Fisher		
	(Rotax 462) SW-TE-0145 & SW-WQ-0159					Long Acres Farm, Sandy	25.10.00P
G-MVRJ	Solar Wings Pegasus XL-Q SW-WQ-0154			10. 4.89	D.J.Cook	Eaglescott	27. 8.00P
	(Rotax 462HP)						
G-MVRL	Aerial Arts Chaser S	CH.801		18. 4.89	K Wildish	Wantage	30. 4.00P
	(Rotax 447)						
G-MVRM	Mainair Gemini/Flash 2A			12. 4.89	G.A.McKay	East Fortune	12. 8.00P
	(Rotax 462) 752-489-7 & W545						
G-MVRN	Rans S-4 Coyote			10. 4.89	C.Briggs	Brafferton, York	28.11.00P
	(Rotax 447) 88-085 & PFA/193-11503						
G-MVRO	CFM Shadow Srs.BD	K.105		3. 4.89	J.R.Fairweather	Hougham, Lincs	27. 7.00P
	(Rotax 447)					t/a G-MVRO Flying Group	
G-MVRP	CFM Shadow Srs.CD	097		7. 4.89	D.R.G.Whitelaw	Oban	27. 7.00P
	(Rotax 503)						
G-MVRR	CFM Shadow Srs.CD	098		7. 4.89	S.P.Christian & M.Mears	Hougham, Lincs	31. 7.00P
	(Rotax 503)						
G-MVRT	CFM Shadow Srs.BD	104		7. 4.89	S.C.Cornock	Lichfield	13. 7.00P
	(Rotax 447)						
G-MVRU	Solar Wings Pegasus XL-Q			12. 4.89	P.J.Edwards	Newmarket	11.10.99P
	(Rotax 462) SW-TE-0166 & SW-WQ-0183						
G-MVRV	Powerchute Kestrel	90210		28. 4.89	G.M.Fletcher	Chesterfield	16. 5.00P
	(Rotax 503)						
G-MVRW	Solar Wings Pegasus XL-Q			12. 4.89	W.H.Mills	Haverfordwest	16. 5.00P
	(Rotax 462) SW-TE-0161 & SW-WQ-0178 (Rebuild 1999 including new factory supplied sailwing)						
G-MVRX	Solar Wings Pegasus XL-Q SW-WQ-0165			12. 4.89	M.Everest	Hailsham	22. 5.00P
	(Rotax 462HP)						
G-MVRY	Medway Hybred 44XLR	MR049/56		12. 4.89	K.Dodman	Cambridge	4. 3.99P
	(Rotax 447)						
G-MVRZ	Medway Hybred 44XLR	MR043/57		9. 5.89	I.Oswald	London SE9	13.10.00P
	(Rotax 503)						
G-MVSB	Solar Wings Pegasus XL-Q			18. 4.89	M.J.Olsen	Middlesbrough	8.10.00P
	(Rotax 462) SW-TE-0184 & SW-WQ-0193						
G-MVSD	Solar Wings Pegasus XL-Q			18. 4.89	J.A.Flock	Kemble	14. 6.99P
	(Rotax 462) SW-TE-0186 & SW-WQ-0195						
G-MVSE	Solar Wings Pegasus XL-Q			18. 4.89	F.McDonagh	Darlington	7. 8.00P
	(Rotax 462) SW-TE-0187 & SW-WQ-0196						
G-MVSG	Aerial Arts Chaser S	CH.804		24. 4.89	M.Roberts	Melksham	20. 8.00P
	(Rotax 377)						
G-MVSI	Medway Hybred 44XLR	MR040/58		18. 4.89	L.Marson	Long Marston	23. 7.95P
	(Rotax 447)					(Stored 1.98)	
G-MVSJ	Aviasud Mistral 072 & BMAA/HB/013			18. 4.89	A.J.Record	Selby	25. 9.00P
	(Rotax 532)						
G-MVSK	Aerial Arts Chaser S	CH.806		27. 4.89	G.A.Inch	Bristol	8. 1.00P
	(Rotax 377)						
G-MVSL	Aerial Arts Chaser S	CH.807		15. 5.89	J.M.Hucker	Abertillery	29. 8.98P
	(Rotax 377)						

Regn	Type	C/n P/I	Date	Owner/operator	Probable Base	CA Expy
G-MVSM	Midland Ultralights Sirocco 377GB (Rotax 377)	MU-023	21. 4.89	J.A.Hambleton	Market Drayton	12.10.99P
G-MVSN	Mainair Gemini/Flash 2A (Rotax 503)	754-589-7 & W547	28. 4.89	P.Shore	South Normanton, Derby	2. 4.00P
G-MVSO	Mainair Gemini/Flash 2A (Rotax 503)	755-589-7 & W548	27. 4.89	A.J.Tyler	Norwich	16. 3.00P
G-MVSP	Mainair Gemini/Flash 2A (Rotax 503)	756-589-7 & W549	27. 4.89	D.R.Buchanan	Pulborough	25. 5.98P
G-MVSR	Medway Hybred 44XLR (Rotax 447)	MR038/59	15. 5.89	G.Tate	Great Orton	25.10.98P
G-MVST	Mainair Gemini/Flash 2A (Rotax 462)	750-589-7 & W543	12. 6.89	G.B.Mountain	Rufforth	19. 4.00P
G-MVSU	Microflight Spectrum (Rotax 503)	008	4. 5.89	R.Nicklin	Otherton, Cannock	28. 1.00P
G-MVSV	Mainair Gemini/Flash 2A (Rotax 503)	757-589-7 & W550	11. 5.89	P.Shelton	St.Michaels	17. 7.00P
G-MVSW	Solar Wings Pegasus XL-Q (Rotax 462HP) SW-TE-0189 & SW-WQ-0198		17. 5.89	P.Devlin	Hungerford	15.11.99P
G-MVSX	Solar Wings Pegasus XL-Q SW-WQ-0199 (Rotax 462)		11. 5.89	A.R.Law	Plymouth	22. 5.00P
G-MVSY	Solar Wings Pegasus XL-Q SW-WQ-0200 (Rotax 462)		11. 5.89	P.L.Cummings & R.J. Turner	Eaglescott	22. 6.00P
G-MVSZ	Solar Wings Pegasus XL-Q SW-WQ-0201 (Rotax 462HP)		11. 5.89	R.Gulliver	Eshott	26. 8.99P
G-MVTA	Solar Wings Pegasus XL-Q SW-WQ-0202 (Rotax 462)		11. 5.89	A.Garlick	Knapthorpe Lodge, Caunton	20. 9.00P
G-MVTC	Mainair Gemini/Flash 2A (Rotax 503)	759-689-7 & W552	30. 5.89	B.D.Bowen	Pontypool	14. 5.00P
G-MVTD	Whittaker MW-6 Merlin PFA/164-11367 (Rotax 503)		11. 5.89	G.J.Green	Matlock	28. 4.97P
G-MVTE	Whittaker MW-6 Merlin PFA/164-11372 (Rotax 503)		17. 5.89	P.D.Burnett	Gravesend	11. 7.96P
G-MVTF	Aerial Arts Chaser S (Rotax 377)	CH.808	30. 5.89	J.Collyer	St.Leonards-on-Sea	15. 7.92P
G-MVTG	Solar Wings Pegasus XL-Q SW-WQ-0204 (Rotax 462)		25. 5.89	D.L.Hadley	Canterbury	15.11.99P
G-MVTI	Solar Wings Pegasus XL-Q SW-WQ-0206 (Rotax 462)		25. 5.89	D.H.Leech	Saffron Walden	30. 8.00P
G-MVTJ	Solar Wings Pegasus XL-Q (Rotax 462) SW-TE-0197 & SW-WQ-0207		25. 5.89	P.D.Rowe	Taunton	1. 9.00P
G-MVTK	Solar Wings Pegasus XL-Q (Rotax 462) SW-TE-0198 & SW-WQ-0208		25. 5.89	S.Davis & S.E.Strangeway	Hungerford/Reading	29.11.00P
G-MVTL	Aerial Arts Chaser S (Rotax 337)	CH.809	13. 6.89	R.J.Grainger	Northampton	20. 3.99P
G-MVTM	Aerial Arts Chaser S (Rotax 447)	CH.810	13. 6.89	C.C.W.Mates	Billericay	8. 8.99P
G-MVUA	Mainair Gemini/Flash 2A (Rotax 462)	760-689-7 & W553	14. 6.89	P.Alexander & S.Hewitt	St Helens/Wigan	26. 3.00P
G-MVUB	Thruster T.300 (Rotax 532)	089-T300-373	13. 6.89	A.R.Hughes	Yatesbury, Wilts	23. 7.97P
G-MVUC	Medway Hybred 44XLR (Rotax 447)	MR046/60	13. 6.89	B.Pounder	Long Acres Farm, Sandy	29. 8.95P
G-MVUD	Medway Hybred 44XLR (Rotax 503)	MR037/55	19. 6.89	B.H.Morton	Great Orton	6. 7.99P
G-MVUF	Solar Wings Pegasus XL-Q (Rotax 462) SW-TE-0203 & SW-WQ-0213		13. 6.89	T.Read	Old Sarum	16. 7.00P
G-MVUG	Solar Wings Pegasus XL-Q (Rotax 462) SW-TE-0204 & SW-WQ-0214		13. 6.89	P.Nicholls	Alton	9. 6.00P
G-MVUH	Solar Wings Pegasus XL-Q (Rotax 462) SW-TE-0205 & SW-WQ-0215		13. 6.89	A.Davis	Macclesfield	17. 8.99P
G-MVUI	Solar Wings Pegasus XL-Q (Rotax 462) SW-TE-0206 & SW-WQ-0216 (Wing incorrectly marked as c/n SW-TE-0216)		13. 6.89	J.K.Edgecombe	Coalville	31. 7.00P
G-MVUJ	Solar Wings Pegasus XL-Q SW-WQ-0217 (Rotax 462)		13. 6.89	I.R.Buckle	Littlemore, Oxon	24. 4.00P
G-MVUL	Solar Wings Pegasus XL-Q SW-WQ-0219 (Rotax 462HP)		13. 6.89	M.Morris t/a G-MVUL Group	Swansea	30. 5.00P
G-MVUM	Solar Wings Pegasus XL-Q SW-WQ-0220 (Rotax 462)		13. 6.89	I.M.Munster	Fiskerton, Nottingham	5.11.95P
G-MVUN	Solar Wings Pegasus XL-Q SW-WQ-0221 (Rotax 462)		13. 6.89	J.A.Crofts	Carmarthen	19. 5.95P

Regn	Type	C/n	P/I	Date	Owner/operator	Probable Base	CA Expy
G-MVUO	AMF Chevvron 2-32C (Konig SD570)	015		14. 6.89	D.Beevers	Pocklington	17. 7.00P
G-MVUP	Aviasud Mistral (Rotax 532) 1087-48 & BMAA/HB/003		83-CQ	10. 8.89	D.G.Salt	Ashbourne, Derbyshire	1. 8.00P
G-MVUR	Hornet RS-ZA HRWA-0050 & ZA107 (Rotax 532) (Originally regd as c/n HRWA-0076; HRWA-0050 was G-MVLK)			3. 7.89	N.J.Frost	Gloucester	20. 5.96P
G-MVUS	Aerial Arts Chaser S (Rotax 377)	CH.813		3. 7.89	H.Poyzer	Eshott	25. 6.00P
G-MVUT	Aerial Arts Chaser S (Rotax 377)	CH.814		4. 7.89	L.L.Perry	Diss	18. 4.00P
G-MVUU	Hornet R-ZA HRWB-0061 & ZA110 (Rotax 462)			13. 7.89	M.J.Allen	St.Helens	17. 8.92P
G-MVVF	Medway Hybred 44XLR (Rotax 447)	MR054/61		11. 7.89	S.F.Carey	Strood, Kent	2. 8.96P
G-MVVG	Medway Hybred 44XLR (Rotax 447)	MR045/62		12. 7.89	C.Smith t/a Avialite Southeast	Hastings	24. 6.94P
G-MVVH	Medway Hybred 44XLR (Rotax 447)	MR047/63		11. 7.89	C.R.Thorne & I.G.Reason	Lyndhurst/Salisbury	25. 6.00P
G-MVVI	Medway Hybred 44XLR (Rotax 447)	MR050/64		12. 7.89	C.J.Newell	Leigh, Surrey	11. 8.00P
G-MVVJ*	Medway Hybred 44XLR (Rotax 447)	MR056/65		12. 7.89	S.D.Bowie (Cancelled by CAA 30.9.98)	Beckenham	5. 5.98P
G-MVVK	Solar Wings Pegasus XL-R (Rotax 447) SW-TB-1414 & SW-WA-1423			11. 7.89	A.Williams	Yate, Bristol	27. 5.00P
G-MVVM	Solar Wings Pegasus XL-R (Rotax 447) SW-TB-1416 & SW-WA-1425			12. 7.89	N.B.Mehew	Oxton, Nottingham	3. 9.00P
G-MVVN	Solar Wings Pegasus XL-Q (Rotax 462) SW-TE-0214 & SW-WQ-0226			11. 7.89	J.R.Francis	Long Marston	12.12.99P
G-MVVO	Solar Wings Pegasus XL-Q (Rotax 462) SW-TE-0215 & SW-WQ-0227			11. 7.89	A.L.Scarlett	Hungerford	5. 9.00P
G-MVVP	Solar Wings Pegasus XL-Q (Rotax 462) SW-TE-0216 & SW-WQ-0228			11. 7.89	B.J.Fallows (Damaged late 1997)	Ammanford	19. 3.98P
G-MVVR	Medway Hybred 44XLR (Rotax 503)	MR058/66		20. 7.89	J.McMillan & A.A.Ellman	Purley	9. 9.96P
G-MVVT	CFM Shadow Srs.CD (Rotax 503) K.101 & PFA/161-11569			26. 7.89	J.N.Fugl	Uckfield	24. 3.00P
G-MVVU	Aerial Arts Chaser S (Rotax 377)	CH.816		19. 7.89	S.Jackson	Eshott	13. 4.99P
G-MVVV	AMF Chevvron 2-32C (Konig SD570)	016	PH-1W9 G-MVVV	11. 5.89	P.R.Turton	Ferndown	20.12.99P
G-MVVW	Aerial Arts Chaser S (Rotax 508)	CH.817		26. 7.89	J.B.Allan	Stanford-le-Hope	30. 4.00P
G-MVVZ	Powerchute Raider (Rotax 447)	90628		25. 7.89	P.R.Sale	Tamworth	19.12.99P
G-MVWB	Powerchute Raider (Rotax 447)	90630		25. 7.89	R.Featherstone	Salisbury	12. 9.95P
G-MVWD	Powerchute Raider (Rotax 447)	90732	9H-ACH G-MVWD	25. 7.89	H.Rota	St.Andrew, Malta	20. 4.96P
G-MVWF	Powerchute Raider (Rotax 447)	90734		25. 7.89	J.Doyle	Castlebar, Co.Mayo	12. 4.93P
G-MVWH	Powerchute Raider (Rotax 447)	90736		25. 7.89	S.Penn	Bridport	11. 8.00P
G-MVWI	Powerchute Raider (Rotax 447)	90737		25. 7.89	C.Charlton	Shrewsbury	16. 8.96P
G-MVWN	Thruster T300 (Rotax 503)	089-T300-374		26. 7.89	T.B.Reakes t/a Whisky November Group Franklyns Field, Chewton Mendip		13. 3.00P
G-MVWP	Thruster T300 (Rotax 503)	089-T300-376		26. 7.89	D.R.G.Whitelaw & C.D.Taylor North Connel t/a Connel Flying Club		2.11.94P
G-MVWR	Thruster T300 (Rotax 503)	089-T300-377		26. 7.89	A.Allan	Muir of Ord	11. 7.99P
G-MVWS	Thruster T300 (Rotax 503)	089-T300-378		26. 7.89	R.J.Humphries	Southampton	15. 8.95P
G-MVWU*	Medway Hybred 44XLR (Rotax 447)	MR057/68		24. 7.89	T.L.Purves (Cancelled as destroyed 16.9.98)	Carrickfergus	7. 7.98P
G-MVWV	Medway Hybred 44XLR (Rotax 447) MR060/69 & BMAA/HB/005			24. 7.89	K.Smith	Rainham	26.11.00P
G-MVWW	Aviasud Mistral 532 (Rotax 532)	0389-81		25. 7.89	P.S.Balmer & B.H.D.Minto Tarn Farm, Cockerham		16. 9.00P
G-MVWX	Microflight Spectrum (Rotax 503)	009		24. 7.89	G.S.Taylor t/a Spectrum Otherton Syndicate	Otherton, Cannock	3.12.99P

Regn	Type	C/n	P/I	Date	Owner/operator	Probable Base	CA Expy
G-MVWZ	Aviasud Mistral	BMAA/HB/008		2. 8.89	B.R.Underwood		
	(Rotax 532) (Originally regd with c/n 1288-70)				Little Battleflats Farm, Ellistown, Coalville		10. 5.00P
G-MVXA	Whittaker MW-6 Merlin	PFA/164-11337		17. 8.89	I.Brewster	Little Gransden	21. 4.00P
	(Fuji-Robin EC-44-PM)						
G-MVXB	Mainair Gemini/Flash 2A			3. 8.89	D.J.Cook	Northwich	19. 6.00P
	(Rotax 462)	762-789-7 & W555					
G-MVXC	Mainair Gemini/Flash 2A			4. 8.89	D.Wood	Arclid Green, Sandbach	27.10.00P
	(Rotax 503)	763-889-7 & W556					
G-MVXD	Medway Hybred 44XLR	MR061/70		3. 8.89	P.R.Millen	Worthing	5. 5.00P
	(Rotax 447)						
G-MVXE	Medway Hybred 44XLR	MR063/71		23. 8.89	A.M.Brittle	Sittles Farm, Alrewas	31. 7.00P
	(Rotax 447)						
G-MVXF*	Weedhopper JC-31A	RAS-01		28. 7.89	R.A.Sammons	Looe	
					(Cancelled by CAA 27.3.99)		
G-MVXG	Aerial Arts Chaser S	CH.820		5. 9.89	R.J.Cook	Glasgow	18. 7.97P
	(Rotax 377)						
G-MVXH	Microflight Spectrum	010		2. 8.89	Medway Microlights Ltd	Stoke, Kent	12. 2.00P
	(Rotax 503)						
G-MVXI	Medway Hybred 44XLR	MR064/72		9. 8.89	G.R.Roach	Stoke, Kent	12.10.00P
	(Rotax 447)						
G-MVXJ	Medway Hybred 44XLR	MR065/73		25. 8.89	P.J.Wilks	Edenbridge	26. 9.90P
	(Rotax 447)						
G-MVXL	Thruster TST Mk.1	8089-TST-122		18. 8.89	K.B.Stokes	Davidstow Moor	30. 8.00P
	(Rotax 503)						
G-MVXM	Medway Hybred 44XLR	MR055/75		17. 8.89	T.Thomson	Hereford	2. 8.97P
	(Rotax 503) (Reported as Medway Raven)						
G-MVXN	Aviasud Mistral	65 & BMAA/HB/002		18. 8.89	B.M.Roberts	Lincoln	25. 8.00P
	(Rotax 532)						
G-MVXP	Aerial Arts Chaser S	CH.822		17. 8.89	E.J.MacPherson	Desborough	29. 5.95P
	(Rotax 377)						
G-MVXR	Mainair Gemini/Flash 2A			22. 8.89	J.D.Bayne	East Fortune	28. 7.00P
	(Rotax 462)	764-889-7 & W557					
G-MVXS	Mainair Gemini/Flash 2A			22. 8.89	J.W.Wood	Tarn Farm, Cockerham	11.12.98P
	(Rotax 503)	766-889-7 & W559					
G-MVXU*	Aviasud Mistral	93 & BMAA/HB/006		29. 8.89	S.J.Fretwell	Rufforth	
					(Stored 8.95; cancelled by CAA 23.4.98)		
G-MVXV	Aviasud Mistral	92 & BMAA/HB/004		22. 8.89	P.H.Ronfell	Tarn Farm, Cockerham	11.12.98P
	(Rotax 532)						
G-MVXW	Rans S-4 Coyote			22. 8.89	M.R.C.Sims & A.A.Castleton	Dunkeswell	20. 7.00P
	(Rotax 447)	89-098 & PFA/193-11545					
G-MVXX	AMF Chevvron 2-	32 018		27. 7.89	C.Dews & H.T.Boal	Ely/Bottisham	9. 4.00P
	(Konig SD570)						
G-MVXZ	TEAM miniMax 91	PFA/186-11429		4. 9.89	P.Harvey	Dursley, Glos	26. 4.93P
	(Arrow GT250R)						
G-MVYB	Solar Wings Pegasus XL-Q			8. 9.89	C.J.Williams	Wisbech	7. 7.97P
	(Rotax 462)	SW-TE-0223 & SW-WQ-0238					
G-MVYC	Solar Wings Pegasus XL-Q	SW-WQ-0239		8. 9.89	I.W.Barlow	Ilkeston	8. 4.00P
	(Rotax 462HP)						
G-MVYD	Solar Wings Pegasus XL-Q			8. 9.89	M.Beake	Long Marston	7. 5.00P
	(Rotax 462)	SW-TE-0225 & SW-WQ-0240					
G-MVYE	Thruster TST Mk.1	8089-TST-123		13. 9.89	S.J.Spavins	St.Albans	4. 7.96P
	(Rotax 503)						
G-MVYG	Hornet R-ZA	HRWB-0067 & ZA119		22. 9.89	H.Knox	Larbert, Stirling	20. 4.96P
	(Rotax 462)						
G-MVYH	Hornet R-ZA	HRWB-0072 & ZA125		22. 9.89	H.Greef	Eshott	13. 1.98P
	(Rotax 462)				(Damaged early 1997)		
G-MVYI	Hornet R-ZA	HRWB-0074 & ZA122		22. 9.89	N.J.Warner	Redditch	21. 9.95P
	(Rotax 462) (A trike unit with c/n HRWB-0074 amended to HRWB-0081 was noted @ Popham 4.96)						
G-MVYJ	Hornet R-ZA	HRWB-0075 & ZA111		22. 9.89	R.Williamson	Great Orton	26. 3.98P
	(Rotax 462) (Trike unit shows deleted c/n HRWB-0070)						
G-MVYK	Hornet R-ZA	HRWB-0076 & ZA117		22. 9.89	P.Asbridge	Rhuallt	22. 7.99P
	(Rotax 462)						
G-MVYL	Hornet R-ZA	HRWB-0077 & ZA115		22. 9.89	J.L.Thomas	Bristol	24. 6.00P
	(Rotax 462)						
G-MVYM	Hornet R-ZA	HRWB-0078 & ZA130		22. 9.89	D.M.Smith	Old Sarum	21. 2.95P
	(Rotax 462)						
G-MVYN	Hornet R-ZA	HRWB-0079 & ZA136		22. 9.89	W.M.Studley	Weston Zoyland	15. 3.00P
	(Rotax 462)						
G-MVYO	Hornet R-ZA	HRWB-0080 & ZA134		22. 9.89	R.W.Swain & C.K.Ford	Barnet	15. 6.97P
	(Rotax 462)						

Regn	Type	C/n	P/I	Date	Owner/operator	Probable Base	CA Expy
G-MVYP	Medway Hybred 44XLR (Rotax 447)	MR071/77		19. 9.89	P.R.Chapman	Swanley	11. 8.00P
G-MVYR	Medway Hybred 44XLR (Rotax 447)	MR068/76		19. 9.89	A.MacDonald	Chorley	28. 8.97P
G-MVYS	Mainair Gemini/Flash 2A (Rotax 503)	770-989-7 & W563		19. 9.89	J.E.Walewdowski	Crosland Moor	9. 7.00P
G-MVYT	Noble Hardman Snowbird Mk.IV (Rotax 532)	SB-022		26. 9.89	D.T.A.Rees	Haverfordwest	22.12.99P
G-MVYU	Noble Hardman Snowbird Mk.IV (Rotax 532)	SB-023		7.11.89	P.J.McEvoy t/a Phoenix Aviation	Romford	26. 6.99P
G-MVYV	Noble Hardman Snowbird Mk.IV (Rotax 532)	SB-024		21. 8.90	D.W.Hayden t/a G-MVYV Group	Swansea	13. 3.99P
G-MVYW	Noble Hardman Snowbird Mk.IV (Rotax 532)	SB-025		22.10.90	T.J.Harrison	Dalton-in-Furness	9. 5.00P
G-MVYX	Noble Hardman Snowbird Mk.IV (Rotax 532)	SB-026		25.11.91	R.McBlain	Kilkerran	2. 5.00P
G-MVYY	Aerial Arts Chaser S (Rotax 508)	CH.824		26. 9.89	J.M.Spatcher	Guildford	31. 7.98P
G-MVYZ	CFM Shadow Srs.BD (Rotax 447)	121		25. 9.89	Erindale Products Ltd	Hougham	17. 7.99P
G-MVZA	Thruster T300 (Rotax 503)	089-T300-379		26. 9.89	C.C.Belcher	Popham	22. 5.00P
G-MVZB	Thruster T300 (Rotax 503)	089-T300-380		26. 9.89	J.F.Kenyon	Holsworthy	29. 6.00P
G-MVZC	Thruster T300 (Rotax 532)	089-T300-381		26. 9.89	R.A.Knight	Chilbolton	27. 9.00P
G-MVZD	Thruster T300 (Rotax 532)	089-T300-382		26. 9.89	T.Pearce t/a G-MVZD Syndicate	Twickenham	5.11.99P
G-MVZE	Thruster T300 (Rotax 532)	089-T300-383		26. 9.89	T.L.Davis	Basingstoke	25. 2.00P
G-MVZG	Thruster T300 (Rotax 532)	089-T300-385		26. 9.89	M.L.Smith (Stored 5.97)	Popham	1. 7.95P
G-MVZI	Thruster T300 (Rotax 503)	089-T300-387		26. 9.89	R.R.R.Whittern	Trowbridge	29. 6.00P
G-MVZJ	Solar Wings Pegasus XL-Q (Rotax 462)	SW-WQ-0241		26. 8.89	M.Price	Shobdon	4. 8.00P
G-MVZK	Quad City Challenger II UK (BMW R.100)	PFA/177-11498		28. 9.89	M.J.Downes	Breidden	7. 7.00P
G-MVZL	Solar Wings Pegasus XL-Q (Rotax 462)	SW-TE-0227 & SW-WQ-0242		4.10.89	G.J.Pearce	Horsham	6. 4.00P
G-MVZM	Aerial Arts Chaser S (Rotax 377)	CH.825		2.11.89	P.S.Herbert	Godalming	18. 9.99P
G-MVZO	Medway Hybred 44XLR (Rotax 503)	MR072/78		25.10.89	P.Smith	Hinton-in-The-Hedges	8. 3.00P
G-MVZP	Murphy Renegade Spirit UK (Rotax 582)	256 & PFA/188-11630		17.10.89	Full Sutton Flying Centre Ltd	Full Sutton	7. 8.95P
G-MVZR	Avidsud Mistral (Rotax 532)	90 & BMAA/HB/011		9.10.89	D.M.Whitham	Crosland Moor	22. 5.00P
G-MVZS	Mainair Gemini/Flash 2A (Rotax 503)	771-1089-7 & W564		17.10.89	S.B.Brady	Rufforth	22. 5.00P
G-MVZT	Solar Wings Pegasus XL-Q (Rotax 462HP)	SW-TE-0228 & SW-WQ-0243		6.10.89	C.J.Meadows	Franklyn's Field, Chewton Mendip	12. 6.00P
G-MVZU	Solar Wings Pegasus XL-Q (Rotax 462)	SW-TE-0229 & SW-WQ-0244		6.10.89	R.D.Proctor	RAF Wittering	1. 6.00P
G-MVZV	Solar Wings Pegasus XL-Q (Rotax 462HP)	SW-TE-0230 & SW-WQ-0245		6.10.89	S.R.Bowsher	Bristol	9. 5.00P
G-MVZW	Hornet R-ZA (Rotax 462)	HRWB-0063 & ZA142		27.10.89	K.W.Warn	Popham	6. 8.00P
G-MVZX	Murphy Renegade Spirit UK (Rotax 582)	PFA/188-11590		18.10.89	G.Holmes	Pickering	30.11.99P
G-MVZY	Aerial Arts Chaser S (Rotax 377)	CH.827		2.11.89	N.W.O'Brien (Damaged mid 1995)	Leicester	30. 4.00P
G-MVZZ	AMF Chevvron 2-32 (Konig SD570)	019		27. 7.89	Lancaster Partners (Holdings) Ltd (B.Lockyear)	Ashcroft Farm, Winsford	29. 3.00P
G-MWAB	Mainair Gemini/Flash 2A (Rotax 503)	772-1089-7 & W565		24.10.89	C.G.Deeley	Lichfield	17. 4.00P
G-MWAC	Solar Wings Pegasus XL-Q (Rotax 462)	SW-TE-0236 & SW-WQ-0260		25.10.89	P.A.Tabberer	Rhuallt	17. 7.00P
G-MWAD	Solar Wings Pegasus XL-Q (Rotax 462)	SW-WQ-0261		25.10.89	R.S.Cochrane	Sutton Meadows, Ely	20. 1.00P

Regn	Type	C/n	P/I	Date	Owner/operator	Probable Base	CA Expy
G-MWAE	CFM Shadow Srs.CD (Rotax 503)	130		24.10.89	D.J.Adams	North Coates	25. 4.00P
G-MWAF	Solar Wings Pegasus XL-R (Rotax 447) SW-TB-1422 & SW-WA-1441			30.10.89	B.B.Boniface	Knutsford	1. 8.00P
G-MWAG	Solar Wings Pegasus XL-R SW-WA-1442 (Rotax 447)			30.10.89	D.Foster	Leek	12.12.99P
G-MWAI	Solar Wings Pegasus XL-R SW-WA-1443 (Rotax 462)			1.11.89	A.G.Spurway	Chard	12.10.00P
G-MWAJ	Murphy Renegade Spirit UK (BMW R.100RS) PFA/188-11438			1.11.89	M.Leavesley "Free Spirit"	Sutton Coldfield	28. 3.00P
G-MWAL	Solar Wings Pegasus XL-Q (Rotax 462) SW-TE-0240 & SW-WQ-0263			2.11.89	A.W.Hill	Bluntisham	21. 9.00P
G-MWAM*	Thruster T300 (Rotax 532)	089-T300-388		14.11.89	S.R.Monkcom (Cancelled 15.12.99 as destroyed)	Long Marston	30. 9.99P
G-MWAN	Thruster T300 (Rotax 532)	089-T300-389		14.11.89	A.R.Tomlinson	Swanton Morley	21. 9.00P
G-MWAP	Thruster T300 (Rotax 503)	089-T300-391		14.11.89	S.F.Chave & A.G.Spurway "Wanda"	Honiton/Chard	2. 6.00P
G-MWAR	Thruster T300 (Rotax 532)	089-T300-392		14.11.89	S.M.Birbeck	Popham	8. 9.00P
G-MWAS	Thruster T300 (Rotax 532)	089-T300-393		14.11.89	A.W.Vaughan (Damaged mid 1994)	Crieff	2. 6.95P
G-MWAT	Solar Wings Pegasus XL-Q SW-WQ-0265 (Rotax 462)			13.11.89	A.R.Hughes	Marlborough	2. 8.00P
G-MWAU	Mainair Gemini/Flash 2A (Rotax 582) 773-1189-7 & W566			7.12.89	L.Roberts	Ammanford	5. 5.00P
G-MWAV	Solar Wings Pegasus XL-R SW-WA-1444 (Rotax 447)			13.11.89	S.P.Waine	Fordingbridge	25. 7.99P
G-MWAW	Whittaker MW-6 Merlin PFA/164-11460 (Rotax 503)			10.11.89	D.J.Flanagan	Hyde	20. 4.00P
G-MWBH	Hornet RS-ZA HRWB-0071 & ZA120 (Rotax 532)			14.11.89	A.F.Neale & C.P.Anderton	Tarn Farm, Cockerham	9. 3.00P
G-MWBI	Medway Hybred 44XLR MR073/79 (Rotax 503)			21.11.89	G.E.Coates	Birmingham	13. 4.00P
G-MWBJ	Medway Puma Sprint MS003/1 (Rotax 447)			21.11.89	C.C.Strong	Buaes	14. 7.00P
G-MWBK	Solar Wings Pegasus XL-Q (Rotax 462) SW-TE-0248 & SW-WQ-0271			16.11.89	P.J.Harrison	Bracknell	22. 7.00P
G-MWBL	Solar Wings Pegasus XL-R/Se (Rotax 447) SW-TB-1424 & SW-WA-1446			16.11.89	C.J.Arthur	Eshott	25. 4.99P
G-MWBM	Hornet R-ZA HRWB-0082 & ZA141 (Rotax 462)			29.11.89	K.D.Shadforth	RAF Dishforth	2. 5.94P
G-MWBN	Hornet R-ZA HRWB-0103 & ZA155 (Rotax 522) (Trike regd as HRWB-0081 but frame restamped as 0103; wing originally ZA143)			21.11.89	J.Batchelor	Benfleet	22. 8.97P
G-MWBO	Rans S-4 Coyote (Rotax 447) 89-097 & PFA/193-11583			29.11.89	D.S.Coutts t/a G-MWBO Group	Linlithgow	26. 4.00P
G-MWBP	Hornet R-ZA HRWB-0083 & ZA144 (Rotax 462)			29.11.89	J.Rossall (Damaged mid 1995)	Poulton-le-Fylde	28. 3.99P
G-MWBR	Hornet RS-ZA HRWB-0084 & ZA145 (Rotax 462)			29.11.89	J.W.Coventry	Davidstow Moor	22. 9.95P
G-MWBS	Hornet R-ZA HRWB-0085 & ZA146 (BMW)			29.11.89	P.D.Jaques	Sandtoft	23. 4.98P
G-MWBU	Hornet R-ZA HRWB-0087 & ZA148 (Rotax 462)			29.11.89	K.C.Wigley	Belper	26.11.96P
G-MWBW	Hornet R-ZA HRWB-0089 & ZA150 (Rotax 462)			29.11.89	C.G.Bentley	Chesterfield	15. 5.00P
G-MWBX	Hornet R-ZA HRWB-0090 & ZA151 (Rotax 462)			29.11.89	J.Johnson	Bootle	22.10.92P
G-MWBY	Hornet R-ZA HRWB-0091 & ZA152 (Rotax 462)			29.11.89	R.M.Hardy	Preston	23. 6.97P
G-MWBZ	Hornet R-ZA HRWB-0092 & ZA153 (Rotax 462) Trike unit originally marked as HRWB-0096; then HRWB-0104 - both overstamped)			29.11.89	T.M.Gilsenan & G.E.C.Burgess	Stock	15. 6.99P
G-MWCA	Hornet R-ZA HRWB-0093 & ZA154 (Rotax 462)			29.11.89	M.J.Knight	Fareham	3. 4.97P
G-MWCB	Solar Wings Pegasus XL-Q SW-WQ-0273 (Rotax 462)			1.12.89	I.P.Joyce	Long Acres Farm, Sandy	5. 6.00P
G-MWCC	Solar Wings Pegasus XL-R/Se (Rotax 447) SW-TB-1387 & SW-WA-1447			1.12.89	J.W.Glendenning	Eshott	5. 9.00P
G-MWCE	Mainair Gemini/Flash 2A (Rotax 503) 775-1289-7 & W568			19.12.89	B.A.Tooze	Shobdon	28. 8.00P

Regn	Type	C/n	P/I	Date	Owner/operator	Probable Base	CA Expy
G-MWCF	Solar Wings Pegasus XL-Q SW-WQ-0276 (Rotax 462)			13.12.89	D.V.Lawrence	Stourbridge	31. 8.00P
G-MWCG	Microflight Spectrum (Rotax 503)	011		15.12.89	P.J.Collicutt	Long Marston	23. 8.99P
G-MWCH	Rans S-6-ESD Coyote II (Rotax 503) 0989-067 & PFA/204-11632 (PFA c/n duplicates Kitfox G-BSFY)			15.12.89	W.Lucy & J.Burns	Eshott	10. 8.00P
G-MWCI	Powerchute Kestrel (Rotax 503)	91245		3. 1.90	E.G.Bray	Clacton	31.10.98P
G-MWCJ	Powerchute Kestrel (Rotax 503)	91246		3. 1.90	B.A.Dowland	Peterborough	16.10.97P
G-MWCK	Powerchute Kestrel (Rotax 503)	91247		3. 1.90	M.A.Avossa	Leicester	7.12.97P
G-MWCL*	Powerchute Kestrel (Rotax 503)	91248		3. 1.90	G.F.Smith (Cancelled by CAA 23.7.99)	Milton Keynes	5. 4.99P
G-MWCN	Powerchute Kestrel (Rotax 503)	91250		3. 1.90	H.J.Goddard	Fleet	2.12.99P
G-MWCO	Powerchute Kestrel (Rotax 503)	91251		3. 1.90	T.F.Bakker	Fairford	17. 5.93P
G-MWCP	Powerchute Kestrel (Rotax 503)	91252		3. 1.90	J.L.Thomas	Bridlington	23.10.99P
G-MWCR	Southdown Puma Sprint (Fuji-Robin EC-44-PM) P.516 & 1121/0070			24. 2.84	S.F.Chave	Honiton	29. 8.00P
G-MWCS	Powerchute Kestrel (Rotax 503)	91253		3. 1.90	B.J.L.Clark t/a Fly High (KSPT)	Maidstone	25.10.98P
G-MWCU	Solar Wings Pegasus XL-R SW-WA-1449 (Rotax 447)			27.12.89	D.A.Bannister	Deenethorpe	29. 9.00P
G-MWCV	Solar Wings Pegasus XL-Q (Rotax 462HP) SW-TE-0256 & SW-WQ-0278			27.12.89	J.B.Hobbs	Long Acres Farm, Sandy	20. 5.00P
G-MWCW	Mainair Gemini/Flash 2A (Rotax 462) 776-0190-7 & W569			29.12.89	B.C.Jones	St.Michaels	6. 5.00P
G-MWCX	Medway Hybred 44XLR (Rotax 503)	MR076/80		8. 1.90	P.A.Harris	Petersfield	31. 3.96P
G-MWCY	Medway Hybred 44XLR (Rotax 503)	MR077/81		15. 1.90	J.K.Masters	Chigwell	15. 5.00P
G-MWCZ	Medway Hybred 44XLR (Rotax 503)	MR078/82		10. 1.90	R.J.Moore	Folkestone	29. 5.00P
G-MWDB	CFM Shadow Srs.CD (Rotax 503)	100		3. 7.89	M.D.Meade	St. Albans	23. 7.00P
G-MWDC	Solar Wings Pegasus XL-R/Se (Rotax 462) SW-TE-0255 & SW-WA-1450			5. 1.90	A.N.Edwards	Great Orton	23. 4.00P
G-MWDD	Solar Wings Pegasus XL-Q SW-WQ-0280 (Rotax 462)			15. 1.90	T.P.Toth	Enstone	28. 8.99P
G-MWDE	Hornet RS-ZA HRWB-0094 & ZA126 (Rotax 532)			10. 1.90	H.G.Reid	Roddige, Fradley	13. 6.98P
G-MWDF*	Hornet RS-ZA HRWB-0095 & ZA155 (Rotax 532)			10. 1.90	Not known (Stored 4.96)	Clench Common	31. 5.92P
G-MWDI	Hornet RS-ZA HRWB-0098 & ZA158 (Rotax 532)			10. 1.90	R.J.Perrin	Tarn Farm, Cockerham	6.11.00P
G-MWDJ	Mainair Gemini/Flash 2A (Rotax 503) 777-0190-7 & W570			17. 1.90	M.Gardiner	Crosland Moor	10. 2.99P
G-MWDK	Solar Wings Pegasus XL-Q SW-WQ-0281 (Rotax 462)			17. 1.90	T.Wicks	Devizes	14.10.00P
G-MWDL	Solar Wings Pegasus XL-Q (Rotax 462) SW-TE-0260 & SW-WQ-0282			17. 1.90	J.N.Whelan	Billericay	30. 6.99P
G-MWDM	Murphy Renegade Spirit UK (Rotax 582) 319 & PFA/188A-11628 (PFA c/n duplicates Streak Shadow G-BRZZ)			18. 1.90	M.A. & S.J.Wood "Iouna"	RAF Laarbruch	6. 3.98P
G-MWDN	CFM Shadow Srs.CD (Rotax 503)	K.102		17. 1.90	D.J.Abbott	St.Albans	13. 8.00P
G-MWDP	Thruster TST Mk.1 (Rotax 503)	8129-TST-124		30. 1.90	J.Walker	Ballymena	5. 5.95P
G-MWDS	Thruster T300 (Rotax 532)	089-T300-395		30. 1.90	M.D.Tulloch	Westhill	8.11.99P
G-MWDZ	Eipper Quicksilver MXL Sport II 022 (Rotax 503)			29. 1.90	R.G.Cook	Newport Pagnell	30. 3.97P
G-MWEE*	Solar Wings Pegasus XL-Q SW-WQ-0147 (Rotax 462)			12.12.88	Not known (Temp unregd 17.11.97)	Sidcup	25. 8.97P
G-MWEF	Solar Wings Pegasus XL-Q (Rotax 462HP) SE-TE-0261 & SW-WQ-0283			30. 1.90	N.R.Williams	Long Marston	5. 9.00P
G-MWEG	Solar Wings Pegasus XL-Q SW-WQ-0284 (Rotax 462)			30. 1.90	R.H.Marshall	Defford	3. 3.95P

Regn	Type	C/n P/I	Date	Owner/operator	Probable Base	CA Expy
G-MWEH	Solar Wings Pegasus XL-Q SW-WQ-0286 (Rotax 462HP)		7. 2.90	B.M.Weinrabe	Borehamwood	10. 9.00P
G-MWEK	Whittaker MW-5 Sorcerer (Rotax 447) PFA/163-11284		20. 2.90	J.T.Francis	Crowthorne, Berks	15.10.00P
G-MWEL	Mainair Gemini/Flash 2A (Rotax 503) 780-0290-7 & W573		13. 2.90	B.L.Benson	Malpas, Cheshire	23. 3.00P
G-MWEN	CFM Shadow Srs.CD K.113 (Rotax 503)		20. 2.90	P.Anning	Torquay	8. 8.00P
G-MWEO	Whittaker MW-5 Sorcerer (Fuji-Robin EC-34-PM) PFA/163-11263		21. 2.90	J Morton t/a Crazy Capers	Ballymena, NI	1.12.00P
G-MWEP	Rans S-4 Coyote (Rotax 447) 89-096 & PFA/193-11616		21. 2.90	A.P.Walsh	Ludham	12. 8.97P
G-MWER	Solar Wings Pegasus XL-Q (Rotax 462) SW-TE-0265 & SW-WQ-0287		1. 3.90	S.V.Stojanovic	Swansea	19. 3.00P
G-MWES	Rans S-4 Coyote (Rotax 447) 89-099 & PFA/193-11737		1. 2.90	R.W.Sage & I.Fleming	Priory Farm, Tibenham	28. 6.00P
G-MWEU	Hornet RS-ZA HRWB-0100 & ZA160 (Rotax 532)		21. 2.90	Tracy A.Simpson	Graveley	11.11.00P
G-MWEV	Hornet RS-ZA HRWB-0101 & ZA161 (Rotax 532) (Stolen 4.95 - Engine No.3799219)		21. 2.90	I.D.McCaig	Tarn Farm, Cockerham	13. 6.95P
G-MWEY	Hornet R-ZA HRWB0104 & ZA135 (Rotax 462)		21. 2.90	J.Kidd	Preston	24. 9.00P
G-MWEZ	CFM Shadow Srs.CD 136 (Rotax 503)		22. 2.90	K.G.Diamond & J.Ball t/a WEZ Group Assets	Redhill	3. 8.00P
G-MWFA	Solar Wings Pegasus XL-R SW-WA-1454 (Rotax 447)		27. 2.90	A.W.Edwards	Davidstow Moor	12.12.98P
G-MWFB	CFM Shadow Srs.CD K.119 (Rotax 503)		1. 3.90	D.P.Cripps	Binstead, IoW	3. 5.00P
G-MWFC	TEAM miniMax 294 & PFA/186-11648 G-BTXC (Rotax 447) G-MWFC		1. 3.90	A.E.Sellers & J.H.Cooling	Fenland	3. 4.00P
G-MWFD	TEAM miniMax 293 & PFA/186-11646 (Rotax 447) (PFA c/n duplicates Shadow G-GORE)		1. 3.90	M.A.Bolshaw	Tarn Farm, Cockerham	7. 6.00P
G-MWFF	Rans S-4 Coyote 89-106		10. 1.90	F.Colman	Eashott	
G-MWFG	Powerchute Kestrel 00358 (Rotax 503)		20. 3.90	J.O.Jones	Llandeilo	13. 5.98P
G-MWFI	Powerchute Kestrel 00360 (Rotax 503)		20. 3.90	S. & G.Millar	Dungannon, Co.Tyrone	27.11.99P
G-MWFL	Powerchute Kestrel 00363 (Rotax 503)		20. 3.90	J.G.Bolitho	Penzance	17. 8.97P
G-MWFN	Powerchute Kestrel 00365 (Rotax 503)		20. 3.90	I.R.Henson	Nottingham	15. 7.93P
G-MWFO*	Solar Wings Pegasus XL-R SW-WA-1455 (Rotax 462)		8. 3.90	Not known Lower Mountpleasant, Chatteris (Temp unregd 17.4.97)		14. 5.97P
G-MWFP	Solar Wings Pegasus XL-R (Rotax 447) SW-TB-1406 & SW-WA-1456		12. 3.90	G.G.Thorpe	Weston Zoyland	12. 8.95P
G-MWFS	Solar Wings Pegasus XL-Q (Rotax 462) SW-TE-0267 & SW-WQ-0289		14. 3.90	A.T.Smith	Tarn Farm, Cocherham	30. 7.00P
G-MWFT	MBA Tiger Cub 440 WFT-02 (Fuji-Robin EC-44-PM)		24.11.83	J.R.Ravenhill	Kemble	30. 3.00P
G-MWFU	Quad City Challenger II UK (Rotax 503) PFA/177-11654		16. 3.90	M.E.Chamberlain	Higher Barn Farm, Houghton	2.11.00P
G-MWFV	Quad City Challenger II UK (Rotax 503) PFA/177-11655		16. 3.90	W.D.Gordon	Dumfries	16. 7.00P
G-MWFW	Rans S-4 Coyote PFA/193-11662 (Rotax 447)		16. 3.90	C.C.B.Soden	Dunkeswell	14. 9.99P
G-MWFX	Quad City Challenger II UK CH2-1189-UK-0485 & PFA/177-11706		20. 3.90	I.M.Walton	Wellesbourne Mountford	21. 6.00P
G-MWFY	Quad City Challenger II UK PFA/177-11668		20. 3.90	P.J.Ladd	Craysmarsh Farm, Melksham	12. 7.00P
G-MWFZ	Quad City Challenger II UK CH2-0190-UK-0506 & PFA/177-11707		20. 3.90	A.Slade	Enfield	
G-MWGA	Rans S-5 Coyote (Rotax 447) 89-092 & PFA/193-11810		20. 3.90	D.B.Casley-Smith	East Kirkby	1.12.99P
G-MWGC	Medway Hybred 44XLR MR087/85 (Rotax 503)		26. 3.90	I.Nicholls	Gravesend	7. 8.99P
G-MWGD	Medway Hybred 44XLR MR088/86 (Rotax 503)		26. 3.90	P.A.Harris (Fitted with new wing after original stolen 12.1994)	Harlow	3.12.94P
G-MWGE*	Medway Hybred 44XLR MR089/87 (Rotax 503)		26. 3.90	A.R.Silvester Horseheath, Haverhill (Damaged Popham 29.2.96; cancelled by CAA 10.9.98)		1. 8.96P
G-MWGF	Murphy Renegade Spirit UK (Rotax 582) 220 & PFA/188-11771		21. 3.90	J.A.Cuthbertson	Malton	26. 9.99P

Regn	Type	C/n	P/I	Date	Owner/operator	Probable Base	CA Expy
G-MWGG	Mainair Gemini/Flash 2A (Rotax 462) 785-0390-7 & W578			26. 3.90	J.R.G.Trumble	Dartmouth	23. 4.00P
G-MWGI	Aerotech MW-5B Sorcerer 5K-0012-02 (Rotax 447)			28. 3.90	B.Barrass	Stamford	3. 9.91P
G-MWGJ	Aerotech MW-5(K) Sorcerer 5K-0014-02 (Rotax 447)			6. 9.90	W.S.S.Lubbock	Callington	29. 4.00P
G-MWGK	Aerotech MW-5(K) Sorcerer 5K-0015-02 (Rotax 447)		(G-MWLV)	19. 9.90	R.M.Thomas	Wombleton	26.11.99P
G-MWGL	Solar Wings Pegasus XL-Q SW-WQ-0293 (Rotax 462)			28. 3.90	J.Walker	Deenethorpe	3. 6.00P
G-MWGM	Solar Wings Pegasus XL-Q W-WQ-0294 (Rotax 462)			28. 3.90	P.J. & L.S.Kirkpatrick	Cambridge	2. 5.00P
G-MWGN	Rans S-4 Coyote (Rotax 447) 89-113 & PFA/193-11709			26. 3.90	R.H.S.Cattle Plaistows. Hemel Hempstead		24. 2.99P
G-MWGO	Aerial Arts 110SX/Chaser 110SX/566 (Rotax 377)			28. 3.90	B.Nicolson	Middlesbrough	28. 4.97P
G-MWGR	Solar Wings Pegasus XL-Q (Rotax 462) SW-TE-0272 & SW-WQ-0296			6. 4.90	M.D.Hurtubise	Long Marston	6. 7.00P
G-MWGS*	Powerchute Kestrel 00366 (Rotax 503) (Cancelled 4.1.91 on sale to Spain: noted 8.99)			26. 4.90	Not known	Dunkeswell	
G-MWGT	Powerchute Kestrel 00367 (Rotax 503)			26. 4.90	G.McAleer	Carrickfergus	19. 5.00P
G-MWGU	Powerchute Kestrel 00368 (Rotax 503)		(9H-) G-MWGU	26. 4.90	M.Pandolfino	Luqa. Malta	19. 7.91P
G-MWGV	Powerchute Kestrel 00369 (Rotax 503)			26.. 4.90	E.G.Bray	Clacton	20. 1.00P
G-MWGW	Powerchute Kestrel 00370 (Rotax 503)			26. 4.90	S.P.Tomlinson	Leominster	13. 7.97P
G-MWGY	Powerchute Kestrel 00372 (Rotax 503)			26. 4.90	C.N.Bond	RAF Manston	29. 7.00P
G-MWGZ	Powerchute Kestrel 00373 (Rotax 503)			26. 4.90	L.J.Lynch	Ventnor, IoW	27. 5.97P
G-MWHC	Solar Wings Pegasus XL-Q (Rotax 462) SW-TE-0274 & SW-WQ-0304			24. 4.90	P.J.Lowery Long Acres Farm, Sandy		14. 5.99P
G-MWHD	Microflight Spectrum 012 (Rotax 503)			18. 4.90	P.B.& M.A.Howson Arclid Green, Sandbach		18. 7.99P
G-MWHE*	Microflight Spectrum 014 (Rotax 503)			18. 4.90	P.J.Taylor Otherton, Cannock (Cancelled by CAA 11.12.98)		3. 9.97P
G-MWHF	Solar Wings Pegasus XL-Q (Rotax 462) SW-TE-0275 & SW-WQ-0305			24. 4.90	N.J.Troke & S.Cox	Swinford, Rugby	17. 6.00P
G-MWHG	Solar Wings Pegasus XL-Q (Rotax 462) SW-TE-0276 & SW-WQ-0306			24. 4.90	I.A.Lumley	Great Orton	11. 9.00P
G-MWHH	TEAM miniMax 326 & PFA/186-11814 (Rotax 447)			23. 4.90	B.F.Crick	Desborough	4. 8.00P
G-MWHI	Mainair Gemini/Flash (Rotax 503) 784-0390-5 & W577			26. 4.90	I.Vardy & M.A.Noakes	Sandtoft	14. 4.97P
G-MWHJ	Solar Wings Pegasus XL-Q (Rotax 462) SW-TE-0277 & SW-WQ-0307			27. 4.90	A.J.Bacon Botany Bay, Horsford, Norwich		7. 3.98P
G-MWHL	Solar Wings Pegasus XL-Q SW-WQ-0308 (Rotax 462)			1. 5.90	T.G.Jackson	London SW11	2. 5.00P
G-MWHM	Whittaker MW-6S Fatboy Flyer (Rotax 532) PFA/164-11463			18. 5.90	D.W. & M.L.Squire	Otherton, Cannock	16. 2.00P
G-MWHO	Mainair Gemini/Flash 2A (Rotax 503) 778-0190-5 & W571			10. 5.90	B.Epps Arclid Green, Sandbach		28. 1.00P
G-MWHP	Rans S-6-ESD Coyote II (Rotax 532) 1089-093 & PFA/204-11768			8. 5.90	J.F.Bickerstaffe Higher Barn Farm, Houghton		1. 6.00P
G-MWHR	Mainair Gemini/Flash 2A (Rotax 503) 787-0590-7 & W580			16. 5.90	P.Jones & B.Brazier	Darwen	31.10.00P
G-MWHS	AMF Chevvron 2-32C 021 (Konig SD570)			18. 5.90	Airshare Flying Clubs Ltd	Abington	26. 2.98P
G-MWHT	Solar Wings Pegasus Quasar TC (Rotax 503) SW-TQ-0005 & SW-WQQ-0314			15. 5.90	E.H.Gatehouse & D.M.Walters Pound Green, Buttonoak, Kidderminster		1. 8.00P
G-MWHU	Solar Wings Pegasus Quasar (Rotax 503) SW-WQQ-0315			15. 5.90	A.F.Frost & S.J.Park	Sywell	16. 9.99P
G-MWHV	Solar Wings Pegasus Quasar (Rotax 503) SW-WQQ-0316			15. 5.90	I.M.J. & A.J.Mitchell Otherton, Cannock		3.12.00P
G-MWHW	Solar Wings Pegasus XL-Q SW-WQ-0317 (Rotax 462)			15. 5.90	P.Brown	Newcastle	20. 7.99P
G-MWHX	Solar Wings Pegasus XL-Q (Rotax 462) SW-TE-0280 & SW-WQ-0318			15. 5.90	N.P.Kelly	Navan, Co.Meath	15. 7.00P

Regn	Type	C/n	P/I	Date	Owner/operator	Probable Base	CA Expy
G-MWHY*	Mainair Gemini/Flash 2A			16. 5.90	G.C.Wright	Dunkeswell	28.11.97P
	(Rotax 462)	788-0590-7 & W581			(Damaged mid 1997: cancelled by CAA 25.8.99)		
G-MWHZ*	Trion J.1	J-001 & BMAA/HB/018		18. 5.90	J.Wibberley	Needham, Harlesdon	
				(Damaged Needham, Norfolk 1990: stored 9.97: cancelled by CAA 9.7.98)			
G-MWIA	Mainair Gemini/Flash 2A			21. 5.90	M.Raj	Otherton, Cannock	29. 5.98P
	(Rotax 503)	789-0690-7 & W582					
G-MWIB	Aviasud Mistral	094 & BMAA/HB/010		16. 5.90	N.W.Finn-Kelcey	Weston Underwood, Olney	14. 6.00P
	(Rotax 532)				"Weston Belle"		
G-MWIC	Whittaker MW-5C Sorcerer			20. 2.90	M.A.C.Stephenson	Totnes	23. 8.99P
	(Rotax 447)	PFA/163-11224			"Freyja"		
G-MWID	Solar Wings Pegasus XL-Q			30. 5.90	A.J.Pike	Lower Mountpleasant, Chatteris	16. 7.96P
	(Rotax 462)	SW-TE-0281 & SW-WQ-0324					
G-MWIE	Solar Wings Pegasus XL-Q			30. 5.90	R.Mercer	Long Marston	17. 6.00P
	(Rotax 462)	SW-TE-0282 & SW-WQ-0325					
G-MWIF	Rans S-6-ESD Coyote II			30. 5.90	S.P.Slade & R.Thorpe	Eshott	1. 3.00P
	(Rotax 503)	1089-095 & PFA/204-11749					
G-MWIG	Mainair Gemini/Flash 2A			4. 6.90	J.Cresswell	Roddige	15. 2.00P
	(Rotax 462)	790-0690-7 & W583					
G-MWIH	Mainair Gemini/Flash 2A			4. 6.90	G.Collins & L.J.Hill	Rufforth	6. 9.00P
	(Rotax 503)	791-0690-5 & W584					
G-MWIK	Medway Hybred 44XLR	MR094/89		7. 6.90	J.L.Gowens	Maidstone	27. 8.99P
	(Rotax 503)						
G-MWIL	Medway Hybred 44XLR	MR096/90		8. 6.90	J.W.Savage	St Albans	13. 9.95P
	(Rotax 447)						
G-MWIM	Solar Wings Pegasus Quasar TC			11. 6.90	P.J.Bates & T.S.Smith	Long Marston	25. 8.00P
	(Rotax 503)	SW-TQ-0008 & SW-WQQ-0326					
G-MWIN	Mainair Gemini/Flash 2A			12. 6.90	C.D.Lingard	Eshott	13.12.99P
	(Rotax 462)	93-0690-7 & W586					
G-MWIO	Rans S-4 Coyote			11. 6.90	R.E.Harris	Leicester	6. 9.00P
	(Rotax 447)	90-117 & PFA/193-11774					
G-MWIP	Whittaker MW-6 Merlin	PFA/164-11360		7. 6.90	D.Beer & B.J.Merrett	Ilfracombe	25. 1.99P
	(Rotax 582)						
G-MWIR	Solar Wings Pegasus XL-Q			8. 6.90	C.E.Dagless	Dereham	18. 5.00P
	(Rotax 462HP)	SW-TE-0283 & SW-WQ-0330					
G-MWIS	Solar Wings Pegasus XL-Q	SW-WQ-0331		8. 6.90	M.Mazure	Edgware	4. 5.00P
	(Rotax 462HP)						
G-MWIT	Solar Wings Pegasus XL-Q			8. 6.90	G.F.Ryland	Oxton, Nottingham	6. 9.00P
	(Rotax 462)	SW-TE-0285 & SW-WQ-0332					
G-MWIU	Solar Wings Pegasus Quasar TC			8. 6.90	M.E.Howard	RAF Halton	7. 3.00P
	(Rotax 503)	SW-TQ-0010 & SW-WQQ-0333					
G-MWIV	Mainair Gemini/Flash			15. 6.90	A.Wales	Rufforth	6. 6.00P
	(Rotax 503)	792-0690-5 & W585					
G-MWIW	Solar Wings Pegasus Quasar			18. 6.90	T.Yates	Alfreton	2.10.99P
	(Rotax 503)	SW-TQ-0011 & SW-WQQ-0334					
G-MWIX	Solar Wings Pegasus Quasar TC			18. 6.90	T.D.Neal	Shobdon	10.12.99P
	(Rotax 503)	SW-TQ-0012 & SW-WQQ-0335					
G-MWIY	Solar Wings Pegasus Quasar			22. 6.90	D.J.Payne	Enstone	30. 5.00P
	(Rotax 503)	SW-TQ-0014 & SW-WQQ-0336					
G-MWIZ	CFM Shadow Srs.CD	096		22.11.88	T.P.Ryan	St. Albans	25. 9.00P
	(Rotax 462)						
G-MWJD	Solar Wings Pegasus Quasar			22. 6.90	A.J.Blackwell	Long Marston	30. 9.00P
	(Rotax 503)	SW-TQ-0016 & SW-WQQ-0339					
G-MWJF	CFM Shadow Srs.BD	K.123		26. 6.90	D.A.Preston	Sowerby Bridge	13. 8.00P
	(Rotax 447)						
G-MWJG	Solar Wings Pegasus XL-R			26. 6.90	M.J.Piggott	Little Gransden	18. 6.00P
	(Rotax 447)	SW-TB-1415 & SW-WA-1472					
G-MWJH	Solar Wings Pegasus Quasar			29. 6.90	N.J.Braund	Bristol	6. 9.00P
	(Rotax 503)	SW-WQQ-0340					
G-MWJI	Solar Wings Pegasus Quasar			29. 6.90	R.J.Howell	Bristol	12. 2.00P
	(Rotax 503)	SW-WQQ-0341					
G-MWJJ	Solar Wings Pegasus Quasar			29. 6.90	E.Daleki	Drayton St.Leonard	5.11.00P
	(Rotax 503)	SW-TQ-0019 & SW-WQQ-0342					
G-MWJK	Solar Wings Pegasus Quasar			29. 6.90	N.P.Chitty	Didcot	10.10.00P
	(Rotax 503)	SW-WQQ-0343					
G-MWJL	AMF Chevvron 2-32 (Konig SD570)	023		16. 7.90	M.Nooshabadi	Co.Meath, Ireland	2. 6.99P
G-MWJM	AMF Chevvron 2-32C (Konig SD570)	024		31. 7.90	Airshare Flying Clubs Ltd	Abington	17. 9.98P
G-MWJN	Solar Wings Pegasus XL-Q			29. 6.90	J.C.Corrall		
	(Rotax 462)	SW-TE-0288 & SW-WQ-0344				Lower Mountpleasant, Chatteris	26. 6.00P
G-MWJO	Solar Wings Pegasus XL-Q			29. 6.90	C.Serra	Wareham, Dorset	11.10.99P
	(Rotax 462HP)	SW-TE-0289 & SW-WQ-0345					

Regn	Type	C/n	P/I	Date	Owner/operator	Probable Base	CA Expy
G-MWJP	Medway Hybred 44XLR (Rotax 503)	MR097/91		29. 6.90	D.W.Beach	Stoke, Kent	14. 5.00P
G-MWJR	Medway Hybred 44XLR (Rotax 503)	MR098/92		28. 6.90	J.Stokes	Stoke, Kent	7 .7.96P
G-MWJS	Solar Wings Pegasus Quasar TC (Rotax 503)	SW-WQQ-0349		6. 7.90	C.R.Ashley	Sittles Farm, Alrewas	27. 6.99P
G-MWJT	Solar Wings Pegasus Quasar TC (Rotax 503)	SW-TQ-0022 & SW-WQQ-0350		16. 7.90	K.V.Rands-Allen Nether Heyford, Northampton		22. 1.00P
G-MWJU	Solar Wings Pegasus Quasar (Rotax 503)	SW-TQ-0023 & SW-WQQ-0351		6. 7.90	S.Baker	Alrewas	30. 1.00P
G-MWJV	Solar Wings Pegasus Quasar (Rotax 503)	SW-TQ-0024 & SW-WQQ-0352		6. 7.90	A.Davies	Torquay	5. 6.00P
G-MWJW	Whittaker MW-5 Sorcerer (Fuji-Robin EC-44-PM)	JDW-02 & PFA/163-11186		11. 5.90	S.Badby	Banbury	1. 6.00P
G-MWJX	Medway Puma Sprint (Rotax 447)	MS009/3		17. 7.90	A.Tristram Pound Green, Buttonoak, Kidderminster		1. 5.00P
G-MWJY	Mainair Gemini/Flash 2A (Rotax 503)	797-0790-7 & W590		16. 7.90	R.E.Parker	Harlow	11. 5.97P
G-MWJZ	CFM Shadow Srs.CD (Rotax 503)	K.132		19. 7.90	D.Mahajan	West Wickham, Kent	23. 7.99P
G-MWKA	Murphy Renegade Spirit UK (Rotax 582) (Incorporates project PFA/188-11690)	PFA/188-11864		26. 7.90	C.E.Neill t/a Downlands Flying Group "Spirit of Lewes"	Deanland	8. 4.00P
G-MWKE	Hornet RS-ZA (Rotax 532) (Trike c/n overstamped on HRWB-0107)	HRWB-0108 & ZA167		30. 7.90	D.R.Stapleton	Blackpool	22.10.00P
G-MWKF*	Hornet R-ZA (Rotax 532) (Trike unit originally stamped as HRWB-0099)	HRWB-0109 & ZA168		30. 7.90	Not known (Trike stored 5.97)	Clench Common	9. 3.91P*
G-MWKO	Solar Wings Pegasus XL-Q (Rotax 462)	SW-WQ-0357		31. 7.90	R.G.Hearsey	Rye	16.10.99P
G-MWKP	Solar Wings Pegasus XL-Q (Rotax 462HP)	SW-TE-0291 & SW-WQ-0358		31. 7.90	G.N.Frost	Daventry	12. 6.00P
G-MWKW	Microflight Spectrum (Rotax 503)	015		3. 8.90	P.B. & M.Robinson	Sutton Meadows, Ely	29. 1.00P
G-MWKX	Microflight Spectrum (Rotax 503)	016		3. 8.90	C.R.Ions	Eshott	25. 7.00P
G-MWKY	Solar Wings Pegasus XL-Q (Rotax 462HP)	SW-TE-0292 & SW-WQ-0362		3. 8.90	C.R.Wright	Roddige, Fradley	17. 3.00P
G-MWKZ	Solar Wings Pegasus XL-Q (Rotax 462HP)	SW-TE-0293 & SW-WQ-0363		3. 8.90	P.L.Cummings	Eaglescott	16.12.99P
G-MWLA	Rans S-4 Coyote (Rotax 447)	89-114 & PFA/193-11787		3. 8.90	B.R.Hunter	Perth	23. 5.00P
G-MWLB	Medway Hybred 44XLR (Rotax 503)	MR104/93		15. 8.90	M.W.Harmer	Long Acres Farm, Sandy	21. 9.99P
G-MWLC*	Medway Hybred 44XLR (Rotax 503)	MR086/94		15. 8.90	G.J.Slater (Rebuilt as G-MWRM 1991; cancelled by CAA 3.12.98)		20. 2.91P*
G-MWLD	CFM Shadow Srs.CD (Rotax 503)	106		9. 5.89	T.J. & M.D.Palmer	Kilmarnock	20.10.00P
G-MWLE	Solar Wings Pegasus XL-R (Rotax 447)	SW-TB-1425 & SW-WA-1474		9. 8.90	D.Stevenson	London Colney	2. 4.00P
G-MWLF	Solar Wings Pegasus XL-R (Rotax 447)	SW-WA-1475		9. 8.90	G.Rainey	Weston Zoyland	13. 3.00P
G-MWLG	Solar Wings Pegasus XL-R (Rotax 447)	SW-TB-1427 & SW-WA-1476		9. 8.90	D.P.Green	Weston Zoyland	17. 5.00P
G-MWLH	Solar Wings Pegasus Quasar (Rotax 503)	SW-WQQ-0364		9. 8.90	R.A.Duncan	Drummiard Farm, Bonnybank	15. 6.00P
G-MWLI	Solar Wings Pegasus XL-Q (Rotax 447)	SW-TQ-0031 & SW-WQQ-0365	G-65-8 G-MWLI	9. 8.90	I.A.MacAdam (Damaged mid 1996)	Bedford	31. 7.96P
G-MWLJ	Solar Wings Pegasus Quasar (Rotax 503)	SW-WQQ-0366		9. 8.90	C.G.Rouse	Chandlers Ford	18. 9.00P
G-MWLK	Solar Wings Pegasus Quasar TC (Rotax 503)	SW-TQ-0033 & SW-WQQ-0367		9. 8.90	R.P.Wilkinson	Charmy Down, Bath	29. 6.00P
G-MWLL	Solar Wings Pegasus XL-Q (Rotax 462)	SW-TE-0287 & SW-WQ-0338		16. 8.90	J.Bacon	Great Yarmouth	28. 8.99P
G-MWLM	Solar Wings Pegasus XL-Q (Rotax 462)	SW-WQ-0322		17. 8.90	R.J.Hawkins	Kettering	28.11.99P
G-MWLN	Whittaker MW-6S Fatboy Flyer (Rotax 503)	PFA/164-11844		16. 8.90	S.J.Field "Red Lips"	Bridgwater	5. 6.92P
G-MWLO	Whittaker MW-6 Merlin (Rotax 503)	PFA/164-11373		21. 8.90	S.P.Ganecki & L.Prew	Otherton, Cannock	14. 6.00P
G-MWLP	Mainair Gemini/Flash (Rotax 503)	801-0990-5 & W594		24. 8.90	J.S.Potts	Kilmarnock	24. 8.99P
G-MWLS	Medway Hybred 44XLR (Rotax 503)	MR081/95		29. 8.90	J.Rochead	Oban	28. 6.00P

Regn	Type	C/n	Date	Owner/operator	Probable Base	CA Expy
G-MWLT	Mainair Gemini/Flash 2A (Rotax 503) 804-0990-7 & W597		31. 8.90	K.Roberts & J.E.Mann	Caernarfon/Wigan	18. 6.00P
G-MWLU	Solar Wings Pegasus XL-R/Se (Rotax 462) SW-TE-0304 & SW-WA-1478		6. 9.90	T.P.G.Ward (Stored 9.97)	Great Orton	14.10.91P
G-MWLW	TEAM miniMax PFA/186-11717 (Rotax 377)		14. 9.90	S.Hobday (Damaged Deanland 4.6.93)	Salisbury	11. 6.93P
G-MWLX	Mainair Gemini/Flash 2A (Rotax 503) 805-0990-7 & W598		5.10.90	G.Good & E.J.Robson	East Fortune	27. 1.00P
G-MWLY	Rans S-4 Coyote PFA/193-11691 (Rotax 447)		20. 9.90	P.J.Burrow	Crediton	3. 6.00P
G-MWLZ	Rans S-4 Coyote (Rotax 447) 90-116 & PFA/193-11887		8.10.90	I.W.Critchley	Stafford	3. 6.00P
G-MWMA	Powerchute Kestrel (Rotax 503)	00398	7.11.90	G.Webb	Selby	24.11.96P
G-MWMB	Powerchute Kestrel (Rotax 503)	00399	7.11.90	D.J.Whysall	Ripley, Derby	17.10.99P
G-MWMC	Powerchute Kestrel (Rotax 503)	00400	7.11.90	K.James	Kemble	11. 6.00P
G-MWMD	Powerchute Kestrel (Rotax 503)	00401	7.11.90	D.J.Jackson	Melton Constable	20.11.91P
G-MWMG	Powerchute Kestrel (Rotax 503)	00404	7.11.90	M.D.Walton	Tregaron	26.10.00P
G-MWMH	Powerchute Kestrel (Rotax 503)	00405	7.11.90	J.D.Smith & A.C.Turnbull	Ferryhill	17.10.99P
G-MWMI	Solar Wings Pegasus Quasar (Rotax 503) SW-TQ-0043 & SW-WQQ-0383		21. 9.90	P.Richardson	Newark	30. 3.00P
G-MWMJ	Solar Wings Pegasus Quasar (Rotax 503) SW-TQ-0044 & SW-WQQ-0384		21. 9.90	D.Webb	Kemble	3. 3.00P
G-MWMK	Solar Wings Pegasus Quasar (Rotax 503) SW-WQQ-0385		21. 9.90	D.H.Lowes-Bird	Kidwelly	15. 5.00P
G-MWML	Solar Wings Pegasus Quasar SW-TQ-0046 & SW-WQQ-0386		21. 9.90	A.Rokker	Cambridge	7. 8.00P
G-MWMM	Mainair Gemini/Flash 2A (Rotax 462) 800-0890-7 & W593		24. 8.90	R.H.Church	Croft Farm, Defford	12. 4.00P
G-MWMN	Solar Wings Pegasus XL-Q (Rotax 462HP) SW-TE-0297 & SW-WQ-0387		2.10.90	N.A.Rathbone & P.A.Arnold	Swinford, Rugby	9. 1.00P
G-MWMO	Solar Wings Pegasus XL-Q (Rotax 462) SW-TE-0298 & SW-WQ-0388		2.10.90	R.S.Wilson	Newmarket	21. 5.00P
G-MWMP	Solar Wings Pegasus XL-Q SW-WQ-0389 (Rotax 462HP)		2.10.90	D.M.Orrock & F.E.Hall	Rushden	28. 7.00P
G-MWMR	Solar Wings Pegasus XL-R SW-WA-1483 (Rotax 462)		2.10.90	J.A.Crofts	Meidrim, Carmarthen	13. 3.00P
G-MWMS	Mainair Gemini/Flash (Rotax 503) 807-1090-5 & W600		3.10.90	C.K.Richardson	East Fortune	18.12.99P
G-MWMT	Mainair Gemini/Flash 2A (Rotax 503) 808-1090-7 & W601		3.10.90	B.Berrington & D.Foxley	Crosby, Liverpool	23. 4.00P
G-MWMU	CFM Shadow Srs.CD 150 (Rotax 503)		2.10.90	A.J.Burton	Market Rasen	9. 4.00P
G-MWMV	Solar Wings Pegasus XL-R (Rotax 462) SW-TE-0307 & SW-WA-1484		5.10.90	G.M.Stevens	Sutton Meadows, Ely	9. 5.00P
G-MWMW	Murphy Renegade Spirit UK (Rotax 532) 254 & PFA/188-11544		21. 8.89	H.Feeney "Spirit of Cornwall"	Long Marston	15.12.99P
G-MWMX	Mainair Gemini/Flash 2A (Rotax 462) 810-1090-7 & W603		17.10.90	G.T.Snoddon	Dundonald, Belfast	19.11.99P
G-MWMY	Mainair Gemini/Flash 2A (Rotax 462) 809-1090-7 & W602		17.10.90	C.W.Lowe	Grove Farm, Raveningham	5. 5.97P
G-MWMZ	Solar Wings Pegasus XL-Q SW-WQ-0393 (Rotax 462)		8.10.90	P.C.Ockwell	Swindon	6. 8.00P
G-MWNA	Solar Wings Pegasus XL-Q SW-WQ-0394 (Rotax 462)		8.10.90	J.M.Kirtley	Eshott	14. 9.99P
G-MWNB	Solar Wings Pegasus XL-Q (Rotax 462) SW-TE-0303 & SW-WQ-0395		8.10.90	P.F.J.Rogers	London SW17	14. 5.00P
G-MWNC	Solar Wings Pegasus XL-Q SW-WQ-0396 (Rotax 462HP)		8.10.90	G.S.Sage	Sleaford	5. 6.00P
G-MWND	Tiger Cub RL5A Sherwood Ranger (Rotax 532) 001 & PFA/237-12229		9.10.90	Tiger Cub Developments Ltd	Doncaster	1. 5.96P
G-MWNE	Mainair Gemini/Flash 2A (Rotax 503) 803-1090-7 & W596		17.10.90	T.C.Edwards	Ware	21. 3.00P
G-MWNF	Murphy Renegade Spirit UK (Rotax 582) PFA/188-11853		15.10.90	D.J.White	Holly Meadow Farm, Bradley	31. 8.99P

Regn	Type	C/n	P/I	Date	Owner/operator	Probable Base	CA Expy
G-MWNG	Solar Wings Pegasus XL-Q			17.10.90	M.A.McClelland	Old Sarum	21. 6.99P
	(Rotax 462HP) SW-TE-0305 & SW -WQ-0399				t/a McClelland Aviation		
G-MWNK	Solar Wings Pegasus Quasar TC			1.11.90	G.S.Lyon	RAF Wyton	1. 8.00P
	(Rotax 503)	SW-WQQ-0403					
G-MWNL	Solar Wings Pegasus Quasar			1.11.90	Creation Company Films Ltd	Popham	30. 7.00P
	(Rotax 503) SW-TQ-0055 & SW-WQQ-0404						
G-MWNO	AMF Chevvron 2-32	025		12.11.90	I.K.Hogg	Kirkbride	30. 4.00P
	(Konig SD570)						
G-MWNP	AMF Chevvron 2-32C	026		31.10.90	D.G.Titterton & D.A.Norwood "Gwenric-J"		
	(Konig SD570)				Ashcroft Farm, Winsford		13. 7.00P
G-MWNR	Murphy Renegade Spirit UK			12.11.90	J.J.Lancaster	Cublington	15. 8.00P
	(Rotax 582)	PFA/188-11926			t/a RJR Flying Group		
G-MWNS	Mainair Gemini/Flash 2A			6.11.90	S.R.Kerr	Grimsby	6. 7.00P
	(Rotax 503)	811-1190-7 & W604					
G-MWNT	Mainair Gemini/Flash 2A			6.11.90	P. & V.C.Reynolds	East Fortune	3. 6.00P
	(Rotax 582)	812-1190-7 & W605					
G-MWNU	Mainair Gemini/Flash 2A			6.11.90	C.C.Muir	Bristol	4. 4.00P
	(Rotax 503)	813-1190-5 & W606					
G-MWNV	Powerchute Kestrel	00406		12.11.90	K.N.Byrne	Isle of Colonsay	13. 3.92P
G-MWNX	Powerchute Kestrel	00408		12.11.90	J.H.Greenroyd	Hebden Bridge	18. 8.00P
	(Rotax 503)						
G-MWNY	Powerchute Kestrel	00409		12.11.90	P.T.T.Williams	Farnham	18. 6.97P
	(Rotax 503)						
G-MWNZ	Powerchute Kestrel	00410		12.11.90	M.J.Boase	Leeds	10. 2.93P
G-MWOC	Powerchute Kestrel	00413		12.11.90	K.J.Foxall	Tamworth	30. 5.00P
G-MWOD	Powerchute Kestrel	00414		12.11.90	T.Morgan	Kidderminster	4.10.00P
	(Rotax 503)						
G-MWOE	Powerchute Kestrel	00415		12.11.90	E.G.Woolnough & P.K.Reason	Halesworth	20. 1.00P
G-MWOF*	Microflight Spectrum	018		13.11.90	Not known	Shobdon	29. 5.96P
	(Rotax 503)				(Temp unregd 4.6.96; on rebuild 6.97)		
G-MWOH	Solar Wings Pegasus XL-R/Se			28.11.90	L R Hodgson	Haltwistle	13. 3.00P
	(Rotax 447)	SW-WA-1485					
G-MWOI	Solar Wings Pegasus XL-R			29.11.90	P.Maller	Cheltenham	30. 5.00P
	(Rotax 447) SW-TB-1430 & SW-WA-1486						
G-MWOJ	Mainair Gemini/Flash 2A			6.12.90	J.K.Nicol	Southport	21. 8.00P
	(Rotax 503)	814-1290-7 & W608					
G-MWOK	Mainair Gemini/Flash 2A			6.12.90	J.C.Miller	East Fortune	5. 7.00P
	(Rotax 462)	815-1290-7 & W609					
G-MWOL	Mainair Gemini/Flash 2A			6.12.90	I.V.Watters	Swansea	31. 1.94P
	(Rotax 503)	816-1290-7 & W610					
G-MWOM	Solar Wings Pegasus Quasar TC			1. 3.91	T.J.Williams	Tuam, Co.Galway	15. 5.00P
	(Rotax 503)	SW-WQQ-0412					
G-MWON	CFM Shadow Srs.CD	K.128		18.12.90	C.J.Ball	Cheltenham	14. 7.00P
	(Rotax 503)						
G-MWOO	Murphy Renegade Spirit UK			14. 9.90	R.C.Wood Lower Mountpleasant, Chatteris		12. 7.00P
	(Rotax 582)	318 & PFA/188-11811					
G-MWOP	Solar Wings Pegasus Quasar TC			31.12.90	A.Baynes	Sywell	2.10.00P
	(Rotax 503) SW-TQC-0059 & SW-WQQ-0410						
G-MWOR	Solar Wings Pegasus XL-Q SW-WQ-0411			21.12.90	I.D.Chantler Long Acres Farm, Sandy		29. 7.00P
	(Rotax 462)						
G-MWOV	Whittaker MW-6 Merlin PFA/164-11301			9. 1.91	S.J.Field	Bridgwater	24.10.95P
	(Rotax 503)						
G-MWOW	CFM Shadow Srs.B	007	83-AG	16. 9.85	Global Aviation Projects Ltd Torrington		2. 7.91P
	(Rotax 447)				(Stored Davidstow Moor 10.95)		
G-MWOX	Solar Wings Pegasus XL-Q SW-WQ-0413			7. 1.91	G.Milo	Popham	16. 6.99P
	(Rotax 462)						
G-MWOY	Solar Wings Pegasus XL-Q			7. 1.91	G.S.Beeby	Sutton Meadows, Ely	17. 4.00P
	(Rotax 462HP) SW-TE-0310 & SW-WQ-0414						
G-MWPA	Mainair Gemini/Flash 2A			9. 1.91	T.Beckham	Eshott	4. 7.00P
	(Rotax 462)	817-0191-7 & W611					
G-MWPB	Mainair Gemini/Flash 2A			3. 1.91	J.Fenton	St.Michaels	4. 6.00P
	(Rotax 503)	823-0191-7 & W617					
G-MWPC	Mainair Gemini/Flash 2A			3. 1.91	I.Shaw	Arclid Green, Sandbach	3. 9.00P
	(Rotax 503)	826-0191-7 & W620					
G-MWPD	Mainair Gemini/Flash 2A			9. 1.91	G.A.McKay	Linlithgow	25. 5.96P
	(Rotax 503)	824-0191-7 & W618					
G-MWPE	Solar Wings Pegasus XL-Q			9. 1.91	E.C.R.Hudson	Upper Stow, Weedon	19. 4.00P
	(Rotax 462HP) SW-TE-0096 & SW-WQ-0416	(Trike ex G-MVGX)					
G-MWPF	Mainair Gemini/Flash 2A			11. 1.91	S.R.Simms	Roddige, Fradley	30. 5.00P
	(Rotax 503)	825-0191-7 & W619					

Regn	Type	C/n	P/I	Date	Owner/operator	Probable Base	CA Expy
G-MWPG	Microflight Spectrum (Rotax 503)	019		9. 1.91	P.F.Craggs	Eshott	11. 7.98P
G-MWPH	Microflight Spectrum (Rotax 503)	020		9. 1.91	S.B.Mance & K.R.Wootton	Wombleton	29.10.00P
G-MWPI	Microflight Spectrum TI (Rotax 503)	021		9. 1.91	B.W.Peacock (Damaged early 1997)	Peterborough	28. 2.97P
G-MWPJ	Solar Wings Pegasus XL-Q (Rotax 462) SW-TE-0312 & SW-WQ-0418			17. 1.91	R.R.Nichol	Carlisle	30. 4.00P
G-MWPK	Solar Wings Pegasus XL-Q (Rotax 462) SW-TE-0313 & SW-WQ-0419			17. 1.91	G.D.Peplow	Shobdon	29. 4.00P
G-MWPN	CFM Shadow Srs.CD (Rotax 503)	K.147		22. 1.91	W.R.H.Thomas	Swansea	11. 6.99P
G-MWPO	Mainair Gemini/Flash 2A (Rotax 503) 827-0191-7 & W621			29. 1.91	T.Mellors	Nottingham	8. 4.00P
G-MWPP	CFM Streak Shadow Srs.M (Rotax 582) K.166-SA & PFA/206-11992		G-BTEM	14. 2.91	W.C.Yates	Higher Barn Farm, Houghton	17. 5.00P
G-MWPR	Whittaker MW-6 Merlin PFA/164-11260			16.10.90	P.J.S.Ritchie	Worthing	
G-MWPS	Murphy Renegade Spirit UK (Rotax 582) PFA/188-11931			18. 2.91	A.R.Broughton-Tompkins (As "0347"in pseudo US Navy c/s)	Elstead	1. 7.98P
G-MWPT	Hunt Avon/Hunt Wing (Fuji-Robin EC-44-PM) JAH-8 & BMAA/HB/015		EI-CKF G-MWPT	18. 2.91	G.A.Murphy (Destroyed in accident ?)	Ballincollig, Cork	10. 5.97P
G-MWPU	Solar Wings Pegasus Quasar TC (Rotax 503) SW-WQQ-0426			20. 2.91	N.J.Holt	Street	16. 6.00P
G-MWPW	AMF Chevvron 2-32C (Konig SD570)	027		26.11.90	E.L.T.Westman	Teangue, Isle of Skye	21.11.00P
G-MWPX	Solar Wings Pegasus XL-R SW-WA-1488 (Rotax 462)			27. 2.91	R.S.Amor	Bristol	19. 5.00P
G-MWPZ	Murphy Renegade Spirit UK PFA/188-11631			18. 3.91	J.Ievers	Pains Castle	24. 2.99P
G-MWRB	Mainair Gemini/Flash 2A (Rotax 503) 819-0191-7 & W613			5. 2.91	A.S.Harvey	RAF Wyton	25. 4.00P
G-MWRC	Mainair Gemini/Flash 2A (Rotax 503) 820-0191-7 & W614			5. 2.91	D.R.Talbot	Chilton Park, Wallingford	31. 7.00P
G-MWRD	Mainair Gemini/Flash 2A (Motavia) 821-0191-7 & W615			5. 2.91	D.M.Law	Redlands, Swindon	14.11.96P
G-MWRE	Mainair Gemini/Flash 2A (Rotax 503) 822-0191-7 & W616			5. 2.91	A.Simon	Dingwall	29. 6.00P
G-MWRF	Mainair Gemini/Flash 2A (Rotax 503) 829-0191-7 & W623			4. 2.91	R.D.Ballard	Bexhill	12. 5.00P
G-MWRG	Mainair Gemini/Flash 2A (Rotax 503) 830-0191-7 & W624			5. 2.91	N.J.Hall	Morpeth	11. 4.00P
G-MWRH	Mainair Gemini/Flash 2A (Rotax 503) 831-0191-7 & W625			5. 2.91	E.G.Astin	Eshott	26. 5.99P
G-MWRI	Mainair Gemini/Flash 2A (Rotax 462) 828-0191-7 & W622			1. 3.91	R.N.Scarr	Marlborough	12.12.99P
G-MWRJ	Mainair Gemini/Flash 2A (Rotax 503) 832-0291-7 & W626			28. 2.91	J.S.Walton	Mold	5.10.00P
G-MWRK	Rans S-6 Coyote II (Rotax 503) 0191-154 & PFA/204-11930			13. 2.91	R.H.Bambury (Wrecked 12.99)	Breighton	6. 5.99P
G-MWRL	CFM Shadow Srs.CD (Rotax 503)	K.152		13. 2.91	A.E.Southern "Shadow Hawk"	Old Sarum	3. 8.00P
G-MWRM	Medway Hybred 44XLR MR086/94/91/S (Rotax 503)		G-MWLC	26. 2.91	M.A.Jones	. Wigan	14. 8.00P
G-MWRN	Solar Wings Pegasus XL-R (Rotax 462) SW-TE-0316 & SW-WA-1489			5. 3.91	D.T.MacKenzie	Downhill, Glasgow	5.12.99P
G-MWRO	Solar Wings Pegasus XL-R SW-WA-1490 (Rotax 462)			5. 3.91	I.D.Stokes	Camelford	8. 6.99P
G-MWRP	Solar Wings Pegasus XL-R SW-WA-1491			1. 3.91	J.Liddiard	Didcot	17. 6.00P
G-MWRR	Mainair Gemini/Flash 2A (Rotax 503) 834-0391-7 & W628			7. 3.91	G.Evans & N Gater	Sandbach	21. 3.00P
G-MWRS	Ultravia Super Pelican	E001-201		9. 5.84	T.B.Woolley	Narborough, Leics	9. 9.87P*
G-MWRT	Solar Wings Pegasus XL-R (Rotax 447) SW-TB-1431 & SW-WA-1492			15. 3.91	G.L.Gunnell	Luton	18. 5.00P
G-MWRU	Solar Wings Pegasus XL-R SW-WA-1493 (Rotax 447)			15. 3.91	J.McIver	West Kilbride	25. 8.96P
G-MWRV	Solar Wings Pegasus XL-R (Rotax 447) SW-TB-1433 & SW-WA-1494			15. 3.91	M.S.Adams	Roddige, Fradley	10.10.00P
G-MWRW	Solar Wings Pegasus XL-Q (Rotax 462) SW-TE-0320 & SW-WQ-0431			25. 3.91	D.A.Linsey-Bloom	Franklyn's Field, Chewton Mendip	17. 6.00P
G-MWRX	Solar Wings Pegasus XL-Q SW-WQ-0432 (Rotax 462)			25. 3.91	M.A.E.Harris	Swansea	6. 4.96P

Regn	Type	C/n	P/I	Date	Owner/operator	Probable Base	CA Expy
G-MWRY	CFM Shadow Srs.CD (Rotax 503)	K.162		26. 3.91	A.W.Hodder	Belle Vue Farm, Yarnscombe	26.10.00P
G-MWRZ	AMF Chevvron 2-32C (Konig SD570)	028		10. 4.91	M.J.Barrett	Davidstow Moor	3. 7.00P
G-MWSA	TEAM miniMax (Rotax 377)	PFA/186-11855		8. 4.91	A.N.Baumber Overseal, Burton-on-Trent "The Flying Cobbler"		13. 6.00P
G-MWSB	Mainair Gemini/Flash 2A (Rotax 582)	837-0591-7 & W631		30. 4.91	T.Slevin	Mansfield	13. 7.97P
G-MWSC	Rans S-6-ESD Coyote II (Rotax 503)	PFA/204-12019		13. 5.91	E.M.Lear	Langport	30. 6.96P
G-MWSD	Solar Wings Pegasus XL-Q (Rotax 462) SW-TE-0319 & SW-WQ-0430			6. 3.91	J.D.Buchanan	Willingham	18. 7.00P
G-MWSE	Solar Wings Pegasus XL-R (Rotax 462) SW-TE-0323 & SW-WA-1496			10. 4.91	Ultra Light Training Ltd	Roddige, Fradley	30. 5.00P
G-MWSF	Solar Wings Pegasus XL-R (Rotax 462) SW-TE-0324 & SW-WA-1497			10. 4.91	V.A.M.Bourne Long Newnton, Malmesbury		12. 3.00P
G-MWSG	Solar Wings Pegasus XL-R (Rotax 462) SW-TE-0325 & SW-WA-1498			10. 4.91	J.Eddon	Pickering	19. 9.99P
G-MWSH	Solar Wings Pegasus Quasar TC (Rotax 503) SW-TQC-0064 & SW-WQQ-0435			30. 4.91	R.Delooze	Warrington	9. 3.00P
G-MWSI	Solar Wings Pegasus Quasar TC (Rotax 503) SW-TQC-0065 & SW-WQQ-0436			23. 5.91	B.J.Kelly & P.J.Prescott	Daventry	22. 7.00P
G-MWSJ	Solar Wings Pegasus XL-Q (Rotax 462)	SW-WQ-0437		12. 4.91	R.A.Barrett	Lower Mountpleasant, Chatteris	29. 5.00P
G-MWSK	Solar Wings Pegasus XL-Q (Rotax 462)	SW-WQ-0438		12. 4.91	J.Doogan t/a Scottglass	Galashiels	5. 9.98P
G-MWSL	Mainair Gemini/Flash 2A (Rotax 503)	835-0491-7 & W629		16. 4.91	C.W.Frost	Rufforth	11. 6.98P
G-MWSM	Mainair Gemini/Flash 2A (Rotax 503)	836-0491-7 & W630		16. 4.91	R.M.Wall & P.A.Garside	St.Michaels	23. 8.00P
G-MWSO	Solar Wings Pegasus XL-R (Rotax 462) SW-TE-0329 & SW-WA-1503			25. 4.91	M.A.Clayton	New Romney	16. 4.00P
G-MWSP	Solar Wings Pegasus XL-R (Rotax 462) SW-TE-0330 & SW-WA-1504			25. 4.91	P.A.Ashton Knapton Lodge, Cauton		9.10.00P
G-MWSR	Solar Wings Pegasus XL-R (Rotax 462) SW-TE-0331 & SW-WA-1505			25. 4.91	M.E.T.Taylor	Newport	7. 8.99P
G-MWSS	Medway Hybred 44XLR (Rotax 503)	MR117/97		7. 5.91	F.S.Ogden West Hoathly, Haywards Heath		6. 8.00P
G-MWST	Medway Hybred 44XLR (Rotax 503)	MR118/98		8. 5.91	A.Ferguson (Damaged mid 1997)	Insch	7. 8.98P
G-MWSU	Medway Hybred 44XLR (Rotax 503)	MR119/99		1. 5.92	S.Jeffrey	Insch	26. 7.00P
G-MWSW	Whittaker MW-6 Merlin	PFA/164-11328		15. 2.91	S.N.F.Warnell	Staines	
G-MWSX	Aerotech MW-5 Sorcerer (Rotax 447)	PFA/163-11549		3. 5.91	A.T.Armstrong	Yelverton	26. 4.00P
G-MWSY	Aerotech MW-5 Sorcerer (Rotax 447)	PFA/163-11218		3. 5.91	J.E.Holloway	Saltash	20. 4.00P
G-MWSZ	CFM Shadow Srs.CD (Rotax 503)	K.158		4. 4.91	P.G.Bibbey	Old Sarum	24. 9.00P
G-MWTA	Solar Wings Pegasus XL-Q (Rotax 462)	SW-WQ-0444		8. 5.91	T.W.Phipps Craysmarsh Farm, Melksham		10. 9.99P
G-MWTB	Solar Wings Pegasus XL-Q (Rotax 462) SW-TE-0333 & SW-WQ-0445			8. 5.91	I.A.Baker	Kettering	24. 8.00P
G-MWTC	Solar Wings Pegasus XL-Q (Rotax 462)	SW-WQ-0446		8. 5.91	P.Nicholson	London SE18	2. 7.00P
G-MWTD	Microflight Spectrum (Rotax 503)	022		13. 5.91	J.V.Harris t/a Group Delta	Ashbourne	18. 4.00P
G-MWTE	Microflight Spectrum (Rotax 503)	023		13. 5.91	R.H.Braithwaite RAF Halton t/a RAF Microlight Flying Association		28. 1.00P
G-MWTF	Mainair Gemini/Southdown Sprint (Fuji-Robin EC-44-PM)	249-684-2		30. 7.84	G.D.C.Buyers	Popham	19. 7.95P
G-MWTG	Mainair Gemini/Flash 2A (Rotax 582)	838-0591-7 & W632		16. 5.91	D.G.Emery & M.R.Smith	Dudley	23. 7.00P
G-MWTH	Mainair Gemini/Flash 2A (Rotax 503)	839-0591-7 & W633		21. 5.91	T.Coughlan	Cumbernauld	9. 6.95P
G-MWTI	Solar Wings Pegasus XL-Q (Rotax 462HP)	SW-WQ-0274		23. 5.91	A.Crozier	East Fortune	15. 5.00P
G-MWTJ	CFM Shadow Srs.CD (Rotax 503)	K.167		16. 5.91	H.F.Blakeman	Crewe	20. 8.00P
G-MWTK	Solar Wings Pegasus XL-R/Se (Rotax 462) SW-TE-0335 & SW-WA-1507			28. 5.91	B.J.Palfreyman	Nottingham	23. 4.00P

Regn	Type	C/n	P/I	Date	Owner/operator	Probable Base	CA Expy
G-MWTL	Solar Wings Pegasus XL-R (Rotax 462) SW-TE-0336 & SW-WA-1508			28. 5.91	B.Lindsay	Chipping Sodbury	27.10.00P
G-MWTM	Solar Wings Pegasus XL-R SW-WA-1509 (Rotax 462)			28. 5.91	I.R.F.King	Tunbridge Wells	4. 5.97P
G-MWTN	CFM Shadow Srs.CD K.153 (Rotax 503)			23. 5.91	M.J.Broom	Long Marston	28. 7.99P
G-MWTO	Mainair Gemini/Flash 2A (Rotax 503) 840-0591-7 & W634			28. 5.91	J.Greenhalgh	St.Michaels	13. 6.00P
G-MWTP	CFM Shadow Srs.CD K.107 (Rotax 503)			23. 5.91	D.A.Crosbie	Sudbury	24. 8.00P
G-MWTR	Mainair Gemini/Flash 2A (Rotax 503) 842-0591-7 & W636			31. 5.91	A.A.Howland	Battle	5.10.00P
G-MWTS	Whittaker MW-6S Fatboy Flyer (Rotax 582) PFA/164-12015			31. 5.91	P.G.Evans & K.N.Lovett	Alford	17. 4.97P
G-MWTT	Rans S-6-ESD Coyote II (Rotax 503) 20391-175 & PFA/204-12016			30. 4.91	L.E.Duffin "Warrior 2"	Insch	16.11.00P
G-MWTU	Solar Wings Pegasus XL-R SW-WA-1501 (Rotax 447)			21. 6.91	J.D.Doran	Mullingar, Co.Westmeath	26. 3.00P
G-MWTY	Mainair Gemini/Flash 2A (Rotax 503) 843-0691-7 & W637			12. 6.91	K.B.Pownall	Stoke-on-Trent	20. 9.99P
G-MWTZ	Mainair Gemini/Flash 2A (Rotax 503) 844-0691-7 & W638			12. 6.91	C.W.R.Felce	Riseley, Bedford	23. 6.00P
G-MWUA	CFM Shadow Srs.CD K.161 (Rotax 503)			10. 6.91	Cloudbase Aviation Services Ltd	Crawley	7. 6.00P
G-MWUB	Solar Wings Pegasus XL-R SW-WA-1510 (Rotax 462)			12. 6.91	N.R.Bray	Hitchin	2. 6.00P
G-MWUC	Solar Wings Pegasus XL-R SW-WA-1511 (Rotax 462)			12. 6.91	J.R.Hall	Bibberne Farm, Stalbridge	6. 8.00P
G-MWUD	Solar Wings Pegasus XL-R SW-WA-1512 (Rotax 462)			12. 6.91	N.A.Martin	Marlborough	6.12.99P
G-MWUE	Solar Wings Pegasus XL-R SW-WA-1513 (Rotax 447)		EI-CGL G-MWUE	13. 6.91	R.M.Balfe	Drogheda, Co.Louth	11. 4.00P
G-MWUF	Solar Wings Pegasus XL-R (Rotax 447) SW-TB-1439 & SW-WA-1514			13. 6.91	J.G.Jackson	Woodley	27. 3.00P
G-MWUG	Solar Wings Pegasus XL-R (Rotax 447) SW-TB-1440 & SW-WA-1515			14. 6.91	G.C.Weighell	Enstone	18. 7.99P
G-MWUH	Murphy Renegade Spirit UK 343 (Built Canada/Saudi Arabia)			12. 6.91	Choicesource Ltd	Inverness	16. 9.00P
G-MWUI	AMF Chevvron 2-32C 029 (Konig SD570)			2. 7.91	B.McFadden t/a Microflight Aviation	Linley Hill, Leven	26. 4.00P
G-MWUJ	Medway Hybred 44XLR MR122/101 (Rotax 503)			27. 6.91	P.C.Cowling	Sleaford	25. 1.98P
G-MWUK	Rans S-6-ESD Coyote II PFA/204-12090 (Rotax 503)			1. 7.91	G.K.Hoult	Long Marston	5.10.99P
G-MWUL	Rans S-6-ESD Coyote II (Rotax 503) 0391-172 & PFA/204-12054			10. 6.91	C.K.Fry	Lychett Minster	17. 8.00P
G-MWUN	Rans S-6-ESD Coyote II (Nose-wheel u/c) (Rotax 503) 0695-841 & PFA/204-12075 (Rebuilt with new Rans airframe as stated) t/a Coyote Flying Group			10. 6.91	M.L.Robinson	Kirkbride	12. 4.00P
G-MWUO	Solar Wings Pegasus XL-Q (Rotax 462) SW-TE-0296 & SW-WQ-0379			26. 6.91	A.P.Slade	High Wycombe	30. 7.00P
G-MWUP	Solar Wings Pegasus XL-R SW-WA-1517 (Rotax 462)			21. 6.91	R.G.Mulford	Gillingham	10. 6.00P
G-MWUR	Solar Wings Pegasus XL-R (Rotax 462) SW-TE-0342 & SW-WA-1518			21. 6.91	A.W.Buchan & C.D.Creasey t/a Nottingham Aerotow Club Knapthorpe Lodge, Causton, Notts		19. 8.00P
G-MWUS	Solar Wings Pegasus XL-R (Rotax 462) SW-TE-0343 & SW-WA-1519			21. 6.91	H.R.Loxton	Weston Zoyland	29. 8.00P
G-MWUU	Solar Wings Pegasus XL-R (Rotax 462) SW-TE-0346 & SW-WA-1521			28. 6.91	B.R.Underwood & P.E.Hadley	Swinford, Rugby	25. 6.00P
G-MWUV	Solar Wings Pegasus XL-R (Rotax 462) SW-TE-0347 & SW-WA-1522			28. 6.91	L.Birkett t/a Blast Clean	Great Orton	25. 6.00P
G-MWUW*	Solar Wings Pegasus XL-R (Rotax 462) SW-TE-0348 & SW-WA-1523			28. 6.91	Ultraflight Microlights Ltd (Cancelled by CAA 16.2.98)	Alrewas	29. 1.98P
G-MWUX	Solar Wings Pegasus XL-Q SW-WQ-0454 (Rotax 462HP)			28. 6.91	B.D.Attwell	Caerphilly	19. 3.00P
G-MWUY	Solar Wings Pegasus XL-Q (Rotax 462) SW-TE-0345 & SW-WQ-0455			28. 6.91	S.Johnstone	Lochwinnoch	26. 7.00P
G-MWUZ	Solar Wings Pegasus XL-Q (Rotax 462) SW-TE-0350 & SW-WQ-0456			28. 6.91	P.Franchi	London NW6	3. 3.00P
G-MWVA	Solar Wings Pegasus XL-Q (Rotax 462) SW-TE-0351 & SW-WQ-0457			28. 6.91	P.C.Hancox	Tewkesbury	28.10.00P

Regn	Type	C/n	P/I	Date	Owner/operator	Probable Base	CA Expy
G-MWVE	Solar Wings Pegasus XL-R (Rotax 447) SW-TB-1441 & SW-WA-1524			18. 7.91	W.A.Keel-Stocker	Long Marston	13. 4.00P
G-MWVF	Solar Wings Pegasus XL-R/Se (Rotax 447) SW-TB-1442 & SW-WA-1525			18. 7.91	M.Tomlinson	Hatherton, Cannock	9. 4.00P
G-MWVG	CFM Shadow Srs.CD (Rotax 503)	151		5. 8.91	Shadow Flight Centre Ltd	Old Sarum	16.10.00P
G-MWVH	CFM Shadow Srs.CD (Rotax 503)	181		5. 8.91	D.J.Cross	Inverness	13. 6.00P
G-MWVI*	Whittaker MW-6 Merlin	PFA/164-11432		1. 9.89	B.H. & P.M.Gilmore (Cancelled by CAA 3.3.99)	Whitminster, Glos	
G-MWVK	Mainair Mercury 849-0891-5 & W643 (Rotax 503)			13. 8.91	J.Northage	Ilkley	10. 7.00P
G-MWVL	Rans S-6 ESD Coyote II (Rotax 503) 0892-341 & PFA/204-12118			13. 8.91 (Originally built with frame c/n 0491-186)	G.G.Hunt	Long Marston	28. 5.00P
G-MWVM	Solar Wings Pegasus Quasar IITC (Rotax 503) SW-TQ-0031 & SW-WX-0020		G-65-8	2. 9.91	J.D.Jones & A.A.Edmonds	Shrewsbury	29. 8.00P
G-MWVN	Mainair Gemini/Flash 2A (Rotax 503) 850-0891-7 & W644			19. 8.91	J.McCafferty	Enstone	20.11.00P
G-MWVO	Mainair Gemini/Flash 2A (Rotax 582) 852-0891-7 & W646			27. 8.91	P.J.Hughes	Chelmsford	11 7.00P
G-MWVP	Murphy Renegade Spirit UK (Rotax 582) PFA/188-11735			22. 8.91	T.B.Woolley "Spirit of Lancashire" (Damaged Redlands, Swindon 3.7.93)	Leicester	29. 4.94P
G-MWVR	Mainair Gemini/Flash 2A (Rotax 503) 855-0991-7 & W650			30. 8.91	G.Cartwright	Northampton	10. 4.00P
G-MWVS	Mainair Gemini/Flash 2A 856-0991-7 & W651			30. 8.91	V.T.Betts	Cannock	13.12.99P
G-MWVT	Mainair Gemini/Flash 2A (Rotax 503) 860-1091-7 & W655			2. 9.91	J.Barlow & C.Osiejuk	Oxton, Nottingham	8.11.00P
G-MWVU	Medway Hybred 44XLR MR123/102 (Rotax 503)			18. 9.91	Medway Microlights Ltd	Stoke, Kent	19. 9.00P
G-MWVW	Mainair Gemini/Flash 2A (Rotax 503) 853-0891-7 & W647			9. 9.91	W.O'Brien	Arclid Green, Sandbach	12. 7.99P
G-MWVY	Mainair Gemini/Flash 2A (Rotax 503) 854-0991-7 & W649			4. 9.91	J.D.Hinton	Tunbridge Wells	3. 5.00P
G-MWVZ	Mainair Gemini/Flash 2A (Rotax 503) 863-1091-7 & W658			4. 9.91	K.T.Leach	Skelmersdale	28. 8.00P
G-MWWA	Solar Wings Pegasus Quasar IITC (Rotax 503) SW-TQC-0073 & SW-WQT-0467			17. 9.91	C.Long	Pontypool	6.10.00P
G-MWWB	Mainair Gemini/Flash 2A (Rotax 503) 864-1091-7 & W659			18. 9.91	D.K.Royle	Guy Lane Farm, Waverton	30. 8.99P
G-MWWC	Mainair Gemini/Flash 2A (Rotax 582) 868-1191-7 & W663			23. 9.91	A. & D.Margereson	Chesterfield	28. 6.00P
G-MWWD	Murphy Renegade Spirit UK (Rotax 582) 344 & PFA/188-11719			23. 9.91	M.H.Moulai "Winning Spirit" (Damaged Windrush, Glos 31.5.99)	Scunthorpe	29. 7.99P
G-MWWE	TEAM miniMax PFA/186-11925 (Rotax 447)			1.10.91	J.Entwistle	Tarn Farm, Cockerham	23. 7.97P
G-MWWG	Solar Wings Pegasus XL-Q SW-WQ-0468 (Rotax 462HP)			3.10.91	A.W.Guerri	Rufforth	17. 7.00P
G-MWWH	Solar Wings Pegasus XL-Q (Rotax 462) SW-TE-0356 & SW-WQ-0469			3.10.91	M.R.Dunnett	Ludham	10. 7.00P
G-MWWI	Mainair Gemini/Flash 2A (Rotax 503) 870-1291-7 & W665			11.10.91	N.R.Osborne	Huddersfield	26. 5.00P
G-MWWJ	Mainair Gemini/Flash 2A (Rotax 503) 865-1191-7 & W660			22.10.91	J.Garcia	Kilmarnock	17. 8.98P
G-MWWK	Mainair Gemini/Flash 2A (Rotax 582) 866-1191-7 & W661			22.10.91	B.N.Thresher	Dunkeswell	7. 4.00P
G-MWWL	Rans S-6-ESD Coyote II (Rotax 503) PFA/204-11849		(G-BTXD)	17.10.91	D.W.Lloyd	Long Acres Farm, Sandy	16. 5.00P
G-MWWM	Kolb Twinstar mk.2 PFA/205-11645 (Rotax 503) (C/n duplicates G-GPST)		(G-BTXC)	17.10.91	D.Jordan	RAF Brize Norton	23. 6.00P
G-MWWN	Mainair Gemini/Flash 2A (Rotax 503) 872-1291-7 & W667			22.10.91	J.Nowill	Dunkeswell	9.10.00P
G-MWWO	Solar Wings Pegasus XL-R/Se (Rotax 447) SW-TB-1443 & SW-WA-1528			22.10.91	J.M.Cooper (Stored 9.97)	Great Orton	7. 7.96P
G-MWWP	Rans S-4 Coyote PFA/193-12073 (Rotax 447)			21.10.91	R.McKinlay	Strathaven	1. 8.00P
G-MWWR	Microflight Spectrum (Rotax 503)	024		23.10.91	C.S.Warr & B.Fukes	Market Rasen	25. 3.00P
G-MWWS	Thruster T300 089-T300-370 (Rotax 532)		EI-BYW	4.11.91	S.P.McCaffrey (Stored 3.97)	Ginge, Wantage	7. 7.95P

Regn	Type	C/n	P/I	Date	Owner/operator	Probable Base	CA Expy
G-MWWT	Thruster Super T300 (Rotax 582)	9012-ST300-503		25.10.91	Tempest Aviation Ltd	Wantage	1. 9.93P
G-MWWV	Solar Wings Pegasus XL-Q (Rotax 462HP)	SW-WQ-0470		30.10.91	R.W.Livingstone	Enniskillen	9.11.00P
G-MWWW*	Whittaker MW.6S Fatboy Flyer	PFA/164-11540		2. 9.91	Not known (Cancelled as destroyed 11.10.96: noted 8.99)	Dunkeswell	
G-MWWX	Microflight Spectrum (Rotax 503)	025		25.10.91	P.Turnbull & B.Smith	Whitley Bay	13. 5.00P
G-MWWZ	Cyclone Chaser S (Rotax 447)	CH.829		29.10.91	G.F.Clews	Roddige, Fradley	17. 6.00P
G-MWXA	Mainair Gemini/Flash 2A (Rotax 503)	873-0192-7 & W668		30.10.91	G.Sipson	Aldermans Green, Coventry	15. 8.97P
G-MWXB	Mainair Gemini/Flash 2A (Rotax 503)	869-1191-7 & W664		6.11.91	N.W.Barnett	Sittles Farm, Alrewas	14. 7.00P
G-MWXC	Mainair Gemini/Flash 2A (Rotax 503)	874-0192-7 & W669		6.11.91	G.Dufton-Kelly	Wirral	12.10.00P
G-MWXD*	Mainair Gemini/Flash 2A (Rotax 462)	876-0192-7 & W671		6.11.91	D.H.Wood (Cancelled as destroyed 27.10.99)	Heysham	6. 5.00P
G-MWXF	Mainair Mercury (Rotax 503)	867-1191-5 & W662		12.11.91	S.M.Hillyer-Jones	Shobdon	14. 6.00P
G-MWXG	Solar Wings Pegasus Quasar IITC (Rotax 503)	SW-TQC-0074 & SW-WQT-0471		7.11.91	J.E.Moseley	Saffron Walden	10. 6.00P
G-MWXH	Solar Wings Pegasus Quasar IITC (Rotax 503)	SW-TQC-0075 & SW-WQT-0472		7.11.91	G.A.Horrocks	Long Marston	20. 7.98P
G-MWXI	Solar Wings Pegasus Quasar IITC (Rotax 503)	SW-WQT-0473		7.11.91	F.Tibone	Abingdon	1. 4.94P
G-MWXJ	Mainair Mercury (Rotax 503)	861-1091-5 & W656		15.11.91	P.L.Parker	Baxby Manor, Husthwaite	18. 2.00P
G-MWXK	Mainair Mercury (Rotax 503)	862-1191-5 & W657		15.11.91	M.P.Wilkinson	Sandtoft	18. 7.96P
G-MWXL	Mainair Gemini/Flash 2A (Rotax 582)	859-1091-7 & W654		12.12.91	C.D.Joyner	Bognor Regis	30. 5.00P
G-MWXN	Mainair Gemini/Flash 2A (Rotax 582)	878-0192-7 & W673		20.11.91	P.I.Miles	Chesterfield	28. 5.00P
G-MWXO	Mainair Gemini/Flash 2A (Rotax 503)	880-0192-7 & W675		25.11.91	R.Pass	Roddige, Fradley	7.11.99P
G-MWXP	Solar Wings Pegasus XL-Q (Rotax 462)	SW-TE-0359 & SW-WQ-0475		26.11.91	A.P.Attfield	Sutton Meadows, Ely	18. 8.99P
G-MWXR	Solar Wings Pegasus XL-Q (Rotax 462)	SW-WQ-0476		26.11.91	G.W.Craig	Insch	12. 4.00P
G-MWXS	Mainair Gemini/Flash 2A (Rotax 503)	883-0292-7 & W678		4.12.91	P.Hall	Clay Cross	18. 7.96P
G-MWXU	Mainair Gemini/Flash 2A (Rotax 582)	882-0192-7 & W677		9.12.91	C.M.Mackinnon	East Fortune	13. 6.00P
G-MWXV	Mainair Gemini/Flash 2A (Rotax 582)	879-1291-7 & W674		9.12.91	Launch Link Systems Ltd	Oxton, Nottingham	23. 4.00P
G-MWXW	Cyclone Chaser S (Rotax 377)	CH.830		9.12.91	K.C.Dodd	Roddige, Fradley	22. 4.00P
G-MWXX	Cyclone Chaser S (Rotax 447)	CH.831	(G-MWEB) (G-MWCD)	9.12.91	R.E.J.Pattenden	Maidstone	3. 6.00P
G-MWXY	Cyclone Chaser S (Rotax 447)	CH.832	(G-MWEC)	19.12.91	A.E.Corfield	Newport	6. 6.00P
G-MWXZ	Cyclone Chaser S (Rotax 508)	CH.836		31.12.91	M.J.A.New "Daedalus"	Hughley, Much Wenlock	25. 4.00P
G-MWYA	Mainair Gemini/Flash 2A (Rotax 462)	886-0292-7 & W681		3. 1.92	R.F.Hunt	St.Michaels	9. 6.00P
G-MWYB	Solar Wings Pegasus XL-Q (Rotax 462)	SW-TE-0364 & SW-WQ-0485		15. 1.92	K.J.Wilson	Steyning	29. 7.00
G-MWYC	Solar Wings Pegasus XL-Q (Rotax 462)	SW-TE-0365 & SW-WQ-0486		15. 1.92	T.E.& A.T.Owen	RAF Mona	20. 6.00P
G-MWYD	CFM Shadow Srs.C (Rotax 503)	K.179		8. 1.92	J.Anderson	Plaistows, Hemel Hampstead	28. 5.00P
G-MWYE	Rans S-6-ESD Coyote II (Rotax 503)	0591-189 & PFA/204-12223		10. 1.92	D.K.Seath	RAF Benson	8. 6.00P
G-MWYG	Mainair Gemini/Flash 2A (Rotax 582)	884-0292-7 & W679		15. 1.92	M.S.McCrudden	Holywood, NI	30. 6.00P
G-MWYH	Mainair Gemini/Flash 2A (Rotax 503)	887-0292-7 & W682		15. 1.92	D.C.Jackson	Nottingham	13. 5.00P
G-MWYI	Solar Wings Pegasus Quasar IITC (Rotax 503)	SW-TQC-0083 & SW-WQT-0488		30. 1.92	T.S.Chadfield	Graveley	1. 4.00P

Regn	Type	C/n	P/I	Date	Owner/operator	Probable Base	CA Expy
G-MWYJ	Solar Wings Pegasus Quasar IITC (Rotax 503) SW-TQC-0084 & SW-WQT-0489			24. 1.92	R.E.Quine	Jurby, IoM	13. 3.00P
G-MWYL	Mainair Gemini/Flash 2A (Rotax 503) 877-0192-7 & W672			17. 1.92	A.Gannon	East Fortune	16. 5.00P
G-MWYM	Cyclone Chaser S 1000 CH.838 (Mosler MM-CB35)			21. 1.92	R.J.Cook	Glasgow	14.12.00P
G-MWYN	Rans S-6-ESD Coyote II (Rotax 503) 0491-185 & PFA/204-12168			22. 1.92	W.R.Tull	Milton-under-Wychwood	6. 5.00P
G-MWYS	CGS Hawk I Arrow (Rotax 447) H-T-470-R447 & BMAA/HB/020			17. 2.93	D.W.Hermiston-Hooper t/a Civilair	Ryde, IoW	
G-MWYT	Mainair Gemini/Flash 2A (Rotax 503) 881-0392-7 & W676			3. 2.92	M.A.Hodgson	Northallerton	17. 9.00P
G-MWYU	Solar Wings Pegasus XL-Q SW-WQ-0491 (Rotax 462)			30. 1.92	Hannah L.Rogers	Hailsham, E.Sussex	17.11.99P
G-MWYV	Mainair Gemini/Flash 2A (Rotax 582) 896-0392-7 & W691			3. 2.92	J.N.Whitworth	Chesterfield	19. 2.00P
G-MWYY	Solar Wings Pegasus XL-Q (Rotax 462) SW-TE-0365 & SW-WQ-0492			17. 2.92	R.D.Allard	Deenethorpe	18. 6.00P
G-MWYZ	Solar Wings Pegasus XL-Q SW-WQ-0474 (Rotax 462HP)			20.11.91	P.V.Stevens	Wantage	15. 5.00P
G-MWZA	Mainair Mercury 888-0292-5 & W683 (Rotax 503)			7. 2.92	A.J.Malham	Rufforth	7. 2.00P
G-MWZB	AMF Chevvron 2-32C 033 (Konig SD570)			10. 2.92	A.J.Pickup	Didcot	18. 8.00P
G-MWZC	Mainair Gemini/Flash 2A (Rotax 503) 899-0492-7 & W694			7. 2.92	G.H.Blaney	Stockport	18. 5.00P
G-MWZD	Solar Wings Pegasus Quasar IITC (Rotax 503) SW-TQC-0086 & SW-WQT-0494			2. 3.92	B.Hamilton	Long Marston	2. 4.00P
G-MWZE	Solar Wings Pegasus Quasar IITC (Rotax 503) SW-TQC-0087 & SW-WQT-0495			17. 2.92	W.A.Donnelly	Cumbernauld	18. 7.00P
G-MWZF	Solar Wings Pegasus Quasar IITC (Rotax 582/40) SW-TQD-0108 & SW-WQT-0496 (Trike c/n duplicates G-MYEK)			17. 2.92	R.G.T.Corney	Clench Common	29. 6.00P
G-MWZG	Mainair Gemini/Flash 2A (Rotax 582) 889-0392-7 & W684			7. 2.92	P.L.Braniff	Belfast	13. 6.00P
G-MWZH	Solar Wings Pegasus XL-R SW-WA-1532 (Rotax 462)			17. 2.92	P.A.Ord	Redcar	17. 4.00P
G-MWZI	Solar Wings Pegasus XL-R (Rotax 462) SW-TE-0367 & SW-WA-1533			17. 2.92	S.A.Oerton	Roddige, Fradley	21. 4.00P
G-MWZJ	Solar Wings Pegasus XL-R/Se (Rotax 462) SW-TE-0368 & SW-WA-1534			17. 2.92	P.Kitchen	Eshott	12. 6.00P
G-MWZL	Mainair Gemini/Flash 2A (Rotax 582) 900-0492-7 & W695			17. 2.92	G.Kerr	East Fortune	24. 6.00P
G-MWZM	TEAM miniMax 91 PFA/186-12211 (Mosler MM-CB40)	G-BUDD G-MWZM		18. 2.92	C.Leighton-Thomas "My Buddy"	Bath	19. 8.97P
G-MWZN	Mainair Gemini/Flash 2A (Rotax 582) 902-0492-7 & W697			25. 2.92	A.G.Marsh	Greenock	13. 2.00P
G-MWZO	Solar Wings Pegasus Quasar IITC (Rotax 503) SW-WQT-0498			26. 2.92	R.Oseland	Roddige, Fradley	29. 3.00P
G-MWZP	Solar Wings Pegasus Quasar IITC (Rotax 503) SW-TQC-0090 & SW-WQT-0499			26. 2.92	C.D.Hogbourne	Long Acres Farm, Sandy	17. 8.00P
G-MWZR	Solar Wings Pegasus Quasar IITC (Rotax 503) SW-WQT-0500			26. 2.92	J.A.Robinson	Kendal	23.7..00P
G-MWZS	Solar Wings Pegasus Quasar IITC (Rotax 503) SW-WQT-0501	EI-CIP G-MWZS		26. 2.92	B.H.A.Van Duykeren Grange Bannow, Co.Wexford		4. 7.00P
G-MWZT	Solar Wings Pegasus XL-R (Rotax 462) SW-TE-0370 & SW-WA-1535			26. 2.92	S.Kilpin	Sutton Meadows, Ely	12. 8.00P
G-MWZU	Solar Wings Pegasus XL-R SW-WA-1536 (Rotax 462)			26. 2.92	D.W.Palmer	Bexhill	8. 6.00P
G-MWZV	Solar Wings Pegasus XL-R SW-WA-1537 (Rotax 462)			26. 2.92	D.J.Newby	Clench Common	8. 8.99P
G-MWZW	Solar Wings Pegasus XL-R (Rotax 462) SW-TE-0373 & SW-WA-1538			26. 2.92	V.Goddard	Calne	16. 6.00P
G-MWZX	Solar Wings Pegasus XL-R (Rotax 462) SW-TE-0374 & SW-WA-1539			26. 2.92	N.M.S.Waters	Arundel	12. 8.99P
G-MWZY	Solar Wings Pegasus XL-R (Rotax 462) SW-TE-0375 & SW-WA-1540			26. 2.92	T.J.Birkbeck & P.G.Moss t/a Vale of York Hang Gliding Club	Rufforth	2. 2.00P
G-MWZZ	Solar Wings Pegasus XL-R (Rotax 462) SW-TE-0376 & SW-WA-1541			26. 2.92	M.P.Shea	Roddige, Fradley	13. 7.00P
G-MXVI	VS.361 Spitfire LF.XVIe CBAF.IX.4394	6850M TE184		17. 2.89	De Cadenet Motor Racing Ltd (As "TE184")	North Weald	27. 3.00P

Regn	Type	C/n	P/I	Date	Owner/operator	Probable Base	CA Expy
G-MYAB	Solar Wings Pegasus XL-R/Se (Rotax 462) SW-TE-0377 & SW-WA-1542			26. 2.92	A.N.F.Stewart (Stored 1.98)	Long Marston	20. 3.97P
G-MYAC	Solar Wings Pegasus XL-Q (Rotax 462) SW-TE-0378 & SW-WQ-0502			26. 2.92	M.A.Garner	Thetford	4.10.00P
G-MYAD	Solar Wings Pegasus XL-Q (Rotax 462HP) SW-TE-0379 & SW-WQ-0503			26. 2.92	P.Byrne	Hacketstown, Ireland	19. 6.00P
G-MYAE	Solar Wings Pegasus XL-Q (Rotax 462) SW-TE-0380 & SW-WQ-0504			26. 2.92	R.J.Waller	Redlands, Swindon	9. 1.99P
G-MYAF	Solar Wings Pegasus XL-Q (Rotax 462) SW-WQ-0505			26. 2.92	K.N.Rigley	Newark	15. 7.00P
G-MYAG	Quad City Challenger II (Rotax 503) PFA/177-12167			25. 2.92	J.W.G.Andrews	Welwyn	20. 8.97P
G-MYAH	Whittaker MW-5 Sorcerer (Rotax 447) PFA/163-11233			2. 3.92	W.G.Tait	Exmouth	12. 5.00P
G-MYAI	Mainair Mercury (Rotax 503) 892-0392-5 & W687			11. 3.92	J.M.Hodgson	Baxby Manor, Husthwaite	6. 5.00P
G-MYAJ	Rans S-6-ESD Coyote II (Tail-wheel u/c) (Rotax 503) 1291-248 & PFA/204-12227			3. 3.92	S.R.Green	Bristol	19. 5.00P
G-MYAK	Solar Wings Pegasus Quasar IITC (Rotax 503) SW-WQT-0506	D-G-MYAK		5. 3.92	R.S.McMaster	Sywell	1. 9.00P
G-MYAL*	Rotec Rally 2B DJC-01			5. 3.92	D.J.Cooper (Cancelled by CAA 29.3.99)	Kings Lynn	
G-MYAM	Murphy Renegade Spirit UK (Rotax 582) PFA/188-11907			6. 3.92	A.F.Reid	Newtownards, NI	7. 7.00P
G-MYAN	Aerotech MW-5(K) Sorcerer 5K-0017-02 (Rotax 447) (Full Lotus floats)	(G-MWNI)		24. 3.92	J.Hollings	Melbourne, Derby	9.10.99P
G-MYAO	Mainair Gemini/Flash 2A (Rotax 503) 894-0392-7 & W689			11. 3.92	D.Collins	Riggend, Airdrie	1. 8.98P
G-MYAP	Thruster T300 (Rotax 582) 9022-T300-501			12. 3.92	R.E.Williams & W.Fletcher (Damaged late 1994)	Swansea	28.11.95P
G-MYAR	Thruster T300 (Rotax 503) 9022-T300-502			12. 3.92	R.J.Ripley	Woolaston	25. 9.99P
G-MYAS	Mainair Gemini/Flash 2A (Rotax 503) 895-0392-7 & W690			11. 3.92	A.N.Duncanson	Redlands, Swindon	8. 5.00P
G-MYAT	TEAM miniMax PFA/186-12017 (Rotax 447)			6. 3.92	M.A.Perry	Rayleigh, Essex	1. 8.00P
G-MYAU	Mainair Gemini/Flash 2A (Rotax 462) 890-0392-7 & W685			25. 3.92	P.P.Allen	Ely	7. 8.00P
G-MYAV	Mainair Mercury 893-0392-5 & W688 (Rotax 503)			23. 3.92	J.Lynch	Baxby Manor, Husthwaite	20. 5.00P
G-MYAW	TEAM miniMax 91 PFA/186-12164 (Rotax 447)			11. 3.92	J.L.Hamer	Hartpury, Glos	1. 4.00P
G-MYAY	Microflight Spectrum 027 (Rotax 503)			13. 3.92	S.A.Clarehugh	Eshott	21.12.99P
G-MYAZ	Murphy Renegade Spirit UK (Rotax 582) PFA/188-12027			16. 3.92	R.Smith	Kilkerran	18. 6.00P
G-MYBA	Rans S-6-ESD Coyote II PFA/204-12210 (Rotax 503)			12. 3.92	M.R.Cann t/a Climsland Climber Society	Dunkeswell	30.11.99P
G-MYBB	Maxair Drifter MD.001 & BMAA/HB/014 (Rotax 503)			10. 4.92	M.Ingleton	Sheerness	12. 6.92P*
G-MYBC	CFM Shadow Srs.CD BMAA/HB/047 (Rotax 503) (Originally regd with c/ns K.195 & PFA/206-12221 - PFA c/n indicates a Streak Shadow incorrectly)			18. 3.92	M.E.Gilbert	Drummiard Farm, Bonnybank	24. 5.00P
G-MYBD	Solar Wings Pegasus Quasar IITC (Rotax 503) SW-WQT-0511			26. 3.92	A.M.Brumpton	Horncastle	11. 6.00P
G-MYBE	Solar Wings Pegasus Quasar IITC (Rotax 503) SW-WQT-0512			26. 3.92	G Heslop	Moor Row	29. 9.00P
G-MYBF	Solar Wings Pegasus XL-Q (Rotax 462) SW-TE-0384 & SW-WQ-0513			26. 3.92	M.R.Williamson	Sutton Meadows, Ely	11.11.00P
G-MYBG	Solar Wings Pegasus XL-Q (Rotax 462) SW-TE-0385 & SW-WQ-0514			26. 3.92	P.A.Henretty & M.Aylett	Northampton	13. 5.00P
G-MYBH*	Eipper Quicksilver GT500 0173			25. 3.92	D.Smith (Cancelled by CAA 18.3.99)	Goole	
G-MYBI	Rans S-6-ESD Coyote II (Rotax 503) 1291.249 & PFA/204-12186			26. 3.92	J.C.O'Donnell	Shotteswell	11.10.00P
G-MYBJ	Mainair Gemini/Flash 2A (Rotax 462) 908-0593-7 & W706			2. 4.92	C.Nicholson	Sandtoft	12. 9.00P
G-MYBL	CFM Shadow Srs.CD K.194 (Rotax 503)			2. 4.92	R.Garrod & S.M.Hart	Stowmarket/Ipswich	8. 1.00P
G-MYBM	TEAM miniMax 91 PFA/186-12212 (Mosler MM-CB35)			3. 4.92	M.K.Dring	East Kirkby	22.10.99P
G-MYBN	Hiway Skytrike mkII/Demon 175 BRL-01			14. 4.92	B.R.Lamming	Seaton, Hull	

Regn	Type	C/n	P/I	Date	Owner/operator	Probable Base	CA Expy
G-MYBO	Solar Wings Pegasus XL-R SW-WA-1545 (Rotax 447)			16. 4.92	K.Sene	Chesham	27. 1.00P
G-MYBP	Solar Wings Pegasus XL-R/Se (Rotax 447) SW-TB-1446 & SW-WA-1546			16. 4.92	N. & J.M.Hodgkinson	Great Orton	5. 7.00P
G-MYBR	Solar Wings Pegasus XL-Q (Rotax 462) SW-TE-0386 & SW-WQ-0517			16. 4.92	M.J.Larbey & G.T.Hunt	Watford	16. 6.00P
G-MYBS	Solar Wings Pegasus XL-Q (Rotax 462) SW-WQ-0518			16. 4.92	J.L.Parker	Maidstone	17. 7.00P
G-MYBT	Solar Wings Pegasus Quasar IITC (Rotax 503) SW-WQT-0519			16. 4.92	I.D.Rutherford	High Wycombe	20. 8.00P
G-MYBU	Cyclone Chaser S (Rotax 447)	CH.837	G-69-15 G-MYBU	28. 4.92	R.L.Arscott	Taunton	21. 1.00P
G-MYBV	Solar Wings Pegasus XL-Q (Rotax 462) SW-TE-0393 & SW-WQ-0522			5. 5.92	G.M.Balaam	Long Acres Farm, Sandy	12.10.00P
G-MYBW	Solar Wings Pegasus XL-Q SW-WQ-0523 (Rotax 462)			5. 5.92	J.S.Chapman	Knaresborough	24. 7.00P
G-MYBX	Solar Wings Pegasus XL-Q SW-WQ-0524 (Rotax 462)		(F-) G-MYBX	5. 5.92	P.A.Mowbray	Newark	28.11.92P*
G-MYBY	Solar Wings Pegasus XL-Q (Rotax 462) SW-TE-0396 & SW-WQ-0525			5. 5.92	P.R.Brooker	Smarden, Kent	12. 8.00P
G-MYBZ	Solar Wings Pegasus XL-Q (Rotax 462) SW-TE-0397 & SW-WQ-0526			5. 5.92	J.M.Todd	Long Marston	27. 9.97P
G-MYCA	Whittaker MW-6 Merlin PFA/164-11821 (Rotax 532)			14. 5.92	R.B.Skinner	Beaworthy, Devon	2. 4.00P
G-MYCB	Cyclone Chaser S (Rotax 447)	CH.839		18. 5.92	E.B.Jones	Crickhowell	10. 9.00P
G-MYCE	Solar Wings Pegasus Quasar IITC (Rotax 503) SW-TQC-0098 & SW-WQT-0527			14. 5.92	J.G.Robinson	Scarborough	20. 6.00P
G-MYCF	Solar Wings Pegasus Quasar IITC (Rotax 503) SW-TQC-0099 & SW-WQT-0528			14. 5.92	I.J.Bratt	Telford	21. 6.00P
G-MYCJ	Mainair Mercury 906-0592-5 & W704 (Rotax 503) (Wing c/n unconfirmed & duplicates G-MYAX)			19. 5.92	C.G.Rodger	East Fortune	24.11.00P
G-MYCK	Mainair Gemini/Flash 2A (Rotax 462) 909-0592-7 & W707			19. 5.92	D.N.Powell	Ince Blundell	27. 8.00P
G-MYCL	Mainair Mercury 910-0592-5 & W708 (Rotax 503)			19. 5.92	Palladium Leisure Ltd	Fenland	10. 6.97P
G-MYCM	CFM Shadow Srs.CD (Rotax 503)	196		20. 5.92	T.Jones	Redhill	20. 5.99P
G-MYCN	Mainair Mercury 901-0492-5 & W696 (Rotax 503)			22. 5.92	P Lowham	Caledon, NI	5. 3.00P
G-MYCO	Murphy Renegade Spirit UK (Rotax 582) PFA/188-12020			28. 5.92	V.A. & C.V.Brierley	Dover	27. 7.00P
G-MYCP	Whittaker MW-6 Merlin PFA/164-11505 (Rotax 532)			2. 6.92	P.Harris	Otherton, Cannock	20. 5.99P
G-MYCR	Mainair Gemini/Flash 2A (Rotax 503) 875-0192-7 & W670			10. 6.92	I.G.Webster	Stoke-on-Trent	10. 2.00P
G-MYCS	Mainair Gemini/Flash 2A (Rotax 503) 911-0592-7 & W710			12. 6.92	G.Penson Baxby Manor, Husthwaite t/a Husthwaite Alpha Group		25. 7.00P
G-MYCT	TEAM miniMax 91 PFA/186-12163 (Rotax 447)			30. 3.92	S.R.Roberts	Stowmarket	2.11.99P
G-MYCU	Whittaker MW-6 Merlin PFA/164-11627 (Rotax 532) (PFA c/n duplicates Streak Shadow G-ORAF)			9. 6.92	R.D.Thomasson	Romford	20. 9.00P
G-MYCV	Mainair Mercury 913-0792-5 & W712 (Rotax 503)			12. 6.92	D.P.Creedy	Crewe	11. 7.00P
G-MYCW	Powerchute Kestrel (Rotax 503)	00420		15. 6.92	C.D.Treffers	Basildon	30. 5.00P
G-MYCX	Powerchute Kestrel (Rotax 503)	00421		15. 6.92	D.Pedlow	Oswestry	24. 7.00P
G-MYCY	Powerchute Kestrel (Rotax 503)	00422		15. 6.92	D.S.Baber	Amersham	18. 8.00P
G-MYCZ	Powerchute Kestrel (Rotax 503)	00423		15. 6.92	A.F.Hardy	Newtownards	10.10.95P
G-MYDA	Powerchute Kestrel (Rotax 503)	00424		15. 6.92	K.J.Greatrix	Sleaford	17.11.00P
G-MYDB	Powerchute Kestrel (Rotax 503)	00425		15. 6.92	Coppard Plant Hire Ltd	Crowborough	28.10.93P
G-MYDC	Mainair Mercury 916-0792-5 & W715 (Rotax 503)			23. 6.92	D.J.Boylan & D.Gordon	Rufforth	12. 9.00P
G-MYDE	CFM Shadow Srs.CD (Rotax 503)	K.187		24. 6.92	D.N.L.Howell	Malvern	8. 2.00P

Regn	Type	C/n	P/I	Date	Owner/operator	Probable Base	CA Expy
G-MYDF	TEAM miniMax 91 PFA/186-12129 (Rotax 447)			24. 6.92	A.R.Mikolajczyk Headon Farm, Notts (Damaged Oxton, Notts 2.5.99)		7. 9.99P
G-MYDI	Solar Wings Pegasus XL-R SW-WA-1557 (Rotax 462HP)			26. 6.92	W.Greenwood Swanborough t/a Southern Hang Gliding Aerotow Group		4. 5.00P
G-MYDJ	Solar Wings Pegasus XL-R SW-WA-1558 (Rotax 462)			1. 7.92	A.M.Webb Swanton Morley t/a Norfolk Aero Tow		7. 5.00P
G-MYDK	Rans S-6-ESD Coyote II (Rotax 503) 0392-276 & PFA/204-12239			21. 4.92	E.Gordon Eshott t/a G-MYDK Group		13. 6.00P
G-MYDL	Aerotech MW-5(K) Sorcerer PFA/163-12106			26. 6.92	S.J.Field	Bridgwater	
G-MYDM	Whittaker MW-6S Fatboy Flyer (Rotax 582) PFA/164-12105			26. 6.92	A.L. & A.R.Roberts	RAF Cranwell	29. 3.00P
G-MYDN	Quad City Challenger II UK (Rotax 462) CH2-1091-UK-0736 & PFA/177-12245			30. 6.92	T.C. & R.Hooks	Newtownards	27. 7.00P
G-MYDO	Rans S-5 Coyote (Rotax 447) 89-110 & PFA/193-12274			6. 7.92	B.J.Benton	Long Marston	15. 6.00P
G-MYDP	Kolb Twinstar Mk.3 PFA/205-12231 (Rotax 503)			15. 7.92	L.G.Horne	Ashford, Kent	26. 4.00P
G-MYDR	Thruster T300 9072-T300-505 (Rotax 582)			21. 7.92	H.G.Soper	Lewes	19. 7.00P
G-MYDS	Quad City Challenger II UK (Rotax 503) CH2-1289-UK-0500 & PFA/177-11716			6. 3.90	A.C.Ryall	Swansea	13. 6.00P
G-MYDT	Thruster T300 9072-T300-506 (Rotax 582)			21. 7.92	A.W.Brandsom Ford Hill Farm, Ternhill		10. 1.96P
G-MYDU	Thruster T300 9072-T300-504 (Rotax 582)			21. 7.92	Euroflight Microlight Club Ltd Dromore, Co.Down		18. 4.00P
G-MYDV	Mainair Gemini/Flash 2A (Rotax 462) 917-0892-7 & W716			29. 7.92	A.Gibson	St.Michaels	27. 8.00P
G-MYDW	Whittaker MW-6 Merlin PFA/164-12184 (Rotax 503)			27. 7.92	A.Chidlow	Mansfield	26. 4.96P
G-MYDX	Rans S-6-ESD Coyote II PFA/204-12238 (Rotax 503)			27. 7.92	R.J.Goodburn Spanhoe "The Ruptured Duck"		26. 5.00P
G-MYDZ	Mignet HM-1000 Balerit 66 (Rotax 582)			3. 8.92	Fleaplanes UK Ltd	Hatfield	12.12.99P
G-MYEA	Solar Wings Pegasus XL-Q (Rotax 462HP) SW-TE-0404 & SW-WQ-0537			28. 7.92	A.M.Taylor	Long Marston	28. 9.00P
G-MYEC	Solar Wings Pegasus XL-Q (Rotax 462HP) SW-TE-0406 & SW-WQ-0539			28. 7.92	D.Young Kemble t/a Pegasus Flight Training		8. 5.00P
G-MYED	Solar Wings Pegasus XL-R (Rotax 462HP) SW-TE-0405 & SW-WA-1559 (Trike may be SW-TE-0403)			28. 7.92	I.A.Clark	Sandtoft	13. 3.00P
G-MYEE*	Thruster TST mk.1 087-TST-206 (Rotax 503) -	ZK-FRW?		11. 8.92	A.P.Gornall Popham (Cancelled as destroyed 16.10.98: dumped Wantage 7.98)		1.12.98P
G-MYEF*	Whittaker MW-6 Merlin PFA/164-11327			28. 5.92	S.Meadowcroft Long Acres Farm, Sandy (Cancelled by CAA 6.3.99: noted 9.99)		
G-MYEG	Solar Wings Pegasus XL-R (Rotax 447) SW-TB-1447 & SW-WA-1560			4. 8.92	D.G.Matthews	London Colney	15.10.00P
G-MYEH	Solar Wings Pegasus XL-R SW-WA-1561 (Rotax 447)			4. 8.92	T.P.Hutchinson	Bridgnorth	11. 3.00P
G-MYEI	Cyclone Chaser S CH.841 (Rotax 447)			18. 8.92	T.Cottrell	Douglas, IOM	18. 4.99P
G-MYEJ	Cyclone Chaser S CH.842 (Rotax 447)			18. 8.92	D.A.Cochrane	Newnham	3. 4.00P
G-MYEK	Solar Wings Pegasus Quasar IITC (Rotax 582/40) SW-TQD-0108 & SW-WQT-0540			7. 8.92	B.A.McWilliams Long Marston (See G-MWZF)		17. 7.00P
G-MYEM	Solar Wings Pegasus Quasar IITC (Rotax 582/40) SW-TQD-0101 & SW-WQT-0542			7. 8.92	D.J.Moore	Oakington, Cambs	7. 8.00P
G-MYEN	Solar Wings Pegasus Quasar IITC (Rotax 582/40) SW-TQD-0105 & SW-WQT-0543			7. 8.92	P.R.Jeffcoat & D.Johnson Upton Snodsbury		24. 1.00P
G-MYEO	Solar Wings Pegasus Quasar IITC (Rotax 582/40) SW-TQD-0106 & SW-WQT-0544			7. 8.92	Avelec Ltd	Enstone	24. 8.88P
G-MYEP	CFM Shadow Srs.CD K.205 (Rotax 503)			13. 8.92	E.M.Middleton	Hereford	15. 4.88P
G-MYER	Cyclone AX2000 B.1052901 & CA.001 (Rotax 582/48)	G-69-27 G-MYER/G-69-5/59-GF		19. 8.92	W.J.Whyte	Insch	24. 6.88P
G-MYES	Rans S-6-ESD Coyote II (Rotax 503) 0392-283 & PFA/204-12254			3. 7.92	W.R.Gilgrist Tarporley t/a Dairy House Flyers		2. 1.01P
G-MYET	Whittaker MW-6 Merlin PFA/164-12318 (Rotax 503)			19. 8.92	M.B.Haine	Christchurch	22. 7.00P
G-MYEU	Mainair Gemini/Flash 2A (Rotax 503) 918-0892-7 & W718			1. 9.92	G.J.Webster & G.J.Williams	Telford	6. 5.00P
G-MYEV	Whittaker MW-6 Merlin PFA/164-11250			25. 8.92	M.M.Ruck	Pontyclun	

Regn	Type	C/n	P/I	Date	Owner/operator	Probable Base	CA Expy
G-MYEX	Powerchute Kestrel (Rotax 503)	00426		28. 8.92	R.S.McFadyen	Tamworth	5.11.00P
G-MYFA	Powerchute Kestrel (Rotax 503)	00429		28. 8.95	D.A.Gardner	Balfron, Glasgow	23. 3.98P
G-MYFE	Rans S-6-ESD Coyote II PFA/204-12232 (Rotax 503)			1. 9.92	K.A.Mitchell	Henley-in-Arden	22. 9.00P
G-MYFG	Hunt Avon Skytrike/Hunt Wing 92040006 & BMAA/HB/017			4. 9.92	S.F.Carey (Cancelled by CAA 16.7.98)	London SE19	
G-MYFH	Quad City Challenger II UK (Rotax 503) CH2-0292-0798 & PFA/177-12282			9. 9.92	R.J. & C.J.Lines	Sandtoft	11. 4.00P
G-MYFI	Cyclone AX3 (Rotax 503)	C.3093159 & CA.002		9. 9.92	C.M.Bulmer & P.M.Voznick	Long Acres Farm, Sandy	5.12.00P
G-MYFJ	Solar Wings Pegasus Quasar IITC (Rotax 582/40)	SW-WQT-0552		11. 9.92	J.Mannion	Kettlethorpe, Lincoln	20. 3.93P*
G-MYFK	Solar Wings Pegasus Quasar IITC (Rotax 582/40) SW-TQD-0113 & SW-WQT-0553			11. 9.92	P.Corke	Long Acres Farm, Sandy	9. 6.99P
G-MYFL	Solar Wings Pegasus Quasar IITC (Rotax 582/40) SW-TQD-0103 & SW-WQT-0541/A (Originally regd as c/n SW-WQT-0554; replacement wing fitted to trike G-MYEL after wing stolen 1.1.93)			11. 9.92	S.B.Wilkes	Roddige, Fradley	30. 5.00P
G-MYFM	Murphy Renegade Spirit UK (Rotax 582)	PFA/188-12249		9. 9.92	A.C.Cale	Long Marston	21.11.00P
G-MYFN	Rans S-5 Coyote (Rotax 447) 89-112 & PFA/193-12273			16. 9.92	D.J.Minary	Rufforth	4. 3.00P
G-MYFO	Cyclone Chaser S (Rotax 377)	CH.843		22. 9.92	A.P.Skipper	Wollaston	22. 5.00P
G-MYFP	Mainair Gemini/Flash 2A (Rotax 503) 920-0992-7 & W719			2.10.92	J.S.Hill & G.H.S.Skilton	Stone	10.11.00P
G-MYFR	Mainair Gemini/Flash 2A (Rotax 503) 921-0992-7 & W720			30. 9.92	M.A.Pugh	London N10	10. 7.97P
G-MYFS	Solar Wings Pegasus XL-R (Rotax 447) SW-TB-1453 & SW-WA-1564			30. 9.92	A.Godber (Damaged mid 1995; stored 4.96)	Alrewas	2. 7.95P
G-MYFT	Mainair Scorcher 922-0992-3 & W234			30. 9.92	M.P.Law	Rochdale	11. 8.99P
G-MYFU	Mainair Gemini/Flash 2A (Rotax 462) 924-1092-7 & W722			7.10.92	S.Meadowcroft	Barton	13. 6.00P
G-MYFV	Cyclone AX3 (Rotax 503)	C.2083050		6.10.92	P.J. Barton	Sandy	24. 3.00P
G-MYFW	Cyclone AX3 (Rotax 503)	C.2083051		13.10.92	T.W.Stewart & D.L.Frankland t/a G-MYFW Flying Group	Eshott	2. 8.00P
G-MYFX	Solar Wings Pegasus XL-Q (Rotax 462)	SW-WQ-0378	(ex ??)	25. 6.93	M.M.Danek	Long Acres Farm, Sandy	19. 3.00P
G-MYFY	Cyclone AX3 (Rotax 503)	C.2083047		1.10.92	P.Rielly & F.J.Lloyd	Tarn Farm, Cockerham	5.11.00P
G-MYFZ	Cyclone AX3 (Rotax 503)	C.2083048		20.10.92	M.L.Smith t/a Buzzard Flying Group	Popham	25.11.00P
G-MYGD	Cyclone AX3 (Rotax 503)	C.2083049		21.10.92	D.Young t/a Kemble Flying Club	Kemble	3.12.00P
G-MYGE	Whittaker MW-6 Merlin PFA/164-11650 (Rotax 532)			20.10.92	M.D. & S.M.North	Manor Farm, Croughton	24. 6.97P
G-MYGF	TEAM miniMax 91 PFA/186-12175 (Rotax 447)			22.10.92	R.D.Barnard	Ley Farm, Chirk	27. 5.00P
G-MYGG*	Mainair Mercury 927-1192-7 & W724 (Rotax 503)			18.11.92	Not known (Crashed nr Sandtoft 31.8.95: wreck stored 5.97)	Sandtoft	17.11.95P
G-MYGH	Rans S-6-ESD Coyote II (Rotax 503) 0692-318 & PFA/204-12335			30.10.92	J.A.Moss	Needham, Harleston	24. 5.00P
G-MYGI	Cyclone Chaser S (Rotax 447)	CH.844		2.11.92	A.D.Stanyer	Sywell	26. 7.99P
G-MYGJ	Mainair Mercury 923-0992-7 & W721 (Rotax 503)			5.10.92	N.E.Parkinson	Arclid Green, Sandbach	22.10.00P
G-MYGK	Cyclone Chaser S (Rotax 508)	CH.846		3.11.92	P.C.Collins	Bath	14.11.95P
G-MYGM	Quad City Challenger II UK (Rotax 503) PFA/177-12261 & CH2-0391-UK-0662			6.11.92	R.Holt	Mill Farm, Hughley, Much Wenlock	29. 7.00P
G-MYGN	AMF Super Chevvron 2-32C (Konig SD.570)	034		29.12.92	Finish Design Ltd t/a Air-Share	Tarn Farm, Cockerham	1. 8.98P
G-MYGO	CFM Shadow Srs.CD (Rotax 503)	K.114		28. 7.92	R.C.S.Mason	Wootton, Bedford	10. 2.000
G-MYGP	Rans S-6-ESD Coyote II (Rotax 503) 0992-349 & PFA/204-12368			10.11.92	J.H.Kempton	Salcombe	14. 2.00P
G-MYGR	Rans S-6-ESD Coyote II PFA/204-12378 (Rotax 503)			16.11.92	R.B.M.Etherington	Totnes	2.3.00P

Regn	Type	C/n	P/I	Date	Owner/operator	Probable Base	CA Expy
G-MYGT	Solar Wings Pegasus XL-R (Rotax 462)	SW-WA-1569		13.11.92	J.J.Hoer t/a Condors Aerotow Syndicate	Dunkeswell	22. 3.00P
G-MYGU	Solar Wings Pegasus XL-R (Rotax 462)	SW-TE-0414 & SW-WA-1570		13.11.92	W.H.J.Knowles	Weston Zoyland	28.10.00P
G-MYGV	Solar Wings Pegasus XL-R (Rotax 462HP)	SW-TE-0415 & SW-WA-1571		13.11.92	D.J.Brixton Bishops Castle, Shropshire t/a Shropshire Tow Group		7. 5.00P
G-MYGZ	Mainair Gemini/Flash 2A (Rotax 582)	928-1192-7 & W726		18.11.92	D.D.Parry	Ware	22.11.00P
G-MYHF	Mainair Gemini/Flash 2A (Rotax 503)	929-1092-7 & W727		25.11.92	J.R.Gibson	St.Michaels	21. 6.00P
G-MYHG	Cyclone AX3 (Rotax 503)	C.2103070		27.11.92	I.McDiarmid t/a G-MYHG Flying Group	Strathaven	10. 6.00P
G-MYHH	Cyclone AX3 (Rotax 503)	C.2103069 & CA.006		30.11.92	M.L.Smith	Popham	8. 4.00P
G-MYHI	Rans S-6-ESD Coyote II (Rotax 503)	PFA/204-12279		8.12.92	L.N.Anderson	Weston Zoyland	15. 8.00P
G-MYHJ	Cyclone AX3 (Rotax 503) (Reported as c/n C.3093157 - see G-MYME)	C.2103073		11.12.92	P.E.Clarke	Long Marston	8. 2.00P
G-MYHK	Rans S-6-ESD Coyote II (Rotax 503)	0692-311 & PFA/204-12349		3.12.92	K.Joynson & M.A.Dunn	Sandtoft	27. 4.00P
G-MYHL	Mainair Gemini/Flash 2A (Rotax 503)	932-0193-7 & W730		21.12.92	J.M.Baines	Preston	3. 2.00P
G-MYHM	Cyclone AX3 (Rotax 503)	C.2103068 & CA.007		18.12.92	A.J.Bergman	Popham	3. 6.00P
G-MYHN	Mainair Gemini/Flash 2A (Rotax 582)	933-0193-7 & W731		29.12.92	D.M.Waddle	Pontefract	7. 5.00P
G-MYHP	Rans S-6-ESD Coyote II (Rotax 503)	0892-313 & PFA/204-12406		8. 1.93	J.M.Swash Sittles Farm, Alrewas "Grass Stripper"		7. 7.00P
G-MYHR	Cyclone AX3 (Rotax 503)	C.2103071	G-68-8 G-MYHR	15. 1.93	G.Humphrey t/a G-MYHR Flying Group	Oldbury	14. 4.99P
G-MYHS	Powerchute Kestrel (Rotax 503) (Frame No.00433/Parachute No.931013/Engine No.4104716)	00433		26. 1.93	R.Kent	Newark	6. 4.00P
G-MYHX	Mainair Gemini/Flash 2A (Rotax 582)	930-1292-7 & W728		2.12.92	G.Tomlinson	Eshott	26.12.99P
G-MYIA	Quad City Challenger II UK (Rotax 503)	PFA/177-12400		21. 1.93	I.J.Arkieson	Ley Farm, Chirk	3.10.00P
G-MYIE	Whittaker MW-6S Fatboy Flyer (Rotax 532)	PFA/164-11800		26. 1.93	P.A.Mercer	St.Michaels	24. 5.00P
G-MYIF	CFM Shadow Srs CD (Rotax 503)	217		2. 2.93	A.W.Shellis & S.D.Taylor	Otherton, Cannock	17. 5.00P
G-MYIH	Mainair Gemini/Flash 2A (Rotax 582)	937-0293-7 & W734		9. 3.93	C.A.Murray Loughton, Essex t/a G-MYIH Flying Group		27. 5.00P
G-MYII	TEAM miniMax 91 (Mosler CB40)	PFA/186-12119		10.11.92	K.R.H.Wingate	Hallwell, Totnes	20. 6.00P
G-MYIJ	Cyclone AX3 (Rotax 503)	C.2103072		8. 2.93	G.A.Breen	Lagos, Algarve	15. 4.00P
G-MYIK	Kolb Twinstar mk.3 (Rotax 582)	PFA/205-12220		13. 1.93	J.Latimer	Altrincham	13. 6.00P
G-MYIL	Cyclone Chaser S (Rotax 508)	CH.849		3. 3.93	R.A.Rawes "Fricky"	RAF Waddington	23. 1.00P
G-MYIM	Solar Wings Pegasus Quasar IITC (Rotax 582/40)	SW-WQT-0579	(EI-) G-MYIM	22. 2.93	D.Forde	Co. Galway, Ireland	15. 5.00P
G-MYIN	Solar Wings Pegasus Quasar IITC (Rotax 582/40)	SW-TQD-0123 & SW-WQT-0580		22. 2.93	M.P.Hadden	Long Marston	1. 8.00P
G-MYIO	Solar Wings Pegasus Quasar IITC (Rotax 582/40)	SW-TQD-0124 & SW-WQT-0581		22. 2.93	K.W.Brock	London SW19	25. 7.00P
G-MYIP	CFM Shadow Srs.CD (Rotax 503)	K.198		16. 3.93	S.S.M.Allardice	Old Sarum	18.10.00P
G-MYIR	Rans S-6-ESD Coyote II (Rotax 503)	0892-344 & PFA/204-12458		17. 3.93	I.R.Westrope	Haverhill, Suffolk	19. 8.00P
G-MYIS	Rans S-6-ESD Coyote II (Rotax 503) (Nose-wheel u/c)	PFA/204-12382		31.12.92	A.J.Wyatt	Haverfordwest	4. 7.00P
G-MYIT	Cyclone Chaser S (Rotax 508)	CH.850		19. 3.93	R.Barringer	Ravensthorpe, Northampton	28. 3.99P
G-MYIU	Cyclone AX3 (Rotax 503)	C.3013084		22. 3.93	P.Duffin	Toomebridge, NI	31. 3.00P
G-MYIV	Mainair Gemini/Flash 2A (Rotax 582)	938-0393-7 & W735		30. 3.93	P.S.Nicholls	Finmere	5. 4.00P
G-MYIX	Quad City Challenger II UK (Rotax 503)	CH2-0191-UK-0615 & PFA/177-12260		5. 1.93	A.Studley	Crewkerne	20. 7.99P

Regn	Type	C/n P/I	Date	Owner/operator	Probable Base	CA Expy
G-MYIY	Mainair Gemini/Flash 2A (Rotax 503) 942-0493-7 & W737		1. 4.93	I.C.Macbeth	Sandbach	22. 6.00P
G-MYIZ	TEAM miniMax 91 (Rotax 447)	PFA/186-12347	31. 3.93	S.E.Richardson	Escrick, York	19. 7.00P
G-MYJB	Mainair Gemini/Flash 2A (Rotax 503) 943-0593-7 & W738		7. 4.93	D.J.A.Sim & J.A.Parry-Sim	RAF Wyton	6.11.99P
G-MYJC	Mainair Gemini/Flash 2A (Rotax 462) 944-0593-7 & W739		7. 4.93	J.E.Cunliffe	Rufforth	14. 4.00P
G-MYJD	Rans S-6-ESD Coyote II (Rotax 503) 0792-324 & PFA/204-12360		23. 4.93	D.M.Newbould	Macclesfield	16.11.00P
G-MYJF	Thruster T.300 (Rotax 582)	9013-T300-509	14. 4.93	B.McConville	Craigavon, NI	24. 9.00P
G-MYJG	Thruster T.300 (Rotax 582)	9043-T300-510	14. 4.93	J.E.L.Goodall	Broadway	17. 7.00P
G-MYJH	Thruster T.300 (Rotax 582)	9013-T300-508	14. 4.93	B.O. & B.C.McCartan	Banbridge, Co.Down	13.12.99P
G-MYJJ	Solar Wings Pegasus Quasar IITC (Rotax 582/40) SW-TQD-0131 & SW-WQT-0591		27. 4.93	J.H.Sparks	Franklyns Field, Chewton Mendip	28. 9.00P
G-MYJK	Solar Wings Pegasus Quasar IITC (Rotax 582/40) SW-WQT-0592		27. 4.93	P.Kneeshaw	Alford	9. 5.00P
G-MYJL	Rans S-6-ESD Coyote II (Nose-wheel u/c) (Rotax 503) 0792-328 & PFA/204-12476		28. 4.93	R.J.Giddings & C.R.Marriott Sutton Meadows, Ely		27. 7.00P
G-MYJM	Mainair Gemini/Flash 2A (Rotax 582) 945-0593-7 & W740		29. 4.93	A.J.Boyd	Bangor, NI	27. 9.00P
G-MYJN	Mainair Mercury 946-0593-7 & W741 (Rotax 503)		29. 4.93	M T Jones Tullamore, Co.Offaly, Ireland		24. 5.95P
G-MYJO	Cyclone Chaser S (Rotax 508)	CH.851	30. 4.93	J.F.Phillips	Liskeard	24. 7.99P
G-MYJP	Murphy Renegade Spirit UK (Rotax 582) 357 & PFA/188-12045		3. 4.91	J.W.E.Pearson Burstom, St.Albans "Cloud Dancer/The Spirit of Luck"		27.10.00P
G-MYJR	Mainair Mercury 947-0593-7 & W742 (Rotax 503)		12. 5.93	T.C.F.Heaney	Epping	27. 1.99P
G-MYJS	Solar Wings Pegasus Quasar IITC 6581 (Rotax 582/40)		19. 5.93	P.J.Barton	Long Acres Farm, Sandy	7. 7.96P
G-MYJT	Solar Wings Pegasus Quasar IITC 6582 (Rotax 582/40)		19. 5.93	G.Stadler	Eshott	12. 9.99P
G-MYJU	Solar Wings Pegasus Quasar IITC 6573 (Rotax 582)		19. 5.93	P.G.Penhaligan	Hemel Hempstead	30. 5.00P
G-MYJW	Cyclone Chaser S (Rotax 508)	CH.856	19. 5.93	P.M.Coppola (Stored 8.96)	East Fortune	10. 9.94P
G-MYJX	Whittaker MW-8 001 & PFA/243-12345 (Rotax 508)		24. 5.93	M.W.J.Whittaker	Doncaster	3.12.95P*
G-MYJY	Rans S-6-ESD Coyote II (Rotax 503) 0692-317 & PFA/204-12346		24. 5.93	F.N.Pearson	Baxby Manor, Husthwaite	23. 8.99P
G-MYJZ	Whittaker MW-5D Sorcerer (Rotax 447)	PFA/163-12385	22. 4.93	P.A.Aston	Newton Abbot	2.12.99P
G-MYKA	Cyclone AX3 (Rotax 503)	C.3013086	25. 5.93	J.Thomas	Long Acres Farm, Sandy	3. 1.00P
G-MYKB	Kolb Twinstar mk.3 (Rotax 582)	PFA/205-12398	31. 3.93	D.Young	Eastbach Farm, Coleford	1. 9.00P
G-MYKC	Mainair Gemini/Flash 2A (Rotax 582) 948-0593-7 & W743		26. 5.93	J.Summersgill	Warrington	22.12.99P
G-MYKD	Cyclone Chaser S (Rotax 447)	CH.857	26. 5.93	J.V.Clewer	Ashford, Kent	9. 8.00P
G-MYKE	CFM Shadow Srs.BD (Rotax 447)	K.031	14. 1.88	M.Hughes Emlyn's Field, Rhuallt t/a MKH Engineering		26.10.96P
G-MYKF	Cyclone AX3 (Rotax 503)	C.3013083	8. 6.93	P.Jones	Tarn Farm, Cockerham	10. 7.00P
G-MYKG	Mainair Gemini/Flash 2A (Rotax 582) 950-0693-7 & W745		21. 6.93	P.G.Angus Higher Barn Farm, Houghton		12.11.00P
G-MYKH	Mainair Gemini/Flash 2A (Rotax 582) 951-0693-7 & W746		21. 6.93	K.G. & G.F.Atkinson Rufforth t/a F.Atkinson & Sons		4. 9.99P
G-MYKI	Mainair Mercury 953-0693-7 & W748 (Rotax 503)		21. 6.93	M.Wilkinson	Glasgow	4.10.98P
G-MYKJ	TEAM miniMax (Rotax 508)	PFA/186-12215	10. 6.93	P.I.Frost	Guilsborough, Northampton	8. 9.00P
G-MYKL	Medway Raven X (Rotax 447)	MRB116/104	6. 7.93	S.Hutchinson	RAF Wyton	24. 9.00P
G-MYKM	Medway Raven X (Rotax 447)	MRB106/105	6. 7.93	G R Holder	Uxbridge	3. 8.94P
				(Thought exported to Australia 1997/98)		

Regn	Type	C/n	P/I	Date	Owner/operator	Probable Base	CA Expy
G-MYKN	Rans S-6-ESD Coyote II PFA/204-12361 (Rotax 503)			23. 6.93	S.E. & L.Hartles "Captain Airfix" Lower Mountpleasant, Chatteris		11.11.00P
G-MYKO	Whittaker MW-6S Fatboy Flyer (Hirth 2706)	PFA/164-11919		25. 6.93	J.Glover	Bristol	27. 7.00P
G-MYKP	Solar Wings Pegasus Quasar IITC 6627 (Rotax 582/40)			7. 7.93	J.Mayer	Stoke-on-Trent	24.10.00P
G-MYKR	Solar Wings Pegasus Quasar IITC 6635 (Rotax 582/40)			7. 7.93	C.Stallard Larkins Farm, Laindon, Essex		26. 8.00P
G-MYKS	Solar Wings Pegasus Quasar IITC 6636 (Rotax 582/40)			7. 7.93	P.W.Sandwith	Pinner	14. 5.00P
G-MYKT	Cyclone AX3 (Rotax 503)	C.3013082		5. 7.93	A.Cooke-Sanderson t/a G-MYKT Group	Popham	8. 7.00P
G-MYKU	Medway Raven X (Rotax 447)	MRB117/107		9. 7.93	M.Woodmansey	Davidstow Moor	18. 6.99P
G-MYKV	Mainair Gemini/Flash 2A (Rotax 503)	954-0793-7 & W749		13. 7.93	J.White & P.Gulliver	Telford	6. 2.00P
G-MYKW	Mainair Mercury (Rotax 503)	960-0893-7 & W755		9. 7.93	N.O.Marsh	Rufforth	1. 3.00P
G-MYKX*	Mainair Mercury (Rotax 503)	961-0893-7 & W756		3. 9.93	L.R.Bain (Cancelled by CAA 27.3.99)	Perth	30.10.99P
G-MYKY	Mainair Mercury (Rotax 503)	962-0893-7 & W757		6. 8.93	R.P.Jewitt	York	14.12.99P
G-MYKZ	TEAM miniMax 91 (Rotax 503)	PFA/186-11841	G-BVAV	26. 7.93	W.W.Vinton	Cinderford	1. 9.00P
G-MYLA	Rans S-6-ESD Coyote II PFA/204-12543 (Rotax 503)			30. 7.93	W.A.Stevens Colchester (Crashed on take-off Cherry Tree Farm, Monewden 6.10.99)		1. 6.00P
G-MYLB	TEAM miniMax 91 (Rotax 532)	PFA/186-12419		2. 8.93	S.Stockill	Buckingham	18.10.00P
G-MYLC	Cyclone Pegasus Quantum 15 (Rotax 503)	6634		9. 8.93	T.E.Pedley	Earlswood	12. 6.98P
G-MYLD	Rans S-6-ESD Coyote II PFA/204-12394 (Rotax 503) (Tail-wheel u/c)			1. 3.93	F.Overall	Priory Farm, Tibenham	27. 6.00P
G-MYLE	Cyclone Pegasus Quantum 15 (Rotax 503)	6609		9. 8.93	Susan E.Powell	Enstone	19.12.00P
G-MYLF	Rans S-6-ESD Coyote II (Rotax 503) 0493-483 & PFA/204-12544			4. 8.93	D.& S.M.Jerwood "Low Flyer"	Newport	16.11.00P
G-MYLG	Mainair Gemini/Flash 2A (Rotax 503)	959-0893-7 & W754		6. 8.93	B.A.Coombe	Weybridge	19. 3.00P
G-MYLH	Cyclone Pegasus Quantum 15 (Rotax 503)	6632		27. 8.93	T.D'Amico	Northampton	10. 7.00P
G-MYLI	Cyclone Pegasus Quantum 15 (Rotax 503)	6645		11. 8.93	E.Jenkins & S.Walters t/a Metropolitan Police SE Area Microlight A/c Club		9. 5.00P
G-MYLJ	Cyclone Chaser S (Rotax 447)	CH.858		24. 8.93	B.W.Atkinson	North Coates	26. 2.00P
G-MYLK	Cyclone Pegasus Quantum 15 (Rotax 503)	6602		27. 8.93	C.L.Minter t/a G-MYLK Group	Deenethorpe	24. 9.00P
G-MYLL	Cyclone Pegasus Quantum 15 (Rotax 462HP)	6650		31. 8.93	N.Demmar	Warminster	21. 3.00P
G-MYLM	Cyclone Pegasus Quantum 15 (Rotax 582/40)	6651	(EC-) G-MYLM	31. 8.93	P.A.Banks	Milton Keynes	29. 2.00P
G-MYLN	Kolb Twinstar mk.3 (Rotax 582)	PFA/205-12430		3. 9.93	C.D.Hatcher	Deenethorpe	14. 6.00P
G-MYLO	Rans S-6-ESD Coyote II PFA/204-12334 (Rotax 503) (Tri-cycle u/c)			9. 9.93	P.G.Rogers	Ince Blundell	3.10.00P
G-MYLP	Kolb Twinstar mk.3 (Rotax 582)	PFA/205-12391	(G-BVCR)	9. 9.93	R.Thompson	Bristol	27. 5.99P
G-MYLR	Mainair Gemini/Flash 2A (Rotax 582)	964-0993-7 & W759		17. 9.93	L.McNaught & L.Kirk	Edinburgh	24. 3.00P
G-MYLS	Mainair Mercury (Rotax 503)	966-0993-7 & W761		5.10.93	D.Burnell-Higgs	Shobdon	6.11.96P
G-MYLT	Mainair Blade (Rotax 582)	967-1093-7 & W762		23. 9.93	A.R.Walsh	Ince Blundell	29. 5.00P
G-MYLV	CFM Shadow Srs.CD (Rotax 503)	220		24. 9.93	G.Gilhead & R.G.M.Proost Old Sarum t/a Aviation for Paraplegics & Tetraplegics Trust		20.12.99P
G-MYLW	Rans S-6-ESD Coyote II (Rotax 503) 1292-401 & PFA/204-12560			4. 8.93	M.J.Phillips	Priory Farm, Tibenham	15. 6.00P
G-MYLX	Medway Raven X (Rotax 447)	MRB113/109		6.10.93	T.M.Knight	Luton	12. 2.00P
G-MYLY	Medway Raven X) (Rotax 447)	MRB001/108		23. 9.93	C.R.Smith	Stanford-le-Hope	3.10.94P

Regn	Type	C/n	P/I	Date	Owner/operator	Probable Base	CA Expy
G-MYLZ	Cyclone Pegasus Quantum 15 (Rotax 462)	6672		6.10.93	J.L.Pollard & K.M.Walter Knapthorpe Lodge, Caunton		21.11.00P
G-MYMB	Cyclone Pegasus Quantum 15 (Rotax 582/40)	6674		6.10.93	C.A.Green "Firebird"	Winterborne Earls	27. 3.00P
G-MYMC	Cyclone Pegasus Quantum 15 (Rotax 582/40)	6675		6.10.93	D.A.Smith & E.Robshaw	Rufforth	20.12.99P
G-MYME	Cyclone AX3 (Rotax 503)	C.3093157		13.10.93	M.L.Smith (See G-MYHJ)	Popham	17.11.00P
G-MYMF	Cyclone AX3 (Rotax 503)	C.3093158		18.10.93	M.McClelland t/a McClelland Aviation	Old Sarum	5.11.00P
G-MYMG*	TEAM miniMax 91	PFA/186-12336		18.10.93	D.Bannister (Cancelled by CAA 18.3.99)	West Kilbride	
G-MYMH	Rans S-6-ESD Coyote II (Rotax 503) 0793-520 & PFA/204-12576			20.10.93	E.O.Otun	Maidenhead	1. 6.00P
G-MYMI	Kolb Twinstar mk.3 (Rotax 582)	PFA/205-12537		21.10.93	R.P.T.Harris	High Wycombe	3. 8.00P
G-MYMJ	Medway Raven X (Rotax 447)	MRB004/110		28.10.93	N.Brigginshaw	Fenland	12. 2.00P
G-MYMK	Mainair Gemini/Flash 2A (Rotax 582) 968-1193-7 & W763			29.10.93	A.Britton	Rickmansworth	27.11.00P
G-MYML	Mainair Mercury (Rotax 503) 969-1193-7 & W765			29.10.93	D.J.Dalley	Weymouth	21.10.98P
G-MYMM	Air Creation Fun 18S GT bis (Rotax 503)	93/001		30. 9.93	A.B.Greenbank Higher Barn Farm, Houghton		25. 7.00P
G-MYMN	Whittaker MW-6 Merlin (Rotax 582)	PFA/164-12124		29.10.93	K.J.Cole	Over Farm, Gloucester	23. 5.00P
G-MYMO	Mainair Gemini/Flash 2A (Rotax 503) 955-0793-7 & W750			24. 6.93	M.D.Sproson	Nottingham	13. 8.00P
G-MYMP	Rans S-6-ESD Coyote II (Rotax 503) 1291-250 & PFA/204-12436		(G-CHAZ)	5.11.93	J.B.Mayes	Newmarket	22.12.00P
G-MYMR	Rans S-6-ESD Coyote II (Rotax 503)	PFA/204-12580		17.11.93	J.Neilands	Ballybofey, Co.Donegal	11.10.99P
G-MYMS	Rans S-6-ESD Coyote II (Rotax 503) 0893-526 & PFA/204-12581			17.11.93	M.R.Johnson & P.G.Briscoe	Long Marston	5. 9.00P
G-MYMT	Mainair Mercury (Rotax 503) 970-1193-7 & W766			19.11.93	W. & C.A.Bradshaw	St.Michaels	9.12.00P
G-MYMV	Mainair Gemini/Flash 2A (Rotax 503) 971-1193-7 & W767			26.11.93	W.A.Edwards	Guy Lane Farm, Waverton	14. 3.00P
G-MYMW	Cyclone AX3 (Rotax 503)	C.3093156		23.11.93	L.J.Perring	Oakley	2.12.99P
G-MYMX	Cyclone Pegasus Quantum 15 (Rotax 582/40)	6705		1.12.93	J.E.McGee	Otherton, Cannock	24.11.98P
G-MYMY	Cyclone Chaser S (Rotax 508)	CH.860		7. 9.93	R.A.Keene	Over, Gloucester	7. 4.99P
G-MYMZ	Cyclone AX3 (Rotax 503)	C.3093154		7.12.93	The Microlight School (Lichfield) Ltd. Roddige, Fradley		15. 4.00P
G-MYNA	CFM Shadow Srs.C (Rotax 447)	K.023		10. 2.88	P.J.Walker	Lincoln	22. 7.00P
G-MYNB	Cyclone Pegasus Quantum 15 (Rotax 582/40)	6719		14.12.93	S.B.C.Wall	Melton Mowbray	1. 5.00P
G-MYNC	Mainair Mercury 973-1293-7 & W769			17.12.93	A.Brotheridge	Redlands, Swindon	1. 4.00P
G-MYND	Mainair Gemini/Flash 2A (Rotax 503) 841-0591-7 & W635			28. 5.91	G.C.Baird	Ludlow	3. 4.00P
G-MYNE	Rans S-6-ESD Coyote II (Rotax 503)	PFA/204-12497		25. 6.93	J.N.W.Moss	Templecombe	20. 5.00P
G-MYNF	Mainair Mercury 974-1293-7 & W770 (Rotax 503)			17. 1.94	E.D.Locke	Barton	24. 1.00P
G-MYNH	Rans S-6-ESD Coyote II (Rotax 462) 0493-487 & PFA/204-12616			30.12.93	E.F. & V.M.Clapham	Oldbury-on-Severn	9. 5.99P
G-MYNI	TEAM miniMax 91 (Mosler MM-CB35)	PFA/186-12314		22. 2.93	J.J.Penney	Neath	17.11.99P
G-MYNJ	Mainair Mercury 972-1293-7 & W768 (Rotax 503)			14. 1.94	S.M.Buchan	Leamington Spa	5. 8.00P
G-MYNK	Cyclone Pegasus Quantum 15 (Rotax 582/40)	6614		17.11.93	N.D.Azevedo	(London N5)	5. 7.00P
G-MYNL	Cyclone Pegasus Quantum 15 (Rotax 582/40)	6648		17.11.93	B.S.Smy	Poringland, Norwich	18. 9.00P
G-MYNM*	Cyclone Pegasus Quantum 15	6723		17.11.93	Not known (Stored 2.97)	Al Rafaah, UAE	
G-MYNN	Cyclone Pegasus Quantum 15 (Rotax 582/40)	6679		17.11.93	P.H.E.Woodliffe-Thomas	Thame	19.11.00P

Regn	Type	C/n P/I	Date	Owner/operator	Probable Base	CA Expy
G-MYNO	Cyclone Pegasus Quantum 15 (Rotax 582/40)	6724	10. 1.94	S.J.Baker	Sutton Meadows, Ely	22. 3.00P
G-MYNP	Cyclone Pegasus Quantum 15 (Rotax 582/40)	6688	17.11.93	R.H.Braithwaite t/a RAF Microlight Flying Association	RAF Cottesmore	12.12.99P
G-MYNR	Cyclone Pegasus Quantum 15 (Rotax 582/40)	6692	17.11.93	D.Pick	Boston	3. 4.00P
G-MYNS	Cyclone Pegasus Quantum 15 (Rotax 582/40)	6694	17.11.93	T.R.Marsh Wing Farm, Longbridge Deverill		13. 2.00P
G-MYNT	Cyclone Pegasus Quantum 15 (Rotax 582/40)	6693	17.11.93	P.A.Vernon	Devizes	20.11.00P
G-MYNU	Cyclone Pegasus Quasar IITC	6695	5. 1.94	R.Sfredda	Luxembourg	
G-MYNV	Cyclone Pegasus Quantum 15 (Rotax 582/40)	6725	10. 1.94	S.C.Jackson	Rufforth	28. 5.00P
G-MYNW	Cyclone Chaser S (Rotax 447)	CH.855	6. 1.94	M.T.G.Pope	Dubai, UAE	30. 1.95P
G-MYNX	CFM Streak Shadow SA-M (Rotax 618) K.193-SA-M & PFA/206-12268		15. 6.92	T.J. & M.D.Palmer	Cumbernauld	23. 6.00P
G-MYNY	Kolb Twinstar mk.3 PFA/205-12478 (Rotax 582)		22.11.93	B.Alexander	Swinford, Rugby	25. 8.98P
G-MYNZ	Cyclone Pegasus Quantum 15 (Rotax 582/40)	6709	18. 1.94	N.S.Lynall	Walsall	11. 3.97P
G-MYOA	Rans S-6-ESD Coyote II (Nose-wheel u/c) (Rotax 503) 0793.523 & PFA/204-12578		23.11.93	R.Powers	Walsall	4. 1.00P
G-MYOB	Mainair Mercury 976-1293-7 & W772 (Rotax 503)		8.12.93	J.C. & B.E.Barnes	Wisbech	19. 9.99P
G-MYOE	Cyclone Pegasus Quantum 15	6668	31. 1.94	J.P.Foret	Aron, France	
G-MYOF	Mainair Mercury 975-1293-7 & W771 (Rotax 503)		3.12.93	B.S.Ogden	Barton	4. 3.00P
G-MYOG	Kolb Twinstar mk.3 PFA/205-12449 (Hirth 2706)		19. 1.94	A.P. de Legh	Redhill	8. 4.00P
G-MYOH	CFM Shadow Srs.CD (Rotax 503)	K.201	27. 1.94	S.C.Smith	Popham	22. 3.00P
G-MYOI	Rans S-6-ESD Coyote II PFA/204-12503 (Rotax 503)		3. 2.94	J.Meijerink Coldharbour Farm, Willingham		7. 8.00P
G-MYOL	Air Creation Fun 18S GT bis 94/001 (Rotax 447)		7. 2.94	I.R.Scott & K.J.O'Grady Roddige, Fradley		7. 7.00P
G-MYOM	Mainair Gemini/Flash 2A (Rotax 582) 981-0294-7 & W777		14. 2.94	A.L.Walmsley	Rufforth	28. 3.99P
G-MYON	CFM Shadow Srs.CD (Rotax 503)	240	12. 1.94	P.M.McNair-Wilson	Old Sarum	28. 2.00P
G-MYOO	Kolb Twinstar mk.3M PFA/205-12200 (Rotax 582)		11. 5.92	P.D.Coppin	Colemore Common	15.10.00P
G-MYOR	Kolb Twinstar mk.3 PFA/205-12602 (Rotax 582)		16. 2.94	J.J.Littler	Chichester	26. 8.00P
G-MYOS	CFM Shadow Srs.CD (Rotax 503)	246	18. 2.94	E.J. & C.A.Bowles	Old Sarum	8. 3.00P
G-MYOT	Rans S-6-ESD Coyote II PFA/204-12668 (Rotax 503) (Tail-wheel u/c)		21. 2.94	S.Moreton	Long Marston	18. 4.00P
G-MYOU	Cyclone Pegasus Quantum 15 (Rotax 582/40)	6726	?. 3.94	D.W.General Wood Machinists Ltd	London Colney	17. 6.00P
G-MYOV	Mainair Mercury 979-0294-7 & W775 (Rotax 503)		1. 3.94	P.Brownrigg	Chester	12. 6.00P
G-MYOW	Mainair Gemini/Flash 2A (Rotax 503) 983-0294-7 & W779		16. 3.94	P.W.F.Coleman Corn Wood Farm, Adversane		16.10.00P
G-MYOX	Mainair Mercury 984-0294-7 & W780 (Rotax 503)		23. 2.94	A.D.Dudding	Sandtoft	20. 4.00P
G-MYOY	Cyclone AX3 (Rotax 503)	C.3123191	23. 2.94	D.O.Herbert t/a Cyclone Flying Group	Shobdon	4. 5.00P
G-MYOZ	Quad City Challenger II UK (Rotax 503) CH2-1093-1045 & PFA/177A-12640		24. 2.94	T.J.Wickham	Bordon, Hants	21. 9.99P
G-MYPA	Rans S-6-ESD Coyote II (Rotax 503) 0893-527 & PFA/204-12678		24. 2.94	L.J.Dutch	Tarn Farm, Cockerham	18. 1.99P
G-MYPC	Kolb Twinstar mk.3 PFA/205-12437 (Rotax 582)		2. 3.94	J.E.Twigge	Newcastle-under-Lyme	5. 7.00P
G-MYPD	Mainair Mercury 982-0294-7 & W778 (Rotax 462)		11. 3.94	A.Bennion	Northwich	14. 7.00P
G-MYPE	Mainair Gemini/Flash 2A (Rotax 582) 985-0394-7 & W781		11. 3.94	J.D.Capewell	East Fortune	21. 3.00P
G-MYPF	Solar Wings Pegasus Quasar IITC SW-WQT-0564		5. 4.94	Articles de Vol Libre	Luxembourg	

Regn	Type	C/n	P/I	Date	Owner/operator	Probable Base	CA Expy
G-MYPG	Solar Wings Pegasus XL-Q SW-WQ-0176 (Rotax 462)			29. 3.89	D.W.Lunn	(Wallington)	26. 5.99P
G-MYPH	Cyclone Pegasus Quantum 15 (Rotax 582/40)	6764		?. 3.94	P.M.J.White	Pickering	4. 6.00P
G-MYPI	Cyclone Pegasus Quantum 15 (Rotax 582/40)	6767		?. 3.94	E.M.Woods	Lydney, Glos	8. 5.00P
G-MYPJ	Rans S-6-ESD Coyote II (Rotax 503) 1293-569 & PFA/204-12692			18. 3.94	A.W.Fish	Eshott	8. 5.00P
G-MYPL	CFM Shadow Srs.CD (Rotax 503) K.213 & BMAA/HB/080			14. 2.94	G.I.Madden	Milton Keynes	28. 8.00P
G-MYPM	Cyclone AX3 (Rotax 503)	C.3123188		23. 3.94	Microflight Ireland Ltd Portrush, Co.Antrim		10. 4.00P
G-MYPN	Cyclone Pegasus Quantum 15 (Rotax 582/40)	6727		12. 4.94	A.H.McBreen	Rugby	14. 6.00P
G-MYPO	Hunt Wing/Experience (Rotax 503) 9409011, BMAA/HB/019 & BMAA/HB/026			28. 3.94	W.I.McMillan	Northwich	11.12.99P
G-MYPP	Whittaker MW-6S Fatboy Flyer PFA/164-12413			11. 4.94	D.S.L.Evans	Gravesend	
G-MYPR	Cyclone AX3 (Rotax 503)	C.3123190		13. 4.94	N.E.Ashton	Ince Blundell	6. 6.00P
G-MYPS	Whittaker MW-6 Merlin PFA/164-11585			19. 4.94	I.S.Bishop	RAF Bicester	
G-MYPT	CFM Shadow Srs.CD (Rotax 503)	K.212		22. 4.94	M.G. & S.A.Collins	Oldbury-on-Severn	23. 6.00P
G-MYPU*	Airwave Microchute UQ/Rave Motor 30 (Rotax 503) 023, PSP.101746 & BMAA/HB/023			22. 4.94	S.E.Jones (Cancelled by CAA 20.7.99)	Cardiff	20. 6.96P
G-MYPV	Mainair Mercury 986-0394-7 & W782 (Rotax 582)			18. 3.94	L.T.Neve	Nazeing	21. 5.00P
G-MYPW	Mainair Gemini/Flash 2A (Rotax 582) 991-0494-7 & W787			3. 5.94	N.A.Porter	Hoddesdon	18. 5.99P
G-MYPX	Cyclone Pegasus Quantum 15 (Rotax 582/40)	6785		28. 4.94	P.J.Callis & M.Aylett Kibworth/Loughborough		21.11.99P
G-MYPY	Cyclone Pegasus Quantum 15 (Rotax 582/40)	6786		12. 5.94	G.& G.Trudgill	(Durham)	6. 8.00P
G-MYPZ	Quad City Challenger II UK (Hirth 2706) CH2-1093-UK-1046 & PFA/177A-12689 (Regd incorrectly as CH2-0194-UK-1046)			2. 3.94	E.G.Astin t/a BFC	Whitby	12. 7.00P
G-MYRA	Kolb Twinstar mk.3 PFA/205-12434 (Rotax 503)			29. 3.94	S.J.Fox & A.P.Pickford	Popham	16. 4.00P
G-MYRB	Whittaker MW-5 Sorcerer PFA/163-11543			14. 4.94	P.J.Careless	Sandy	
G-MYRC	Mainair Blade 988-0594-7 & W784 (Rotax 462)			1. 6.94	A.T.Hayward	Ince Blundell	11. 8.00P
G-MYRD	Mainair Blade 989-0594-7 & W785 (Rotax 582)			20. 5.94	W.G.Minns	Burwash, East Sussex	11. 8.99P
G-MYRE	Cyclone Chaser S (Rotax 337)	CH.863	G-69-18 G MYRE	10. 5.94	M.P.Dodgson	Eshott	24. 7.99P
G-MYRF	Cyclone Pegasus Quantum 15 (Rotax 462HP)	6795		13. 5.94	J.D.Gray	Eshott	22. 8.99P
G-MYRG	TEAM miniMax PFA/186-11891			17. 5.94	D.G.Burrows	Presteigne	1. 3.00P
G-MYRH	Quad City Challenger II UK (Rotax 582) CH2-1093-1044 & PFA/177A-12690			10. 3.94	R.T.Hall	Thorney Island	11. 2.00P
G-MYRI	Medway Hybred 44XLR MR180/841 (Rotax 503)			23. 5.94	K.Angel	Belvedere	1. 9.00P
G-MYRJ	Quad City Challenger II UK (Hirth 2706.R05) CH2-1093-1042 & PFA/177A-12658			28. 3.94	H.F.Breakwell & P.Woodcock Sittles Farm, Alrewas		20. 7.99P
G-MYRK	Murphy Renegade Spirit UK (Rotax 582) 215 & PFA/188-11425			3.10.89	P.Crowhurst	Kettering	16. 7.00P
G-MYRL	TEAM miniMax 91 PFA/186-11967 (Rotax 447)			17. 5.94	J.N.Hanson	Prestwich	15. 9.00P
G-MYRM	Cyclone Pegasus Quantum 15 (Rotax 582/40)	6800		26. 5.94	R.C.Budden	Old Sarum	28. 1.00P
G-MYRN	Cyclone Pegasus Quantum 15 (Rotax 582/40)	6801		26. 5.94	M.H.Rollins	Solihull	23.11.00P
G-MYRO	Cyclone AX3 (Rotax 503)	C.4043211		6. 6.94	R.I.Simpson & R.Tarplee	Broadstairs	21. 8.00P
G-MYRP	Letov LK-2M Sluka (Rotax 447) PFA/263-12725 & 0209			6. 6.94	J.W.Hiestand	Dereham	4. 8.00P
G-MYRR	Letov LK-2M Sluka (Rotax 447) (Regd with c/n 05)	0205		10. 6.94	R.Riley	Ashford, Kent	21. 7.00P
G-MYRS	Cyclone Pegasus Quantum 15 (Rotax 582/40)	6803		13. 6.94	R.M.Summers	Insch	8. 5.00P
G-MYRT	Cyclone Pagasus Quantum 15 (Rotax 582/40)	6732		1. 3.94	M.C.Taylor	Coleford	22. 3.00P

Regn	Type	C/n	P/I	Date	Owner/operator	Probable Base	CA Expy
G-MYRU	Cyclone AX3 (Rotax 503)	C.4043210		7. 6.94	L.W. & C.Scarlett	Eshott	8.10.00P
G-MYRV	Cyclone AX3 (Rotax 503)	C.4043209		8. 6.94	M.Gardiner	Crosland Moor	4. 7.99P
G-MYRW	Mainair Mercury 999-0694-7 & W795 (Rotax 503)			17. 6.94	G.C.Hobson	St.Michaels	5. 7.00P
G-MYRX	Mainair Gemini/Flash 2A (Rotax 462) 995-0694-7 & W792			22. 6.94	L.J.Latter	London N19	23. 8.95P
G-MYRY	Cyclone Pegasus Quantum 15 6813 (Rotax 582/40)			15. 6.94	P.G.Jackson & D.Roberts	Shobdon	27. 8.99P
G-MYRZ	Cyclone Pegasus Quantum 15 6812 (Rotax 582/40)			15. 6.94	C.Judd Lark Engine Farmhouse, Prickwillow, Ely		27. 6.00P
G-MYSA	Cyclone Chaser S CH.864 (Rotax 508)			15. 6.94	D.W.M.Hamer	Banbury	3. 9.00P
G-MYSB	Cyclone Pegasus Quantum 15 6809 (Rotax 582/40)			22. 6.94	D.Margereson	Chesterfield	10. 8.00P
G-MYSC	Cyclone Pegasus Quantum 15 6811 (Rotax 582/40)			22. 6.94	A.R.Way	Dunkeswell	13. 2.99P
G-MYSD	Quad City Challenger II CH2-1093-1043 & PFA/177A-12688			23. 6.94	C.E.Bell	Oakham	
G-MYSG	Mainair Mercury 993-0694-7 & W790 (Rotax 503)			12. 7.94	B.M.Jones	Shifnal	30. 4.00P
G-MYSH	Mainair Blade 994-0694-7 & W791 (Rotax 582)			12. 7.94	J.Lamont	NK	13. 9.95P
G-MYSI	HM.14/93 PFA/255-12700			18. 7.94	A.R.D.Seaman	Dagenham	
G-MYSJ	Mainair Gemini/Flash 2A (Rotax 503) 1001-0894-7 & W797			2. 8.94	L.Cottle Baxby Manor, Husthwaite		9. 8.99P
G-MYSK	TEAM miniMax 91 PFA/186-12203 (Rotax 447)			25. 7.94	A.D.Bolshaw	Wolverhampton	27.10.00P
G-MYSL	Aviasud Mistral 66 & BMAA/HB/007 (Rotax 532)		83-DE	27. 2.92	P.C.Piggott & M.E.Hughes Little Battleflats Farm, Ellistown, Coalville		21. 7.00P
G-MYSM	CFM Shadow Srs.CD (Rotax 503) K.243 & BMAA/HB/049			22. 3.94	L.W.Stevens	Grantham	14. 9.99P
G-MYSN	Whittaker MW-6S Fatboy Flyer (Rotax 532) PFA/164-12285			27. 7.94	T.A.Dockrell	Weston-super-Mare	11.10.99P
G-MYSO	Cyclone AX3 (Rotax 503)	C.4043215		1. 8.94	M.L.Smith	Popham	10. 3.00P
G-MYSP	Rans S-6-ESD Coyote II (Rotax 503) 0392-284 & PFA/204-12265			26. 5.92	G.C.Holmes	Sittle Farm, Alrewas	17.12.98P
G-MYSR	Cyclone Pegasus Quantum 15 6837 (Rotax 582)			?. 8.94	D.O.Crane	Lutterworth	13. 6.00P
G-MYST	Aviasud Mistral (Rotax 532) 0489-83, GB.01 & BMAA/HB/012			11. 7.89	T.E.Taylor	Otherton, Cannock	5. 8.98P
G-MYSU	Rans S-6-ESD Coyote II PFA/204-12753 (Rotax 503)			5. 8.94	K.W.Allan	Leven	11. 3.00P
G-MYSV	Aerial Arts Chaser S CH.812 (ex Korea) (Rotax 377)			24. 8.94	R J Sims & I G Reason	Salisbury	13. 3.00P
G-MYSW	Cyclone Pegasus Quantum 15 6834 (Rotax 582)			13. 7.94	D.A.Southern	Thornton Cleveleys	21. 8.00P
G-MYSX	Cyclone Pegasus Quantum 15 6832 (Rotax 503)			13. 7.94	J.L.Treves	London Colney	23. 7.00P
G-MYSY	Cyclone Pegasus Quantum 15 6864 (Rotax 582)			15. 8.94	C.Lamb	Rye	2.10.99P
G-MYSZ	Mainair Mercury 1006-0894-7 & W802 (Rotax 503) (C/n confirmed but see G-MYYY)			2. 9.94	N.Cox	Shobdon	18. 9.00P
G-MYTA	TEAM miniMax 91 PFA/186-12461 (Rotax 447)			20. 5.94	R.E.Gray	Oxted, Surrey	13. 6.00P
G-MYTB	Mainair Mercury 1004-0894-7 & W800 (Rotax 582)			19. 8.94	P.J.Higgins	Fenland	7. 4.00P
G-MYTC	Solar Wings Pegasus XL-Q SW-WQ-0246 (ex)			28. 9.94	M.J.Edmett	London N3	
G-MYTD	Mainair Blade (Rotax 582) 1002-0894-7 & W798			18. 8.94	D.M.Dunphy	Barton	5. 8.00P
G-MYTE	Rans S-6-ESD Coyote II PFA/204-12718 (Rotax 503)			22. 7.94	J.A.Way t/a The Rans Flying Group	Lydd	9.11.00P
G-MYTG	Mainair Blade (Rotax 582) 1008-0994-7 & W804			16. 9.94	P.Lenk	Barton	1. 2.00P
G-MYTH	CFM Shadow Srs.CD 089 (Rotax 503)			7.11.88	J.E.Neil Sheriff Hall, Balgone, Berwick		22. 7.00P
G-MYTI	Cyclone Pegasus Quantum 15 6874 (Rotax 582/40)			6.10.94	J.Madhvani Plaistows, Hemel Hampstead		21. 2.00P

Regn	Type	C/n	P/I	Date	Owner/operator	Probable Base	CA Expy
G-MYTJ	Cyclone Pegasus Quantum 15 (Rotax 582/40)	6877		29. 9.94	T.J.Cale	Croft Farm, Defford	24. 5.00P
G-MYTK	Mainair Mercury (Rotax 503)	1009-1094-7 & W805		29. 9.94	D.A.Holroyd	London W14	19.10009P
G-MYTL	Mainair Blade (Rotax 582)	1010-1094-7 & W807		4.10.94	S.Ostrowski	Davidstow Moor	26. 4.00P
G-MYTM	Cyclone AX3 (Rotax 503)	C.3123189		13. 4.94	T.S.Mangat	Long Marston	3. 8.00P
G-MYTN	Cyclone Pegasus Quantum 15 (Rotax 503)	6878		30. 9.94	R.Redman	Grantham	19. 3.00P
G-MYTO	Quad City Challenger II UK (Hirth 2705.R06)	PFA/177-12583		22. 7.94	J.P.Bennett	RAF Wyton	20. 2.00P
G-MYTP	CGS Arrow Flight Hawk II (Rotax 503) H-CGS-489-P & PFA/266-12801	215		6.10.94	R.J.Turner	Otherton, Cannock	8. 5.97P
G-MYTR	Solar Wings Pegasus Quasar IITC (Rotax 582/40)	6880		11.10.94	I.Jones	Dunkeswell	31. 1.00P
G-MYTS*	Hunt Wing/Avon (Rotax 447) 92009014 & BMAA/MB/032			12.10.94	C.Jenkins (Cancelled by CAA 30.9.98)	Ballina, Co.Mayo	12. 1.96P*
G-MYTT	Quad City Challenger II (Rotax 503) PFA/177-12761			11.10.94	R.J.Shave t/a Challenger G-MYTT	Dunkeswell	19.10.99P
G-MYTU	Mainair Blade (Rotax 582)	1011-1094-7 & W808		21.10.94	R.M.A.Woodward	Stony Stratford	19.10.00P
G-MYTV	Hunt Wing/Avon (Rotax 503) 92040010 & BMAA/HB/029			13.10.94	P.J.Sutton	Bristol	21. 8.00P
G-MYTW	Mainair Blade (Rotax 582)	1012-1194-7 & W809		4.11.94	J.Parker	Fenland	27.11.97P
G-MYTX	Mainair Mercury (Rotax 503)	1003-0894-7 & W799		23. 9.94	R.Steel	York	24. 9.00P
G-MYTY	CFM Streak Shadow Srs.M (Rotax 912UL) PFA/206-12607 (Possibly c/n K.242)			11. 7.94	Skydrive Ltd	Leamington Spa	31. 8.00P
G-MYTZ	Air Creation Fun 18S GT bis (Rotax 503)	94/003		7.11.94	J.K.Evans	Husbands Bosworth	15. 3.00P
G-MYUA	Air Creation Fun 18S GT bis (Rotax 503)	94/002		8.11.94	D.Mahajan Lower Mountpleasnt. Chatteris		31. 7.99P
G-MYUB	Mainair Mercury (Rotax 503)	1014-1194-7 & W812		14.12.94	T.A. & C.M.Ross Arclid Green, Sandbach		9. 7.00P
G-MYUC	Mainair Blade (Rotax 462)	1015-1294-7 & W813		16.11.94	A.D.Clayton	St.Michaels	4.11.00P
G-MYUD	Mainair Mercury (Rotax 582)	1016-1294-7 & W814		24.11.94	S.A.Noble	Audley End	13. 2.00P
G-MYUE	Mainair Mercury (Rotax 582)	1017-1294-7 & W815		22.11.94	R.J.Speight	Amersham	22. 7.00P
G-MYUF	Murphy Renegade Spirit	PFA/188-12795		16.11.94	C.J.Dale	Beverley	13. 9.99P
G-MYUG*	Hunt Wing/Avon BMAA/HB/038 & 9409034			21.11.94	C.W.Green (Cancelled 6.5.99 as WFU with Permit pending)	High Wycombe	AC
G-MYUH	Solar Wings Pegasus XL-Q (Rotax 462)	6810		28.11.94	K.S.Daniels	London Colney	28. 8.99P
G-MYUI	Cyclone AX3 (Rotax 503) (Frame stamped with c/n 0102822; possibly rebuilt)	C.4043213		13.12.94	R. & M.Bailey Plaistows. Hemel Hempstead		13. 3.99P
G-MYUJ	Meridian Ultralights Maverick (Rotax 503) 402 & PFA/259-12750			30.12.94	K.Anderson "69"	Stafford	12.12.97P
G-MYUK	Mainair Mercury (Rotax 462)	1020-0195-7 & W818		12.12.94	S.Lear	London N15	28.11.97P
G-MYUL	Quad City Challenger II UK (Rotax 503) PFA/177-12687			10. 1.95	A.G.Easson	Perth	16. 2.00P
G-MYUM	Mainair Blade (Rotax 582)	1018-1294-7 & W816		24.11.94	M.E.Keefe	St.Michaels	10. 1.00P
G-MYUN	Mainair Blade (Rotax 582)	1019-0195-7 & W817		5.12.94	P.Harper	St.Michaels	17. 1.00P
G-MYUO	Cyclone Pegasus Quantum 15 (Rotax 582)	6911		23. 1.95	D.J.Harris (Damaged late 1997)	St.Albans	15. 7.00P
G-MYUP	Letov LK-2M Sluka (Rotax 447) 829409x24, PFA/263-12785 & UK.2			20.12.94	R.D.Proctor	RAF Wyton	27.11.99P
G-MYUR	Hunt Wing/Avon BMAA/HB/034 (Rotax 582)			24. 1.95	S.D.Pain	Rayne	5.10.00P
G-MYUS	CFM Shadow Srs.CD (Rotax 503)	257		26. 1.95	G.Gilhead & R.G.M.Proost t/a Aviation for Paraplegics and Tetraplegics Trust	Old Sarum	15. 7.00P
G-MYUT*	Hunt Wing/Experience 9409039 & BMAA/HB/042			26. 1.95	R.A.Kehoe (Cancelled by CAA 23.6.98)	Chelmsford	
G-MYUU	Cyclone Pegasus Quantum 15 (Rotax 462)	6917		30. 1.95	Lynette J.Ryals	Enstone	13. 4.00P

Regn	Type	C/n	P/I	Date	Owner/operator	Probable Base	CA Expy
G-MYUV	Cyclone Pegasus Quantum 15 6918 (Rotax 582)			6. 2.95	D.Baillie	Great Orton	27. 6.00P
G-MYUW	Mainair Mercury 1024-0295-7 & W822 (Rotax 503)			7. 2.95	G.Suckling	Saffron Walden	11. 7.00P
G-MYUY	Airwave Microchute UQ/Reggae Motor 30 (Rotax 503) PSP.104006			9. 2.95	S.E.Jones	Cardiff	19.10.95P*
G-MYUZ	Rans S-6-ESD Coyote II (Rotax 503) 1293-568 & PFA/204-12741			5. 1.95	B.Davies	Sittles Farm, Alrewas	16. 4.00P
G-MYVA	Kolb Twinstar mk.3 PFA/205-12756 (Rotax 582)			13. 2.95	S.P.Read	Henstridge	20. 6.00P
G-MYVB	Mainair Blade 1021-0195-7 & W819 (Rotax 582)			15.12.94	P.C.Watson	Arclid Green, Sandbach	23. 4.00P
G-MYVC	Cyclone Pegasus Quantum 15 6904 (Rotax 582)			13. 2.95	G.Lace	Liverpool	17. 5.99P
G-MYVE	Mainair Blade 1027-0295-7 & W825 (Rotax 582)			8. 2.95	C.W.Laskey t/a Blue Blade Syndicate G-MYVE	Risca, Newport	8. 3.00P
G-MYVG	Letov LK-2M Sluka (Rotax 447) PFA/263-12786 & 829409x26			15. 2.95	M.Tormey	Co.Meath, Ireland	8.12.99P
G-MYVH	Mainair Blade 1028-0295-7 & W826 (Rotax 582)			21. 2.95	D.Sugden	Liversedge	27. 3.00P
G-MYVI	Air Creation Fun 18S GT bis 94/004 (Rotax 503)			17. 2.95	P.Osborne t/a Northampton Aerotow Club	Northampton	15. 6.99P
G-MYVJ	Cyclone Pegasus Quantum 15 6974 (Rotax 582/40)			24. 2.95	G.R.Hall	Canterbury	27. 4.00P
G-MYVK	Cyclone Pegasus Quantum 15 6970 (Rotax 582/40)			27. 2.95	D.J.Parrish	Long Acres Farm, Sandy	9. 4.00P
G-MYVL	Mainair Mercury 1030-0395-7 & W828 (Rotax 462)			1. 3.95	T.Pollard	Cambourne, Cornwall	7. 7.99P
G-MYVM	Cyclone Pegasus Quantum 15 6893 (Rotax 582/40)	G-69-17 G-MYVM		9. 3.95	A.F.A.Marreiros	Lisboa, Portugal	27. 4.97P
G-MYVN	Cyclone AX3 C.4043212 (Rotax 503)			16. 3.95	F.Watt	Insch	6. 6.00P
G-MYVO	Mainair Blade 1013-1194-7 & W811 (Rotax 582)			8.11.94	S.S.Raines	Shobdon	11. 2.00P
G-MYVP	Rans S-6-ESD Coyote II PFA/204-12828 (Rotax 503)			27. 3.95	T.Ellison & C.E.Hormaeche	Newcastle	29.11.99P
G-MYVR	Cyclone Pegasus Quantum 15 6980 (Rotax 582)			21. 3.95	M.P.Wimsey	Louth	26. 4.00P
G-MYVS	Mainair Mercury 1037-0495-7 & W835 (Rotax 462)			12. 4.95	P.S.Flynn	Sandtoft	25. 4.00P
G-MYVT	Letov LK-2M Sluka (Rotax 447) PFA/263-12835 & 829409x25			17. 3.95	J.Hannibal	Kidderminster	9.11.00P
G-MYVU*	Medway Budget Raven MRB126/108 (Rotax 447)			3. 4.95	Not known (Temp unregd 25.10.95)	Chislehurst, Kent	9. 4.96P
G-MYVV	Medway Hybred 44XLR MR127/109 (Rotax 503)			3. 4.95	A.I.Dawson	Chesterfield	24. 2.99P
G-MYVW	Medway Raven X MRB128/110 (Rotax 447)			15. 5.95	J.C.Woolgrove	Beckenham	5. 6.97P
G-MYVX	Medway Hybred 44XLR MR129/111 (Rotax 503)			3. 4.95	S.J.Martin	Belvedere, Kent	29. 7.00P
G-MYVY	Mainair Blade 1033-0495-7 & W831 (Rotax 582)			29. 3.95	N.Purdy	Sutton-in-Ashfield	30. 6.00P
G-MYVZ	Mainair Blade 1034-0495-7 & W832 (Rotax 582)			31. 3.95	M.Morris	Preston	27. 4.00P
G-MYWA	Mainair Mercury 1035-0495-7 & W833 (Rotax 503)			30. 3.95	D.James	Neath	7. 5.00P
G-MYWB*	Edel Corniche/Scorpion 004 & BMAA/HB/071			31. 3.95	P.F.Funnell (Cancelled by CAA 7.8.98)	Cranbrook, Kent	
G-MYWC	Hunt Wing/Avon 9409038 & BMAA/HB/043 (Rotax 503)			3. 4.95	F.J.C.Binks	Saffron Walden	7. 7.00P
G-MYWD	Thruster T.600N 9035-T600-511 (Rotax 503)		(G-MYOJ)	18. 4.95	G.J.Slater	Clench Common	17. 3.00P
G-MYWE	Thruster T.600T 9035-T600-512 (Rotax 503)		(G-MYOK)	18. 4.95	P.J.Reed	Dunkeswell	9. 1.00P
G-MYWF	CFM Shadow Srs.CD (Rotax 503) K.248 & BMAA/HB/068			18. 4.95	M.A.Newman	Saxmundham	8. 1.00P
G-MYWG	Cyclone Pegasus Quantum 15 6998 (Rotax 582/40)			20. 4.95	N.S.McNaughton	Auchincruive, Ayr	1. 9.00P
G-MYWH	Hunt Wing/Experience 9409025 & BMAA/HB/037			20.12.94	G.N.Hatchett	Gloucester	

Regn	Type	C/n	P/I	Date	Owner/operator	Probable Base	CA Expy
G-MYWI	Cyclone Pegasus Quantum 15 (Rotax 582)	7006		1. 5.95	M.B.Chapman	Wellingborough	12. 6.00P
G-MYWJ	Cyclone Pegasus Quantum 15 (Rotax 582)	6919		24. 1.95	W.C.Jones	Long Acres Farm, Sandy	27. 3.00P
G-MYWK	Cyclone Pegasus Quantum 15 (Rotax 582/40)	7011		1. 5.95	W.P.Byrne	Belfast	25. 9.00P
G-MYWL	Cyclone Pegasus Quantum 15 (Rotax 582)	6995		2. 5.95	J.S.Hamilton	Edenbridge, Kent	19. 6.00P
G-MYWM	CFM Shadow Srs.CD (Rotax 503)	K.227 & BMAA/HB/056		9. 5.95	R.E.Peirse	Kingston, Royston	23. 7.00P
G-MYWN	Cyclone Chaser S (Rotax 508)	CH.865		9. 5.95	J.E.Borrill	Fort William	22. 8.00P
G-MYWO	Cyclone Pegasus Quantum 15 (Rotax 582)	6932		9. 5.95	B.D.Avery	Chippenham	10. 9.00P
G-MYWP	Kolb Twinstar mk.3 (Rotax 582)	PFA/205-12561		7. 3.95	B.J.M.Albiston	Long Marston	12.10.00P
G-MYWR	Cyclone Pegasus Quantum 15 (Rotax 582/40)	7002		10. 5.95	T.A.Chambers	Long Marston	11. 8.00P
G-MYWS	Cyclone Chaser S (Rotax 447)	6946 & CH.866		17. 5.95	M.H.Broadbent	Bexhill-on-Sea	6. 8.00P
G-MYWT	Cyclone Pegasus Quantum 15 (Rotax 582/40)	6997		19. 5.95	H.Hall	Willenhall	9. 7.99P
G-MYWU	Cyclone Pegasus Quantum 15 (Rotax 582)	7024		25. 5.95	J.R.Buttle	Dunkeswell	23. 7.00P
G-MYWV	Rans S-4C Coyote (Rotax 447)	093-212 & PFA/193-12826		30. 5.95	A.H.Trapp	Bewdley, Worcs	7. 7.00P
G-MYWW	Cyclone Pegasus Quantum 15 (Rotax 503)	7021		30. 5.95	K.J.Gay	Bangor, Co.Down	7. 7.00P
G-MYWX	Cyclone Pegasus Quantum 15 (Rotax 582)	7019		6. 6.95	D.J.Revell	Lower Mountpleasnt, Chatteris	13. 7.00P
G-MYWY	Cyclone Pegasus Quantum 15 (Rotax 582)	6982		20. 3.95	D.Young	Kemble	24. 9.00P
G-MYWZ	Thruster TST mk.1 (Rotax 503)	8128-TST-115	G-MVMJ	22. 2.93	W.H.J.KNowles	Tiverton	24. 5.00P
G-MYXA	TEAM miniMax 91 (Rotax 447)	PFA/186-12266		13. 6.95	G.M.Johnson	Huntingdon	18. 5.00P
G-MYXB	Rans S-6-ESD Coyote II (Rotax 503)	PFA/204-12787		20. 6.95	A.Aldridge	Swanton Morley	26. 4.00P
G-MYXC	Quad City Challenger II UK	CH2-0294-UK-1099		16. 5.95	K.N.Dickinson	Higher Barn Farm, Houghton	
G-MYXD	Cyclone Pegasus Quasar IITC (Rotax 582)	7029		21. 6.95	C.Lee	Long Acres Farm, Sandy	30. 8.00P
G-MYXE	Cyclone Pegasus Quantum 15 (Rotax 582)	7061		23. 6.95	D.Little	Crawley	7. 9.00P
G-MYXF	Air Creation Fun 18S GT bis (Rotax 503)	94/005		23. 6.95	T.A.Morgan	Popham	11.10.99P
G-MYXG	Rans S-6-ESD Coyote II (Rotax 503)	PFA/204-12879		29. 6.95	G.H.Lee	Higher Barn Farm, Houghton	18. 5.00P
G-MYXH	Cyclone AX3 (Rotax 503)	7028		3. 7.95	E.G.White	Wantage	18. 9.00P
G-MYXI	Cook Aries 1	BMAA/HB/048		4. 7.95	H.Cook	Newport, Gwent	
G-MYXJ	Mainair Blade (Rotax 582)	1048-0795-7 & W846		17. 7.95	J.A.Horn	Durham	12. 6.00P
G-MYXK	Quad City Challenger II (Rotax 503)	CH2-1194-1254 & PFA/177A-12877		11. 7.95	V.Vaughan & N.O'Brien Mullinahone, Co.Tipperary		4. 7.00P
G-MYXL	Mignet HM-1000 Balerit (Rotax 582)	112		11. 7.95	R.W.Hollamby	Bardown, Wadhurst	17. 7.00P
G-MYXM	Mainair Blade (Rotax 582)	1047-0795-7 & W845		19. 7.95	S.C.Hodgson	Chesterfield	7. 8.00P
G-MYXN	Mainair Blade (Rotax 582)	1046-0795-7 & W844		27. 7.95	M.R.Sands	Peterlee	19. 7.00P
G-MYXO	Letov LK-2M Sluka (Rotax 447)	8295s001 & PFA/263-12873		27. 7.95	K.H.A.Negal	London SW7	24. 3.00P
G-MYXP	Rans S-6-ESD Coyote II (Rotax 503)	PFA/204-12886		31. 7.95	K.J.Lywood	Bradford-on-Avon	6.10.00P
G-MYXR	Murphy Renegade Spirit UK	PFA/188-12755		2. 8.95	S.Hooker	Ashford, Kent	
G-MYXS	Kolb Twinstar mk.3 (Rotax 582)	PFA/205-12528		4. 5.94	R.Coar Higher Barn Farm, Houghton (On rebuild 3.99)		11. 7.97P
G-MYXT	Cyclone Pegasus Quantum 15 (Rotax 582)	7073		4. 8.95	D.M.Mackenzie	Beauly, Inverness	26. 9.99P

Regn	Type	C/n	P/I	Date	Owner/operator	Probable Base	CA Expy
G-MYXU	Thruster T.300 (Rotax 582)	9024-T300-513		16. 8.95	D.W.Wilson	Collone, Co.Armagh	18.12.99P
G-MYXV	Quad City Challenger II UK (Rotax 503)	CH2-1194-UK-1243		19. 7.95	A.Hipkin	Bewdley, Worcs	18. 6.00P
G-MYXW	Cyclone Pegasus Quantum 15 (Rotax 582)	7090		24. 8.95	M.A.Pantling	Gillingham	4.12.99P
G-MYXX	Cyclone Pegasus Quantum 15 (Rotax 582)	7081		25. 8.95	J.H.Arnold	Milverton, Taunton	13.11.00P
G-MYXY	CFM Shadow Srs.CD (Rotax 503)	K.245 & BMAA/HB/059		29. 8.95	N.H.Townsend	Old Sarum	21. 7.00P
G-MYXZ	Cyclone Pegasus Quantum 15 (Rotax 582)	7023		21. 6.95	I.Fernihough	Ashbourne	24. 8.00P
G-MYYA	Mainair Blade (Rotax 462)	1052-0995-7 & W850		1. 9.95	J.N.Hanson	St.Michaels	17. 9.99P
G-MYYB	Cyclone Pegasus Quantum 15 (Rotax 582)	7079		4. 9.95	A.L.Johnson	Long Acres Farm, Sandy	17.10.00P
G-MYYC	Cyclone Pegasus Quantum 15 (Rotax 582)	7094		12. 9.95	B.Kirkland	Tarn Farm, Cockerham	26. 2.00P
G-MYYD	Cyclone Chaser S (Rotax 447)	CH.7099		15. 9.95	D.Kingslake	Long Acres Farm, Sandy	7.11.00P
G-MYYE	Hunt Wing/Hunt Avon (Fuji-Robin EC-44-PM)	BMAA/HB/041		21. 9.95	P.J.Dickinson	Stoke-on-Trent	
G-MYYF	Quad City Challenger II UK (Rotax 503)	PFA/177-12811		27. 9.95	G.Ferries	Insch	16.11.00P
G-MYYG	Mainair Blade (Rotax 462)	1054-0995-7 & W852		4.10.95	P.McCormick	Shobdon	23.10.00P
G-MYYH	Mainair Blade (Rotax 582)	1056-1095-7 & W854		3.10.95	B.Hunter	Bridlington	13. 3.00P
G-MYYI	Cyclone Pegasus Quantum 15 (Rotax 582)	7101		28. 9.95	S.Etches	Sandtoft	23. 7.99P
G-MYYJ	Hunt Wing/Hunt Avon (Rotax 503)	BMAA/HB/033		29. 9.95	M.J.Slater (Stored 5.97)	Clench Common	
G-MYYK	Cyclone Pegasus Quantum 15 (Rotax 582)	7100		2.10.95	L.Scarse	Melksham	1. 5.00P
G-MYYL	Cyclone AX3 (Rotax 503)	7110		4.10.95	P.M.Dewhurst & K.Meredith-Jones	Sywell	9.11.00P
G-MYYM	Trekking Microchute/Motor 27	TH10124M		17.10.95	S.E.Jones t/a Motor Gliders Group	Cardiff	
G-MYYN	Cyclone Pegasus Quantum 15 (Rotax 582)	7022		3.10.95	Kwik, Kwek Kwak SA	Marbella, Spain	2.10.96P
G-MYYO	Medway Raven X (Rotax 447)	MRB134/114		5.10.95	B.F.Rimington	Basingstoke	8. 5.00P
G-MYYP	AMF Chevvron 2-32C (Konig SD570)	036		31.10.95	G.A.Pentelow	Rothwell Lodge, Kettering	5.11.00P
G-MYYR	TEAM miniMax 91 (Rotax 447)	PFA/186-12724		31.10.95	P.Palmer	Crosland Moor	7.11.00P
G-MYYS	TEAM miniMax	PFA/186-11989		7.11.95	J.R.Hopkinson	Chesterfield	
G-MYYT	Hunt Wing/Experience	BMAA/HB/065		14.11.95	E.Finnamore	Tullamore, Co.Offauy	
G-MYYU	Mainair Mercury (Rotax 503)	1062-1295-7 & W862		17.11.95	G.V.Willder	Arclid Green, Sandbach	26. 3.00P
G-MYYV	Rans S-6-ESD Coyote IIXL (Rotax 503)	0896-1026XL & PFA/204-12943		17.11.95	B.W.Drake	Long Marston	16. 7.00P
G-MYYW	Mainair Blade (Rotax 582)	1051-0895-7 & W849		8. 8.95	M.J.Naylor	Glenfield, Leics	3.10.00P
G-MYYX	Cyclone Pegasus Quantum 15 (Rotax 582)	7126		17.11.95	M.L.Johnston	Glasgow	3. 4.00P
G-MYYY	Mainair Blade (Rotax 582) (Incorrectly stamped with wing c/n W802 - see G-MYSZ)	1031-0495-7 & W829		15. 3.95	D.A.Lane	Barton	30. 3.00P
G-MYYZ	Medway Raven X (Rotax 447)	MRB135/116		10. 1.96	S.G.Beeson	Stoke-on-Trent	8. 9.99P
G-MYZA	Whitaker MW-6 Merlin	PFA/164-11396		17. 7.95	D.C.Davies	Lover Farm	21. 6.00P
G-MYZB	Cyclone Pegasus Quantum 15 (Rotax 582)	7124		22.11.95	P.A.Bass	Northampton	14.12.90P
G-MYZC	Cyclone AX3 (Rotax 503)	7125		5.12.95	A.B.Simpson	Blackpool	28. 5.00P
G-MYZE	TEAM miniMax 91 (Global GMT-35)	PFA/186-12570		28. 9.95	R.B.M.Etherington	Totnes	11. 4.00P
G-MYZF	Cyclone AX3 (Rotax 503)	7133		11.12.95	R.L.H.Alexander	Holywood, NI	12. 3.00P
G-MYZG	Cyclone AX3 (Rotax 503)	7137		11. 1.96	R.A.Johns	Weston Zoyland	9. 1.00P
G-MYZH	Chargus Titan 38	JPA-1		16. 1.96	P.A.James	Crawley	

Regn	Type	C/n	P/I	Date	Owner/operator	Probable Base	CA Expy
G-MYZI	Tiger Cub RL5A-LW Sherwood Ranger PFA/237-12947			17. 1.96	K.F.Crumplin	Wells	
G-MYZJ	Cyclone Pegasus Quantum 15 (Rotax 582)	7150		24. 1.96	P.Millar	Coatbridge	16. 4.00P
G-MYZK	Cyclone Pegasus Quantum 15 (Rotax 582/40)	7157		5. 2.96	T.D.Grieve	Hamilton	11. 7.99P
G-MYZL	Cyclone Pegasus Quantum 15 (Rotax 582/40)	7158		5. 2.96	Flight Aid Ltd	Ilminster	20. 7.00P
G-MYZM	Cyclone Pegasus Quantum 15 (Rotax 582/40)	7159		5. 2.96	D.Hope	Uckfield	16. 4.00P
G-MYZN	Whittaker MW-6S-LW Fatboy Flyer (Rotax 582)	PFA/164-12431		31. 1.96	M.K.Shaw	RAF Halton	8. 5.00P
G-MYZO	Medway Raven X (Rotax 447)	MRB136/115		12. 2.96	B.C.Kealy	London SE12	4. 5.00P
G-MYZP	CFM Shadow Srs.DD (Rotax 582)	249 & PFA/161-12914		7. 2.96	R.M.Davies & P.I.Hodgson	Amersham	13. 7.99P
G-MYZR	Rans S-6-ESD Coyote II XL (Rotax 503)	PFA/204-12958		9. 2.96	S.E.J.McLaughlin	Sutton Meadows, Ely	27. 4.00P
G-MYZS	Airwave Rave/Vega 1	001 & BMAA/HB/054		16. 2.96	Paratrike Ltd	Colchester	
G-MYZT	Airwave Rave/Vega 2	002		16. 2.96	Paratrike Ltd	Colchester	
G-MYZU	Airwave Rave/Scorpion	005		16. 2.96	Paratrike Ltd	Colchester	
G-MYZV	Rans S-6-ESD Coyote II XL (Rotax 503)	PFA/204-12946		26. 2.96	D.R.Gooby & B.P.Harrison	Dunkeswell	26. 6.00P
G-MYZW	Cyclone Chaser S (Rotax 508)	7165		27. 2.96	C.J.Meadow	Shepton Mallet	26. 4.00P
G-MYZX	Cyclone Chaser S (Rotax 508)	7172		28. 2.96	A.J.Blake	Buxton	1. 4.97P
G-MYZY	Cyclone Pegasus Quantum 15 (Rotax 582)	7156		8. 2.96	D.D.Appleford	Swindon	23. 4.00P
G-MZAA	Mainair Blade (Rotax 462)	1059-1195-7 & W857		24.10.95	J.C.Kitchen	London SE15	6. 1.00P
G-MZAB	Mainair Blade (Rotax 582)	1043-0695-7 & W841		26. 5.95	S.M.Holroyd	Rufforth	8. 6.00P
G-MZAC	Quad City Challenger II CH2-0294-1100 & PFA/177A-12716			21. 7.95	M.N.Calhaem	Fradswell, Stafford	4. 5.00P
G-MZAD	Mainair Blade (Rotax 912)	1061-1295-7 & W861		29.11.95	T.Kidd (Stored 4.97)	Oxton, Notts	
G-MZAE	Mainair Blade (Rotax 582)	1063-1295-7 & W863		4.12.95	A.C.Rowlands	Dalscote, Nether Heyford	21. 3.00P
G-MZAF	Mainair Blade (Rotax 582)	1045-0795-7 & W843		1.12.95	G.C.Brown	Barton	19. 5.00P
G-MZAG	Mainair Blade (Rotax 582)	1042-0695-7 & W840		26. 5.95	I.D.Milne	St.Michaels	30.12.98P
G-MZAH	Rans S-6-ESD Coyote II (Nose-wheel u/c) (Rotax 503) 0393-470 & PFA/204-12553 (Rebuilt with new fuselage - c/n not known)			3. 9.93	D.G.Matthews	Long Marston	15. 6.00P
G-MZAI	Mainair Blade (Rotax 912UL)	1065-0196-7 & W867		4.12.95	P. & M.Boultby	Oxton, Notts	5. 8.00P
G-MZAJ	Mainair Blade (Rotax 582)	1067-0196-7 & W869		20.12.95	K.W.Palmer	Benfleet	5. 2.00P
G-MZAK	Mainair Mercury (Rotax 503)	1070-0296-7 & W872		15. 1.96	S.J.Joseph	Cheshunt	9. 4.00P
G-MZAL	Mainair Blade	1076-0396-7 & W878		21. 2.96	T.Dunn	Nottingham	28. 4.00P
G-MZAM	Mainair Blade (Rotax 582)	1044-0695-7 & W842		31. 5.95	B.K.Robinson	Droitwich	11. 8.00P
G-MZAN	Cyclone Pegasus Quantum 15 (Rotax 582/40)	7188		7. 3.96	R.R.Hadley t/a Zanco Syndicate	Dunkeswell	30. 4.00P
G-MZAO	Mainair Blade (Rotax 912UL)	1069-0296-7 & W871		15. 3.96	P.A.B. & B.A.Morgan	Sandy	7. 4.00P
G-MZAP	Mainair Blade (Rotax 582)	1036-0495-7 & W834		31. 3.95	J.G.Lloyd	Harlow	28. 2.00P
G-MZAR	Mainair Blade (Rotax 582)	1072-0296-7 & W874		13. 2.96	T.R.Southall	Shobdon	24. 3.00P
G-MZAS	Mainair Blade (Rotax 582)	1049-0895-7 & W847		15. 8.95	T.Carter	Long Marston	25. 8.00P
G-MZAT	Mainair Blade (Rotax 582)	1060-1195-7 & W860		29.11.95	P.Carmassi	Southport	7. 4.00P
G-MZAU*	Mainair Blade (Rotax 582)	1064-0196-7 & W864		29.11.95	I.Caslin & I.Simpson (Cancelled 8.5.99 as Destroyed)	Carlisle	28. 4.99P
G-MZAV	Mainair Blade (Rotax 582)	1078-0396-7 & W881		11. 3.96	D.L.Pollitt	St.Michaels	8. 5.00P

Regn	Type	C/n	P/I	Date	Owner/operator	Probable Base	CA Expy
G-MZAW	Cyclone Pegasus Quantum 15 (Rotax 503)	7160		14. 2.96	M.J.Mawle	Kemble	13. 3.00P
G-MZAX	Cyclone Pegasus Quantum 15	7152		11. 3.96	Kwik Kwek Kwak SA	Marbella, Spain	
G-MZAY	Mainair Blade (Rotax 462)	1077-0396-7 & W880		15. 3.96	M.D.Harris	Earls Barton, Northampton	13. 3.99P
G-MZAZ	Mainair Blade (Rotax 462)	1040-0595-7 & W838		26. 5.95	P.J.Kay	Barton	30. 6.00P
G-MZBA	Mainair Blade (Rotax 912UL)	1068-0296-7 & W870		15. 3.96	M.K.Mitchell	Hertford	27. 3.98P
G-MZBB	Cyclone Pegasus Quantum 15 (Rotax 582/40)	7139		13. 3.96	C.D.C.Ashdown	Largs	24. 7.00P
G-MZBC	Cyclone Pegasus Quantum 15 (Rotax 582)	7077		15. 8.95	B.M.Quinn	Barlow, Sheffield	30. 3.00P
G-MZBD	Rans S-6-ESD Coyote II XL (Rotax 503) 0795-850XL & PFA/204-12957			15. 3.96	S P Yardley	Rugeley	9. 2.00P
G-MZBE	CFM Streak Shadow SA-M PFA/206-12905 (Rotax 618)			18. 3.96	N.J.Bushell	Southampton	16.11.00P
G-MZBF	Letov LK-2M Sluka (Rotax 447)	PFA/263-12881		18. 3.96	B.Boylan	Coleraine, NI	25. 1.00P
G-MZBG	Whittaker MW-6S Fatboy Flyer (Rotax 503)	PFA/164-12891		20. 3.96	A.W.Hodder	RAF Cranwell	1. 6.00P
G-MZBH	Rans S-6-ESD Coyote II PFA/204-12244 (Rotax 503)			21. 3.96	D.Sutherland	Breighton	10. 5.00P
G-MZBI	Cyclone Pegasus Quantum 15 (Rotax 582/40)	7189		21. 3.96	C.A.Campbell	Kirkhill, Inverness	9. 5.99P
G-MZBK	Letov LK-2M Sluka 8295s 002 & PFA/263-12872			26. 3.96	R.Painter	Bridgnorth	
G-MZBL	Mainair Blade (Rotax 582)	1080-0496-7 & W883		11. 4.96	J.R.Webster	Ormskirk	18. 6.00P
G-MZBM	Cyclone Pegasus Quantum 15 (Rotax 582/40)	7196		12. 4.96	Flight Aid Ltd	Dunkeswell	31. 5.00P
G-MZBN	CFM Shadow Srs.CD 069 & BMAA/HB/073 (Rotax 503) (Manufacturer's c/n duplicates G-MTWP - was 'WP rebuilt ?)			22. 4.96	Cloudbase Aviation Services Ltd Redhill		19. 6.00P
G-MZBO	Cyclone Pegasus Quantum 15 (Rotax 582)	7218		3. 5.96	A.M.Dalgetty	Perth	24. 7.00P
G-MZBP	Airwave Microchute UQ/Motor 27 BMAA/HB/028 and/or BMAA/HB/075			29. 3.96	V.G.Pearson	Guildford	
G-MZBR	Southdown Raven	2232/0082		24. 5.96	D.M.Lane	Stourbridge	
G-MZBS	CFM Shadow Srs.D PFA/161-13008 (Rotax 582/47)			14. 5.96	P.B.Merritt	Newbury	17. 6.99P
G-MZBT	Cyclone Pegasus Quantum 15 (Rotax 912)	7224		22. 5.96	T.M.Clark	Guildford	20. 7.99P
G-MZBU	Rans S-6-ESD Coyote II XL (Rotax 503) PFA/204-12992			30. 5.96	J.B.Marshall	Scarborough	3.10.00P
G-MZBV	Rans S-6-ESD Coyote II XL (Rotax 503) 0396-950XL & PFA/204-13009			30. 5.96	R.Hatton	Douglas, IoM	20. 9.00P
G-MZBW	Quad City Challenger II UK (Rotax 582) PFA/177-12971			19. 2.96	R.T.L.Chaloner	Grisborough, Cleveland	28.11.00P
G-MZBX	Whittaker MW-6S-LW Fatboy Flyer (Rotax 503) PFA/164-12563			16. 5.96	S.Rose & P.Tearall	Ilford/Camberley	17.10.00P
G-MZBY	Cyclone Pegasus Quantum 15 7227 (Rotax 582) (C/n 7224 reported - see G-MZBT)			30. 5.96	D.M.Holmam	Northwich	29. 7.00P
G-MZBZ	Quad City Challenger II UK PFA/177-12928			11. 3.96	J.Flisher	Honiton	
G-MZCA	Rans S-6-ESD Coyote II XL (Rotax 503) 0396-953XL & PFA/204-12997			31. 5.96	S.J.Everett, K.Kettles & F.Williams Stratford-upon-Avon		13. 7.00P
G-MZCB	Cyclone Chaser S (Rotax 447)	7220		4. 6.96	G.P.Hodgson	Bolton	1. 8.00P
G-MZCC	Mainair Blade (Rotax 912UL)	1086-0696-7 & W889		7. 6.96	D.E.McGauley	Ince Blundell	18. 7.00P
G-MZCD	Mainair Blade (Rotax 582)	1087-0696-7 & W890		10. 6.96	J.R.Caylow	Nottingham	30. 6.00P
G-MZCE	Mainair Blade (Rotax 462)	1088-0696-7 & W891		17. 6.96	P.Hayes	Ince Blundell	15.12.99P
G-MZCF	Mainair Blade (Rotax 462)	1089-0696-7 & W892		30. 8.96	J.White	Ince Blundell	29. 8.97P
G-MZCG	Mainair Blade (Rotax 462)	1090-0696-7 & W893		17. 6.96	M.J.Wilson	Childwall	19.11.00P
G-MZCH	Whittaker MW-6S Fatboy Flyer PFA/164-12131			7. 6.96	E.J.Blake	Totnes	

Regn	Type	C/n	P/I	Date	Owner/operator	Probable Base	CA Expy
G-MZCI	Cyclone Pegasus Quantum 15 (Rotax 503)	7231		10. 6.96	P.H.Risdale	Wollaston	13. 7.00P
G-MZCJ	Cyclone Pegasus Quantum 15 (Rotax 582/40)	7233		14. 6.96	A.W.Hay	Insch	19. 7.00P
G-MZCK	AMF Chevvron 2-32C (Konig SD570)	038		11. 7.96	Finish Design Ltd	Cambridge	9. 7.97P
G-MZCL	Ultrasports Tripacer/Moyes Mega II	JAJ-01		21. 6.96	J.A.Jones	Winchester	
G-MZCM	Cyclone Pegasus Quantum 15 (Rotax 582)	7219		3. 5.96	A.J.Harper	Croughton	10. 6.00P
G-MZCN	Mainair Blade (Rotax 582)	1079-0396-7 & W882		27. 6.96	P.C.Nelstrop	Barton	31. 1.00P
G-MZCO	Mainair Mercury (Rotax 462)	1091-0796-7 & W894		26. 6.96	E.Rush	Congleton	14. 8.00P
G-MZCP	Solar Wings Pegasus XL-Q (Rotax 462) SW-TE-0434 & SW-WQ-0576			11. 2.93	C.A.Palmer	Clench Common	25. 6.00P
G-MZCR	Cyclone Pegasus Quantum 15 (Rotax 503)	7234		28. 6.96	J.E.P.Stubberfield	Kenley	8. 5.00P
G-MZCS	TEAM miniMax 91	PFA/186-12646		20.12.95	D.T.J.Stanley	Cheltenham	14. 6.00P
G-MZCT	CFM Shadow Srs.CD (Rotax 503)	277		11. 7.96	W.G.Gill	Plaistows, Hemel Hampstead	16. 9.97P
G-MZCU	Mainair Blade (Rotax 462)	1082-0496-7 & W885		1. 5.96	K.D.Curtis	Lowestoft	15. 8.00P
G-MZCV	Cyclone Pegasus Quantum 15 (Rotax 503)	7235		11. 7.96	B.S.Toole	Rhuallt	8. 8.00P
G-MZCX	Hunt Wing/Avon Skytrike (Rotax 503) (Originally regd with c/n 9510055)	BMAA/HB/072		17. 7.96	R.Harrison	Higher Barn Farm, Houghton	28. 4.00P
G-MZCY	Cyclone Pegasus Quantum 15 (Rotax 582)	7236		19. 7.96	B.G.Simons	Craysmarsh Farm, Melksham	30. 8.00P
G-MZCZ	Hunt Wing/Experience (Originally regd with c/n 9409024)	BMAA/HB/039		24. 7.96	C.Kiernan	Mostrim, Co.Longford	
G-MZDA	Rans S-6-ESD Coyote II XL (Nose-wheel u/c) (Rotax 503) 0386.951 & PFA/204-13019			29. 7.96	J.Dent & W.C.Lombard	Thirsk/Northallerton	9. 9.99P
G-MZDB*	Cyclone Pegasus Quantum 15 (Rotax 912)	7237		31. 7.96	Not known (Temp unregd 15.11.96)	Marlborough	26. 7.97P
G-MZDC	Cyclone Pegasus Quantum 15 (Rotax 582)	7246		2. 8.96	M.T.Jones	Witney	11.11.00P
G-MZDD	Cyclone Pegasus Quantum 15 (Rotax 503)	7114	G-69-23	11. 7.96	L.A.Hosegood	Swindon	19. 2.00P
G-MZDE	Cyclone Pegasus Quantum 15 (Rotax 582)	7238		12. 7.96	D.J.Taylor	St.Neots	26. 1.00P
G-MZDF	Mainair Blade (Rotax 462)	1093-0896-7 & W896		15. 8.96	T.D.Thompson	Knutsford	13. 4.00P
G-MZDG	Rans S-6-ESD Coyote II XL (Rotax 503)	PFA/204-13030		7. 8.96	M.J.Rhodes t/a Barton Heritage Flying Group	Barton	26. 4.00P
G-MZDH	Cyclone Pegasus Quantum 15 (Rotax 912)	7248		12. 8.96	R.Gill	Knapthorpe Lodge, Caunton	24. 9.00P
G-MZDI	Whittaker MW-6S Fatboy Flyer Srs.A (Rotax 503) PFA/164-11929		G-BUNN	15. 8.96	G.T.Harris	East Grinstead	10.11.99P
G-MZDJ	Medway Raven X (Rotax 447)	MRB138/119		19. 8.96	R.Bryan & S.Digby	Bristol	1. 5.00P
G-MZDK	Mainair Blade (Rotax 582) (C/n reported as 1084-0696-7)	1084-0596-7 & W887		9. 5.96	K.J.Miles	St.Michaels	29. 5.00P
G-MZDL	Whittaker MW-6S Fatboy Flyer	PFA/164-12412		19. 8.96	C.D. & S.J.Wills	Andover	23..6.00P
G-MZDM	Rans S-6-ESD Coyote II XL (Rotax 503) 0396-954XL & PFA/204-13022			2. 9.96	M.E.Nicholas	Chilbolton	25. 8.99P
G-MZDN	Cyclone Pegasus Quantum 15 (Rotax 582)	7255		5. 9.96	T D Dyson	Addlestone	16. 3.99P
G-MZDO	Cyclone AX3 (Rotax 503)	7252		11. 9.96	I.P.Noonan	Weston Zoyland	28. 4.00P
G-MZDP	AMF Chevvron 2-32C (Konig SD570)	020		3. 4.90	A.S.Nicol & A.S.Gunn t/a G-MZDP Group (Damaged mid 1995)	Billericay	16. 3.96P
G-MZDR	Rans S-6-ESD Coyote II XL (Rotax 503) PFA/204-13012			8. 8.96	R.Pyper & P.McGill	Newtownards/Holywood	28.11.00P
G-MZDS	Cyclone AX3 (Rotax 503)	7253		16. 9.96	A.B.Askew	Kettering	7.11.00P
G-MZDT	Mainair Blade (Rotax 582)	1096-0996-7 & W899		19. 9.96	G.Sipson	Otherton, Cannock	25. 7.00P
G-MZDU	Cyclone Pegasus Quantum 15 (Rotax 912)	7260		19. 9.96	G.A.Breen	Lagos, Portugal	26.10.00P

Regn	Type	C/n	P/I	Date	Owner/operator	Probable Base	CA Expy
G-MZDV	Cyclone Pegasus Quantum 15 (Rotax 582)	7199		9. 4.96	P.M.Wilkinson	Great Orton	19. 5.00P
G-MZDW	Trekking Microchute UQ/Motor 27	BMAA/HB/078		23. 9.96	C.Kiernan	Mostrim, Co.Longford	
G-MZDX	Letov LK-2M Sluka	PFA/263-12882		30. 9.96	R.P.Stonor	London W3	22. 2.00P
G-MZDY	Cyclone Pegasus Quantum 15 (Rotax 462HP)	7263		2.10.96	E.R.Bone	Newmarket	22.10.00P
G-MZDZ	Hunt Avon/Wing 9501042 & BMAA/HB/045			23.10.96	E.W.Laidlaw	Langholm, Dumfries	
G-MZEA	Quad City Challenger II	CH2-0294-1101 & PFA/177A-12728		22. 4.96	G.S.Cridland	Thorney Island	9. 2.00P
G-MZEB	Mainair Blade (Rotax 462)	1074-0396-7 & W876		22. 7.96	G.R.Barker	Epping	21. 7.00P
G-MZEC	Cyclone Pegasus Quantum 15 (Rotax 582/40)	7278		24.10.96	A.B.Godber	Bradley Ashbourne, Derby	10.11.00P
G-MZED	Mainair Blade (Rotax 582)	1092-0796-7 & W895		3. 7.96	P.Lavender	Barton	25. 9.00P
G-MZEE	Cyclone Pegasus Quantum 15 (Rotax 582)	7245		9. 8.96	D.R.Willson	Oakham	28. 8.00P
G-MZEF*	Mainair Blade (Rotax 462)	1094-0896-7 & W897		12. 8.96	D.A.Bolton (Cancelled as destroyed 19.2.99)	Rochdale	23. 9.99P
G-MZEG	Mainair Blade (Rotax 582)	1095-0896-7 & W898		8. 8.96	J.Jasinczuk	Otherton, Cannock	5. 9.00P
G-MZEH	Cyclone Pegasus Quantum 15 (Rotax 582/40)	7259		19. 9.96	P.S.Hall	Sywell	16.10.00P
G-MZEI	Whittaker MW-5D Sorcerer (Rotax 447)	PFA/163-12011		28.10.96	W.G.Reynolds (U S Navy c/s)	Overstrand	27. 6.00P
G-MZEJ	Mainair Blade (Rotax 462)	1097-0996-7 & W900		8.10.96	D.Jones	Liverpool	18. 6.00P
G-MZEK	Mainair Mercury (Rotax 462)	1098-1096-7 & W901		14.10.96	M.Whiteman-Heywood	Bewdley	4.11.00P
G-MZEL	Cyclone AX3 (Rotax 503)	7250		30.10.96	T.I.Bull	Tarn Farm, Cockerham	26. 3.00P
G-MZEM	Cyclone Pegasus Quantum 15 (Rotax 912)	7277		8.11.96	C.A.W.Godfrey	London W4	6. 1.00P
G-MZEN	Rans S-6-ESD Coyote II (Nose-wheel u/c) (Rotax 503) 1294.705 & PFA/204-12823			9. 7.96	P.Bottomley	Damyns Hill, Upminster	15. 3.00P
G-MZEO	Rans S-6-ESD Coyote II XL (Rotax 503)	PFA/204-13046		19.11.96	J.R.Dobson t/a G-MZEO Group	Eshott	23. 3.00P
G-MZEP	Mainair Rapier (Rotax 503)	1103-1296-7 & W906		13.12.96	A.J. & M.S.Haworth	Arclid Green, Sandbach	10. 3.00P
G-MZER	Cyclone AX2000 (HKS.700E)	7251	G-69-28 G-MZER	4.12.96	B.H.Stephens t/a Sarum AX2000 Group	Old Sarum	18. 3.00P
G-MZES	Letov LK-2M Sluka (Rotax 447) 8296K10 & PFA/263-13064			5.12.96	M.F.Cottam	Lincoln	14. 6.00P
G-MZET	Cyclone Pegasus Quantum 15 (Rotax 503)	7288		9.12.96	D.L.Walker	Medernach, The Netherlands	17. 2.99P
G-MZEU	Rans S-6-ESD Coyote II XL (Rotax 503)	PFA/204-13023		23.12.96	W S S Lubbock	Callington	16.11.99P
G-MZEV	Mainair Rapier (Rotax 503)	1101-1296-7 & W904		7. 1.97	I.D.Woolley	Barton	5. 5.00P
G-MZEW	Mainair Blade (Rotax 462)	1105-0197-7 & W908		13. 1.97	M.Rhodes	Arclid Green, Sandbach	5. 2.00P
G-MZEX	Cyclone Pegasus Quantum 15 (Rotax 582/40)	7292		19.11.96	J.Wittering	Uttoxeter	30. 1.00P
G-MZEY	Micro Avn B.22S Bantam (Rotax 582)	96-002	ZK-TII	7. 1.97	F.D.Hatton t/a Pound Green Syndicate	Pound Green, Kidderminster	9. 6.00P
G-MZEZ	Cyclone Pegasus Quantum 15 (Rotax 912)	7285		8.11.96	E.Daleki	Oakley	17. 2.00P
G-MZFA	Cyclone AX2000 (Rotax 582/48)	7301		17.12.96	P.J.Howard	Ennis, Co.Clare	16. 1.00P
G-MZFB	Mainair Blade (Rotax 462)	1108-0197-7 & W911		7. 1.97	R.J.Allarton	Newark	3. 6.99P
G-MZFC	Letov LK-2M Sluka (Rotax 447)	PFA/263-13063		7. 1.97	J.van der Broek	Long Marston	26. 8.00P
G-MZFD	Mainair Rapier (Rotax 462)	1109-0197-7 & W912		24. 1.97	R.Gill	Knapthorpe Lodge, Caunton	19. 3.00P
G-MZFE	Hunt Avon/Wing 9507049 & BMAA/HB/061 (Rotax 503)			16. 1.97	G.J.Latham	Sittles Farm, Alrewas	10. 6.00P
G-MZFF	Hunt Avon/Wing 960458 & BMAA/HB/074			22. 1.97	B.J.Adamson	Stockport	
G-MZFG	Cyclone Pegasus Quantum 15 (Rotax 582/40)	7305		21. 1.97	P.Smith	Ulverston	20.11.00P

Regn	Type	C/n	P/I	Date	Owner/operator	Probable Base	CA Expy
G-MZFH	AMF Chevvron 2- (Konig SD570)	32C 039		27. 3.97	Finish Design Ltd Tarn Farm, Cockerham t/a Air-Share		21. 4.98P
G-MZFI	Lorimer Iolaire (BMW)	BMAA/HB/035		30. 1.97	H.Lorimer	Mauchline, Ayr	
G-MZFK	Whittaker MW-6 Merlin (Rotax 532)	PFA/164-11626		10. 2.97	K.Worthington	Chorley	19.11.00P
G-MZFL	Rans S-6-ESD Coyote II XL (Rotax 503) 0696-999XL & PFA/204-13041			12. 2.97	D.L.Robson & U.Y.S.O'Reilly	Eshott	19. 8.00P
G-MZFM	Cyclone Pegasus Quantum 15 (Rotax 582/40)	7310		21. 2.97	T.Holford	Cannock	26. 4.00P
G-MZFN	Rans S-6-ESD Coyote II PFA/204-12977 (Rotax 503)			26. 2.97	C.J. & W.R.Wallbank Ley Farm, Chirk		14. 9.99P
G-MZFO	Thruster T.600N (Rotax 503)	9037-T600N-001		4. 3.97	Mainair Sports Ltd	Barton	8. 4.00P
G-MZFP	Thruster T.600T (Rotax 503)	9047-T600T-002		4. 3.97	A.R.Emerson Priory Farm, Tibenham (Damaged on take-off Priory Farm 25.6.99)		12. 5.00P
G-MZFR	Thruster T.600N (Rotax 503)	9047-T600N-003		4. 3.97	H.Larmour Shobdon t/a Blue Bird Syndicate		18. 5.00P
G-MZFS	Mainair Blade 1110-0297-7 & W913 (Rotax 582) (Regd with Trike c/n 1010-0297-7)			8. 1.97	S.P.Stone & F.A.Stephens Baxby Manor, Husthwaite		25. 3.00P
G-MZFT	Cyclone Pegasus Quantum 15 (Rotax 912)	7264		2.10.96	J.F.Woodham	Otherton	13. 3.00P
G-MZFU	Thruster T.600N (Rotax 503)	9047-T600N-004		4. 3.97	Thruster Air Services Ltd	Wantage	25.11.00P
G-MZFV	Cyclone Pegasus Quantum 15 (Rotax 912)	7324		13. 3.97	G.J.Slater	Deenethorpe	22. 4.00P
G-MZFW	Mainair Rapier 1111-0297-7 & W914 (Rotax 462)			17. 1.97	C.S.M.Hallam	Rochdale	23. 4.99P
G-MZFX	Cyclone AX2000 (Rotax 582/48)	7322		14. 3.97	Flylight Airsports Ltd	Sywell	30. 4.99P
G-MZFY	Rans S-6-ESD Coyote II XL (Rotax 503)	PFA/204-13043		17. 3.97	L.G.Tserkezos	Reigate	22. 6.00P
G-MZFZ	Mainair Blade 1119-0497-7 & W922 (Rotax 582/2V)			2. 4.97	S.M.Park Rufforth t/a Phoenix Flying Group		16. 6.00P
G-MZGA	Cyclone AX2000 (Rotax 582/48)	7303		17.12.96	Microflight Ireland Ltd	Mullaghmore	18. 5.00P
G-MZGB	Cyclone AX2000 (Rotax 582/48)	7302		28. 1.97	P.Hegarty Magherafelt, Co.Londonderry		31. 3.00P
G-MZGC	Cyclone AX2000 (Rotax 582/2V)	7304		20.12.96	Carol E.Walls	Mullaghmore	23. 1.99P
G-MZGD	Rans S-5 Coyote 89.095 & PFA/193-13096			1. 4.97	A.G.Headford	Barton	3 .5.00P
G-MZGE	Medway Hybred 44XLR (Rotax 503)	MR143/125		8. 4.97	Eclectic Computer Software Ltd Stoke, Kent		27. 5.99P
G-MZGF	Letov LK-2M Sluka (Rotax 447) 8296K008 & PFA/263-13073			8. 4.97	G.Lombardi	RAF Wyton	27. 9.00P
G-MZGG	Cyclone Pegasus Quantum 15 (Rotax 503)	7327		10. 4.97	A.J.Ridell	Graveley	17. 4.00P
G-MZGH	Hunt Avon/Hunt Wing	BMAA/HB/070		20.12.96	G.C.Horner Tyldesley, Manchester		
G-MZGI	Mainair Blade 1117-0397-7 & W920 (Rotax 912UL)			11. 4.97	N.E.King	Bolton	8. 6.00P
G-MZGJ	Kolb Twinstar Mk.3	PFA/205-12421		16. 4.97	P.Coppock	Kemble	12. 8.99P
G-MZGK	Cyclone Pegasus Quantum 15 (Rotax 582/40)	7331		30. 4.97	G.C.Weighell	Enstone	14. 5.00P
G-MZGL	Mainair Rapier 1104-0197-7 & W907 (Rotax 503)			18.12.96	L.R.Fox	Aylesbury	7. 3.00P
G-MZGM	Cyclone AX2000 (Rotax 582/48)	7334		1. 5.97	W.G.Dunn	Winkleigh, Devon	2. 7.00P
G-MZGN	Cyclone Pegasus Quantum 15 (Rotax 503)	7332		2. 5.97	R.J.Townsend Long Acres Farm, Sandy		16. 6.00P
G-MZGO	Cyclone Pegasus Quantum 15 (Rotax 582/40)	7320		20. 3.97	S.F.G.Allen Knapthorpe Lodge, Caunton		16. 5.00P
G-MZGP	Cyclone AX2000 (Rotax 582/48)	7333		7. 5.97	M.W.Taylor	Insch	12. 6.00P
G-MZGR	TEAM miniMax	PFA/186-12323		8. 5.97	K.G.Seeley	Reading	
G-MZGS	CFM Shadow Srs.DD	PFA/161-13050		8. 5.97	C.S.Robinson	Newtownards	10. 8.99P
G-MZGT	RH7B Tiger Light (5/8ths scale Tiger Moth)	PFA/230-13013		10. 3.97	J.B.McNab	Coventry	
G-MZGU	Arrowflight Hawk II (UK) (Rotax 503)	PFA/266-13075		8. 5.97	Arrowflight Aviation Ltd	Cowes, IoW	27. 7.99P
G-MZGV	Cyclone Pegasus Quantum 15 (Rotax 582/40)	7339		12. 6.97	J.I.Greenshields	Dunkeswell	22. 6.99P

Regn	Type	C/n	P/I	Date	Owner/operator	Probable Base	CA Expy
G-MZGW	Mainair Blade (Rotax 462)	1112-0297-7 & W915		19. 2.97	R.Almond	Bury St.Edmunds	19. 5.00P
G-MZGX	Thruster T.600N (Rotax 503)	9057-T600N-005		28. 4.97	R.L.Barton	Arclid Green, Sandbach	19. 7.00P
G-MZGY	Thruster T.600N (Rotax 503)	9057-T600N-006		28. 4.97	M.J.& A.R.Wolldridge	Newbury	12. 8.98P
G-MZGZ	Thruster T.600N (Rotax 503)	9057-T600N-007		28. 4.97	K.Hanson t/a G-MZGZ Group	Dunkeswell	29.10.00P
G-MZHA	Thruster T.600T (Rotax 503)	9057-T600T-008		28. 4.97	R.V.Buxton	Feshiebridge	29. 7.00P
G-MZHB	Mainair Blade (Rotax 462)	1114-0297-7 & W917		19. 2.97	R.J.Butler	Guy Lane Farm, Waverton	22. 3.00P
G-MZHC	Thruster T.600T	9067-T600T-009		13. 5.97	Thruster Air Services Ltd	Wantage	21. 3.00P
G-MZHD	Thruster T.600T	9067-T600T-010		13. 5.97	B.E.Foster	Tain, Ross-shire	4. 1.99P
G-MZHE	Thruster T.600N (Rotax 503)	9067-T600N-011		13. 5.97	K.R.Jenkins	Dunkeswell	5. 1.00P
G-MZHF	Thruster T.600N (Rotax 503)	9067-T600N-012		13. 5.97	R.G.Noble	Chipping Norton	18. 6.00P
G-MZHG	Whittaker MW-6T	PFA/164-11420		16. 6.97	M.G.Speers	Douglas, IoM	21. 9.00P
G-MZHI	Cyclone Pegasus Quantum 15 (Rotax 582/40)	7337		27. 5.97	P R Hope t/a Quantum HI Group	Knapthorpe Lodge, Caunton	3. 7.00P
G-MZHJ	Mainair Rapier (Rotax 462)	1123-0697-7 & W926		17. 6.97	T.D.Guest	Shifnal	22. 6.00P
G-MZHK	Cyclone Pegasus Quantum Super Sport 15 (Rotax 582/40)	7352		24. 6.97	B.J.Partridge	Sutton Meadows	19. 7.00P
G-MZHL	Mainair Rapier (Rotax 503)	1126-0797-7 & W929		30. 6.97	A.N.W.Fletcher	Bodmin	23. 7.00P
G-MZHM	Team Himax 1700R (Rotax 447)	PFA/272-12912		8. 1.97	M.H.McKeown	Enniskillen	27. 4.00P
G-MZHN	Cyclone Pegasus Quantum 15 (Rotax 462HP)	7351		27. 6.97	T.G.Jones	Rhuallt	10. 8.98P
G-MZHO	Quad City Challenger II	PFA/177-12936		15. 7.97	J.Pavelin	Barling	20. 5.00P
G-MZHP	Cyclone Pegasus Quantum 15 (Rotax 582/40)	7353		15. 7.97	A.S.Findley	Cardington	20. 8.00P
G-MZHR	Cyclone AX2000 (Rotax 582)	7307		7. 3.97	A.M.Hemmings	Sandtoft	1. 5.00P
G-MZHS	Thruster T.600T (Rotax 503)	9077-T600T-013		4. 7.97	D.Mahajan	Lower Mountpleasant, Chatteris	15.10.00P
G-MZHT	Whittaker MW-6 Merlin (Rotax 503)	PFA/164-11244		12. 6.97	S.J.Smith	Bristol	20.12.99P
G-MZHU	Thruster T.600T	9077-T600T-019		4. 7.97	M.S.Shelton	Stoneacre Farm, Farthing Corner	11. 6.00P
G-MZHV	Thruster T.600T	9077-T600T-018		4. 7.97	K.M.Jones	Leicester	29. 7.00P
G-MZHW	Thruster T.600N	9077-T600N-017		4. 7.97	K.N.Hopewell	Queniborough	1. 5.00P
G-MZHX	Thruster T.600N	9077-T600N-016		4. 7.97	Thruster Air Services Ltd	Wantage	
G-MZHY	Thruster T.600N	9077-T600N-015		4. 7.97	J.R.North t/a West Lancashire Microlight School	Ince Blundell	11. 5.00P
G-MZHZ	Thruster T.600N	9077-T600N-014		4. 7.97	G.E.Hillyer-Jones	Shobdon	29. 6.00P
G-MZIA	Team Himax 1700R	PFA/272-13020		25. 4.97	I.J.Arkieson	Meols, Wirral	
G-MZIB	Cyclone Pegasus Quantum 15 (Rotax 582/40)	7354		15. 7.97	S.Murphy	Trim, Ireland	2. 9.00P
G-MZIC	Cyclone Pegasus Quantum 15 (Rotax 503)	7348		24. 6.97	Helen M.Squire & C.F.Two t/a Swansea Airsports Services	Swansea	22. 7.00P
G-MZID	Whittaker MW-6 Merlin	PFA/164-11383		15. 7.97	M.G.A.Wood	Tadcaster	
G-MZIE	Cyclone Pegasus Quantum 15 (Rotax 582/40)	7359		6. 8.97	Flylight Airsports Ltd	Sywell	25. 8.00P
G-MZIF	Cyclone Pegasus Quantum 15 (Rotax 503)	7355		16. 7.97	P.Simpson	Weston Favell, Northampton	20. 8.00P
G-MZIH	Mainair Blade (Rotax 462)	1128-0797-7 & W931		16. 7.97	E.Scarisbrick	Preston	5. 8.00P
G-MZII	TEAM miniMax 88 (Rotax 377)	PFA/186-11842		19. 3.97	G.F.M.Garner	Clench Common	21. 2.00P
G-MZIJ	Cyclone Pegasus Quantum 15 (Rotax 582/40)	7362		14. 8.97	B.Errington-Weddle	North Shields	15. 9.00P
G-MZIK	Cyclone Pegasus Quantum 15 (Rotax 582/40)	7368		8. 9.97	D.Kiddy & P.Davies	Torquay/Totnes	11.10.00P
G-MZIL	Mainair Rapier (Rotax 462)	1132-0897-7 & W935		1. 9.97	A.J.Varga	Rufforth	8. 9.00P
G-MZIM	Mainair Rapier (Rotax 462)	1124-0697-7 & W927		9. 6.97	M.J.McKegney	Sandtoft	9. 7.00P

Regn	Type	C/n	P/I	Date	Owner/operator	Probable Base	CA Expy
G-MZIN*	Whittaker MW-6 Merlin PFA/164-12820 (Rotax 503)			9. 9.97	R.F.Bayford Newnham, St.Neots (Crashed Newnham 28.3.99: cancelled by CAA 1.12.99)		20.10.99P
G-MZIP	Murphy Renegade Spirit UK (Rotax 532) 216 & PFA/188-11426			4. 7.89	C.I.Bates Long Marston		1.11.99P
G-MZIR	Mainair Blade 1134-0997-7 & W937 (Rotax 582)			18. 9.97	I.Callaghan Davidstowe t/a Moorland Flying Club		28. 9.99P
G-MZIS	Mainair Blade 1115-0397-7 & W918 (Rotax 462)			17. 2.97	K.R.McCartney Saltburn-by-the-Sea		23. 3.00P
G-MZIT	Mainair Blade 1129-0897-7 & W932 (Rotax 912UL)			16. 7.97	K.M.Jones Tring		24. 7.00P
G-MZIU	Cyclone Pegasus Quantum 15 7371 (Rotax 582/40)			15.10.97	S.F.Winter Calne		5.10.00P
G-MZIV	Cyclone AX2000 7372 (Rotax 582/48)			21.10.97	C.J.Tomlin Desborough		16.10.00P
G-MZIW	Mainair Blade 1127-0797-7 & W930 (Rotax 462)			16. 7.97	N.Creeney St.Michaels		11. 9.00P
G-MZIX	Mignet HM-1000 Balerit 130			23. 9.97	P.E.H.Scott Stockbridge		13. 2.00P
G-MZIY	Rans S-6-ESD Coyote II XL (Rotax 503) 1096-1050XL & PFA/204-13184			29. 9.97	P.A.Bell Barton		16.10.00P
G-MZIZ	Murphy Renegade Spirit UK (Rotax 582) 257 & PFA/188-11701		G-MWGP	21.10.92	J.G.McMinn Movenis, Co.Londonderry		16.11.00P
G-MZJA	Mainair Blade 1135-0997-7 & W938 (Rotax 582)			30. 9.97	R.Cookson Wirral		1.12.99P
G-MZJB	Aviasud Mistral 047		(ex ?)	30. 9.97	D.M.Whitham Crosland Moor		
G-MZJC*	Micro Avn B.22S Bantam 97-011		ZK-JIK	14.10.97	A.S.Moore Stafford (Cancelled by CAA 17.12.99)		3.11.99P
G-MZJD	Mainair Blade 1130-0897-7 & W933 (Rotax 503)			7. 8.97	R.J.Davey Sleaford		20. 8.00P
G-MZJE	Mainair Rapier 1136-1097-7 & W939 (Rotax 503)			17.10.97	J.E.Davies Southport		23.11.99P
G-MZJF	Cyclone AX2000 7378 (Rotax 582/48)			2.12.97	J.A.R.Hartley Long Marston		1.12.00P
G-MZJG	Cyclone Pegasus Quantum 15 7335 (Rotax 462)			2. 5.97	J.Gamlen Oakley		28. 5.00P
G-MZJH	Cyclone Pegasus Quantum 15 7350 (Rotax 503)			25. 6.97	J.Hardy Kettering		17. 7.00P
G-MZJI	Rans S-6-ESD Coyote II XL (Rotax 503) 1096-1046XL & PFA/204-13221			3.11.97	A.T.Morgan Rayne Hall Farm, Rayne		18.12.98P
G-MZJJ	Meridian Ultralights Maverick PFA/259-13016			5.11.97	N.B.Kirby Dunkeswell		1.10.99P
G-MZJK	Mainair Blade 1100-1196-7 & W903 (Rotax 582)			19.11.96	A.H.Kershaw Bury		2. 4.00P
G-MZJL	Cyclone AX2000 7363 (Rotax 503)			11. 8.97	A.J.Longbottom Smeathorpe, Honiton		28.10.00P
G-MZJM	Rans S-6-ESD Coyote II XL 1096.1049XL & PFA/204-13215			19.11.97	R.J.Hopkins Popham		29. 3.00P
G-MZJN	Cyclone Pegasus Quantum 15 7376 (Rotax 582/40)			11.11.97	J.Nelson Knapthorpe Lodge, Caunton		16.11.00P
G-MZJO	Cyclone Pegasus Quantum 15 7338 (Rotax 582/40)			17. 6.97	D.C.Lennard Richmond, Surrey		1. 7.98P
G-MZJP	Whittaker MW-6S Fatboy Flyer PFA/164-13049			21.10.97	D.J.Burton & C.A.J.Funnell Brighton		
G-MZJR	Cyclone AX2000 7385			11.11.97	Cyclone Airsports Ltd Manton t/a Pegasus Aviation		25. 5.00P
G-MZJS	Meridian Ultralights Maverick (Jabiru 2200A) PFA/259-13017			12.12.97	R.D.Barnard Stockport (Damaged Sleap 17.5.99)		5.10.99P
G-MZJT	Cyclone Pegasus Quantum 15 7399 (Rotax 912)			23.12.97	C.M.Theakstone Sywell		23.12.00P
G-MZJU	Cyclone Pegasus Quantum 15 7382			23.12.97	L.M.King Telford		18. 2.99P
G-MZJV	Mainair Blade 1141-0198-7 & W944 (Rotax 912)			7. 1.98	M.A.Roberts West Malling		3. 2.99P
G-MZJW	Cyclone Pegasus Quantum 15 7390			27. 1.98	I.D.Stokes Camelford		27. 1.00P
G-MZJX	Mainair Blade 1139-0198-7 & W942			9. 1.98	R.G.Hearsey & D.B.Limbrick Rye t/a HAL Microlight Club		29. 4.00P
G-MZJY	Cyclone Pegasus Quantum 15 7394 (Rotax 912)			23.12.97	S.G Payne Sandy t/a Yankee Syndicate		23.12.99P
G-MZJZ	Mainair Blade 1121-0597-7 & W924 (Rotax 912UL)			23. 6.97	P.Crosby Ince Blundell		22. 6.00P
G-MZKA	Cyclone Pegasus Quantum 15 7380 (Rotax 912)			1.12.97	A.S.R.McSherry West Kilbride		26.11.00P

Regn	Type	C/n	P/I	Date	Owner/operator	Probable Base	CA Expy
G-MZKB*	Kolb Twinstar Mk.3 PFA/205-13160			18. 7.97	K.R.Blades	Louth	19.11.98P
	(Rotax 582)				(Cancelled by CAA 17.4.99)		
G-MZKC	Cyclone AX2000	7398		22. 1.98	A.G. & G.L.Higgins	Bitteswell	1. 2.00P
G-MZKD	Cyclone Pegasus Quantum 15	7404		19. 3.98	S.J.E.Smith	Newcastle	18. 4.00P
G-MZKE	Rans S-6-ESD Coyote II XL			19. 1.98	I.Findlay	Eshott	8. 3.00P
	PFA/204-13248						
G-MZKF	Cyclone Pegasus Quantum 15	7407		21. 1.98	G.J.Slater	Clench Common	24. 2.00P
G-MZKG	Mainair Blade 1145-0198-7 & W948			23. 1.98	P.Olsson	Ulverston	10. 2.99P
G-MZKH	CFM Shadow Srs.DD	292-DD		23. 1.98	K.D.Mitchell	Shoreham	8. 3.00P
G-MZKI	Mainair Rapier 1147-0298-7 & W950			12. 2.98	C.A.Benjamin	Rufforth	18. 5.00P
G-MZKJ	Mainair Blade 1039-0595-7 & W837			19. 5.95	L.G.M.Maddick	Barton	2. 8.00P
	(Rotax 582)						
G-MZKK	Mainair Blade 1140-0198-7 & W943			12. 2.98	D.L.Handley	Lydd	23. 2.00P
	(Rotax 912)						
G-MZKL	Cyclone Pegasus Quantum 15	7360		18. 8.97	S.Pearce & K.J.Fish		
	(Rotax 582/40)					Knapthorpe Lodge, Caunton	31. 8.00P
G-MZKM	Mainair Blade 1133-0897-7 & W936			15. 8.97	C.Bodill	Nottingham	22. 8.00P
	(Rotax 912UL)						
G-MZKN	Mainair Rapier 1138-1297-7 & W941			12.12.97	G.Craig	Dundonald, Belfast	23. 1.00P
G-MZKO	Mainair Blade 1131-0897-7 & W934			5. 8.97	A.M.Durose	Nottingham	19. 6.00P
	(Rotax 503)						
G-MZKP	Thruster T.600N	9038-T600N-020		27. 1.98	Thruster Air Services Ltd	Wantage	
G-MZKR	Thruster T.600N	9038-T600N-021		27. 1.98	Thruster Air Services Ltd	Margaretting	19 .6.00P
G-MZKS	Thruster T.600N	9038-T600N-022		27. 1.98	D.Clarke	Swanton Morley	18. 7.00P
	(Rotax 582)				t/a David Clarke Microlight Aircraft		
G-MZKT	Thruster T.600T	9038-T600T-023		27. 1.98	M.J.O'Connor	Margaretting	7. 7.00P
G-MZKU	Thruster T.600T	9038-T600T-024		27. 1.98	A.S.Day	RAF Wyton	1.10.99P
G-MZKV	Mainair Blade 1144-0198-7 & W947			28. 1.98	M.P.J.Moore	Stoke-on-Trent	18. 3.00P
	(Rotax 912)						
G-MZKW	Quad City Challenger II			22. 3.94	K.W.Warn	Newbury	18.10.00P
	(Hirth 2705 R06) PFA/177-12518						
G-MZKX	Cyclone Pegasus Quantum 15	7395		15. 1.98	T.J.Hector	Royston	14. 1.00P
G-MZKY	Cyclone Pegasus Quantum 15	7403		16. 1.98	G.N.S.Farrant	Wallingford	28. 1.00P
G-MZKZ	Mainair Blade 1137-0298-7 & W940			18. 2.98	R.P.Wolstenholme	Warrington	15. 6.00P
G-MZLA	Cyclone Pegasus Quantum 15	7415		27. 2.98	D.A.Morgan	Dunkeswell	12. 3.00P
G-MZLB	Hunt Wing/Experience	BMAA/HB/058		25. 2.98	M.ffrench	New Ross, Ireland	
G-MZLC	Mainair Blade 1146-0298-7 & W949			26. 2.98	J.Melsher	Mold	6. 4.00P
	(Rotax 912)						
G-MZLD	Cyclone Pegasus Quantum 15-912	7416		24. 3.98	B.Kirkland	Blackpool	15. 3.00P
G-MZLE	Meridian Ultralights Maverick		G-BXSZ	27. 2.98	A.A.Plumridge	Yevlverton	8.11.00P
	PFA/259-12955						
G-MZLF	Cyclone Pegasus Quantum 15	7417		30. 3.98	J.H.Tope & B J Harper	Newton Abbot	31. 3.00P
	(Rotax 503-2V)						
G-MZLG	Rans S-6-ESD Coyote II XL (Nose-wheelu/c)			3. 3.98	R.H.J.Jenkins	Liverpool	20. 5.00P
	0897-1143XL & PFA/204-13192						
G-MZLH	Cyclone Pegasus Quantum 15	7426		1. 4.98	R.J.Philpotts	Stourbridge	24. 5.00P
G-MZLI	Mignet HM-1000 Balerit	133		5. 3.98	D.S.Tye	Oban	22. 3.99P
G-MZLJ	Cyclone Pegasus Quantum 15	7421		20. 3.98	M.H.Colin & A.C.Jones	Otherton	19. 3.99P
G-MZLK	Hunt Avon Skytrike/Solar Wings Typhoon			9. 3.98	J.A.Jones	Winchester	3. 9.00P
	T285-1471						
G-MZLL	Rans S-6-ESD Coyote II PFA/204-13067			23. 9.97	J.A.Willats & G.W.Champion	Crawley	26. 8.00P
G-MZLM	Cyclone Pegasus AX2000	7425		22. 4.98	P.Bennett	Swinford	30. 4.00P
G-MZLN	Cyclone Pegasus Quantum 15	7431		14. 4.98	P.Thomson	Deenethorpe	24. 4.00P
	(Rotax 503)				t/a G-MZLN Flying Group		
G-MZLO	CFM Shadow Srs.D	K.298-D		1. 4.98	CFM Aircraft Ltd	Leiston	24.10.99P
G-MZLP	CFM Shadow Srs.D	K.299-D		1. 4.98	CFM Aircraft Ltd	Parkham	25. 3.00P
G-MZLR	Cyclone Pegasus XL-Q	7441		28. 5.98	T.I.Courtney	Jacksdale	31. 5.00P
	(Rotax 462HP)						
G-MZLS	Cyclone Pegasus AX2000	7428		6. 7.98	G.Forster	Market Rasen	5. 7.00P
G-MZLT	Cyclone Pegasus Quantum 15	7438		24. 4.98	C.S.Bourne	Stone	22. 4.00P
	(Rotax 912)						
G-MZLU	Cyclone Pegasus AX2000	7439		28. 7.98	M.L.Smith	Verwood	20. 7.00P
G-MZLV	Cyclone Pegasus Quantum 15	7437		29. 4.98	C.J.Finnigan	(BFPO 140)	6. 7.00P
G-MZLW	Cyclone Pegasus Quantam 15	7440		28. 4.98	G.Clipston	Kettering	27. 4.00P
G-MZLX	Micro Avn B.22S Bantam	97-013	ZK-JIV	9.12.97	R.Smith	Bedford	14.12.98P
	(Rotax 582)						
G-MZLY	Letov LK-2M Sluka PFA/263-13065			20. 4.98	C.S.Warr	Market Rasen	28. 7.00P
G-MZLZ	Mainair Blade 1154-0498-7 & W957			21. 4.98	S.R.Winter	Broxbourne	14. 5.00P
	(Rotax 912)						
G-MZMA	Solar Wings Pegasus Quasar IITC	6611		1. 9.93	C.M.Addison	Knapthorpe Lodge, Caunton	11.11.99P
	(Rotax 582/40)						

Regn	Type	C/n P/I	Date	Owner/operator	Probable Base	CA Expy
G-MZMB	Mainair Blade 1149-0398-7 & W952		5. 3.98	G.Faulkner	Otherton, Cannock	29. 3.00P
G-MZMC	Cyclone Pegasus Quantum 15 7206 (Rotax 912)		10. 5.96	J.J.Baker	Deenethorpe	29. 5.00P
G-MZMD	Mainair Blade 1148-0398-7 & W951 (Rotax 912)		5. 3.98	T.Gate	Clitheroe	3. 4.00P
G-MZME	Medway Hybred 44XLR EclipseR 151/129E		28. 4.98	T.Bowles	Liverpool	24. 9.00P
G-MZMF	Cyclone Pegasus Quantum 15 (HKS) 7387		30. 4.98	J.W.Teesdale	Rufforth	2. 9.00P
G-MZMG	Cyclone Pagasus Quantum 15 7446		27. 5.98	P.Baker	Bath	27. 5.00P
G-MZMH	Cyclone Pegasus Quantum 15 7402 (Rotax 912)		27. 1.98	M.Hurtubise	Leamington Spa	19. 2.00P
	(Exhibited at PFA Cranfield 7.99 with Ballistic Recovery system fitted)					
G-MZMI	CFM Streak Shadow PFA/206-13205		30. 4.98	M.A.Hayward	Liskeard	
G-MZMJ	Mainair Blade 1155-0598-7 & W958 (Rotax 912)		8. 5.98	S.Miles	Sutton-in-Ashfield	22. 6.00P
G-MZMK	AMF Chevvron 2-32C 040		19. 5.98	K.D.Calvert	Park Farm, Eaton Bray	22. 6.00P
G-MZML	Mainair Blade 1158-0698-7 & W961 (Rotax 912)		19. 5.98	M.J.Allan	East Fortune	11. 6.00P
G-MZMM	Mainair Blade 1162-0698-7 & W965 (Rotax 912)		19. 5.98	J.F.Shaw	York	12. 7.00P
G-MZMN	Cyclone Pegasus Quantum 15 7445 (Rotax 912)		21. 5.98	W.H.J.Knowles	Tiverton	27.10.00P
G-MZMO	TEAM miniMax 91 PFA/186-12951		20. 5.98	I.M.Ross	Banchory	
G-MZMP	Mainair Blade 1160-0698-7 & W963 (Rotax 582-2V)		20. 5.98	C E Stott	East Fortune	28.11.00P
G-MZMR	Rans S-6-ESA Coyote II PFA/204-13315		21. 5.98	E.W.McMullan	Ballyclare, NI	
G-MZMS	Rans S-6-ES Coyote II (Nose-wheel u/c) 1298-1203ES & PFA/204-13294		26. 5.98	J.W.Barr	Malvern	21.10.00P
G-MZMT	Cyclone Pegasus Quantum 15 7449		18. 6.98	C.I.D.H.Garrison	Sutton Meadows	16. 6.00P
G-MZMU	Rans S-6-ESD Coyote II PFA/204-13242		5. 6.98	S.Cox	Hinckley	30. 9.00P
G-MZMV	Mainair Blade 1152-0496-7 & W955		30. 3.98	R.Nicklin	Wolverhampton	11. 5.00P
G-MZMW	Mignet HM-1000 Balerit 125 (Rotax 582)		2.10.96	M.E.Whapham	Corn Wood Farm, Adversane	6.11.99P
G-MZMX	Cyclone AX2000 7451		8. 9.98	R.H.Braithwaite t/a RAF Microlight Flying Association	RAF Halton	10.10.00P
G-MZMY	Mainair Blade 1153-0498-7 & W956		16. 3.98	C.J.Millership	Stoke-on-Trent	14. 5.00P
G-MZMZ	Mainair Blade 1081-0496-7 & W884 (Rotax 582)		22. 4.96	M.K.O'Donnell	Rainham, Essex	17. 5.00P
G-MZNA	Quad City Challenger II UK EI-CLE (Rotax 503) CH2-0894-UK-1193		19. 3.98	R.S.O'Carroll	Craigavon, NI	11.10.99P
G-MZNB	Cyclone Pegasus Quantum 15 7456 (Rotax 912)		17. 7.98	W.D.Fanshawe	Old Sarum	3. 8.00P
G-MZNC	Mainair Blade 1161-0698-7 & W964 (Rotax 912)		22. 6.98	A.Costello	Manchester	22. 6.00P
G-MZND	Mainair Rapier 1170-0898-7 & W973 (Rotax 912)		24. 6.98	S.D.Hutchinson	Preston	12. 7.00P
G-MZNE	Whittaker MW-6-2 Fatboy Flyer PFA/164-13120		26. 6.98	V.E.Booth	Croft Farm, Defford	18 .7.00P
G-MZNG	Cyclone Pegasus Quantum 15 7457 (Rotax 912)		11. 8.98	G.G.Rowley	Penrith	13. 8.00P
G-MZNH	CFM Shadow Srs.DD K.297-DD		30. 6.98	D.J.Goldsmith	Edenbridge	15. 7.00P
G-MZNI	Mainair Blade 1163-0698-7 & W966 (Rotax 912)		3. 7.98	D.Armstrong	Ruislip	9. 8.99P
G-MZNJ	Mainair Blade 1168-0798-7 & W971		6. 7.98	G.E.Cole	Chepstow	11. 8.00P
G-MZNK	Mainair Blade 1164-0798-7 & W967 (Rotax 912)		6. 7.98	D.S.Taylor & Taylor Refrigeration Ltd	Maidstone	11.11.99P
G-MZNL	Mainair Blade 1165-0798-7 & W968 (Rotax 912)		6. 7.98	R.P.Taylor & Taylor Refrigeration Ltd	Folkestone	11.11.99P
G-MZNM	TEAM miniMax 91 PFA/186-12304		10. 7.98	N.P.Thomson	North Berwick	
G-MZNN	TEAM miniMax 91 PFA/186-13125		10. 7.98	D.M.Dronsfield	Thornton-Cleveleys	
G-MZNO	Mainair Blade 1167-0798-7 & W970		9. 6.98	R.C.Colclough	Stoke-on-Trent	3. 8.00P
G-MZNP	Cyclone Pegasus Quantum 15 Super Sport (HKS) (Rotax 912) 7466		22. 7.98	O.W.Achurch	Northampton	4.11.99P
G-MZNR	Cyclone Pegasus Quantum 15 7465		17. 8.98	E.S.Wills	Paignton	13. 8.00P
G-MZNS	Cyclone Pegasus Quantum 15 7473 (Rotax 912)		31. 7.98	Cyclone Airsports t/a Pegasus Aviation	Marlborough	30.11.00P
G-MZNT	Cyclone Pegasus Quantum 15 7470 (Rotax 912)		25. 9.98	M.P.Lewis	Market Harborough	22. 9.99P
G-MZNU	Mainair Rapier 174-0898-7 & W977		5. 8.98	D.M.Hepworth	West Linton	2. 9.00P
G-MZNV	Rans S-6-ESD Coyote II PFA/204-12884		7. 8.98	D.E.Rubery & A.P.Thomas	Lower Wasing Farm, Brimpton	2. 9.00P
G-MZNW	Thruster T.600N HKS 9098-T600N-025		10. 8.98	Thruster Air Services Ltd	Shobdon	5. 7.00P

Regn	Type	C/n	P/I	Date	Owner/operator	Probable Base	CA Expy
G-MZNX	Thruster T.600N	9098-T600N-026		10. 8.98	D.Clarke t/a David Clarke Microlight Aircraft	Swanton Morley	28. 9.00P
G-MZNY	Thruster T.600N (Rotax 582)	9098-T600N-027		10. 8.98	P.Young t/a Thruster Group (Crashed Congham 7.7.99 & extensively damaged)	Swanton Morley	19. 6.00P
G-MZNZ	Letov LK-2M Sluka	PFA/263-13274		21. 4.98	K.T.Vinning (Cf/f 13.10.99)	Stratford-upon-Avon	
G-MZOA	Thruster T.600T	9108-T600T-028		10. 8.98	Thruster Air Services Ltd	Wantage	
G-MZOB	Thruster T.600T	9098-T600T-029		10. 8.98	Thruster Air Services Ltd	Wantage	
G-MZOC	Mainair Blade (Rotax 912)	1172-0898-7 & W975		10. 8.98	G.M.Prowling	Sowerby Bridge	1. 9.99P
G-MZOD	Cyclone Pegasus Quantum 15 (Rotax 912)	7435		28. 4.98	J.W.Mann	Witney	26. 4.00P
G-MZOE	Cyclone AX2000	7472		17. 9.98	York Microlight Centre Ltd	Rufforth	2.10.00P
G-MZOF	Mainair Blade (Rotax 462)	1122-0697-7 & W925		5. 6.97	A.P.S.John, T.D.Holland-Martin & P.J.Bossom t/a Overbury Farms	Tewkesbury	28. 7.00P
G-MZOG	Cyclone Pegasus Quantum 15 (Rotax 912)	7471		12.10.98	T.S.Sayers	Bristol	13.10.00P
G-MZOH	Whittaker MW-5D Sorcerer	PFA/163-13060		14. 8.98	D.M.Precious	Camelford	18. 8.00P
G-MZOI	Letov LK-2M Sluka	PFA/263-13238		17. 8.98	K.P.Taylor	Welwyn Garden City	6. 6.00P
G-MZOJ	Cyclone Pegasus Quantum 15	7478		9.11.98	A.C. Lane	Long Acres Farm, Sandy	15.11.00P
G-MZOK	Whittaker MW-6 Merlin (Rotax 582)	PFA/164-11568		24. 8.97	T.A.Willcox	Bristol	5. 7.00P
G-MZOM	CFM Shadow Srs.DD	302-DD		8. 9.98	CFM Aircraft Ltd	Leiston	9. 4.00P
G-MZON	Mainair Rapier	1180-1098-7-W983		11. 9.98	K.A.Armstrong	Brough	5.10.00P
G-MZOP	Mainair Blade (Rotax 912)	1178-0998-7-W981		11. 9.98	P.Barrow	Arclid Green, Sandbach	15.10.00P
G-MZOR	Mainair Blade (Rotax 912)	1173-0898-7-W976		21. 9.98	Mainair Microlight School Ltd	Barton	21. 9.00P
G-MZOS	Cyclone Pegasus Quantum 15 (Rotax 912)	7458		6.10.98	J.P.Appleby	Swinford	11.10.99P
G-MZOT	Letov LK-2M Sluka	PFA/263-13346		21. 9.98	J.R.Walter	Hollybush, Ayr	1 .8.00P
G-MZOV	Cyclone Pegasus Quantum 15	7512		9. 3.99	J.C.Tunstall	Banbury	17. 3.00P
G-MZOW	Cyclone Pegasus Quantum 15	7502		9. 3.99	G.R.Craig	Insch	30 .3.00P
G-MZOX	Letov LK-2M Sluka	PFA/263-13415		15. 2.99	C.M.James	Canterbury	
G-MZOY	TEAM miniMax 91	PFA/186-12526		29. 3.99	E.F.Smith	Egremont	
G-MZOZ	Rans S-6-ESD Coyote II XL (Nose-wheel u/c)	1096-1052XL & PFA/204-13168		20. 5.98	D.C. & S.G.Emmons	Reading	13. 8.00P
G-MZPB	Mignet HM-1000 Balerit (Rotax 582)	124		4.10.96	P.M.Baker	Corn Wood Farm, Adversane	20.11.99P
G-MZPD	Cyclone Pegasus Quantum 15 (Rotax 582)	7013		9. 5.95	P.M.Dewhurst	Sywell	31. 5.99P
G-MZPH	Mainair Blade	1177-0998-7-W980		26. 8.98	P.M.Hopewell	Loughborough	11.10.00P
G-MZPJ	TEAM miniMax 91	PFA/186-12277		23.11.92	P.R.Jenson	Sittles Farm, Alrewas	18. 5.00P
G-MZPW	Solar Wings Pegasus Quasar IITC (Rotax 582)	6892		26.10.94	D.R.Griffiths	Sherborne	18. 4.00P
G-MZRC	Cyclone Pegasus Quantum 15	7482		25.11.98	R.J.Cook	(Glasgow)	15.11.99P
G-MZRH	Cyclone Pegasus Quantum 15 (Rotax 582/40)	7269		11.10.96	A.J.Boulton	Roddige, Fradley	21.11.99P
G-MZRM	Cyclone Pegasus Quantum 15 (Rotax 912)	7455		10. 7.98	M.R.Mosley	Retford	9. 7.00P
G-MZRS	CFM Shadow Srs.CD (Rotax 503)	141		4. 4.90	M.R.Lovegrove	Croft Farm, Defford	8. 8.98P
G-MZSC	Cyclone Pegasus Quantum 15 (Rotax 503)	7370		3.10.97	R.J.Greaves	Hockliffe	11.10.00P
G-MZSD	Mainair Blade (Rotax 912)	1179-0998-7 & W978		21. 8.98	D.Sampson	Edinburgh	9.11.00P
G-MZSM	Mainair Blade (Rotax 582)	1000-0794-7 & W796		15. 7.94	P.R.Anderson	Oxton, Nottingham	23. 8.00P
G-MZTA	Mignet HM-1000 Balerit (Rotax 582)	120		14. 5.96	A.Fusco t/a Sky Light Group	Burwash	8. 5.00P
G-MZTS	Aerial Arts Chaser S (Rotax 377)	CH703	G-MVDM	19. 3.96	D.G.Ellis	Tamworth	22. 7.00P
G-MZUB	Rans S-6-ESD Coyote II XL	PFA/204-13244		30. 4.98	B.O.Dowsett	Astwood	30. 7.00P
G-MZZT	Kolb Twinstar Mk.3	PFA/205-12596		1. 5.98	P.I.Morgans	Milford Haven	17.11.00P
G-MZZY	Mainair Blade (Rotax 912UL)	1050-0895-7 & W848		13.11.95	A.Mucznik	Oxton, Nottingham	28. 2.99P
G-MZZZ*	Whittaker MW-6S Fatboy Flyer (Rotax 532)	PFA/164-11908		21.12.90	P.M.N.Richardson (Cancelled by CAA 29.3.99)	Haywards Heath	

G-NAAA – G-NZZZ

Regn	Type	C/n	P/I	Date	Owner/operator	Probable Base	CA Expy
G-NAAA	MBB Bo.105DBS-4 (Rebuilt with new pod S.912 1993)	S.34/912	G-BUTN G-AZTI/EI-BTE/G-AZTI/EC-DRY/G-AZTI/D-HDAN	6. 4.99	Bond Air Services	Blackpool	21. 2.02T
G-NAAB	MBB Bo.105DBS-4	S.416	D-HDMO D-HSTP/D-HDMO	23. 3.99	Bond Air Services	Aberdeen	8..4.02t
G-NAAS	Aerospatiale AS.355F1 Twin Squirrel	5203	G-BPRG G-NWPA/G-NAAS/G-BPRG/N370E	23. 3.90	Northumbria Ambulance Service NHS Trust	Blyth	18. 4.99T
G-NAAT*	Folland Gnat T.1	FL.507	XM697	27.11.89	Hunter Wing Ltd (As "XM697": open storage 1.97)	Bournemouth	
G-NACA	Norman NAC-2 Freelance 180	2001		23.11.87	NDN Aircraft Ltd (Stored 6.99)	Coventry	AC
G-NACI	Norman NAC-1 Freelance 180	NAC.001	G-AXFB	20. 6.84	L.J.Martin (Stored 10.95)	Bembridge	7. 4.94P
G-NACL	Norman NAC-6 Firemaster 65 (Note - fitted with rudder/marks of G-NACM 2.96)	6001	G-BNEG	23. 4.87	EPA Acft Co Ltd (Stored 3.99)	Sandown	5.12.90P*
G-NACO	Norman NAC-6 Firemaster 65	6004		2.12.87	EPA Acft Co Ltd (Stored 3.99)	Bournemouth	27. 8.92A
G-NACP	Norman NAC-6 Fieldmaster 34	6005		2.12.87	EPA Acft Co Ltd (Stored 3.99)	Bournemouth	6. 9.93A
G-NADS	TEAM miniMax 91	PFA/186-12995		8. 2.99	P.M.Spencer	(Thornton-Cleveleys)	
G-NANA	VPM M-16 Tandem Trainer (Arrow GT1000R)	PFA G/112-1249		29.11.94	J.W.P.Lewis	Haverfordwest	31. 8.00P
G-NARO	Cassutt Racer (Continental O-200-A) (Aka Musso Racer Original)	M.14372	G-BTXR N68PM	14. 4.98	D.A.Wirdnam	Redhill	7.10.00P
G-NASA	Lockheed T-33A-5-LO	580-6350	RDAF DT-566/51-8566 (As "91007" in USAF c/s)	3. 6.91	De Havilland Aviation Ltd	Swansea	7. 5.87P
G-NASH	Grumman-American AA-5A Cheetah	AA5A-0617	(G-BFWL) N26477	13. 9.78	J.J.Woodhouse t/a Flying Services	Blackbushe	14.10.99T
G-NATT	Rockwell Commander 114A	14538	N5921N	14. 1.80	Northgleam Ltd	Woodford	3. 9.01T
G-NATX	Cameron O-65 HAFB	1681		3. 3.88	A.G.E.Faulkner "National Express Rapide"	Willenhall, W.Midlands	5. 5.91T
G-NATY	Folland Gnat T.1	FL.548	8642M XR537	19. 6.90	F.C.Hackett-Jones (Displayed by Bournemouth Museum as "XR537/T")	Bournemouth	
G-NAVO*	PA-31-325 Navajo C/R	31-8212031	G-BMPV N4109V	6. 7.90	Air Care (South West) Ltd (Crashed 1999: cancelled as destoyed 29.12.99)	Plymouth	24. 7.99T
G-NAVY*	DH.104 Sea Devon C.20 (Dove 6)	04406	XJ348 G-AMXX	6. 1.82	Flugausstellung L & P Junior Museum (As "XJ348" in Royal Navy c/s)	Hermeskeil, Germany	23. 1.87
G-NBDD	Robin DR.400/180 Regent	1103	F-BXVN	26. 9.88	J.N.Binks	Sherburn-in-Elmet	28.12.00
G-NCFC	PA-38-112 Tomahawk	38-81A0107	N737V G-BNOA/N23272	14. 1.99	Light A/c Leasing (UK) Ltd	Norwich	21. 9.02T
G-NCFE	PA-38-112 Tomahawk	38-80A0081	G-BKMK OO-GME/(OO-HKD)/N9676N	1. 7.99	APB Leasing Ltd	Welshpool	12. 2.01T
G-NCFR	BAe HS.125 Srs.700B	257054	G-BVJY RA-02802/G-BVJY/C6-BET	28. 4.97	Chauffair (CI) Ltd	Farnborough	25. 3.00T
G-NCUB	Piper J3C-65 Cub (L-4H-PI)	11599	G-BGXV F-BFQT/OO-GAB/43-30308	6. 7.84	N.Thomson t/a G-NCUB Flying Group	Grove Farm, Raveningham	25. 8.00P
G-NDGC	Grob G-109	6150		7. 4.83	M.Newton "Babs"	Lydd	24. 5.02
G-NDNI	Norman NDN-1 Firecracker	001		30. 3.77	N.W.G.Marsh (Stored 7.97)	Coventry	AC
G-NDOL	Europa Avn Europa 44 & PFA/247-12594 (Subaru EA81)			30.11.93	S.Longstaff	(Sheffield)	12. 5.00P
G-NDRW	Colt AS-80 mk.II Hot-Air Airship	2085		2.12.91	Huntair Ltd "NDR"	(Germany)	21. 1.00A
G-NEAL	PA-32-260 Cherokee Six	32-1048	G-BFPY N5588J	7.11.83	V.Walker t/a VSD Group	(Kingswinford)	30. 7.00
G-NEAT	Europa Avn Europa 65 & PFA/247-12642 (Rotax 912UL)			28. 6.94	M.Burton	Nympsfield	13. 6.00P
G-NEEL	Rotorway Exec 90 (RW 162)	5002		7. 8.90	M.B.Sims	Bagby	17. 6.98P
G-NEGS	Thunder Ax7-77 HAFB	1059		18. 3.87	M.Rowlands "Hot-Shot"	Ashton-in-Makerfield	4. 6.00A
G-NEIL	Thunder Ax3 Maxi Sky Chariot HAFB	379		2.12.81	N.A.Robertson "Neil"	Combe Hay Manor, Bath	8. 6.00A
G-NEPB	Cameron N-77 HAFB	1264		7. 3.86	The Post Office (Royal Mail North East) "Royal Mail"	Leeds	5. 3.97A
G-NERC	PA-31-350 Navajo Chieftain	31-7405402	G-BBXX N66869	26. 4.94	Natural Environment Research Council (Op Air Atlantique)	Coventry	21. 5.01T
G-NERI*	PA-28-181 Archer II	28-7890483	G-BMKO N31880	19. 3.93	Not Known (Cancelled as destoyed 24.11.98: wreck stored 12.98)	Bristol	10.4.98T
G-NESI	Van's RV-6	PFA/181-13381		24.11.98	G.Ness	(Wakefield)	

Regn	Type	C/n	P/I	Date	Owner/operator	Probable Base	CA Expy
G-NESU	PBN BN-2B-20 Islander	2260	G-BTVN	30. 5.95	Northumbria Police Authority	Newcastle	20. 2.00T
					(Op North East Air Support Unit)		
G-NESV	Eurocopter EC.135 T1	0067		4. 2.99	Northumbria Police Authority	Newcastle	30. 3.02T
G-NETY	PA-18-150 Super Cub	1809108	N4159K	8. 9.95	N.B.Mason	Rendcomb	19. 1.02
G-NEUF	Bell 206L-1 Long Ranger II	45548	G-BVVV	20.11.98	Yendle Roberts Ltd	(Henley-on-Thames)	6. 9.98
			D-HUGO/OE-KXT/C-GLMM				
G-NEVS	Aero Designs Pulsar XP PFA/202-12283			12.11.93	N.Warrener	(Stockport)	
G-NEWR	PA-31-350 Navajo Chieftain	31-7952129	N35251	23. 8.79	Eastern Air Executive Ltd	Sturgate	8. 1.00T
G-NEWS	Bell 206B JetRanger III	2547	N18098	29.11.78	Abington Aviation Ltd	(Abington)	3. 4.00
G-NEWT	Beechcraft 35 Bonanza	D-1168	G-APVW	28. 2.90	J.A.West	Sibson	8. 9.02
	(Modified to C35 engine status)		EI-BIL/G-APVW/N9866F/4X-ACL/ IDF/AF 0604/ZS-BTE				
G-NEWZ	Bell 206B Jet Ranger III	4475	C-GBVZ	28. 1.98	Peter Press Ltd	Southampton	2. 4.01T
G-NFLC	HP.137 Jetstream 1	222	G-AXUI	12.12.95	Cranfield University	Cranfield	3. 6.00T
			G-8-9		(National Flying Laboratory Centre)		
G-NGRM	Spezio DAL-1 Tuholer	134	N6RM	14. 8.90	S.H.Crook	Redhill	1. 2.99P
	(Lycoming O-290-G)				(Crashed near Le Touquet 24.7.99 following an engine failure)		
G-NHRH	PA-28-140 Cherokee	28-22807	OY-BIC	19. 5.82	J.E.Parkinson	Newcastle	23. 4.01
			SE-EZP				
G-NHRJ	Europa Avn Europa XS PFA/247-13112			30. 9.99	D.A.Lowe	(Telford)	
G-NHVH	Maule M.5-235C Lunar Rocket	7276C	N5634N	4. 7.80	Commercial Go-Karts Ltd	Exeter	21. 2.02
G-NICH	Robinson R-22 Beta	0937		4. 1.89	Skyhopper Ltd & D.J.Pearce	Booker	5. 5.01T
G-NICK*	PA-18-95 Super Cub (L-18C-PI)18-2065		PH-CWA	17.10.79	I.Woolacott	Headcorn	26. 6.85P
	(Frame No.18-2085)		R.Neth AF R-79/8A-79/52-2465 "Jose" (On rebuild 2.96)				
G-NIGE	Luscombe 8E Silvaire	3525	G-BSHG	6. 6.90	Gardan Party Ltd	Popham	20.19.00P
	(Continental C85)		N72098/NC72098				
G-NIGL	Europa Avn Europa	PFA/247-12775		6. 7.95	N.M.Graham	(Southampton)	
G-NIGS	Thunder Ax7-65 HAFB	1663		30. 1.90	A.N.F.Pertwee "Bang Sai"	Frinton-on-Sea	19. 6.97A
G-NIKE	PA-28-181 Archer II	28-8390086	N4315N	4. 7.89	Key Properties Ltd	White Waltham	8. 9.01T
G-NINA	PA-28-161 Cherokee Warrior II	28-7716162	G-BEUC	29. 7.88	P.A.Layzell	Old Buckenham	28.10.00
			N3507Q				
G-NINB	PA-28-180G Cherokee Challenger	28-7305234	SE-KHR	16. 7.99	P.A. Layzell	Old Buckenham	28. 7.02T
			OY-DLR/CS-AHY/N11C				
G-NINE	Murphy Renegade 912	448 & PFA/188-12191		16. 6.93	R.F.Bond	Old Sarum	29. 5.00P
	(Rotax 912)						
G-NIOS	PA-32R-301 Saratoga SP	32R-8513004	N4381Z	28. 9.90	L.A.Dingemans & D.J.Everett	Stapleford	13. 5.02
			N105DX/N4381Z		t/a Plant Aviaton		
G-NIPA	Slingsby Nipper T.66 RA.45 Srs.3	S.120/1627	G-AWDD	7. 6.96	R.J.O.Walker	(Lincoln)	3.11.93P
	(Acro/VW1834)						
G-NIPP	Slingsby Nipper T.66 RA.45 Srs.3	S.103	G-AVKJ	17. 1.00	T.Dale	(Stamford Bridge)	
G-NIPY	Hughes 369HS	124-0676S	OH-HMD	26.11.97	Jet Aviation (Northwest) Ltd	Liverpool	8.12.00T
			SE-JAK/N65BL/N9232F				
G-NISR	Rockwell Turbo Commander 690A	11243	HB-GFS	10. 7.85	Ziad Isma'il Bilbeisi	Fairoaks	13. 9.00
G-NITA	PA-28-180 Cherokee C	28-2909	G-AVVG	16. 1.84	T.Clifford	(Dunstable)	17.11.97T
	(Used spare Frame No.28-3807S)						
G-NJAG	Cessna 207 Skywagon	207-00093	D-EMDN	2. 8.78	G.H.Nolan	Biggin Hill	17. 6.00T
			(N91152)				
G-NJIA	BAe 146 Srs 300	E-3161	B-1775	7.99R	British Airways plc		
G-NJIB	BAe 146 Srs 300	E-3174	B-1776	7.99R	British Airways plc		
G-NJIC	BAe 146 Srs 300	E-3202	B-1781	7.99R	British Airways plc		
G-NJID	BAe 146 Srs 300	E-3165	B-1777	7.99R	British Airways plc		
G-NJIE	BAe 146 Srs 300	E-3209	B-1778	7.99R	British Airways plc		
G-NJSH	Robinson R-22 Beta	0780		19. 4.88	A J.Hawes	Sywell	19. 6.00
G-NLEE	Cessna 182Q Skylane II	182-65934	G-TLTD	1.12.93	J.S.Lee	Booker	27. 9.02
			N759EL				
G-NMHS	Eurocopter AS.355N Twin Squirrel	5502	G-DPPS	26. 3.98	North Midlands Helicopter Support Unit	Ripley	29. 3.01T
			F-WYMM				
G-NNAC	PA-18-135 Super Cub	18-3820	PH-PSW	19. 5.81	P.A.Wilde	Bagby	14. 8.00T
	(L-21B-PI) (Frame No.18-3820)		R.Neth AF R-130/54-2420 t/a PAW Flying Services				
G-NOBI	Spezio HES-1 Tuholer Sport	162	N1603	28.11.90	A.D.Pearce	(Lydney)	27. 7.00P
	(Continental C125)						
G-NOCK	Reims Cessna FR182 Skylane RGII 0036		G-BGTK	18. 1.94	R.D.Masters	Top Farm, Royston	17.11.00
			(D-EHZB)				
G-NODE	Gulfstream AA-5B Tiger	AA5B-1182	N4533L	22. 5.81	Strategic Telecom Networks Ltd	(Hook)	5. 7.02T
G-NODY	American General AG-5B Tiger	10076	N1194C	3.10.91	Curd & Green Ltd (Op Cabair)	Elstree	12. 3.01T
G-NOIR	Bell 222	47031	G-OJLC	9. 8.91	Arlington Securities plc	Blackbushe	31. 5.00T
			G-OSEB/G-BNDA/A40-CG				
G-NONI	Grumman-American AA-5 Traveler	AA5-0383	G-BBDA	1. 8.88	P.T.Harmsworth	Exeter	26. 4.01
			(EI-AYL)/G-BBDA		t/a November India Flying Group		
G-NOOR	Commander 114B	14656		6. 2.98	As-Al Ltd	Guernsey	19. 5.01

Regn	Type	C/n	P/I	Date	Owner/operator	Probable Base	CA Expy
G-NORD	SNCAC NC.854	7	F-BFIS	20.10.78	W.J.McCollum (On rebuild) (Magherafelt, Co.Londonderry)		27. 5.82P
G-NOSE	Cessna 402B	402B-0823	N98AR G-MPCU/SE-IRL/OO-TAT/(OO-SEL)/N3946C	23. 4.96	Atlantic Air Transport Ltd	Coventry	11. 5.00T
G-NOTE	PA-28-181 Archer III	2843082	D-ESPI N9282N	19. 9.97	General Aeroplane Trading Co Ltd	Elstree	18. 9.00T
G-NOTT	Nott ULD/2 HAFB	06		11. 6.86	J.R.P.Nott	London NW3	
G-NOTY	Westland Scout AH.1	F.9630	XT624	5.11.97	R.P.Coplestone Draycott Farm, Chiseldon		7. 2.00P
G-NOVO	Colt AS-56 Hot-Air Airship	1067		20. 5.87	Astec Group plc	Cheltenham	29. 4.97A
G-NOWW	Mainair Blade 912	1227-1299-7-W1020		10.12.99	C Bodill	Nottingham	
G-NPKJ	Van's RV-6 (Tail-wheel u/c)	PFA/181-13138		12. 2.98	K.Jones	Netherthorpe	21. 2.00P
G-NPNP	Cameron N-105 HAFB	2959	G-BURX	18. 1.93	Virgin Airship & Balloon Co Ltd "National Power II"	Telford	18. 8.98A
G-NPWR*	Cameron RX-100 HAFB	2849		13. 7.92	R S Kent "Nuclear Electric 2" (Balloon Preservation Group 7.98)	Lancing	21.11.96A
G-NRDC*	Norman NDN-6 Fieldmaster	004		8. 6.81	Not known (Stored 3.99)	Sandown	17.10.87P
G-NROY	PA-32RT-300 Lance II	32R-7985070	G-LYNN G-BGNY/N30242	26.11.93	R.L.West, J.E.Dixon & W.Wells t/a Roy West Cars	Norwich	6. 1.02
G-NSEW	Robinson R-44 Astro	0615		6. 7.99	Pebblestar Ltd	Harefield	8..7.02T
G-NSHR	Robinson R-22 Beta-II	2809		8. 5.98	F.G.Sytner	Leicester	14. 5.01T
G-NSOF	Robin HR.200-120B	334		4. 6.99	Northamptonshire School of Flying Ltd	Sywell	14 .6.02T
G-NSTG	Reims Cessna F.150F (Wichita c/n 63499) (Tail-wheel conversion)	0058	G-ATNI	16. 8.89	N.S.Travers-Griffin "Iris"	Blackpool	23. 8.01
G-NTEE	Robinson R-44 Astro	0024		14.12.93	Central Aviation (Helicopters) Ltd	Nottingham	3. 2.00T
G-NUTS*	Cameron Mr Peanut 35SS HAFB	711		18. 2.81	British Balloon Museum & Library "Mr Peanut II"	Newbury	1. 4.84A
G-NUTY	Aerospatiale AS.350B Ecureuil	1490	G-BXKT F-GXRT/N333FH/N5797V	20. 7.98	Arena Aviation Ltd	Redhill	10. 9.00T
G-NVBF	Lindstrand LBL-210A HAFB	249		19. 5.95	Virgin Balloon Flights Ltd (London SE16)		14. 5.00T
G-NVSA	DHC-8-311 Dash Eight	451	C-GDNG	20.11.98	Brymon Airways Ltd	Plymouth	20.11.01T
G-NVSB	DHC-8-311 Dash Eight	517	C-GHRI	14. 1.99	Brymon Airways Ltd (Delftblue Daybreak t/s)	Plymouth	13. 1.02T
G-NVSC	DHC-8-311 Dash Eight	519	C-FDHO R		Brymon Airways Ltd (For delivery 2000)	Plymouth	
G-NWAC	PA-31-310 Turbo Navajo	31-7612040	G-BDUJ N59814	18. 2.94	North West Air Charters Ltd	Liverpool	5. 8.02
G-NWPS	Eurocopter EC.135T 1	0063		15.10.98	North West Police Authority (Colwyn Bay)		11. 2.02T
G-NYTE	Reims Cessna F.337G Super Skymaster (Wichita c/n 01465)	0056	G-BATH N10631	12. 5.86	I.M.Latiff	Little Staughton	9. 6.00T
G-NZGL	Cameron O-105 HAFB	1361		3. 9.86	P.G.Vale "Nazgul"	Kidderminster	28. 5.00A
G-NZSS	Boeing-Stearman E75 (N2S-5) Kaydet (Lycoming R-680)	75-8611	N4325 Bu.43517/42-109578 (As "343251/27" in USAAC c/s)	31. 1.89	Ace Aviation Ltd	Swanton Morley	6. 1.02T

G-OAAA – G-OZZZ

Regn	Type	C/n	P/I	Date	Owner/operator	Probable Base	CA Expy
G-OAAA	PA-28-161 Warrior II	2816107	N9142N	8. 9.93	Halfpenny Green Flight Centre Ltd	Halfpenny Green	15. 9.02T
G-OAAC	Airtour AH-77B HAFB	010		13. 9.88	Army Air Corps, Historic A/c Board of Management "Go AAC"	AAC Middle Wallop	10. 1.00A
G-OAAL	PA-38-112 Tomahawk	38-78A0623	N4471E	25.10.88	Cardiff Wales Aviation Services Ltd	Cardiff	15.12.00T
G-OABB	SAN Jodel D150 Mascaret	01	F-BJST F-WJST	21. 1.97	A.B.Bailey	Popham	12. 3.00
G-OABC	Colt 69A HAFB	1159		17.11.87	P.A.C.Stuart-Kregor	Newbury	26. 6.00A
G-OABO	Enstrom F-28A	097	G-BAIB	10. 7.98	ABO Ltd	Goodwood	2. 6.01T
G-OABR	American General AG-5B Tiger	10124	C-GZLA N256ER	15. 4.98	Abraxas Aviation Ltd	Elstree	23. 4.01
G-OACE	Valentin Taifun 17E	1017	D-KCBA	22. 1.87	J.E.Dallison	Enstone	27. 4.02
G-OACG	PA-34-200T Seneca II	34-7870177	G-BUNR EI-CFI/N9245C	10. 3.94	Cega Aviation Ltd	Goodwood	9.11.01T
G-OACI	Socata MS.893E Rallye 180GT	13086	G-DOOR EI-BHD/F-GBCF	5. 5.98	A.M.Quayle	Alderney	6. 4.01
G-OACP	OGMA DHC.1 Chipmunk 20 (Lycoming O-360)	OGMA.35	(CS-DAO) FAP 1345	20. 8.96	Aeroclub de Portugal	(Lisbon)	19.12.99
G-OADY	Beechcraft 76 Duchess	ME-56	N5022M	27.10.86	Multiflight Ltd	Leeds-Bradford	31. 1.02T
G-OAER	Lindstrand LBL-105A HAFB	359		4. 3.96	T.M.Donnelly "Aero"	Doncaster	31. 1.02T
G-OAFC*	Airtour AH-56	011		15. 6.89	P J Donnellan (Balloon Preservation Group 12.98)	Lancing	

Regn	Type	C/n	P/I	Date	Owner/operator	Probable Base	CA Expy
G-OAFT	Cessna 152 II	152-85177	G-BNKM N6161Q	19. 4.88	Bobbington Air Training School Ltd	Halfpenny Green	18.11.02T
G-OAHC	Beechcraft F33C Bonanza	CJ-133	G-BTTF PH-BND	2. 9.91	V.D.Speck	Clacton	18. 5.01
G-OAJB	Cyclone AX2000 (Rotax 582/48)	7281	G-MZFJ	16. 2.99	A.J.Blackwell	Long Marston	8. 4.99P
G-OAJS	PA-39 Twin Comanche C/R	39-15	G-BCIO N49JA/N57RG/G-BCIO/N8860Y	9. 3.94	Go-AJs Ltd	Sherburn-in-Elmet	16. 3.01
G-OAKJ	BAe Jetstream 3202	795	G-BOTJ G-OAKJ/G-BOTJ/G-31-795	20. 7.89	Air Kilroe Ltd	Manchester	31. 8.00T
G-OALD	Socata TB-20 Trinidad	490	N54TB F-GBLL	17. 3.88	D.A.Grief t/a Gold Aviation	Biggin Hill	24. 5.00
G-OAMG	Bell 206B JetRanger III	2901	G-COAL	25. 2.86	Alan Mann Helicopters Ltd	Fairoaks	18. 5.01T
G-OAML	Cameron AML-105 HAFB	3881		4.12.96	Cheqair Ltd	Long Stratton	16. 4.00A
G-OAMP	Reims Cessna F177RG Cardinal (Wichita c/n 00098)	0006	G-AYPF	30.11.93	G.Hamilton & R.Sheldon t/a Vale Aero Gp	Liverpool	6. 7.00
G-OAMS	Boeing 737-37Q	28548		9.12.97	British Regional Airlines Ltd Manchester (Rendezvous t/s)		9. 1.01T
G-OAMT	PA-31-350 Navajo Chieftain	31-7752105	G-BXKS N350RC/EC-EBN/N27230	23. 1.98	AM & T Solutions Ltd	Bristol	18.11.00T
G-OAMY	Cessna 152 II	152-84639	N6214M	5. 8.85	Cardiff Wales Aviation Services Ltd	Cardiff	12.11.00T
G-OANI	PA-28-161 Warrior II	28-8416091	N43570	8. 1.91	J.F.Mitchell	(Burgess Hill)	8. 9.97
					(Damaged Upton Farm, Dover 16.6.96; wreck at Oxford 9.96)		
G-OANN	Zenair CH.601HDS	PFA/162-12932		2. 2.96	P.Noden	(Stoke-on-Trent)	
G-OAPB	Colt Bottle 14 SS HAFB	4406		9.11.98	Airborne Images Ltd	Singapore	24.11.99A
G-OAPE	Cessna T303 Crusader	T303-00245	N303MF D-INKA/N9960C/M303HW/N9960C	3. 2.99	C.Twiston-Davies & P L Drew	Jersey	8. 2.02
G-OAPR	Brantly B-2B	446	(G-BPST) N2280U	21. 4.89	E.D.Ap Rees t/a Helicopter International Magazine	Weston-super-Mare	26. 6.01
G-OAPW	Glaser-Dirks DG-400	4-268		17. 4.90	D.T.S.Walsh "434"	(Dunstable)	10. 6.02
G-OARA	PA-28R-201 Arrow	28-37002	N802ND N9622N	28.10.98	London School of Flying Ltd	Elstree	19.11.01T
G-OARC	PA-28RT-201 Arrow IV	28R-7918009	G-BMVE N3071K	17. 8.99	ARC Precision Engineering Ltd	Bournemouth	9.11.02T
G-OARG	Cameron C-80 HAFB	3379		20.10.94	G. & R.Madelin	Farnham/London SW15	5.12.99A
G-OART	PA-23-250 Aztec D	27-4293	G-AXKD N6936Y	26.11.93	Levenmere Ltd (Op Skydrift)	Old Buckenham	15. 3.00T
G-OARV	ARV-1 Super 2 (Hewland AE75)	001 & PFA/152-11060		18. 6.84	N.R.Beale	(Leamington Spa)	12.10.87P
					(Rebuilt with Kit No.008 1986; stored Sproughton 1.91)		
G-OASH	Robinson R-22 Beta	0761	N2627Z	13. 6.88	J.C.Lane (Op Heliflight)	Halfpenny Green	18. 6.00T
G-OASP	Aerospatiale AS.355F2 Twin Squirrel	5479	F-GJAJ F-WYMH	3. 8.95	Avon & Somerset Constabulary & Gloucestershire Constabulary	Filton	9. 9.01T
G-OATD*	Short SD.3-30 Var.100	SH.3096	N332SB G-BKSV/G-14-3096	23. 2.89	Wingspares Ltd	Shoreham	
					(Damaged Belfast Harbour 27.11.89; fuselage in open store 12.94)		
G-OATS	PA-38-112 Tomahawk	38-78A0007	N9659N	14. 3.78	Truman Aviation Ltd	Nottingham	28. 8.00T
G-OATV	Cameron V-77 HAFB	2149		14. 2.90	W.G.Andrews	Plymouth	23.10.93A
G-OAUS	Sikorsky S-76A	760219	(G-BKGU) N3122M	11. 8.82	Darley Stud Management Co Ltd Blackbushe (Op by Air Hanson)		2.10.00T
G-OAWS	Cameron Colt 77A HAFB	4340		23. 4.98	Auto Windscreens Ltd	Chesterfield	30. 4.00A
G-OAXA	Cameron Cup-90 HAFB	4750		24.12.99	Cameron Balloons Ltd	Bristol	
G-OBAL	Mooney M.20J (201LM)	24-1601	N56569	27.11.86	Britannia Airways Ltd (Op Britannia Flying Club)	Luton	24. 3.02T
G-OBAM	Bell 206B JetRanger III	4511	N6379U	25. 5.99	Shawford Park Helicopters Ltd	(London WC2)	4 .7.02T
G-OBAN	SAN Jodel D.140B Mousquetaire II	80	G-ATSU F-BKSA	20. 2.92	S.R.Cameron	North Connel	3. 3.01
G-OBAT*	Reims Cessna F.152 II	1771	G-OENT G-OBAT/(D-EMIN)	25. 7.80	M.Entwistle	Coventry	10. 1.93T
					(Damaged Sladbury's Farm, Holland-on-Sea 11.12.92; cancelled by CAA 8.3.99)		
G-OBAY	Bell 206B JetRanger	276	G-BVWR C-GNXQ/N4714R	27. 7.98	Helixair Ltd	Blackpool	2. 3.00T
G-OBBC	Colt 90A HAFB	1358		11. 5.89	R.A. & M.A.Riley "Beeb" (BBC in the Midlands titles)	Bromsgrove	13. 2.00A
G-OBBO	Cessna 182S Skylane	18280534	N7247Z	8. 6.99	F.Friedenberg	Denham	21. 6.02
G-OBDA	Diamond DA-20-A1 Katana	10260		2. 7.98	Diamond Aircraft Industries GmbH	Gamston	30. 7.01T
G-OBEN	Cessna 152 II	152-81856	G-NALI G-BHVM/N67477	16. 8.93	Airbase Aircraft Ltd	Shoreham	26. 3.00T

Regn	Type	C/n	P/I	Date	Owner/operator	Probable Base	CA Expy
G-OBEV	Europa Avn Europa	PFA/247-12813		3. 2.98	M.B.Hill & N.I.Wingfield	(Dursley)	
G-OBEY	PA-23-250 Aztec C	27-2569	G-BAAJ SE-EIU	11. 5.79	Creaton Aircraft Services Ltd	Halfpenny Green	4. 8.86T
G-OBFC	PA-28-161 Warrior II	2816118	N9252X	15. 7.96	Bournemouth Flying Club Ltd	Bournemouth	27. 7.02T
G-OBFS	PA-28-161 Warrior III	2842039	N41274	4.12.98	Bournemouth Flying Club Ltd	Bournemouth	3.12.01T
G-OBGC	Socata TB.20 Trinidad	1898		13. 5.99	Bidford Airfield Ltd	Bidford/Bickmarsh	12 .5.02T
G-OBHD	Short SD.3-60 Var.100	SH.3714		20. 1.87	Jersey European Airways Ltd	Exeter	5. 3.00T
			G-OBHD/G-BNDK/G-14-3714				
G-OBIB	Colt 120A HAFB	4229		9. 1.98	The Aerial Display Co Ltd (Michelin titles)	Looe	16.11.99A
G-OBIG	Aerospatiale AS.355F1 Twin Squirrel	5157	G-SVJM G-BOPS/I-MOST	28. 8.96	Plane Talking Ltd (Op Cabair Helicopters)	Elstree	22. 5.00T
G-OBIL	Robinson R-22 Beta	0792		10. 5.88	C.A.Rosenberg	Abergavenny	3. 7.00T
G-OBIO	Robinson R-22 Beta	1402	N7724M	29. 6.98	A.E.Churchill	(Huntingdon)	20. 7.01
G-OBJB	Lindstrand LBL 90A HAFB	640		12.11.99	2B Designs Ltd	(Andover)	22.11.00A
G-OBJH	Colt 77A HAFB	2569		11. 3.94	UK Petroleum Products Ltd t/a Eurogas & Corralgas	Alcester	16. 7.00
G-OBLC	Beechcraft 76 Duchess	ME-249	N6635R	3. 6.87	Pridenote Ltd	(Knaresborough)	31.10.02T
G-OBLK	Short SD.3-60 Var.100	SH.3712	G-BNDI	20. 1.87	Jersey European Airways Ltd	Exeter	11. 2.00T
			G-OBLK/G-BNDI/G-14-3712				
G-OBLN	DH.115 Vampire T.11 (Regd with Nacelle No.DHP.48700)	15664	XE956	14. 9.95	De Havilland Aviation Ltd (As "XE956": on rebuild 2.96)	Bridgend	
G-OBMF	Boeing 737-4Y0	23868		14.10.88	British Midland Airways Ltd	East Midlands	11.11.01T
G-OBMH	Boeing 737-33A	24460		19. 3.90	British Midland Airways Ltd	East Midlands	21. 3.02T
G-OBMJ	Boeing 737-33A	24461		22. 3.90	British Midland Airways Ltd	East Midlands	27. 3.02T
G-OBMM	Boeing 737-4Y0	25177		4.12.91	British Midland Airways Ltd	East Midlands	6. 4.02T
G-OBMO	Boeing 737-4Q8	26280		13. 3.92	British Midland Airways Ltd	East Midlands	29. 4.02T
G-OBMP	Boeing 737-3Q8	24963		8. 1.92	British Midland Airways Ltd	East Midlands	19. 3.02T
G-OBMR	Boeing 737-5Y0	25185	XA-RJS	7. 5.96	British Midland Airways Ltd	East Midlands	4. 6.02T
G-OBMS	Reims Cessna F.172N Skyhawk II	1584	OO-BWA (OO-HWA)/D-EBYX	16. 4.84	D.Beverley & A N Macdonald	Sherburn-in-Elmet	10. 6.02
G-OBMW	Grumman-American AA-5 Traveler	AA5-0805	G-BDFV	4. 7.79	Fretcourt Ltd	Sherburn-in-Elmet	25. 2.00
G-OBMX	Boeing 737-59D	25065	SE-DNE (SE-DND)	23. 9.93	British Midland Airways Ltd	East Midlands	22. 9.02T
G-OBMZ	Boeing 737-53A	24754	SE-DNC	22. 9.93	British Midland Airways Ltd	East Midlands	20. 9.02T
G-OBNF	Cessna 310K	310K-0109	F-BNFI N7009L	20. 7.94	P.H.Johnson t/a Fadmoor Flying Group	Boonhill, Fadmoor	20. 5.00T
G-OBPL	Embraer EMB-110P2 Bandeirante	110-199	PH-FVB	27.11.98	Comed Aviation Ltd	Blackpool	6.12.00T
			G-OEAB/G-BKWB/G-CHEV/(PT-GLR)				
G-OBRY	Cameron N-180 HAFB	3010		1. 3.93	Bryant Group plc	Solihull	6. 4.00T
G-OBTS	Cameron C-80 HAFB	3589		18. 4.95	Bedford Tyre Service (Chichester) Ltd "Hi-Q"	Chichester	23. 6.00A
G-OBUD*	Colt 69A HAFB	698		26. 6.85	British Balloon Museum & Library "Budweiser"	Newbury	1. 2.90A
G-OBUS*	PA-28-181 Archer II	28-7990242	G-BMTT N3002K	4. 8.86	Northbrook College (Crashed Goodwood 18. 4.89; instructional airframe 8.97)	Shoreham	14. 8.89T
G-OBUY	Colt 69A HAFB	2031		7. 8.91	Virgin Airship & Balloon Co Ltd "Virgin Megastore"	Telford	25. 8.00A
G-OBWA	BAC One-Eleven 518FG	BAC.232	G-BDAT G-AYOR	1.12.92	British World Airlines Ltd (Iberia Regional Air Nostrum titles)	Southend	12. 4.00T
G-OBWB	BAC One-Eleven 518FG	BAC.202	G-BDAS G-AXMH	8.12.92	British World Airlines Ltd	Southend	18. 4.02T
G-OBWC	BAC One-Eleven 520FN	BAC.230	G-BEKA	8.12.92	British World Airlines Ltd	Southend	11.10.01T
			4X-BAR/G-16-22/G-BEKA/PP-SDR (Open storage Southend 5.99)				
G-OBWD	BAC One-Eleven 518FG	BAC.203	G-BDAE G-AXMI	14. 1.93	British World Airlines Ltd	Southend	14. 4.02T
G-OBWE	BAC One-Eleven 531FS	BAC.242	G-BJYM TI-LRI/TI-1095C	7. 4.93	British World Airlines Ltd	Southend	26. 5.02T
G-OBWL	BAe ATP	2057	G-11-057	26. 9.97	British World Airlines Ltd (CityJet c/s)	Southend	25. 9.00T
G-OBWM	BAe ATP	2058	G-11-058	22.12.97	British World Airlines Ltd	Southend	21.12.00T

Regn	Type	C/n	P/I	Date	Owner/operator	Probable Base	CA Expy
G-OBWN	BAe ATP	2059	G-BVEO	22.12.98	British World Airlines Ltd	Southend	21.12.02T
			G-11-059				
G-OBWO	BAe ATP	2060	(EI-COS)	6. 6.98	British World Airlines Ltd	Southend	15. 6.01T
			G-11-060				
G-OBWP	BAe ATP	2051	G-BTPO	8.10.99	Trident Aviation Leasing Services (Jersey) Ltd		
			G-5-051			Southend	17.10.02T
G-OBWR	BAe ATP	2053	G-BUWP	8.10.99	Trident Jet (Jersey) Ltd	Southend	20. 4.00T
			G-11-053				
G-OBWZ	Boeing 737		N699PU	11.99R	Britsh World Airlines	Southend	
G-OBYB	Boeing 767-304ER	28040		17. 5.96	Britannia Airways Ltd	Luton	16. 5.02T
G-OBYC	Boeing 767-204ER	28041	D-AGYC	14. 4.99	Britannia Airways Ltd	Luton	25. 4.02T
			G-OBYC				
G-OBYD	Boeing 767-304ER	28042		4. 3.97	Britannia Airways Ltd	Luton	3. 3.00T
G-OBYE	Boeing 767-304ER	28979	D-AGYE	26. 2.98	Britannia Airways Ltd	Luton	28.10.02T
			G-OBYE				
G-OBYG	Boeing 767-304ER	29137		13. 1.99	Britannia Airways Ltd	Luton	12. 1.02T
G-OBYI	Boeing 767-304ER	29138		1. 2.00	Britannia Airways Ltd	Luton	
G-OBYT	Agusta-Bell 206A JetRanger	8237	G-BNRC	30. 1.95	Sloane Helicopters Ltd	Sywell	12. 7.00T
			Oman AF 601				
G-OCAA	HS.125 Srs.700B	257091	G-BHLF	22. 4.92	Magec Aviation Ltd (Op for CAA)	Luton	28. 4.00T
G-OCAD	Sequoia Falco F8L PFA/100-12114			8. 6.92	C.W.Garrard	Leicester	28. 3.00P
	(Lycoming IO-320)				t/a Falco Flying Group		
G-OCAM	Gulfstream AA-5A Cheetah AA5A-0741		G-BLHO	24. 3.94	Plane Talking Ltd (Op Cabair)	Elstree	4.10.00T
			OO-RTJ/OO-HRN				
G-OCAR	Colt 77A HAFB	1099		6. 8.87	S.C.J.Derham (Bridgnorth)		25. 8.00A
					"Toyota"		
G-OCAT	Eiri PIK.20E	20226	(D-KGAT)	19.11.79	D.Bonucchi (Croxley Green)		13. 5.01
			G-OCAT				
G-OCAW	Lindstrand Bananas SS HAFB	388		22. 5.96	Flying Pictures Ltd	Fairoaks	1. 8.97A
G-OCBB	Bell 206B JetRanger II	969	G-BASE	16.11.90	Corby Motor Group Ltd	Sywell	30.10.00T
			N18093				
G-OCBS	Lindstrand LBL 210A HAFB	602		21. 7.99	G.Binder	Sonnenbuhl, Germany	20. 7.00A
G-OCDB	Cessna 550 Citation II	550-0601	G-ELOT	20. 8.92	Paycourt Ltd	Birmingham	28. 2.00T
			(N1303M)		(Op Eurojet)		
G-OCDS	Aviamilano F.8L Falco Srs.II	114	G-VEGL	6. 9.85	C.O.P.Barth	Hartenholm, Germany	11. 8.02
			OO-MEN/I-VEGL				
G-OCEA	Short SD.3-60 Var.100	SH.3762	N162CN	26.10.95	BAC Express Airlines Ltd	(Horley)	26. 3.00T
			N162SB/G-BRMX				
G-OCFR	Gates Learjet 35A	35A-614	G-VIPS	15. 6.92	Chauffair (CI) Ltd Heathrow/Farnborough		12. 4.00T
			G-SOVN/HB-VJC/G-PJET/N3815G				
G-OCIN	Cessna 150K	15071728	EI-CIN	6. 4.99	F.McGovern	(Wicklow, Ireland)	26 .4.02
			G-BSXG/N6228G				
G-OCJK	Schweizer Hughes 269C (300C)	S.1294	N69A	10.12.87	P.Crawley	Shipley	27. 5.00
G-OCJS	Cameron V-90 HAFB	2805		24. 4.92	C.J.Sandell	Sevenoaks	29. 4.00T
G-OCJW	Cessna 182R Skylane II	182-68316	G-SJGM	18. 4.97	C.J.Ward	Wellesbourne Mountford	9. 7.00
			N357WC				
G-OCME*	BN-2A Mk.III-1 Trislander	262	G-AYWI	14. 5.86	Eccles Demolition Ltd		
			G-51-262			Tenax Road, Trafford Park	29. 5.87
					(Damaged Hale, Cheshire 9.2.87; stored in scrapyard 1.93)		
G-OCND*	Cameron O-77 HAFB	1020		6. 2.84	K A Kent "CND Airborne"	Lancing	N/E(A)
					(Balloon Preservation Group 7.98)		
G-OCPC	Reims Cessna FA.152 Aerobat	0343		20. 1.78	Westward Airways (Lands End) Ltd St.Just		12. 8.02T
G-OCPF	PA-32-300 Cherokee Six	32-7640082	G-BOCH	22. 9.97	Syndicate Clerical Services Ltd (Exeter)		8. 9.00
			N9292K				
G-OCPS	Colt 120A HAFB	2047		27. 5.92	CPS Fuels Ltd "CPS Gas"	Norwich	19. 5.00T
G-OCRI	Colomban MC-15 Cri-Cri			24. 6.92	M.J.J.Dunning	(Coventry)	
		524 & PFA/133-12288					
G-OCSB	Cessna 525 Citation Jet	525-0177	N1280A	28. 1.98	Kestrel Aviation Ltd	Guernsey	4 .2.02T
			(RP-C717)/N1280A/N5163C				
G-OCSI	Embraer EMB-110P2 Bandeirante		G-BHJZ	29.12.94	Air Tabernacle Ltd	Bembridge	3. 7.98T
		110-270	PT-SBH		(Op Willow Air) (Overseas Courier Service titles)		
G-OCST	Agusta-Bell 206B JetRanger III	8694	N39AH	14.12.94	G.J.Plumstead	Bristol	7. 1.01T
			VR-CDG/G-BMKM		t/a Fieldgrove Trading (Op Polo Aviation)		
G-OCTA	BN-2A Mk.III-2 Trislander	1008	VR-CAA	14. 7.87	Aurigny Air Services Ltd	Guernsey	17. 7.00T
			DQ-FCF/G-BCXW		(ITEX c/s)		
G-OCTI	PA-32-260 Cherokee Six	32-288	G-BGZX	26. 7.88	D.G.Williams	Redhill	23. 4.01T
			9XR-MP/5Y-ADH/N3427W				
G-OCTU	PA-28-161 Cadet	2841280	N91997	16.11.89	Plane Talking Ltd	Elstree	13.12.01T
G-OCUB	Piper J3C-90 Cub (L-4J-PI)	13248	OO-JOZ	21. 4.81	C.A.Foss & P.A.Brook	Shoreham	23. 6.98P
	(Frame No.13078)		PH-NKC/PH-UCH/45-4508		t/a Florence Flying Group "Florence"		
	(Official c/n of 13215 is 45-4475/PH-UCW and was rebuilt as PH-UCH)						

Regn	Type	C/n	P/I	Date	Owner/operator	Probable Base	CA Expy
G-ODAC	Reims Cessna F.152 II	1824	G-BITG	19.12.96	T.M. & M.L.Jones	Egginton	22. 7.01T
					(Op Derby Aero Club)		
G-ODAD	Colt 77A HAFB	2001		20. 2.91	K.Meehan "Odyssey"	Much Wenlock	17. 7.00A
G-ODAM	Gulfstream AA-5A Cheetah	AA5A-0818	G-FOUX	16.11.88	Stop & Go Ltd	Biggin Hill	22. 3.02T
			N8488H		(Op London Aviation)		
G-ODAT	Aero L-29 Delfin	194227	ES-YLV	28. 7.99	DAT Enterprises Ltd	(Robertsbridge)	12.10.00P
			Estonian AF/Soviet AF				
G-ODBN	Lindstrand Flowers SS HAFB	389		22. 5.96	Flying Pictures Ltd	Fairoaks	15. 6.00A
					"Sainsbury's Flowers"		
G-ODCS	Robinson R-22 Beta-II	2828		19. 5.98	E.Simpson	Kintore, Inverurie	1. 6.01T
					t/a Gibb Helicopters		
G-ODDY	Lindstrand LBL-105A HAFB	042		15. 7.93	P.& T.Huckle	Oakwood	25. 7.00A
G-ODEB	Cameron A-250 HAFB	4328		23. 4.98	A.Derbyshire	(Stafford)	7. 4.99T
G-ODEL	Falconar F-11-3	PFA/32-10219		14. 8.78	G.F.Brummell	(Bedford)	17. 7.89P
	(Continental O-200-A)				(Damaged Little Gransden 4.9.88; on rebuild)		
G-ODEN	PA-28-161 Cadet	2841282	N92004	22.11.89	J.Appleton	Denham	18.12.01T
					t/a Holmes Rentals (Op Denham School of Flying)		
G-ODGS	Avtech Jabiru UL	PFA/274A-13472		2. 8.99	D.G.Salt	(Ashbourne)	
G-ODHL	Cameron N-77 HAFB	1538		22. 2.88	DHL Intl (UK) Ltd "DHL"	Hong Kong	17. 6.94A
G-ODIG	Bell 206B JetRanger II	2142	G-NEEP	11. 6.93	Vallely Engineering Ltd	(Leeds)	30.10.98T
			N777FW/N3CR				
G-ODIN	Mudry CAARP CAP-10B	192	F-GDTH	16.12.93	T.W.Harris	(Hunstanton)	1. 5.00
G-ODIY	Colt 69A HAFB	1786		12. 6.90	P.Glydon	Barnt Green, Birmingham	18. 3.99A
G-ODJG	Europa Avn Europa	PFA/247-12889		3. 5.96	D.J.Goldsmith	(Edenbridge)	
G-ODJH	Mooney M.20C Ranger	690083	G-BMLH	19. 1.93	R.M.Schweitzer		13. 7.02
			N9293V		(Amsterdam, The Netherlands)		
G-ODLY	Cessna 310J	310J-0077	G-TUBY	21. 3.88	R.J.Huband	Gloucestershire	3. 6.00
			G-ASZZ/N3077L				
G-ODMC	Aerospatiale AS.350B1 Ecureuil	2200	G-BPVF	17.10.89	D.M.Coombs t/a DM Leasing Co	Denham	25.10.01T
G-ODOC	Robinson R-44 Astro	0372		27. 8.97	Gas & Air Ltd	Thaxted, Essex	21. 9.00T
G-ODOG	PA-28R-200 Cherokee Arrow II	28R-7235197	EI-BPB	2. 8.96	Advanced Investments Ltd	Sibson	22.10.02
			G-BAAR/N11C				
G-ODOT	Robinson R-22 Beta-II	2779		23. 1.98	Farm Aviation Ltd	Booker	17. 2.01T
G-ODSK	Boeing 737-37Q	28537		23. 7.97	British Midland Airways Ltd		
						East Midlands	27. 7.00T
G-ODTW	Europa Avn Europa	PFA/247-12890		7. 9.95	D.T.Walters	(Longfield, Kent)	
G-ODUS	Boeing 737-36Q	28659	D-ADBX	17. 3.98	British Regional Airlines Ltd	Manchester	15. 4.01T
					(Waves & Cranes t/s)		
G-ODVB	CFM Shadow Srs.DD	300-DD	G-MGDB	3.11.98	D.V. Brunt	Plaistows, Hemel Hempstead	15. 3.00P
G-OEAC	Mooney M.20J (201)	24-1636	N57656	16. 6.88	D.Teece & R.Hodges	Nottingham	1. 7.00
					t/a DR Airgroup		
G-OEAT	Robinson R-22 Beta	0650	G-RACH	8. 1.98	C.Y.O.Seeds Ltd	(Didcot)	21. 1.02T
G-OECH	Gulfstream AA-5A Cheetah	AA5A-0836	G-BKBE	24. 1.89	Plane Talking Ltd	Elstree	1. 5.00T
			(G-BJVN)/N26952		(Op London School of Flying)		
G-OEDB	PA-38-112 Tomahawk	38-79A0167	G-BGGJ	9. 5.89	Air Delta Bravo Ltd	Cranfield	21. 5.00T
			N9694N		(Op Bonus Aviation)		
G-OEDP	Cameron N-77 HAFB	2189		28.12.89	M.J.Betts	Norwich	13. 6.00A
					"Eastern Counties Press"		
G-OEGG	Cameron Egg 65SS HAFB	2140		4.12.89	Virgin Airship & Balloon Co Ltd		
	(Cadbury's Creme Egg shape)				"Cadburys Creme Egg"	Telford	25. 3.00A
G-OEGL	Christen Eagle II	001	N46JH	12. 1.98	D.I.Cooke & J.Penfold	Swanborough Farm	31. 3.00P
	(Lycoming IO-360)				(Damaged landing Popham 18.6.99: noted Little Gransden 9.99)		
G-OEJA	Cessna 500 Citation	500-0264	G-BWFL	2. 8.96	Eurojet Aviation Ltd	Birmingham	20. 7.00T
			F-GLJA/N205FM/N5264J				
G-OERR	Lindstrand LBL-60A HAFB	469		30. 6.97	Lindstrand Balloons Ltd	Oswestry	9. 1.00
G-OERS	Cessna 172N Skyhawk II	172-68856	G-SSRS	24. 5.94	E.R.Stevens	Leicester	29.10.99T
			N734HA				
G-OERX	Cameron O-65 HAFB	4004		23. 1.96	R.Roehsler	Vienna, Austria	27. 2.97A
G-OEST	BAe Jetstream 320	2836	OH-JAD	18. 6.99	Air Kilroe	Manchester	20 .6.00T
			N836JX/CG-FGLH/G-31-836/N332QJ/G-31-836				
G-OEWA	DH.104 Dove 8	04528	G-DDCD	10. 6.98	D.C.Hunter	East Midlands	
			G-ARUM				
G-OEYE	Rans S-10 Sakota	PFA/194-11955		25. 4.91	R J McCarthy	(Stafford)	19. 5.00P
	(Rotax 582-2V)				"Dancing Doll"		
G-OEZY	Europa Avn Europa 42 &	PFA/247-12590		8. 8.95	A.W.Wakefield	Conington	27. 6.00P
	(Rotax 912UL)						
G-OFAS	Robinson R-22 Beta	0559		17. 6.86	J.L.Leonard	Shoreham	11. 4.02T
					t/a Findon Air Services		
G-OFBJ	Thunder Ax7-77A HAFB	2050		2. 9.91	N.D.Hicks "Blue Horizon"	Alton	25. 9.99A
G-OFCM	Reims Cessna F.172L	0839	G-AZUN	21.10.81	FCM Aviation Ltd	Guernsey	31. 3.00
			(OO-FCB)				

Regn	Type	C/n	P/I	Date	Owner/operator	Probable Base	CA Expy
G-OFER	PA-18-150 Super Cub	18-7709058	N83509	29.12.89	Mary S.W.Meagher	Edgehill	2. 3.00
G-OFFA	Pietenpol Aircamper	PFA/047-13181		3.11.98	D.J. Street t/a Offa Group	(Chinnor)	
G-OFHL	Aerospatiale AS.350B Ecureuil	1805	EI-BPM G-BLSP	25. 6.93	Ford Helicopters Ltd	Brentwood	15. 7.02T
G-OFIL	Robinson R-44	0555		15. 1.99	P.& J.Twigg	(Gloucester)	2. 2.02T
G-OFIN	Aerospatiale AS.355F2 Twin Squirrel	5480	G-DANS G-BTNM	18. 6.99	Salehurst Aviation Ltd (Robertsbridge)		14. 6.02T
G-OFIT	Socata TB-10 Tobago	938	G-BRIU	11. 9.89	P.Hennessy t/a GFI Aviation Group	White Waltham	19. 1.02T
G-OFIZ*	Cameron Can 80SS HAFB	2106		30.10.89	British Balloon Museum & Library Newbury "Andrews Can"		2.12.91A
G-OFJC	Eiri Pik-20E	20291	OH-641	19. 3.93	M.J.Aldridge	Tibenham	3. 6.02
G-OFJS	Robinson R-22 Beta	0699	G-BNXJ	28. 5.91	Burman Aviation Ltd	Gloucestershire	26.10.02
G-OFLG	Socata TB-10 Tobago	11	G-JMWT F-GBHF	11.12.91	R.Noble Ltd	(Teddington)	2. 8.01T
G-OFLI	Colt 105A HAFB	991		20. 1.87	Virgin Airship & Balloon Co Ltd Telford "Virgin Atlantic"		22.11.90A
G-OFLT	Embraer EMB-110P1 Bandeirante	110-211	G-MOBL (G-BGCS)/PT-GMD	11.12.90	Flightline Ltd	Southend	1. 1.01T
G-OFLY	Cessna 210M Centurion II	210-61600	(D-EBYM) N732LQ	13.10.79	A.P.Mothew	Southend	7. 5.01
G-OFMB	Rand Robinson KR-2	7808	N5337X	29. 4.97	F.M. & S.I.Burden	(Bracknell)	
G-OFOA	BAe 146 Srs.100	E-1006	EI-COF/SE-DRH/G-BKMN/G-ODAN	3. 3.98	Formula One Adminstration Ltd	(London SW7)	14. 7.00
G-OFOR	Thunder Ax3 Maxi Sky Chariot HAFB	596		5.10.84	T.J.Ellenreider, G.D.Bartram & P.Spellward "Go For It"	Bristol	17. 4.97A
G-OFOX	Denney Kitfox	PFA/172-11523		1.11.89	P.R.Skeels	Barton	
G-OFRA	Boeing 737-36Q	29327		5. 5.98	British Regional Airlines Ltd Manchester (Sterntaler/Bauhaus t/s)		17. 5.01T
G-OFRB*	Everett Gyroplane Srs.2 (Rotax 503)	006	(G-BLSR)	7. 8.85	R.M.Savage t/a Roger Savage (Photography) "Little Patty" (Cancelled by CAA 9.6.99)	Kemble	17. 6.92P
G-OFRT	Lockheed L.188CF Electra	1075	N347HA N423MA/N23AF/N64405/SE-FGC/N5537	29.10.91	Dart Group plc t/a Channel Express	Bournemouth	28.10.01T
G-OFRY	Cessna 152 II	152-81420	G-BPHS N49971	8. 2.93	Devon School of Flying Ltd	Dunkeswell	23. 8.01T
G-OFTI	PA-28-140 Cherokee Cruiser	28-7325201	G-BRKU N15926	11. 6.90	P.E.Richardson	Kings Farm, Thurrock	28. 9.02T
G-OGAN	Europa Avn Europa	PFA/247-12734		28. 7.94	M.A.Jackson t/a G-OGAN Group (Cf/f 12.11.99)	(Ingham, Lincoln)	
G-OGAR	PZL SZD-45A Ogar	B-601	SP-0004	29. 1.90	N.C.Grayson	Boscombe Down	9. 6.00
G-OGAS*	Westland WG.30 Srs.100	008	G-17-1 G-OGAS/G-BKNW	23. 3.83	Westland Helicopters Ltd (Open storage 9.97)	Yeovil	19. 5.88T
G-OGAV	Lindstrand LBL-240A HAFB	074		4. 2.94	C.J.Sandell t/a Out of this World Balloons	Sevenoaks	18. 5.00T
G-OGAZ	Aerospatiale SA.341G Gazelle 1	1274	G-OCJR G-BRGS/F-GEQA/N341SG/(N341P)N341SG/N47295	12. 1.94	I.M.& S.M. Graham t/a Killochries Fold	(Kilmalcolm)	7. 3.00T
G-OGBA	Boeing 737-4S3	25596	G-OBMK	4. 4.97	GB Airways Ltd (Waves & Cranes t/s)	Gatwick	7. 5.02T
G-OGBB	Boeing 737-34S	29108		27. 1.98	GB Airways Ltd (Dove/Colum t/s)	Gatwick	26. 1.01T
G-OGBC	Boeing 737-34S	29109	N1787B	26. 2.98	GB Airways Ltd (Cockerel of Lowicz/Koguty Lowickie t/s)	Gatwick	25. 2.01T
G-OGBD	Boeing 737-3L9	27833	OY-MAR D-ADBJ/OY-MAR	16. 3.98	GB Airways Ltd (Martha Masanabo/Ndebele t/s)	Gatwick	12. 3.01T
G-OGBE	Boeing 737-3L9	27834	OY-MAS	24.11.98	GB Airways Ltd (Crossing Borders t/s)	Gatwick	17.12.01T
G-OGCA	PA-28-161 Warrior II	28-8016262	N8154L	16. 8.90	Aerohire Ltd (Op Midland Flight Centre)	Halfpenny Green	7. 7.02T
G-OGEE	Christen Pitts S-2B Special (Lycoming AEIO-540)	5200	OH-SKY	1. 6.95	Management Consultancy Services Inc Ltd & GB-European Ltd	(Ipswich)	28. 6.01
G-OGEM	PA-28-181 Archer II	28-8190226	N83816	10. 3.88	GEM Rewinds Ltd	Coventry	8. 5.00T
G-OGET	PA-39-160 Twin Comanche C/R	39-87	G-AYXY N8930Y	14. 3.83	P.G.Kitchingman	White Waltham	21.12.01
G-OGGS	Thunder Ax8-84 HAFB	1595		1. 9.89	G.Gamble & Sons (Quorn) Ltd "Gamblis Quorn"	Loughborough	10. 2.95T
G-OGHH	Enstrom 480	5015		14. 2.96	Silver Lining Finance SA,	(Luxembourg)	12. 3.02T
G-OGHL	Aerospatiale AS.355F1 Twin Squirrel	5164	N5796S	18. 4.97	Grampian Helicopter Charter Ltd	Cumbernauld	27. 5.00T
G-OGIL*	Short SD.3-30 Var.100	SH.3068	G-BITV G-14-3068	23. 1.89	North East Aircraft Museum (Damaged Newcastle 1.7.92)	Usworth	21. 4.93T

Regn	Type	C/n	P/I	Date	Owner/operator	Probable Base	CA Expy
G-OGJS	Rutan Puffer Cozy PFA/159-11169 (Lycoming O-360)			27. 1.89	G.J.Stamper	Carlisle	14. 9.98P
G-OGOA	Aerospatiale AS.350B Ecureuil	1745	G-PLMD G-NIAL	16. 1.90	Lomas Helicopters Ltd	Lake, Bideford	23. 5.02T
G-OGOB	Schweizer Hughes 269C (300C)	S.1315	G-GLEE G-BRUW/N86G	2.10.90	Kingfisher Helicopters Ltd	Longdown	25. 3.02T
G-OGOG	Robinson R-22 Beta	1475	G-TILL	2. 7.97	D.Thomas t/a Lake Services	Lake, Bideford	9.10.02T
G-OGOS	Everett Gyroplane (VW1834)	004	7Q-YES G-OGOS	30. 7.84	N.A.Seymour	(Norwich)	12. 9.90
G-OGRK	Aerospatiale AS.355F1 Twin Squirrel	5185	G-BWZC (G-MOBZ)/N107KF/N5799R	26. 3.99	Kelwaiver Ltd	Stapleford	12. 2.00T
G-OGTS	Air Command 532 Elite (Rotax 532) 0432 & PFA G/104-1125			19.12.88	GTS Engineering (Coventry) Ltd Coventry t/a GTS Cars		1.10.90P
G-OHAJ	Boeing 737-36Q	29141		2. 6.98	British Regional Airlines Ltd Manchester (Delftblue Daybreak t/s)		15. 6.01T
G-OHAL	Pietenpol Aircamper PFA/47-12840			25.11.90	H.C.Danby	(Sudbury)	
G-OHCP	Aerospatiale AS.355F1 Twin Squirrel	5249	G-BTVS G-STVE/G-TOFF/G-BKJX	14. 3.94	Cabair Helicopters Ltd	Elstree	19. 2.01T
G-OHDC	Colt Film Cassette SS HAFB (Agfa Film shape)	2633		8. 8.94	Flying Pictures Ltd "Agfa"	Fairoaks	26. 8.99A
G-OHEA*	HS.125 Srs 3B/RA	25144	G-AVRG G-5-12	25.11.86	Cranfield University (Dumped 7.99)	Cranfield	7. 8.92T
G-OHIG	Embraer EMB.110-P1 Bandeirante	110-235	G-OPPP XC-DAI/PT-SAB	29..3 95	Air Tabernacle Ltd (Fuselage to Valley Nurseries, Alton, Hants 4.99)		26. 5.98T
G-OHHI	Bell 206L-1 Long Ranger	45552	G-BWYJ D-HOBD/D-HGAD	30. 4.98	I.R.Chisholm t/a Bradmore Helicopters	Costock	25. 2.00T
G-OHKS	Cyclone Pegasus Quantum 15	7505		24. 3.99	Cyclone Airsports Ltd t/a Pegasus Aviation	Marlborough	
G-OHLL	Robinson R-22 Beta	1087	G-CHAL	2.12.97	Plane Talking Ltd	Elstree	26. 4.01T
G-OHMS	Aerospatiale AS.355F1 Twin Squirrel	5194	N367E	15. 6.90	South Western Electricity plc	Bristol	23. 6.02T
G-OHNA	Mainair Blade 912 1189-0199-7-W992			6.11.98	P.A. Lee	(Harlow)	4 .3.00P
G-OHSA	Cameron N-77 HAFB	4269		2. 2.98	D.N. & L.J.Close (HSA Healthcare titles)	Andover	9. 4.00A
G-OHWV	Raj Hamsa X'Air 582 (5) BMAA/HB/121			18.11.99	H.W.Vasey	(Newquay)	
G-OIBM	Rockwell Commander 114	14295	G-BLVZ SX-AJO/N4957W	14.10.88	I.Rosewell	Blackbushe	4. 7.00
G-OIBO	PA-28-180 Cherokee C	28-3794	G-AVAZ	21. 1.87	Britannia Airways Ltd	Luton	24. 3.00T
G-OICE	Cessna 525 Citation Jet	G525-0028	N1330S	5.10.93	Airshare Holdings Ltd	Oxford	17.10.00T
G-OICO	Lindstrand LBL-42A HAFB	566		3.11.98	Virgin Airship & Balloon Co Ltd Telford		12.11.99A
G-OICV*	Robinson R-22 Beta	0991	G-BPWH	11. 2.93	Helicentre Ltd (Damaged Blackpool 18.7.99: cancelled as wfu 19.11.99)	Blackpool	3. 3.01
G-OIDW	Reims Cessna F.150G	0188	N70163 D-EGTI	24. 4.90	I.D.Wakeling Franklyns Field, Chewton Mendip		5. 8.99
G-OIEA	PA-31P Pressurised Navajo	31P-7300141	G-BBTW N7660L	13. 7.89	Skyrock Aviation Ltd "Anastasia"	Cardiff	19.10.96
G-OIFM	Cameron Dude 90SS HAFB (Radio One FM DJ's Head & 'phones)	2841		18. 6.92	L.N.Mastis West Bloomfield, MI, USA "Cool Dude"		29. 5.99A
G-OIMC	Cessna 152 II	152-85506	N93521	15. 5.87	East Midlands Flying School Ltd East Midlands		28. 6.02T
G-OINK	Piper J3C-65 Cub (L-4J-PI) (Frame No.12643)	12613	G-BILD G-KERK/F-BBQD/44-80317	22. 3.83	A.R.Harding Newton Green, Sudbury		19. 7.99P
G-OINV	Bae 146 Srs…	E-3171		.00R	British Regional Airlines		
G-OIOZ	Thunder AX9-120 S2 HAFB	4434		17.11.98	The Flying Doctors Hot Air Balloon Co Ltd (Spire FM titles)	Salisbury	18. 3.00T
G-OISO	Reims Cessna FRA.150L Aerobat (Modified to FA.150 standard)	0213	G-BBJW	3. 4.90	Valerie J.Wilce t/a Les Oiseaux Poplar Hall Farm, Elmsett		26. 8.02T
G-OITN	Aerospatiale AS.355F1 Twin Squirrel	5088	N400HH N5788B	3.10.89	Independent Television News Ltd Redhill		13.12.01T
G-OITV	Enstrom 280C Shark	1038	G-HRVY G-DUGY/G-BEEL	9. 4.96	M.A.Crook & A.Wright	Barton	19. 9.99T
G-OJAB	Avtech Jabiru SK PFA/274-13031 (Jabiru 2200)			19. 9.96	ST Aviation Ltd Southery, Downham Market		14. 4.99P
G-OJAC	Mooney M.20J (201)	24-1490	N5767E	20. 8.90	Hornet Engineering Ltd	Biggin Hill	22. 1.00T
G-OJAE	Hughes 269C	90-0966	N1101W	12. 2.90	J.A. & C.M.Wilson Slaithwaite, Huddersfield		17. 9.02
G-OJAV	BN-2A Mk.III-2 Trislander	1024	G-BDOS (4X-CCI)/G-BDOS	6. 6.90	Air Tabernacle Ltd (Op Sky Trek)	Lydd	25.11.00T
G-OJBB	Enstrom 280FX	2084		14. 6.99	Adenstar Developments Ltd	Shoreham	23. 6.02T
G-OJBM	Cameron N-90 HAFB	2899		28. 9.92	P.Spinlove	Chalfont St.Giles	23. 9.93A

Regn	Type	C/n	P/I	Date	Owner/operator	Probable Base	CA Expy
G-OJBW	Lindstrand J & B Bottle SS HAFB	436		26. 8.97	Justerini & Brooks Ltd (London SW1)		27. 7.00A
G-OJCB	Agusta-Bell 206B JetRanger II	8554		7. 4.78	R & M International Engineering Ltd		
						Dereham	7. 5.99T
G-OJCM*	Rotorway Exec 90	5117		4. 8.92	Not known	Chester	28. 6.96P
	(RI 162)				(Damaged Whitchurch, Shropshire 25.9.95; stored 3.96)		
G-OJCW	PA-32RT-300 Lance II	32R-7985062	N3016K	9. 1.80	P.G.Dobson t/a CW Group	Blackbushe	19. 5.01T
G-OJDA	EAA Acrosport 2	PFA/72-11067		1. 4.98	D.B.Almey	Fenland	17. 6.00P
G-OJDC	Thunder Ax7-77 HAFB	875		9. 1.89	Julia Crosby	Brighton	29. 7.99A
G-OJEG	Airbus A.321-231	1015	D-AVZN	14.5.99	Monarch Airlines Ltd	Luton	13. 5.02T
G-OJEN	Cameron V-77 HAFB	3302		26. 5.94	Jensport Ltd	Bedale	18. 7.96A
G-OJGT	Maule M.5-235C Lunar Rocket	7285C	LN-AEL	30. 6.98	J.G.Townsend Draycott Farm, Chiseldon		23. 7.01
			(LN-BEK)/N5635V				
G-OJHB	Colt Flying Ice Cream Cone SS HAFB	2591		23. 6.94	Benedikt Haggeney GmbH		
						Ennigerloh, Germany	16. 2.00A
G-OJHL	Europa Avn Europa	PFA/247-13039		12. 5.97	J.H.Lace "Lady Lace"	Prestwick	1. 9.00P
G-OJIL	PA-31-350 Navajo Chieftain	31-7625175	OY-BTP	28. 5.97	Redhill Aviation Ltd	Southend	7.12.00T
					(Op Redhill Charters)		
G-OJIM	PA-28R-201T Turbo Arrow III	28R-7703200	N38299	4. 8.86	B.J.Campbell & M.Arnell	Aberdeen	13.12.01
					t/a Piper Arrow Group,		
G-OJJB	Mooney M.20K (252TSE)	25-1161		12. 8.88	Fly Over Ltd (Roma-Urbe, Italy)		17. 5.01
G-OJJF	Druine D.31 Turbulent	378 & 31	00-30	6. 1.97	J.J.Ferguson (Bideford)		
	(VW1300)						
G-OJMR	Airbus A.300B4-605R	605	F-WWAY	3. 5.91	Monarch Airlines Ltd	Luton	2. 5.02T
G-OJNB	Lindstrand LBL-21A HAFB	085		14. 2.94	Justerini & Brooks Ltd	London SW1	27. 7.00A
G-OJON	Taylor JT.2 Titch III	PFA/3208		6.10.78	J.H.Fell (Great Massingham)		
	(Continental C90)				(Under build at owner's home ?)		
G-OJPB	HS.125 Srs.F600B	25258	VP-CJP	25. 9.97	Widehawk Aviation Ltd	Cambridge	9.11.00T
			VR-CJP/G-BFAN/G-AZHS				
G-OJRH	Robinson R-44 Astro	0321		11. 4.97	Holgate Construction Ltd		
						Emley Moor, Huddersfield	10. 4.00
G-OJSW	Boeing 737-8Q8	28218		11.12.98	Sabre Airways Ltd "Tinks"	Gatwick	10.12.01T
G-OJSY	Short SD.3-60 Var.100	SH.3603	N368MQ	26. 3.86	BAC Leasing Ltd	Exeter	22. 4.00T
			G-BKKT		(Stored 10.99)		
G-OJTA	Stemme S-10V	14-018	D-KGDA	18. 9.95	O.J.Truelove	St Mawgan	31. 3.02
					t/a OJT Associates		
G-OJTW	Boeing 737-36N	28558	(G-JTWF)	26. 4.97	British Midland Airways Ltd		
						East Midlands	1. 5.00T
G-OJVA	Van's RV-6	PFA/181-12292		6. 9.96	J.A.Village	(Sheffield)	30. 9.00P
G-OJVH	Reims Cessna F.150H	0356	G-AWJZ	27. 3.81	Yorkshire Light Acft Ltd	Leeds-Bradford	17. 5.01T
G-OJWE	Cameron A-210 HAFB	4081		20. 2.97	John Weatherill Electronics Ltd		
					(Damaged North Ferriby, Hull 20.7.97)	Pocklington	27. 4.98T
G-OJWS	PA-28-161 Warrior II	28-7816415	N6377C	13. 7.88	L.E.Guernieri	Denham	10. 7.00
G-OKAG	PA-28R-180 Cherokee Arrow	28R-30075	N3764T	15. 4.88	N.F. & B.R.Green	Stapleford	3. 4.00T
G-OKAY	Pitts S-1E Special	12358	N35WH	27. 5.80	D S T Eggleton	(Sudbury)	28. 3.00P
	(Lycoming IO-360)						
G-OKBT	Colt 25A Sky Chariot mk.II HAFB	2301		10.11.92	British Telecommunications plc	Thatcham	11. 4.00A
					"Skypiper II"		
G-OKCC	Cameron N-90 HAFB	1741		6. 5.88	D.J.Head	Newbury	25. 7.00A
G-OKDN	Boeing 737-8Q8	28226		27. 7.98	Air Berlin GmbH	Berlin-Tegel	26. 7.01T
G-OKED	Cessna 150L	150-74250	N19223	29. 1.93	Haimoss Ltd	Old Sarum	14.11.99T
					(Op Old Sarum Flying Club)		
G-OKEN	PA-28R-201T Turbo Arrow III	28R-7703390	N47518	20.10.87	W.B.Bateson	Blackpool	25. 2.00T
G-OKES	Robinson R-44 Astro	0053		16. 3.94	Direct Helicopters (Southend) Ltd		
						Southend	11. 5.00T
G-OKEV	Europa Avn Europa	PFA/247-13091		11. 6.97	K.A.Pilcher	Halfpenny Green	26 .9.00P
	(Tri-cycle u/c)						
G-OKEY	Robinson R-22 Beta	2004		14. 1.92	Key Properties Ltd	Denham	12. 8.01
G-OKIS	Tri-R Kis	PFA/239-12248		15. 6.92	B.W.Davies	Fenland	30. 3.99P
	(CAM.100)				t/a Junipa Sales (Aviation) Ltd (Stored 8.98)		
G-OKMA	Tri-R Kis	PFA/239-12808		22.11.95	K.Miller	(Coventry)	
G-OKPW	Tri-R Kis	PFA/239-12359		17. 8.93	K.P.Wordsworth	Shoreham	12. 2.98P
	(Jabiru 3300)						
G-OKYA	Cameron V-77 HAFB	1259		4. 3.87	D.J.B.Woodd	BFPO.17, Germany	
	(Replacement envelope c/n 3331)				t/a Army Balloon Club "Fly Army II"		
G-OKYM	PA-28-140 Cherokee	28-23303	G-AVLS	10. 5.88	B.Marshall	Humberside	8. 7.00
			N11C				
G-OLAH	Short SD.3-60 Var.100	SH.3604	G-BPCO	14. 8.91	Gill Aviation Ltd	Newcastle	27.12.01T
			G-RMSS/G-BKKU				
G-OLAU	Robinson R-22 Beta	1119		5. 9.89	Thistle Aviation Ltd	Booker	25. 3.02

Regn	Type	C/n	P/I	Date	Owner/operator	Probable Base	CA Expy
G-OLAW	Lindstrand LBL-25A Cloudhopper HAFB	170		9.12.94	George Law Plant Ltd "Law Hopper"	Kidderminster	24. 4.97A
G-OLBL	Lindstrand LBL-90A HAFB	419		24. 2.97	A.Geudon t/a Alois Geudon Balloons	Mossingen, Germany	8. 4.00A
G-OLDD	BAe 125-800B	258106	PK-RGM PK-WSJ/G-5-580	11. 3.99	Gold Air International Ltd.	Cambridge	19..8.00T
G-OLDM	Cyclone Pegasus Quantum 15 (Rotax 912)	7589		10.12.99	P A B & B A Morgan	Ongar	11.12.00P
G-OLDN	Bell 206L LongRanger	45077	G-TBCA G-BFAL/N64689/A6-BCL	2.10.84	Von Essen Aviation Ltd.	(Taunton)	29. 5.00T
G-OLDV*	Colt 90A HAFB	2592		5. 5.94	Virgin Airship & Balloon Co Ltd "LDV" (Cancelled 29.6.99 as WFU)	Telford	10.11.98A
G-OLEE	Reims Cessna F.152 II	1797		11. 9.80	Aerohire Ltd (Op South Warwickshire F/School)	Wellesbourne Mountford	30. 5.99T
G-OLEO	Thunder Ax10-210 Srs.2 HAFB	3974		9. 1.97	P.J.Waller	Norwich	15. 3.00T
G-OLFC	PA-38-112 Tomahawk	38-79A0995	G-BGZG	6.12.85	M.W.Glencross	Luton	21. 5.01T
G-OLFT	Rockwell Commander 114	14274	G-WJMN N4954W	28. 3.85	B.C.Richens & B.N.Woodward	Redhill	25. 1.99
G-OLGA	CFM Starstreak Shadow SA.II	PFA/206-13164		15.10.97	N.F.Smith	Halstead	20. 4.99P
G-OLIN*	PA-30-160 Twin Comanche B	30-1716	OY-DLC G-AWMB/N8569Y	22.12.81	Not known (Crashed Stapleford 16.8.87; stored 1992)	(Henstridge)	3. 3.88T
G-OLIZ	Robinson R-22 Beta	0779		29. 9.98	L T Alderman t/a Randall Photographic	Baldock, Herts	5. 8.01T
G-OLJT	Mainair Gemini/Flash 2A (Rotax 503)	570-887-5 & W359	G-MTKY	16. 9.98	L.J.Taylor	Darlington	21.12.99P
G-OLLE	Cameron O-84 HAFB	1520		15. 4.87	N.A.Robertson "Golly IV"	Combe Hay Manor, Bath	9. 9.00A
G-OLLI	Cameron O-31 HAFB (Special Shape - Golly)	196		11. 5.76	N.A.Robertson "Golly III"	Combe Hay Manor, Bath	17. 7.97A
G-OLLY	PA-31-350 Navajo Chieftain	31-7405418	G-BCES N66916	27. 1.76	Barnes Olson Aeroleasing Ltd (Op Bristol Flying Centre)	Bristol	6. 5.01T
G-OLMA	Partenavia P.68B	159	G-BGBT	15. 4.85	C.M.Evans	Plymouth	15. 5.99T
G-OLOW	Robinson R-44 Astro	0100		3.10.94	R.C.Hields t/a Hields Aviation	Sherburn-in-Elmet	17.11.00
G-OLPG	Colt 77A HAFB	2568		11. 3.94	UK Petroleum Products Ltd t/a Eurogas & Corralgas	Leeds	11. 5.99
G-OLRT	Robinson R-22 Beta	1378	N4014R	21. 5.90	A.J. & P.D.Morgan t/a Morhire	Cardiff	29. 7.02T
G-OLSC*	Cessna 182A	34078	G-ATNU EI-ANC/N6078B	19. 8.87	Not known	St.Merryn	3. 7.93
			(Crashed Knettishall 6.6.93; for film use as "G-ATCX" - fuselage stored 4.94)				
G-OLSF	PA-28-161 Cadet	2841284	G-OTYJ G-OLSF/N92008	23.11.89	Plane Talking Ltd	Elstree	22. 1.02T
G-OLVR*	Clutton FRED Srs.II (Continental A65)	PFA/29-10321		17.11.78	C.P.Whitwell (Cancelled by CAA 23.12.99)	Wyberton	2. 6.00P
G-OLYD	Beechcraft 58 Baron	TH-1427	N7255H ZS-LYC/N7255H	12. 9.97	I.G.Lloyd	Gamston	13.10.00
G-OLYN	Sky 260-24 HAFB	088		24. 4.98	C.J.Sandell	Sevenoaks	2. 9.00T
G-OMAC	Reims Cessna FR.172E Rocket	0022	PH-HAI (PH-KRC)/D-EDDC	3. 7.84	R.J.Knibbs t/a RK Consultants	Maypole Farm, Chislet	5.11.01
G-OMAF	Dornier 228-200	8112	D-CAAD	16. 2.87	Cobham Leasing Ltd (Op for Ministry of Agriculture & Fisheries/Fisheries Patrol)	Bournemouth	22. 6.02T
G-OMAK	Airbus A.319-132 CJ	913	F-WWIF G-OMAK/F-WWIF/G-OMAK/D-AVYL	7. 1.99	Alkharafi Aviation 2000 Ltd	(Jersey)	7. 1.03T
G-OMAP	Rockwell Commander 685	12036	F-GIRX F-OCGX/F-ZBBU/N6525V	4.11.94	Cooper Aerial Surveys Ltd	Sandtoft	6. 4.00A
G-OMAR	PA-34-220T Seneca III	34-8233142	N82033	17. 6.88	Redhill Aviation Ltd t/a Redhill Flying Club	Redhill	19.10.00T
G-OMAT	PA-28-140 Cherokee D	28-7125139	G-JIMY G-AYUG	27. 8.87	R.B.Walker t/a Midland Air Training School	Coventry	3.11.00T
G-OMAX	Brantly B.2B	473	G-AVJN	7. 8.87	P.D.Benmax	Costock, Leics	9.12.99
G-OMDD	Cameron Thunder AX8-90 S2 HAFB	4345		2. 4.98	M.D.Dickinson	(Bristol)	
G-OMDG	Hoffmann H-36 Dimona	3510	OE-9215	19.11.98	P.Turner t/a Mendip Dimona Group	Halesland	7.12.01
G-OMDH	MDH Hughes 369E (500E)	0293E		14.11.88	Stiltgate Ltd	Booker	28. 4.01T
G-OMDR	Agusta-Bell 206B JetRanger III	8610	G-HRAY G-VANG/G-BIZA	8.12.97	Aeromega Ltd	Stapleford	15.12.00T
G-OMEC	Agusta-Bell 206B JetRanger III	8716	G-OBLD	16. 1.90	Kallas Ltd	(Monaco)	21.10.01
G-OMEL	Robinson R-44 Astro	0073	G-BVPB	30. 9.96	Nedair Ltd	Blackpool	2.11.00
G-OMGD	BAe HS.125 Srs.700B	257184	9K-AGA YI-AKG/9K-AGA/G-5-12	28.12.94	Magec Aviation Ltd	Luton	21. 2.00T

Regn	Type	C/n	P/I	Date	Owner/operator	Probable Base	CA Expy
G-OMGE	BAe 125 Srs.800B	258197	G-5-696	1. 7.91	Marconda Services Ltd	Luton	22. 5.00T
			G-BTMG				
G-OMGG	BAe 125 Srs.800B	258058	N125JW	21.11.94	Magec Aviation Ltd	Luton	23.11.00T
			G-5-637/N125JW/VH-NMR/ZK-EUI/(ZK-EUR)/G-5-510				
G-OMHC	PA-28RT-201 Arrow IV	28R-7918105	N3072Y	10. 2.81	M.R.Shelton	Tatenhill	6. 5.02T
					t/a Tatenhill Aviation		
G-OMHI	Mills MH-1	MH.001		8.10.97	J.P.Mills	(Stockport)	
G-OMIA	Socata MS.893A Rallye Commodore 180		D-ENME	21. 7.98	P.W.Portelli	Elstree	23. 8.01
		12074	F-BUGE/(D-ENMH)				
G-OMIG	WSK SBLim-2	622047	6247	10.11.92	Classic Aviation Ltd	Duxford	18. 5.99P
			(Polish AF)		(Op by The Old Flying Machine Co)		
	(Built Aero Vodochody as CS.102; later rebuilt in Poland)		(As "6247"in Soviet AF c/s)				
G-OMIK	Europa Avn Europa	PFA/247-12991		12. 1.98	M.J.Clews	(Maidenhead)	
G-OMJB	Bell 206B JetRanger II	2051	N315JP	20. 4.89	Coventry Helicopter Centre Ltd	Coventry	7. 6.01T
			N712WG/N712WC/N9989K				
G-OMJT	Rutan LongEz 968 & PFA/74A-10703			14.10.92	M.J.Timmons	Prestwick	31. 7.99P
	(Lycoming O-235)						
G-OMKF	Aero Designs Pulsar	PFA/202-11866		15. 1.91	M.K.Faro	Henstridge	28. 6.00P
	(Rotax 582)						
G-OMMG	Robinson R-22 Beta	1041	G-BPYX	25. 2.94	Abraxas Aviation Ltd	Denham	27. 1.01T
G-OMMM	Colt 90A HAFB	2328		20. 1.93	3M Health Care Ltd	Loughborough	4. 5.00A
G-OMNH	Beechcraft 200 Super King Air		N108BM	19. 8.98	Maynard & Harris Holdings Ltd	Norwich	20. 8.00T
		BB-108	RP-C1979/TR-LWC				
G-OMNI	PA-28R-200 Cherokee Arrow II		G-BAWA	3. 1.84	Excel Automation Ltd	Gloucestershire	8. 6.00T
		28R-7335130					
G-OMOG	Gulfstream AA-5A Cheetah	AA5A-0793	G-BHWR	4. 3.88	Solent Flight Aircraft Ltd	Southampton	15. 4.02T
			N26892				
G-OMPS*	PA-28-161 Warrior II	28-8016050	G-BOHP	14. 2.89	Not known Montpellier/Frejorques, France		29. 3.94T
			N8079Z		(Crashed Tours 20.8.92; wreck in open store 5.97)		
G-OMRB	Cameron V-77 HAFB	2184		29. 8.90	M.R.Bayne "Harlequin" Dunnington, Yorks		13. 8.00A
G-OMRG	Hoffmann H-36 Dimona	36132	G-BLHG	15.11.88	M.R.Grimwood	Gloucestershire	7. 2.00
G-OMSG	Robinson R-22 Beta-II	2738		8.10.97	S.Freedman	Gloucestershire	23.10.00T
G-OMUC	Boeing 737-36Q	29405		29. 6.98	British Regional Airlines Ltd	Manchester	16. 7.01T
					(Dove/Colum t/s)		
G-OMUM	Rockwell Commander 114	14067	PH-JJJ	24. 1.97	Armadafleet Ltd	Blackbushe	3. 3.00
			(PH-MMM)/N4737W				
G-OMWE	Zenair CH.601HD	PFA/162-12740	G-BVXU	21. 3.97	Mid-West Engines Ltd	Gloucestershire	14. 7.00P
	(Mid-West AE.100R)						
G-OMXS	Lindstrand LBL-105A HAFB	172		7.12.94	Virgin Airship & Balloon Co Ltd	Telford	1. 4.97A
					"Mazda"		
G-ONAF	Naval Acft Factory N3N-3	-	N45192	31. 1.89	R.P.W.Steele & J.D.Hutchinson	Sandown	30. 8.02
	(Wright Whirlwind R.760)		Bu.4406				
G-ONAV	PA-31-310 Turbo Navajo C	31-7812004	G-IGAR	29. 1.93	Panther Aviation Ltd	Booker	11. 5.00T
			D-IGAR/N27378				
G-ONCB	Lindstrand LBL-31A HAFB	393		4. 6.96	Flying Pictures Ltd	Fairoaks	6. 9.99A
G-ONCL	Colt 77A HAFB	1637		4. 4.90	D.R.Pearce	Slimbridge	14. 2.00A
G-ONEB	Westland Scout AH.1	F.9761	G-BXOE	21. 1.98	N.E.Bailey Draycott Farm, Chiseldon		23. 3.00P
			XW798				
G-ONET	PA-28-180 Cherokee E	28-5802	G-AYAU	3. 6.98	J.Blackburn & J.J.Feeney	Elstree	4. 8.02T
G-ONFL	Meridian Ultralights Maverick						
	(Rotax 503) 402 & PFA/259-12750		G-MYUJ	27.11 98	K.M.Dando	Long Marston	11. 2.00P
G-ONGC	Robin DR.400/180R Remorquer	1385	EI-CKA	11.11.98	Norfolk Gliding Club Ltd	Tibenham	3.12.01
			SE-GHM				
G-ONHH	Forney F-1A Aircoupe	5725	G-ARHA	13.12.89	R.D.I.Tarry	(Kettering)	5. 3.01P
			N3030G		"Easy Rider"		
G-ONIX	Cameron C-80 HAFB	4411		12. 8.98	Hillwalk Ltd	Pewsey	10. 8.00A
G-ONKA	Aeronca K	K283	N19780	21.10.91	N.J.R.Minchin Manor Farm, Tongham		22. 6.00P
	(Lycoming O-145)		NC19780		"Aggnes"		
G-ONMT	Robinson R22 Beta-II	2963		20. 7.99	Redcourt Enterprises Ltd	(Lanark)	2 .8.02T
G-ONON	Rotary Air Force RAF 2000 GTX-SE			13. 8.99	M.S.R.Allen	(Oakham)	
		PFA G/13-1313					
G-ONOW	Bell 206A JetRanger	605	G-AYMX	8. 8.88	J.Lucketti	Fenland	27. 4.00T
G-ONPA(2)	PA-31-350 Navajo Chieftain		N89PA	6. 5.98	Anglo American Airmotive Ltd	Bournemouth	15.10.01T
		31-7952110	N35225				
G-ONTV	Agusta-Bell 206B JetRanger III	8733	D-HUNT	1. 4.98	Castle Air Charters Ltd		7. 4.01T
			TC-HKJ/(D-HSAV)/I-GPFP/I-PIEF		Trebrown, Liskeard		
G-ONUN	Van's RV-6A	PFA/181-12976		20. 2.96	R.E.Nunn	(Herne Bay)	2 .8.00P
G-ONUP	Enstrom F-28C	348	G-MHCA	18. 1.00	R.E.Harvey	(West Deeping)	
			G-SHWW/G-SMUJ/G-BHTF				
G-ONYX	Bell 206B Jet Ranger III	4160	G-BXPN	22. 1.98	D.C. & A.J.Burgoyne	Halfpenny Green	10. 3.01T
			N18EA/D-HOBA/(D-HOBE)		t/a Burgoyne Group		

Regn	Type	C/n	P/I	Date	Owner/operator	Probable Base	CA Expy
G-ONZO	Cameron O-77 HAFB	1089		13.11.84	K.Temple "Gonzo"	Diss	19. 7.99A
G-OOAA	Airbus A.320-231	291	F-WWBZ	11. 4.92	Air 2000 Ltd	Manchester	14. 4.02T
G-OOAB	Airbus A.320-231	292	F-WWDN	24. 4.92	Air 2000 Ltd	Manchester	23. 4.02T
G-OOAC	Airbus A.320-231	327	F-WWDQ	15. 9.92	Air 2000 Ltd	Manchester	14. 9.02T
G-OOAD	Airbus A.320-231	336	F-WWIG	24. 9.92	Air 2000 Ltd	Manchester	23. 9.02T
G-OOAE	Airbus A.321-112	852	(G-UNIF) D-AVZG	14. 7.98	Air 2000 Ltd	Manchester	13. 7.01T
G-OOAF	Airbus A.321-211	677	G-UNID G-UKLO/D-AVZO	4.12.98	Air 2000 Ltd	Manchester	
G-OOAH	Airbus A.321-211	781	G-UNIE D-AVZK	4. 1.99	Air 2000 Ltd	Manchester	2. 3.01T
G-OOAI	Airbus A.321-211	1006	D-AVZJ	30. 4.99	Air 2000 Ltd	Manchester	29. 4.02T
G-OOAJ	Airbus A.321-211	1017	D-AVZM	12. 5.99	Air 2000 Ltd	Manchester	11. 5.02T
G-OOAL	Boeing 767-38A	29617		29. 3.99	Air 2000 Ltd	Manchester	29 .3.02T
G-OOAN	Boeing 767-39HER	26256	G-UKLH	26. 1.99	Air 2000 Ltd	Manchester	4 .4.00T
G-OOAO	Boeing 767-39HER	26257	G-UKLI	11. 1.99	Air 2000 Ltd	Manchester	14. 4.00T
G-OODE	SNCAN Stampe SV-4C (Gipsy Major 10)	500	G-AZNN F-BDGI	9. 5.77	A.R.Radford	Redhill	4. 7.02T
G-OODI	Pitts S-1D Special (Lycoming IO-360)	KH.1	G-BBBU	23.12.80	M.J.Walden	Cheddington	4. 5.00P
G-OODW	PA-28-181 Archer II	28-8490031	N4332C	14. 7.87	Goodwood Road Racing Co Ltd	Goodwood	18.11.02T
G-OOER	Lindstrand LBL-25A Cloudhopper HAFB 125			15. 8.94	Airborne Adventures Ltd	Skipton	18.10.95A
G-OOGA	Gulfstream GA-7 Cougar	GA7-0111	SE-IEA N758G	3. 2.86	Plane Talking Ltd (Op Denham School of Flying)	Denham	25.11.01T
	(C/n confirmed correct although YV-1334P is registered with same)						
G-OOGI	Gulfstream GA-7 Cougar	GA7-0077	G-PLAS G-BGHL/N789GA	16. 1.95	Plane Talking Ltd	Biggin Hill	10. 8.00T
G-OOGO	Grumman-American GA-7 Cougar GA7-0049		N762GA	12.11.97	Leonard F.Jollye (Brookmans Park) Ltd Elstree		2.12.00T
G-OOGS	Gulfstream American GA-7 Cougar GA7-0105		G-BGJW N737G	19. 6.98	Bournemouth Flying Club Ltd	Bournemouth	
G-OOJB	Cessna 421C Golden Eagle III 421C-1006		G-BKSO N6333X	13. 3.91	Melman Investments Ltd	Guernsey	26. 5.00
G-OOJC	Bensen B.8MR	PFA G/101-1303		4.12.98	J.R.Cooper	Swansea	
G-OOJP	Commander 114B	14567	N92JT	24.12.99	Plato Management Ltd	Oxford	
G-OOLE	Cessna 172M Skyhawk II	172-66712	G-BOSI N80714	25. 8.89	P.S.Eccersley	Humberside	15. 1.01
G-OONE	Mooney M.20J (205)	24-3039		31. 7.87	J.H.Donald & K.B.Moore	Cumbernauld	8. 4.00
G-OONI	Thunder Ax7-77 HAFB	1534		9. 3.90	Fivedata Ltd "Bridesnightie"	Todmorden, Lancs	4. 8.96A
G-OONY	PA-28-161 Warrior II	28-8316015	N83071	26. 7.89	D.A.Field & P.B.Jenkins	Compton Abbas	24. 9.01T
G-OOOA	Boeing 757-28AER	23767	C-FOOA G-OOOA (x3)/C-FOOA (x2)	6. 3.87	Air 2000 Ltd	Manchester	6. 4.01T
G-OOOB	Boeing 757-28AER	23822	C-FOOB G-OOOB (x9)	19. 2.87	Air 2000 Ltd	Manchester	28. 4.01T
G-OOOC	Boeing 757-28AER	24017	C-FRYL C-FXOC/G-OOOC (x7)	19. 1.88	Air 2000 Ltd	Manchester	27. 4.02T
G-OOOD	Boeing 757-28AER	24235	C-GRYU G-OOOD (x4)/C-FXOD (x4) (Leased Aero Continte 11.99)		Air 2000 Ltd	Manchester	27.10.02T
G-OOOG	Boeing 757-23AER	24292	C-FOOG G-OOOG (x5)	29. 3.89	Air 2000 Ltd	Manchester	29.10.01T
G-OOOI	Boeing 757-23AER	24289	N510SK EC-EMV/EC-247	19.10.89	Air 2000 Ltd	Manchester	19.10.02T
G-OOOJ	Boeing 757-23AER	24290	N510FP EC-EMU/EC-248	19.10.89	Air 2000 Ltd	Manchester	1.11.02T
G-OOOM	Boeing 757-225	22612	SE-DUN G-OOOM/N523EA	19.10.89	Air 2000 Ltd	Manchester	13.12.02T
G-OOOO	Mooney M.20J (205)	24-3046	N205EE	25. 1.88	Pergola Ltd	Weston, Ireland	7. 7.00
G-OOOS	Boeing 757-236ER	24397	G-BRJD EC-ESC/Fuji-Robin EC-349/G-BRJD	14. 5.91	Air 2000 Ltd	Manchester	18.10.02T
G-OOOU	Boeing 757-2Y0ER	25240		30. 8.91	Air 2000 Ltd	Manchester	24.10.02T
G-OOOV	Boeing 757-225	22211	N521EA	12. 2.92	Air 2000 Ltd	Manchester	17. 2.00T
G-OOOW	Boeing 757-225	22611	N522EA	20. 1.92	Air 2000 Ltd	Manchester	20. 1.00T
G-OOOX	Boeing 757-2Y0	26158		24. 2.93	Air 2000 Ltd	Manchester	22. 3.00T
G-OOOY	Boeing 757-28A	28203		21. 5.98	Air 2000 Ltd	Manchester	20. 5.01T
G-OOSE	Rutan VariEze	1536 & PFA/74-10326		7.12.78	B.O.Smith & J.A.Towers (Under construction 8.91)	Yearby	
G-OOSY	DH.82A Tiger Moth (Composite rebuild)	85831	F-BGFI Fr AF/DE971	6. 9.94	M.Goosey (On rebuild 9.94)	Eccleshall, Stafford	

Regn	Type	C/n	P/I	Date	Owner/operator	Probable Base	CA Expy
G-OOTC	PA-28R-201T Turbo Arrow III	28R-7703086	G-CLIV N3011Q	18. 1.94	H.Daines Electronics Ltd	(Beccles)	9. 1.03
G-OOUT	Colt Flying Shuttlecock SS HAFB 1938			16. 5.91	Shiplake Investments Ltd "Shuttlecock"	(Switzerland)	26.11.98A
G-OOXP	Aero Designs Pulsar XP PFA/202-11915 (Rotax 912)			25.10.90	T.D.Baker	Corby	18. 4.96P
G-OPAG	PA-34-200 Seneca	34-7250348	N506DM G-BNGB/F-BTQT/(F-BTMT)	16.10.90	A.H.Lavender	Biggin Hill	10. 4.00
G-OPAL	Robinson R-22 Beta	0535	N23750	11. 2.86	Heli Air Ltd	Wellesbourne Mountford	13. 4.01T
G-OPAM	Reims Cessna F.152 II (Reverted to Tri-cycle u/c 1999)	1536	G-BFZS	5. 9.86	PJC (Leasing) Ltd "Little Red Rooster"	Stapleford	17. 6.00T
G-OPAT	Beechcraft 76 Duchess	ME-304	G-BHAO	6.12.82	R.D.J.Axford	Booker	30. 1.00
G-OPAZ	Pazmany PL-2	PFA/69-10673		20. 3.98	K.Morris	(Salisbury)	
G-OPDM	Enstrom 280FX Shark	2021	N8627Q PH-GBL/N650PG	7. 1.98	Southern Air Ltd	Shoreham	15. 1.01T
G-OPDS	Denney Kitfox mk.4 PFA/172A-12259 (Rotax 582)			8. 1.93	P.D.Sparling	Popham	27. 6.00P
G-OPEP	PA-28RT-201T Turbo Arrow IV	28R-7931070	OY-PEP N2217Q	3.12.97	A.J.Keen	(Castletown, IOM)	12. 1.01T
G-OPFT	Cessna 172R Skyhawk II	172-80316	N9491F	11. 3.98	Rankart Ltd	Oxford	19. 3.01T
G-OPFW	HS.748 Srs.2A/266	1714	G-BMFT VP-BFT/VR-BFT/G-BMFT/5W-FAO/G11-10 (Parcelforce c/s)	1. 7.98	Emerald Airways Ltd	Liverpool	16. 2.01T
G-OPHT	Schleicher ASH 26E	26105		6. 2.97	Scheibler Filters Ltd "T1"	Gamston	11. 3.00
G-OPIC	Reims Cessna FRA.150L Aerobat	0234	G-BGNZ PH-GAB/D-EIQE	20. 6.95	S.J.Burke t/a Peak Aviation Photography	Bodmin	10.12.99T
G-OPIK	Eiri PIK-20E Srs.1	20233	PH-651	27. 1.82	A.J.McWilliam	Newtownards	18.10.02
G-OPIP*	Avtech Jabiru UL	0253		14 .4.99	P.Simpson (Cancelled by CAA 28.6.99)	(Potters Bar)	
G-OPIT	CFM Streak Shadow (Rotax 532) K.126-SA & PFA/161A-11624			22.11.89	W.M.Kilner Higher Barn Farm, Houghton		23. 6.00P
G-OPJC	Cessna 152 II	152-82280	N68354	7. 6.88	PJC (Leasing) Ltd	RAF Henlow	9.10.00T
G-OPJD	PA-28RT-201T Turbo Arrow IV	28R-8231028	N8097V	2.10.89	A.C.Gradidge & M.J.S.Worley	Southampton	15.12.01T
G-OPJH	Rollason Druine D.62B Condor RAE/619		G-AVDW	15. 4.97	P.J.Hall	Old Sarum	9.12.01
G-OPJK	Europa Avn Europa 17 & PFA/247-12487 (Rotax 912UL)			29. 4.93	P.J.Kember Laddingford, Paddock Wood "The First of the Many"		14. 4.00P
G-OPLB	Cessna 340A II	340-0486	G-FCHJ G-BJLS/(N6315X)	11. 7.95	Ridgewood Ltd	Chester	13. 5.00
G-OPLC	DH.104 Dove 8	04212	G-BLRB VP962	10. 1.91	W.G.T.Pritchard & I.D'Arcy-Bean (Op Mayfair Dove)	Redhill/Biggin Hill	30. 3.00T
G-OPME	PA-23-250 Aztec D	27-4099	G-ODIR G-AZGB/N878SH/N10F	31. 3.94	Oxspeed Ltd	Lydd	26. 9.01T
G-OPMT	Lindstrand LBL-105A HAFB	052		30. 9.93	Pace Micro Technology Ltd "Pace"	Shipley	31. 7.99A
G-OPNH	Stoddard-Hamilton Glasair IIRG PFA/149-13011		G-CINY	14.10.98	P N Haigh	Crosland Moor	
G-OPNI	Bell 206B Jet Ranger	83	G-BXAA F-GKYR/HB-XOR/G-BHMV/VH-SJJ/VH-FVR	24. 4.96	P & I Data Services Ltd	Denham	30. 5.99
				(Crashed 2 miles off-shore from Lyme Regis 5.4.99)			
G-OPPL	Gulfstream AA-5A Cheetah	AA5A-0867	G-BGNN	11.10.85	J.P.E.Walsh t/a Walsh Aviation (Op Cabair)	Elstree	8. 8.00T
G-OPSF	PA-38-112 Tomahawk	38-79A0998	EI-BLT G-BGZI	13.10.82	Panshanger School of Flying Ltd	High Cross, Ware	17. 8.00T
G-OPSL	PA-32R-301 Saratoga SP	32R-8013085	G-IMPW N8186A	4. 1.99	Photonic Science Ltd	(Robertsbridge)	15. 1.00
G-OPST	Cessna 182R Skylane II	182-67932	N9317H	16. 6.88	Lota Ltd	Shoreham	9. 7.00
G-OPTS	Robinson R-22 Beta-II	2712		16. 7.97	ZB Ltd	(Stockport)	17. 7.00T
G-OPUB	Slingsby T-67M Firefly 160	2002	G-DLTA G-SFTX	18.10.96	P.M.Barker	Bagby	3. 2.01T
G-OPUP	Beagle B.121 Pup 2	B121-062	G-AXEU (5N-AJC)	31.10.84	A.Brinkley Standalone Farm, Meppershall t/a Brinkley Light Aircraft Services		4. 2.01
G-OPUS	Avtech Jabiru SK PFA/274-13343			16. 7.98	Opus Software Ltd	Nottingham	16. 2.99P
G-OPWK	Grumman-American AA-5A Cheetah	AA5A-0663	G-OAEL N26706	26. 5.92	A.H.McVicar	Carlisle	6. 9.02T
G-OPWS	Mooney M.20K (231)	25-0663	N1162W	12. 4.91	A.R.Mills	Fowlmere	10. 7.00
G-OPYE	Cessna 172S Skyhawk	172S-8059	N653SP	19. 2.99	Pye Consulting Group Ltd	Blackpool	25 .2.02T
G-ORAC	Cameron Van-110SS HAFB	4577		22. 6.99	Virgin Airship & Balloon Co Ltd (RAC Titles)	Telford	6 .7.00A
G-ORAF	CFM Streak Shadow (Rotax 532) K.134-SA & PFA/161A-11627 (PFA c/n duplicates MW6 G-MYCU)			18. 5.90	A.P.Hunn	(Norwich)	1.10.99P
G-ORAL	HS.748 Srs.2A/334SCD	1756	G-BPDA G-GLAS/9Y-TFS/G-11-8 (Reed Aviation c/s) "John J Goodall"	13.08.99	Emerald Airways Ltd	Liverpool	12.11.02T

Regn	Type	C/n	P/I	Date	Owner/operator	Probable Base	CA Expy
G-ORAR	PA-28-181 Archer II	2890224	N9255G	6. 6.95	P.N. & S.M.Thornton	Goodwood	26. 6.01T
G-ORAY	Reims Cessna F.182Q Skylane II	0132	G-BHDN	18. 3.94	G A Barret	Gamston	27. 8.01
G-ORDN*	PA-28R-200 Cherokee Arrow II		G-BAJT	21. 7.89	Not known	Stapleford	9. 4.99
		28R-7235294			(Damaged Stapleford 27.5.96; open store 5.97)		
G-ORDO	PA-30-160 Twin Comanche B	30-1648	N8485Y	19. 4.91	C.A.Ringrose	Biggin Hill	28. 4.00
G-ORED	PBN BN-2T Turbine Islander	2142	G-BJYW	10. 1.85	Red Devils Aviation Ltd	AAC Netheravon	25. 9.00A
G-OREV	Revolution Helicopters Mini 500	0112		8. 8.96	R.H.Everett	Thruxton	AC
G-ORFC	Jurca MJ.5 Sirocco	PFA/2210		16. 5.85	D.J.Phillips	Lasham	9. 5.00P
	(Lycoming O-290)						
G-ORFH	Aerospatiale/Alenia ATR-42-300	346	F-WWEI	29.12.93	Gill Aviation Ltd	Newcastle	28.12.02T
					(Op Air France Express)		
G-ORHE	Cessna 500 Citation	500-0220	(N619EA)	25. 3.96	R.H.Everett	Thruxton	22. 5.00T
	(Unit No.220)		G-OBEL/G-BOGA/N932HA/N93WD/N5220J				
G-ORIG	Glaser-Dirks DG-800A	8-39-A29		5. 4.94	I.Godfrey "386"	Lasham	17.11.00
G-ORIX	ARV K1 Super 2	034 & PFA/152-12424	G-BUXH	16. 9.93	Burel Air Ltd	(Cheltenham)	15.12.00P
	(Norton AE.100R)		(G-BNVK)				
G-ORJB	Cessna 500 Citation	500-0364	G-OKSP	2. 7.92	L'Equipe Air Ltd	Gamston	20.10.01T
	(Unit No.392)		N40DA/N20WP/(N221JB)/N221AC/HB-VFF/N36892				
G-ORJW	Laverda F.8L Falco Srs.4	403	(PH-)	2.12.85	W.R.M.Sutton	Seppe, The Netherlands	1. 9.01
			G-ORJW/D-ELDV/D-ELDY				
G-ORMA	AS.355F1 Twin Squirrel	5192	G-SITE	9.11.98	Autopilot Ltd	Elstree	7. 6.01T
			G-BPHC/N365E				
G-ORMB	Robinson R-22 Beta	1607		14.12.90	R.M.Bailey	Cumbernauld	24. 2.00T
G-ORMG	Cessna 172R Skyhawk II	172-80344	N9518F	25. 9.98	J.R.T.Royle	Andrewsfield	30. 9.01
G-OROB	Robinson R-22 Beta	0965	G-TBFC	11. 6.90	R.Culff	Redhill	25. 6.95T
			N80287		t/a Corniche Helicopters (Spares use 9.97)		
G-OROD	PA-18-150 Super Cub	18-7856	SE-CRD	27. 6.89	R.J.O.Walker Griffins Farm, Temple Bruer		10. 3.02
G-ORON	Colt 77A HAFB	1149		8. 3.88	J.Charley	Wymeswold	29. 9.99A
					t/a Orion Hot Air Balloon Group		
G-OROZ	Aerospatiale AS.350B2 Ecureuil	2617		26. 2.92	Fisher Engineering Ltd	Enniskillen	30. 4.01
G-ORPR	Cameron O-77 HAFB	2341		26. 6.90	T.Strauss & A.Sheehan	(London SW1)	5. 8.00A
					"Batman"		
G-ORSP	Beechcraft A36 Bonanza	E-2723	N56037	26.10.92	C.W.Makin t/a Makins	(Garforth)	7. 1.02
G-ORTM	Glaser-Dirks DG-400	4-209		6. 3.87	D.P.Holdcroft	(Brackley)	29. 4.00
G-ORTW	Lindstrand AM.25000 HAFB	304		15. 8.95	Lindstrand Balloons Ltd	Oswestry	9. 4.96E
G-ORVB	McCulloch J.2	039	(G-BLGI)	2. 8.89	R.V.Bowles (On overhaul 7.91)	Coventry	AC
			(G-BKKL)/Bahrain Public Security BPS-3/N4329G				
G-ORVR	Partenavia P.68B	115	G-BFBD	2.10.95	Cheshire Flying Services Ltd	Liverpool	17. 3.02T
					t/a Ravenair		
G-OSAL	Cessna 421C Golden Eagle II		OY-BEC	13. 7.83	M.D.Thorpe	Leeds-Bradford	13. 1.99T
		421C-0218	SE-GZI/N5471G		t/a Yorkshire Helicopters		
G-OSCA	Cessna 500 Citation	500-0270	G-SWET	31. 1.96	Oscar Aviation Ltd	Fairoaks	20. 6.00T
	(Unit No.270)		N4238X/N68CB/N72BC/N712N/N712J/N5270J				
G-OSCC	PA-32-300 Cherokee Six	32-7540020	G-BGFD	27.11.84	BG & G Airlines Ltd	Jersey	27. 6.02
			D-EOSH/N32186				
G-OSCH	Cessna 421C Golden Eagle III		G-SALI	13. 9.95	Sureflight Aviation Ltd	(Birmingham)	8.11.00
		421C-0706	N26552				
G-OSCO	TEAM miniMax	PFA/186-12878		24.12.96	P.J.Schofield	(Sproston, Crewe)	
G-OSDI	Beechcraft 58 Baron	TH-1111	G-BHFY	27. 7.84	D.Darling	Wellesbourne Mountford	27. 4.02
G-OSEA	PBN BN-2B-26 Islander	2175	G-BKOL	27. 8.85	W.T.Johnson & Sons (Huddersfield) Ltd		
						Crosland Moor	23. 3.01
G-OSEE	Robinson R-22 Beta	0917		11. 1.89	Burman Aviation Ltd	Cranfield	13.10.02
G-OSFA	Diamond HK.36TC Super Dimona	36-649		15. 6.99	Diamond Aircraft Industries GmbH Enstone		19 .7.02T
G-OSFC	Reims Cessna F.152 II	1872	G-BIVJ	31. 1.86	Stapleford Flying Club Ltd	Stapleford	12. 6.00T
G-OSGB	PA-31-350 Navajo Chieftain		G-YSKY	25.01.99	Gold Air International Ltd	Cambridge	1. 5.00T
		31-7952155	N3529D				
G-OSHL	Robinson R-22 Beta	1000		19. 4.89	Sloane Helicopters Ltd	Sywell	27. 8.01T
G-OSII	Cessna 172N Skyhawk II	172-67768	G-BIVY	17.10.95	K.J.Abrams	(Great Dunmow)	14. 3.02T
			N73973				
G-OSIP	Robinson R-22 Beta-II	2916		9. 2.99	Heli Air Ltd	Tatenhill	3 .3.02
G-OSIS	Pitts S-1S Special	PFA/09-12043		19. 9.94	M.C.Boddington & I.M.Castle	Sywell	
G-OSIX	PA-32-260 Cherokee Six	32-499	G-AZMO	5. 8.86	A.E.Whittie	Blackpool	7. 4.02T
			SE-EYN				
G-OSKP	Enstrom 480	5002	F-GSOT	6. 6.94	Churchill Stairlifts Ltd	(Runcorn)	25. 3.00
			G-OSKP/N480EN				
G-OSKY	Cessna 172M Skyhawk II	172-67389	A6-KCB	27. 2.79	Skyhawk Leasing Ltd		
			N73343			Wellesbourne Mountford	8. 7.00T
G-OSLO	Schweizer Hughes 269C	S.1360	N7507L	15. 3.89	AH Helicopter Services Ltd Newton Abbot		3. 3.01T
G-OSMD	Bell 206B JetRanger II	2034	G-LTEK	12. 2.99	Stuart Aviation Ltd	White Waltham	7. 5.01T
			G-BMIB/ZS-HGH				

Regn	Type	C/n	P/I	Date	Owner/operator	Probable Base	CA Expy
G-OSMR	Lake LA-4-200 Buccaneer	650	EI-BNB N1057L	13. 3.96	J.P.Billingham	Gloucestershire	6. 7.02
G-OSMS	Robinson R-22 Beta	1528	G-BXYW HA-MIU/N528SH	22. 2.99	Heli Air Ltd	Cardiff	22. 9.01T
G-OSMT	Europa Avn Europa	PFA/247-12705		15. 6.94	S.M.Thomas	(Stockton-on-Tees)	
G-OSND	Reims Cessna FRA.150M Aerobat	0272	G-BDOU	16.10.84	Wilkins & Wilkins Special Auctions Ltd	RAF Henlow	30. 1.00T
G-OSNI	PA-23-250 Aztec C	27-3852	G-AWER N6556Y	2. 7.98	Marham Investments Ltd (Castletown, IoM)		17. 5.01T
G-OSOE	HS.748 Srs.2A/275	1697	G-AYYG	17.11.97	Emerald Airways Ltd	Liverpool	10.11.02T
			ZK-MCF/C-GRCU/ZK-MCF/G-AYYG/(x3)/G-11-9 (Securicor Omega Express titles)				
G-OSOO	MDH Hughes 369E (500E)	0298E		10. 5.89	Tyrone Fabrication Ltd	Dungannon, Co.Tyrone	25. 5.01T
G-OSOW	PA-28-140 Cherokee	28-23780	G-AVWH	13. 6.94	Go-Hog Flying Ltd	Bournemouth	3. 8.00T
					(Op Airbourne School of Flying)		
					(Crashed on take-off Bournemouth 10.12.99 & destroyed)		
G-OSPS	PA-18-95 Super Cub (L-18C-PI)		OO-SPS	9. 7.92	J.W.Macleod	Felthorpe	28. 3.99
	(Frame No.18-1527)	18-1555	G-AWRH/OO-HMI/ALAT 51-15555				
G-OSST	Colt 77A HAFB	737		28.10.85	British Airways plc	Heathrow	10.10.96A
					"Concorde II"		
G-OSTA	Auster 5 J/1 Autocrat	1957	G-AXUJ PH-OTO	22. 7.99	D & M Nelson	Coldharbour Farm, Willingham	1. 4.01
G-OSTC	Gulfstream AA-5A Cheetah	AA5A-0848	N26967	22. 4.91	5th Generation Designs Ltd	Goodwood	29. 9.00T
G-OSTU	Gulfstream AA-5A Cheetah	AA5A-0807	G-BGCL	18. 4.95	Airhouse Corporation Ltd	Blackbushe	3. 7.00T
G-OSTY	Reims Cessna F.150G	0129	G-AVCU	21. 3.97	C.R Guggenheim	Bournemouth	15.12.02T
					(Op Airbourne School of Flying)		
G-OSUP	Lindstrand LBL-90A HAFB	098		17. 3.94	T.J.Orchard	Booker	15. 4.00T
					t/a British Airways Balloon Club "Goes Up"		
G-OSUS	Mooney M.20K (231)	25-0429	OY-SUS (N3597H)	7.11.94	J.B. & M.O.King	Goodwood	25.11.00
G-OSVO	Cameron Hopper Servo 30SS HAFB	3077		30. 4.93	Servo & Electronic Sales Ltd	Lydd	26. 6.97A
					"Twocon"		
G-OSVY	Sky 31-24 HAFB	104		28. 5.98	Virgin Airship & Balloon Co Ltd	Telford	11. 3.00A
					(Ordnance Survey titles)		
G-OTAC	Robinson R-22 Beta-II	2737		8.10.97	Aviation Corporation plc	Cheltenham	23.10.00T
G-OTAF	Aero L-39ZO Albatros	232337	N40VC	9. 2.95	C.P.B.Horsley	Duxford	25. 4.00P
			N159JC/(N4321X)/Chad AF TT-ROB/Libyan Arab AF 2337				
	(Note:- at one time carried marks "28-04" for flying sequences of a James Bond film but Aero L-39 tail unit used for static shots and which remains at Breighton is c/n 731004 and most recently was "2804" of the German AF. This explains various German language marks on the unit. These are two separate aircraft.						
G-OTAL	ARV1 Super 2	024	G-BNGZ	10. 9.87	N.R.Beale	Shotteswell	21. 6.00P
	(Rotax 912)						
G-OTAM	Cessna 172M Skyhawk II	172-64098	N29060	13. 2.89	G.V.White	Swanton Morley	28.10.01T
G-OTAN	PA-18-135 Super Cub (L-21B-PI)		OO-TAN	28.10.96	S.D.Turner	Kings Farm, Thurrock	13. 4.00
	(Frame No.18-3850)	18-3845	(OO-DPD)/R.Neth AF R-155/54-2445				
G-OTBY	PA-32-300 Six	32-7940219	N2932G	14. 2.91	GOTBY Ltd	Jersey	29. 3.00
G-OTCH	CFM Streak Shadow			28.10.93	H.E.Gotch	Redhill	11.10.00P
	(Rotax 582)	K.207 & PFA/206-12401					
G-OTDB	MDHC Hughes 369E	0204E	G-BXUR HA-MSC	7. 4.98	D.E.McDowell	(Wantage)	9. 7.01T
G-OTED	Robinson R-22HP	0209	G-BMYR ZS-HLG	17. 1.96	Andrews Heli-Lease Ltd	Denham	17. 2.02T
G-OTEL	Thunder Ax8-90 HAFB	1790		13. 6.90	D.N.Belton	Chard	3.12.92A
G-OTFT	PA-38-112 Tomahawk	38-78A0311	G-BNKW N9274T	14. 3.97	N.Papadroushotis	Elstree	9. 4.00T
G-OTGT	Cessna 560 Citation V	560-0517		22 .6.99	Ferron Trading Ltd	Jersey	17 .6.00
G-OTHE	Enstrom 280C-UK Shark	1226	G-OPJT G-BKCO	22. 9.87	GTS Engineering (Coventry) Ltd	Coventry	27. 6.02
G-OTHL	Robinson R-22 Beta	0738	G-DSGN	28.11.94	London Helicopter Centre Ltd	Redhill	2. 3.00T
G-OTIM	Bensen B.8MV	PFA G/101-1084		5. 6.90	T.J.Deane	(Tilehurst, Reading)	
G-OTNT	Cameron Cider Bottle 120SS HAFB	3067		9. 7.93	A.J.Round	Wantage	24. 8.95A
G-OTOE	Aeronca 7AC Champion	7AC-4621	G-BRWW N1070E/NC1070E	2. 4.90	J.M.Gale Coombe Farm, Spreyton, Crediton		10. 5.95P
					(Damaged Coombe Farm 31. 5.95)		
G-OTOO	Stolp SA.300 Starduster Too	PFA/035-13352		26. 8.98	I.M.Castle	(Market Harborough)	
G-OTOY	Robinson R-22 Beta	0888	G-BPEW	5. 9.97	Tickstop Ltd	Kimpton Park, Hitchin	4. 9.00T
G-OTRG	Cessna TR182 Turbo-Skylane RG II	R182-00766	(N736SU)	14. 3.79	M.J. & A.M.Bonnick t/a Thermodata Components Standalone Farm, Meppershall		22.10.01
G-OTRV	Van's RV-6	PFA/181-13302		27. 5.98	W.R.C.Williams-Wynne	(Tywyn)	2 .6.00P
G-OTSP	Aerospatiale AS.355F1 Twin Squirrel	5177	G-XPOL G-BPRF/N363E	31. 3.98	Aeromega Ltd	Boreham, Essex	23. 2.00T
					(Op Essex Police Air Support Unit)		

Regn	Type	C/n	P/I	Date	Owner/operator	Probable Base	CA Expy
G-OTTI	Cameron OTTI 34SS HAFB	3490		23. 3.95	Ballonverbung Hamburg GmbH Kiel, Germany		17. 7.99A
G-OTTO	Cameron Katalog 82SS HAFB	2843		15. 6.92	Ballonverbung Hamburg GmbH Kiel, Germany		14. 7.99A
	(New envelope 1999 - c/n not known)				"Otto Versand Katalog"		
G-OTUG	PA-18-150 Super Cub	18-5352	(G-BKNM)	17. 2.83	B.F.Walker	Nympsfield	16. 7.01
	(Frame No.18-5424)		PH-MBA/ALAT 18-5352				
G-OTUP	Lindstrand LBL-180A HAFB	111		28. 3.94	Airborne Adventures Ltd	Skipton	19. 2.96T
G-OTVS*	Britten-Norman BN-2T Turbine Islander		G-BPBN	14. 2.83	Headcorn Parachute Club Ltd	Headcorn	18. 5.90
		419	G-BCMY		(Damaged Headcorn 11.3.89; open store 3.96)		
G-OTWO	Rutan Defiant	114		24. 6.87	A.J.Baggarley	Shoreham	10. 9.99P
	(Lycoming O-320)				(Stored Lydd 5.99)		
G-OURO	Europa Avn Europa 16 & PFA/247-12522			13.12.93	D.Pitt	Kemble	16.12.99P
	(NSI EA-81/100) (Tri-cyle u/c)						
G-OURS	Sky 120-24 HAFB	168		22.12.99	M P A Sevrin	Saint Etienne, Belgium	9.12.00
G-OUVI	Cameron O-105 HAFB	1766		4. 5.89	P.Spellward "Uvistat II"	Bristol	31. 3.94A
					t/a Bristol University Hot Air Ballooning Society		
G-OUZO	Airbus A.320-231	449	EI-VIR	8.11.95	Virgin Atlantic Airways Ltd	Gatwick	7.11.01T
			N449RX/SX-BSV/N449RX/F-WWIG "Spirit of Melina"				
G-OVAA	Colt Jumbo SS HAFB	1426		11. 5.89	Virgin Airship & Balloon Co Ltd	Telford	21. 9.96A
	(Conventional HAFB with nose/wings/tail of Virgin 747)				"Virgin Jumbo II"		
G-OVAX	Colt AS-80 Mk II Hot-Air Airship			3. 7.89	H.Dahloff	Rangendingen, Germany	17. 5.00A
		1501			"Vax Airship"		
G-OVBF	Cameron A-250 HAFB	3494		1. 3.95	Virgin Balloon Flights Ltd	Northampton	31. 8.00T
					"Virgin Oscar"		
G-OVBJ	Bell 206B Jet Ranger III	2734	G-BXDS	19. 2.98	Aeromega Helicopters (Engineering) Ltd		
			OY-HDK/N661PS			Stapleford	9. 7.00T
G-OVET	Cameron O-56 HAFB	3939		25. 6.96	E.J.A.Macholc	Saltburn-by-the-Sea	15. 5.01A
G-OVFM	Cessna 120	14720	N2119V	29. 4.88	G.Stevenson	Nottingham	27. 7.00P
	(Continental O-200-A)		NC2119V		t/a Commair Group		
G-OVFR	Reims Cessna F.172N Skyhawk II	1892		23. 5.79	Western Air (Thruxton) Ltd	Thruxton	13. 5.01T
G-OVID	Light Aero Avid Flyer	NMFC.11760	N879UP	31. 5.91	J.M.Walsh & D.F.Chamberlain		
	(Rotax 532)					Haverfordwest	30. 9.99P
G-OVMC	Reims Cessna F.152 II	1667		29. 5.79	J.A.Lyons	Gloucestershire	16. 8.01T
					t/a Staverton Flying School		
G-OVNR	Robinson R-22 Beta	1634		24.12.90	S.Lancaster & L.Clarke	Breighton	14. 5.00T
					t/a Rally Repaints		
G-OWAC	Reims Cessna F.152 II	1678	G-BHEB	25. 2.80	Barnes Olson Aeroleasing Ltd	Bristol	30. 4.01T
			(OO-HNW)		(Op Bristol Flying Centre)		
G-OWAK	Reims Cessna F.152 II	1677	G-BHEA	25. 2.80	A.S.Bamrah	Blackbushe	23.11.01T
					t/a Falcon Flying Services (Op European Flyers)		
G-OWAL	PA-34-220T Seneca III	3448030	D-GAPN	7. 7.98	Capistrano Investments Ltd	Biggin Hill	1. 9.01
			N9163K				
G-OWAR	PA-28-161 Warrior II	28-8616054	TF-OBO	18. 2.88	Bickertons Aerodromes Ltd	Denham	27. 3.00T
			N9521N		(Op Denham School of Flying)		
G-OWAX	Beechcraft Super King Air 200	BB-302	N86Y	4. 1.00	Dawcroft Ltd	(Ulverston)	
			N300BW/N600CP				
G-OWAZ	Pitts S-1C Special	43JM	G-BRPI	22.11.94	P.E.S.Latham	RAF Shawbury	13.12.99P
	(Lycoming O-320)		N199M		"Tiny Dancer"		
G-OWCG	Bell 222	47041	G-VERT	12. 8.94	Phoenix Helicopter Charters Ltd		
			G-JLBZ/G-BNDB/A40-CH (Op Air Hanson)			Blackbushe	9. 3.00T
G-OWDB	HS.125 Srs.700B	257040	G-BYFO	18. 2.99	Bizair Ltd.	Jersey	25 .4.00
			HB-VMD/VP-BPE/VR-BPE/N47TJ/EC-ETI/EC-375/G-OWEB/HZ-RC1				
G-OWEL	Colt 105A HAFB	1773		18. 5.90	S.R.Seager	Aylesbury	16. 3.98T
G-OWEN	K & S Jungster 1	PFA/44-10124		13.11.78	R.C.Owen	Danehill	
	(Continental C90)						
G-OWET	Thurston TSC-1A2 Teal	037	C-FNOR	28. 9.94	D.Nieman	Turweston	10. 5.02
			(N1342W)				
G-OWGC	Slingsby T-61F Venture T.2	1875	XZ555	14. 8.91	Wolds Gliding Club Ltd	Pocklington	1.11.00
G-OWIN	IRMA BN-2A-8 Islander	653	EI-AWM	22. 3.83	North London Parachute Centre Ltd		
			G-AYXE			Chatteris	1. 6.00A
G-OWIZ	Luscombe 8A Silvaire	3071	N71644	18.10.89	R.J.Pearson	(Cere-La-Ronde, France)	2. 8.99P
	(Continental A65)		NC71644				
G-OWLC	PA-31 Turbo Navajo	31-679	G-AYFZ	13. 6.91	Top Nosh Ltd	Jersey	1. 8.00
			N6771L				
G-OWND	Robinson R-44 Astro	0644		26. 8.99	W.N.Dore	(Warwick)	7. 9.02T
G-OWOW	Cessna 152 II	152-83199	G-BMSZ	10. 5.95	A.S.Bamrah	Blackbushe	5.11.01T
			N47254		t/a Falcon Flying Services (Op European Flyers)		
G-OWWW	Europa Avn Europa	PFA/247-12683		9. 6.94	W.R.C. & J.F.Williams-Wynne		
						(Tywyn, Gwynedd)	
G-OWYN	Aviamilano F.14 Nibbio	208	HB-EVZ	2. 2.87	D.Kynaston Coldharbour Farm, Willingham		18. 8.99P
			I-SERE				
G-OXBY	Cameron N-90 HAFB	1993	PH-DUM	9. 6.94	C.A.Oxby "The Zit"	Doncaster	

Regn	Type	C/n	P/I	Date	Owner/operator	Probable Base	CA Expy
G-OXKB	Cameron Jaguar XK8 Sports Car 110SS HAFB 3941			9. 7.96	Flying Pictures Ltd "Jaguar XK8"	Fairoaks	8. 8.99T
G-OXLI*	BAe Jetstream 4100	41003		5. 2.91	FR Aviation Ltd (Fuselage noted 5.99)	Bournemouth	
G-OXTC	PA-23-250 Aztec D	27-4344	G-AZOD N697RC/N6976Y	31. 5.89	A.S.Bamrah t/a Falcon Flying Services	Biggin Hill	15. 6.98T
G-OXVI	VS.361 Spitfire LF.XVIe CBAF.IX.4262	7246M TD248		22. 8.89	Silver Victory BVBA (As "TD248/D" in 41 Sqn c/s) (Karel Bos)	Antwerp-Deurne, Belgium	5. 5.00P
G-OYAK	SPP Yakovlev C.11 171205 (C/n quoted as 1701139 and/or 690120)		EAF 705 OK-KIH	25. 2.88	A.H.Soper (As "27" in Soviet AF c/s)	Earls Colne	5 1.00P
G-OYES	Mainair Blade 912 1186-1198-7-W989			12.11.98	M.Irving	(Ware)	4. 3.00P
G-OZAR	Enstrom 480	5007	G-BWFF	31. 7.95	Lancroft Air Ltd	(Oswestry)	5. 8.01T
G-OZBB	Airbus A.320-212	0389	C-FTDW G-OZBB (x 4)/F-WWDI	21. 3.94	Monarch Airlines Ltd	Luton	28 .4.02T
G-OZBC	Airbus A.321-231	633	D-ASSE D-AVZJ/F-WWIJ	24. 4.97	Monarch Airlines Ltd	Luton	23. 4.00T
G-OZEE	Light Aero Avid Speed Wing mk.4 (Rotax 582) PFA/189-12308			18. 4.94	S.C.Goozee	Newton Peveril	4. 9.00P
G-OZLN	Moravan Zlin Z.242L	0651	OK-XNA (SE-KMM)	2.10.92	R.L.McDonald	Edinburgh	28. 3.02
G-OZOI	Cessna R182 Skylane RGII R182-01950		G-ROBK	31. 5.85	J.R. & F.L.Gibson Fleming t/a Ranston Farms	Ranston, Blandford Forum	28. 6.01
G-OZOO	Cessna 172N Skyhawk II 172-67663		G-BWEI N73767	17.11.99	Atlantic Bridge Aviation Ltd	Lydd	26. 8.01T
G-OZRH	BAe 146 Srs.200	E-2047	N188US N364PS	29. 1.96	Flightline Ltd (Op Alpine Flightline: Lufthansa c/s)	Stansted	1. 2.02T
G-OZZI	Avtech Jabiru SK PFA/274-13176			15. 8.97	A.H.Godfrey & E.J.Stradling	(Weston-Super-Mare)	22. 6.00P

G-PAAA – G-PZZZ

Regn	Type	C/n	P/I	Date	Owner/operator	Probable Base	CA Expy
G-PACE	Robin R.1180T Aiglon	218		16.10.78	Millicron Instruments Ltd	Cranfield	14.10.00
G-PACL	Robinson R-22 Beta	1893	N2314S	17.12.91	R.Wharam	(Rotherham)	3. 2.01T
G-PADI	Cameron V-77 HAFB	1809		18. 8.88	R.F.Penney	Watford	3. 4.00A
G-PADS	Commander 114B	14637	N60987	15. 1.98	J.D'Arcy Mounter	Guernsey	27. 1.01T
G-PAGS	Aerospatiale SA.341G Gazelle 1 1155		G-OAFY G-SFTH/G-BLAP/N62406	11. 3.96	P.A.G.Seers	North Weald	7.11.99T
G-PAIZ	PA-12 Super Cruiser	12-2018	N3215M	11. 4.94	B.R.Pearson (Carries "NC3215M" on tail)	Eaglescott	11. 6.00T
G-PALL	PA-46-350P Malibu Mirage	4636091	G-RMST	4. 3.99	Pressurised A/c Leasing Ltd	Booker	1. 4.00
G-PALS	Enstrom 280C-UK-2 Shark	1191	N5688M	17. 7.80	G.Firbank Eastwood End Farm, Adlington, Macclesfield		22. 8.99
G-PAMS	Ted Smith Aerostar 601P 61P-0275-060		G-GAIR N90488	27. 7.89	P.A.Brook	Lydd	7.12.01
G-PAPS	PA-32R-301T Turbo Saratoga SP 32R-8529005		F-GELX N4385D	8. 7.97	Pump & Plant Services Ltd	Halfpenny Green	23. 7.00
G-PARI	Cessna 172RG Cutlass II 172RG-0010		N4685R	19.11.79	Applied Signs Ltd	Tatenhill	16. 2.02
G-PARR*	Colt Bottle 90SS HAFB 1953 (Old Parr Whisky bottle shape)			15. 3.91	British Balloon Museum & Library Newbury "Old Parr"		29. 9.94A
G-PASB*	MBB Bo.105D S.135 (Original pod from 1994 rebuild; see G-WMAA) G-BDMC/D-HDEC (On rebuild 3.96)		VH-LSA	2. 3.89	The Helicopter Museum Weston-super-Mare		
G-PASC	MBB Bo.105DBS/4	S.421	G-BNPS N4929M/D-HDMT	27.10.89	Police Aviation Services Ltd (Op Lincolnshire Ambulance Service)	RAF Waddington	27. 9.02T
G-PASD	MBB Bo.105DBS/4	S.656	G-BNRS N14ES/N4572Q/D-HDTZ	27.10.89	Police Aviation Services Ltd	Gloucestershire	26. 6.00T
G-PASF	Aerospatiale AS.355F1 Twin Squirrel 5033		G-SCHU N915EPFA G/1N5777H	7. 3.91	Police Aviation Services Ltd (Op Northumbria Police Air Support Unit)	Newcastle	16.12.01T
G-PASG	MBB Bo.105DBS/4	S.819	G-MHSL D-HFCC	7.12.92	Police Aviation Services Ltd	Gloucestershire	12. 5.02T
G-PASH	Aerospatiale AS.355F1 Twin Squirrel 5040		F-GHLI LX-HUPFA G/1F-GHLI/N356E	17. 5.96	Police Aviation Services Ltd	Gloucestershire	24. 3.01T
G-PASS	Boeing MDH MD.902 Explorer 900-00056		N9234P	12.10.98	Police Aviation Services Ltd (Op Sussex Police 4.99)	Shoreham	19. 4.02T
G-PASU	PBN BN-2T Turbine Islander	2144	5T-BSA G-BJYY	27. 5.93	Police Aviation Services Ltd	Gloucestershire	10. 7.00T
G-PASV	PBN BN-2B-21 Islander	2157	G-BKJH HC-BNR/G-BKJH	26. 2.92	Police Aviation Services Ltd	Teesside	18. 7.00T
G-PASX	MBB Bo.105DBS/4	S.814	D-HDZX	20.12.89	Police Aviation Services Ltd (Op Sussex Police Helicopter Unit)	Shoreham	10. 1.02T
G-PATF	Europa Avn Europa PFA/247-12757			5. 1.99	E P Farrell	(Beaconsfield)	

Regn	Type	C/n	P/I	Date	Owner/operator	Probable Base	CA Expy
G-PATG	Cameron O-90 HAFB	3856		13. 3.96	P.A. & A.J.A.Bubb	Guildford	21. 5.00A
					"Purple Rain"		
G-PATN	Socata TB-10 Tobago	307	G-LUAR	25. 3.97	A.T.Paton	Blackbushe	23.11.00
G-PATP	Lindstrand LBL-77A HAFB	471		8. 7.97	P.Pruchnickyj	Weston Turville, Bucks	31. 7.00
G-PATS	Europa Avn Europa	PFA/247-12888		19. 7.95	D.J.G.Kesterton	(Milton Keynes)	
G-PATZ	Europa Avn Europa	PFA/247-12625		2. 6.98	H.P.H.Griffin	White Waltham	
G-PAVL	Robin R.3000/120	170		22.11.96	Newcharter (UK) Ltd	Biggin Hill	6. 2.00T
G-PAWL	PA-28-140 Cherokee	28-24456	G-AWEU	8. 9.82	A.E.Davies t/a G-PAWL Group	Barton	13. 5.01
G-PAWS	Gulfstream AA-5A Cheetah	AA5A-0806	N2623Q	8. 2.82	Plane Talking Ltd	Elstree	11. 5.01T
G-PAXX	PA-20-135 Pacer	20-1107	(G-ARCE)	20. 5.83	D.W. & M.R.Grace	Truro	1. 6.01
			F-BLLA/CN-TDJ/F-DADR				
G-PAZY	Pazmany PL-4A	PFA/17-10378	G-BLAJ	20.11.89	C.R.Nash	(Fordingbridge)	3.10.95P
	(Continental A65)						
G-PBBT	Cameron N-56 HAFB	1535		23. 6.87	E.C.Moore "Little Book"	Great Missenden	21. 9.96A
G-PBEL	CFM Shadow Srs.DD	305-DD		27.10.98	P.C.Bell	(Maidstone)	
G-PBES	Robinson R-22 Beta	1491	G-EXOR	17. 3.95	B.C.Seedle	Blackpool	14. 3.00T
			G-CMCM		t/a Brian Seedle Helicopters		
G-PBUS	Avtech Jabiru SK	PFA/274-13269		18. 8.98	G.R.Pybus	Durham	6. 5.00P
G-PBYY	Enstrom 280FX	2077	G-BXKV	15. 8.97	Southern Air Ltd	Shoreham	28. 8.00
			D-HHML				
G-PCAF	Pietenpol Aircamper	PFA/47-12433		1. 6.94	C.C. & F.M.Barley	(Farnborough)	
G-PCDP	Moravan Zlin Z.526F Trener Master	1163	SP-CDP	24.10.94	R.A.Mills	Fairoaks	16. 7.01
					t/a Zlin Group		
G-PCOM	PA-30-160 Twin Comanche B	30-1053	HB-LDD	15.10.97	H. & P.Robinson	(Cheltenham)	21. 5.01
			N7957Y				
G-PCUB*	PA-18-135 Super Cub	18-3874	(PH-KER)	16. 2.81	M.J.Wilson	Turweston	28. 3.98
	(L-21B-PI) (Frame No.18-3893)		R.Neth AF R-184/54-2474 (Op Florence Flying Group)				
	(Regd incorrectly as c/n 18-3674)				(Cancelled by CAA 10.3.99)		
G-PDGG	Aeromere F.8L Falco Srs.3	208	OO-TOS	6. 1.98	P.D.G.Grist	Sibson	7. 5.01
			I-BLIZ				
G-PDHJ	Cessna T182R Turbo Skylane II	T182-68092	N6888H	3. 1.85	P.G.Vallance Ltd	Charlwood/Redhill	5.11.00
G-PDMH	Cessna 340A II	340A-0461	N6282N	20. 4.98	D.R.C.Knight	(Thame)	22. 4.01
			G-RITA/N6282N				
G-PDOC	PA-44-180 Seminole	44-7995090	G-PVAF	17.12.85	T.White	Newcastle	5. 5.01T
			N2242A		t/a Medicare		
G-PDOG	Cessna O-1E Bird Dog	24550	F-GKGP	25. 9.98	N.D.Needham Old Manor Farm, Anwick		AC
	(Regd as Cessna 305C)		ALAT		(As "24550/GP" in South Vietnamese AF c/s)		
G-PDSI	Cessna 172N Skyhawk II	172-70420	N739BU	4. 1.88	P.A.Hosey & A Clements	Lasham	2. 2.01T
					t/a DA Flying Group		
G-PDWI	Revolution Helicopters Mini-500	0248		14. 2.97	P.Waterhouse	(Stockport)	
G-PEAK	Agusta-Bell 206B JetRanger II	8242	G-BLJE	7. 3.94	Leisure Park Management Ltd	Goodwood	9. 2.00T
			SE-HBW				
G-PEAL	Aerotek Pitts S-2A Special	2048	N81LF	11. 5.88	Plymouth Executive Aviation Ltd Plymouth		21. 2.92T
	(Lycoming AEIO-360)		N48KA		(Damaged nr Kidderminster 28.6.91; stored 9.97)		
G-PEAT	Cessna 421B Golden Eagle	421B-0432	G-BBIJ	5. 4.84	Golden Airways Ltd	Cambridge	12. 8.01T
			N41073				
G-PEGG	Colt 90A HAFB	1550		28. 6.89	Ballon Vole Association		
						Fontaine Les Dijon, France	29. 4.00A
G-PEGI	PA-34-200T Seneca II	34-7970339	N2907A	27.11.89	Tayflite Ltd	Dundee/Manchester	20. 7.01T
G-PEKT	Socata TB-20 Trinidad	532	N24AS	28. 7.89	A.J.Dales	(Hull)	24. 2.02
G-PELG	Mudry CAP.231	11	G-OPPS	6. 4.99	J.P.M.Groot		
			F-GGYN/F-WZCI/G-OPPS			Zuid-Scharwoude, The Netherlands	20. 7.00
G-PENN	Gulfstream AA-5B Tiger	AA5B-0996	(I-TIGR)	4. 7.80	L.F.Banks	Denham	30. 9.01T
			N3756L				
G-PENT	Bell 206B Jet Ranger III	3958	G-IIRB	12. 7.99	Flying Tonight Ltd	(Oswestry)	29. 6.02
			N903CA				
G-PERR*	Cameron Bottle 60SS HAFB	699		28. 1.81	British Balloon Museum	Newbury	3. 6.84A
					"Perrier" (Stored 9.93)		
G-PERZ	Bell 206B Jet Ranger III	4411	N6272T	7. 1.97	D.J.Gilmour	Redhill	27. 2.00T
					t/a Intrepid Aviation Co		
G-PEST	Hawker Tempest II	12202	HA604	9.10.89	Tempest Two Ltd	Sandtoft	AC
	(Built Bristol) (Regd with c/n "1181")		(RIAF)/MW401		(On rebuild 11.96)		
G-PETR	PA-28-140 Cherokee Cruiser	28-7425320	G-BCJL	23. 9.85	Marnham Investments Ltd		
						(Castletown, IOM)	22. 1.00
G-PFAA	EAA Model P2 Biplane	PEB/03 & PFA/1338		19. 9.78	E.W.B.Comber	Willingham	1. 6.00P
	(Continental PC90)						
G-PFAD*	Wittman W.8 Tailwind	PFA/31-10259		19. 9.78	Not known	Priory Farm, Tibenham	21. 4.87P
	(Continental PC60)				(Stored 8.93)		
G-PFAF	Clutton FRED Srs.II	PFA/29-10310		30.10.78	M.S.Perkins	(Hinckley)	

Regn	Type	C/n	P/I	Date	Owner/operator	Probable Base	CA Expy
G-PFAG	Evans VP-1 (VW1600)	PFA/7022		13.11.78	J.A.Hatch	Netherthorpe	30. 6.89P
G-PFAH	Evans VP-1 (VW1834)	PFA/7004		23.11.78	J.A.Scott	Chestnut Farm, Tipps End	20. 7.00P
G-PFAL	Clutton FRED Srs.II (VW1600)	PFA/29-10243		7.12.78	J.M.Robinson (Stored 4.96)	Bann Foot, Lough Neagh	27. 7.88P
G-PFAO	Evans VP-1	PFA/7008		12.12.78	P.W.Price	(Cheadle)	
G-PFAP	Phoenix Currie Wot (Continental O-200-A) (Built as an SE-5A rep)	PFA/58-10315		12.12.78	J.H.Seed (As "C1904/Z" in RFC c/s) Black Spring Farm, Castle Bytham		17.12.96P
G-PFAR	Isaacs Fury II (Continental O-200-A)	PFA/11-10220		18.12.78	K.M.Potts (As "K2059" in 25 Sqdn RAF c/s)	Dunkeswell	26. 1.99P
G-PFAT	Monnett Sonerai II (VW1834)	PFA/15-10312		26.10.78	H.B.Carter (St.Clement, Jersey) (Stored Newcastle 5.93)		24.10.92P
G-PFAW	Evans VP-1 (VW1834)	PFA/62-10183		18.12.78	R.F.Shingler	Forest Farm, Welshpool	6.10.00P
G-PFAY	EAA Biplane	PFA/1525		18.12.78	A.K.Lang & A.L.Young (Stoke-sub-Hamdon) (Project abandoned 5.98)		
G-PFML	Robinson R-44 Astro	0082		9. 9.94	Helicopter Training & Hire Ltd	Belfast	9.10.00T
G-PGAC	Dyn'Aero MCR-01 Ban-bi	PFA/301-13186		27. 1.99	G.A.Coatesworth	Cambridge	
G-PGUY	Sky 70-16 HAFB	131	G-BXZJ	13.12.99	J L Guy t/a Black Sheep Balloons	Skipton	4.10.00
G-PHAA	Reims Cessna F.150M Commuter	1159	G-BCPE	19. 6.97	PHA Aviation Ltd	Elstree	17. 3.01T
G-PHEL	Robinson R-22 Beta	1669	G-RUMP N2405T	15. 8.96	Focal Point Communications Ltd	Denham	30. 4.00
G-PHIL	Brookland Hornet (VW1600)	17		7. 7.78	A.J.Philpotts (Stored 5.90)	St.Merryn	11. 8.89P
G-PHON	Cameron Phone SS HAFB (Motorola Microtac Mobile Phone)	2505	G-BTEY	13.12.91	Redmalt Ltd "Motorola Microtac"	Witham, Essex	14. 7.97A
G-PHOT	Thunder & Colt Film Cassette SS HAFB	4507		3. 2.99	Flying Pictures Ltd	Fairoaks	11. 2.00A
G-PHSI	Colt 90A HAFB	2181		12. 5.92	P.H.Strickland & Simpson (Piccadilly) Ltd "Daks"	Bedford/London W1	8. 7.99A
G-PHTG	Socata TB-10 Tobago	1008		15.11.89	A.J.Baggarley	Goodwood	14.10.02
G-PHYL	Denney Kitfox Mk.4	PFA/172A-12189		14. 9.98	J.Dunn (C/f/f 3.12.99)	(Basingstoke)	
G-PIAF	Thunder Ax7-65 HAFB	1885		19.11.90	L.Battersey "No Regrets/La Vie en Rose"	Newbury	24. 3.94A
G-PICT	Colt 180A HAFB	1723		22. 3.90	J.L.Guy	Skipton	29. 6.00T
G-PIDG	Robinson R-44 Astro	0678		23.11.99	T.Pidgley	(Virginia Water)	9.12.02
G-PIDS	Boeing 757-225	22195	N505EA	9. 1.95	Airtours Intnl Airways Ltd	Manchester	23. 2.01T
G-PIEL	Menavia Piel CP.301A Emeraude	218	G-BARY F-BIJR	17.11.88	P.R.Thorne	Cublington	17. 2.00P
G-PIES*	Thunder Ax7-77Z HAFB	263		13. 2.80	Not known	(Nottingham)	N/E(A)
G-PIET	Pietenpol Air Camper	PFA/47-12267		1. 4.93	N.D.Marshall	RAF Halton	
G-PIGG	Lindstrand Flying Pig SS HAFB	473		18. 8.97	Iris Heidenreich	Remscheid, Germany	31.10.99A
G-PIGS	Socata Rallye 150ST	2696	G-BDWB	13. 6.88	D.Hodgson t/a Boonhill Flying Group	Wombleton	24. 4.00
G-PIGY	Short SC.7 Skyvan 3A-100	SH.1943	LX-JUL 5T-MAM/(G-14-111)	21.12.95	Hunting Aviation Ltd	Oxford/Weston-on-the-Green	28. 1.00T
G-PIIX	Cessna P210N Pressurised Centurion II	P210-00130	G-KATH (N4898P)	12. 6.95	J.R.Colthurst	(Hungerford)	17. 2.02
G-PIKE	Robinson R-22 Mariner	1718M		18. 3.91	Sloane Helicopters Ltd	Sywell	23.11.00T
G-PIKK	PA-28-140 Cherokee	28-22932	G-AVLA N11C/(N9509W)	19. 8.88	L.P. & I.Keegan	Dundee	4. 3.01
G-PILE	Rotorway Exec 90 (RI 162)	5143		27. 7.93	J.B.Russell	Magheramorne, Co.Antrim	5.11.98P
G-PILL	Light-Aero Avid Flyer mk.4	PFA/189-12333		12. 8.97	D.R.Meston	Old Sarum	29. 2.00P
G-PINE	Thunder Ax8-90 HAFB	1546		30. 5.89	J.A.Pine	London W4	15. 8.92A
G-PING	Gulfstream AA-5A Cheetah	AA5A-0878	G-OCWC G-WULL/N27153	6.12.95	Plane Talking Ltd (Op London School of Flying)	Elstree	4. 6.00T
G-PINT	Cameron Barrel 60 SS HAFB (Wells Brewery Beer Barrel shape)	794		4. 1.82	D.K.Fish "Charles Wells"	Bedford	13. 2.98A
G-PINX	Lindstrand Pink Panther SS HAFB	032		23. 4.93	L.V.Mastis	West Bloomfield, Mi.,USA	30. 5.99A
G-PIPR	PA-18-95 Super Cub (Frame No.18-832)	18-826	G-BCDC 4X-ANQ/IDF/AF/4X-ADE	11.10.96	D.S.Sweet	Dunkeswell	15. 7.01T
G-PIPS	Van's RV-4 (Tri-cycle u/c)	PFA/181-11836		3. 8.90	C.J.Marsh (F/f 25.5.99)	Bembridge	17. 6.00P
G-PIPY	Cameron Scottish Piper 105SS HAFB	3815		30. 1.96	Cameron Balloons Ltd Almondsbury, Glos (To Muir Moffat) "The Scotsman"		19.12.99A

Regn	Type		C/n	P/I	Date	Owner/operator		Probable Base	CA Expy
G-PITS	Pitts S-2AE Special (Lycoming IO-360)	PFA/09-11001			4. 7.85	T.McManus & D.F.van Lonkhuyzen t/a The Eitlean Group		Weston, Ireland	18. 8.99P
G-PITZ	Pitts S-2A Special (Lycoming AEIO-360)		100ER	N183ER	2.10.87	A.K.Halvorsen		Barton	21. 3.00P
G-PIXI	Cyclone Pegasus Quantum 15 (Rotax 912)		7557		27. 8.99	D.L.Goode		Enstone	6. 9.00P
G-PIXS	Cessna 336 Skymaster		336-0130	N86648	9. 9.88	Atlantic Bridge Aviation Ltd (Stored 11.97)		Lydd	29. 1.95T
G-PIZZ	Lindstrand LBL 105A HAFB		629		27. 7.99	HD Bargain SRL		Firenze, Italy	2..8.00A
G-PJMT	Neico Lancair 320 (Tri-cycle u/c)	PFA/191-12348			8. 5.98	M.T.Holland		Exeter	7. 1.00
G-PJRT*	BAe Jetstream 4100		41002		5. 2.91	British Aerospace (Operations) Ltd (Stored 7.97 - cancelled as PWFU 27.3.99)		Prestwick	1. 5.94S
G-PJTM	Reims Cessna FR.172K Hawk II		0611	EI-CHJ G-BFIF	13.10.98	P J McNamara t/a Jane Air		Haverfordwest	12.10.01T
G-PKPK	Schweizer Hughes 269C (300C)		S.1454	EI-CAR N69A	3. 8.93	C.H.Dobson		(Louth)	14. 9.02T
G-PLAC	PA-31-350 Chieftain		31-8052038	G-OLDA G-BNDS/N131PP/N3550N	23.12.98	Vale Aviation Ltd		(London SW1)	7.10.00T
G-PLAH	BAe Jetstream 3102		640	G-LOVA G-OAKA/G-BUFM/G-LAKH/G-BUFM/N410MX/G-31-640	1.11.99	Osprey Aviation Ltd		Southampton	26. 7.00T
G-PLAN	Reims Cessna F.150L Commuter		1066	PH-SPR	11. 8.78	D.A.Johnson t/a G-PLAN Flying Group		Barton	25.11.02
G-PLAT	Beechcraft 200 Super King Air	BB-487		N8PY N198SC/PT-OYR/N40QN/VH-NIC/N40QN/N400N/N243KA	27. 4.99	Bevair Services Ltd		(Godalming)	5. 5.00T
G-PLAY	Robin R.2112		170	F-ODIT	1. 8.79	D.R.Austin		High Cross, Ware	20.12.97
G-PLEE	Cessna 182Q Skylane II	182-66570		N95538	4.12.87	Sunderland Parachute Centre Ltd t/a Peterlee Parachute Centre		Peterlee	11. 3.00
G-PLIV	Pazmany PL-4 (Continental A65)	PFA/17-10155			19.12.78	B.P.North		(Aylesbury)	
G-PLMB	Aerospatiale AS.350B Ecureuil		1207	G-BMMB C-GBEW/(N36033)	26. 3.86	PLM Dollar Group Ltd		Inverness	15. 2.01T
G-PLMC	Aerospatiale AS.350B Ecureuil		1731	G-BKUM	23. 8.88	PLM Dollar Group Ltd		Cumbernauld	3.11.01T
G-PLMH	Eurocopter AS.350B2 Ecureuil		2156	F-WQDJ G-PLMH/HB-XTE/F-WQPK/HB-XTE	9. 1.95	PLM Dollar Group Ltd		Inverness	25. 2.01T
G-PLMI	Aerospatiale SA.365C1 Dauphin 2	5001		F-GFYH F-WZAE	19. 6.95	PLM Dollar Group Ltd		Inverness	8. 7.00T
G-PLOW	Hughes 269B		67-0317	G-AVUM	13. 9.83	Sulby Aerial Surveys Ltd (Cockpit section only stored Bruntingthorpe 8.97)		Sywell	29.11.92
G-PLPC	Schweizer Hughes 269C (300C)		S.1558	G-JMAT	14. 4.97	Power Lines, Piper & Cables Ltd		Carluke, Lanark	3. 6.01
G-PLUG*	Colt 105A HAFB		1958		17. 4.91	British Balloon Museum & Library		Newbury	14. 8.95T
G-PLUS	PA-34-200T Seneca II		34-8070111	N81406	25. 3.80	C.G.Strasser t/a Skycabs		Jersey	9. 5.01
G-PLXI	BAe ATP (Development a/c with PW 127D engines)		2001	G-MATP (G-OATP)	26. 8.94	British Aerospace (Aircraft) Ltd (Stored 10.97)		Woodford	2.12.92P
G-PMAM	Cameron V-65 HAFB		1155		29. 5.85	P.A.Meecham "Tempus Fugit"		Milton-under-Wychwood	3. 8.00A
G-PMAX	PA-31-350 Navajo Chieftain		31-7305006	G-GRAM G-BRHF/N7679L	7.7.99	AM & T Aviation Ltd		Bristol	5. 2.98T
G-PMNF	VS.361 Spitfire HF.IX	CBAF.10372		SAAF TA805	29. 4.96	P.R.Monk (On rebuild 1995 as "TA805")		(Maidstone)	
G-PNEU	Colt Bibendum 110SS HAFB		4223		5. 1.98	The Aerial Display Co Ltd		Looe	22.11.99A
G-PNNI	PA-28-181 Archer III		2843278	N41651	22.10.99	Dorset Aircraft Leasing Ltd		(London SW10)	21.10.02
G-PNUT*	Cameron Mr.Peanut 35SS HAFB		643	N400AB G-PNUT	4. 2.80	British Balloon Museum & Library "Mr.Peanut" (Stored)		Newbury	
G-POAH	Sikorsky S-76B		760399		30. 3.92	The Peninsula & Oriental Steam Navigation Co Ltd (Op P&O Aviation Ltd)		Stansted	17. 5.01T
G-POLT	Robinson R-44 Astro		0370		24. 9.97	Lyntonworth Ltd		Solihull	24. 9.00T
G-POLY	Cameron N-77 HAFB		428		13. 7.78	D.M.Barnes, N.F.Biggs, J.L.Hinton, M.A.C.Life & D.J.Thornley t/a The Empty Wallets Balloon Group "Polywallets"		Bristol	4. 8.00A
G-POND	Oldfield Baby Lakes (Continental A80)		01	N87ED	2.10.90	A Stegner		Sulzemoos, Germany	16.12.99P
G-POOH	Piper J3C-65 Cub (Frame No.7015)		6932	F-BEGY NC38324	17.10.79	P. & H.Robinson Upper Harford Farm, Bourton-on-the-Water			8. 4.01
G-POOL	ARV1 Super 2		025	G-BNHA	28. 8.87	P.A.Dawson (Stored 6.97)		Kemble	9. 9.90T
G-POOP	Dyn'Aero MCR-01 Ban-bi	PFA/301-13190			5.11.97	P.Bondar		Cambridge	6. 9.000
G-POPA	Beechcraft A36 Bonanza		E-2177	N7007F N7204R	20. 5.92	C.J.O'Sullivan		Southend	28. 1.02
G-POPE	Eiri PIK.20E Srs.1		20257		5. 3.80	C.J.Hadley "PE"		Membury/Bidford	6. 6.01

Regn	Type	C/n	P/I	Date	Owner/operator	Probable Base	CA Expy
G-POPI	Socata TB-10 Tobago	315	G-BKEN (G-BKEL)	20. 4.90	I.S.Hacon & C.J.Earle	Seething	27. 3.01
G-POPP*	Colt 105A HAFB	1776		1. 3.91	Flying Pictures Ltd "Champagne Mercier" (Cancelled as WFU 5.2.99)	Fairoaks	21.11.96A
G-POPS	PA-34-220T Seneca III	34-8133150	N8407H	11. 6.90	Alpine Ltd	Jersey	4. 5.02
G-POPW	Cessna 182S Skylane	182-80204	N9451F	10. 7.98	D.L. Price	(Kimbolton)	15. 7.01
G-PORK	Grumman-American AA-5B Tiger	AA5B-0625	EI-BMT G-BFHS	28. 2.84	J.W. & B.A.Flint (Crashed on take-off Eaglescott 13.7.99: on repair 8.99)	Southampton	27. 5.02T
G-PORT	Bell 206B JetRanger III	2784	N37AH N39TV/N397TV/N2774R	23. 8.89	Image Computer Systems Ltd (Op Fast Helicopters)	Thruxton	4. 8.01T
G-POSH	Colt 56A HAFB	822	G-BMPT	10. 6.86	B.K.Rippon	Didcot	23. 7.00A
G-POTT	Robinson R-44 Astro	0383		21.11.97	Ranc Care Homes Ltd	(Ilford)	27.11.00T
G-POWL	Cessna 182R Skylane II	182-67813	N9070G D-EOMF/N6265N	11.11.82	Hillhouse Estates Ltd	Bowldown Farm, Tetbury	27. 4.01
G-POWR	Agusta A.109E Power	11014	G-BXUD	20. 7.98	Powersene Ltd	Shoreham	16. 6.01T
G-PPAH	Enstrom 480	5032		9. 3.98	Cumbrian Seafoods Ltd	Hexham	8. 4.01
G-PPLH	Robinson R-22 Beta	1007		11. 5.89	Status Investments Ltd	(Sheffield)	27. 4.02T
G-PPPP	Denney Kitfox mk.3 (Rotax 582)	771 & PFA/172-11830		9. 1.91	S.P.Woodhouse & S.A.Tuff	Goosedale Farm, Market Bosworth	14. 5.02P
G-PPTS	Robinson R-44 Clipper (Float equipped)	0664		14.10.99	Superstore Ltd	(Runcorn)	2.11.02T
G-PRAG	Brugger MB.2 Colibri (VW1835)	PFA/43-10362		29.11.78	D.Frankland t/a Colibri Flying Group	RAF Mona	17. 8.00P
G-PRET	Robinson R-44 Astro	0381		8.10.97	First Degree Air Ltd	(Walsall)	15.10.00T
G-PREY	Pereira Osprey II 88 & PFA/070-10193 (Lycoming IO-320)		G-BEPB	28. 9.99	D.W.Gibson	(Doseley)	8. 6.98P
G-PRII	Hawker Hunter PR.Mk.11	41H-670690	N723WT A2616/WT723	14. 7.99	Stick & Rudder Aviation Ltd	Ostend, Belgium	1. 9.00P
G-PRIM	PA-38-112 Tomahawk	38-78A0669	N2398A	28. 1.87	Braddock Ltd	White Waltham	25.12.01T
G-PRNT	Cameron V-90 HAFB	2819		23. 3.92	E.K.Gray	Droitwich	7. 3.00A
G-PROD	Eurocopter AS.350B2 Ecureuil	2825		7. 2.95	Prodrive Ltd	Banbury	29. 3.01T
G-PROM	Aerospatiale AS.350B Ecureuil	1486	G-MAGY G-BIYC	11.10.96	JPM Ltd	Horsham	23.10.02T
G-PROP	Gulfstream AA-5A Cheetah	AA5A-0845	G-BHKU (OO-HTF)	16. 2.84	Fortune Technology Ltd	Elstree	28. 5.01T
G-PROV	Hunting P.84 Jet Provost T.52A (T.4)	PAC/W/23905	Sing.AF352 S.Yemen AF 104/G-27-7/XS228	13.12.83	D.S.Milne	(Banchory)	10.12.99P
G-PRSI	Cyclone Pegasus Quantum 15	7492		17.12.98	P.R.Stevens	(New Milton)	16.12.99P
G-PRTT	Cameron N-31 HAFB	1374		6.11.86	J.M.Albury "Baby Pritt"	Cirencester	14.11.99A
G-PRXI	VS.365 Spitfire PR.XI (C/n quoted as 6S/501431)	6S/583003	PL983 G-15-109/N74138/PL983	6. 6.83	Wizzard Investments Ltd (As "PL983" in 4 Sqdn, 2 TAF c/s)	North Weald	22. 5.93P
G-PSFT	PA-28-161 Warrior II	28-8416021	G-BPDS N4328P	1. 8.96	SFT Europe Ltd	Bournemouth	6.11.00T
G-PSIC	North American P-51C-10 Mustang (Composite from major components P-51D IDF/AF 13)	103-26778	N51PR 43-25147	16. 4.98	Patina Ltd (Op by The Fighter Collection) "Princess Elizabeth" (As "2106449/HO-W" in 487th FS/362nd FS USAAF c/s)	Chino, USA	AC
G-PSON	Colt Cylinder One SS HAFB (Panasonic Battery Shape)	1780	PH-SON	14. 3.95	M.E.White	Dublin	7. 8.99A
G-PSRT	Piper PA-28-151 Cherokee Warrior	28-7615225	G-BSGN N9657K	18. 3.99	P.A.S.Dyke	Little Gransden	13. 6.99T
G-PSST	Hawker Hunter F.58A	HABL-003115	J-4104 G-9-317/A2568/XF947	12. 2.97	Heritage Aviation Developments Ltd "Miss Demeanour"	Kemble	22.10.00P
G-PSUE	CFM Shadow Srs.CD (Rotax 503)	K.139	G-MYAA	1. 4.99	P.F.Lorriman	Stoke, Kent	18. 4.00P
G-PTAG	Europa Avn Europa (Jabiru 3300) (Tri-cycle u/c)	PFA/247-13121		14.12.98	R.C.Harrison	(Market Raisen)	
G-PTRE	Socata TB-20 Trinidad	762	G-BNKU	14. 6.88	Trantshore Ltd	Rochester	21. 4.01
G-PTWB	Cessna T303 Crusader	T303-00306	G-BYNG G-PTWB/N6312V	6.12.84	F.Kratky t/a FK Global Aviation.	Denham	10. 3.00
G-PTWO	Pilatus P.2-05	600-30	U-110 A-110	26. 2.81	Rentair Ltd (As "U-110" in Swiss AF c/s)	(Jersey)	12. 8.94P
G-PTYE	Europa Avn Europa 1 & PFA/247-12496 (Rotax 912UL)			22. 1.96	J.Tye "Harriet"	Holly Meadow Farm, Bradley	17. 6.00P
G-PUBS*	Colt Beer Glass 56SS HAFB	037		7. 6.79	Not known "Beer Glass"	NK	
G-PUDL	PA-18-150 Super Cub	18-7292	SE-CSE	24. 2.98	R.A.Roberts	(Billingshurst)	24. 2.01
G-PUDS	Europa Avn Europa (Tri-cycle u/c)	PFA/247-12999		9.10.97	I.Milner	(Appleby-in-Westmorland)	10.11.00
G-PUFF	Thunder Ax7-77 Bolt HAFB	165		17.11.78	C.A.Gould t/a Intervarsity Balloon Club "Puffin II"	Ipswich	20. 8.99A
G-PUFN	Cessna 340A II	340A-0114	N532KG N532KC/N5477J	4.12.96	The Puffin Club Ltd	Leicester	15.12.02T

Regn	Type	C/n	P/I	Date	Owner/operator	Probable Base	CA Expy
G-PULL*	PA-18-150 Super Cub	18-5356	PH-MBB	17. 2.83	R.A.Yates	Sibsey	2. 4.89A
	(Frame No.18-5429)		ALAT 18-5356		(Crashed Eaglescott 13.6.86; stored 8.90)		
G-PUMA	Aerospatiale AS.332L Super Puma	2038	F-WMHB	31. 1.83	Bond Helicopters Ltd	Aberdeen	12. 4.00T
G-PUMB	Aerospatiale AS.332L Super Puma	2075		31. 1.83	Bond Helicopters Ltd	Aberdeen	15. 5.00T
G-PUMD	Aerospatiale AS.332L Super Puma	2077	F-WXFD	31. 1.83	Bond Helicopters Ltd	Aberdeen	23. 8.02T
G-PUME	Aerospatiale AS.332L Super Puma	2091		3. 8.83	Bond Helicopters Ltd	Aberdeen	6. 9.00T
G-PUMG(2)	Aerospatiale AS.332L Super Puma	2018	F-ODOS	3. 8.83	Bond Helicopters Ltd	Aberdeen	14. 5.02T
G-PUMH	Aerospatiale AS.332L Super Puma	2101		3. 8.83	Bristow Helicopters Ltd	Aberdeen	22. 5.01T
G-PUMI	Aerospatiale AS.332L Super Puma	2170		27. 1.86	Bristow Helicopters Ltd	Aberdeen	21. 5.02T
G-PUMK	Aerospatiale AS.332L Super Puma	2067	LN-OMF	23. 3.90	Bond Helicopters Ltd	Aberdeen	2. 8.00T
			G-PUMK/LN-OMF/F-WXFP				
G-PUML	Aerospatiale AS.332L Super Puma	2073	LN-ODA	20. 7.90	Bond Helicopters Ltd	Aberdeen	4. 7.00T
			G-PUML/LN-OMG				
G-PUMM	Eurocopter AS.332L-2 Super Puma	2477		29. 7.98	Bond Helicopters Ltd	Aberdeen	21. 9.02T
G-PUMN	Eurocopter AS.332L Super Puma	2484	LN-OHF	16. 7.99	Bond Helicopters Ltd	Aberdeen	
G-PUMO	Eurocopter AS.332L-2 Super Puma	2467		30. 9.98	Bond Helicopters Ltd	Aberdeen	25.10.02T
G-PUNK	Thunder Ax8-105 HAFB	1719		28. 3.90	D.J.Farrar	Leeds	15. 5.99T
G-PUPP	Beagle B.121 Pup 2	B121-174	G-BASD	23.11.93	P.A.Teichman	Elstree	16. 4.02
			(SE-FOG)/G-BASD				
G-PURR	Gulfstream AA-5A Cheetah	AA5A-0794	G-BJDN	22. 2.82	N.Bass	Elstree	2. 9.02T
			N26893		t/a Nabco Retail Display		
G-PURS	Rotorway Exec 152	3827		19. 1.90	J.E.Houseman	Clitheroe	5. 6.96P
	(RW152)						
G-PUSH	Rutan LongEz	PFA/74A-10740		11. 7.83	E.G.Peterson	(Nottingham)	
G-PUSI	Cessna T303 Crusader	T303-00273	N3479V	26. 7.88	Walter Swinburn Ltd	Oxford	18. 5.00T
G-PUSS	Cameron N-77 HAFB	1577		6.10.87	The Balloon Club Ltd	Bristol	21. 5.00A
					t/a Bristol Balloons "Dick Whittington"		
G-PUSY	Tiger Cub RL-5ALW Sherwood Ranger		G-MZNF	25. 6.99	B.J.Chester-Master	(Moccas)	4.10.00P
		PFA/237-12964					
G-PUTT	Cameron Golfball 76SS HAFB	2060	LX-KIK	8. 8.95	D.P.Hopkins Pidley, Huntingdon		
					t/a Lakeside Lodge Golf Centre		
G-PVBF	Lindstrand LBL-260S HAFB	504		7. 4.98	Virgin Balloon Flights Ltd (London SE16)		29. 4.02T
G-PVCU	Cameron N-77 HAFB	4376		22. 5.98	R.G.March Market Harborough		14. 5.00A
					(Coldseal titles)		
G-PVET	DHC.1 Chipmunk 22	C1/0017	WB565	23. 5.97	Connect Properties Ltd	(Abingdon)	9. 9.00T
					(As "WB565")		
G-PWBE	DH.82A Tiger Moth	LES.1	VH-KRW	23. 7.99	P.W.Beales	(Bridgend)	AC
	(This ex-Australian Tiger Moth was one of 11 aircraft, given c/ns LES.1 to LES.11, which was constructed						
	by Lawrence Engineering Services from ex-RAAF spares in the late 1950s. VH-KRW was first registered to						
	K.R.Wilson, Queensland on 6.2.59 and has no known previous identity)						
G-PWEL	Robinson R-22 Beta-II	2982		1. 9.99	DJP Ltd	(Shrewsbury)	19..9.02
G-PYCO	Dassault Falcon 2000	78	F-WMMJ	21. 4.99	Charyo Corporation Ltd	Jersey	20..4.02
G-PYLN	Cameron Pylon 80SS HAFB	2958	G-BUSO	18. 1.93	Virgin Airship & Balloon Co Ltd	Telford	25. 4.97A
	(Electricity Pylon shape)						
G-PYOB	Aerospatiale SA.341G Gazelle 1	1145	G-IYOB	8. 8.95	MW Helicopters Ltd.	Stapleford	23. 7.00
			G-WELA/G-SFTD/G-RIFC/G-SFTD/N641HM/N341BB/F-WKQH					
G-PYRO	Cameron N-65 HAFB	567		8. 1.80	A.C.Booth "Pyromania"	Bristol	4. 8.99A
G-PZAZ	PA-31-350 Navajo Chieftain		G-VTAX	18. 1.95	Air Medical Ltd	Oxford	22. 5.00T
		31-7405214	(G-UTAX)/N54266				
G-PZIZ	PA-31-350 Navajo Chieftain		G-CAFZ	30.10.98	Air Medical Ltd	Oxford	22. 3.02T
		31-7405429	G-BPPT/N54297				

G-RAAA – G-RZZZ

Regn	Type	C/n	P/I	Date	Owner/operator	Probable Base	CA Expy
G-RACA*	Hunting-Percival P.57 Sea Prince T.1		WM735	2. 9.80	Not known	Long Marston	4.11.80P*
		P57/49			(Open storage 10.99)		
G-RACO	PA-28R-200 Cherokee Arrow II		N1498X	12. 9.91	Graco Group Ltd	Barton	2. 2.01
		28R-7535300					
G-RACY	Cessna 182S Skylane	18280588	N7273Y	19.10.99	N.J.& P.D.Fuller	Cambridge	4.11.02
G-RADA	Soko P-2 Kraguj	024	30140	25. 9.96	Steerworld Ltd	Fairoaks	17. 6.00P
			(Yugoslav AF)				
G-RADI	PA-28-181 Archer II	28-8690002	N2582X	6. 5.98	G.S. & D.V.Foster	Leven, Linley Hill	21. 5.01
			N9608N				
G-RAEM	Rutan LongEz	557 & PFA/74A-10638		15. 3.82	G.F.H.Singleton	(Matlock)	18. 6.93P
	(Lycoming O-235)				t/a Easy Group		
G-RAES	Boeing 777-236ER	27491	(G-ZZZN)	10. 6.97	British Airways plc	Heathrow	9. 6.00T
					(Delftblue Daybreak t/s)		
G-RAFA	Grob G-115A	8081	D-EGVV	2. 3.89	RAF College Flying Club Ltd		
						RAF Cranwell	31. 3.01T
G-RAFB	Grob G-115A	8079	D-EGVV	2. 3.89	RAF College Flying Club Ltd		
						RAF Cranwell	22. 3.01T

Regn	Type		C/n	P/I	Date	Owner/operator		Probable Base	CA Expy
G-RAFC	Robin R.2112 Alpha		192		19. 5.80	J.E.Churchill		Conington	25. 6.01
						t/a RAF Charlie Group			
G-RAFE	Thunder Ax7-77 Bolt HAFB		176		18.12.78	L.P.Hooper		Bristol	29. 8.00A
						t/a Giraffe Balloon Syndicate			
G-RAFF	Gates Learjet 35A		35A-504	N8568B	12. 6.84	Graff Aviation Ltd		Coventry	26. 6.00T
				N10871		(Op Aerocharter (Midlands) Ltd)			
G-RAFG	Slingsby T-67C		2076		2.11.89	Arrow Flying Ltd		(Alton)	30. 3.02T
G-RAFI	Hunting-Percival P.84 Jet Provost T.4		8458M	XP672	18.12.92	R.J.Everett		North Weald	11. 3.00P
			PAC/W/17641			(As "XP672/03")			
G-RAFT	Rutan LongEz	PFA/74A-10734			9. 8.82	B.Wronski		Gloucestershire	19. 7.96P
	(Continental O-240-A)					"A Craft of Graft" (For dismantling 9.99)			
G-RAFW	Mooney M.20E Super 21		805	G-ATHW	14.11.84	Vinola (Knitwear) Manufacturing Co Ltd			
				N58810				Leicester	14. 7.01
G-RAGG	Maule M.5-235C Lunar Rocket		7260C	N5632M	8. 9.95	P.Ragg		(Austria)	12.10.01
G-RAGS	Pietenpol Aircamper	PFA/47-11551			8. 6.94	R.F.Billington		(Kenilworth)	
G-RAID	Douglas AD-4NA Skyraider		7722	F-AZED	7. 6.93	Patina Ltd		Duxford	25. 8.99P
	(SFERMA c/n 42)			TR-K../Fr AF 42/Bu.126922 (Op B J S Grey/The Fighter Collection)					
						(As "126922/AK/402" in VA-176 Sqn USN c/s)			
G-RAIL	Colt 105A HAFB		1434		31. 3.89	Ballooning World Ltd		London NW1	31.10.96T
						"Railfreight"			
G-RAIN	Maule M.5-235C Lunar Rocket		7262C	N5632J	26. 7.79	D.S.McKay & J.A.Rayment			
								Hinton-in-the-Hedges	22. 9.01
G-RAIX	CCF T-6J Texan (Harvard 4)	CCF4...		G-BIWX	16. 2.98	M.R.Paul & P.A.Shaw		Lee-on-Solent	14. 3.00P
	(Possibly c/n CCF4-409 ex 51-17227)			MM53846/RM-22/51-17 (As "KP584")					
G-RAJA	Raj Hamsa X'Air 582 (2)				13. 9.99	S.R.Roberts	Priory Farm, Stowmarket		
			456 & BMAA/HB/118			t/a Priory Flyers			
G-RAJS	General Avia F22-C		023		22. 4.99	R.A.J.Spurrell		(London W6)	28. 6.02
G-RALD	Robinson R-22HP		0218	G-CHIL	25. 1.96	Heli Air Ltd			
				(G-BMXI)/N9074K				Wellesbourne Mountford/Denham	18. 2.02T
G-RAMI	Bell 206B JetRanger III		2955	N1080N	18.10.90	M.D.Thorpe		Coney Park, Leeds	10. 2.00T
						t/a Yorkshire Helicopters			
G-RAMP	Piper J3C-65 Cub		6658	N35941	5. 7.90	J.Whittall			
				NC35941			Brickhouse Farm, Frogland Cross		18. 2.99P
G-RAMS	PA-32R-301 Saratoga SP	32R-8013134		N8271Z	17.10.80	Air Tobago Ltd		Gamston	30. 5.02
G-RAMY	Bell 206B JetRanger		1401	N59554	22. 9.95	A.Drewry		Fenland	15.10.01T
G-RANA	Cameron Cheese 82SS HAFB		1996	I-IORE	4.10.95	Consorzio Per La Tutela del Formaggio			
				G-BSFM				Milan, Italy	21. 5.97A
G-RAND*	Rand Robinson KR-2		RLW-01		19.10.78	R.L.Wharmby		(Milton Keynes)	
						(Cancelled 19.4.99 as WFU)			
G-RANS	Rans S-10 Sakota	PFA/194-11537			17. 8.89	J.D.Weller		Egginton	23. 6.00P
	(Rotax 532)								
G-RANZ	Rans S-10 Sakota	PFA/194-11536			2.11.89	R.J.Humphries		Hannington	12. 5.97P
	(Rotax 532)								
G-RAPA	PBN BN-2T-4R Defender 4000			N360WT	11. 5.82	Britten-Norman Ltd		Bembridge	31. 7.91T
			2115 & 4001	G-RAPA/G-51-2115/G-BJBH (Stored 8.99)					
G-RAPH	Cameron O-77 HAFB		1673		21. 3.88	P.B.D.Bird & M.E.Mason		Bristol	28. 5.00T
						"Walsal Litho"			
G-RAPP	Cameron H-34 HAFB		2380		16. 8.90	Cameron Balloons Ltd		St.Louis, USA	30. 6.00A
G-RARB	Cessna 172N Skyhawk II	172-72334		G-BOII	4. 6.96	Richlyn Aviation Ltd		Biggin Hill	10. 4.00T
				N4702D					
G-RARE	Thunder Ax5-42 SS HAFB		266		20. 2.80	Justerini & Brooks Ltd		London SW1	14. 8.88A
	(J & B Rare Whisky Bottle shape)					"J & B Hamish"			
G-RASC*	Evans VP-2	V2-1178 & PFA/63-10422			14.12.78	E Phillips		(Soothill, Batley)	29. 5.94P
	(Continental C90)					(Crashed Bagby 9.7.95)			
G-RATE	Gulfstream AA-5A Cheetah	AA5A-0781		G-BIFF	11. 6.84	J.Appleton		Blackbushe	13.11.01T
				(G-BIBR)/N26879		t/a Holmes Rentals			
G-RATZ	Europa Avn Europa	PFA/247-12582			16. 6.95	W.Goldsmith		(Boldon Colliery)	23. 8.00P
	(Rotax 912UL)								
G-RAVE	Southdown Raven X		2232/0219	G-MNZV	22.12.98	M.J.Robbins		Tunbridge Wells	15.12.95P
	(Rotax 447)								
G-RAVL	HP.137 Jetstream 200		208	G-AWVK	2.12.86	Cranfield University		Cranfield	26. 2.94A
				N1035S/G-AWVK					
G-RAYA	Denney Kitfox mk.4	PFA/172A-12403			14.12.92	A.K.Ray		(Stone)	
G-RAYE	PA-32-260 Cherokee Six	32-460		G-ATTY	30. 5.96	F.J.Wadia		Edinburgh	8. 8.00
G-RAYS	Zenair CH.250	RED.001 & PFA/24-10460			26.10.78	Acro Engines & Airframes Ltd		Yearby	
	(Lycoming O-235)								
G-RAZA	Eurocopter AS.365N2 Dauphin 2		6476	N585RH	21. 5.99	Banco Real SA			17. 6.00
				G-RAZA/3A-MGS/N373QC				Grand Cayman, Cayman Islands	
				(Original UK registration issued 21. 5.99: sold as N585RH 5. 8.99 & restored 16.12.99)					
G-RBBB	Europa Avn Europa	PFA/247-12664			6. 5.94	T.J.Hartwell	Sackville Lodge, Riseley		7. 5.99P
	(Rotax 912UL)								

Regn	Type	C/n	P/I	Date	Owner/operator	Probable Base	CA Expy
G-RBMV	Cameron O-31 HAFB	4658		27. 7.99	P.D.Griffiths	Romsey	20. 7.00
G-RBOS*	Colt AS-105 Hot-Air Airship	390		9. 2.82	The Science Museum	Wroughton	6. 3.87A
G-RBOW	Thunder Ax7-65 HAFB	1439		24. 4.89	A.C.Hall	Melton Mowbray	22. 8.00A
					"Rain-Beau-Lune"		
G-RCED	Rockwell Commander 114	14241	VR-CED	19. 6.92	Echo Delta Ltd	Guernsey	13. 5.01
			N4917W				
G-RCEJ	BAe 125 Srs.800B	258021	VR-CEJ	15. 6.95	TAG Aviation Charter (UK) Ltd		
			G-GEIL/G-5-15			Farnborough	14. 6.00T
G-RCHA	PA-28-181 Archer IV	2843094	N9269S	30. 7.97	R.Kay	Jersey	6. 8.00T
G-RCMC	Murphy Renegade 912			1. 2.93	R.C.M.Collisson	Turweston	30. 6.00P
	(Rotax 912)	485 & PFA/188-12483					
G-RCMF	Cameron V-77 HAFB	1618		23.11.87	Mouldform Ltd	Loughborough	19. 8.97A
					"Mouldform I/Mayfly"		
G-RCML	Sky 77-24 HAFB	148		9. 3.99	R.C.M.Sarl	Luxembourg	5 .3.00
G-RDBS	Cessna 550 Citation II	550-0094	G-JETA	7. 5.99	Redbus Charter Aviation Ltd	Filton	21. 6.00T
	(Unit No.101)		(N26630)				
G-RDCI	Rockwell Commander 112A	345	G-BFWG	15. 5.85	P.Turner	(Hull)	5. 2.01T
			ZS-JRX/N1345J				
G-RDVE	Airbus A.320-231	163	OY-CND	26. 2.97	Airtours International Airways Ltd		
			F-WWDU			Manchester	2. 3.00T
G-READ	Colt 77A HAFB	1158	EI-BYI	16.11.87	J.Keena	Athlone, Co.Westmeath	2. 5.00A
			G-READ		(Flying as "EI-BYI" 9.98)		
G-REAH	PA-32R-301 Saratoga SP	32R-8413017	G-CELL	15. 8.94	M.Q.Tolbod & S.J.Rogers	Blackbushe	5. 8.00
G-REAP	Pitts S-1S Special	PFA/09-11557		7. 2.90	R.Dixon	Netherthorpe	22. 9.00P
	(Lycoming O-360)				"The Grim Reaper"		
G-REAS	Van's RV-6A	PFA/181-12188		16. 8.94	E.J.D.Proctor	Shobdon	27. 6.00P
	(Lycoming O-320)						
G-REAT	Grumman-American GA-7 Cougar		N29699	6.10.78	Goodtechnique Ltd	Leeds-Bradford	18. 7.00T
		GA7-0033					
G-REBK	Beechcraft B200 Super King Air		D-IHAP	22. 5.97	Gold Air International Ltd	Cambridge	17. 6.01T
		BB-1202	N44VM/N7207M				
G-REBL	Hughes 269B	67-0318	N9493F	25. 7.89	GTS Engineering (Coventry) Ltd	Gamlingay	9.10.95
					(Stored 3.97)		
G-RECK	PA-28-140 Cherokee B	28-25656	G-AXJW	17. 3.88	R.J.Grantham & D.Boatswain		
			N11C		Clutton Hill Farm, High Littleton	29. 7.01
G-REDB	Cessna 310Q	310Q-0811	G-BBIC	17. 6.93	Vectair Aviation 1995	Goodwood	22. 3.01T
			N69600				
G-REDC	Cyclone Pegasus Quantum 15	7572		30. 9.99	Red Communications Ltd	(Huntingdon)	28. 9.00P
G-REDD	Cessna 310R II	310R-1833	G-BMGT	2.10.96	G.Wightman	(Kendal)	17.12.01T
			ZS-KSY/(N2738X)				
G-REDX	Experimental Aviation Berkut			27. 1.95	G.V.Waters	Norwich	23. 6.00P
	(Lycoming 180hp) 002 & PFA/252-12481				(F/f 15.5.99)		
G-REEC	Sequoia F.8L Falco	654	LN-LCA	2. 7.96	J.D.Tseliki		
	(Lycoming IO-320)				Kittyhawk Farm, Deanland, E Sussex	17. 8.00P
G-REEK	Grumman-American AA-5A Cheetah			12. 9.77	J.& A.Pearson	Dundee	10.12.01
		AA5A-0429					
G-REEM	Aerospatiale AS.355F1 Twin Squirrel		G-EMAN	9. 3.98	Heliking Ltd	Redhill	9.10.00T
		5175	G-WEKR/G-CHLA/N818RL/C-FLXH/N818RL/N818R/N5798U				
G-REEN	Cessna 340	340-0063	G-AZYR	2. 2.84	E. & M.Green	Guernsey	5. 9.02
			N5893M				
G-REES	SAN Jodel D.140C Mousquetaire III		F-BMFR	23. 4.80	W.H.Greenwood	Swanborough Farm, Lewes	21.10.99
		156					
G-REFI*	Enstrom 280C-UK Shark	1090	N638H	2. 5.89	Not known	Coventry	15.10.95
					(Destroyed Dublin 22. 9.95; stored for rebuild 1.97)		
G-REID*	Rotorway Scorpion 133	1147	G-BGAW	7.12.81	G.F.Burridge & S.B.Evans	Bedford	18. 3.91P
					(Cancelled by CAA 19.4.99)		
G-RENE	Murphy Renegade 912	PFA/188-12030		6.11.91	P.M.Whitaker	(Ilkley)	27. 7.00P
	(Rotax 912)						
G-RENO	Socata TB-10 Tobago	249		10.12.81	Lamond Ltd	Birmingham	21. 5.01T
G-RENT	Robinson R-22 Beta	0758	N2635M	17. 3.88	Rentatruck (Self Drive) Ltd	Newtownards	12. 6.94T
					(Op Helicopter Training & Hire) (Damaged Newtownards 30.9.92)		
G-REPM	PA-38-112 Tomahawk	38-79A0354	N2528D	8. 1.87	Nultree Ltd (Stored 8.99)	Chilbolton	9.10.95T
G-REST	Beechcraft P35 Bonanza	D-7171	G-ASFJ	14.12.82	C.R.E.S.Taylor	Biggin Hill	8. 9.02
G-RETA	CASA I-131E Jungmann 2000	2197	E3B-305	24. 3.80	N.S.C.& G.English	Dereham	11.11.99P
G-REXS	PA-28-181 Archer II	28-8090102	N8093Y	14. 1.80	M.R.Shelton	Tatenhill	18. 6.01T
					t/a Tatenhill Aviation		
G-REZE	Rutan VariEze	PFA/74-11086		28. 9.89	S.D.Brown & S.P.Evans	Biggin Hill	29. 8.96P
	(Continental O-200-A)				(Destroyed Bembridge 19.11.95)		
G-RFDS	Agusta A109A II	7411	N1YU	24. 5.99	Castle Air Charters Ltd	Trebrown	20. 7.02
			VP-CLA/VR-CLA/G-BOLA/VR-CMP/G-BOLA				
G-RFIL	Thunder Colt 77A HAFB	1496		16. 4.98	G.Davis	(Reading)	1. 4.00T

Regn	Type	C/n	P/I	Date	Owner/operator	Probable Base	CA Expy
G-RFIO	Aeromot AMT-200 Super Ximango	200-048		6. 3.95	G.McLean & R.P.Beck	Rufforth	30. 6.01
G-RFSB	Sportavia Fournier RF5B Sperber	51045	N55HC	2.12.88	S.W.Brown	Sibson	1. 4.01
G-RGEN	Cessna T337D Turbo Super Skymaster	T337-1062	G-EDOT G-BJIY/9Q-CPF/PH-JWL/N86056	24. 5.96	R.J.Willies	Top Farm, Royston	30.11.02
G-RGUS*	Fairchild 24R-46A Argus III (UC-61K-FA)	1145	(PH-) G-RGUS/ZS-UJZ/ZS-BAY/KK527/44-83184 (As "44-83184/7" in USAAC c/s; on rebuild 8.98)	16. 9.86	Fenlands Ltd	Sturgate	15. 5.93
G-RHCB	Schweizer 269C-1	0036	N201WL	20. 3.98	Oxford Aviation Services Ltd	Oxford	
G-RHHT	PA-32RT-300 Lance II	32R-7885190	N36476	3. 7.78	R.W. & M.Struth	Southend	18.12.99T
G-RHYS	Rotorway Exec 90 (RI 162)	5140		8.11.93	A.K.Voase & K.Matthews	(Hornsea)	7.12.00P
G-RIAN	Agusta-Bell 206A JetRanger	8056	G-SOOR G-FMAL/G-RIAN/G-BHSG/PH-FSW	16. 9.87	Thorneygrove Ltd	Newcastle	22.12.02T
G-RIAT	Robinson R-22 Beta-II	2684		27. 5.97	D.K.Griffiths t/a Pinetree Car Centre	Cardiff	2. 6.00T
G-RIBS	Diamond DA.20-A1 Katana	10143	G-BWWM	7. 7.97	J.T.H.McAlpine t/a West London Models	Oxford	16.11.02
G-RIBV	Cessna 560 Citation Ultra	560-0506	N50820	17. 3.99	Rothmans International Tobacco (UK) Ltd	Bournemouth	16. 3.02T
G-RICA	American General AG-5B	10164	N132U	7. 9.99	Plane Talking Ltd	Elstree	5.10.02T
G-RICC	Aerospatiale AS.350B2 Ecureuil	2559	G-BTXA	30.10.91	Specialist Helicopters Ltd	Inverness	8. 2.01T
G-RICE	Robinson R-22 Beta	2509	N93MK	14. 3.97	Warwickshire Flying Training Centre Ltd	Coventry	3. 4.00T
G-RICK	Beechcraft 95-B55 Baron	TC-1472	G-BAAG	23. 5.84	James Jack (Invergordon) Ltd (Damaged Stornoway 8.12.98-& remains Blackbushe 4.99)	Inverness	16. 6.99T
G-RICO	American-General AG-5B Tiger	10162	N130U	14. 5.99	Dynasty Trading Ltd	(London SE10)	31. 5.02T
G-RICS	Europa Avn Europa	PFA/247-12747		19. 3.96	R.G.Allen t/a The Flying Property Doctor	Kemble	22. 8.00P
G-RIDE	Stephens Akro (Lycoming AIO-360)	111	N81AC N55NM	10. 8.78	R.Mitchell t/a Mitchell Aviation (PSA c/s) (Stored 3.95)	RAF Cosford	13. 8.92P
G-RIFB	Hughes 269C	116-0562	N7428F	17. 5.90	J.C.McHugh & Son (Civil Eng) Continentalractors Ltd	Romford	16.10.99
G-RIFN	Mudry CAP.10B	276		6. 6.96	S.A.W.Becker	Goodwood	30. 6.02
G-RIGB	Thunder Ax7-77 HAFB	1201		16. 3.88	Antrum & Andrews Ltd t/a Duck Lane Productions "Rigby"	London W1	15. 2.96A
G-RIGH	PA-32R-301 Saratoga	32R-3246123	N41272	23.12.98	G M R & I H L Graham t/a Rentair	Fowlmere	22.12.01T
G-RIGS	PA-60-601P Aerostar 61P-0621-7963281		N8220J	18. 5.79	G G Caravatti & P G Penati Monza, Italy		2.12.01
G-RILY*	Monnett Sonerai IIL (VW1834)	PFA/15-10353		20.12.78	Not known Hill Farm, Nayland (Stored 4.95: cancelled by CAA 26.3.97)		5.10.89P
G-RIMM	Westland Wasp HAS.Mk.1 (Official records quote "ex NZ3907")	F9605	NZ3908 XT435	11. 3.99	P.A.Shaw & M.P.Grimshaw	RNAS Yeovilton	27. 7.00P
G-RINO	Thunder Ax7-77 HAFB	975		24. 6.87	D.J.Head "Cerous"	Newbury	5. 3.94T
G-RINS	Rans S6-ESD Coyote II (Rotax 582)	PFA/204-13361		15. 3.99	D.Watt Laidthwaite Farm, Cumbria (Damaged landing at Base 28.6.99)		13. 5.00p
G-RINT	CFM Streak Shadow (Rotax 582) K199-SA & PFA/206-12251			7.12.93	D. & J.S.Grint	Shoreham	3.11.00P
G-RIPS	Cameron Action Man/Parachutist 110SS HAFB	4092		29. 4.97	Virgin Airship & Balloon Co Ltd "Action Man"	Telford	24. 6.98A
G-RISE	Cameron V-90 HAFB	2395		21. 9.90	D.L.Smith "Rise N' Shine"	Newbury	21.11.98T
G-RIST	Cessna 310R II	310R-1294	G-DATS (N6128X)	28. 4.81	J.M.Jackson	Bournemouth	22. 6.01
G-RIVR	Thruster T.600N (Rotax 582-UL) (Exhibited on floats at Microlight Trade weekend 5.99 at Popham: flew into PFA Cranfield 1.7.99 fitted with conventional wheeled u/c & then exhibited on full LOTUS floats)	9029-T600N-031		3.12.99	Thruster Air Services Ltd	Wantage	7.12.00P
G-RIVT	Van's RV-6 (Lycoming O-320)	PFA/181-12743		31. 7.95	N.Reddish	Netherthorpe	28. 5.00P
G-RIZE	Cameron O-90 HAFB	3163		13.12.93	S.F.Burden Noordwijk, The Netherlands		23. 5.00A
G-RIZI	Cameron N-90 HAFB	3080		12. 5.93	R.Wiles	Wadhurst	18. 9.95A
G-RIZZ	PA-28-161 Warrior II	28-7816494	D-EMFW N9563N	11. 2.99	Northamptonshire School of Flying Ltd	Sywell	21. 3.02T
G-RJAH	Boeing-Stearman D75N1 (PT-27BW) Kaydet (Continental W670)	75-4041	N75957 RCAF FJ991/42-15852 (As "44" in US Army c/s)	6. 4.90	R.J.Horne	Rendcomb	16. 7.99
G-RJCP	Commander 114B	14606	N6001M	3. 7.96	W.P.J.Davison	(Solihull)	30. 8.02
G-RJGR	Boeing 757-225	22197	N701MG N507EA	22.11.94	Airtours International Airways Ltd	Manchester	1. 2.01T
G-RJMS	PA-28R-201 Arrow III	28R-7837059	N6223H	19. 1.88	M.G.Hill	Crosland Moor	20. 4.00
G-RJWW	Maule M.5-235C Lunar Rocket	7250C	G-BRWG N5632H	6.10.87	PAW Flying Services Ltd	Sandtoft	25. 9.00T

Regn	Type	C/n	P/I	Date	Owner/operator	Probable Base	CA Expy
G-RJXA	Embraer EMB-145EP	145-136		18. 6.99	British Midland Airways Ltd		
						East Midlands	17. 6.02T
G-RJXB	Embraer EMB-145EP	145-142		23. 6.99	British Midland Airways Ltd		
						East Midlands	27. 6.02T
G-RJXC	Embraer EMB-145EP	145-153	PT-SEE	15. 7.99	British Midland Airways Ltd		
						East Midlands	14. 7.02T
G-RJXD	Embraer EMB-145EP	145-207		4. 2.00	British Midland Airways Ltd		
						East Midlands	
G-RKET	Taylor JT.2 Titch	PFA/3223	G-BIBK	25. 8.99	P.A.Dunley	RAF Valley	
G-RLFI	Reims Cessna FA.152 Aerobat	0340	G-DFTS	17. 1.90	Tayside Aviation Ltd	Aberdeen/Dundee	18.11.01T
G-RLMC	Cessna 421C Golden Eagle II	421C-0118	PH-SBI D-IMAZ/I-CCNN/N3849C	9. 3.88	R.D.Lygo	Fairoaks	17. 1.00
G-RMAC	Europa Avn Europa	PFA/247-12717		3. 7.97	P.J.Lawless	(Bath)	
G-RMAN	Aero Designs Pulsar	PFA/202-13071		6. 6.97	M.B.Redman	(Wilton, Salisbury)	
G-RMAX	Cameron C-80 HAFB	4705		6.12.99	M Quinn & D Curtain	Dublin, Ireland	16.11.00A
G-RMCT	Short SD.3-60 Var.100	SH.3656	EI-BPD G-BLPU/G-14-3656	27.11.92	Gill Aviation Ltd	Newcastle	21.12.99T
G-RMIT	Van's RV-4 (Tri-cycle u/c)	PFA/181-12207		4. 9.96	J.P.Kloos Truleigh Manor Farm, Edburton		9. 5.00P
G-RMUG	Cameron Nescafe Mug 90SS HAFB	3450		3. 5.95	Nestle UK Ltd "Nescafe"	Croydon	8. 7.00A
G-RNAS*	DH.104 Sea Devon C.20 (Dove 6)	04473	XK896	16.11.82	Not known	Filton	3. 7.84
					(As "XK896" in RN c/s: with Fire Station 10.98)		
G-RNBW	Bell 206B Jet Ranger II	2270	F-GQFH F-WQFH/HB-XUF/F-GFBP/N900JJ/N16UC	9. 1.98	Rainbow Helicopters Ltd	Whimple	22. 2.01T
G-RNEE	Cameron R-420 HAFB	4426		15. 9.98	Bondbaste Ltd	Bristol	
G-RNGO	Robinson R-22 Beta	3035		19. 1.00	MC Air Ltd	(Birmingham)	
G-RNIE	Cameron Ball 70SS HAFB	2333		3. 8.90	Virgin Airship & Balloon Co Ltd Telford "Schwarzenegger"		16. 5.97A
G-RNLD	Agusta A.109C	7633	I-ANAG	21. 6.96	Irvine Aviation Ltd	Elstree	25. 7.02
G-RNLI	VS.236 Walrus 1	S2/5591	W2718	13.12.90	R.E.Melton	Great Yarmouth	
					(As "W2718/AA5Y" in 751 Sqn RN c/s; on rebuild 6.95)		
G-RNRM	Cessna A185F Skywagon	A185-02541	N1826R	20. 1.87	A T Usher	Dunkeswell	2. 4.99
					t/a Royal Navy & Royal Marines Sport Parachute Association		
G-ROAM	Schempp-Hirth Nimbus 4DM	22/32		24. 9.96	B.A.Eastwell	Lasham	29. 4.00
G-ROAR	Cessna 401	401-0166	G-BZFL G-AWSF/N4066Q	8. 3.82	Special Scope Ltd	Woodford	16. 9.02
G-ROBD	Europa Avn Europa	PFA/247-12671		23. 2.94	R.D.Davies	(Cowbridge)	
G-ROBN	Robin R.1180T Aiglon	220		16. 8.78	Bustard Flying Group Ltd	Boscombe Down	13. 8.00T
G-ROBT	Hawker Hurricane I (Built Gloster)	-	P2902	19. 9.94	R.A.Roberts	Moat Farm, Milden	
					(On rebuild by Hawker Restorations Ltd from remains salvaged in 1988 from wreck site at Dunkirk Beach; to be "P2902/DX-X")		
G-ROBY	Colt 17A Cloudhopper HAFB	483		7. 2.83	Virgin Airship & Balloon Co Ltd Telford " Cloudhopper"		26. 9.92A
G-ROCH	Cessna T303 Crusader	T303-00129	N4962C	29. 3.90	R.S.Bentley	Cambridge	7. 6.02
G-ROCK	Thunder Ax7-77 HAFB	781		25. 2.86	M.A.Green "Rocky"	Rednal	23. 4.00A
G-ROCR	Schweizer Hughes 269C	S.1336	N219MS	14. 6.90	Oxford Aviation Services Ltd	Oxford	28. 1.00T
G-RODD	Cessna 310R II	310R-0544	G-TEDD G-MADI/N87396/G-MADI/N87396	2.10.89	RJ Herbert Engineering Ltd	Marshland, Wisbech	1. 8.02
G-RODG	Avtech Jabiru XL	PFA/274A-13379		14. 4.99	I.M.Donnelly	(Aboyne)	19. 5.00P
G-RODI	Isaacs Fury (Lycoming O-290)	PFA/11-10130		22.12.78	M.R.Baker	Westfield Farm, Hailsham, E.Sussex	17. 8.95P
					(As "K3731" in 43 Sqdn c/s; stored 3.97)		
G-ROGG	Robinson R-22 Beta	1487		31. 8.90	Burman Aviation Ltd	Cranfield	9. 9.99T
G-ROGY	Cameron Concept 60 HAFB	3055		11. 5.93	A.A.Laing "Cameron Voyager"	Aberdeen	3. 5.97A
G-ROIN	Aerospatiale AS.350BA Ecureuil	2344	F-GMAR N516AJ	5. 6.98	C.C.Blake	Redhill	23. 6.01T
G-ROLA	PA-34-200T Seneca II	34-7670066	N4537X G-ROLA/N4537X	4.12.85	Deer Hill Aviation Ltd & Goss Challenges Ltd 	Exeter	23.11.01T
G-ROLF	PA-32R-301 Saratoga SP	32R-8113018	N83052	7. 1.81	P.F.Larkins	High Cross, Ware	29. 3.02
G-ROLL	Aerotek Pitts S-2A Special (Lycoming AEIO-360)	2175	N31444	20. 2.80	N.Lamb t/a Aerial & Aerobatic Services (Marlboro' titles)	Booker	13. 8.01A
G-ROLO	Robinson R-22 Beta	1226		24. 1.90	Plane Talking Ltd (Op Cabair Helicopters)	Elstree	22.12.01T
G-ROMA*	Hughes 369HS	13-0442S	G-ROPI G-ROMA/G-ONPP/OY-HCP/D-HGER	16. 1.84	Helicopters (Northern) Ltd	Sywell	27.10.95T
					(Damaged early 1993; to March Helicopters for spares; pod in store 6.96: cancelled by CAA 16.12.99)		
G-ROME	III Sky Arrow 650TCC	011		26. 5.99	Sky Arrow (Kits) UK Ltd	Thruxton	16. 6.02T
G-ROMS	Lindstrand LBL-105G HAFB	401		13. 9.96	International Balloons Ltd	Oswestry	24. 8.99A
G-ROMW	Cyclone AX2000	7486		4. 2.99	Financial Planning (Wells) Ltd	Wells	3. 2.00P
G-RONA	Europa Avn Europa (Rotax 912UL)	PFA/247-12588		17. 1.95	C.M.Noakes "Mr Jake"	Tatenhill	17. 6.00P

Regn	Type	C/n	P/I	Date	Owner/operator	Probable Base	CA Expy
G-RONG	PA-28R-200 Cherokee Arrow II 28R-7335148		N16451	14. 6.90	E.Tang	Elstree	22. 9.02
G-RONI	Cameron V-77 HAFB	2349		27. 7.90	R.E.Simpson t/a Elbow Beach Balloon Club "Roni"	Great Missenden	15. 5.99A
G-RONN	Robinson R-44 Astro	0267	N770SC G-RONN/D-HIRR	8. 1.98	R Hallam & S E Watts	Leicester	15. 2.01
G-RONS	Robin DR.400/180 Regent	2088		17. 7.91	R. & K.Baker	Newcastle	10. 8.00
G-RONW	Clutton FRED Srs.II PFA/29-10121 (VW1834)			18.12.78	K.Atkinson	Haverfordwest	29. 3.00P
G-ROOK	Reims Cessna F.172P Skyhawk II	2081	PH-TGY G-ROOK	12. 1.81	Rolim Ltd	Aberdeen	7.11.02
G-ROOV	Europa Avn Europa XS PFA/247-13204 (Correct c/n is PFA/247-13214)			16. 7.98	D.K.Richardson (Cf/f 17.11.99)	(Malvern)	
G-ROPA*	Europa Avn Europa PFA/247-12396			27.11.92	R.G.Gray (Cancelled by CAA 9.4.99)	(London N1)	
G-RORI	Folland Gnat T.1	FL.549	8621M XR538	18.10.93	D.S.Milne	(Banchory)	10.12.99P
G-RORO	Cessna 337B Super Skymaster	337-0554	G-AVIX N5454S	8. 1.80	H.D.Hezlett (Damaged landing Castle Rock, N Ireland 25.6.99)	Ronaldsway	15. 7.00
G-RORY	Focke-Wulf Piaggio FWP.149D (Piaggio c/n 338)	014	G-TOWN D-EFFY/90+06/BB+394	2. 8.88	Bushfire Investments Ltd	Booker	6.10.02
G-ROSE	Evans VP-1	PFA/7031		22. 1.79	A.P.M.Long	(Leighton Buzzard)	
G-ROSI	Thunder Ax7-77 HAFB	1284		29. 6.88	J.E.Rose "Rosi"	Abingdon	21. 9.96A
G-ROSS	Practavia Pilot Sprite 132 & PFA/05-10404			28. 2.80	A.D.Janaway	(Wellington)	
G-ROTI	Luscombe 8A (Continental A65)	2117	N45590 NC45590	18. 4.89	R.Ludgate & A.L.Chapman Old Hay,Paddock Wood		9.10.97P
G-ROTR	Brantly B.2B	403	N2192U	9.12.91	P.G.R.Brown	(Crediton)	17.11.02
G-ROTS	CFM Streak Shadow K.120-SA & PFA/161A-11603			21.12.89	P.White	Caernarfon	9. 6.00P
G-ROUP	Reims Cessna F.172M Skyhawk II	1451	G-BDPH	23. 5.84	Stapleford Flying Club Ltd	Blackbushe	23. 4.00T
G-ROUS	PA-34-200T Seneca II	34-7870187	N9412C	26. 4.78	Oxford Aviation Services Ltd	Oxford	8.12.99T
G-ROUT	Robinson R-22 Beta	1241	N8068U	23. 1.90	Ramsgill Aviation Ltd	(Bingley)	25. 9.00T
G-ROVE	PA-18-135 Super Cub 18-3846 (L-21B-PI) (Frame No.18-3853)		PH-VLO (PH-DKF)/R-156/54-2446	6. 5.82	S.J.Gaveston	(Pembury)	21. 7.98T
G-ROVY	Robinson R22 Beta-II	2957		9. 7.99	R.Rice	(Warwick)	15. 7.02T
G-ROWE	Reims Cessna F.182P Skylane II	0007	OO-CNG	18.12.95	D.Rowe	Liverpool	15. 2.02
G-ROWI	Europa Europa XS PFA/247-13482			16. 6.99	R.M.Carson	(Cheltenham)	
G-ROWL	Grumman-American AA-5B Tiger AA5B-0595		(N28410)	26.10.77	Airhouse Corporation Ltd	Elstree	9. 5.01T
G-ROWN	Beechcraft 200 Super King Air BB-684		G-BHLC N27L/N8511L/G-BHLC	13.10.87	Valentia Air Ltd.	Oxford	27. 3.01T
G-ROWS	PA-28-151 Warrior	28-7715296	N8949F	15. 9.78	Mustarrow Ltd	Manchester	2. 3.00
G-ROZI	Robinson R-44 Astro	0252		26. 3.96	Vitapage Ltd	(Tring)	29. 4.02T
G-ROZY	Cameron R-36 Gas Free Balloon	1141		20. 5.85	Jacques W.Soukup Enterprises Ltd Beaulieu Court, Wilts		N/E(A)
G-RPEZ	Rutan LongEz	PFA/74A-10746		3. 4.84	B.A.Fairston & D.Richardson (Stored uncomplete 1.94)	Booker	
G-RRCU	CEA DR.221B Dauphin	129	F-BRCU	9.12.99	Merlin Flying Club Ltd	Hucknall	AC
G-RRGN	VS.390 Spitfire PR.XIX	6S/594677	G-MXIX PS853	23.12.96	Rolls-Royce plc (As "PS853/C" in 2nd TAF/PRU c/s)	Filton	28. 8.99P
G-RRSG(2)*	Thunder Ax7-77 HAFB	874		24. 9.86	M.T.Stevens "Silver Ghost" (Cancelled as destroyed 18.11.99)	Solihull	1. 8.97A
G-RSCJ	Cessna 525 Citation Jet	525-0298		15. 1.99	SMD Investments Ltd	Jersey	15. 2.00T
G-RSFT	PA-28-161 Warrior II	28-8616038	G-WARI N9276Y	15.12.95	SFT Europe Ltd	Bournemouth	22. 2.01T
G-RSKR	PA-28-161 Warrior II	28-7916181	G-BOJY N3030G	27. 4.95	Southern Air Ltd, P.M.Forte, R.Sherwin-Smith, G R.Stammers & R.W.Broad	Shoreham	25. 5.00T
G-RSSF	Denney Kitfox mk.2 PFA/172-12125 (Rotax 582)			9.10.92	R.W.Somerville	Comber, NI	15. 5.97P
G-RSVP	Robinson R-22 Beta-II	2788		5. 2.98	Pearce Enterprise Ltd	(Tonbridge)	8. 3.01T
G-RSWO	Cessna 172R Skyhawk II	172-80206	N9401F	25. 2.98	New Century Services Ltd t/a Printcentre	(Sunderland)	2. 3.01T
G-RSWW	Robinson R-22 Beta	1775	N40815	16. 5.91	R.S.Weston-Woods Brands Hatch, Dartford t/a Woodstock Enterprises		21. 5.00T
G-RTBI	Thunder Ax6-56 HAFB	2584		19. 4.94	P.J.Waller	Norwich	25. 5.95A
G-RTWI	Cameron R-550 HAFB	4384		3. 6.98	Spirit of Peace Ltd	(Chippenham)	
G-RTWW	Robinson R-44 Astro	0438		20. 3.98	R.Woods t/a Rotorvation	(Longfield)	30. 4.01T
G-RUBB	Gulfstream AA-5B Tiger AA5B-0928		(G-BKVI) OO-NAS/(OO-HRC)	20. 9.83	D.E.Gee	Blackbushe	23.11.01

Regn	Type	C/n	P/I	Date	Owner/operator	Probable Base	CA Expy
G-RUBI	Thunder Ax7-77 HAFB	1051		27. 2.87	G.Warren	Norwich	20.11.93A
					t/a Warren & Johnson "Rubicon Computer Systems"		
G-RUBY	PA-28RT-201T Turbo Arrow IV		G-BROU	5. 1.90	R.Harman	Tatenhill	16. 6.02
		28R-8331037	N4306K		t/a Arrow Aircraft Group		
G-RUDD	Cameron V-65 HAFB	844		19. 5.82	N.A.Apsey	High Wycombe	20. 5.00A
					"Smilie" (Kodak titles)		
G-RUDI*	QAC Quickie Q.2	PFA/94A-11209		3. 9.91	R.Brandenberger	(Wilmslow)	
	(Revmaster 2100D)				(Cancelled by CAA 8.4.99)		
G-RUFF	Mainair Blade 912	1203-0799-7-W1006		18. 6.99	C.G.P.Holden	(Chesterfield)	27 .7.00P
G-RUFS	Avtech Jabiru UL	PFA/274A-13359		19.11.99	J.W.Holland	(Swindon)	
G-RUGS	Campbell Cricket Mk.4	PFA G/103-1307		11. 2.99	J.L.G.Mclane	(York)	
G-RUIA	Reims Cessna F.172N Skyhawk II	1856	PH-AXA(3)	4.10.79	Knockin Flying Club Ltd		
						Knockin, Shropshire	13. 7.01
G-RUMM	Grumman F8F-2P Bearcat	D.1088	NX700HL	20. 3.98	Patina Ltd	Duxford	1. 7.00P
			NX700H/N1YY/N4995V/Bu.121714 (Op The Fighter Collection)				
			(As "21714/201B" in USN c/s)				
G-RUMN	Grumman-American AA-1A Trainer		N87599	30. 5.80	D.W.Reast	Nottingham	17. 3.00
		AA1A-0086	D-EAFB/(N9386L)				
G-RUMT	Grumman F7F-3P Tigercat	C.167	N7235C	6. 4.98	Patina Ltd (Op The Fighter Collection)		
			BuA.80425		(As "80425 4-WT" in US Marines c/s) Duxford		5. 7.00P
G-RUMW	Grumman FM-2 Wildcat	5765	N4845V	15. 4.98	Patina Ltd (Op The Fighter Collection)		
			BuA.86711		(As "F" in FAA c/s)	Duxford	28. 6.00P
G-RUNG	SAAB-Scania SF.340A	340A-086	F-GGBV	3. 6.97	Aurigny Air Services Ltd	Guernsey	5. 6.00T
			SE-E86				
G-RUNT	Cassutt Racer IIIM			12. 4.83	Coulson Flying Services Ltd		
	(Lycoming O-235) 161149 & PFA/34-10860					(Croft, Skegness)	24. 8.96P
G-RUSA	Cyclone Pegasus Quantum 15	7517		7. 4.99	J.Rankin	(Edinburgh)	
G-RUSO	Robinson R-22 Beta	1387		25. 5.90	R.M.Barnes-Gorell	Thruxton	6. 4.02T
G-RUSS*	Cessna 172N Skyhawk 100	172-68563	N733UR	30. 6.80	Not known (Wings stored 1.99)	Southend	19. 9.86T
G-RVAN	Van's RV-6	PFA/181-12657		25. 4.97	D.Broom	Panshanger	22. 4.00P
	(Lycoming IO-320) (Tail-wheel u/c)						
G-RVAW	Van's RV-6	PFA/181-13234		24.11.97	A.A.Wordsworth	(Sutton-in-Ashfield)	
G-RVBA	Van's RV-8A	PFA/303-13309		26.10.99	S.Hawksworth	(Nuneaton)	
G-RVCL	Van's RV-6	PFA/181A-13439		18. 2.99	C.T.Lamb	(Stamford)	
G-RVDJ	Van's RV-6	PFA/181-12938		8. 2.99	J.D.Jewitt	(Selby)	1. 9.00P
G-RVEE	Van's RV-6	PFA/181-12262		16. 2.93	J.C.A.Wheeler	Perth	22.12.00P
	(Tri-cycle u/c)						
G-RVET	Van's RV-6	PFA/181-12852		9. 3.98	D.R.Coleman	Biggin Hill	4.10.00P
					(F/f 28.8.99)		
G-RVGA	Van's RV-6A	PFA/181-13079		11. 5.98	D.P.Dawson	Rush Green	20. 8.00P
G-RVHT	Cessna 550 Citation II	550-0441	N221GA	17.11.99	Ravenheat Manufacturing Ltd		
			HB-VKS/VR-CCE/N56PC/N50LM/N1220J			Leeds-Bradford	22.11.00T
G-RVIA	Van's RV-6A	PFA/181-12289		13. 8.97	A.J.Rose	Perth	26.10.00P
G-RVIB	Van's RV-6	PFA/181-13220		22. 6.99	I.M.Belmore	(Horsham)	
G-RVIN	Van's RV-6	PFA/181-13236		28.11.97	N.Reddish	Netherthorpe	9. 6.00P
G-RVIT	Van's RV-6	PFA/181-12422		1. 5.95	P.J.Shotbolt	Fenland	29. 7.00P
	(Lycoming O-360)						
G-RVIV	Van's RV-4	PFA/181-12366		31.12.97	G.S.Scott Truleigh Manor Farm, Edburton		9 .5.00P
					(F/f 16.3.99)		
G-RVMJ	Van's RV-4	PFA/181-13433		16. 2.99	M.J.de Ruiter	(Craigavon, NI)	
G-RVMZ	Van's RV-8	PFA/303-13395		12.11.99	M.W.Zipfell	(Bury St.Edmunds)	
G-RVRA	PA-28-140 Cherokee Cruiser		G-OWVA	14. 1.97	Cheshire Flying Services Ltd	Liverpool	12. 3.00T
		28-7625038	N4459X		t/a Ravenair		
G-RVRB	PA-34-200T Seneca II	34-7970440	G-BTAJ	24. 2.97	Cheshire Flying Services Ltd	Manchester	3. 6.01T
			N22MJ/N45113		t/a Ravenair		
G-RVRC	PA-23-250 Aztec E	27-7405336	G-BNPD	14.10.97	Cheshire Flying Services Ltd	Manchester	22.12.00T
			N101VH/N40591		t/a Ravenair		
G-RVRD	PA-23-250 Aztec E	27-4634	G-BRAV	16. 3.98	Cheshire Flying Services Ltd	Manchester	9.11.02T
			G-BBCM/N14021		t/a Ravenair		
G-RVRF	PA-38-112 Tomahawk	38-78A0714	G-BGEL	21.11.97	Cheshire Flying Services Ltd	Liverpool	7. 5.00T
					t/a Ravenair		
G-RVRG	PA-38-112 Tomahawk	38-79A1092	G-BHAF	3. 8.98	Cheshire Flying Services Ltd	Manchester	4. 7.02T
					t/a Ravenair		
G-RVRV	Van's RV-4	PFA/181-13024		29. 9.98	P Jenkins	(Nairn)	
G-RVSA	Van's RV-6A	PFA/181-12574		19. 5.99	W.H.Knott	(Inverness)	
G-RVSX	Van's RV-6	PFA/181-13090		18. 9.97	R.L. & V.A.West	(Worthing)	
G-RVVI	Van's RV-6	PFA/181-12418		26. 1.93	J.E.Alsford & J.N.Parr	Sibson	
G-RWHC	Cameron A-180 HAFB	2700		16. 4.92	J.J.Rudoni & A.C.K.Rawson	Stafford	13. 4.00T
					t/a Wickers World Hot Air Balloon Co		
G-RWIN	Rearwin 175 Skyranger	1522	N32391	12. 9.90	G.Kay	Yew Tree Farm, Lymm Dam	15. 6.98P
	(Continental A75)		NC32391				

Regn	Type	C/n	P/I	Date	Owner/operator	Probable Base	CA Expy
G-RWSS	Denney Kitfox mk.2　PFA/172-12008 (Rotax 582)			16. 4.91	R.W.Somerville	Comber, Newtownards	14. 6.93P
G-RWWW	Westland WS-55 Whirlwind HCC.12	8727M WA/418	XR486	21. 6.90	Whirlwind Helicopters Ltd　Redhill (As "XR486" in Queens Flight c/s: stored 9.97)		25. 8.96P
G-RXUK	Lindstrand LBL-105A HAFB	232		29. 3.95	P.A.Hames "Rank Xerox"	Reading	3. 3.00A
G-RYAL	Avtech Jabiru UL　PFA/274A-13365			6. 7.99	A.C.Ryall	(Cardiff)	

G-SAAA - G-SZZZ

Regn	Type	C/n	P/I	Date	Owner/operator	Probable Base	CA Expy
G-SAAB	Rockwell Commander 112TC	13002	G-BEFS N1502J	5.12.79	C.L.Walton	(Reading)	28. 6.00
G-SAAM	Cessna T182R Turbo Skylane II	182-68200	G-TAGL G-SAAM/N2399E	23. 5.84	H.C.Danby & M.D.Harvey	Earls Colne	15.11.01
G-SABA	PA-28R-201T Turbo Arrow III	28R-7703268	G-BFEN N38745	22. 8.79	R.J.Howard	Sherburn-in-Elmet	21. 4.01
G-SABR	North American F-86A-5NA Sabre (Regd with c/n 151-083)	151-43547	N178 N68388/48-178	6.11.91	Golden Apple Operations Ltd　Duxford (Op by The Old Flying Machine Co) (As "8178/FU-178" in 4th Fighter Wing USAF c/s)		10. 6.99P
G-SACB	Reims Cessna F.152 II	1501	G-BFRB	7. 3.84	Sky Pro Ltd	Barton	16. 2.00T
G-SACD	Reims Cessna F.172H	0385	G-AVCD	13. 6.83	Northbrook College of Design & Technology (Op Sky Leisure Aviation)　Shoreham		27. 7.00T
G-SACF*	Cessna 152 II	152-83175	G-BHSZ N47125	21. 3.85	T M & A L Jones (Derby A/C)　Egginton (Damaged Egginton 21.3.97 - fuselage noted 8.99)		8. 6.95T
G-SACH	Stoddard-Hamilton Glastar	PFA/295-13088		27. 8.99	R.S.Holt	(Evesham)	
G-SACI	PA-28-161 Warrior II	28-8216123	N81535	26. 7.89	PJC (Leasing) Ltd	Stapleford	28. 4.02T
G-SACK	Robin R.2160	316		2. 5.97	Sherburn Aero Club Ltd	Sherburn-in-Elmet	14. 5.00T
G-SACO	PA-28-161 Warrior II	28-8416085	N4358Z	1. 6.89	D.C. & M.Brooks　Oxford t/a The Barn Gallery		23. 7.01
G-SACR	PA-28-161 Cadet	2841046	N91618	6. 2.89	Sherburn Aero Club Ltd	Sherburn-in-Elmet	19. 2.01T
G-SACS	PA-28-161 Cadet	2841047	N91619	6. 2.89	Sherburn Aero Club Ltd	Sherburn-in-Elmet	19. 2.01T
G-SACT	PA-28-161 Cadet	2841048	N9162D	6. 2.89	Sherburn Aero Club Ltd	Sherburn-in-Elmet	19. 2.01T
G-SACU	PA-28-161 Cadet	2841049	N9162X	6. 2.89	Sherburn Aero Club Ltd	Sherburn-in-Elmet	19. 2.98T
			(Damaged landing Sherburn-in-Elmet 29.6.96: wrecked fuselage only stored 9.99)				
G-SACZ	PA-28-161 Warrior II	28-7916258	N2098N	26. 7.89	Lima Delta Aviation Ltd	Shoreham	15. 4.02
G-SADE	Reims Cessna F.150L	0752	G-AZJW	28. 5.91	N.E.Sams　Cranfield (Op Billins Air Services)		21. 9.97T
G-SAEW	Aerospatiale AS.355F2 Twin Squirrel	5435	N244BB N244BH	20.12.96	Veritair Ltd　Cardiff Heliport (Op South & East Wales ASU)		30. 1.00T
G-SAFE	Cameron N-77 HAFB	511		14. 2.79	P.J.Waller "The High Flyer"	Norwich	21. 4.91A
G-SAFR	Saab 91D Safir	91-382	PH-RLR	10.10.95	B.Johansson	Bruntingthorpe	AC
G-SAGA	Grob G-109B	6364	OE-9254	28. 6.90	G-GROB Ltd	Booker	16. 7.02
G-SAGE	Luscombe 8A Silvaire (Continental A65)	2581	G-AKTL N71154/NC71154	15. 8.90	R.J.P.Herivel	Alderney	9.12.00P
G-SAHI	FLS Sprint 160	001		21.10.80	Sunhawk Ltd	North Weald	30. 4.94P
	(Lycoming O-235) (Design originally known as Trago Mills SAH-1)						
G-SAIR	Cessna 421C Golden Eagle III	421C-0471	G-OBCA N6812C	1. 4.86	R G Wharton	(Inverurie)	21. 4.00
G-SAIX	Cameron N-77 HAFB	626	N386CB	14. 1.99	C.Walther, B.Sevenich, B. & S.Harren　Aachen, Germany		21. 2.00A
G-SALA	PA-32-300 Six	32-7940106	(G-BHEJ) N2184Z	17.10.79	Stonebold Ltd	Elstree	16. 3.01
G-SALL	Reims Cessna F.150L	0682	PH-LTY D-ECPH	19. 1.79	D.& P.A.Hailey	Thruxton	7. 8.00T
G-SAMG	Grob G-109B	6278		16. 5.84	T.Holloway　RAF Bicester t/a RAFGSA		20. 4.02
G-SAMI	Cameron N-90 Sainsbury Strawberry SS HAFB	3907	G-BWSE	21. 8.96	Flying Pictures Ltd	Fairoaks	30.11.99A
G-SAMM	Cessna 340A II (RAM-conversion)	340A-0742	N37TJ N2671A	7. 3.88	M.R.Cross	Exeter	24. 6.00
G-SAMY	Europa Avn Europa　PFA/247-12901			17. 8.95	K.R.Tallent	(Chertsey)	
G-SAMZ	Cessna 150D	150-60536	G-ASSO N4536U	19. 4.84	N.E.Sams	Cranfield	9. 2.01T
G-SAND	Schweizer Hughes 269C (300C)	S.1399		17. 8.89	Aerocroft Ltd	Oxford	5.11.01T
G-SANS	Robinson R-22 Beta	2012	G-BUHX	31.10.97	J.E. & M.J.Morris　Cheltenham t/a The Type Marketing Co		6. 7.01T
G-SARA	PA-28-181 Archer II	28-7990039	N21270	6. 4.81	R.P.Lewis　Shoreham (Op Airbase Flying Club)		16. 4.01T
G-SARH	PA-28-161 Warrior II	28-8216173	N8232Q	18. 2.91	Sussex Flying Club Ltd	Shoreham	6. 2.01T
G-SARK	BAC.167 Strikemaster 84	EEP/JP/1931	N2146S	13. 1.95	Sark Intl Airways Ltd	Biggin Hill	AC
			Sing.AF 311/G-27-140 (A.Gjertsen Classic Jets Aircraft) (Noted 6.99)				

Regn	Type	C/n	P/I	Date	Owner/operator	Probable Base	CA Expy
G-SARO	Saro Skeeter AOP.12	S2/5097	XL812	17. 7.78	Major F.F.Chamberlain (As "XL812")	Old Buckenham	18. 4.00P
G-SASK	PA-31P Pressurised Navajo	31P-39	G-BFAM SE-GLV/OH-PNF	30.10.97	Middle East Business Club Ltd (Guernsey)		30. 8.91T
G-SATL	Cameron Sphere 105SS HAFB	2696		5.12.91	Ballonverbung Hamburg GmbH Kiel, Germany		29. 4.97A
G-SAUF	Colt 90A HAFB (New envelope c/n 2492 1990/1)	1497		25. 5.89	K.H.Medau	Baden, Germany	8. 7.99A
G-SAWI	Piper PA-32RT-300T Turbo Lance	32R-7887069	OY-CJJ N36719	23. 6.99	S.A.& K.J.Williams	(Droitwich)	6 .7.02
G-SAXO	Cameron N-105 HAFB	3864		1. 4.96	Flying Pictures Ltd (Citroen Saxo titles)	Fairoaks	25. 5.00A
G-SBAE	Reims Cessna F.172P Skyhawk	2200	D-EOCD(3)	3. 6.98	British Aerospace (Operations) Ltd	Blackpool	16. 7.01T
G-SBAS	Beechcraft B200 Super King Air	BB-1007	SE-IVZ N777GA/G-BJJV	16.11.90	Gama Aviation Ltd	Fairoaks	20.12.00T
G-SBLT	Steen Skybolt	MH-01		14. 4.92	S.D.Arnold t/a Skybolt Group	Coventry	
G-SBMO	Robin R.2160I	116	EI-BMO SE-GSZ	12. 2.99	D.Henderson, U.Simpson & M.Mannion	Weston	26. 4.02T
G-SBUS	PADC BN-2A-26 Islander	3013	G-BMMH RP-C578	31.10.86	Isles of Scilly Skybus Ltd	St.Just	17. 4.00T
G-SBUT	Robinson R-22 Beta-II	2739	G-BXMT	18. 5.98	Princepro Ltd	(Alfreton)	6.10.00T
G-SCAH	Cameron V-77 HAFB	788		18. 1.82	D.P.Busby "Orpheus" (Balloon Preservation Group 7.98)	Lancing	24. 7.87A
G-SCAN	Vinten Wallis WA-116 Srs.100 (Rotax 532)	001		5. 7.82	K.H.Wallis (Stored 5.99)	Reymerston Hall	10. 7.91P
G-SCAT	Reims Cessna F.150F (Tail-wheel conversion) (Wichita c/n 63455) (G-ATMN)	0054	G-ATRN	15. 9.86	G.D.Cooper	Biggin Hill	26. 3.02T
G-SCBI	Socata TB-20 Trinidad	1908	F-OIGV	10. 8.99	S.C.Brown t/a Ace Services	Enstone	17. 8.02T
G-SCFO	Cameron O-77 HAFB	1131		3. 5.85	M.K.Grigson "Southern Counties" (Balloon Preservation Group 7.98)	Lancing	24. 5.95A
G-SCLX	FLS Aerospace Sprint 160	002	G-PLYM	14. 7.94	Sunhawk Ltd	North Weald	3. 7.00T
G-SCOW	Aerospatiale AS.355F2 Twin Squirrel	5346	ZS-HSW G-POON/G-MCAL	19. 5.99	B.K.Scowcroft	(Windermere)	14 .9.02T
G-SCOX	Enstrom F-28F	771	N330SA G-BXXW/JA7823	3. 9.98	S.Cox	(Barnsley)	14. 9.01T
G-SCPL	PA-28-140 Cherokee Cruiser	28-7725160	G-BPVL N1785H	4. 5.89	Aeroshow Ltd	Gloucestershire	5. 8.01T
G-SCRU	Cameron A-250 HAFB	3935	G-BWWO	30. 9.96	Societe Bombard SARL	Meursanges, France	3.10.99A
G-SCTA	Westland Scout AH.1	F.9701	XV126	18.12.95	B.H.& E.F.Austen t/a Austen Associates (As "XV126/X" in AAC c/s)	Oaksey Park	24. 6.00P
G-SCTT*	HPR.7 Dart Herald 210	173	F-BLOY F-OCLY/HB-AAK/G-ASPJ (Stored 8.97)	30. 8.88	Channel Express Group plc	Bournemouth	27. 7.99T
G-SCUB	PA-18-135 Super Cub (L-21B-PI) (Frame No.18-3849)	18-3847	PH-GAX R.Neth AF R-157/54-2447	13.12.78	N.D. & Mrs.C.L.Needham t/a N.D.Needham (Farms) Old Manor Farm, Anwick (As "54-2447" in US Army c/s)		15. 8.00
G-SCUD	Montgomerie-Bensen B.8MR	PFA G/101-1294		18. 8.97	D.Taylor	Belper	
G-SCUL	Rutan Cozy	PFA/159-13212		28. 5.98	K.R.W.Scull	(Usk)	
G-SDEV	DH.104 Sea Devon C.20 (Dove 6)	04472	XK895	29. 3.90	Wyndeham Press Group plc (As "XK895/CU19" in 771 Sqn RN c/s)	Shoreham	17. 9.99
G-SDLW	Cameron O-105 HAFB	2460		11. 3.91	P.J.Smart	Bath	15. 5.99A
G-SEAB	Republic RC-3 Seabee	413	N6210K NC6210K	6. 5.88	Barbara A.Farries (On rebuild 10.99)	Nottingham	AC
G-SEAI	Cessna U206G Stationair II Seaplane	U206-04059	N756FQ	20. 3.92	Aerofloat Ltd	Cumbernauld	8. 6.98T
G-SEAT	Colt 42A HAFB	817		28. 5.86	Virgin Airship & Balloon Co Ltd "Virgin Atlantic"	Telford	28. 7.88A
G-SEED	Piper J3C-90 Cub (L-4H-PI) (Frame No.10932) (Official identity is c/n 12499/44-80203 and probably rebuilt 1945)	11098	EI-BAP F-BFBZ/44-80203/43-29807	28. 1.80	J.H.Seed Black Spring Farm, Castle Bytham, Grantham		14. 4.00P
G-SEEK	Cessna T210N Turbo-Centurion II	210-64579	N9721Y	14.10.83	A.Hopper	Sibson	15. 2.02
G-SEGA	Cameron Sonic 90SS HAFB (Sonic The Hedgehog shape)	2896		16. 9.92	Virgin Airship & Balloon Co Ltd "Sonic The Hedgehog"	Telford	24. 4.97A
G-SEGO	Robinson R-22 Beta	0871	N9081N	12.10.88	Burman Aviation Ltd	Cranfield	13.11.00T
G-SEJW	PA-28-161 Warrior II	28-7816469	N9557N	19. 4.78	Keen Leasing Ltd	Aldergrove/Ronaldsway	19. 4.00T
G-SELL	Robin DR.400/180 Regent	1153	D-EEMT	7. 3.85	A.Burbidge t/a G-SELL Regent Group	Tatenhill	14. 6.00
G-SELY	Agusta-Bell 206B Jet Ranger III	8740		26. 7.96	Petrochem Aviation Services Ltd	Fairoaks	15. 9.02T
G-SEMI	PA-44-180 Seminole	44-7995052	G-DENW N21439	23. 2.99	T.Hiscox	Halfpenny Green	22.12.02T

424

Regn	Type	C/n	P/I	Date	Owner/operator	Probable Base	CA Expy
G-SENA	Rutan LongEz	1325	F-PZSQ / F-WZSQ	11.11.96	G.Bennett	(Great Yarmouth)	
G-SEND	Colt 90A HAFB	2100		2.12.91	Redmalt Ltd "Motorola III"	Witham, Essex	4. 6.99T
G-SENV	PA-34-220T Seneca V	3449135		28. 9.99	Technical Flight Services Ltd	Bournemouth	26.10.02T
G-SENX	PA-34-200T Seneca II	34-7870356	G-DARE G-WOTS/G-SEVL/N36742	15. 5.95	JG Computer Services Ltd & Maze Computers Ltd	Cardiff	30. 5.01T
G-SEPA	Eurocopter AS.355N Twin Squirrel	5525	G-METD G-BUJF/F-WYMF	25. 7.96	The Metropolitan Police	Fairoaks/Lippitts Hill, Loughton	4. 8.02T
G-SEPB	Eurocopter AS.355N Twin Squirrel	5574	G-BVSE	1. 2.95	The Metropolitan Police	Fairoaks/Lippitts Hill, Loughton	1. 3.01T
G-SEPC	Eurocopter AS.355N Twin Squirrel	5596	G-BWGV	29.11.95	The Metropolitan Police	Fairoaks/Lippitts Hill, Loughton	20. 3.02T
G-SEPT	Cameron N-105 HAFB	1880		22.11.88	P.Gooch "Septodont"	Alresford	8. 6.00A
G-SERA	Enstrom F-28A-UK	103	G-BAHU EI-BDF/G-BAHU	14. 3.91	W.R.Pitcher t/a Enstrom Associates	Leatherhead	12. 3.00
G-SERL	Socata TB-10 Tobago	109	G-LANA EI-BIH	28. 5.92	R.J. & G.J.Searle	Rochester	26. 3.00
G-SEUK	Cameron TV 80SS HAFB (Samsung Computer Shape)	3810		12. 4.96	Flying Pictures Ltd "Samsung"	Fairoaks	24. 3.00A
G-SEVA	Replica Plans SE.5A (Continental C90)	PFA/20-10955		19. 6.85	I.D.Gregory (As "F-141/G" in 141 Sqn RFC c/s)	Boscombe Down	20.12.00P
G-SEVE	Cessna 172N Skyhawk II	172-69970	N738GR	10. 1.90	MK Aero Support Ltd	Andrewsfield	28. 1.01T
G-SEXI	Cessna 172M Skyhawk II	172-63806	N1964V	21. 4.92	General Airline Ltd t/a European Flyers	Blackbushe	13. 8.01T
G-SEXY	American AA-1 Yankee (Regd as c/n 0042 incorrectly)	AA1-0442	G-AYLM	30. 6.81	I.C.Kenyon (Liverpool Flying School c/s) (Damaged Burscough, Lancs 11.2.94; stored 1.97)	Liverpool	17. 3.95
G-SFBH	Boeing 737-46N	28723		28. 5.97	British Midland Airways Ltd	East Midlands	5. 6.00T
G-SFHR	PA-23-250 Aztec F	27-8054041	G-BHSO N2527Z	24. 6.82	Comed Aviation Ltd	Blackpool	22.11.01T
G-SFOX	Rotorway Exec 90 (RW5055)	5059	G-BUAH	11.10.93	Magpie Computer Services Ltd (Stored Chester 7.97)	Crabtree Farm, Crowborough	8.12.00P
G-SFPA	Reims Cessna F406 Caravan II	0064		11.11.91	Secretary of State for Scotland Dept of Agriculture & Fisheries (Op Fisheries Protection Agency)	Prestwick	12. 3.00T
G-SFPB	Reims Cessna F406 Caravan II	0065		11.11.91	Secretary of State for Scotland Dept of Agriculture & Fisheries (Op Fisheries Protection Agency)	Prestwick	26. 4.00T
G-SFRY	Thunder Ax7-77 HAFB	1667		23. 1.90	K.J.Baxter & P.Szczepanski	Birmingham	4.11.99A
G-SFTA*	Westland SA.341G Gazelle 1	1039	"G-BAGJ" G-SFTA/HB-XIL/G-BAGJ/(XW858)	10. 9.82	North East Aircraft Museum (Crashed nr Alston, Cumbria 7.3.84; rebuilt to static condition in Army c/s)	Usworth	24. 2.86
G-SFTZ	Slingsby T-67M Firefly 160	2000		7. 2.83	Airborne Services Ltd (Damaged landing Compton Abbas 4.8.99; on repair 1.00)	Compton Abbas	24. 1.02T
G-SGAS	Colt 77A HAFB	2073		31.10.91	SGL Ltd t/a Shellgas South West Area "Shell Gas"	Barton	16. 7.00A
G-SGSE	PA-28-181 Archer II	28-7890332	G-BOJX N3774M	2.12.96	Mountune Racing Ltd	Andrewsfield	4. 9.00
G-SHAA	Enstrom 280-UK Shark	1011	N280Q	8. 7.88	C.J.& D.Whitehead t/a ELT Radio Telephones	(Burnley)	17.11.01T
G-SHAH	Reims Cessna F.152 II	1839	OH-IHA SE-IHA	7. 2.97	E.Alexander	Andrewsfield	24. 4.00T
G-SHAM	Beechcraft C90 King Air	LJ-819	N2063A	12. 4.99	Aerospeed Ltd	Southampton	20. 5.00T
G-SHAW	PA-30-160 Twin Comanche B	30-1221	LN-BWS	21. 3.78	E.R.Meredith & M.D.Faiers	Gloucestershire	6. 4.01
G-SHCB	Schweizer Hughes 269C-1	0038	N41S	28. 6.96	Oxford Aviation Services Ltd	Oxford	7.10.02T
G-SHCC	Bell 206B JetRanger II	1172	N280C	14.11.88	R & M International Engineering Ltd.	Dereham	30. 4.01T
G-SHED	PA-28-181 Archer II	28-7890068	G-BRAU N47411	12. 6.89	P.T.Crouch & R.M.Gingell	Gloucestershire	14. 8.01
G-SHIM	CFM Streak Shadow (Rotax 582) K.228-SA & PFA/206-12501			19. 5.93	E.G.Shimmin	Little Down Farm, Milson	13. 9.00P
G-SHIP*	PA-23-250 Aztec F	27-7654015	N62490	18. 1.77	Not known (Crashed Keystone 4.12.83; displayed in "paint-ball" Woodland 11.92)	Hockley Heath, Solihull	1. 7.85T
G-SHIV	Gulfstream GA-7 Cougar	GA7-0092	N713G	22.11.84	Westley Aircraft Ltd	Cranfield	18. 1.98T
G-SHNN	Enstrom 280C Shark	1119	N51685	22. 5.89	C.J.Roberts t/a CJ Services	Northwich, Cheshire	28. 4.98

Regn	Type	C/n	P/I	Date	Owner/operator	Probable Base	CA Expy
G-SHOE*	Cessna 421C Golden Eagle II	421C-0123	G-BHGD D-IASC/OE-FLR/N3862C	15. 1.81	Not known	Southampton	1. 5.86T
					(Damaged Deauville, France 8.11.85; fuselage on fire dump 9.96)		
G-SHOG	Colomban MC-15 Cri-Cri (JPX PUL-212)	001	G-PFAB F-PYPU	3.10.96	V.S.E.Norman (Mitsubishi Shogun titles - see SECTION 4)	Rendcomb	20.12.99P
G-SHOT	Cameron V-77 HAFB	972		14.12.83	E.C.Moore "Buckshot"	Great Missenden	20. 5.97A
G-SHOW*	Morane-Saulnier MS.733 Alcyon	125	F-BMQJ Fr.AF 125/MZ	1.10.80	Not known (Status unknown)	MK	24. 5.83P
G-SHPP	Hughes 269A (TH-55A)	36-0481	N80559 64-18169	24. 7.89	R.P.Bateman	White Waltham	15.12.02
G-SHRK	Enstrom 280C-UK Shark	1173	N373SA G-BGMX/EI-CCS/G-SHXX/G-BGMX/EI-BHR/G-BGMX/(F-GBOS)	6. 1.97	D.R.Kenyon t/a Aviation Bureau	Redhill	26. 9.02T
G-SHRL	Jodel D.18	PFA/169-12217		18. 9.92	M.W.Kilvert & G.Trevor	(Newtown, Powys)	
G-SHSH	Europa Avn Europa	PFA/247-12722		7. 4.98	D.G.Hillam	(Birkenhead)	
G-SHSP	Cessna 172S	172S-8079	N6535P N9552Q	25. 3.99	Shropshire Aero Club Ltd	Sleap	25. 3.02T
G-SHSS	Enstrom 280C-UK Shark	1060	N6892X G-SHSS/EI-CHG/G-SHSS/G-BENO t/a St. Angelo Helicopters	11.10.89	R.J.Patten	St. Angelo	11.11.00T
G-SHUG	PA-28R-201T Turbo Arrow III	28R-7703048	N1026Q	17. 5.88	Nicola E.Rennie	Booker	10. 7.00T
G-SHUU	Enstrom 280C-UK-2 Shark	1221	G-OMCP G-KENY/G-BJFG/N8617N	16.10.89	D.Ellis	Wigan	23. 6.01
G-SIAL	Hawker Hunter F.58	41H-697457	J-4090	2.10.95	Classic Aviation Ltd	(Scampton)	27. 9.99P
			(To represent a 'Black Diamond'/111 Sqdn machine but still in ex-Swiss scheme 8.99)				
G-SIGN	PA-39 Twin Comanche C/R	39-8	OY-TOO N8853Y	9. 2.78	D.Buttle	Blackbushe	10.12.99
G-SIIB	Aviat Pitts S-2B Special (Lycoming AEIO-540)	5218	G-BUVY N6073U	24. 3.93	G.Ferriman	Jericho Farm, Lambley	30. 4.02
G-SIII	Extra EA.300	058	D-ETYE	10. 1.95	Firebird Aerobatics Ltd (MG F titles)	RAF Halton	22. 1.01T
G-SILS	Pietenpol Air Camper	PFA/47-13331		29. 6.98	D.Silsbury	Ivybridge	
G-SIMI	Cameron A-315 HAFB	3391		10. 3.95	Balloon School (Intl) Ltd t/a Balloon Safaris	Petworth	7. 4.00T
G-SIMN	Robinson R-22 Beta-II	2769		10.12.97	Simlot Ltd	(Jersey)	22.12.00T
G-SION	PA-38-112 Tomahawk II	38-81A0146	N23661	30. 1.91	F.N.Dunstan t/a Naiad Air Services (Op Avon Flying School)	Hinton-in-The-Hedges	28.12.00T
G-SIPA	SIPA 903	63	G-BGBM F-BGBM	31. 5.83	G.K.Brothwood & P.R.Tonks t/a Mersey SIPA Group	Liverpool	14. 2.89P
G-SIRR	North American P-51D-25NA Mustang	122-39798	N51RR (N151MC)/TNI-AU F-3../44-73339 t/a Intrepid Aviation Co	3. 2.97	D.J.Gilmour	North Weald	11. 5.00P
			(As "474008/VF-R" in 4th FG/1336th FS USAAF c/s)				
	(A/c adopted identity of c/n 122-40548/44-74008/RCAF 9274/N8676E/N76AF/(N151MC) during 1982-84 rebuild)						
G-SIVA	MDC Hughes 369E (500E)	0372E		21. 1.94	Southern Air Ltd	Headcorn	22. 3.02T
G-SIXC	Douglas DC-6A/B	45550	N93459 N90645/B-1006/XW-PFZ/B-1006	20. 3.87	Atlantic Air Transport Ltd	Coventry	4. 4.02T
G-SIXD	PA-32-300 Cherokee Six D	32-7140007	HB-OMH N8615N	25. 3.98	G-SIXD Ltd (Carries Swiss Cross on fin)	Kings Farm, Thurrock	28. 7.01
G-SIXX	Colt 77A HAFB	1327		21.10.88	P.B.D.Bird & R.J.Maud	Bristol	12. 1.99A
G-SIXY	Van's RV-6	PFA/181-13368		9. 3.99	C.J.Hall & C.R.P.Hamlett	(Cambridge)	
G-SIZE	Lindstrand LBL-310A HAFB	028		9. 6.93	Adventure Balloon Co Ltd	London W7	1. 6.00T
G-SJAB	PA-39-160 Twin Comanche C/R	39-85	(N) G-AYWZ/N8928Y	14. 9.81	J.L.Way t/a Smith & Way	Blackpool	24. 9.01
G-SJCH	PBN BN-2T-4S Islander	4006	G-BWPK	18.11.99	Britten-Norman Ltd.	Bembridge	AC
G-SJDI	Robinson R-44 Astro	0626		16. 7.99	Total Asset Ltd	Liverpool	2. 8.00T
G-SJMC	Boeing 767-31KER	27205	N6038E	16. 3.94	Airtours Intl Airways Ltd	Manchester	15. 3.00T
G-SKAN	Reims Cessna F.172M Skyhawk II	1120	G-BFKT F-BVBJ	8. 7.85	Bustard Flying Club Ltd	Boscombe Down	1. 4.01T
G-SKID	Lake LA-4-200 Buccaneer	680	G-BMGY N39RG/G-BWKS/G-BDDI/N1087L	4.11.99	D.J.Lindsey Wood	Bournemouth	9. 1.98T
G-SKIE	Steen Skybolt	AACA/357	ZK-DEN	29. 8.97	S.Gray	Rushett Farm, Chessington	20.10.00P
G-SKIL	Cameron N-77 HAFB	2264		19. 3.90	Sky Trek Ballooning Ltd "Skillball"	Longfield, Kent	27. 7.00T
G-SKIS	Tri-R Kis	PFA/239-12630		3. 2.94	S.D.Barnard	(Coalville)	
G-SKYC	Slingsby T-67M Firefly	2009	G-BLDP	13. 6.97	T.W.Cassells	Bagby	7.10.02T
G-SKYD	Christen Pitts S-2B Special (Lycoming AEIO-540)	5057	N5331N	15.10.92	S.D.Harris t/a G-SKYD Syndicate	Redhill	6. 3.02
G-SKYE	Cessna TU206G Turbo Stationair 6 II	U206-04568	(G-DROP) N9783M	1. 8.79	P.M.Hall t/a RAF Sport Parachute Association	Weston-on-the-Green	5. 4.01
G-SKYG	III Sky Arrow 650 TC	C008		15.12.98	G.F.Smith	(Milton Keynes)	13. 1.02
G-SKYH*	Cessna 172N Skyhawk 100	172-68098	A6-GRM N76034	20. 2.79	Not known (Crashed Connaught, Ireland 21.7.91; stored 4.96)	Abbeyshrule, Ireland	9. 8.91T

Regn	Type	C/n	P/I	Date	Owner/operator	Probable Base	CA Expy
G-SKYI	Air Command 532 Elite (Rotax 532)	0430		1. 9.88	P.J.Troy-Davies	Royston	29. 5.91P
G-SKYL	Cessna 182S Skylane	182-80176	N4104D	19. 6.98	Skylane Aviation Ltd	Sherburn-in-Elmet	24. 6.01
G-SKYR	Cameron A-180 HAFB	2826		31. 3.92	PSH Skypower Ltd "Candy Floss"	Pewsey, Wilts	29. 4.00T
G-SKYT	III Sky Arrow 650TC (Rotax 912)	C.004		6. 9.96	I.R.Malby	Thruxton	26. 2.00T
G-SKYX	Cameron A-210 HAFB	4613		22. 6.99	PSH Skypower Ltd	Pewsey, Wilts	14. 6.00T
G-SKYY	Cameron A-250 HAFB	3402		9. 3.95	PSH Skypower Ltd "City of Southampton"	Pewsey, Wilts	28. 3.00T
G-SKYZ	PA-34-200T Seneca II	34-7870260	N31712	20. 1.95	Park Aeroleasing Ltd	Humberside	15. 3.01T
G-SLAC	Cameron N-77 HAFB	2295		7. 6.90	The Scottish Life Assurance Co "Scottish Life"	Manchester	20. 4.97A
G-SLCE	Cameron C-80 HAFB	4022		24. 2.97	Z.Bayat	Bristol	18.10.00T
G-SLEA	Mudry/CAARP CAP.10B	124		19.12.80	P.D.Southerington	Cranwell North	13. 4.00
G-SLII	Cameron O-90 HAFB	2388		20. 9.90	R.B. & A.M.Harris "Mad Dash"	Huntingdon	24. 7.00A
G-SLNE	Agusta A.109A II	7393	G-EEVS G-OTSL	23. 7.96	Sloane Helicopters Ltd	Sywell	3. 7.00T
G-SLOW	Pietenpol Aircamper	PFA/047-13488		8.10.99	C.Newton	(Brackley)	
G-SLTN	Socata TB-20 Trinidad	763	HB-KBR	6. 8.99	S.N.Adamson	(Warlingham)	15. 9.02T
G-SLYN	PA-28-161 Warrior II	28-8116204	N161WA N8373K	12. 4.89	G.E.Layton	Dunkeswell	25. 5.01
G-SMAF	Sikorsky S-76A	760149	N130TL N5425U	6. 9.88	Air Harrods Ltd	Stansted	3.10.00T
G-SMAN	Airbus A.330-243	261	F-WWKR	26. 3.99	Monarch Airlines Ltd	Luton	25. 3.01T
G-SMBM	Cyclone Pegasus Quantum 15	7602		24. 1.00	B.J.Mould	(Oswestry)	
G-SMDB	Boeing 737-36N	28557		15. 3.97	British Midland Airways Ltd	East Midlands	20. 3.00T
G-SMDH	Europa Avn Europa XS	PFA/247-13367		8.10.98	S.W.Pitt	(Petersfield)	
G-SMDJ	Eurocopter AS.350B2 Ecureuil	3187		21. 4.99	Denis Ferranti Hoverknights Ltd (Bangor)		12. 8.02
G-SMIG	Cameron O-65 HAFB	922		6. 6.83	G.Green & R.W.Taaffe Kowloon, Hong Kong t/a The Hong Kong Balloon & Airship Club "San Miguel Brewery"		28. 7.87A
G-SMIT*	Messerschmitt Bf.109G-6/U-2	163824	Luftwaffe 163824	10.12.79	Australian War Memorial Mitchell, Canberra, ACT, Australia (Displayed in Treloar Warfare Technology Centre 1996)		
G-SMJJ	Cessna 414A Chancellor II	414A-0425	N2694H	24. 3.81	Gull Air Ltd	Guernsey	30. 5.00
G-SMTC	Colt Flying Hut SS HAFB	1828		7. 1.91	Shiplake Investments Ltd	(Switzerland)	23. 9.93A
G-SMTH	PA-28-140 Cherokee C	28-26916	G-AYJS	28. 9.90	T.I.Mason & C.J.Mewis	Gloucestershire	14. 1.02
G-SNAK	Lindstrand LBL-105A HAFB	404		23. 9.96	Ballooning Adventures Ltd	Hexham	N/E(T)
G-SNAP	Cameron V-77 HAFB	1217		29.11.85	C.J.S.Limon "Snapshot"	Great Missenden	26. 6.97A
G-SNAX	Colt 69A HAFB	1680		6. 3.90	United Biscuits (UK) Ltd "Phileas Fogg II"	Consett	16. 7.97A
G-SNAZ	Enstrom F-28F	761	G-BRCP	31.10.94	Thornhill Aviation Ltd	Barton	5. 1.02T
G-SNDY	Piper J3C-65 Cub	3751	N25797 NC25797	1. 3.90	R.R.K.Mayall (Stored 4.94)	Carlisle	
G-SNEV	CFM Streak Shadow SA (Rotax 582)	PFA/206-13042		17. 9.96	N.G.Smart	(Feltham)	26. 1.99P
G-SNOW	Cameron V-77 HAFB (Fitted with replacement envelope 1989 - c/n 2050 which was the original G-BSDX)	541	(G-BGWA)	21. 6.79	M.J.Ball	Clitheroe	29. 5.00A
G-SOAR	Eiri PIK-20E	20214		21. 6.79	F.W.Fay "AR"	Bidford	7. 6.02
G-SOEI	HS.748 Srs.2A/242	1689	ZK-DES	25. 2.98	Emerald Airways Ltd (Securicor Omega Express titles)	Liverpool	17. 4.01T
G-SOFA	Cameron N-65 HAFB	968		30. 8.83	M.J.Axtell	Todmorden	10. 6.90A
G-SOFT	Thunder Ax7-77 HAFB	1339		5.12.88	A.J.Bowen "Enterprise Software"	Edinburgh	11. 9.99A
G-SOHI	Agusta A.109E	11045		23. 4.99	Tri-Ventures Group Ltd	Elstree	28. 4.02T
G-SOKO	Soko P-2 Kraguj	003	G-BRXK 30149 Yugoslav Army	6. 1.94	M.R.Keen	Liverpool	4. 7.97P
G-SOLA	Star-Lite SL-1 203TG & (Rotax 447)	PFA/175-11311		9. 6.88	J.P.Lethaby "A Star Is Born" (Stored 6.93)	(Lynton, Devon)	31. 3.93P
G-SOLD	Robinson R-22 Alpha	0471	N8559X	16. 5.85	J.F.H.James	Banbury	12. 6.00
G-SOLH	Bell 47G-5	2639	G-AZMB CF-NJW	5. 3.97	Sol Helicopters Ltd	Elstree	13. 2.00T
G-SOLO	Anvil-Pitts S-2S Special (Lycoming AEIO-540)	AA/1/1980		30. 5.80	Landitfast Ltd	Denham	6. 4.96P
G-SONA	Socata TB-10 Tobago	151	G-BIBI	24.10.80	C.D.Brack	(York)	17. 5.02
G-SONY	Aero Commander 200D	358	G-BGPS 5Y-AFT/N2985T	24.11.88	General Airline Ltd t/a European Flyers	Blackbushe	27. 7.01
G-SOOC	Hughes 369HS (500C)	111-0354S	G-BRRX N9083F	6.10.93	Repetek Ltd	Dungannon, Co.Tyrone	14.10.02
G-SOOE	Hughes 369E (500E)	0227E		27. 4.87	R.W.Nash	Rochester	26. 5.02

Regn	Type	C/n	P/I	Date	Owner/operator	Probable Base	CA Expy
G-SOOK	Sukhoi SU-26M	04-01	RA-0401 DOSAAF30	23. 3.95	V.Rahmani "30"	(London SW6)	25. 6.00P
G-SOOM	Glaser-Dirks DG-500M	5E42-M20		14. 5.92	R.L.McLean & J.Ellis t/a Glaser-Dirks UK "112"	Rufforth	2. 6.01
G-SOOS	Colt 21A Cloudhopper HAFB	1263		7. 6.88	P.J.Stapley	Redcar	25. 3.95A
G-SOOT	PA-28-180 Cherokee C	28-4033	G-AVNM N11C	19. 8.88	J.A.Bridger	Exeter	26. 8.01T
G-SOPP	Enstrom 280FX	2024	G-OSAB N86259	23.10.97	F.P. & M.Sopp & L.A.Moore Jefferies Farm, Billingshurst		18. 5.01
G-SORT	Cameron N-90 HAFB	2878		13. 7.92	A.Brown "Streamline"	Bristol	8. 8.98A
G-SOUL	Cessna 310R II	310R-0140	N5020J	27. 6.88	Atlantic Air Transport Ltd	Coventry	10. 6.01T
G-SOUP	Cameron C-80 HAFB	3387		24.10.94	M.G.Barlow (Not built)	(Skipton)	
G-SPAM	Light Aero Avid Aerobat (Rotax 582) 829 & PFA/189-12074			9. 5.91	R.W.Fair	(Chester)	26. 8.00P
G-SPEE	Robinson R-22 Beta	0939	G-BPJC	20. 7.94	Speed Helicopters Ltd	Redhill	28. 9.00T
G-SPEL	Sky 220-24 HAFB	045		26. 7.96	T.G.Church t/a Pendle Balloon Co	Blackburn	5.12.99T
G-SPEY	Agusta-Bell 206B JetRanger III	8608	G-BIGO	1. 4.81	Castle Air Charters Ltd Trebrown, Liskeard		13. 5.02T
G-SPFX	Rutan Cozy	PFA/159-13113		30. 4.97	B.D.Tutty	(Gillingham, Kent)	
G-SPIN	Aerotek Pitts S-2A Special (Lycoming AEIO-360)	2110	N5CQ	13. 3.80	C.A.Morris Top Farm, Royston t/a Barmoor Aviation		22. 4.02T
G-SPIT	VS.379 Spitfire FR.XIVe 6S/649205		(G-BGHB)	2. 3.79	Patina Ltd Duxford Indian AF T-20/MV293 (Op The Fighter Collection) (As "MV293/OI-C"" in 2 Sqn c/s)		6. 5.00P
G-SPOG	San Jodel DR.1050 Ambassadeur	155	G-AXVS F-BJNL	25. 9.95	A.C.Frost (Ware) (Damaged Stonacre Farm, Bredhurst 17.2.91: on rebuild 1995)		13. 6.77S
G-SPOL	MBB Bo.105DBS-4	S-392	VR-BGV D-HDLH	23. 3.90	Bond Air Services Glasgow Heliport (Op Strathclyde Police Air Support Unit)		5. 6.02T
G-SPOR	Beechcraft B200 Super King Air	BB-1557	N57TL N57TS	3. 9.99	Select Plant Hire Co. Ltd	Southend	19 .9.02T
G-SPUR	Cessna 550 Citation II	550-0714	N593EM N12035	27.10.98	Amsail Ltd	(Brentwood)	15.11.00T
G-SPYI	Bell 206B Jet Ranger III	3689	G-BVRC G-BSJC/N3175S	9. 5.96	A.J.Sinclair	Bournemouth	29. 6.02T
G-SROE	Westland Scout AH.1	F.9508	XP907	26.10.95	Bolenda Engineering Ltd (As "XP907")	Ipswich	31.10.00P
G-SRVO	Cameron N-90 HAFB	3551		10. 4.95	Servo & Electronic Sales Ltd "Connect One"	Lydd	15. 6.00A
G-SSCL	MDC Hughes 369E (500E)	0491E	N684F	25. 4.98	Shaun Stevens Continentalractors Ltd	(Maidstone)	29. 7.01
G-SSFC	PA-34-200 Seneca	34-7450016	G-BBXG N56647	28. 4.94	SFC (Air Taxis) Ltd	Stapleford	26. 3.01T
G-SSFT	PA-28-161 Warrior II	28-8016069	G-BHIL N80821	16. 7.86	SFT Europe Ltd	Bournemouth	15. 3.01T
G-SSGS	Europa Avn Europa (Rotax 912UL)	082		25. 1.94	G. & S.G.Schwetz t/a SGS Partnership "Fledermaus"	Old Sarum	19. 7.00P
G-SSIX	Rans S-6-116 Coyote II (Rotax 582)	PFA/204A-12749		5. 9.94	T.J.Bax	Old Sarum	8. 4.00P
G-SSKY	PBN BN-2B-26 Islander	2247	G-BSWT	11. 5.92	Isles of Scilly Skybus Ltd	St.Just	29. 4.00T
G-SSSC	Sikorsky S-76C	760408		26.10.93	Bond Helicopters Ltd	Aberdeen	13. 1.01T
G-SSSD	Sikorsky S-76C	760415		26.10.93	Bond Helicopters Ltd	Aberdeen	22.12.02T
G-SSSE	Sikorsky S-76C	760417		23.11.93	Bond Helicopters Ltd	Aberdeen	2. 2.00T
G-SSTI	Cameron N-105 HAFB	3238		30. 3.94	British Airways plc "Concorde" (Active 1.00)	Heathrow	26. 6.99T
G-SSWA	Short SD.3-30 Var.100	SH3042	D-CTAG	15.10.99	Streamline Aviation (SW) Ltd Exeter G-BHHU/OY-MUC/G-BHHU/N181AP/N332MV/G-BHHU/G-14-3042		15.10.99T
G-SSWT	Short SD.3-30 Var.100	SH3095	4X-CSQ	2. 6.98	Freshleave Ltd Exeter G-BNYA/G-BKSU/G-14-3095 (Damaged landing Luton 13.2.99)		18. 6.00T
G-SSWU	Short SD.3-30 Var.100	SH3076	C-FYXF	24. 2.99	Streamline Aviation (SW) Ltd Exeter G-BIYH/N181AP/N338MV/G-BIYH/G-14-3076		7. 3.00TC
G-SSWV	Sportavia Fournier RF5B Sperber	51032	N55WV	31. 5.90	E.C.Neighbour & J.A.Melville Camphill t/a Skylark Flying Group		4. 8.00P
G-SSWX	Short SD.3-60 Var.200	SH.3715	N711PM G-BNDL/G-14-3715	19.10.99	Streamline Aviation (SW) Ltd	Exeter	2.12.00TC
G-STAT	Cessna U206F Stationair II	U206-03485	A6-MAM N8732Q	20. 2.79	Wingglider Ltd	Hibaldstow	11. 9.98
G-STAV	Cameron O-84 HAFB	2913		29. 9.92	F.Horsfall	Moreton-in-Marsh	27. 3.00A
G-STEF	Hughes 369HS	114-0673S	G-BKTK OY-HCL/OO-JGR	7.11.84	Source Ltd	Bournemouth	4. 3.02T

Regn	Type	C/n	P/I	Date	Owner/operator	Probable Base	CA Expy
G-STEM	Stemme S-10V	14-027		2. 7.97	Warwickshire Aerocentre Ltd		
						Husbands Bosworth	15. 7.00
G-STEN	Stemme S-10	10-32	D-KGCH	9. 1.92	W.A.H.Kahn "4"	Lasham	19. 3.01
G-STEP	Schweizer Hughes 269C	S.1494		1.10.90	M.Johnson	Neath	29.10.00
G-STER	Bell 206B JetRanger III	4116	OO-EGA	23. 3.94	P.J.Brown	Redhill	24. 3.00T
					t/a P.J.Brown Civil Engineer & Haulage Contractors		
G-STEV	CEA Jodel DR-221 Dauphin	61	F-BOZD	9. 3.82	S.W.Talbot	Long Marston	25. 2.02
G-STMP	SNCAN Stampe SV-4A	241	F-BCKB	11. 3.83	A.C.Thorne	(Yelverton)	
					(On overhaul Ivybridge 5.93)		
G-STOW	Cameron Wine Box-90 SS HAFB	4420		2.10.98	I.Martin & D.Groombridge	Bristol	19. 8.99A
					t/a Flying Enterprises Partnership (Stowells of Chelsea titles)		
G-STOX	Bell 206B JetRanger II	1513	G-BNIR N59615	27. 4.89	Burman Aviation Ltd	Cranfield	7. 6.02T
G-STOY	Robinson R-22 Beta	0700		10.11.87	Burman Aviation Ltd	Cranfield	29.11.99T
G-STPI	Cameron A-250 HAFB	4102		26. 2.97	A.D.Pinner	Northampton	24. 4.00T
					(Central Auto Supplies c/s)		
G-STRK	CFM Streak Shadow (Rotax 582) K.143-SA & PFA/161-11762			4. 4.90	E.J.Hadley	(Arch, Switzerland)	17. 6.00P
G-STRM	Cameron N-90 HAFB	3568		3. 7.95	B.G.Jones	Devizes	8. 8.97T
					t/a High Profile Balloons		
G-STUA	Aerotek Pitts S-2A Special (Lycoming AEIO-360)	2164	N13GT	6. 3.91	Rollquick Ltd	White Waltham	21. 3.00T
G-STUB	Christen Pitts S-2B Special (Lycoming AEIO-540)	5163	N260Y	5. 5.94	R.N.Goode & T.L.P.Delaney	White Waltham	19. 6.00
G-STVN*	HPR.7 Dart Herald 210	188	F-BOIZ F-OCLZ/HB-AAL	30. 8.88	Dart Group plc	Bournemouth	24.10.99T
					t/a Channel Express (Cancelled as PWFU 8.4.97)		
G-STWO	ARV1 Super 2 002 & PFA/152-11048 (Hewland AE75)			24. 4.85	G.E.Morris	Gloucestershire	16. 9.00P
G-STYL	Pitts S-1S Special (Lycoming-O-320)	GJSN-1P	N665JG	26. 1.88	C.A.Wills	Mitchells Farm, Wilburton	21.12.00P
G-SUEE	Airbus A.320-231	363	G-IEAG F-WWBX	23. 9.93	Airtours International Airways Ltd	Manchester	18. 3.00T
G-SUEZ	Agusta-Bell 206B Jet Ranger II	8319	SU-YAE YU-HAZ	16. 9.98	Aerospeed Ltd	Southampton	16. 5.02T
G-SUIT	Cessna 210N Centurion II	210-64576	N9698Y	17.11.92	Edinburgh Air Centre Ltd	Edinburgh	3. 3.02T
G-SUKI	PA-38-112 Tomahawk	38-79A0260	G-BPNV N2313D	22. 5.91	Western Air (Thruxton) Ltd	Thruxton	20. 5.02T
G-SULL*	PA-32R-301 Saratoga SP	32R-8113002	N82818	19. 6.86	The Fire Service College	Moreton-in-Marsh	27. 7.95T
					(Crashed Crowfield 1.2.95: in Fire Service use 8.98)		
G-SULY*	Monnett Moni	PFA/142-11208		15. 7.87	M.J.Sullivan	(London W13)	
					(Cancelled by CAA 4.5.99)		
G-SUMT	Robinson R-22 Beta	2147	G-BUKD N23381	24. 9.92	Frankham Brothers Ltd	Leicester	7. 9.01
G-SUNY	Robinson R-44 Astro	0540		8.12.98	PS Helicopter Ltd (Kingston-Upon-Thames)		13.12.01T
G-SUPA	PA-18-150 Super Cub (Frame No.18-5512)	18-5395	PH-BAJ PH-MBF/ALAT 18-5395	13.12.78	J.M. Roach t/a Supa Group	Welshpool	1.12.01
G-SURG	PA-30-160 Twin Comanche B	30-1424	G-VIST G-AVHZ/N8287Y	18. 6.90	A.R.Taylor	Turweston	20. 1.02T
G-SURV	PBN BN-2T-4S Defender 4000	4005	G-BVHZ	14. 4.94	Britten-Norman Ltd	Bembridge	7. 7.02T
G-SUSI	Cameron V-77 HAFB	1133		22. 7.85	J.H.Dyden "Susi"	Okehampton	5. 5.00A
G-SUSY	North American P-51D-25NA Mustang	122-39232	N12066	23. 7.87	P.J.Morgan "Susy" (As "472773/AJ-C" in 354th FG USAF c/s)	Sywell	20. 5.00P
G-SUSX	MDH MD 902 Explorer	900-00065	N3065W	19. 1.00	Sussex Police Authority	Shoreham	
G-SUTN	III Sky Arrow 650TC	C007		27. 8.98	G.C.Sutton	Headcorn	18.10.01
G-SUZI	Beechcraft 95-B55 Baron	TC-1574	N3573C	11. 3.84	Bebecar (UK) Ltd	Elstree	7. 7.01
G-SUZN	PA-28-161 Warrior II	28-8016187	N3573C N9540N	16. 1.91	E.Reed	Teesside	17. 3.00T
					t/a The St.George Flying Club		
G-SUZY	Taylor JT.1 Monoplane (VW1600)	PFA/55-10395		1.12.78	D.I.Law	Dunkeswell	4. 8.98P
G-SVBF	Cameron A-180 HAFB	3587		2. 6.95	Virgin Balloon Flights Ltd (London SE16) "Virgin Sierra"		22. 4.00T
G-SVEA	PA-28-161 Warrior II	28-7916082	N30299	16.12.98	A.Hastings & E.Lowery t/a Avion Aviation	Birmingham	15.12.01T
G-SVIP	Cessna 421B Golden Eagle II	421B-0820	G-BNYJ N4686Q/D-IMVB/N1590G	12. 3.97	Stephenson Marine Co Ltd	Southampton	28.11.00T
G-SVIV	SNCAN Stampe SV-4C (Gipsy Major)	475	N65214 F-BDBL	7. 8.90	A.J.Clarry & S.F.Bancroft	Thruxton	12. 6.99
G-SWEB	Cameron N-90 HAFB	2413		1.10.90	South Western Electricity plc "SWEB"	Bristol	4. 8.00T

Regn	Type	C/n	P/I	Date	Owner/operator	Probable Base	CA Expy
G-SWEL	Hughes 369HS	61-0328S	G-RBUT C-FTXZ/CF-TXZ	18. 7.96	I.C. & L.E.Stilwell	Leamington Spa	13. 3.00
G-SWIF	VS.552 Swift F.7	VA.9597	XF114	1. 6.90	Heritage Aviation Developments Ltd (Stored 9.98)	Scampton	AC
G-SWIM*	Aerocar Super Coot	PFA/18-11486		21. 8.90	R.J.Hopkins (Cancelled by CAA 14.4.99)	(Exmouth)	
G-SWIS*	FFW DH.100 Vampire FB.6	658	J-1149	21. 5.91	Hunter Wing Ltd (As "J-1149" in Swiss AF c/s: stored 9.97)	Bournemouth	
G-SWJW	Airbus A.300B4-203	302	OH-LAB F-WZMY	19. 5.98	OY Air Scandic International Aviation AB	Manchester	18. 5.01T
G-SWOT	Phoenix Currie Super Wot (Continental O-200-A)	PFA/3011		10. 9.80	D.Watt (As "C3011/S" in SE.5A guise)	Conington	15.11.99P
G-SWPR	Cameron N-56 HAFB	829		16. 3.82	A.Brown "Post Code"	Bristol	5. 7.95A
G-SWSH	Revolution Helicopters Mini-500	0049		10.10.95	Aerial Enterprises Ltd	(London SW19)	
G-SWUN	Pitts S-1M Special (Lycoming O-320)	338-H	G-BSXH N14RM	18. 4.95	T.G.Lloyd (Stored 3.97)	Little Gransden	5. 6.92P
G-SYCO	Europa Avn Europa (NSI EA-81/118)	PFA/247-12540		27.11.95	J.T.Fillingham	Kemble	8. 6.00P
G-SYFW	WAR Focke-Wulf 190 rep (Continental O-200-A) 269 & PFA/81-10584			28. 2.83	M.R.Parr Les Padins Farm, St.Saviour, Guernsey (As "WNo.7334/2+1" in Luftwaffe c/s; stored 1.98)		29. 6.87P
G-SYPA	Aerospatiale AS.355F2 Twin Squirrel	5193	LV-WHC F-WYMS/G-BPRE/N366E	25. 9.96	South Yorkshire Police Authority	Sheffield City	2. 4.00T

G-TAAA – G-TZZZ

Regn	Type	C/n	P/I	Date	Owner/operator	Probable Base	CA Expy
G-TAAL	Cessna 172R Skyhawk	17280733	N9535G	11. 8.99	Eagle Cruise Aviation. Ltd	(London W14)	6. 9.02T
G-TABS	Embraer EMB.110P1 Bandeirante	110-212	G-PBAC F-GCLA/F-OGME/F-GCLA/PT-GME	18. 8.98	Skydrift Ltd	Southend	21.10.99T
G-TACE*	HS 125 Srs.403B	25223	G-AYIZ F-BSSL/PJ-SLB/G-AYIZ/G-5-15	23. 1.81	British Aerospace plc (Open store 10.95)	Dunsfold	16. 7.86F
G-TACK	Grob G-109B	6279		30. 5.84	A.P.Mayne	Exeter	4. 5.02
G-TAFF	CASA I-131E Jungmann	1129	G-BFNE E3B-148	7. 9.84	A.Horsfall	Breighton	11. 5.00P
G-TAFI	Dornier Bucker Bu133C Jungmeister	24	N2210 HB-MIF/SwAF U-77	27. 1.93	R.J.Lamplough	North Weald	30. 7.97P
G-TAGS	PA-28-161 Warrior II	28-8416026	N4329D	6. 5.88	Oxford Aviation Services Ltd	Oxford	3. 8.00T
G-TAIL	Cessna 150J	150-70152	N60220	21. 4.89	Not known (Damaged Southend 4.1.98 - removed 6.98)	Blackpool	15. 1.98T
G-TAIR	PA-34-200T Seneca II	34-7970055	N3059H	17.11.87	D.I.G. & J.de Souza t/a Branksome Dene Garage	Bournemouth	3. 3.00T
G-TAMY	Cessna 421B Golden Eagle	421B-0512	SE-FNS N2BH/N69865	14.11.77	Malcolm Enamellers (Midlands) Ltd	Halfpenny Green	2. 6.00
G-TAND	Robinson R-44 Astro	0478		12. 6.98	Southwest Helicharter Ltd	Gloucestershire	2. 7.01T
G-TANI	Gulfstream GA-7 Cougar	GA7-0107	G-VJAI G-OCAB/G-BICF/N8500H/N29707	18. 5.95	S.Spier (Op Denham School of Flying)	Denham	1. 2.02T
G-TANK	Cameron N-90 HAFB	3625		20. 6.95	Hoyers (UK) Ltd	Huddersfield	26. 6.00A
G-TANS	Socata TB-20 Trinidad	1870	F-GRBX	25. 9.98	K.& G.Threfall t/a Tettenhall Leisure	Halfpenny Green	24. 9.01
G-TAPE	PA-23-250 Aztec D	27-4054	G-AWVW OY-RPF/G-AWVW/N6799Y	7.10.83	D.J.Hare (Op Merlix Air)	Fairoaks	11. 2.00T
G-TARN	Pietenpol Air Camper	PFA/47-13349		3. 8.98	P.J.Heilbron	(Guildford)	
G-TART	PA-28-236 Dakota	28-7911261	N2945C	18.12.90	Dateworld Ltd	Bournemouth	18. 6.00
G-TARV	ARV.1 Super 2	PFA/152-12627		1. 6.94	M.F.Filer	(Bristol)	
G-TASH	Cessna 172N (modified)	172-70531	PH-KOS N739GL	4.11.98	A. Ashpitel	Popham	30.11.01T
G-TASK	Cessna 404 Titan II	404-0829	PH-MPC SE-IHL/N6806Q	10. 3.93	Bravo Aviation Ltd (Op Air Atlantique)	Coventry	8. 7.00T
G-TATT	Gardan GY-20 Minicab	PFA/56-10347		30.11.78	P.W.Tattershall t/a Tatt's Group	(Clitheroe)	
G-TATY	Robinson R-44 Astro (C/n 0626 also suggested)	0627		27. 7.99	W.R.Walker	Denham	2. 8.02T
G-TAXI	PA-23-250 Aztec E	27-7305085	N40270	6. 4.78	M.L.D.Levi & S.Waite t/a SWL Leasing	Bagby	22. 9.01T
G-TAYI	Grob G.115	8008	(D-ENFT) G-TAYI/G-DODO/D-ENFT	12. 9.90	K.P.Widdowson	(Doncaster)	10. 7.00
G-TAYS	Reims Cessna F.152 II	1697	G-LFCA	28.10.91	Tayside Aviation Ltd	Aberdeen/Dundee	28. 5.01T
G-TBAG	Murphy Renegade 912	PFA/188-11912		11.12.90	M.R.Tetley	Newton-on-Rawcliffe, Yorks	12.10.00P
G-TBBC	Cyclone Pegasus Quantum 15	7583		6.12.99	Big Bamboo Co Ltd	Durham	
G-TBEE	Dyn'Aero MCR-01 Ban-bi	PFA/301-13514		30.11.99	A.D.S.Baker	(Brighton)	

Regn	Type	C/n	P/I	Date	Owner/operator	Probable Base	CA Expy
G-TBGL	Agusta A.109A II	7412	G-VJCB G-BOUA	6. 1.99	Thomas Bolton Group Ltd (Stoke-on-Trent)		8.12.00T
G-TBIC	BAe 146 Srs.200	E-2025	N167US N349PS	15. 1.97	Flightline Ltd (Aer Lingus Commuter c/s)	Dublin	16. 1.00T
G-TBIO	Socata TB-10 Tobago	340	F-BNGZ	10. 2.83	P G Sherry & A J Simmonds	(Northwich)	20. 4.02T
G-TBMW	Murphy Renegade Spirit PFA/118-11725		(G-MYIG)	20.10.98	S J Spavins	(St Albans)	
G-TBRD	Canadair CL-30 (T-33AN) Silver Star mk.3 	T33-261	N33VC/G-JETT/G-OAHB/CF-IHB/CAF 133261/RCAF 21261	18.12.96	Golden Apple Operations Ltd. (Op The Old Flying Machine Co; as "54-21261" in USAF c/s)	Duxford	AC
G-TBXX	Socata TB-20 Trinidad	276		16. 3.82	D.A.Phillips & C.S.Swaine	Headcorn	21. 5.00
G-TBZI	Socata TB-21 Trinidad TC	871	N21HR	25. 7.96	W.R.M.Beesley	Blackbushe	14.11.02
G-TBZO	Socata TB-20 Trinidad	444		8. 8.84	D.L.Clarke & M.J.M.Hopper	Shoreham	24. 4.00
G-TCAN	Colt 69A HAFB	1996		19. 7.91	H.C.J.Williams "Toucan"	Bristol	7. 4.97A
G-TCAP	BAe 125 Srs 800B	258115	G-5-599	24. 4.96	British Aerospace plc R. Saudi AF 104/G-5-665/RSAF 104/G-BPGR/G-5-599	Warton	28. 8.00
G-TCDI	HS.125 Srs.F400B	25248	N792A	10.10.96	Aravco Ltd G-5-707/G-SHOP/G-BTUF/G-5-707/D-CFCF	Farnborough	19.12.00T
G-TCMP	Robinson R-22 Beta	0890		3.11.88	Thornhill Aviation Ltd	Shoreham	19. 2.01T
G-TCOM	PA-30-160 Twin Comanche C	30-1967	N555JC N8810Y	29. 1.96	C.A.C.Burrough	Blackbushe	9. 4.02
G-TCSL*	Rockwell Commander 112A	322	N506CA	17. 9.92	The Works Night Club (Damaged Spanhoe 5.12.94)	(Corby)	7.10.95
G-TCTC	PA-28RT-201T Turbo Arrow IV	2831001	N9130B	1.12.89	S.C.Tysoe t/a STMS	Leicester	26. 3.02
	(Originally built as N9524N c/n 28R-8631006)						
G-TCUB	Piper J3C-65 Cub (NE-2)	13970	N9039Q	31. 7.87	C.Kirk	Wyberton	13. 4.01
	(Frame No.13805)		N67666/NC67666/Bu.29684/45-55204				
G-TDFS	IMCO Callair A.9	1200	G-AVZA SE-EUA/N26D	8.10.86	Dollarhigh Ltd t/a TD Flight Services	Sturgate	11.12.00A
G-TDTW	CCF Hawker Hurricane	-	RCAF 5450	R	Hawker Restorations Ltd (Composite rebuild 6.96) Moat Farm, Milden		
G-TEAL	Thurston TSC-1A1 Teal	15	C-GDQD	8.12.92	K.Heeley	Crosland Moor	AC
	(Damaged Crosland Moor 3.93; wings only stored 9.96 - fuselage on rebuild off-site)						
G-TEBZ	PA-28R-201 Cherokee Arrow III	28R-7737050	N105CC	7. 1.00	R.W.Tebby t/a S.F.Tebby & Son	Bristol	
G-TECC	Aeronca 7AC Champion	7AC-5269	N1704E NC1704E	26. 6.91	T.E.C.Cushing	Little Snoring	18.10.00P
G-TECH	Rockwell Commander 114	14074	G-BEDH N4744W	8. 8.85	P.A.Reed	Elstree	7. 8.00
G-TECK	Cameron V-77 HAFB	625		21. 3.86	G.M.N.Spencer "Spring Fever"	Watford	21. 7.00A
G-TEDF	Cameron N-90 HAFB	2634		8. 8.91	Fort Vale Engineering Ltd	Nelson	9. 7.00A
G-TEDS	Socata TB-10 Tobago	57	G-BHCO	29. 3.83	E.W.Lyon	Halfpenny Green	11. 3.02
G-TEDY	Evans VP-1 (VW1834)	PFA/62-10383	G-BHGN	4.10.90	N.K.Marston "The Plank"	(Harrow)	1. 7.97P
G-TEDZ	Nipper T.66 Srs.3B (Fairey c/n 30)	PFA/25-11051		27. 2.96	C.J.D.Edwards	Crosland Moor	28. 7.00P
G-TEEZ	Cameron N-90 HAFB	4005		27.11.96	Fresh Air Ltd	London NW2	13. 3.00T
G-TEFC	PA-28-140 Cherokee F	28-7325088	OY-PRC N15530	18. 6.80	A.R.Knight	Andrewsfield	14. 3.02
G-TEHL	CFM Streak Shadow Srs.M (Rotax 503)	185	G-MYJE	20.11.98	A.K. Paterson	Sleaford	13. 7.00P
G-TELY	Agusta A.109A II	7326	N1HQ N200SH	10. 3.89	Castle Air Charters Ltd Trebrown, Liskeard		23. 7.02T
G-TEMP	PA-28-180 Cherokee E	28-5806	G-AYBK	15. 5.89	M.J.Groome t/a Bev Piper Group	Andrewsfield	8. 7.01T
G-TEMT	Hawker Tempest II	420	HA586 (RIAF)/MW763	9.10.89	Tempest Two Ltd (On rebuild 11.96: to be "MW763/HF-A" in 183 Sqn c/s)	Sandtoft	
G-TENT	Auster 5 J/1N Alpha	2058	G-AKJU TW513	1. 2.90	R.C.Callaway-Lewis	Oaksey Park	26. 8.02
G-TERN	Europa Avn Europa	PFA/247-12780		18. 7.97	J.E.G.Lundesjo	White Waltham	5. 9.00P
G-TERY	PA-28-181 Archer II	28-7990078	G-BOXZ N22402	13. 1.89	T.Barlow	Barton	26. 6.98T
G-TEST	PA-34-200 Seneca	34-7450116	OO-RPW G-BLCD/PH-PLZ/N41409	28. 7.89	Stapleford Flying Club Ltd	Stapleford	23.12.01T
G-TEWS	PA-28-140 Cherokee B	28-25128	G-KEAN G-AWTM	23. 5.88	M.J.Tew t/a G-TEWS Flying Group	Barton	1. 7.01T
G-TFCI	Reims Cessna FA.152 Aerobat	0358		25.10.79	Tayside Aviation Ltd	Dundee	11. 6.01T
G-TFOX	Denney Kitfox mk.2 (Rotax 582)	PFA/172-11817		3. 6.91	F.A.Bakir	Barton	12.12.99P
G-TFRB	Air Command 532 Elite Sport 0628 & PFA G/104-1167			26. 4.90	F.R.Blennerhassett	Wingate, Hartlepool	6. 8.98P

Regn	Type	C/n	P/I	Date	Owner/operator	Probable Base	CA Expy
G-TFUN	Valentin Taifun 17E	1011	D-KIHP	28.12.83	G.F.Wynn & D.H.Evans	Blackpool	7. 7.00
					t/a North West Taifun Group		
G-TGAS	Cameron O-160 HAFB	1315		12. 8.87	Zebedee Balloon Service Ltd	Hungerford	26. 5.00T
G-TGER	Gulfstream AA-5B Tiger	AA5B-0952	G-BFZP	20. 2.86	Photonic Science Ltd	Biggin Hill	26. 3.00T
G-TGRS	Robinson R-22 Beta	1069	G-DELL	5.11.97	A.L.Ramsden	Shobdon	21. 9.01T
			N80466		t/a Tiger Helicopters		
G-THCL	Cessna 550 Citation II	550-0563	N1298P	15.10.87	Tower House Consultants Ltd	Jersey	7. 1.01
G-THEA	Boeing-Stearman E75 (N2S-5) Kaydet		(EI-RYR)	18. 3.81	C.M.Ryan	Leicester	4.11.02
	(Lycoming R-680)	75-5736A	N1733B/USN Bu.38122 (As "33" in Navy c/s: noted 9.99)				

(Converted by Eastern Stearman at Swanton Morley 1997/98: the plate shows c/n 75-5736 which corresponds to N2PP ex 42-17573 - and also records BuA No.38122 [c/n 75-7744] ex N5714N. This is now confirmed as ex N1733B. The a/c has a non-standard c/n 75-5736A. The original airframe c/n 75-5736 was built as a USN N2S-5 in 1943 and sold in 5.47. It was stored for some time before becoming N1733B. After many years crop-dusting it was rebuilt by N.Norigan at Fresno, California in 1974 during which parts from N2S-4 c/n 75-7743/BuA38122 (and possibly from 75-7744/N5714N) were incorporated. The two aircraft which emerged post-1974 rebuild were thus: (i) c/n 75-5736 -N244E,later N2PP, and (ii) c/n 75-5736A - N1733B. The plate on G-THEA is an amalgam of the c/n 75-5736 and the original identity of c/n 75-7743. It was sold to Chris Ryan in 5.97 after five years of inactivity and arrived at Swanton Morley for rebuild in 7.97. Although registration EI-RYR was reserved in 3.98, and applied to the a/c, registered ownership was transferred officially by CAA to C M Ryan on 31.8.99 under marks G-THEA. The a/c was delivered to Dublin 19.11.99 as G-THEA and will operate in those marks from Weston)

Regn	Type	C/n	P/I	Date	Owner/operator	Probable Base	CA Expy
G-THEL	Robinson R-44 Astro	0159	G-OCCB	2. 9.98	London Helicopter Centre Ltd	Redhill	3. 5.01T
			G-STMM				
G-THEO	TEAM miniMax 91	PFA/186-13099		9. 2.99	T.Willford	Blandford Forum	
G-THLS	MBB Bo.105DBS-4	S.80/859	G-BCXO	20. 2.92	Bond Air Services	RAF St.Mawgan	27. 2.01T
	(Rebuilt with new pod c/n S.859 1992)		D-HDCE		(Op by Trinity House Lighthouse Service)		
G-THOM	Thunder Ax6-56 HAFB	366		14. 7.81	T.H.Wilson "Macavity"	Diss	22. 6.00A
G-THOS	Thunder Ax7-77 HAFB	769		20. 2.86	C.E.A.Breton	Bristol	12.10.99A
G-THOT	Avtech Jabiru SK	PFA/274-13159		16. 9.97	N.V.Cook	(Cranleigh)	6. 1.00P
G-THRE	Cessna 182S Skylane	18280454	N2391A	6. 5.99	S.J.G.Mole	(Halesowen)	5. 5.02
G-THSL	PA-28R-201 Arrow III	28R-7837278	N36396	11. 9.78	D.M.Markscheffel	Southend	28. 4.00
G-THUN	Republic P-47D Thunderbolt-			18. 6.99	Patina Ltd	Duxford	7. 7.00P
					(Op The Fighter Collection: as "226413/ZU-N" in 56th FG USAAF c/s)		

(Note 1: Composite re-build from wreck of original N47DD plus new P-47N fuselage identification unknown)
(Note 2: "Original" N47DD is c/n 399-55731 ex Peruvian AF 119/Peruvian AF 545/45-49192 and is also exhibited statically at Duxford in the American Air Museum.)

Regn	Type	C/n	P/I	Date	Owner/operator	Probable Base	CA Expy
G-THZL	Socata TB-20 Trinidad	534	F-GJDR	9. 5.96	Ewan Ltd	Gloucestershire	1. 8.02T
			N65TB				
G-TICL	Airbus A.320-231	169	OY-CNG	10.12.96	Airtours International Airways Ltd		
			F-WWIH			Manchester	11.12.02T
G-TIDS	SAN Jodel 150 Mascaret	44	OO-GAN	15. 4.86	J.B.Dovey	Crowfield	27. 4.99P
G-TIGA	DH.82A Tiger Moth	83547	G-AOEG	5. 6.85	D.E.Leatherland	Nottingham	20. 8.01T
			T7120				
G-TIGB	Aerospatiale AS.332L Super Puma	2023	G-BJXC	31. 3.82	Bristow Helicopters Ltd	Aberdeen	27. 4.01T
			F-WTNM		"City of Aberdeen"		
G-TIGC	Aerospatiale AS.332L Super Puma	2024	G-BJYH	14. 4.82	Bristow Helicopters Ltd	Aberdeen	17. 5.02T
			F-WTNJ		"Royal Burgh of Montrose"		
G-TIGE	Aerospatiale AS.332L Super Puma	2028	G-BJYJ	15. 4.82	Bristow Helicopters Ltd	Aberdeen	7. 6.01T
			F-WTNM		"City of Dundee"		
G-TIGF	Aerospatiale AS.332L Super Puma	2030	F-WKQJ	15. 4.82	Bristow Helicopters Ltd	Aberdeen	27. 6.00T
					"Peterhead"		
G-TIGG	Aerospatiale AS.332L Super Puma	2032	F-WXFT	15. 4.82	Bristow Helicopters Ltd	Aberdeen	1. 8.01T
					"Macduff"		
G-TIGH*	Aerospatiale AS.332L Super Puma	2034	F-WXFL	15. 4.82	Bristow Helicopters Ltd	Aberdeen	24. 8.92T
				(Damaged 100m NE of Shetland Isles 14.3.92; used as Escape trainer 12.95)			
G-TIGI	Aerospatiale AS.332L Super Puma	2036	F-WTNP	15. 4.82	Bristow Helicopters Ltd	Aberdeen	5. 9.02T
					"Fraserburgh"		
G-TIGJ	Aerospatiale AS.332L Super Puma	2042	VH-BHT	15. 4.82	Bristow Helicopters Ltd	Aberdeen	29. 6.02T
			G-TIGJ		"Rosehearty"		
G-TIGL	Aerospatiale AS.332L Super Puma	2050		15. 4.82	Bristow Helicopters Ltd	Aberdeen	9.12.02T
					"Portsoy"		
G-TIGM	Aerospatiale AS.332L Super Puma	2045		15. 4.82	Bristow Helicopters Ltd	Aberdeen	1. 8.00T
					"Banff"		
G-TIGO	Aerospatiale AS.332L Super Puma	2061	F-WMHH	18. 2.83	Bristow Helicopters Ltd	Scatsta	30. 3.00T
					"Royal Burgh of Arbroath"		
G-TIGP	Aerospatiale AS.332L Super Puma	2064		11. 3.83	Bristow Helicopters Ltd	(China)	8. 5.00T
					"Carnoustie"		
G-TIGR	Aerospatiale AS.332L Super Puma	2071	F-WTNW	11. 3.83	Bristow Helicopters Ltd	(Vietnam)	19. 5.02T
					"Stonehaven"		
G-TIGS	Aerospatiale AS.332L Super Puma	2086		6. 5.83	Bristow Helicopters Ltd	Aberdeen	27. 6.02T
					"Findochty"		

Regn	Type	C/n	P/I	Date	Owner/operator	Probable Base	CA Expy
G-TIGT	Aerospatiale AS.332L Super Puma	2078		6. 5.83	Bristow Helicopters Ltd "Portknockie"	Aberdeen	2. 5.01T
G-TIGV	Aerospatiale AS.332L Super Puma	2099	LN-ONC G-TIGV/LN-ONC/G-TIGV/LN-OPF/G-TIGV	12. 1.84	Bristow Helicopters Ltd.	Aberdeen	25. 6.01T
G-TIGZ	Aerospatiale AS.332L Super Puma	2115	C-GQKK G-TIGZ	8. 8.84	Brintel Helicopters Ltd t/a British International Helicopters	Aberdeen	14.10.00T
G-TIII	Aerotek Pitts S-2A Special (Lycoming AEIO-360)	2196	G-BGSE N947	27. 2.89	D.G.Cowden	Redhill	14. 7.01
G-TIKO	Hatz CB-1	PFA/143-13396		9. 7.99	K.Robb t/a Tiko Architecture	(Yeovil)	
G-TILE	Robinson R-22 Beta	1100		4. 8.89	M.J.Webb & C.R.Woodwiss	Coventry	16. 2.02T
G-TILI	Bell 206B Jet Ranger II	2061	F-GHFN N7037A/XC-BOQ	6. 3.96	C.I.Threlfall t/a CIM Helicopters Ream Hill Farm, Weeton, Preston		22. 4.02
G-TIMB	Rutan VariEze (Continental O-200-A)	PFA/74-10795	G-BKXJ	11. 6.85	T.M.Bailey "Kitty"	Shoreham	14. 6.00P
G-TIME	PA-61P Aerostar 601P	61P-0541-230	(N8058J)	21. 7.78	T & G Engineering Co Ltd	(West Byfleet)	21.12.02
G-TIMJ*	Rand Robinson KR-2 (VW1834)	PFA/129-11112		25.11.85	N.Seaton (Cancelled by CAA 4.5.99)	Bidford	
G-TIMK	PA-28-181 Archer II	28-8090214	OO-TRT PH-EAS/OO-HLN/N8142H	25. 8.81	T.Baker	Halfpenny Green	12. 2.00
G-TIMM	Folland Gnat T.1	FL.519	8618M XP504	19. 2.92	T.J.Manna t/a Kennet Aviation (As "XM693")	Cranfield	23. 2.00P
G-TIMP	Aeronca 7BCM Champion (Continental C85)	7AC-3392	N84681 NC84681	14. 8.92	T.E.Phillips "Nancy" Hill Farm, Nayland		17. 1.99P
G-TIMS	Falconar F-12A	PFA/22-12134		1.10.91	T.Sheridan	Wellingborough	
G-TIMW*	PA-28-140 Cherokee C	28-26404	G-AXSH	22. 3.85	Taylor Aircraft Servics Ltd Sywell (Crashed nr Netherthorpe 25.3.90; stored 3.91)		15. 5.91T
G-TIMY	Gardan GY-80-160 Horizon	36	I-TIKI	17. 1.00	R.G.Whyte	(Rugby)	
G-TINA	Socata TB-10 Tobago	67		30.10.79	A.Lister	Old Buckenham	13. 8.01
G-TING	Cameron O-120 HAFB	4007		4.10.96	Floating Sensations Ltd Thatcham, Berks		5.11.99T
G-TINS	Cameron N-90 HAFB	1626		27. 1.88	J.R.Clifton	Brackley	15. 8.99A
G-TINY	Moravan Zlin Z.526F Trener Master	1257	OK-CMD G-TINY/YR-ZAD	4.94	Air V8 Ltd	North Weald	17. 8.98
G-TIPS	Tipsy Nipper T.66 Srs.5 (Jabiru) (Rebuild of Fairey c/n 50)	PFA/25-12696	OO-VAL 9Q-CYJ/90-CYJ/(OO-CYJ)/(OO-CCD)	27. 3.95	R.F.L.Cuypers	Keiheuvel, Belgium	10. 5.00P
G-TJAY	PA-22-135 Tri-Pacer	22-730	N730TJ N2353A	11. 5.93	D.D.Saint Garston Farm, Marshfield		22. 7.01
G-TJHI	Cessna 500 Citation I (Unit No.363)	500-0354	G-CCCL N51GA/G-BEIZ/(N5363J)	17. 1.92	Trustair Ltd	Blackpool	21. 7.01T
G-TJPM	BAe 146 Srs.300QT	E-3150	SE-DIM G-BRGK	4. 7.94	TNT Express Worldwide (UK) Ltd Stansted (Skypak International Couriers c/s)		3. 7.00T
G-TKAY	Europa Avn Europa	PFA/247-12804		2. 6.99	A.M.Kay	(Hertford)	29. 7.00P
G-TKGR	Lindstrand Racing Car SS HAFB	380		28. 8.96	Brown & Williamson Tobacco Corporation (Export) Ltd "Team Green" Louisville, KY, USA		20. 8.99A
G-TKIS	Tri-R Kis 029 & (Lycoming O-290) (Tail-wheel variant)	PFA/239-12358		23.12.93	J.L.Bone	Biggin Hill	15.12.00P
G-TKPZ	Cessna 310R II	310R-1225	G-BRAH N1909G	19. 3.90	Fraggle Leasing Ltd	Edinburgh	1. 4.02T
G-TLDK	PA-22-150 Tri-Pacer	22-4726	N6072D	27. 1.97	A.M.Thomson	(King's Lynn)	
G-TLME	Robinson R-44 Astro	0062		13. 4.94	TJB Associates Ltd	Blackpool	22. 7.00T
G-TMCC	Cameron N-90 HAFB	4327		30. 3.98	Prudential Assurance Co Ltd Bristol "The Mall/Cribbs Causeway"		11. 2.00A
G-TMDP	Airbus A.320-231	168	OY-CNF (D-ADSL)/OY-CNF/F-WWIF	19.11.96	Airtours International Airways Ltd	Manchester	19.11.02T
G-TMKI	Percival P.56 Provost T.1	PAC/F/268	WW453	1. 7.92	B.L.Robinson, (As "WW453/W-S" in RAF c/s)	(Clevedon)	
G-TNTB	BAe 146 Srs.200QT	E-2067	G-5-067 (N145AC)/(G-BNFG)	3. 3.87	TNT Express Worldwide (UK) Ltd	Luton	17. 9.02T
G-TNTD	BAe 146-Srs 200QT	E-2109	RP-C481 G-TNTD/SE-DHM/G-BOMJ/G-5-109	29.12.89	GD Express Worldwide NV Amsterdam, The Netherlands		AC
G-TNTE	BAe 146 Srs.300QT	E-3153	G-BRPW	8. 6.90	TNT Express Worldwide (UK) Ltd	Luton	5. 6.02T
G-TNTG	BAe 146 Srs.300QT	E-3182	G-BSUY	21.10.91	TNT European Airlines Ltd	Luton	1.10.02T
G-TNTI	Airbus A.300B4-203	155	N72987 TC-ALR/N72987/(N987C)/N224EA/F-GBNS	12.10.99	TNT Express Worldwide (UK) Ltd Stansted		18.10.02T
G-TNTK	BAe 146 Srs.300QT	E-3186	G-BSXL G-6-186	30. 1.92	TNT European Airlines Ltd	Luton	10.10.01T
G-TNTL	BAe 146 Srs.300QT	E-3168	RP-C479 G-TNTL/G-BSGI/(RP-C479)/G-BSGI/G-6-168	7. 2.92	TNT European Airlines Ltd	Luton	27.10.00T
G-TNTM	BAe 146 Srs.300QT	E-3166	RP-C480 G-TNTM/G-BSLZ/G-6-166	28. 2.92	TNT European Airlines Ltd	Luton	27.10.00T
G-TNTN	Thunder Ax6-56 HAFB	1991		25. 4.91	H.M.Savage & J.F.Trehern	Edinburgh	29. 4.92A

Regn	Type	C/n	P/I	Date	Owner/operator	Probable Base	CA Expy
G-TNTR	BAe 146 Srs.300QT	E-3151	SE-DIT G-BRGM	4. 7.94	TNT Express Worldwide (UK) Ltd Luton (XP Parcel System c/s)		3. 7.00T
G-TNTS	Airbus A.300B4-103	124	G-CEXC N407U/N407UA/N220EA/F-GBNO	10. 2.00	TNT Express Worldwide (UK) Ltd Stansted		
G-TOAD	SAN Jodel D.140 Mousquetaire	27	F-BIZG	27. 9.88	J.H.Stevens	Headcorn	25.10.98
G-TOAK	Socata TB-20 Trinidad	468	N83AV	5.12.89	R.Chown	Teesside	4. 7.02
G-TOBA	Socata TB-10 Tobago	625	N600N	4. 4.91	E.J.Downing Farley Farm, Winchester		31. 7.00
G-TOBE*	PA-28R-200 Cherokee Arrow II	28R-7435148	G-BNRO N40979	25.11.87	Not known Headcorn (Damaged nr Cranbrook, Kent 6.3.92; stored 8.96)		6. 3.94
G-TOBI	Reims Cessna F.172K	0792	G-AYYB	5. 1.84	G.Hall	Henstridge	14. 7.02
G-TOBY*	Cessna 172B	47852	G-ARCM N6952X	8. 4.81	Northbrook College Shoreham (Damaged Sandown 15.10.83; instructional airframe 10.96)		28. 4.85
G-TODD	ICA IS-28M2A	59		18. 4.86	C.I.Roberts & C.D.King	Shobdon	7. 9.01
G-TODE	Ruschmeyer R90-230RG	016	D-EEAX	20. 6.94	Tode Ltd	Denham	8.10.00
G-TOFT	Colt 90A HAFB	1693		8. 3.90	C.S.Perceval "Bumble" Great Missenden		17. 6.00A
G-TOGA*	PA-32-301 Saratoga	32-8006028	G-BIEG N81852	15.11.82	Not known Blackpool (Damaged Belmont, Lancs 29. 8.93; status unknown)		1. 2.95
G-TOGO	Van's RV-6	PFA/181A-13447		6. 4.99	G.Schwetz	(Southampton)	
G-TOMG	Hunting P.84 Jet Provost T.4	9030M PAC/W/19987	XR674	31. 8.94	Kingspride Associates Ltd Lydd (Sword's Aerobatic Team c/s: as "XW428") (Crashed Woolaston Grange, Lydney, Glos 1.8.99 & destroyed)		26.11.99P
G-TOMS	PA-38-112 Tomahawk	38-79A0453		22. 1.79	Polawood Aviation Ltd Wellesbourne Mountford		5. 8.00T
G-TOOL	Thunder Ax8-105 HAFB	1670		29. 3.90	W.J.Honey "Trademaster" Bristol		5. 7.00A
G-TOPC	Aerospatiale AS.355F1 Twin Squirrel	5313	I-LGOG 3A-MCS/D-HOSY/OE-BXV/D-HOSY	29. 7.97	Bridge Street Nominees Ltd (Hemel Hempstead)		6.11.00T
G-TOPS	Aerospatiale AS.355F1 Twin Squirrel	5151	G-BPRH N360E/N5794F	7. 5.91	Sterling Helicopters Ltd Norwich		7.12.01T
G-TORE	Hunting-Percival P.84 Jet Provost T.3A	PAC/W/9212	XM405	14. 6.91	Butane Buzzard Aviation Corporation Ltd (Op Kennet Aviation: as "42": stored 7.96) Cranfield		5. 5.95P
G-TORS	Robinson R-22 Beta	3021		4. 1.00	GT Investigations (International) Ltd NK		
G-TOSH*	Robinson R-22 Beta	0933	N2629S	14. 3.97	Heli Air Ltd Blackpool (Cancelled by CAA 29.12.99)		20. 3.00T
G-TOTO	Reims Cessna F.177RG Cardinal	0049	G-OADE G-AZKH	29. 8.89	W.G.Walton	Blackbushe	14. 8.97
G-TOUR	Robin R.2112	187		9.10.79	Mardenair Ltd	Goodwood	12. 3.01T
G-TOWS	PA-25-260 Pawnee C (Mod 4 blade Hoffman propeller)	25-4853	PH-VBT D-EAVI/N4370Y	17. 7.91	Lasham Gliding Society Ltd Lasham		23.12.00
G-TOYS	Enstrom 280C-UK-2 Shark	1218	G-BISE	17. 6.82	Stephenson Aviation Ltd Goodwood (Stored 4.96)		26. 2.94T
G-TOYZ	Bell 206B Jet Ranger III	3949	G-RGER N75EA/JA9452/N32018	21.11.96	P.B.Ellis Blackpool		29. 9.00T
G-TPSL	Cessna 182S	182-80398	N23700	11.12.98	A.N.Purslow	Blackbushe	17.12.01T
G-TPTS	Robinson R-44 Astro	0457		24. 4.98	Superstore Ltd	(Runcorn)	6. 5.01
G-TRAC	Robinson R-44 Astro	0598		10. 5.99	C.Sharples	(Newbury)	9. 6.02T
G-TRAM	Cyclone Pegasus Quantum 15	7552		29. 7.99	T.F.J.Roach Knapthorpe Lodge, Caunton		28. 7.00P
G-TRAN	Beechcraft 76 Duchess	ME-408	G-NIFR N1808A	15. 3.93	G T & J M Peck Guernsey		7. 9.01T
G-TRCY	Robinson R-44 Astro	0668		22.10.99	T.Fletcher	(Newark)	18.11.02
G-TREC	Cessna 421C Golden Eagle III	421C-0838	G-TLOL (N2659K)	2. 7.96	C.P.Lockyer	Coventry	18 2.00
G-TRED	Cameron Colt Bibendum 110SS HAFB	4222		12.12.97	The Aerial Display Co Ltd	Looe	23. 9.99A
G-TREE	Bell 206B JetRanger III	2826	N2779U	15. 6.87	LGH Aviation Ltd Fairoaks (Op Alan Mann Helicopters)		9.12.02T
G-TREK	Jodel D.18 182 & PFA/169-11265 (Limbach L.2000)			1. 5.92	R.H.Mole	Leicester	1. 8.00P
G-TREN	Boeing 737-4S3	24796	G-BRKG	3. 4.91	GB Airways Ltd Gatwick (Blue Poole t/s)		11. 7.02T
G-TRIB	Lindstrand HS-110 Hot Air Airship (Rotax 582)	174	(N...)	23. 1.95	J Addison Melton Mowbray		17. 8.99A
G-TRIC	DHC.1 Chipmunk 22A	C1/0080	G-AOSZ WB635	18.12.89	D.M.Barnett North Weald (As "18013" in RCAF c/s)		7. 9.00
G-TRIM	Monnett Moni 00258T & PFA/142-11012			16. 2.84	J.E.Bennell	(High Wycombe)	
G-TRIN	Socata TB-20 Trinidad	1131		25. 6.90	Isnet Ltd	Cambridge	7. 1.00
G-TRIO	Cessna 172M Skyhawk II	172-66271	G-BNXY N9621H	30. 7.91	C.M.B.Reid Biggin Hill		30.12.99T
G-TRIX	VS.509 Spitfire Trainer IX CBAF.9590		(G-BHGH) IAC161/G-15-174/PV202 (As "PV202/5R-Q" in 33 Sqdn c/s)	2. 7.80	R.A.Roberts Goodwood		13. 6.00P
G-TROP	Cessna T310R II	T310R-1381	N4250C	31.12.86	D E Carpenter	Shoreham	29. 4.02T

434

Regn	Type	C/n	P/I	Date	Owner/operator	Probable Base	CA Expy
G-TROY	North American T-28A Fennec	142/174-545	F-AZFV FrAF No 142/51-7692	21. 4.99	S.G.Howell & S.Tilling	Duxford	
G-TRUC*	Cassutt Speed One (Possibly a re-registration of G-MARY)	PFA/34-11400		20. 6.89	J.A.H.Chadwick (Cancelled by CAA 4.5.99)	(London NW8)	
G-TRUE	MDH Hughes 369E	0490E	N6TK ZK-HFP	12. 9.94	B.M.Christie t/a Horizon Helicopter Hire	Goodwood	28.10.00T
G-TRUK	Stoddard-Hamilton Glasair IIRG (Lycoming O-320)	575R & PFA/149-11015		23. 7.84	M.P.Jackson	Fairoaks	26. 4.00P
G-TRUX	Colt 77A HAFB	1860		13.11.90	Highway Truck Rental Ltd	Gateshead	2.12.99A
G-TSAM	BAe 125 Srs.800B	258028	G-5-12	31. 1.85	British Aerospace (Operations) Ltd	Warton	13. 6.00
G-TSAR	Beechcraft 58 Baron	TH-1698	N81287	9. 2.94	Thornfield Enterprises Ltd	Guernsey	24. 3.00
G-TSFT	PA-28-161 Warrior II	28-8216117	G-BLDJ N9632N	5. 4.89	SFT Europe Ltd	Bournemouth	7. 2.02T
G-TSGJ	PA-28-181 Archer II	28-8090109	N8097W	12. 9.88	A.Dove & A.D.S.Peat t/a Golf Juliet Flying Club	Teesside	23.11.00
G-TSIX	North American AT-6C-1NT Harvard IIA	88-9725	FAP1535 SAAF7183/EX289/41-33262 (As "111836/JZ/6" in USN c/s)	19. 3.79	J.Zemlik	Breighton	29. 1.00P
G-TSKY	Beagle B.121 Pup Srs.2	B121-010	OE-CFM HB-NAA/G-AWDY/HB-NAA/G-AWDY	6. 4.98	R.G.Hayes	Elstree	7. 5.01T
G-TSMI	Rockwell Commander 114	14249	OO-TSM	8. 6.93	J.J.J.C.Herbaux	St.Ghislain, Belgium	26. 9.02
G-TTAM*	Taylor JT.2 Titch (VW1600)	PFA/3229		14.12.78	C.H.Morris (Cancelled by CAA 28.4.99)	(Polegate, E.Sussex)	
G-TTDD	Zenair CH.701 STOL	PFA/187-13106		1. 9.97	D.B.Dainton & V.D.Asque	Sackville Farm, Riseley	9. 2.00T
G-TTFN	Cessna 560 Citation V	560-0537	N5181V	19.11.99	Corporate Administration Management Ltd	Shoreham	18.11.02T
G-TTHC	Robinson R-22 Beta	1196		21.12.89	P.N.Briggs t/a North West Auto Engineering	Bristol	27. 5.02T
G-TTIM	Cassutt Racer IIIM	PFA/34-13116		10. 7.98	J.D.Llewellyn	(Coalville)	
G-TTMC	Airbus A.300B4-203	299	OH-LAA (LX-LGP)/F-WZMX	25. 4.98	OY Air Scandic International Aviation AB	Manchester	29. 4.01T
G-TTOY	CFM Streak Shadow SA (Rotax 618)	233-SA & PFA/206-12805		15. 4.96	S.Marriott	Old Sarum	19. 7.00P
G-TTWO*	Colt 56A HAFB	087		14. 5.80	R S Kent "Tea 4 Two" (Balloon Preservation Group 7.98)	Lancing	1. 9.87A
G-TUBB	Avtech Jabiru UL-450 (Jabiru 2200A)	PFA/274A-13484		1.10.99	A.H.Bower	Kemble	14.11.00P
G-TUDR	Cameron V-77 HAFB	1135		20. 5.85	Jacques W.Soukup Enterprises Ltd "Tudor Rose/HVIIIR"	Chippenham	21. 3.99A
G-TUGG	PA-18-180 Super Cub (Frame No.18-8497)	18-8274	PH-MAH N5451Y	10. 1.83	Ulster Gliding Club Ltd	Bellarena	30. 3.01
G-TUGY	Robin DR.400/180 Regent	2052	D-EPAR	27. 4.98	J.M.Airey	Saltby	19. 5.01T
G-TUKE	Robin DR.400/160 Major 80	1542		2. 6.81	J.W.F. & S.M.Tuke t/a Tukair Acft Charter	Headcorn	18. 3.02T
G-TULL	Avtech Jabiru UL	PFA/274A-13535		29.10.99	W.R.Tull	(Chipping Norton)	
G-TUNE	Robinson R-22 Beta	0818	N60661 G-OJVI/(G-OJVJ)	12. 1.99	Ecurie Ecosse (Scotland) Ltd (Pitlochry)		7. 2.02T
G-TURF	Reims Cessna F.406 Caravan II	0020	PH-FWF (EI-CND)/PH-FWF/F-WZDS (Air Atlantic c/s)	17.10.96	Atlantic Air Transport Ltd	Coventry	21.11.00T
G-TURK	Cameron Sultan 80SS HAFB	1711		12. 4.88	Forbes Europe Inc "Suliman"	Balleroy, Normandy	18. 6.00A
G-TURN	Steen Skybolt (Lycoming IO-360)	003 & PFA/64-11349		14. 7.88	R.C.Berger	Turweston	24. 2.00P
G-TUSK	Bell 206B Jet Ranger 4	4406	G-BWZH N53114	13. 1.97	Zeuros Ltd	Blackbushe	23. 2.00T
G-TVAA	Agusta A.109E Power	11052		24. 9.99	Sloane Helicopters Ltd (for Thames Valley Air Ambulance)	Sywell	23. 2.00T
G-TVBF	Lindstrand LBL-310A HAFB	439		2. 4.97	Virgin Balloon Flights Ltd (London SE16)		20. 4.00T
G-TVII	Hawker Hunter T.7	41H-693834	XX467 RJAF 836/RSAF 70-617/G-9-214/XL605 (Carries "XX467" in TWU c/s)	8.12.97	G.R.Montgomery	Kemble	
G-TVIJ	CCF Harvard 4 (T-6J-CCF Texan)	CCF4-442	G-BSBE Moz PLAF 1730 FAP 1730/AA+652/52-8521 (As "28521/TA-521" in USAF c/s)	10.12.93	R.W.Davies	Little Robhurst Farm, Woodchurch	26. 5.00P
G-TVSI	Campbell Cricket (Rotax 503)	CA/340	G-AYHH	8. 4.82	C.Smith	Kemble	16. 4.98P
G-TVTV	Cameron TV 90SS HAFB	2357		14. 9.90	J.Krebs	Erfstadt, Germany	2. 6.99A
G-TWEL	PA-28-181 Archer II	28-8090290	N81963	12. 6.80	International Aerospace Engineering Ltd	Cranfield	22. 4.02T
G-TWEY	Colt 69A HAFB	700		24. 7.85	N.Bland	Didcot	9. 1.99A

Regn	Type	C/n	P/I	Date	Owner/operator	Probable Base	CA Expy
G-TWIG	Reims Cessna F.406 Caravan II	0014	PH-FWD F-WZDS	21.10.98	Highland Airways Ltd	Inverness	22.10.01T
G-TWIN	PA-44-180 Seminole	44-7995072	N30267	6.11.78	Bonus Aviation Ltd	Cranfield	25. 3.00T
G-TWIZ	Rockwell Commander 114	14375	SE-GSP N5808N	9. 5.90	B.C.& P M Cox	Redhill	5. 7.02
G-TWTD	CCF Hawker Sea Hurricane X	CCF/41H/8020	(Russia) AE977	6. 5.94	Hawker Restorations Ltd Moat Farm, Milden		
G-TXSE	Rotary Air Force RAF 2000 GTX-SE (Subaru EJ22)	PFA G/113-1271		1. 3.96	Software Development International Ltd Long Acre Farm, West Clandon (Damaged in ground incident & stored Henstridge 4.99)		1. 1.98P
G-TYGA	Gulfstream AA-5B Tiger	AA5B-1161	G-BHNZ (D-EGDS)/N4547L	22. 2.82	G.J.Wilmshurst	Biggin Hill	29. 1.01T
G-TYNE	Socata TB-20 Trindad	1523	F-GRBM F-WWRW/CS-AZH/F-OHDE	6.11.97	D.T.Watkins	Newcastle	19.11.00
G-TYPO	Robinson R-22 Beta	1040	G-JBWI	9. 8.99	J.E.& M.J.Morris t/a The Type Marketing Co	Gloucestershire	19. 7.01T
G-TYRE	Reims Cessna F.172M Skyhawk II	1222	OY-BIA	16. 2.79	J.A.Lyons t/a Staverton Flying School	Gloucestershire	2. 9.00T
G-TZII	Thorp T.211B	PFA/305-13285		2. 6.99	AD Aerospace Ltd	Barton	

G-UAAA – G-UZZZ

Regn	Type	C/n	P/I	Date	Owner/operator	Probable Base	CA Expy
G-UAPA	Robin DR.400/140B Major	2213	F-GMXC	11. 1.95	Aeromarine Ltd Owslebury, Southampton		10. 6.01
G-UAPO	Ruschmeyer R90-230RG	019	D-EECT	2. 3.95	S.J.Green	Lagoa, Portugal	21. 6.01
G-UCCC	Cameron Sign 90SS HAFB	3918		5. 7.96	Flying Pictures Ltd "Unipart Car Care Centres"	Fairoaks	6. 9.99A
G-UDAY	Robinson R-22 Beta	1101		4. 8.89	Newmarket Plant Hire Ltd	Cambridge	11. 5.02T
G-UDGE	Thruster T.600N (Rotax 503UL)	9099-T600N-037	G-BYPI	17. 9.99	L.J.Appleby	(Keyworth, Notts)	20. 9.00P
G-UEST	Bell 206B JetRanger II	1484	G-RYOB G-BLWU/ZS-PAW	8. 9.89	E.& S.Vandyk	(Newbury)	20. 1.00T
G-UESY	Robinson R-22 Beta-II	2801		13. 3.98	EW Guess (Holdings) Ltd	(Stamford)	2. 4.01
G-UFCA	Cessna 172S Skyhawk	172S8313	N2461P	26. 1.00	Oxford Aviation Services Ltd	Oxford	
G-UFCB	Cessna 172S Skyhawk	172S8318	N455SP	25. 1.00	Oxford Aviation Services Ltd	Oxford	
G-UFLY	Reims Cessna F.150H	0264	G-AVVY	29. 9.89	Westair Flying Services Ltd	Blackpool	16.11.01T
G-UIDA*	Star-Lite SL-1 211 & PFA/175-11440 (Rotax 447)		G-BRKK	23. 9.91	I.J.Widger (Rancho Palos Verdes, California) (Cancelled by CAA 1.6.99)		11. 3.99P
G-UIDE	Jodel Wassmer D.120 Paris-Nice	262	F-BMIY	27. 5.80	S.T.Gilbert (Burnham, Slough) (Damaged Aldbury, Bucks 10.9.88)		16. 6.89P
G-UILD	Grob G-109B	6419		28. 1.86	Runnymede Consultants Ltd Longbridge Deverill		22. 3.01
G-UILE	Neico Lancair 320	PFA/191-12538		17. 1.94	R.J.Martin	(Alresford, Hants)	
G-UINN	Stolp SA.300 Starduster Too (Lycoming 0-360)	HB.1980-1	EI-CDQ C-GTLJ	16. 3.98	J.D.H.Gordon	(Galashiels)	21. 5.99P
G-UJAB	Avtech Jabiru UL	PFA/274A-13373		27. 1.99	C.A.Thomas	(Huntingdon)	19. 8.00P
G-UKAC	BAe 146 Srs.300	E-3142	G-5-142	25.10.89	KLM UK Ltd	Stansted	19.11.01T
G-UKAG	BAe 146 Srs.300	E-3162	G-6-162	28.11.90	Air UK Ltd	Stansted	11.12.02T
G-UKFA	Fokker F.100.620	11246	N602RP C-FICY/PH-EZB	1. 7.92	KLM UK Ltd	Norwich	12.10.02T
G-UKFB	Fokker F.100.620	11247	N602TR C-FICW/PH-EZC	1. 7.92	KLM UK Ltd	Norwich	12. 8.02T
G-UKFC	Fokker F.100-620	11263	N602DG C-FICL/PH-EZF	1. 7.92	KLM UK Ltd	Norwich	27. 7.02T
G-UKFD	Fokker F.100-620	11259	C-FICP PH-EZJ	22. 7.92	KLM UK Ltd	Norwich	9.11.02T
G-UKFE	Fokker F.100-620	11260	C-FICQ PH-EZK	22. 7.92	Air UK Ltd	Inverness	30.11.02T
G-UKFF	Fokker F.100-620	11274	PH-ZCK (G-FIOB)/PH-ZCK/PH-EZB/(PH-KLK)	9.11.93	Air UK Ltd	Norwich	8.11.00T
G-UKFG	Fokker F.100-620	11275	PH-ZCL (G-FIOC)/PH-ZCL/PH-EZV/(PH-KLL)	19.11.93	KLM UK Ltd	Norwich	18.11.00T
G-UKFH	Fokker F.100-620	11277	PH-ZCM (G-FIOD)/PH-ZCM/PH-EZW/(PH-KLN)	29. 9.93	KLM UK Ltd	Norwich	28. 9.00T
G-UKFI	Fokker F.100-620	11279	PH-ZCN (G-FIOE)/PH-ZCN/PH-EZX/(PH-KLO)	12.10.93	KLM UK Ltd	Norwich	11.10.00T
G-UKFJ	Fokker F.100-620	11248	F-GIOV C-FICB/PH-INC/PH-EZD	30. 1.96	KLM UK Ltd	Norwich	22. 2.02T
G-UKFK	Fokker F.100-620	11249	F-GIOX C-FICO/PH-INA/PH-EZE	19. 2.96	KLM UK Ltd	Norwich	1. 4.02T

Regn	Type	C/n	P/I	Date	Owner/operator	Probable Base	CA Expy
G-UKFL	Fokker F.100-620	11268	PH-KLC	14. 8.97	KLM UK Ltd	Norwich	18. 8.00T
			F-GIDT/F-OGDI/F-GIDT/F-OGQI/PH-KLC				
G-UKFM	Fokker F.100-620	11269	PH-KLD	27.10.98	KLM UK Ltd.	Stansted	25.11.01T
			F-GIDQ/PH-KLD				
G-UKFN	Fokker F.100-620	11270	PH-KLE	16. 6.97	KLM UK Ltd	Norwich	21. 7.00T
			F-GIDP/PH-KLE				
G-UKFO	Fokker F.100-620	11271	PH-KLG	20.10.97	KLM UK Ltd	Norwich	20.10.00T
			F-GIDO/PH-KLG				
G-UKFP	Fokker F.100-620	11272	PH-KLH	27.10.98	KLM UK Ltd.	Stansted	28.10.01T
			F-GIDN/F-OGQA/PH-KLH				
G-UKFR	Fokker F.100-620	11273	PH-KLI	21. 3.97	KLM UK Ltd	Norwich	26. 3.00T
			F-GIDM/F-OGQB/PH-KLI				
G-UKHP	BAe 146 Srs.300	E-3123	G-5-123	26.10.88	KLM UK Ltd	Stansted	26. 2.02T
G-UKID	BAe 146 Srs.300	E-3157	G-6-157	28. 2.90	KLM UK Ltd	Stansted	6. 3.02T
G-UKOZ	Avtech Jabiru SK	PFA/274-13310		16. 6.99	D.J.Burnett	(Wallingford)	
G-UKRB	Colt 105A HAFB	1769		10.12.90	Virgin Airship & Balloon Co Ltd	Telford	16. 5.97A
					"Lloyds Bank II"		
G-UKRC	BAe 146 Srs.300	E-3158	G-BSMR	14. 2.91	KLM UK Ltd	Stansted	24. 2.02T
			G-6-158				
G-UKSC	BAe 146 Srs.300	E-3125	G-5-125	26.10.88	KLM UK Ltd "City of Innsbruck"	Stansted	9. 3.02T
G-UKTA	Fokker F.27-050	20246	PH-KXF	22. 2.95	KLM UK Ltd "City of Norwich"	Norwich	21. 2.01T
G-UKTB	Fokker F.27-050	20247	PH-KXG	21. 3.95	KLM UK Ltd "City of Aberdeen"	Norwich	21. 3.01T
G-UKTC	Fokker F.27-050	20249	PH-KXH	25. 1.95	KLM UK Ltd "City of Bradford"	Norwich	25. 1.01T
G-UKTD	Fokker F.27-050	20256	PH-KXT	20. 1.95	KLM UK Ltd "City of Leeds"	Norwich	19. 1.01T
G-UKTE	Fokker F.27-050	20270	PH-LXJ	14. 2.95	KLM UK Ltd "City of Hull"	Norwich	14. 2.01T
G-UKTF	Fokker F.27-050	20271	PH-LXK	31. 1.95	KLM UK Ltd "City of York"	Norwich	31. 1.01T
G-UKTG	Fokker F.27-050	20276	PH-LXP	28. 2.95	KLM UK Ltd "City of Durham"	Norwich	28. 2.01T
G-UKTH	Fokker F.27-050	20277	PH-LXR	28. 3.95	KLM UK Ltd "City of Amsterdam"	Norwich	28. 3.01T
G-UKTI	Fokker F.27-050	20279	PH-LXT	17. 3.95	Air UK Ltd "City of Stavanger"	Norwich	16. 3.01T
G-UKTJ	Aerospatiale/Alenia ATR-72-202	509		19.12.97	KLM UK Ltd	Norwich	18.12.00T
G-UKTK	Aerospatiale/Alenia ATR-72-202	519	F-WWLQ	30. 1.98	KLM UK Ltd	Norwich	29. 1.01T
G-UKTL	Aerospatiale/Alenia ATR-72-202	523	F-WWLD	10. 3.98	KLM UK Ltd	Stansted	9. 3.01T
					(Damaged at Norwich 14.5.98)		
G-UKTM	Aerospatiale/Alenia ATR-72-202	508	F-WWLU	23. 4.98	KLM UK Ltd	Stansted	22. 4.01T
G-UKTN	Aerospatiale/Alenia ATR-72-202	496	F-WWLT	4. 6.98	KLM UK Ltd	Stansted	3. 6.01T
G-UKUK	Head Ax8-105 HAFB	248	N8303U	1. 9.97	P.A.George	Princes Risborough	3. 4.00A
G-ULAB	Robinson R-22 Beta	2444	N8311Z	18. 8.94	I.R.Chisholm	Costock, Loughborough	10. 9.00T
					t/a Bradmore Helicopter Leasing		
G-ULAS	DHC.1 Chipmunk 22	C1/0554	WK517	14. 6.96	Search & Management Services Ltd	Booker	12. 8.02
					(As "WK517")		
G-ULIA	Cameron V-77 HAFB	2860		30. 4.99	J.M.Dean	Oswestry	17 .7.00A
G-ULLS	Lindstrand LBL-90A HAFB	434		18. 2.97	Tanswell of Towcester Ltd	Towcester	21.12.99A
G-ULPS	Everett Gyroplane Srs.1	007	G-BMNY	13. 7.93	The Aziz Corporation Ltd	Winchester	25. 4.00P
	(VW1835)						
G-ULTR	Cameron A-105 HAFB	4100		24. 2.97	P.Glydon	Birmingham	15. 5.00T
					(Ultrafilter titles)		
G-UMBO	Colt Jumbo SS HAFB	747		2. 4.86	Virgin Airship & Balloon Co Ltd	Telford	21. 5.96A
	(Special shape with nose/tail/wings of Virgin 747)				"Virgin Jumbo"		
	(Built as c/n 816 but amended: replacement envelope c/n 1645 fitted 1990)						
G-UMMI	PA-31-310 Turbo Navajo	31-7912060	G-BGSO	11. 8.92	J.A, A.G.M, D.T.A. & J.A.Rees		
			N3519F		t/a Messrs Rees of Poynston West	Haverfordwest	1. 8.00T
G-UNGE	Lindstrand LBL-90A HAFB	122	G-BVPJ	6.12.96	M.T.Stevens	Solihull	25. 7.00A
					t/a Silver Ghost Balloon Club		
G-UNIA	Airbus A.330-2..		F-WW..	R	Leisure International Airways Ltd		
					(For delivery 2.00)	Manchester	
G-UNIB	Airbus A.330-2..		F-WW..	R	Leisure International Airways Ltd		
					(For delivery 2.00)	Manchester	
G-UNIG	Airbus A.321-211		D-AVZ.	R	Leisure International Airways Ltd		
						Manchester	
G-UNIH	Airbus A.321-211		D-AVZ.	R	Leisure International Airways Ltd		
						Manchester	
G-UNII	Airbus A.3..-...			R	Leisure International Airways Ltd		
						Manchester	
G-UNIJ	Airbus A.3..-...			R	Leisure International Airways Ltd		
						Manchester	
G-UNIP	Cameron Oil Container SS HAFB	2532		15. 3.91	Balloon Preservation Group	Lancing	7.11.96A
	(Unipart Sureflow Oil Can)				"Unipart Oil" (For restoration 12.98)		
G-UNIT	Partenavia P.68B	23	G-BCNT	21.10.93	Aliservice SRL	(Pordenone, Italy)	16.12.01T
G-UNIV	Montgomerie-Parsons Two-Place Gyroplane	G-BWTP		3. 8.99	Dept of Aerospace Engg, University of Glasgow		
	PFA G/08-1276					(Glasgow)	

Regn	Type	C/n	P/I	Date	Owner/operator	Probable Base	CA Expy
G-UNNY	BAC 167 Strikemaster mk.87 (Regd with c/n "601")	PS.70	G-AYHR	19. 3.98	Gone Flying Ltd	Duxford	1. 3.00P
			OJ4/Kenya 601/G-27-141/G-AYHR/G-27-191				
G-UNRL	Lindstrand RR-21 HAFB	260		25. 5.95	Virgin Airship & Balloon Co Ltd "Virgin Cola"	Telford	23. 7.99A
G-UNYT	Robinson R-22 Beta	0985	G-BWZV	17.11.97	Cambridge Helicopters Ltd	Cambridge	13.11.00T
			G-LIAN				
G-UPHL	Cameron Concept 80 HAFB	3002		23. 2.93	Uphill Motor Co Ltd (Uphill Motors titles)	Langford, Somerset	8. 9.00T
G-UPMW	Robinson R-22 Beta	1982		31.12.91	Burman Aviation Ltd	Newcastle/Cranfield	5. 2.01T
G-UPPP	Colt 77A HAFB	852		4. 8.86	M.Williams "Nugget"	Wadhurst	25. 3.95A
G-UPPY	Cameron DP-80 Hot-Air Airship	2274		29. 3.90	Jacques W.Soukup Enterprises Ltd "Jacques Soukup" Beaulieu Court, Wilts/Great Missenden		27. 8.94A
G-UPUP	Cameron V-77 HAFB	1828		21. 7.89	S.R.Burden "Fantasia"	Noordwijk, The Netherlands	23. 5.00T
G-URCH	Rotorway Exec 162F	6414		1.10.99	D.L.Urch	(Winscombe)	AC
G-UROP	Beechcraft B55 Baron	TC-2452	N64311	17. 9.90	Pooler International Ltd	Sleap	27. 2.00
G-URRR	Air Command 582 Sport	0630 & PFA G/104-1200		13. 6.90	L.Armes	(Basildon)	
G-URUH*	Robinson R-44 Astro	0354		3. 7.97	Heli Air Ltd (Cancelled by CAA 29.12.99)	Wellesbourne Mountford	10. 8.00T
G-USAM	Cameron Uncle Sam SS HAFB	1120		20. 5.85	Jacques W.Soukup Enterprises Ltd		
	(Uncle Sam head shape) (New envelope 1999 - c/n not known)					S.Dakota, USA	27. 6.00A
G-USFT	PA-23-250 Aztec F	27-7654174	G-BEGV	8. 5.97	SFT Europe Ltd	Bournemouth	4. 9.00T
			N62720				
G-USGB	Colt 105A HAFB	1130		26. 8.87	Virgin Airship & Balloon Co Ltd "Virgin Replica"	Telford	22.11.92A
G-USIL	Thunder Ax7-77 HAFB	1587		22. 8.89	Window on the World Ltd "Mantis"	London SE1	27. 5.99A
G-USMC	Cameron Chestie 90SS HAFB	1251		24. 4.86	Jacques W.Soukup Enterprises Ltd		
	(US Marine Corps Bulldog shape)					S.Dakota, USA	15. 6.00A
G-USSR	Cameron Doll 90SS HAFB (Russian Doll shape)	2273		29. 3.90	Jacques W.Soukup Enterprises Ltd "Matrioshka"	(USA)	9. 6.00A
G-USSY	PA-28-181 Archer II	28-8290011	N8439R	7.11.88	Western Air (Thruxton) Ltd	Thruxton	11. 2.01T
G-USTA*	Agusta A.109A	7170	G-MEAN	3.12.96	Markoss Aviation Ltd	Biggin Hill	21. 4.00T
			G-BRYL/G-ROPE/G-OAMH				
	(Damaged Bedlam Street, Hurstpierpoint 27.3.99 -stored Biggin Hill 4.99: cancelled as wfu 5.8.99)						
G-USTB	Agusta A.109A	7163	D-HEEG	9. 5.97	Newton Aviation Ltd.	Redhill	26. 6.00T
			(D-HEEF)/VR-CKN/HB-XKM				
G-USTE	Robinson R-44 Astro	0315		11. 3.97	Westleigh Developments Ltd	Whetstone, Leics	6. 4.00
G-USTV*	Messerschmitt Bf.109G-2/Trop (Erla built)	10639	8478M RN228/Luftwaffe	26.10.90	RAF Museum (As "6" in Luftwaffe III/JG77 c/s)	Hendon	30. 5.98P
	(Damaged Duxford 12.10.97: to be rebuilt to static display standard for eventual display at RAF Museum)						
G-USTY	Clutton FRED Srs.III (VW1834)	PFA/29-10390		11.10.78	R.T.Mosforth t/a GUSTY Group	(Sheffield)	9. 6.97P
G-USUK*	Colt 2500A HAFB	1100		1. 6.87	Virgin Atlantic Airways Ltd "Virgin Atlantic Flyer" (Gondola displayed 1.99 - remainder stored)	Duxford	19. 8.87P
G-UTSI	Rand-Robinson KR-2	KBG-01		2.10.89	K.B.Gutridge	Biggin Hill	
G-UTSY	PA-28R-201 Cherokee Arrow III	28R-7737052	N3346Q	29. 8.86	Arrow Aviation Ltd	Southend	8. 2.02
G-UTZY	Aerospatiale SA.341G Gazelle 1	1307	G-BKLV N341SC	21.12.87	Goldcalm Ltd	(London SW1)	4. 3.01T
G-UVIP	Cessna 421C Golden Eagle III	421C-0603	G-BSKH N88600	23.11.98	Capital Trading Aviation Ltd	Exeter	2.11.01T
G-UZEL	Aerospatiale SA.341G Gazelle 1	1413	G-BRNH YU-HBO	21.11.89	S.E.Hobbs (UK) Ltd	Biggin Hill	30. 4.00
G-UZLE	Colt 77A HAFB	2021		1. 8.91	Flying Pictures Ltd "John Courage"	Fairoaks	25. 5.00A

G-VAAA – G-VZZZ

Regn	Type	C/n	P/I	Date	Owner/operator	Probable Base	CA Expy
G-VAEL	Airbus A.340-311	015	F-WWJG	15.12.93	Virgin Atlantic Airways Ltd "Maiden Toulouse"	Gatwick	14.12.02T
G-VAGA	PA-15 Vagabond (Lycoming O-145)	15-248	N4458H NC4458H	14.11.80	I.M.Callier	(Windsor)	29. 8.98P
G-VAIR	Airbus A.340-313	164	F-WWJA	21. 4.97	Virgin Atlantic Airways Ltd "Maiden Tokyo"	Gatwick	20. 4.00T
G-VAJT	Socata MS.894E Rallye 220GT	12195	EI-BAB	25. 7.89	W.M.Patterson		
			(S9-NAF)/EI-BAB/(G-BLPN)/EI-BAB(Manorcunningham, Co.Donegal)				29. 9.01
G-VALS	Pietenpol Aircamper	PFA/47-13157		30. 7.97	I.G.& V.A.Price	(Liphook)	

Regn	Type	C/n	P/I	Date	Owner/operator	Probable Base	CA Expy
G-VANS	Van's RV-4 (Lycoming O-320)	355	N16TS	7. 9.92	T.R.Grief	Bagby	3. 2.00P
G-VANZ	Van's RV-6A	PFA/181-12531		15. 7.93	S.J.Baxter	(Macclesfield)	
G-VARG	Varga 2150A Kachina	VAC 157-80	OO-RTY N80716	14. 5.84	A.C.Fletcher	Sherburn-in-Elmet	19. 6.02
G-VASA	PA-34-200 Seneca	34-7350080	G-BNNB N15625	29. 3.96	V.Babic	Bournemouth	15.12.99T
G-VAST	Boeing 747-41R	28757		17. 6.97	Virgin Atlantic Airways Ltd "Ladybird"	Heathrow	16. 6.00T
G-VAUN	Cessna 340 II	340-0538	D-IOWS N5148J	25.11.77	K.L.Burnett	Humberside	16.11.01
G-VBAC	Short SD.3-60 Var.100	SH.3736	VH-MJU G-BOEJ/G-14-3736	15. 9.97	BAC Leasing Ltd (Op BAC Express)	Exeter	15. 9.00T
G-VBEE	Boeing 747-219B	22723	ZK-NZW	5. 4.99	Virgin Atlantic Airways Ltd "Honeypie"	Gatwick	4 .4.02T
G-VBIG	Boeing 747-4Q8	26255		10. 6.96	Virgin Atlantic Airways Ltd "Tinker Belle"	Gatwick	9. 6.02T
G-VBUS	Airbus A.340-311	013	F-WWJE	26.11.93	Virgin Atlantic Airways Ltd "Lady in Red"	Gatwick	25.11.00T
G-VCAT	Boeing 747-267B	22872	B-HIE VR-HIE	16.10.98	Virgin Atlantic Airways Ltd "Wild Thing"	Heathrow	21.10.01T
G-VCED	Airbus A.320-231	193	OY-CNI F-WWIX	21. 1.97	Airtours International Airways Ltd	Manchester	30. 1.00T
G-VCIO	EAA Acrosport 2	PFA/72-12388		9.10.97	R.F.Bond (Corsham, Wilts) (Under construction 1999)		
G-VCJH*	Robinson R-22 Beta	1569		26.10.90	Great Northern Helicopters Ltd (Damaged Booker 13.7.99: cancelled by CAA 13.11.99)	Booker	13. 1.00T
G-VCML	Beechcraft 58 Baron	TH-1346	N2289R	31.10.97	St.Angelo Aviation Ltd	Lydd	27.11.00T
G-VCSI*	Rotorway Exec	3660		25.10.90	Not known (Stored 5.94)	Ley Farm, Chirk	
G-VDIR	Cessna T310R II	310R-0211	N5091J	31. 1.91	Southern Air Ltd	Shoreham	2.11.00T
G-VELA	SIAI-Marchetti S.205-22R (Confirmed as S.208A Waco Vela)	4-149	N949W	30.10.89	K.R.Allen t/a G-VELA Partnership	Gamston	29. 4.02
G-VELD	Airbus A.340-313X	214	F-WWJY	16. 3.98	Virgin Atlantic Airways Ltd "African Queen"	Gatwick	15. 3.01T
G-VENI	FFW DH.112 Venom FB.50 (FB.1)	733	J-1523	8. 6.84	Lindsay Wood Promotions Ltd (Op Source Classic Jet Flight: as "WE402")	Bournemouth	29.11.99P
G-VENM	FFW DH.112 Venom FB.50 (FB.1)	824	G-BLIE J-1614	16. 6.99	T.J.Manna (As "J-1614" in Swiss AF c/s)	Cranfield	AC
G-VERA	Garden GY-201 Minicab	PFA/56-12236		7. 6.94	D.K.Shipton	(Peterborough)	
G-VETA	Hawker Hunter T.7	41H-693751	G-BVWN XL600	2. 7.96	Jet Heritage Ltd	Bournemouth	18. 5.00P
G-VETS	Enstrom 280C-UK Shark	1015	G-FSDC G-BKTG/OY-HBP	11. 9.95	C.Upton	Barton	28. 7.02
G-VEZE	Rutan Varieze	PFA/74-10285		2. 9.77	S.D.Brown, S.Evans & M.Roper (West Wickham/Haywards Heath)		
G-VFAB	Boeing 747-4Q8	24958		28. 4.94	Virgin Atlantic Airways Ltd "Lady Penelope"	Gatwick	27. 4.00T
G-VFAR	Airbus A.340-313X	225	(G-VPOW) F-WWJZ	12. 6.98	Virgin Atlantic Airways Ltd "Diana"	Gatwick	
G-VFLY	Airbus A.340-311	058	F-WWJE	24.10.94	Virgin Atlantic Airways Ltd "Dragon Lady"	Gatwick	23.10.00T
G-VFSI	Robinson R-22 Beta	1785	N4081L	19.12.96	Survey & Construction (Roofing) Ltd	Redhill	18.12.99T
G-VGIN	Boeing 747-243B	19732	N747BL B-2440/N358AS/I-DEMU	30. 1.86	Virgin Atlantic Airways Ltd "Scarlet Lady"	Gatwick	1.10.02T
G-VHOL	Airbus A.340-311	002	F-WWAS	30. 5.97	Virgin Atlantic Airways Ltd "Jetstreamer"	Gatwick	29. 5.00T
G-VHOT	Boeing 747-4Q8	26326		12.10.94	Virgin Atlantic Airways Ltd "Tubular Belle"	Gatwick	11.10.00T
G-VIBA	Cameron DP-80 Hot Air Airship	1729		28. 5.91	Jacques W.Soukup Enterprises Ltd Beaulieu Court, Wilts/Great Missenden		3. 2.99A
G-VIBE	Boeing 747-219B	22791	ZK-NZZ 9M-MHH/ZK-NZZ/N6108N	24. 9.99	Virgin Atlantic Airways Ltd	Gatwick	23. 9.02T
G-VICC	PA-28-161 Warrior II	28-7916317	G-JFHL	3. 3.92	A.W.Collett	Turweston	4. 8.01T
G-VICE	MDH Hughes 369E (500E)	0365E	D-HLIS	16. 5.95	Controlled Demolition Group Ltd	Barton	21. 8.01
G-VICI	FFW DH.112 Venom FB.50 (FB.1)	783	HB-RVB (G-BMOB)/J-1573	6. 2.95	Lindsay Wood Promotions Ltd (Op Source Classic Jet Flight: as "J-1573" in Swiss AF c/s)	Bournemouth	24.11.99P
G-VICM	Beechcraft F33C Bonanza	CJ-136	PH-BNG	3. 7.91	Velocity Engineering Ltd	Elstree	20. 5.00
G-VICS	Commander 114B	14655	N655V	3. 2.98	Millennium Aviation Ltd	Guernsey	18. 3.01

Regn	Type	C/n	P/I	Date	Owner/operator	Probable Base	CA Expy
G-VICT	PA-31-310 Navajo	31-7401211	G-BBZI N7590L	10. 9.99	Victoria Wharf Ltd	Plymouth	7. 7.00T
G-VICW	Beechcraft 200 Super King Air BB-561		G-ECAV N36GA/N963JC	5.10.99	Victoria Wharf Ltd	Plymouth	4. 6.00T
G-VIEW	Vinten Wallis WA-116L Srs.100 (Limbach L2000)	002		5. 7.82	K.H.Wallis (Stored 5.99)	Reymerston Hall	6.10.85P*
G-VIIA	Boeing 777-236ER	27483	N5022E (G-ZZZF)	3. 7.97	British Airways plc (Waves of the City t/s)	Gatwick	2. 7.00T
G-VIIB	Boeing 777-236ER	27484	N5023Q (G-ZZZG)	23. 5.97	British Airways plc	Heathrow	22. 5.00T
G-VIIC	Boeing 777-236ER	27485	N5013R (G-ZZZH) (Reported as ex N5016R)	6. 2.97	British Airways plc	Heathrow	5. 2.00T
G-VIID	Boeing 777-236ER	27486	(G-ZZZI)	18. 2.97	British Airways plc	Heathrow	17. 2.00T
G-VIIE	Boeing 777-236ER	27487	(G-ZZZJ)	27. 2.97	British Airways plc	Heathrow	26. 2.00T
G-VIIF	Boeing 777-236ER	27488	(G-ZZZK)	19. 3.97	British Airways plc	Heathrow	18. 3.00T
G-VIIG	Boeing 777-236ER	27489	(G-ZZZL)	9. 4.97	British Airways plc	Heathrow	8. 4.00T
G-VIIH	Boeing 777-236ER	27490	(G-ZZZM)	7. 5.97	British Airways plc	Heathrow	6. 5.00T
G-VIIJ	Boeing 777-236ER	27492	(G-ZZZP)	29.12.97	British Airways plc (Mountain of the Birds/Benyhone Tartan t/s)	Gatwick	28.12.00T
G-VIIK	Boeing 777-236ER	28840		3. 2.98	British Airways plc (Animals and Trees t/s)	Gatwick	2. 2.01T
G-VIIL	Boeing 777-236ER	27493		13. 3.98	British Airways plc (Wings t/s)	Heathrow	12. 3.01T
G-VIIM	Boeing 777-236ER	28841		26. 3.98	British Airways plc (Waves & Cranes t/s)	Gatwick	25. 3.01T
G-VIIN	Boeing 777-236ER	29319		21. 8.98	British Airways plc (Whale Rider t/s)	Heathrow	20. 8.01T
G-VIIO	Boeing 777-236	29320		26. 1.99	British Airways plc (Chelsea Rose t/s)	Gatwick	25.01.02T
G-VIIP	Boeing 777-236	29321		9. 2.99	British Airways plc (Dove/Colum t/s)	Heathrow	8. 2.02T
G-VIIR	Boeing 777-236ER	29322		18.3.99	British Airways plc (Mountain of the Birds/Benyhone Tartan t/s)	Gatwick	17. 3.02T
G-VIIS	Boeing 777-236ER	29323		1.4.99	British Airways plc (Chelsea Rose t/s)	Heathrow	31. 3.02T
G-VIIT	Boeing 777-236ER	29962		26. 5.99	British Airways plc (Rendezvous t/s)	Heathrow	25. 5.02T
G-VIIU	Boeing 777-236ER	29963		28. 5.99	British Airways plc (Delftblue Daybreak t/s)	Heathrow	27. 5.02T
G-VIIV	Boeing 777-236ER	29964		29. 6.99	British Airways plc (Union Flag t/s)	Gatwick	28. 6.02T
G-VIIW	Boeing 777-236	29965		30. 7.99	British Airways plc (Union Flag t/s)	Heathrow	29. 7.02T
G-VIIX	Boeing 777-236	29966		11. 8.99	British Airways plc (Union Flag t/s)	Gatwick	10 .8.02T
G-VIIY	Boeing 777-236	29967		22.10.99	British Airways plc (Union Flag t/s)	Heathrow	21.10.02T
G-VIKE	Bellanca 17-30A Super Viking 300A	79-30911	N302CB	8. 7.80	W.G.Prout	(Fareham)	27. 6.99
G-VIKY	Cameron A-120 HAFB	3068		27. 4.93	D.W.Pennell	Broadway	2. 6.00A
G-VILL	Carmichael Lazer Z.200 (Lycoming AEIO-360)	10	G-BOYZ	10. 6.96	M.G.Jefferies (Global Village titles)	Little Gransden	13. 7.00P
G-VINO	Sky 90-24 HAFB	102		25. 2.98	Fivedata Ltd	Todmorden	13. 3.00A
G-VINS	Cameron N-90 HAFB	4731		12. 1.00	PSH Skypower Ltd	Pewsey	
G-VIPI	BAe 125 Srs.800B	258222	G-5-745	27. 7.92	Yeates of Leicester Ltd	Southampton	16. 9.00T
G-VIPP	PA-31-350 Navajo Chieftain	31-7952244	G-OGRV G-BMPX/N3543D	6. 8.93	Capital Trading Aviation Ltd	Filton	26. 8.00T
G-VIPY	PA-31-350 Navajo Chieftain	31-7852143	EI-JTC G-POLO/N27750	10.10.97	Capital Trading Aviation Ltd	Filton	12.10.00T
G-VIRG	Boeing 747-287B	21189	N354AS LV-LZD/N1791B	14. 6.84	Virgin Atlantic Airways Ltd "Maiden Voyager"	Gatwick	1. 8.02T
G-VITE	Robin R.1180T Aiglon	219		16.10.78	D.C.Perrett & D.T.Scrutton t/a G-VITE Flying Group	Stapleford	20. 4.00
G-VIVA	Thunder Ax7-65 Bolt HAFB	190		28.11.78	R.J.Mitchener	Andover	18. 3.99A
G-VIVI	Taylor JT.2 Titch	PFA/60-12405		4.11.96	D.G.Tucker	Hill Farm, Nayland	
G-VIVM	BAC P.84 Jet Provost T.5 PAC/W/23907		G-BVWF XS230	25. 3.96	Flight Test Associates Ltd	Woodford	5. 9.00P
G-VIXN	HS.110 Sea Vixen FAW.2 (TT)	10145	8828M XS587	5. 8.85	P.G.Vallance Ltd (As "XS587/252/V" in RN c/s)	Charlwood, Surrey	AC
G-VIZZ	Sportavia RS.180 Sportsman	6018	D-EFBK	25.10.79	M.J.Revill t/a Exeter Fournier Group	Exeter	20. 7.01

Regn	Type	C/n	P/I	Date	Owner/operator	Probable Base	CA Expy
G-VJAB	Avtech Jabiru UL	PFA/274-13322		25. 6.98	ST Aviation Ltd	Downham Market	24.10.00P
G-VJET	Avro 698 Vulcan B.2		XL426	7. 7.87	R.J.Clarkson	Southend	
					t/a The Vulcan Restoration Trust (As "XL426" 5.99)		
G-VJFK	Boeing 747-238B	20842	VH-EBH	4. 2.91	Virgin Atlantic Airways Ltd	Gatwick	3. 3.00T
					"Boston Belle"		
G-VJIM	Colt Jumbo 77SS HAFB	1298	(G-BPJI)	7. 8.89	L.V.Mastis	W Bloomfield, Mi., USA	31. 7.00A
					"Jumbo Jim" (Virgin Atlantic titles)		
G-VKID	Airbus A.320-214	1130	F-WWIR	16.12.99	Virgin Atlantic Airways Ltd	Gatwick	AC
					"Sundance Kid"		
G-VLAD	Yakovlev Yak-50	791502	D-EIVR	14.11.88	M.B.Smith	Duxford	11 8.00P
			N51980/DDR-WQR/DM-WQR				
G-VLAX	Boeing 747-238B	20921	VH-EBI	1. 5.91	Virgin Atlantic Airways Ltd	Gatwick	26. 5.02T
					"California Girl"		
G-VLCN	Avro 698 Vulcan B.2		XH558	6. 2.95	C.Walton Ltd (As "XH558") Bruntingthorpe		AC
G-VMAX	Mooney M.20K	25-0504	ZS-KYP	12. 2.86	Aerokits GmbH (Neubrandenburg, Germany)		27. 5.02T
			N9716G				
G-VMDE(2)	Cessna P210N Pressurised Centurion II	P210-00088	(N4717P)	20. 7.78	Royton Express Deliveries (Welwyn) Ltd	North Weald	26. 4.00
G-VMED	Airbus A.320-214	0978	F-WWDC	16. 4.99	Virgin Atlantic Airways Ltd	Gatwick	15 .4.02T
G-VMIA	Boeing 747-123	20108	EI-CAI	23. 3.90	Virgin Atlantic Airways Ltd	Kemble	7. 5.02T
			VH-EEI/G-HIHO/(LX-NCV)/N14939/N9669 (For scrapping 1.00)				
G-VMJM	Socata TB-10 Tobago	1361	G-BTOK	21. 4.92	J.H.Michaels	Denham	20. 4.01
G-VMPR	DH.115 Vampire T.11	15621	8196M	13. 3.95	J.N.Kerr & J.Jones	Swansea	15. 2.00P
			XE920		(As "XE920/A" in 603 Sqdn c/s))		
G-VMSL	Robinson R-22 Alpha	0483	G-KILY	5. 2.98	L.L.F.Smith	Booker	18.12.00T
			N8561M				
G-VNOM	FFW DH.112 Venom FB.50 (FB.1)	842	J-1632	13. 7.84	T.J.Mann	Cranfield	AC
					(As "J-1632" in Swiss AF c/s))		
G-VOAR	PA-28-181 Archer III	2843011	N9256Q	3.11.95	Jones Samuel Ltd	Leicester	15.12.01
					t/a JSE Systems		
G-VODA	Cameron N-77 HAFB	2208		8. 2.90	Vodafone Group plc "Vodafone"	Newbury	1. 4.00A
	(New envelope 12.97)						
G-VOID	PA-28RT-201 Arrow IV	28R-8118049	ZS-KTM	17. 8.87	Newbus Aviation Ltd	Shoreham	3.12.99
			N83232				
G-VOLH	Airbus A.321-211 ·	823	(EC-)	15. 5.98	Airtours International Airways Ltd		
			D-AVZX			Manchester	14. 5.01T
G-VOLT	Cameron N-77 HAFB	2157		8.11.89	National Power plc	Swindon	25. 4.97A
					"National Power"		
G-VOTE	Ultramagic M-77 HAFB	77-164		10. 3.99	Window on the World Ltd (London SE1)		6 .4.00A
G-VPII	Evans VP-2	PFA/63-10262	(G-EDIF)	4.10.88	V.D.J.Hitchings Rayne Hall Farm, Rayne		
	(Continental A65)				(Wings stored 2.92)		
G-VPSJ	Europa Avn Europa	PFA/247-12520		29. 7.93	J.D.Bean	(Oxford)	
G-VPUF	Boeing 747-219B		ZK...	R	Virgin Atlantic Airways Ltd	Gatwick	
					(For delivery 10.99)		
G-VROE	Avro 652A Anson T.21	3634	G-BFIR	3. 3.98	Air Atlantique Ltd	Coventry	4. 6.00P
			7881M/WD413		(As "WD413" in RAF Transport Command c/s)		
G-VRST	PA-46-350P Malibu Mirage	4636189		7.12.98	Winchfield Development Ltd	Fairoaks	11. 2.02
G-VRUM	Boeing 747-267B	23048	B-HIF	2.11.98	Virgin Atlantic Airways Ltd	Gatwick	1.11.01T
			VR-HIF/N6066U		"Calypso Queen"		
G-VRVI	Cameron O-90 HAFB	2522		27. 2.91	Cooling Services Ltd "Daikin" Portishead		1. 8.00A
G-VSBC	Beechcraft B200 Super King Air	BB-1290	N3185C	17. 6.93	Vickers Shipbuilding & Engineering Ltd		
			JA8859/N3185C			Walney Island	21. 6.00
G-VSEA	Airbus A.340-311	003	F-WWDA	7. 7.97	Virgin Atlantic Airways Ltd	Gatwick	6. 7.00T
					"Plane Sailing"		
G-VSFT	PA-23-250 Aztec F	27-7754144	G-TOMK	23. 4.96	SFT Europe Ltd	Bournemouth	4. 5.01T
			G-BFEC/N63823				
G-VSKY	Airbus A.340-311	016	F-WWJH	21. 1.94	Virgin Atlantic Airways Ltd	Gatwick	20. 1.00T
					"China Girl"		
G-VSSS	Boeing 747-219B		ZK...	R	Virgin Atlantic Airways Ltd	Gatwick	
					(For delivery 1.00)		
G-VSUN	Airbus A.340-313	114	F-WWJI	30. 4.96	Virgin Atlantic Airways Ltd	Gatwick	29. 4.02T
			(F-GLZJ)		"Rainbow Lady"		
G-VTAN	Airbus A.320-214	0764	G-BXTA	29. 4.99	Virgin Atlantic Airways Ltd	Gatwick	29. 4.01T
G-VTEN*	Vinten-Wallis WA.117 Venom	UMA-01 & 003		22. 4.85	K.H.Wallis	Reymerston Hall	3.12.85P*
	(Continental O-200-B)				(Unmarked frame stored 5.99)		
G-VTII	DH.115 Vampire T.11	15127	WZ507	9. 1.80	De Havilland Aviation Ltd	Swansea	13. 8.95P
	(Fuselage No.DHP40273)				(As "WZ507")		
G-VTOL*	Hawker Siddeley Harrier T.52	B3/41H/735795	ZA250	27. 7.70	British Aerospace plc	Brooklands	2.11.86S
			G-VTOL		(On loan to Brooklands Museum 10.96)		
G-VTOP	Boeing 747-408	28194		28. 1.97	Virgin Atlantic Airways Ltd	Gatwick	17. 3.00T
					"Austin Powered"		

Regn	Type	C/n	P/I	Date	Owner/operator	Probable Base	CA Expy
G-VULC	Avro 698 Vulcan B.2A		N655AV	27. 2.84	Radarmoor Ltd Wellesbourne Mountford		
			G-VULC/XM655		(As "XM655") (Noted 5.99)		
G-VVBF	Colt 315A HAFB	4058		3. 3.97	Virgin Balloon Flights Ltd (London SE16)		2. 6.00T
G-VVBK	PA-34-200T Seneca II	34-7570303	G-BSBS	26. 1.89	Magyar Construction Co Ltd(Douglas, IOM)		30.10.01
			G-BDRI/SE-GLG				
G-VVIP	Cessna 421C Golden Eagle III		G-BMWB	7. 7.92	Capital Trading Aviation Ltd	Filton	30. 4.01T
		421C-0699	N2655L				
G-VXLG	Boeing 747-41R	29406		30. 9.98	Virgin Atlantic Airways Ltd	Heathrow	20. 9.01T
					"Ruby Tuesday"		
G-VYGR	Colt 120A HAFB	2479		24. 9.93	A.van Wyk	Caxton	31. 3.00T
G-VZZZ	Boeing 747-219B	22722	ZK-NZV	7. 7.99	Virgin Atlantic Airways Ltd	Gatwick	6 .7.02T
					"Morning Glory"		

G-WAAA – G-WZZZ

Regn	Type	C/n	P/I	Date	Owner/operator	Probable Base	CA Expy
G-WAAC	Cameron N-56 HAFB	492		14. 2.79	N.P.Hemsley	Crawley	26. 6.97A
					t/a Whacko Balloon Group "Whacko"		
G-WACB	Reims Cessna F.152 II	1972		16. 9.86	Wycombe Air Centre Ltd	Booker	24. 2.02T
G-WACE	Reims Cessna F.152 II	1978		16. 9.86	Wycombe Air Centre Ltd	Booker	23. 4.02T
G-WACF	Cessna 152 II	152-84852	N628GH	20. 1.87	Wycombe Air Centre Ltd	Booker	24.11.00T
			(LV-PMB)/N628GH				
G-WACG	Cessna 152 II	152-85536	ZS-KXY	4.11.86	Wycombe Air Centre Ltd	Booker	3. 4.01T
			(N93699)				
G-WACH	Reims Cessna FA.152 Aerobat	0425		18. 6.87	Wycombe Air Centre Ltd	Booker	4. 8.02T
G-WACI	Beechcraft 76 Duchess	ME-289	N6703Y	26. 7.88	Wycombe Air Centre Ltd	Booker	14.11.00T
G-WACJ	Beechcraft 76 Duchess	ME-278	N6700Y	3. 1.89	Wycombe Air Centre Ltd	Booker	6. 5.02T
G-WACL	Reims Cessna F.172N Skyhawk II	1912	G-BHGG	19. 6.89	Wycombe Air Centre Ltd	Booker	20. 4.01T
G-WACO	Waco UPF-7	5400	N29903	28. 1.87	R.G.Vincent	Gloucestershire	13. 5.90
			NC29903		t/a RGV (Aircraft Services) & Co		
					(Damaged Liverpool 15.4.89; on rebuild 4.97)		
G-WACP	PA-28-180 Cherokee Archer	28-7405007	G-BBPP	5. 4.89	Wycombe Air Centre Ltd	Booker	9. 7.01T
			N9559N				
G-WACR	PA-28-180 Archer	28-7505090	G-BCZF	18.12.86	Wycombe Air Centre Ltd	Booker	9. 7.00T
			N9517N				
G-WACT	Reims Cessna F.152 II	1908	G-BKFT	24. 6.86	Wycombe Air Centre Ltd	Booker	5.10.00T
G-WACU	Reims Cessna FA.152 Aerobat	0380	G-BJZU	10. 7.86	Wycombe Air Centre Ltd	Booker	9. 6.00T
G-WACW	Cessna 172P Skyhawk II	172-74057	N5307K	16. 5.88	Wycombe Air Centre Ltd	Booker	16. 6.00T
G-WACY	Reims Cessna F.172P Skyhawk II	2217	F-GDOZ	3.10.86	Wycombe Air Centre Ltd	Booker	14. 1.02T
G-WACZ	Reims Cessna F.172M Skyhawk II	1311	G-BCUK	19. 5.86	Professional Air Training Ltd		
						Bournemouth	22. 4.02T
G-WADI	PA-46-350P Malibu Mirage	4636205		8. 5.99	Albatross Air Ltd	(London EC4)	
G-WADS	Robinson R-22 Beta	1224	G-NICO	25. 4.96	Pyramid Precision Eng Ltd	Blackpool	3. 3.02
G-WAGG	Robinson R-22 Beta-II	2960		7. 7.99	J.B.Wagstaff	Costock	15 .7.02
					t/a N.J.Wagstaff Leasing)		
G-WAIR	PA-32-301 Saratoga	32-8506010	N2607X	14. 1.91	P.H.Burtwhistle (Thorne, Doncaster)		13. 5.00
			N9577N		t/a Thorne Aviation		
G-WAIT	Cameron V-77 HAFB	2390		20.11.90	C.P.Brown	Ely	24. 7.99A
G-WALS	Cessna A152 Aerobat	A152-0843	N4614A	27. 9.88	Redhill Aviation Ltd	Redhill	5. 2.01T
					t/a Redhill Flying Club		
G-WARA	PA-28-161 Warrior III	2842021	N9289N	3. 9.97	Solent Flight Aircraft Ltd	Southampton	14. 9.00T
G-WARB	PA-28-161 Warrior III	2842034	N41286	4. 9.98	London School of Flying Ltd	Elstree	7. 9.01T
G-WARC	PA-28-161 Warrior III	2842035	N41244	11. 9.98	London School of Flying Ltd	Elstree	13. 9.01T
G-WARD	Taylor JT.1 Monoplane			1.12.80	R.P.J.Hunter	Redhill	22. 2.00P
	(VW1834)	WB.VI & PFA/1407			(Damaged Redhill 17.9.99)		
G-WARE	PA-28-161 Warrior II	28-8416080	N4357L	21. 7.89	W.B.Ware	Bristol	17.11.01
G-WARF	Cessna 182S	18280546	N7089F	10. 6.99	Victoria Wharf Ltd	Plymouth	30. 6.02T
G-WARK	Schweizer Hughes 269C (300C)	S.1354		13.11.89	K.Sutcliffe	(Halifax)	15. 4.99T
G-WARO	PA-28-161 Warrior II	2842015	N92946	24.10.97	London School of Flying Ltd	Elstree	23.10.00T
G-WARP	Cessna 182F	182-54633	G-ASHB	6. 6.95	R.M.Burnett	AAC Netheravon	14. 7.01
			N3233U		t/a Army Parachute Association		
G-WARR	PA-28-161 Warrior II	28-7916321	N3074U	15. 9.88	T.J. & G.M.Laundy	RAF Halton	1. 1.01T
					(Op RAF Halton Aeroplane Club)		
G-WARS	PA-28-161 Warrior III	2842022	N9281X	7.11.97	London School of Flying Ltd	Elstree	6.11.00T
G-WARU	PA-28-161 Warrior III	2842023	N92880	6.11.97	Solent Flight A/c Ltd	Southampton	6.11.00T
G-WARV	PA-28-161 Warrior III	2842036	N41247	9.10.98	London Aviation Ltd	Biggin Hill	13.10.01T
G-WARW	PA-28-161 Warrior III	2842037	N41254	17.11.98	London School of Flying Ltd.	Elstree	19.11.01T
G-WARX	PA-28-161 Warrior III	2842038	N4126D	15.12.98	C.M.A.Clark	(Rednal)	20.12.01
G-WARY	PA-28-161 Warrior III	2842024	N9287X	13.11.97	London School of Flying Ltd	Elstree	18.11.00T
G-WARZ	PA-28-161 Warrior III	2842025	N92944	26.11.97	London Aviation Ltd	Elstree	27.11.00T
G-WASH	Cameron N-850 HAFB	1451		3. 3.87	Noble Adventures Ltd	Bristol	18. 8.87P
G-WASP	Brantly B-2B	445	G-ASXE	7. 2.77	N.J.R.Minchin Hill Top Farm, Godalming		9. 9.02

Regn	Type	C/n	P/I	Date	Owner/operator	Probable Base	CA Expy
G-WATS	PA-34-220T Seneca III	34-8333058	G-BOVJ N8202J	3. 2.89	Oxford Aviation Services Ltd	Oxford	26. 5.01T
G-WATT	Cameron Cooling Tower SS HAFB	2158		8.11.89	National Power plc "Enterprise"	Swindon	22. 8.96A
G-WAVE(2)	Grob G-109B	6381		1. 8.85	M.L.Murdoch Park Farm, Eaton Bray		21. 2.01
G-WAZZ	Pitts S-1S Special (Lycoming O-360)	7-0332	G-BRRP N3TD	17. 6.94	D.T.Knight	White Waltham	13. 7.00P
G-WBAT*	Wombat Gyrocopter (Rotax 532)	CJ-001	G-BSID	31. 5.90	C.D.Julian (Cancelled by CAA 12.7.99)	St.Merryn	4. 3.97*
G-WBMG	Cameron N Ele 90SS HAFB	3086	G-BUYV	5. 7.93	M.Sevrin Court St.Etienne, Belgium		25. 6.00A
G-WBPR	BAe 125 Srs.800B	258085	G-5-551	29. 9.87	Granada Group plc	Luton	13.11.00
G-WBTS	Falconar F-11W-200 PFA/32-10070 (Continental O-200-A)		G-BDPL	22.10.90	W.C.Brown	White Waltham	13. 7.00P
G-WCAT	Colt Flying Mitt SS HAFB	1744		30. 5.90	I.Chadwick "Washcat" t/a Balloon Preservation Flying Group	Horsham	N/E(A)
G-WCEI	Socata MS.894E Rallye 220GT	12141	G-BAOC	28. 5.85	R.A.L.Lucas	Walney Island	12. 7.01
G-WDEB	Thunder Ax7-77 HAFB	1606		26. 9.89	W.de Bock "Landplan"	Peterborough	16. 7.00A
G-WDEV	Westland SA.341G Gazelle 1	WA/1098	G-IZEL G-BBHW	30. 9.98	MW Helicopters Ltd	Stapleford	21.11.99T
G-WEAC	BN-2A mk.III-2 Trislander	1042	5H-AZD G-BEFP/(4X-CCL)/G-BEFP/N30WA/JA6401/G-BEFP (Op Woodgate Executive Air Services)	16.12.94	Keen Leasing Ltd	Aldergrove	12.12.02T
G-WELI	Cameron N-77 HAFB	1078		26. 9.84	M.A.Shannon "Wellie"	Southampton	27. 7.00A
G-WELL	Beechcraft E90 King Air	LW-198	N202CC (N7PB)/N202CC	18. 7.85	Colt Transport Ltd	Goodwood	5. 6.00T
G-WELS	Cameron N-65 HAFB	1297		7. 4.86	K.J.Vickery "Talisman"	Billingshurst	26. 6.92A
G-WEND	PA-28RT-201 Arrow IV	28R-8118026	PH-SYL N8296L	8.11.82	C.P.Edgar t/a G-WEND Group	Prestwick	20. 5.02
G-WERY	Socata TB-20 Trinidad	305		2. 4.82	G.L.Appleyard & M.T.Jenkins t/a WERY Flying Group Sherburn-in-Elmet		3. 4.00
G-WEST	Agusta A.109A	7213		21. 1.81	Westland Helicopters Ltd	Yeovil	28. 3.02
G-WESX	CFM Streak Shadow (Rotax 582) K.116-SA & PFA/161A-11561			2. 2.90	D.J.Sagar Croft Farm, Defford		5. 9.00P
G-WETI	Cameron N-31 HAFB	449		27.11.78	C.A.Butter & J.J.T.Cooke "Puddleduck"	Marsh Benham	5. 7.88A
G-WFEP	Aerospatiale/Alenia ATR-42-300	149	N4210G F-WWEV	9. 2.98	Gill Airways Ltd (KLMuk c/s)	Newcastle	26. 2.01T
G-WFFW	PA-28-161 Warrior II	28-8116161	N8342A	26.10.93	N.F.Duke	Bournemouth	27.11.99
G-WFOX	Robinson R-22 Beta-II	2826		2. 6.98	Heli-Air Ltd Wellesbourne Mountford (Damaged Tatenhill 7.7.99)		25. 6.01T
G-WGAL	Bell 206B JetRanger III	3165	G-OICS N678TM	22. 3.93	Watkiss Group Aviation Ltd	Biggleswade	19. 3.01
G-WGCL	Rockwell Commander 685	12043	CS-AQO N57028	7.11.95	Cooper Aerial Surveys Ltd	Sandtoft	20. 5.98A
G-WGCS	PA-18-95 Super Cub (L-18C-PI) (Frame No.18-1500)	18-1528	(G-BLSV) ALAT F-MBCH/51-15528	21.12.84	S.C.Thompson Newells Farm, Bolney		5. 7.00P
G-WGHB	Canadair (CL-30) T-33AN Silver Star mk.3	T33-640	CF-EHB/CAF 133640/RCAF 21640	9. 5.74	R.H.& G.C. Cooper	Sandtoft	13. 6.77P
G-WGSC	Pilatus PC-6/B2-H4 Turbo-Porter	848	OE-ECS	2. 1.90	D.M.Penny Movenis, Co.Londonderry (Op Wild Geese Parachute Centre)		23. 3.01
G-WHAT	Colt 77A HAFB	1911		15. 3.91	M.A.Scholes "Chad"	London SE25	1. 8.00A
G-WHAZ	Agusta-Bell 206A Jet Ranger	8112	OH-HRE G-WHAZ/OH-HRE	26. 6.97	J.E.Mills	(Maidstone)	28. 7.00
G-WHDP	Cessna 182S	182-80178	N178TC	12. 5.98	Heatherford Ltd	Elstree	14. 5.01T
G-WHEE	Cyclone Pegasus Quantum 15 (Rotax 912)	7510		26. 3.99	N & R Harwood	Littlehampton	25 .3.00P
G-WHIM	Colt 77A HAFB	1476		10. 4.89	D.L.Morgan	Ilford	20. 8.00A
G-WHIS	Beechcraft Baron 58	TH-1922	N31622	24. 1.00	G.R.Kinally t/a GKL Management Services	(Cranleigh)	
G-WHOG	CFM Streak Shadow (Rotax 618) K.253-SA & PFA/206-12776			21. 9.94	B.R.Cannell "Wart Hog"	Old Sarum	29. 7.00P
G-WHRL	Schweizer 269C	S 1453	EC-GGX CS-HDG/G-WHRL/N41S	19. 4.90	G.Wood t/a Graham Wood Decorators	(York)	26 .8.02T
G-WHST	Eurocopter AS.350B2 Ecureuil	2915	G-BWYA	9. 8.96	Hawkrise Ltd	Sutton Coldfield	26. 9.02T
G-WHZZ	Aero L-39C Albatross	433114	(RussAF 84)	6.12.99	B J Berry	(Dublin, Ireland)	
G-WIBB	Jodel D.18 PFA/169-11640 (Subaru EA81)			18. 6.96	J.& D.Wibberley Priory Farm, Tibenham		6. 4.00P
G-WIBS	CASA I-131E Srs 2000	2005	E3B-401	25. 3.99	C Willoughby	(Ashford)	
G-WILD	Aerotek Pitts S-1T Special (AEIO-360)	1017	ZS-LMM	6.12.85	The Aerobatics Co Ltd	White Waltham	1. 5.01A
G-WILG	WSK PZL-104 Wilga 35A	62153	G-AZYJ	15. 4.97	M.H.Bletsoe-Brown	Sywell	29. 9.00

Regn	Type	C/n	P/I	Date	Owner/operator	Probable Base	CA Expy
G-WILS	PA-28RT-201T Turbo Arrow IV		PH-DPD	16. 1.96	W.S.Stanley & V.F.A.Dimock		
		28R-8431005	N4330W			Gloucestershire	22. 3.02T
G-WILY	Rutan LongEz 1200 & PFA/74A-10724			8. 6.83	W.S.Allen & B.Wronski	Gloucestershire	28. 3.00P
	(Lycoming O-320)				"Time Flies"		
G-WIMP	Colt 56A HAFB	755		13. 2.86	T.& B.Chamberlain	York	2. 6.00A
G-WINE	Thunder AX7-77Z HAFB	472		25.11.82	S.M.Miles	Lancing	17. 6.97A
					(Balloon Preservation Group 12.98)		
G-WINK	Grumman-American AA-5B Tiger		N74658	14.12.90	B.S.Cooke	Elstree	22. 3.00
		AA5B-0327					
G-WINS	PA-32-300 Cherokee Six	32-7640065	N8476C	24. 4.91	Cheyenne Ltd	Jersey	26. 2.00
G-WIRE	Aerospatiale AS.355F1 Twin Squirrel		G-CEGB	22. 1.90	National Grid Co plc	Oxford	12. 6.00T
		5312	G-BLJL				
G-WIRL	Robinson R-22 Beta	0671		27. 7.87	C.A.Rosenberg	Shobdon	12. 8.02T
G-WISH	Lindstrand Cake SS HAFB	006		14.12.92	Oxford Promotions (UK) Ltd	Kentucky, USA	18. 4.00A
	(Birthday Cake shape)						
G-WISP*	Robinson R-44 Astro	0566		16. 3.99	Heli-Air Ltd	Redditch	
	(Damaged Bridstow, Ross-on-Wye 13.8.99: cancelled as destroyed 17.11.99)						
G-WIXI	Avions Mudry CAP.10B	279		27. 1.98	J.M. & E.M.Wicks		
						Boones Farm, High Garrett	26. 7.01
G-WIZA	Robinson R-22 Beta	0861	G-PERL	16.11.94	Burman Aviation Ltd	Cranfield	12. 1.01T
			N90815		(Op Burman Helicopters)		
G-WIZB	Grob G.115A	8104	EI-CAD	2. 9.98	A.G.Wisbey	Sywell	22.10.01T
G-WIZD	Lindstrand LBL-180A HAFB	066		12.11.93	T.H.Wilson	Diss	28. 9.99T
G-WIZO	PA-34-220T Seneca III	34-8133171	N8413U	16.12.86	B.J.Booty	(Trowbridge)	5. 2.01T
G-WIZR	Robinson R-22 Beta-II	2799		9. 3.98	J.D.Forbes-Nixon & N.H.Taylor	Bristol	25. 3.01T
					t/a Clifton Helicopter Hire		
G-WIZY	Robinson R-22 Beta	0566	G-BMWX	26. 8.97	Central Aviation (Helicopters) Ltd		
			N24196			Nottingham	5. 6.00T
G-WIZZ	Agusta-Bell 206B JetRanger II	8540		7.12.77	Rivermead Aviation Ltd	(Reading)	3.10.02T
G-WJAN	Boeing 757-21K	28674		18. 3.97	Airtours Intl Airways Ltd	Manchester	19. 3.00T
G-WKRD	Eurocopter AS.350B2 Ecureuil	2668	G-BUJG	16. 3.99	Wickford Development Co	Wickford	22. 9.01T
			G-HEAR/G-BUJG				
G-WLAC	PA-18-150 Super Cub	18-8899	G-HAHA	2. 6.98	White Waltham Airfield Ltd		
			G-BSWE/N9194P			White Waltham	14. 6.01T
G-WLGA	WSK PZL-104 Wilga 80	CF21910932	EC-FYY	8.11.96	A.J.Renham	Morgansfield, Fishburn	2. 3.00
			F-GMLR				
G-WLLY	Bell 206B JetRanger	405	G-OBHH	24. 3.93	Blue Five Aviation Ltd	Redhill	13. 7.02T
			G-WLLY/G-RODY/G-ROGR/G-AXMM/N1469W				
G-WLMS	Mainair Blade 912 1223-0999-7-W1016			23. 9.99	J.R.North	(Preston)	26 .9.00P
G-WMAA	MBB Bo.105DBS-4	S.135/914	G-PASB	8. 9.94	Bond Air Services	RAF Cosford	29. 9.00T
	(Rebuilt with new airframe S.914 1994)		VH-LSA/G-BDMC/D-HDEC		(Op West Midlands Air Ambulance)		
G-WMAN	Aerospatiale SA.341G Gazelle 1	1277	ZS-HUR	4. 8.99	J.Wightman	(Ballynahinch, NI)	AC
			N4491R/YV-54CP				
G-WMCC*	BAe Jetstream Srs 3102-01	601	G-31-601	22. 9.83	Not known	Birmingham	
			(N....)/G-TALL/G-31-601				
	(Cancelled as sold USA 11.97 but derelict Fire Station 3.98)						
G-WMID	MDH MD.902 Explorer	900-00062	N3063T	12.10.99	West Midlands Police Authority		
						Birmingham	AC
G-WMPA	Aerospatiale AS.355F2 Twin Squirrel			7. 2.89	West Midlands Police Authority		
		5401				Birmingham	10. 5.01T
G-WMTM	Gulfstream AA-5B Tiger	AA5B-1035	N4517V	8. 1.91	Susan A.Westhorp	Bournemouth	10. 8.02T
					(Carries "4517V"on fin)		
G-WNGS	Cameron N-105 HAFB	4385		15. 7.98	Redmalt Ltd	Witham	4. 9.00A
					(Motorola Wings titles)		
G-WOLF	PA-28-140 Cruiser	28-7425439	OY-TOD	20. 3.80	Werewolf Aviation Ltd	Elstree	4. 2.02
G-WOOD	Beechcraft 95-B55A Baron	TC-1283	SE-GRC	17. 9.79	T.D.Broadhurst	Sleap	10.12.01
			G-AYID/SE-EXK		t/a Baron Aviation		
G-WOOF	Enstrom 480	5027		3. 3.98	Westover Park Ltd	Guernsey	6. 4.01
G-WOOL	Colt 77A HAFB	2044		23. 2.93	T.G.Pembrey, N.P.Helmsley & C.L.Pembrey		
					t/a Whacko Balloon Group	Steyning	9. 9.99
G-WORM	Thruster T600N 9109-T600N-039			5.10.99	Thruster Air Services Ltd	(Wantage)	
G-WOTG	PBN BN-2T Turbine Islander	2139	(ZF444)	10.11.83	P.M.Hall	Weston-on-the-Green	30. 1.00
			G-WOTG/G-BJYT		t/a RAF Sport Parachute Association		
G-WPAS	MDH MD.900 Explorer	900-00053		1. 7.98	Police Aviation Services Ltd	Devizes	28.10.01T
					(Op Wiltshire Police/Ambulane Authority)		
G-WREN	Aerotek Pitts S-2A Special	2229	N947	28. 1.81	Northamptonshire School of Flying Ltd		
	(Lycoming AEIO-360)					Sywell	31. 3.02T
G-WRFM	Enstrom 280C-UK Shark	1202	G-CTSI	21. 4.89	A.J.MacFarlane	Goodwood	19. 5.01
			G-BKIO/(G-BKHN)/SE-HLB		t/a Skywalker Enterprises		
G-WRIT	Colt 77A HAFB	1328		15. 9.88	G.Pusey "Legal Eagle"	Seville, France	23. 2.00A
G-WRWR	Robinson R-22 Beta-II	2964		20. 7.99	Choppertech Ltd	(Petworth)	

Regn	Type	C/n	P/I	Date	Owner/operator	Probable Base	CA Expy
G-WSEC	Enstrom F-28C	398	G-BONF N51661	19.12.88	M.J.Easey	Town Farm, Hoxne, Eye	10.12.01
G-WSFT	PA-23-250 Aztec F	27-7754059	G-BTHS N62824	18. 6.86	SFT Europe Ltd	Bournemouth	15. 6.01T
G-WSKY	Enstrom 280C-UK-2 Shark	1037	G-BEEK	25. 7.83	M.I.Edwards	Brandon, Suffolk	23. 4.00
G-WUFF	Europa Avn Europa	PFA/247-12942		19. 1.99	M.A.Barker.	(Doncaster)	
G-WULF	WAR Focke-Wulf 190 204 & PFA/81-10328 (Continental O-200-A)			24. 2.78	S.N.Lester (As "8+-" in Luftwaffe c/s)	Popham	22. 6.00P
G-WURL	Robinson R-22 Beta-II	2740	G-BXMS	13.10.97	Heli Air Ltd Wellesbourne Mountford (At Sywell as EC-GGC with March Helicopters by 7.99)		15.10.00T
G-WVBF	Lindstrand LBL-210A HAFB	312		6.12.95	Virgin Balloon Flights Ltd (London SE16)		1. 5.00T
G-WWAL	PA-28R-180 Cherokee Arrow	28R-30461	G-AZSH N4612J	23.10.98	C.& G.Clarke	White Waltham	23. 8.02T
G-WWAS	PA-34-220T Seneca III	34-8133222	G-BPPB N83270	2. 3.95	D.Intzevidis	Athens, Greece	10. 9.01
G-WWIZ	Beechcraft 58 Baron	TH-429	G-GAMA G-BBSD	18.10.96	Chase Aviation Ltd	Bournemouth	16. 6.02T
G-WWWG	Europa Avn Europa 40 & PFA/247-12597 (Exhibited at PFA Cranfield 7.99 as "G-DSEL" with Wilksch-CITEC WAM120 engine)			31. 7.95	Chloe F.Williams-Wynne Talybont, Gwynedd		10.11.98P
G-WYAT	CFM Streak Shadow SA	PFA/206-12993		9. 6.97	M.G.Whyatt	(High Peak, Derbyshire)	5. 5.00P
G-WYCH	Cameron Witch 90SS HAFB (Witch on broomstick plus cat!)	1330		30. 9.86	Jacques W.Soukup Enterprises Ltd (USA) "Hilda"		13. 7.99A
G-WYMP	Reims Cessna F.150J	0521	G-BAGW SE-FKM	26. 2.82	R.Hall	Full Sutton	18. 8.99T
G-WYMR*	Robinson R-44 Astro	0439		15. 4.98	Heli Air Ltd Wellesbourne Mountford (Cancelled by CAA 29.12.99)		30. 4.01T
G-WYNN	Rand Robinson KR-2 PFA/129-11141 (Originally regd as c/n PFA/129-11093; probably composite of both projects)			28. 8.85	W.Thomas	(Wrexham)	
G-WYNS	Aero Designs Pulsar XP PFA/202-11976 (Rotax 912)			22. 2.91	S.L.Bauza	(Palma de Mallorca)	27. 4.98P
G-WYND	Wittman W.8 Tailwind	PFA/031-12407		2. 8.99	R.S.Marriott & C.Clark t/a Forge Group	(Scunthorpe)	
G-WYNT	Cameron N-56 HAFB	1038		3. 4.84	S.L.G.Williams "Gwyntoedd Dros Cymru/Winds over Wales"	Bristol	21. 3.98A
G-WYPA	MBB Bo.105DBS/4	S.815	D-HDZY	27.10.89	West Yorkshire Police Authority Carr Gate, Wakefield		19.12.01T
G-WYSP	Robinson R-44 Astro	0657		17. 9.99	Heli Air Ltd Wellesbourne Mountford		
G-WYZZ*	Air Command 532 Elite 0429 & PFA G/104-1103		G-BPAK	22. 1.90	C.H.Gem (Cancelled by CAA 22.3.99)	(London SW9)	27. 3.90P
G-WZOL	Tiger Cub RL5B LWS Sherwood Ranger PFA/237-12887		G-MZOL	20. 1.99	G.W.F.Webb Coldharbour Farm, Willingham		
G-WZZZ	Colt AS-42 Hot Air Airship 459 (Rebuilt 1984/85 using new AS-56 envelope c/n 607)			10.12.82	Lindstrand Balloons Ltd "Kit Kat"	Oswestry	17. 2.00A

G-XAAA – G-XZZZ

Regn	Type	C/n	P/I	Date	Owner/operator	Probable Base	CA Expy
G-XALP	Schweizer Hughes 269C (300C)	S.1314		27. 6.88	J.Rawding t/a Helicopter Experience	Wickenby	13. 8.00T
G-XANT	Cameron N-105 HAFB	3003		4. 3.93	Flying Pictures Ltd "Citroen Xantia"	Fairoaks	21.11.96A
G-XARV	ARV1 Super 2	010	G-OPIG G-BMSJ	8.11.95	N.R.Beale	Shotteswell	3.10.00P
G-XAYR	Raj Hamsa X'Air 582 (6)	BMAA/HB/122		4. 1.00	M.J.Kaye & S.Litchfield	(Mexborough)	
G-XBHX	Boeing 737-36N	28572		21. 5.98	British Regional Airlines Ltd Manchester (Grand Union t/s)		4. 6.01T
G-XCEL	Aerospatiale AS.355F1 Twin Squirrel 5324		G-HBAC G-HJET/F-GEOX/F-WYMC/OY-HDL	16. 5.95	Tri-Ventures Group Ltd	Denham	23. 1.00T
G-XCUB	PA-18-150 Super Cub	18-8109036		1. 5.81	M.C.Barraclough	Selborne, Alton	26. 4.01
G-XENA	PA-28-161 Warrior II	28-7716158	N3486Q	29. 6.98	Braddock Ltd	Stockbridge	10. 5.02T
G-XIIX*	Robinson R-22 Beta	0736		8. 2.88	Helitech (Luton) Ltd (Cancelled as wfu 16.11.99)	Luton	21. 3.97T
G-XITD*	Cessna 310G	310G-0048	G-ASYV HB-LBY/N8948Z	15.10.87	Not known Arbury College, Cambridge (Crashed Leavesden 14.7.88; instructional airframe 1.92)		14. 9.86
G-XLTG	Cessna 182S Skylane	182-80234	N9571L	17. 7.98	GX Aviation Ltd	(London W5)	30. 7.01
G-XLXL	Robin DR.400/160 Knight	813	G-BAUD	3. 1.92	R.Pykett & D.Shutter t/a 40-40 Aero Group	Gamston	5. 5.00
G-XMAN	Boeing 737-36N	28573		18. 6.98	British Regional Airlines Ltd Manchester (Golden Khokhloma t/s)		7. 7.01T
G-XPBI	Letov LK-2M Sluka	PFA/263-13341		4.12.98	P.Bishop (Noted 5.99)	Swanton Morley	29. 3.01P

Regn	Type	C/n	P/I	Date	Owner/operator	Probable Base	CA Expy
G-XPTS*	Robinson R-44 Astro	0433		11. 3.98	Heli Air Ltd Wellesbourne Mountford		4. 6.01T
					(Cancelled by CAA 29.12.99)		
G-XPXP	Aero Designs Pulsar XP			30. 3.92	B.J.Edwards Belle Vue Farm, Yarnscombe		22. 5.00P
	(Rotax 912) 218 & PFA/202-11958						
G-XRAY	Rand Robinson KR-2 PFA/129-11227			30. 4.87	R.S.Smith	(Inverurie)	
G-XRMC	BAe 125 Srs.800B	258180	G-5-675	3. 7.90	RMC Group Services Ltd	Farnborough	11.12.00
G-XRXR	Raj Hamsa X-Air 582 (1) BMAA/HB/102			13. 9.99	I.S.Walsh	(Ivybridge)	
G-XSDJ	Europa Avn Europa XS PFA/247-13378			3. 2.99	D.N.Joyce	(Berkeley)	
G-XSFT	PA-23-250 Aztec F	27-7754103	G-CPPC	18. 6.86	SFT Europe Ltd	Bournemouth	1. 6.00T
			G-BGBH/N63773				
G-XSKY	Cameron N-77 HAFB	2508		26. 3.91	T.D.Gibbs	Billingshurst	11. 8.00A
G-XTEC	Robinson R-22 Beta	1478	G-BYCK	23.10.98	Simax Services Ltd (Bury St. Edmunds)		11.11.01T
			N101EJ				
G-XTEK	Robinson R-44 Astro	0647		11. 8.99	Xitec Software plc (Milton Keynes)		31..8.02T
G-XTOR	BN-2A Mk.III-2 Trislander	359	G-BAXD	1. 4.96	Aurigny Air Services Ltd	Guernsey	5. 7.00T
	(New fuselage from c/n 1065/N3266G (NTU) fitted 2.96)						
G-XTRA	Extra EA.230	012A	D-EDLF	21. 1.87	I.A.Scott	(Vaxholm, Sweden)	19. 4.00P
	(Lycoming AEIO-360)						
G-XTRS	Extra EA.300/L	047	D-EXJH	8.10.98	D.J.& L.F.Daly	Inverness	23. 9.01
	(Lycoming AEIO-540) (Tail-wheel u/c)						
G-XTUN	Westland-Bell 47G-3B1	WA/382	G-BGZK	11. 5.99	Zonk! Aviation Ltd (London SW6)		29. 5.00
	(Line No.WAP/81)		XT223		(As "XT223" in Army Air Corps c/s)		
G-XVIE	VS.361 Spitfire LF.XVIe CBAF.IX.3807		8073M	3. 7.92	Historic Flying Ltd	Audley End	
			7281M/7257M/TB252		(Stored 7.97: as "TB252/GW-H")		
G-XWWF	Lindstrand LBL-56A HAFB	595		25. 2.99	D.D.Maimone	Guildford	19 .4.00A
					"WWF"		
G-XXEA	Sikorsky S-76C	760492		21.12.98	T.C.Elworthy, Director of Royal Travel		
					(Op Queen's Flight)	Blackbushe	4. 1.01T
G-XXIV	Agusta-Bell 206B JetRanger III	8717		27. 4.89	Hampton Printing (Bristol) Ltd	Bristol	28. 6.01T
G-XXVI	Sukhoi SU-26M	0410	CCCP-0401	2. 4.93	A.N.Onn & T.R.G.Barnby	Headcorn	29. 5.00P

G-YAAA – G-YZZZ

Regn	Type	C/n	P/I	Date	Owner/operator	Probable Base	CA Expy
G-YAKA	Yakovlev Yak-50	822303	LY-ANJ	10.11.94	J.Griffin	Compton Abbas	29. 4.00P
			DOSAAF 80				
G-YAKI	IAV-Bacau Yakovlev Yak-52	866904	LY-ANM	20. 9.94	Yak One Ltd	Popham	5. 1.00P
			DOSAAF 100		(As "100" in DOSAAF c/s)		
G-YAKM	Yakovlev Yak-55M	920506	RA-01333 R		Mrs B.Abela	White Waltham	
			DOSAAF 40		"40"		
G-YAKO	Yakovlev Yak-52	822203	RA-01493	8. 5.99	M.K.Shaw	(Mallorca, Spain)	16 .6.00P
G-YAKS	Aerostar Yakovlev Yak-52	9311708		16.12.93	Two Bees Associates Ltd "2"	North Weald	25. 3.00P
G-YAKX	Aerostar Yakovlev Yak-52	9111307		13. 3.96	The X Fliers Ltd	(Farnham)	25. 5.00P
			RA-9111307/DOSAAF 27 (As "27" in DOSAAF c/s)				
G-YAKY	Aerostar Yakovlev Yak-52	844109	LY-AKX	26. 2.96	T.K.Butcher & I.A.Reid	Duxford/Clacton	2.12.00P
			DOSAAF 24		t/a Kilo Yankee Group (As "52" in DOSAAF c/s)		
G-YANK	PA-28-181 Archer II	28-8090163	N81314	19. 3.93	Janet A.Millar-Craig	Tatenhill	2. 5.02
					t/a G-YANK Flying Group		
G-YAWW	PA-28RT-201T Turbo Arrow IV		N2929Y	15.11.90	Barton Aviation Ltd	Barton	1. 5.00
		28R-8031024					
G-YBAA	Reims Cessna FR.172J Rocket	0579	5Y-BAA	15.11.84	H.Norman	Bourn	26.10.00
G-YCII	LET Yakovlev C.11	2511108	F-AZPA	13. 1.00	R.W.Davies	(Ashford)	
			Egyptian AF				
G-YCUB	PA-18-150 Super Cub	1809077	N4993X	23. 8.96	F.W.Rogers Garage (Saltash) Ltd		
			N4157T			Dunkeswell	14. 1.00
G-YEAR	Revolution Helicopters Mini-500	0050		6.10.95	D.J.Waddington	(Preston)	AC
	(Rotax 582)						
G-YELL	Murphy Rebel PFA/232-12381			1. 5.95	A.D.Keen	(Totnes)	
G-YEOM	PA-31-350 Chieftain	31-8352022	N41108	3. 1.89	Foster Yeoman Ltd	Bristol	16. 3.99
G-YEWS*	Rotorway Exec 152	DGP-1 & 3850		22. 6.89	D.G.Pollard		
		(Stored 8.95 - cancelled by CAA 22.3.99) Yews Hotel, Great Glen, Leicester					17. 6.93P
G-YFLY	VPM M-16 Tandem Trainer VPM16-UK114		G-BWGI	14.10.96	A.J.Unwin	Kemble	11. 7.00P
	(Arrow GT1000R)						
G-YIII	Reims Cessna F.150L	0827	PH-CEX	5. 6.80	Sherburn Aero Club Ltd Sherburn-in-Elmet		21. 8.00T
G-YIIK	Robinson R-44 Astro	0640		9. 8.99	The Websiteshop (UK) Ltd	Denham	15 .8.02T
G-YJBM	Airbus A.320-231	362	G-IEAF	28. 9.93	Airtours International Airways Ltd		
			F-WWIN			Manchester	26. 1.00T
G-YJET	Montgomerie-Bensen B.8MR		G-BMUH	25. 9.96	A.Shuttleworth	Barton	19. 4.00P
	(Rotax 582) PFA G/101-1072						
G-YKEN	Robinson R-22 Beta-II	2875		22.10.98	S M & Y J Kenmore	Denham	5.11.01
G-YKSZ	Aerostar Yakovlev Yak-52	9311709		16.12.93	J.N. & C.J.Carter	Old Buckenham	12. 5.00P
					(As "01" in Soviet AF c/s)		

Regn	Type	C/n	P/I	Date	Owner/operator	Probable Base	CA Expy
G-YLYB	Cameron N-105 HAFB	4482		15. 1.99	Virgin Airship & Balloon Co Ltd Telford (Lloyds TSB titles)		7. 1.00A
G-YMBO	Robinson R-22 Mariner	2054M	OY-HFR	21. 8.95	J.Robinson	(Bridlington)	10. 9.01T
G-YMMA	Boeing 777-236ER (RR Trent)	30302		7. 1.00	British Airways plc (Union Flag t/s)	Heathrow	
G-YMMB	Boeing 777-236ER	30303		18. 1.00	British Airways plc (Union Flag t/s)	Heathrow	
G-YMMC	Boeing 777-236ER	30304		4. 2.00	British Airways plc	Heathrow	
G-YMMD	Boeing 777-236ER	30305		.00R	British Airways plc (For delivery 2.00)	Heathrow	
G-YMME	Boeing 777-236ER	30306		.00R	British Airways plc (For delivery 3.00)	Heathrow	
G-YMMF	Boeing 777-236ER	30307		. 00R	British Airways plc (For delivery 5.00)	Heathrow	
G-YMMG	Boeing 777				British Airways plc (For delivery 2000/2002)	Heathrow	
G-YMMH	Boeing 777				British Airways plc (For delivery 2000/2002)	Heathrow	
G-YMMI	Boeing 777				British Airways plc (For delivery 2000/2002)	Heathrow	
G-YMMJ	Boeing 777				British Airways plc (For delivery 2000/2002)	Heathrow	
G-YMMK	Boeing 777				British Airways plc (For delivery 2000/2002)	Heathrow	
G-YMML	Boeing 777				British Airways plc (For delivery 2000/2002)	Heathrow	
G-YMMM	Boeing 777				British Airways plc (For delivery 2000/2002)	Heathrow	
G-YMMM	Boeing 777				British Airways plc Heathrow (For delivery 2000/2002)		
G-YMMO	Boeing 777				British Airways plc Heathrow (For delivery 2000/2002)		
G-YMMP	Boeing 777				British Airways plc Heathrow (For delivery 2000/2002)		
G-YMYM	Lindstrand Ice Cream Cone SS HAFB 007			7. 7.93	Lindstrand Balloons Ltd	USA	1. 3.97A
G-YNOT	Rollason Druine D.62B Condor RAE/649		G-AYFH	10.11.83	A.Littlefair	Lymington	13. 6.00P
G-YOGI	Robin DR.400/140B Major	1090	G-BDME	1.10.86	R.M. & A.M.Gosling Stones Farm, Wickham St.Pauls, Essex		19. 4.01
G-YORK	Reims Cessna F.172M Skyhawk II	1354	PH-LUY F-WLIT	14.12.78	P.F.Donegan	(Dublin, Ireland)	6. 7.00
G-YOYO	Pitts S-1E Special PFA/09-10885 (Lycoming O-360)		G-OTSW G-BLHE	22. 5.96	J.D.L.Richardson	Exeter	21. 7.00P
G-YPSY	Andreasson BA.4B PFA/38-10352 (Continental O-200-A)			7. 6.78	C.W.N.Huke & A.N.M.Cox (Colchester) (Damaged Bagby 31. 8.93)		16.11.00P
G-YRAT*	VPM M-16 Tandem Trainer VPM16-UK104 (Arrow GT1000R)			16.11.92	A.J.Unwin Kemble (Damaged nr Kemble 23. 2.96; stored 6.97)		31. 8.96P
G-YRIL	Luscombe 8E Silvaire (Continental O-200-A)	5945	N1318B NC1318B	3. 2.92	C.Potter	North Weald	4.10.00P
G-YROI	Air Command 532 Elite (Rotax 532)	0002	N532CG	3. 9.87	W.B.Lumb Melrose Farm, Melbourne		17.12.90P
G-YROS	Montgomerie-Bensen B.8M (HAPI 60-6M) PFA G/101-1004			29. 1.81	N.B.Gray Worsley, Manchester		6. 6.97P
G-YROY	Montgomerie-Bensen B.8MR (Rotax 532) PFA G/101A-1145			12. 9.89	R.D.Armishaw	Insch	3.10.00P
G-YSFT	PA-23-250 Aztec F	27-7754038	G-BEJT N62805	1.12.87	SFT Europe Ltd	Bournemouth	19. 4.00T
G-YSON	Eurocopter EC.120B	1068		14. 1.00	McAlpine Helicopters Ltd	Oxford	
G-YSTT	PA-32R-301 Saratoga IIHP	3246056	N848T	4. 8.97	A.W.Kendrick	Halfpenny Green	5. 8.00
G-YTUK	Cameron A-210 HAFB	4640		30. 9.99	Societe Bombard SRL	Beaune, France	3.10.00A
G-YUGO*	HS.125 Srs.1B/R-522	25094	G-ATWH HZ-BO1/G-ATWH	25. 8.88	British Aerospace plc Dunsfold (Open store 9.97)		19. 4.91
G-YULL	PA-28-180 Cherokee E	28-5603	G-BEAJ 9H-AAC/N2390R	30. 3.79	Fortescue Investments & Consulting Ltd Gloucestershire/Guernsey		18. 9.00
G-YUMM	Cameron N-90 HAFB	2723		12.12.91	Wunderbar Ltd "Boulevard"	York	6.11.99A
G-YUPI	Cameron N-90 HAFB	1602		12. 1.88	MCVH SA	Brussels, Belgium	22.11.98A
G-YURO*	Europa Avn Europa 001 & PFA/220-11981 (Rotax 912UL)			6. 4.92	Yorkshire Air Museum	Elvington	9. 6.95P
G-YVBF	Lindstrand LBL-317S HAFB	505		2. 4.98	Virgin Balloon Flights Ltd	London SE16	13. 3.00T
G-YVET	Cameron V-90 HAFB	3182		11.10.93	K.J.Foster	Coleshill, Birmingham	9. 7.00A

G-ZAAA – G-ZZZZ

Regn	Type	C/n	P/I	Date	Owner/operator	Probable Base	CA Expy
G-ZABC	Sky 90-24 HAFB	062		10. 4.97	Rishtons (Chichester) Ltd	Chichester	7. 5.00A
G-ZACH	Robin DR.400/100 Cadet	1831	G-FTIO	20.10.92	A.P.Wellings	Sandown	22. 7.01
G-ZAIR	Zenair CH.601HD (Rotax 912UL)	PFA/162-12194		21. 2.92	Speedfreak Ltd	Crosland Moor	22. 6.00P
G-ZAPD	Short SD.3-60 Var.100	SH.3741	G-OLGW G-BOFK/G-14-3741	6. 8.92	Titan Airways Ltd	Stansted	4. 8.00T
G-ZAPJ	Aerospatiale/Alenia ATR-42-312	113	EI-CIQ DQ-FEQ/F-WWEJ	17. 5.96	Titan Airways Ltd	Stansted	19. 5.02T
G-ZAPK	BAe 146 Srs.200QC	E-2148	G-BTIA ZS-NCB/G-BTIA/G-6-148/G-PRIN	25. 4.96	Titan Airways Ltd	Stansted	17. 4.00T
G-ZAPM	Boeing 737-33A	27285	DQ-FJD N102AN/CS-TKG	2. 6.99	Titan Airways Ltd	Stansted	2 .6.02T
G-ZAPN	BAe 146-Srs.200QC	E-2119	ZK-NZC G-BPBT	20. 9.99	Titan Airways Ltd	Stansted	15.11.02T
G-ZAPS	Hughes 269C	90-0041	G-AYLX	26.11.99	D.R.Kenyon t/a Aviation Bureau	Redhill	13. 1.03T
G-ZAPY	Robinson R-22 Beta	0788	G-INGB	8. 7.98	Heli Air Ltd	Wellesbourne Mountford	6. 8.01T
G-ZARI	Grumman-American AA-5B Tiger	AA5B-0845	G-BHVY N28835	7. 3.86	ZARI Aviation Ltd	(Esher)	25. 2.01
G-ZARV	ARV1 Super 2	PFA/152-13035		26. 2.97	P.R.Snowden	Cambridge	23. 2.01
G-ZAZA	PA-18-95 Super Cub (L-18C-PI)	18-2041	D-ENAS R.Neth AF R-66/52-2441 (Adrian Swire)	1. 5.84	Airborne Taxi Services Ltd	Wantage	11. 4.00P
G-ZBED	Robinson R-22 Beta	1684	N63993 F-GHHM	18.11.99	A.Harrison (Bedding) Ltd	(Leeds)	17.11.02T
G-ZBHH	Hughes 269C	129-0869	G-GINZ F-GINZ/SE-HMX/PH-HAN/C-GFKF/N1091N t/a Biggin Hill Helicopters	20. 8.99	The Hughes Helicopter Co Ltd Biggin Hill		28. 5.01T
G-ZBRA	Thunder Ax10-160 HAFB	1530		4. 4.91	Zebra Ballooning Ltd "Zebra"	Maidstone	2. 2.96T
G-ZEBO	Thunder Ax8-105 Srs.2 HAFB	2197		22. 5.92	S.M.Waterton "Gazebo"	Borehamwood	20. 4.00T
G-ZEBR	Colt 210A HAFB	2272		10. 9.92	Zebra Ballooning Ltd "Zebra II"	Maidstone	19. 3.00T
G-ZEIN	Slingsby T-67M-260 Firefly	2234		19. 7.95	RV Aviation Ltd	Blackbushe	25. 3.02T
G-ZENO	Gates Learjet 35A	35A-429	G-GAYL G-ZING	16. 5.96	Northern Executive Aviation Ltd	Manchester	19. 3.00T
G-ZEPI	Colt GA-42 Gas Airship	878	G-ISPY (G-BPRB)	9. 4.92	Lindstrand Balloons Ltd	Oswestry	12. 5.93A
G-ZEPY	Colt GA-42 Gas Airship	1299	G-BSCU	6. 2.92	Keelex 195 Ltd	Telford	8. 8.97A
G-ZERO	Grumman-American AA-5B Tiger	AA5B-0051	OO-PEC	3. 9.80	D.M.Ashford t/a G-ZERO Syndicate	Southampton	6. 2.02T
G-ZIGI	Robin DR.400/180 Regent	2107		19.11.91	R.J.Dix	Bodmin	5. 3.01
G-ZIPA	Rockwell Commander 114A (Originally laid down as c/n 14436)	14505	G-BHRA N5891N	3. 9.98	M.F.Luke	Goodwood	26. 1.01
G-ZIPI	Robin DR.400/180 Regent	1557		22. 2.82	H.U. & D.C.Stahlberg	Rochester	11. 5.01
G-ZIPY	Wittman W.8 Tailwind (Lycoming O-235)	PFA/31-11339		29. 5.91	M.J.Butler Ranksborough Farm, Langham		14. 9.00P
G-ZIZI	Cessna 525 Citationjet	525-0345	N5185V	10.11.99	Ortac Air Ltd	Guernsey	17.11.02T
G-ZLIN	Moravan Zlin Z.326 Trener Master 916 (Modified to Z.526 standard) (C/n confirmed but duplicates I-ETRM)		G-BBCR OH-TZF	30. 6.81	N.J.Arthur	Finmere	6.10.01
G-ZLOJ	Beechcraft A36 Bonanza	E-1677	ZS-LOJ N6748J	11. 9.98	C.J.Parker Shacklewell Lodge, Empingham/Denham		12.11.01
G-ZLYN	Moravan Zlin Z.526F Trener Master	1255	OK-CMC YR-ZAB	4. 8.95	Air V8 Ltd	North Weald	17. 8.98
G-ZONK	Robinson R-44 Astro	0179	G-EDIE	16. 7.97	CCB Aviation Ltd	(Marlborough)	25. 6.01T
G-ZOOI	Lindstrand LBL-105A HAFB	390		22. 5.96	Flying Pictures Ltd	Fairoaks	
G-ZOOL	Reims Cessna FA152 Aerobat	0357	G-BGXZ	11.11.94	A.S.Bamrah t/a Falcon Flying Services (Op European Flyers)	Blackbushe	17. 2.01T
G-ZORO	Europa Avn Europa	PFA/247-12672		20. 6.95	N.T.Read	(Gillingham, Kent)	
G-ZSFT	PA-23-250 Aztec F	27-7954063	G-SALT G-BGTH/N2551M	5. 4.89	SFT Europe Ltd	Bournemouth	8. 3.01T
G-ZTED	Europa Avn Europa	PFA/247-12492		30. 4.96	J.J.Kennedy & E.W.Gladstone	(Edinburgh)	
G-ZULU	PA-28-161 Warrior II	28-8316043	N4292X	25. 2.88	R.W.Tebby t/a S.F.Tebby & Son (Op Bristol Flying Centre)	Bristol	19. 6.00T
G-ZUMY*	Task Silhouette	25		30.12.93	P.M.Wells (Cancelled by CAA 4.5.99)	(Aylesbury)	
G-ZVBF	Cameron A-400 HAFB	4280		21. 1.98	Virgin Balloon Flights Ltd	London SE16	15. 3.00T
G-ZZAG	Cameron Z-77 HAFB	4588		6. 4.99	T.Charlwood	Chichester	4 .5.00A
G-ZZIP	Mooney M.20J (205)	24-3167	N1086N	14. 6.91	H.T.El-Kasaby	Southend	23. 6.01
G-ZZZA	Boeing 777-236	27105	N77779	20. 5.96	British Airways plc "Sir Frank Whittle"	Heathrow	19. 5.02T

Regn	Type	C/n	P/I	Date	Owner/operator	Probable Base	CA Expy
G-ZZZB	Boeing 777-236	27106	N77771	28. 3.97	British Airways plc "Sir William Sefton Branker"	Heathrow	27. 3.00T
G-ZZZC	Boeing 777-236	27107	N5014K	11.11.95	British Airways plc (Rendezvous t/s)	Heathrow	10.11.01T
G-ZZZD	Boeing 777-236	27108		28.12.95	British Airways plc "Wilbur Wright/Orville Wright"	Heathrow	27.12.01T
G-ZZZE	Boeing 777-236	27109		12. 1.96	British Airways plc "Sir Arthur Whitten Brown/Sir John Alcock"	Heathrow	11. 1.02T

SECTION 2

IRELAND

This year the Register has been compiled from information contained in "Irish Air Letter". This is the monthly journal of current and historical Irish aviation and is editored/published by Paul Cunniffe, Karl E Hayes and Eamon C Power, 20 Kempton Way, Navan Road, Dublin 7. In addition, data is also taken from the "Overseas Registers" Section found in our own monthly "Air-Britain News". The information supplied is current up to 6 January 2000. I am very grateful to these gentlemen for the information.

As before, no official C of A data is available and, therefore, it is difficult to determine the status of many aircraft. Nonetheless, I have retained the system introduced last year in an attempt to denote which aircraft have been reported as either active (A) or extant (E) during 1999. The system does not extend to commercial airline aircraft, which should all be active in theory, or where it is self evident from the text. Details relating to other preserved or non-currently registered Irish civil aircraft are shown and marked with an asterisk.

In addition, considerably new information has emerged from the excellent publication "70 Years of the Irish Civil Register" published by BN Historians last Autumn 1999. Thank you to the Author and Air-Britain member, Peter J Hornfleck, for allowing me to use this.

Regn	Type	C/n	P/I	Date	Owner/operator	Probable Base	Remarks
EI-ABI(2)	DH.84 Dragon 2	6105	EI-AFK G-AECZ/AV982/G-AECZ	12. 8.85	Aer Lingus plc "Iolar"	Abbeyshrule	A 8.99
EI-ADV	PA-12 Super Cruiser (Lycoming O-235)	12-3459	NC4031H	11. 5.48	R.E.Levis (Badly damaged in force landing Maynooth, Weston 8.7.99)	Weston	
EI-AFE	Piper J3C-90 Cub	16687	OO-COR D-ELAB/N9954F/EI-AFE/NC79076	11. 3.49	J.Conlon (On rebuild 4.96)	Kildare	
EI-AFF	BA L.25C Swallow II (Pobjoy Cataract II)	406	G-ADMF	18. 5.49	J.Molloy, J.J.Sullivan & B.Donoghue (Damaged Coonagh 24.10.61; on rebuild 4.96)	Ashbourne	
EI-AGD	Taylorcraft Plus D	108	G-AFUB HL534/G-AFUB	26. 5.53	B. & K.O'Sullivan (On rebuild 4.96)	Abbeyshrule	
EI-AGJ	Auster 5 J/1 Autocrat	2208	G-AIPZ	3.11.53	T.G.Rafter (On rebuild 6.96)	Ballyboughal, Co.Dublin	
EI-AHI(2)	DH.82A Tiger Moth	85347	G-APRA DE313	17. 9.93	High Fidelity Flyers	Harriston Nurney, Monasterevin	
EI-AKM	Piper J3C-65 Cub	15810	N88194 NC88194	17.11.58	Setanta Flying Group (Stored)	Kilmoon	
EI-ALH	Taylorcraft Plus D	106	G-AHLJ HH987/G-AFTZ	5. 5.60	N.Reilly	Ballyjamesduff	
EI-ALP	Avro 643 Cadet (Genet Major)	848	G-ADIE	12. 9.60	J.C.O'Loughlin (Engine seizure 12.6.77; awaiting spares & stored in poor condition 8.99)	Weston	
EI-ALU*	Avro 631 Cadet	657	G-ACIH	14. 3.61	M P Cahill (Under restoration 4.96)	Brittas Bay	
EI-AMF*	Taylorcraft Plus D	157	G-ARRK G-AHUM/LB286	26. 4.62	Not known (Fuselage partly restored 4.98)	Carr Farm, Newark	
EI-AMK	Auster 5 J/1 Autocrat	1838	G-AGTV	19. 9.62	Irish Aero Club (Wfu after engine failure 5.79; sold 4.95; stored 1998 for Air Corps Museum)	Newcastle,Dublin	
EI-AMY	Auster J/1N Alpha	2634	G-AJUW	9. 4.63	T.Lennon (For rebuild 4.92)	Maynooth, Co.Kildare	
EI-ANA*	Taylorcraft Plus D	206	G-AHCG LB347	29. 8.63	N.Reilly (Stored 4.92)	Ballyjamesduff, Co.Cavan	
EI-AND	Cessna 175A	56444	G-APYA N6944E	29. 8.63	M. & A.Cooke (Crashed Irish Sea nr Formby Point, Lancs 30.10.94)	Not known	
EI-ANN*	DH.82A Tiger Moth	83161	G-ANEE T5418	6.10.64	Not known (Damaged Culmullen 18.10.64; stored 5.96 for restoration using parts of EI-AOP)	Abbeyshrule	
EI-ANT	Champion 7ECA Citabria	7ECA-38		13. 1.65	Talbury Ltd "The Colonel"	Trim	A 8.98
EI-ANY	PA-18-95 Super Cub	18-7152	G-AREU N3096Z	18.11.64	The Bogavia Group	Weston	A 8.98
EI-AOB	PA-28-140 Cherokee	28-20667		28. 4.65	J.Surdival, L.Moran, J.Kilcoyne & J.Cowell	Waterford	A 8.99
EI-AOK(2)	Reims Cessna F.172G	0208		14. 3.66	D.Bruton (Open store 5.99)	Abbeyshrule	A 8.99
EI-AOP*	DH.82A Tiger Moth	84320	G-AIBN T7967	24. 9.65	Not known (Stored 5.96)	Abbeyshrule	
EI-AOS	Cessna 310B	35578	G-ARIG EI-AOS/G-ARIG/N5378A	1.11.65	Joyce Aviation Ltd (Wfu and to scrapyard)	Kildimo	

Regn	Type	C/n	P/I	Date	Owner/operator	Probable Base	Remarks
EI-APF	Reims Cessna F.150G	0112		6. 3.66	Sligo Aero Club Ltd	Strandhill	A 8.98
EI-APS(2)	Schleicher ASK 14	14008	(EI-114) G-AWVV/D-KOBB	24.11.69	SLG Group	Gowran Grange	
EI-ARH(2)	Slingsby T.56 SE5 rep (Lycoming O-235)	1590	G-AVOT	22. 6.67	L.Garrison (Reported 5.86)	Flabob, CA, USA	
EI-ARM	Slingsby T.56 SE5 rep (Lycoming O-235) (Regd with c/n 1595, ex G-AVOY)	1594	G-AVOX	22. 6.67	M L Putman (Reported by FAA as N912AC 10.99)	Sanger, Texas. USA	
EI-ARW	SAN Jodel DR.1050 Ambassadeur	118	F-BJJH	14. 8.67	P.Walsh & P.Ryan (Damaged nr Carnmore 28.7.86; stored 4.96)	Abbeyshrule	
EI-ASR(2)	McCandless M.4 Gyroplane (VW) (c/n M4/4 also quoted)	M.4/5	G-AXHZ	29. 9.69	G.J.J.Fasenfeld Sion Mills, Strabane (Sold to R.McGregor; stored 4.96)		
EI-AST	Reims Cessna F.150H	0273		30. 1.68	P.McKenna	Galway	E 8.98
EI-ASU*	Beagle A.61 Terrier 2	B.633	G-ASRG WE599	10. 1.68	C Lebroda & Pnts (On rebuild 4.96)	Trim	
EI-ATJ	Beagle B.121 Pup 2	B121-029	G-35-029	10. 2.69	L.O'Leary	Waterford	E 8.98
EI-ATK	PA-28-140 Cherokee	28-24120	G-AVUP	18.10.68	Mayo Flying Club	Abbeyshrule	
					(Damaged Connaught 14.2.87; stored - spares use 4.96)		
EI-ATK*	PA-28-Cherokee 140	28-24120	G-AVUP	18.10.68	Mayo Flying Club	Castlebar	
					(Damaged Connaught 14.2.87: airframes stored Abbeyshrule 9.99)		
EI-ATL	Aeronca 7AC Champion	7AC-4674	N1119E	22. 9.69	Kildare Flying Club	Abbeyshrule	
					(Damaged Weston 26.11.75; used for spares in restoration of EI-AVB)		
EI-ATP*	Phoenix Luton LA-4A Minor	PAL/1124	G-ASCY	29. 8.69	E Batchelor Miami International (Displayed in Concourse 10.94 as EI-ATP/N924GB)		
EI-ATS	Socata MS.880B Rallye Club	1582		20. 4.70	ATS Group (Stored 4.96)	Abbeyshrule	
EI-AUC	Reims Cessna FA150K Aerobat	0040		10. 4.70	Garda Aviation Club Ltd	Weston	
					(Badly damaged in force landing north of Weston 15.7.99)		
EI-AUE	Socata MS.880B Rallye Club	1359	G-AXHU	1. 4.70	Kilkenny Flying Club Ltd	Waterford	A11.99
EI-AUG	Socata MS.894A Rallye Minerva 220	11080		17. 6.70	K.O'Leary	Rathcoole	
EI-AUJ	Socata MS.880B Rallye Club	1370	G-AXHF F-BNGV	12. 6.70	Ormond Flying Club Ltd (Stored 3.98)	Abbeyshrule	E 8.98
EI-AUM	Auster 5 J/1 Autocrat	2612	G-AJRN	11. 9.70	T.G.Rafter Ballyboughal, Co.Dublin (On rebuild 6.96)		
EI-AUO	Reims Cessna FA.150K Aerobat	0074		2. 3.70	Kerry Aero Club Ltd	Waterford	A 6.99
EI-AUP*	Socata MS.880B Rallye Club	1143	G-AVVK	30. 9.70	Not known (Damaged Coonagh 1.9.83; stored - spares use 5.99)	Abbeyshrule	
EI-AUS	Auster J/5F Aiglet Trainer	2779	G-AMRL	17.11.70	T.Stevens & T.Lennon (On rebuild 4.95)	Powerscourt	
EI-AUT	Forney F-1A Aircoupe	5731	G-ARXS D-EBSA/N3037G	21.12.70	Joyce Aviation Ltd (To N.Glass & A.Richardson?) (Stored 8.97) Bann Foot, Lough Neagh, NI		
EI-AUY*	Morane-Saulnier MS.502 Criquet (Argus AS.10)	338	F-BCDG Fr.Mil	30.11.70	G Warner Duxford (Imperial War Museum as "CF+HF" in Luftwaffe c/s)		
EI-AVB	Aeronca 7AC Champion (Continental A65)	7AC-1790	7P-AXK ZS-AXK	14. 6.71	J D Cooper Thonotosassa, Florida,USA (Reported by FAA as N151JC 10.99 c/n 7AC-71790)		
EI-AVC	Reims Cessna F.337F Super Skymaster (Wichita c/n 01355)	N4757 0032		26. 8.71	Christy Keane (Saggart) Ltd Abbeyshrule (Reported as broken up 9.99)		
EI-AVM	Reims Cessna F.150L	0745		3. 3.72	J.Cowell	Castlebar	
EI-AWD	PA-22-160 Tri-Pacer	22-6411	G-APXV N9437D	17. 1.73	J.P.Montcalm Carrigtwohill, Co.Cork (Blown over in gales Cork 12.81; stored 1989)		
EI-AWE	Reims Cessna F.150L	0877		22. 2.73	D.Bruton (Fuselage stored 7.99)	Abbeyshrule	
EI-AWH	Cessna 210J Centurion	210-59067	G-AZCC (EI-AWH)/G-AZCC/5N-AIE/N1734C/(N6167F)	19. 1.73	Rathcoole Flying Club Ltd	Rathcoole	
EI-AWP	DH.82A Tiger Moth (Regd with c/n 19577)	85931	F-BGCL Fr.AF/DF195	4. 7.72	Anne.P.Bruton	Abbeyshrule	
EI-AWR	Malmo MFI-9 Junior	010	LN-HAG (SE-EBW)	12. 6.73	M.Bevan & P.Byrne	Powerscourt	
EI-AWU	Socata MS.880B Rallye Club	880	G-AVIM	12. 1.74	Longford Aviation Ltd	Rosnakil	E 8.98
EI-AYA	Socata MS.880B Rallye Club	2256	G-BAON	27. 7.73	Limerick Flying Club (Coonagh) Ltd	Coonagh	A 8.99
EI-AYB	Gardan GY-80-180 Horizon	156	F-BNQP	5.10.73	J.B.Smith (Restored 1999 after re-build)	Abbeyshrule	
EI-AYD	Grumman-American AA-5 Traveler	0380	G-BAZE N5480L	9. 7.73	P.Howick, H.Martini & V.O'Rourke	Powerscourt	
EI-AYF	Reims Cessna FRA.150L Aerobat	0218		26. 3.74	K.A.O'Connor	Weston	A 8.98
EI-AYI	Morane MS.880B Rallye Club	189	F-OBXE	21.11.73	J.McNamara	Trim	
EI-AYK	Reims Cessna F.172M Skyhawk II	1092		25. 3.74	D.Gallagher	Waterford	A 3.99
EI-AYL(2)	Beagle A.109 Airedale	B.507	G-ARRO (EI-AVP)/G-ARRO	12. 3.74	J.Ronan (Stored for rebuild 1999)	Abbeyshrule	
EI-AYN	IRMA BN-2A-8 Islander	704	G-BBFJ	26. 3.74	Galway Aiation Services Ltd (Op Aer Arann) "Inis-Mor"	Connemara	

Regn	Type	C/n	P/I	Date	Owner/operator	Probable Base	Remarks
EI-AYO(2)	Douglas DC-3A-197	1911	N655GP	5. 3.76	The Science Museum	Wroughton	
			N65556/N255JB/N8695E/N333H/NC16071				
EI-AYR	Schleicher ASK 16	16022	(EI-119)	5. 4.74	Kilkenny Airport Ltd	Kilrush	A 7.99
EI-AYS	PA-22-108 Colt	22-8448	G-ARKT	28. 6.74	M.F.Skelly	Abbeyshrule	
					(Open stored 8.99)		
EI-AYT(2)	Socata MS.894A Rallye Minerva 220		G-AXIU	6. 8.74	K.A.O'Connor	Abbeyshrule	
		11065			(Damaged Palklasmore 12.11.89; stored 11.98)		
EI-AYV	SEEMS MS.892A Rallye Commodore 150		F-BLSP	27. 8.74	P.Murtagh	Strandhill	
		10482			(Open stored 2.84 - wind damaged 1.85 & scrapped 1986)		
EI-AYY	Evans VP-1 MD-01 & SAAC-03			18. 8.75	M.Donoghue	Newcastle	A10.98
	(VW1500)						
EI-BAG*	Cessna 172A	172-47571	G-ARAV	7. 8.74	Cork Parachute Club	Portadown, Belfast	
			N9771T		(Damaged 3.10.76: on rebuild 4.96)		
EI-BAJ	SNCAN Stampe SV-4C	171	F-BBPN	17.10.74	Dublin Tiger Group	Trim	
					(Reported badly damaged in force landing in 8.99)		
EI-BAL*	Beagle A.109 Airedale	B.515	G-ARZS	17.10.74	S.Bruton (Stored 9.99)	Abbeyshrule	
EI-BAO	Reims Cessna F.172G	0278	G-ATNH	11. 2.75	D.Bruton	Abbeyshrule	A 8.99
EI-BAR	Thunder Ax8-105 HAFB	014	G-BCAM	26. 2.75	J.Burke & V.Hourihane	Cahir	
					"Rockwell" (WFU)		
EI-BAS	Reims Cessna F.172M Skyhawk II	1262		2. 5.75	Falcon Aviation Ltd	Waterford	A 6.99
EI-BAT	Reims Cessna F.150M	1196		2. 5.75	K.A.O'Connor	Weston	A10.99
EI-BAV	PA-22-108 Colt	22-8347	G-ARKO	30. 4.75	J.Davy	Moynes	A 8.98
EI-BAY*	Cameron O-84 HAFB	16	G-AYJZ	28. 5.75	British Balloon Museum & Library		
	(Original canopy replaced by c/n 433)				"Godolphin"	Newbury, UK	
EI-BBC	PA-28-180 Cherokee B	28-1049	G-ASEJ	18. 6.75	Piper Aero Club Ltd	Strandhill	A 8.98
EI-BBD	Evans VP-1 VP-1-No.2 & SAAC-02			13. 8.76	The Volksplane Group	Celbridge	
	(VW1600)				(Damaged 12.9.81: on rebuild 1999)		
EI-BBE	Champion 7FC Tri-Traveler	7FC-393	G-APZW	7. 9.75	P.Forde & D.Connaire	Galway	
	(Tail-wheel conversion to 7EC Traveler status)						
EI-BBG	Socata Rallye 100ST	2592		27.10.75	Weston Ltd	Weston	
					(Stored unmarked 8.99)		
EI-BBI	Socata Rallye 150ST	2663		13.10.75	Kilkenny Airport Ltd	Kilkenny	A12.99
EI-BBJ	Socata MS.880B Rallye 100S	2361	F-BUVX	7.11.75	Weston Ltd	Weston	A 5.98
EI-BBK	Beagle A.109 Airedale	B.509	G-ARXB	18.11.75	H.F.Igoe	Abbeyshrule	A 3.99
			(EI-ATE)/G-ARXB				
EI-BBN*	Reims Cessna F.150M	1281		27. 2.76	Sligo North West Aero Club Ltd		
						Strandhill	
				(Cancelled as destroyed 23.6.98: fuselage in Club hangar 8.99)			
EI-BBO	Socata MS.893E Rallye 180GT	12522	F-BVNM	8. 3.76	G.P.Moorhead	Hacketstown	
EI-BBV	Piper J3C-65 Cub (L-4J-PI)	13058	D-ELWY	14. 6.76	F.Cronin	Weston	
	(Frame No.12888)		F-BEGB/44-80762		(Stored 5.97)		
EI-BCE	BN-2A-26 Islander	519	G-BDUV	14. 9.76	Galway Aviation Services Ltd	Inverin	A104.99
					(Op Aer Arann) "Inis-Meain"		
EI-BCF	Bensen B-8M Gyrocopter	47941	N....	24. 8.76	P.Flanagan	Kilrush	
	(McC.O-100)				(Stored 1997)		
EI-BCH	GEMS MS.892A Rallye Commodore 150		G-ATIW	17. 9.76	B Foley	Weston	
		10561			(Dismantled 4.99)		
EI-BCJ(2)	Aeromere F.8L Falco 3	204	G-ATAK	19. 1.77	D.Kelly	Abbeyshrule	
			D-ENYB		(On rebuild 5.99)		
EI-BCK	Reims Cessna F.172N Skyhawk II	1543		22.11.76	K.A.O'Connor	Weston	A12.99
EI-BCL	Cessna 182P Skylane II 182-64300		N1366M	22.11.76	L.Burke	Newcastle	A 5.99
	(Reims assembled with c/n 0045)						
EI-BCM	Piper J3C-65 Cub (L-4H-PI)	11983	F-BNAV	26.11.76	Kilmoon Flying Group	Trim	
			N9857F/44-79687				
EI-BCN	Piper J3C-65 Cub (L-4H-PI)	12335	F-BFQE	26.11.76	Snowflake Flying Group	Trim	
			OO-PIE/44-80039				
EI-BCO	Piper J3C-65 Cub	"1"	F-BBIV	26.11.76	J.Molloy	Kilmoon	
					(Not converted and remains stored)		
EI-BCP	Rollason Druine D.62B Condor	RAE/618	G-AVCZ	27. 1.77	A.Delaney	Dolla	
EI-BCS	Socata MS.880B Rallye 100T	2550	F-BVZV	4. 2.77	Organic Fruit & Vegetables of Ireland Ltd		
						Waterford	A 8.98
EI-BCU	Socata MS.880B Rallye 100T	2595	F-BXTH	10. 2.77	Weston Ltd (Dismantled 12.98)	Weston	
EI-BCW	Socata MS.880B Rallye Club	1783	G-AYKE	18. 4.77	Kilkenny Flying Club	Abbeyshrule	
					(Stored 6.97)		
EI-BDH	Socata MS.880B Rallye Club	1270	G-AWOB	18. 7.77	Munster Wings Ltd	Abbeyshrule	
					(Damaged Cork 5.12.78: status uncertain - thought scrapped)		
EI-BDK	Socata MS.880B Rallye 100T	2561	F-BXMZ	10. 8.77	Limerick Flying Club (Coonagh) Ltd		
					(Airframe stored 9.99)	Abbeyshrule	
EI-BDL	Evans VP-2			7. 9.77	P.Buggle	Kilrush	
	(VW) V2-2101 & PFA/7213 & SAAC-04						

Regn	Type	C/n	P/I	Date	Owner/operator	Probable Base	Remarks
EI-BDM	PA-23-250 Aztec D	27-4166	G-AXIV N6826Y	10.10.77	G.A.Costello t/a Executive Air Services	Waterford	
	(WFU & scrapped Shannon 4.85: fuselage to SE Aviation Enthusiasts' Museum & stored 4.96)						
EI-BDP*	Cessna 182P Skylane	182-60867	G-AZLC N9327G	14.11.77	O.Bruton	Abbeyshrule	
	(Damaged 1988: cancelled 27.11.98 as WFU: wings only 8.99)						
EI-BDR	PA-28-180 Cherokee C	28-3980	G-BAAO LN-AEL/(SE-FAG)	8.12.77	Cherokee Group	Farranfore	A11.99
EI-BEA	Socata Rallye 100ST	3007		28. 2.78	Weston Ltd	Weston	
	(Stored in poor condition 8.99)						
EI-BEN	Piper J3C-65 Cub (L-4J-PI) (Frame No.12376)	12546	G-BCUC F-BFMN/44-80250	28. 4.78	J.J.O'Sullivan	Weston	A 8.98
EI-BEO	Cessna 310Q II	310Q-0233	D-ICEG N7733Q	13. 4.78	C.Keane	Carrickfin	
	(Stored 1995; status uncertain 1997)						
EI-BEP	Socata MS.892A Rallye Commodore 150	11947	F-BTJT	14. 4.78	H.Lynch & J.O'Leary	Abbeyshrule	
	(Stored 4.96)						
EI-BFB*	Socata Rallye 100ST	3044		12. 6.78	Weston Ltd	Weston	
	(Crashed nr Weston 18.10.87; wreck stored 2.95)						
EI-BFE	Reims Cessna F.150G	0158	G-AVGM	3. 8.78	Joyce Aviation Ltd	Waterford	E 8.98
	(Stored dismantled 1.99)						
EI-BFF	Beechcraft A23-24 Musketeer Super III	MA-352	G-AXCJ	20. 8.78	P.Furlong	Waterford	A 6.99
EI-BFI	Socata Rallye 100ST	2618		10.8.78	J O'Neill	Abbeyshrule	
	(Crashed 14.12.85; stored 4.99 for spares)						
EI-BFM	Socata MS.893E Rallye 180GT	12958	F-GARN	12.10.78	Limerick Flying Group (Coonagh) Ltd	Coonagh	A 5.99
EI-BFO	Piper J3C-90 Cub (L-4J-PI) (Frame No.12531 - regd as c/n 8911)	12701	F-BFQJ N79856/NC79856/44-80405	11. 9.78	D.Gordon	Weston	
EI-BFP	Socata Rallye 100ST	2942	F-GARR	6.10.78	Weston Ltd	Weston	A12.98
EI-BFR	Socata Rallye 100ST	2429	F-OCVK	9.11.78	J.Power	Waterford	A 8.98
EI-BFV	Socata MS.880B Rallye 100T	2415	F-BVAH	2. 2.79	Ormond Flying Club Ltd	NK	
	(Stored 8.94: status unknown)						
EI-BGA	Socata Rallye 100ST	2549	G-BCXC F-OCZQ	23.11.78	J.J.Frew	Mullaghmore, NI	
EI-BGB	Socata MS.880B Rallye Club	1913	G-AZKB	22. 1.79	Limerick F/C (Coonagh) Ltd	Abbeyshrule	
	(Stored 3.98)						
EI-BGC	Socata MS.880B Rallye Club	1265	F-BRDC	22.12.78	P.Moran	Roscommon	
	(Thought WFU & cannibalised)						
EI-BGD	Socata MS.880B Rallye Club	2287	F-BUJI (D-EKHD)	18.12.78	N.Kavanagh	Abbeyshrule	
	(Stored 3.98)						
EI-BGF	PA-28R-180 Cherokee Arrow	28R-30121	SE-FAS	30. 1.79	Arrow Group	NK	
	(Crashed into Mynydd Prescelly nr Haverfordwest, Dyfed 6.10.83)						
EI-BGG	Socata MS.892E Rallye 150GT	12824	F-GAFS	30. 1.79	J.Dowling & M.Martin	Abbeyshrule	A 8.99
EI-BGJ	Reims Cessna F.152 II	1664		14. 5.79	Sligo Aero Club Ltd	Strandhill	A 6.98
EI-BGS	Socata MS.893E Rallye 180GT	12675	F-BXTY	25. 4.79	M.Farrelly	Abbeyshrule	
	(Damaged Claive 3.91; wreck stored 4.96)						
EI-BGT	Colt 77A HAFB	041		14. 5.79	K.Haugh	Dublin	
	(Has new envelope c/n 1092 - original to EI-BBM)				"Spitit of Ireland" (Ryan Air c/s)		
EI-BGU	Socata MS.880B Rallye Club	875	F-BONM	9. 5.79	M.F.Neary	Abbeyshrule	
	(Wreck stored 9.99)						
EI-BHB*	Socata MS.887 Rallye	2162	F-BUCH	7. 6.79	Hotel Bravo Flying Club Ltd	Abbeyshrule	
	(Cancelled 29.11.99: open store 5.99)						
EI-BHC	Reims Cessna F.177RG Cardinal (Wichita c/n 00117)	0010	G-AYTG	11. 7.79	B.J.Palfrey & ptnrs	Dublin	A 1.00
					"Hot Chocolate" "90"		
EI-BHF	Socata MS.892A Rallye Commodore 150	10742	F-BPBP	10. 7.79	B.Mullen	Strandhill	
EI-BHI	Bell 206B JetRanger II	906	G-BAKX	14. 8.79	J.Mansfield	Rathcoole	
EI-BHK	Socata MS.880B Rallye Club	1307	F-BRJE	20. 8.79	D.Bruton	Abbeyshrule	A 8.99
EI-BHL	Beechcraft E90 King Air	LW-321	N60253	7. 9.79	Stewart Singlam Fabrics Ltd	Plymouth	A 1.00
EI-BHM	Reims Cessna F.337E Super Skymaster (Wichita c/n 01217)	0004	OO-PDC OO-PDG	1.11.79	Ross Flying Group	Bolton St, Dublin	
	(to Dublin College of Technology: instructional airframe 1993)						
EI-BHN	Socata MS.893A Rallye Commodore 180	11422	F-BRRO	11.10.79	T.Garvan	Hacketstown	
	(On overhaul 6.96)						
EI-BHP	Socata MS.893A Rallye Commodore 180	11459	F-BSAA	12.10.79	Spanish Point Flying Club	Spanish Point	
EI-BHT	Beechcraft 77 Skipper	WA-77		17.10.79	Waterford Aero Club Ltd	Waterford	A 8.98
EI-BHV	Aeronca 7EC Traveler	7EC-739	G-AVDU N9837Y	30.10.79	E.P.O'Donnell & Pntrs	Clonmel	E 9.99
EI-BHW	Reims Cessna F.150F (Wichita c/n 62671)	0013	G-ATMK	22.11.79	R.Sharpe	Weston	
EI-BHY	Socata Rallye 150ST	2929	F-GARL	19.11.79	Liberty Flying Group	Cork	A 7.99
EI-BIB	Reims Cessna F.152 II	1724		30.11.79	Galway Flying Club Ltd	Galway	A12.99

Regn	Type	C/n	P/I	Date	Owner/operator	Probable Base	Remarks
EI-BIC	Reims Cessna F.172N Skyhawk II	1965	(OO-HNZ)	15. 2.80	Oriel Flying Group Ltd	Abbeyshrule	
					(Damaged Castlebar 13.4.95: open store 9.99)		
EI-BID	PA-18-95 Super Cub (L-18C-PI)	18-1524	D-EAES	30.11.79	S.Coghlan & P.Ryan	Galway	A 8.98
	(Possibly c/n 18-1571 ex 51-15571)		ALAT/51-15524				
EI-BIG	Moravan Zlin 526 Trener Master	1086	D-EBUP	7.12.79	P.von Lonkhuyzen		
			OO-BUT			Rushett Farm, Chessington, UK	
					(Damaged 9.91; stored 10.97)		
EI-BIJ	Agusta-Bell 206B JetRanger II	8432	G-BCVZ	29. 1.80	Medavia Properties Ltd	Dublin Heliport	A 2.99
					(Op Celtic Helicopters Ltd)		
EI-BIK	PA-18-180 Super Cub	18-7909088	N82276	1. 2.80	Dublin Gliding Club Ltd	Gowran Grange	A 5.99
EI-BIM	Morane MS.880B Rallye Club	305	F-BKYJ	28. 3.80	D.Millar (Stored 6.97)	Abbeyshrule	
EI-BIO	Piper J3C-65 Cub (L-4J-PI)	12657	F-BGXP	27. 5.80	Monasterevin Flying Group		
			OO-GAE/44-80361			Harristown Nurney, Monasterevin	A 5.99
EI-BIR	Reims Cessna F.172M Skyhawk II	1225	F-BVXI	24. 3.80	B.Harrison, K.Brereton, P.Rogers & F.Maher		A 8.98
						Clonbullogue	
EI-BIS	Robin R.1180TD Aiglon	268		14. 5.80	The Robin Aiglon Group	Abbeyshrule	A 8.99
EI-BIT	Socata MS.887 Rallye 125	2169	F-BULQ	18. 3.80	Spanish Point Flying Club		
						Spanish Point, Co.Clare	
EI-BIU	Robin R.2112A Alpha	175		14. 5.80	Wicklow Flying Group	Weston	E 8.98
EI-BIV	Bellanca 8KCAB Super Decathlon	464-79	N5032Q	3. 6.80	Aerocrats Flying Group Ltd	Weston	A 8.99
EI-BIW	Socata MS.880B Rallye Club	1144	F-BPGB	19. 5.80	E.J.Barr	Buncrana	
					(Crashed on t/o Rosnakil 10.8.86 & scrapped 1990)		
EI-BJB	Aeronca 7DC Champion	7AC-925	G-BKKM	16. 4.80	W.Kennedy	Thurles	E 9.99
	(Continental C85)		EI-BJB/N82296/NC82296				
EI-BJC	Aeronca 7AC Champion	7AC-4927	N1366E	2. 4.80	E.Griffin	Blackwater	
	(Continental A65)		NC1366E				
EI-BJI	Reims Cessna FR.172E Rocket	0040	G-BAAS	23. 5.80	Irish Parachute Club Ltd	Dublin	
			SE-FBW/OY-DKN (Crashed Edenderry 9.82; probably scrapped pre 1990)				
EI-BJJ	Aeronca 15AC Sedan	15AC-226	(G-BHXP)	6. 6.80	O.Bruton	Abbeyshrule	
			EI-BJJ/N1214H		(Stored 3.98)		
EI-BJK	Socata Rallye 110ST	3226	F-GBKY	8. 7.80	Jordan Larkin Flying Group	Weston	A 5.98
EI-BJM	Cessna A152 Aerobat	A152-0936	N761CC	18. 9.80	Leinster Aero Club Ltd	Dublin	A10.99
EI-BJO	Cessna R172K Hawk XP II	R172-3340	N758TD	6. 8.80	P.Hogan & G.Ryder	Galway	A 7.99
EI-BJS	Gulfstream AA-5B Tiger	AA5B-0979	G-BFZR	3. 9.80	P.Morrissey	Newcastle	A 9.98
EI-BJT	PA-38-112 Tomahawk	38-78A0818	G-BGEU N9650N	16.10.80	S.Corrigan & W.Lennon	Abbeyshrule	A 8.99
EI-BJW*	DH.104 Dove 6	04485	G-ASNG	7.11.80	Waterford Airport Fire Service Waterford		E 3.99
			HB-LFF/G-ASNG/HB-LFF/G-ASNG/PH-IOM (No external marks)				
EI-BKC	Aeronca 15AC Sedan	15AC-467	N1394H	5.11.80	J.Lynch	Birr	
EI-BKE*	Morane MS.885 Super Rallye	278	F-BKUN	9. 2.81	Not known	Abbeyshrule	
			F-WKUN (Crashed Ballyclumack, Wexford 5.4.81; wreck stored 4.96)				
EI-BKF	Reims Cessna F.172H	0476	G-AVUX	4.12.80	E.McEllin	Castlebar	
EI-BKK	Taylor JT.1 Monoplane	PFA/1421	G-AYYC	2. 2.81	Waterford Aero Club	Waterford	E 1.99
	(VW1500)				(Stored dismantled 1.99)		
EI-BKN	Socata Rallye 100ST	3035	F-GBCK	18. 2.81	Weston Ltd	Weston	A 5.98
EI-BKS	Eipper Quicksilver	IMA-001		15. 4.81	Irish Microlight Aircraft Ltd	Shannon	
	(Yamaha KT100SD)						
EI-BKT	Agusta-Bell 206B JetRanger III	8562	D-HAFD HB-XIC	6. 4.81	Irish Helicopters Ltd	Dublin	A12.99
EI-BKU	Socata MS.892A Rallye Commodore 150	10990	F-BRLG	21. 5.81	Limerick Flying Club (Coonagh) Ltd		
					(Open stored 5.99)	Abbeyshrule	
EI-BLB	SNCAN Stampe SV-4C	323	F-BCTE	27. 7.81	J.E.Hutchinson & R.A.Stafford		
					(Crashed Drumsna, Carrick-on-Shannon 1.6.97)	Abbeyshrule	
EI-BLD	MBB Bo.105DB	S.381	D-HDLQ	21. 7.81	Irish Helicopters Ltd	Dublin	A10.99
EI-BLE	Eipper Quicksilver	IMA-003		20. 8.81	R.P.St.George-Smith	Kilkenny	
	(Yamaha KT100SP)						
EI-BLN	Eipper Quicksilver MX	MX.01		26. 8.81	O.J.Conway & B.Daffy	Ennis	
	(Cuyana 340)						
EI-BLU	Evans VP-1	SAAC-05		13.10.81	S.Pallister	Kilkenny	
	(VW)						
EI-BLW*	PA-23-250 Aztec C	27-3173	G-BBAV	16.11.81	Shannon Executive Aviation	Shannon	
			PH-KNV/LN-NPD/SE-EPW				
			(Dismantled 1995: extant Engineering School, Airport Industrial Estate 9.99)				
EI-BMA	Socata MS.880B Rallye Club	1965	F-BTJR	26. 1.82	W.Rankin & M.Kelleher	Abbeyshrule	
					(Airframe stored 9.99)		
EI-BMB	Socata MS.880B Rallye 100T	2505	G-BJCO F-BVLB	5. 1.82	Glyde Court Developments Ltd	Weston	A 5.98
EI-BMF	Laverda F.8L Super Falco Srs.IV	416	G-AWSU	28. 1.82	M.Slazenger & H.McCann	Powerscourt	A 5.99
EI-BMH	Socata MS.880B Rallye Club	1277	(G-BIDS) F-BSTJ	19. 2.82	N.S.Bracken	Donegal	

Regn	Type	C/n	P/I	Date	Owner/operator	Probable Base	Remarks
EI-BMI	Socata TB-9 Tampico	203	F-GCOV	12. 5.82	Ashford Flying Group	Weston	A 3.99
EI-BMJ	Socata MS.880B Rallye 100T	2594	F-BXTG	10. 3.82	Weston Ltd	Weston	E 5.98
EI-BMM	Reims Cessna F.152 II	1899		10. 3.82	P.Redmond	Weston	
EI-BMN	Reims Cessna F.152 II	1912		10. 3.82	BMN Group	Abbeyshrule	A 4.99
EI-BMU	Monnett Sonerai IIL (VW2100)	01224		19. 5.82	A.Fenton	Ballyshannon	
EI-BMV	American Avn AA-5 Traveler	AA5-0200	G-BAEJ	28. 7.82	E.Tierney & K.A.Harold (Damaged Brittas Bay 3.93; stored 9.99)	Abbeyshrule	
EI-BMW	Maddock Skytrike/Hiway Vulcan LM-100 (Fuji-Robin)			1. 6.82	L.Maddock	Carlow	
EI-BNA	McDonnell-Douglas DC-8-63CF	45989	LX-ACV (CX-BOU)/TF-ACV/LX-ACV/N779FT	15. 4.83	Aer Turas Teoranta "City of Dublin"	Marana, USA (Stored 11.99)	
EI-BNF	Eurowing Goldwing (Fuji-Robin)	-		22. 9.82	N Irwin (WFU & scrapped 1985)	Cork	
EI-BNH	Hiway Skytrike (Fuji-Robin EC-25-PS)	AS.09		18.10.82	M.Martin	Tullamore	
EI-BNJ	Evans VP-2 (VW2000)	-		24. 1.83	G.A.Cashman (WFU & thought dismantled 1996)	Bartlemy	
EI-BNK	Cessna U206F Stationair	U206-01706	G-HILL PH-ADN/D-EEXY/N9506G	23.12.82	Irish Parachute Club Ltd	Clonbulloge	A 8.99
EI-BNL	Rand Robinson KR-2 (VW2000)	-		13. 1.83	K.Hayes	Birr	
EI-BNP	Rotorway Exec 145	-		1. 3.83	R.L.Renfroe (Not completed 1989)	Letterkenny	
EI-BNR*	American Avn AA-5 Traveler	AA5-0203	N9992Q CS-AHM	12. 4.83	Victor Mike Flying Group Ltd Abbeyshrule (Crashed 21.2.88; open store for spares 5.99)		
EI-BNT	Cvjetkovic CA-65			23. 3.83	B.Tobin & P.G.Ryan	(Tallaght)	
EI-BNU	Socata MS.880B Rallye Club	1204	F-BPQV	7. 4.83	P.A.Doyle	Coonagh	A 8.99
EI-BOA	Pterodactyl	-		3. 5.83	A.Murphy	Athenry	
EI-BOE	Socata TB-10 Tobago	301	F-GDBL	12. 9.83	P.Byron, K.Lawford, L.Naye, E.Murtagh, G.Haughey, M.Verling & J.Byron	Weston	A10.99
EI-BOH	Eipper Quicksilver (Yamaha 970cc)	-		8. 9.83	J.Leech (Status unknown - though dismantled)	Waterford	
EI-BOP*	Socata MS.892A Rallye Commodore 150	11748	G-BKGS F-BSXS	13. 3.84	Not known (Crashed Coonagh 29.3.86; open store for spares 5.99)	Abbeyshrule	
EI-BOR	Bell 222A	47021	LN-OSB	24. 2.84	Westair Aviation Ltd (Op for GPA Grp plc)	Shannon	A11.99
EI-BOV	Rand Robinson KR-2 (VW1835)	SAAC-11		7. 5.84	G.O'Hara & G.Callan "Kitty Hawk" (Damaged Carnmore 3.91 on re-build 1999)	NK	
EI-BOX	Box Duet (Rotax 503)	-		12.10.84	Dr.K.Riccius (Status unknown - thought still under construction)	(Newcastle)	
EI-BPE	Viking Dragonfly (VW1835)	SAAC-16		15.10.84	G.G.Bracken	Castlebar	
EI-BPJ	Cessna 182A Skylane	34949	G-BAGA N4849D	4.12.84	Falcon Parachute Club Ltd (Damaged pre 7.95; fuselage open store 9.99)	Abbeyshrule	
EI-BPL	Reims Cessna F.172K	0758	G-AYSG	28. 3.85	Phoenix Flying Ltd	Shannon	A11.99
EI-BPN	Flexiform Striker (Fuji Robin)	-		12. 3.85	P.H.Collins	Dunlaoghaire	
EI-BPO	Southdown Puma (Fuji-Robin EC-44-PM - E/No.82-00108)	1923		12. 3.85	A.Channing (Also quoted as Southdown Sailwing c/n 1924)	Clane	
EI-BPP	Eipper Quicksilver MX (Cuyana 430)	3207		12. 3.85	J.A.Smith (Stored 8.93)	Abbeyshrule	
EI-BPT	Skyhook Sabre (Solo 210)	-		26. 3.85	T.McGrath Status unknown: thought dismantled)	Glounthane	
EI-BPU	Hiway Demon (Fuji-Robin EC-25-PS)	-		26. 3.85	A.Channing	Artane	
EI-BRH	Mainair Gemini/Flash (Fuji-Robin EC-44-PM)	316-585-3		15. 5.85	J.Deeney	Carrigaline	
EI-BRK	Flexiform Trike (Fuji Robin)	LM.102		17. 6.85	L.Maddock (WFU & scrapped 1994)	Hacketstown	
EI-BRS	Cessna P172D	P172-57173	G-WPUI G-AXPI/9M-AMR/N11B/(N8573X)	2. 9.85	D.& M.Hillary	Weston	A 5.98
EI-BRT*	Flexwing M17727 (Fuji-Robin EC-44-PM)	990059		5.11.85	Not known (Stored 8.97)	Ballymore Eustace	
EI-BRU	Evans VP-1 V-12-84-CQ & SAAC-18 (VW1600)			5.11.85	Home Bru Flying Group	Weston	
EI-BRV	Hiway Demon/Skytrike (Fuji-Robin EC-25-PS)	NK		5.11.85	M.Garvey & C.Tully	Kells	
EI-BRW	Hovey Delta Bird (VW 1300)	NK		5.11.85	A & E Aerosport (Originally regd as Ultra-Lite Deltabird but is a Bimax Osprey: the a/c was built for the "Blue Max" film. It crashed nr Fermoy 1986 & dismantled with remains to Bartlemy)	Curraglass	

Regn	Type	C/n	P/I	Date	Owner/operator	Probable Base	Remarks
EI-BRX	Reims Cessna FRA.150L Aerobat	0160	G-BACM	9. 1.86	Trim F/C Ltd	Trim	
EI-BSB	Wassmer Jodel D.112	1067	G-AWIG F-BKAA	23. 6.87	J.M.Finnan & M.O'Reilly	Kilrush	
EI-BSC	Reims Cessna F.172N Skyhawk II	1651	G-NIUS	10.12.85	S.Phelan	Weston	A 9.99
EI-BSD	Enstrom F-28A	153	G-BBHE	10. 2.86	Clarke Aviation Ltd	Waterford	A 8.98
EI-BSF*	Avro 748 Srs.1/105	1544	EC-DTP G-BEKD/LV-HHF/LV-PUM	28. 5.86	Ryanair Ltd "Spirit of Tipperary" Dublin (Cabin crew trainer 11.95)		
EI-BSG	Bensen B-80 Gyrocopter (McC.4318)	-		30. 1.86	J.Todd (Stored 3.90)	(Riverstick)	
EI-BSK	Socata TB-9 Tampico	618		9. 4.86	Weston Ltd	Weston	A 7.99
EI-BSL	PA-34-220T Seneca III	34-8233041	N8468X	27. 6.86	P Greenan	Weston	A10.98
EI-BSN	Cameron O-65 HAFB	1278		14. 4.86	W.G.Woollett "Erin-Go-Bragh"	Birr	
EI-BSO	PA-28-140 Cherokee B	28-25449	C-GOBL N8241W	16. 4.86	H.M.Hanley	Na Minna	A12 99
EI-BSF*	Avro 748-Srs 1A/105	1544	EC-DTP G-BEKD/LV-HHF/LV-PUM	28. 5.86	Aer Rianta	Dublin	
	(Wings & tail removed & scrapped 10.92: used as cabin trainer: for fire training 9.99 in all-white c/s)						
EI-BSU	Champion 7KCAB Citabria	124	N1621G	15. 6.87	S. & S.Donohue	Proudstown	
EI-BSV	Socata TB-20 Trinidad	579	G-BMIX	15. 8.86	J.Condron	Abbeyshrule	A 8.99
EI-BSW	Solar Wings Pegasus XL-R (Rotax 447)	SW-TB-1124&SW-WA-1122		22. 6.87	E.Fitzgerald	Waterford	
EI-BSX	Piper J3C-65 Cub (Frame No.8999)	8912	G-ICUB F-BEGT/NC79805/45-4515/42-36788	25. 3.86	J. & T.O'Dwyer	Gowran Grange	
	(Official c/n 13255 is incorrect as a/c probably rebuilt c.1945)						
EI-BTX	McDonnell Douglas DC9-82 (MD-82)	49660	(N59842)	23. 3.88	Air Tara Ltd (Leased Aeromexico)	Mexico City, Mexico	
EI-BTY(2)	McDonnell Douglas DC9-82 (MD-82)	49667	N12844	6. 5.88	Air Tara Ltd (Leased Aeromexico)	Mexico City, Mexico	
EI-BUA	Cessna 172M Skyhawk II	172-65451	N5458H	8. 8.86	Skyhawks Flying Club Ltd	Dublin	A 6.98
EI-BUC	Jodel D.9 Bebe (VW 1500)	PFA/929	G-BASY	20. 1.87	D.Lyons	Thurles	A 5.99
EI-BUF	Cessna 210N Centurion II	210-63070	G-MCDS G-BHNB/N6496N	18.12.86	210 Group	Abbeyshrule	A 8.99
EI-BUG	Socata ST-10 Diplomate	125	G-STIO OH-SAB	4. 2.87	J.Cooke	Weston	A 8.98
EI-BUH	Lake LA-4-200 Buccaneer	543	G-PARK G-BBGK/N39779	27. 5.87	T.Henderson Lough Derg Marina, Killaloe		A 5.99
EI-BUJ	Socata MS.892A Rallye Commodore 150	10737	G-FOAM G-AVPL	27. 2.87	T.Cunniffe (Damaged pre 1992: stored 3.98)	Abbeyshrule	
EI-BUL	Whittaker MW.5 Sorcerer (Citroen 602cc)	1		4. 3.87	J.Culleton	Mountmellick, Co.Laois	
EI-BUN	Beechcraft 76 Duchess	ME-371	(EI-BUO) N37001	26. 6.87	L.O'Connor, M.Mellett & K.O'Driscoll	Weston	A 8.99
EI-BUO	Aero Composites Sea Hawker (Lycoming O-320) (Now regd as Glass S.005E)	80		25. 8.87	C.Donaldson & C.Lavery Langford Lodge (Displayed Ulster Aviation Society Museum 1999)		
EI-BUR	PA-38-112 Tomahawk	38-79A0363	G-BNDE N2541D	10. 7.87	Westair Aviation Ltd	Shannon	A11.99
EI-BUS	PA-38-112 Tomahawk	38-79A0186	G-BNDF N2439C	10. 7.87	Westair Aviation Ltd	Shannon	A11.98
EI-BUT	GEMS MS.893A Rallye Commodore 180	10559	SE-IMV F-BNBU	30. 7.87	T.Keating (Galerien c/s)	Weston	A 7.99
EI-BUW	Noble-Hardman Snowbird IIIA (Rotax 532)	SB-F001	77-DS (French)	8. 9.87	TIFC & IS Ltd (Damaged Dromiskin, Co.Louth 1.6.92: status unknown)	Dundalk	
EI-BUX	Agusta A.109A	7147	N790SC (N466MP)/N790SC/N72521	10. 6.88	Orring Ltd	Rathcoole	
EI-BVB	Whittaker MW.6 Merlin (Rotax)	1		14. 9.87	R.England	Mallow	
EI-BVF	Reims Cessna F.172N Skyhawk II	1777	G-BGHJ	30.10.87	First Phantom Group Ltd (Damaged by gales Dublin 3.12.99)	Dublin	
EI-BVJ(2)	AMF Chevvron 2-32 (Konig SD570)	009		16. 2.88	S.J.Dunne Bolybeg, Ballymore Eustace		
EI-BVK	PA-38-112 Tomahawk	38-79A0966	OO-FLG OO-HLG/N9705N	2. 3.88	Pegasus Flying Group Ltd	Weston	A 5.98
EI-BVT	Evans VP-2 (VW 1834) V2-2129/PFA/7221 & SAAC-20		G-BEIE	29. 4.88	P.Morrison	Cobh	
EI-BVY	Heintz Zenith CH.200AA-RW (Lycoming O-320)	2-582		7. 6.88	J.Matthews, M.Skelly & T.Coleman	Abbeyshrule	A11.98
EI-BWD	McDonnell Douglas DC-9-83 (MD-83)	49575	9Y-THT EI-BWD/EC-EFJ/EC-102 (Leased Trans World Airlines)	13. 4.88	Airplanes IAL Ltd Kansas City, USA		
EI-BWH	Partenavia P.68C	212	G-BHJP	11.12.87	K.Buckley	Cork	A 7.99

Regn	Type	C/n	P/I	Date	Owner/operator	Probable Base	Remarks
EI-BXA	Boeing 737-448	24474		28. 6.89	Aer Lingus plc "St.Conleth/Connlaodh"	Dublin	
EI-BXB	Boeing 737-448	24521		27.10.89	Aer Lingus plc "St.Gall"	Dublin	
EI-BXC	Boeing 737-448	24773		26. 4.90	Aer Lingus plc "St.Brendan/Breandan"	Dublin	
EI-BXD	Boeing 737-448	24866		1. 6.90	Aer Lingus plc "St.Colman"	Dublin	
EI-BXI	Boeing 737-448	25052		29. 4.91	Aer Lingus plc "St.Finnian" (Leased Ryan International 11.99)	Dublin	
EI-BXK	Boeing 737-448	25736		14. 4.92	Aer Lingus plc "St.Calmin" (Leased Ryan International 12.99)	Dublin	
EI-BXL	Polaris F1B OK350 Microlight (Rotax 503)	M.561628		27. 6.91	M.McKeon	Lough Gowna	
EI-BXO	Fouga (Valmet) CM-170 Magister (C/n FM-28 quoted)	213	N18FM FM-28	21.11.88	G.W.Connolly (Stored Swords, Dublin 4.96)	Saggart	
EI-BXT	Rollason Druine D.62B Condor	RAE/626	G-AVZE	24. 8.88	S.Bruton	Abbeyshrule	A 8.99
EI-BXX	Agusta-Bell 206B JetRanger III	8560	G-JMVB G-OIML	15.11.88	Westair Aviation Ltd	Shannon	A11.99
EI-BYA	Thruster TST Mk.1	8504	G-MNDA	1. 2.89	E.Fagan	Ballyheelan	
EI-BYF	Cessna 150M Commuter	150-76654	N3924V	20.11.89	Twentieth Air Training Group Ltd	Dublin	A 7.99
EI-BYG	Socata TB-9 Tampico Club	928		23. 8.89	Weston Ltd	Weston	A12.99
EI-BYJ	Bell 206B JetRanger II	1897	N49725	23. 6.89	Celtic Helicopters Ltd	Dublin Heliport	A 9.99
EI-BYL	Heintz Zenith CH-250 (Lycoming 0-320) (C/n quoted as c/n A2-866)	MS/FAS 2866	(EI-BYD)	14. 6.89	M.Guckian	Strandhill	A 3.98
EI-BYR	Bell 206L-3 Long Ranger III	51284	(EI-LMG) EI-BYR/D-HBAD	15. 8.89	Donloe Management Services Ltd	Dublin	A 7.99
EI-BYX	Champion 7GCAA Citabria	7GCAA-40	N546DS	4. 4.90	P.J.Gallagher	Coonagh	A 8.99
EI-BYY	Piper J3C-85 Cub (Frame No.12322) (Regd with c/n 22288 and officially ex G-AKTJ/N3595K/NC3595K)	12494	EC-AQZ HB-OSG/44-80198	12. 4.90	V.Murphy	Thurles	A 8.99
EI-BZE	Boeing 737-3Y0	24464		2. 8.89	Paloma Developments (PAL) (Leased Philippine Airlines)	Manila	
EI-BZF	Boeing 737-3Y0	24465		7. 8.89	Pergola Ltd (Leased Philippine Airlines)	Manila	
EI-BZJ	Boeing 737-3Y0	24677		29. 3.90	Pergola Ltd (Leased Philippine Airlines)	Manila	
EI-BZL	Boeing 737-3Y0	24680		4.10.90	GECAS Technical Services Ltd (Leased Philippine Airlines)	Manila	
EI-BZM	Boeing 737-3Y0	24681		15.10.90	GECAS Technical Services Ltd (Leased Philippine Airlines)	Manila	
EI-BZN	Boeing 737-3Y0	24770		30.10.90	Airplanes Finance Ltd (Leased Philippine Airlines)	Manila	
EI-CAA*	Reims Cessna FR.172J Rocket	0486	G-BHTW 5Y-ATO	17. 8.89	O.Bruton (Damaged 1993/94: canc 27.11.98 as WFU: open store 9.99)	Abbeysrule	
EI-CAC	Grob G-115A	8092		22.10.89	G.Müller	Weston	A 8.99
EI-CAE	Grob G-115A	8105		5. 4.90	D.Kehoe	Waterford	A 8.98
EI-CAN	Aerotech MW.5(K) Sorcerer (Rotax 447)	5K-0011-02	(G-MWGH)	15. 6.90	V.Vaughan	Abbeyshrule	
EI-CAP	Cessna R182 Skylane RGII	R182-00056	G-BMUF N7342W	27. 4.90	M.J.Hanlon	Weston	A11.98
EI-CAQ	Allocated to Aer Lingus 2.3.91 for Flight Simulator testing using "c/n" 1.666 (1666 also quoted)						
EI-CAU	AMF Chevvron 2-32 (Konig SD32)	022		14.11.90	J.Farrant	Rathcoole	
EI-CAW	Bell 206B JetRanger	780	N2947W	11. 7.90	Celtic Helicopters (Maintenance Servicss) Ltd	Dublin Heliport	
EI-CAX	Cessna P210N Pressurized Centurion II	P210-00215	(EI-CAS) G-OPMB/N4553K	9. 7.90	J.Rafter	Naul	A 7.99
EI-CAY	Mooney M.20C Ranger	690074	N9272V	14.11.90	Ranger Flights Ltd	Dublin	
EI-CAZ*	Fairchild-Hiller FH-227D	519	SE-KBR C-FNAK/CF-NAK/(N701U)/N2735R	23. 9.91	Norwich Airport Fire Service	Norwich, UK	
EI-CBJ	DHC-8-102 Dash Eight	215	C-GFCF	25. 5.90	Aerfi Jetprop Ltd (Leased US Air)	(USA)	
EI-CBK	ATR 42-312	199	F-WWEM	25. 7.90	GPA-ATR Ltd (Leased Italair Ltd)	(Italy)	
EI-CBR	McDonnell Douglas DC-9-83 (MD-83)	49939		3.12.90	Airplanes 111 Ltd (Leased Avianca)	Bogota, Columbia	
EI-CBS	McDonnell Douglas DC-9-83 (MD-83)	49942		10.12.90	GECAS Technical Services Ltd "Ciudad De Cucuta" (Leased Avianca)	Bogota, Columbia	

Regn	Type	C/n	P/I	Date	Owner/operator	Probable Base	Remarks
EI-CBY	McDonnell Douglas DC-9-83 (MD-83)	49944		30. 7.91	GECAS Technical Services Ltd "Ciudad De Barranquilla" Bogota, Columbia (Leased Avianca)		
EI-CBZ	McDonnell Douglas DC-9-83 (MD-83)	49945		13. 8.91	GECAS Technical Services Ltd "Ciudad Santiago De Cali" Bogota, Columbia (Leased Avianca)		
EI-CCA	Beechcraft 19A Musketeer Sport	MB-411	G-AWTR N2758B	18. 7.90	P.F.McCoole	Coonagh	A 6.99
EI-CCC	McDonnell Douglas DC-9-83 (MD-83)	49946		27. 9.91	Airplanes 111 Ltd Bogota, Columbia "Ciudad De Pereira" (Leased Avianca)		
EI-CCD	Grob G-115A	8108	D-EIUD or D-EIWD ?	15. 8.90	MOD Aviation Ltd	Weston	A 8.98
EI-CCE(2)	McDonnell Douglas DC-9-83 (MD-83)	49947		19. 9.91	GECAS Technical Services Ltd (Leased Avianca) Bogota, Columbia		
EI-CCF	Aeronca 11AC Chief (Continental A65)	11AC-S-40	N3826E NC3826E	10. 1.91	L.Murray & Ptnrs	Rathkenny	E 7.99
EI-CCH	Piper J3C-65 Cub	7278	N38801 NC38801	24. 1.91	J.Matthews & Ptnrs	Trim	A 8.99
EI-CCJ	Cessna 152 II	152-80174	N24251	9.10.90	M.P.Cahill (Op Irish Aero Club) (Stored 2.95)	Dublin	
EI-CCK	Cessna 152 II	152-79610	N757BM	9.10.90	M.P.Cahill (Damaged pre 1995)	Newcastle	
EI-CCL	Cessna 152 II	152-80382	N24791	9.10.90	M.P.Cahill	Dublin	
					(Damaged Bray Head, Co.Wicklow 4.5.93; status uncertain)		
EI-CCM	Cessna 152 II	152-82320	N68679	9.10.90	E Hopkins	Newcastle	
EI-CCV	Cessna R172K Hawk XPII	R172-3039	N758EP	2. 3.91	Kerry A/C Ltd	Farranfore	
EI-CCY	Grumman-American AA-1B Trainer	AA1B-0617	G-BDYC	19. 3.91	N.F. & C.Whisler (Crashed Galway/Carnmore 5.11.94; wreck stored 4.96)	Galway	
EI-CDB	Boeing 737-548	24919	EI-BXF	27. 5.91	Aer Lingus plc "St.Albert/Ailbhe"	Dublin	
EI-CDC	Boeing 737-548	24968	EI-BXG	19. 6.91	Aer Lingus plc "St.Munchen/Maincin"	Dublin	
EI-CDD	Boeing 737-548	24989	EI-BXH	3. 7.91	Aer Lingus plc "St.Macartan/Macarthain"	Dublin	
EI-CDE	Boeing 737-548	25115	PT-SLM EI-CDE/(EI-BXJ)	21. 5.91	Aer Lingus plc "St.Jarlath/Iarflaith"	Dublin	
EI-CDF	Boeing 737-548	25737		23. 3.92	Aer Lingus plc "St.Cronan"	Dublin	
EI-CDG	Boeing 737-548	25738		7. 4.92	Aer Lingus plc "St.Moling"	Dublin	
EI-CDH	Boeing 737-548	25739		14. 4.92	Aer Lingus plc "St.Ronan"	Dublin	
EI-CDP	Cessna 182L	182-58955	G-FALL OY-AHS/N4230S	20. 5.91	Irish Parachute Club Ltd	Clonbulloge	
EI-CDV	Cessna 150G	150-66677	N2777S	17. 7.91	K.A.O'Connor	Weston	E 5.98
EI-CDX	Cessna 210K Centurion	210-59329	G-AYGN N9429M	14. 8.91	Falcon Aviation Ltd	Waterford	A 9.99
EI-CDY	McDonnell Douglas DC-9-83 (MD-83)	49948		27. 9.91	GECAS Technical Services Ltd (Leased Avianca) Bogata, Columbia		
EI-CEG	Socata MS.893E Rallye 180GT	13083	SE-GTS	31.10.91	M.Farrelly	Powerscourt	
EI-CEK	McDonnell Douglas DC-9-83 (MD-83)	49631	EC-FMY EC-113/EI-CEK/EC-EPM/EC-261	13.12.91	Airplanes IAL Finance Ltd Turin, Italy (Leased Eurofly)		
EI-CEN	Thruster T.300 (Rotax 582)	9012-T300-500		2. 3.92	P.J.Murphy	Macroom	
EI-CEP	McDonnell Douglas DC-9-83 (MD-83)	53122		14. 4.92	GECAS Technical Services Ltd (Leased Avianca) Bogota, Columbia		
EI-CEQ	McDonnell Douglas DC-9-83 (MD-83)	53123		14. 4.92	GECAS Technical Services Ltd "Ciudad De Leticia" Bogota, Columbia (Leased Avianca)		
EI-CER	McDonnell Douglas DC-9-83 (MD-83)	53125	N9017P	20. 5.92	Airplanes 111 Ltd Bogota, Columbia (Leased Avianca)		
EI-CES	Taylorcraft BC-65	2231	G-BTEG N27590/NC27590	25. 3.92	N.O'Brien	Kilkenny	
EI-CEX	Lake LA-4-200 Buccaneer	1115	N8VG N3VC/N8544Z	18. 5.92	Derg Developments Ltd Lough Derg Marina, Killaloe		A 8.99
EI-CEY	Boeing 757-2Y0	26152		10. 8.92	Pergola Ltd Bogota, Columbia (Leased Avianca)		
EI-CEZ	Boeing 757-2Y0	26154		18. 9.92	Airplanes Holdings Ltd Bogota, Columbia (Leased Avianca)		
EI-CFE	Robinson R-22 Beta	1709	G-BTHG	15. 5.91	Toriamos Ltd	Weston	A10.99

Regn	Type	C/n	P/I	Date	Owner/operator	Probable Base	Remarks
EI-CFF	PA-12 Super Cruiser (Lycoming O-235)	12-3928	N78544 NC78544	23. 5.91	J.O'Dwyer & J.Molloy	Gowran Grange	A 5.99
EI-CFG	Rousseau Piel CP.301B Emeraude	112	G-ARIW F-BIRQ	1. 6.91	Southlink Ltd (Stored 1.99)	Waterford	
EI-CFH	PA-12 Super Cruiser (Lycoming O-320)	12-3110	(EI-CCE) N4214M/NC4214M	1. 6.91	G.Treacy	Shinrone	A10.99
EI-CFM	Cessna 172P Skyhawk II	172-74656	N53000	19. 5.92	Hibernian Flying Club (Damaged in gales Cork 24.12.97)	Cork	
EI-CFN	Cessna 172P Skyhawk II	172-74113	N5446K JA4172/N5446K	10. 5.92	B.Fitzmaurice & G.O'Connell	Weston	A11.99
EI-CFO	Piper J3C-65 Cub	11947	OO-RAZ OO-RAF/44-79651	13. 5.92	J.Mathews & Ptnrs (USAAF c/s)	Trim	E 8.98
EI-CFP	Cessna 172P Skyhawk II	172-74428	N52178	15. 7.91	K A O'Connor	Weston	A10.99
EI-CFV	Socata MS.880B Rallye Club	1850	G-OLFS G-AYYZ	13. 5.92	Kilkenny Flying Club "Liverbird"	Kilkenny	A 8.99
EI-CFX	Robinson R-22 Beta	0793	G-OSPI	16. 6.92	Glenwood Transport Ltd	Weston	
EI-CFY	Cessna 172N Skyhawk II	172-68902	N734JZ	18. 6.92	K.A.O'Connor	Weston	A 7.99
EI-CFZ	McDonnell Douglas DC-9-83 (MD-83)	53120	N6206F	29. 7.92	Airplanes 111 Ltd (Leased Avianca)	Bogota, Columbia	
EI-CGB	TEAM miniMax	SAAC-36		20. 8.92	M.Garvey	Abbeyshrule	
EI-CGC	Stinson 108-3 Station Wagon	108-5243	OO-IAC OO-JAC/N3B	17. 7.92	Anne P.Bruton	Abbeyshrule	A 5.99
EI-CGD	Cessna 172M Skyhawk II	172-62309	OO-BMT N12846	30. 7.92	W.Phelan & M.Casey	Weston	A11.99
EI-CGE*	Hiway Demon/Skytrike (Fuji-Robin EC-25PS-04))	NK		19. 8.92	T Carr (Temp unregd 11.2.97)	Kilpedder	
EI-CGF	Luton LA-5 Major PAL-1124/ PFA/1208 & SAAC-19		G-BENH	31. 7.92	F.Doyle & J.Duggan	(Newlands)	A10.99
EI-CGG	Ercoupe 415C (Continental C75)	3147	N2522H NC2522H	10. 9.92	Irish Ercoupe Group	Weston	A 5.98
EI-CGH	Cessna 210N Centurion II	210-63524	N6374A	16.11.92	J.J.Spollen	Abbeyshrule	A 8.99
EI-CGI	McDonnell Douglas DC-9-83 (MD-83)	49624	EC-279 EC-EKM/EC-178	19.10.92	Airplanes IAL Ltd (Leased Nouvelair, Tunisie)	Monastir, Tunisia	
EI-CGJ	Solar Wings Pegasus XL-R (Rotax 447)	SW-WA-1506	G-MWTV	5. 4.93	P.Hearty (Crashed Portarlington late 1995: status unknown)	Portarlington	
EI-CGM	Solar Wings Pegasus XL-R (Rotax 447)	SW-WA-1502	G-MWVC	14.11.92	Microflight Ltd	Ballyfore	
EI-CGN	Solar Wings Pegasus XL-R (Rotax 447)	SW-WA-1529	G-MWXM	14.11.92	V.Power	Donamore, New Ross	
EI-CGO	McDonnell Douglas DC-8-63AF	45924	N353AS (N791AL)/SE-DBH/OY-SBM/HS-TGZ/SE-DBH	25. 4.89	Aer Turas Teoranta	Dublin	
EI-CGP	PA-28-140 Cherokee C	28-26928	G-MLUA G-AYJT	25.11.92	G.Cashman (Op Euroair Training)	Cork	A12.99
EI-CGQ	Aerospatiale AS.350B Ecureuil	2076	G-BUPK JA9740	21. 1.93	Caulstown Air Ltd	Dublin Heliport	A10.99
EI-CGT	Cessna 152 II	152-82331	G-BPBL N16SU/N68715	10.12.92	J.J.Dunne	Stamullen	
EI-CGV	Piper J/5A Cub Cruiser	5-624	G-BPKT N35372/NC35372	11.12.92	J5 Grp	Trim	A 6.99
EI-CGX	Cessna 340	340-0106	(EI-CHH) N51388/G-BALM/N4553L	27. 3.93	Meckfield Construction Co Ltd (Crashed nr Knock 19.8.94: stored Galway 1.95)	Dublin	
EI-CHF	PA-44-180 Seminole	44-7995112	G-BGJB N3046B	22. 2.93	A.Barlow (Op Euroair Training)	Waterford	A 8.98
EI-CHK	Piper J3C-65 Cub	23019	C-FHNS CF-HNS/N1492N/NC1492N	10. 3.93	N.Higgins	Longwood	A 7.99
EI-CHM	Cessna 150M Commuter	150-79288	G-BSZX N714MU	2. 3.93	K.A.O'Connor	Waterford	A 8.99
EI-CHN	Socata MS.880B Rallye Club	901	G-AVIO	22. 2.93	Limerick Flying Club (Coonagh) Ltd	Coonagh	A 8.98
EI-CHP	DHC-8-103 Dash Eight	258	VH-FNQ C-GFRP	7. 4.93	Airplanes Jetprop Finance Ltd (Leased US Air Express)	Harrisburg, PA, USA	
EI-CHR	CFM Shadow Srs.BD (Rotax 447)	063	G-MTKT	20. 5.93	J.Smith	Laytown	
EI-CHS	Cessna 172M Skyhawk II	172-66742	G-BREZ N80775	26. 4.93	Kerry Aero Club Ltd	Farranfore	A11.99
EI-CHT	Solar Wings Pegasus XL-R (Rotax 447) (Possibly c/n SW-TB-1449)	1449		16. 4.93	G.W.Maher	Loughlinstown	
EI-CHV	Agusta A.109A II	7149	VR-BMM HB-XTJ/D-HASV	10. 6.93	Celtic Helicopters Ltd	Dublin Heliport	A 8.99

Regn	Type	C/n	P/I	Date	Owner/operator	Probable Base	Remarks
EI-CIA	Socata MS.880B Rallye Club	1218	G-MONA	26. 4.93	G.Hackett & C.Mason	Thurles	A11.99
			G-AWJK				
EI-CIF	PA-28-180 Cherokee C	28-2853	G-AVVV	12. 6.93	AA Flying Group	Weston	A10.99
			N8880J (Rebuilt 1967 with spare frame c/n 28-3808S - dismantled 12.98)				
EI-CIG	PA-18-150 Super Cub	18-7203	G-BGWF	12. 6.93	K.A.O'Connor	Weston	A 8.99
	(Frame No.18-7360)		ST-AFJ/ST-ABN		(Thought derelict fuselage by 12.98		
EI-CIH	Ercoupe 415CD	4834	OO-AIA	25. 6.93	J.T.Haycock	Weston	A 5.98
	(Continental C85)		(PH-NDO)/N94723/NC94723				
EI-CIJ	Cessna 340	340-0304	G-BBVE	2. 7.93	Airlink Airways Ltd	Sligo	A12.99
			N69451				
EI-CIK	Mooney M.20C Mark 21	2620	G-BFXC	2. 7.93	A & P Aviation Ltd	Galway	A 8.99
			9H-ABD/G-BFXC/OH-MOA/N1349W				
EI-CIM	Light Aero Avid mk.IV	1125D		17. 8.93	P.Swan	Weston	A10.98
	(Rotax 582)						
EI-CIO	Bell 206L-3 Long Ranger III	51436	JA6075	24.10.93	Sean Quinn Properties Ltd	Ballyconnel	A 7.99
			N65460				
EI-CIR(2)	Cessna 551 Citation II	551-0174	N60AR	29.11.93	Air Group Finance Ltd	Dinard, France	
	(Built as Cessna 550 EI-CIR(1) c/n 550-0128) EI-CIR(1)/F-WLEF/9A-BPU/RC-BPU/YU-BPU/N220LA/N536M/N2631V						
EI-CIV	PA-28-140 Cherokee Cruiser		G-BEXY	20.11.93	G.Cashman & E.Callanan	Abbeyshrule	A11.99
		28-7725232	N9639N		(Damaged in gales Cork 24.12.97)		
EI-CIW	McDonnell Douglas DC-9-83	49785	HL-7271	30.12.93	Carotene Ltd	(USA)	
	(MD-83)				(Leased TWA)		
EI-CIZ	Steen Skybolt	001	G-BSAO	12.12.93	J.Keane	Coonagh	A 8.99
	(Lycoming IO-360)		N303BC				
EI-CJB	Boeing 767-35HER	26388	S7-AAV	23.12.93	Hikone Ltd	Malpensa, Italy	
			(I-AEJE)		(Leased Air Europe Italy)		
EI-CJC	Boeing 737-204ADV	22640	G-BJCV	25. 1.94	Ryanair Ltd	Dublin	
			CS-TMA/G-BJCV/C-GCAU/G-BJCV/C-GXCP/G-BJCV (Hertz Car Rental titles)				
EI-CJD	Boeing 737-204ADV	22966	G-BKHE	18. 2.94	Ryanair Ltd	Dublin	
			(G-BKGU)		(Eirecell titles		
EI-CJE	Boeing 737-204ADV	22639	G-BJCU	10. 3.94	Ryanair Ltd	Dublin	
			EC-DVE/G-BJCU		(Jaguar titles)		
EI-CJF	Boeing 737-204ADV	22967	G-BTZF	24. 3.94	Ryanair Ltd	Dublin	
			G-BKHF/(G-BKGV)				
EI-CJG	Boeing 737-204ADV	22058	G-BGYK	25. 3.94	Ryanair Ltd	Dublin	
			PP-SRW/G-BGYK/(G-BGRV)				
EI-CJH	Boeing 737-204ADV	22057	G-BGYJ	30. 3.94	Ryanair Ltd	Dublin	
			(G-BGRU)/N8278V				
EI-CJI	Boeing 737-2E7	22875	G-BMDF	8. 7.94	Ryanair Ltd	Dublin	
			(PK-RI.)/G-BMDF/4X-BAB/N4570B				
EI-CJK	Airbus A.300B4-103	020	F-BUAR	13. 1.94	Airplanes Holdings Ltd	Filton	
			D-AMAY/(F-WLGB)		(Stored 12.99)		
EI-CJR	SNCAN Stampe SV-4A	318	G-BKBK	28. 2.94	C.Scully & P.Ryan	Galway	A 8.98
			OO-CLR/F-BCLR				
EI-CJS	Jodel Wassmer D.120A Paris-Nice	339	F-BOYF	28. 2.94	K.Houlihan	Kilrush	A 8.98
EI-CJT	Slingsby Cadet III	830 & PCW-001	G-BPCW	25. 2.94	J.Tarrant	Rathcoole	
	(VW 1835)		XA288				
EI-CJV	Moskito 2	004	D-MBGM	12. 3.94	Peril, Kingston, Hanly & Fitzgerald		
	(Rotax 582)					Coonagh	
EI-CJZ	Whittaker MW-6S Fatboy Flyer		G-MWTW	24. 3.94	M.McCarthy	Watergrasshill	
	(Rotax 503)	PFA/164-11493					
EI-CKG	Hunt Avon	92009013		2. 7.94	B.Kenny	Clara	
	(Rotax 447)						
EI-CKH	PA-18-95 Super Cub	18-7248	G-APZK	3. 6.94	G.Brady & C.Keenan	Weston	
EI-CKI	Thruster TST mk.1	8078-TST-091	G-MVDI	3. 6.94	S.Pallister	Brannockstown	
	(Rotax 503)						
EI-CKJ	Cameron N-77 HAFB	3305		6. 7.94	F.Meldon	Blackrock	
					"Goodfellas"		
EI-CKM	McDonnell Douglas DC-9-83	49792	TC-INC	10. 8.94	Airplanes Finance Ltd	Olbia, Sardinia	
	(MD-83)		EI-CKM/(D-ALLW)/EI-CKM/XA-RPH/EC-FFP/EC-733/XA-RPH				
					(Leased Meridiana)		
EI-CKN	Whittaker MW-6S Fatboy Flyer	BCA.8942		29. 7.94	F.Byrne & M.O'Carroll	Kilrush	
	(Rotax 462)						
EI-CKP	Boeing 737-2K2ADV	22296	PH-TVS	7.10.94	Ryanair Ltd	Dublin	
			PP-SRV/PH-TVS/LV-RBH/PH-TVS/LV-RAO/PH-TVS/EC-DVN/PH-TVS				
EI-CKQ	Boeing 737-2K2ADV	22906	PH-TVU	20. 2.95	Ryanair Ltd	Dublin	
			G-BPLA/PH-TVU/C-FCAV/PH-TVU				
EI-CKR	Boeing 737-2K2ADV	22025	PH-TVR	4. 5.95	Ryanair Ltd	Dublin	
			C-FICP/PH-TVR/(D-AJAA)/PH-TVR				
EI-CKS	Boeing 737-2T5ADV	22023	PH-TVX	1. 6.95	Ryanair Ltd	Dublin	
			OE-ILE/PH-TVX/G-BGTW				

Regn	Type	C/n	P/I	Date	Owner/operator	Probable Base	Remarks
EI-CKT	Mainair Gemini/Flash 307-585-3 & W47 (EC-44-PM)		G-MNCB	27. 9.94	C.Burke	Bartlemy	
EI-CKU	Solar Wings Pegasus XL-R (Rotax 447) SW-TB-1434 & SW-WA-1500		G-MWVB	14.10.94	M.O'Regan	Edenderry	
EI-CKX	Wassmer Jodel D.112	1166	G-ASIS F-BKNR	7.12.94	J.Greene	Castle Dermott	
EI-CKZ	Jodel D.18 (VW1834)	229		5. 4.95	J.O'Brien	Glen of Imal	
EI-CLA	HOAC DV-20 Katana	20106		24. 3.95	Weston Ltd	Weston	A 3.99
EI-CLB	Aerospatiale/Alenia ATR-72-212	423	F-WWEB	23. 2.95	Tarquin Ltd	Rome-Fiumicino	
					"Lago di Bracciano" (Leased Avianova: Alitalia c/s)		
EI-CLC	Aerospatiale/Alenia ATR-72-212	428	F-WWEF	24. 2.95	Tarquin Ltd	Rome-Fiumicino	
					"Fiume Simeto" (Leased Avianova: Alitalia c/s)		
EI-CLD	Aerospatiale/Alenia ATR-72-212	432	F-WWEL	3. 3.95	Tarquin Ltd	Rome-Fiumicino	
					(Leased Avianova: Alitalia c/s)		
EI-CLF	Fairchild-Hiller FH-227E	505	SE-KBP	12. 7.95	Ireland Airways Holdings Ltd		
			C-FNAI/CF-NAI/PP-BUK/N7802M (Stored 8.99)			Dinard, France	
EI-CLG	BAe 146 Srs.300	E-3131	G-BRAB	7. 6.95	Aer Lingus Ltd	Dublin	
			HS-TBL/G-BRAB/G-11-131 "St.Finbarr/Fionnbar"				
EI-CLH	BAe 146 Srs.300	E-3146	G-BOJJ	2. 6.95	Aer Lingus Ltd	Dublin	
			I-ATSC/G-BOJJ/G-6-146 "St.Aoife"				
EI-CLI	BAe 146 Srs.300	E-3159	G-BVSA	19. 4.95	Aer Lingus Ltd	Dublin	
			I-ATSD/G-6-159/G-5-159 "St.Eithne"				
EI-CLJ	BAe 146 Srs.300	E-3155	G-BTNU	1. 3.96	Aer Lingus Ltd	Dublin	
			(G-BSLS)/G-6-155 "St.Senan/Seanen"				
EI-CLL	Whittaker MW-6S Fatboy Flyer (Rotax 503)	1069		2. 4.95	M.McCarthy	Watergrasshill	
EI-CLQ	Reims Cessna F.172N Skyhawk II	1653	G-BFLV	26. 5.95	K.Dardis & Ptnrs	Abbeyshrule	A11.99
EI-CLR	Boeing 767-3YOER	25411	SE-SKY	23. 6.99	Airplanes Funding 1 Ltd (GPA House)	NK	
			XA-EDE/XA-TJD/SE-DKY/EI-CLR/XA-SKY/PT-TAF/EI-TVP/(EI-CEA)				
EI-CLS	Boeing 767-325ER	26262	(N808AM) N171LF	28. 7.95	ILFC Ireland Ltd	Malpensa, Italy	
					(Leased Air Europe Italy)		
EI-CLT	Bell 206B JetRanger	1727	N90158	17. 7.95	Mistwood Ltd	Cloghran Heliport	A10.99
EI-CLW	Boeing 737-3Y0	25187	XA-SAB	10. 6.95	Airplanes Finance Ltd	Pescara, Italy	
					(Leased Air One)		
EI-CLY	BAe 146 Srs.300	E-3149	G-BTZN	16. 4.97	Aer Lingus Ltd	Dublin	
			N146PZ/ZP-CCY/N146PZ/G-BTZN/HS-TBN/G-11-149 "St.Eugene"				
EI-CLZ	Boeing 737-3Y0	25179	XA-RJR N3521N	27. 7.95	Airplanes Finance Ltd	Pescara, Italy	
					(Leased Air One)		
EI-CMB	PA-28-140 Cherokee Cruiser 28-7725094		G-BELR N9541N	5. 9.95	Kestrel Flying Group Ltd	Dublin	A10.99
EI-CMF	CFM Streak Shadow K.260 & SAAC 50 (Rotax 582) (Possible re-build as G-MTFY has c/n 50)		G-MTFY	13. 9.95	O.Williams	Galway	
EI-CMI	Robinson R-22 Beta	1129	G-BRRZ N8050N	30.11.95	Santail Ltd (To USA 11.99?)	Leeds-Bradford	
EI-CMJ	Aerospatiale/Alenia ATR-72-210	467	F-WWLU	21.12.95	Tarquin Ltd	Milan-Linate, Italy	
					"Fiume Volturno" (Leased Avianova)		
EI-CMK	Eurowing Goldwing ST 76 & SAAC-57 (Fuji-Robin EC-PM-34)			22.12.95	M.Garrigan	Clondara, Longford	
EI-CML	Cessna 150M	150-76786	G-BNSS N45207	5. 1.96	K.A.O'Connor	Weston	A 8.99
EI-CMM	McDonnell Douglas DC-9-83 (MD-83)	49937	G-COES N30010	1. 2.96	Irish Aerospace Ltd (Leased Eurofly)	Turin, Italy	
EI-CMN	PA-12 Super Cruiser (Lycoming O-235)	12-1617	N2363M NC2363M	26. 1.96	D.Graham & Ptnrs	Birr	E 8.98
EI-CMR	Rutan LongEz (Lycoming O-235)	1716		2. 5.96	F. & C.O'Caoimh (F/f 25.10.99)	Waterford	
EI-CMS	BAe 146 Srs.200A	E-2044	N184US N361PS	24. 4.96	Cityjet Ltd (Air France c/s)	Dublin	
EI-CMT	PA-34-200T Seneca II	34-7870088	G-BNER N2590M	23. 4.96	Atlantic Air Ltd	Cork	A11.99
EI-CMU	Mainair Mercury 1071-0296-7 & W873 (Rotax 462)			3. 5.96	J.Deeney	Carrigaline	
EI-CMV	Cessna 150L	150-72747	G-MSES N1447Q	17. 5.96	K.A.O'Connor	Weston	A11.98
EI-CMW	Rotorway Exec (RW162D)	3550		13. 5.96	B.McNamee	Dunboyne	
EI-CMY	BAe 146 Srs.200A	E-2039	N177US N356PS	19. 6.96	Cityjet Ltd (Air France c/s)	Dublin	
EI-CMZ	McDonnell Douglas DC-9-83 (MD-83)	49390	9Y-THN	20. 7.96	Airplanes Finance Ltd (Leased Eurofly)	Turin, Italy	

Regn	Type	C/n	P/I	Date	Owner/operator	Probable Base	Remarks
EI-CNA	Letov LK-2M Sluka (Rotax 447)	8295S005		28. 6.96	G.Doody	Portlaoise	A 8.98
EI-CNB	BAe 146 Srs.200A	E-2046	(EI-CMZ) N187US/N363PS	3. 8.96	Cityjet Ltd (Leased Malmo Aviation)	Dublin	
EI-CNC	Team miniMax 1600 (Rotax 447)	514		10. 9.96	A.M.S.Allen	Trim	
EI-CNG	Air & Space 18-A Gyroplane	18-75	G-BALB N6170S	10. 9.96	P.Joyce	Newmarket-on-Fergus	
EI-CNI	BAe 146 RJ85	E-2299	G-6-299	26.11.96	Peregrine Aviation Leasing Co Ltd "Lombardia" (Leased Azzurra Air)	Bergamo, Italy	
EI-CNJ	BAe 146 RJ85	E-2300	G-6-300	2.12.96	Peregrine Aviation Leasing Co Ltd "Piemonte" (Leased Azzurra Air)	Bergamo, Italy	
EI-CNK	BAe 146 RJ85	E-2306	G-6-306	8. 5.97	Peregrine Aviation Leasing Co Ltd "Lazio" (Leased Azzurra Air)	Bergamo, Italy	
EI-CNL	Sikorsky S-61N Mk.II	61746	G-BDDA ZS-RBU/G-BDDA/N91201/G-BDDA	19.12.96	Bond Helicopters (Ireland) Ltd Shannon (Op Irish Marine Emergency Service)		A12.98
EI-CNM	PA-31-350 Navajo Chieftain 31-7305107		N1201H G-BBNT/N74958	16.12.96	M.Goss (Irish Air Transport titles)	Dublin	A12.99
EI-CNN	Lockheed L.1011-385-1 Tristar	1024	VR-HHV G-BAAA	30. 1.97	Aer Turas Teoranta (Leased Air Scandic)	Manchester	
EI-CNO	McDonnell Douglas DC-9-83 (MD-83)	49672	EC-FTU EC-487/EC-EJQ/EC-150	19. 2.97	Airplanes Finance Ltd Monastir, Tunisia (Leased Nouvelair Tunisie)		
EI-CNQ	BAe 146 Srs.200	E-2031	G-OWLD N173US/N353PS	2. 7.97	Cityjet Ltd (Op Business City Express) (Air France c/s)	Dublin	
EI-CNR	McDonnell Douglas DC-9-83 (MD-83)	53199	SE-DLU N13627	10. 4.97	Aircraft Finance Trust Ireland Ltd (Leased Eurofly)	Milan, Italy	
EI-CNS	Boeing 767-3Q8ER	27600	N6005C	16. 4.97	ILFC (Ireland) Ltd (Leased Air Europe Italy)	Malpensa, Italy	
EI-CNT	Boeing 737-230ADV	22115	D-ABFC	5.12.96	Ryanair Ltd (News of the World/The Sun c/s)	Dublin	
EI-CNU	Cyclone Pegasus Quantum 15 (Rotax 912)	7326		10. 4.97	M.Ffrench	Donamore, New Ross	A11.99
EI-CNV	Boeing 737-230ADV	22128	D-ABFX (D-ABFW)	26. 3.97	Ryanair Ltd	Dublin	
EI-CNW	Boeing 737-230ADV	22133	D-ABHC (B-)/D-ABHC/(D-ABHB)	31. 5.97	Ryanair Ltd	Dublin	
EI-CNX	Boeing 737-230ADV	22127	D-ABFW N5573K/(D-ABFU)	4. 7.97	Ryanair Ltd	Dublin	
EI-CNY	Boeing 737-230ADV	22113	D-ABFB N5573K	10.10.97	Ryanair Ltd (Kilkenny - Cream of Irish Beer c/s)	Dublin	
EI-CNZ	Boeing 737-230ADV	22126	D-ABFU (D-ABFT)	5.11.97	Ryanair Ltd	Dublin	
EI-COA	Boeing 737-230ADV	22637	CS-TES D-ABHX	16.12.97	Ryanair Ltd	Dublin	
EI-COB	Boeing 737-230ADV	22124	D-ABFR	16. 1.98	Ryanair Ltd	Dublin	
EI-COD	Aerospatiale/Alenia ATR-42-312	052	N4203G F-WWEG	24. 7.97	Duntington Ltd (Leased Italair)	(Italy)	
EI-COE	Europa Avn Europa (Jabiru 2200)	286		29. 5.97	F.Flynn	(Urlanmore)	
EI-COG	Gyroscopic Gyroplane	G.120		11. 3.98	R.C.Fidler & D.Bracken	Letterkenny	A 8.98
	(Imported from Australia during 1996 and flown without marks in 8.97; design is 2-seat side by side open cockpit gyro and the quoted c/n G.120 may be the type designation)						
EI-COH	Boeing 737-430	27001	D-ABKB (VT-S)/D-ABKB	6. 6.97	Flightlease (Ireland) Ltd (Leased Air One)	Rome-Fiumicino, Italy	
EI-COI	Boeing 737-430	27002	D-ABKC	13.11.97	Challey Ltd (Leased Air One)	Pescara, Italy	
EI-COJ	Boeing 737-430	27005	D-ABKK (D-ABKF)	13.11.97	Challey Ltd (Leased Air One)	Pescara, Italy	
EI-COM	Whittaker MW-6S Fatboy Flyer (Rotax 582)	1		10.10.97	M. Watson	Clonbullogue	
EI-CON	Boeing 737-2T5	22396	PK-RIW EI-CON/PK-RIW/VT-EWF/A40-BM/C-GVRE/(EI-B)/G-BHVH	21. 7.97	Ryanair Ltd	Dublin	
EI-COO	Carlson Sparrow II (Rotax 532)	302		13. 8.97	D.Logue	Weston	
EI-COP	Reims Cessna F.150L Commuter	1058	G-BCBY PH-TGI/(G-BCBY)	26. 6.97	High Kings Flying Group Ltd	Greigs, Navan	A 8.99
EI-COQ	BAe 146 RJ70	E-1254	9H-ACM (9H-ABW)/G-BVRJ/G-6-254	17.10.97	Peregrine Aviation Leasing Co Ltd (Leased Azzurra Air)	Bergamo, Italy	

Regn	Type	C/n	P/I	Date	Owner/operator	Probable Base	Remarks
EI-COT	Reims Cessna F.172N Skyhawk II	1884	D-EIEF	24.11.97	Kawasaki Distributors (Ireland) Ltd		
						Newcastle	A 7.99
EI-COV	BAe 125 Srs.700B	257178	N621S	28. 5.98	Wilton Bridge Ltd	Dublin	
			N700CJ/G-5-747/VH-LMP/G-5-570/G-BMYX/G-5-530/4W-ACM/G-5-14					
EI-COX	Boeing 737-230ADV	22123	D-ABFP	9. 1.98	Ryanair Ltd	Dublin	
EI-COY	Piper J-3C-65 Cub	22519	N3319N	5.11.97	P.McWade	Abbeyshrule	A 8.98
			NC3319N				
EI-COZ	Piper PA-28-140C Cherokee	28-26796	G-AYMZ	5.11.97	G Cashman	Cork	A 8.99
			N11C				
EI-CPB	McDonnell Douglas DC-9-83 (MD-83)	49940	TC-IND	27.11.97	Irish Aerospace Ltd	Milan, Italy	
			G-TTPT/N30016		(Leased Eurofly)		
EI-CPC	Airbus A.321-211	815	D-AVZT	8. 5.98	ILFC	Dublin	
					"St.Fergus/Faergus" (Leased Aer Lingus)		
EI-CPD	Airbus A.321-211	841	D-AVZA	19. 6.98	ILFC	Dublin	
					"St.Davnet/Damhnat" (Leased Aer Lingus)		
EI-CPE	Airbus A.321-211	926	D-AVZQ	11.12.98	ILFC	Dublin	
					"St.Enda/Eanna" (Leased Aer Lingus)		
EI-CPF	Airbus A.321-211	991	D-AVZE..	9. 4.99	Aer Lingus Ltd	Dublin	
					"St Ida/Ide"		
EI-CPG	Airbus A.321-211	1023	D-AVZR	28. 5.99	Aer Lingus Ltd	Dublin	
					"St.Aidan"		
EI-CPH	Airbus A.321-211	1094	F-WWDD	22.11.99	Aer Lingus Ltd	Dublin	
			D-AVZA		"St.Dervilla"		
EI-CPI	Rutan LongEz (Lycoming O-235)	17		18.12.97	D.J.Ryan	Waterford	A 8.99
					"Lady Elizabeth"		
EI-CPJ	BAe 146-RJ70	E-1258	9H-ACN	27. 3.98	Peregrine Aviation Leasing Co Ltd		
			(9H-ABX)/G-6-258		"Puglia"	Bergamo, Italy	
					(Leased Azzura Air)		
EI-CPK	BAe 146-RJ70	E-1260	9H-ACO	27. 3.98	Peregrine Aviation Leasing Co Ltd		
			(9H-ABY)/G-6-261		(Leased Azzura Air)	Bergamo, Italy	
EI-CPL	BAe 146-RJ70	E-1267	9H-ACP	31. 3.98	Peregrine Aviation Leasing Co Ltd		
			(9H-ABZ)/G-6-267		(Leased Azzura Air)	Bergamo, Italy	
EI-CPM	SAAB 2000	028	SE-KCF	18. 3.98	Cityjet Ltd	Dublin	
			F-GMVR/(V7-9509)/SE-028 (Air France c/s)					
EI-CPN	Auster J/4	2073	G-AIJR	1. 4.98	E.Fagan	Killykeen	A.5.99
EI-CPO	Robinson R-22B2 Beta	2775	G-BXUJ	23. 9.98	Santail Ltd	Weston	A 9.99
EI-CPP	Piper J-3C-65 Cub (Rebuilt Glasthule, Dublin 1994/1998)	12052	G-BIGH	23. 3.98	E.Fitzgerald	Newcastle	
			F-BFQV/OO-GAS/OO-GAZ/44-79756					
EI-CPR	Short SD.3-60 Var.200	SH.3713	G-OBOH	1. 2.99	Comhfhorbairt (Gaillimh) Teo	Dublin	
			G-BNDJ/G-14-3713		(Op Aer Arann)		
EI-CPS	Beechcraft 58 Baron	TH-862	G-BEUL	21. 5.98	F.Doherty	Donegal	A12.99
EI-CPT	Aerospatiale/Alenia ATR-42-312	191	C-GIQS	12. 6.98	GPA-ATR Ltd	Milan, Italy	
			(ZS-NYP)/C-GIQS/F-WWEA (Leased to Italair Spa)					
EI-CPW	SAAB 2000	016	F-GTSC	12. 6.98	DB Export Leasing GmbH	Dublin	
			D-ADSC/SE-016		(Cityjet Ltd) (Op Air France)		
EI-CPX	III Sky Arrow 650T K.122 & SAAC-67			24. 6.98	N.Irwin	Cork	A12.99
EI-CPY	BAe 146 Srs.100	E-1003	N246SS	13. 7.98	CityJet Ltd	Dublin	
			(N631AW)/N246SS/G-5-14/G-SCHH/G-5-14/G-SCHH/(G-BIAF)					
EI-CRB	Lindstrand LBL-90A HAFB	550		23. 9.98	J.& C.Concannon	Tuam	
EI-CRC	Boeing 737-46BR	24124	EC-HCP	29.10.98	Aer Lingus Ltd	Wichita, USA	
			EI-CRC/EC-GNC/SU-SAB/EC-GHF/EC-309/SU-SAA/EC-FYG/EC-655/N689MA/G-BOPK					
					(Leased Ryan International)		
EI-CRD	Boeing 767-31BER	26259	B-2565	29.10.98	ILFC Ireland Ltd	(Italy)	
					(Leased EuroFly Italy)		
EI-CRE	McDonnell Douglas DC-9-83 (MD-83)	49854	D-ALLL	11.12.98	Crane Aircraft Ltd	Olbia, Sardinia	
					(Leased Meridiana)		
EI-CRF	Boeing 767-31B	25170	B-2566	4.12.98	ILFC Ireland Ltd	Rome	
					(Leased Eurofly)		
EI-CRG	Robin DR.400-180R	2021	D-EHEC	11.12.98	D & B Lodge	Waterford	
EI-CRH	McDonnell Douglas DC-9-83 (MD-83)	49935	HB-IKM	10. 2.99	Airplanes 111 Ltd	Olbia, Sardinia	
			G-DCAC/N3004C		(Leased Meridiana)		
EI-CRJ	McDonnell Douglas DC-9-83 (MD-83)	53013	D-ALLP	27. 1.99	C A Aviation Ltd	Olbia, Sardinia	
					(Leased Meridiana)		
EI-CRK	Airbus A.330-301	070	(EI-NYC)	18.11.94	Aer Lingus Ltd	Dublin	
			F-WWKV		"St Brigid/Brighid"		
EI-CRL	Boeing 767-343ER	30008	(I-DEIB)	22. 3.99	GECAS Technical Services Ltd Rome, Italy		
					"Leonardo da Vinci" (Leased Alitalia)		
EI-CRM	Boeing 767-343	30009		8. 4.99	GECAS Technical Services Ltd Rome, Italy		
					(Leased Alitalia) ·		
EI-CRN	Boeing 737-228	23008	F-GBYI	18. 2.99	Rancemont Ltd	Sicily	
					(Leased Air Sicilia)		

Regn	Type	C/n	P/I	Date	Owner/operator	Probable Base	Remarks
EI-CRO	Boeing 767-3Q8ER	29383		16. 4.99	ILFC Ireland Ltd	Rome, Italy	
					(Leased Alitalia TEAM).		
EI-CRP	Boeing 737-73S	29078	N1014S	15. 4.99	Pembroke B737-7006 Leasing Ltd	(Italy)	
			N60436/N1787B		(Leased Azzurra Air)		
EI-CRQ	Boeing 737-73S	29080	N1782B	14. 4.99	Pembroke B737-7006 Leasing Ltd	(Italy)	
			N1786B.		(Leased to Azzurra Air)		
EI-CRR	Aeronca 11AC Chief	11AC-1605	OO-ESM	13. 4.99	L.Maddock & Ptnrs	Killamaster	
			. (OO-DEL)/OO-ESM				
EI-CRS	Boeing 777-2Q8	29908		15. 7.99	ILFC (Ireland) Ltd	Malpensa Italy	
					(Leased Air Europe Italy)		
EI-CRT	Boeing 777-2Q8	28676		8.10.99	ILFC (Ireland) Ltd	Malpensa Italy	
					(Leased Air Europe Italy)		
EI-CRU	Cessna 152	85621	G-BNSW	21. 9.99	W.Reilly	Inis Mor	
			N94213				
EI-CRV	Hoffman H.36 Dimona	3674	OE-9319	2. 6.99	Falcon Aviation Ltd	Waterford	
			HB-2081				
EI-CRW	McDonnell Douglas DC-9-83	49951	HB-IKN	8. 4.99	Airplanes IAL Ltd	Olbia, Sardinia	
	(MD-83)		G-GMJM/N13627		(Leased Meridiana)		
EI-CRX	Socata TB-9	1170	F-GKUL	21. 5.99	Hotel Bravo Flying Club Ltd	Weston	A 8.99
EI-CRY	Medway EclipseR	160/138		2. 6.99	G.A.Murphy	Rathcoole	
EI-CRZ	Boeing 737-36E	26322	EC-GGE	14. 4.99	ILFC Ireland Ltd	Pescara, Italy	
			EC-798		(Leased to Air One)		
EI-CSA	Boeing 737-8AS	29916	N5537L	12. 3.99	Ryanair Ltd	Dublin	
			N1786B				
EI-CSB	Boeing 737-8AS	29917	N1786B	16. 6.99	Ryanair Ltd	Dublin	
EI-CSC	Boeing 737-8AS	29918	N1786B	25. 6.99·	Ryanair Ltd	Dublin	
EI-CSD	Boeing 737-8AS	29919	N1786B	9. 8.99	Ryanair Ltd	Dublin	
EI-CSE	Boeing 737-8AS	29920	N1786B	31. 8.99	Ryanair Ltd	Dublin	
EI-CSF	Boeing 737-8AS		R		Ryanair Ltd	Dublin	
					(For delivery 3.00)		
EI-CSG	Boeing 737-8AS		R		Ryanair Ltd	Dublin	
					(For delivery 3.00)		
EI-CSH	Boeing 737-8AS		R		Ryanair Ltd	Dublin	
					(For delivery 3.00)		
EI-CSI	Boeing 737-8AS		R		Ryanair Ltd	Dublin	
EI-CSJ	Boeing 737-8AS		R		Ryanair Ltd	Dublin	
EI-CSK	BAe 146 Srs.200A	E-2062	N810AS	3. 4.98	Jet Acceptance Corp	Dublin	
			N880DV/G-5-062/N406XV/(G-BNDR)/G-5-062				
					(Leased Aer Lingus Commuter"St.Ciara")		
EI-CSL	BAe 146 Srs.200A	E-2074	N812AS	8. 5.98	Jet Acceptance Corp	Dublin	
			N881DV/G-5-074/G-BNND/HS-TBQ/G-BNND/N146SB/N192US/N368PS/(G-BNND)/G-5-074				
					(Leased Aer Lingus Commuter "St.Cormac")		
EI-CSM	Boeing 737-8AS		R		Ryanair Ltd	Dublin	
EI-CSN	Boeing 737-8AS		R		Ryanair Ltd	Dublin	
EI-CSO	Boeing 737-8AS		R		Ryanair Ltd	Dublin	
EI-CSO	Boeing 737-8AS		R		Ryanair Ltd	Dublin	
EI-CSR	Boeing 737-8AS		R		Ryanair Ltd	Dublin	
EI-CSS	Boeing 737-8AS		R		Ryanair Ltd	Dublin	
EI-CST	Boeing 737-8AS		R		Ryanair Ltd	Dublin	
EI-CSU	Boeing 737-36E	27626	EC-GGZ	14. 4.99	ILFC Ireland Ltd	Pescara, Italy	
			EC-799		(Lsd Air One)		
EI-CSV	Boeing 737-8AS		R		Ryanair Ltd	Dublin	
EI-CSW	Boeing 737-8AS		R		Ryanair Ltd	Dublin	
EI-CSX	Boeing 737-8AS		R		Ryanair Ltd	Dublin	
EI-CSY	Boeing 737-8AS		R		Ryanair Ltd	Dublin	
EI-CSZ	Boeing 737-8AS		R		Ryanair Ltd	Dublin	
EI-CTA	Boeing 737-8AS		R		Ryanair Ltd	Dublin	
EI-CTB	Boeing 737-8AS		R		Ryanair Ltd	Dublin	
EI-CTC	Medway EclipseR	158/137		2. 6.99	C.Brogan	Rathcoole	
EI-CTD	Airbus A.320-211	085	F-GJVZ	6. 5.99	Aerco Ireland Ltd	Italy	
			F-WWDF		(Leased Air Europe)		
EI-CTG	Stoddard-Hamilton SH-2R Glasair RG	721R	N721WR	3. 6.99	K.Higgins	Galway	A 8.99
EI-CTI	Cessna FRA150L	0261	G-BCRN	29. 4.99	D.Bruton	Abbeyshrule	A10.99
EI-CTJ	McDonnell-Douglas DC-9-82	53147	HL7547	11. 6.99	GECAS Technical Services Ltd		
	(MD-82)		HL7203		(Leased Nouvelair, Tunisie)	Monastir, Tunisia	
EI-CTK	Sikorsky S-61N	61-489		28. 4.99	Irish Helicopters Ltd	Dublin	
EI-CTL	Aerotech MW-5B Sorcerer		G-MTFH	21. 5.99	M.Wade	Kilrush	
	(Fuji-Robin EC-44-PM) SR102-R440B-07						
EI-CTM	BAe 146 Srs.300	E-3129	G-JEAL	23. 3.99	Trident Aviation Leasing	Dublin	
			G-BTXN/HS-TBM/G-5-129 (Leased Aer Lingus Ltd) "St.Fiacre/Fiacra"				

Regn	Type	C/n	P/I	Date	Owner/operator	Probable Base	Remarks
EI-CTN	BAe 146 Srs.300	E-3169	G-BSNS R		Aer Lingus Ltd (For delivery 5.00)Dublin		
			EC-FHU/G-6-169/G-BSNS/N887DV/G-BSNS/(N887DW)G-6-165				
EI-CTO	BAe 146 Srs.300	E-3193	G-BUHC R		Aer Lingus Ltd	Dublin	
			G-BTMI/G-6-193		(For delivery 6.00)		
EI-CTT	PA-28-Cherokee 161	28-7716305	N38974	14. 7.99	M.Farrell	Connaught	
EI-CTW	Boeing 767-341ER	30342		8.12.99	GECAS Technical Services Ltd		
					(Leased Eurofly: Alitalia c/s 12.99) Milan, Italy		
EI-CTX	Boeing 737-228	23006	F-GBYG	26. 8.99	Rancemont Ltd	Olbia, Sardinia	
					(Leased Air Sicilia)		
EI-CUA	Boeing 737-4K5	24901	D-AHLR	29. 9.99	Indigo Aviation Leasing Ltd	Rome, Italy	
					(Leased Blue Panorama)		
EI-CUB	Piper J3C-65 Cub	16010	G-BPPV	17. 7.91	J.Connelly & Ptnrs	Galway	E 5.99
			N88392/NC88392				
EI-CUC	Airbus A.320-214	1152	F-WWBS	OOR	GECAS Technical Services Ltd		
					(For lease Volare)		
EI-CUE	Cameron N-105 HAFB	4683		16. 9.99	Bord Telecom Eireann "EIRCOM"	Dublin	A 9.98
EI-CUF	McDonnell Douglas DC-9-82 (MD-82)	49507	B-2123	27. 9.99	GECAS Technical Services Ltd	Shannon	
EI-CUG	Bell 206B JetRanger	4177	N248BC	21.10.99	J.O'Reilly & B.McNamara	Dublin	A12.99
			N118GC				
EI-CUJ	Cessna 172N Slyhawk II	172-71985	G-BJGO	19.11.99	M.Casey & Ptnrs	Cork	A12.99
			N6038E				
EI-CUK	Airbus A.320-214	1198	R		GECAS Technical Services Ltd	Shannon	
					(For lease Volare)		
EI-CVA	Airbus A.320-…	1242	R		Aer Lingus Ltd	Dublin	
					(For delivery 6.00)		
EI-CVB	Airbus A.320-…		R		Aer Lingus Ltd	Dublin	
					(For delivery 2.01)		
EI-CVC	Airbus A.320-…		R		Aer Lingus Ltd	Dublin	
					(For delivery 4.01)		
EI-CVD	Airbus A.320-…		R		Aer Lingus Ltd	Dublin	
					(For delivery 5.01)		
EI-CVE	Airbus A.320-…		R		Aer Lingus Ltd	Dublin	
					(For delivery 5.02)		
EI-CVF	Airbus A.320-…		R		Aer Lingus Ltd	Dublin	
					(For delivery 7.02)		
EI-DAB	Cessna 550 Citation Bravo	550-0917	N5079V R		Gold Air International Ltd	Biggin Hill	
EI-DLA	McDonnell Douglas DC-10-30	46958	N883LA	22. 6.94	GECAS Technical Services Ltd		
			EI-DLA/RP-C2003/(RP-C2000)/(PH-DTM)			Houston, USA	
					(Leased Continental Airlines)		
EI-DUB	Airbus A.330-301ER	055	F-WWKP	6. 5.94	Aer Lingus plc	Dublin	
					"St.Patrick/Padraig"		
EI-DWN	Cessna 421C Golden Eagle III	421C-0641	N422GC	5. 4.96	Dawn Meats (Waterford) Ltd	Waterford	A11.99
			N307SP/ZS-KEP/N88582				
EI-EAA	Airbus A.300B4-203F	150	F-WQGT	2. 4.98	Air Contractors (Ireland) Ltd	Dublin	
			SU-BCC/F-WZMD		(DHL titles)		
EI-EAB	Airbus A.300B4-203F	199	F-WQFO R		Air Contractors (Ireland) Ltd	Dublin	
			SU-BDF/(SU-BCD)/F-WZMF (DHL titles)				
EI-EAC	Airbus A.300B4-203F	250	N10970	20.11.98	Air Contractors (Ireland) Ltd	Dublin	
			N970C/F-WZMU		(Leased Household Commercial Services) (DHL titles)		
EI-EAD	Airbus A.300B4-203F	289	N13972	18. 5.99	Air Contractors (Ireland) Ltd	Dublin	
			N972C/F-WZMM Dublin (Leased Household Financial Services)				
EI-EAT	Airbus A.300B4-203F	116	F-WQFR	16.12.97	Air Contractors (Ireland) Ltd	Dublin	
			D-ASAY/SU-BCB/F-WZES (DHL titles)				
EI-ECA	Agusta A.109A II	7387	N109RP	28. 2.97	Backdrive Ltd	Drogheda	A11.99
			JA9662		(Op Ace Helicopters Ltd)		
EI-EDR	PA-28R-200 Cherokee Arrow II	28R-7435265	G-BCGD	19.11.87	Victor Mike Flying Club Ltd	Dublin	A10.99
			N9628N				
EI-EEC	PA-23-250 Aztec E	27-7554045	G-SATO	6. 2.92	Westair Aviation Ltd	Shannon	A12.99
			G-BCXP/N54257				
EI-EIO	PA-34-200T Seneca II	34-7670274	N6257J	1.10.91	K.A.O'Connor	Weston	A11.99
EI-ELL	Medway EclipseR	157/136		2. 6.99	Microflex Ltd	Rathcoole	
EI-EWR	Airbus A.330-202	330	F-W… R		Aer Lingus Ltd (For delivery 4.00)Dublin		
EI-EXP	Short SD.3-30 Var.100	SH.3092	G-BKMU	23. 7.92	Ireland Airways Holdings Ltd		
			SE-IYO/G-BKMU/G-14-3092/EI-BEH/EI-BEG/G-BKMU/G-14-3092				
					(To Valley Nurseries, Alton, Hants 3.99)		
EI-FKC	Fokker F.27-050	20177	PH-EXC	23. 2.90	Aer Lingus Ltd	Dublin	
					"St.Fidelma/Feideilme"		
EI-FKD	Fokker F.27-050	20181	PH-EXG	12. 4.90	Aer Lingus Ltd	Dublin	
					"St.Mel"		

Regn	Type	C/n	P/I	Date	Owner/operator	Probable Base	Remarks
EI-FKE	Fokker F.27-050	20208	PH-EXA	28. 1.91	Aer Lingus Ltd "St.Pappin/Paipan"	Dublin	
EI-FKF	Fokker F.27-050	20209	PH-EXE	8. 2.91	Aer Lingus Ltd "St.Ultan"	Dublin	
EI-GER	Maule MX7-180A Star Rocket (Tail-wheel u/c)	20006C		7. 1.94	P.J.L.Ryan	Trim	A 7.99
EI-GFC	Socata TB-9 Tampico	141	G-BIAA	9.10.93	B.McGrath, J.Ryan & D.O'Neill	Waterford	A 8.98
EI-GHL	Bell 206B Jet Ranger III	3379	N16Q N2069A	4. 2.97	Marwing Trading Ltd (Op ICC Bank)	Dromahane	A10.99
EI-GHP	Cessna 550 Citation	0897		R	Gold Air International Ltd	Biggin Hill	
EI-GSM	Cessna 182S	182-80188	N9541Q	17. 6.98	Westpoint Flying Group Ltd	Dublin	A12.99
EI-GWY	Cessna 172R Skyhawk	172-80162	N9497F	31.12.97	Galway Flying Club Ltd	Galway	A 6.99
EI-HAM	Light-Aero Avid Flyer (Rotax 582)	1072-90		18.11.96	H.Goulding	Bray	
EI-HCA	Boeing 727-225F	20382	N8839E	15. 4.94	Air Contractors (Ireland) Ltd "Eagle/Iolar"	Dublin	
EI-HCB	Boeing 727-223F	19492	N6817 EI-HCB/N6817	2. 9.95	Air Contractors (Ireland) Ltd	Dublin	
EI-HCC	Boeing 727-223F	19480	N6805	26. 9.95	Air Contractors (Ireland) Ltd	Dublin	
EI-HCD	Boeing 727-223F	20185	N6832	8.11.95	Air Contractors (Ireland) Ltd	Dublin	
EI-HCI	Boeing 727-223F	20183	N6830	23. 5.95	Air Contractors (Ireland) Ltd	Dublin	
EI-HCS	Grob G-109B	6414	G-BMHR	18. 8.95	H.Sydner Boleybeg, Ballymore Castle		A 5.99
EI-HER	Bell 206B JetRanger III	3408	G-HIER G-BRFD/N2069N	1. 7.94	SELC Ireland Ltd & Ptnrs	Belmullet	A 2.99
EI-IRV	Aerospatiale AS.350B Ecureuil	1713	D-HENY	7.10.96	Rathalope Ltd	Weston	A 9.99
EI-JAK	Avtech Jabiru UL 0144 & SAAC-68			9. 7.98	S.Walshe	Waterford	A 8.98
EI-JBC	Agusta A.109A	7126	F-GATN	24. 7.97	Medeva Properties Ltd	Dublin	A 7.99
EI-JFK	Airbus A.330-301	086	F-GMDE	11. 7.95	Aer Lingus plc "St.Colmcille"	Dublin	
EI-JWM	Robinson R-22 Beta	1386	G-BSLB	21.11.92	C.Shiel	Weston	A11.99
EI-LAX	Airbus A.330-202	269	F-WWKV	29. 4.99	Aer Lingus Ltd "St.Mella"	Dublin	
EI-LCH	Boeing 727-281F	20466	N903PG N527MD/HL7355/JA8332 "Sylvia"	6. 2.95	Air Contractors (Ireland) Ltd	Dublin	
EI-LIT	MBB Bo.105S	S.434	A6-DBH Dubai 105/D-HDMH	20. 2.96	Irish Helicopters Ltd	Cork	A11.99
EI-LRS	Schweizer Hughes 269C	S.1701	N41S	6. 3.95	Lynch Roofing Systems Ltd	Galway	
EI-MAC	Robinson R-22 Beta	1433	G-OHHL	18. 4.97	McAuliffe Trucking Ltd	Castleisland	
					(W/O after in-flight break-up en-route Weston to Sligo 27.8.99)		
EI-MCF	Cessna 172R (Allocation awaits confirmation)	80799	N2469D	R12.99	Galway Flying Club	Carnmore	
EI-MER	Bell 206B	4513	N60507	28. 9.99	Mercury Engineering Ltd	Dublin	A12.99
EI-MES	Sikorsky S-61N	61776	G-BXAE LN-OQO	27. 3.97	Bond Helicopters (Ireland) Ltd (Op Irish Marine Emergency Service)	Shannon	A12.99
EI-MIP	Aerospatiale SA.365N Dauphin 2	6119	G-BLEY F-WTNM	20. 3.96	Bond Helicopters (Ireland) Ltd	Cork	A 9.98
EI-ONE	Bell 206B JetRanger	1761	EI-CJM N281C/N49582	30. 5.96	TCI Aircraft Ltd	Westpoint	A 6.98
EI-ORD	Airbus A.330-301	059	(EI-USA) F-GMDD	6. 6.97	Aer Lingus plc "St.Maeve/Maedbh"	Dublin	A 5.99
EI-PAL	Cessna 550m Citation Bravo	550-0935		R	Gold Air International Ltd	Biggin Hill	
EI-PAT	BAe.146 Srs 200	E-2030	G-ZAPL G-WLCY/N172US/N352US (Leased Cityjet)	11.10.99	Brimstage Ltd	Dublin	
EI-PMI	Agusta-Bell 206B JetRanger III	8614	EI-BLG G-BIGS	19. 9.96	Ping Golf Equipment Ltd	Dublin	A 8.99
EI-POD	Cessna 177B Cardinal	177B-02729	N1444C	3. 8.95	Trim Flying Club Ltd	Trim	A 7.99
EI-RMC	Bell 206B Jet Ranger	488	G-BWLO N2290W	16.12.99	Westair Aviation Ltd	Shannon	
EI-RRR	HS.125 Srs 700A	257170/NA0318	N80CL N819M/G-5-14	11.10.99	Star Air (Ireland) Ltd	Dublin	A12.99
EI-RYR	Boeing-Stearman E75 (N2S-5) Kaydet				See G-THEA in SECTION 1		
EI-SAR	Sikorsky S-61N (Mitsubishi c/n M61-001)	61-143	G-AYOM N4585/JA9506/N94565	26. 6.98	Bond Helicopters (Ireland) Ltd (Op Irish Marine Emergency Service)	Shannon	A12.98
EI-SAT	Steen Skybolt	1	N52DH	22.10.99	Capt B.O'Sullivan	- Trim	
EI-SHN	Airbus A.330-301	054	F-WWKJ	27. 4.94	Aer Lingus plc "St.Flannan"	Dublin	
EI-STR	Bell 430	53282	N44504	R	Westair Aviation (Noted as N44504 Dublin Heliport 24.8.99)	Shannon	
EI-SXT	Canadair CL.600 Challenger 3R	5159	C-FTNN C-GLWR	25. 4.95	Sextant Ireland Ltd Zurich, Switzerland		A11.98
EI-TAR	Bell 222A	47029	N121NN N121NC/N120NC	10. 9.98	Westair Ltd (Leased Confucious Ltd)	Jersey	A11.99
EI-TKI	Robinson R-22 Beta	1195	G-OBIP	22. 8.91	J.McDaid	Weston	A 4.99

466

Regn	Type	C/n	P/I	Date	Owner/operator	Probable Base	Remarks
EI-TLB	Airbus A.300B4-103	012	F-GIJU	2. 4.96	Airplanes Holdings Ltd	Filton	
			G-BMNC/D-AMAX/F-WLGC (Stored 12.99)				
EI-TLF	Airbus A.320-231	476	F-WWBR	10. 6.94	TransAer International Airlines Ltd		
					(Reserved as G-	2.00)	
EI-TLG	Airbus A.320-231	428	C-GMPG	20. 5.94	TransAer International Airlines Ltd		
			EI-TLG/C-GMPG/EI-TLG/(D-ANDY)/N391LF/F-WWIL				(Libya)	
					(Leased Libyan Arab Airlines 12.99)		
EI-TLH	Airbus A.320-231	247	G-OALA	22.12.94	TransAer International Airlines Ltd		
			EI-TLH/N247RX/F-WWDK				(Cuba)	
					(Leased Cubana 11.98/5.01)		
EI-TLI	Airbus A.320-231	405	N141LF	26. 5.95	TransAer International Airlines Ltd		
			HC-BTV/N441LF/F-WWDK			Philadelphia, USA	
					(Leased Trasnmeridian)		
EI-TLJ	Airbus A.320-231	257	N257RX	29. 9.95	TransAer International Airlines Ltd		
			LZ-ABA/F-WWBI		(Leased Cubana 11.98)	(Cuba)	
EI-TLK	Airbus A.300B4-203	161	N226GE	12. 3.97	GECAS Technical Services Ltd		
			TC-JUV/N226EA/F-GBNU			Karachi, Pakistan	
					(Leased TransAer/Pakistan International)		
EI-TLL	Airbus A.300B4-203	158	N225GE	20. 6.97	GECAS Technical Services Ltd		
			TC-JUY/N225EA/F-GBNT Karachi, Pakistan				
					(Leased TransAer/Pakistan International)		
EI-TLM	Airbus A.300B4-203	046	RP-C8882	18. 9.97	TransAer International Airlines Ltd		
			SX-BEB/F-WZER/F-WZEK/F-WLGB			Karachi, Pakistan	
					(Leased TransAer/Pakistan International)		
EI-TLO	Airbus A.320-232	758	F-WWDC	9. 1.98	TransAer International Airlines Ltd		
					(Leased Britannia Airways)	Luton	
EI-TLP	Airbus A.320-232	760	F-WWDD	20. 1.98	TransAer International Airlines Ltd		
					(Leased Shorouk Air)	NK	
EI-TLQ	Airbus A.300B4-203	131	6Y-JMK	2. 4.98	Airplanes Finance Ltd Karachi, Pakistan		
			G-BIMB/F-WZEL		(Leased Pakistan International Airways)		
EI-TLR	Airbus A.320-231	414	B-HYR	16. 6.98	TransAer International Airlines Ltd		
			VR-HYR/F-WWIU		(Leased Khalifa)	Dublin	
EI-TLS	Airbus A.320-231	430	(N430CR)	19. 8.98	TransAer International Airlines Ltd		
			B-HYS/VR-HYS/F-WWBH (Leased Khalifa)			Cologne, Germany	
EI-TLT	Airbus A.320-231	415	B-HYV	23. 4.99	TransAer International Airlines Ltd -		
			VR-HYV/F-WWBL		(Leased Libyan Arab Airlines)	(Libya)	
EI-TVA	Boeing 737-43Q	28489	(OO-VEJ)	21.11.98	Aldebaran FSE-One Corp	Shannon	
			B-18671		(Leased Virgin Express (Ireland) Ltd)		
EI-TVB	Boeing 737-43Q	28493	(OO-VEK)	9.12.98	Virgin Express (Ireland) Ltd	Shannon	
			B-18676				
EI-TVC	Boeing 737…			R	Virgin Express (Ireland) Ltd	Shannon	
EI-TVD	Boeing 737- .			R	Virgin Express (Ireland) Ltd	Shannon	
EI-TVE	Boeing 737-			R	Virgin Express (Ireland) Ltd	Shannon	
EI-TVF	Boeing 737-			R	Virgin Express (Ireland) Ltd	Shannon	
EI-TVG	Boeing 737-			R	Virgin Express (Ireland) Ltd	Shannon	
EI-TVH	Boeing 737-			R	Virgin Express (Ireland) Ltd	Shannon	
EI-TVH	Boeing 737-			R	Virgin Express (Ireland) Ltd	Shannon	
EI-TVJ	Boeing 737-			R	Virgin Express (Ireland) Ltd	Shannon	
EI-TVK	Boeing 737-			R	Virgin Express (Ireland) Ltd	Shannon	
EI-TVL	Boeing 737-			R	Virgin Express (Ireland) Ltd	Shannon	
EI-TVM	Boeing 737-			R	Virgin Express (Ireland) Ltd	Shannon	
EI-TVN	Boeing 737-36N	28586	N1768B	19. 1.99	Virgin Express (Ireland) Ltd	Shannon	
EI-TVO	Boeing 737-46M	28333	OO-VEB	6. 5.99	Virgin Express (Ireland) Ltd	- Shannon	
			(OO-EBB)				
EI-TVP	Boeing 737-3M8	25041	OO-LTL	30. 6.99	Tombo Aviation Netherlands BV	Shannon	
					(Op Virgin Express (Ireland) Ltd)		
EI-TVQ	Boeing 737-36N	28568	OO-VEG	R	Virgin Express (Ireland) Ltd	Shannon	
					(For delivery 1.00)		
EI-TVR				R	Virgin Express (Ireland) Ltd	Shannon	
EI-TVS				R	Virgin Express (Ireland) Ltd	Shannon	
EI-TVT				R	Virgin Express (Ireland) Ltd	Shannon	
EI-TVU				R	Virgin Express (Ireland) Ltd	Shannon	
EI-TVV				R	Virgin Express (Ireland) Ltd	Shannon	
EI-TVW				R	Virgin Express (Ireland) Ltd	Shannon	
EI-TVX				R	Virgin Express (Ireland) Ltd	Shannon	
EI-TVY				R	Virgin Express (Ireland) Ltd	Shannon	
EI-TVZ				R	Virgin Express (Ireland) Ltd	Shannon	
EI-UFO	PA-22-150 Tri-Pacer	22-4942	G-BRZR	12. 2.94	W.Treacy	Trim	A 8.99
	(Tail-wheel conversion)		N7045D				
EI-VIP	Hughes 269C	21-1024	G-BOTS	27. 3.95	Cloughran Helicopter Club Ltd	Weston	
			EI-VIP/G-BOTS/N13048/(N229SC)/N1105Z (Crashed Loughshinney 19.6.98)				

Regn	Type	C/n	P/I	Date	Owner/operator	Probable Base	Remarks
EI-WAC	PA-23-250 Aztec E	27-4683	G-AZBK N14077	26. 5.95	Westair Aviation Ltd	Shannon	A10.99
EI-WAV	Bell 430	49028	N4213V	24.12.97	Westair Aviation Ltd	Shannon	A12.99
EI-WCC	Robinson R-22 Beta	1044	G-OLUM	30.10.93	Westair Aviation Ltd	Shannon	
EI-WDC	HS.125 Srs.3B	25132	G-OCBA	2. 7.94	Westair Aviation Ltd	Shannon	A12.99
	EI-WDC/G-OCBA/G-MRFB/G-AZVS/OY-DKP						
EI-WGV	Gulfstream G.1159 Gulfstream V	505	N505GV	21.11.97	Westair Aviation Ltd "Born Free"	Shannon	A 1.99
EI-WHE	Beechcraft B200 Super King Air	BB-1569	VP-CHE N20505	7. 5.98	Westair Aviation Ltd	Shannon	
EI-WRN	PA-28-Cherokee Warrior 151	28-7615212	G-BDZX N9559N	10.99	B.A.Carpenter (Op Westair Aviation Ltd)	Shannon	A10.99
EI-XMA	Robinson R-22 Beta	0681	G-BNVC	20.10.87	Westair Aviation Ltd (Automobile Association c/s)	Dublin	
EI-XMC	Robinson R-22 Beta	1655		17. 5.91	McAuliffe Photographic Laboratories Ltd		
	(Crashed Dingle Harbour, Co.Kerry 31.5.92; wreck to store)					Dublin	

Registrations awaited:

Regn	Type	C/n	P/I	Date	Owner/operator	Probable Base	Remarks
EI-...	Bensen B8MV	PFA G/01-1044	G-BKZJ	R.99	(Cancelled by UK CAA 22.12.98)		
EI-	Bell 206B JetRanger	488	G-BWLO N2290W	R.99	(Cancelled by UK CAA 2.12.99)		
EI	Hornet RS-ZA (Rotax 532)	HRWB-0052 & ZA137	G-MWAH	R.99	(Cancelled by UK CAA 17.12.99)		
EI-TV?	Boeing 737-36N	28671	00-VEH	R	Virgin Express (Ireland) Ltd	Shannon	
EI-TV?	Boeing 737-36N	28670	00-VEX	R	Virgin Express (Ireland) Ltd	Shannon	

SECTION 3

AIRCRAFT WHICH FAILED TO MAKE SECTIONS 1 & 2 IN 1999

These are the UK & Ireland registrations added and removed since the last edition.

UNITED KINGDOM

Regn	Type	C/n	P/I	Date	Owner/operator	Cancellation Details
G-BCMC @	Bell 212	30639	9Y-THL	9. 7.99	Bristow Helicopters Ltd	To EC-- 4. 8.99
	HK-4103X/G-BCMC/(EC-GHO)/EC-294/G-BCMC/EC-GCS/EC-932/G-BCMC/9Y-THL/G-BCMC/9M-ATU/VR-BFI/G-BCMC/N18090					
G-BGCZ @	Bell 212	30668	ZH815	18.11.99	Bristow Helicopters Ltd	To ZH815 18.11.99
	- G-BGCZ/LZ-CAJ/G-BGCZ/5N-AJS/G-BGCZ/VR-BFM/N18090					To ZH814 17.11.99
G-BGMH @	Bell 212	30512	ZH814	17.11.99	Bristow Helicopters Ltd	
	- G-BGMH/9Y-THH/G-BGMH/VR-BGH/G-BGMH/5N-AJZ/G-BGMH/EP-HBU/VR-BGH/N7099J/PK-OAK/VR-HGL/N7099J					
G-BLZJ	Aerospatiale AS.332L Super Puma	2123	LN-OMI	30. 9.99	Bristow Helicopters Ltd	To LN- 16.12.99
	G-PUMJ/LN-OMI/G-BLZJ/LN-OMI/G-BLZJ/LN-OMI					
G-BTLC	Aerospatiale AS.365N2 Dauphin 2	6406	ZJ164	22.12.99	Bond Helicopters Ltd	To ZJ164 22.12.99
G-BTPA @	BAe ATP	2007	EC-GYE	15. 7.99	British Aerospace (Operations) Ltd	
	G-BTPA/N377AE)					To EC-HGB 26. 8.99
G-BTPD @	BAe ATP	2011	EC-GYR	13.10.99	British Aerospace (Operations) Ltd	
	G-BTPD					To EC-HGD 3.11.99
G-BTPE @	BAe ATP	2012	EC-GZH	30. 7.99	British Aerospace (Operations) Ltd	
	G-BTPE/(N382AE)					To EC-HGE 10. 9.99
G-BYFS	Airbus A.320-231	230	A40-MA	27. 3.99	Airtours Intl Airways Ltd	To D-AFRO 14. 4.99
	N230RX/SX-BSJ/N230RX/F-WWOI					
G-BYFZ	Cessna TU.206G Turbo Stationair	U206-05128	EC-ESG	8. 3.99	Bob Crowe Aircraft Sales Ltd	To N206TG 9. 3.99
			N4855U			
G-BYHF	Dornier Do.328-100	3050	N350AD	18. 3.99	Suckling Aviation (Cambridge) Ltd	
	D-CAOT/(D-CDXR)					To N350AD 13. 9.99
G-BYKH	Aerospatiale AS.355F2 Twin Squirrel	5169	SX-HNP	27. 7.99	Alan Mann Helicopters Ltd	To G-EMHH 3. 8.99
	VR-CCM/N57967					
G-BYMS	Agusta A.109E Power	11053		3. 8.99	Sloane Helicopters Ltd	To G-DPPH 17.11.99
G-BYPI	Thruster T600N	9089-T600N-037		17. 8.99	Thruster Air Services Ltd	To G-UDGE 17. 9.99
G-BYRI	Boeing 737-229	20910	OO-SDD	16.10.99	European Aviation Air Charter Ltd	To G-CEAF 13. 1.00
G-BYRW	PA-23-250C Aztec	27-3788	F-BOXQ	22. 9.99	D.C.Hanss	To N2209P 24. 9.99
			N6500Y			
G-BYSH	WSL PZL Koliber 160A	04990080	SP-WGH	12.10.99	PZL International Aviation Marketing & Sales plc	To G-LOKM 26.11.99
G-CBRI	Eurocopter EC-120B	1027		6. 5.99	McAlpine Helicopters Ltd	To G-IGPW 31. 7.99
G-DEBZ	Boeing 737-3S3	24059	RP-C4006	10. 5.99	Debonair Airways Ltd	To N 22.12.99
	EC-FGG/EC-711/G-BNPB/C-FGHT/G-BNPB					
G-DPSI	Robinson R.44 Astro	0661		21.10.99	Focal Point Communications Ltd	To G-DSPI 25.10.99
G-EZYS	Boeing 737-33V	29342		9.11.99	easyJet Airline Co Ltd	To HB- 13.12.99
G-HWPH	Agusta A.109E Power	11951		24. 6.99	Sloane Helicopters Ltd	To G-HPWH 9. 8.99
G-ISPL	Robinson R-22 Mariner	1771M	SE-JAL	3. 2.99	Selectpile Ltd	To OH- 10.12.99
G-MSKJ	Bae Jetstream 4100	41034	N434MX	21. 9.99	Trident Turboprop (Dublin) Ltd	To ZS-OMF 30. 9.99
G-NTOO @	Aerospatiale AS.365N2 Dauphin 2	6372		22.12.99	Bond Helicopters Ltd	To ZJ165 22.12.99
G-OMAK	Airbus A.319-132	913	F-WWIF	20. 5.99	Alkharafi Aviation 2000 Ltd	To F-WWIF 9. 6.99
	(Note: A/c appeared in this Section last year - the above date heralded a short lived restoration)					
G-OZAP	Hughes 369HS	33-0461S	G-FBHH	19. 2.99	G.R.Lloyd	To N846D 12. 8.99
			N2186K/PK-AVH/PK-PDO			

@ = Restored

IRELAND

Regn	Type	C/n	P/I	Date	Owner/operator	Cancellation Details
EI-CTE	McDonnell-Douglas DC-9-82	49517	B-2133	26. 4.99	GECAS Technical Services Ltd	To EC-HFS 30. 7.99
EI-CTF	McDonnell-Douglas DC-9-82	49521	B-2137	26. 4.99	GECAS Technical Services Ltd	To EC-HFT 7. 8.99
EI-CTH	Sud SE.313B Alouette	1430	F-GKML	17.12.99	Independent Helicopters	To G- 21.12.99
			ALAT 1430			
EI-CTP	McDonnell Douglas DC-9-82	49509	B-2125	9. 6.99	GECAS Technical Services Ltd	To EC-... 20.10.99
EI-CTQ	McDonnell Douglas DC-9-82	49519	B-2135	9. 6.99	GECAS Technical Services Ltd	To EC-HGJ 21. 9.99
EI-CTV	McDonnell Douglas DC-9-82	49501	B-2107	23. 7.99	GECAS Technical Services Ltd.	To EC-... 5.10.99

SECTION 4

PART 1 – ALPHABETICAL TYPE INDEX (UK & IRELAND)

ACES HIGH _CUBY:_ G-BVNA
ACRO _ADVANCED:_ G-BPAA
ADAM _RA.14 LOISIRS:_ G-BHIK
ADVANCED AIRSHIP CORPN _ANR-1:_ G-MAAC
ADVANCED TECHNOLOGIES _CH1 ATI:_ G-BXZN
AERIAL ARTS (including CYCLONE)
110/130SX (wing)/ALPHA/AVENGER (combi): G-MMSZ MMYL MMZI MNDE MNEK MNEL MNIT MNJV MNLW MNMY MNTT MNWL MNZS MVBC
CHASER: G-MNTD MNXC MNYD MNYE MNYF MTCP MTDD MTDE MVDK MVDL MVDN MVDP MVDR MVGA MVGF MVGG MVGH MVGI MMGJ MVGK MVHA MVHN MVID
G-MVIE MVJF MVJG MVJH MVJI MVJJ MVJK MVKY MVKZ MVLA MMLB MVLC MVLD MVLE MVLF MVLG MVLH MVLS MVLT MVLU MVLW MVML MVMM MVOA MVOD
G-MVOP MVRG MVRL MVSG MVSK MVSL MVTF MVTL MVTM MVUS MVUT MVVU MVVW MVXG MVXP MVYY MVZM MVZY MWGO MWWZ MWXW MWXX MWXY MWXZ MWYM
G-MYBU MYCB MYEI MYEJ MYFO MYGI MYGK MYIL MYIT MYJO MYJW MYKD MYLJ MYMY MYNW MYSA MYSV MYWN MYWS MYYD MYZW MYZX MZCB MZTS
AERO-VODOCHODY - see CZL/LET
L-29 DELFIN: G-BYCT DELF DLFN MAYA ODAT WHZZ
L-39 ALBATROS: G-OTAF
AERO COMMANDER (including ROCKWELL/GULFSTREAM production)
_200:_ G-SONY   _500S SHRIKE:_ G-BDAL   _560:_ G-ARDK
_680/685/690:_ G-AWOE NISR OMAP WGCL
AERO COMPOSITES _SEA HAWKER:_ EI-BUO
AERO DESIGNS _PULSAR:_ G-BSFA BTDR BTRF BTWY BUDI BUJL BULM BUOW BUSR BUYB BUZB BVJH BVLN BVSF BVTW BXDU BYJL DESI EPOX IIAN LUEL
G-MCMS NEVS OMKF OOXP RMAN WYNS XPXP
AERO-DIFUSION - see JODEL
AERO DYNAMICS _SPARROWHAWK:_ G-BOZU
AEROCAR (including TAYLOR)
MINI IMP: G-BLWW   _SOOPER COOT;_ G-COOT SWIM
AERODYNE - see RAVEN
AEROMERE - see AVIAMILANO & including LAVERDA homebuilts)
F.8L FALCO: EI-BCJ EI-BMF
AEROMOT _AMT-200 SUPER XIMANGO:_ G-BWNY JTPC KHOM RFIO
AERONCA -see CHAMPION
_C-3/100:_ G-ADRR ADYS AEFT AESB AETG AEVS AEXD   _K:_ G-ONKA
11AC CHIEF/11CC SUPER CHIEF: G-AKTK AKUO AKVN BJEV BJNY BPRA BPRX BPXY BRCW BRFJ BRWR BRXF BRXL BSTC BTFL BTRI BTSR BUAB BUTF
G-IIAC IVOR EI-CCF EI-CRR   _15AC SEDAN:_ G-AREX EI-BJJ EI-BKC
A65TAC/O-58B/L-3 GRASSHOPPER (including _65C SUPER CHIEF_): G-BRHP BRPR BTRG BTUV
AEROSPACE DEVELOPMENTS _AD.500:_ G-BECE
AEROSPATIALE - see ATR/SOCATA/SUD AVIATION & including EUROCOPTER production
AS.332 SUPER PUMA: G-BKZE BKZG BKZH BLPM BLXR BMCW BMCX BOZK BRXU BSOI BTCT BUZD BWMG BWWI BWZX CHCC PUMA PUMB PUMD PUME PUMG
G-PUMH PUMI PUMK PUML PUMM PUMN PUMO TIGB TIGC TIGE TIGF TIGG TIGH TIGI TIGJ TIGL TIGM TIGO TIGP TIGR TIGS TIGT TIGV TIGZ
AS.350B ECUREUIL: G-BMAV BRVO BVJE BVXM BWFY BXGA BXNE BXNJ BXNY BXOG BXOK BXPG BXPJ BYZE COPT CWIZ DRHL EJOC FIBS HLEN
G-IIPM JOSS LHPL MSDJ MSKM ODMC OFHL OGOA OROZ NUTY PLMB PLMC PLMH PROD RICC ROIN SMDJ WHST WKRD EI-CGQ IRV
AS.355 TWIN SQUIRREL: G-BOOV BPRI BPRJ BPRL BSTE BSYI BTIS BVLG BXBT BYPA BYZA BZGC CAMB CCAO CLIP CPOL DANZ DOOZ ECOS EMAN
G-EMHH EPOL FFRI FTWO GMPA GRID HARO ICSG JETU KGMT LCON LECA LENI LINE LOUN MOBI NAAS NMHS OASP OBIG OFIN OGHL OGRK OHCP OHM*
G-OITN OROM ORMA OTSP PASF PASH REEM SAEW SASU SCOW SEPA SEPB SEPC SYPA TOPC TOPS WIRE MPA XCEL
AEROSPORT
SCAMP: G-BKFL BKPB BOOW   _WOODY PUSHER:_ G-AWWP AYVP BSFV
AEROSTAR - see TED SMITH & YAKOVELEV
AEROSTRUCTURE (including SOUTHDOWN)
PIPISTRELLE: G-MJTM MNPI
AEROTEC/AEROTEK - see PITTS
AEROTECH - see WHITTAKER
AES _SKY RANGER:_ G-MJHB
AESL - see VICTA
AGUSTA - see BELL
_A.109:_ G-BVCJ BVNH BWNZ BWZI BXCB BXIV BXWD DPPH GVIP HPWH JRSL POWR RFDS RNLD SLNE SOHI TBGL TELY TVAA USTA USTB WEST EI-BUX
EI-CHV EI-ECA EI-JBC
AILES DE K _FLYAIR:_ G-BUHP
AIR COMMAND
503 COMMANDER: G-BMZA BOAS BOIK BPAO BPMC
532 ELITE/582 SPORT:
G-BOGV BOGW BOHG BOJF BOKF BOOJ BPGC BPPR BPPU BPRS BPSB BPTH BPUE BPUG BPUI BPYW BREM BRGO BRKS BRKX BRLB BRLK BRMM BROF BRSF
G-BSAR BSCB BSND BSRZ BSSN BSXP BTCB BVVY BWTY KENB KLIK OGTS SKYI TFRB URRR WYZZ YROI
AIR CREATION _FUN 18 GT:_ G-MYMM MYOL MYTZ MYUA MYVI MYXF
AIR & SPACE _18A:_ G-BVWK BVWL EI-CNG

AIRBUS INDUSTRIE
A.300B: G-BYDH BYYS CEAA CEAB CEXH CEXI HLAA HLAB HLAC MAJS MONR MONS OJMR SWJW TNTI TNTS TTMC EI-CEB EI-CJK EI-CPC EI-CPD
EI-CPE EI-CPF EI-EAA EI-EAB EI-EAC EI-EAD EI-EAT EI-TLB EI-TLK EI-TLL EI-TLM EI-TLQ EI-TLR EI-TLS
A.319: G-EUOA EUOB EUOC EUOD EUOE EUOF EUOG EUOH EUOI EUOJ EUOK EUOL EUOM EUON EUOO EUOP EUOR EUOS EUOT EUOU EUOV EUOW EUOX
G-EUOY EUOZ EUPA EUPB EUPC EUPD EUPE EUPF EUPG EUPH EUPI EUPJ EUPK EUPL EUPM EUPN EUPO EUPP EUPR EUPS EUPT EUPU EUPV
G-EUPW EUPX EUPY EUPZ OMAK
A.320: G-BXKA BXKB BUSB BUSC BUSD BUSE BUSF BUSG BUSH BUSI BUSJ BUSK BVYA BVYB BVYC BXKC BXKD BXRX BYTH COEZ CRPH CVYD CVYE
G-CVYG DJAR EPFR MEDA MEDB MEDD MIDK MIDP MIDR MIDS MIDV MIDW MIDX MIDY MIDZ MONW MONX MPCD OOAA OOAB OOAC OOAD OOAI OOAJ OUZO
G-BB RDVE SUEE TICL TMDP UNIH VCED VKID VMED VTAN EI-CTD EI-CUC EI-CUK EI-CVA EI-CVB EI-CVC EI-CVD EI-CVE EI-CVF EI-TLF EI-TLG
EI-TLH EI-TLI EI-TLJ EI-TLO EI-TLP
A.321: G-DHJH EUOA EUOB EUOC EUOD EUOE EUOF EUOG EUOH EUOI EUOJ EUOK EUOL EUOM EUON EUOP EUOR EUOS EUOT EUOU EUOV EUOW EUOX
G-EUOY EUOZ JSJX MIDA MIDC MIDE MIDF MIDH MIDI MIDJ MIDK MIDL MIDM MIDN MIDO MIDT MIDU NIKO OOAE OOAF OOAH OZBD UNIG UNIH UNIJ
G-VOLH YJBM EI-CPC EI-CPD EI-CPE EI-CPF EI-CPG EI-CPH
A.330: G-CSJS EOMA MDBD MLJL MOJO SMAN UNIA UNIB EI-CRK EI-EI-DUB EI-EWR EI-JFK EI-LAX EI-ORD EI-SHN
A.340: G-VAEL VAIR VBUS VELD VFAR VFLY VHOL VSEA VSKY VSUN

AIRCO:
DH.2: G-BFVH   *DH.6:* G-EAML   *DH.9:* G-EAQM

AIRMARK see CASSUTT
TSR.3: G-AWIV

AIRSPEED
AS.40 OXFORD: G-AHTW AITB AITF   *AS.57 AMBASSADOR:* G-ALZO
AIRSPEED *300 MODEL HAFB:* G-FYGJ

AIRTOUR
AH-31 HAFB: G-BKVY   *AH-56 HAFB:* G-BKVW BKVX BLVA BLVB BSGH BWPL OAFC   *AH-77 HAFB:* G-BLYT BOBH IVAC OAAC

AIRWAVE
MERLIN (wing): G-MMIJ   *MICROCHUTE/TREKKING:* G-MYPU MYUY MYYM MZBP MZDW
NIMROD (wing): G-MBCX MBJG MBJL MNIW MNZY   *RAVE:* G-MYZS MYZT MYZU

ALLPORT *HAFB:* G-BJIA BJSS

AMERICAN AEROLIGHTS (including ELECTRAFLYER)
EAGLE/DOUBLE EAGLE: G-MBCU MBEP MBGB MBHE MBIO MBJD MBJK MBJN MBKY MBNK MBNT MBOD MBRB MBRS MBTY MBWE MBWY MBYD MBYO MBYR
G-MBYX MJAE MJBL MJBN MJBV MJCX MJEO MJFP MJIO MJLY MJNM MJNO MMJB MMTV MNBL MNSS
AMERICAN AVIATION - see GRUMMAN-AMERICAN
AMETHYST Ax6-56 HAFB: G-BFLP
AMF *CHEVVRON:* G-MNFL MTFG MTRJ MVGC MVGD MVGE MVIP MVOO MVUO MVVV MVXX MVZZ MWHS MWJL MWJM MWNO MWNP MWPW MWRZ MWUI MWZB MYGN
G-MYYP MZCK MZDP MZFH EI-BVJ CAU
ANDERSON *EA-1 KINGFISHER AMPHIBIAN:* G-BUTE BXBC
ANDREASSON (including CROSBY)
BA.4B: G-AWPZ AYFV BEBS BEBT BFXF YPSY

ANEC
II: G-EBJO   *IV MISSEL THRUSH:* G-FBPI
ARBITER SERVICES *TRIKE:* G-MNWL
ARKLE - see MITCHELL
ARMSTRONG-WHITWORTH see GLOSTER
SEAHAWK: G-JETH   *AW.650 ARGOSY:* G-APRL BEOZ
ARROW *ACTIVE:* G-ABVE
ARROWFLIGHT - see CGS
ARV *ARV1 SUPER 2:* G-BMDO BMOK BMWE BMWF BMWM BNGV BNGW BNGX BNGY BNHB BNHD BNHE BNVI BOGK BPMX BSRK BWBZ COWS DEXP ERMO OARV
G-ORIX OTAL POOL STWO TARV XARV ZARV

AEROSPATIALE/ALENIA
ATR-42: G-BUEA BUPS BVEC BVED BVEF BVJP BXBV BXEG BXEH ORFH WFEP ZAPJ EI-CBK COD CPT
ATR-72: G-BVTJ BVTK BWDA BWDB BWTL BWTM BXTN BXXA BXYV BYTO BYTP UKTJ UKTK UKTL UKTM UKTN EI-CBD EI-CLB EI-CLC EI-CLD EI-CMJ
AUSTER (including TAYLORCRAFT production)
Model E III: G-AHLI AHLK AREI BUDL
Model G/H 4/5/5D/ALPHA 5: G-AGLK AIKE AJGJ AJHJ AJVT AJXC AJXV AJXY AKOW AKPI AKSY AKSZ AKWS AKWT AKXP ALBJ ALBK ALFA ALNV
G-ALXZ ALYB ALYG AMVD ANFU ANHR ANHS ANHU ANHW ANHX ANIE ANIJ ANIS ANLU ANRP AOCP AOCR AOCU AOFJ AOVW APAF APAH APBE APBW APRF
G-APTU BDFX BICD BXKX
Srs 5 J/1 AUTOCRAT/J/1N ALPHA & KINGSLAND/CROFTON SPECIAL: G-AGTO AGTT AGVN AGXN AGXU AGXV AGYD AGYH AGYK AGYT AHAL AHAM AHAP
G-AHAT AHAU AHAV AHCK AHCL AHHH AHHP AHHT AHHU AHSO AHSP AHSS AHST AIBH AIBM AIBR AIBW AIBX AIBY AIFZ AIGD AIGF AIGP AIGR AIGT
G-AIGU AIJI AIJZ AIPV AIRC AIZU AIZY AJAE AJAJ AJAS AJDW AJEB AJEE AJEH AJEI AJEM AJIH AJIS AJIT AJIU AJIW AJPZ AJRB AJRC AJRE
G-AJUD AJUE AJUL AJYB AMTM APIK APJZ APKM APKN APTR APUK ARRL ARUY ASEE BLPG BRKC BVGT JAYI OSTA TENT EI-AGJ AMK AMY AUM
Srs 5 J/1B AIGLET: G-AMKU ARBM   *Srs 5 J/1U WORKMASTER:* G-AGVG APMH APSR   *Srs 5 J/2 ARROW:* G-AJAM AWLX BEAH
Srs 5 J/4: G-AIJK BIJM BIJS BIJT BIPR EI-CPN
Srs 5 J/5B/G/P/V AUTOCAR: G-AOBV AOFM AOHZ AOIY APUW ARKG ARLY ARNB ARUG ASFK AXMN
Srs 5 J/5F/K/L AIGLET TRAINER: G-AMMS AMRF AMTA AMUI AMUJ AMYD AMZI AMZT AMZU ANWX AOFS APVG BGKZ EI-AUS
Srs 5 J/5Q/R ALPINE: G-ANXC AOGV AOZL APCB   *6A/AOP.6/TUGMASTER:* G-ARDX ARGB ARGI ARHM ARIH ARRX ARXU ARYD ASEF ASIP ASNB ASOC
G-ASTI BKXP BNGE
AOP.9/11/BEAGLE E.3: G-ASCC AVHT AVXY AXRR AXWA AYUA AZBU BDFH BGBU BGKT BGTC BJXR BKVK BUCI BURR BWKK BXON   *B.4:* G-AMKL-
AVENGER *HAFB:* G-BHMJ BHMK BIGR BIPW BIRK BIRL BIRM BIXS
AVIA *FL.3:* G-AGFT

AVIAMILANO (including AEROMERE/LAVERDA/SEQUOIA production)
F.8L FALCO: G-BICN BVDP BWYO BYLL CWAG FALC GANE KYNG OCAD OCDS ORJW PDGG REEC
F.14 NIBBIO: G-OWYN
AVIASUD *MISTRAL:* G-MGAG MVSJ MVUP MVWW MVWZ MVXN MVXV MVZR MWIB MYSL MYST MZJB
AVIONS LOBET *GANAGOBIE:* G-BAMG
AVIONS MUDRY - see CAARP
AVRO (including HSA & BAe production)
TRIPLANE: see ROE
504K/L: G-EASD EBJE ECKE ABAA ADEV BYKW   *534 BABY:* G-EACQ   *594 AVIAN:* G-EBOV EBZM ACGT   *621 TUTOR:* G-AHSA
631/643 CADET: EI-ALP ALU   *652A ANSON/NINETEEN:* G-AGPG AGWE AHKX AMDA APHV AVVO AWRS AWSA AYWA BFIR BSMF VROE
683 LANCASTER: G-ASXX BVBP LANC   *685 YORK:* G-AGNV ANTK   *694 LINCOLN:* G-APRJ   *698 VULCAN:* G-BLMC VJET VLCN VULC
748: G-ARAY ARMX ATMI ATMJ AVXI AVXJ AYIM BEJD BGMN BGMO BIUV BNJK BORM BPNW BVOU BVOV OJEM OPFW ORAL OSOE SOEI EI-BSF
AVRO (CANADA) *CF-100 CANUCK:* G-BCYK
AVTECH *JABIRU SK/UL:* G-BXAO BXNU BXSI BYBM BYBZ BYCC BYCZ BYFC BYIA BYIF BYIM BYJD BYJF BYKY BYNL BYNR BYTK BYTV BYYL BYYT BYZS
G-BZAP COVE CSDJ DMAC JABA JACO JAXS JBSP JPMA KKER LEEE LUMA LYPG MGCA ODGS OJAB OPIP OPUS OZZI PBUS RODG RUFS RYAL THOT TUBB
G-TULL UKOZ UJAB VJAB EI-JAK

B

A - see BRITISH KLEMM & KLEMM

EAGLE 2: G-AFAX   *SWALLOW 2:* G-ADPS AEVZ AFCL AFGC AFGD AFGE AFHC EI-AFF
BAC (BRITISH AIRCRAFT CO) (including KRONFELD & PROCTOR)
DRONE: G-ADPJ AEDB
BAC see HUNTING
ONE-ELEVEN: G-ASYD AVMH AVMI AVMJ AVMK AVML AVMM AVMN AVMO AVMP AVMR AVMS AVMT AVMU AVMV AVMW AVMX AVMY AVMZ AWYV AXLL AYOP
G-AZMF BEJM HKIT IIIH OBWA OBWB OBWC OBWD OBWE EI-BWJ
BAC-SUD/AEROSPATIALE *CONCORDE:* G-AXDN BBDG BOAA BOAB BOAC BOAD BOAE BOAF BOAG SSST
BAe - see HAWKER SIDDELEY AVIATION (HSA) & including HANDLEY-PAGE & SCOTTISH AVIATION production)
JETSTREAM (to Srs.32): G-ATXJ AXXU BBYM BKUY BLKP BRGN BUJT BWWW BXLM BYMA BYRA BYRM CBEA IJYS JSSD LOVB NFLC OAKJ OBWN OBWO
G-OEST PLAH RAVL WMCC
JETSTREAM 41: G-BWUI GCJL JMAC MAJA MAJB MAJC MAJD MAJE MAJF MAJG MAJH MAJI MAJJ MAJK MAJL MAJM MSKJ OXLI PJRT
ATP (including JETSTREAM 61): G-BRLY BTTO BTZG BTZJ BUKJ BUWM BUWP CORP MANA MANB MANC MANE MANF MANG MANH MANJ MANL MANM MANO
G-MANP MANU MAUD OBWL OBWM OBWP OBWR OEDJ PLXI WISS
BAe 146 variants: G-BKMN BLRA BOMK BPNT BSNR BSNS BTTP BUHC BXAR BXAS BZAT BZAU BZAV BZAW BZAX BZBA BZBB BZBC DEBC DEBE DEBF DEBG
G-DEBH DEFK DEFL DEFM FLTA GNTZ JEAJ JEAK JEAM JEAO JEAR JEAS JEAT JEAU JEAV JEAW JEAX JEBA JEBB JEBC JEBD JEBE LUXE MANS MABR
G-MIMA NJIA NJIB NJIC NJID NJIE OFOA OINV OZRH TBIC TJPM TNTB TNTD TNTE TNTG TNTL TNTM TNTR UKAC UKAG UKHP UKID UKRC UKSC
G-ZAPK ZAPL ZAPN EI-CLG EI-CLH EI-CLI EI-CLJ EI-CLY EI-CMS EI-CMY EI-CNB EI-CNI EI-CNJ EI-CNK EI-CNQ EI-COF EI-COQ EI-CPJ
EI-CPK EI-CPL EI-CPY EI-CSK EI-CSL EI-CTM EI-CTN EI-CTO EI-PAT
BARNES *AVON (Trike):* G-MJGO
BARNETT *ROTORCRAFT J4B:* G-BRVR BRVS BWCW
BARRITAULT - see GARDAN
BAT *FK-23 BANTAM:* G-EACN
BEAGLE - see AUSTER
BEAGLE-AUSTER see SCOTTISH AVIATION
D.4, *D.5 HUSKEY:* G-ASNC ATCD ATMH AVOD AVSR AWSW AXBF   *D.6:* G-ARCS ARDJ   *E.3* - see AUSTER AOP.9/11
A.61 TERRIER: G-ARLO ARLP ARLR ARNO ARSL ARTM ARUI ASAJ ASAK ASAN ASAX ASBU ASCD ASDK ASDL ASEG ASKJ ASMZ ASOI ASOM ASUI ASYG
G-ASYN ASZE ASZX ATBU ATDN ATHU AVCS AVYK AYDW AYDX EI-ASU
A.109 AIREDALE: G-ARNP ARNR AROJ ARXC ARXD ARYZ ASAI ASBH ASBY ASRK ASWB ATCC AVKP AWGA EI-AYL BAL BBK
B.121 PUP: G-AVDF AVLM AVLN AVZN AVZP AWKM AWKO AWVC AWWE AWYJ AWYO AXCX AXDU AXDV AXDW AXEV AXHO AXIA AXIE AXIF AXJH AXJI
G-AXJJ AXJO AXMW AXMX AXNL AXNM AXNN AXNP AXNR AXNS AXOJ AXOZ AXPA AXPB AXPC AXPM AXPN AXSC AXSD AXTZ AXUA AZCK AZCL AZCN AZCP
G-AZCT AZCU AZCV AZCY AZCZ AZDA AZDG AZEU AZEV AZEW AZEY AZFA AZGF AZSW BAKW BASP BDCO IPUP JIMB OPUP PUPP TSKY EI-ATJ
B.206: G-ARRM ASWJ ATZO BSET HRHI FLYP
BEDE
BD.4: G-BEKL BKZV BOPD BYLS   *BD.5:* G-BCOX BDTT BGLB BJPI BUTP BYFB
BEECHCRAFT
17 TRAVELER/UC-43: G-BRVE BUXU   *18/3NM, 3TM & C-45:* G-ASUG BKGL BKGM BKRN BSZC
23 MUSKETEER/SUNDOWNER: G-ASBB ASJO ASWP ATBI AWFZ AWTS AWTV AYYU BAHO BARH BARI BASN BBSB BBTX BBTY BUXN DJHB GUCK EI-BFF
EI-CCA   *24R SIERRA:* G-BBSC BBVJ BBXU BYDG   *33 DEBONAIR/33 BONANZA:* G-BGSW BTHW BTZA BYRT COLA ENSI GRYZ HOPE MOAC OAHC VICM
35 BONANZA/("V" tail): G-APTY ARKJ ARZN ASJL ATSR BBTS BONZ EHMJ NEWT REST   *36 BONANZA:* G-BMYD BSEY JLHS MAPR ORSP POPA ZLOJ
55/56/58 BARON: G-ASDO ASOH AWAH AWAJ AYKA AYPD AZDK AZXA BFLZ BLJM BLKY BMLM BNBY BNUN BNVZ BRTN BTFT BWRP BXDF BXNG BXPM
G-BYDY DAFY FABM FLAK FLTZ FRBY IOCO JOYS MOSS OLYD OSDI RICK SUZI TSAR UROP VCML WHIS WOOD WWIZ EI-CPS
60 DUKE: G-IASL   *65/70/80 QUEEN AIR:* G-ASDA AVDR AVDS AWKX KEAB KEAC TUBS WJPN
76 DUCHESS: G-BGHP BGRG BGVH BHGM BIMZ BMJT BNTT BNUO BNYO BODX BOFC BOZP BRPU BXHD BXMH BXSK BXWA BXXT BYNY GBSL GCCL JLRW
G-OADY OBLC OPAT TRAN WACI WACJ EI-BUN EI-CMX   *77 SKIPPER:* EI-BHT
90 KING AIR: G-BMKD BVRS DEXY FLTI SHAM WELL EI-BHL   *95 TRAVEL AIR:* G-ASMF ASYJ ATRC
200/350 SUPER KING AIR: G-BGRE BPPM BVMA BXMA BYCK BYCP CEGR CLOW FPLA FPLB FRYI HAMA IMGL KMCD MAMD OMNH OWAX PLAT REBK ROWN
G-SBAS SPOR VICW VSBC WRCF EI-WHE

BELL:
P-63 KINGCOBRA: G-BTWR
BELL HELICOPTERS (including AGUSTA/WESTLAND (47D/G)/AGUSTA (47H/J & 206) production)
47D/G: G-ARXH ASOL AXKN AXKO AXKS AXKW AXKX AXKY AYOE BAXS BBRI BBVP BEGA BFEF BFVM BFYI BGID BGMU BGZK BHAR BHBE BHNV BLGR
G-BPAI BPDY CHOP CIGY GGTT MASH MINX SOLH XTUN   *47H/J:* G-ATFV AZYB BFPP EURA
206 JET RANGER: G-AVII AVSZ AYMW BAKS BAML BARP BAUN BBCA BBNG BBOR BEWY BIZB BKEW BKZI BLCA BLGV BLZN BNYD BOLO BORV
G-BOTM BPIE BPWI BSBW BSDU BTFX BTHY BUZZ BVGA BWVE BWZW BXAY BXKL BXLI BXNS BXNT BXRY BXUF BXZX BYBA BYBC BYBI BYSE CCLY CHGL
G-CITZ CODE COIN CORC CORN CORT CPTS CRPS CTPW DBMW DENN DNCN DOFY DORB ELLI FINS FOXM GAND GHCL GUST HEBE HELE HMPH HMPT HSDW
G-INVU IOIO ISKY JAHL JBDB JEKP JETX JIMW JLEE JWBI JWLS KLEE LGRM LILY MCPI MFMF MILI MOTA NEWS NEWZ OAMG OBEY OBAM OBYT OCBB
G-OCST ODIG OJCB OMDR OMEC OMJB OOOW ONTV ONYX OPNI OSMD OVBJ PEAK PENT PORT RAMI RAMY RIAN RNBW SELY SHCC SPEY SPYI STER STOX
G-SUEZ TILI TOYZ TREE UEST WGAL WHAZ WIZZ WLLY XXIV EI-BHI EI-BIJ EI-BKT EI-BXX EI-BYJ EI-CAW EI-CLT EI-CUG EI-GHL EI-HER
EI-MER EI-ONE EI-PMI EI-RMC   *206L LONG RANGER:* G-BXIB CSWL ECAW ELIT EYRE IANG LEEZ NEUF OHHI OLDN EI-BYR EI-CHL EI-CIO
212: G-BCMC BFER BIXV BWLE BWOS   *214ST SUPER TRANSPORT:* G-BKFN BKFP   *222:* G-NOIR OWCG EI-BOR EI-TAR
407: G-DCDB   *430:* EI-WAV   *UH-1H IROQUOIS:* G-HUEY
BELLANCA- see CHAMPION
17-30 SUPER VIKING: G-VIKE
BENES-MRAZ *M.1 SOKOL:* G-AIXN BWRG
BENSEN (including CAMPBELL-BENSEN & MONTGOMERIE-BENSEN)
B.7/B.8 GYROCOPTER: G-APSY APUD ARTJ ASCT ASME ASNY ASWN ASYP ATLP ATOZ AWAS AWDW AWLM AWPY AXBG AXCI AZAZ BCGB BDJF BGIO BHEM
G-BHKE BIFN BIGP BIGX BIHX BIPY BIVK BIVL BIZT BJAO BJSU BJZY BKBS BKNY BKUS BLGO BLLA BLLB BMBW BMOT BMYF BMZW BNBU BNCV BNJL
G-BOTZ BOUV BOWZ BOZW BPBA BPCV BPFK BPIF BPNN BPOO BPSK BPTV BRBS BRCF BREA BREU BRFW BRHL BRHM BRHU BRXN BSBX BSJB BSMG BSMX
G-BSNI BSNL BSNY BSPJ BSZM BTAH BTBL BTFW BTIG BTJN BTJS BTST BTSU BTTD BUJK BUPF BVAZ BVIF BVJF BVKJ BVMG BVPX BWAH BWEY BWJN
G-BWSZ BXCL BXDC BYTS HAGS INCH JOEL OOJC OTIM SCUD YJET YROS YROY EI-BCF EI-BSG
BETTS *TB.1:* G-BVUG
BINDER - see PIEL
BIRDMAN
CHEROKEE (Wing): G-MBJO   *WT-11 CHINOOK:* G-MMKE
BLACKBURN
B.2: G-ACBH ADFV AEBJ   *MONOPLANE:* G-AANI
BLAKE *BLUETIT:* G-BXIY
BLERIOT *XI:* G-AANG BPVE BWRH LOTI
BOEING
B-17G FLYING FORTRESS: G-BEDF   *B-29 SUPERFORTRESS:* G-BHDK
707: G-APFG APFJ BFEO D2-TOU EL-AJT AKJ   *727:* G-BNNI BPND EI-HCA EI-HCB EI-HCC EI-HCD EI-HCI EI-LCH EI-SKY
737: G-BGDA BGDB BGDE BGDJ BGDL BGDO BGDP BGDR BGDS BGDT BGDU BGJE BKYA BKYB BKYH BKYN BKYP BNNK BNNL BSNV BSNW BUHJ BUHK BUHL
G-BVKA BVKB BVKC BVKD BVNM BVNN BVNO BVZE BVZG BVZH BVZI BYYF BYYG BYZJ BYZN BZZA BZZB CEAC CEAD CEAE CEAF DOCA DOCB DOCC DOCD
G-DOCE DOCF DOCG DOCH DOCI DOCJ DOCK DOCL DOCM DOCN DOCO DOCP DOCR DOCS DOCT DOCU DOCV DOCW DOCX DOCY DOCZ GBTA GBTB ECAS EZYB
G-EZYC EZYD EZYF EZYG EZYH EZYI EZYJ EZYK EZYL EZYM EZYO EZYP EZYR GFFA GFFB GGFC GGFD GGFE GGFF GGFG GGFI GGFJ IGOA IGOB
G-IGOC IGOD IGOE G-IGOF IGOG IGOH IGOI IGOJ IGOK IGOL IGOM IGOP IGOR LFJB MONG MONV MSKA MSKB MSKC MSKD MSKE OAMS OBMD OBMF
G-OBMG OBMH OBMJ OBMK OBML OBMM OBMO OBMP OBMR OBMV OBMZ OBWZ ODSK ODUS OFRA OGBA OGBB OGBC OGBD OGBE OHAJ OJSW OJTW OKDN OMUC SFBH SMDB
G-TREN XBHX XMAN ZAPM EI-BXA EI-BXB EI-BXC EI-BXD EI-BXI EI-BXK EI-BZE EI-BZF EI-BZJ EI-BZL EI-BZM EI-BZN EI-CDB EI-CDC EI-CDD
EI-CDE EI-CDF EI-CDH EI-CHH EI-CJC EI-CJD EI-CJE EI-CJF EI-CJG EI-CJH EI-CJI EI-CKK EI-CKP EI-CKQ EI-CKR EI-CKS EI-CLK EI-CLW
EI-CLZ EI-CNT EI-CNV EI-CNW EI-CNX EI-CNY EI-CNZ EI-COA EI-COB EI-COH EI-COI EI-COJ EI-CON EI-COX EI-CRC EI-CRN EI-CRP EI-CRQ
EI-CRZ EI-CSA EI-CSB EI-CSC EI-CSD EI-CSE EI-CSF EI-CSG EI-CSH EI-CSI EI-CSJ EI-CSM EI-CSN EI-CSO EI-CSP EI-CSR EI-CSS EI-CST
EI-CSU EI-CSV EI-CSW EI-CSX EI-CSY EI-CSZ EI-CTA EI-CTB EI-CTX EI-CUA EI-TVA EI-TVB EI-TVC EI-TVD EI-TVE EI-TVF EI-TVG EI-TVH
EI-TVI EI-TVJ EI-TVK EI-TVL EI-TVM EI-TVN EI-TVO EI-TVP EI-TVQ
747: G-AWNP BDXA BDXB BDXC BDXE BDXF BDXG BDXH BDXI BDXJ BDXK BDXL BDXM BDXN BDXO BDXP BNLA BNLB BNLC BNLD BNLE BNLF BNLG BNLH
G-BNLI BNLJ BNLK BNLL BNLM BNLN BNLO BNLP BNLS BNLT BNLU BNLV BNLW BNLX BNLY BNLZ BYGA BYGB BYGC BYGD BYGE BYGF BYGG BYGH
G-BYGI BYGJ BYGK CIVA CIVB CIVC CIVD CIVE CIVF CIVG CIVH CIVI CIVJ CIVK CIVL CIVM CIVN CIVO CIVP CIVR CIVS CIVT CIVU CIVV CIVW
G-CIVX CIVY CIVZ GAFX VAST VBEE VBIG VCAT VFAB VGIN VHOT VIBE VIRG VJFK VLAX VMIA VRUM VTOP VXLG VZZZ EI-BZA
757: G-BIKA BIKB BIKC BIKD BIKF BIKG BIKH BIKI BIKJ BIKK BIKL BIKM BIKN BIKO BIKR BIKS BIKT BIKU BIKV BIKW BIKX BIKY BIKZ BMRA
G-BMRB BMRC BMRD BMRE BMRF BMRG BMRH BMRI BMRJ BPEA BPEB BPEC BPED BPEE BPEF BPEI BPEJ BPEK BPET BYAD BYAE BYAF BYAH BYAI BYAJ
G-BYAK BYAL BYAN BYAO BYAP BYAR BYAS BYAT BYAU BYAW BYAX BYAY BCPEL BPEM BPEN BPEO BPEP BPER BPES CPEL CPEM CPEN CPEO CPEP
G-CPER CPES CPET CPEU CPEV CPEW CPEX CPEY CPEZ DAJB FCLA FCLB FCLC FCLD FCLE FCLF FCLG FCLH FCLI FCLJ FCLK JALC LCRC MCEA MONB
G-MONC MOND MONE MONJ MONK OOOA OOOB OOOC OOOD OOOG OOOI OOOJ OOOM OOOS OOOU OOOV OOOW OOOX OOOY PIDS RJGR WJAN EI-CEY EI-CEZ
EI-CJX EI-CJY EI-CLU
767: G-BNWA BNWB BNWC BNWD BNWE BNWF BNWG BNWH BNWI BNWJ BNWK BNWL BNWM BNWN BNWO BNWP BNWR BNWS BNWT BNWU BNWV BNWW BNWX BNWY
G-BNWZ BNYS BOPB BRIF BRIG BYAA BYAB BZHA BZHB BZHC DAJC DIMB OBYB OBYC OBYD OBYE OBYG OBYH OBYI OOAN OOAO SJMC UKLI EI-CLR
EI-CLS EI-CNS EI-CRD EI-CRF EI-CRL EI-CRO EI-CRM EI-CTW
777: G-RAES VIIA VIIB VIIC VIID VIIE VIIF VIIG VIIH VIIJ VIIK VIIL VIIM VIIN VIIO VIIP VIIR VIIS VIIT VIIU VIIV VIIX VIIY VIIZ
G-YMMA YMMB YMMC YMMD YMME YMMF YMMG YMMH YMMI YMMJ YMMK YMML YMMM YMMN YMMO YMMP ZZZA ZZZB ZZZC ZZZD ZZZE EI-CRS EI-CRT

BOEING-STEARMAN *75 KAYDET/N2S/N3N/PT-13/PT-17*: G-AROY AWLO AZLE BAVO BIXN BNIW BPTB BRHB BRSK BRTK BRUJ BSDS BSGR BSWC BTFG
  G-BTGA BUKE ERIX IIIG ILLE ISDN NZSS ONAF RJAH EI-RYR
BOLAND *52 HAFB:* G-BYMW
BOLKOW (including MALMO & MBB production)
  Bo.207: G-EFTE
  Bo.208 JUNIOR: G-ASFR ASZD ATDO ATRI ATSI ATSX ATTR ATUI ATVX ATZA ATXZ AVKR AVLD AVZI BIJD BOKW BSME CLEM ECGO EI-AWR
  Bo.209 MONSUN: G-AYPE AZBB AZDD AZOA AZOB AZRA AZTA AZVA AZVB BLRD
BOND *SKY DANCER:* G-BLUK
BONSALL *DB-1 MUSTANG:* G-BDWM
BOWERS *FLY BABY:* G-BFRD BNPV BUYU
BRADSHAW *HAB-76:* G-AXXP
BRANDLII *BX-2 CHERRY:* G-BXUX
BRANTLY
  B.2: G-ASHD ASXD ATFG AVIP AWDU AWIO AXSR BPIJ OAPR OMAX ROTR WASP   *305:* G-ASXF
BREMNER - see MITCHELL WING
BRIGHTON *Ax7-65 HAFB:* G-AVTL
BRISTOL
  BOXKITE: G-ASPP   *BABE:* G-EASQ   *F.2B FIGHTER:* G-AANM ACAA AEPH   *M.1C REP.:* G-BLWM BWJM   *105 BULLDOG:* G-ABBB
  149 BOLINGBROKE (BLENHEIM): G-BPIV MKIV   *156 BEAUFIGHTER:* G-DINT   *171 SYCAMORE:* G-ALSX HAPR
  175 BRITANNIA: G-ANCF AOVF AOVT   *192 BELVEDERE:* G-BRMB
BRITISH KLEMM - see BA & KLEMM
  L.25 SWALLOW: G-ACXE
BRITTEN *SHERIFF:* G-FRJB
BRITTEN-NORMAN (including IRMA & PILATUS production):
  BN.1F: G-ALZE
  BN.2A/B/T ISLANDER/DEFENDER: G-AWNT AXHE AXUB AXZK AYRU AYYW BCEN BEEG BELF BFNU BIIP BJOP BJSA BJWO BLDV BLNJ BLNL BNXA BPC
  G-BSPY BSWR BUBN BVFK BVHX BVHY BVSJ BVSL BWNF BWNG BWPM BWPR BWPU BWPV BWPW BWPX BWYW BWYX BWYY BWYZ BWZF CHES CIAS HPAA IS
  G-JSAT JSPC LEAP LOTO MAFF NESU ORED OSEA OTVS OWIN PASU PASV RAPA SBUS SJCH SSKY SURV WOTG EI-AYN EI-BCE
  BN.2A/III TRISLANDER: G-AZLJ BBYO BCCU BDOT BDTN BDTO BDWV BEDP BEFO BEPH BEPI BEVR BEVT BEVV JOEY OCME OCTA OJAV WEAC XTOR
BROCHET
  MB.50 PIPISTRELLE: G-AVKB BADV   *MB.84:* G-AYVT
BROOKLAND
  HORNET: G-BRPP MIKE PHIL   *MOSQUITO:* G-AWIF BGEX
BROOKLANDS - see OPTICA
BROOKS *PULSAR:* G-MBOK
BRUGGER *MB.2/MB.3 COLIBRI:* G-BKCI BKRH BNDP BNDT BOBF BPBP BRWV BSUJ BUDW BUTY BVIS BVVN BXVS HRLM KARA PRAG
BUCKER including *CASA* & *DORNIER* production)
  Bu.131 JUNGMANN (CASA 1.131): G-BECT BECW BEDA BHPL BHSL BIRI BJAL BPDM BPTS BPVW BRSH BSAJ BSFB BSLH BTDT BTDZ BUCC BUCK BU
  G-BUTA BUVN BUVP BVPD BWHP BXBD BYIJ CDRU DUDS EHBJ EMJA JGMN JUNG RETA TAFF WIBS
  Bu.133 JUNGMEISTER: G-AEZX AXMT AYSJ BSZN BUKK BUTX BVGP BVXJ TAFI   *Bu.181 BESTMANN (ZLIN Z.381):* G-AMYA
BUG: G-BXTV
BUSBY *HAFB:* G-FYGF
BUSHBY-LONG - see LOEHLE
  MIDGET MUSTANG: G-AWIR BDGA BXHT MIDG
BVS *Special HAFB:* G-BJUB

C

CAARP - including <u>PIEL</u> & <u>MUDRY</u> production)

<u>CAP.10:</u> G-BECZ BKCX BLVK BRDD BXBK BXBU BXFE BXRA BXRB BXRC BYFY CAPI CAPX CZCZ GDTU LORN MOZZ ODIN RIFN SLEA WIXI
<u>CAP.20/21:</u> G-BIPO BPPS   <u>CAP.231:</u> G-PELG
<u>CAB</u> - see <u>GARDAN</u>
<u>CALLAIR</u> <u>A.9:</u> G-TDFS
<u>CAMBRIDGE HOT-AIR BALLOONING ASSOCIATION</u> <u>HAFB:</u> G-BBGZ
<u>CAMERON</u> - see <u>CAMERON-COLT/CAMERON-THUNDER</u>
 Airship (Gas)
<u>DG-14:</u> G-BTFB   <u>DG-19:</u> G-BKIK BPWT   <u>D-38:</u> G-BGEP   <u>DP-50:</u> G-BMEZ   <u>DP-70:</u> G-BPFF BRDT   <u>DP-80:</u> G-BTBR UPPY VIBA
<u>DP-90:</u> G-BVJJ BXKY   <u>D-96:</u> G-BAMK BKNL
 Balloon (Gas)
<u>R-15:</u> G-CICI   <u>R-36:</u> G-ROZY   <u>R-42:</u> G-BLIO   <u>R-77:</u> G-BUFA BUFC BUFE BVJO   <u>R-150:</u> G-BVUO   <u>R-420:</u> G-JNEE RNEE
<u>R-550:</u> G-RTWI   <u>R-900:</u> G-CWCW
 Balloon (Hot Air)
<u>RW-9:</u> G-BVOG   <u>H-20/P-20/V-20:</u> G-BIBS BJUV BOYO BPRU BRCJ BRCO   <u>H-24:</u> G-BRLU BSCK BVCY
<u>N-31/O-31/S-31/V-31:</u> G-BAGI BDSO BEJK BEUY BGHS BKIZ BMST BKIX BPUB BRMT BVFB COOP LEAU LLYD PRTT RBMV WETI
<u>H-34:</u> G-BRKL BRWY BUCB BVZX BXYI BYNW EROS FZZI IAMP RAPP
<u>N-42/O-42/V-42:</u> G-AZER BCDL BCEU BISH BKNB BMWU BPHD BUPP BVLC BWEE BWGX BXJH BXTG BYRK HOPI
<u>N-56/O/56/V-56:</u> G-AZKK BADU BYU BCAP BCOJ BCXZ BDPK BDSF BDUI BDUZ BDYH BECK BEEH BELX BEND BENN BERT BEXX BEXZ BFAB BFFT BFKL
G-BFME BGLX BGOI BGUY BHGF BHSN BICU BKLC BKRS BKZF BLWX BMOJ BNIF BOWM BRIR BRSA BRSL BTHZ BUVG BYSL BZKK HOFM HOOV LENN OVET
G-PBBT SWPR WAAC WYNT EI-BBM
<u>N-65/O-65/V-65:</u> G-AZIP AZUP AZUV AZXB BAOW BBGR BBYR BCFC BCFN BCRI BDFG BDGP BDRK BDSK BEIF BETP BGJU BHKH BHNC BHND BHOT
G-BHOU BIBO BIGL BISW BIWK BIWU BIYI BJAW BJNX BJWJ BJZA BKGR BKWR BKXX BLEP BLJF BLXY BLZB BMCD BMJN BMKY BMPD BMVW BMYJ BNAN
G-BNAU BNAW BOAL BOOB BOWV BPGD BPPA BPXF BREH BRMI BROE BROG BSAS BSGP BTUH BWBA BWHB BWHG BWJC BXGY BXUU GLUE HENS JOIN KAFE
G-MUIR NATX OERX PMAM PYRO RUDD SMIG SOFA WELS EI-BSN EI-BVC
<u>CONCEPT C-60/70/80/PM-80:</u> G-BTZU BUYC BVDM BVDY BVEK BVEN BVGJ BVSV BVSW BVUE BVUU BVWE BVZN BWAO BWGP BWRT BXJP BXJZ BXLG
G-BXOT BXSC BXSJ BYER BYIV BYIW BYIX BYJJ BYJX BYTJ EVET OARG OBTS ONIX RMAX ROGY SLCE SOUP UPHL
<u>N-77/O-77/V-77/Z-77:</u> G-BAXF BBCK BBOC BBOL BCNP BCRE BCZO BDAC BDBI BDNZ BDSE BFUG BFYK BGAZ BGHV BHDV BHHB BHHK BHHN BHII
G-BHYO BIDU BIEF BIET BIRY BJGK BKCT BKIC BKNP BKPN BKRI BKTR BKWW BKZB BLFY BLIP BLJH BLLD BLPP BLSH BLVN BLXF BLZS BMAD BMCK
G-BMKJ BMKP BMKW BMLJ BMLW BMOH BMPP BMTN BMTX BMVO BMZB BNCB BNCH BNCJ BNCK BNCM BNDN BNDV BNEO BNES BNFG BNFO BNGJ BNGN BNHI
G-BNIN BNIU BNJG BNKT BNMA BNMG BNNC BNNE BNPE BNTW BNTZ BNUC BOAU BOBR BOEK BOFF BOGP BOJB BOJD BOJU BOOZ BORB BORN BOSV BOTW
G-BOWB BOWL BOXG BOZN BPAE BPBU BPBV BPBY BPDF BPDG BPHH BPHJ BPIM BPLF BPLV BPPP BPSH BPSR BPTD BPVC BPVM G-BPWC BPYI BPYS
G-BPYT BPYV BRAJ BRBO BREL BRFE BRFO BRHC BRIB BRIE BRKW BRLX BRMU BRMV BRNW BROB BRRF BRRO BRRR BRRW BRSD BRTV BRUE BRUV BRWH
G-BRZA BRZT BSBI BSBM BSBR BSDX BSEV BSGY BSHO BSHT BSIC BSIJ BSKD BSLI BSMS BSUV BSWJ BSWV BSWY BSXM BSYJ BTAG BTIX BTJH BTKZ
G-BTOI BTOP BTPT BTRX BTWJ BTWM BTXW BTZV BUAF BUAM BUDU BUES BUEV BUGD BUGP BUGS BUHM BUNG BUOX BUPI BUTJ BUWU BUWY BUZK BVBS
G-BVBU BVDR BVFF BVHK BVIM BVLI BVMF BVUK BVXB BWAJ BWAN BWHC BWKV BWPB BWPC BWTJ BWYN BXAX BXSX BXTJ BXVT BYBN BYHY BYLY BYNJ
G-BYRF CBKT CCAR CCSC CEJA CGOD CHOK CHUK CRAK CTGR DASU DRYI EIIR ENNY EPDI ERIK FABB FELT FUZY GEES GEEZ GEUP GUNS HARE HENY
G-HGAS HORN HOST IDDI JLMW KEYY KODA KTEE LAZR LEGO LEND LEXI LIDD LIOT LOAG LOAN LOLL LOSS LUBE MAMO MILE MITS MITZ MOFF MOKE
G-MRTY NEPB OATH OCND ODHL OEDP OHSA OJEN OKYA OMRB ONZO ORPR PADI POLY PUSS PVCU RAPH RCMF RONI SAFE SAIX SCAH SCFO SHOT SKIL
G-SLAC SNOW SUSI TECK TUDR UPUP ULIA VODA VOLT WAIT WELI XSKY ZZAG EI-CKJ
<u>O-84:</u> G-AYAJ AYVA AZBH AZNT AZRN AZSP BAGY BAKO BALD BAST BBLL BCEZ BNET BNFP BNXR BOWU BOYM BREX BRGD BSKE BSKU BSMK BUYN
G-BVXD BWLN KEYB MOSY OLLE STAV EI-BAY
<u>LTSB-90/N-90/O-90/V-90/Z-90:</u> G-BMFU BMJZ BNBR BNII BNJX BOWK BPSO BPUJ BPZO BRGE BROH BROY BRPJ BRZC BSCA BSNJ BSSO BSWX BTBP
G-BTCM BTFU BTHF BTJU BTTB BTTL BTWV BTXF BUAJ BUFJ BUFX BUGY BUIE BUIU BUIZ BUOE BUUO BUVW BVBX BVDX BVEJ BVFP BVHO BVHR BVKV
G-BVMR BVOC BVOP BVPK BVTN BWAU BWBC BWDU BWIP BWJI BWNO BWNS BWPT BWUU BWVU BWYC BXAM BXBS BXCS BXJO BXVV BYDT BYHC BYIU BYJC
G-BYKX BYMY BYNN BYOK BYOX CHAA COMP CONC CPSF CTEL CXCX DHLB DIAL DRYS ELLE ENUS FBNW FOGG GLAW GOCX GOGW HBUG HTVI IGEL IGLE
G-ILES INSR ITOI IWON JULU LAGR LTSB MANI MFLI MOFZ OJBM OJBW OXBY PATG PKCC PRNT RISE RIZE RIZI SLII SORT SRVO STRM SWEB TANK
G-TEDF TEEL TINS TMCC VINS VRVI YUMM YUPI YVET   <u>RX-100:</u> G-NPWR
<u>A-105/N-105/O-105/AML-105/RX-105:</u> G-BAVU BLSX BMEE BMOV BMVI BNFN BOTD BOTK BOYY BPBW BPJE BRFR BRLL BRZB BSNZ BTEA BTFM BTIZ
G-BTKW BTPB BTRL BTOU BUHU BULD BUPT BUWF BUWW BVCA BVEU BVHV BVNR BVUA BVXA BVXP BWDH BWEW BWKF BWOW BWPZ BWRY BWSU BXBM BXBR
G-BXBY BXEN BXGC BXWY BXXG BXXL BXYG BYFB BYFJ BYHU BYIL BYMX BYNX BYPD CAMP CLIC DRGN ENRY FOWS GFAB HONK JSON LBNK NPNP NZGL
G-OAML OUVI SAXO SDLW SEPT SSTI ULTR WNGS XANT YLYB EI-CUE
<u>A-120/N-120/O-120/RTW-120:</u> G-BNEX BOBB BOHL BOZY BPSS BPTX BPZK BRXA BSYB BTEE BTKN BTUU BTXS BUDV BUFT BURN BVSO BVXF BWAG
G-BWKD BWLD BWYS BXNL BXVJ BXWI BYSV FLOA GHIA HOTT LOBO MEUP MOFB TING VIKY   <u>N-133:</u> G-BWAA
<u>A-140/O-140:</u> G-BVPU BVYU BWTE BYLU GAIW GDXK   <u>N-145:</u> G-DENT HIBM
<u>A-160/N-160/O-160:</u> G-BNIE BOBD BPCN BPJZ BPLE BRIM BYHW TGAS   <u>AT-165:</u> G-BIAZ
<u>A-180/N-180:</u> G-BPPJ BPSZ BPYY BRTH BRVC BRZI BSEX BSLG BSWD BSWZ BSYD BSZY BTBS BTCW BTYE BUAU BUJR BUKC BVKL BWBR BWHW BXMM
G-OBRY RWHC SKYR SVBF   <u>A-200:</u> G-BWYL BXOS
<u>A-210:</u> G-BLSU BRVX BTCK BTXV BUAY BUEE BUHY BUOC BUVK BUYH BVBN BVRM BWZK BXBA BXJC BXNM BXRM BXWZ BXXF BXZG BXZH BYDI BYJV
G-BYMG CVBF FLYE JOJO LPGI OJWE SKYX YTUK
<u>A-250:</u> G-BUBR BUXE BUXR BUZY BVIG BVUD BVYR BWKU BWKX BWZJ BXPK HIUP LORA MOLI ODEB OVBF SCRU SKYY STPI
<u>A-275:</u> G-BWML BXIC BXKJ BXMW BXTE BXYL   <u>A-315:</u> G-SIMI   <u>AS-250:</u> G-BYHX   <u>A-340:</u> G-BWPA KVBF KYBF RANG   <u>A-375:</u> G-BWNH
<u>A-400:</u> G-ZVBF   <u>N-1250:</u> G-WASH

SHAPE	REGISTRATION(S)	SHAPE	REGISTRATION(S)
ACTION MAN PARACHUTIST	G-RIPS	JAGUAR XK8 SPORTS CAR	G-OXKB
APPLE	G-BWSO	KATALOG	G-OTTO
BALL	G-RNIE	KOOKABURRA	G-CHKL
BEER BARREL	G-PINT	KP CHOC DIPS TUB	G-DIPI
BEER CAN	G-IBET	LIGHTBULB	G-BVWH
BEETHOVEN BUST	G-BNJU	MACAW	G-BRWZ
BELLS WHISKY BOTTLE	G-BUUU	MICKEY MOUSE	G-MOUS
BENIHANA	G-BMVS	MOBILE PHONE	G-PHON
BERENTZEN BOTTLE	G-KERN KORN	MONSTER TRUCK	G-BWMU
BERTIE BASSETT	G-BXAL	MOUNTIE	G-BXSW
BIERKRUG	G-BXFY	MR.PEANUTNUTS	G-PNUT
BRADFORD AND BINGLEY	G-BWMY	MUG	G-RMUG
BUDWEISER CAN	G-BPFJ	N ELE	G-WBMG
BULB	G-BVWI	OIL CAN	G-UNIP
BUS	G-BUSS	OTTI	G-OTTI
CADBURY'S CARAMEL BUNNY	G-BUNI	PERRIER BOTTLE	G-PERR
CADBURY'S CRÈME EGG	G-OEGG	PIG	G-HOGS
CAN	G-OFIZ	POT	G-CHAM
CARROTS	G-BWSP HUCH	PRINTER	G-BYFK
CART	G-BYDU	REAL FRUIT	G-BXJL
CHAMPION SPARK PLUG	G-BETF	ROBINSON'S BARLEY WATER	G-BKES
CHATEAU DE BALLEROY	G-BKBR BTCZ		
CHEESE	G-RANA	RUPERT BEAR	G-BTML
CHESTIE	G-USMC	RUSSIAN DOLL	G-USSR
CHICK	G-BYEI	SAMSUNG COMPUTER	G-SEUK
CIDER BOTTLE	G-OTNT	SANTA MARIA SHIP	G-BPSP
CLUB	G-BWNP	SATURN	G-DREX
COCA COLA BOTTLE	G-BXSA BXSB	SAUCER	G-GUFO
COOLING TOWER	G-WATT	SCOTTISH PIPER	G-PIPY
COTTAGE	G-COTT	SIGN	G-UCCC
CUP	G-OAXA	SONIC THE HEDGEHOG	G-SEGA
DOLL	G-BVDF	SPHERE	G-BVFU BYJW IBBC SATL
DOUGLAS LURPAK BUTTERMAN	G-BXCK	STARTAC	G-HAND
DRACULA SKULL	G-DRAC	STRAWBERRY	G-BXTF SAMI
DUDE	G-OIFM	SULTAN	G-TURK
EAGLE	G-BVMJ	TEMPLE	G-BMWN
ELEPHANT	G-BLRW BMKX BPRC	TENNENT'S LAGER GLASS	G-BTSL
EXPANSION JOINT	G-BIUL	THOMAS	G-BXND
FABERGE EGG	G-BNFK	TRAINER'S SHOE	G-BUDN
FIRE EXTINGUISHER	G-BVYJ	TRUCK	G-BLDL DERV
FORBES' MAGAZINE	G-BPOV	TV	G-TVTV
FREDDO	G-BYSU	UFO	G-BUFO
FURNESS BUILDING	G-BSIO	UNCLE SAM	G-USAM
GOLFBALL	G-BXKK PUTT	VAN	G-ORAC
GOLLY	G-OLLI	WITCH	G-WYCH
GRAND ILLUSION	G-MAGC	WINE BOX	G-STOW
HARD HAT	G-BXAP		
HARLEY DAVIDSON MOTOCYCLE	G-BMUN		
HELIX OIL CAN	G-HLIX		
HOFMEISTER LAGER BEAR	G-HEYY		
HOME SPECIAL	G-BWZP BYST		
HOPPER SERVO	G-OSVO		

CAMPBELL including BENSEN & EVERETT production
COUGAR: G-BAPS
CRICKET: G-AXPZ AXRC AXVL AXVM AYCC AYHI AYPZ AYRA AYRC BHBA BKVS BORG BRLF BTEI BTMP BUIG BULT BVDJ BVIT BVLD BVOH BWCE BWSD G-BWUA BWUZ BXCJ BXEM BXHU BXUA BYMO BYMP GYRO RUGS TVSI
CANADAIR
RJ100 (CL.600-2B19): G-JECA JECB MSKK MSKL MSKM MSKN MSKO MSKP
CL.600 Challenger 3R: EI-SXT
CARLSON SPARROW: G-BSUX BVVB EI-COO
CASA - see BUCKER (1.131 JUNGMANN), HEINKEL (2.111) & JUNKERS (C.352L)
CASSUTT including MUSSO/SPECIAL
RACER: G-BDTW BEUN BKCH BNJZ BOMB BOXW BPVO BPVX BUFK BWEC BXMF FRAY MARY NARO RUNT TTIM TRUC
CAUDRON
G.III: G-AETA   C.270 LUCIOLE: G-BDFM
CCF - see HAWKER & NORTH AMERICAN
CEA (CENTRE EST AVIATION) - see JODEL

<u>CENTRAIR</u> *MOTO-DELTA:* G-MBPJ

<u>CESSNA</u> (including <u>REIMS</u> [F.prefix] production)

C.165 AIRMASTER: G-BTDE

120/140: G-AHRO AJJS AJJT AKTS AKUR AKVM ALOD ALTO ANGK BHLW BJML BOCI BPHW BPHX BPKO BPUU BPWD BPZB BRJC BRPE BRPF BRPG BRPH
G-BRUN BRXH BSUH BTBV BTBW BTEW BTOS BTVG BTYW BTYX BUHO BUHZ BUJM BUKO BVUZ BYCD GAWA HALJ JOLY OVFM

150: G-APXY APZR ARAU ARFI ARFO ARJM ARRY ASMS ASMU ASMW ASST ASUE ASYP ASZB ASZU ATEF ATHV ATHZ ATIE ATKF ATMC ATML ATMM ATMY
G-ATNE ATNL ATOE ATOF ATRK ATRL ATRM ATUF ATYM ATZY AVAR AVCU AVEM AVEN AVER AVGU AVHM AVIA AVIB AVIT AVJE AVMD AVMF AVNC
G-AVPH AVUG AVUH AVVL AVVW AVVX AVZU AWAW AWAX AWBX AWCM AWCO AWCP AWEO AWES AWFF AWFH AWGK AWLA AWMT AWOT AWPJ AWPP AWPU AWRK
G-AWTJ AWTX AWUG AWUH AWUJ AWUK AWUL AWUN AWUO AWUT AWUU AXGG AXPF AYBD AYEY AYGC AYKL AYRF AYRK AYYF AZLH AZLY AZLZ AZXC BABB
G-BABC BABH BAEU BAHI BAIK BAIP BAMC BAXU BAXV BAYO BAYP BAZS BBBC BBCI BBDT BBJX BBKA BBKB BBKE BBKY BBNJ BBTT BBTZ BCBX BCCC
G-BCRT BCTW BCUH BCUJ BCZN BDBU BDFJ BDFZ BDOD BDSL BDTX BDUM BDUO BDZC BEIG BELT BEOK BEWP BFFY BFGW BFIY BFLM BFOG BFSR BFVU
G-BFWL BGBI BGEA BHIY BIFY BIOC BJOV BLVS BMBB BMLX BMXJ BNFI BOBV BOIV BOMN BORY BOTP BOUJ BOUZ BOVS BOVT BPAB BPAW BPAX BPCJ
G-BPEM BPGB BPGY BPGZ BPNA BPOS BPRP BPUX BPWG BPWM BRBH BRJT BRLR BRNC BRTJ BSBZ BSEJ BSJU BSJZ BSKA BSSB BSYV BSYW BSZU
G-BSZV BTES BTGP BTHE BTIN BTSN BTTE BTYC BUCS BUCT BUGG BUJU BUNS BURH BWGU BWII BWVL CSBM CSFC DENA DENB DENC DEND ECBH EJMG
G-FAYE FFEN FINA GBLR GFLY GLED HFCB HFCI HIVE HULL HUNY IANJ INGR JWDS LFSF LUCK MABE NSTG OCIN OIDW OJVH OKED OSTY PHAA PLAN
G-SADE SALL SAMZ SCAT TAIL UFLY WYMP YIII EI-APF EI-AST EI-AVM EI-AWE EI-BAT EI-BFE EI-BHW EI-BYF EI-CDV EI-CHM EI-CML EI-CMV
EI-COP

A150 AEROBAT: G-AXRT AXRU AXSW AXUF AYBW AYCF AYOZ AYRO AZID AZJY AZKV AZOZ AZUZ AZZX BACC BACN BABD BACO BACP BAEP BAEV BAEZ
G-BAII BAIN BAOP BAPH BAPI BAPJ BAUY BBCF BBEO BBKF BBKU BBNX BBNY BBTB BBTK BBXB BCDY BCFR BCKU BCKV BCTU BCUY BCVG BCVH BDAI
G-BDEX BDNR BDOW BDRD BEIA BEKN BEMY BEOE BEOY BFGG BFGX BFGZ BFIE BFRR BHRH BJTB BLPH BMEX BOFW BOFX BOYU BPJW BPRO BTFS BUCA
G-BUTT CLUB FMSG HFCA OISO OPIC OSND EI-AUC EI-AUO EI-AYF EI-BRX EI-CTI

152: G-BFEK BFFC BFFE BFFW BFHT BFHU BFHV BFKG BFKH BFLU BFOE BFOF BFRL BFSB BFXH BGAA BGAB BGAD BGAE BGBP BGFX BGGO BGGP BGHI
G-BGIB BGLG BGNT BGSX BHAA BHAI BHAV BHCP BHDM BHDR BHDS BHDU BHDW BHEC BHFC BHFI BHHG BHIN BHNA BHPX BHPY BHRB BHRM BHRN BHSA
G-BHUI BHWA BHWB BHWS BHYX BHZH BICG BIDH BIJW BIJX BIJY BILR BILS BIOK BIOM BITF BITH BIUM BIXH BIZG BJKX BJKY BJNF BJVJ BJVT
G-BJWH BJYD BKAZ BKFC BKGW BKTV BKWY BLJO BLWV BLZE BLZH BLZP BMCN BMCV BMFZ BMGG BMJB BMJC BMJD BMMM BMSJ BMTA BMTB BMTJ BMTL
G-BNMC BNMD BNME BNMF BNNR BNOZ BNPY BNPZ BNRK BNRL BNSI BNSM BNSN BNSU BNSV BNUL BNUS BNUT BNXC BNYL BNYN BOAI BODO BOFL BOFM
G-BOGC BOGG BOHI BOHJ BOIO BOIP BOIR BOIW BOKY BOLV BOLW BONW BOOI BORI BORJ BORO BOTB BOTG BOYL BOZR BPBG BPBJ BPBK BPEO BPFZ
G-BSHE BSRC BSTO BSTP BSWH BSZI BSZO BSZW BTAL BTCE BTDW BTFC BTGH BTGR BTGW BTGX BTIK BTVW BTVX BTYT BUEF BUEG BVTM BWEU BWEV
G-BWNB BWNC BWND BXGE BXJM BXRN BXTB BXUZ BXVB BXVY BXWC BYFA BYMH BYMJ BZEC CHIK CPFC CWFY DACF DESY DRAG ENTT ENTW FIGA FIGB
G-HART HFCL HFCT IAFT IBRO IRAN KAFC KATT LAMS LSMI MASS OAFT OBAT OBEN ODAC OFRY OIMC OLEE OPAM OPJC OSFC OVMC OWAC OWAK OWOW
G-RICH SACB SACF SHAH TAYS WACB WACE WACF WACG WACT EI-BGJ EI-BIB EI-BMM EI-BMN EI-CCJ EI-CCK EI-CCL EI-CCM EI-CGT EI-CRU

A152 AEROBAT: G-BFGL BFKF BFMK BFRV BFZN BFZT BFZU BGAF BGLN BHAC BHAD BHED BHEN BHJA BHJB BHMG BIHE BILJ BILK BIMT BLAC BLAX
G-BMUO BMYG BOPW BOPX BOSO BOYB BRCD BRUM FIFE FLIP JEET JONI LEIC MPBH OCPC RLFI TFCI WACH WACU WALS ZOOL EI-BJM

170: G-AORB APVS AWOU BCLS

172/SKYHAWK: G-APSZ ARID ARLU ARMO ARMR AROA ARWH ARWO ARWR ARYI ARYK ARYS ARZD ARZE ASFA ASIB ASMJ ASNW ASOK ASPI ASSS ASUH
G-ASUP ASVM ASWL ATAF ATFY ATGO ATKT ATKU ATLM ATSL ATWJ AVBZ AVEC AVHH AVIC AVIS AVJF AVJI AVKG AVPI AVTP AVVC AVZV AWBW AWGD
G-AWGJ AWGR AWLF AWMP AWUX AWUZ AWVA AXBH AXBJ AXDI AXSI AXVB AXWF AYCT AYRG AYRT AYUV AZDZ AZJV AZKW AZKZ AZLM AZLV AZTK AZTS
G-AZUM AZXD AZZV BAAL BAEO BAEW BAEY BAIW BAIX BANX BAOB BAOS BAVB BAXY BAZT BBDH BBJD BBJY BBJZ BBKI BBKZ BBNZ BBOA BBTG BBTH
G-BCCD BCEC BCHK BCOL BCPK BCRB BCUF BCVJ BCYR BCZM BDCE BDNU BDZD BEBI BEHV BEMB BENK BEUX BEWR BEZK BEZO BEZR BEZV BFGD BFKB
G-BFMX BFOV BFPH BFPM BFRS BFTH BFTX BFZV BGAG BGBR BGIU BGIY BGLO BGMP BGND BGNS BGRO GSHW BHAW BHCC BHCM BHDX BHDZ BHIH BHMI
G-BHPZ BHSB BHUG BHUJ BHVR BHYP BHYR BIBW BIDF BIGJ BIHI BIIB BIIE BING BIOB BITM BIZF BJDE BJDW BJGY BJVM BJWI BJWW BJXZ BKCE
G-BKEP BKEV BKHZ BKII BKIJ BKLO BKLP BKRB BLHJ BLVW BMCI BMHS BMIG BMTS BMVJ BNKD BNKE BNRR BNST BNTP BNXD BNYM BOEN BOHH BOIL
G-BOIX BOIY BOJR BOJS BOLI BOLX BOLY BOMS BOMT BONO BONR BONS BOOL BORW BOUE BOUF BOVG BOYP BPML BPRM BPTL BPVA BPVY BPWS BRAK
G-BRBI BRBJ BRCM BRWX BRZS BSEP BSHR BSNG BSOG BSOO BSPE BSTM BTMA BTMR BTRE BUAN BUJN BULH BUOJ BURD BUZN BWJP BXGH BXLJ
G-BXOI BXSD BXSE BXSM BXSR BXXD BXXK BYBD BYEA BYEB BYEN BYES BYET BYNA BZBF BZZD BZGH CBOR CCCC CFLY CLUX COCO CSCS CURR DCKK
G-DEMH DENR DODD DRAM DRBG DREY DUVL ECGC ENII ENOA ETDC EWUD FNLD FNLY GBFF GBLP GRAY GWYN GYAV GZDO HILS ICOM IZSS IZZY JFWI
G-JONE JONZ JVMD LANE LAVE LOOK MALK MELT MICK MILA OBMS OERS OFCM OOLE OPFT OPYE ORMG OSII OSKY OTAM OVFR OZOO PDSI RARB ROOK
G-ROUP RSWO RUIA RUSS SACD SBAE SEVE SEXI SHSP SKAN SKYH TAAL TASH TOBI TOBY TRIO TYRE UFC UFCB WACL WACW WACY WACZ YORK
EI-AOK EI-AYK EI-BAG EI-BAO EI-BAS EI-BCK EI-BIC EI-BIR EI-BKF EI-BPL EI-BRM EI-BRS EI-BSC EI-BUA EI-BVF EI-CFM EI-CFN EI-CFP
EI-CFY EI-CGD EI-CHS EI-CLQ EI-COT EI-CUJ EI-GWY EI-MCF

172RG CUTLASS: G-BHYC ILU IXI PARI EI-BPC

R172 HAWK XP/FR172 ROCKET: G-AWCN AWDR AWWU AWYB AXBU AYGX AYJW BARC BBKG BBXH BCTK BDOE BEZS BFFZ BFIG BFIU BFSS BHYD BLMX
G-BLPF BPCI BPWR BTMK BXYY DAVD DIVA FANL JANS LOYA OMAC PJTM YBAA EI-BJI EI-BJO EI-CCV

175/SKYLARK: G-APZS ARCV AREB ARFG ARFL ARML ARMN AROC ARRG ARUZ ARWS OTOW EI-AND

177(RG) CARDINAL: G-AYPG AYPH AYPI AYSX AYSY AZTF AZTW AZVP BAGN BAIS BAJA BAJB BAJE BBHI BBJV BCUW BEBN BFGF BFIV BFMH BPSL
G-BRDO BRPS BTSZ BUJE FIJJ LNYS OAMP TOTO EI-BHC EI-POD

180/SKYWAGON: G-ARAT ASIT AXZO BEOD BETG BMAF BNCS BOIA BTSM BUPG DAPH

(R)182/SKYLANE (RG): G-ARAW ASLH ASNN ASRR ASSF ASUL ASXZ ATCX ATLA ATPT ATTD AVCV AVDA AVGY AVID AXNX AXZU AYOW AYWD AZNO
G-BAAT BAFL BAHD BAHX BAMJ BBGX BBYH BBYS BCWB BDBJ BDIG BEKO BFOD BFSA BFZD BGAJ BGFH BGPA BGVT BHDP BHEO BHIB BHIC BHVP BHYA
G-BIRS BJDI BJVH BKHJ BKKN BKKO BLEW BMMK BMUD BMNO BNOX BNRY BOPG BOPH BOTH BOWO BPUM BRKR BRRK BSDW BSSR BTHA BUVO BWMC BWRR
G-BXEZ BXZM BYEG G BYEM CBIL DOVE DRGS EEZS EIWT EOHL GEAR GOZO HRNT HUFF IBZS IFAB IOPT IRPC ISEH JBRN JENI JOON KWAX LEGG
G-LSKW MILN MISH MLAS NLEE NOCK OBBO OCJW OKOS OLSC OPST ORAY OTRG OZOI PDHJ PLEE POWL POWR RACY ROWE SAAM SKYL THRE TPSL WARF
G-WARP WHDP XLTG EI-AOD EI-BCL EI-BPJ EI-CAP EI-CDP EI-GSM

185 SKYWAGON/AG CARRYALL: G-AYNN BBEX BDKC BKPC BLOS BWWF BXRH BYBP RNRM   *188 AG WAGON/AG TRUCK/T.188 AG HUSKY:* G-AZZG BHTD

190/195: G-BSPK BTBJ   *205:* G-ASNK ASOX

206 SUPER SKYLANE/SUPER SKYWAGON/STATIONAIR: G-ASVN ATCE ATLT AWUA AYCJ AZRZ BAGV BATD BFCT BGED BGWR BJRW BMHC BMOF BNRI BOFD
G-BPGE BRID BSMB BSUE BXDB BXRO BYIC DROP EESE SEAI SKYE STAT EI-BGK EI-BNK   *207 SKYWAGON/STATIONAIR 8:* G-NJAG PARA

208 CARAVAN: G-EELS ETHY

210 CENTURION: G-ASXR BBRY BENF BEYV BNZM BSGT BVZM IKIS MANT OFLY PIIX SEEK SUIT VMDE EI-AWH EI-BUF EI-CAX EI-CDX EI-CGH

T303 CRUSADER: G-BKXG BSPF BXRI CRUS CRUZ CYLS DOLY EDRY GAME IKAP INDC JUIN OAPE PTWB PUSI ROCH   _305 BIRD DOG (L-19):_ G-PDOG
_310:_ G-APNJ ARBC ARCI AVDB AXLG AYGB AYND AZRR AZUY AZYM BALN BARG BARV BBBX BBHG BBXL BCTJ BGTT BGXK BHEH BIFA BJMR BKSB BMMC
G-BODY BPIL BRIA BTFF BTGN BTYK BWYE BWYG BWYH BXUY BXYF EGEE EGLT FFOR FFWD FISH GREN IMLI MIWS MPBI OBNF ODLY REDB REDD RIST
G-RODD SOUL TKPZ TROP VDIR XITD EI-AOS EI-BEO
320 SKYKNIGHT: G-AZCI BKRD   _335:_ G-FITZ   _336 SKYMASTER:_ G-ASLL ATAH PIXS
337 SUPER SKYMASTER: G-ATCU ATID ATSM AXFG AXHA AZKO AZLO AZRW BARD BBBL BCBZ BFGH BFJR BMJR BNNG BOWD BTVV HIVA NYTE RGEN
G-RORO EI-AVC EI-BHM   _340:_ G-BISJ BVES FEBE LAST LIZA OPLB PUFN PDMH REEN SAMM VAUN EI-CGX EI-CIJ
_401/402:_ G-AVKN AWWW AZFR AZRD BXJA DACC DOBN EYES MAPP NOSE ROAR
404 TITAN/AMBASSADOR/COURIER: G-BWLF EXEX ILGW KIWI MIND TASK
406 CARAVAN II: G-BVJT BYLR DFLT LEAF MAFA MAFB SFPA SFPB SURF TWIG   _414/CHANCELLOR:_ G-DYNE SMJJ
421/GOLDEN EAGLE: G-BAGO BBUJ BDCS BDYF BDZU BFTT BHKJ BKNA BLST BMLZ BTDK CSNA CJEA EAGL FTAX FWRP GILT HASI JACK JDTI KWLI
G-MUVG OOJB OSAL OSCH PEAT RLMC SAIR SHOE TAMY TREC UVIP VVIP EI-DWN
425/441 CONQUEST I/II: G-BNDY FCAL FPLC FRAX FRAZ   _500/501 CITATION 1:_ G-CITI DJAE LOFT OEJA ORHE ORJB OSCA TJHI
525 CITATIONJET: G-BVCM IUAN OCSB OICE RSCJ ZIZI
550/CITATION BRAVO/551 CITATION II: G-BFRM BJIR BWOM ESTA FJET FLVU JCFR JETJ OCDB RDBS RVHT SPUR THCL EI-CIR EI-DAB EI-GHP
EI-PAL   _560 CITATION V:_ G-CZAR OTGT RIBV TTFN   _650 CITATION III:_ G-HNRY   _750 CITATION X:_ G-HERS
CFM _(STREAK) SHADOW:_ G-BONP BROI BRSO BRWP BRZZ BSMN BSOR BSPL BSRX BSSV BTDD BTEL BTGT BTKP BTZZ BUGM BUIL BULJ BUOB BUTB BUVX
G-BUWR BUXC BVDT BVFR BVLF BVOR BVPY BVTD BWAI BWCA BWHJ BWOZ BWPS BXFK BXVD BXWR BXXZ BXZV BXZY BYAZ BYCI BYFI BYOO CAIN DMWX
G-FAME GORE HLCF LYNK MEOW MGGT MGPH MGTW MGUY MJVF MMWT MNCM MNER MNIS MNSV MNTK MNTP MNVJ MNVK MNWK MNWY MNXX MNZJ MNZP MNZR
G-MNZZ MTBE MTCA MTCT MTDU MTDX MTFU MTFZ MTGN MTGV MTGW MTHS MTHT MTHV MTKR MTMX MTMY MTMZ MTSG MTTH MTWH MTWK MTWL MTWM MTWN
G-MWDB MWDN MWEN MWEZ MWFB MWIZ MWJF MWJZ MWLD MWMU MWON MWOW MWPH MWPP MWRL MWRY MWSZ MWTJ MWTN MWTP MWUA MWVG MWVH MWYD MYBC
G-MYBL MYCM MYDE MYEP MYGO MYIF MYIP MYKE MYLV MYNA MYNX MYOH MYON MYOS MYPL MYPT MYSM MYTH MYTY MYUS MYWF MYWM MYXY MYZP MZBE
G-MZBN MZBS MZCT MZGS MZKH MZRS MZLO MZLP MZMI MZNH MZOM ODVB OLGA OPIT ORAF OTCH PBEL PSUE RINT ROTS SHIM SNEV STRK TEHL TTOY
G-WESX WHOG WYAT EI-CHR EI-CMF
CGS (including ARROWFLIGHT)
HAWK: G-MWYS MYTP MZGU
CHAMPION/AERONCA (including BELLANCA production)
7AC/7DC CHAMPION: G-AJON AKTO AKTR AOEH ATHK AVDT AWVN BGWV BPFM BPGK BRAR BRCV BRER BRFI BRWA BRXG BTGM BTNO BTRH BUYE BVCS
G-CHMP HAMP JTYE LEVI OTOE TECC EI-ATL EI-AVB EI-BJB EI-BJC
7BCM (L-16): G-BFAF TIMP   _7EC TRAVELER:_ G-ARAP EI-BBE BHV   _7FC TRI-TRAVELER:_ G-APYT APYU ARAS
CITABRIA/DECATHLON/SCOUT: G-AYXU BAYZ BBEN BBXY BDBH BFHP BGGA BGGB BGGC BGGD BITA BIZW BKBP BOID BOIN BOLG BOTO BPMM BRJW
G-BSLW BTXX BUGE BVLT EXPL HUNI EI-ANT EI-BIV EI-BSU EI-BYX
CHANCE-VOUGHT - see VOUGHT
CHARGUS _T.225/T.250 (Trike):_ G-MBEU MBJG MMRY
CHASLE _YC-12 TOURBILLON:_ G-AYBV
CHICHESTER-MILES _LEOPARD:_ G-BRNM
CHILTON _DW.1/1A/1B/2:_ G-AESZ AFGH AFGI AFSV AFSW BWGJ DWIA DWIB
CHRISLEA
LC.1 AIRGUARD: G-AFIN   _CH.3 SUPER ACE:_ G-AKUW AKVF AKVR
CHRISTEN
EAGLE: G-BPZI EEGL EGAL EGEL EGLE EGUL ELKA OEGL   _A-1 HUSKY:_ G-BUVR
CHRIS TENA _MINI COUPE:_ G-BPDJ
CIERVA
_C.8L:_ G-EBYY   _C.24:_ G-ABLM   _C.30A AUTOGIRO (AVRO 671):_ G-ACUU ACWM ACWP
CIVILIAN _CAC.1 COUPE:_ G-ABNT
CLUTTON-TABENOR _FRED:_ G-BBBW BDBF BDSA BGAH BGFF BGHZ BISG BITK BKAF BKDP BKEY BKVF BKZT BLNO BMAX BMMF BMOO BMSL BNZR BOLS
G-BPAV BSSJ BTCO BVCO BWAP BYLA FRED MANX OLVR PFAF PFAL RONW USTY
COLT - see COLTING
Airship (Gas) _GA-42:_ G-MATS ZEPI ZEPY
Airship (Hot Air) _AS-42:_ G-WZZZ   _AS-56:_ G-BNKF BTXH NOVO   _AS-80:_ G-BORF BPCF BPGT BPKN BROL BTSW NDRW OVAX
_AS-105:_ G-BNAO BTFD BUKV BWKE BWMV BXEY BXNV BXYF RBOS   _AS-120:_ G-BXKU
Balloon (Gas) _AA-1050:_ G-BWVM
Balloon (Hot Air)
14A Cloudhopper: G-BHKN BHKR BHOJ BHPN BVKX
17A Cloudhopper: G-BIDV IYT BJWV BKBO BKIU BKWE BKXM BLHI BONV BOSG BPXH BRBU HELP ROBY
21A Cloudhopper: G-BKIV BLXG BMKI BNFM BNPI BNZJ BOLN BOLP BOLR BPFX BSAK BSIG BTNN BTXM BUEU BWBJ SOOS
25A Sky Chariot: G-BSOF BVAO OKBT
31A Air Chair: G-BHIG BLOB BPGJ BRKP BROJ BSDV BSMM BVTL BXXU DHLZ DOWN HOUS IMAN LBCS MUTE
_42A/R:_ G-BJZR BVHP SEAT
_56A/B/C/D:_ G-BGIP BHEX BHGX BHRY BICM BIFP BISX BIXW BJXP BJYF BKSD BLCH BLLW BLOT BMNX BMYA BPDE BRVV BTZY BUGO BVCN BVOZ
G-BVUC BVYL CFBI ILEE MERC POSH TTWO WIMP
_69A:_ G-BLEB BLUY BOSF BOVW BPAH BSHC BSHD BTMO BVDD COLR FZZY JBJB OABC OBUD OBUY ODIY SNAX TCAN TWEY
_77A/C:_ G-BGOD BIGT BKOW BLSK BLTA BMYN BNGP BOCF BOGT BOHD BORA BORE BORT BPEZ BPFB BPJK BRLT BRVF BRVU BSCI BSUB BSUK BSZL
G-BTDS BTTS BTVH BTXB BTZR BTZS BUJH BUKS BULF BURG BUVB BUVE BUVS BUVT BUYO BUZF BVAX BXFN BXIE BYFX CURE DING DRAW DURX FLAGX
G-GGOW GOBT HOME HOTI HOTZ HRZN IMAG JONO LOWA LSHI MAUK MKAK OAWS OBJH OCAR ODAD OLPG ONCL ORON OSST READ RFIL SGAS SIXX TRUXX
G-UPPP UZLE WHAT WHIM WOOL WRIT EI-BGT
_90A:_ G-BLWE BMLU BOBU BPUW BRFF BRFH BRHG BRRU BSIU BTCS BTMH BTPV BVEI BXUW EXPR FOWL HWKR IRLY JNNB OBBC OLDV OMMM PEGG PHSIX
G-SAUF SEND TOFT
_105A:_ G-BLHK BLMZ BMBS BNAG BPZS BRUH BSBK BSCC BSHS BSNU BTAV BTHX BURL BUSV BWMA BWRM BXOV BXWO BYIO DYNG HSHS OFLI PLUG
G-RAIL TIKI USGB   _120A:_ G-BOJO BXAI BXCO BYDJ BYPV OBIB OCPS VYGR   _180A:_ G-BOGR BONK BSUU CUCU PICT

210A: G-BTYZ BUGN BULN BUXA BVSR ZEBR   240A: G-BNAP BVCZ BVVT IGLA LCIO   260A: G-HUGO   300A: G-RAPE
315A: G-KAUR VVBF   2500A: G-USUK
SPECIAL SHAPES

SHAPE	REGISTRATION(S)	SHAPE	REGISTRATIONS(S)
AGFA FILM CASSETTE	G-OHDC	HOP	G-MALT
APPLE	G-BRZV	HOT DOG	G-BVKG
ARIEL BOTTLE	G-BNHN	HUT	G-SMTC
BEER GLASS	G-BNHL PUBS	ICE CREAM CONE	G-BWBE BWBF OJHB
BIBENDUM	G-GRIP PNEU TRED	J & B WHISKEY BOTTLE	G-JANB
BLACK KNIGHT	G-BNMI	JUMBO JET	G-BRDP OVAA UMBO VJIM
BOTTLE	G-BOTL BVHU OAPB	KINDERMOND	G-BMUL
BUDWEISER CAN	G-BUET BVIO	MAXWELL HOUSE COFFEE JARS	G-BVBJ BVBK
CAN	G-BXPR	MICKEY MOUSE	G-BTRB
CHEESE	G-BRZU	MONTGOLFIERE	G-BPHV
CLOWN	G-GWIZ	OLD PARR WHISKY BOTTLE	G-PARR
COMPAC COMPUTERISED HEAD	G-HEAD	PANASONIC BATTERY	G-PSON
DRACHENFISCH	G-BMUJ	PAPER BAG	G-BNAH
EGG	G-BWWL	PIG	G-BUZS
FINANCIAL TIMES	G-ETFT FTFT	PIGGY BANK	G-BWBV BXVW
FIRE EXTINGUISHER	G-CHUB	SANTA CLAUS	G-HOHO
FLAME	G-BLKU	SATZENBRAU BOTTLE	G-BIRE
FLYING MITT	G-WCAT	SHUTTLECOCK	G-OOUT
FLYING YACHT	G-AXXJ	SKOL LAGER CAN	G-BTUN
GAS FLAME	G-BGOO	SNOWFLAKE	G-BNBP
GOLF BALL	G-BJUY	SPARKASSE BOX	G-BXKH
GORDON'S GIN BOTTLE	G-BUYG	STORK	G-BRGP
HAND	G-BUDM	UFO	G-BMUK
		WORLD	G-DHLI

COLTING _Ax7-77 HAFB:_ G-BHBB BLUE
COLOMBAN (including _ZENAIR_)
 MC.12/15 CRI-CRI: G-BOUT BWFO CRIC OCRI SHOG
COMMANDER - see ROCKWELL
COMMONWEALTH - see NORTH AMERICAN
COMPER _CLA.7 SWIFT:_ G-ABTC ABUS ACTF LCGL
CONSOLIDATED-VULTEE - see STINSON
CONVAIR _L-13A:_ G-BGHE
COOK _ARIES P:_ G-MYXI
CORBEN
 BABY ACE: G-BTSB BUAA   _JUNIOR ACE:_ G-BSDI
CORBY _CJ-1 STARLET:_ G-BVVZ ILSE
COSMOS _TRIKE:_ G-MVCK
COUGAR _(Wing):_ G-MMUJ
CRANFIELD _A.1-200 EAGLE:_ G-COAI
CRAWFORD _DHCA.1:_ G-DJIM
CREMER _HAFB:_ G-BIWH BJGL BJLX BJLY BJRP BJRR BJRV BJVB
CROSBY - see ANDREASSON
CUB PROSPECTOR - see PIPER
CULVER _LCA CADET:_ G-CDET
CURRIE (including TURNER)
 WOT: G-APNT ARZW ASBA AVEY AYMP AYNA BANV BDFB BEBO BFAH BFWD BGES BKCN BLPB BXMX CWBM CWOT MINI PFAP SWOT
CURTISS
 _JN-4D:_ G-ECAB   _ROBIN C.2:_ G-BTYY HFBM   _P-40 KITTYHAWK/TOMAHAWK:_ G-KITT TOMA
CURTISS-WRIGHT _TRAVEL AIR 12Q:_ G-AAOK
CUTLASS - see SKYHOOK
CVJETKOVIC _CA-65 SKYFLY HAFB:_ G-BWBG
CYCLONE AIRSPORTS- see AERIAL ARTS/CHARGUS/PEGASUS AVIATION/SOLAR WINGS (AVIATION)
 70 (Trike): G-MMYL MNMY
 _AX3:_ G-BUTC BVJG BVRY MGRW MYFI MYFV MYFW MYFY MYFZ MYGD MYHG MYHH MYHJ MYHM MYHR MYIJ MYIU MYKA MYKF MYKT MYME MYMF MYMW MYMZ
G-MYOY MYPM MYPR MYRO MYRU MYRV MYSO MYTM MYUI MYVN MYXH MYYL MYZC MYZF MYZG MZDO MZDS ZELE
 _AX2000:_ G-BYJM JONY MGUN MYER MZER MZFA MZFX MZGA MZGB MZGC MZGM MZGP MZHR MZIV MZJF MZJL MZJR MZKC MZLS MZLU MZMX MZOE OAJB
G-ROMW   _Cyclone (Wing):_ G-MBOK   _TS.440 (Wing):_ G-MBDU   _VORTEX (Wing):_ G-MJWH   _TITAN 38 (Trike):_ G-MBDU MBEV MYZH
CZL _AERO 45/145:_ G-APRR ATBH AYLZ

DALOTEL _DM-165 VIKING:_ G-BILA

DART _KITTEN:_ G-AEXT

<u>DASSAULT</u>
 <u>FALCON 20/200:</u> G-BGOP FFRA FRAD FRAE FRAF FRAH FRAI FRAJ FRAK FRAL FRAM FRAO FRAP FRAR FRAS FRAT FRAU FRAW FRBA
 <u>FALCON 900:</u> G-EVES GPWH MLTI JCBG OPWH   <u>FALCON 2000:</u> G-GEDI JCBI PYCO
<u>DAVIS</u> <u>DA-2:</u> G-BPFL
<u>DE HAVILLAND</u> - see <u>AIRCO/HAWKER SIDDELEY AVIATION</u> & including <u>FFW/MORANE/MOTH CORPORATION</u> production
 <u>DH.51:</u> G-EBIR   <u>DH.53 HUMMING BIRD:</u> G-EBHX EBQP
 <u>DH.60/60G/60M/60X MOTH:</u> G-AAAH AACD AADR AAEG AAHI AAHY AAMX AALY AAMY AANF AANL AANO AANV AAOR AAWO ABAG ABDX ABEV ABSD ABW
 G-ATBL EBLV EBWD EBZN   <u>DH.60GIII MOTH MAJOR:</u> G-ABZB ACXB ADHD ACGZ BVNG   <u>DH.71 TIGER MOTH:</u> G-ECDX
 <u>DH.80A PUSS MOTH:</u> G-AAZP ABLS AEOA
 <u>DH.82A TIGER MOTH:</u> "G-ABUL" ACDA ACDC ACDI ACDJ ACMD ADGT ADGV ADIA ADJJ ADNZ ADPC ADWJ ADWO ADXT AFGZ AFVE AFWI AGEG AGHY
 G-AGNJ AGPK AGYU AGZZ HAAN AHIZ AHLT AHMN AHOO AHPZ AHUF AHUV AHVU AHVV AIDS AIRI AIRK AIVW AIXJ AJHS AJHU AJOA AJTW AJVE AK
 G-AKXS ALBD ALIW ALJL ALNA ALND ALRI ALTW ALUC ALVP ALWS ALWW AMBB AMCK AMCM AMHF AMIU AMNN AMTF AMTK AMTV AMVS ANCS ANCX AN
 G-ANDM ANDP ANEH ANEJ ANEL ANEM ANEN ANEW ANEZ ANFC ANFI ANFL ANFM ANFP ANFV ANFW ANHK ANIX ANJA ANJD ANJK ANKK ANKT ANKV AN
 G-ANLD ANLH ANLS ANLX ANMY ANNB ANNE ANNG ANNI ANNK ANNN ANOO ANOH ANON ANON ANOO ANOR ANPC ANPE ANPK ANRF ANRM AN
 G-ANRX ANSM ANTE ANZU ANZZ AOAA AOBH AOBO AOBX AODT AOEI AOEL AOES AOET AOGI AOGR AOHY AOIL AOIM AOIS AOJJ AOJK AOUR AOZH AP
 G-APAM APAO APAP APBI APCC APFU APGL APIH APJO APLU APMX APPN ARAZ AREH ARTL ASKP ASPV AVPJ AXAN AXBW AXBZ AXXV AYDI AYIT AZ
 G-AZGZ AZZZ BAFG BBRB BEWN BFHH BHLT BHUM BJAP BJZF BMPY BNDW BPAJ BPHR BRHW BTOG BUJY BWIK BWMK BWMS BWVT BXMN BYLB BYTN DH
 G-DHZF EMSY ERDS ISIS MOTH OOSY PWBE TIGA EI-AHI EI-ANN EI-AOP EI-AWP
 <u>DH.82B QUEEN BEE:</u> G-BLUZ   <u>DH.83/C FOX MOTH:</u> G-ACCB ACEJ AOJH   <u>DH.84 DRAGON:</u> G-ACET ACIT EI-ABI
 <u>DH.85 LEOPARD MOTH:</u> G-ACLL ACMA ACMN ACOJ ACUS AIYS APKH
 <u>DH.87B HORNET MOTH:</u> G-ADKC ADKK ADKM ADLY ADMT ADND ADNE ADOT ADRH ADSK ADUR AELO AESE AHBL AHBM
 <u>DH.88 COMET:</u> G-ACSP ACSS
 <u>DH.89A DRAGON RAPIDE:</u> G-ACYR ACZE ADAH AEML AGJG AGSH AGTM AHAG AHED AHGD AIDL AIUL AIYR AJBJ AJCL AKDW AKIF AKOE AKRP ALAX
 G-ALXT   <u>DH.90 DRAGONFLY:</u> G-AEDT AEDU   <u>DH.94 MOTH MINOR:</u> G-AFNG AFNI AFOB AFOJ AFPN
 <u>DH.98 MOSQUITO:</u> G-ASKC AWJV MOSI   <u>DH.100 VAMPIRE:</u> G-DHXX FBIX MKVI SWIS
 <u>DH.104 DOVE/DEVON:</u> G-AHRI ALCU ALFT ALFU AMXT ANAP ANDX ANOV ANUW ANVU APSO ARBE ARBH ARDE AREA ARHW ARHX ARJB AVVF BLRN BVX
 G-DEVN DHDV DVON HBBC KOOL NAVY OEWA OPLC RNAS SDEV EI-BJW
 <u>DH.106 COMET:</u> G-ALYW ALYX AOJT APAS APDB APMB APYD BDIW BDIX   <u>DH.110 SEA VIXEN:</u> G-CVIX VIXN
 <u>DH.112 VENOM:</u> G-BLID BLKA BLSD DHSS DHTT DHUU GONE VENI VENM VICI VNOM
 <u>DH.114 HERON:</u> G-ANUO ANXB AORG AOTI HRON   <u>DH.115 VAMPIRE TRAINER:</u> G-DHAV DHVV DHWW DHYY DHZZ DUSK HELV OBLN VMPR VTII
 <u>DH.121 TRIDENT</u> - see <u>HAWKER SIDDELEY</u>
 <u>DH.125</u> - see <u>HAWKER SIDDELEY</u>
<u>DE HAVILLAND (AUSTRALIA)</u> <u>DHA.3 DROVER:</u> G-APXX
<u>DE HAVILLAND (CANADA)</u> - including <u>BOMBARDIER</u> production
 <u>DHC.1 CHIPMUNK:</u> G-AKDN ALWB AMUF ANWB AOFE AOJR AOJZ AORW AOSF AOSK AOSO AOSU AOSY AOTD AOTF AOTR AOTY AOUO AOUP AOZP APLO
 G-APPA APPM APYG ARGG ARMB ARMC ARMD ARMF ARMG ARWB ATHD ATVF BAPB BARS BAVH BBMN BBMO BBMR BBMT BBMV BBMW BBMX BBMZ BBNA BE
 G-BBND BBRV BBSS BCAH BCCX BCEY BCGC BCHL BCHV BCIH BCIW BCKN BCOI BCOO BCOU BCOY BCPU BCRX BCSA BCSB BCSL BCXN BCYJ BCYM BC
 G-BDBP BDCC BDDD BDET BDEU BDRJ BFAW BFAX BFDC BHRD BNZC BPAL BTWF BVBT BVTX BVWP BVZZ BWHI BWJY BWJZ BWMX BWNK BWNT BWOX BW
 G-BWTO BWUN BWUT BWUV BWVY BWVZ BXCP BXCT BXCV BXDA BXDG BXDH BXDI BXDM BXDP BXEC BXGL BXGM BXGO BXGP BXGX BXHA BXHF BXIA BX
 G-BXNN BYHL BYSJ CHPY CPMK DHCC DHCI HAPY JAKE MAJR OACP PVET TRIC ULAS
 <u>DHC.2 BEAVER:</u> G-BUCJ BVER   <u>DHC.6 TWIN OTTER:</u> G-BIHO BVVK   <u>DHC.7 DASH SEVEN:</u> G-BRYA BRYD
 <u>DHC.8 DASH EIGHT:</u> G-BRYH BRYI BRYJ BRYM BRYO BRYP BRYR BRYS BRYT BRYU BRYV BRYW BRYY BRYX BRYZ BXPZ JEDA JEDB JEDC JEDD JEDX
 G-JEDY NVSA NVSB NVSC EI-CBJ EI-CHP
<u>DEMON</u> - see <u>HIWAY</u>
<u>DENNEY</u> <u>KITFOX:</u> G-BNYX BONY BPII BPKK BRCT BSAZ BSCG BSCH BSCM BSES BSFX BSFY BSGG BSHK BSIF BSIK BSLJ BSMO BSRT BSSF BSUZ BS
 G-BTAT BTBG BTBN BTDC BTDN BTFA BTIF BTIP BTIR BTKD BTMT BTMX BTNR BTOL BTSV BTTY BTVC BTWB BUDR BUIC BUKF BUKP BULZ BU
 G-BUOL BUPW BUWS BUYK BUZA BVAH BVCT BVEY BVGO BWAR BWHV BWSJ BWSN BWWZ BWYI BXCW BXWH CJUD CRES CTOY DJNH ELIZ EYAS FOXC FO
 G-FOXE FOXG FOXI FOXS FOXX FOXZ FSHA HOBO HUTT KAWA KFOX KITF KITY LACR LEED LESJ LEZJ LOST OFOX OPDS PHYL PPPP RAYA RWSS RS
 G-RWSS TFOX
<u>DEPERDUSSIN</u> <u>MONOPLANE:</u> G-AANH
<u>DESIGNABILITY</u> - see <u>JORDAN</u>
<u>DESOUTTER</u> <u>DESOUTTER 1:</u> G-AAPZ
<u>DEWOITINE</u> <u>D.27:</u> F-AZJD
<u>DIAMOND</u> - see <u>HOAC</u>
<u>DORNIER</u> - see <u>BUCKER</u>
 <u>DO.27:</u> G-BMFG BNMK   <u>DO.28/SKYSERVANT:</u> G-ASUR BWCO BXTK   <u>228:</u> G-BMMR BUXT MAFE MAFI OMAF   <u>328:</u> G-BWIR BWWT BYHG BYMK BYML BY
<u>DORRINGTON</u> <u>SKYCYCLE D2:</u> G-BUOP
<u>DOUGLAS</u> see <u>McDONNELL DOUGLAS</u>
 <u>AD-4 SKYRAIDER:</u> G-RAID
 <u>DC-3/C-47 DAKOTA/SKYTRAIN:</u> G-ALWC AMCA AMHJ AMPO AMPP AMPY AMPZ AMRA AMSN AMSV AMYJ ANAF APML BGCG BHUB BVOL DAKK DAKS EI-AYM
 <u>DC-6:</u> G-APSA SIXC   <u>DC-8:</u> EI-BNA EI-CGO
<u>DR 107 ONE DESIGN:</u> G-IDDI
<u>DRAGON</u> <u>77 HAFB:</u> G-BKRZ
<u>DRAGON</u> <u>Srs 150/200:</u> G-MJSL MJUZ MJVY MMAC MMAE MMAI MMML MMNH MMPR MNJF
<u>DRAGONFLY</u> <u>MPA:</u> G-BDFU
<u>DRAGONFLY</u> <u>250:</u> G-MJLK
<u>DRAYTON</u> <u>B-56 HAFB:</u> G-BITS
<u>DRUINE</u> (including <u>ROLLASON</u> production)
 <u>D.5 TURBI:</u> G-AOTK APBO APFA
 <u>D.31 TURBULENT:</u> G-AJCP APIZ APNZ APOL APTZ APUY APVN APVZ APWP ARBZ AREZ ARGZ ARIM ARJZ ARLZ ARMZ ARNZ ARRU ARRZ ASDB ASFX
 G-ASHT ASMM ASPU ASSY ASTA ATBS AVPC AWBM AWDO AWFR AWMR AWWT BFXG BGBF EGMA BKXR BLTC BRIZ BUKH BVLU BWID OJJF

D.62 CONDOR: G-ARHZ ARVZ ASEU ASRB ASRC ATAU ATAV ATOH ATUG ATVW AVAW AVEX AVJH AVKM AVMB AVOH AVXW AWAT AWEI AWFN AWFO AWFP
G-AWSN AWSP AWSS AWST AXGS AXGU AXGV AXGZ AYFC AYFD AYFE AYFF AYFG AYZS BADM BUOF OPJH YNOT EI-BCP EI-BXT
DYN'AERO _MCR-01 BAN-BI:_ G-BYEZ BYTM CUTE LMLV PGAC POOP TBEE

E_{AA}

ACROSPORT: G-BJHK BKCV BLCI BPGH BPKI BSHY BTAK BTWI BVVL OJDA VCIO
BIPLANE: G-ATEP AVZW AYFY BBMH BPUA BRUU PFAA FFAY
EAGLE - see AMERICAN AEROLIGHTS
EAVES (EUROPEAN) _HAFB:_ G-BJDK BJFB BJFC BJGF BJGG BJIC BJJE BJMI BJRB BJRC BJRD BJTW FYBP FYDC FYDN FYEL FYFA FYFG FYFH FYFI
ECLIPSE _SUPER EAGLE:_ G-BGWZ
EDGAR PERCIVAL (including LANCASHIRE AIRCRAFT production)
EP.9 PROSPECTOR: G-APWZ APXW ARDG
EDGLEY (including BROOKLANDS/FLS/OPTICA production)
OPTICA: G-BMPF BMPL BOPM BOPN BOPO BOPR TRAK
EDWARDS _HELICOPTER:_ G-ASDF
EH INDUSTRIES _EH-101:_ G-EHIL
EIPPER _QUICKSILVER:_ G-MBBM MBCK MBFO MBYM MJAM MJBI MJBT MJCL MJDU MJDW MJFH MJHU MJHX MJIR MJJB MJJK MJKH MJNV MJPV MJUJ MJVP
G-MJVT MJVU MJZL MMBU MMCG MMEG MMIL MMMG MMNB MMNC MMND MMSE MMWC MMYR MNCO MTDO MWDZ MYBH EI-BKS EI-BLE EI-BLN EI-BOH EI-BPP
EIRI _PIK-20E:_ G-BGZL BHFR BHIJ BHNP OCAT OFJC OPIK POPE SOAR
EKW _C-3605:_ G-DORN
ELECTRAFLYER - see AMERICAN AEROLIGHTS
ELISPORT _CH-7 ANGEL:_ G-HALO
ELMWOOD _CA-05 CHRISTAVIA:_ G-MRED
EMBRAER
EMB-110 BANDEIRANTE: G-BGYT FLTY LOOT OBPL OCSI OFLT OHIG TABS
EMB-145: G-EMBA EMBB EMBC EMBD EMBE EMBF EMBG EMBH EMBI EMBJ EMBK EMBL EMBM EMBN EMBO ERJA ERJB RJXA RJXB RJXC RJXD
ENGLISH ELECTRIC
WREN: G-EBNV   _CANBERRA:_ G-BURM BVIC BVXC BXOD   _LIGHTNING:_ G-BTSY
ENSIGN _CROSSLEY RACER:_ G-BKRU
ENSTROM
_F-28:_ G-BAAU BAWI BBIH BBIN BBPM BBPN BBPO BBXO BBZS BDKD BHAX BONG BPPL BRZG BSHX BSHZ BURI BWOV BXLV BXLW BXLX BXXB BYKF
G-BZHI DICE MHCE MHCJ OABO SCOX SERA SNAZ WSEC
280C SHARK/280FX: G-BEYA BGWS BIBJ BPXE BRPO BSDZ BSIE BSLV BWSK BXEE BXFD BXRD CKCK COLL DDOD ECHO GKAT HDIX HYST IDUP MEYO
G-MHCB MHCD MHCF MHCG MHCH MHCI MHCK MHCL OITV OJBB ONUP OPDM OTHE PALS PBYY REFI SHAA SHNN SHRK SHSS SHUU SOPP TOYS VETS WRFM
G-WSKY EI-BSD   _480:_ G-BWMD GUAY HADA IGHH IJBB LADD LIVR OGHH OSKP OZAR PBTT PPAH WOOF
ERCOUPE (including ALON/FORNEY production)
_415:_ G-ARHB ARHC ARHF AROO ASNF AVIL AVTT BKIN COUP EGHB ERCO HARY ONHH EI-AUT EI-CGG EI-CIH
EUROCOPTER - see AEROSPATIALE/SUD AVIATION/MBB
_EC.120:_ G-BXYD CBNB ECZZ IGPW YSON   _EC.135:_ G-BXXV CCAU CHSU EMAS HDDP NESV NWPS
EUROPA AVIATION _EUROPA:_ G-BVGF BVIZ BVJN BVKF BVLH BVLV BVOS BVOW BVRA BVUV BVVH BVVP BVWM BWCV BWDP BWDX BWEG BWFH BWFX BWGH
G-BWIJ BWIV BWJH BWKG BWNL BWON BWRO BWUP BWVS BWWB BWYD BWRA BWZT BXCH BXDY BXEF BXFG BXGG BXHY BXII BXIJ BXLK BXLZ BXNC BXOB
G-BXTD BXUM BYFG BYIK BYPM BYJI BYPK BYSA BZAM CHAV CHEB CHET CHUG CROY CUTY DAMY DAYI DAYS DLCB DONZ DRMM EENI EESA EIKY EMIN
G-EMSI EOFS EORJ FELL FIZY FLOR FLOX FLYT GBXS HOFC IBBS INAV IOWE IVET JOST JULZ KIMM KITS KWIP LABS LACE LAMM MFHI MIME MKPU
G-MUZO NDOL NEAT NHRJ NIGL OBEV ODJG ODTW OEZY OGAN OJHL OKEV OMIK OPJK OSMT OURO OWWW PATF PATS PATZ PTAG PTYE PUDS RATZ RBBB
G-RICS RMAC ROBD RONA ROOV ROPA ROWI SAMY SHSH SMDH SSGS SYCO TERN TKAY VPSJ WUFF WWWG XSDJ YURO ZORO ZTED EI-COE
EUROWING _GOLDWING:_ G-MBDG BMFZ MBJA MBON MBPM MBPX MBZH MJAJ MJAY MJDP MJEG MJOE MJPO MJRL MJRO MJRS MJRV MJSY MJUT MJUU MJUY
G-MJWB MJWS MMBN MMLE MMTZ MMWL MNNS MNZU EI-BNF EI-CMK
EVANS
_VP-1:_ G-AYUJ AYXW BAAD BAFH BAJC BAPP BBPK BBXZ BCTT BDAH BDAR BDTB BDTL BDUL BEHJ BEIS BEKM BFAS BFHX BFJJ BGEE BGFK BGLF
G-BHKA BHMT BHYV BICT BIDD BIFO BINO BKFI BLCW BLKK BLWT BMJM BVAM BVEL BVJU BVPI BVUT BWFJ PFAG PFAH PFAO PFAW ROSE TEDY
EI-AYY EI-BBD EI-BLU EI-BRU
_VP-2:_ G-BCVE BEFV BEHX BEVP BEYN BFFB BFYL BGFC BGPM BHUO BHXL BHZF BJVC BJZB BMSC BPBB BTAZ BTHJ BTSC BUGI BUKZ BVPM BXOC
G-RASC VPII EI-BNJ EI-BVT
EVERETT - see CAMPBELL
GYROPLANE: G-BIPI BKPK BMZN BMZP BMZS BOUU BOUX BSJW BSRL BTMV BTVB BUAI BUZC BWCK LAXY MICY OFRB OGOS ULPS
EXPERIENCE _TRIKE:_ G-MYLU
EXPERIMENTAL AVIATION _BERKUT:_ G-REDX
EXTRA
_EA.230/260:_ G-EXTR XTRA   _EA.300:_ G-EXEA HIII IICM IITI IIZI MIII SIII XTRS

F_{AIRCHILD} _24/ARGUS:_ G-AIZE AJOZ AJPI AJSN BCBH BCBL FANC LEPF RGUS

FAIREY
FLYCATCHER: G-BEYB   _FIREFLY:_ G-ASTL   _FULMAR:_ G-AIBE   _GANNET:_ G-BMYP   _SWORDFISH:_ G-AJVH BMGC
ULTRA-LIGHT HELICOPTER: G-AOUJ OPJJ
FAIRTRAVEL - see PIEL
FALCONAR _F-9/F-11/F-12:_ G-AWHY AXDY AYEG BGHT ODEL TIMS WBTS
FARNELL _TRIKE:_ G-MJKO

FEWSDALE TIGERCRAFT _GYROPLANE:_ G-ATLH
FFA _AS.202 BRAVO:_ G-BNTE BNTF BNTH BNTI BNTJ BNTK BNTL BNTM BNTN BNTO
FFW - see DE HAVILLAND
FIAT _G.46:_ G-BBII
FIESELER STORCH - see MORANE-SAULNIER
 _MS.500:_ G-FIST
FISHER _FP202U KOALA/SUPER KOALA:_ G-BTBF BUVL MMTY
FLAGLOR _SKY SCOOTER:_ G-BDWE
FLEET _80 CANUCK:_ G-FLCA
FLEXIFORM - see MAINAIR
 HILANDER (Wing): G-MJAN   _SEALANDER (Wing):_ G-MBBY MBDJ MBGA MBIA MBLO MJFK MMFL MMGU
 STRIKER (Wing)/DUAL STRIKER: G-MBDE MBHK MBPZ MBWF MBZO MJER MJFB MJFI MJIA MJIC MJIF MJJO MJMN MJMX MJTP MJUM MJVN MJWI MJWN
 G-MJXX MJYP MJZO MJZU MMAL MMAN MMAX MMBS MMCJ MMCZ MMDK MMDN MMDT MMEJ MMFD MMFE MMFG MMFH MMFK MMFV MMGH MMGI MMHY MMJG MMKM
 G-MMMR MMMW MMNT MMPL MMPT MMRW MMWG MMWN MMWS MMYV MNZY MTFK EI-BPN   _TRIKE:_ EI-BRK
FLEXIWING _M17727:_ EI-BRT
FLS-(including TRAGO MILLS production)
 EDGLEY SPRINT: G-BVNU BXWU BXWV FLSI SAHI SCLX
FOCKE WULF - see PIAGGIO
 _FW.190:_ G-FOKW
FOKKER (including FAIRCHILD-HILLER production):
 D.VII: G-BFPL   _DR.1:_ G-ATJM BVGZ   _E.III:_ G-AVJO   _S.11 INSTRUCTOR:_ G-BEPV BIYU
 F-27 FRIENDSHIP/FH-227: G-BAUR BCDN BCDO BHMW BHMY BMXD BNCY BNIZ BVOB CEXA CEXB CEXD CEXE CEXF JEAD JEAE JEAF JEAH JEAI JEAP
 EI-CAZ EI-CLF
 _F.27-050:_ G-UKTA UKTB UKTC UKTD UKTE UKTF UKTG UKTH UKTI EI-FKC EI-FKD EI-FKE EI-FKF
 _F.28-0070:_ G-BVTE BVTF BVTG
 F.28-4000 FELLOWSHIP: G-BXRE
 _F.100-620/650:_ G-BVJA BVJB BVJC BVJD BXWE BXWF BYDN BYDO BYDP UKFA UKFB UKFC UKFD UKFE UKFF UKFG UKFH UKFI UKFJ UKFK UKFL UKFM
 G-UKFN UKFO UKFP UKFR
FOLLAND _GNAT:_ G-BVPP FRCE GNAT MOUR NAAT NATY RORI TIMM
FORNEY - see ERCOUPE
FOSTER-WIKNER _GM.1 WICKO:_ G-AFJB
FOUGA _CM-170 MAGISTER:_ EI-BXO
FOURNER
 _RF3:_ G-ATBP AYJD BCWK BFZA BHLU BIIA BIPN BLXH BNHT
 _RF4D:_ G-AVHY AVKD AVLW AVNX AVNZ AVWY AWBJ AWEK AWEL AWEM AWGN AWLZ AYHY BHJN IIF BUPJ BXLN IVEL F-BMKC
 RF5/RF5B SPERBER: G-AYME AZJC AZPF AZRK AZRM BACE BEVO BJXK BLAA BPWK KCIG RFSB SSWV
 _RF6B:_ G-BKIF BLWH BOLC GANJ   _RF7:_ G-LTRF
FRED - see CLUTTON
FUJI _FA.200:_ G-BAPM BBGI BBNV BBRC BBZN BBZO BCFF BCKS BCKT BCNZ BDFR BDFS BEUK BFGO FUJI HAMI KARI KARY MCOX

G͟ADFLY _HDW-1:_ G-AVKE

GAERTNER _Ax4 SKYRANGER HAFB:_ G-BSGB
GARDAN (including CAB & BARRITAULT production):
 GY-20 MINICAB: G-ATPV AVRW AWEP AWUB AWWM AZJE BANC BBFL BCER BCNC BCPD BDGB BGKO BGMJ BGMR BRGW TATT VERA
 GY-80 HORIZON: G-ASJY ASZS ATGY ATJT AVMA AVRS AWAC AZAW AZRX AZYA BCVW BFAA BJAV BKNI BYBL BYME BYPE GYBO TIMY EI-AYB
GARDNER _T-M SCOUT:_ G-MJTD MTKM
GARLAND-BIANCHI - see PIEL
GATES _LEARJET:_ G-GJET HUGG JETG JETN LEAR LJET MURI OCFR RAFF ZENO
GAZEBO _AX6-65 HAFB:_ G-BCGP
GAZELLE - see SOUTHERN MICROLIGHT
GEMINI - see MAINAIR
GENERAL AIRCRAFT _GAL.42 CYGNET:_ G-AGBN
GENERAL AVIA _F22:_ G-FZZA RAJS
GLASER-DIRKS
 _DG-400:_ G-BLJD BLRM BNCN BNXL BPIN BPXB BRTW BYTG SBOM DGDG DGLM DIRK HAJJ INCA LEES OAPW ORTM
 _DG-500M:_ G-BRRG SOOM   _DG-600:_ G-KOFM   _DG-800:_ G-BVJK BXBSH BXUI BYEC DGIV MSIX ORIG
GLOBE _GC-1B SWIFT:_ G-AHUN ARNN
GLOSTER - including ARMSTRONG-WHITWORTH production
 GLADIATOR: G-AMRK GLAD   _METEOR:_ G-ARCX BPOA BWMF JETM LOSM METE
GOLDMARQUE _GYR (Wing):_ G-MJKO
GOULD _Mk.1:_ G-OULD
GOULD-TAYLORCRAFT - see TAYLORCRAFT
GRANGER _ARCHEOPTERYX:_ G-ABXL
GRASSHOPPER including SERVOTEC
 GRASSHOPPER: G-ARVN AWRP AXFM AZAU
GREAT LAKES see OLDFIELD
 2T-1A SPORT TRAINER: G-BIIZ BUPV
GREEN _S-25 HAFB:_ G-BSON
GREGA - see PIETENPOL

GREGORY *FREE SPIRIT:* G-FSII
GRIFFITHS *GH.4:* G-ATGZ
GROB
  G-109: G-BIXZ BJVK BJZX BLMG BLUV BMCG BMFY BMGR BMLK BMLL BMMP BRCG BXSP BXXG BYJH CHAR DKDP IPSI KEMC LULU NDGC SAGA SAMG
  G-TACK UILD WAVE EI-HCS
  G-115/HERON/TUTOR: G-BOPT BOPU BPKF BVHC BVHD BVHE BVHF BVHG BYDB BYFD BYUA BYUB BYUC BYUD BYUE BYUF BYUG BYUH BYUI BYUJ BYUK
  G-BYUL BYUM BYUN BYUO BYUP BYUR BYUS BYUT BYUU BYUV BYUW BYUX BYUY BYUZ BYVA BYVB BYVC BYVD BYVE BYVF BYVG BYVH BYVI BYVJ BYVK
  G-BYVL BYVM BYVN BYVO BYVP BYVR BYVS BYVT BYVU BYVV BYVW BYVX BYVY BYVZ BYWA BYWB BYWC BYWD BYWE BYWF BYWG BYWH BYWI BYWJ
  G-BYWK BYWL BYWM BYWN BYWO BYWP BYWR BYWS BYWT BYWU BYWV BYWW BYWX BYWY BYWZ BYXA BYXB BYXC BYXD BYXE BYXF BYXG BYXH BYXI BYXJ
  G-BYXK BYXL BYXM BYXN BYXO BYXR BYXS BYXT BYXX BYXY BYXZ BYYA BYYB MERF RAFA RAFB TAYI WIZB EI-CAC EI-CAE EI-CCD
GRUMMAN
  F-6F HELLCAT: G-BTCC   *F-7F TIGERCAT:* G-RUMT   *F-8F BEARCAT:* G-RUMM   *FM-2 WILDCAT:* G-RUMW   *TBM-3 AVENGER:* G-BTDP
  G.44 WIDGEON: G-DUCK   *G-159 GULFSTREAM I:* G-BNCE
  G-1159 GULFSTREAM II/III/IV/V: G-DNVT HARF EI-CMF CNP CRY CUB CYM
GRUMMAN-AMERICAN (including AMERICAN AVIATION, AMERICAN-GENERAL & GULFSTREAM-AMERICAN production)
  AA-1 YANKEE/TRAINER/LYNX: G-AYFX AYHA AYLP AZKS BBFC BBWZ BCIL BCLW BDLS BDNW BDNX BERY BEXN BFOJ BTLP RUMN SEXY EI-CCY
  AA-5/AG-5 TRAVELER/CHEETAH/TIGER: G-AZMJ AZVG BAFA BAJN BAJO BAOU BASG BASH BAVR BAVS BBBI BBCZ BBDL BBDM BBLS BBRZ BBSA BBUE
  G-BBUF BCCJ BCCK BCEE BCEF BCEO BCEP BCIJ BCIK BCLI BCLJ BCPN BCRR BDCL BDFY BDLO BDLR BEBE BEZC BEZF BEZG BEZH BEZI BFIJ BFIN
  G-BFLW BFLX BFPB BFTF BFTG BFVS BFXW BFXX BFZO BGCM BGFG BGFI BGPH BGPK BGVV BGVW BGVY BHKV BHLX BHZK BHZO BIAY BIBT BIPA BIPV
  G-BIVV BIWW BJAJ-BJDO BKPS BLFW BLSF BMYI BNVB BOXU BOZO BOZZ BPIZ BSTR BTII BTUZ BXCY BXCZ BXHH BXOO BXOX BXTT BYDX CCAT CCOL
  G-CHTA DAVO DINA DOEA DONI ERRY ESTE GAJB GIRY GOCC IDEA IFLI IRIS JAZZ JENN JUDY JWDG KINE LSFI MALC MELD MILY MOGI MSTC NASH
  G-NODE NODY NONI OABR OBMW OCAM ODAM OECH OMOG OPPL OPWK OSTC OSTU PAWS PENN PING PORK PROP PURR RATE REEK RICA RICO ROWL RUBB
  G-TGER TYGA WINK WMTM ZARI ZERO EI-AYD EI-BJS EI-BMV EI-BNR
  GA-7 COUGAR: G-BGNV BGON BGSY BLHR BOGS BOOE BOXR CYMA EENY FLII GABD GENN GOTC HIRE OOGA OOGI OOGO REAT SHIV TANI
GRYPHON SAILWINGS - see WASP/WILLGRESS
  GRYPHON: G-MJGO MMYC
GS *TRIKE:* G-MJHR
GUIDO: G-BJSP
GULFSTREAM-AMERICAN - see GRUMMAN-AMERICAN
GYROFLIGHT - see BROOKLAND
GYROSCOPIC ROTORCRAFT *GYROPLANE:* EI-COG

H

ADLAND *WILLOW:* G-MMMH

HALLAM *FLECHE:* G-FLCT
HANDLEY PAGE see BAe
  0/400 Rep: G-BKMG   *HP.39 GUGNUNC:* G-AACN   *HP.81 HERMES:* G-ALDG
HANDLEY PAGE (READING)
  HPR.7 DART HERALD: G-APWA APWJ ASKK ASVO ATDS ATIG AVEZ AVPN BAZJ BBXJ BEYF BEYK CEAS CEXP GNSY SCTT STVN
HAPI *CYGNET SF-2A:* G-BRZD BWFN BXCA BXHJ BYYC CYGI
HARKER *DH/WASP:* G-MJSZ
HATZ *CB-1:* G-BRSY BXXH HATZ TIKO
HAWKER - see W.A.R & including CCF production
  CYGNET: G-CAMM EBJI EBMB   *AUDAX:* G-BVVI   *DEMON:* G-BTVE   *FURY (Biplane):* G-BKBB   *TOMTIT:* G-AFTA   *HART:* G-ABMR
  HIND: G-AENP   *NIMROD:* G-BURZ BWWK   *HURRICANE:* G-AMAU BKTH BWHA BYDL HURI HURR HURY KAMM ROBT TDTW TWTD
  TEMPEST: G-BSHW PEST TEMT   *FURY/SEA FURY:* G-AGHB BTTA BUCM BWOL EEMV
  HUNTER: G-BNCX BUEZ BVGH BVMB BVVC BWAF BWFR BWFS BWFT BWGK BWGL BWGM BWGN BWIU BWKB BWOU BXFI BXKF BXNZ EGHH FFOX GAII HNTR
  G-HPUX HVIP KAXF PRII PSST SIAL TVII VETA
HAWKER SIDDELEY AVIATION: (see AVRO and including DE HAVILLAND/BAe/RAYTHEON HAWKER production):
  HS.121 TRIDENT: G-ARPH ARPK ARPO ARPP ARPZ AVFB AVFE AVFG AVFJ AVFK AVFM AVYE AWZI AWZJ AWZK AWZM AWZO AWZS AWZU AWZX AWZZ
  HS.125: G-ARYB ARYC ASNU ASSM ATPD AWYE AXDM BGYR BLSM BLTP BMIH BOCB BTAB BWSY BYHM DBAL DEZC ETOM FANN GDEZ HCFR ICFR IFTC
  G-IFTE JETI LORI NCFR OCAA OHEA OJPB OLDD OMGD OMGE OWDB RCEJ SUFC SVLB TACE TCAP TCDI TSAM VIPI WBPR XRMC YUGO EI-COV EI-RRR
  EI-WDC   *HARRIER:* G-VTOL
HEAD *Ax8-105 HAFB:* G-UKUK
HEATH *PARASOL:* G-AFZE
HEINKEL *He 111 (CASA 2.111):* G-AWHB
HEINTZ *ZENITH/ZENAIR CH.200/250/300:* G-BIRZ BPTO BTXZ DUNN GFKY RAYS EI-BVY EI-BYL
HELIO *SUPER COURIER:* G-BAGT BGIX
HELTON *LARK 95:* G-LARK
HILL - see MAXAIR
HILLER *UH-12 (360):* G-APKY ASAZ ASTP ATKG BBAZ BEDK
HINDUSTAN *PUSHPAK:* G-AVPO BXTO
HISPANO - see MESSERSCHMITT
HIWAY
  DEMON (Wing): G-MBAL MBDD MBEU MBFK MBFU MBIT MBPU MBTE MBUA MBVV MBXJ MBZA MJAV MJDJ MJDR MJHM MJHV MJKF MJMA MJMD MJMT MJNK
  G-MJNT MJOU MJPE MJRP MJSO MJXE MJXY MJYY MMEI MMHD MMHP MMLH MMNW MMRH MMTD MNCA MNME MTHD MWXE MYBN EI-BPU EI-BRV
  EI-CGE   *EXCALIBUR (Wing):* G-MBAA
  SKYTRIKE: G-MBAA MBCI MBCL MBDD MBFK MBGP MBGW MBIA MBIT MBJF MBJS MBKZ MBLM MBPU MBTE MBVS MBVV MBXF MBXJ MJAN MJAP MJAV MJCW
  G-MJDJ MJDR JMHV MJMA MJMD MJMS MJMT MJMU MJNK MJNT MJOU MJPE MJPP MJSO MJUM MJXY MJYY MMBJ MMBS MMCV MMEF MMEI MMHK MMHL MMHP
  G-MMLH MMOO MMRH MMUR MNME MYBN EI-BMW EI-BNH EI-BRV

483

SUPER SCORPION (Wing): G-MBGW MBVS MJCW MMEF MMHK MMHL   *VULCAN (Wing):* G-MBIZ MJAP MMRY EI-BMW

HOAC (including <u>DIAMOND</u> production)
DV-20 KATANA: G-BWEH BWFD BWFE BWFI BWFV BWGY BWGZ BWIO BWLP BWLS BWLT BWLV BWPY BWTA BWYM BXBW BXGH BXJV BXJW BXMZ BXOF BXPB
G-BXPC BXPD BXPE BXTP BXTR BXTS BYFL BYMB KATA OBDA OSFA RIBS EI-CLA

HOFFMANN *H.36 DIMONA/HK.36 SUPER DIMONA:* G-BKPA BLCV BNUX BXGI BYRL IMOK KOKL LIDA LIDR LYDA OMDG OMRG EI-CRV

HORIZON *1:* G-DOGZ

HORNET
Trike: G-MBCX MBHJ MBJL MJDA MJIB MJWN MMHD MMNM   *INVADER (Trike):* G-MMHY MMMW
DUAL TRAINER/RAVEN (Combi): G-MNRI MNRJ MNRK MNRL MNRM MTDA MTGX MTHU MTJX MTMP MTMR MTRK MTRL MTXE MTXY MVHZ
R/RS (Combi): G-MVUR MVUU MVYG MVYH MVYI MVYJ MVYK MVYL MVYM MVYN MVYO MVZW MWBH MWBM MWBN MWBP MWBR MWBS MWBU MWBW MWBX MWBY
G-MWBZ MWCA MWDE MWDF MWDI MWEU MWEV mwey MWKE MWKF

HOVEY
BETA BIRD: G-BMOX   *HOVEY DELTA BIRD:* EI-BRW   *WD-II/III WHING DING:* G-MBAB MBTS MNVO

HOWARD *SPECIAL T-MINUS:* G-BRXS

HOWES *Ax6 HAFB:* G-BDWO

HUGHES (including <u>SCHWEIZER</u> (269) & <u>McDONNELL DOUGLAS</u> (369) production)
269 (Srs 300): G-BATT BAUK BAXE BMWA BOVX BOVY BOXT BPJB BPPW BPPY BRFP BRTT BSML BSVR BUEX BWAV BWDV BWNJ BWWJ BWZJ BXHI BXMY
G-BXRP BXTL BXUP ECLI GINZ GIRO HFLA IBHH HAS JMDI LEMJ MARE OCJK OGOB OJAE OSLO OZAP PKPK PLOW PLPC REBL RHCB RIFB ROCR SAND
G-SHCB SHPP STEP WARK WHRL XALP ZAPS ZBHH EI-LRS EI-VIP
369 (Srs 500): G-AYIA AZVM BPLZ BRTL BTRP CSPJ DADS DIZZ DRAR ERIS GASC GEEE HAUS HKHM HSOO IDWR JETZ LIBS LINC LOGO MRAJ NIPY
G-OMDH OSOO OTDB ROMA SIVA SOOC SOOE SSCL STEF SWEL TRUE VICE

HUNT *WING/AVON/EXPERIENCE:* G-MGTR MGUX MMGT MNCA MWPT MYFG MYPO MYTV MYUG MYUR MYUT MYWE MYWH MYYE MYYJ MYYT MZCX MZCZ MZDZ
G-MZFE MZFF MZGH MZLB MZLK EI-CKG

HUNTAIR *PATHFINDER:* G-MBWG MBYK MBYL MJBZ MJDE MJDH MJFM MJJA MJOC MJTY MJUV MJWK MJXS MMBV MMCB MMDR MMWB

HUNTING - see <u>PERCIVAL</u> & including <u>BAC</u> production
P.84 JET PROVOST/BAC.145/167 STRIKEMASTER: G-AOBU AOHD AYHR BKOU BVEZ BVSP BVTC BWBS BWCS BWDR BWEB BWGF BWGS BWGT BWOF BWOT
G-BWSG BWSH BWUW BWZE BWZZ BXBH BXBI BXDL BXFP BXFS BXFU BXFV BXFW BXFX BYED JETP JPRO JPTV JPVA KNOT PROV RAFI SARK TOMG TORE
G-UNNY VIVM

HYBRED - see <u>MEDWAY</u>

I

AU-BACAU - see <u>YAKOVLEV</u>

ICA (<u>INTREPRINDEREA DE CONSTRUCTII AERONAUTICE</u>) *IS.28B2/M2:* G-BKAB BKXN BMMV BMOM BROM TODD

III (<u>INITIZIATIVE INDUSTRIALI ITALIAN</u>) *SKY ARROW:* G-BXGT BYCY BYZR CIAO ROME SKYG SKYT SUTN EI-CPX

IMCO - see <u>CALLAIR</u>

INTERAVIA *70TA HAFB:* G-BUUT

ISAACS
FURY: G-ASCM AYJY BBVO BCMT BEER BIYK BKFK BKZM BMEU BPWY BTPZ BWWN BZAS PFAR RODI   *SPITFIRE:* G-BBJI BXOM

J

ODEL - see <u>FALCONAR/ROBIN</u> & including <u>CEA</u> & <u>WASSMER</u> production)

D.9 BEBE (including D.92): G-AVPD AWFT AXKJ AXYU AZBL BAGF BDEI BDNT BGFJ BURE KDIX EI-BUC
D.11 (including D.112/D.117/D.119 & AERO D.1190S): G-ARDO ARNY ASJZ ASXY ATIN ATIZ ATJN ATWB AVPM AWFW AWMD AWVB AWVZ AWWI
G-AXAT AXCG AXCY AXFN AXHV AXTX AXWT AXXW AXZT AYBP AYBR AYCP AYEB AYGA AYHX AYKJ AYKK AYKT AYMU AYWH AYXP AZFF AZHC AZII AZKP
G-AZVL BAAW BAKR BAPR BARF BATJ BAUH BAZM BBPS BCGW BCLU BDBV BDDG BDIH BDJD BDMM BEDD BEZZ BFEH BFGK BFNG BFXR BGEF BGTX BGWO
G-BHCE BHEL BHFF BHHX BHKT BHNL BHNX BIAH BIDX BIEO BIOU BIPT BITO BIVB BIVC BIWN BIYW BIZY BJOT BKAO BKIR BMIP BOOH BPFD BRCA
G-BRVZ BVEH BVPS BVVE BWMB DAVE EI-BSB EI-CKX
D.18: G-BODT BPJN BRZO BSBP BSYA BTRZ BUAG BUPR BWVC BWVV BXFC HERS SHRL TREK WIBB EI-CKZ
D.120 PARIS-NICE: G-ASPF ASXU ATLV AVLY AVYV AXNJ AYGG AYLV AYRS AZEF AZGA AZLF BACJ BANU BCGM BDDF BDEH BDWX BFOP BGZY BHGJ
G-BHNK BHPS BHXD BHXS BHZV BICR BIEN BJFM BJOE BJYK BKAE BKCW BKCZ BKGB BKJS BKPX BMDS BMID BMLB BMYU BOWP BYBE DIZO UIDE
EI-CJS   *D.140 MOUSQUETAIRE:* G-ARDZ ARLX AROW ARRY ATKX AYFP BJOB BSPC BWAB DCXL OBAN REES TOAD
150 MASCARET/SUPER MASCARET: G-ASKL ASRT AVEF AZBI BACL BFEB BHEG BHEZ BHVF BIDG BKSS BLAT BLXO BMEH BVSS BVST DISO EDGE FARR
G-IEJH JDLI MASC OABB TIDS
DR.100/1050/M1/1051/M1 AMBASSADEUR SICILE/SICILE RECORD/EXCELLENCE: G-ARFT ARRD ARRE ARUH ARXT ASXS ATAG ATEV ATFD ATGE ATGP
G-ATHX ATIC ATJA ATLB ATWA AVGJ AVGZ AVHL AVJK AVOA AWEN AWUE AWVE AWWN AWWO AXLS AXSM AXUK AXUY AYEH AYEJ AYEV AYEW AYGD AYJA
G-AYKD AYLC AYLF AYLL AYUT AYYO AYYT AYZK AZAD AZOU AZWF BAEE BDMW BEAB BEYZ BFBA BGBE BGRI BHHE BHOL BHSY BHTC BHUE BIOI BKDX
G-BLKM BLRJ BLUL BPLH BTHH BTIW BXIO BXYJ BYCS BYFM IOSI JODL JWBB JWIV SPOG EI-ARW
DR.200: G-AYDZ   *DR.220/221 (2+2/DAUPHIN):* G-AVOM BANA BFHR BHRW BLCT BLLH BMKF BUTH CPCD GOSS RRCU STEV
DR.250: G-ATTM BCGG BJBO BKPE BSZF BUVM BXCG BYEH   *DR.253 REGENT:* G-AWYL AXWV AYUB BOSM BYHP
DR.315 PETIT PRINCE/DR.340 MAJOR/DR.360 CHEVALIER/KNIGHT/REMORQUEUR: G-AXDK AYCO AZIJ AZJN BGVB BICP BLAM BLGH BLHH BOEH BOZV
G-BVYG BVYM BXOU DRSV DRZF KIMB
JORDAN *DUET:* G-MBWH MJTO
JUNKERS *Ju.52/3m (CASA.352L):* G-BFHD BFHF
JURCA
MJ.2 TEMPETE: G-ASUS AYTV   *MJ.5 SIROCCO:* G-AZOS BFXM BUGC CLAX ORFC

K

K & S *SA.102.5 CAVALIER:* G-AZHH BCMJ BCRK BDKJ BDLY BJAN BUNJ BWSI   *JUNGSTER:* G-BLDC OWEN

KAY *GYROPLANE:* G-ACVA
KEN BROCK *KB-2:* G-BSEG BUYT BUZV BVMN BVUJ
KENSINGER *KF:* G-ASSV
KIS *CRUISER:* G-BYZD
KLEMM - see BA & BRITISH KLEMM
  L.25: G-AAUP AAXK   *KL.35:* G-BVXI BWRD
KNIGHT - see PAYNE
KOLB *TWINSTAR:* G-BUZT KOLB BYTA MWWM MYDP MYIK MYKB MYLN MYLP MYMI MYNY MYOG MYOO MYOR MYPC MYRA MYVA MYWP MYXS MZGJ MZKB MZZT
KRONFELD - see BAC

L

L A MOUETTE *PROFIL (Wing):* G-MVCK

LAFAYETTE *HI-NUSKIE:* G-MBWI
LAKE *LA-4/LA-250/BUCCANEER RENEGADE/SKIMMER:* G-BASO BOLL LAKE OSMR SKID EI-BUH EI-CEX
LANCAIR - see NEICO
LANCASHIRE AIRCRAFT - see EDGAR PERCIVAL
LANCASHIRE *MICRO-TRIKE:* G-MJXX MJYW MJZO MMFG MMPL
LATULIP *LM-3X:* N6FL
LAVERDA - see AVIAMILANO
LAVOCHKIN *LA-9:* G-BWUD
LAZAIR - see ULTRAFLIGHT
LAZER - see STEPHENS
LEDERLIN *380L LADYBUG:* G-AYMR
LEOPOLDOFF *L-6:* G-BYKS   *L-7:* G-AYKS
LET - see YAKOVLEV
  L-200A/D MORAVA: G-ASFD BNBZ   *Z-37 CMELAK:* G-AVZB KDLN
LETOV *LK-2M SLUKA:* G-BYLJ MYRP MYRR MYUP MYVG MYVT MYXO MZBF MZBK MZDX MZES MZFC MZGF MZLY MZNZ MZOI MZOT MZOX XPBI EI-CNA
LE VIER *COSMIC WIND:* G-ARUL BAER
LIGHT AERO *AVID FLYER/SPEEDWING/AEROBAT:* G-BSPW BTGL BTHU BTKG BTMS BTNP BTRC BUFV BUIR BUJJ BUJV BULC BULY BUON BUSZ BUZE BUZM
  G-BVAA BVBR BVBV BVFO BVHT BVIV BVLW BVSN BVYX BWCI BWLW BWRC BWZD BXNA EFRY ELKS FOLD IJAC IMPY LAPN LORT MOTT OVID OZEE PILL
  G-SPAM EI-CIM
LIGHTNING - see SOUTHDOWN
LILLIPUT *TYPE 1:* G-HONY
LINDSTRAND
Airship (Hot Air)
AS-2: G-BYPC   *HS-110:* G-BWLH HSTH TRIB
Balloon (Hot Air)
LBL-9: G-BVRP   *LBL-14:* G-BWBB BWEO BWER BXAJ BXEP   *LBL-21/RR-21:* G-BVRL BYEY OJNB UNRL
LBL-25 CLOUDHOPPER: G-BVUI BXHM BYYJ OLAW OOER   *LBL-31 AIR CHAIR:* G-BVOJ BWHD BXIZ BXUH ONCB   *LBL-42:* G-BWCG
LBL-56: G-COSY XWWF   *LBL-60:* G-OERR   *LBL-69:* G-BVDS BVGG BVIR BWLA BYKA LBLI
LBL-77: G-BUBS BUWI BUZR BVPV BVRR BWAW BWBO BWEP BWFK BWKZ BWMH BWTU BXDR BXDX BYJG BYKW BYLW BYRZ BYYE BYYR HUNK ICEY ICKY
  G-MERE PATP
LBL-90: G-BVAG BVWW BVXG BVZT BWBT BWRV BWTN BWWE BWZU BXLF BXXO BXZF BXZI BYEP CLAG DUGI FLEW MRKT OBJB OLBL OSUP ULLS UNGE
  EI-CRB
LBL-105: G-BUUN BUYJ BVDO BVON BVOO BVRU BWGA BWOK BWRZ BWSB BWTB BWWY BXDZ BXHE BXHP BXJG BXSO BXUO BYFU BYIY BYJN BYJZ BYLX
  G-ENRI GULF ICOI ICOZ LPAD OAER ODDY OMXS OPMT OICO PIZZ RDMS RXUK SNAK ZOOI
LBL-120: G-BVLZ BWDM BWEA   *LBL-150:* G-BVEW BXCM   *LBL-180:* G-BVBM BVIX BWCL EVNT GVBF KNOB OTUP WIZD
LBL-203: G-BXGK   *LBL-210:* G-BVLL BVML BXNX DVBF FVBF HVBF JVBF NVBF OCBS WVBF   *LBL-240:* G-BXBL OGAV
LBL-260: G-PVBF   *LBL-310:* G-SIZE TVBF   *LBL-317:* G-YVBF   *LBL-330:* G-BXVE   *AM.25000:* G-ORTW   *AM.32000:* G-GLBL
SPECIAL SHAPES

SHAPE	REGISTRATION	SHAPE	REGISTRATIONS
ARMCHAIR	G-LAZY	G144	G-BVHN
AUDI SALOON CAR	G-BWRU	ICE CREAM CONE	G-YMYM
BABY BEL	G-BXUG	J & B BOTTLE	G-OJBW
BANANAS	G-OCAW	LOZENGE	G-BVID
BATTERY	G-MAXX	MOUNTAIN DEW CAN	G-MDEW
BENZ	G-BWTF	PIG	G-PIGG
BIRTHDAY CAKE	G-WISH	PINK PANTHER	G-PINX
BUDWEISER CAN	G-BXHN	PHARMACIST	G-BYJY
BUNNY	G-FLUF	RACING CAR	G-TKGR
DIET PEPSI CAN	G-DIET	SYRUP BOTTLE	G-BXUB
FLOWERS	G-ODBN	TELEWEST SPHERE	G-BXHO

LOCKHEED (including CANADAIR production)
  10 ELECTRA: G-LIOA   *18 LODESTAR:* G-BMEW   *414 HUDSON:* G-BEOX
  L.188 ELECTRA: G-BYEF CEXS CHNX FIJR FIJV FIZU LOFB LOFC LOFD LOFE OFRT EI-HCF   *L.749 CONSTELLATION:* G-CONI
  L.1011 TRISTAR: G-BBAE BBAF BBAH BBAI BBAJ EI-CNN   *T-33A:* G-BYOY NASA TBRD WGHB
LOEHLE *5151 MUSTANG:* G-BTSD

LORIMER _IOLAIRE:_ G-MZFI
LOVEGROVE - see BENSEN
AV-8 Gyroplane: G-BXXR
LUSCOMBE _8 SILVAIRE/MASTER/RATTLER:_ G-AFUP AFYD AFZK AFZN AGMI AHEC AICX AJAP AJJU AJKB AKPG AKTI AKTM AKTN AKTT AKUF AKUG AKUH
G-AKUI AKUJ AKUK AKUL AKUM AKUP AKVP BNIO BNIP BPOU BPPO BPVZ BPZA BPZC BPZE BRDJ BRGF BRGG BRHX BRHY BRJA BRJK BRKA BRPZ BRRB
G-BRSW BRUG BSHH BSHI BSNE BSNT BSOE BSOX BSSA BSTX BSUD BSYF BSYH BTCH BTCJ BTDF BTIJ BTJA BTJB BTJC BUAO BUKT BULO BVEP
G-BVGW BVGY BVMD BWOB DAIR KENM LUSC LUSI LUST NIGE OWIZ ROTI SAGE YRIL
LUTON
LA-4/A MINOR/PARKER CA-4/PHOENIX DUET: G-AFIR AMAW ARIF ARXP ASAA ASEA ASEB ASML ASXJ ATCJ ATCN ATFW ATKH ATWS AVDY AVUO AWIP
G-AWMN AXGR AXKH AYDY AYSK AZHU AZPV BANF BBCY BBEA BCFY BDJG BDZY BIJS BKHR BRWU EI-ATP
LA-5A MAJOR: G-ARAD ASWH AYXO BCKP EI-CGF
LUTON - see ROLLASON
LVG _C.VI:_ G-AANJ

MACAIR _MERLIN:_ G-BTAD BWEN

McCANDLESS _M.4:_ G-ARTZ ATXX AXVN BIPZ BVLE EI-ASR
McCULLOGH _J.2:_ G-ORVB
McDONNELL-DOUGLAS
_DC-9/MD-82/83/87:_ EI-BTX EI-BTY EI-BWD EI-CBR EI-CBS EI-CBY EI-CBZ EI-CCC EI-CCE EI-CDY EI-CEK EI-CEP EI-CEQ EI-CFZ EI-CGI
EI-CIW EI-CKM EI-CMM EI-CMZ EI-CNR EI-CPB EI-CRE EI-CRH EI-CRJ EI-CRW EI-CTJ EI-CUF
_DC-10:_ G-BEBL BYDA DCIO DMCA GOKT LYON MULL EI-DLA
McDONNELL-DOUGLAS HELICOPTERS - see MD HELICOPTERS
MAINAIR -see PEGASUS/FLASH
BLADE: G-BY CW BYHN BYHO BYHS BYJB BYKC BYKD BYLK BYNM BYON BYOS BYOW BYRO BYRP BYRR BYTL BYTU BYZB BZAA BZAL BZDD MAIN MYRC
G-MYRD MYSH MYTD MYTG MYTL MYTU MYTW MYUC MYUM MYUN MYVB MYVE MYVH MYVO MYVV MYVZ MYXJ MYXM MYXN MYYA MYYG MYYH MYYW MYYY MZAA
G-MZAB MZAD MZAE MZAF MZAG MZAI MZAJ MZAL MZAM MZAP MZAR MZAS MZAT MZAU MZAY MZAZ MZBA MZBL MZCC MZCD MZCE MZCF MZCG MZCN MZCU
G-MZDF MZDK MZDT MZEB MZED MZEF MZEG MZEJ MZEW MZFB MZFS MZFZ MZGI MZGW MZIH MZIR MZIS MZIT MZIW MZJA MZJD MZJK MZJV MZJX MZJZ
G-MZKG MZKJ MZKK MZKM MZKO MZKV MZKZ MZLC MZLZ MZMB MZMD MZMJ MZML MZMM MZMP MZMV MZMY MZMZ MZNC MZNI MZNJ MZNK MZNL MZNO MZOC
G-MZOF MZOP MZOR MZPH MZSD MZSM MZZY OHNA OYES RUFF WLMS
GEMINI/FLASH (Combi): G-MJYF MJZD MMDP MMKL MMOW MMPO MMSP MMUE MMUO MMUS MMUT MMUW MMVP MMWA MMXC MMXD MMXG MMXH MMXJ MMXK
G-MMXL MMXT MMXU MMXV MMZA MMZC MMZD MMZE MMZF MMZJ MMZK MMZM MMZN MMZV MNAE MNBD MNBF MNBG MNBN MNBP MNBR MNBS MNBT MNBV
G-MNBV MNBW MNCF MNCG MNCJ MNDC MNDF MNDM MNEF MNEG MNEH MNET MNEV MNEY MNFE MNFF MNFH MNFJ MNFK MNFM MNFN MNFP MNGK MNGL MNGM
G-MNGN MNGT MNGU MNGW MNGZ MNHZ MNIA MNID MNIE MNIF MNIG MNIH MNII MNIP MNIX MNIZ MNJU MNKL MNLI MNLX MNLY MNMG MNMH MNMI MNMJ
G-MNMO MNMV MNNE MNNF MNNI MNNK MNNL MNNP MNNR MNNU MNNV MNPC MNPG MNPX MNRW MNRX MNRY MNSA MNSE MNSI MNSJ MNSR MNTI MNTS MNTU
G-MNXU MNYJ MNYK MNZB MNZC MNZD MNZE MNZF MTAB MTAC MTAE MTAF MTAG MTAH MTAR MTBC MTBD MTBG MTBH MTBI MTBJ MTBW MTBX MTBY MTCC
G-MTCE MTCU MTCW MTDF MTDR MTDW MTDY MTEH MTEJ MTEK MTEN MTEY MTFF MTFI MTFJ MTFX MTGA MTGH MTGO MTHW MTHY MTHZ MTIA MTIB MTIC
G-MTIL MTIM MTIN MTJA MTJB MTJC MTJD MTJE MTJF MTJK MTJL MTJM MTJT MTJV MTJW MTJY MTJZ MTKN MTKO MTKV MTKW MTKX MTKZ MTLB MTLC
G-MTLD MTLL MTMA MTMC MTML MTMT MTMV MTMW MTNC MTNG MTNH MTNI MTNJ MTNL MTNM MTNX MTNY MTPA MTPB MTRA MTRB MTRF MTRZ MTSB MTSC
G-MTTI MTTM MTTP MTTR MTTS MTTW MTUV MTVG MTVH MTVI MTVJ MTWF MTWG MTWR MTWS MTWX MTXM MTXP MTXS MTXZ MTZG MTZH MTZL MTZM
G-MTZO MTZV MTZW MTZX MTZY MTZZ MVAA MVAB MVAD MVAO MVAP MVBD MVBF MVBG MVBH MVBI MVBK MVBL MVBM MVBO MVCE MVCF MVCY MVDA
G-MVDT MVEH MVEJ MVEK MVEL MVEO MVEP MVER MVES MVET MVEV MVEW MVGM MVHE MVHF MVHG MVHH MVIB MVIC MVLH MVIX MVIY MVIZ MVJA MVJB
G-MVJC MVJE MVJL MVKC MVLL MVLR MVMN MVMO MVMR MVMT MVMU MVMV MVMX MVMY MVMZ MVNM MVNK MVNX MVNY MVNZ MVOB MVOF MVON MVOR MVPA
G-MVPB MVPD MVPE MVPI MVPO MVRA MVRB MVRC MVRD MVRM MVSN MVSO MVSP MVST MVSV MVTC MVUA MVXB MVXC MVXR MVXS MVYS MVZS MWAB MWAU
G-MWCE MWCW MWDJ MWEL MWGG MWHI MWHO MWHR MWHY MWIA MWIG MWIH MWIN MWIV MWJY MWLP MWLT MWLX MWMM MWMS MWMT MWMX MWMY MWNE MWNS
G-MWNT MWNU MWOJ MWOK MWOL MWPA MWPB MWPC MWPD MWPF MWPO MWRB MWRC MWRD MWRE MWRF MWRG MWRH MWRI MWRJ MWRR MWSB MWSL MWSM MWTG
G-MWTH MWTO MWTR MWTY MWTZ MWVN MWVO MWVR MWVS MWVT MWVW MWVY MWVZ MWWB MWWC MWWI MWWJ MWWK MWXA MWXB MWXC MWXD MWXL MWXN
G-MWXN MWXO MWXS MWXU MWXV MWYA MWYG MWYH MWYL MWYT MWYV MWZC MWZG MWZL MWZN MYAO MYAS MYAU MYBJ MYCK MYCR MYCS MYDV MYEU MYFP
G-MYPE MYPW MYRX MYSJ OLJT EI-BRH EI-CKT
GEMINI (Trike): G-MBST MBTF MBTG MJYP MMAJ MMAR MMFC MMHR MMIR MMIV MMJT MMKM MMKU MMLP MMMD MMOB MMRO MMRP MMRW MMSC MMSO
G-MMTB MMTG MMTL MMTM MMTX MMUX MMXW MNGB MNMC MNUM MTBY MWTF
MERCURY: G-MWVK MWXF MWXJ MWXK MWZA MYAI MYAV MYCJ MYCL MYCN MYCV MYDC MYGG MYGJ MYJN MYJR MYKI MYKW MYKX MYKY MYLS MYML MYMT
G-MYNC MYNF MYNJ MYOB MYOF MYOV MYOX MYPD MYPV MYRW MYSG MYSZ MYTB MYTK MYTX MYUB MYUD MYUE MYUK MYUW MYVL MYVS MYWA MYYU MZAK
G-MZCO EI-CMU   _RAPIER:_ G-BYBV BYOZ BZAB MZEP MZEV MZFD MZFW MZGL MZHJ MZHL MZIL MZIM MZJE MZKN MZND MZNU MZON
SCORCHER SOLO: G-MNDD MNNM MNPV MNPY MNPZ MNRE MNRF MNRG MNRZ MVBE MYFT MZKI MZKN   _STARLET:_ G-MYLT
TRI-FLYER (Trike): G-MBCJ MBDJ MBGA MBHK MBIZ MBPG MBPZ MBUK MBWF MBZA MBZO MJEE MJEY MJFK MJHR MJIF MJJO MJMN MJMR MJMX MJRP
G-MJTP MJXE MJYV MJYX MJZH MJZU MMAL MMAN MMCM MMCZ MMDK MMDN MMDT MMEJ MMFD MMFE MMFK MMFV MMJG MMKR MMMB MMNW MMTD MMTO MMUG
G-MMUH MMWG MMWN MMYV MNFA MNFR MNGB MNIW MNJD MNJG MNUI MNXB MNZY MVBC
MAINAIR/FLEXIFORM _RAPIER 1+1 (Combi):_ G-MJYV MMAW
MALMO - see BOLKOW
MANNING-FLANDERS _MF.1:_ G-BAAF
MANTA _PFLEDGE (Wing):_ G-MBNY
MANUEL _LADYBIRD:_ G-MJPB
MARQUART _MA.5 CHARGER:_ G-BHBT BVJX
MARTIN _MONOPLANE:_ G-AEYY
MASQUITO _Masquito M.58:_ G-MASX MASY MASZ
MAULE
M.4 ROCKET: G-MAWL   _M.5 LUNAR ROCKET:_ G-BHJK BICX BIES BPMB BVFT BVFZ FAMY KRIS NHVH OJGT RAGG RAIN RJWW

M.6 SUPER ROCKET: G-BKGC MOUL
 M.7 SUPER/STAR ROCKET/STARCRAFT: G-BSKG BSKO BSKT BTMJ BTWN BTXT BUEO BUEP BUXD BVIK BVIL CROL GROL HIND ITON LOFM EI-GER
MAX HOLSTE _MH.1521M BROUSSARD:_ G-BWGG WLR
MAXAIR
 DRIFTER: G-MYBB   _HUMMER:_ G-MJZX MMAP MMZZ MNIM MTMJ
MBA (MICRO BIPLANE AVIATION) _TIGER CUB:_ G-MBUE MJRU MJSP MJSU MJSV MJUC MJUF MJUW MJWF MJWG MJWJ MJWW MJXD MJXJ MJZC MJZE MMAG
 G-MMAK MMAM MMBH MMBT MMCX MMEY MMFN MMFS MMFT MMGF MMGL MMHN MMIE MMIH MMIM MMIX MMJS MMJV MMKP MMLB MMLF MMLM MMOF MMSW MMUM
 G-MMVG MNJC MNKM MWFT
MBB
 _Bo.105:_ G-AZOR BAMF BATC BCXO BFYA BGKJ BTHV BTKL BUIB BUXS CDBS DCCH DNLB EYNL NAAA NAAB PASB PASC PASD PASG PASX SPOL THLS
 G-WMAA WYPA EI-BLD   _BK.117:_ G-DCPA
MD HELICOPTERS _MD.900 EXPLORER:_ G-BXZK PASS SUSX WMID WPAS
MEA _MISTRAL TRAINER:_ G-MBET MBOH
MEDWAY - see SOUTHDOWN
 ECLIPSE R: G-BYXV BYXW BZGE EI-CRY EI-CTC EI-ELL
 HALF PINT (Trike): G-MMSZ MMZI MNDE MNEK MNEL MNJV MNLW MNTT
 HYBRED (Trike/Combi/R 44XLR): G-BYBJ BYBO BYRH MGOM MJVE MMEK MMKG MMKH MMTK MNCU MNCV MNEI MNFW MNJK MNMN MNWR MNXN MNXO MTDJ
 G-MTFC MTJG MTJP MTLX MTNE MTNF MTUX MVCD MVDB MVDC MVDJ MVEE MVGB MVGL MVGY MVIF MVKB MVMK MVPF MVPG MVPL MVRY-MVRZ MVSI MVSR
 G-MVUC MVUD MVVF MVVG MVVH MVVI MVVR MVWV MVXD MVXE MVXI MVXJ MVXM MVYP MVYR MVZO MWBJ MWCX MWCY MWCZ MWGC MWGD MWIK MWIL MWJP
 G-MWJR MWJX MWLB MWLS MWRM MWSS MWST MWSU MWUJ MWVU MYRI MYVV MYVX MZGE MZME
 PUMA SPRINT: G-MWBI   _REBEL:_ G-BYPP BYSS
MENAVIA - see PIEL
MERCURY _DART:_ G-BKKS
MERIDIAN ULTRALIGHTS _MAVERICK:_ G-BXSZ BYCV MYUJ MZJJ MZJS MZLE ONFL
MESSERSCHMITT - see NORD and including HISPANO production)
 _Bf.109:_ G-AWHS BOML BWUE BYDS SMIT
MICRO AVIATION _B-22 BANTAM:_ G-BXZU MZEY MZJC MZLX
MICROFLIGHT _SPECTRUM:_ G-MVJM MVSU MVWX MVXH MWCG MWHD MWKW MWKX MWOF MWPG MWPH MWPI MWTD MWTE MWWR MWWX MYAY
MIDLAND ULTRALIGHTS _SIROCCO:_ G-MNDU MNDV MNDW MNRT MTEO MTJN MTRC MVSM
MIGNET
 HM.14/HM.19 POU-DU-CIEL: G-ADRG ADRX ADRY ADVU ADXS ADYV ADZW AEBB AEEH AEFG AEGV AEHM AEJZ AEKR AEMY "AEOF" AEOH AFFI BWRI
 G-MYSI   _HM.293:_ G-AXPG   _HM-1000 BALERIT:_ G-MRAM MYDZ MYXL MZIX MZLI MZMW MZPB MZTA
MIKOYAN (including WSK-PZL)
 MiG-15 (Lim-2): G-BMZF OMIG   _MiG-17 (Lim 5):_ G-BWUF   _MiG-21:_ G-BRAM
MILES
 M.2H HAWK MAJOR: G-ADMW   _M.2L HAWK SPEED SIX:_ G-ADGP   _M.3 FALCON:_ G-AEEG   _M.5 SPARROWHAWK:_ G-ADNL
 M.11A WHITNEY STRAIGHT: G-AERV AEUJ   _M.12 MOHAWK:_ G-AEKW
 M.14A HAWK TRAINER 3: G-AFBS AHUJ AIUA AJRS AKAT AKKR AKKY AKPF ANWO   _M.17 MONARCH:_ G-AFJU AFLW AFRZ   _M.18:_ G-AHKY
 M.38/48 MESSENGER: G-AGOY AHUI AIEK AILL AJOC AJOE AJWB AKBO AKEZ AKIN AKIS AKVZ ALAH
 M.65 GEMINI: G-AKDK AKEK AKEL AKER AKGD AKGE AKHP AKHZ AKKB AKKH   _M.75 ARIES:_ G-AOGA   _M.100 STUDENT:_ G-MIOO
MILLS _MH-1:_ G-OMHI
MIRAGE - see ULTRAFLIGHT
MITCHELL
 WING B-10: G-MMJA MNJW   _WING U-2:_ G-MMNS
MITCHELL-PROCTER - see PROCTER
 KITTIWAKE: G-ATXN AWGM BBRN BBUL
MITSUBISHI
MONG _SPORT:_ G-BTOA
MONNETT
 MONI: G-BMVU INOW MONI SULY TRIM EI-BMU
 SONERAI: G-BGEH BGLK BICJ BJBM BJLC BKDC BKFA BKNO BLAI BMIS BOBY BSGJ BVCC CCOZ PFAT RILY
MONOCOUPE _90A:_ G-AFEL
MONTGOMERIE-BENSEN - see BENSEN & PARSONS
MOONEY _M.20/M.252:_ G-APVV ASUB ATOU AWLP BCJH BDTV BDVU BHBH BHJI BIBB BIWR BJHB BKMA BKMB BPCR BPFC BPKL BSXI BVZY BWJG BWTW
 G-BXML BYDD BYEE CERT DBYE DESS DEST DPUK FLYA GCKI GJKK GTPL JAKI JDIX JENA MALS MOON MUNI OBAL ODJH OEAC OJAC OJJB OONE OOOO
 G-OPWS OSUS RAFW ZZIP EI-CAY EI-CIK
MORANE-SAULNIER - see DE HAVILLAND/FIESELER and including GEMS/MORANE/PZL/SEEMS & SOCATA production
 TYPE N: G-AWBU   _MS.317:_ F-BCNL   _MS.502/505:_ G-BIRH BPHZ EI-AUY   _MS.733 ALCYON:_ G-MSAL SHOW
 MS.880/885/887/892/894 RALLYE/GALERIEN/GALOPIN: G-ARTT ARXW ASAT ASAU AVIN AVPK AVTV AVVJ AVZX AWAA AWKT AWOA AWXY AWYX AXAK
 G-AXCL AXCM AXCN AXGC AXGE AXHG AXHS AXHT AXIT AXOH AXOS AXOT AYDG AYET AYFJ AYRH AYTA AYYX AZEE AZGI AZGL AZKC AZKE AZMZ AZUT
 G-AZVF AZVH AZVI AZYD BAAI BAOG BAOH BAOJ BAOM BBAK BBED BBGC BBHX BBLM BCAC BCLT BCOR BCST BCUL BCVC BCXB BDEC BDWH BECA BECB
 G-BECC BEIL BERA BERC BETO BEVB BEVC BEVW BFAK BFDF BFGS BFTZ BGKC BGKD BGMT BGPZ BGSA BGZO BHWK BIAC BIIK BIOR BIPS BIRB BJDF
 G-BKBF BKGA BKGT BKJF BKOA BKVA BKVB BLGS BLIY BOJL BPJD BRDN BTIU BTOW BTUG BUDO BUGX BUKR BVAI BVAN BVWA BWWG BXLR BXLS BXZT
 G-BYPN BYSI BZAJ EXIT FARM GIGI KHRE KOLI LOKM MELV OACI OMIA PIGS VAJT WCEI EI-ATS EI-AUE EI-AUG EI-AUJ EI-AUP EI-AWU EI-AYA
 EI-AYI EI-AYT EI-AYV EI-BBG EI-BBI EI-BBJ EI-BBO EI-BCH EI-BCS EI-BCU EI-BCW EI-BDH EI-BDK EI-BEA EI-BEP EI-BFB EI-BFI EI-BFM
 EI-BFP EI-BFR EI-BFV EI-BGA EI-BGB EI-BGC EI-BGD EI-BGG EI-BGS EI-BGU EI-BHB EI-BHF EI-BHK EI-BHN EI-BHP EI-BHY EI-BIM EI-BIT
 EI-BIW EI-BJK EI-BKE EI-BKN EI-BKU EI-BMA EI-BMB EI-BMH EI-BMJ EI-BNG EI-BNU EI-BOP EI-BUJ EI-BUT EI-CEG EI-CFV EI-CHN EI-CIA
MOSKITO _MOSKITO 2:_ EI-CJV
MOSSCRAFT _MA.1/MA.2:_ G-AFHA AFJV
MOTH CORPORATION - see DE HAVILLAND
MOTO-DELTA - see CENTRAIR

MOULT *(Trike):* G-MTFK
MOYES MEGA *(Wing):* G-MZCL
MSS - see EUROWING
MUDRY - see CAARP
MURPHY
 REBEL: G-BUTK BVHS BWCY BWFZ BWLL BYBK DIKY LJCC YELL
 RENEGADE/SPIRIT: G-BTHN BTKB BWPE BYBU FIRZ MGOO MVZP MVZX MWAJ MWDM MWGF MWKA MWMW MWNF MWNR MWOO MWPS MWPZ MWUH MWVP MWWD
 G-MYAM MYAZ MYCO MYFM MYJP MYRK MYUF MYXR MZIP MZIZ NINE RCMC RENE TBAG TBMW

N
ANCHANG - see YAKOVLEV

NASH - see PROCTER
NAVAL AIRCRAFT FACTORY - see BOEING-STEARMAN
NEICO *LANCAIR 235/320/IV:* G-BSPX BSRI BUNO BUST BVLA FOPP PJMT UILE
NICOLLIER *HN.700 MENESTREL:* G-BVHL MINS
NIEUPORT
 SCOUT 17/23: G-BWMJ   *28:* G-BSKS
NIMROD - see AIRWAVE
NOBLE HARDMAN *SNOWBIRD:* G-MTRY MTXL MVCI MVCJ MVIL MVIM MVIN MVIO MVOI MVOJ MVOL MVYT MVYU MVYV MVYW MVYX EI-BUW
NOORDUYN - see NORTH AMERICAN
NORD see SNCAC
 1002 PINGOUIN: G-ASTG ASUA ATBG   *1101 NORALPHA:* G-ATDB ATHN BAYV SMD   *1203 NORECRIN:* G-BAYL BEDB BHXJ
 3202: G-BIZK BIZM BPMU   *3400:* G-BOSJ
NORMAN
 NAC-1 FREELANCE: G-NACA NACI   *NDN-1 FIRECRACKER/TURBO FIRECRACKER:* G-NDNI
 NAC-6 FIELDMASTER/FIREMASTER: G-NACL NACO NACP NRDC
NORTH AMERICAN - see LOEHLE & including CCF/FENNEC production)
 T-6/AT-16 HARVARD/TEXAN): G-AZBN AZSC BBHK BDAM BGHU BGOR BGPB BHTH BICE BIWX BJST BKRA BMJW BRBC BRLV BRVG BRWB BSBG BTKI
 G-BTXI BUKY BWUL CTKL DDMV ELMH HRVD JUDI RAIX TSIX TVIJ
 B-25 MITCHELL: G-BWGR BYDR   *P-51 MUSTANG:* G-BIXL BTCD HAEC LYNE MSTG MUST PSIC SIRR SUSY
 NA-64 YALE: G-BYNF   *F-86 SABRE:* G-SABR   *T-28/A TROJAN/FENNEC:* G-TROY
NOSTALGAIR *N.3 PUP:* G-BVEA
NOTT-CAMERON *ULD-1/2/3 HAFB:* G-BLJN BNXK NOTT
NOVA *VERTEX:* G-BYLI, BYZT

O
LDFIELD *BABY LAKES:* G-BBGL BGEI BGLS BKCJ BKHD BMIY BRKO BSXY BTZL BWMO POND

OMEGA BALLOONS
 0-20: G-AXMD   *56:* G-AXAO AYAL   *84:* G-AXJB AXVU
OPTICA - see EDGLEY
ORD-HUME - see LUTON
ORIENTAL *HAFB:* G-BINY
ORLICAN *L-40 META-SOKOL:* G-APUE APVU AROF
OSPREY (CHOWN) *HAFB:* G-BJHP BJHW BJID BJLE BJND BJNH BJPL BJRA BJRG BJSC BJSD BJSF BJSI BJTN BJTY BJUE BJUI BJUU FYAV FYBD FYBE
 G-FYBF FYBG FYBH FYBI FYBJ FYBR FYCL FYCV FYCZ FYDF FYDO FYDS FYDW FYEV FYFN

P
AKES *JACKDAW:* G-MBOF

PANTHER - see ULTRASPORTS/SOLAR WINGS
PARKER *CA-4:* G-AFIU
PARNALL *ELF:* G-AAIN   *PIXIE:* G-EBJG
PARSONS -(including MONTGOMERIE production)
 GYROPLANE: G-BTFE BUWH BVOD BVPH IIXX IVYS UNIV
PARTENAVIA
 P.64B OSCAR: G-BMDP
 P.68: G-BCDK BCPO BFBU BGXJ BHBZ BHJS BIFZ BMOI ENCE FJMS HUBB KWIK OLMA ORVR UNIT EI-BWH
PAYNE *Ax6-62 HAFB:* G-AZRI BFMZ
PAYNE KNIGHT *TWISTER:* G-APXZ BRAX
PAZMANY
 PL-1: G-BDHJ   *PL-2:* G-OPAZ   *PL-4:* G-BMMI BRFX FISK PAZY PLIV
PEARSON *HAFB:* G-BIXX

PEGASUS
XL-P: G-MMYA
XL-Q: G-DEAN MGCB MNKO MTNO MTNP MTPN MTPO MTPS MTRU MTRV MTTD MTTE MTTX MTTZ MTUN MTUP MTUR MTUS MTUT MTUY MTVX MTXH MTXI
G-MTXJ MTXK MTYA MTYC MTYD MTYE MTYF MTYH MTYI MTYL MTYM MTYN MTYP MTYR MTYS MTYT MTYU MTZP MTZR MTZS MTZT MVAW MVAX MVAY MVCL
G-MVCM MVCN MVCO MVCP MVCR MVCS MVCT MVCV MVEX MVEZ MVFA MVFB MVFC MVFD MVFE MVFF MVFG MVGT MVGU MVGV MVGW MVHO MVHP MVHR MVHS
G-MVHT MVHU MVHV MVHW MVHX MVHY MVIA MVJD MVJN MVJO MVJP MVJR MVJS MVJT MVJU MVJW MVJX MVKE MVKF MVKG MVKN MVKO MVKP MVKS MVKT
G-MVKU MVKV MVKW MVKX MVLX MVLY MVMA MVMB MVMC MVPR MVPS MVPU MVPW MVPS MVPY MVRH MVRI MVRJ MVRU MVRW MVRX MVSB MVSD MVSE MVSW
G-MVSX MVSY MVSZ MVTA MVTG MVTI MVTJ MVTK MVUF MVUG MVUH MVUI MVUJ MVUL MVUM MVUN MVVN MVVO MVVP MVYB MVYC MVYD MVZJ MVZL MVZT
G-MVZU MVZV MWAC MWAD MWAL MWAT MWBK MWCB MWCF MWCV MWDD MWDK MWDL MWEE MWEF MWEG MWEH MWER MWFS MWGL MWGM MWGR MWHC MWHF MWHG
G-MWNG MWOR MWOX MWOY MWPE MYPG MWPJ MWPK MWRV MWRW MWRX MWSD MWSJ MWSK MWTA MWTB MWTC MWTI MWUO MWUX MWUY MWUZ MWVA MWWG MWWH
G-MWWV MWXP MWXR MWYB MWYC MWYU MWYY MYAC MYAD MYAE MYAF MYBF MYBG MYBR MYBS MYBV MYBW MYBX MYBY MYBZ MYEA MYEC MYED MYFX MYTC
G-MYUH MZCP MZLR
XL-R: G-MGPD MMOH MMTC MMTR MNAN MNAO MNAR MNAU MNAW MNAX MNAY MNAZ MNBA MNBB MNBC MNEM MNGG MNHB MNHC MNHD MNHE MNHF MNHI
G-MNHJ MNHK MNHL MNHM MNHN MNHP MNHR MNHS MNHT MNHU MNHV MNMK MNUX MNVB MNVC MNVE MNWW MNWX MNYB MNYC MNYT MNYU MNYV MNYW MNYX
G-MNZK MNZL MTAA MTAI MTAJ MTAO MTAT MTAV MTAW MTAX MTAY MTAZ MTBA MTBL MTBU MTCG MTCH MTCN MTCO MTCR MTCX MTDG MTDH MTDI MTDP
G-MTDS MTDT MTDV MTEB MTEC MTED MTEE MTER MTES MTET MTEU MTEV MTEW MTEX MTFA MTFB MTFE MTFM MTFO MTFP MTFR MTFT MTGJ MTGK MTGL
G-MTGM MTHG MTHH MTHI MTHJ MTHN MTHO MTIE MTIH MTII MTIJ MTIO MTIP MTIR MTIS MTIU MTIV MTIW MTIX MTIY MTIZ MTJH MTJR MTJS MTKG
G-MTOH MTOI MTOJ MTOK MTOL MTOM MTON MTOO MTOP MTOR MTOS MTOT MTOU MTOW MTOX MTOY MTOZ MTPP MTPR MTRM MTRN MTRO MTRR MTRS MTSN
G-MTSO MTSP MTSR MTSS MTSU MTSV MTSX MTSY MTSZ MTTA MTTB MTTU MTUA MTUI MTUJ MTUK MTUL MTUB MTVC MTVK MTVL MTVM MTVN MTVO MTWA
G-MTWB MTWC MTWD MTWE MTYY MTZI MTZJ MTZK MVAR MVAS MVAT MVAU MVAV MVBJ MVBY MVBZ MVCA MVCB MVDU MVDV MVDW MVDX MVDY MVDZ MVEA
G-MVEC MVED MVEF MVEG MVFP MVFR MVFS MVFT MVFV MVFW MVFX MVGN MVGO MVGP MVGR MVGS MVKH MVKJ MVKK MVKL MVKM MVKK MVKM MWAF MWAG
G-MWAI MWAV MWBL MWCC MWCU MWDC MWFA MWFO MWFP MWJG MWLE MWLF MWLG MWLU MWMR MWMV MWOH MWOI MWPXMWRN MWRO MWRP MWRT MWRU MWSE
G-MWSF MWSG MWSO MWSP MWSR MWTM MWTU MWUB MWUC MWUD MWUE MWUF MWUG MWUP MWUR
MU.2/MARQUISE: N33EW N747SY   *MU.300 DIAMOND:* N70XX MWUS MWUU MWUV MWUW MWVE MWVF MWWO MWZH MWZI MWZJ MWZT MWZU MWZV MWZW MWZX
G-MWZY MWZZ MYAB MYBO MYBP MYDJ MYDJ MYEG MYEH MYFS MYGT MYGU MYGV EI-BSW EI-CGJ EI-CGM EI-CGN EI-CHT EI-CKU
XL-S: G-MNAF MNHH   *BANDIT:* G-MVLM
FLASH: G-MNDO MNGF MNJH MNJJ MNJK MNJL MNJN MNJO MNJP MNJR MNKP MNKR MNKS MNKV MNKW MNKX MNND MNNY MNNZ MNPA MNPB MNSH MNSN
G-MNUD MNUE MNVF MNVG MNVH MNWP MNWU MNWW MNXP MNYA MNYZ MNZA MNZO MTCK
PHOTON: G-MNIK MNIU MNKB MNKC MNKD MNKE MNKG MNKH MNKK MNNG MNUJ MNVY MNVZ MNXB MTAL
QUASAR variants: G-MWHT MWHU MWHV MWIM MWIU MWIW MWIX MWIY MWJD MWJH MWJI MWJJ MWJK MWJS MWJT MWJU MWJV MWLH MWLJ MWLK MWMI
G-MWMJ MWMK MWML MWNK MWNL MWOM MWOP MWPU MWSH MWSI MWTK MWTL MWVM MWWA MWXG MWXH MWXI MWYI MWYJ MWZD MWZE MWZF MWZO MWZP MWZR
G-MWZS MYAK MYBD MYBE MYBT MYCE MYCF MYEK MYEM MYEN MYEO MYFJ MYFK MYFL MYIM MYIN MYIO MYJJ MYJK MYJS MYJT MYJU MYKP MYKR MYKS
G-MYNU MYPF MYTR MYXD MZMA MZPW
QUANTUM 15 variants: G-BYEU BYDM BYDZ BYEW BYFF BYFG BYIS BYIZ BYJK BYKT BYLC BYMF BYMI BYMT BYND BYND BYOG BYOV BYPB BYPJ
G-BYPL BYRJ BYRU BYSX BYTC BYYN BYYP BYYY BZAI DINO EDMC EMLY EOFW FFUN JGSI MCJL MGDL MGDM MGEF MGFK MGFO MGGG MGGV MGMC MGTG
G-MROC MYLC MYLE MYLH MYLI MYLK MYLL MYLM MYLZ MYMB MYMC MYMD MYMX MYNB MYNK MYNL MYNM MYNN MYNO MYNP MYNR MYNS MYNT MYNV MYNZ
G-MYOE MYOU MYPH MYPI MYPN MYPX MYPY MYRF MYRM MYRN MYRS MYRT MYRY MYRZ MYSB MYSC MYSR MYSW MYSX MYSY MYTI MYTJ MYTN MYUO MYUU
G-MYYI MYYK MYYN MYYX MYYZ MYZJ MYZK MYZL MYZM MYZY MZAN MZAW MZAX MZBB MZBC MZBI MZBM MZBO MZBT MZBY MZCI MZCJ MZCM MZCR MZCV
G-MZCY MZDB MZDC MZDD MZDE MZDH MZDN MZDU MZDV MZDY MZEC MZEE MZEH MZEM MZET MZEX MZEZ MZFG MZFM MZFV MZGG MZGK MZGN MZGO MZGV
G-MZHI MZHK MZHN MZHP MZIB MZIC MZIE MZIF MZIJ MZIK MZIU MZJG MZJH MZJN MZJO MZJT MZJU MZJW MZJY MZKA MZKD MZKF MZKL MZKX MZKY
G-MZLA MZLD MZLF MZLH MZLJ MZLN MZLT MZLV MZMC MZMF MZMG MZMH MZNP MZMN MZMT MZNB MZNG MZNR MZNS MZNT MZOD MZOG MZOJ MZOS
G-MZOV MZOW MZPD MZRC MZRH MZRM MZSC OAKS OLDM PIXI PRSI REDC RUSA SMBM TBBC TRAM WHEE EI-CNU   *STORM (Wing):* G-MMUR
TYPHOON (Wing): G-MBCI MBCJ MBCL MBGP MBJS MBOK MBPG MBTJ MBUK MJCU MJEE MJMR MJPP MJVE MMBJ MMBZ MMCV MMDX MMKG MMKH MMLI
G-MMPU MMTK MMUG MMUK MNCU MNCV MNEI MNFA MNFR MNGD MNSD MNZI MZLK
PENN-SMITH *GYROPLANE:* G-AXOM
PERCIVAL - see HUNTING
P.1 GULL: G-ACGR ADPR   *P.6 MEW GULL:* G-AEXF   *P.10 VEGA GULL:* G-AEZJ   *P.16 Q SIX:* G-AFFD
P.28/31/34/44 PROCTOR: G-AHTE AHVG AHWO AKIU AKZN ALCK ALJF ANPP ANXR
P.40 PRENTICE: G-AOKH AOKL AOKO AOKZ AOLK AOLU APIT APIU APIY APJB APPL
P.56 PROVOST: G-ASMC AWPH AWRY AWVF BDYG BGSB BKFW BLIW BTDH KAPW MOOS TMKI
P.57/66 PRINCE/SEA PRINCE/PEMBROKE: G-AMLZ BNPH BNPU BXES DACA GACA RACA
PEREIRA *OSPREY:* G-BEPB BVGI GEOF PREY
PHANTOM - see SKYRIDER
PHILLIPS *ST.1 SPEEDTWIN:* G-DPST EMNI GPST
PHOENIX - see CURRIE WOT/LUTON
PM-3 DUET: G-AYTT
PIAGGIO (including FOCKE WULF production)
P.149: G-BPWW RKD RORY   *P.166:* G-APWY
PICCARD
HAFB: G-ATTN   *Ax6:* G-AWCR AZHR
PIEL (including COOPAVIA/MENAVIA/ROUSSEAU/SCINTEX production & BINDER/FAIRTRAVEL variants):
CP.301/328 EMERAUDE: G-APNS ARDD ARRS ARSJ ARUV ASCZ ASLX ASMT ASVG ASZR AXXC AYCE AYEC AYTR AZGY AZYS BBKL BCCR BDCI BDDZ
G-BDKH BHRR BIDO BIJU BIVF BKFR BKNZ BKUR BLHL BLRL BPRT BSVE BXAH BXYE DENS PIEL EI-CFG
CP.1310/1315 SUPER EMERAUDE: G-ASMV ASNI BANW BCHP BGVE BHEK BJCF BJVS BLXI BXRF
PIETENPOL (including GREGA
AIR CAMPER: G-ADRA BBSW BKVO BMDE BMLT BNMH BPOL BRXY BSVZ BUCO BUXK BUZO BVYY BWAT BWVB BWVF BXZO BYFT BYKG BYLD BYZY ECOX
G-EDFS IMBY OFFA OHAL PCAF PIET RAGS SILS SLOW TARN VALS
PIK (POLYTECKNIKKOJEN ILMAILUKERHO - see EIRI/SIREN)

489

PILATUS

P.2: G-BLKZ BONE CJCI PTWO *P.3:* G-BTLL *PC.6 PORTER:* G-BYNE WGSC

PIPER - see TED SMITH

J/2 CUB: G-AEXZ AFFH JTWO

J/3C CUB(L-4/0-59): G-AFDO AGAT AGIV AGVV AHIP AIIH AISS AISX AJAD AJAO AJES AKAZ AKIB AKRA AKTH AKUN ASPS ATKI ATZM AXGP AXH
G-AXHR AXVV AYCN AYEN BAET BBHJ BBLH BBUU BBXS BCNX BCOB BCOM BCPH BCPJ BCUB BCXJ BDCD BDEY BDEZ BDHK BDJP BDMS BDOL BECN BED
G-BEUI BFBY BFDL BFHI BFZB BGPD BGSJ BGTI BGXA BHPK BHPT BHVV BHXY BHZU BIJE BILI BJAF BJAY BJSZ BJTO BKHG BLPA BMKC BOTU BOX
G-BPCF BPUR BPVH BPYN BREB BROR BSAX BSBT BSFD BSNF BSTI BSVH BSVJ BSYO BTBX BTET BTSP BTUM BTZX BVAF BVPN BWEZ CCUB COPS CUB
G-CVIL FRAN HEWI KIRK LIVH LOCH NCUB OCUB OINK POOH RAMP SEED SNDY TCUB EI-AFE EI-AKM EI-BBV EI-BCM EI-BCN EI-BCO EI-BEN
EI-BFO EI-BIO EI-BSX EI-BYY EI-CCH EI-CFO EI-CHK EI-COY EI-CPP EI-CUB

J/4A CUB COUPE: G-AFGM AFWH AFZA BRBV BSDJ BUWL *J/5A CUB CRUISER:* G-BRIL BRLI BSDK BSXT BTKA BWUG EI-CGV

PA-12 SUPER CRUISER: G-AMPG ARTH AWPW AXUC BCAZ BOWN BSYG PAIZ EI-ADV CFF CFH

PA-15/PA-17 VAGABOND: G-AKTP ALEH ALGA ALIJ AMYL ASHU AWKD AWOF AWOH BCVB BDVA BDVB BDVC BIHT BLMP BOVB BRJL BRPY BRSX BSFW
G-BSMV BSWG BTBY BTCI BTFJ BTOT BUKN BUXX FKNH VAGA *PA-16 CLIPPER:* G-BAMR BBUG BIAP BSVI BSWF N5240H N5718H

PA-18 SUPER CUB(L-18/L-21): G-AMEN APZJ ARAM ARAN ARAO ARCT AREO ARGV ARVO ASCU ATRG AVOO AWMF AXGA AXLZ AYPM AYPO AYPP AYPR
G-AYPS AYPT AZRL BAFS BAFT BAFV BAKV BBOL BBYB BCFO BCMD BEOI BEUA BEUU BFFP BGPN BGWH BGYN BHGC BHOM BHPM BIDJ BIDK BIID BI
G-BIMM BIRH BITA BIYJ BIYR BIYY BIZV BJBK BJCI BJEI BJFE BJIV BJLH BJTP BJWX BJWZ BKET BKJB BKRF BKTA BKVM BLGT BLHM BLIH BLL
G-BLLO BLMI BLMR BLMT BLPE BLRC BMAY BMEA BMKB BNXM BOOC BPJG BPJH BPUL BROZ BRRL BSGC BSHV BTBU BTDX BTDY BTUR BUBA BVIE BV
G-BVMI BVRZ BWHH BWOR BWUB BWUC CUBB CUBJ CUBP FUZZ GCUB GDAM HACK HELN JCUB KAMP LION NETY NICK NNAC OFER OROD OSPS OTAN OTU
G-PCUB PIPR PUDL PULL ROVE SCUB SUPA TUGG WGCS WLAC XCUB YCUB ZAZA EI-ANY EI-BID EI-BIK EI-CIG EI-CKH

PA-20 PACER/PA-22 conversions: G-APYI ARBS ARGY ARNK ATBX AVDV BFAO BFMR BIYP BSED BTLM BUOI BUXV BXBB GGLE PAXX

PA-22 TRI-PACER/CARIBBEAN/COLT: G-APTP APUR APXR APXT APXU APYN APZL APZX ARAI ARAX ARBV ARCC ARCF ARDS ARDT ARDV AREL ARET
G-AREV ARFB ARFD ARGO ARHN ARHP ARHR ARIK ARIL ARJC ARJE ARJF ARJH ARKK ARKM ARKN ARKP ARKR ARKS ARND ARNE ARNG ARNH ARNI ARN
G-ARNL ARON ARSU ARSW ARSX ARYH ASSE ATXA AWLI AZRS BHCW BMCS BNED BOAK BRNX BTIC BTKV BTWU BUVA BWWU HALL TJAY TLDK EI-AWD
EI-AYS EI-BAV EI-UFO

PA-23/PA-27 APACHE/AZTEC: G-APMY ARBN ARCW ARHL ARJR ARJS ARJT ARJU ARJV ARTD ARYF ASEP ASER ASHH ASHV ASMO ASMY ASND ASRI
G-ATFF ATHA ATJR ATMU ATOA AVKZ AXDC AXOG AXZP AYBO AYMO AYSA AYWY AZRG AZSZ AZXG AZYU BADI BADJ BAED BAPL BATN BATX BAUA BAU
G-BAUJ BAUW BAVL BAVZ BAXP BBCC BBCW BBDO BBEW BBEY BBGB BBGE BBHF BBIF BBMJ BBNO BBRA BBRJ BBTJ BBTL BBVG BCBG BCBM BCCE BCK
G-BCRP BEXO BDAX BFBB BFJK BFVP BFWE BGTG BGWW BHNG BICY BJNZ BJXX BKJW BKVT BLLM BMFD BMOL BNUV BRAV BSVP BXPS BYRW CALL CSF
G-ESKU ESKY FOTO HFTG JANK JTCA KEYS KSFT LIZZ MLFF MOLY OART OBEY OPME OSNI OXTC RVRC RVRD SFHR SHIP TAPE TAXI USFT VSFT WSF
G-XSFT YSFT ZSFT EI-BDM EI-BLW EI-EEC EI-WAC

PA-24/PA-26 COMANCHE: G-APUZ APXJ ARBO ARDB ARFH ARHI ARIE ARLK ARUO ARXG ARYV ASEO ATIA ATJL ATNV ATOY AVCM AVGA AXMA AXTO
G-AYED AZKR AZWY BAHG BAHJ BRDW BRXW BUTL BWNI BYTI DISK KSVB MOTO

PA-25 PAWNEE: G-ASIY ASKV ASLK ASVP ATFR AVPY AVXA AXED AZPA BAUC BCBJ BDDS BDDT BDPJ BDWL BEHS BEII BENL BEPN BETL BETM BEXK
G-BFEV BFEW BFPS BFRX BFRY BFSC BFSD BHUU BILL BLDG BNZV BPWL BSTH BUXY BVYP BXST CMGC DSGC LYND TOWS

PA-28-140/160 CHEROKEE/CHALLENGER/CRUISER/FLITE-LINER: G-ARUR ARVT ARVU ARVV ARYR ASFL ASHX ASII ASIJ ASIL ASKT ASLV ASPK ASF
G-ASSW ASUD ASVZ ASWX ATAS ATDA ATEM ATEZ ATHI ATHR ATIS ATJF ATJG ATLW ATMW ATNB ATOI ATOJ ATOK ATOL ATOM ATOO ATOP ATC
G-ATOS ATOT ATPN ATRO ATRP ATRR ATTF ATTG ATTI ATTK ATTU ATTV ATTX ATUB ATUD ATUL ATVK ATVL ATVO ATVS ATXM ATYS ATZK AXAX AVB
G-AVBH AVBS AVBT AVFP AVFR AVFX AVFZ AVGC AVGD AVGE AVGG AVGH AVGK AVLB AVLC AVLD AVLE AVLF AVLG AVLH AVLI AVLJ AVLR AVN
G-AVNO AVNP AVNR AVNS AVNU AVNW AVOZ AVPV AVRK AVRP AVRT AVRU AVRY AVRZ AVSA AVSB AVSC AVSD AVSE AVSF AVSI AVSP AVUS AVUT AVL
G-AVUT AVUU AVWA AVWD AVWE AVWG AVWI AVWJ AVWL AVWM AVYL AVYM AVYP AVYR AVZR AWBE AWBG AWBH AWBS AWDP AWET AWEV AWEX AWIT AWF
G-AWSL AWSM AWTL AWTM AWXR AWXS AXAB AXIO AXJV AXJX AXMP AXOR AXSG AXSZ AXTA AXTC AXTJ AXTL AXTP AXZD AXZF AYAA AYAB AYAR AYA
G-AYAW AYEE AYEF AYIF AYIG AYJP AYJR AYKW AYKX AYMK AYMN AYNF AYNJ AYPJ AYPV AYRM AYUH AYWE AZDX AZEG AZFC AZLN AZMX AZRH AZW
G-AZWD AZWE AZZO BABG BAFU BAGX BAHE BAHF BAJR BAKH BAMM BASJ BASL BATV BATW BAWK BAXZ BBBK BBBN BBBY BBDB BBDC BBEC BBEF BBE
G-BBHY BBIL BBIX BBKX BBPY BBYP BBZF BCDJ BCGI BCGJ BCGN BCGT BCJM BCJN BCJP BCLL BDGY BDSH BDWY BEAC BEEU BEEV BEFF BEYO BE
G-BFBF BFPE BFXK BGAX BGPU BGRC BGVU BHXK BIFB BIHG BIYX BODM BOFY BOHM BOSR BOSU BRBW BRGI BRPK BRPL BRWO BSEF BSER BSGD BSL
G-BSLU BSSE BSTZ BTEX BTGO BTON BTVR BULR BUTZ BUUX BUYY BWYB BXJD BXPL BXVU BXYM BYCA CGHM CJBC DAKS DENE DEVS DIAT DLTR FIA
G-RECK SCPL SMTH SOOT TEFC TEMP TEWS TIMW WOLF YULL EI-AOB EI-ATK EI-BBC EI-BDR EI-BSO EI-CGP EI-CIV EI-CMB EI-COZ

PA-28-151/161 CHEROKEE WARRIOR/CADET: G-BCIR BCRL BCTF BDGM BDPA BEBZ BEFA BELP BFBR BFDK BFMG BFNI BFNJ BFNK BFWB BFXD BFXE
G-BFYB BFYM BFZG BGKS BGOG BGPJ BGPL BGVK BGYG BGYH BHFK BHJO BHOR BHRC BHVB BICW BIEY BIIT BIUW BJBW BJBX BJBY BJCA BJSV BJ
G-BLEJ BLVL BMFP BMKR BMTR BMUZ BNCR BNEL BNJM BNJT BNMB BNNO BNNS BNNT BNNY BNNZ BNOE BNOF BNOG BNOH BNOI BNOJ BNOK BNOL BNC
G-BNON BNOO BNOP BNOR BNOS BNOT BNOU BNOV BNOW BNRG BNSY BNSZ BNTD BNXE BNXT BNXU BNZB BNZZ BOAH BOBA BOBB BODC BODD BODE BOE
G-BODR BOER BOFZ BOHA BOHO BOHR BOIG BOJW BOJZ BOKB BOKK BOKL BOKM BOKN BOKO BOKP BOKR BOKS BOKT BOKU BOKX BOMY BOPC BORK BOF
G-BOSP BOTF BOTI BOTN BOUP BOUR BOVH BOVK BOXA BOXB BOXC BOYH BOYI BOZI BPAC BPAF BPAU BPBM BPCK BPDT BPDU BPEL BPFH BPHB BPH
G-BPHL BPID BPIU BPJO BPJP BPJR BPJS BPJT BPJU BPMK BPKR BPMF BPMR BPMV BPOM BPPN BPRY BPWA BPWE BRBA BRBB BRBD BRBE BRC
G-BRDG BRDM BRFH BRJV BRRM BRRN BRSE BRSG BRTM BRTX BRUB BRXC BRZP BSAW BSBA BSCV BSCY BSFK BSGL BSHP BSIB BSJX BSLE BSLK BSL
G-BSMZ BSOK BSOZ BSPI BSPM BSSC BSSR BSSW BSSX BSVF BSVG BSVM BSXA BSXB BSXC BSYZ BSZT BTAW BTBC BTDV BTFO BTGY BTID BTIH BT
G-BWOJ BXAB BXJJ BXJX BXLY BXNH BXTX BXTY BXTZ BYHH BYHI BYKN BYKO BYKR BYXU BYZM CBAL CDON CLAC CLEA CPTM CWFZ DENH DOME EDG
G-EGLD EGTR EKKL ELZY ESFT ESSX ETDA FIZZ FLAV FLEN FMAM FOXA GFCA GFCB GFCF GFTA GFTB GHRX GRRC GUSS HMED HMES IKBP ISDB JAM
G-JASE JAVO KART KBPI KDET KNAP LACA LACB LAZL LBMM LORC LSFT MAND MAYO MSFT NINA NSFT OAAA OANI OBFC OCTU ODEN OGCA OJWS OMF
G-OONY OTYJ OWAR PSFT PSRT RIZZ RSFT RSKR ROWS SACI SACO SACR SACS SACT SACU SACZ SARH SEJW SLYN SSFT SUZN TAGS TSFT VICC WAF
G-WARB WARC WARE WARO WARR WARS WARU WARV WARW WARX WARY WARZ WFFW XENA ZULU EI-CTT EI-WRN

PA-28-180/181 CHEROKEE ARCHER: G-ATAA BCCF BDSB BEIP BEMW BEXW BEYL BFDI BFMM BFSY BFVG BGBG BGTJ BGVZ BGWM BHNO BHWZ BHYS
G-BOSE BOXY BPAY BPFI BPGU BPOT BPTE BPXA BPYO BRBG BRBX BRME BRNV BRUD BRXD BSCS BSEU BSIM BSIZ BSKW BSNX BSVB BSXS BSZJ BTA
G-BTGZ BTKX BTYI BUMP BVNS BVOA BWPH BWUH BXEX BXIF BXOZ BXRG BXRJ BXTW BXWO BYFP BYHK BYKL BYSP CHAS CHIP CIFR DENK DIXY DJ
G-EFIR EHLX EMAZ EPJM ERNI FBRN GASP IBBO ILLY IMVA JACS JADJ JANA JANT JCAS JJAN JOYT JOYZ KAIR KEES KEMI KEVB KITE LACD LOF
G-MALA MASF MDAC MERI NERI NIKE NINB NOTE OBFS OBUS OGEM OODW ORAR PIPA PNNI RADI RCHA REXS SARA SGSE SHED SVEA TERY TIMK TSG
G-TWEL USSY VOAR WACP WACR YANK

PA-28-236 (TURBO) DAKOTA: G-BGXS BHTA BNYB BOKA BPCX BRKH BWSX BXCC DAKO FRGN FWPW KOTA LEAM TART
PA-28R/28RT CHEROKEE ARROW: G-AVWN AVWO AVWR AVWT AVWU AVWV AVXF AVYS AVYT AWAZ AWBA AWBB AWBC AWEZ AWFB AWFC AWFD AWFJ AXCA
G-AXWZ AYAC AYII AYPU AYRI AZAJ AZDE AZFI AZFM AZNL AZOG AZRV AZSF AZSH AZWS BAAZ BAHS BAIH BAMY BAPW BAWG BAZU BBDE BBEB BBEL
G-BBFD BBIA BBZH BBZV BCGS BCJO BCOP BCPG BEOH BEWX BFDO BFLI BFTC BFZH BGKU BGKV BGOL BGVN BHAY BHEV BHFJ BHGY BHIR BHWY BIDI
G-BIKE BIZO BKCB BKFZ BKXF BLXP BMGB BMHT BMHZ BMIV BMJG BMKK BMLS BMNL BMOE BMOP BMPR BNEE BNJR BNNX BNSG BNTC BNTS BNVT BNZG
G-BOBA BOET BOGM BOIC BOJH BOJI BONC BOOG BOUS BOWY BOYV BPBO BPXJ BPZM BREP BRLG BRMS BRRJ BSLD BSNP BSPN BTLG BTRT BUND BUNH
G-BUUM BVDH BWMI BWNM BVXC BXYO BXYP BXYR BXYS BXYT BYKP BYYO DAAH DDAY DIZY DMCS DNCS DONS DORA ECJM EDVL EMAK EPTR FBWH FULL
G-GDOG GEHP GHRW GPMW GYMM HALC HERB IBFW IJOE ISCA JANO JEFS JESS JMTT LAOL LBRC LEEM LFSE MACK MEAH MEGA MEME MERL MRST OARC
G-ODOG OJIM OKAG OKEN OMHC OMNI OOTC OPEP OPJD ORDN RACO RJMS RONG RUBY SABA SHUG TCTC TEBZ THSL TOBE UTSY VOID WEND WILS WWAL
G-YAWW EI-BGF EI-EDR
PA-30/39 TWIN COMANCHE: G-ASMA ASON ASRH ASRO ASSB ASSP ASWW ATET ATEW ATMT ATSZ ATWR ATXD AVAU AVCX AVJJ AVKL AVPR AVPS AVUD
G-AVVI AWBN AWBT AXAU AXRO AYAF AYLB AYSB AYZE AZAB AZBC BAKJ BAWN BAWU BFUF BKCL BLOR COMB LADI LARE OAJS OGET OLIN ORDO PCOM
G-SHAW SIGN SJAB SURG TCOM
PA-31/31T NAVAJO/CHIEFTAIN/CHEYENNE: G-AYEI BBZI BEZL BFIB BFOM BHGA BIYO BJLO BLFZ BMBC BMGH BPYR BTAX BTLE BVYF BWDE BWHF
G-BXKS CITY EEAC EHJM EMAX EPED FILL GLTT GLUG GTAX HTAX HVRD IFIT IKPS ILEA ISFC JAJK LIDE LYDD MOHS MRMR NAVO NERC NEWR NWAC
G-OAMT OIEA OJIL OLLY ONAV ONPA OSGB OWLC PLAC PMAX PZAZ PZIZ SASK UMMI VICT VIPP YEOM EI-CNM
PA-32 CHEROKEE SIX/LANCE/SARATOGA (SP): G-ATES ATJV ATRW ATRX AVFS AVFU AVTJ AVTK AVUZ AZDJ AZTD BADO BAGG BAXJ BBFV BBSM BDWP
G-BEHH BEZP BFUB BFYC BGUB BHBG BHGO BIWL BJCW BKEK BKMT BMDC BMEV BMJA BNJF BOGO BOON BOTV BPVI BPVN BRGT BRHA BRNZ BSTV BSUF
G-BSYC BTCA BVBG BVEB BVWZ BXWP BYFR BYPU CCSW CTCP DCAV DENI DIGI DIWY EENA ELLA ETBY FRAG GOMM GOTO HDEW HERO HYLT IFFR ILTS
G-IMPW JPOT KFRA KNOW LADE LLTT LLYY LUNA MCAR MOLL MOVI NIOS NROY NEAL OCPF OCTI OJCW OSCC OSIX OTBY PAPS RAMS RAYE REAH RHHT
G-RIGH ROLF SALA SAWU SIXD SULL TOGA WAIR WINS WYST
PA-34 SENECA: G-AZIK AZOL AZOT AZVJ BABK BACB BAIG BAKD BANK BASM BASX BATR BBLU BBNH BBNI BBPX BBXK BBZJ BCDB BCGA BCID BCVY
G-BDEF BDUN BEAG BEHU BEJV BETT BEVG BFKY BFLH BGFT BGLW BHFH BHYE BHYF BHYG BLWD BLYK BMDK BMJO BMNT BMUT BNEI BNEN BNRX BOCG
G-BOCP BOCR BOCS BOCT BOCU BOCV BOCW BOCX BOCY BOFE BOIZ BOJK BOPV BORH BOSD BOUK BOUL BOUM BOWE BPAD BPON BPXX BRHO BRXO BSDN
G-BSGK BSHA BSII BSOY BSPG BSUW BTGU BTGV BUBU BVDN BVEV BWDT BXPV BXUT BXXY BYKM CAHA CEGA CHEM CLOS CLUE CTWW DARA
G-DCEA DSID ELBC EMER EXEC FILE FLYI GAFA GFEY GFCD GUYS HCSL HMJB IFLP JANN JLCA LORD MAIK MAIR MAXI MPWT OACG OMAR OPAG OWAL
G-PEGI PLUS POPS ROLA ROUS RVRB SENV SENX SKYZ SSFC TAIR TEST VASA VVBK WATS WIZO WWAS EI-BSL EI-CMT EI-EIO
PA-38 TOMAHAWK: G-BFVF BGBK BGBN BGBW BGBY BGEK BGGE BGGF BGGG BGGI BGGL BGGM BGGN BGIG BGKY BGLA BGRK BGRL BGRM BGRN BGRR
G-BGRX BGSH BGSI BGVL BGWN BGWU BGXB BGXN BGXO BGZF BGZJ BGZW BHCZ BJNN BJUR BJUS BJYN BKAR BKAS BKCY BLWP BMKG BMML BMNP BMSF
G-BMTO BMTP BMVL BMVM BMXL BNCO BNEK BNGR BNGS NBHG BNIM BNKH BNNU BNPL BNPM BNSL BNUY BNVD BNXV BNYK BNYV BOBJ BOBK BOBL BOCC
G-BODP BODS BOEC BOIN BOHS BOHT BOHU BOLD BOLE BOLF BOMO BOMZ BOUD BOZM BPBR BPER BPES BPHI BPIK BPJF BPPD BPPE BPPF BRFL BRFN
G-BRHR BRHT BRJR BRLO BRLP BRMJ BRML BRNJ BRSJ BRTA BSFE BSKC BSKK BSKL BSOT BSOU BSVV BSVW BSVX BSVY BSYK BSYL BSYM BTAP
G-BTAR BTAS BTEV BTFP BTIL BTJK BTJL BTND BTOD BTOM BVBL BVHM BVLP BWNR BWNU BWNV BWSC BXET BXZU BYLE BYMC BYMD CWFA CWFB DFLY
G-DTOO DYOU EDNA EMMS EORG ENGR GTHM JEFF LFSA LFSB LFSD MSFC NCFC NCFE OAAL OATS OEDB OLFC OPSF OTFT PRIM REPM PVRF PVRG SION
G-SUKI TOMS EI-BJT EI-BUR EI-BUS EI-BVK
PA-44 SEMINOLE: G-BGCO BGSG BGTF BHFE BHRP BOHX BRUI BRUX DENZ FRST FSFT GSFT GHSI HSFT PDOC SEMI TWIN EI-CHF
PA-46 MALIBU: G-BMBE BXER BYLM BYSO CUPN DODI HYHY JCAR MICZ PALL VRST WADI
PIPER *CP.1 METISSE:* G-BVCP
PITTS *S.1/2 SPECIAL:* G-AXNZ AZCE AZPH BADW BADZ BBOH BETI BHSS BIRD BKDR BKPZ BLAG BMTU BOEM BOXH BOXV BOZS BPDV BPLY BPRD
G-BPVP BPZY BRAA BRAW BRBN BRCE BRCI BRJN BRRS BRVL BRVT BRZL BRZX BSDB BSRH BTEF BTOO BTTR BTUK BTUL BUAW BUWJ BVFN BVSZ BXAF
G-BXAU BXFB BXTI BYIP BYIR BYJP EWIZ FLIK FOLY FORZ HISS ICAS IIII IIIL IIIR IIIT IIIX ITII JAWZ KITI LITZ LOOP MAGG MINT OGEE
G-OKAY OODI OSIS OWAZ PEAL PITS PITZ REAP ROLL SIIB SKYD SOLO SPIN STUA STUB STYL SWUN TIII WAZZ WILD WREN YOYO
PIXIE - see SKYHOOK
PLUMB *BGP.1 BIPLANE:* G-BGPI FUNN
POBER *P-9 PIXIE:* G-BUXO
POLARIS *F1B OK350:* EI-BXL
PORTERFIELD
 CP-50: G-AFZL   *CP-65:* G-BVWY
PORTSWOOD *HAFB:* G-FYBS FYBX
POTTIER *P.80S:* G-BTYH
POWERCHUTE
 KESTREL: G-MVRV MWCI MWCJ MWCK MWCL MWCN MWCO MWCP MWCS MWFG MWFI MWFL MWFN MWGS MWGT MWGU MWGW MWGY MWGZ MWMA MWMB MWMC
 G-MWMD MWMG MWMH MWNV MWNX MWNY MWNZ MWOC MWOD MWOE MYCW MYCX MYCY MYCZ MYDA MYDB MYEX MYFA MYHS
 RAIDER: G-MTVZ MVHB MVHC MVMD MVNA MVNB MVNC MVNE MVNI MVNK MVNL MVNM MVVZ MVWB MVWD MVWF MVWH MVWI
PRACTAVIA *PILOT SPRITE:* G-AXRK AZZH BALY BCVF BCWH BILF ROSS
PRICE
 Ax7-77 HAFB: G-BLEL BMDJ   *TPB.2 HAFB:* G-BULE
PRIVATEER - see SLINGSBY
PROCTER - see MITCHELL
 PETREL: G-AXSF
PROTECH *PT-2C SASSY:* G-EWAN
PTERODACTYL - see SOLEAIR
 PFLEDGLING/PTRAVELER: G-MBAW MBHZ MBKB MBLN MJBX MJST MMWJ EI-BOA
PUTZER *ELSTER B:* G-APVF BMWV LUFT
PZL
 PZL-101 GAWRON: SP-CHD   *PZL-104 WILGA:* G-BKWG BTNS BUNC BWDF BXBZ BXMU WILG WLGA
 PZL-110 KOLIBER - see MORANE-SAULNIER   *PZL SZD-45A OGAR:* G-BEBG BKTM BMFI OGAR

QAC *QUICKIE/TRI-Q:* G-BKFM BKSE BMFN BMVG BMZG BNCG BNJO BOBS BPMW BPNL BPUC BSPA BSSK BUBC BUOO BUXM BVYT BWIT BWIZ BXOY

G-KUTU KWKI RUDI
QUAD-CITY *CHALLENGER:* G-BYKU CAMR IBFC MGAA MGRH MVZK MWFU MWFV MWFX MWFY MWFZ MYAG MYDN MYDS MYFH MYGM MYIA MYIX MYOZ MYPZ
G-MYRH MYRJ MYSD MYTO MYTT MYUL MYXC MYXK MYXV MYYF MZAC MZBW MZBZ MZEA MZHO MZKW MZNA

R.A.F. - see REPLICA PLANS & SLINGSBY

BE.2E: G-BVGR   *SE-5A:* G-EBIA EBIB EBIC BKDT
RAJ HAMSA *X'AIR 582:* G-BYCL BYHV BYJU BYLN BYLT BYMM BYMR BYNT BYOH BYOJ BYOR BYPO BYPW BYRV BYSY BYTW BYTT BYTZ BYYM BYYR BYZF
G-BYZW BZAF BZAK HARI OHWV RAJA XAYR XRXR
RAND ROBINSON *KR.2:* G-BEKR BFKC BLOU BMFL BMMD BNAD BNML BOLZ BOTT BOUN BPIH BPRR BRJX BRJY BRSN BTGD BUDF BUDS BURF BUWT BVIA
G-BVZJ BWNN BXXE BYLP DGWW JCMW KISS KRII OFMB RAND TIMJ UTSI WYNN XRAY EI-BNL EI-BOV
RANGO - including RANGO-SAFFERY
Model Free Balloons: G-BHAL BIAL BIIX BJAS BJNP FYEJ FYEM FYEU FYFT FYFW FYFY FYGA FYGB FYGI FYGK
NA 24 (Model Airship): G-FYEB   *NA-36/Ax3:* G-BJRH
RANS
S4/S-5 COYOTE: G-MVPJ MVPZ MVRN MVXW MWBO MWEP MWES MWFF MWFW MWGA MWGN MWIO MWLA MWLY MWLZ MWWP MYDO MYWV MZGD
S6 COYOTE II: G-BSMU BSSI BSTT BSUA BSUT BTNW BTXD BUOK BUTM BUWK BVCL BVFM BVIN BVOI BPW BVRK BVUM BVZO BVZV BWHK BWWP BWYR
G-BXCU BXRZ BXWK BYBR BYCM BYCN BYCO BYIB BYID BYJO BYKE BYMN BYMU BYMV BYNP BYOT BYOU BYPZ BYRG BYRS BYSN BYZO BZBC BZBX CHAZ
G-IZIT MGEC MGND MWCH MWHP MWIF MWRK MWSC MWTT MWUK MWUL MWUN MWVL MWWL MWYE MWYN MYAJ MYBA MYBI MYDK MYDX MYES MYFE MYFN MYGH
G-MYGP MYGR MYHI MYHK MYHP MYIR MYIS MYJD MYJL MYJY MYKN MYLA MYLD MYLF MYLO MYLW MYMH MYMP MYMR MYMS MYNE MYNH MYOA MYOI MYOT
G-MYPA MYPJ MYSP MYSU MYTE MYUZ MYVP MYXB MYXG MYXP MYYV MYZR MZAH MZBD MZBH MZBU MZBV MZCA MZDA MZDG MZDM MZDR MZEN MZEO MZEL
G-MZFL MZFN MZFY MZIY MZJI MZJM MZKE MZLG MZLL MZMP MZMS MZMU MZNV MZOZ MZUB RINS G-SSIH
S-7 COURIER: G-BVNY BWKJ BWMN KATI   *S-9 CHAOS:* G-BPUS BSEE
S-10 SAKOTA: G-BRPT BRSC BRZW BSBV BSGS BSMT BSNN BSWB BSWI BTCR BTGG BTJX BTKS BTWZ BUAX BUGH BUKB BULW BVCB BVFA BVHI BWIA
G-BWIL BYRE JSCL OEYE RANS RANZ   *S-12:* G-BZAO
RAVEN-EUROPE *MFM FS-57A HAFB:* G-BRUZ
RAVEN - see SOUTHDOWN
VECTOR: G-MBTW MJAZ
RAYTHEON HAWKER - see HAWKER SIDDELEY AVIATION
REARWIN
175 SKYRANGER: G-BTGI RWIN   *7000 SPORTSTER:* NC14485   *8125 CLOUDSTER:* G-BVLK   *8500 SPORTSTER:* G-AEOF
9000L SPORTSTER: G-BGAU
REECE *SKY RANGER:* G-MJRR
REID & SIGRIST *RS.4 DESFORD:* G-AGOS
REIMS - see CESSNA
RENEGADE - see MURPHY
REPLICA PLANS *SE-5A:* G-BDWJ BIHF BKER BMDB BUOD BUWE INNY SEVA
REPUBLIC *P-47 Thunderbolt:* G-THUN   *RC-3 SEABEE:* G-SEAB
REVOLUTION HELICOPTERS *MINI-500:* G-BWCZ HIAH MSOO OREV PDWI SWSH YEAR
RH7B *TIGER LIGHT:* G-MZGT
RICH *PROTOTYPE GLIDER:* G-BKEX
RIDOUT *HAFB:* G-BIRP BIWF BIWG BJMX BJMZ BJNA
RIGG *HAFB:* G-BHLJ BIAR
ROBIN
DR.400/2+2/PETIT PRINCE/EARL/KNIGHT/MAJOR/REGENT: G-BAEB BAEM BAEN BAFP BAFX BAGC BAGR BAGS BAHL BAJY BAJZ BAKM BALF BALG BALH
G-BALI BALJ BAMS BAMT BAMU BAMV BANB BAPV BAPX BAZC BBAX BBAY BBCH BBCS BBDP BBJU BBMB BCXE BDUY BEUP BFJZ BGRH BGWC BHAJ BHFS
G-BHJU BHLE BHLH BHOA BIHD BIZI BJUD BKDH BKDI BKDJ BKVL BNFV BNXI BOGI BPHG BPTT BPZP BRBK BRBL BRBM BRNT BRNU BSDG BSDH BSFF
G-BSLA BSSP BSVS BSYU BSZD BTRU BUGJ BUYS BXRT BYHT BYIT CONB DUDZ EGGS EHMM ELEN EYCO FCSP FILO FTIL FTIM FTIN FUEL GBUE HANS
G-IEYE IOOI JBDH JEDH JMTS JUDE LARA LEOS MIFF NBDD ONGC RONS SELL TUGY TUKE UAPA XLXL YOGI ZACH ZIGI ZIPI EI-CRG
DR.500: G-LISE MOTI
HR.100 ROYALE/SAFARI/TIARA: G-AZHB AZHK BAEC BAPY BAWR BAYR BBAW BBCN BBIO BBPW BEUD BGTP BLHN BLWF BVMZ BWPG BXWB HRIO MPWI
HR.200/CLUB: G-BBOE BCCB BCCY BDJN BETD BFBE BGXR BLTM BNIK BUWZ BVMM BWFG BWPG BWVG BXDT BXGW BXOR BXVK BYLG BYLH BYNK BYSG
G-GORF NSOF   *R.1180T AIGLON:* G-BGHM BIRT BJVV GBAO GDER GEEP PACE ROBN VITE EI-BIS
R.2100/R.2112 ALPHA: G-BGBA BICS BIVA BKXA PLAY RAFC TOUR EI-BIU   *R.2160:* G-BLWY BVYO BWZG BYBF BYMZ BYOF MATT SACK SBMO
R.3000: G-BLYP BOLU ENNI PAVL
ROBINSON *REDWING:* G-ABNX

ROBINSON
R-22 ALPHA/BETA/MARINER: G-BJUC BLDK BLME BLTF BNRZ BNUZ BOAM BOCN BODZ BOEW BOEX BOEZ BOVR BOXX BOYC BOYX BPGV BPIT BPNF BPNI
G-BPTP BPTZ BRBY BRHN BRKN BRLD BROX BRRY BRTI BRVI BRWD BRXV BSCE BSCL BSEK BSGF BSIN BSIT BSXN BSZS BTBA BTDI BTHI BTNA BTNB
G-BTOC BTVU BUBW BVGS BVPR BWAK BWHY BWTH BXLA BXOA BXRK BXSG BXSY BXTU BXUC BXWJ BXXN BXYK BYCF BYCK BYCU BYHD BYHE BYOP BYTD
G-BYTE BYZP BYZZ CHIS CHYL CNDY CRAY DAAM DEER DELT DERB DHGS DIRE DLDL DMCD DODB DODR EIBM ELFI EPAR ERBL ETIN FAGN FIRS FLYU
G-FOGY FOLI FUSI GDAY GEGE GJCD GSFC HBMW HERA HIEL HIPO HONI HRHE HUMF HURN HVRS IBED ICCL IGAD IHSB IIRF ILYS INKS IORG ISMO
G-ISPL JARA JERS JHEW JONH JRBH JSAK JWFT KENN KEVN KILY KRAY LAIN LAND LEDA LIDS LIPE MAVI MDKD MFHT MICH MOGY MRSN MUFY NHSR
G-NICH NJSH OASH OBIL OBIO ODCS ODOT OEAT OFAS OFJS OGOG OHLL OICV OKEY OLAU OLIZ OLRT OMMG OMSG ONMT OPAL OPTS ORMB OROB OSEE
G-OSHL OSIP OSMS OTAC OTED OTHL OTOY OVNR PACL PBES PHEL PIKE PPLH PWEL RACH RALD RENT RIAT RICE RNGO ROGG ROUT ROVY RSVP RSWW
G-RUSO SANS SBUT SIMN SOLD SPEE STOY SUMT TCMP TGRS TILE TORS TOSH TTHC TUNE TYPO UDAY UESY ULAB UNYT UPMW VCJH VFSI VMSL WADS
G-WAGG WFOX WIRL WIZA WIZR WIZY WRWR WURL XIIX XTEC YKEN YMBO ZAPY EI-CFE EI-CFX EI-CMI EI-CPO EI-JWM EI-MAC EI-TKI EI-WCC
EI-XMA EI-XMC
R-44 ASTRO/CLIPPER: G-BVMC BWVH BXKI BXPY BXUK BXUN BYCE BYKK CHAP CLKE DCSE DSPI EYET FABI FLYZ FODI HALE HEPY HREH HRHS ICAB
G-IFDM IFTS INDY IVIV JANI LATK LUKY MGAN MURY NSEW NTEE ODOC OFIL OJRH OKES OLOW OMEL OPAO OWND PFML PIDG POLT POTT PRET PPTS
G-RONN ROZI RTWW SJDI SUNY TAND TATY THEL TPTS TRAC TRCY URUH USTE WISP WYMR WYSP XTEK XPTS YIIK YKDD ZONK EI-CPO
ROCKWELL - see AERO COMMANDER & including COMMANDER AIRCRAFT
COMMANDER 112/114: G-BDAK BDFC BDFW BDIE BDKW BDLT BDYD BEBU BEDG BENJ BEPY BERI BERW BFAI BFPO BFRA BFXS BFZM BGBZ BHRO BHSE
G-BIOJ BIUO BKAY BLTK BMJL BMWR BOLT BPTG BUSW BVNL BYKB CRIL DANT DASH DIME EHXP ERIC FATB FLPI GRIF HILO HMBJ HPSE HPSM HROI
G-IMPX JILL JURG LADS LIMA LITE NATT NOOR OIBM OLFT OMUM OOJP PADS RCED RDCI RJCP SAAB TCSL TECH TSMI TWIZ VICS ZIPA
ROE
TRIPLANE: G-ARSG
ROLLASON - see DRUINE
BETA: G-AWHX BADC BETE BUPC
ROMAIN *COBRA BIPLANE:* G-MNLH
ROOSTER - see LIGHTWING
ROTEC *RALLY 2B:* G-MBAP MBAZ MBGS MBMG MJEH MJOD MJPA MVRF MYAL
ROTARY AIR FORCE *RAF 2000:* G-BUYL BVSM BWAD BWAE BWHS BWTK BWWS BXAC BXEA BXEB BXGS BXKM BXMG BYDW BYIN BYJA IRAF ONON TXSE
ROTORWAY *SCORPION/EXEC:* G-BHHZ BJBZ BNZL BNZO BPCM BPNC BRGX BRNP BSGV BSRP BSUR BTVF BUJZ BURP BUSN BVOY BVTV BWJK BWLY BWUJ
G-BYNI BYNJ CHTG ESUS FLIT IROY KENI KONE LUKY MAMC MPWH NEEL OJCM PILE PURS REID RHYS SFOX URCH VCSI YEWS EI-CMW
ROUSSEAU - see PIEL
RUSCHMEYER *R90:* G-TODE UAPO
RUTAN
COZY: G-BXDO BXVX COZI LOAT OGJS SCUL SPFX   *DEFIANT:* G-OTWO
LONG-EZ/VARIEZE: G-BEZE BEZY BIMX BKST BKVE BKXO BLLZ BLMN BLRH BLTS BLZM BMHA BMIM BMUG BNCZ BNUI BOOX BPWP BRFB BSIH BUPA
G-BVAY BVKM EEZE EMMY EZOS HAIG IPSY LASS LEZE LUKE MUSO OMJT OOSE PUSH RAEM RAFT REZE RPEZ SENA TIMB VEZE WILY EI-CMR EI-CPI
RYAN *ST3KR/PT-22:* G-AGYY BTBH BYPY

S AAB

32 LANSEN: G-BMSG   *91 SAFIR:* G-ANOK BCFW BKPY HRLK SAFR
SF.340: G-GNTA GNTB GNTC GNTD GNTE GNTF GNTG GNTH GNTI GNTJ LGNA LGNB RUNG   *2000:* EI-CPM EI-CPQ EI-CPW
SABRE - see SKYHOOK
SABRE (Wing): G-MJDA MJFX MJIB MJMI MJNY MMNM EI-BPT
SAFFERY *HAFB:* G-BERN BFBM BHRI BIHU BINF BINU BIVT BNHP FYGM
SAI *KZ.VIII:* G-AYKZ
SAN - see JODEL
SAUNDERS-ROE (SARO) *SKEETER:* G-APOI AWSV BJWC BKSC BLIX HELI SARO
SCALLAN *HAFB:* G-FYEO FYEZ
SCHEIBE
SF.23 SPERLING: G-BCHX   *SF.24A MOTORSPATZ:* G-BBKR
SF.25 FALKE/MOTORFALKE/SUPER FALKE/SLINGSBY T.61/VENTURE: G-AVIZ AXEO AXIW AXJR AYBG AYSD AYUM AYUN AYUP AYUR AYYK AYYL AYZU
G-AYZW AZHD AZHE AZIL AZMC AZMD AZPC AZYY BADH BAIZ BAKY BAMB BDZA BECF BEGG BFPA BFUD BGMV BHSD BIGZ BKVG BLCU BLTR BLZA BMBZ
G-BMVA BODU BPIR BPZU BRRD BRWT BSEL BSUO BSWL BSWM BTDA BTRW BTTZ BTUA BTWC BTWD BTWE BUDA BUDB BUDC BUDT BUED BUEK BUFG BUFN
G-BUFP BUFR BUGL BUGT BUGV BUGW BUGZ BUHA BUHR BUIH BUJA BUJB BUJI BUJX BUNB BUXJ BVKK BVKU BVLX BWTR BXAN BXMV BXWS BXXC FEFE
G-FHAS KAOM KDEY KDFF KFAN KGAO MFMM OWGC   *SF.27MB:* G-BSUM   *SF.28 TANDEM FALKE:* G-BARZ BYEJ
SCHEMPP-HIRTH
JANUS CM: G-BMBJ BXJS   *3DM/4DM:* G-BPMH MOAK ROAM
SCHLEICHER
ASK14: G-BKSP BSIY EI-APS   *ASK16:* G-BCHT BCTI EI-AYR   *ASH26E:* G-BWBY DAVT OPHT
SCHWEIZER - see HUGHES
SCOBLE - see SOUTHERN MICROLIGHT
SCINTEX - see PIEL
SCOTTISH AVIATION
BULLDOG: G-ASAL AXEH AXIG BCUO BCUS BCUV BDOG BHXA BHZR BHZS BHZT BPCL BULL BWIB BXGU CCOA JWCM
TWIN PIONEER: G-APRS AZHJ BBVF
SCRUGGS *HAFB:* G-BILE BILG BINI BINL BINM BINX BIPH BISL BISM BISS BIST BIWB BIWC BIWD BJEN
SE - see R.A.F./SLINGSBY/REPLICA PLANS
SEEMS - see MORANE-SAULNIER
SEQUOIA - see AVIAMILANO
SERVOTEC - see CIERVA

SHARP & SONS _TARTAN (Trike):_ G-MBDE
SHAW _TWIN-EZE:_ G-IVAN
SHEFFIELD _TRIDENT:_ G-MBNV
SHERRY _BUZZARD:_ G-MMNN
SHERWOOD RANGER - see TIGER CUB
SHIELD _XYLA:_ G-AWPN
SHORT - see EMBRAER
  S.16 SCION: G-ACUX AEZF   _SA.6 SEALAND:_ G-AKLW   _SC.5 BELFAST:_ G-BEPS BFYU HLFT   _SC.7 SKYVAN:_ G-BKMD BVXW PIGY
  _SD.3-30:_ G-BDBS BGNH BJLK BKIE BLCP BNTX BSBH DACS IOCS LEDN OATD OGIL SSWA SSWT SSWU EI-EXP
  _SD.3-60:_ G-BKMX BLZT BNMT BNMU BNMW BNYI BPFN BPFR BVMX CBAC CEAL CLAS DASI EXPS KBAC LEGS OBHD OBLK OJSY OLAH RMCT SSWX UBAC
  G-VBAC ZAPD EI-CPR
SIAI-MARCHETTI
  _S.205:_ G-AVEH AYXS BBRX BFAP VELA   _SF.260:_ G-BAGB MACH
SIGMA - see SOUTHDOWN
SIKORSKY - see WESTLAND
_S-52_ - see VERTICAL AVIATION TECHNOLOGIES
  _S-61:_ G-ATBJ ATFM AYOY BBHL BBHM BBVA BCEA BCEB BCLC BCLD BDIJ BDOC BEIC BEJL BFFJ BFFK BFMY BFRI BGWJ BGWK BHOH BIMU BPWB
  G-BXSN LAWS EI-BLY EI-CNL EI-MES EI-SAR
  _S-76:_ G-BHBF BHGK BIBG BIEJ BISZ BITR BJFL BJGX BJVX BMAL BOND BOYF BTLA BURS BUXB BVKR BWDO BXZS BYDF BYOM CBJB CHCD DRNT
  G-EWEL HARH JCBA JCBJ OAUS POAH SMAF SSSC SSSD SSSE UKLS XXEA
SIPA _901/903/91:_ G-AMSG ASXC ATXO AWLG BBBO BBDV BDAO BDKM BGME BHMA SIPA
SIREN _PIK-30:_ G-BMMJ
SKY
  _21:_ G-BYCB   _25:_ G-BXWX   _31:_ G-BWOY BXVP OSVY   _56:_ G-BWYP   _65:_ G-BWDY BWLM BWUS BXFZ BXKO BXUS DUNG   _70:_ G-PONY
  _77:_ G-BWSL BXHL BXVG BXXP CLRK KSKY LOWS MAGL RCML   _80:_ G-BYBS BYOI
  _90:_ G-BWKR BXGD BXJT BXJU BXLP BXPP BXVR BXWL CLOE CZAG LEAS VINO ZABC
  _105:_ G-BWDZ BWJE BWOA BWPP BWUM BXCN BXDV BXIW BXVN BXXS BYNV DONG   _120:_ G-BWIX BWJR BWPF BWPI BWYU BXDW BXLC BXWG BYEX OURS
  _140:_ G-BWHM BYKZ   _160:_ G-BWUK BWVP BXZZ BYHZ   _180:_ G-BWIW BWSF BXVL   _200:_ G-BWEL BWST BXIH   _220:_ G-BWRW BXDH EGUY SPEL
  _240:_ G-BXUE MRLN   _260:_ G-KTKT OLYN   _SPECIAL SHAPE FLYING MAP:_ G-MAPS
SKYCRAFT - see WHEELER
SKYFOX _CA-25N GAZELLE:_ G-IDAY
SKYHOOK
  SAILWINGS TR1 (Trike)/PIXIE: G-MJFX MJNU MJNY MMVS MNGH   _SAILWINGS TR2 (Trike):_ G-MBVW
  SAILWINGS CUTLASS (Wing): G-MBHJ MBVW MJNH MJNU MNUI   _SAILWINGS ZEUS (Wing):_ G-MMVS MNGH
SKYRAIDER _GYROCOPTER:_ G-BUUS
SKYRIDER _HAFB:_ G-BJTF
SKYRIDER _AIRSPORTS PHANTOM:_ G-MJKX MJSE MJSF MJTE MJTX MJTZ MJUR MJUX MJVX MMKX MNCS MTTN
SKYSALES _S-31 HAFB:_ G-BDYM
SKYTRIKE - see HIWAY
SLINGSBY see FOURNIER/SCHEIBE/SOPWITH/TIPSY
  T.7/T.21/T.29/T.31 MOTOR CADET/TUTOR: G-AXMB AYAN AZSD BCYH BDSM BEMM BMDD BNPF BODG BODH BOKG BOOD BPIP BRTZ BRVJ BUAC BVFS
  EI-CJT   _T.56 SE.5 rep:_ EI-ARH ARM
  T.67/T.67M FIREFLY: G-BIOW BIZN BJIG BJNG BJXA BJXB BJZN BKAM BKTZ BLLP BLLR BLLS BLLV BLPI BLRF BLRG BLTT BLTU BLTV BLTW BLUX
  G-BLVI BNSO BNSP BNSR BOCL BOCM BONT BONU BUUA BUUB BUUC BUUD BUUE BUUF BUUG BUUI BUUJ BUUK BUUL BWGO BWXA BWXB BWXC BWXD BWXE
  G-BWXF BWXG BWXH BWXI BWXJ BWXK BWXL BWXM BWXN BWXO BWXP BWXR BWXS BWXT BWXU BWXV BWXW BWXX BWXY BWXZ BXKW BYBX BYOA BYOB BYRY
  G-BYYG DLTA EFSM FORS HONG KONG OPUB RAFG SFTZ SKYC ZEIN
SMAN _PETREL AMPHIBIAN:_ G-GULL
SMD - see SOUTHERN MICROLIGHT
SMITH _DSA-1 MINIPLANE:_ G-BTGJ
SMYTH _SIDEWINDER:_ G-BRVH
SNCAC (AEROCENTRE) - (including NORD production)
  _NC854/858:_ G-BCGH BDJR BDXX BGEW BIUP BJEL BJLB BPZD NORD
SNCAN - see NORD/STAMPE
SNIAS - see SUD/AEROSPATIALE
SOCATA - see MORANE-SAULNIER
  ST.10 DIPLOMATE: G-AZIB BBTU HOLY EI-BUG
  TB.9 TAMPICO/TB.10 TOBAGO: G-BGXC BGXD BGXT BHDE BHER BHGP BHIT BHJF BHOZ BIAK BIBA BITE BIXA BIXB BIZE BIZR BJDT BJKF BKBN
  G-BKBV BKBW BKCR BKIA BKIB BKIS BKIT BKTY BKUE BKVC BLCG BLCM BLYE BMEG BMYC BMZE BNDR BNIJ BNRA BOIT BOIU BPGX BRIV BSDL BTHR
  G-BTIE BTWX BTZP CFME CONL COCL DAND EDEN GBHI GHZJ GMSI GOLF HALP HILT IGGL JURE MOOR MRTN OFIT OFLG PATN PHTG POPI RENO SERL
  G-SONA TBIO TEDS TINA TOBA VMJM EI-BMI EI-BOE EI-BSK EI-BYG EI-CRX EI-GFC
  TB.20/21/200 TRINIDAD/TOBAGO XL: G-BLXA BLYD BNXX BPAS BPFG BPTI BRYN BSCN BTEK BTZO BXLT BXVA BYJS CORB CPMS DLOM EGHR EGJA
  G-EWFN FITI FIFI GDGR GOOD HGPI JDEE KKDL KKES OALD OBGC PEKT PTRE SCBI SLTN TANS TBXX TBZI TBZO THZL TOAK TRIN TYNE WERY
  EI-BSV
SOKO _P-2 KRAGUJ:_ G-BSXD RADA SOKO
SOLAR WINGS - see PEGASUS
SOMERS-KENDALL _SK.1:_ G-AOBG
SOPWITH
  CAMEL: G-AWYY BFCZ BPOB   _PUP/DOVE:_ G-ABOX APUP BIAU EAGA EAVX EBKY   _TABLOID SCOUT:_ G-BFDE   _TRIPLANE:_ G-BOCK BWRA
  "1 ½" STRUTTER REP: G-BIDW
SORRELL _SNS-7 HYPERBIPE:_ G-HIPE

SOUTHDOWN - see MEDWAY
  LIGHTNING (Wing): G-MBGX MBKC MBLU MBMT MJEY MJHC MJHZ MJIZ MJRT MJZH MMAS MMDF MMEO MMKR MMKZ MMMI
  PIPISTRELLE - see AEROSTRUCTURE
  PUMA/PUMA SPRINT (Combi-unit): G-MBZJ MBZN MJCE MJEB MJHZ MJRT MJTR MJUE MJVN MJYT MMAO MMAR MMAZ MMBL MMCI MMCM MMCW MMES
  G-MMGP MMHE MMHF MMII MMIR MMIV MMIW MMJD MMJM MMJT MMKD MMKV MMLV MMMD MMPG MMPH MMRN MMST MMSV MMTH MMTI MMTM MMTZ MMUA MMUJ
  G-MMUV MMVA MMVI MMVO MMVX MMVZ MMWH MMWI MMWX MMWZ MMXN MMXO MMXP MMYF MMYI MMYJ MMYO MMYT MMYU MMYY MMYZ MMZR MMZW MMZX MNAV
  G-MNBE MNBH MNBM MNCI MNCK MNCL MNCP MNDG MNDP MNDY MNDZ MNFB MNFG MNFX MNFZ MNGR MNGS MNGX MNHL MNJD MNJG MNJS MNKU MNMC MNSB
  G-MNUM MTTK MVAF MVOS MWCR
  RAVEN/HORNET DUAL TRAINER/RAVEN: G-MGOD MMRT MMVH MNFD MNJB MNJT MNKZ MNLB MNLE MNLK MNLL MNLM MNLN MNLO MNLT MNLU MNLV MNLZ
  G-MNMD MNMU MNNA MNNB MNNC MNNN MNNO MNRP MNRS MNSL MNSW MNSX MNSY MNTC MNTE MNTF MNTG MNTM MNTN MNTO MNTY MNUH MNUT MNUU MNUW
  G-MNVN MNVP MNWA MNWG MNXA MNXD MNXE MNXF MNXG MNXI MNYG MNYI MNYL MNYM MNYP MNYS MNZW MTAP MTBB MTBK MTBN MTBO MTBZ MTCM MTHC
  G-MTID MTIK MTJI MTMK MTMO MTNB MTPC MTRT MTRW MTSD MTYV MTYW MTYX MVOS MYKL MYKM MYKU MYLX MYLY MYMJ MYVU MYVW MYYO MYYZ MYZO
  G-MZBR MZDJ RAVE EI-BPO   SIGMA (Wing): G-MBDM MBLM
  SPRINT (Wing)/PUMA: G-MBST MBTF MBTG MMAJ MMDP MMHR MMKU MMLP MMMB MMOB MMRO MMRP MMSO MMTB MMTG MMTL MMTO MMTX MMUH MMUX MMXW
  G-MWTF   WILD CAT (Trike): G-MJUE MMDF
SOUTHERN
  AEROSPORTS SCORPION: G-MBNH   FLYER: G-MJCN MICROLIGHT (SMD) GAZELLE (Trike): G-MMGU MMPT   MICROLIGHT (SMD) VIPER: G-MMHS
  SOUTHERN MARTLET: G-AAYX
SPAD XIII: G-BFYO
SPARTAN
  ARROW: G-ABWP   CRUISER: G-ACYK   THREE-SEATER: G-ABYN
SPEZIO DAL-1 TUHOLER/SPORT: G-NGRM NOBI
SPORTAVIA - see FOURNIER
  RS.180 SPORTSMAN: G-VIZZ
SQUIRES LIGHTFLY: G-MNNG
STAAKEN Z-1/Z-21A FLITZER: G-BVAW BYYZ FLIZ
STAMPE (including SNCAN/AIA production)
  SV.4A/B/C: G-AIYG AMPI ASHS ATIR AWEF AWIW AWXZ AXHC AXNW AXRP AYCG AYCK AYDR AYGE AYIJ AYJB AYWT AYZI AZCB AZGC AZGE AZNK
  G-AZSA AZTR BAKN BALK BEPC BEPF BHFG BHYI BIMO BKRK BKSX BMNV BNYZ BPLM BRXP BTIO BWEF BWRE BWRS BYDK EEUP FORC FORD GMAX HJSS
  G-OODE STMP SVIV EI-BAJ BLB CJR
STARCK AS.80: G-BJAE
STAR-LITE SL-1: G-BUZH FARO SOLA UIDA
STEARMAN - see BOEING-STEARMAN
STEEN SKYBOLT: G-BGRT BIMN BRIS BUXI BVXE BWPJ KEST SBLT SKIE TURN EI-CIZ EI-SAT
STEER TERROR (Trike): G-MBNY
STEMME S-10: G-BVYZ BXGZ BXHR CHLT JCKT JULS LINA OJTA STEM STEN
STEPHENS AKRO/LAZER 200: G-BMZZ BRHZ BWKT LAZA RIDE VILL
STERN ST.80 BALADE: G-BWVI
STEVENDON SKYREACHER HAFB: G-BIWA
STINSON
  RELIANT: G-BUCH   HW-75/105 VOYAGER: G-AFYO BMSA   108 STATION WAGON: G-BHMR BPTA BRZK EI-CGC
STITS SA.3A PLAYBOY: G-BDRL BGLZ BVVR
STODDARD-HAMILTON
  GLASAIR: G-BMIO BODI BOVU BSAI BUBT BUHS CINY IIRG KRES KSIR LAIR LASR OPNH TRUK EI-CTG
  GLASTAR: G-BYEK CBCL CTEC IARC LAZZ LEZZ LSTR SACH
STOLP
  SA.100 STARDUSTER: G-BSZG N40D
  SA.300 STARDUSTER TOO: G-BNNA BOBT BPCE BRVB BSZB BTGS BUPB DUST JIII KEEN OTOO UINN EI-CDQ
  SA.500 STARLET: G-AZTV   SA.750 ACRODUSTER TOO: G-BLES BUGB   SA.900 V-STAR: G-BLAF
STRIKER - see FLEXIFORM
STRIPLIN
  LONE RANGER: G-MBDL MBJM   SKY RANGER: G-MJKB
STROJNIK S-2A: G-BMPS
SUD AVIATION - see GARDAN/SOCATA & including AEROSPATIALE/SOKO/WESTLAND production
  SE.3130 ALOUETTE II/SA.315 LAMA: G-BSFN BSFS BSFU BVSD LAMA   SA.321 SUPER FRELON: F-BTRP
  SA.341 GAZELLE: G-BAGL BCHM BKLS BXJK BXTH BXZD BXZE EHUP FDAV GAZA GAZI GAZZ HTPS LOYD MANN OGAZ PAGS PYOB SFTA UTZY UZEL
  G-WDEV WMAN   SA.365 DAUPHIN 2: G-BKXD BLEZ BLUM BLUN BTEU BTNC BTUX BXLL BXPA HEMS MLTY PLMI RAZA EI-MIP
SUKHOI
  SU-26M: G-SOOK XXVI
SUPER SCORPION - see HIWAY
SUPERMARINE - see VICKERS-SUPERMARINE
SURREY FLYING SERVICES AL-1: G-AALP
SUSSEX Balloon (Gas): G-AWOK
SWALLOW AEROPLANE SWALLOW B: G-MJNS
SWEARINGEN SA-227 METRO III: G-BUKA
SZD (SZYBOWCOWY ZAKLAD DOSWIADCZALNY) - see PZL
SZEP HFC-125: G-BCPX

T

ARJANI *(Trike):* G-MJCU

TASK *SILHOUETTE:* G-ZUMY

TAYLOR

JT.1 MONOPLANE: G-APRT AWGZ AXYK AYSH AYUS BBBB BBDN BDAD BDAG BDJB BDKU BDNC BDNG BDNO BEEW BEHM BEUM BEVS BEYW BFBC BFDZ
G-BFOU BFRF BGCY BGHY BILZ BJMO BKEU BKHY BLDB BMAO BMET BNAR BRUO BUXL BVDE BXTC BYAV CDGA CJIM CRIS DIPS DRAY SUZY WARD
EI-BKK   *JT.2 TITCH:* G-AYZH BABE BARN BCSY BDRG BFID BGCX BGMS BIAX BKWD BVNI EVAN MISS MOLE OJON RKET TTAM VIVI

TAYLOR - see AEROCAR

TAYLOR-WATKINSON *DINGBAT:* G-AFJA

TAYLORCRAFT (AUSTER) - see *AUSTER*

TAYLORCRAFT

PLUS C/D: G-AHCR AHGW AHGZ AHSD AHUG AHWJ AHXE AIXA EI-AGD ALH AMF ANA

BC-12D/BL-65/DF-65/DCO-65: G-AHNR AKVO BIGK BOLB BPHO BPHP BPPZ BPTC BREY BRIH BRIY BRPX BRXE BSCW BSDA BTFK BTMF BVDZ BVRH
G-BVXS BWLJ EI-CES   *F-19/F-21/F-22:* G-BPJV BRIJ BVOX BWBI

TEAM

HIMAX: G-MZHM MZIA

MINIMAX: G-BVSB BVSX BVYK BXCD BXSU BYBW BYFV BYII BYJE BYYX MVXZ MWFC MWFD MWHH MWLW MWSA MWWE MWZM MYAT MYAW MYBM MYCT MYDF
G-MYGF MYGL MYII MYIZ MYKJ MYKZ MYLB MYMG MYNI MYRG MYRL MYSK MYTA MYXA MYYR MYYS MYZE MZCS MZGR MZII MZMO MZNM MZNN MZOY MZP
G-NADS OSCO THEO EI-CGB EI-CNC

TED SMITH - (including PIPER production)

AEROSTAR 601: G-MOVE PAMS RIGS TIME

TEMAN *MONO-FLY:* G-MMJX MMPZ

THERMAL AIRCRAFT *104 HAFB:* G-BRAP

THORN *COAL GAS BALLOON:* G-ATGN

THORP including VENTURE

T-18: G-BLIT BSVN BYBY   *T-211:* G-BTHP BXPF BXPO BYJF TZII

THRUSTER

TST: G-DRUM MNWB MTGB MTGC MTGD MTGE MTGF MTGP MTGR MTGS MTGT MTGU MTKA MTKB MTKD MTKE MTLM MTLN MTLO MTLR MTNR MTNS MTNT MTN
G-MTNV MTNW MTPT MTPU MTPV MTPW MTPX MTPY MTSH MTSI MTSJ MTSK MTSL MTSM MTST MTUB MTUC MTUD MTUE MTUF MTUG MTVP MTVR MTVS MTV
G-MTVV MTWY MTWZ MTXA MTXB MTXC MTXD MTZA MTZB MTZC MTZD MTZE MTZF MVAG MVAH MVAI MVAJ MVAK MVAL MVBP MVBS MVBT MVBU MVDD MVD
G-MVDF MVDG MVDH MVFJ MVFK MVFL MVFM MVFN MVFO MVHI MVHJ MVHK MVHL MVIR MVIS MVIU MVIV MVIW MVME MVMG MVMH MVMI MVOT MVOU MVO
G-MVOW MVOX MVOY MVXL MVYE MWDP MYWZ EI-BYA EI-CKI

T.300/SUPER T300: G-MGWH MVUB MVWN MVWP MVWR MVWS MVZA MVZB MVZC MVZD MVZE MVZG MVZI MWAM MWAN MWAP MWAR MWAS MWDS MWWS MWWT
G-MYAP MYAR MYDR MYDT MYDU MYJF MYJG MYJH MYXU EI-CEN

T.600: G-BYFN BYPF BYPG BYPH BYPI BZBG FJCE INGE MYWD MYWE MZFO MZFP MZFR MZFU MZGX MZGY MZGZ MZHA MZHC MZHD MZHE MZHF MZHS
G-MZHU MZHV MZHW MZHX MZHY MZHZ MZKP MZKR MZKS MZKT MZKU MZNW MZNX MZNY MZOA MZOB RIVR UDGE WORM

THRUXTON *JACKAROO:* G-ANFY ANZT AOEX AOIR

THUNDER

AA-1050 Gas FB: G-BSRJ   *AS-33 Airship:* G-ERMS   *0.5:* G-BBOD   *Ax3 SKY CHARIOT:* G-BHUR BJGE BJVF BKBD BKFG BKIY NEIL OFOR
Ax4-31: G-LORY   *Ax5-42:* G-BDAY BEEP BEMU BLOV

Ax6-56: G-BBCP BBDJ BBOO BBOY BCCH BCFU BDVG BEEE BEJB BERD BETH BFOS BFOZ BGPF BGWY BGZZ BHAM
G-BHTG BHXT BIIL BIZU BJVU BKUJ BLWB BPSJ BPUF BUSY BVRI BVUH DICK LDYS LIFE RTBI THOM TNTN

Ax7-65: G-BBDJ BCCG BGST BHEU BHHH BHIS BHOO BHZX BJHT BJSW BJZC BLCY BLGX BLKJ BLTN BLUI BMHJ BTAN BTXK BZBH FUND NIGS PIAF
G-RBOW VIVA

Ax7-77: G-BAIR BAWW BAXK BBOX BCAN BCAR BCAS BCIN BCNR BCSX BCZI BDGH BDGO BDMO BDON BEVI BFIX BGRS BHAT BHSP BIGF BKDK BKUU
G-BLAD BLAH BLET BLZF BMCC BMJS BMKV BMMU BMMW BMMY BMOG BMUU BMVT BMYS BNBL BNBV BNBW BNCC BNCU BNGO BNHO BNMX BNXZ BNZK BOAⅣ
G-BOIJ BORD BOSB BPBZ BPGF BPHU BPNU BPVU BPYK BPYZ BRDC BRDE BRLS BROA BRVN BRWF BRXB BRZE BSAV BSBN BSCF BSCO BSOJ BSZH BTA
G-BTHK BTRR BTSX BTTW BTVA BTWS BUDK BUIN BUKI BULB BUNV BUPU BUYI BVDB BWED BYNU GASS GGGG GHIN HOWE LENS LYTE MLWI NEGS OFB
G-OJDC OONI ORDY PIES PUFF RAFE RIGB RINO ROCK ROSI RRSG RUBI SFRY SOFT THOS USIL WDEB WINE

Ax8-84: G-BOHF BSPB INGA ISTT OGGS

Ax8-90: G-BORR BOTE BRTT BRVY BSKI BSTK BSTY BTJD BTPX BTRO BUJW BUXW BUYD BVDW BVGX BVKH BVLS BVWB BWKW GEMS HAZE HOPS KBKB
G-OMDD OTEL PINE

Ax8-105: G-BJMW BPZZ BSCX BSFJ BTBB BTHM BTTK BUBL BUBY BUEI BUYM BVGB BVPA BWJB BYLV PUNK THOR TOOL ZEBO EI-BAR

Ax9-120: G-BTMN BTOZ BTRN BTUJ BUAT BULK BVKZ BVSY FABS IOAZ   *Ax9-140:* G-BTJO   *Ax10-160:* G-BPSI ZBRA

Ax10-180: G-BTJF BTNL BTYF BUNZ BUVZ BVUF BWNX   *Ax10-210:* G-BWUR OLEO   *AX11-225:* G-BXAD   *AX11-250:* G-BXVF

SPECIAL SHAPES

SHAPE	REGISTRATION	SHAPE	REGISTRATIONS
FILM CASSETTE	G-PHOT	JUMBO JET	G-UMBO
FORK LIFT TRUCK	G-BWBH	WHISKY BOTTLE	G-RARE
ICE CREAM	G-ICES		

THURSTON *TAWNEY OWL:* G-APWU

THURSTON *TEAL:* G-OWET TEAL

TIGER *HAFB:* G-BIMK

TIGER CUB - see MBA

RL5A SHERWOOD RANGER: G-GKFC HVAN MWND WZOL PUSY

TIPSY - including COBELAVIA/SLINGSBY production

TRAINER/B/BELFAIR: G-AFJR AFSC AFVN AFWT AISA AISC APIE APOD   *JUNIOR:* G-AMVP

T.66 NIPPER: G-APYB ARBG ARBP ARDY ARFV ARXN ASXI ASZV ATBW ATKZ ATUH AVKI AVKK AVXC AVXD AWDA AWJE AWJF AWLR AWLS AXLI
G-AXZM AZBA BLMW BRIK BRPM BWCT BWHR BYLO CORD ENIE NIPA NIPP TEDZ TIPS

TRAGO MILLS - see FLS
TREKKING - see AIRWAVE
TRI-FLYER - see MAINAIR SPORTS
TRI-R KIS: G-BVTA BVZD BXJI MANW OKIS OKMA OKPW SKIS TKIS
TRIDENT - see SHEFFIELD
TRION J.1: G-MWHZ
TRIPACER - see ULTRASPORTS
TROTTER Ax3-90 HAFB: G-BRBT
TURLEY- see RAVEN
TURNER SUPER T-40A: G-BRIO
TURNER - see CURRIE
TWAMLEY TRIKE: G-MBGF MJWI

U AS SOLAR/STORM BUGGY (Trike): G-MJBS
ULTIMATE AIRCRAFT 10 DASH 200: G-BOFO

ULTRAFLIGHT
  LAZAIR: G-MBYI MNRD MTDN MTFL MVGZ   MIRAGE: G-MBRH MBSX MBXX MBYT
ULTRAMAGIC H-77/M-77 HAFB: G-BXPT DWPH VOTE
ULTRASPORTS - see SOUTHDOWN
  TRIPACER: G-MBAL MBBY MBDE MBFU MBLU MBPY MBTJ MBZA MJER MJFB MJFI MJHC MJHM MJHZ MJIA MJIC MJIZ MMEO MMFL MMIJ MMMI MMMR MMPU
  G-MMUK MNGD MNSD MTHD MZCL
  ULTRASPORTS/SOLAR WINGS PANTHER (combi TRIPACER/TYPHOON): G-MBZK MJIY MJPU MJWZ MJYC MMBY MMDS MMGS MMHZ MMJF MMKA MMLX MMMN
  G-MMNX MMOK MMRJ MMRK MMRL MMRR MMRZ MMSA MMSG MMSH MMTA MMTC MMTS MMTT MMUN MMVC MMVF MMWO MMYN MMZG MMZP MNAH MNAI MNAJ MNAK
  G-MNAM MNBI
ULTRAVIA
  SUPER PELICAN: G-MWRS   PELICAN CLUB: G-BWWA
UNICORN HAFB: G-BINR BINS BINT BIWJ BJGM BJLF BJLG BJSX FYEK

V ALENTIN TAIFUN 17E: G-BMSE OACE TFUN
VAN'S
  RV-3: G-BVDC   RV-4: G-BOHW BROP BULG BVDI BVLR BVRV BVUN BVVS BXPI BXRV FTUO MAXV PIPS RMIT RVMJ RVRV VANS
  RV-6: G-BUEC BUTD BVCG BVRE BXJY BXVM BXVO BXWT BXYN BXYX BYDV BYEL EDRV EYOR GLUC GRIN HOPY KELL NESI NPKJ OJVA ONUN OTRV
  G-REAS RIVT RVAN RVAW RVCL RVDJ RVEE RVET RVGA RVIA RVIB RVIN RVIT RVIV RVSA RVSX RVVI SIXY TOGO VANZ   RV-8: G-DUDE RVBA RVMX
VARGA 2150A KACHINA: G-BLHW BPVK CHTT DJCR VARG
VAN DEN BEMDEN Balloon (Gas): G-BBFS BDTU BIHP BWCC
VENTURE - see THORP
VERTICAL AVN TECHNOLOGIES S-52-3 HUMMINGBIRD: G-BVBD BVBO
VICKERS
  FB-5 GUNBUS: G-ATVP   FB.27 VIMY rep: "G-AWAU"   60 VIKING rep: "G-EBED"   V.600 VIKING: G-AGRU AGRW AIVG
  V.668 VARSITY: G-BEDV BHDD   V.700/800 VISCOUNT: G-ALWF AMOG AOHL AOJC AOJD AOYR APIM AZLP AZLS AZNA AZNC BAPF
  V.950/1 VANGUARD/MERCHANTMAN: G-APEK APEP   VC-10: G-ARVF ARVM ASGC
VICKERS-SUPERMARINE
  WALRUS/SEAGULL: G-AIZG RNLI
  SPITFIRE/SEAFIRE: G-AIST AISU AWII AWIJ BJSG BKMI BMSB BRAF BRDV BRMG BRRA BRSF BSKP BUAR BUOS BUWA BWEM BXHZ BXVI BYDE CCIX
  G-CCVV CTIX FXII FXIV HFIX HVDM IXCC LFIX LFVB LFVC MKIX MKVB MKXI MXVI OXVI PMNF PRXI RRGN SPIT TRIX XVIE
  SWIFT: G-SWIF
VICTA - including AESL production
  AIRTOURER: G-ATCL ATEX ATHT ATJC AWDE AWMI AWVG AXIX AYLA AYMF AYWM AZBE AZHI AZHT AZMN AZOE AZOF AZRP AZTN BANY
VIKING DRAGONFLY: G-BKPD BNEV BRKY DKGF EI-BPE
VOISIN REP: G-BJHV
VOLMER
  VJ.22 SPORTSMAN: .G-BAHP   VJ-24: G-MBBZ
VOUGHT F4U CORSAIR: G-BXUL FGID N179PT
VPM
  M-14 SCOUT: G-BUEN   M-16 TANDEM TRAINER: G-BUPM BUZL BVRD BVWX BXEJ BXIX CVPM DBDB NANA POSA YFLY YRAT
VULTURE Tx3 HAFB: G-BICC

W ACO
  UPF-7: G-WACO   YKS-7: G-BWAC
WAG-AERO
  CUBY ACROTRAINER: G-BLDD BTWL   SPORT TRAINER: G-BVMH   WAG-A-BOND: G-BNJA
WALLBRO MONOPLANE: G-BFIP
WALLINGFORD (WMB) HAFB: G-BGZN BIAI BIBX BILB

WALLIS - (including BEAGLE-WALLIS/VINTEN production)
 WA.116/WA.122: G-ARRT ARZB ASDY ATHM ATTB AVJV AVJW AXAS AYVO BAHH BGGU BGGV BGGW BKLZ BLIK BMJX SCAN VIEW VTEN
 WA.201: G-BNDG
W.A.R.
 FOCKE-WULF 190: G-BSLX SYFW WULF   *P-47 THUNDERBOLT:* G-BTBI
WARD *P45 GNOME:* G-AXEI
WASP *GRYPHON (Wing):* G-MBPY MJYW
WASSMER - see JODEL
 WA.41 SUPER BALADOU: G-ATSY ATZS AVEU   *WA.52 PACIFIC/EUROPA:* G-AZYZ BTLB   *WA.81 PIRANHA:* G-BKOT
WATKINSON - see TAYLOR-WATKINSON
WEEDHOPPER
 JC-24: G-BHWH MBAD MBPW MTNK   *JC-31:* G-MVXF
WEST *Ax3-15 HAFB:* G-BCFD
WESTERN
 20: G-AYMV   *O-31:* G-AZPX   *O-56:* G-AZUX   *O-65:* G-AZBT AZJI AZOO BBCB BBUT
WESTLAND - (see SUD AVIATION & including SIKORSKY production)
 LYSANDER: G-AZWT LIZY   *WS.51 DRAGONFLY:* "G-AJOV" BRMA   *WS.51/2 WIDGEON:* G-ANLW AOZE APTW
 WS.55 WHIRLWIND: G-ANFH ANJV AODA APWN AYNP AYXT AYZJ BDBZ BEBC BJWY BKHA BVGE RWWW   *WS.58 WESSEX:* G-ATBZ AVNE AWOX AZBY BYRC
 WG.13 LYNX: G-BEAD LYNX   *WG.30:* G-BGHF BIWY BKGD BKKI BKXY BLLF ELEC HAUL KATE OGAS
 SCOUT: G-BKLJ BWHU BWJW BWLX BXOE BXRL BXRR BXRS BXSL BYKJ BYNZ BYRX CRUM KAXL NOTY ONEB SCTA SROE   *WASP:* G-BMIR KAWW RIMM
WESTLAND-AGUSTA - see EH INDUSTRIES
WESTLAND-BELL - see BELL
WHE *AIRBUGGY:* G-AXYX AXYZ AXZA AXZB
WHEELER - see FLYLITE
 SCOUT/SKYCRAFT: G-MBAR MBBB MBOU MBRE MBUZ MJAL MNKN MNMS
WHEELER *SLYMPH:* G-ABOI
WHITTAKER - including AEROTECH
 MW.2B EXCALIBUR: G-BDDX
 MW.4/5/SORCERER: G-MBTH MMGV MMMM MNXZ MTAS MTBP MTBR MTBS MTBT MTDK MTFN MTHB MTLZ MTRX MVHM MVNN MVNO MVNP MVNR MVNS MVNT
 G-MVNU MWEK MWEO MWGI MWGJ MWGK MWIC MWJW MWLN MWSX MWSY MYAH MYAN MYDL MYDW MYJZ MYRB MZEI MZOH EI-BUL EI-CAN EI-CTL
 MW.6 MERLIN/MW.6S FATBOY FLYER/MW.6T: G-BUOA BYTX MGCK MNMW MTMD MTRE MTTF MTXO MURR MVPH MVPM MVPN MVTD MVTE MVXA MWAW MWHM
 G-MWIP MWLO MWOV MWPR MWSW MWTS MWVI MWWW MYCA MYCP MYCU MYDM MYEF MYET MYEV MYGE MYIE MYKO MYMN MYPP MYPS MYSN MYZA MYZN MZBG
 G-MZBX MZCH MZDI MZDL MZFK MZFS MZHG MZHT MZID MZIN MZJP MZNE MZOK MZZZ EI-BVB EI-CJZ EI-CKN EI-CLL EI-COM
 MW.7: G-BOKH BOKI BOKJ BPUP BREE BRMW BSXX BTFV BTUS BWVN   *MW.8:* G-MYJX
WILLGRESS - see GRYPHON
 GRYPHON: G-MBPS
WILLIAMS *KFZ-1 TIGERFALCK:* G-KFZI
WILLIAMS (WESTWIND) *HAFB:* G-FYAN FYAO FYAU FYDI FYDP FYFJ
WILLS *AERA:* G-BJKW
WINDSOR *HAFB:* G-BJGD
WITTMAN *TAILWIND:* G-BCBR BDAP BDBD BDJC BJWT BMHL BNOB BOHV BOIB BPYJ CIPI JBPR PFAD WYND ZIPY
WITTY *SPHINX HAFB:* G-BJLV
WOLF *W-II BOREDOM FIGHTER:* G-BMZX BNAI
WOMBAT *GYROCOPTER:* G-BFYP WBAT
WOOD *DUET:* G-DUET
WOODS - see AEROSPORT
WSK-PZL - see MIKOYAN
 SB Lim-2: G-OMIG
 MIELEC TS-11 ISKRA: G-BXVZ

Y AKOVLEV - including ACROSTAR/IAU-BACAU/LET/NANCHANG production

 YAK-1: G-BTZD   *YAK-3:* G-BTHD BWOE   *YAK-11:* G-BTUB BTZE DYAK IYAK KYAK OYAK YCII
 YAK-18: G-BMJY BVFX BVVF BVVG BVVX BXZB   *YAK-50:* G-BTZB BVVO BWFM BWJT BWWH BWWX BWYK BXNO FUNK IVAR VLAD YAKA
 YAK-52: G-BVMU BVOK BVVA BVVW BVXK BWFP BWOD BWSV BWSW BWVR BWVX BXAK BXAV BXID BXJB CCCP YAKI YAKS YAKX YAKO YAKY YKSZ
 YAK-55: G-YAKM

Z EBEDEE *V-31 HAFB:* G-BXIT

ZENAIR - see HEINTZ/COLOMBAN
 CH-600/CH.601/ZODIAC: G-BRII BRJB BUTG BUZG BVAB BVAC BVPL BVVM BVZR OBYJT BYLF BYPR CLEO OANN OMWE ZAIR
 CH-701: G-BRDB BTMW BXIG BYEO EOIN FAMH TTDD
ZLIN
 226/326/526 TRENER/TRENER MASTER/AKROBAT: G-AWJX AWJY AWSH BEWO BEZA BIVW BKOB BLMA BPNO BUPO EJGO TINY ZLIN ZLYN EI-BIG
 Z.242: G-BWTC BWTD OZLN   *Z.381* - see *BUCKER Bu 181 BESTMANN*   *Z.50L:* G-MATE

PART 2 - MISCELLANEOUS INDICES

In certain circumstances the Civil Aviation Authority may permit the operation of an aircraft without the need to carry regulation size national registration letters. These conditions are referred to as "exemptions". The CAA will issue to each operator an Exemption Certificate which is usually valid for two years. The basic requirements are that the owner undertakes to notify the CAA of the markings carried and may not, without specific permission of the overseas country, fly overseas.

In the case of aircraft wearing military marks the authority of the relevant department at the Ministry of Defence is required for UK markings whilst an equivalent establishment must sanction any overseas markings to be carried. Below are details of aircraft, including gliders, known to be wearing military marks currently as compiled from member's observations. The information includes any BAPC, Class B, and overseas registered aircraft known to be in the UK & Ireland. Full details of BAPC markings are carried in SECTION 5. In addition we provide separate listings of aircraft which carry fictitious registrations and also those with no known external markings.

(i) - MILITARY MARKINGS

Country	Serial	Code	Regn	Type

UNITED KINGDOM - RAF unless otherwise shown

	Serial	Code	Regn	Type
	168		G-BFDE	Sopwith Tabloid Scout rep. (RNAS)
	304		BAPC.62	Cody Biplane (RFC)
	687		BAPC.181	RAF BE.2b (RFC)
	1701		BAPC.117	RAF BE.2c rep. (RFC)
	2345		G-ATVP	Vickers FB.5 Gunbus rep. (RFC)
	2882		BAPC.234	Vickers FB.5 Gunbus rep. (RFC)
	3066		G-AETA	Caudron G.III (RNAS)
	5964		BAPC.112	DH.2 rep. (RFC)
	6232		BAPC.41	RAF BE.2c rep. (RFC)
	A1742		BAPC.38	Bristol Scout D rep. (RFC)
	A4850		BAPC.176	SE.5A rep. (RFC)
	A7317		BAPC.179	Sopwith Pup rep. (RFC)
	A8226		G-BIDW	Sopwith 1 1/2-Strutter rep. (RFC)
	B415		BAPC.163	AFEE 10/45 Rotabuggy rep.
	B595	"W"	G-BUOD	SE.5A rep. (RFC)
	B1807	"A7"	G-EAVX	Sopwith Pup (RFC) - intended marks
	B2458	"R"	G-BPOB	Sopwith Camel rep. (RFC)
	B3459	"2"	G-BWMJ	Nieuport Scout 17/23 rep (RFC)
	B4863	"G"	G-BLXT	SE.5A (RFC)
	B6291		G-ASOP	Sopwith Camel (RFC)
	B6401		G-AWYY	Sopwith Camel rep. (RFC)
	B7270		G-BFCZ	Sopwith Camel rep. (RFC)
	C1904	"Z"	G-PFAP	SE.5A (Currie Wot) (RFC)
	C3011	"S"	G-SWOT	SE.5A (Currie Wot) (RFC)
	C4451		BAPC.210	Avro 504J rep. (RFC)
	C4918		G-BWJM	Bristol M.1C rep.
	C4994		G-BLWM	Bristol M.1C rep. (RFC)
	C9533	"M"	G-BUWE	SE.5A rep. (RFC)
	D276	"A"	BAPC.208	SE.5A rep. (RFC)
	D3419		BAPC.59	Sopwith Camel rep. (RFC)
	D7889		G-AANM	Bristol F.2B Fighter - intended marks
	D8084	"S"	G-ACAA	Bristol F.2B Fighter
	D8096	"D"	G-AEPH	Bristol F.2B Fighter
	D8781		G-ECKE	Avro 504K rep (RFC)
	E449		G-EBJE	Avro 504K
	E2466		BAPC.165	Bristol F2B Fighter
	F141	"G"	G-SEVA	SE.5A rep. (RFC)
	F235	"B"	G-BMDB	SE.5A rep. (RFC)
	F904	"H"	G-EBIA	SE.5A (RFC)
	F938		G-EBIC	SE.5A (RFC)
	F943		G-BIHF	SE.5A rep. (RFC)
	F943		G-BKDT	SE.5A rep. (RFC)
	F5447	"N"	G-BKER	SE.5A rep. (RFC)
	F5459	"Y"	G-INNY	SE.5A rep. (RFC)
	F5459	"Y"	BAPC.142	SE.5A rep. (RFC)
	F5475		BAPC.250	SE.5A rep. (RFC)
	F8010	"Z"	G-BDWJ	SE.5A rep. (RFC)
	F8614		G-AWAU	Vickers FB.27A Vimy rep.
	H1968		BAPC.42	Avro 504K rep.

Country	Serial	Code	Regn	Type
	H3426		BAPC.68	Hawker Hurricane rep.
	H5199		G-ADEV	Avro 504K
	J7326		G-EBQP	DH.53 Humming Bird - intended marks
	J9941		G-ABMR	Hawker Hart II
	K1786		G-AFTA	Hawker Tomtit
	K1930		G-BKBB	Hawker Fury II
	K2050		G-ASCM	Hawker (Isaacs) Fury
	K2059		G-PFAR	Hawker (Isaacs) Fury
	K2060		G-BKZM	Hawker (Isaacs) Fury
	K2075		G-BEER	Hawker (Isaacs) Fury
	K2227		G-ABBB	Bristol Bulldog IIA
	K2567		G-MOTH	DH.82 Tiger Moth
	K2572		G-AOZH	DH.82A Tiger Moth
	K2587		G-BJAP	DH.82A Tiger Moth
	K3215		G-AHSA	Avro Tutor
	K3731		G-RODI	Hawker (Isaacs) Fury
	K4232		SE-AZB	Cierva C.30A (Avro Rota)
	K4235	"KX-H"	G-AHMJ	Cierva C.30A (Avro Rota)
	K4259	"71"	G-ANMO	DH.82A Tiger Moth
	K5054		G-BRDV	Supermarine Spitfire Prototype rep.
	K5054		BAPC.190	Supermarine Spitfire rep.
	K5054		BAPC.214	Supermarine Spitfire rep.
	K5414	"XV"	G-AENP	Hawker Hind
	K5600		G-BVVI	Hawker Audax
	K5673		BAPC.249	Hawker Fury I rep.
	K7271		BAPC.148	Hawker Fury rep.
	K8203		G-BTVE	Hawker Demon I
	K8303	"D"	G-BWWN	Hawker (Isaacs) Fury
	K9853	"QV-H"	G-AIST	Supermarine Spitfire IA - see AR213
	K9926	"JH-C"	BAPC.217	Supermarine Spitfire rep.
	L1070	"XT-A"	BAPC.227	Supermarine Spitfire rep.
	L1679	"JX-G"	BAPC.241	Hawker Hurricane 1 rep.
	L1710	"AL-D"	BAPC.219	Hawker Hurricane rep.
	L2301		G-AIZG	Supermarine Walrus 1 (RN)
	L6906		G-AKKY	Miles Magister
	N500		G-BWRA	Sopwith Triplane rep. (RNAS)
	N546		BAPC.164	Wight Quadruplane rep.
	N1854		G-AIBE	Fairey Fulmar 2 (RN)
	N3194	"GR-Z"	BAPC.220	Supermarine Spitfire rep.
	N3289	"QV-K"	BAPC.65	Supermarine Spitfire rep.
	N3313	"KL-B"	BAPC.69	Supermarine Spitfire rep.
	N5182		G-APUP	Sopwith Pup (RNAS)
	N5195		G-ABOX	Sopwith Pup (RNAS)
	N5492	"B"	BAPC.111	Sopwith Triplane rep. (RNAS)
	N6181		G-EBKY	Sopwith Pup (RNAS)
	N6290		G-BOCK	Sopwith Triplane rep. (RNAS)
	N6452		G-BIAU	Sopwith Pup rep. (RNAS)
	N6466		G-ANKZ	DH.82A Tiger Moth
	N6740		G-AISY	DH.82A Tiger Moth
	N6797		G-ANEH	DH.82A Tiger Moth
	N6847		G-APAL	DH.82A Tiger Moth
	N6848		G-BALX	DH.82A Tiger Moth
	N6965	"FL-J"	G-AJTW	DH.82A Tiger Moth
	N6985		G-AHMN	DH.82A Tiger Moth
	N9191		G-ALND	DH.82A Tiger Moth (RN)
	N9192	"RCO-N"	G-DHZF	DH.82A Tiger Moth
	N9389		G-ANJA	DH.82A Tiger Moth
	P2793	"SD-M"	BAPC.236	Hawker Hurricane rep.
	P2902	"DX-X"	G-ROBT	Hawker Hurricane I
	P3059	"SD-N"	BAPC.64	Hawker Hurricane rep.
	P3208	"SD-T"	BAPC.63	Hawker Hurricane rep.
	P3386	"FT-I"	BAPC.218	Hawker Hurricane rep.
	P6382	"C"	G-AJRS	Miles Magister
	P7350	"BA-Y"	G-AWIJ	Vickers Supermarine 329 Spitfire F.IIA
	P8140	"ZF-K"	BAPC.71	Supermarine Spitfire rep.
	P8448	"UM-D"	BAPC.225	Supermarine Spitfire rep.
	R1914		G-AHUJ	Miles Magister
	R3821	"UX-N"	G-BPIV	Bristol Blenheim IV
	R4897		G-ERTY	DH.82A Tiger Moth

Country	Serial	Code	Regn	Type
	R4959	"59"	G-ARAZ	DH.82A Tiger Moth
	S1287	"5"	G-BEYB	Fairey Flycatcher rep. (FAA)
	S1579	"571"	G-BBVO	Hawker Nimrod (Isaacs Fury) (RN)
	T5424		G-AJOA	DH.82A Tiger Moth
	T5672		G-ALRI	DH.82A Tiger Moth
	T5854		G-ANKK	DH.82A Tiger Moth
	T5879		G-AXBW	DH.82A Tiger Moth
	T6066		G-ANJK	DH.82A Tiger Moth
	T6313		G-AHVU	DH.82A Tiger Moth
	T6390		G-ANIX	DH.82A Tiger Moth
	T6562		G-ANTE	DH.82A Tiger Moth
	T6818	"91"	G-ANKT	DH.82A Tiger Moth
	T6953		G-ANNI	DH.82A Tiger Moth
	T6991		G-ANOR	DH.82A Tiger Moth
	T7230		G-AFVE	DH.82A Tiger Moth
	T7245		G-ANEJ	DH.82A Tiger Moth
	T7281		G-ARTL	DH.82A Tiger Moth
	T7404	"04"	G-ANMV	DH.82A Tiger Moth
	T7471		G-AJHU	DH.82A Tiger Moth
	T7842		G-AMTF	DH.82A Tiger Moth
	T7909		G-ANON	DH.82A Tiger Moth
	T7997		G-AHUF	DH.82A Tiger Moth
	T8191		G-BWMK	DH.82A Tiger Moth
	T9707		G-AKKR	Miles Magister
	T9738		G-AKAT	Miles Magister
	V1075		G-AKPF	Miles Magister
	V3388		G-AHTW	Airspeed Oxford 1
	V6028	"GB-D"	G-MKIV	Bristol Blenheim IV
	V6799	"SD-X"	BAPC.72	Hawker Hurricane rep.
	V7476	"LE-D"	BAPC.223	Hawker Hurricane rep.
	V9441	"AR-A"	G-AZWT	Westland Lysander IIIA
	V9545	"BA-C"	G-BCWL	Westland Lysander IIIA
	V9673	"MA-J"	G-LIZY	Westland Lysander III
	W2718	"AA5Y"	G-RNLI	Supermarine Walrus (RN)
	W5856	"A2A"	G-BMGC	Fairey Swordfish II
	W9385	"YG-L"	G-ADND	DH.87B Hornet Moth
	Z2033	"N/275"	G-ASTL	Fairey Firefly TT.1
	Z???1	"XR-T"	G-HURI	Hawker Hurricane IIB
	Z5053		G-BWHA	Hawker Hurricane IIB
	Z5252	"GO-B"	G-BWHA	Hawker Hurricane IIB
	Z7015	"7-L"	G-BKTH	Hawker Sea Hurricane IB (RN)
	Z7197		G-AKZN	Percival Proctor III
	AA908	"UM-W"	BAPC.230	Supermarine Spitfire rep.
	AB910	"ZD-C"	G-AISU	Vickers Supermarine 349 Spitfire LF.VB
	AE977		G-TWTD	Hawker Sea Hurricane X
	AP507	"KX-P"	G-ACWP	Cierva C.30A (Avro Rota)
	AR213	"PR-D"	G-AIST	Supermarine Spitfire IA - see K9853
	AR501	"NN-A"	G-AWII	Supermarine Spitfire Vc
	AR614	"DU-Z"	G-BUWA	Supermarine Spitfire Vc
	BB807		G-ADWO	DH.82A Tiger Moth
	BE417	"AE-K"	G-HURR	Hawker Hurricane IIB
	BE421	"XP-G"	BAPC.205	Hawker Hurricane rep.
	BL924	"AZ-G"	BAPC.242	Supermarine Spitfire VB rep.
	BM597	"JH-C"	G-MKVB	Supermarine Spitfire VB
	BR600	"SH-V"	BAPC.222	Supermarine Spitfire rep.
	BR600	"JP-A"	BAPC.224	Supermarine Spitfire rep.
	(NOTE: Another "BR600" Spitfire rep. was in open storage Dunkeswell 11.95)			
	BW881		G-KAMM	Hawker Hurricane XIIA
	CB733		G-BCUV	Scottish Bulldog
	DE208		G-AGYU	DH.82A Tiger Moth
	DE470	"16"	G-ANMY	DH.82A Tiger Moth
	DE623		G-ANFI	DH.82A Tiger Moth
	DE673		G-ADNZ	DH.82A Tiger Moth
	DE970		G-AOBJ	DH.82A Tiger Moth
	DE992		G-AXXV	DH.82A Tiger Moth
	DF112		G-ANRM	DH.82A Tiger Moth
	DF128	"RCO-U"	G-AOJJ	DH.82A Tiger Moth
	DF155		G-ANFV	DH.82A Tiger Moth
	DG590		G-ADMW	Miles Hawk Major

Country	Serial	Code	Regn	Type
	DR613		G-AFJB	Foster-Wikner Wicko (Warferry)
	DR628		N18V	Beechcraft Traveler
	EM720		G-AXAN	DH.82A Tiger Moth
	EN224		G-FXII	Supermarine Spitfire XII - intended marks
	EN343		BAPC.226	Supermarine Spitfire rep.
	EN398	"WO-A"	BAPC.184	Supermarine Spitfire IX rep.
	EP120	"AE-A"	G-LFVB	Supermarine Spitfire VB
	FB226	"MT-A"	G-BDWM	N-A Mustang (Bonsall Mustang)
	FE695	"94"	G-BTXI	N-A Harvard IIB
	FE905		LN-BNM	N-A Harvard IIB
	FE992	"K-T"	G-BDAM	N-A Harvard IIB
	FH153		G-BBHK	N-A Harvard IIB
	FJ777		G-BRTK	Boeing-Stearman Kaydet
	FJ992		G-BPTB	Boeing-Stearman Kaydet
	FR886		G-BDMS	Piper Cub
	FT323	"GN"	FAP 1513	N-A Harvard III
	FT375		G-BWUL	N-A Harvard IIB
	FT391		G-AZBN	N-A Harvard IIB
	FX301	"FD-NQ"	G-JUDI	N-A Harvard III
	HB275		G-BKGM	Beechcraft Expeditor
	HB751		G-BCBL	Fairchild Argus III
	HM580		G-ACUU	Cierva C.30A (Avro Rota)
	KB889	"NA-I"	G-LANC	Avro Lancaster X
	KD345	"130"	G-FGID	Vought FG-1D Corsair (RN)
	KG391	"AG"	G-BVOL	Douglas Dakota III
	KJ351		BAPC.80	Airspeed Horsa II
	KP584		G-RAIX	N-A Harvard IV
	LB312		G-AHXE	Taylorcraft Plus D (Auster I)
	LB367		G-AHGZ	Taylorcraft Plus D (Auster I)
	LB375		G-AHGW	Taylorcraft Plus D (Auster I)
	LF789		BAPC.186	DH.82B Queen Bee
	LF858		G-BLUZ	DH.82B Queen Bee
	LS326	"L/2"	G-AJVH	Fairey Swordfish II
	LZ766		G-ALCK	Percival Proctor III
	MAV467	"R-O"	BAPC.202	Supermarine Spitfire V rep.
	MH434	"PK-K"	G-ASJV	Supermarine Spitfire IXB
	MH486	"FF-A"	BAPC.206	Supermarine Spitfire rep.
	MH777	"RF-N"	BAPC.221	Supermarine Spitfire rep.
	MJ627	"9G-P"	G-BMSB	Supermarine Spitfire IX
	MJ730	"GZ-?"	G-HFIX	Supermarine Spitfire IXe
	MJ751	"DU-V"	BAPC.209	Supermarine Spitfire rep.
	MJ832	"DN-Y"	BAPC.229	Supermarine Spitfire rep.
	MK732	"OU-U"	G-HVDM	Supermarine Spitfire IXc
	MK805	"SH-B"	*	Supermarine Spitfire IX rep.
				* Built by TDL Rep. Aircraft, in 64 Sqn c/s, as "SH-B"/"Peter John III"
	MK912	"MN-P"	G-BRRA	Supermarine Spitfire IX
	ML407	"OU-V"/"NL-D"	G-LFIX	Supermarine Spitfire IX
	ML417	"2I-T"	G-BJSG	Supermarine Spitfire IXe
	MP425		G-AITB	Airspeed Oxford I
	MT438		G-AREI	Auster III
	MT928	"ZX-M"	G-BKMI	Supermarine Spitfire VIIIc
	MV262		G-CCVV	Supermarine Spitfire XIV - intended marks
	MV293	"OI-C"	G-SPIT	Supermarine Spitfire XIVe
	MV370	"EB-Q"	G-FXIV	Supermarine Spitfire XIV
	MW763	"HF-A"	G-TEMT	Hawker Tempest II
	MW800	"HF-V"	G-BSHW	Hawker Tempest II
	NH238	"D-A"	G-MKIX	Supermarine Spitfire IX
	NJ673		G-AOCR	Auster V
	NJ695		G-AJXV	Auster IV
	NJ703		G-AKPI	Auster V
	NJ719		G-ANFU	Auster V - intended marks
	NL750		G-AOBH	DH.82A Tiger Moth
	NL785		G-BWIK	DH.82A Tiger Moth
	NM181		G-AZGZ	DH.82A Tiger Moth
	NS519		G-MOSI	DH.98 Mosquito 35 (RAF/USAAF)
	NX534		G-BUDL	Auster III
	NX611	"LE-C/DX-C"	G-ASXX	Avro Lancaster B.VII
	PL344	"Y2-B"	G-IXCC	Supermarine Spitfire IXe
	PL965	"R"	G-MKXI	Supermarine Spitfire PR.XI

Country	Serial	Code	Regn	Type
	PL983		G-PRXI	Supermarine Spitfire XI
	PP972		G-BUAR	Supermarine Seafire III
	PR772		G-BTTA	Hawker Iraqi Fury
	PS853	"C"	G-RRGN	Supermarine Spitfire PR.XIX
	PT462	"SW-A"	G-CTIX	Supermarine Spitfire IX
	PV202	"5R-Q"	G-TRIX	Supermarine Spitfire IX
	PZ865	"Q"	G-AMAU	Hawker Hurricane IIc
	RG333		G-AIEK	Miles Messenger
	RG333		G-AKEZ	Miles Messenger
	RM221		G-ANXR	Percival Proctor IV
	RN201		G-BSKP	Supermarine Spitfire XIV - intended marks
	RN218	"N"	G-BBJI	Isaacs Spitfire
	RR232		G-BRSF	Supermarine Spitfire IXc
	RT486	"PF-A"	G-AJGJ	Auster 5
	RT610		G-AKWS	Auster 5A
	RX168		G-BWEM	Supermarine Seafire L.III - intended marks
	SM520		G-BXHZ	Supermarine Spitfire HF.IX
	SM845		G-BUOS	Supermarine Spitfire XVIIIe
	SM969	"D-A"	G-BRAF	Supermarine Spitfire XVIII
	SX336		G-BRMG	Supermarine Seafire XVII
	TA634	"8K-K"	G-AWJV	DH.98 Mosquito TT.35
	TA719		G-ASKC	DH.98 Mosquito TT.35
	TA805		G-PMNF	Supermarine Spitfire IX
	TB252	"GW-H"	G-XVIE	Supermarine Spitfire XVIe
	TD248	"D"	G-OXVI	Supermarine Spitfire XVIe
	TE184		G-MXVI	Supermarine Spitfire XVIe
	TE517		G-CCIX	Supermarine Spitfire IXe - intended marks
	TJ398		BAPC.70	Auster V
	TJ565		G-AMVD	Auster V
	TJ569		G-AKOW	Auster V
	TJ672	"TS-D"	G-ANIJ	Auster V
	TJ704	"JA"	G-ASCD	Auster AOP.6 (RN)
	TS291		BGA.852	Slingsby T.8 Tutor
	TS423	"YS-L"	G-DAKS	Douglas Dakota III
	TS798		G-AGNV	Avro 685 York C.1
	TW439		G-ANRP	Auster V
	TW467	"ROD-F"	G-ANIE	Auster V
	TW511		G-APAF	Auster V (Army)
	TW536	"TS-V"	G-BNGE	Auster AOP.6
	TW591		G-ARIH	Auster AOP.6 (Army)
	TW641		G-ATDN	Auster AOP.6
	TX183		G-BSMF	Avro Anson C.19
	VF512	"PF-M"	G-ARRX	Auster AOP.6
	VF516		G-ASMZ	Auster AOP.6
	VF526	"T"	G-ARXU	Auster AOP.6 (Army)
	VF548		G-ASEG	Auster AOP.6
	VF581		G-ARSL	Auster AOP.6
	VL348		G-AVVO	Avro Anson C.19/2
	VL349		G-AWSA	Avro Anson C.19/2
	VM360		G-APHV	Avro Anson C.19/2
	VP955		G-DVON	DH.104 Devon C.2/2
	VP981		G-DHDV	DH.104 Devon 8 (BoBMF c/s)
	VR192		G-APIT	Percival Prentice T.1
	VR249	"FA-EL"	G-APIY	Percival Prentice T.1
	VR259	"M"	G-APJB	Percival Prentice T.1
	VS356		G-AOLU	Percival Prentice T.1
	VS610	"K-L"	G-AOKL	Percival Prentice T.1
	VS623		G-AOKZ	Percival Prentice T.1
	VT871		G-DHXX	DH.100 Vampire FB.6
	VX118		G-ASNB	Auster AOP.6
	VX147		G-AVIL	Ercoupe 415
	VX926		G-ASKJ	Auster AOP.6
	VZ345		D-CATA	Hawker Sea Fury T.20 (RN)
	VZ467	"A"	G-METE	Gloster Meteor F.8
	VZ638	"HF"	G-JETM	Gloster Meteor T.7 (RN)
	VZ728		G-AGOS	Reid & Sigrist Bobsleigh
	WA591		G-BWMF	Gloster Meteor T.7 - intended marks
	WB531		G-BLRN	DH.104 Devon C.2/2
	WB533		G-DEVN	DH.104 Devon C.2/2

Country	Serial	Code	Regn	Type
	WB565	"X"	G-PVET	DHC.1 Chipmunk T.10 (Army)
	WB571	"34"	G-AOSF	DHC.1 Chipmunk T.10
	WB585	"M"	G-AOSY	DHC.1 Chipmunk T.10
	WB588	"D"	G-AOTD	DHC.1 Chipmunk T.10
	WB615		G-BXIA	DHC.1 Chipmunk T.10
	WB652		G-CHPY	DHC.1 Chipmunk T.10
	WB654		G-BXGO	DHC.1 Chipmunk T.10
	WB660		G-ARMB	DHC.1 Chipmunk T.10
	WB671		G-BWTG	DHC.1 Chipmunk T.10
	WB697		G-BXCT	DHC.1 Chipmunk T.10
	WB702		G-AOFE	DHC.1 Chipmunk T.10
	WB703		G-ARMC	DHC.1 Chipmunk T.10
	WB711		G-APPM	DHC.1 Chipmunk T.10
	WB726	"E"	G-AOSK	DHC.1 Chipmunk T.10
	WB763	"14"	G-BBMR	DHC.1 Chipmunk T.10
	WD286	"J"	G-BBND	DHC.1 Chipmunk T.10
	WD288		G-AOSO	DHC.1 Chipmunk T.10
	WD292		G-BCRX	DHC.1 Chipmunk T.10
	WD305		G-ARGG	DHC.1 Chipmunk T.10
	WD310		G-BWUN	DHC.1 Chipmunk T.10
	WD331		G-BXDH	DHC.1 Chipmunk T.10
	WD363		G-BCIH	DHC.1 Chipmunk T.10
	WD373	"12"	G-BXDI	DHC.1 Chipmunk T.10
	WD379	"K"	G-APLO	DHC.1 Chipmunk T.10
	WD390		G-BWNK	DHC.1 Chipmunk T.10
	WD413		G-BFIR	Avro Anson C.21
	WE402		G-VENI	DH.112 Venom FB.1
	WE569		G-ASAJ	Beagle Terrier (Auster T.7)
	WE571	"Y"	G-ASAK	Beagle Terrier (Auster T.7)
	WF877		G-BPOA	Gloster Meteor T.7
	WG307		G-BCYJ	DHC.1 Chipmunk T.10
	WG316		G-BCAH	DHC.1 Chipmunk T.10
	WG321		G-DHCC	DHC.1 Chipmunk T.10
	WG348		G-BBMV	DHC.1 Chipmunk T.10
	WG350		G-BPAL	DHC.1 Chipmunk T.10
	WG407	"67"	G-BWMX	DHC.1 Chipmunk T.10
	WG422		G-BFAX	DHC.1 Chipmunk T.10
	WG465		G-BCEY	DHC.1 Chipmunk T.10
	WG469		G-BWJY	DHC.1 Chipmunk T.10
	WG472		G-AOTY	DHC.1 Chipmunk T.10
	WG719	"705"	G-BRMA	Westland Dragonfly HR.5
	WG754	"912/CU"	N99870	Westland Dragonfly HR.5
	WJ237	"113/0"	G-BLTG	Hawker (WAR) Sea Fury rep. (RN)
	WJ358		G-ARYD	Auster AOP.6
	WJ680	"CT"	G-BURM	EE Canberra TT.18
	WJ945	"21"	G-BEDV	Vickers Varsity T.1
	WK126	"843"	N2138J	EE Canberra TT.18
	WK163		G-BVWC	EE Canberra B.2(mod)
	WK511		G-BVBT	DHC.1 Chipmunk T.10 (RN)
	WK512	"A"	G-BXIM	DHC.1 Chipmunk T.10 (Army)
	WK517		G-ULAS	DHC.1 Chipmunk T.10
	WK522		G-BCOU	DHC.1 Chipmunk T.10
	WK549		G-BTWF	DHC.1 Chipmunk T.10
	WK586	"V"	G-BXGX	DHC.1 Chipmunk T.10 (Army)
	WK590	"69"	G-BWVZ	DHC.1 Chipmunk T.10
	WK609		G-BXDN	DHC.1 Chipmunk T.10
	WK611		G-ARWB	DHC.1 Chipmunk T.10
	WK622		G-BCZH	DHC.1 Chipmunk T.10
	WK624	"M"	G-BWHI	DHC.1 Chipmunk T.10
	WK628		G-BBMW	DHC.1 Chipmunk T.10
	WK630		G-BXDG	DHC.1 Chipmunk T.10
	WK633	"B"	G-BXEC	DHC.1 Chipmunk T.10
	WK638	"83"	G-BWJZ	DHC.1 Chipmunk T.10
	WK640	"C"	G-BWUV	DHC.1 Chipmunk T.10
	WK642		G-BXDP	DHC.1 Chipmunk T.10
	WL505		G-FBIX	DH.100 Vampire FB.9
	WL505		G-MKVI	DH.100 Vampire FB.6
	WL626	"P"	G-BHDD	Vickers Varsity T.1
	WM167		G-LOSM	AW Meteor NF.11

Country	Serial	Code	Regn	Type
	WP788		G-BCHL	DHC.1 Chipmunk T.10
	WP790	"T"	G-BBNC	DHC.1 Chipmunk T.10
	WP795	"901"	G-BVZZ	DHC.1 Chipmunk T.10 (RN)
	WP800	"2"	G-BCXN	DHC.1 Chipmunk T.10
	WP803		G-HAPY	DHC.1 Chipmunk T.10
	WP808		G-BDEU	DHC.1 Chipmunk T.10
	WP809	"778"	G-BVTX	DHC.1 Chipmunk T.10 (RN)
	WP840	"O"	G-BXDM	DHC.1 Chipmunk T.10
	WP843	"F"	G-BDBP	DHC.1 Chipmunk T.10
	WP844		G-BWOX	DHC.1 Chipmunk T.10
	WP851		G-BDET	DHC.1 Chipmunk T.10
	WP856	"904"	G-BVWP	DHC.1 Chipmunk T.10 (RN)
	WP857	"24"	G-BDRJ	DHC.1 Chipmunk T.10
	WP859		G-BXCP	DHC.1 Chipmunk T.10
	WP860	"6"	G-BXDA	DHC.1 Chipmunk T.10
	WP896	"M"	G-BWVY	DHC.1 Chipmunk T.10
	WP901		G-BWNT	DHC.1 Chipmunk T.10
	WP903		G-BCGC	DHC.1 Chipmunk T.10 (Queens Flight)
	WP920		G-BXCR	DHC.1 Chipmunk T.10
	WP925	"C"	G-BXHA	DHC.1 Chipmunk T.10
	WP928		G-BXGM	DHC.1 Chipmunk T.10
	WP929	"F"	G-BXCV	DHC.1 Chipmunk T.10
	WP930		G-BXHF	DHC.1 Chipmunk T.10
	WP971		G-ATHD	DHC.1 Chipmunk T.10
	WP977		G-BHRD	DHC.1 Chipmunk T.10
	WP983	"B"	G-BXNN	DHC.1 Chipmunk T.10
	WP984	"H"	G-BWTO	DHC.1 Chipmunk T.10
	WR410	"N"	G-BLKA	DH.112 Venom FB.4
	WR410		G-DHUU	DH.112 Venom FB.1
	WR421		G-DHTT	DH.112 Venom FB.1
	WT327		G-BXMO	EE Canberra B.6
	WT333		G-BVXC	EE Canberra B(I).8
	WT722	"878"	G-BWGN	Hawker Hunter T.8C (RN)
	WV198	"K"	G-BJWY	Sikorsky Whirlwind HAR.21
	WV318		G-FFOX	Hawker Hunter T.7B
	WV372	"R"	G-BXFI	Hawker Hunter T.7
	WV493	"29"/"A-P"	G-BDYG	Percival Provost T.1
	WV494	"04"	G-BGSB	Percival Provost T.1
	WV666	"O-D"	G-BTDH	Percival Provost T.1
	WV740		G-BNPH	Hunting Percival Pembroke C.1
	WW453	"W-S"	G-TMKI	Percival Provost T.1
	WZ507		G-VTII	DH.115 Vampire T.11
	WZ553	"40"	G-DHYY	DH.115 Vampire T.11
	WZ589		G-DHZZ	DH.115 Vampire T.55
	WZ662		G-BKVK	Auster AOP.9 (Army)
	WZ706		G-BURR	Auster AOP.9 (Army)
	WZ711		G-AVHT	Auster AOP.9 (Army)
	WZ729		G-BXON	Auster AOP.9
	WZ819		BGA.3498	Slingsby T.38 Grasshopper
	WZ847		G-CPMK	DHC.1 Chipmunk T.10
	WZ868	"H"	G-ARMF	DHC.1 Chipmunk T.10
	WZ868	"H"	G-BCIW	DHC.1 Chipmunk T.10 (wreck)
	WZ879	"73"	G-BWUT	DHC.1 Chipmunk T.10
	WZ882		G-BXGP	DHC.1 Chipmunk T.10
	XA880		G-BVXR	DH.104 Devon C.2 (RAE)
	XD693	"Z-Q"	G-AOBU	Percival Jet Provost T.1
	XE665	"876"	G-BWGM	Hawker Hunter T.8C (RN)
	XE677		G-HHUN	Hawker Hunter F.4
	XE685	"861/VL"	G-GAII	Hawker Hunter GA.11 (RN)
	XE689	"864/VL"	G-BWGK	Hawker Hunter GA.11 (RN)
	XE897		G-DHVV	DH.115 Vampire T.55
	XE920	"A"	G-VMPR	DH.115 Vampire T.11
	XE956		G-OBLN	DH.115 Vampire T.11
	XF114		G-SWIF	Supermarine Swift F.7
	XF375	"05"	G-BUEZ	Hawker Hunter F.6A
	XF515	"R"	G-KAXF	Hawker Hunter F.6A
	XF516	"F"	G-BVVC	Hawker Hunter F.6A
	XF597	"AH"	G-BKFW	Percival Provost T.1
	XF603	"H"	G-KAPW	Percival Provost T.1

Country	Serial	Code	Regn	Type
	XF690		G-MOOS	Percival Provost T.1
	XF836	"J-G"	G-AWRY	Percival Provost T.1
	XF877	"J-X"	G-AWVF	Percival Provost T.1
	XG160	"U"	G-BWAF	Hawker Hunter F.6A
	XG232		G-BWIU	Hawker Hunter F.6
	XG452		G-BRMB	Bristol Belvedere HC.1
	XG547	"T-S/S-T"	G-HAPR	Bristol Sycamore HR.14
	XG775	"VL"	G-DHWW	DH.115 Vampire T.11 (RN)
	XH558		G-VLCN	Avro Vulcan B.2
	XH568		G-BVIC	English Electric Canberra B.2/B.6
	XJ347		G-AMXT	DH.104 Sea Devon C.20
	XJ348		G-NAVY	DH.104 Sea Devon C.20 (RN)
	XJ729		G-BVGE	Westland Whirlwind HAR.10
	XJ763	"P"	G-BKHA	Westland Whirlwind HAR.10
	XJ771		G-HELV	DH.115 Vampire T.55
	XK416		G-AYUA	Auster AOP.9
	XK417		G-AVXY	Auster AOP.9
	XK895	"CU-19"	G-SDEV	DH.104 Sea Devon C.20 (RN)
	XK896		G-RNAS	DH.104 Sea Devon C.20 (RN)
	XK940		G-AYXT	Westland Whirlwind HAS.7
	XL426		G-VJET	Avro Vulcan B.2
	XL502		G-BMYP	Fairey Gannet AEW.3 (RN)
	XL572	"83"	G-HNTR	Hawker Hunter T.7
	XL573		G-BVGH	Hawker Hunter T.7
	XL577		G-BXKF	Hawker Hunter T.7
	XL602		G-BWFT	Hawker Hunter T.8M
	XL613		G-BVMB	Hawker Hunter T.7A
	XL616	"D"	G-BWIE	Hawker Hunter T.7A
	XL621		G-BNCX	Hawker Hunter T.7
	XL714		G-AOGR	DH.82A Tiger Moth
	XL809		G-BLIX	Saro Skeeter AOP.12 (Army)
	XL812		G-SARO	Saro Skeeter AOP.12
	XL929		G-BNPU	Hunting Percival Pembroke C.1
	XL954		G-BXES	Hunting Percival Pembroke C.1
	XM223		G-BWWC	DH.104 Devon C.2
	XM365		G-BXBH	Hunting Jet Provost T.3A
	XM370		G-BVSP	Hunting Jet Provost T.3A
	XM376	"27"	G-BWDR	Hunting Jet Provost T.3A
	XM378		G-BWZE	Hunting Jet Provost T.3A
	XM424		G-BWDS	Hunting Jet Provost T.3A
	XM470		G-BWZZ	Hunting Jet Provost T.3
	XM478		G-BXDL	Hunting Jet Provost T.3A
	XM479	"54"	G-BVEZ	Hunting Jet Provost T.3A
	XM553		G-AWSV	Saro Skeeter AOP.12
	XM575		G-BLMC	Avro Vulcan B.2A
	XM655		G-VULC	Avro Vulcan B.2A
	XM685	"PO/513"	G-AYZJ	Westland Whirlwind HAS.7
	XM693		G-TIMM	Folland Gnat T.1
	XM697		G-NAAT	Folland Gnat T.1
	XM819		G-APXW	Lancashire Acft EP.9 (Army)
	XN351		G-BKSC	Saro Skeeter AOP.12 (Army)
	XN441		G-BGKT	Auster AOP.9
	XN459		G-BWOT	Hunting Jet Provost T.3A
	XN470		G-BXBJ	Hunting Jet Provost T.3A
	XN498	"16"	G-BWSH	Hunting Jet Provost T.3A
	XN510		G-BXBI	Hunting Jet Provost T.3A
	XN629	"49"	G-BVEG	Hunting Jet Provost T.3A
	XN637	"03"	G-BKOU	Hunting Jet Provost T.3
	XP242		G-BUCI	Auster AOP.9 (Army)
	XP254		G-ASCC	Auster AOP.11
	XP279		G-BWKK	Auster AOP.9 (Army)
	XP282		G-BGTC	Auster AOP.9
	XP355	"A"	G-BEBC	Westland Whirlwind HAR.10
	XP672	"03"	G-RAFI	Hunting Jet Provost T.4
	XP772		G-BUCJ	DHC.2 Beaver AL.1 (Army)
	XP907		G-SROE	Westland Scout AH.1
	XP924		G-CVIX	DH.110 Sea Vixen D.3
	XR240		G-BDFH	Auster AOP.9 (Army)
	XR241		G-AXRR	Auster AOP.9 (Army)

Country	Serial	Code	Regn		Type
	XR246		G-AZBU		Auster AOP.9
	XR267		G-BJXR		Auster AOP.9
	XR486		G-RWWW		Westland Whirlwind HCC.12 (Queens Flight c/s)
	XR537	"T"	G-NATY		Folland Gnat T.1
	XR595	"M"	G-BWHU		Westland Scout AH.1 (Army)
	XR673		G-BXLO		Hunting Jet Provost T.4
	XR724		G-BTSY		EE Lightning F.6
	XR944		G-ATTB		Wallis WA.116
	XR991		G-MOUR		Folland Gnat T.1 (Yellowjacks c/s)
	XR993		G-BVPP		Folland Gnat T.1 (Red Arrows c/s)
	XS101		G-GNAT		Folland Gnat T.1 (Red Arrows c/s)
	XS165	"37"	G-ASAZ		Hiller UH-12E (RN)
	XS587	"252/V"	G-VIXN		DH.110 Sea Vixen FAW.2
	XS765		G-BSET		Beagle Basset CC.1
	XS770		G-HRHI		Beagle Basset CC.1 (Queens Flight c/s)
	XT223		G-BGZK		Westland Sioux AH.1 (Army)
	XT653		BGA.3469		Slingsby T.45 Swallow
	XT788		G-BMIR		Westland Wasp HAS.1
	XV121		G-BYKJ		Westland Scout AH.1 (Army)
	XV126	"X"	G-SCTA		Westland Scout AH.1 (Army)
	XV130	"R"	G-BWJW		Westland Scout AH.1 (Army)
	XV134		G-BWLX		Westland Scout AH.1 (Army)
	XV140		G-KAXL		Westland Scout AH.1 (Army)
	XV268		G-BVER		DHC.2 Beaver (Army)
	XV613		G-BXRS		Westland Scout AH.1
	XW281	"U"	G-BYNZ		Westland Scout AH.1 (Royal Marines)
	XW289	"73"	G-JPVA		BAC Jet Provost T.5A
	XW293	"Z"	G-BWCS		BAC Jet Provost T.5
	XW310	"37"	G-BWGS		BAC Jet Provost T.5A
	XW324		G-BWSG		BAC Jet Provost T.5
	XW325	"E"	G-BWGF		BAC Jet Provost T.5A
	XW333	"79"	G-BVTC		BAC Jet Provost T.5A
	XW355	"20"	G-JPTV		BAC Jet Provost T.5A
	XW423	"14"	G-BWUW		BAC Jet Provost T.5A
	XW428		G-TOMG		BAC Jet Provost T.4
	XW431	"A"	G-BWBS		BAC Jet Provost T.5A
	XW433		G-JPRO		BAC Jet Provost T.5A (CFS)
	XW613		G-BXRS		Westland Scout AH.1 (Army)
	XW635		G-AWSW		Beagle Husky
	XW784	"VL"	G-BBRN		Mitchell-Procter Kittiwake (RN)
	XX110		BAPC.169		BAC/Sepecat Jaguar GR.1
	XX263	"263"	BAPC.152		BAe Hawk T.1A
	XX297		BAPC.171		BAe Hawk T.1 (Red Arrows)
	XX467		G-TVII		Hawker Hunter T.7 (TWU)
	XX725	"GU"	BAPC.150		BAC/Sepecat Jaguar GR.1
	XZ363	"A"	BAPC.151		BAC/Sepecat Jaguar GR.1A
	ZA368	"AJ-P"	BAPC.155	\	Panavia Tornado GR.1
	ZA634	"C"	G-BUHA		Slingsby T-61F Venture T.2
	ZA663		G-BUFP		Slingsby T-61F Venture T.2
	ZD472	"01"	BAPC.191		BAe Harrier GR.5
	G-17-3		G-AVNE		Westland Wessex 60
	G-29-1		G-APRJ		Avro Lincoln
		"F"	G-RUMW		Grumman FM-2 Wildcat (RN/FAA)
		"AL-K"	G-HURR		Hawker Hurricane XII
		"VO-B"	G-BYDR		N-A B-25D Mitchell II
		"42"	G-TORE		Hunting Jet Provost T.3A
	G-48/1		G-ALSX		Bristol Sycamore
	U-0247		G-AGOY		Miles Messenger - intended marks
	W-2		BAPC.85		Weir W-2

OTHER ARMED FORCES

AUSTRALIA

	Serial	Code	Regn	Type
	A2-4		VH-ALB	Supermarine Seagull
	A16-199	"SF-R"	G-BEOX	Lockheed Hudson IIIA
	A17-48		G-BPHR	DH.82A Tiger Moth
	361		N36SF	Hawker Sea Fury FB.11 (RAN)
	WH588	"NW/114"	G-EEMV	Hawker Sea Fury FB.11 (RAN)

Country	Serial	Code	Regn	Type

BELGIUM
	HD-75		N75/G-AFDX	Hanriot HD.1

CANADA
	622		N6699D	Piasecki HUP-3 Retreiver (RCN)
	671		G-BNZC	DHC.1 Chipmunk
	920	"QN-."	CF-BXO	Supermarine Stranraer
	16693	"693"	G-BLPG	Auster J/1N (Painted as AOP.6)
	18013		G-TRIC	DHC.1 Chipmunk
	18393		G-BCYK	Avro Canada CF.100 Canuck IV
	20310	"310"	G-BSBG	N.A. Harvard IV

CHINA
	1219	"57"	G-BVVG	Nanchang CJ-6A
	2028	"69"	G-BVVF	Nanchang CJ-6A
	1532008	"08"	G-BVFX	Nanchang CJ-6A

FRANCE
	73		G-BWRF	Morane-Saulnier MS.505 Criquet
	120	"3"	G-AZGC	Stampe SV-4C
	124		G-BOSJ	Nord 3400
	143		G-MSAL	Morane-Saulnier MS.733 (Aeronavale)
	185	"44-CA"	G-BWLR	Max Holste Broussard
	192	"44-GI"	G-BKPT	Max Holste Broussard
	316/315-SN		F-GGKR	Max Holste Broussard
	394		G-BIMO	Stampe SV-4C
	396		G-BWRE	Stampe SV-4C
	18-5395	"CDG"	G-CUBJ	Piper L-18C Super Cub (ALAT)
	MS.824		G-AWBU	Morane-Saulnier N rep.
	1/4513		G-BFYO	SPAD XII rep.
	(F-GGKG)	"315-SQ"	G-BWGG	Max Holste Broussard

GERMANY
	1+4		G-BSLX	WAR FW190 Scale rep.
	3		G-BAYV	Nord 1101 (Messerschmitt guise)
	3 (Red)		G-BOML	Messerschmitt Bf.109 (HA.1112)
	6 (Black)		G-USTV	Messerschmitt Bf.109G-2
	7		G-BWRD	Klemm Kl.35D
	8+-		G-WULF	WAR FW190 Scale rep.
	14		BAPC.67	Messerschmitt Bf.109 rep.
	14+		G-BBII	Fiat G-46
	114		G-BSMD	Nord 1101 (Messerschmitt guise)
	152/17		G-ATJM	Fokker DR.1 rep.
	422/15		G-AVJO	Fokker E-III rep.
	425/15		G-BWRJ	Fokker DR.1 rep.
	425/17		BAPC.133	Fokker DR.1 rep.
	626/8		N6268	Fokker D.VII (Travel Air 2000)
	D5397/17		G-BFXL	Albatros D.VA rep.
	1227	"DG+HO"	G-FOKW	Focke-Wulfe FW190A-5
	1480	"6"	BAPC.66	Messerschmitt Bf.109 rep.
	6357	"6"	BAPC.74	Messerschmitt Bf.109 rep.
	7198/18		G-AANJ	LVG C.VI
	AM+YA		G-AMYA	Bucker (Zlin) 181 Bestmann
	BU+CC		G-BUCC	CASA I-131E Jungmann
	BU+CK		G-BUCK	CASA I-131E Jungmann
	CC+43		G-CJCI	Pilatus P.2 (Arado Ar.96B guise)
	CF+HF		EI-AUY	Fieseler Storch (MS.502)
	D604		G-FLIZ	Staaken Flitzer
	D692		G-BVAW	Staaken Flitzer
	F+IS		G-BIRW	Fieseler Storch (MS.505)
	LG+01		G-AYSJ	Bucker 133 Jungmeister
	LG+03		G-AEZX	Bucker 133 Jungmeister
	NJ+C11		G-ATBG	Messerschmitt Bf.108 (Nord 1002)
	RJ+NP		G-BFHF	Junkers (CASA) Ju52/3m
	S4+A07		G-BWHP	CASA I-131E Jungmann
	S5+B06		G-BSFB	CASA I-131E Jungmann

Country	Serial	Code	Regn	Type
	TA+RC		G-BPHZ	Fieseler Storch (MS.505)
	TQ+BC		LV-ZAU	Focke-Wulf FW.44J Steiglitz
	2+1	"7334"	G-SYFW	WAR FW190 Scale rep.
	28+10		G-BWTT	Aero L-39ZO Albatros
	6J+PR		G-AWHB	Heinkel (CASA) He.111H-16
	97+04		G-APVF	Putzer Elster B
	-		G-BFPL	Fokker D.VII rep. (Skull & crossbones c/s)

HUNGARY
	503		G-BRAM	MiG 21PF (Russian c/s)

IRELAND
	177		G-BLIW	Percival Provost T.51

ITALY
	MM12822		G-FIST	Fieseler Fi 156C Storch
	W7		G-AGFT	Avia FL.3

JAPAN
	24		BAPC.83	Kawasaki Ki 100-1b
	2-134		114700 (French)	NA T-6G Texan

THE NETHERLANDS
	BI-005		G-BUVN	CASA I-131E Jungmann
	E-15		G-BIYU	Fokker S.11 Instructor
	R-151		G-BIYR	Piper L-21B Super Cub
	R-163		G-BIRH	Piper L-21B Super Cub
	R-167		G-LION	Piper L-21B Super Cub
	S-9		G-BUVF	DHC.2 Beaver

NEW ZEALAND
	NZ3009		ZK-AMH	Curtiss P-40E Kittyhawk
	NZ5648	"648"	G-BXUL	Vought FG-1D Corsair
		"192"	G-BYCX	Westland Wasp HAS.1

NORTH KOREA
	01420		G-BMZF	MiG-15

NORWAY
	321		G-BKPY	Saab Safir
	423 & 427		G-AMRK	Gloster Gladiator#

PORTUGAL
	85		G-BTPZ	Hawker (Isaacs) Fury
	1377		G-BARS	DHC.1 Chipmunk
	1747		G-BGPB	CCF Harvard 4

REPUBLIC OF SOUTH AFRICA
	92		G-BYCX	Westland Wasp HAS.Mk.1 (Navy)

RUSSIA
	01		G-YKSZ	Yak 52
	07		G-BMJY	Yak 18
	09		G-BVMU	Yak 52 (DOSAAF)
	26		G-BVXK	Yak 52 (DOSAAF)
	27		G-OYAK	Yak 11
	27		G-YAKX	Yak 52 (DOSAAF)
	42			Yak 52
	50		G-BWJT	Yak 50 (DOSAAF)
	52		G-YAKY	Yak 52 (DOSAAF)
	52		LY-AMP	Yak-52 (DOSAAF)
	55		G-BVOK	Yak 52 (DOSAAF)
	69		G-BTZB	Yak 50
	72		G-BXAV	Yak 52 (DOSAAF)
	74		G-BXID	Yak 52 (DOSAAF)

Country	Serial	Code	Regn	Type
	100		G-YAKI	Yak 52 (DOSAAF)
	139		G-BWOD	Yak 52 (DOSAAF)
	6247		G-OMIG	MiG-15 (Korean War c/s)
	853007		G-BVVO	Yak 50
	-		G-BTUB	Yak 11

SPAIN

	E3B-143		G-JUNG	CASA I.131 Jungmann
	E3B-153	"781-75"	G-BPTS	CASA I.131 Jungmann
	E3B-350	"05-97"	G-BHPL	CASA I.131 Jungmann
	E3B-369	"781-32"	G-BPDM	CASA I.131 Jungmann
	-	"781-25"	G-BRSH	CASA I.131 Jungmann
	-	"781-26"	G-BUOR	CASA I.131 Jungmann

SWEDEN

	32028		G-BMSG	SAAB 32 Lansen

SWITZERLAND

	A-10		G-BECW	CASA I-131E Jungmann
	A-57		G-BECT	CASA I-131E Jungmann
	A-806		G-BTLL	Pilatus P.3
	C-552		G-DORN	EKW C-3605
	J-1149		G-SWIS	DH.100 Vampire FB.6
	J-1573		G-VICI	DH.112 Venom FB.50
	J-1605		G-BLID	DH.112 Venom FB.50
	J-1611		G-DHTT	DH.112 Venom FB.50
	J-1614		G-BLIE	DH.112 Venom FB.50
	J-1632		G-VNOM	DH.112 Venom FB.50
	J-1758		G-BLSD	DH.112 Venom FB.50
	J-4031		G-BWFR	Hawker Hunter F.58
	J-4058		G-BWFS	Hawker Hunter F.58
	J-4066		G-BXNZ	Hawker Hunter F.58
	J-4081		G-BWKB	Hawker Hunter F.58
	J-4083		G-EGHH	Hawker Hunter F.58
	J-4090		G-SIAL	Hawker Hunter F.58
	U-80		G-BUKK	Bucker Jungmeister
	U-95		G-BVGP	Bucker Jungmeister
	U-110		G-PTWO	Pilatus P.2
	U-1234		G-DHAV	DH.115 Vampire T.11
	V-54		G-BVSD	SE.3130 Alouette II

UNITED STATES OF AMERICA

	2		G-AZLE	Boeing-Stearman Kaydet (US Army)
	5		G-BEEW	Taylor Monoplane (Boeing P-26A) (US Army)
	14		G-ISDN	Boeing-Stearman Kaydet (US Army)
	23		N49272	Fairchild PT-23 Cornell (USAAC)
	26		G-BAVO	Boeing-Stearman Kaydet (US Army)
	27		G-AGYY	Ryan PT-21 (USAAC)
	27		G-BRVG	NA SNJ-7 Texan (US Navy)
	28		N8162G	Boeing-Stearman Kaydet (US Army)
	33		G-THEA	Boeing-Stearman Kaydet (US Navy)
	43	"SC"	G-AZSC	NA AT-16 Texan (USAAF)
	44		G-BWHH	Piper L-21B Super Cub (US Army)
	44		G-RJAH	Boeing-Stearman Kaydet (US Army)
	49		G-KITT	Curtiss TP-40M Kittyhawk (US Army)
	54		G-BCNX	Piper L-4H (USAF)
	85		G-BTBI	Republic P-47 Thunderbolt Scale rep. (USAF)
	112		G-BSWC	Boeing-Stearman Kaydet (US Army)
	118		G-BSDS	Boeing-Stearman Kaydet (US Army)
	208		N75664	Boeing-Stearman Kaydet
	243		G-BUKE	Boeing-Stearman Kaydet (US Army)
	379		G-ILLE	Boeing-Stearman Kaydet (US Army)
	441		G-BTFG	Boeing-Stearman Kaydet (US Navy)
	526		G-BRWB	NA T-6G Texan (USAF)
	624	"D-39"	G-BVMH	Piper L-4 (Wag-Aero Cuby) (USAAC)
	669		N75TL	Boeing-Stearman Kaydet (US Army)
	854		G-BTBH	Ryan PT-22 (US Army)
	855		N56421	Ryan PT-22 (US Army)

Country	Serial	Code	Regn	Type
	897	"E"	G-BJEV	Aeronca Chief (US Navy)
	985		G-ERIX	Boeing-Stearman Kaydet (US Navy)
	1164		G-BKGL	Beechcraft C-45 (US Army)
	1180		G-BRSK	Boeing-Stearman Kaydet (US Navy)
	2807	"V-103"	G-BHTH	NA T-6G Texan (US Navy)
	6531	"5"	G-BSKS	Nieuport 28C-1 (US AEF)
	7797		G-BFAF	Aeronca L-16A (US Army)
	8178	"FU-178"	G-SABR	NA F-86A Sabre (USAF)
	8242	"FU-242"	N196B	NA F-86A Sabre (USAF)
	02538		N33870	Fairchild PT-19 Cornell (USAAC)
	14863	"TA-863"	G-BGOR	NA AT-6D Texan (USAAF)
	16136	"205"	G-BRUJ	Boeing-Stearman Kaydet (US Navy)
	18263	"822"	N38940	Boeing-Stearman Kaydet (USAAC)
	28521	"TA-521"	G-TVIJ	NA T-6J Harvard (USAF)
	29261		G-CDET	Culver Cadet (USAAF) (Not used as NC29261)
	31145	"G-26"	G-BBLH	Piper L-4B (US Army)
	31171		N7614C	NA B-25J Mitchell (US Marines)
	31952		G-BRPR	Aeronca L-3C Grasshopper (US Army)
	34037		N9115Z	NA B-25N Mitchell (USAAF)
	38674		G-MTKM	Thomas-Morse S4 Scout Scale rep. (USASC)
	40467	"19"	G-BTCC	Grumman F6F Hellcat (US Navy)
	41386		G-MJTD	Thomas-Morse S4 Scout Scale rep. (USASC)
	46214	"3-X"	CF-KCG	Grumman TBM-3E Avenger (USN)
	53319	"RB/319"	G-BTDP	Grumman TBM-3R Avenger (US Navy)
	54137	"69"	G-CTKL	Noorduyn Harvard IIB (US Navy)
	80425	"4- WT"	G-RUMT	Grumman F7F-3P Tigercat (USN)
	80480	"E-44"	G-BECN	Piper L-4J (USAAC)
	91007	"TR-007"	G-NASA	Lockheed T-33A (USAF)
	93542	"LTA-542"	G-BRLV	NA T-6 Texan (USAF)
	111836	"JZ/6"	G-TSIX	NA AT-6C Texan (US Navy)
	111989		N33600	Cessna L-19A Bird Dog (US Army)
	115042	"TA-042"	G-BGHU	NA T-6G Texan (USAF)
	115302	"TP"	G-BJTP	Piper L-18C Super Cub (US Marines)
	115684		G-BKVM	Piper L-21A Super Cub (US Army)
	124485	"DF-A"	G-BEDF	Boeing B-17G Flying Fortress (USAAC)
	122351		G-BKRG	Beechcraft C-45G
	126603		G-BHWH	Weedhopper JC-24C (US Navy)
	126922	"AK-402"	G-RAID	Douglas AD-4NA Skyraider (US Navy)
	151632		G-BWGR	NA TB-25N Mitchell (USAF)
	21714	"201B"	G-RUMM	Grumman F8F-2P Bearcat (USN)
	217786	"177"	G-BRTK	Boeing-Stearman Kaydet (USAAF)
	226413	"ZU-N"	N47DD	Republic P-47D Thunderbolt (USAAF)
	226671	"MX-X"	N47DD	Republic P-47D Thunderbolt (USAAF)
	231983	"IY-G"	F-BDRS	Boeing B-17G Flying Fortress (USAAF)
	236800	"A-44"	G-BHPK	Piper L-4A (USAAF)
	237123		BAPC.157	Waco CG-4A Hadrian
	243809		BAPC.185	Waco CG-4A Hadrian
	252983		N66630	Schweizer TG-3A
	269097		G-BTWR	Bell P-63A Kingcobra (USAAF)
	314887		G-AJPI	Fairchild UC-61 Forwarder (USAAF)
	315509	"W7-S"	G-BHUB	Douglas C-47A Dakota (USAAF)
	329405	"A-23"	G-BCOB	Piper L-4H (USAAC)
	329417		G-BDHK	Piper L-4A Cub (USAAC)
	329471	"F-44"	G-BGXA	Piper L-4H (USAAC)
	329601	"D-44"	G-AXHR	Piper L-4H (USAAC)
	329854	"R-44"	G-BMKC	Piper L-4H (USAAC)
	329934	"B-72"	G-BCPH	Piper L-4H (USAAC/French)
	330238	"A-24"	G-LIVH	Piper L-4H (USAAC)
	330485	"C-44"	G-AJES	Piper L-4H (USAAC)
	343251	"27"	G-NZSS	Boeing-Stearman Kaydet (USAAC)
	413573	"B6-V"	N6526D	NA P-51D Mustang (USAAC)
	436021		G-BWEZ	Piper L-4 Cub (US Army)
	454467	"J-44"	G-BILI	Piper L-4J (US Army)
	454537	"J-04"	G-BFDL	Piper L-4J (US Army)
	461748	"Y"	G-BHDK	Boeing B-29A Superfortress (USAF)
	463209	"WZ- "	BAPC.255	NA P-51D Mustang (USAAF)
	463221	"G4-S"	G-BTCD	NA P-51D Mustang (USAAF)
	472216	"AJ-L"	G-BIXL	NA P-51D Mustang (USAAF)
	472218	"WZ-I"	G-HAEC	NA P-51D Mustang (USAAF)

Country	Serial	Code	Regn	Type
	472773	"AJ-C"	G-SUSY	NA P-51D Mustang (USAAF)
	474008	"VF-R"	G-PSIC	NA P-51D Mustang (USAAF)
	479744	"M-49"	G-BGPD	Piper L-4H (USAAC)
	479766	"D-63"	G-BKHG	Piper L-4H (USAAC)
	480015	"M-44"	G-AKIB	Piper L-4H (USAAC)
	480133	"B-44"	G-BDCD	Piper L-4J (USAAC)
	480321	"H-44"	G-FRAN	Piper L-4J (USAAC)
	480636	"A-58"	G-AXHP	Piper L-4J (USAAC)
	480752	"E-39"	G-BCXJ	Piper L-4J (USAAC)
	483868	"N"	N5237V	Boeing B-17G Flying Fortress (USAF)
	493209		G-DDMV	NA T-6G Texan (Calif ANG)
	607327	"L-09"	G-ARAO	Piper (L-21B) Super Cub (US Army)
	3-1923		G-BRHP	Aeronca O-58B Grasshopper (US Army)
	18-2001		G-BIZV	Piper L-18C Super Cub (US Army)
	41-33275	"CE"	G-BICE	NA AT-6C Texan (USAAC)
	42-17786	"25"	CF-EQS	Boeing-Stearman PT-17 (US Army)
	42-58678	"IY"	G-BRIY	Taylorcraft L-2A (USAAC)
	42-78044		G-BRXL	Aeronca L-3F (US Army)
	42-84555	"EP-H"	G-ELMH	NA AT-6D Harvard (USAAC)
	44-30861		N9089Z	NA B-25J Mitchell (USAAC)
	44-63507		NL51EA	NA P-51D Mustang
	44-79609	"PR"	G-BHXY	Piper L-4H (USAAC)
	44-80594		G-BEDJ	Piper L-4J (USAAC)
	44-83184	"7"	G-RGUS	Fairchild UC-61K Forwarder (USAAC)
	51-7545	Fennec No.119	N14113	NA T-28B Trojan
	51-7962	Fennec No.142	F-AZFV	NA T-28B Trojan
	51-11701A	"AF258"	G-BSZC	Beechcraft C-45H (USAF)
	51-15227	"10"	G-BKRA	NA T-6G Texan (US Navy)
	52-8543	"66"	G-BUKY	NA (CCF) Harvard IV (US Navy)
	54-2447		G-SCUB	Piper L-21B Super Cub (US Army)
	54-21261		G-TBRD	Lockheed T-33A (USAF)
	146-11042	"7"	G-BMZX	SPAD rep. (Wolf W.II) (US Army/AEF)
	146-11083	"5"	G-BNAI	SPAD rep. (Wolf W.II) (US Army/AEF)
	I-492		G-BPUD	Ryan PT-22 (US Army)
		"H-57"	G-AKAZ	Piper L-4A (USAAF)
		"K-33"	G-BJLH	Piper L-18C Super Cub (US Army)

YUGOSLAVIA

Country	Serial	Code	Regn	Type
	30140		G-RADA	Soko Kraguj
	30146		G-BSXD	Soko Kraguj
	30149		G-SOKO	Soko Kraguj

(ii) - FICTITIOUS MARKINGS - AUTHENTIC, REPRODUCTION & MOCK-UP (STATIC)

Regn	Code	Type	Comments
"K.158"		Austin Whippet rep	See BAPC.207
"G-EAOU"		Vickers Vimy rep	See NX71MY in SECTION
"G-EASQ"		Bristol 30/46 Babe III rep	See BAPC.87
"G-EBED"		Vickers 60 Viking IV rep	See BAPC.114)
"G-AAAH"		DH.60G Moth rep	See BAPC.168)
"G-AACA"		Avro 504K rep	See BAPC.177)
"G-ABUL"		DH.82A Tiger Moth	C/n 83805) ex XL717/G-AOXG/T7291
			Fleet Air Arm Museum RNAS Yeovilton
"G-ACDA"		DH.82A Tiger Moth	N3529 based Old Rhinebeck, New York
"G-ACDR"		DH.82A Tiger Moth	C/n 86536) ex N9295
			Denton, Texas, USA
"G-ACSS"		DH.88 Comet model	See BAPC.216
"G-ACSS"		DH.88 model	See BAPC.257
"G-ADRG"		Mignet HM.14 Pou-Du-Ciel	See BAPC.77
"G-ADRX"		Mignet HM.14 Pou-Du-Ciel	See BAPC.231
"G-ADRY"		Mignet HM.14 Pou-Du-Ciel	See BAPC.29
"G-ADVU"		Mignet HM.14 Pou-Du-Ciel	See BAPC.211
"G-ADYV"		Mignet HM.14 Pou-Du-Ciel	See BAPC.243
"G-ADZW"		Mignet HM.14 Pou-Du-Ciel	See BAPC.253
"G-AEOF"		Mignet HM.14 Pou-Du-Ciel	See BAPC.22
"G-AFAP"		CASA 352L (Junkers Ju52/3m)	c/n 163 ex Sp AF T2B-272
			RAF Museum, Cosford (Original British Airways c/s)

Regn	Code	Type	Comments
"G-AFFI"		Mignet HM.14 Pou-Du-Ciel	See BAPC.76
"G-AFUG"		Luton LA.4 Minor	See BAPC 97
"G-AJOV"		Westland WS-51 Dragonfly HR.3 c/n WA/H/80 ex WP495	
			RAF Museum, Cosford (BEA c/s)
"G-AMSU"		Douglas C-47A Dakota 3	See G-AMPP in SECTION 1
"G-AOXL"		DH.114 Heron 2	See G-ANUO in SECTION 1
"G-BABF"		PA-23-250	Used 1999 to portray "crashed" a/c in TV episode of *"The Bill"*- actually G-BADI (qv)
"G-CARS"		Pitts S-2A Special	See BAPC.134
"G-CDBS"		MBB Bo.105D	See G-BCXO in SECTION 1
"G-DRNT"		Sikorsky S-76A	Petak Offshore Industry Training Centre, Norwich
"G-MAZY"		DH.82A Tiger Moth	H.Hodgson, Winthorpe "Maisie" (Cotswold Acft Restoration Group) (Composite ex Newark components & G-AMBB/T6801; also reported ex DE561 lost at sea 1942; rebuilt for static display & loaned Newark Air Museum 3.97)
"G-SHOG"		Colomban MC-15 Cri-Cri	V.S.E.Norman, Rendcomb (Static model 1999)

(iii) - NO EXTERNAL MARKINGS

Regn	Type	Comments
G-AANI	Blackburn Monoplane	
G-AANG	Bleriot XI	
G-BWJM	Bristol M.1C rep.	
G-ASPP	Bristol Boxkite rep.	
G-AANH	Deperdussin Monoplane	
G-EBNV	English Electric Wren	
G-BAAF	Manning-Flanders MF.1	
G-ARSG	Roe Triplane IV rep.	
G-BFIP	Wallbro Monoplane	

SECTION 5

PART 1 - BRITISH AIRCRAFT PRESERVATION COUNCIL

Once again we include the register of the British Aircraft Preservation Council (BAPC). This was devised in 1967 to give identity to the numerous anonymous aircraft held by various public and private collections. Since then the scope has been extended to identify static and taxiable reproductions, film extras and "plastic" display pieces. All exhibits based in Museums are usually on display. There has been very little new information this year - just some tinkering around the edges. Special thanks to Nigel Ponsford for his input.

BAPC No.	Identity	Type	C/n	P/I	Owner/operator	Probable Base
1					See G-ARSG in SECTION 1	
2					See G-ASPP in SECTION 1	
3					See G-AANG in SECTION 1	
4					See G-AANH in SECTION 1	
5					See G-AANI in SECTION 1	
6	14	Roe Triplane Type IV rep			The Aeroplane Collection Ltd	Manchester
		(JAP 9hp)			(On loan to Manchester Museum of Science & Industry)	
					"Bullseye Avroplane"	
7		Southampton University Aircraft			Southampton Hall of Aviation	Southampton
		("Sumpac") Manpowered				
8		Dixon Ornithopter			The Shuttleworth Collection	Old Warden
					(Stored 1.90)	
9		Bleriot XI Monoplane rep			The Midland Air Museum	Coventry
		(Humber) (Conv to 1911 Humber Bleriot Monoplane; assembled from some original parts Old Warden 1959)				
10		Hafner R.II Revoplane			Mrs E.Hafner	AAC Middle Wallop
		(Salmson 45hp)			(On loan to Museum of Army Flying)	
11					See G-EBNV in SECTION 1	
12		Mignet HM.14 Pou-Du-Ciel			The Aeroplane Collection	Manchester
		(Scott A2S)			(On loan to Manchester Museum of Science & Industry)	
13		BAPC 13 Mignet HM.14 Pou-Du-Ciel			Brimpex Metal Treatments Ltd	(Sheffield)
		(Douglas 600cc)			(Under restoration 3.96)	
14		Addyman Standard Training Glider			A.Lindsay & N.H.Ponsford	(Selby)
					(Stored 3.98)	
15		Addyman Standard Training Glider			N.H.Ponsford	Wigan
		(Yorkshire Aeroplanes rebuild)	YA2		(Stored 3.98)	
16		Addyman Ultralight		·	A.Lindsay & N.H.Ponsford	(Selby)
					(Stored incomplete 3.98)	
17		Woodhams Sprite			BB Aviation	Canterbury
					(Project active 1960/65 but not completed: stored 3.98)	
18		Killick Gyroplane			A.Lindsay & N.H.Ponsford	(Selby)
					(Stored 12.99)	
19	B4	Bristol F2B Fighter			Musee Royal De L'Armee	Brussels, Belgium
		(Rebuilt to static condition by Skysport Engineering 6.89 with parts from J8264)				
					(As "66" in Belgian AF c/s)	
20		Lee Richards Annular Biplane rep			Newark Air Museum	Winthorpe
		("Those Magnificent Men in Their Flying Machines"film) (Stored 3.98)				
21		Thruxton Jackaroo			M.J.Brett	Not known
		(Used as spares in rebuild of G-APAL; status unknown)				
22	"G-AEOF"	Mignet HM.14 Pou-Du-Ciel	WM.1		R.R.Mitchell	Schiphol, The Netherlands
		(Scott A2S) (Fictitious registration adopted in 1964; loaned to Aviodome and stored 1992)				
23		Allocation cancelled - originally used by half scale SE.5 rep at Newark Air Museum				
24		Allocation cancelled - originally used by 2/3 scale Currie Wot rep at Newark Air Museum				
25		Nyborg TGN.III Sailplane			Paul Williams	Warwick
					(On rebuild 1.92)	
26		Auster AOP.6 - fuselage frame only since scrapped Swansea				
27		Mignet HM.14 Pou-Du-Ciel			M J Abbey (Under construction 1988)	
28		Wright Flyer rep			Leeds Corn Exchange	Leeds
29	"G-ADRY"	Mignet HM.14 Pou-Du-Ciel			Brooklands Museum	Brooklands
		(Anzani "V") (Built by P.D.Roberts, Swansea 1960/78)				
30		DFS Grunau Baby			Not known (Destroyed by fire Swansea 1969)	
31		Slingsby T.7 Tutor			Not known (Believed scrapped Swansea)	
32		Crossley Tom Thumb			Midland Air Museum	Coventry
					(Not completed Banbury 1937: stored 4.96)	
33		DFS 10849 Grunau Baby IIB		VN148	Russavia Collection	Bishops Stortford
				LN+ST	(On rebuild as BGA.2400 1978; status unknown)	

BAPC No.	Identity	Type	C/n	P/I	Owner/operator	Probable Base
34		DFS 10849 Grunau Baby IIB	030892	RAFGSA.281	D.Elsdon	Hazlemere, Bucks
				RAFGGA	GK.4/LZ+AR	
		(On rebuild as BGA.2362; status unknown but possibly used for spares)				
35		EoN AP.7 Primary	EoN/P/063		Not known (ex Russavia Collection)	
					(On rebuild as BGA.2493 8.89)	Pocklington
36		Fieseler Fi 103 V1 model			Kent Battle of Britain Museum	Hawkinge
		("Operation Crossbow" film) (On loan from Shuttleworth Trust)				
37		See G-BXIY in SECTION 1				
38	A1742	Bristol Scout D rep			K Williams & M Thorn	Solihull
		(80 hp Gnome)			(For restoration 11.97)	
39		Addyman Zephyr sailplane			A Lindsay & N.Ponsford	(Selby)
		(Parts held for eventual rebuild 3.98)				
40		Bristol Boxkite rep	BM.7281		Bristol City Museum & Art Gallery	
		(Gnome)			("Those Magnificent Men in Their Flying Machines"film) Clifton, Bristol	
41		RAF BE.2C rep	6232		Yorkshire Air Museum	Elvington
					(Stored 3.98)	
42	H1968	Avro 504K rep			Yorkshire Air Museum	Elvington
		(Stored 3.98)				
43		Mignet HM.14 Pou-Du-Ciel			Newark Air Museum	Winthorpe
		(Scott A2S)			(Stored 3.96)	
44	L6906	Miles M.14A Magister			See G-AKKY in SECTION 1	
45		Pilcher Hawk glider rep			Lord Braye/Percy Pilcher Museum	
		(Built by AWA apprentices 1957/58)				Stanford Hall, Rugby
46		Mignet HM.14 Pou-Du-Ciel			Not known	Tump Farm, Coleford, Glos
					(Probably scrapped; status uncertain)	
47	BAPC 47	Watkins CHW Monoplane			National Museum of Wales	Cardiff
		(Watkins 40hp)				
48		Pilcher Hawk glider rep			Museum of Transport	Kelvin Hall, Glasgow
		(Built by No.2175 Sqdn ATC, Glasgow 1966)			(Stored 3.96)	
49		Pilcher Hawk glider (1896 original)			National Museum of Scotland - Museum of Flight	
		(Rebuilt after fatal crash Stanford Hall, Leics 30.9.1899)				East Fortune
50		Roe Triplane Type I			The Science Museum	South Kensington, London
		(JAP 9hp) (1909 original)				
51		Vickers FB.27 Vimy IV	13		The Science Museum	South Kensington, London
		(RR Eagle VIII 360hp)				
52		Lilienthal Glider Type XI			The Science Museum	South Kensington, London
		(1895 original)			(Stored 6.94)	
53		Wright Flyer rep			The Science Museum	South Kensington, London
54		JAP/Harding Monoplane			The Science Museum	South Kensington, London
		(JAP Anzani 45hp) (Modified Bleriot XI built by J.A.Prestwich & Co 1910)				
55		Levasseur-Antoinette Developed			The Science Museum	South Kensington, London
		Type VII Monoplane (1910 original) (Antoinette V8 50hp)				
56		Fokker E.III	210/16		The Science Museum	South Kensington, London
		(Oberusal 100hp) (Captured in Somme 1916; reported as ex XG4 of RFC) (Skeletal airframe)				
57		Pilcher Hawk glider rep			The Science Museum	Wroughton
		(Built Martin & Miller, Edinburgh 1930)			(Stored 6.94)	
58	15-1585	Yokosuka MXY7 Ohka model 11			The Science Museum	RNAS Yeovilton
					(Loaned to Fleet Air Arm Museum)	
59	D3419	Sopwith F1 Camel rep		"F1921"	Cosford Aerospace Museum	RAF Cosford
					(Stored 3.96)	
60		Murray M.1 Helicopter			The Aeroplane Collection	Weston-super-Mare
		(JAPJ99 36hp)			(On loan to The Helicopter Museum) (Stored 3.96)	
61		Stewart Ornithopter			Lincolnshire Aviation Heritage Centre	
					"Bellbird II" (Stored 12.96) Tumby Woodside, Lincs	
62	304	Cody Type V Bi-plane			The Science Museum	South Kensington, London
		(Austro-Daimler 120hp) (1912 original)				
63	P3208	Hawker Hurricane model		"L1592"	Hawkinge Aeronautical Trust	Hawkinge
		("Battle of Britain" film)			(Kent Battle of Britain Museum: as "SD-T"in 501 Sqdn c/s)	
64	P3059	Hawker Hurricane model			Hawkinge Aeronautical Trust	Hawkinge
		("Battle of Britain" film)			(Kent Battle of Britain Museum: as "SD-N" in 501 Sqdn c/s)	
65	N3289	Supermarine Spitfire model			Hawkinge Aeronautical Trust	Hawkinge
		("Battle of Britain" film)			(Kent Battle of Britain Museum: as "DW-K" in 610 Sqdn c/s)	
66		Messerschmitt Bf109	1480			Hawkinge
		(Hispano HA.1112) model ("Battle of Britain" film) (Kent Battle of Britain Museum as "6")				
67	14	Messerschmitt Bf109			Hawkinge Aeronautical Trust	Hawkinge
		(Hispano HA.1112) model (Battle of Britain" film)			(Kent Battle of Britain Museum)	
					(As "14"; JG52 c/s: probably previously as "KM+JI")	
68	H3426	Hawker Hurricane model			Not known	(Coventry)
		("Battle of Britain" film)			(Status uncertain; stored 12.94)	

BAPC No.	Identity	Type	C/n	P/I	Owner/operator	Probable Base
69	N3313	Supermarine Spitfire rep		"MH314"	Hawkinge Aeronautical Trust	Hawkinge
		("Battle of Britain" film)		"N3313"	(Kent Battle of Britain Museum)	
					(As "KL-B" in 54 Sqn c/s)	
70	TJ398	Auster AOP.5	TAY/33153	"GALES"	Aircraft Preservation Society of Scotland/	
					Museum of Flight	East Fortune
71	P8140	Supermarine Spitfire model		"P9390"	Norfolk & Suffolk Avn Museum "Nuflier"	Flixton
		("Battle of Britain" film)		"N3317"	(As "ZP-" in 74 Sqn c/s)	
72	V6779	Hawker Hurricane model		"KIT 3"	Gloucestershire Aviation Collection	
					Gloucestershire	
					(Under rebuild 1998 as "SD-X" of 501 RAAF Sqdn)	
73		Hawker Hurricane rep			Not known	(Bishops Stortford)
					(Displayed at "Queens Head" Public House; status unconfirmed)	
74		Messerschmitt Bf109	6357		Hawkinge Aeronautical Trust	Hawkinge
		(Hispano HA.1112) rep ("Battle of Britain" film)			(Kent Battle of Britain Museum as "6")	
75					See G-AEFG in SECTION 1	
76	"G-AFFI"	Mignet HM.14 Pou-Du-Ciel			Yorkshire Air Museum	Elvington
		(Scott) (Modern reproduction)				
77	"G-ADRG"	Mignet HM.14 Pou-Du-Ciel			Stondon Transport Museum & Garden Centre	
		(Citroen 425cc) (Modern reproduction)			Lower Stondon	
78					See G-AENP in SECTION 1	
79	ZI-4	Fiat G.46-4b	71	FHE	T P Luscombe/British Air Reserve	
				MM53211	(Not constructed)	
80	KJ351	Airspeed AS.58 Horsa II			Museum of Army Flying	AAC Middle Wallop
		(Composite from LH208, TL659, 8569M & others)				
81		RFD (Hawkridge) Dagling	10471	BGA.493	Russavia Collection	Hemel Hempstead
					(On rebuild)	
82		Hawker Afghan Hind	41H/81899		RAF Museum	Hendon
		(RR Kestrel)			(R.Afghan AF c/s)	
83	8476M	Kawasaki Ki 1001b			Cosford Aerospace Museum	RAF Cosford
84		Mitsubishi Ki 46III (Dinah)	5439	(ATAIU/SEA)	Cosford Aerospace Museum	RAF Cosford
		(ex Jap Army AF/81st Sentai)			(Allotted 8484M)	
85	W2	Weir W2			Museum of Flight/Royal Museum of Scotland	
		(Weir Dryad II 50hp)				East Fortune
86		DH.82A Tiger Moth			Yorkshire Acft Preservation Society	
					(Status unknown)	(Acaster Malbis)
87	"G-EASQ"	Bristol 30/46 Babe III rep	1		Bristol Aero Collection	Kemble
		(Construction commenced in 1970s by W.Sneesby)				
88	102/17	Fokker DR.1 5/8th rep			Fleet Air Arm Museum	RNAS Yeovilton
		(Modified Lawrence Parasol airframe)				
89		Cayley Glider rep			Manchester Museum of Science & Industry	
					Manchester	
90		Colditz Cock rep			Lincolnshire Avn Heritage Centre	East Kirkby
		(BBC "The Colditz Story" film)				
91		Fieseler Fi 103R-IV			Lashenden Air Warfare Museum	Headcorn
		(Believed a genuine piloted version)				
92		Fieseler Fi 103 (V1)			RAF Museum	Hendon
93		Fieseler Fi 103 (V1)			Imperial War Museum	Duxford
94	8583M	Fieseler Fi 103 (V1)		418947	Cosford Aerospace Museum	Cosford
					(P/I unconfirmed)	
95		Gizmer Autogyro			F.Fewsdale	(Darlington)
					(Status unknown)	
96		Brown Helicopter			North East A/c Museum	Sunderland
					(Stored 3.98)	
97	"G-AFUG"	Luton LA.4 Minor			North East A/c Museum	(Stoke-on-Trent)
		(JAP J99)			(Under restoration by K Fern 3.98)	
98	997	Yokosuka MXY7 Ohka model 11		8485M	Manchester Museum of Science & Industry	
					Manchester	
99	8486M	Yokosuka MXY7 Ohka model 11			Cosford Aerospace Museum	RAF Cosford
100		Clarke Chanute biplane glider			The Science Museum	Hendon
		(Loaned to RAF Museum)				
101		Mignet HM.14 Pou-Du-Ciel			Newark Air Museum	Winthorpe
		(Fuselage stored 3.98)				
102		Mignet HM.14 Pou-Du-Ciel			Not constructed - parts to BAPC.75	
103		Hulton Hang-glider			Personal Plane Services Ltd	Booker
		(Built E.A.S.Hulton, London 1969)			("Blue Max" Movie A/c Museum 3.96)	
104		Bleriot XI		G-AVXV	Sold as F-AZIN 1992	
105		Bleriot XI	54		Arango Collection Los Angeles, California, USA	
		(Anzani "V" 25hp)				
		(Composite from original components including c/n 54; built by L.D.Goldsmith in 1976 @ RAF Colerne)				
106	164	Bleriot XI			Royal Aeronautical Society	RAF Cardington
		(Anzani 40hp) (1910 original) (Allotted 9209M)			(On loan to RAF Museum: stored 10.95) †	

BAPC No.	Identity	Type	C/n	P/I	Owner/operator	Probable Base
107	433	Bleriot XXVII			Royal Aeronautical Society	Hendon
		(1911 original) (Allotted 9202M)			(On loan to RAF Museum)	
108		Fairey Swordfish IV		HS503	Cosford Aerospace Museum	RAF Cosford
		(Identity not confirmed)			(Stored 3.96)	
109		Slingsby T.7 Cadet	28	BGA.679	RAF Museum	(RAF Henlow)
					(Allotted 8599M: presumed stored; status unconfirmed)	
110	5125/18	Fokker D.VII rep			Leisure Sport Ltd	(Thorpe Park, Surrey)
					(JG1 c/s) (Sold 10.87)	
111	N5492	Sopwith Triplane rep			Fleet Air Arm Museum	RNAS Yeovilton
					("B" Flt/10 Sqdn RNAS c/s)	
112	5964	De Havilland DH.2 rep			Museum of Army Flying	AAC Middle Wallop
113	B4863	RAF SE.5A rep			Leisure Sport Ltd	(Thorpe Park, Surrey)
					(As "G" in 56 Sqdn c/s) (Sold 10.87)	
114	"G-EBED"	Vickers 60 Viking IV rep		"R4"	Brooklands Museum	Brooklands
		("The Land Time Forgot" film)				
115		Mignet HM.14 Pou-Du-Ciel			I Hancock	Flixton
		(Douglas 500cc)			(On loan to Norfolk & Suffolk Aviation Museum)	
116		Santos-Dumont Demoiselle XX rep			Flambards Triple Theme Park	(Helston)
		(JAP J99)			(Sold 1993)	
117	1701	RAF BE.2C rep			Friends of Biggin Hill	Orpington
		(Gipsy Major for taxying)			(Stored 3.96)	
		(Built Ackland & Shaw for "Wings" BBC TV 1976)				
		(Two similar a/c were built but only one has appeared on the BAPC register)				
118	C19/15	Albatros D.V static rep			North Weald A/c Restoration Flt	North Weald
119		Bensen B.7 Gyroglider			North East A/c Museum	Sunderland
120					See G-AEJZ in SECTION 1	
121					See G-AEKR in SECTION 1	
122	1881	Avro 504 rep			Not known	Not known
		(Ford 1300 for taxying)			(Status unknown)	
		(Built by PPS Booker for "Wings" BBC TV in 1976)				
123	P641	Vickers FB.5 Gunbus	1186/2	ZS-UHN	A.Topen	Cranfield
		(Built IES Projects Ltd 1975 for "Shout at the Devil" film;				
		small components only remain & stored 3.90)				
124		Lilienthal Glider Type XI rep			The Science Museum	South Kensington, London
		(Display reproduction of BAPC.52)				
126		Rollason-Druine D.31 Turbulent			Midland Air Museum	Coventry
		(Static airframe)				
127		Halton MPA			C.Roper	Filching Manor, Wannock
					(On loan to the Foulkes-Halbard Collection) "Jupiter"	
128		Watkinson CG-4 rotorcraft			The Helicopter Museum	Weston-super-Mare
129		Blackburn " 1911 Monoplane rep			Flambards Triple Theme Park	(Helston)
		(Built for TV series "The Flambards")			"Mercury" (Sold 1993)	
130		Blackburn 1911 Monoplane rep			Yorkshire Air Museum	Elvington
		(Built for TV series "The Flambards")				
131		Pilcher Hawk glider rep			C.Paton	(London E)
		(Built by C.Paton for film 1972)			(Status unknown; probably stored)	
132		Bleriot XI EMK010 & PFA/8810864			Not known	
		(Anzani 25hp) (L.D.Goldsmith 1976 rebuild from original components; rebuilt again by EMK in 1982				
		& initially allotted G-BLXI; reported as sold to unidentified Musee de l'Automobile, France in 1986;				
		possibly the same a/c as BAPC.189)				
133	425/17	Fokker DR.1 model			Kent Battle of Britain Museum	Hawkinge
134		Pitts S.2A		"G-RKSF"	Toyota	(Northampton)
					See "G-CARS" in SECTION 4	
135	C4912	Bristol M.1C Monoplane rep			Leisure Sport Ltd	(Thorpe Park, Surrey)
					(150 Sqdn c/s) (Sold 10.87)	
136	619	Deperdussin 1913 floatplane rep			Planes of Fame Air Museum Chino, California, USA	
137	8151	Sopwith Baby floatplane rep			Leisure Sport Ltd	(Thorpe Park, Surrey)
		(Built FEM Displays Ltd 1978)			(RNAS c/s) (Sold 10.87)	
138	2292	Hansa Brandenberg W.29 rep			Not known	(Thorpe Park, Surrey)
		(Ford 1300 for taxying)			(Status unknown; sold prior to 10.87)	
139	DR1/17	Fokker DR.1 Triplane rep			Leisure Sport Ltd (Jasta II c/s) (Sold 10.87)	
140	3	Curtiss 42A R3C2 rep			Planes of Fame Air Museum Chino, California, USA	
					(US Army c/s)	
141	5	Macchi M.39 rep			Fighter Jets & Air Racing Museum	
		(Gipsy Queen for taxying)			Chino, California, USA	
142	F5459	AF SE.5A rep			Not known	(Switzerland)
					(As "Y") (Sold 1.5.93)	
143		Paxton MPA			R.A.Paxton	(Gloucestershire)
					(Status unknown; presumed stored)	
144		Weybridge MPA			Not known "Mercury"	(Cranwell)
		(Previously "Dumbo" rebuilt)			(Status unknown)	

BAPC No.	Identity	Type	C/n	P/I	Owner/operator	Probable Base
145		Oliver MPA			Not known	(Warton)
					(Status unconfirmed, possibly scrapped)	
146		Pedal Aeronauts MPA			Not known "Toucan"	Not known
					(Status uncertain: centre section/power train only departed London Colney 1995)	
147	LHS-1	Bensen B7 Gyroglider			Norfolk & Suffolk Aviation Museum	Flixton
148	K7271	Hawker Fury II rep			High Ercall Aviation Museum	High Ercall
					(1 Sqdn c/s) (Stored 10.98)	
149		Short S.27 rep			Fleet Air Arm Museum	RNAS Yeovilton
					(Stored 4.98)	
150	XX725	BAC/Sepecat Jaguar GR.1 model	"XX718" "XX732"		RAF Exhibition, Production & Transportation Unit (As "GU" in 54 Sqdn c/s))	(RAF St.Athan)
					(Extant 9.96)	
151	XZ226	BAC/Sepecat Jaguar GR.1A model	"XX824"		RAF Exhibition, Production & Transportation Unit (As "A" in 41 Sqdn c/s)	(RAF St.Athan)
					(Extant 7.96)	
152	XX226	BAe Hawk T.1A model	"XX262" "XX162"		RAF Exhibition, Production & Transportation Unit (As "74 in 74 Sqdn c/s)	(RAF St.Athan)
					(Extant 9.96)	
153		Westland WG33			The Helicopter Museum	Weston-super-Mare
		(Engineering mock-up)			(Stored 2.98)	
154		Druine D.31 Turbulent	PFA/1654		Lincolnshire Aviation Society	East Kirkby
					(Unfinished: stored 3.96)	
155	ZA446	Panavia Tornado GR.1 model	"ZA446" "ZA600/ZA322" (As "AJ-P")		RAF Exhibition, Production & Transportation Unit	(RAF St.Athan)
156	S1595	Supermarine S.6B rep			Museum of Flying Santa Monica, California, USA	
157	237123	WACO CG-4A Hadrian			Yorkshire Air Museum	Elvington
					(Fuselage frame section only & tail pieces ex 456476)	
158		Fieseler Fi 103 (V1)			Defence Explosives Ordnance Disposal School	
						Lodge Hill Camp, Chattenden
159		Yokosuka MXY7 Ohka model 11			Defence Explosives Ordnance Disposal School	
						Lodge Hill Camp, Chattenden
160		Chargus 18/50 Hang-Glider			National Museum of Scotland-Museum of Flight	
						East Fortune
161		Stewart MP Ornithopter			Stewart "Coppelia" (Stored 1991) (Lincolnshire)	
162		Goodhart MPA			The Science Museum	Wroughton
					"Newbury Manflier" (Parts only stored 9.93)	
163	B415	Hafner AFEE 10/42 Rotabuggy rep			Wessex Aviation Society	AAC Middle Wallop
					(On loan to Museum of Army Flying)	
164	N546	Wight Quadruplane Type 1 rep			Southampton Hall of Aviation	Southampton
165	E2466	Bristol F.2B Fighter			RAF Museum	Hendon
		(RR Falcon rep)			(22 Sqdn c/s)	
166	"D7889"	Bristol F.2B Fighter		G-AANM	Aero Vintage Ltd	St.Leonards-on-Sea
					(Under restoration 8.95)	
167		RAF SE.5A rep			TDL Replicas Ltd (Stored 12.97)	Lowestoft
168	"G-AAAH"	DH.60G Moth rep	8058		Yorkshire Ar Museuml	Elvington
					"Jason"	
169	XX110	BAC/Sepecat Jaguar GR.1			No.1 School of Technical Training	RAF Halton
		(Engine systems static demonstration airframe)			(Extant 11.93)	
170		Pilcher Hawk glider rep			Not known	Strathallan
		("Kings Royal" BBC film; built 1983 by A.Gourlay)			(Stored 3.93)	
171	XX297	BAe Hawk T.1 model	"XX262"		RAF Exhibition, Production & Transportation Unit	(RAF St.Athan)
172		Chargus Midas Super E Hang-Glider			The Science Museum	Wroughton
173		Birdman Grasshopper Hang-Gglider			The Science Museum	Wroughton
		(Power assisted)				
174		Bensen B.7 Gyro-glider			The Science Museum	Wroughton
175		Volmer VJ-23 Swing-wing			Manchester Museum of Science & Industry	
		(McCulloch 9hp)				Manchester
176	A4850	RAF SE.5A scale rep			Barton Aviation Heritage	Barton
		(Currie Wot basic airframe built by Slingsby for "The Blue Max" film)				
177	"G-AACA"	Avro 504K rep	"G1381"		Brooklands Museum	Brooklands
		(Clerget 130hp)			(Brooklands School of Flying c/s)	
178		Avro 504K rep	"E373"		By-gone Times Antique Warehouse Eccleston, Lancs	
					(German marks)	
179	A7317	Sopwith Pup rep			Epping Forest Council	Coventry
		("Wings" film)			(With Midland Air Museum as "A7317" 6.99)	
180		McCurdy Silver Dart rep			Reynolds Pioneer Museum	
					(Delivered 4.94) Wetaskiwin, Alberta, Canada	
181	687	RAF BE.2b			RAF Museum	Hendon
		(Renault V8) (Restoration from original components)				

BAPC No.	Identity	Type	C/n	P/I	Owner/operator	Probable Base
182		Wood Ornithopter			Manchester Museum of Science & Industry (Stored 3.96)	Manchester
183		Zurowski ZP.1 (Panhard 850cc)			Newark Air Museum (Polish AF c/s)	Winthorpe
184	EN398	Supermarine Spitfire IX model (Built by Specialised Mouldings Ltd 1985)			R.J.Lamplough (As "WO-A")	North Weald
185	243809	WACO CG-4A Hadrian			Museum of Army Flying (Restoration from original unidentified components)	AAC Middle Wallop
186	LF789	DH.82B Queen Bee (Correct identity not known)	K3584		De Havilland Aircraft Museum (As "R2-K")	Salisbury Hall, London Colney
187		Roe Type I Biplane rep (ABC 24hp) (Built by M.L.Beach)			Brooklands Museum	Brooklands
188		McBroom Cobra 88 Hang-Glider			The Science Museum	Wroughton
189		Bleriot XI rep (Anzani) (Some original parts ex Goldsmith Trust)			Not known (Status uncertain; see BAPC.132) (Sold at Christies 31.10.86, probably to France)	
190	K5054	Supermarine Spitfire prototype rep			P.Smith (Stored 8.95) (On loan to Barton Aviation Heritage)	Barton
191	ZD472	BAe Harrier GR.7 model			RAF Exhibition, Production & Transportation Unit (As Code "01") (Extant 5.96)	(RAF St.Athan)
192		Weedhopper JC24			N.Dykes	Bacup, Lancs
193		Hovey WDII Whing Ding			N.Dykes	Bacup, Lancs
194		Santos Dumont Type 20 Demoiselle rep (ABC Scorpion 30hp) ("Those Magnificent Men in Their Flying Machines" film)	24 bis PPS/DEM/1		RAF Museum (On loan to Brooklands Museum)	Brooklands
195		Birdman Sports Moonraker 77 Hang-Glider (Built c.1977)			National Museum of Scotland-Museum of Flight	East Fortune
196		Southdown Sailwings Sigma 2m Hang-Glider (Built c.1980)			National Museum of Scotland-Museum of Flight	East Fortune
197		Scotkites Cirrus III Hang-Glider (Built 1977)			National Museum of Scotland-Museum of Flight East Fortune	
198		Fieseler Fi 103 (V1)	477663		Imperial War Museum	South Lambeth, London
199		Fieseler Fi 103 (V1)	442795		The Science Museum	South Kensington, London
200		Bensen B.7 Gyroglider (Composite of three airframes)			Not known (Stored 11.93)	(Leeds)
201	BAPC 201	Mignet HM.14 Pou-Du-Ciel			Caernarfon Air World	Caernarfon
202	MAV467	Vickers Supermarine Spitfire V model ("A Piece of Cake" film)			Maes Artro Village (As "RO")	Llanbedr
203	"G-AFIN"	Chrislea LC.1 Airguard rep			The Aeroplane Collection (Burnt 1998?)	Wigan
204		McBroom Hang-Glider			The Aeroplane Collection (On loan to Newark Air Museum: stored 3.98)	Winthorpe
205	BE421	Hawker Hurricane IIc model			RAF Museum (As "XP-G" in 174 Sqn c/s)	Hendon
206	MH486	Vickers Supermarine Spitfire IX model			RAF Museum (As"FF-A" in 132 Sqn c/s)	Hendon
207	"K.158"	Austin Whippet rep	"G-EAGS"		K.Fern t/a Vintage & Rotary Wing Collection (To North East Aircraft Museum)	Sunderland
208	D276	RAF SE.5A rep (Built AJD Engineering)			Prince's Mead Shopping Precinct	Farnborough, Hants
209	MJ751	Vickers Supermarine Spitfire LF.IXC model ("Piece of Cake" film)			Museum of D-Day Aviation (As "DU-V" in 321 Sqn c/s)	Shoreham
210	C4451	Avro 504J rep (Gnome Monosoupape 100hp) (Built AJD Engineering)			Southampton Hall of Aviation	Southampton
211	"G-ADVU"	Mignet HM.14 Pou-Du-Ciel (Built by Ken Fern/Vintage & Rotary Wing Collection 1993; in North East Aircraft Museum 4.98)			I.Burns t/a Burns Garage	Sunderland
212		Bensen B.6 Gyrocopter (Stored 2.98)			The Helicopter Museum	Weston-super-Mare
213		Cranfield Vertigo MP Helicopter (Stored 2.98)			The Helicopter Museum	Weston-super-Mare
214	K5054	Supermarine Spitfire prototype model			The Spitfire Society (On loan to Tangmere Military Aviation Museum)	Tangmere
215		Airwave Hang Glider prototype			Southampton Hall of Aviation	Southampton
216	"G-ACSS"	DH.88 Comet model (Taxying)			G.Gayward t/a Trout Lake Air Force	Home Park, Kings Langley
217	K9926	Vickers Supermarine Spitfire I rep			RAF Inspectorate of Recruiting (As "JH-C" in 317 Sqn c/s)	RAF Bentley Priory
218	P3386	Hawker Hurricane IIc model			RAF Inspectorate of Recruiting (As "FT-I"in 43 Sqn c/s)	RAF Bentley Priory
219	L1710	Hawker Hurricane I model			RAF Memorial Chapel (As "AL-D" in 79 Sqn c/s)	Biggin Hill

BAPC No.	Identity	Type	C/n	P/I	Owner/operator	Probable Base
220	N3194	Vickers Supermarine Spitfire I model			RAF Memorial Chapel (As "GR-Z" in 92 Sqn c/s)	Biggin Hill
221	MH777	Vickers Supermarine Spitfire LF.IX model			RAF Museum (As "RF-N" in 303 Sqn c/s)	RAF Northolt
222	BR600	Vickers Supermarine Spitfire IX model			RAF Museum (As "SH-V in 64 Sqn c/s)	RAF Uxbridge
223	V7467	Hawker Hurricane I model			RAF Museum (As "LE-D"in 242 Sqn c/s)	RAF Coltishall
224	BR600	Vickers Supermarine Spitfire V model (Built by TDL Replicas)			Stakis Ambassador Hotel (As "JP-A" in 64 Sqn c/s)	Norwich Airport
225	P8448	Vickers Supermarine Spitfire IX model			RAF Museum (As "UM-D" in 52 Sqn c/s)	RAF Cranwell
226	EN343	Vickers Supermarine Spitfire XI model			RAF Museum (PRU c/s)	RAF Benson
227	L1070	Vickers Supermarine Spitfire IA model			RAF Museum (As "XT-A" in 603 Sqn c/s)	Edinburgh
228		Olympus Hang Glider			North East A/c Museum (Stored 3.98)	Sunderland
229	MJ832	Vickers Supermarine Spitfire IX model	"L1096"		RAF Museum "City of Oshawa" (As "DN-Y" in 416 Sqn c/s)	RAF Digby
230	AA908	Vickers Supermarine Spitfire rep (Built by TDL Replicas 1993)	"AA908"		Eden Camp Modern History Theme Museum (As "GE-P" in 152 Sqn c/s) Old Malton, N.Yorks	
231	"G-ADRX"	Mignet HM.14 Pou-Du-Ciel (Probably built Ulverston 1936 with Anzani engine; on rebuild at HM Prison, Haverigg, Millom 3.94 with modern DAF engine, from original remains acquired from Torver, Cumbria)			South Copeland Avn Group	Haverigg, Millom
232		Airspeed AS.58 Horsa I/II (Composite airframe from unidentified components)			De Havilland Heritage Museum Salisbury Hall, London Colney	
233		Broburn Wanderlust Sailplane (Built 1946)			Museum of Berkshire Avn	Woodley
234	GBH-7	Vickers FB.5 Gunbus rep (Built 1985 for "Gunbus" film)			Barton Aviation Heritage (Stored 3.98)	Barton
235		Fieseler Fi 103 V1 model (Built TDL Replicas 1993)			Eden Camp Modern History Theme Museum Old Malton, N.Yorks	
236	P2793	Hawker Hurricane model (Built TDL Replicas 7.93)			Eden Camp Modern History Theme Museum (As "SD-M" in 501 Sqn c/s) Old Malton, N.Yorks	
237		Fieseler Fi 103 (V1) (Stored 11.93)			RAF Museum	RAF Cardington
238		Waxflatter Ornithopter rep ("Young Sherlock Holmes" film & built by PPS)			Personal Plane Services Ltd ("Blue Max" Movie Acft Museum 7.96)	Booker Ť
239		Fokker D.VIII 5/8 Scale rep			Norfolk & Suffolk Avtn Museum	Flixton
240		Messerschmitt Bf.109G model (Built D.Thorton 1994)			Yorkshire Air Museum	Elvington
241	L1679	Hawker Hurricane I model (Built Aerofab 1994)			Tangmere Military Aviation Museum (As "JX-G" in 1 Sqn c/s)	Tangmere
242	BL924	Vickers Supermarine Spitfire VB rep (Built TDL Reps 1994)			Tangmere Military Aviation Museum (As "AZ-G" in 234 Sqn c/s)	Tangmere
243	"G-ADYV"	Mignet HM.14 Pou-Du-Ciel (Scott A2S) (Modern reproduction built Bill Francis; stored 8.95)			P.Ward	Malvern Wells
244		Solar Wings Typhoon Hang-Glider (Wing only) (Built 1981)			National Museum of Scotland - Museum of Flight East Fortune	
245		Electraflyer Floater Hang-Glider (Wing only) (Built 1979)			National Museum of Scotland - Museum of Flight East Fortune	
246		Hiway Cloudbase Hang-Glider (Built 1978)			National Museum of Scotland - Museum of Flight East Fortune	
247		Albatros ASG.21 Hang-Glider (Built 1977)			National Museum of Scotland - Museum of Flight East Fortune	
248		McBroom Hang-Glider (Built 1974)			Museum of Berkshire Aviation	Woodley
249	K5673	Hawker Fury I model			Brooklands Museum (As "A" Flt in 1 Sqn c/s)	Brooklands
250	F5475	RAF SE.5A rep			Brooklands Museum "1st Battalion Honourable Artillery Company" (As "A" in 41 Sqn c/s)	Brooklands
251		Hiway Spectrum Hang-Glider (Built 1980)			Manchester Museum of Science & Industry (Stored 3.98)	Manchester
252		Flexiform Wing Hang-Glider (Built 1982)			Manchester Museum of Science & Industry (Stored 3.98)	Manchester
253	"G-ADZW"	Mignet HM.14 Pou-Du-Ciel (Modern reproduction built in 1990s)			H.Shore (On loan to The Island Aeroplane Co Collection)	Sandown

BAPC No.	Identity	Type	C/n	P/I	Owner/operator	Probable Base
254	R6690	Supermarine Spitfire 1 rep			No.609 (West Riding) Squadron Association (On loan to Yorkshire Air Museum) (As "PR-A" in 609 Sqdn c/s)	Elvington
255	463209	NA P-51D Mustang model		"88"	American Air Museum (As "WZ-S" in 78th FS c/s)	Duxford
256		Santos Dumont Type 20 Demoiselle rep (Built J Aubot 1996/97)			Brookland Museum	Brooklands
257	"G-ACSS	DH.88 model			Galleria Leisure Experience "Grosvenor House"	Hatfield
258		Adams Balloon (14,000 cu.ft) (Built GQ Parachutes)			British Balloon Museum & Library	Newbury
		(Note: A Gloster Gamecock, under construction 1999 at Jet Age Museum, Gloucestershire, is reported as BAPC 258)				
259						
260						
261		GA Hotspur rep			Museum of Army Flying	AAC Middle Wallop
		(Comprises anonymous cockpit of Mk.1 ex Airborne Forces Museum, Aldershot and rear end of Mk.II, HH379, ex RAF Hendon - under rebuild 1999)				

PART 2- IRISH AVIATION HISTORICAL COUNCIL

The IAHC Register came into existence with similar objectives to the BAPC. There has been no fresh information this year.

IAPC No.	Identity	Type	C/n	P/I	Owner/operator	Probable Base
1		Mignet HM.14 Pou-Du-Ciel			South East Aviation Enthusiasts Group "Patrick" (Stored 4.96)	New Ross, Wexford
2		Aldritt Monoplane			Foulkes-Halbard Collection (Under restoration 4.98)	Filching Manor, Wannock
3		Mignet HM.14 Pou-Du-Ciel (1937 original but unflown)			M.Donohoe (On rebuild 4.96)	Delgany, Co.Wicklow
4		Hawker Hector		IAAC...	D.McCarthy (Believed components on rebuild in Florida, USA)	NK
5		Not known			Not known	
6		Ferguson Monoplane rep (Built Capt J.Kelly Rogers 1974; original engine)			Ulster Folk & Transport Museum (On loan from Irish Aviation Museum)	Holywood, Belfast
7		Sligo Concept			G.O'Hara (Stored incomplete 8.91)	Sligo
8		O'Hara Autogyro			G.O'Hara (Stored unflown 8.91)	Sligo
9		Ferguson Monoplane rep (Built L.Hannah 1980)			Ulster Folk & Transport Museum (Stored 4.98)	Holywood, Belfast

SECTION 6

OTHER AIRCRAFT LOCATED IN UK & IRELAND

Many thanks to Peter Budden, Richard Cawsey, Mike Cain, Paul Hewins & Bernard Martin for continually updating this section. Appreciation goes to Dennis Clement for his valuable oversight and additional contributions.

Regn	Type	C/n	P/I	Owner/operator	Probable Base
UNITED ARAB EMIRATES					
A6-ALG	MBB Bo.105	S-94		Not known	Bourn
	(Non-airworthy pod is white with red/black stripes and on rebuild for Aerogulf 1999)				
A6-HHH	Gulfstream G.1159C Gulfstream IV	1011	(A6-DLF) N17581	Government of Dubai (Noted 4.99)	Farnborough
MUSCAT & OMAN					
A40-AB	Vickers VC-10-1103	820	G-ASIX	Brooklands Museum	Brooklands
CANADA					
CF-BXO	V-S.304 Stranraer		RCAF 920 CV-209	RAF Museum (As "920/QN-" in RCAF c/s)	Hendon
CF-EQS	Boeing-Stearman A75N1 (PT-17-BW) Kaydet	75-1728	41-8169	IWM Collection/American Air Museum (As "42-17786/25" in USAAF c/s)	Duxford
CF-KCG	Grumman TBM-3E Avenger AS.3	2066	RCN326 Bu.69327	IWM Collection (As "46214/3-X 69327" in USN c/s: sold 1999 ?)	Duxford
C-FDFC	Bristol 170 Freighter 31M	13218	G-BISU ZK-EPH/NZ5912/ZK-BVI/NZ5912/G-18-194	British Airways Employees	Enstone
	(Damaged Enstone 18.7.96; wreck in open store 4.97)				
C-FLNP	Cessna 172M	61809	CF-LNP N12099	Not known (Noted 8.99)	Denham
C-FQIP	Lake LA-4-200 Buccaneer	679		Not known (Noted 6.99)	Elstree
C-GCYL	PA-31-300 Navajo	31-688		Not known	Warton
C-GYZI	Cameron N-77 HAFB	269		Balloon Preservation Group "Aeolus" (Inflated 5.99)	Lancing
RCAF 9893	Bristol 149 Bolingbroke IVT	-		IWM Collection (Stored 3.96)	Duxford
RCAF 9940	Bristol 149 Bolingbroke IVT	-		Museum of Flight/Royal Museum of Scotland (Stored 3.96)	East Fortune
PORTUGAL					
CS-AUM	Beech F33A Bonanza	CE-763		Not known	Blackbushe
CS-AQW	Reims Cessna F.172N Skyhawk II	1914	(G-BOJJ) CS-AQW	C.Wagner/Cormack (Aircraft Services) Ltd (Stored 3.99)	Cumbernauld
CS-DAQ	OGMA DHC.1 Chipmunk T.20	OGMA-57	FAP 1367	(R.Farrer) (On overhaul Spanhoe 3.96; sold overseas 1997 ?)	(Bedfordshire)
FAP 1366	OGMA DHC.1 Chipmunk T.20	OGMA-58		(R.Farrer) (On overhaul Spanhoe 3.96; sold overseas 1997 ?)	(Bedfordshire)
FAP 1513	North American AT-6D-NT Harvard III	88-14555	SAAF 7426 EX884/41-33857	Air Engineering Services (As "FT323/GN") (On rebuild 4.95)	Swansea
GERMANY					
D-CACY	Hawker Sea Fury FB.11	ES.3617	G-BWOL	The Old Flying Machine Company	Duxford
D-CATA	Hawker Sea Fury T.20	ES.8503	D-FATA G-9-30/VZ345	Fleet Air Arm Museum (As "VZ345" in RN c/s)	Brough
	(Damaged Boscombe Down 17.4.85: stored 9.95)				
D-EALX	Cessna F.150L	0766	OE-ALX	Not known (Noted 9.99)	Nayland
D-EASB	Cessna 177RG Cardinal	177RG-0776	N1603H	C.Hardiman (Wreck stored 9.96)	Shobdon
D-EAXX	MS.885 Super Rallye	260	F-BKUI	Not known (Stored 6.99)	Thurrock
D-EAZO	Bucker Bu.131 Jungmann	52	HB-UTK SwAF A-41	J.Koch (On rebuild 2.97)	Sandown
D-ECLY	Reims Cessna FR.172E Rocket	0046		Not known (Noted 9.99)	Whiterashes
D-EFFA	Ruschmeyer R90	018		Not known (Noted 11.99)	Bournemouth
D-EFJD	Bolkow Bo.209 Monsun	126		Not known (Noted 11.99)	Old Sarum
D-EFTH	Cessna 195B	16087	N195MB N2102C	J.Koch (Last noted 2.97)	Sandown
	(Should have returned to Germany with owner on closure of Sandown Museum in 1998)				
D-EFTI	Bolkow 207	219		Mark Hayles	(Market Rasen)
D-ELOP	PA-24-250 Comanche	24-3489	N8297P	Not known (Noted 10.99)	Slinfold
D-ERCH	Mooney M.20M	27-0210		Not known (Noted 9.99)	Biggin Hill

Regn	Type	C/n	P/I	Owner/operator	Probable Base
D-ESEW(3)	Extra EA.300/L	91		Not known (Noted 8.99)	Sherburn-in-Elmet
	(Conversion of original EA.330 c/n 01 also regd D-ESEW (No2)				
D-EXGC	Extra EA.200	27		Not known (Noted 11.99)	Andrewsfield
D-EXLH	PA-28			Not known (Noted 10.99)	Seething
D-GCWB	PA-34 Seneca	3448070		Not known (Noted 12.99)	Biggin Hill
D-HCKV	Agusta A.109A-11	7345	N109C	The Global Travel Group	Chester
			N2GN	(Noted 8.99)	
D-HEED	Agusta A.109A	7201	N3983N	Not known	Liskeard
			HB-XNF/I-PATZ	(Stored 1997)	
D-HMED	MBB Bo.105			Not known (Noted 12.99)	Bourn
				(Non-airworthy pod is white/green carries "Polizei" titles)	
D-HMQV	Bolkow Bo.102 Helitrainer	6216		The Helicopter Museum	Weston-super-Mare
	(Development aircraft)				
D-HMUR	MBB Bo.105			Not known (Noted 1999)	Bourn
	(Non-airworthy pod is S.91)				
D-HOAY	Kamov Ka.26	7001309	DDR-SPY	The Helicopter Museum	Weston-super-Mare
			DM-SPY		
D-IFSB	DH.104 Dove 6	04379	D-CFSB	De Havilland Aircraft Museum	
			G-AMXR/N4280V		Salisbury Hall,London Colney
D-NFBU	Hang-glider			Not known (Noted 1.99)	Edburton
D-OPHA	Fire Balloons 3000 HAFB	057	D-TALCID	R S Kent t/a Balloon Preservation Group	Lancing
				"Talcid" (Stored 7.98)	
D-PAMGAS	Cameron N-90 HAFB	1288		A Kirk t/a Balloon Preservation Group	Lancing
				"Pamgas" (Stored 7.98)	
D-0369	Glasflugel H201 Standard Libelle	289		Not known "J" (Noted 8.99)	Dunstable
V7+1H	Aero Focke-Wulf Fw.189A-1 Uhu	0112100		J.Pearce	Lancing
				(For rebuild ex Russia 2.92: to Czech Republic for rebuild 1995)	
+4	Messerschmitt Bf.109E	WerkeNr 1190		Imperial War Museum	Duxford
				(For static rebuild 2.99: confirmed long-term resident/rebuild in IWM Bldg 66)	
3579	Messerschmitt Bf.109E-4	3579		C.Charleston	Chino, California, USA
				(Op Santa Monica Museum of Flying) (On rebuild 5.99)	
	(Imported ex Murmansk late 1992; coded 14 (white) ex I/LG2, or 4/JG51)				
8347	Messerschmitt Bf.109F-4 (Erla b.)	8347		D.Price	Colchester
				(Op Santa Monica Museum of Flying)	
	(Wreck found Lubjan, 75 ml SE St.Petersburg; coded 10 (Yellow) ex II/JG54; also reported as WNo.8147)				
				(On rebuild or spares by C.Charleston 12.94)	
	(Note: One of these Craig Charleston 109s went to the USA earlier in 1999)				

ANGOLA

D2-TOU	Boeing 707-351C	18964	5Y-BFB	Central Training Establishment	Manston
			5A-DJS/TF-VLP/N88TF/VR-HGQ/(VR-HGR)/N363US (Fire Training use 4.96)		

SPAIN

EC-AOY	Aero-Difusion Jodel D.1190-S Compostela			G.Janney	Dunkirk, Canterbury
		E.56		(On rebuild 9.97)	
EC-AOZ	PA-20-135 Pacer			Not known	Farley Farm, Winchester
				(On rebuild 6.99)	
EC-AXZ	Bell 47J	2079		Not known	Lower Upham
				(Boom only - used for spares 5.99)	
EC-FVM	Edgley EA-7 Optica	021		Not known (Stored 12.98)	Farnborough
B2I-103	CASA 2.111B (Heinkel He.111)	17		The Old Flying Machine Co	Duxford
				(Marked as "B2I-27":confirmed external Eastern end resident 1999)	
C4E-88 (Sp.AF)	Messerschmitt Bf.109E	-	Sp AF 6-88	R.Lamplough	Denford Manor, Hungerford
				(Poor condition - stored 12.93)	
ES1-16	CASA I-133L Jungmeister	?		J.Sykes (On rebuild 3.94)	Stretton

LIBERIA

EL-AJT	Boeing 707-344BA	18891	(N7000Y)	Omega Air (Spares use 2.97)	Manston
			3B-NAE/VP-WKW/ZS-SAD/LX-LGR/ZS-SAD/ZS-DYL		
EL-AKJ	Boeing 707-321C	19375		Omega Air (Open store 1.00)	Southend
			(PP-BRR)/EL-AKJ/9Q-CSW/5N-TAS/N864BX/OB-R-1243/HK-2473/HK-2473X/N473RN/N473PA		
EL-WXA	Bristol 175 Britannia 253F	13508	9Q-CJH	Britannia Aircraft Preservation Trust	Kemble
			CU-T120/G-BDUP/XM496 (Stored 8.99: as "XM496" in RAF c/s)		

ESTONIA

ES-YLK	Aero L-29A Delfin	194521	Est.AF	Not known	Enniskillen
			Soviet AF	(Noted 8.97)	
ES-YLV	Aero L-29A Delfin	194227		Not known	Manston
ES-ZLA	Aero L-39 Albatros	931520		AS Murket	North Weald
ES-ZLB	Aero L-39 Albatros	931822		Not known	Manston

FRANCE

Regn	Type	C/n	P/I	Owner/operator	Probable Base
F-AZJD	Dewoitine D.27-SA (P & W R985)	SA-290 & 322	F-AZBF (F-AZBC)/HB-RAC/U-290	The Old Flying Machine Co (Noted 1999)	Duxford
F-BBQE	Morane-Saulnier MS.315 (Reported as ex F-BCNL)	7603/345		J.Koch (On rebuild 2.97)	Sandown
F-BBSO	Auster 5	1792	G-AMJM TW452	C.J.Baker (Frame dismantled 4.98)	Carr Farm, Newark
F-BDRS	Boeing B-17G-95DL Flying Fortress	32376	N68269 NL68269/44-83735	IWM Collection/American Air Museum "Mary Alice" (As "231983/IY-G" in 401st BG/615th BS USAAF c/s)	Duxford
F-BFUT	Auster J/1N Alpha	3357		T.Cox (On rebuild: see G-AJEI)	Bristol
F-BGEQ	DH.82A Tiger Moth	86305	Fr.AF NL846	Brooklands Museum (On rebuild 11.93)	Rushett Farm, Chessington
F-BGNR	Vickers Viscount 708	35	(OY-AFO)	Not known (OY-AFN)/F-BGNR (Stored 2.99)	Rotary Farm, Hatch
F-BGNX	DH.106 Comet 1XB			See G-AOJT in SECTION 1	
F-BMCY	Potez 840	02	N840HP F-BJSU/F-WJSU	Shetland Fire Service (Damaged Sumburgh 29.3.81; extant 12.95)	Sumburgh
F-BMKC	Sportavia Fornier RF4D	4006		Not known (Spares use 2.95)	Biggin Hill
F-BSGM	Dornier Do.27A-4	524	WGAF 57+63	Real Aviation	(Kent)
F-BTGV	Aero Spacelines 377SGT Super Guppy	201 001	N211AS	British Aviation Heritage Collection (Airbus Skylink c/s) (Stored 9.97)	Bruntingthorpe
F-BTRP	Sud SA.321F Super Frelon (Converted from SA.321 c/n 116)	01	F-WMHC F-BTRP/F-WKQC/F-OCZV/F-RAFR/F-OCMF/F-BMHC/F-WMHC	The Helicopter Museum (As "F-OCMF" in Olympic Airways c/s)	Weston-super-Mare
F-BVGB	Airbus A.300B2-1C	06	F-WVGB	Channel Express Air Services Ltd (Completely broken up 1999)	Bournemouth
F-BVGC	Airbus A.300B2-1C	07	F-WVGC	Channel Express Air Services Ltd (Broken up 1999)	Bournemouth
F-GCCZ	Eurococpter SA.341 Gazelle			Not known (Noted 12.99)	
F-CCHG	Wassmer WA.21 Javelot	19		Not known (Noted 6.99)	Yeatsall Farm, Abbotts Bromley
F-GALL	Beechcraft 58P Baron	TJ-83		T.Hayselden (Doncaster) Ltd (Noted 2.96)	Sandtoft
F-GDPA	Cessna 172RG Cutlass	172RG-1091	N9945B	Not known (Wreck stored 12.96)	Shobdon
F-GFDG	Aerospatiale SA.341 Gazelle	1204		MW Helicopters (Noted 12.99)	Stapleford
F-GFLD	Beechcraft C90 King Air	LJ-741	HB-GGW I-AZIO	RFS Aircraft Engineering (Stored unmarked 1.00)	Southend
F-GFNO	Robin ATL	16	F-WFNO	Not known (Noted 6.98)	Kemble
F-GFRO	Robin ATL	64		Not known (Noted 6.98)	Gloucestershire
F-GGKR	Max Holste 1521M Broussard	316	F-WGKR Fr Mil	Not known (As "316/315-SN" 1.99)	Duxford
F-GGTJ	Aerospatiale SA.341 Gazelle	1473		MW Helicopters (Noted 12.99)	Stapleford
F-GHOB	Chaize CS.2200-F12 HAFB	30		M.Hammond "Hobicat" (Active 6.97)	Lindfield, W.Sussex
F-GHRI	Colt AS-261 Hot-Air Airship	1380	F-WGGM G-BPLD	British Balloon Museum & Library (Stored 1997)	Newbury
F-GOBF	SIAI-Marchetti SF.260	116	BF8431 Philippines AF	C.D.Weiswall (As "BF8431") (Noted 8.99)	Elstree
F-HMFI	Farman F.40	6799		RAF Museum (On rebuild 10.95 to F.141 status ?)	RAF Cardington
"F-OCMF"				See F-BTRP above	
F-OGVR	Aerospatiale AS.350 Ecureuil	2773		Not known (Noted 12.99)	NK
F-PYOY	Heintz Zenith 100	52		B.Featherstone (Noted 1.00)	Southend
F-PYVA	Colomban MC-15 Cri-Cri	371		Not known (Stored 8.96 - current status uncertain)	Guernsey
F-PYYV	Rutan LongEz	1046		Not known (Noted 2.99)	Poplar Hall Farm, Elmsett
F-WGTX	Heli Atlas			Intora Firebird plc (Current status uncertain)	Southend
F-WGTY	Heli Atlas			Intora Firebird plc (Current status uncertain)	Southend
50-BH	Fisher FP-202 Super Koala	-		K.Riches t/a MUL International (Stored off airfield 1.92: status unknown)	(Guernsey)
114700 (Fr.AF)	North American T-6G-NH Texan	182-387	51-14700	Aces High Ltd (As "2-134" in Japanese AF c/s: wreck stored 3.96	North Weald

HUNGARY

Regn	Type	C/n	P/I	Owner/operator	Probable Base
HA-ACL	Dornier Do.28D-2	4125	D-IDRC	Not known (Noted 11.99)	Hibaldstow
			WGAF 58+50	(In basic GAF camo marked "Hibaldstow Skydive")	
HA-JAM	Yaskovlev Yak-55M	910104		Not known (Noted 5.99)	White Waltham
HA-LAY	LET 410UVP	841326	UR67100	Not known (Noted 9.99)	Hinton-in-The-Hedges
HA-MEP	WSK-PZL Antonov AN-2R	1G190-25		V.S.E.Norman t/a Aerosuperbatics	Rendcomb
				(Utterly Butterly/St.Ivel titles) (Noted 8.98)	
HA-MKA	WSK-PZL Antonov AN-2R	1G186-29	OM-JIR	Not known (Noted 5.99)	White Waltham
			OK-JIR		
HA-MKE	WSK-PZL Antonov AN-2R	1G158-34	UR-07714	Air Foyle (Noted 12.99)	White Waltham
			CCCP-07714		
HA-MKF	WSK-PZL Antonov AN-2TP	1G233-43	OM-248	Transair	White Waltham
			OM-UIN/OK-UIN (Noted 6.99)		
HA-PPY	Aerospatiale SA.341G Gazelle			Not known (Noted 12.99)	NK

SWITZERLAND

Regn	Type	C/n	P/I	Owner/operator	Probable Base
HB-IVR	Canadair CL-604 Challenger	5318	HB-IKQ	Sintec SA	Luton
			(TC-DHE)/C-FYYH/C-GLXO		
HB-NAV	Beagle B.121 Pup 2	B121-155	G-AZCM	447 ATC Sqdn	Henley-on-Thames
				(Fuselage only stored 12.94)	
HB-PNE	PA-28RT-201T Turbo Arrow IV	28R-8231051	PH-HJM	Not known	Thurrock
			N8206B	(Noted 12.99 - for UK Register)	
HB-XPR	Bell 206 JetRanger			Not known (Noted 12.99)	NK
C-558 (Sw.AF)	EKW C-3605	338		Not known (Stored 4.99)	Little Gransden

SAUDI ARABIA

Regn	Type	C/n	P/I	Owner/operator	Probable Base
HZ-123	Boeing 707-138B	17696	"17696"	Not known (Open store 1.00)	Southend
			HZ-123/N138MJ/N220M/N138TA/(N112TA)/C-FPWV/CF-PWV/VH-EBA/N31239		
HZ-DG1	Boeing 727-51	19124	N604NA	Dallah Avco	Stansted
			(N5604)/N478US (Noted 12.97)		
HZ-KAA	Grumman Gulfstream IV	1294	(HZ-MAL)	Mawarid Ltd	Farnborough
			N416GA	(Noted 10.99)	
HZ-SAK1	Boeing 707-351B	18586	VR-BOR	Al Wisar Trading (Stored 2.97)	Manston
			VR-BMV/G-BSZA/EL-SKD/N351SR/N651TF/VR-CAO/VR-HGO/N353US		
HZ-SJP3	Canadair CL-604 Challenger	5346	N604JP	Jouannou & Parskevaides	Farnborough/Riyadh

ITALY

Regn	Type	C/n	P/I	Owner/operator	Probable Base
I-LIOI	Agusta E-101	50009		Not known (Noted 12.99)	NK
I-LUST	Enstrom 280FX Shark	2026	N88CV	Not known (Noted 9.99)	Shoreham
I-TOMI	Nardi FN.305D		I-UEBI	Kermit Weeks	Booker
				(With PPS for pre-delivery restoration)	
I-4818	Groppino Microlight	?		Not known	Gloucestershire
				(Moved to Germany with Mid-West Engines Ltd 1999?)	
MM53432	N.A. AT-6D-NT Harvard	88-16086	42-84305	D.Baker	Swansea
	(Plates marked "88-3160" and "AF33-038-2117")			(Coded "RM-11") (On rebuild 5.95)	
MM54-2372	PA-18-95 Super Cub	18-3572	I-EIXM	Not known (Open store 7.95)	Kesgrave, Ipswich
			54-2372	(Coded "EI-184")	

JAPAN

Regn	Type	C/n	P/I	Owner/operator	Probable Base
JA7684	Enstrom F28F			Not known (Noted 4.99)	Shoreham

NORWAY

Regn	Type	C/n	P/I	Owner/operator	Probable Base
LN-AMY	North American AT-6D Harvard	88-16849	(LN-LCS)	The Old Flying Machine Co	Duxford
			(LN-LCN)/N10595/42-85068 (SEAC/RAF c/s 1.99)		
LN-BNM	Noorduyn AT-16-ND Harvard IIB	14-639	R.Dan AF	RAF Museum	Hendon
			31-329/FE905/42-12392 (As "FE905" in RAF/RCAF c/s)		
LN-FOI(3)	Lockheed L-188C Electra	2005	(LN-MOF)	(Air Atlantique Ltd)	Coventry
			N31231/ZK-TEA/(ZK-BMP)/N9724C (Fred Olsen c/s: stored 6.99)		
LN-FOL(2)	Lockheed L-188C Electra	1116	N669F	(Air Atlantique Ltd)	Coventry
			N404GN/N6126A (DHL c/s: stored 6.99)		
LN-FON(2)	Lockheed L-188C Electra	1128	N342HA	(Air Atlantique Ltd)	Coventry
			N417MA/OB-R-1138/HP-684/N417HA/CF-ZST/N7142C		
			(DHL c/s: stored 6.99)		
LN-FOO	Lockheed L-188C Electra	1098	N345HA	(Air Atlantique Ltd)	Coventry
			N5541B/N12VG/N5541/SE-FGB/N5541 (DHL titles: stored 6.99)		

ARGENTINA

Regn	Type	C/n	P/I	Owner/operator	Probable Base
LQ-BLT	MBB Bo.105			Not known	Bourn

(Non-airworthy pod is the old airframe and carries "Policia" titles - it crashed 13.06.96 and was shipped to UK and rebuilt with airframe S.915 - basically all the dynamics etc were taken out of one airframe and put into the other with some replacment and refurbishment en route. So this is the discarded shell of S.863 and is now earmarked for the North East Aircraft Museum)

Regn	Type	C/n	P/I	Owner/operator	Probable Base
LV-RIE	Nord 1002 Pingouin	-		R.J.Lamplough (Stored 3.97)	North Weald

LITHUANIA

Regn	Type	C/n	P/I	Owner/operator	Probable Base
LY-ABQ	Yakovlev Yak-52	866915	DOSAAF 111	A.Hyatt "15" (Noted 10.99)	Leicester
LY-ABV	Yakovlev Yak-52	8910004		Not known (Noted 4.99)	Little Gransden
LY-ABW	Antonov AN-2	1G195-26	CCCP-68121	Not known (Noted 8.99)	Oaksey ParK
LY-ABZ	Yakovlev Yak-52	9611914		Not known (Noted 5.99)	Panshanger
LY-AFA	Yakovlev Yak-52	822608	DOSAAF 110	Not known "110" (Noted 9.99)	Barton
LY-AFB	Yakovlev Yak-52	822610	DOSAAF 112	Termikas Co "112" (Noted 1.99)	Little Gransden
LY-AFJ	Yakovlev Yak-52	9712003		Not known "58" (Noted 4.99)	White Waltham
LY-AFK	Yakovlev Yak-52	877415	DOSAAF 27	Not known (Noted 10.99)	Halfpenny Green
LY-AFV	Yakovlev Yak-52	899915		A Fraser (Noted 1.00)	RAF Halton
LY-AFX	Yakovlev Yak-52	899413		D Hawkins (Noted 9.99)	Compton Abbas
LY-AFZ	Yakovlev Yak-50	842706	DOSAAF 24	Not known	Little Gransden
LY-AKW	Yakovlev Yak-52	855601	DOSAAF 56	A.Harris "56" (Noted 1.99)	Swanton Morley
LY-AGG	Yakovlev Yak-50		DOSAAF 107	Not known (Noted 10.99) "Svetlana"	Old Sarum
LY-AHB	Yakovlev Yak-52	9812106		Not known (Noted 1.00)	North Weald
LY-AHB	Yakovlev Yak-52	9812106		Not known (Noted 1.00)	North Weald
LY-AHE	Yakovlev Yak-52	822710	DOSAAF 100	Not known "10" (Noted 10.99)	Little Gransden
LY-AHF	Yakovlev Yak-52			Not known (Noted 5.99)	Galway
LY-AID	Yakovlev Yak-52	822603	DOSAAF 105	Not known "105" (Red) (Noted 5.99)	Gloucestershire
LY-AIE	Yakovlev Yak-52	899907	DOSAAF	Not known (Noted 12.99)	Breighton
LY-AIH	Yakovlev Yak-18T		RA-44527	Not known (Noted 12.99)	White Waltham
LY-AKC	Yakovlev Yak-52			Not known (Noted 10.99)	Little Gransden
LY-AKW	Yakovlev Yak-52	855601	DOSAAF 56	Not known "56"	Swanton Morley
LY-ALJ	Yakovlev Yak-52	8910115	DOSAAF 132	D.Hawkins (Noted 4.99)	Compton Abbas
LY-ALM	Yakovlev Yak-52	669012		Not known "114" (Blue) (Noted 12.99) "Tatiyana II"	Old Sarum
LY-ALN	Yakovlev Yak-52	800708	DOSAAF	D.Lewendon "52" (Noted 7.99)	Bickmarsh

(Regd as c/n 800910 but wears c/n plate from 800708 - see LY-AMP below)

Regn	Type	C/n	P/I	Owner/operator	Probable Base
LY-ALO	Yakovlev Yak-52	844815	DOSAAF 135	Sky Associates (UK) Ltd (Noted 10.99)	Little Gransden
LY-ALS	Yakovlev Yak-52	855509	DOSAAF 69 DOSAAF 49	M.Jefferies "69" "Once a Knight" (Noted 2.99)	North Weald
LY-ALT	Yakovlev Yak-52	822704	DOSAAF 121	Titan Airways Ltd (Noted 10.99)	North Weald
LY-ALU	Yakovlev Yak-52	9011107	DOSAAF 124	S.Goodridge (Noted 7.98)	Exeter
LY-AMJ	Yakovlev Yak-18T	22202047812	DOSAAF	Not known (Noted 11.99)	Earls Colne
LY-AMP	Yakovlev Yak-52	800708	DOSAAF 52	B Brown "52" (Noted 7.98)	Breighton

(Wears c/n plate 856103 but offically registered as 800708 - see LY-ALN above)

Regn	Type	C/n	P/I	Owner/operator	Probable Base
LY-AMS	Yakovlev Yak-52	844306	DOSAAF 51(red)	Willowair Flying Club (Noted 1.00)	Southend
LY-AMU	Yakovlev Yak-52	833901	DOSAAF 42(red)	G.Sharp "42" (Noted 5.98)	North Weald
LY-ANG	Yakovlev Yak-52	832409	DOSAAF 81	Not known (Noted 5.98)	North Weald
LY-ANI	Yakovlev Yak-52	9411812	DOSAAF	Not known (Noted 7.98)	Little Gransden
LY-AOB	Yakovlev Yak-52	9211517	DOSAAF	M.Schwarz (Noted 8.99) (Polydron c/s)	Kemble
LY-AOC	Yakovlev Yak-52	811308	DOSAAF 30(?)	T Boxhall (Noted 10.99)	Headcorn
LY-AOK	Yakovlev Yak-52	877404	DOSAAF 16	I.Vaughan (Noted 3.99)	Nottingham
LY-AOO	Yakovlev Yak-18T	22202040425		Not known (Noted 8.98)	Sturgate
LY-AOT	Yakovlev Yak-50	853101		Not known (Noted 12.98)	White Waltham
LY-AOX	Yakovlev Yak-52	833708	DOSAAF 122	J & J Van der Luit	Biggin Hill

(Previously reported as c/n 877604 - correct position unconfirmed) (Noted 8.97)

Regn	Type	C/n	P/I	Owner/operator	Probable Base
LY-AOZ	Yakovlev Yak-52			Not known (Noted 11.97)	Biggin Hill
LY-APP	Yakovlev Yak-18P			Alan Hyatt (Noted 11.99)	Headcorn
LY-ASA	Antonov AN-2T	1G139-49	UR-70290 CCCP-70290	Not known (Damaged landing Portcurno, Cornwall 23.6.99)	Turweston
LY-FKD	Yakovlev Yak-12M	210999	SP-FKD	M Jefferies (Noted 8.99)	Oaksey Park
LY-JDR	Yakovlev Yak-55M		DOSAAF	Not known (Noted 10.99) (As "JD-R/J-DR in US c/s) "Oh Rats"	White Waltham

Regn	Type	C/n	P/I	Owner/operator	Probable Base

UNITED STATES OF AMERICA

Regn	Type	C/n	P/I	Owner/operator	Probable Base
N1EF	Cessna 525 Citationjet	0167		Micromure plc	Guernsey
N1FD	Socata TB-200	1614		Not known (Noted 10.99)	Fairoaks
N2CL	PA-28RT-201T Turbo Arrow IV	28R-8131054	N8333S	Speedbird Air Inc (Noted 11.99)	Elstree
N2FU	Gates Lear Jet 31	31-027	N30LJ	Motor Racing Development Corp	Biggin Hill
			N91201	(Noted 8.97)	
N2MD	Piper J3C-65 Cub	17521	N70515	V.S.E.Norman	Rendcomb
			NC70515	(Noted 7.97) (G-BSVJ reserved)	
N3CX	Sikorsky S-76B	76-0324	N762TC	Not known (Noted 9.98)	East Midlands
N3TQ	Cessna 310Q	310Q-0752	N1534T	Not known (Noted 2.99)	Blackbushe
N5LL	PA-34 Navajo	7812041	N27495	Not known (Noted 1999)	NK
N5NN	Cessna 421C Golden Eagle III	421C-0446	G-BRIT	Mistair Inc	Elstree
			N6713C	(Noted 9.97) (Old Britannia Airways c/s)	
N6FL	Latulip LM-3X	LM-3X-1001		J.Parkins	Bidford
	(Rotax 377) (Aeronca 7AC scale rep)			(Stored 9.95 - USAAF c/s)	
N6NE	Lockheed Jetstar 731	5006/40	(VR-CCC)	Aerospace Finance Leasing Inc	Southampton
			N6NE/N222Y/N731JS/N227K/N12R/N9280R		
				(Damaged Southampton 27.11.92; on fire dump 11.99)	
N7SY	Hunting Percival P.57 Sea Prince	P57/71	G-BRFC	Bournemouth Aviation Museum	Bournemouth
			WP321	(Noted 12.99)	
N9AY	Cessna 421C Golden Eagle III	421C-0844	G-NSGI	D & J Aviation (Noted 2.99)	Elstree
			N421EL/XA-RAE/N421EB/(N21MW)/N421EB/N2659Z		
N11ZP	American Blimp A60	11		Not known (Noted 11.99)	Cardiff
				(Sanyo c/s)"	
N12FU	Gates Lear Jet 60	60-027	N4230S	B.Ecclestone/Motor Racing Development Corporation	
			XA-ICA/N4027S (Noted 8.97)		Biggin Hill
N12NM	Cessna 501 Citation I/SP	501-0257	OE-FLY	Pektron Aviation Inc/L'Equipe Air	Gamston
	(Unit No.660)		N500NW/(N992NW)/N2631V (Noted 9.99)		
N12ZP	American Blimp A60	12		Not known	White Waltham
				(Goodyear c/s) "Spirit of Europe 2"	
N15FH	Cessna 340A II	340A-0722	G-CMAC	F.R.Foran & D.Hanley (Noted 8.99)	Liverpool
			G-JIMS/G-PETE/N2667N		
N18E	Boeing 247D	1722	NC18E	The Science Museum	Wroughton
			NC18/NC13340		
N18V	Beechcraft UC-43-BH Traveler	6869	NC18	R.J.Lamplough	North Weald
			Bu 32898/FT507/44-67761 (As "PB1": moted 11.99)		
N19F	Cessna 337A Super Skymaster	337A-0289	N6289F	Not known	Shoreham
	(Robertson STOL conversion)			(Stored 1.99)	
N20RJ	Beechcraft H35 Bonanza	D-5193	N7945D	Not known (Noted 10.99)	Shobdon
N22CG	Cessna 441			M.Klinge (Noted 8.99)	Prestwick
N22GA	Cessna 550 Citation II	0031	RP-C296	ILMOR Engineering Inc	Coventry
N25PJ	Cessna 340A II	340A-0912	HB-LNM	Not known	Guernsey
			LN-TEA/N27026 (Noted 1.99)		
N27BG	Cessna 340A	340A-0656		B Gregory (Noted 9.99)	Cardiff
N27MW	Beechcraft B58 Baron	TH995		Not known (Noted 11.99)	Fairoaks
N31NB	PA-31-310 Navajo B	31-7401239	G-OSFT	N.Brown	Deenethorpe
			G-MDAS/5N-AEP/G-BJCZ/N61427 (Noted 7.99)		
N31RB	Grumman-American AA-5B Tiger	AA5B-0156		Forest Aviation Ltd (Noted 6.99)	Bournemouth
N33EW	Mitsubishi MU-2B-60	1519S.A.	N331W	King Aviation	Southend
			N33TW/N434MA (Noted 1.00)		
N33CJ	Cessna 525 Citationjet	0245	N5214J	Starna Aviation	Ronaldsway
N33PV	Partenavia P.68TC	347-33TC		Not known (Noted 10.99)	Henstridge
N34FA	SOCATA TB-20 Trinidad	866		Not known (Noted 1.00)	Southend/Coventry
N36NB	Beechcraft A36 Bonanza	E-2274	F-GKTZ	Air Bickerton Inc	Biggin Hill
			N7249H		
N36SF	Hawker Iraqi Fury FB.11	37539	Iraqi AF 315	J.Bradshaw	Kemble
			(As "361" in composite RAN/RCN/RN/Dutch c/s)		
	(Still present for sale 9.99 apparently no longer officially on US Register)				
N37WC	Cessna 401	401-0183	N917WS	R.H.Durston/Durston Air Service	Blackpool
			N4083Q	(Noted 11.99)	
N40BJ	Dornier Bucker Bu.133 Jungmeister	4	G-AYFO	K.Weeks	Booker
			HB-MIO/U-57	(On rebuild by PPS 3.96 as G-AYFO)	
N40D	Stolp SA-100 Starduster 1	4258549		Not known (Noted 9.96)	Biggin Hill
N43SV	Boeing PT-13D Kaydet	75-5541		Not known (As "796")	Rendcomb
N45AW	PA-28RT-201T Turbo Arrow IV	28R-8431003	N43230	Powersway Aviation (Noted 11.99)	White Waltham
N45CD	PA-28-161 Warrior II	28-7916467	PH-AND	Not known	Old Sarum
			N2841J	(Noted 4.98)	
N45JB	Dassault Falcon 100	203	XA-TBL	Barron International Holdings	London/Gibraltar
			N100CT/VR-CLA/N267FJ/F-WZGJ		
N46EA	Percival P.66 Pembroke C.1	P66/83	8452M	P.G.Vallance Ltd	Charlwood, Surrey
	(Regd with c/n K66-046)		XK885	(Stored 6.97)	

Regn	Type	C/n	P/I	Owner/operator	Probable Base
N47BK	PA-32RT-301T Turbo Saratoga	3257046	N41283	B Kreiskey (Noted 12.99)	Blackbushe
N47DD	Republic P-47D-40RA Thunderbolt		Peru AF 119	American Air Museum	Duxford
	(Composite rebuild)	399-55731	FAP 545/45-49192	"Oregons Britannia"	
				(As "226413/ZU-N" in 56th FG USAAF c/s)	
N47DG	Republic P-47G Thunderbolt	21962	N42354	Flying A Services	Earls Colne
			42-25068	(Noted 1996)	
N47FK	Douglas C-47A Dakota III	9700	EC-FNS	Not known (Noted 7.99)	North Weald
			EC-187/N2669A/C-FEEX/CF-EEX/N308FN/N3PG/N3W/N7V/NC49538/42-23838		
				(Active with Tony Holden/Dakota Club UK 7.99)	
N47FL	Douglas C-47A Dakota III	13087	EC-FIN	MLP Aviation	North Weald
			EC-659/N7164E/C-GCTE/C-GXAV/(N92A)/C-GXAV/CAF 12952/RCAF 968/42-93202		
				(To USA 11.99 ?)	
N51CV	Beech 200C Super King Air	BL-49	Z-TAM	Aerospace Financial Services	Jersey
N52NW	Grumman G.1159 Gulfstream II	52	N211MT	Global Trading Ltd	Bristol/Lulsgate
			N711MT/(N52TJ)/(N52NE)/N5SJ/N38KM/N69SF/C-FFNM/CF-FNM		
N55BN	Beechcraft 95-B55 Baron	TC-1572	G-KCAS	C.Butler	White Waltham
			G-KCEA/N2840W (Noted 12.99)		
N55EN	Beechcraft 95-E55 Baron	TE-942		Not known (Noted 3.99)	Elstree
N58GT	Beech B58 Baron (winglets)	TH-1090	HB-GIK	Not known (Noted 6.99)	Southend
N60B	Rockwell Commander 690			Not known (Noted 9.99)	Gamston
N60FM	Boeing 727-27	19535	N7294	Aimes Co (Stored 2.99)	Lasham
N60GM	Cessna 421C Golden Eagle III	0328		Not known (Noted 10.99)	Ronaldsway
N60NB	Mitsubishi Mu-2B Marquise	1528SA	5Y-VIZ	Dogfox Aviation (Noted 1.00)	Southend
N60VB	Ted Smith Aerostar 600A	60-0182-080		Not known (Noted 9.99)	Henstridge
N61HB	PA-34-220T Seneca	3449091		Holding & Barnes Ltd (Noted 5.99)	Thurrock
N61SL	Antonov An-2	1G/17527		S Lungren (Noted 6.99)	White Waltham
N65TD	IAI 1125A Astra-SPX	093		Helios Ltd/Vitol SA	Luton
N66SW	Cessna 340	340-0011	N5035Q	Cabledraw Inc (Noted 9.98)	Elstree
N70AA	Beechcraft 70 Queen Air	LB-35	G-KEAA	Trygon Ltd	Southend
			G-REXP/G-AYPC (Noted 1.00)		
N70VB	Ted Smith Aerostar 600A	60-0446-150	C-GVHQ	Not known	Blackbushe
			N9805Q	(Noted 5.99)	
N70XX	Mitsubishi MU.300 Diamond 1	A052SA	I-FRAB	Lovair Inc	Luton
			HB-VHT/N352DM (Noted 10.96)		
NX71MY	Vickers Vimy rep	01		Greenco (UK) Ltd/K.Snell	Kemble
				(Noted 5.99: as "G-EAOU" - see SECTION 4)	
N71VE	NA Rockwell Turbo Commander 690	11043	N71VT	Cooper Aerial Surveys Ltd	Gamston
			N2VQ/N2VA	(Noted 9.99)	
N74BF	Stoddard-Hamilton Glasair	2274		Not known (Noted 1.00)	Bournemouth
N74DC	Pitts S-2A Special	2228	I-ALAT	D.Cockburn (Noted 3.99)	Elstree
N74PM	Agusta A.109			Not known (Noted 12.99)	
N75	Hanriot HD.1	75	G-AFDX	RAF Museum	Hendon
			OO-APJ/H-1/75 (As "HD-75" in Belgian AF c/s)		
N75TL	Boeing-Stearman A75N1 (N2S-4) Kaydet		N5148N	Not known	Headcorn/Goudhurst, Kent
		75-3616	Bu.37869	(As "669" in US Army c/s) (Noted 7.98)	
N76TH	Sikorsky S-76B	76-0373		Turbine Helicopters	Leeds-Bradford
				(Noted 12.99)	
N79AP	Beechcraft 58P Baron	TJ-206	VH-ORP	R & B Services Ltd	Southend
			ZK-TML/N6648Z (Noted 1.00)		
N79EL	Beechcraft 400A Beechjet	RK-214		Edra Lauren Leasing/DFS Furniture	East Midlands
N80BA	Pitts S-2A Special	648-4		T.Stronge (Noted 6.97)	Newtownards
N80CP	PA-31T-620 Cheyenne II	31T-7920040	N23185	Not known (Noted 8.99)	Thruxton
N80RF	Beechcraft 60 Duke	P-17	(G-BMSO)	MLP Aviation/E.Lundquist	Elstree
			I-DUKA/F-BRAX/HB-GDO (Noted 5.98)		
N86Y	Beechcraft 200 Super King Air	BB-302	N300BW	York International Corporation	Farnborough
			N600CP	(Noted 9.99)	
N88PL	PA-46-310P Malibu	46-8508099		D.Clark Grove Fields Farm/Wellesbourne Mountford	
				(Noted 8.99)	
N90AQ	Gates Learjet 60			Sterling Jets (Noted 8.99)	Prestwick
N90MD	PA-46-350P Malibu Mirage	4622086	G-BUPN	Not known	Gloucestershire
			N91884		
	(A/c crashed near Seattle w/e 23.10.99. It left Gloucester on 14.10.99 to Wick and then on to US for				
	Turbine conversion, but apparently "went into a hill nr Seattle")				
N93GS	Grumman G-21A Goose	B-76	C-FBAE	T.Friedrich "Caribbean Clipper"	Elstree
	(PW R-985)		CF-BAE/CF-FEM/RCAF 392/Bu.37823 (Noted 7.97)		
N95D	PA-34-220T Seneca III	34-49060		Not known (Noted 10.99)	Welshpool
N97CN	Agusta A.109C	7657		Not known (Noted 10.99)	Redhill
N97RJ	PA-31 Turbo Navajo	31-7300956	G-SKKB	JRB Aviation Ltd	Southend
			G-BBDS/N7565L (Noted 1.00)		
N99ET	Socata TB-10 Tobago	226	G-BJDG	E.A.Terris	Oxford
			F-BNGR	(Noted 7.96)	

Regn	Type	C/n	P/I	Owner/operator	Probable Base
N101AP	Beechcraft B200 King Air			Nigel Webb (Confirmed by owner 10.99)	Cranfield
N109AB	Agusta A.109			Not known (Noted 12.99)	
N109TW	Agusta A.109C	7650	D-HCKM	Tom Walkinshaw Racing (Noted 12.99)	Oxford
N109UK	Agusta A.109	7304		Not known (Noted 12.99)	Ware
N112JS	Cessna 550 Citation II (Unit No.032)	550-0032	N905EM	Hamlin Jet Ltd/Flamingo 500 Inc	Luton
				N50US/N66ES/N55BP/N810SG/N810SC/N3251M (Noted 10.97)	
N112WG	Westland WG-30-100	012		The Helicopter Museum (Stored 8.98)	Weston-super-Mare
N114WG	Westland WG-30-100	014	G-EFIS G-17-18	The Helicopter Museum (Noted 8.98)	Weston-super-Mare
N116WG	Westland WG-30-100	016	(G-BLLG)	The Helicopter Museum (Stored 8.98)	Weston-super-Mare
N118WG	Westland WG-30-100	018		The Helicopter Museum (Stored 8.98)	Weston-super-Mare
N125GP	Gates Learjet 31A	31A-162	N162LJ N525GP	Damon Hill	Dublin
N125XX	BAe HS.125 Srs.700A	NA0254 & 257075	N124AR	Connex Aviation/Ambrion Aviation	Luton
				N125TR/N125AM/(G-BHKF)/G-5-13 (Noted 6.99)	
N126NH	Bell 412HP	36067	OE-XLL	Bell Helicopter Textron Ltd	Redhill
				D-HHJJ/N7078L (Noted 9.96)	
N133H	Agusta A.109C	7609	N1NQ	Graff Aviation Ltd (Noted 12.99)	Fairoaks
N139DB	PA-23-250 Aztec E	27-4611	G-AYUL N13992	Not known (Noted 12.99)	Welshpool
N139DP	Bell P-39Q-5BE Airacobra	?	(New Guinea) 42-19993	The Fighter Collection (As "219993" in USAAC c/s) "Brooklyn Bum 2nd" (On rebuild in USA for delivery)	Duxford
N139XX	Gates Learjet 60	60-139	N233FX	Corporate Jets Ltd	Prestwick
N142TW	Beech 58	TH-1841		Not known (Noted 7.99)	Fairoaks
N145DF	Cessna 501 I/SP	501-0055		Ambrion Aviation	Luton
N146GA	Cessna 425 Conquest I	425-0074	HB-LPU N6845Y	Davis Aircraft Operations Inc (Noted 12.99)	Edinburgh
N147DC	Douglas C-47A-75-DL Dakota	19347	"G-AGHY"	Aces High (US) Inc	North Weald
				G-DAKS/TS423/42-100884 (As "TS423" 1999)	
N150JC	Beechcraft A35 Bonanza	D.2084	N8674A	M.Hornblower (On rebuild with AeroFab Restorations 8.99)	Hurstbourne Tarrant, Hants

(History as follows:

Regd. . . . N8674A   Built 1949 Regd.   . . . N150JC   G A Cooley, Amarillo, Texas
Regd. . . . N150JC   Weimar Hydrophonics Inc., Weimar, Texas
Regd. . . . N150JC   Blake F Hunter, Leesburg, Florida
Regd. . . . N150JC   Michael Hornblower, Aberdeen, Scotland
Based at Ford in 1979 & temporarily based at Lee-on-Solent the same year. Based at Aberdeen by middle
of 1981. Capt. Hornblower was the Managing Director of Peregrine Air Services and also owned Hawk
Aviation both of which were based at Aberdeen. The aircraft was kept at the premises of either company.
On climb-out from Wick 18.6.83 a sudden power loss was experienced and, with the u/c already retracted,
a/c forced-landed straight ahead, slid over ditch through perimeter wire fence and slewed through 180
degrees. It came to rest in a barley field. There was no injury to the four occupants. The cause of
power loss was attributed to the fuel pump. The engine was a Continental E185- 11. Damage was to lower
fuselage structure, aft of engine, leading edge of port wing and tip tank and bent propeller)

Regn	Type	C/n	P/I	Owner/operator	Probable Base
N159M	Dasssult Falcon 50EX	276	F-WWHB	Motorola Inc (Noted 12.99)	Farnborough
N172AM	Cessna 172M	64993	G-BXHG	R S Bartlett (Noted 5.99)	Seething
N177CE	Cessna 177RG Cardinal	177RG-1308	N52914	Not known (Noted 5.99)	Farnborough
N180BB	Cessna 180K			Not knwn (Noted 7.99)	Humberside
N181WW	Beagle B.206 Srs.1	B.018	G-BCJF	Not known	Biggin Hill
				N181WW/G-BCJF/XS773 (Open Store 2.99)	
N185F	Agusta A.109			Not known (Noted 12.99)	
N190RM	Beechcraft E90 King Air	LW-1	N64RJ N64RA/N934K	R & M Aviation Inc (Noted 11.97)	Norwich
N195AL	Beech 300 Super King Air	FA-102	C-FPCC	Ian Woosnam (Noted 1.00)	Jersey
N196B	North American F-86A-5-NA Sabre	151-43611	48-242	American Air Museum (As "8242/FU-242" in USAF c/s)	Duxford
N201XJ	Mooney M.20J	240494		Not known (Noted 10.98)	NK
N206NS	Bell 206B JetRanger	4474		Biztech (Noted 12.99)	Blackbushe
N208MK	Cessna 206B	00276		Not known (Noted 1999)	Jersey
N209AA	Bell 206B JetRanger			Not known (Noted 12.99)	Sywell
N210MP	Cessna T210N Turbo Centurion II	T210-63193	(G-BPGO) N210MP	Welback Estates Ltd (Noted 7.99)	Compton Abbas
N220SC	PA-31T Navajo	8120041		Not known (Noted 1999)	Guernsey
N228CX	Socata TBM-700	84		B.Holmes (Noted 1.00)	Southend/Cannes
N237TD	Beech 95	TD-237	HB-GOC	Not known (Noted 1999)	Gloucestershire
N250MC	PA-23-250 Aztec E	27-7305142	EI-BXP	Oilsearch (US) Inc	East Midlands
				G-BSFL/PH-NOA/9M-AUS/PH-NOA/N40378 (Noted 8.99)	

Regn	Type	C/n	P/I	Owner/operator	Probable Base
N250TP	Beechcraft A36 Bonanza (Allison 250-B17)	E-2408	N416HC N600TT/N3107K (Willie Carson) (Noted 9.99)	Minster Enterprises Inc	Tatenhill
N252JP	Hughes 369E	0346E		Not known (Noted 12.99)	Banchory
N252JS	Grumman Gulfstream V	525	N594GA	Smurfitt Group	Dublin
N260KH	SIAI-Marchetti SF-260D	739	I-SMAD	Cheyne Motors Ltd (Noted 5.99)	Old Sarum
N260QB	Aerotek Pitts S-2S Special	3002		D.Baker (Noted 2.99)	Exeter
N273TB	Beech 58 Baron	TH-305		Not known (Noted 8.99)	Welshpool
N281Q	Enstrom F.28A	266		Stephenson Aviation Ltd (Wreck stored 1999)	Goodwood
N285RA	Consolidated PBY-5A Catalina	2087	N212DM	Not known (Noted 5.99)	North Weald
	G-BPFY/N212DM/G-BPFY/N212DM/C-FHNH/CF-HNH/F-ZBAV/N5555H/N2864D/Bu.64017				
N295SS	PA-46 Malibu	46-36174		Not known (Noted 1.00)	Fairoaks
N310KZ	Cessna 310R	310R-1861	G-BHKY (N3156M)	Not known (Noted 1999)	NK
N310QQ	Cessna 310Q	310Q-0695	N8048Q G-BAUE	Not known (Noted 11.99)	Elstree
N311DG	Cessna 560 Citation V	560-0167	N211DG (167WE)/N20CN/(N68873)	Woodlands Ltd	Manchester
NL314BG	North American P-51D-20NA Mustang	-	C-GZQX	Flying A Services/David Arnold (Noted 1996)	Earls Colne
	(Regd with c/n 122-39599 ex C-FBAU/44-73140 which crashed/dbf 7.7.84; possibly a composite rebuild)				
N316MJ	Cessna 525	0297		Reynard Motorsport (Noted 8.99)	Oxford
N320MR	PA-30-160 Twin Comanche	30-1917		Not known (Noted 11.99)	Elstree
N321DH	Pilatus PC.XII	116	HB-FQJ	Not known (Noted 3.97)	Farnborough
N321GN	Cessna 550 Citation II			Not known (Noted 8.99)	Jersey
N331SJ	Gates Lear Jet 31A	31A-113	N31LJ	Sterling Jet (Noted 12.98)	Prestwick
N340SC	Cessna 340	340-0363		Not known (Noted 11.99)	North Weald
N340YP	Cessna 340A II	340A-0990	VR-CHR G-OCAN/D-ICIC/(N3970C)	Not known (Noted 12.99)	Biggin Hill
N345TG	Cessna 421	1067		Not known (Noted 10.99)	Guernsey
N347GS	Gates Lear Jet 60	60-026	N60LJ N700GS/N60LJ/N4026Z (Noted 4.97)	Heron 550 Inc	Farnborough
N352AE	Dassault Falcon 900B	172	F-WWFD N177FJ	Fayair Inc	Stansted/White Plains, New York
N356PA	Boeing 727-225A	20626		Kiwi International Airlines (Open storage 1.00)	Southend
N358E	Eurocopter AS.355 Twin Squirrel			Not known (Noted 12.99)	NK
N360Q	Lockheed L.188CF Electra	1112	N360WS N360Q/N8LG/PT-DZK/N777DP/N129US	Air Atlantique Ltd (Noted 7.97)	Coventry
N365GL	Aerospatiale SA365N2 Dauphin II	6431		Multiflights Ltd	Leeds-Bradford
N367M	Raytheon Hawker 800XP	258367	N3236E	Dudmaston Ltd/Bruno de Mico	Luton/Milan
N370SA	PA-23-250F Aztec	27-8054005	G-BKVN	R K Pugh (Noted 1.00)	Guernsey/Shoreham
N372SA	Cessna 172	0550	G-BHVC	Not known (Noted 2.99)	High Cross
N395TC	Commander 114TC	20003		Not known (Noted 8.99)	Denham
N402R	Cessna 402B II	402B-1364	G-BTVY N402R/N888EE/(N4609A)	Not known (Noted 1.97)	Cardiff
N407FD	Siai-Marchetti SF-260D	772		M.Clarke (As "MC-04" in French AF c/s; noted 7.98)	Newcastle
N407RB	Bell 407			Not known (Noted 12.99)	
N407NZ	Bell 407			Not known (Noted 12.99)	
N413JB	Cameron v-56 HAFB	723		D P Busby "Midnight Aurora" (Balloon Preservation Group 7.98)	Lancing
N417CL	Canadair CL-601-3A Challenger	5107	C-GLWZ	Electronic Data Systems Corp	Farnborough
N421CA	Cessna 421	0153		Not known (Noted 9.99)	Gamston
N423RS	Consolidated PBY-5A Catalina	1785	CF-JJG N4002A/BuAer48423 (Greenpeace c/s)	Plane Sailing (Noted 2.99)	Duxford
N425DR	Cessna 425 Conquest	425-0199	VP-BPR	Not known (Noted 1999)	Booker
N425TV	Cessna 425 Conquest I	425-0176	ZS-LDR N6873T	Not known (Noted 12.98)	Aberdeen
N430AP	Bell 430			Not known (Noted 12.99)	
N456CD	Beechcraft 200 King Air	BB-456		Not known (Noted 11.99)	Blackbushe
N459LJ	Gates Learjet 45	45-009	N984GC	Stealth Aviation	Jersey
N473BS	PA-28RT-201T Turbo Arrow IV	28R-8631003	G-BNYY N25WA/N77860/G-BNYY/N9129X/N9517N	B.Strickland (Noted 1.00)	Southend
N480E	Enstrom 480			Not known (Noted 12.99)	
N485A	Enstrom 480			Not known (Noted 12.99)	
N500LN	Howard 500	500-113	N381RD	D.Baker (Active 7.99)	Exeter
	(Conversion of Lockheed PV-1 Ventura c/n 5560) N206G/N200G/N539N/SAAF 6417/FP579/Bu.34670				
N501D	Cessna 501 Citation I/SP (Unit No.511)	501-0298	VR-CMS N65M/OE-FIW/I-GERA/(PH-JOB)/N26498 (Noted 6.98)	Cirrus Aviation Inc	Guernsey

Regn	Type	C/n	P/I	Owner/operator	Probable Base
N502TC	PA-30-160 Twin Comanche	30-881	G-BMSX	Not known	Blackbushe
			N502TC/N7802Y (Noted 11.99)		
N504KH	Aerospatiale SA.341G Gazelle			Not known (Noted 12.99)	NK
N510PS	Cessna 310N	310N-0054	G-AWTA	Heliscott Ltd	Walton Wood, Pontefract
			EI-ATB/N4154Q (Noted 7.99)		
N511VA	MDH MD.600N			Not known (Noted 1999)	Redhill
			(Same owner as N97CN Agusta A.109C)		
N519MC	PA-28-140 Cherokee Cruiser	28-7325519	G-BBID	Not known (Noted 11.99)	Elstree
N525RA	Cessna 525 Citation			The Estate of the late Christopher Dawes	Jersey
			(With Aviation Beauport 1999)		
N527EW	Cessna 500 Citation 1/SP	0322	N769EW	Rockville Investments (Noted 8.99)	Jersey
N560MM	Cessna 560 Citation V	560-0235	N129PJ	Sagesoft Ltd	Luton
			N52RG/N22RG/N1288D (Noted 8.99)		
N600PV	MDH MD.600N			Cumbrian Seafoods Ltd	(Maryport)
			(Noted 9.99)		
N606LG	American Blimp A60	016		Not known (Noted 1.99)	Halfpenny Green
N611VA	Agusta A.109			Not known (Noted 12.99)	
N624TC	Cessna T303 Crusader	303-00130	EC-DRR	Not known	Prestwick
			N4971C	(Dumped 12.98)	
N666GA	Gulfstream AA-5B Tiger	AA5B-1136		Mr.Fasano (Noted 8.97)	Enniskillen
N666LP	PA-46 Malibu	46-36130		Not known (Noted 1.99)	Guernsey
N669MM	Bellanca			Not known (Noted 8.99)	Rendcomb
N699PU	Boeing 737			Not known	Southend
			(Noted 11.99 - reserved for Britsh World Airlines as G-OBWZ)		
N700JJ	Socata TBM-700	2	F-GLBA	JCT Aviation Ltd (Noted 1.98)	Fairoaks
N707KS	Boeing 707-321B	20025	N728Q	Kalair Corporation	Stansted
			N886PA	(Noted 5.97)	
N707TJ	Boeing-Stearman A75N1 (N2S-1) Kaydet		N9PK	V.S.E.Norman "Honey"	Rendcomb
	(PW R-985 450hp)	75-950	N50057/Bu.3173 t/a Aerosuperatics Ltd (Noted 6.99)		
N709EL	Beechcraft 400A Beechjet	RK-52	(N709EW)	Edra Lauren Leasing/DFS Furniture	East Midlands
			N709JB	(Noted 9.98)	
N709PC	Boeing 707-323B	20175	N8436	Omega Air (Stored 5.99)	Shannon
			(Guyana Airlines c/s)		
N720B	Bell 206L LongRanger			Not known (Noted 12.99)	Dublin
N735CX	Cessna 182Q Skylane II	182-65329		B.Holmes (Noted 1.00)	Barnard Farm, Thurrock
	(Mod to Advanced Lift 260 STOL)		(Reported at Kings Farm, Thurrock: same strip ?)		
N736GX	Cessna 172 tail-wheel			Not known (Noted 10.99)	Headcorn
N766AM	Aerospatiale AS.355N Twin Sqirrel	5601		Beacon Energy (Aviation) Ltd	Beacon Farm, Leics
			(Noted 12.99)		
N768WM	Boeing-Stearman B75N-1 Kaydet (N2S-3)		G-ROAN	V.S.E.Norman	Rendcomb
		75-7394	N4685N/Bu.07790 (On overhaul 7.97)		
N772H	Cessna T337GP Super Skymaster II		N1ZG	R.M.English & Co	Full Sutton
	(Converted to Riley Rocket)	P337-0265	(Noted 7.97)		
N773DC	Beechcraft 58 Baron	TH-755	G-BDWK	DC Energy Ltd	Gamston
			(G-BEET)	(Noted 9.99)	
N797HG	PA-46-310P Malibu	46-8408064	N43644	Not known (Noted 1.99)	Guernsey
N800LA	Cessna 550 Citation II	550-0295	N483G	Hamlin Jet	Luton
			N68876		
N800VM	Beech 76 Duchess	ME-318	G-BHGM	Not known (Noted 1999)	Gloucestershire
N800VP	Beechcraft 95-B55 Baron	TC-1805		Shipping & Airlines (Noted 9.99)	Biggin Hill
N816RL	Beechcraft E90 King Air	LW-187	N66BP	L'Equipe Air Ltd/Gamston Aviation	
			N816EP/N900MH/N2187L (Noted 8.99)		Gloucestershire
N829CB	Cessna 550 Citation Bravo	550-0829	N5096S	JJB Sports (Noted 1.00)	Blackpool
N836TP	Beechcraft A36TP Bonanza	E-2124	N6770M	Velcourt East plc (Noted 8.99)	Anwick
N840LE	Gulfstream 690C Commander 840	11709	N690BA	O.Henriksen	Guernsey
			ZS-KZM/N5961K (Noted 1.99)		
N841WS	Cessna 550 Citation Bravo	550-0849	N5086W	Walter Scott & Ptnrs	Edinburgh
N882JH	Maule MX-7	23056C		Not known (Noted 10.99)	Henstridge
N900CB	Cessna 421C Golden Eagle III	421C-0837	VP-CPR	Fifty North (Chris Ryecroft)	
			VR-CPR/N2659F (Noted 1.99)		Leeds-Bradford/Guernsey
N904RE	Rotec Rally III	25513		Not known (Stored 8.95)	Bantry
N909RM	Mooney M.20J (201)	24-0636		I.M.Johnson (Noted 10.99)	Southend
N951SF	Beechcraft 56TC Baron	TG-83	N23PB	Not known (Noted 11.99)	Elstree
N966SW	Cessna 560 Citation V Ultra	560-0284	N5108G	Terry Coleman Ltd	Manchester
N973BB	Mitsubishi Mu-2B Marquise	1509SA		Red Apple Aviation (Noted 8.99)	Jersey
N980HB	Commander 980			HBC Aviation (Noted 12.99)	Guernsey
N991RV	Dassault Falcon 10	24	N301JJ	Eddie Irvine	Dublin
			F-GBTI/N1924V/N116FJ/F-WJML		
N997JB	Partenavia P.68C-TC	288-20-TC	F-GROG	Not known	St.Just
			HB-LSB/F-GEQD/N60CH/YV-2318P (Noted 10.99)		

Regn	Type	C/n	P/I	Owner/operator	Probable Base
N999DF	Cessna 441 Conquest II	441-0185	N999DB	Semitool Europe Inc	Cambridge
				N441CM/(N2724R) (Noted 6.96)	
N999MH	Cessna 195B	7168	OH-CSE	E Detiger (Last noted 7.98: departed ?)	NK
N999PJ	Morane-Saulnier MS.760 Paris 2	089	F-BJLY	R.J.Lamplough (Noted 5.97)	North Weald
N1012W	Beechcraft 58 Baron	TH-305		Not known	Welshpool
				(Stored 7.97) (Reserved as N273TR 6.97)	
N1024L	Beechcraft 60 Duke	P-78	C-FOPH	R.Ogden	Farnborough
				CF-OPH/N1024L/CF-OPH (Noted 11.99)	
N1027G	Maule M7	23032C		Not known (Noted 5.99)	NK
N1065B	Beechcraft B.55 Baron			Not known (Noted 5.99)	Rochester
N1086L	Lake LA- 4		C-FQIP	Not known (Noted 11.99)	Elstree
N1089D	Hughes 369			Not known (Noted 12.99)	
N1096C	Schweizer-Hughes 369C			Technical Exponents Ltd	Denham
				(Noted 11.99)	
N1092H	Beechcraft C90 King Air			Not known (Noted 8.99)	Blackbushe
N1134K	Luscombe 8AE Silvaire (Cont C85)	3861	NC1134K	M.Masters	Lower Upham
				(Damaged Turweston 28.8.96: noted 10.97)	
N1158V	Cessna 310J	0172		Not known (Noted 10.99 in poor condition)	Popham
N1172X	PA-34-200T Seneca II	34-7570228		Not known (Noted 1.99)	Shoreham
N1207V	Bell 430	49017		Not known (Noted 10.98)	Fairoaks
N1234T	Beechcraft C33A Bonanza	CE-141		Not known (Noted 6.97)	Fairoaks
N1325M	Boeing-Stearman E75 (N2S-5) Kaydet	75-8484	Bu.43390	R.W.Sage Priory Farm, Tibenham	
				t/a Blackbarn Aviation (Stored 7.98)	
NC1328	Fairchild 24KS	3310		R.W.Sage Priory Farm, Tibenham	
				t/a Blackbarn Aviation (Stored 9.97)	
N1344	Ryan PT-22-RY Recruit	2086	41-20878	Mrs.H.Mitchell	RAF Cosford
				t/a PT Flt (Noted 3.95)	
N1350J	Rockwell Commander 112B	516		G.Richards (Noted 5.99)	Cardiff
N1351H	PA-32-300 Cherokee Six	32-7740034		Not known (Noted 1.99) "Gabriel"	Shoreham
N1407J	Rockwell Commander 112A	407		Not known (Noted 12.99)	Blackbushe
N1553N	Beech C90A King Air	LJ-1238		Exxtor Brokerage (Noted 2.99)	Guernsey
N1565B	Beechcraft 400 Beechjet	RJ-65		A.Ogden & Sons plc (Noted 12.97)	Leeds-Bradford
N1745M	Cessna 182P Skylane II	182-64424		Not known (Noted 3.99)	Cardiff
N1778X	Cessna 210L Centurion	210-60798		Not known (Noted 8.99)	Jersey
N1937Z	Cessna 172RG			Not known (Noted 9.99)	Ronaldsway
N1944A	Douglas C-47	19677		Not known (Noted 8.99)	Booker
N2000M	Cessna 560 Citation V	560-0146	(N6877Q)	Siebe Inc (Noted 12.99)	Farnborough
N2099L	Beechcraft Baron	TC-1983		Not known (Noted 12.98)	Blackbushe
N2121T	Gulfstream AA-5B Tiger	AA5B-1031		J.Siebols (Noted 1.00)	Southend
N2109L	Eurocopter AS.355 Twin Squirrel			Not known (Noted 12.99)	
N2138J	English Electric Canberra TT.18	WK126		Biggles Air Inc	Gloucestershire
	(Built Avro)	R3/EA3/6640 (Loaned to Gloucestershire Avn Collection 4.96) (As "WK126/843")			
N2187V	Cessna 140	14416		Not Known (Noted 6.99)	White Waltham
N2273Q	PA-28-181 Cherokee Archer II	28-7790389		Not known (Noted 6.99)	Panshanger
N2366D	Cessna 170			Not known (Noted 6.99)	Turweston
N2379C	Cessna 182	00170		Not known (Nolted 8.99)	Ledbury
N2495Q	PA-34-200T Seneca II	34-7770188		Not known (Noted 1.99)	Alderney
N2548T	Navion Model H	254		Not known (Noted 11.99)	Guernsey
NC2612	Stinson Junior SR	8754		A.L.Young (Stored 4.98)	Henstridge
N2652P	PA-22-150 Tri-Pacer	22-2992		Anne Lait "Jeff Jeff" (Noted 5.98)	Weston
N2657N	Cessna 421C Golden Eagle	421C-0811	G-TELL	Not known	Thurrock
			N2657N	(Noted 9.99)	
N2668Z	Cessna 340A II	340A-0731		Not known (Noted 6.97)	Luton
N2675Y	Cessna 340	340-0760		Not known (Noted 1.00)	Fairoaks
N2706X	Cessna 335	335-0018		Not known (Noted 11.99)	Elstree
N2923N	PA-32-300 Cherokee Six	32-7940207		G.Semler Buttermilk Hall Farm, Blisworth	
				(Noted 12.99)	
N2929W	PA-28-151 Cherokee Warrior	28-7415457	OO-GPE	R.Lobell	Elstree
			N9619N	(Noted 10.99)	
N2967N	PA-32-300 Six	32-7940242		Not known (Noted 1.99) Guernsey/Bournemouth	
N3023W	Beechcraft V35B Bonanza	D-9517		Not known (Noted 9.99)	Guernsey
N3036A	PA-34-200T Seneca II	34-7970003		Biggles Aviation (Noted 11.98)	Birmingham
N3044B	PA-34-200T Seneca II	34-7970012		Not known (Noted 5.97)	East Winch
N3188H	Ercoupe 415C	3813	NC3188H	Not known Maypole Farm, Chislet	
				(Damaged c 7.92: stored for spares 5.98)	
N3536N	Mooney M.20			Not known (Noted 8.99)	Stapleford
N3839H	Ted Smith Aerostar	61P-0569-7963247	G-RACE	Not known (Noted 5.99)	Elstree
N3922B	Boeing-Stearman E75 (PT-17) Kaydet	75-5805	42-17642	Eastern Stearman Ltd	Swanton Morley
	(Cont W670)			(Noted 7.97)	
N3995W	PA-32-260 Cherokee Six	32-963		Not known (Noted 5.98)	Blackbushe

Regn	Type	C/n	P/I	Owner/operator	Probable Base
N4050S	Sikorsky YUH-60A Blackhawk	70-005		Westland Helicopters Ltd	Yeovil
				(Apprentice Training/Installation Trials 3.93)	
N4085E	PA-18-150 Super Cub	18-7809059		Not known (Noted 6.97)	Top Farm, Royston
N4173T	Cessna 320D Skyknight	320D-0073		J.Irwin (Noted 7.99)	Cranfield
N4232Y	Cessna F150G	0098	D-EBYW	Not known (Noted 1.00)	Stapleford
N4306Z	PA-28-161 Warrior II	28-8316073		USAF Flying Club (Noted 5.99)	RAF Lakenheath
N4337K	Cessna 150K	150-71583	G-BTSA	M Barlett	Branscombe
			N6083G	(Noted 6.99)	
N4422P	PA-23-160 Geronimo	23-1936		Not known (Noted 1.00)	Stansted
N4504J	PA-31 Navajo	80522204	SE-BFM	Not known (Noted 1.00)	Bournemouth
N4565L	Douglas DC-3-201A	2108	LV-GYP	390th BG Memorial Air Museum	Framlingham
	(Regn N3TV reserved but NTU)		LV-PCV/N129H/N512/N51D/N80C/NC21744		
				(Damaged in gales 10.87 & 25.1.90; on rebuild 8.97)	
N4596N	Boeing-Stearman E75 (PT-13D) Kaydet	42-17782		N.Mason & D.Gilmour	North Weald
	(Lyc R680-7)	75-5945		t/a Intrepid Avn Co (Noted 12.98) (US Mail c/s)	
N4599W	Rockwell Commander 112TC	13089		Not known (Noted 7.99)	Haverfordwest
N4647J	PA-28R-180 Cherokee Arrow	28R-30541		R.Breckell (Noted 9.99)	Barton
N4698W	Rockwell Commander 112TC-A	13274		W.Haynes (Noted 9.99)	Gamston
N4806E	Douglas A-26B-45DL Invader	27451	44-34172	A-26 Europe Inc (R & R Cadman)	Manston
				(3rd BW c/s) (Stored 3.95) "Kunsan Killer"	
N4893K	Cessna 185A	1850240		Not known (Noted 1.99)	Hinton-in-The Hedges
N4990T	Thunder Ax7-65B	123		British Balloon Museum & Library	Newbury
				"Stormy Weather" (Noted 6.99)	
N5025J	Hiller UH-12B	726	G-AVAJ	C.R.James	Whitehall Farm, Benington
			Thai AF 116	t/a Flight "C" Helicopters (Stored 4.93)	
N5052P	PA-24-180 Comanche	24-56	G-ATFS	T.A.G.Randell	Nuthampstead
			N5052P	(Stored 2.97)	
N5057V	Boeing-Stearman PT-13D Kaydet	75-5598	42-17435	V.S.E.Norman	Rendcomb
				"Charlie Brown" (Noted 5.99)	
N5092P	PA-24-180 Comanche	24-101		Not known	Little Staughton
				(Rear fuselage stored 9.96)	
N5107N	Boeing E75 Stearman	75-7166		Not known (Noted 2.99)	Swanton Morley
N5115C	Robinson R-22 Beta	1564	G-NABS	Burman Aviation Ltd	Cranfield
				(W/off 30.6.91 Cumbernauld as G-NABS, US reg canx 10.96; wreck stored 2.97)	
NC5171N	Lockheed 10A Electra			See G-LIOA in SECTION 1	
N5237V	Boeing B-17G-95DL Flying Fortress	32509	(N6466D)	RAF Museum	Hendon
			N5237V/Bu.77233/44-83868 (As "483868/N" in 94th BG USAAF c/s)		
N5240H	PA-16 Clipper	16-44	NC5240H	D.Hillier (Noted 10.99)	Slinfold
N5345N	Boeing-Stearman PT-13D Kaydet	75-5718	42-17555	Eastern Stearman Ltd	Swanton Morley
				(On rebuild 5.99 - for Holland)	
N5419	Bristol Scout D re	-		Bristol Aero Collection	Kemble
	(Built Leo Opdycke 1983)			(As "N5419" in RFC c/s)	
N5428C	Cessna 170A	19462		P.Norman (Noted 7.99)	Audley End
N5632R	Maule 5-235C Lunar Rocket	7244R		D.Group (Noted 8.99)	Stowes Farm, Tillingham
N5644L	American AA-1 Yankee	AA1-0044		S.Matterface (Noted 10.97)	Biggin Hill
N5647S	Maule			Not known	Yeatsall Farm, Abbotts Bromley
				(Noted 6.99)	
N5668H	Maule MX7-180 Star Rocket	11028C		Not known (Noted 10.99)	Headcorn
N5718H	PA-16 Clipper	16-323		Paul Penn-Sayers	Scaynes Hill, Haywards Heath
				(Stored 6.95)	
N5730H	PA-16 Clipper	342		Not known (Noted 6.99)	Cork Farm, Streethay
N5820T	Westland WG-30	004	G-BKFD	The Helicopter Museum	Weston-super-Mare
			G-17-28	(Stored 8.98)	
N5824H	PA-38-112 Tomahawk II	38-81A0118	D-EFFX	Lakenheath F/C (Noted 1.99)	RAF Lakenheath
N5832M	Aero Dynamics Sparrowhawk	8411-2		Not known (Noted 6.96)	Swanton Morley
N5840T	Westland WG-30	006	G-BKFF	The Helicopter Museum	Weston-super-Mare
			G-17-30	(Stored 8.98)	
N5880T	Westland WG-30	009		The Helicopter Museum	Weston-super-Mare
				(Stored 8.98)	
N6003F	Commander 114B	14590		Not known (Noted 3.99)	Exeter
N6010Y	Commander 114B	14589		Not known (Noted 8.98)	Biggin Hill
N6107Y	Commander 114B	14627		Not known (Noted 1.99)	Guernsey
N6182G	Cessna 172N Skyhawk II	172-73576		Not known (Noted 9.99)	Andrewsfield
N6191K	Republic RC-3 Seabee	382	NC6191K	D.T.Smollett	Bratton Clovelly, Okehampton
				(Noted 5.96)	
N6268	Travel Air Model 2000	707	NC6268	Bianchi Aviation Film Services Ltd	Booker
				(As "Fokker D.VII 626/8" in Ernst Udet c/s)	
				(Blue Max Movie Acft Museum 7.96)	
N6339U	PA-28-236 Cherokee Dakota	28-8011089	OO-JFD	Thistle Aviation Inc	Booker
			F-GCMV/OO-HLM/N8152S (Noted 8.99)		

Regn	Type	C/n	P/I	Owner/operator	Probable Base
N6526D	North American P-51D-25NA Mustang	RCAF 9289		RAF Museum	Hendon
		122-39874	44-73415	(As "413573/B6-V" in 361st FS/357th FG USAAF c/s)	
	(Composite - mainly based on ex AURI airframe)				
N6632L	Beechcraft C23 Musketeer	M-2188		Not known (Noted 12.99)	White Waltham
N6699D	Piasecki HUP-3 Retriever	51	RCN 622	The Helicopter Museum	Weston-super-Mare
			USN/51-16622	(Noted 8.98) (As "622" in RCN c/s)	
N6834L	Cessna T310R II	310R-2137		P.Basch/Tropair Engineering Ltd	Leeds-Bradford
				(Noted 12.98)	
N6907E	Cessna 175	56407		Not known (Noted 3.99)	Elstree
N7027E	Hawker Tempest V	-	EJ693	K.Weeks	Hurstbourne Tarrant, Hants
				(On rebuild by Aerofab 10.95)	
N7070A	Cessna S550 Citation SII	S550-0068	N4049	Omega Air Inc	Dublin
			N404G/N1272Z	(Noted 10.98)	
N7133J	Mooney M.20C Mark 21	3116	G-BJAK	Not known	Belle Vue Farm, Huntshaw
			OO-CAB/OO-VLB/N5814Q	(Noted 4.96)	
N7148R	Beechcraft B55 Baron	TC-2028	N2198L	Not known	Fairoaks/Guernsey
			C-GWFD/N2198L/D-IGRW/N2198L	(Noted 3.98)	
N7219L	Beechcraft B55 Baron	TC-717		Not known (Noted 8.99)	Kemble
N7263S	Cessna 150H	150-67963		Not known (Noted 9.96)	Elstree
N7269A	Cessna 182			Not known (Noted 7.99)	Oxford
N7348P	PA-24-250 Comanche	24-2526		J.Bown (Noted 10.99)	Netherthorpe
N7374A	Cessna A150M Aerobat 135	A150-0726		J.Thomas	Branscombe
	(Tail-wheel conversion)			"Turnin' Tricks" (Noted 7.98)	
N7423V	Mooney			Not known (Noted 6.99)	Turweston
N7564J	PA-28R-180			Not known (Noted 9.99)	Barton
N7614C	North American B-25J/PBJ-1J Mitchell		44-31171	Imperial War Museum/American Air Museum	Duxford
		108-37246		(As "31171" in US Marines c/s)	
N7777G	Lockheed L.749A-79 Constellation			See G-CONI	
N7801R	Bell 407			Not known (Noted 12.99)	
N7813M	PA-28-180 Cherokee D	28-5227	G-AZYF	Not known	Leicester
			5Y-AJK/N7813N	(Noted 5.98)	
N7832P	PA-24-250 Comanche	24-3052		Not known (Noted 1.99)	Elstree/Guernsey
N7997E	Cessna 150	17797		Flt C Helicopters	Bramford, Ipswich
				(Stored 9.92)	
N8075U	Cessna 150G	150-65381	N4081J	G.Sargeant & J.Winder	Hundon
				(Last noted as N4081J 7.97 - departed ?)	
N8153E	PA-28RT-201T Turbo Arrow IV 28R-8131185			Not known (Noted 9.99)	Caernarfon
N8162G	Boeing-Stearman PT-17 Kaydet	75-323	YS-177P	Eastern Stearman Ltd	Swanton Morley
			N52061/40-1766 (As "28" in US Army c/s) (Noted 5.99)		
N8190U	Boeing 707-341C	19321	4K-AZ3	Not known	Southend
			N107BW/PP-VJS/(FAB2405)/PP-VJS (Open store as "4K-AZ3" 1.00)		
				(Azerbaijanan Airlines c/s)	
N8258F	Beech B36TC	EA-513		Not known (Noted 3.99)	Elstree
N8360Y	PA-28-181 Archer II	28-8190195		Not known (Noted 7.99)	Booker
N8471Y	PA-28-236 Dakota	28-8211019		Not known (Noted 10.99)	Panshanger
N8713Z	Cessna U.206			Not known (Noted 7.99)	White Waltham
N8728A	Aero Dynamics Sparrow Hawk II 87005-26			F.Beckett/Highland Aero Dynamics Ltd	
	(Rotax 532)	(Status uncertain but believed unmarked specimen stored 10.95)			Swanton Morley
N8754J	Christen A-1 Husky	1160	(ex)	A.Febrache (Noted 7.98)	Guernsey
N8862V	Bellanca 17-31ATC Turbo Viking	31022		M Hales (Noted 9.99)	Wickenby
N8911Y	PA-30-160 Twin Comanche C/R	39-66	G-AYFT	Not known (Noted 12.99)	Blackbushe
N9050T	Douglas C-47A-10DK Dakota 3	12472	5N-ATA	J.Woodhouse/Dakota's American Bistro	Fleet
			PH-MAG/G-AGYX/KG437/42-92648		
				(Parts displayed in restaurant 3.96)	
N9059H	Reims Cessna F.172N Skyhawk II	1815	OY-CBZ	A.Nutbrown	Jersey
			D-EOSS	(Noted 7.99)	
N9089Z	North American TB-25J-25NC Mitchell		"HD368"	Aces High Ltd	North Weald
		108-34136	N9089Z	(As "44-30861" in USAAF c/s) "Bedsheet Bomber"	
			44-30861	(G-BKXW reserved 1983 but NTU; stored 5.99)	
N9115Z	North American TB-25N-20NC Mitchell		44-29366	RAF Museum	Hendon
		108-32641		(As "34037" in USAAF c/s; allotted 8838M)	
N9122N	PA-46-310P Malibu	46-8097		Not known (Noted 8.98)	Booker
N9146N	Cessna 401B/RAM conv.	401B-0010		Not known (Noted 5.98)	Weston
N9232Y	PA-31P Navajo	8414018		Anglo American Airmotive	Bournemouth
				(Noted 1.00)	
N9249C	"PA Arrow"			Not known (Noted 8.99)	RAF Lakenheath
N9281D	PA-34 Seneca	3449002		Not known (Noted 1.00)	Jersey
N9303W	PA-28-235 Cherokee B	28-10981		R.K.Spence (Noted 1.97)	Cardiff
N9381P	PA-24-260 Comanche C	24-4882		Not known (Noted 1.99)	Guernsey
N9469P	PA-24-260 Comanche C	24-4979		Not known (Noted 12.98)	Guernsey
N9325N	PA-28R-200 (Lopresti Version) 28R-25025			Hiam Mercado	Panhanger

Regn	Type	C/n	P/I	Owner/operator	Probable Base
N9606H	Fairchild M.62A-4 Cornell (PT-26-FA)	FH768		Rebel Air Museum	Earls Colne
	(Quoted p/i thought unlikely) T43-4361		42-14361 (C/n T43-3642?) (On rebuild 3.96)		
N9668H	Maule MX7			Not known (Noted 9.99)	Headcorn
N9677N	Hughes 369			Not known (Noted 12.99)	
N9694Q	Cessna 172M	172-65778		Not known (Noted 9.97)	Elstree
N9727G	Cessna 180	180-52227	G-FESC	B Richardson (Noted 7.99)	Slinfold Farm
N9861M	Maule M.4			Not known (Noted 10.99)	Headcorn
N9987Q	Westland WS-51 Dragonfly HR.5	WA/H/56	7703M WG725	Flambards Village Theme Park (As "WG754/912/CU")	Helston
N11824	Cessna 150L	150-75652		Not known (On rebuild 8.97)	Framlingham
N12006	Raven S.50A	111		British Balloon Museum & Library "Cheers" (Noted 1.99)	Newbury
N12426	SNCAN Stampe SV-4C	677	F-BGGT	D.Kaberry	
	(Lyc VO-360)		Fr AF (Damaged Middleton Sands, Heysham 16.7.94; status uncertain)		
N14113	North American T-28B Trojan	174-398	FA Haiti 1236	Radial Revelations Ltd (USN c/s)	Duxford
			N14113/FrAF 119/51-7545 (As "51-7545 Fennec No.119" 1.99)		
N14234	HP.137 Jetstream	234	N102SC	British Aerospace plc	East Fortune
	(Conv to Jetstream 31 mobile display unit) N1BE/(N200SE)/G-BBBV/G-8-12 (On loan to Museum of Flight 3.96)				
NC14485	Rearwin 7000 Sportster	403		Not known (Stored 8.94)	Thruxton
NC16403	Cessna C.34 Airmaster	322		Alan House Lower Wasing Farm, Brimpton (Resident since 1988 !)	
NC16676	Fairchild 24C-8F	3101		R.W.Sage Priory Farm ,Tibenham t/a Blackbarn Aviation (Stored 9.97)	
NC18028	Beechcraft D17S	147	NC18028	P.H.McConnell (Noted 5.99)	Popham
N21381	PA-34-200 Seneca	34-7350274	F-BUTM F-ETAL	Not known (Noted 5.97)	Dunkeswell
N23659	Beechcraft 58 Baron	TH-893		P.R.Earp (Noted 8.99)	Guernsey
N23840	Beechcraft C24R Sierra 200	MC-556		A.Hall (Noted 4.99)	Liverpool
N27597	PA-31-350 Navajo	31-7852073		Matair (Noted 1.00)	Southend
N33600	Cessna L-19A-CE Bird Dog	22303	51-11989	Museum of Army Flying AAC Middle Wallop (As "111989" in US Army c/s)	
N33870	Fairchild M62A (PT-19-FA) Cornell	T40-237	G-BTNY N33870/US Army	R.Lamplough North Weald (As "02538" in US Army c/s) (On rebuild 1999)	
NC33884	Aeronca 65CA Chief	CA.14101		N.A.Evans (Noted 7.99)	Branscombe
N36362	Cessna 180	180-31691		W Burgess (Noted 12.99)	Sibson
N38049	Beechcraft A236 Bonanza			Not known (Noted 9.99)	RAF Mona
N38273	PA-28R-201 Cherokee Arrow III	28R-7737086		L.Slater (Noted 12.99)	Blackbushe
N38940	Boeing-Stearman A75N1 (PT-17) Kaydet	75-1822	(G-BSNK) N38940/N55300/41-8263	R.W.Sage Priory Farm, Tibenham t/a Blackbarn Aviation (As "18263/822" in US Army c/s) (Noted 8.97)	
	(Cont R670)				
N41098	Cessna 421B Golden Eagle	421B-0448		Not known (Noted 7.98)	Biggin Hill
N43069	PA-28-161 Warrior II	28-8316075		D.Wards (Noted 1.99)	RAF Lakenheath
N44504	Bell 407			Not known (Noted 12.99)	(Ireland)
N46294	1990 Steen Skybolt	SB-1990		Not known (Noted 9.99)	Kings Farm, Thurrock
N47914	PA-32-300 Six	32-7840018		Not known (Noted 1.00)	Alderney
N49272	Fairchild M.62/PT-23-HO Cornell	HO-437	42-.....	R.E.Mitchell RAF Cosford t/a PT Flt (As "23" in USAAC c/s) (Noted 6.96)	
	(Cont W670) (Marked as being ex US Army 43-437)				
N50029	Cessna 172	28807	LX-AIB N6707A	E.Byrd Cardiff (Noted 2.99)	
N50755	Boeing-Stearman D75N1 (PT-27) Kaydet	75-4020	RCAF FJ970	Eastern Stearman Ltd	Swanton Morley
	(Rebuilt with new fuselage 1993, original fuselage frame stored Carleton Rode, Norfolk 8.93; now marked as A75N1 "211672" (sic); noted 4.94)				
N53091	Boeing-Stearman A75N1 (PT-17) Kaydet	75-2795	41-25306	Eastern Stearman Ltd Swanton Morley (On rebuild 5.99)	
N54211	PA-23-250E	27-7554006	G-ITTU	Not known (Noted 11.99)	Elstree
N54922	Boeing-Stearman A75N1 (N2S-4) Kaydet	75-3491	Bu.30054	V.S.E.Norman "Sweetie" Rendcomb (Crunchie c/s) (Damaged White Waltham 12.7.99)	
	(PW985-14B)				
N52245	Bell 407			Not known (Noted 12.99)	
N56421	Ryan PT-22-RY Recruit	1539	41-15510	R.E.Mitchell t/a PT Flt RAF Cosford (As "855" in US Army c/s) (Noted 6.96)	
N56462	Maule M.6-235	7409C		Not known (Noted 5.99)	Old Buckenham
N56643	Maule M.5-180C	8086C		Not known (Noted 6.97)	Langar
N58566	Vultee BT-15-VN Valiant	10670	42-41882	R.E.Mitchell t/a PT Flt RAF Cosford (US Army c/s) (Noted 6.96)	
N60526	Beechcraft E55 Baron	TE-1159		Not known (Noted 3.99)	Elstree
N61422	PA-31-310 Turbo Navajo B Panther	31-7401236		Swiftair Inc (Noted 11.99)	Elstree
N61787	Piper Cub			Not known (Noted 8.99)	Rendcomb

Regn	Type	C/n	P/I	Owner/operator	Probable Base
N61970	PA-24 Comanche			Not known (Noted 9.99)	Gamston
	(Former mount of owner of Slinfold and possibly replaced by D-ELOP qv)				
N62842	Boeing-Stearman PT-17 Kaydet	?		R.W.Sage	Priory Farm, Tibenham
	(Registration not confirmed - if so then ex RCAF FJ801 [75-3851] t/a Blackbarn Aviation (Stored 10.97)				
N63590	Boeing-Stearman N2S-3 Kaydet	75-7143	Bu.07539	R.W.Sage	Priory Farm, Tibenham
				t/a Blackbarn Aviation (Stored 10.97)	
N65200	Boeing-Stearman D75N1 Kaydet	75-3817	FJ767	Eastern Stearman Ltd (Noted 2.99)	Swanton Morley
N66630	Schweizer TG-3A	63	42-52983	Imperial War Museum	Duxford
	(P/i assumed but unconfirmed)			(As "252983" in USAAC c/s)	
N68200	Boeing-Stearman PT-17 Kaydet	75-7415	Bu.07811	Eastern Stearman Ltd	Swanton Morley
				(For spares use 10.95)	
N68427	Boeing-Stearman A75N1 (N2S-4) Kaydet	Bu.55771		R.W.Sage	Priory Farm, Tibenham
		75-5008		t/a Blackbarn Aviation (Stored 10.97)	
N70727	DHC.1 Chipmunk 22	C1/0783	9M-ANN	L.A.Groves	Stubbington
			FM1026/WP909	t/a Crofton Aeroplane Services	
				(For spares or rebuild)	
N72127	Cessna 206			Not known (Noted 9.99)	Nayland
N73410	Boeing-Stearman B75N1 (N2S-3) Kaydet	Bu.38140		R.W.Sage	Priory Farm, Tibenham
		75-7761		t/a Blackbarn Aviation (Stored 10.97)	
N76402	Cessna 140	10828	NC76402	C.Murgatroyd Standalone Farm, Meppershall	
				(Noted in damaged state 1.99)	
N79863	Grumman F6F-5K Hellcat	A-11008	Bu.79863	Flying A Services (Noted 5.98)	North Weald
N80302	PA-34-220T Seneca III	34-8233055		Ambrian Aviation (Noted 6.98)	Elstree
N80533	Cessna 172	66640		Not known (Noted 6.99)	Old Sarum
N82507	PA-28RT-201 Arrow IV	28R-8018100		Not known	Stapleford
				(Damaged Earls Colne 7.3.93; on rebuild 4.99)	
N83196	PA-28RT-201T Turbo Arrow IV	28R-8118045		P Lane (Noted 12.98)	Leeds-Bradford
N90005	Gulfstream G.1159C Gulfstream IV	1103	N433GA	GECC/Siebe plc (Noted 3.98)	Heathrow
N91384	Rockwell Commander 690A	11118	SE-FLN	Coopers Aerial Surveys Ltd	Sandtoft
				(Noted 11.99)	
N91457	PA-38-112 Tomahawk II	38-82A0034		Falcon Flying Services (Noted 1.99)	Biggin Hill
N96240	Beechcraft D18S (3TM)	CA-159	G-AYAH	Visionair International Aviation	North Weald
			N6123/RCAF 1559 "Snapdragon" (Stored 12.98)		
N97121	Embraer EMB-110P1 Bandeirante	110-334	PT-SDK	Guernsey Fire Services (Noted 1.99)	Guernsey
N99153	North American T-28C Trojan	252-52		Norfolk & Suffolk Aviation Museum	Flixton
			Zaire AF FG-289/Congo AF FA-289/Bu.146289 (As "146289/2W")		
				(Crashed Limoges, France 14.12.77; fuselage only)	

AUSTRIA
OE-FBC	LET L-200D Morava	171120	OK-RFW	M.Emery (Spares use)	Hertford
				(Status uncertain - reported reverted to OK-RFW 10.74)	

CZECH REPUBLIC
OK-JIY	Yakovlev C.11	-	(Egypt AF)	Personal Plane Svs Ltd	(High Wycombe)
	(Probably c/n 172673; stored 3.96 for rebuild)				

BELGIUM
OO-48	Jodel D.9	519		Not known (Noted 7.99)	Benington
	(Built Etienne de Schrevel, Gent 1970-77) (VW1600)				
OO-ARK	Cameron N-56 HAFB	276		R S Kent "Princess Alex"	Lancing
				(Balloon Preservation Group 7.98)	
OO-BDO(2)	Cameron N-90 HAFB	1960	(LX-PRO)	I M Martin "Profo"	Lancing
				(Balloon Preservation Group 7.98)	
OO-DOL	Beechcraft C35 Bonanza	D-3346	OO-JAN	Not known Hurstbourne Tarrant, Hants	
	(Engine swapped with N150JC qv)			(On rebuild 8.99 with AeroFab Restorations)	
	(History as follows: US Export Certificate Issued 6.11.52, Regd. OO-JAN (NTU),				
	Regd.20.11.53 OO-DOL Cogea Nouvelle, Ostend-Middlekerke, CofR Number 936, CofA Issued 1954				
	Regd. OO-DOL Etablissement Cost, Regd. OO-DOL Autostrade Motors S.A.				
	Regd. OO-DOL Autostrade Motors, Antwerp-Deurne, Regd. OO-DOL Etablissement F Casteels, Brussels-Grimbergen				
	cc 27.9.96 as sold in UK - delivered by road 19.7.95)				
OO-FAN	Beechcraft 56TC Baron	TG-10	G-AZOJ	Not known (Stored 10.97)	Shoreham
			N5443U		
OO-JAT	Cameron Zero 25 Airship	1407		Balloon Preservation Group	Farnborough
				(On loan to Farnbrough Air Sciences Trust 7.98)	
OO-MHB	PA-28-236 Dakota	28-8011143	G-BMHB	Not known	Blackpool
			D6-PAD/N81321/N9593N (Damaged Southend 20.10.90; stored 6.96)		
OO-NAT	MS.880B Rallye Club	2253	G-BAOK	Not known Grimmet Farm, Maybole	
				(Noted dismantled in a container 8.99)	
OO-VPC	Cessna 182P Skylane II	182-63928	D-EHTW	Not known	Romsey
	(Reims-assembled c/n 0019)		N9859E (Damaged Maasbree, Holland 26.7.94; wreck in store 1.96)		

DENMARK

Regn	Type	C/n	P/I	Owner/operator	Probable Base
OY-ANZ	Maule M.5-210C Strata Rocket	6027C	D-EMKK N15B	Not known	East Winch
				(Damaged in gales 11/12.4.82; on rebuild 9.97)	
OY-JRR	DHC.2 Turbo Beaver III	1632/TB-18	N911CC	Ipswich Parachute Centre	Elmsett/Windrush
			C-FUKK/CF-UKK (Noted 6.96)		
OY-BOB	Omega O-80	01	G-AWWO	British Balloon Museum & Library	Newbury
				"Blue Strike" (Noted 1999)	
OY-BOW(2)	Colting 77A	77A-014		British Balloon Museum & Library	Newbury
				(Noted 1999)	
OY-MUA	EMBRAER Bandeirante			IPM (Europe) Ltd (Noted 1.00)	Southend
OY-PBA	Pilatus PC-6/B-4-H2 Turbo-Porter	678	LN-VIT	Not known	Langar
			HB-FEY/I-ALPJ/HB-FEY (Noted 6.99)		

ARUBA

Regn	Type	C/n	P/I	Owner/operator	Probable Base
P4-ABU	Airbus A.310	431	P4-DPD V8-DPD	Praeda AVV (Noted 12.99)	Bournemouth
P4-FDH	Boeing 707-351B	18586	HZ-SAK1	Omega Air (Open store 1.00)	Southend
			VR-BOR/VR-BMV/G-BSZA/EL-SKD/N351SR/N651TF/VR-CAO/VR0HGO/N353US		
P4-SKI	Boeing 727-212	21460	VP-CBQ	Precision Air/FR Aviation Group	Bournemouth
			VR-CBQ/HZ-DA5/9V-SGF (Noted 12.99)		
P4-TBN	Boeing 707-3L6B	21049	A6-HPZ	TBN Aircraft	Southend
			(A6-HHP)/9M-TDM/N62393 (Open store 1.00)		

THE NETHERLANDS

Regn	Type	C/n	P/I	Owner/operator	Probable Base
PH-COL	Neico Lancair	399		Not known (Noted 3.99)	Shoreham
PH-NLH	Hawker Hunter T.7	41H-695342			
	(A/c stored Exeter for many years before being scrapped. The forward fuselage is with a collection at Eaglescott, North Devon 9.99 and is currently up for disposal. The wings are at Long Marston, Warwickshire as part of "XJ714")				
PH-NLK	PA-23-160 Apache	23-1694	OY-DCG SE-CKW	Not known	Burgh-le-Marsh, Skegness
				(Wreck stored 10.93)	
PH-SRX	Robin DR.400/140B	1401		Not known (Noted 10.99)	Rochester
B-163 (R Neth AF)	Noorduyn AT-16 Harvard IIB	14-664	FE930	G.King (On rebuild to SNJ standard 6.95)	
			42-12417	Thameside Avn Museum, Coalhouse Fort, East Tilbury	

RUSSIA

Regn	Type	C/n	P/I	Owner/operator	Probable Base
RA-01153	Yakovlev Yak-18T	22202047817		Not known (Noted 7.99)	Haverfordwest
RA-01193	Yakovlev Yak-50			Not known (Noted 10.99)	Halfpenny Green
RA-01249	Yakovlev Yak-52			Not known	Perth
RA-01276	Sukhoi Su-29			Not known	White Waltham
				(Noted 8.99 as "RA01276")	
RA-01277	Sukhoi Su-29	80-02		Not known (Noted 8.96)	White Waltham
RA-01278	Sukhoi Su-29	80-05		Not known	White Waltham
RA-01333	Yakovlev Yak-55M	920506	DOSAAF 40	Mrs B.Abela "40"	White Waltham
				(Noted 6.99) (G-YAKM reserved)	
RA-01370	Yakovlev Yak-18T	NK		F.M.Govern (Noted 12.99)	Oxford
RA-01378	Yakovlev Yak-52	833004	DOSAAF 14	T.Evans	Wellesbourne Mountford
	(Composite with c/n 833805/DOSAAF 134 which is now N54GT) (Open storage - unflyable 5.98)				
RA-01401	Sukhoi Su-26	"30"		Not known	White Waltham
RA-01404	Sukhoi Su-31	01-04		Not known	White Waltham
RA-01410	Sukhoi Su-26	78-03		Not known	White Waltham
RA-01480	Sukhoi Su-31	02-04		L.Perry (Noted 5.98)	White Waltham
RA-01493	Yakovlev Yak-52			D Featherby (Noted 7.98)	White Waltham
RA-01496(2)	Sukhoi Su-29	78-03	RA-7803	R.Goode (Noted 12.95)	White Waltham
RA-01564	Yakovlev Yak-52			Not known (Noted 12.99)	White Waltham
RA-01607	Sukhoi Su-29	77-02	RA-7702	S Jones (Noted 7.98)	White Waltham
RA-01608	Sukhoi Su-31	01-04	RA-0104	R.Goode "03" (Noted 11.97)	White Waltham
RA-01609	Sukhoi Su-29	75-03	RA-7503	Not known	White Waltham
	(Modified 5.99 with 3-bladed propeller)				
RA-01610	Sukhoi Su-29	78-02	RA-7802	P.Williams (Noted 12.99)	White Waltham
RA-01641	Antonov An-2R	IG190-47		Not known	Wellesbourne Mountford
RA-02050	Yakovlev Yak-52	855907	DOSAAF 107	Not known	Old Sarum
				"Tatiyana" "107" (Damaged 1998 - departed ?)	
RA-02135	Aeropract A-21M Solo	01		Not known (Noted 3.97)	Newcastle, Co.Wicklow
RA-02149	Yakovlev Yak-52			Not known (Noted 6.99)	White Waltham
RA-02209	Yakovlev Yak-52	9111311	DOSAAF 31	P.Scandrett "31" (Noted 7.99)	Rendcomb
RA-02293	Yakovlev Yak-52	9011013	DOSAAF 115	A.Tyler (Noted 10.99)	Halfpenny Green
RA-02386	Sukhoi Su-29M			Not known	White Waltham
RA-02622	Yakovlev Yak-52	9612001	LY-AFH	Not known	White Waltham
	(Also reported as RA-02620 with same c/n)			(Noted 5.99)	

Regn	Type	C/n	P/I	Owner/operator	Probable Base
CCCP-19731	Antonov An-2	IG165-45	-	Prererval	Hooton Park
RA-22521	Yakovlev Yak-52	9211612	DOSAAF 04	D.Squires "04" (Noted 9.97)	Wellesbourne Mountford
RA-4147	Reims Cessna FA.337G Super Skymaster (Cessna c/n 01589)	00070	G-BOYR PH-RPE	Not known (Noted 7.99)	Haverfordwest
RA-44400	Yakovlev Yak-18T			Not known (Noted 12.99)	White Waltham
RA-44445	Yakovlev Yak-55			Not known (Noted 12.99)	White Waltham
RA-44463	Yakovlev Yak-52	888912	DOSAAF	Not known (As "N/123" in FAA Sea Fury c/s) (Noted 6.99)	RNAS Yeovilton
RA-44464	Yakovlev Yak-52	9111415	DOSAAF 50	Not known "50" (Noted 12.98)	White Waltham
RA-44465	Yakovlev Yak-55			Barbelle Aviation (Noted 9.97)	White Waltham
RA-44467	Technoavia Yak-18T	15-33	CCCP-44467	Not known ((Noted 7.96)	Little Gransden
RA-44470	Technoavia Yak-18T	18-33		B.Austen (Noted 8.99)	Oaksey Park
RA-44480	Technoavia Yak-18T	08-34	CCCP-44480	R.Goode (Noted 11.99)	White Waltham
RA-44483	Technoavia Yak-18T	10-34	DOSAAF 221	R.Goode (Noted 11.95)	White Waltham
RA-44485	Technoavia SM-92 Finist	03		M.A.Crymble (Noted 12.99)	RAF Cranwell
RA-44488	Technoavia SM-93			Not known (Noted 3.98)	White Waltham
RA-44506	Yakovlev Yak-18T			Not known (Noted 11.99)	(White Waltham)
RA-44508	Sukhoi Su-31			Not known (Noted 8.99: as "RA44508")	White Waltham
RA-44510	Yakovlev Yak-55			T Shears (Noted 11.99)	White Waltham
RA-44514	Yakovlev Yak-52			Not known (Noted 5.99) "48"	Manston
RA-44515	Yakovlev Yak-52	9111515		M.Stebbing "65" (Noted 2.99)	Poplar Hall Farm, Elmsett
RA-44516	Yakovlev Yak-52	9111506		Not known "56" (Noted 12.98)	White Waltham
RA-44518	Yakovlev Yak-50			M Revill (Noted 5.99)	White Waltham
RA-44525	Yakovlev Yak-55	901103		Not known (Noted 10.99)	White Waltham
RA-44527	Yakovlev Yak-18T			Not known (Noted 7.99)	NK
RA-44531	Sukhoi Su-26			Not known (Noted 12.99)	(White Waltham)
RA-44533	Yakovlev Yak 50			Not known (Noted 6.99)	(White Waltham)
RA-44534	Yakovlev Yak-52	812203		Not known (Noted 8.99)	White Waltham
RA-44536	Yakovlev Yak-18T	22202034143	LY-AMI DOSAAF	M Webb (Noted 12.99)	White Waltham
RA-76401	Ilyushin Il-76TD	1023412399	CCCP-76401	Heavylift Cargo Airlines Ltd/Volga-Dnepr (Noted 4.97)	Stansted
RA-76758	Ilyushin Il-76TD	0073474203	CCCP-76758	Heavylift Cargo Airlines Ltd/Volga-Dnepr (Noted 2.97)	Stansted
RA-81854	Yakovlev Yak-18T	22202054812		Not known (Noted 12.99)	White Waltham
RA-82042	Antonov An-124-100 Ruslan	9773054055093	CCCP-82042	Heavylift Cargo Airlines Ltd/Volga-Dnepr (Noted 7.98)	Stansted
RA-82043	Antonov An-124-100 Ruslan	9773054155101	CCCP-82043	Heavylift Cargo Airlines Ltd/Volga-Dnepr (Noted 9.97)	Stansted
RA-82044	Antonov An-124-100 Ruslan	9773054155109	CCCP-82044	Heavylift Cargo Airlines Ltd/Volga-Dnepr (Noted 5.99)	Stansted
RA-82045	Antonov An-124-100 Ruslan	9773052255113	CCCP-82045	Heavylift Cargo Airlines Ltd/Volga-Dnepr (Noted 8.97)	Stansted
RA-82046	Antonov An-124-100 Ruslan	9773052255117	CCCP-82067	Heavylift Cargo Airlines Ltd/Volga-Dnepr (Noted 8.97)	Stansted
RA-82047	Antonov An-124-100 Ruslan	9773053259121	CCCP-82068	Heavylift Cargo Airlines Ltd/Volga-Dnepr (Noted 9.99)	Stansted
03 (red)	Mil Mi-24D Hind D	3532461715415		Hawarden Air Services (Stored 4.98)	Chester
04 (red)	Mikoyan MiG-23ML Hind D	024003607		Hawarden Air Services (Noted 11.97)	Chester
05 (blue)	Yakovlev Yak-50	832507	YL-CBH DOSAAF 05	Hawarden Air Services (Noted 11.97)	Chester
05 (red)	Yakovlev Yak-50	832507	YL-YAK	Hawarden Air Services (Noted 11.95)	Chester
06 (yellow)	Mil Mi-24D Hind D	3532464505029		Hawarden Air Services (Stored11.97)	Chester
09 (green)	Yakovlev Yak-52	811202	YL-CBI DOSAAF 09	Hawarden Air Services (Noted 11.96)	Chester
20 (black)	Yakovlev Yak-52	790404	YL-CBJ DOSAAF 20	Hawarden Air Services (Noted 11.97)	Chester
20	Lavochkin La-11	-		The Fighter Collection (Still awaiting rebuild 12.99)	Duxford
23 (red)	Mikoyan MiG-27D	83712515040		Hawarden Air Services (Stored 7.98)	Chester
35 (red)	Sukhoi Su-17M-3 Fitter H (Reported as Su-22M-3; and possibly 25103)	25102		Hawarden Air Services (Stored 7.98)	Chester
50 (red)	Mikoyan MiG-23ML	023003508		Hawarden Air Services (Stored 7.98)	Chester
53 (Soviet AF)	Curtiss P-40B Tomahawk	2380	41-13390	The Fighter Collection (On rebuild in Chino 3.96)	Duxford
54 (red)	Sukhoi Su-17 Fitter C	69004		Hawarden Air Services (Stored 7.98)	Chester
56 (Red)	Yakovlev Yak-52	811504	DOSAAF	Not known (Noted 5.95)	Chester

Regn	Type	C/n	P/I	Owner/operator	Probable Base
71 (red)	Mikoyan MiG-27D	61912507006		Hawarden Air Services (Stored 4.98)	Chester
NK	Mil Mi-24RKR Hind	3532424810853		Hawarden Air Services (Stored 7.98)	Chester
00153	Yakovlev Yak-18T	22202047817		Not known (Noted 1997)	Haverfordwest
30151	Soko Kraguj		30151	Not known	Bournemouth
			Yugoslav AF	(Noted 12.98)	
RK858 (Sov AF)	V-S Spitfire F.IX	CBAF.9746		The Fighter Collection	Duxford
				(Imported 9.92; wreck recovered from Russia; stored 3.96)	

SWEDEN

Regn	Type	C/n	P/I	Owner/operator	Probable Base
SE-AZB	Avro 671 Cierva C.30A Autogiro		K4232	RAF Museum	Hendon
			R3/CA.954	(As "K4232")	
SE-BZP	Stinson V-77 Reliant	6375	OO-NUT	Not known	(East Anglia)
			FB536	(Noted 1.99)	
SE-BNN	Saab 91A Safir	91130	OY-DBT	L.de Jonge	Luxters Farm, Hambledon
			OO-MUG/OO-HUG/PH-UEB/SE-BNN	(Stored 10.97)	
SE-CNH	PA-38 Tomahawk			Not known (Wrecked 4.99)	Little Staughton
SE-ESM	Cessna 182H Skylane	18256480	N8380S	Carey Shaw (Noted 8.99)	Old Buckenham
SE-EXL	Beechcraft 95-B55 Baron	TC-1287		Not known (Noted 9.99)	Biggin Hill
SE-GVH	PA-38-112 Tomahawk	38-78A0053		Not known	Little Staughton
				(Open storage unmarked 4.97 & used in rebuild of G-CGFC as G-BLNN 1990/1)	
SE-IIV	PA-24-260C Comanche			Not known (Noted 9.99)	Gamston
SE-JDU	Aerospatiale AS.355 Twin Squirrel	1594	LN-OTO	Not known (Noted 12.99)	NK
SE-LBR	Yakovlev YAK-50	791602	DOSAAF	Not known (Noted 10.99)	Rochester

POLAND

Regn	Type	C/n	P/I	Owner/operator	Probable Base
SP-CHD	PZL-101A Gawron	74134		J.Koch	Sandown
SP-FBO	Antonov AN-2T	1G108-55	PLW-0855	Not known (Noted 5.98)	Priory Farm, Tibenham
SP-SAY	Mil Mi-2	529538125		The Helicopter Museum	Weston-super-Mare
				(Noted 8.98)	
008 (Polish AF)	WSK SBLim 2A	1A09-008		G.P.Hinckley	Channons Hall, Tibenham
				(Stored 8.96)	

SUDAN

Regn	Type	C/n	P/I	Owner/operator	Probable Base
ST-AHZ	PA-31-310 Turbo Navajo	31-473	G-AXMR	Not known	Elstree
			N6558L	(Fire practice; burnt-out fuselage remains 11.97)	

ICELAND

Regn	Type	C/n	P/I	Owner/operator	Probable Base
TF-ABP	Lockheed L.1011-385-100 Tristar	1045	VR-HOG	British Aviation Heritage Collection	
			N323EA	(Istanbul Airlines c/s)	Bruntingthorpe
				(Stored 1.00)	
TF-TOA	PA-28R-200	28R-7635029		Not known (Noted 8.99)	Elstree

UKRAINE

Regn	Type	C/n	P/I	Owner/operator	Probable Base
UR-67199	LET L-410UVP Turbolet	790305	CCCP-67199	Not known (Noted 6.99)	Langar
UR-67433	LET L-410UVP Turbolet			Not known (Noted 1999)	Hinton-in-The-Hedges
				(UK based 6 months a year)	
UR-67477	LET L-410UVP Turbolet	841302	CCCP-67477	Not known	Sibson
				(Universal Avia c/s) (Noted 8.97)	
UR-67519	LET L-410UVP Turbolet	851423	CCCP-67519	East West Aviation Ltd (Noted 9.95)	Wymeswold
UR-78755	Ilyushin IL-76MD	0083484531	CCCP-78755	Air Foyle UK	Luton
				(Op for Oil Spill Response Ltd) (Noted 12.96)	

AUSTRALIA

Regn	Type	C/n	P/I	Owner/operator	Probable Base
VH-ALB	Supermarine 228 Seagull V	-	A2-4	RAF Museum (As "A2-4")	Hendon
VH-ASM	Avro 652A Anson I	72960	W2068	RAF Museum (As "W2068/68" in RAF c/s)	Hendon
VH-BRC	Short S.24 Sandringham IV	SH.55C		The Science Museum	Southampton
			VP-LVE	(On loan to Southampton Hall of Aviation)	
			N158C/VH-BRC/ZK-AMH/JM715 (Ansett c/s) "Beachcomber"		
VH-FHJ	Cessna 560 Citation V Ultra	560-0278	N2HJ	Eagle Airways/F.Hackett-Jones	Guernsey
			N5103J	"Cuillon of True Flight" (Noted 6.97)	
VH-SNB	DH.84A Dragon	2002	VH-ASK	Museum of Flight/Royal Museum of Scotland	
			A34-13		East Fortune
VH-UQB	DH.80A Puss Moth	2051	(G-ABDW)	Museum of Flight/Royal Museum of Scotland	
			VH-UQB/G-ABDW		East Fortune
VH-UTH	GAL Monospar ST-12	ST12/36		Newark Air Museum	Winthorpe
				(On rebuild by Cotswold Acft Restoration Grp, Innsworth 7.95)	
VH-UUP	Short S.16 Scion 1			See G-ACUX in SECTION 1	
VH-WGL	Short SC.7 Skyvan Srs.3M	SH.1914	Sing AF 701	Not known (Noted 10.98)	Fairoaks
			9V-BNJ/Sing AF 701/G-14-86		

Regn	Type	C/n	P/I	Owner/operator	Probable Base
VH-YOT	Skyfox Gazelle CA25N (Rotax 912)	CA25N030		Not known (Noted 8.97)	Dunkirk, Canterbury

BAHAMAS/BERMUDA

Regn	Type	C/n	P/I	Owner/operator	Probable Base
VP-BBK	Beechcraft B200 Super King Air	BB-1519	VR-BBK N10827	Videovision Ltd (Noted 2.99)	Guernsey
VP-BCC	Canadair CL.601 Challenger 3R	5162	VR-BCC C-FTNE/C-GLXF	Consolidated Contractors (UK) Ltd (Noted 11.99)	Farnborough
VP-BCI	Canadair CL.601 Challenger 3R	5193	VR-BCI N604D/C-GLYK	Consolidated Contractors (UK) Ltd (Noted 8.99)	Farnborough
VP-BDB	Cessna 560 Citation	0503	(ZS-FCB) N88059	Fegotila Ltd (Noted 1.00)	Gloucestershire
VP-BHJ	Dassault Falcon 900B	138	VR-BHJ	F.Hackett-Jones/Eagle Airways Ltd (Noted 1.99)	Guernsey
VP-BIE	Canadair CL.601 Challenger 1A	3016	N601CL N1107Z/N4562Q/C-GLWV	Inflite Executive Charter (Noted 8.98)	Stansted
VP-BIF	Boeing 727-1H2	20533	VP-BKC VR-BKC/HZ-122/N228G/N320HG	USAL Inc (Noted 1999)	Stansted/Heathrow
VP-BIR	Sikorsky S.76	0430		Air Hanson (Noted 1999) (Based on yacht in Mediterranean during Summer & in UK during Winter)	Blackbushe
VP-BIS	Grumman Gulfstream IV	1150	N151G V8-SRI/V8-009/V8-ALI/N433GA	ISPAST Group Ltd	Luton
VP-BJV	Grumman G-1159 Gulfstream II	186	N17582 D-AFKG/5N-AML/VR-BJV	Uniexpress Jet Services (Noted 3.98)	Heathrow
VP-BKK	HS.125 Srs.400A/731	25238	VR-BKK N808V/N125GC/G-TOPF/G-AYER/9K-ACR/G-AYER	Air 125 Ltd/Business Real Estates (Noted 3.97)	Southampton
VP-BKQ	Bell 430	49008	N62833	Jud Investments Co Ltd (Noted 7.99)	Fairoaks
VP-BLK	Gulfstream 690C Commander 840	11672	VR-BLK OE-FIT/D-IKOM/(N5924K)	Control Techniques (Bermuda) Ltd (Noted 8.99)	Welshpool
VP-BLS	Pilatus PC-XII	176	N176BS VP-BLS/HB-FSL	B.L.Schroeder (Noted 10.99)	Fairoaks
VP-BMF	Dassault Falcon 50	205	F-WWHB	Sally Navigation	Farnborough
VP-BMZ	Gulfstream 690D Commander 900	15033	VR-BMZ G-MFAL/N49GA/(N5925N)	Aviatica Trading Co Ltd/Marlborough Fine Art Ltd (Noted 7.99)	Fairoaks
VP-BNJ	Dassault Falcon 900B	120	VR-BNJ F-WWFN	Triair (Bermuda) Ltd/Silver Sand Ltd (Noted 10.99)	Farnborough
VP-BNM	Cessna 425 Conquest I	425-0027	VR-BNM N181AA/HI-598SP/N97DA/(N711EF)/N97DA/N67720	Rig Design Services Ltd (Noted 10.96)	Fairoaks
VP-BNU	Robin DR400/180 Regent	2047	VR-BNU G-BTDU	N.French (Noted 1.99)	Biggin Hill
VP-BNZ	Gulfstream G.1159A Gulfstream III	452	VR-BNZ N633P/N27R/N331GA	Dennis Vanguard (International) Ltd (Noted 11.97)	Coventry
VP-BOO	McDonnell Douglas MD-87	49778	VR-BOO N806ML	Interlocutary Ltd/Ford Motor Co Ltd (Noted 9.99)	Stansted
VP-BOP	McDonnell Douglas MD-87	49725	VR-BOP N802ML	Interlocutary Ltd/Ford Motor Co Ltd (Noted 9.99)	Stansted
VP-BPS	Consolidated 28-5ACF (PBY-5A) Catalina	1997	VR-BPS G-BLSC/C-FMIR/N608FF/CF-MIR/N10023/Bu.46633	Not known (Crashed Southampton Water 27.7.98: dismantled 6.99)	(Lasham)
VP-BPW	Dassault Falcon 900B	135	VR-BPW F-WWFJ	N.Somers/Tower House Consultants Ltd (Noted 8.99)	Jersey/Southampton
VP-BQK	Agusta A.109A II	7410	VR-BKQ	Patriot Aviation (Bermuda) Ltd (Noted 12.99)	Sywell
VP-BSA	Dassault Falcon 50	196	D-BNJH	Shell Aircraft Ltd (Noted 11.99)	Heathrow
VP-BSL	Dassault Falcon 50	209	N96DS	Shell Aircraft Ltd (Noted 1998)	Stansted
VP-BSI	BAe 125 Srs.800B	258073	VR-BSI N802MM/G-5-532/G-BVBH/D-CFVW/G-5-532	Group 4 Securities Ltd (Noted 11.97)	Gloucestershire
VP-BUS	Gulfstream G.1159C Gulfstream IV	1127	VR-BUS VR-BLR/N427GA	AEC International Ltd/BP Flight Operations Ltd (Noted 12.99)	Farnborough

CAYMAN ISLANDS

Regn	Type	C/n	P/I	Owner/operator	Probable Base
VP-CAM	Canadair Cl-601-3A Challenger	5090	N400KC N818TH/N818LS/N404CB/N601CB/C-GLXF	Qamar Ltd	Jersey
VP-CAS	BAe 125 Srs.800A	258167	VR-CAS N125AS/G-5-662/N125AS/G-5-662	Cavalier Air Corpn/A.Senna (Noted 5.97)	Southampton
VP-CAT	Cessna 501 Citation 1/SP (Unit No.637)	501-0232	VR-CAT VR-CHF/N35TL/N853KB/N2616C/(N2616G)	Kestrel Avn/Aviation Jet (Noted 3.99)	Elstree
VP-CBE	Cessna 550 Citation II (Unit No.119)	550-0108	N4EK (N65SA)/N4EK/N4TL/(N2665P)	Eurojet Ltd (Noted 12.98)	Birmingham

Regn	Type	C/n	P/I	Owner/operator	Probable Base
VP-CBM	Cessna 550 Citation II	550-0729	VR-CBM N1210V	Bernard Matthews plc (Noted 1.00)	Norwich
VP-CBW	Gulfstream G.1159C Gulfstream IV	1096	VR-CDW N17589	Rolls-Royce plc (Noted 4.99)	Farnborough
VP-CBX	Grumman Gulfstream V	511	N511GA	Aravco	Farnborough
VP-CCK	Agusta A.109A II	7357	VR-CCK N109JD/N90GA (Noted 4.99)	Tarmac plc	Wolverhampton/Sywell
VP-CCT	Beechcraft C90-1 King Air	LJ-1028	VR-CCT G-BKFY/N6420H (Op Corgi Toys) (Noted 4.99)	Corgi Investments Ltd	Oxford
VP-CCW	McDonnell Douglas MD.600N			Not known (Noted 12.99)	NK
VP-CDA	BAC One-Eleven 488GH	BAC.259	G-MAAH PK-TAL/G-BWES/PK-TAL/G-BWES/5N-UDE/LX-MAM/HZ-MAM	Not known (Noted 1999)	Bournemouth
VP-CDW	Cessna 650 CitationJet	650-7034	N4360S XA-SWM/N1264E	Grosvenor Estates/Duke of Westminster	Chester
VP-CED	Cessna 525	0870		Iceland Foods (Noted 4.99)	Chester
VP-CFG	Cessna 501 Citation I/SP (Unit No.577)	501-0176	VR-CFG (VR-CIA)/N49LC/N44LC/N6779L (Noted 2.99)	Alpha Golf Aviation Ltd	Oxford
VP-CFI	Dassault Falcon 50EX	278	F-WWHD	Williams Grand Prix Engineering Ltd (Noted 1999)	Oxford
VP-CHC	Sikorsky S-76C	760377	G-BXGR I-PRLT/N62375/JA6692 (Noted 9.97)	Williams Grand Prix Engineering Ltd	Oxford
VP-CHJ	Agusta A.109C	7634	VR-CHJ VR-CEC/3A-MSG (Noted 12.99)	Eagle Airways	Guernsey
VP-CIC	Canadair CL.601 Challenger 3A	5011	VR-CIC N602UK/N611MH/JA8283/N603CC/C-GLXD (Noted 8.98)	TGC Avn Ltd/Fakhar Ltd	Stansted
VP-CIS	Cessna 525 CitationJet	525-0252	N740JV (N5223P)	Flightline Ltd (Noted 1.00)	Southend/Guernsey
VP-CIZ	Agusta A.109C	7662	VR-CIZ HB-XYY	Williams Grand Prix Engineering Ltd (Noted 11.97)	Oxford
VP-CJB	Cessna 501 Citation I/SP (Unit No.564)	501-0155	VR-CJB N800DW/N110TP/N110TV/(N108CT)/N2617B (Noted 11.97)	Brown Pestell Ltd	Biggin Hill
VP-CJR	Cessna 550 Citation II (Unit No.388)	550-0354	VR-CJR N121C/N121CG (Noted 7.97)	Broome & Wellington (Aviation) Ltd/Air Kilroe	Manchester
VP-CMF	Gulfstream G.1159C Gulfstream IV	1062	VR-CMF N688H/N462GA/N17583 (Noted 10.97)	Aravco Ltd/Sheikh Mohammed Fakhry	Heathrow
VP-CMO	Cessna 500 Citation (Unit No.070)	500-0070	VR-CMO YV-707CP/N600MT/N500TD/N570CC (Noted 9.99)	Tunstall Group	Leeds-Bradford
VP-CNM	Cessna 550 Ciation Bravo	550-0857	N51246	Nigel Mansell	Jersey/Exeter
VP-CNP	Grumman Gulfstream III	496	N843HS (N99SU)/N99SC/N89AB/N89AE/N21NY/N310SL/N327GA	Fitzwilton plc	Dublin
VP-COM	Cessna 500 Citation (Unit No.318)	500-0318	VR-COM N944B/N518CC/N5318J (Noted 8.97)	Rapid 3864 Ltd (C.McGill)	Biggin Hill
VP-CPO	Canadair CL.601 Challenger 3R	5165	VR-CPO C-FTOH/C-GLXO (Noted 8.98)	P & O Containers Ltd	Stansted
VP-CPT	BAe 125 Srs.1000B	259004	G-LRBJ G-5-779	Reno Investments Inc (Noted 1.99)	Biggin Hill
VP-CRB	Gates Learjet 60	60-125	N60LR	Lisane Ltd	Jersey
VP-CRX	Canadair CL600-2AI2	3052	N801GC N603HJ/B-4007/C-GDCQ/C-GLWT (Noted 4.99)	Avia Carriers	Luton
VP-CRY	Grumman Gulfstream IV	1176	N176G V8-008/N468GA	Avia Carriers	Luton/Moscow
VP-CSC	Cessna 560 Citation V Ultra	560-0439	(N39LX) N50612	Stadium City Ltd (Noted 1.99)	Humberside
VP-CSN	Cessna 560 Citation V Ultra	560-0401	N401CV	Scottish & Newcastle Breweries Ltd (Noted 12.98)	Edinburgh
VP-CTF	Cessan 550 Citation II	550-0716	VP-CTE (N800KC)/N4VR/N1205A	Not known	Jersey/Chester
VP-CWA	Agusta A.109			Not known (Noted 12.99)	NK
VP-CYM	Gulfstream G.1159C Gulfstream IV	1090	VR-CYM N466GA	Jet Fly Aviation Ltd (Noted 5.99)	Heathrow

FALKLAND ISLANDS & DEPENDENCIES

Regn	Type	C/n	P/I	Owner/operator	Probable Base
VP-FAZ	DHC.6-310 Twin Otter	748	C-GEOA (FAP-2029)/C-GEOA (Noted 5.98)	British Antarctic Survey	Oxford
VP-FBB	DHC.6-310 Twin Otter	783	C-GDKL	British Antarctic Survey (Noted 8.99)	Oxford
VP-FBC	DHC.6-310 Twin Otter	787	C-GDIU	British Antarctic Survey (Noted 8.99)	Oxford
VP-FBL	DHC.6-310 Twin Otter	839	C-GDCZ	British Antarctic Survey (Noted 8.99)	Oxford

Regn	Type	C/n	P/I	Owner/operator	Probable Base

KENYA
| VP-KJL | Miles M.38 Messenger 4A | - | G-ALAR RH371 | Miles Acft Collection (For rebuild off-site 3.96) | Woodley |

RHODESIA/NYASALAND
| VP-YKF | DH.104 Dove 6 | 04292 | 3D-AAI VQ-ZJC/G-AMDD | South East Avn Enthusiasts Grp New Ross, Ireland (Damaged 9.8.82; stored 3.97) (As "IAC 176") | |

BERMUDA
VR-BEA	BAC One-Eleven 524FF	BAC.195	RP-C1185 D-AMUR/G-AXSY/D-AMUR	European Aviation Ltd (Stored 7.97)	Bournemouth
VR-BEB	BAC One-Eleven 527FK	BAC.226	RP-C1181 PI-C1181	European Aviation Ltd (Open stored 11.99)	Bournemouth
VR-BEP	Westland WS-55 Whirlwind 3	WA.83	G-BAMH XG588	East Midlands Aeropark (As "XG588 in SAR c/s) "Cormorant"	East Midlands
VR-BEU	Westland WS-55 Whirlwind 3	WA.493	G-ATKV EP-HAN/G-ATKV	The Helicopter Museum (Stored for spares 8.98)	Weston-super-Mare
VR-BMB	HS.125 Srs.400B	25240	VR-BKN I-GJBO/G-AYLI/G-5-11	Not known (With Fier Service 5.99)	Stansted

INDIA
| HA557 (RIAF) | Hawker Tempest II (Reported as "HA577") | 12205 | MW404 | C.P.B.Horsley (On rebuild by Osprey Aviation 9.96) | Dunsfold |

MEXICO
XA-NAA	MBB Bo.105			Not known (Noted 12.99)	Bourn
	(Non-airworthy pod is the orange one with the pegasus logo (as operated by Transportes Aereos Pegaso))				
XA-NAN	MBB Bo.105			Not known (Noted 12.99)	

BURKINA FASA
| XT-BBE | Boeing 727-14 | 18990 | N21UC N2741A/(N975PS)/D-AHLP/N975PS | Not known (Stored 6.97) | Lasham |

LATVIA
YL-BAB	Boeing 737-236	22032	G-BGJK (YL-BAB/G-BGJK)	Transaero (Stored 1.00)	Southend
YL-LEU	WSK-PZL Antonov AN-2R	1G165-45	CCCP-19731 SP-ZFP/CCCP-19731	Hawarden Air Services (Noted 11.97 as "CCCP-19731")	Chester
YL-LEV	WSK-PZL Antonov AN-2R	1G148-29	CCCP-07268	Hawarden Air Services (Noted 4.98 as "CCCP-07268")	Chester
YL-LEW	WSK-PZL Antonov AN-2R	1G182-28	CCCP-56471	Hawarden Air Services (Noted 4.98 as "CCCP-56471")	Chester
YL-LEX	WSK-PZL Antonov AN-2R	1G187-58	CCCP-54949	Hawarden Air Services (Noted 4.98 as "CCCP-54949")	Chester
YL-LEY	WSK-PZL Antonov AN-2R	1G173-11	CCCP-40784	Hawarden Air Services (Noted 4.98 as "CCCP-40784")	Chester
YL-LEZ	WSK-PZL Antonov AN-2R	1G165-47	CCCP-19733	Hawarden Air Services (Noted 4.98 as "CCCP-19733")	Chester
YL-LFA	WSK-PZL Antonov AN-2R	1G172-20	CCCP-40748	Hawarden Air Services (Noted 4.98 as "CCCP-40748")	Chester
YL-LFB	WSK-PZL Antonov AN-2R	1G173-12	CCCP-40785	Hawarden Air Services (Noted 4.98 as "CCCP-40785")	Chester
YL-LFC	WSK-PZL Antonov AN-2R	1G206-44	CCCP-17939	Hawarden Air Services (Noted 4.98 as "CCCP-17939")	Chester
YL-LFD	WSK-PZL Antonov AN-2R	1G172-21	CCCP-40749	Hawarden Air Services (Noted 4.98 as "CCCP-40749")	Chester
YL-LHN	Mil Mi-2	524006025	CCCP-20320	Hawarden Air Services (Noted 4.98 as "CCCP-20320")	Chester
YL-LHO	Mil Mi-2	535025126	CCCP-20619	Hawarden Air Services (Noted 3.96)	Chester
YL-MIG	Aviatika MAI-890 Baby MIG	037		Hawarden Air Services (Stored 7.97)	Chester
YL-	Aviatika MAI-890 Baby MIG	034		Hawarden Air Services (Noted 10.93)	Cumbernauld
YL-	Aviatika MAI-890 Baby MIG	038		Hawarden Air Services (Stored 5.95)	Chester
YL-	Aviatika MAI-890 Baby MIG	039		Hawarden Air Services (Noted 10.93)	Cumbernauld
YL-	Aviatika MAI-890 Baby MIG	042		R.J.Everett (Noted 7.94)	Sproughton
YL-	Aviatika MAI-890 Baby MIG	043		Hawarden Air Services (Noted 10.93)	Cumbernauld
YL-	Aviatika MAI-890 Baby MIG	069		Pilatus Britten-Norman Ltd (As G-51-890-69) (Noted 5.96)	Bembridge

Regn	Type	C/n	P/I	Owner/operator	Probable Base

NICARAGUA

Regn	Type	C/n	P/I	Owner/operator	Probable Base
YN-CCN	Boeing 707-123B	18054	5B-DAO	Omega Air (Aeronica c/s)	Shannon
			G-BGCT/N7526A	(Stored 5.99)	

SERBIA

Regn	Type	C/n	P/I	Owner/operator	Probable Base
YU-DMN	UTVA-66		JRV51182	Not known	Biggin Hill
				(Noted 11.97: as "51182" in Serbia AF c/s)	
YU-DMT	UTVA-66		JRV51...	Not known (Stored with above)	Biggin Hill
YU-HCE	Bell 212	5173		Not known (For rebuild 12.98)	Redhill
YU-HEH	Aerospatiale SA.341G Gazelle	011	JRV12619	Not known	Stapleford
	(Built SOKO)			(Noted 10.99)	
YU-HEI	Aerospatiale SA.341 Gazelle	126	JRV126..	Not known	Stapleford
	(Built SOKO)			(Noted 11.99)	
YU-HEK	Aerospatiale SA.341 Gazelle	012	JRV12620	Not known	Stapleford
	(Built SOKO)			(Noted 1999)	
YU-YAB	Soko Galeb G-2A		JRV...	Note known (Noted 5.99)	North Weald

NEW ZEALAND

Regn	Type	C/n	P/I	Owner/operator	Probable Base
ZK-MCV	VS Spitfire Vc		A-58-178	Historic Flying Ltd	Audley End
				(On rebuild 12.99)	
ZK-RMH	Curtiss P-40E-1-CU Kittyhawk	19669	NZ3009	The Old Flying Machine Co	Duxford
			ET482/41-25158	(Noted 4.99: as "NZ3009")	

REPUBLIC OF SOUTH AFRICA

Regn	Type	C/n	P/I	Owner/operator	Probable Base
ZS-JVL	Lockheed C-130 Hercules	4676		Safair (Op Air Contractors)	East Midlands
				(Noted 11.99)	
ZS-LFB	Beechcraft F.33A Bonanza	CE-971	N18384	Not known (Noted 8.99)	Shobdon
ZS-RSI	Lockheed L.100-30 Hercules	4600	F-GIMV	Safair (Op Hunting Cargo Airlines)	East Midlands
			ZS-RSI/TN-..../F-GDAQ/F-WDAQ/ZS-RSI/C-FNWY/ZS-RSI		
			(Last noted 2.97 - presumably ZS-JVL (qv) is a replacement)		
ZS-VFW	SNCAN Stampe SV-4C	186	G-AXCZ	Not known	Bristol
			F-BCFG	(Stored 10.95)	
ZU-BVB	Avtech Jabiru			Not known (Noted 7.99)	Shoreham
				"Joolie Bird"	

EQUATORIAL GUINEA

Regn	Type	C/n	P/I	Owner/operator	Probable Base
3C-AAW	Fokker F.27 Friendship 600	10394	HZ-KA8	Trygon Ltd (Stored 1.00)	Southend

AZERBAIJAN

Regn	Type	C/n	P/I	Owner/operator	Probable Base
4K-AZ3	Boeing 707-341C	19321	N107BV	ALG Inc	Southend
			PP-VJS/(FAB2405)/PP-VJS (Open store 1.00)		

ISRAEL

Regn	Type	C/n	P/I	Owner/operator	Probable Base
4X-DZH	Beech A36			Not known (Noted 11.99)	Elstree
Israel	Hawker Hurricane IV	-	KZ191	R.J.Lamplough (For rebuild 3.96)	North Weald

CYPRUS

Regn	Type	C/n	P/I	Owner/operator	Probable Base
5B-DBE	Boeing 727-30	18371	9M-SAS	Aimes Co (Noted 8.99)	Luton
			V8-BG2/V8-BG1/V8-UHM/N727CH/VS-UHM/VR-UHM/VR-BHP/N727CH/D-ABIQ		

NIGERIA

Regn	Type	C/n	P/I	Owner/operator	Probable Base
5N-ABJ	Boeing 707-3F9C	20474		Not known	Shannon
				(Stored 5.97; being broken up 1.98)	
5N-ANO	Boeing 707-3F9C	21428		Nigerian Airways (Stored 5.99)	Dublin
5N-AOK	BAC One-Eleven 320L-AZ	BAC.113	G-BKAW	Fire Training College	Chorley
			G-AVBY	(Noted 9.98)	
5N-ATU	Beechcraft A90 King Air	LJ-136	F-BFRE	Not known	Gamston
			HB-GDF	(On fire dump 1.97)	
5N-AVC	PA-31-350 Navajo Chieftain	31-7305122	NAF 1003	Shoreham Airport Fire Service	Shoreham
			N74970	(Open store 10.96)	
5N-BAB	BAC One Eleven 414EG	BAC.127	EI-BWT	Not known	Bournemouth
			N174FE/G-AZED/(N174FE)/G-AZED/(G-AZDG)/D-ANDY/G-16-3		
			(ADC Airlines c/s) (Open store 1.00)		
5N-HTC	BAC One-Eleven 208AL	BAC.049	EI-ANE	Not known	Southend
			(Hold-Trade Air c/s) (Open store 1.00)		
5N-MXX	Boeing 707-323C	18940	N1088V	Merchant Express c/s	Southend
			PP-VLP/N7561A (Open store 1.00)		

Regn	Type	C/n	P/I	Owner/operator	Probable Base

UGANDA
5X-UUW	Westland Scout Srs.1	F9617	G-17-1	R.Dagless (Stored 6.93)	East Dereham

KENYA
5Y-SIL	Cameron A-140 HAFB	138	F-BTVO	British Balloon Museum & Library	Newbury
			F-WTVO/G-AZUW "Cumulo Nimbus" (Stored 1998)		

JAMAICA
6Y-JQK	BN-2A Mk.III-2 Trislander			see G-BEVV in SECTION 1	

GHANA
9G-DAN	Westland Wessex	WA/739		Not known (Noted 9.99)	Honey Crock Farm, Redhill
G-102	Scottish Avn Bulldog 120/122	BH120-226		Not known (Stored 8.99)	Hurstbourne Tarrant, Hants
G-108	Scottish Avn Bulldog 120/122	BH120-372	G-BCUP	Not known (Stored 8.99)	Hurstbourne Tarrant, Hants

DEMOCRATIC REPUBLIC OF KINSHASA
9Q-CBW	Boeing 707-329C	20200	9Q-CBS	Not known	Southend
			OO-SJO	(Open store 1.00)	

SECTION 7

PART 1 - BRITISH GLIDING ASSOCIATION

The Register includes the Certificate of Airworthiness reference number as issued by the British Gliding Association. This is usually found below the tailplane in small characters. We include, also, the corresponding "three-letter" coding (or "trigraph system") sometimes marked on the tails. Codes marked + denote that gliders are known to be wearing their respective trigraphs. BGA Competition Numbers etc are shown where known to be carried and details are contained in SECTION 8. The official BGA list is extended by including non-current gliders and those with recently lapsed Certificates of Airworthiness (CA) for which no cancellation details are known but may survive. These are identified by "*" in the CA expiry column. I have decided this year to break with tradition and present the BGA number first which is, after all, the prime reference followed by the three letter Code. However, the Glider Index is still referenced by Code but I have included a helpful de-code courtesy of Richard Cawsey.

Thanks, again, to Phil Butler and Wal Gandy for updating the BGA register. We are also especially grateful to BGA's Secretary, Barry Rolfe for providing access. The official information is current to 27.1.00. Further comments and material have been provided by Richard Causey and Tony Morris.

BGA No/Code	Type	C/n	P/I	Date	Owner/operator	Probable Base	CA Expy
162	Manuel Willow Wren	.		9.34	M.L.Beach "The Willow Wren"	Dunstable (Extant 7.97)	*
231/AAA	Abbott-Baynes Scud II (Built Slingsby)	215B	G-ALOT BGA.231	8.35	Brooklands Museum (Stored 1999)	Brooklands	9.95*
236/(AAF)	Slingsby T.6 Kite 1	27A	G-ALUD BGA.236/(BGA.222)	11.35	Not known (Stored pending rebuild 12.95)	Dunstable	*
251/AAX	Slingsby T.6 Kite 1	227A	(ex RAF) BGA.251	3.36	R.Boyd	Rivar Hill	8.00
260/ABG	Schleicher Rhonsperber	32-16		5.36	F.K.Russell t/a Rhonsperber Syndicate	Dunstable	9.00
266/(ABN)	Slingsby T.1 Falcon 1 Waterglider	237A		5.36	Windermere Steamboat Museum (On display 5.95)	Windermere	*
277/ABZ	Grunau Baby 2 (Built F.Coleman)	?	RAFGSA.270 BGA.277/G-ALKU/BGA.277	8.36	J.L.Smoker & Ptnrs . Weston-on-the-Green		7.95*
283/ACF	Abbott-Baynes Scud III	2	G-ALJR BGA.283	12.36	L.P.Woodage "Scud III" Dunstable		4.00
285/ACH	Slingsby T.6 Kite 1	247A	G-ALNH BGA.285	12.36	E.B.Scott AAC Middle Wallop (On loan to The Museum of Army Flying) (As "G285/E" in 1 GTS RAF c/s: on display 5.94)		5.99*
310/ADJ	Slingsby T.6 Kite 1 (Rebuilt 1982 with components from BGA.327 c/n 285A)	258B		2.37	A.M.Maufe	Tibenham	8.99
337/AEM	Schleicher Rhonbussard	620	G-ALME BGA.337	4.38	C.Wills & S.White	Booker	11.00
378/AGE	Slingsby T.12 Gull I	312A	G-ALPJ BGA.378	9.38	T.Smallwood & Ptnrs "900"	Booker	6.00
394/AGW	Slingsby T.6 Kite 1 (Rebuild of BGA.317 c/n 277A)	331A		3.39	J.S.Allison	RAF Halton	5.00
400/AHC	Slingsby T.6 Kite 1 (Wings from Special T.6 c/n 355A)	336A	VD165 BGA.400	5.39	R.Hadlow & Ptnrs (As "F" in 1 GTS RAF c/s)	Brooklands	4.97
416/AHU	Scott Viking 1	114	G-ALRD BGA.416	6.39	L.Glover (As "G-ALRD")	Husbands Bosworth	10.00
418/AHW	Slingsby T.13 Petrel 1	348A	G-ALNP BGA.418	.39	R.I.Davidson	Husbands Bosworth	5.97
442/AJW+	Slingsby T.8 Tutor	MHL/RC/8	G-ALMX BGA.442	8.46	M.Hodgson	Dunstable	8.98
448/(AKC)	DFS 108-68 Weihe	000348	G-ALJW BGA.448/LO+WQ	6.47	D.Philips (Damaged Thun, Switzerland 20.7.79: on rebuild 1994)	Solihull	*
449/AKD	DFS/70 Olympia-Meise	227	LF+VO	7.47	L.S.Phillips (Stored)Perranporth		5.85*
466/AKW	Slingsby T.8 Tutor	MHL/RT/7		11.46	D.Kitchen	Tibenham	7.96
470/(ALA)	Short Nimbus	S.1312		.47	Ulster Folk & Transport Museum (Stored 6.97) Holywood, Belfast		8.75*
485/ALR	Slingsby T.8 Tutor	513	G-ALPE BGA.485	11.46	M.H.Birch	Booker	6.97
490/ALW	Hutter H-17A (Built D.Campbell)	-	G-ALRK BGA.490	8.48	G.Saw & N.I.Newton . (As "G-ALRK")	Booker	4.00
491/ALX)	Hawkridge Dagling	08471		2.47	N.H.Ponsford (Stored 1.98)	(Breighton)	*

BGA No/Code	Type	C/n	P/I	Date	Owner/operator	Probable Base	CA Expy
493/(ALZ)	Hawkridge Nacelle Dagling	10471		7.47	P. & D.Underwood	Eaton Bray	*
					(Also allotted BAPC.81: on rebuild 12.95)		
503/AMK+	EoN AP.5 Olympia 2	EoN/0/003	G-ALJP	5.47	D.T.Staff	Booker	5.95*
			BGA.503				
507/AMP	EoN AP.5 Olympia 2	EoN/0/008	G-ALJO	6.47	M.Briggs	Cranfield	6.95*
			BGA.507				
509/AMR+	EoN AP.5 Olympia 2	EoN/0/011	G-ALLA	5.47	B.Perkins	Rhigos	10.97
			BGA.509				
511/AMT+	EoN AP.5 Olympia 2	EoN/0/005	G-ALLM	5.47	E.W.Burgess	Lyveden	7.97
			BGA.511				
514/AMW+	EoN AP.5 Olympia 2	EoN/0/015	G-ALKM	6.47	M R.Fox	Pocklington	10.00
			BGA.514				
538/ANW+	EoN AP.5 Olympia 2B	EoN/0/040	G-ALNE	7.47	D.C.Phillips	Snitterfield	4.00
			BGA.538				
544/APC+	EoN AP.5 Olympia 2	EoN/0/046	G-ALMJ	9.47	N.G.Oultram	Seighford	5.00
			BGA.544				
561/APV	EoN AP.5 Olympia 2B	EoN/0/032	G-ALKN	6.47	A.Kepley	Crowland	8.78*
			BGA.561		t/a Fenland & West Norfolk Avtn Museum (Stored 8.97)		
565/APZ	Slingsby T.25 Gull 4	505	G-ALPB	.	E.A.Arthur	Tibenham	8.99
			(BGA.565)				
570/AQE	Slingsby T.21B	538	G-ALNJ		Not known	Camphill	*
			BGA.570				
			(Crashed on landing Ridgewell 12.6.80: stored pending rebuild 10.97)				
572/(AQG)	Slingsby T.21B Sedbergh TX.1	539	8884M	.	RAF Museum	RAF Cardington	*
			VX275/BGA.572		(Stored 5.93)		
573/AQH	Slingsby T.21B	540	G-ALJU	.	Not known	(To Zimbabwe)	9.90*
			BGA.573				
578/AQN+	Hawkridge Grunau Baby 2B	G.3348	G-ALSO	.48	R G Hood	Bicester	7.99
			BGA.578				
580/(AQQ)	EoN AP.7 Primary	EoN/P/003	G-ALPS	.	Imperial War Museum	Duxford	*
			BGA.580		(Stored)		
588/AQY	EoN AP.7 Primary	EoN/P/011		.	N.H.Ponsford	(Breighton)	*
					(Stored 1.98)		
589/(AQZ)	EoN AP.7 Primary	EoN/P/012	G-ALMN	.	Not known	(Farnborough)	4.51*
			BGA.589		(Stored 1992)		
599/ARK+	Slingsby T.30A Prefect	548	PH-1	.	K.M.Fresson	Parham Park	7.99
			BGA.599/G-ALLF/BGA.599 (As "G-ALLF")				
601/ARM+	Slingsby T.21B	543	G-ALKX	8.48	South London Gliding Centre		
			BGA.601			Kenley	5.00
614/ASB	Slingsby T.21B	549	RNGSA	9.48	J.L.Rolls & Ptnrs	Talgarth	6.00
			G-ALLT/BGA.614		"T42"		
615/ASC	Grunau Baby 2B	G-4848	G-ALMM	2.49	C.D.Stainer & Ptnrs	Rufforth	8.94*
	(Built Hawkridge)		BGA.615		(Stored 8.95 - possibly sold in Germany)		
625/ASN	Slingsby T.30B Prefect	567	G-ALPC	1.49	G.Martin	Rhigos	5.99
			BGA.625				
628/(ASR)	EoN AP.8 Baby	EoN/B/004	G-ALRU	3.49	Not known	Aston Down	*
			BGA.628		(Crashed Bardney 28.5.71; stored 8.99)		
629/AST	EoN AP.8 Baby	EoN/B/005	G-ALRH	3.49	EoN Baby Syndicate	Chipping	9.96
	(Currently regd as G-ALRH)		BGA.629		"Liver Bird"(As "G-ALRH": dismantled 3.99)		
643/ATH	Slingsby T.15 Gull III	364A	TJ711	11.49	Brooklands Museum	Brooklands	9.94*
					(Stored 1999)		
646/ATL	Slingsby T.21B	536	G-ALKS	6.50	G.Markham (Stored 3.97)	Enstone	7.96
651/ATR	Slingsby T.13 Petrel 1	361A	EI-101	7.50	G.Saw	Booker	4.00
			IGA.101/IAC.101/BGA.651/G-ALPP				
655/ATV	Zlin 24 Krajanek	101	G-ALMP	4.50	N.Barr	Lasham	6.00
			OK-8592		(As "OK-8592")		
663/AUD	Slingsby T.26 Kite 2B	727		1.52	R.S.Hooper "663"	Dunstable	4.00
666/AUG	Slingsby T.21B	643		6.51	Cambridge University GC		
						Gransden Lodge	6.00
668/AUJ	Slingsby T.21B	639		6.51	Not known	Rufforth	6.86*
	(Built Aero & Engineering)				(Damaged Feshiebridge 16.7.85: stored 7.97)		
673/AUP	Slingsby T.21B	636	(RNGSA.N21?)	7.51	The Solent T21 Group		
						Lee-on-Solent	5.00
678/AUU+	EoN AP.5 Olympia	EoN/0/076		4.52	J.M.Lee	Parham Park	8.00
680/AUW	Avia 40P	117		8.52	F.Ragot	Booker	7.98
684/AVA	Abbott-Baynes Scud III	3		1.53	E.A.Hull	Dunstable	6.00
685/AVB+	Slingsby T.34 Sky	644	G-644	2.53	R.Moyse	Lasham	3.00
686/AVC+	Slingsby T.34 Sky	670		3.53	P.J.Teagle	Sutton Bank	8.00
					"Kinder Scout II"		
687/AVD+	Eon AP.5 Olympia 2	EoN/0/092		3.53	A.C.Jarvis	Parham Park	7.98

BGA No/Code	Type	C/n	P/I	Date	Owner/operator	Probable Base	CA Expy
689/AVF+	Slingsby T.26 Kite 2A	728	RAFGSA.294 BGA.689	4.53	P.M.Warren "Percy"	Cross Hayes	8.00
694/AVL	Slingsby T.34 Sky	671	G-671	5.53	M.P.Wakem	Long Mynd	5.00
698/AVQ	Slingsby T.34 Sky	645	G-645	8.53	Miss A.G.Veitch & B.Middleton "Gertie" "G"	Easterton	6.00
701/AVT	Slingsby T.30B Prefect	857	AGA... BGA.701	1.53	Booker GC	Booker	5.00
711/AWD	Slingsby T.21B	950		9.54	D.B.Brown t/a T.21 Syndicate	Chipping	6.00
724/	Slingsby T.41 Skylark 2	997			Not known "391" (Under restoration 8.99)	Dunstable	
726/AWU+	EoN AP.5 Olympia 2	EoN/O/082		5.55	M J Riley	Cranfield	3.00
729/AWX+	Slingsby T.41 Skylark 2	946		1.56	A.G.Leach	Cranfield	7.99
731/AWZ+	Slingsby T.7 Cadet	SSK/FF/169	RA847	1.57	R.Moyse	Lasham	5.00
733/AXB+	Slingsby T.41 Skylark 2	926		2.55	A.L.Shaw	Lyveden	4.00
735/AXD+	Slingsby T.43 Skylark 3	1014		.55	F.G.T.Birlison	Aston Down	5.00
736/AXE+	Slingsby T.43 Skylark 3	1029		3.57	R.J.Hopkins & Ptnrs	Snitterfield	5.98
740/AXJ	Slingsby T.42A Eagle 2	994		.55	P.C.Horn t/a The Eagle Syndicate	Parham Park	2.00
742/AXL	Slingsby T.43 Skylark 3	1030		6.56	M.Chalmers & Ptnrs	Kingston Deverill	2.00
745/AXP+	Slingsby T.41 Skylark 2	949		4.55	M.Sanderson	Milfield	3.99
747/AXR+	Slingsby T.41 Skylark 2	945		.56	Lincolnshire GC	Strubby	3.00
750/AXU+	Slingsby T.41 Skylark 2	944		3.55	M.A.Langhurst	Halesland	6.95*
759/AYD+	Slingsby T.41 Skylark 2	1048		.56	B.Milburn	Currock Hill	6.00
761/AYF+	Slingsby T.43 Skylark 3B	1058		9.56	A.Jenkins	Enstone	10.99
763/AYH+	Slingsby T.43 Skylark 3B	1066		.56	A.Griffiths	Crowland	6.00
778/AYY	Slingsby T.41 Skylark 2C	1073		.56	H.Johnson "33"	Long Mynd	6.96
780/AZA+	Slingsby T.42 Eagle 3	1085	RNGSA 2-08 BGA.780		J.M.Crewe	Weston on the Green	7.00
782/AZC	Slingsby T.21B	1096		5.57	C.Stachulla	(Augsberg)	8.00
785/AZF	Slingsby T.30B Prefect	1100		.56	L.J.Smith t/a The Prefect Syndicate	Culdrose	3.96*
789/AZK	Slingsby T.8 Tutor	-	VM650	6.57	Not known (Stored 5.93)	Croft, Skegness	7.90*
793/AZP	Slingsby T.41 Skylark 2	999		1.57	G.Dixon & Ptnr "136"	Currock Hill	8.97
794/AZQ	Slingsby T.8 Tutor	-	VM687	.57	J.M.Brookes (As "VM687")	Strubby	10.98
795/AZR+	EoN AP.5 Olympia 2	EoN/O/101		7.58	S.Mooring	Dunstable	7.95*
797/AZT	EoN AP.5 Olympia 2	EoN/O/063	ZS-GCM	3.57	J.Starling	Camphill	8.00
802/AZY+	Slingsby T.41 Skylark 2	963		4.57	A.J.Jackson	Burn	6.97
804/BAA	Slingsby T.8 Tutor	931	XE761 VM589	5.57	A.Chadwick	Rufforth	3.97

(A Cadet TX.1 purporting to be "BGA.804 ex VM589" is stored by Midland Air Museum, Coventry 12.97: this came from Perranporth in 1968)

BGA No/Code	Type	C/n	P/I	Date	Owner/operator	Probable Base	CA Expy
806/BAC	Slingsby T.43 Skylark 3B	1101	RNGSA CU19 BGA.806	6.58	M.Stokeld	Carlton Moor	5.97
810/BAH+	Slingsby T.41 Skylark 2	1104		7.58	B.Jackson	Cranfield	9.97
814/BAM+	Slingsby T.41 Skylark 2	1108		1.58	B.H.Thwaites	Wormingford	3.00
815/BAN	Slingsby T.30B Prefect	1120		1.58	J.S.Allison	RAF Halton	5.00
822/BAV+	Slingsby T.41 Skylark 2B	1113		2.58	T.Cushion	Kingston Deverill	7.97
823/BAW+	Slingsby T.43 Skylark 3B	1126		2.58	D.Heslop	North Weald	8.00
825/BAY+	Slingsby T.42B Eagle 3	1116		3.58	M.Lodge	Cranwell	8.00
826/BAZ+	Slingsby T.41 Skylark 2	1112		3.58	W.Fuller	Currock Hill	5.99
827/BBA+	Slingsby T.41 Skylark 2	1128		3.58	M.Bosher	Winthorpe	5.99
828/BBB+	Slingsby T.42B Eagle 3	1118		4.58	I.K.Mitchell	North Hill	8.00
833/(BBG)	Slingsby T.8 Tutor	-	VW535	9.57	Not known (On rebuild 12.95)	Dunstable	*
834/BBH+	EoN Olympia 2	EoN/O/041	BGA.539	8.57	J.W.Bonham	Cranfield	6.99
841/BBQ+	Slingsby T.42B Eagle 3	1115		5.58	Eagle Syndicate	Milfield	6.00
844/BBT+	Slingsby T.43 Skylark 3B	1134	RAFGSA.234 BGA.844	.58	J.P.Gilbert	Wormingford	5.00
845/BBU+	Slingsby T.41 Skylark 2B	1135		.58	J.A.Timpany	Bicester	5.00
852/(BCB)	Slingsby T.8 Tutor	-	TS291	7.58	Royal Museum of Scotland - Museum of Flight (On display: as "TS291")	East Fortune	*
856/BCF	Slingsby T.21B (Built Leighton Park School)	1		10.58	P.Underwood (Blown over Haddenham 14.6.80: stored 12.95)	Eaton Bray	*
858/BCH+	Slingsby T.8 Tutor	SSK/FF/489	VM547	9.58	N.James	Lyveden	5.99
860/BCK	EoN AP.5 Olympia 2B	EoN/O/081		4.59	C.D.Street	Lasham	7.99

547

BGA No/Code	Type	C/n	P/I	Date	Owner/operator	Probable Base	CA Expy
861/BCL+	Slingsby T.43 Skylark 3B	1139		9.58	R.Aylett	Bidford	5.96
864/BCP+	Slingsby T.43 Skylark 3B	1140		11.58	M Cummings	Milfield	3.00
867/BCS	Slingsby T.43 Skylark 3B	1144		12.58	M.Wright & Ptnrs "549"	Wormingford	5.00
869/BCU	Slingsby T.21B	1148		1.59	Not known "2" (Stored)	North Connel	*
870/BCV+	Slingsby T.43 Skylark 3B	1195		4.59	W R Davis "155"	Challock	2.99
871/BCW+	Slingsby T.43 Skylark 3B	1147		3.59	I.Tittenson	Bidford	10.97
872/BCX	Slingsby T.41 Skylark 2B	1197		4.59	G W Haworth	Tibenham	5.00
873/BCY+	Slingsby T.45 Swallow	1198		4.59	D.C Urwin "T45"	Talgarth	7.00
875/BDA	Slingsby T.21B	1205	AGA.7 BGA.875	6.59	W Grobkinsey (Stored 8.98)	Edgehill	5.00
880/BDF+	Slingsby T.42B Eagle 3	1213		9.59	D.C.Phillips	Long Mynd	7.00
886/BDM	Slingsby T.21B	1216		11.59	D.G.Cooper	Wormingford	7.98
890/BDR+	Slingsby T.45 Swallow	1243		6.60	R.J.Shallcross	Waldershare Park	8.00
895/BDW	Slingsby T.8 Tutor TX.2	-	VM637	4.59	R.Patrick & Ptnrs (On rebuild 1.96: probably to be "VM637")	Winthorpe	6.93*
896/BDX+	Slingsby T.41 Skylark 2 (Built C Hurst)	CH.095/1		6.59	H D Maddams	Wormingford	6.00
899/BEA+	Slingsby T.41 Skylark 2	1194		7.59	M.L.Ryan	Hullavington	9.00
902/BED	Slingsby T.12 Gull I	-	(Not known)	5.59	Royal Museum of Scotland - Museum of Flight East Fortune		
904/BEF+	Slingsby T.8 Tutor (Frame No.SSK/FF 934)	-	(ex RAF)	10.59	D.Chaplin (Tutor Syndicate)	Sutton Bank	5.96
909/BEL+	EoN AP.5 Olympia 2B	EoN/O/126		12.59	J.G.Gilbert & Ptnrs	Wormingford	3.00
910/BEM+	Slingsby T.45 Swallow	1221		2.60	I.D.Smith	Kingston Deverill	8.97
914/BER+	Slingsby T.43 Skylark 3B	1225		3.60	K.V.Payne	Bryngwyn Bach	2.99
916/BET	Slingsby T.43 Skylark 3B	1227		3.60	A.C.Robertson & Ptnrs "600"	Feshiebridge	5.98
920/BEX+	Slingsby T.43 Skylark 3F	1229		4.60	P.J.Mortimer	Rivar Hill	7.99
921/BEY	Slingsby T.45 Swallow	1230		4.60	R.C.Martin	Lasham	5.99
922/BEZ+	Slingsby T.43 Skylark 3F	1232		4.60	R.G.Gillow	Perranporth	7.00
924/BFB	Slingsby T.45 Swallow	1235		5.60	Essex & Suffolk GC	North Weald	8.99
925/BFC+	Slingsby T.43 Skylark 3F	1239		5.60	Strathclyde GC	Strathaven	8.99
926/BFD	Slingsby T.21B	1240	RAFGSA BGA.926	5.60	B.Jaessing	(Hamburg)	7.96*
927/BFE+	Slingsby T.43 Skylark 3F	1244		6.60	Essex Skylark Gliding Syndicate (I.F.Barnes)	North Weald	5.00
929/BFG	Slingsby T.43 Skylark 3F	1245		7.60	T.J.Wilkinson "161"	Sackville Farm, Riseley	6.99
933/BFL+	Slingsby T.41 Skylark 2B	1220		5.60	D G Coats	Milfield	8.99
936/BFP	Schleicher Ka7 Rhonadler	702/60		5.60	Dartmoor GC (Damaged Brent Tor 15.11.95)	Brent Tor	4.96*
945/BFY+	Slingsby T.21B	1251	RAFGGA.515 RAFGSA.286/BGA.945	9.60	D.M.Hayes & Ptnrs	Sutton Bank	10.99
948/BGB	Slingsby T.21B (Robin EC-33)	1274	RAFGSA.282 BGA.948	11.60	Shenington GC (Stored 8.98)	Edgehill	12.97
950/BGD+	Slingsby T.43 Skylark 3F	1276		11.60	Essex University GC	Wormingford	8.99
953/BGG	Slingsby T.21B	1294		12.60	West Wales Gliding Trust	Templeton	3.98
954/BGH+	Slingsby T.43 Skylark 3F	1295		12.60	Denbigh GC	Lleweni Parc	5.00
957/BGL+	Slingsby T.43 Skylark 3F	1296		3.61	C.Willey & Ptnrs	Eaglescott	4.00
960/BGP+	Slingsby T.21B	1297	RAFGSA.283 BGA.960	1.61	Bannerdown GC	RAF Keevil	6.00
962/BGR+	EoN AP.5 Olympia 2B	EoN/O/124		6.60	M.H.Gagg	Cosford	1.00
964/BGT	DFS/30 Kranich II (Built AB Flygplan)	087	SE-STF Fv.8226	.60	C.Wills	Booker	6.00
968/BGX	EoN AP.5 Olympia 2	EoN/O/123	(BGA.892)	8.60	C.Kominski	Eaglescott	7.97*
969/BGY+	Slingsby T.21B	558	SE-SHM	8.60	P.J.Wilby	Wormingford	8.98
973/BHC+	EoN AP.5 Olympia 2B	EoN/O/138		1.61	M Pedwell	Bidford	6.00
985/BHQ	Slingsby T.43 Skylark 3F	1304		4.61	R.Furness "760"	Cranfield	5.96
988/BHT+	Slingsby T.43 Skylark 3F	1306		4.61	K.Chichester & Ptnrs	Camphill	6.00
990/BHV+	Slingsby T.45 Swallow	1308	NEJSGSA.4 BGA.990	4.61	S.Thom	Lyveden	3.00
996/BJB+	Slingsby T.43 Skylark 3F (Built Jones, Pentelow & Saint)	SSK/JPS/1		4.61	R.A.Mills	Turweston	9.99
997/BJC+	EoN AP.5 Olympia 2B	EoN/O/135		4.61	A.Vidion & Ptnrs	Lyveden	6.00
998/BJD+	SZD-9 bis Bocian 1D	P-391		5.61	D.L.Martlew (Bocian Syndicate)	Lasham	12.99
1000/BJF+	Slingsby T.21B	1309		6.61	Dukeries GC	Gamston	4.00
1004/BJK	Slingsby T.43 Skylark 3F	1311		7.61	F.J.Wiseman & Ptnrs	Wormingford	4.00

BGA No/Code	Type	C/n	P/I	Date	Owner/operator	Probable Base	CA Expy
1008/BJP+	Slingsby T.45 Swallow	1316		9.61	S R Grant	Stow Maries	8.99
1009/BJQ+	Slingsby T.49A Capstan	1314		.	L.Glover & Ptnrs		
						Husbands Bosworth	10.00
1014/BJV	Slingsby T.21B	556	SE-SHK	1.62	Royal Museum of Scotland - Museum		
					of Flight	East Fortune	*
1015/BJW	Slingsby T.43 Skylark 3G	1321		3.62	J.B.Strzebrakowski	Crowland	3.00
					"198"		
1017/BJY+	Slingsby T.45 Swallow	1324		3.62	C.Devine	Portmoak	9.99
1018/BJZ	Slingsby T.45 Swallow	1325		3.62	J.P.Marshall	North Connel	11.96*
1019/BKA+	Slingsby T.50 Skylark 4	1326	EI-117	6.62	Staffordshire GC	Seighford	5.00
			BGA.1019				
1021/BKC+	DFS 108-68 Weihe	231	SE-SNE	4.61	B.Briggs	Cranwell	9.96*
	(Built AB Flygindustri)		Fv.8312				
1023/BKE+	Slingsby T.43 Skylark 3F	1715/CR/1		7.61	G.Smith	Kingston Deverill	5.00
	(Built C Ross)						
1027/BKJ+	Schleicher Ka6CR	565/59	9G-AAR	7.61	P.M.Hogan		
						Sandhill Farm, Shrivenham	6.00
1028/BKK	EoN AP.5 Olympia 2	EoN/O/139	RNGSA.CU11	7.61	J.Bradley	Thruxton	7.99
			BGA.1028				
1029/BKL+	EoN AP.5 Olympia 2B	EoN/O/134		6.61	J.S.Orr	Lasham	5.00
1031/BKN+	Schleicher Ka7 Rhonadler	1091/61		9.61	East Sussex GC "B"	Ringmer	4.00
1032/BKP	Slingsby T.45 Swallow	1203		10.61	E.Traynor	(Currock Hill)	10.96*
1035/BKS+	EoN AP.5 Olympia 2B	EoN/O/144		11.61	N W Woodward	Booker	3.00
1037/BKU+	EoN AP.5 Olympia 2B	EoN/O/153		1.62	D. & C.MacKay	Aboyne	4.00
1039/BKW+	Schleicher Ka6 Rhonsegler	295	OH-RSA	10.62	I.M.Hembling	Rattlesden	4.00
1040/BKX+	EoN AP.5 Olympia 2B	EoN/O/148		3.62	E.T.Samways & Ptnrs	Old Sarum	6.00
1043/BLA	Slingsby T.50 Skylark 4	1331		5.62	I.A.Masterton "327"	Portmoak	5.00
1047/BLE+	Slingsby T.50 Skylark 4	1335	RNGSA 1-228	6.62	S.Frank	Easterton	5.00
			BGA.1047		"228"		
1050/BLH+	Slingsby T.50 Skylark 4	1338	RAFGSA	7.62	M.D.Cohler	Rufforth	4.00
			BGA.1050				
1051/BLJ+	EoN AP.6 Olympia 419X	EoN/4/009		3.62	G.Balshaw & Ptnrs	Lleweni Parc	10.96*
					"Big Bird"		
1052/BLK	EoN AP.6 Olympia 419X	EoN/4/007	G-APSX	4.62	C.J.Abbott & Ptnrs	Long Mynd	5.00
					"Wild Goose" "67"		
1055/BLN+	EoN AP.5 Olympia 2B	EoN/O/152		5.62	M.R.Derwent	Cranwell	3.00
1056/BLP	EoN AP.5 Olympia 2B	EoN/O/149		3.62	D.Birtwhistle & Ptnrs	Chipping	5.95*
					(Stored 9.97)		
1057/BLQ+	EoN AP.5 Olympia 2 Special	EoN/O/042	RAFGSA 145	7.62	R.C Patrick & Ptnrs	Winthorpe	5.00
			BGA.540				
1059/BLS	EoN AP.5 Olympia 2B	EoN/O/151		7.62	D.J.Wilson	Seighford	5.00
	(EoN rebuild of BGA.897 [EoN/O/128])						
1061/BLU	Slingsby T.45 Swallow	1340		7.62	Not known (Stored 1.98)	Burn	7.94*
1063/BLW+	Slingsby T.50 Skylark 4	1342		8.62	A.J.Preston	Dunstable	5.00
1066/BLZ	Slingsby T.50 Skylark 4	1346		11.62	R.M Lambert	Easterton	5.00
1077/BML	Slingsby T.45 Swallow	1328		6.62	Dartmoor GS	Burnford Common	7.97*
1078/BMM	SZD-9bis Bocian 1D	P-397		10.62	D.R.Wilcox	Crowland	8.00
1081/BMQ+	Slingsby T.21B	1351		11.62	I H Davies	Seighford	10.00
1085/BMU	Slingsby T.21B (T)	1355	9G-ABD	12.62	D.Woolerton & Ptnrs	East Kirkby	9.97
	(Rotax 503)		BGA.1085		"Spruce Goose"		
1087/BMW+	Slingsby T.50 Skylark 4	1357		12.62	M.J.R.Lindsay	Tibenham	6.98
1088/BMX	Slingsby T.50 Skylark 4	1358	RAFGSA.308	1.63	S.R.Stanwix	Kingston Deverill	4.00
			BGA.1088		(789 Syndicate)		
1089/BMY	Slingsby T.50 Skylark 4	1361		1.63	J.Page "163"	Sutton Bank	4.98
1091/BNA	Shenstone Harbinger Mk.2	1		12.62	A.C.Wood	Camphill	7.97*
1093/BNC	DFS 108-68 Weihe	1	SE-SHU	3.63	K.S.Green	Lasham	9.00
	(Built AB Kockums Flygindustri)						
1094/BND+	Schleicher Ka6CR	1157		3.63	E.G.Harris	Tibenham	5.00
1095/BNE+	Slingsby T.50 Skylark 4	1343	N70TN	4.63	M.Rossiter & Ptnrs	Usk	5.00
			C-FOUO/CF-OUO				
1098/BNH+	Schleicher Ka6CR	6115		3.63	Bath, Wilts & N.Dorset GC		
						Kingston Deverill	3.00
1100/BNK+	Slingsby T.50 Skylark 4	1362		2.63	E.D.Weekes & Ptnrs	Bicester	5.00
1102/BNM	Slingsby T.50 Skylark 4	1367		3.63	D.Hertzburg	North Weald	6.00
	(Reported as "BMN")						
1103/BNN+	Slingsby T.50 Skylark 4	1366		3.63	J R Robinson	Pocklington	12.98
1104/BNP	Slingsby T.50 Skylark 4	1368		3.63	A.R.Worters "653"	Milfield	6.00
1105/BNQ+	Slingsby T.50 Skylark 4	1369		3.63	R Pye	Chipping	4.00
1106/BNR+	Slingsby T.49B Capstan	1370		8.63	A.R.Bushnell	Crowland	5.00
1107/BNS	Slingsby T.45 Swallow	1373	XS652	3.63	York GC Swallow Syndicate		
			BGA.1107		(As "XS652")	Rufforth	4.00

BGA No/Code	Type	C/n	P/I	Date	Owner/operator	Probable Base	CA Expy
1109/BNU	Slingsby T.45 Swallow	1377		5.63	K.D.Bagshaw	Lasham	5.97*
1115/BPA+	Slingsby T.50 Skylark 4	1383		5.63	D.Penney	Lasham	12.99
1116/BPB	Slingsby T.50 Skylark 4	1384	RNGSA BGA.1116 "255"	6.63	A.J.Hall	Lasham	7.00
1117/BPC+	Slingsby T.50 Skylark 4	1389		7.63	J.L.Grayer & Ptnr	Ringmer	3.00
1118/BPD	Slingsby T.49B Capstan	1390	(RNGSA.N55)	7.63	Culdrose GC Culdrose	3.00	
1119/BPE+	Slingsby T.50 Skylark 4	1391		6.63	D.H.Scales	Currock Hill	4.00
1121/BPG	Slingsby T.50 Skylark 4	1393		7.63	R.M.Neill & Ptnrs "741"	Long Mynd	11.99
1123/BPJ	Slingsby T.50 Skylark 4	1360		4.63	M.Cooper "809" (Damaged Challock 26.3.97)	Challock	3.98*
1124/BPK+	Slingsby T.50 Skylark 4	1381		6.63	D.Crowhurst	Crowland	6.00
1125/BPL+	EoN AP.5 Olympia 2B	EoN/0/136	G-APXC	6.63	D.Harris & Ptnrs	Camphill	5.97*
1127/BPN	Oberlerchner Standard Austria	003	OE-0496	6.63	R.K.Avery & Ptnrs "571"	Eaglescott	7.98
1131/BPS+	Slingsby T.49B Capstan	1399		9.63	Capstan Gliding Group	Aboyne	2.00
1132/BPT	Slingsby T.49B Capstan	1400		10.63	J.E.Neville	Laurencekirk	2.95*
1133/BPU	Slingsby T.49B Capstan	1402		11.63	I.T.Godfrey t/a Capstan Syndicate	Dunstable	3.98
1134/BPV	Slingsby T.49B Capstan	1404		12.63	C R Partinton "N31"	Currock Hill	7.00
1135/BPW+	Slingsby T.49B Capstan	1408		1.64	Ulster GC	Bellarena	7.00
1136/BPX	Slingsby T.45 Swallow	1397	XS859 BGA.1136	1.64	F.Pape & Ptnrs "859"	Rufforth	7.98
1138/BPZ+	Slingsby T.50 Skylark 4	1406		3.64	A.Pattermore & Ptnrs	Rivar Hill	7.00
1143/BQE	Slingsby T.7 Cadet	-	RAFGSA.273 RA905	8.63	M.L.Beach (As "RA905")	RAF Halton	3.00
1144/BQF	Slingsby T.21B	1168	XN189	10.63	Connel GC "1"	North Connel	8.00
1147/BQJ	DFS/30 Kranich II (Built Schleicher)	821	RAFGSA.215 D-11-0442(?)	11.63	M.C.Russell (As "D-11-3224"; stored 3.96)	Bishops Stortford	*
1148/BQK+	Schleicher Ka7 Rhonadler	7120		12.63	R.B Armitage (Damaged Waldershare Park 21.8.95)	Challock	6.96*
1149/BQL	Schleicher Ka6CR	725/60	D-7117	12.63	R.O.Toop	Eaglescott	7.00
1150/BQM+	EoN AP.10 460 Srs.1B	EoN/S/002	RAFGSA.276	12.63	A.Duncan	Portmoak	2.00
1152/BQP+	Slingsby T.30B Prefect	646	RAFGSA.159	2.64	A.Downie (On rebuild 8.99)	Dunstable	9.00
1153/BQQ	EoN AP.5 Olympia 2B (Rebuilt 1993 using wings from BGA.678)	EoN/0/121	RAFGSA.244	2.64	P.R.Brinson "Dopey"	Nympsfield	7.00
1155/BQS+	EoN AP.10 460 Srs.1	EoN/S/008		3.64	P.Williams	Snitterfield	4.97*
1156/BQT+	EoN AP.10 460 Srs.1	EoN/S/007	BGA.2666 AGA.6/BGA.1156	1.64	J.H.May	Seighford	4.97*
1157/BQU	Schleicher Ka7 Rhonadler	7141	RNGSA AR66 BGA.1157	4.64	Portsmouth Naval GC (RNGSA.N27) Lee-on-Solent		3.00
1162/BQZ+	Slingsby T.50 Skylark 4	1416		4.64	G.Colledge	Edgehill	6.99
1163/BRA+	Slingsby T.49B Capstan	1417		4.64	K.R.Brown	Nympsfield	6.00
1164/BRB	Slingsby T.51 Dart 15	1423	RAFGSA.334 BGA.1164	4.64	M.Sansom "T51"	Gallows Hill	2.00
1165/BRC+	Slingsby T.45 Swallow 1	1407		5.64	J.R.Smalley	Kirton-in-Lindsey	4.00
1166/BRD+	Slingsby T.51 Dart 15	1425	RAFGSA.335 BGA.1166	5.64	V.Day	Lyveden	8.00
1167/BRE+	Slingsby T.45 Swallow 2	1415		5.64	A.Swannock & Ptnrs	Gamston	6.99
1169/BRG	Slingsby T.45 Swallow	1410		5.64	A.W.F.Edwards	Gransden Lodge	2.00
1172/BRK	EoN AP.10 460	EoN/S/001	G-APWL BGA.1172/G-APWL/RAFGSA.268/G-APWL (As "G-APWL/243")	4.64	D.G.Andrew	North Hill	4.00
1173/BRL	EoN AP.5 Olympia 2B	EoN/0/132		5.64	A.Cutts & Ptnrs	Ridgewell	3.99
1174/BRM+	Schleicher Ka7 Rhonadler	776/60	D-4635	5.64	D.S.Driver	Currock Hill	1.00
1177/BRQ+	EoN AP.10 460 Srs.1C	EoN/S/003	G-ARFU	6.64	J.Steel & Ptnrs	Falgunzeon	8.96*
1180/BRT	Slingsby T.51 Dart 15	1430		6.64	H.E.Birch & Ptnrs	Dishforth	4.00
1181/BRU+	Slingsby T.51 Dart 15	1429		6.64	M.Charlton	Currock Hill	2.00
1183/BRW+	Slingsby T.49B Capstan	1413		6.64	A.West & Ptnrs	Lasham	11.00
1185/BRY+	Slingsby T.51 Dart 15	1434		7.64	S.Wilkinson & Ptnrs	Kirton-in-Lindsey	5.00
1187/BSA+	Slingsby T.51 Dart 15	1405		7.64	N G Oultram	Camphill	6.00
1189/BSC	Slingsby T.50 Skylark 4	1422		8.64	A.Etchells "H23"	Bidford	10.00
1191/BSE+	Slingsby T.49B Capstan	1414		9.64	D.A Bullock	Bicester	2.00
1193/BSG	Slingsby T.50 Skylark 4	1436		9.64	North Wales GC	Bryngwyn Bach	4.99
1194/BSH+	Slingsby T.50 Skylark 4	1444		11.64	M Mathieson	Wormingford	7.99
1196/BSK+	Slingsby T.49B Capstan	1418		10.64	Kermit Syndicate	Lleweni Parc	4.00
1197/BSL+	Slingsby T.51 Dart 17	1445		10.64	C.J.Owles	Tibenham	7.00
1198/BSM	Slingsby T.51 Dart 15	1439		10.64	M.Robertson "597"	Strathaven	9.97*
1201/BSQ	EoN AP.10 460 Srs.1	EoN/S/014		5.64	K.G.Ashford Husbands Bosworth "463"		7.00

BGA No/Code	Type	C/n	P/I	Date	Owner/operator	Probable Base	CA Expy
1202/BSR+	Slingsby T.50 Skylark 4	1443		12.64	D.Johnstone	Rattlesden	1.00
1203/BSS	Slingsby T.49B Capstan	1449		12.64	J.F.Rogers "T49"	Booker	6.00
1204/BST	Slingsby T.49 Capstan	1451		1.65	P H Pickett	Husbands Bosworth	8.00
1206/BSV+	Slingsby T.51 Dart 15	1454		7.65	G.G.Butler	Snitterfield	2.97*
1207/BSW+	Slingsby T.51 Dart 17R	1459		2.65	B.L.Owen	Tibenham	5.00
1208/BSX+	Slingsby T.45 Swallow	1461	OO-ZWC	4.65	P.Brownlow & Ptnrs		
			F-OTAN-C5/BGA.1208			Sackville Farm, Riseley	5.00
1209/BSY+	Slingsby T.50 Skylark 4	1448		4.65	G B Dennis	Nympsfield	2.00
1210/BSZ+	Slingsby T.50 Skylark 4	1460		4.65	B.Ling	Lleweni Parc	5.00
1211/BTA+	Slingsby T.45 Swallow	1473		6.65	M.Morley	Odiham	8.00
1214/BTD+	DFS/49 Grunau Baby 2C	?	(ex RAFGSA)	8.64	Bidford Gliding Centre	Bidford	5.97*
1217/BTG+	EoN AP.10 460 Srs.1	EoN/S/024		2.65	A.W Hearney	Strubby	9.99
1218/BTH	Slingsby T.21B	JHB/2		3.65	M.Lake (As "WB981")	Aston Down	5.00
	(Built J.Hulme: restored 1995 with wings from BGA.3238/WB981)						
1219/BTJ+	Schleicher Ka6CR	6367		3.65	D.Keith	Kingston Deverill	5.00
1220/BTK	Slingsby T.50 Skylark 4	1364	SE-SZW	3.65	J.A.Lewis & Syndicate	Lasham	7.96*
					"368"		
1222/BTM	Schleicher Ka6CR	6174		3.65	P.Maller "211"	Aston Down	4.00
1223/BTN+	EoN AP.10 460 Srs.1	EoN/S/022	AGA.15	4.65	S.C.Thompson	Parham Park	10.00
			BGA.1223				
1225/BTQ+	EoN AP.10 460 Srs.1	EoN/S/029		4.65	P.Etherington & Ptnrs		
						Husbands Bosworth	2.97*
1230/BTV	DFS/68 Weihe	0-00358	RAFGGA	5.65	Not known	Cranwell	5.93*
1237/BUC+	Slingsby T.49B Capstan	1472		6.65	Lakes GC	Walney Island	1.00
1239/BUE+	Slingsby T.50 Skylark 4	1468		7.65	D.Holt & I.H.Davies	Seighford	4.00
1240/BUF	Slingsby T.51 Dart 17R	1469		7.65	C.H.Brown & Ptnrs "366" Chipping		3.00
1241/BUG+	EoN AP.10 460 Srs.1	EoN/S/028		5.65	A.Rowson & Ptnrs	Long Mynd	3.97*
1242/BUH	Eon AP.10 460 Srs.1	EoN/S/021	G-ASMP	.65	A.E.Lawrence		
			(Damaged Gransden Lodge 29. 6.95) Sackville Farm, Riseley				5.96*
1244/BUK	EoN AP.10 460 Srs.1	EoN/S/027		5.65	M.Hodgson	Booker	6.97*
1245/BUL+	Slingsby T.51 Dart 17R	1470		7.65	A.Parrish & Ptnr		
						Husbands Bosworth	6.00
1247/BUP	Slingsby T.51 Dart 17R	1478		9.65	D.S.Carter "837"	Enstone	6.99
1249/BUR+	Slingsby T.49B Capstan	1482		11.65	Denbigh GC	Lleweni Parc	7.00
1251/BUT+	Slingsby T.43 Skylark 3F	VRT.1		7.65	I.Bannister	Chipping	5.00
	(Built V.R.Tull & Ptnrs)				t/a Sky Syndicate		
1253/BUV+	EoN AP.10 460 Srs.1	EoN/S/030		7.65	S.H.Gibson	Dunstable	4.00
1254/BUW	Slingsby T.21B	NK	RAFGSA.242	8.65	J.N.Wardle	Lasham	9.00
1257/BUZ+	Schleicher Ka6CR	6418		8.65	R.Leacroft	Lyveden	10.00
1259/BVB+	Schleicher Ka7 Rhonadler	7230		9.65	York Gliding Centre	Rufforth	6.00
	(Modified to ASK 13 standard)						
1260/BVC	Slingsby T.51 Dart 17R	1479		3.66	R.M.Hitchin & Ptnrs		
						Kingston Deverill	2.00
1262/BVE+	Slingsby T.51 Dart 17R	1483		11.65	P.Leach & Ptnr		
					"61" Sandhill Farm, Shrivenham		7.00
1263/BVF+	Slingsby T.45 Swallow	1481		11.65	Pershore F/C	Bidford	6.00
1265/BVH+	Slingsby T.51 Dart 17R	1485		12.65	D.J.Simpson	Halesland	6.00
1266/BVJ+	Slingsby T.51 Dart 17R	1486		1.66	R.& M.Weaver	Usk	12.99
1268/BVL	Slingsby T.51 Dart 15	1487		1.66	D.Stabler & Ptnrs "404" Tibenham		8.99
1269/BVM	Slingsby T.51 Dart 17R	1492		1.66	N.H.Ponsford	(Breighton)	5.89*
					"150" (Stored 12.99)		
1270/BVN+	EoN AP.10 460 Srs.1	EoN/S/023		3.65	F J Clarke & Ptnrs	North Hill	10.99
1273/BVR+	Schleicher Ka6CR	6441		10.65	R.C Cannon & Ptnrs	Lasham	3.00
1274/BVS+	SZD-9 bis Bocian 1D	F-831		??.??	Spilsby Soaring	Spilsby	6.00
1278/BVW	EoN AP.6 Olympia 403	EoN/4/001	RAFGSA.306	8.65	J.B. & K.D.Dumville	Camphill	7.99
			G-APEW				
1279/BVX+	Schleicher Ka6CR	6439		10.65	C.G.Stoves	Burn	6.00
1280/BVY+	LET L-13 Blanik	173121		10.65	Strathclyde GC	Strathaven	6.00
1281/BVZ+	Schleicher Ka6CR	6446		10.65	J.C.Taggart	Bellarena	3.00
1283/BWB	EoN AP.10 460 Srs.1	EoN/S/036		12.65	S Metcalfe "B96"	Tibenham	6.00
1284/BWC	Schleicher Ka6CR	6449		12.65	M.E.Hazlewood "424"	Lasham	4.00
1286/BWE+	EoN AP.10 460 Srs.2	EoN/S/035		12.65	C.Hughes	Nympsfield	8.00
1288/BWG	EoN AP.10 465 Srs.2	EoN/S/038		12.65	K.S.Green & Ptnr "465"	Lasham	4.97*
1290/BWJ+	Slingsby T.51 Dart 17R	1495		2.66	D.Godfrey & Ptnrs "377" Edgehill		7.96*
1291/BWK+	Slingsby T.45 Swallow	1493		2.66	K.Hubbard & Ptnrs	North Hill	5.00
1293/BWM	Slingsby T.51 Dart 17R	1500		4.66	P.L. & L.E.Poole "182"	Lasham	8.96*
1295/BWP	Slingsby T.51 Dart 17R	1501		3.66	D Champion "861"	Parham Park	4.00
1296/BWQ+	Slingsby T.51 Dart 15	1505		3.66	C.Uncles	Halesland	6.00
1298/BWS	Slingsby T.51 Dart 17R	1502		4.66	R.D.Broom & E.A.Chalk Cranfield		8.00
					"517"		

BGA No/Code	Type	C/n	P/I	Date	Owner/operator	Probable Base	CA Expy
1299/BWT	Slingsby T.51 Dart 15R	1508		4.66	R.Parker "163" (Stored)	RAF Dishforth	8.96*
1300/BWU+	EoN AP.10 460 Srs.1	EoN/S/034		1.66	P.Berridge	Ridgewell	7.00
1303/BWX+	EoN AP.5 Olympia 2B (Built from spares)	101		2.66	P.Kent	Seighford	5.99
1308/BXC+	EoN AP.10 460 Srs.1	EoN/S/006		4.66	D.D.Copeland "781"	Dunstable	4.96*
1310/BXE+	Slingsby T.51 Dart 15R	1509		5.66	M.P.Holburn	Currock Hill	5.97*
1312/BXG	Slingsby T.51 Dart 17R	1512		5.66	B.W.Compton "686"	Usk	3.00
1313/BXH+	Slingsby T.51 Dart 17R	1516		6.66	B.Crow	Usk	2.00
1315/BXK	Slingsby T.21B	1510		6.66	Not known (Damaged Falgunzeon 18.5.80; stored 10.93)	Rufforth	*
1316/BXL	Slingsby T.51 Dart 17R	1517		6.66	W.R.Longstaff & Ptnr "121"	Feshiebridge	5.98
1317/BXM	Slingsby T.51 Dart 17R	1521		7.66	C.A.P.Ellis "9"	Ridgewell	7.98
1319/BXP+	Slingsby T.45 Swallow 2	1522		7.66	Carlton Moor GC	Carlton Moor	4.00
1321/BXR	LET L-13 Blanik	173301	G-ATPX	5.66	Not known (Stored 7.98)	Cranfield	12.92*
1323/BXT+	Schleicher Ka6CR	6492		4.66	J.& A.Briggs	Tibenham	3.00
1325/BXV	LET L-13 Blanik	173304	G-ATRA	5.66	Blanik Syndicate (As "G-ATRA")	Husbands Bosworth	4.00
1326/BXW+	LET L-13 Blanik	173305	G-ATRB	6.66	K A Hale	Bidford	6.00
1328/BXY+	EoN AP.10 460 Srs.1	EoN/S/042		6.66	G.K.Stanford	Brent Tor	8.00
1330/BYA+	Slingsby T.51 Dart 17R	1518		7.66	J.A.Thomson & D.Archer	Easterton	1.00
1331/BYB+	Slingsby T.45 Swallow	1525		7.66	Surrey Hills GC "352"	Kenley	7.97*
1332/BYC+	Slingsby T.51 Dart 17R	1526		8.66	G.Woodman	Sandhill Farm, Shrivenham	4.00
1334/BYE+	EoN AP.10 463 Srs.1	EoN/S/044		9.66	C.Bushell	Long Mynd	3.00
1336/BYG	Slingsby T.51 Dart 17R	1535	RAFGSA BGA.1336	11.66	W.T.Emery "225"	Rufforth	6.00
1338/BYJ	Slingsby T.45 Swallow	1568		2.67	D.I.Johnstone t/a Swallow Soaring Group	Strathaven	11.96*
1339/BYK+	Slingsby T.45 Swallow	1566		1.67	G.E.Williams	Seighford	7.00
1340/BYL+	Schleicher Ka6CR	6517		7.66	J.P.Bedingfield	Lleweni Parc	9.00
1341/BYM+	Schleicher Ka6CR	6518	RAFGSA.381 BGA.1341	7.66	K.S.Smith	Rattlesden	9.00
1348/BYU	Schleicher Ka6CR	6525	XW640 BGA.1348	9.66	M.K.Collingham Syndicate "350"	Dunstable	8.99
1351/BYX	Schleicher Ka6E	4055		12.66	J.Dent & D.B.Andrews	Chipping	2.00
1352/BYY	Slingsby T.21B	628	RAFGSA.338 BGA.1352/WB967	11.66	Not known (Under rebuild 11.99)	RAF Bicester	
1354/BZA+	Slingsby T.21B	1162	RAFGSA.318 XN183	11.66	A Hill	Wattisham	10.99
1355/BZB+	EoN AP.10 460 Srs.1	EoN/S/047		10.66	D.C.Ratcliffe Syndicate	Parham Park	5.00
1356/BZC+	Slingsby T.51 Dart 17R	1563		2.67	A.N.Ely	Strubby	6.00
1359/BZF	Slingsby T.51 Dart 17R	1570		3.67	P.C.Gill & Ptnrs "311"	Ridgewell	9.00
1360/BZG	Slingsby T.49B Capstan	1581	(RNGSA.N54)	4.67	Culdrose GC	Culdrose	4.00
1361/BZH	Slingsby T.51 Dart 17R	1580		4.67	C.Long "406"	Bidford	7.97*
1362/BZJ	Slingsby T.51 Dart 17R	1567		4.67	D.M.Steed "Anastasia" "362"	Enstone	8.98
1364/BZL+	Slingsby T.45 Swallow	1596		7.67	Cairngorm Swallow Syndicate	Feshiebridge	8.00
1365/BZM	Slingsby T.45 Swallow	1597		7.67	F.Webster	Arbroath	5.97*
1367/BZP	SZD-24-4A Foka 4	W-301		1.67	I.K.Mitchell "F4"	Halesland	3.97*
1368/BZQ	Schleicher Ka6CR	6551		2.67	A.Holland "453"	North Hill	8.99
1369/BZR+	EoN AP.10 460 Srs.1	EoN/S/049		2.67	G.Wardell "471"	Camphill	10.00
1370/BZS+	EoN AP.10 460 Srs.1	EoN/S/052		2.67	R.Hutchinson	Carlton Moor	4.97*
1373/BZV+	EoN AP.10 460 Srs.1	EoN/S/046		2.67	I.Smith	Lasham	6.00
1374/BZW	EoN AP.10 460 Srs.1	EoN/S/053		3.67	J.Bradley & Ptnrs "Z11"	Lleweni Parc	4.97*
1375/BZX+	Schleicher Ka6CR	6571		3.67	Leeds University GC	Rufforth	7.99
1376/BZY	Slingsby T.31B (Rebuild of BGA.1175)	SSK/FF1817	BGA.1175	3.67	A.L.Higgins t/a The Blue Brick Syndicate	Cranfield	7.00
1377/BZZ	SZD-24-4A Foka 4	W-308		3.67	M.Hudson & Ptnrs "77"	Booker	4.00
1379/CAB+	EoN AP.10 460 Srs.1	EoN/S/033	RAFGSA.344	3.67	P.Green & Ptnr	Pershore	10.98
1380/CAC	Schleicher Ka6E	4054		3.67	L.I.Rigby "994"	Crowland	2.00
1381/CAE	Schleicher Ka6E	4076		4.67	P.P.Brightman & G D A.Green "5"	Dunstable	5.00
1382/CAF	EoN AP.5 Olympia 2B	EoN/O/131	RAFGSA.254	4.67	G.D.Griffiths	Brent Tor	2.00
1383/CAG	Schleicher Ka6E	4080		4.67	S.Beaumont "715"	Crowland	6.00

BGA No/Code	Type	C/n	P/I	Date	Owner/operator	Probable Base	CA Expy
1386/CAK	EoN AP.5 Olympia 2B	EoN/O/122	RAFGSA.246	3.67	P.Hatfield	Rufforth	4.00
					t/a Olympia 2B Syndicate "117"		
1389/CAN+	EoN AP.10 460 Srs.1	EoN/S/050		3.67	R.Russon	Snitterfield	2.97*
1391/CAQ	Schempp-Hirth SHK	37		3.67	M.A.Thorne "812"	Old Sarum	5.00
1392/CAR	Schempp-Hirth SHK-1	40		4.67	P.Gentil & M.Gresty	Aston Down	3.00
					"422"		
1393/CAS	Schleicher Ka6E	4029	RAFGSA.372	5.67	R.F.Tindall "372" Gransden Lodge		1.95*
1394/CAT+	EoN AP.10 460 Srs.1	EoN/S/051		5.67	A.Jackson & Ptnrs		
						Sackville Farm, Riseley	4.97*
1396/CAV+	Schleicher ASK13	13015		5.67	M.Cuming	Edgehill	8.00
1397/CAW	LET L-13 Blanik	173202	RAFGSA.357	5.67	Not known	Enstone	2.83*
			G-ASZK		"357" (Stored - spares use 6.96)		
1398/CAX+	Slingsby T.45 Swallow	1598		7.67	R.B Armitage	Waldershare Park	5.00
1400/CAZ	Slingsby T.51 Dart 17WR	1611		7.68	J.M.Young & Ptnrs "702"Easterton		5.98
1401/CBA	Slingsby T.51 Dart 17WR	1612		7.68	D.Bennett & P.H.Pickett		
					"679"	Snitterfield	4.00
1410/CBK	Grunau Baby III	-	RAFGSA.378	9.68	N.H.Ponsford	Breighton	4.83*
	(Built Sfg. Schaffin)		D-4676		(Op Real Aeroplane Club) (Stored 1.98)		
1412/CBM	Schleicher Ka6CR	6607		7.67	R.H.Moss "343"	Nympsfield	11.99
1413/CBN+	SZD-30 Pirat	W-320		5.67	B.C.Cooper	Burn	4.00
1414/CBP+	SZD-24C Foka	W-198	OY-BXR	7.67	G.Sutton	Sutton Bank	4.00
1416/CBR+	Aeromere M.100S	044		7.67	K.George & Ptnrs	Wormingford	4.97*
1417/CBS	EoN AP.5 Olympia 2B	EoN/O/143	RAFGSA.291	7.67	G.Moden & Ptnrs	Edgehill	9.94*
	(Possibly kit-built) (Cn incorrect as '143 was BGA.1034 & sold Zambia) (Stored 6.95)						
1419/CBU	Schempp-Hirth SHK-1	53	D-8441	10.67	M.Dodd "905"	Shobdon	12.99
1420/CBV	EoN AP.10 460 Srs.1	EoN/S/055		6.67	J.Sharples & Ptnr "362"	Burn	10.96*
1421/CBW+	Schleicher ASK13	13034		8.67	Stratford-upon-Avon GC		
						Snitterfield	2.00
1423/CBY+	Schleicher Ka6CR	960	RAFGSA.322	10.67	G.Martin	Talgarth	6.00
			D-3222				
1425/CCA+	Schleicher Ka6E	4126		10.67	R.K.Forrest	Nympsfield	3.00
1426/CCB+	Schempp-Hirth SHK-1	52		7.67	R.M.Johnson	Milfield	7.00
1427/CCC	Schleicher ASK13	13035	RAFGSA.R83	11.67	RAFGSA Centre	Bicester	6.00
			BGA.1427				
1428/CCD	Schleicher Ka6E	4127		12.67	M.H.Phelps "373"	H.Bosworth	4.00
1429/CCE+	Schleicher ASK13	13047		12.67	Oxford GC	Weston-on-the-Green	3.00
1430/CCF+	Schleicher ASK13	13042		12.67	Norfolk GC	Tibenham	2.00
1431/CCG+	Schleicher Ka6E	4125		12.67	G.A.Fudge	Kenley	3.00
1433/CCJ	Schleicher Ka6CR	6145	RAFGSA.323	10.67	P.Green "878"Weston-on-the-Green		4.99
1435/CCL	Schleicher Ka6E	4129		3.68	M.T.Stanley "47"	Sutton Bank	1.00
1436/CCM+	Schleicher ASK13	13053		2.68	Burn GC	Burn	4.00
1437/CCN+	SZD-9 bis Bocian 1E	P-431		3.68	South London Gliding Centre		
						Kenley	4.00
1438/CCP	Schleicher ASK13	13052		2.68	DRA GC "L99"	Odiham	2.00
1440/CCR+	Schleicher Ka6E	4149		2.68	A E Burgess	Enstone	9.00
1441/CCS+	Slingsby T.41 Skylark 2	1008	PH-230	3.68	S.L.Benn	Cranfield	10.97*
1442/CCT+	Schleicher ASK13	13057		3.68	Stratford-upon-Avon GC		
						Snitterfield	1.00
1443/CCU	Schleicher Ka6E	4122		3.68	D.C.Findlay	Keevil	2.00
1444/CCV	Schleicher Ka6E	4160		3.68	C.J.Nicholas	Ridgewell	6.00
1445/CCW+	Schleicher ASK13	13051		3.68	J E.Hart & Ptnrs	Sutton Bank	2.00
1446/CCX+	Schleicher ASK13	13054		3.68	Trent Valley GC		
						Kirton-in-Lindsey	3.00
1447/CCY+	Schleicher ASK13	13050		3.68	D.Woolf & Ptnrs	Long Mynd	4.00
1448/CCZ+	Schleicher ASK13	13070		3.68	Trent Valley GC		
						Kirton-in-Lindsey	7.00
1449/CDA+	Schleicher Ka6E	4136		3.68	F.Bick & Ptnrs	Aboyne	3.00
1450/CDB+	Schleicher Ka6E	4137		3.68	K.L.Holburn	Currock Hill	6.00
1451/CDC+	Schleicher K8B	8743		3.68	Enstone Eagle GC	Enstone	3.99
1452/CDD	Schleicher Ka6E	4165		3.68	D.T.Staff	Booker	3.99
1454/CDF	Schleicher Ka6E	4162		3.68	J.Reid & Ptnrs "683"	Upavon	4.97*
1455/CDG+	FFA Diamant 18	35		3.68	J.A.Luck	Cranfield	6.00
1456/CDH	Schempp-Hirth HS.2 Cirrus	10		4.68	A.A.Jenkins "619"	Enstone	1.00
1457/CDJ+	Schleicher ASK13	13077		4.68	Southdown GC	Parham Park	5.00
1458/CDK+	Schleicher K8B	8747		5.68	Burn GC	Burn	9.00
1464/CDR+	Scheibe Bergfalke III	5625		8.68	N.M Neil Hinton-in-the-Hedges		4.00
1468/CDV+	Schleicher Ka6E	4159		5.68	Not known	Cranfield	4.87*
					(Wreck stored 7.97)		
1469/CDW+	FFA Diamant 18	033		8.68	J.McIver	Falgunzeon	12.99
1470/CDX	SZD-30 Pirat	W-392		5.68	S.Cynalski "303"	Rufforth	6.00
1472/CDZ+	Schleicher Ka6E	4177		5.68	J R Minnis	North Weald	11.00

BGA No/Code	Type	C/n	P/I	Date	Owner/operator	Probable Base	CA Expy
1473/CEA+	Schempp-Hirth HS.2 Cirrus	21	XZ405 BGA.1473/D-8437	8.68	M.Whitton	Long Mynd	4.00
1474/CEB+	SZD-9 bis Bocian 1E	P-433		5.68	Bath, Wilts & N.Dorset GC Kingston Deverill		6.00
1475/CEC	Schempp-Hirth HS.2 Cirrus	22		7.68	C.R.Ellis "782"	Long Mynd	12.99
1476/CED	Schleicher Ka6E	4196		6.68	H.G.Williams & Ptnrs "18"	Snitterfield	3.00
1479/CEG	Schleicher Ka6E	4203		6.68	J.C.Boley	Halesland	3.96*
1480/CEH+	Wassmer WA.22 Super Javelot	68	F-OTAN-C6 F-CCLU	7.68	E.Hill & Ptnrs	Camphill	4.00
1481/CEJ+	Schleicher ASK13	13102		8.68	Devon & Somerset GC	North Hill	4.00
1482/CEK	Slingsby T.21B (T) (Robin EC34PM s/n 82-00676)	1151	RAFGSA.369	7.68	D.Woolerton	East Kirkby	11.99
1483/CEL	Schleicher Ka6E	4174		8.68	Essex & Suffolk GC "JD"	Wormingford	7.00
1484/CEM+	Schleicher Ka6E	4212		8.68	V D Long	Tibenham	7.00
1485/CEN+	SZD-30 Pirat	W-393	SP-2520	7.68	A.Bogan	Kirton-in-Lindsey	2.99
1487/CEQ	Schleicher Ka6E	4230		8.68	C.L.Lagden & Ptnrs "458"	Ridgewell	7.00
1492/CEV	Scheibe Bergfalke II	184	???	8.68	A.Lewis (Stored 10.96)Jurby, IoM		12.93*
1493/CEW+	Schleicher Ka6E	4209		8.68	J.W.Richardson "177"	Dunstable	5.00
1494/CEX+	Schleicher ASK13	13108		9.68	Newcastle & Teesside GC Carlton Moor		11.00
1495/CEY+	Schleicher Ka6E	4222		8.68	S.N.Longland & Ptnrs Gransden Lodge		3.00
1497/CFA+	Schleicher ASK13	3113		10.68	Booker GC	Booker	3.00
1498/CFB	Schleicher ASK13	13110		10.68	Not known (Crashed Ashbourne 7.10.79: wrecked)	Burn	*
1499/CFC+	Schleicher Ka7 Rhonadler	470	RAFGSA.387 F-OTAN-C1	11.68	J H Mare	Edgehill	9.99
1500/CFD	LET L-13 Blanik	173214	G-ATCG	10.68	M D White "B1"	Burn	2.00
1502/CFF+	Schleicher K8B	8765		10.68	Norfolk GC	Tibenham	4.00
1503/CFG+	Schleicher ASK13	13115		10.68	Soaring Service	Seighford	2.00
1506/CFK+	Schempp-Hirth HS.2 Cirrus	38		11.68	C.V Webb & Ptnrs	Sleap	11.99
1507/CFL+	Schleicher Ka6E	4215		10.68	Bath, Wilts & N.Dorset GC Kingston Deverill		6.00
1508/CFM+	Schleicher ASK13	13121		12.68	Vale of White Horse GC Sandhill Farm, Shrivenham		5.00
1513/CFS+	Glasflugel H.201 Standard Libelle	83		4.70	J.L.H.Pegman "271"	Currock Hill	5.00
1514/CFT	Slingsby T.59A Kestrel 17	1729		3.73	J.A.Kane "62"	Carlton Moor	4.00
1518/CFX+	Glasflugel H.201 Standard Libelle	274		2.72	A.R Head & Ptnrs	Gransden Lodge	3.00
1519/CFY+	Glasflugel H.201 Standard Libelle	270		3.72	C.W.Stevens "862"	Camphill	3.00
1522/CGB+	Schleicher Ka6E	4247		12.68	M.S Colebrook & Ptnrs	Bembridge	3.00
1524/CGD	Schleicher Ka6E	4202		1.69	I F Smith "418"	Lasham	9.00
1525/CGE	Schleicher Ka6E	4246		1.69	R.J.Brown	Bellarena	4.00
1528/CGH	Schleicher K8B	8772		2.69	Surrey & Hants GC "153"	Lasham	2.00
1529/CGJ+	Schleicher K8B	8773		2.69	Nene Valley GC	Upwood	3.00
1530/CGK	Schleicher Ka6E	4261		3.69	J.A.F.Barnes & Ptnrs "124"	Wormingford	8.00
1532/CGM+	FFA Diamant 18	053		5.69	M.C.Ogglesby Hinton-in-The Hedges		3.00
1533/CGN	Schleicher Ka6E	4173		3.69	K.R Brown & Ptnr "309"	Nympsfield	9.99
1535/CGQ+	Schleicher ASK13	13153		4.69	Oxford GC	Weston-on-the-Green	2.00
1536/CGR	Schleicher ASK13	13142		3.69	Bristol & Glos GC	Nympsfield	12.96*
					"913" (Damaged nr Nympsfield 2.6.96)		
1537/CGS+	FFA Diamant 18	055		7.69	C.J.Wimbury	Ringmer	3.00
1538/CGT	Schempp-Hirth SHK-1	38	D-1966	4.69	G.Jones & B.W.Svenson "449"	Pocklington	1.00
1539/CGU+	EoN AP.5 Olympia 2B	EoN/O/115	RAFGSA.228	4.69	M.Skinner & Ptnrs	Pocklington	8.97*
1540/CGV+	PIK-16C Vasama	48		4.69	D.J.Osborne & Ptnrs	Currock Hill	7.00
1542/CGX+	Bolkow Phoebus C	869		4.69	W.N.Smith & Ptnrs Sackville Farm, Riseley		5.00
1543/CGY	Schempp-Hirth HS.2 Cirrus	51		4.69	R.Munday & Ptnrs "337"	Eaglescott	5.00
1544/CGZ+	Schempp-Hirth SHK	39		5.69	M.C.Ridger	Saltby	1.00
1546/CHB	Schleicher Ka6E	4235		5.69	D.J.Jones	Weston-on-the-Green	4.00
					"577"		
1547/CHC	Bolkow Phoebus C	858		5.69	D.Garner Syndicate	Rhigos	9.00
1549/CHE+	Slingsby T.41 Skylark 2 (Built Doncaster Sailplane Services)	DSS.002		6.69	M.S.Howey	Burn	3.00

BGA No/Code	Type	C/n	P/I	Date	Owner/operator	Probable Base	CA Expy
1550/CHF+	SZD-9 bis Bocian 1E	P-432		5.69	T.J.Wilkinson		
			(Damaged Sackville 27. 8.95)			Sackville Farm, Riseley	8.96*
1551/CHG	SZD-30 Pirat	B-294		6.69	Culdrose GC (RNGSA.N52) Culdrose		3.00
1553/CHJ	Bolkow Phoebus 17C	879		6.69	D.C.Austin	Sutton Bank	2.00
1554/CHK	EoN AP.5 Olympia 2B	NK	RAFGSA	6.69	Oly Gliding Syndicate Halesland		4.00
1555/CHL+	SZD-30 Pirat	B-295		6.69	W.Sage & Syndicate	Rufforth	2.00
1559/CHQ	Slingsby T.31B	1186	XN247	6.69	N.H.Ponsford	(Selby)	7.82*
					(Stored 1.98)		
1562/CHT	Schleicher ASW15	15013		8.69	J.N.Kelly & Ptnrs "846" Lasham		5.00
1563/CHU+	Schleicher K8B	8794		8.69	H B Chambers	Easterton	3.00
					(Highland GC Syndicate)		
1565/CHW+	Schleicher ASK13	13187		8.69	Dorset GC	Gallows Hill	3.00
1567/CHY+	Slingsby T.45 Swallow	RG.103		9.69	J.L.H.Pegman & Ptnrs		
	(Built R.Greenslade from kit)					Currock Hill	7.00
1568/CHZ	Schleicher Ka6E	4153	N6916	9.69	M.Uphill "357"	Usk	5.99
1570/CJB	Bolkow Phoebus C	919		12.69	T.J.Wilkinson		
					"764" Sackville Farm, Riseley		6.00
1571/CJC	Ginn-Lesniak Kestrel	1		10.69	P.G.Fairness & K Burns		
						Strathaven	10.00
1572/CJD	Schleicher ASK13	13182		10.69	Shenington GC "S14" Edgehill		1.00
1574/CJF	Schleicher K8B	8803		11.69	Surrey & Hants GC "474" Lasham		2.00
1575/CJG+	Wassmer WA.21 Javelot II	38	F-OTAN-C4	1.70	R S Hanslip	Burn	4.00
			F-CCEZ				
1577/CJJ+	Bolkow Phoebus C	913		1.70	P Maddocks	Falgunzeon	8.99
1578/CJK+	Schempp-Hirth SHK	35	RAFGSA.25	2.70	R.H.Short	Lyveden	8.00
1579/CJL	Schempp-Hirth SHK-1	42	OO-ZLG	2.70	M.F.Brook "222"	Camphill	3.00
1580/CJM+	Schleicher K8B	8814		3.70	Surrey & Hants GC	Lasham	3.00
1581/CJN	Schempp-Hirth SHK-1	55		3.70	G.Kench	Dunstable	10.99
1582/CJP+	Schleicher ASW15	15041		3.70	C.Pain	Cranfield	2.00
1584/CJR	Schempp-Hirth HS.2 Cirrus	87		3.70	J.H.Stanley "83"	Lasham	3.00
1591/CJY+	Schleicher Ka6CR	555	(RAFGSA)	4.70	Bristol & Glos GC	Nympsfield	1.00
1595/CKC+	Bolkow Phoebus C	936	(BGA.1590)	4.70	S.J.Bennett	Bidford	10.00
1596/CKD+	SZD-30 Pirat	B-327		4.70	P.H.Turner	Gamston	4.98
1598/CKF	Glasflugel H.201 Standard Libelle	101		4.70	S.M.Turner "961"	Crowland	7.00
	(Note BGA.3371 also wears "CKF" being the owner's initials)						
1601/CKJ	Slingsby T.30B Prefect	740	PH-197	4.71	Not known (Stored) Crosshill		4.90*
1603/CKL+	Schleicher Ka6E	4336		4.70	I.Lowes & Ptnrs	Milfield	7.00
1605/CKN+	SZD-9 bis Bocian 1E	P-496		5.70	Strubby GC "Enola Gay" Strubby		1.00
1606/CKP+	Schleicher ASW15	15058		7.70	M.G.Shaw & Ptnrs	Portmoak	10.00
1608/CKR+	Schleicher ASK13	13247		7.70	Essex GC	North Weald	1.00
1611/CKU+	Schleicher ASK13	13243		8.70	Essex GC	North Weald	5.00
1612/CKV+	Schleicher ASK13	13253		8.70	Black Mountain GC	Talgarth	7.00
1613/CKW+	Schleicher K8B	8836		9.70	D.R Crompton	Bidford	6.98
1615/CKY	Glasflugel H.201 Standard Libelle	139		8.70	P G Mullis "743"	Snitterfield	4.00
1616/CKZ	Schempp-Hirth HS.4 Standard Cirrus	52	RAFGSA	8.70	M.E.Kingston	Dunstable	5.00
			BGA.1616		"724"		
1617/CLA+	Schempp-Hirth HS.4 Standard Cirrus	63		11.70	J.A.Wight & D.Dye	Nympsfield	11.00
1622/CLF+	Schleicher Ka7 Rhonadler	931	D-5062	1.71	P.Morgan & Ptnrs	Tibenham	10.00
1623/CLG+	Schempp-Hirth SHK-1	36	RAFGSA.27	1.71	J.E.Kenny	Bembridge	4.00
1624/CLH	Schempp-Hirth HS.4 Standard Cirrus	77			P.C.Bray & Ptnrs "252"Nympsfield		1.00
1625/CLJ	EoN AP.7 Primary	EoN/P/035	WP267	2.71	Not known	Bicester	2.72*
					(Stored 8.99)		
1626/CLK+	Schleicher Ka7 Rhonadler)	607	D-5714	2.71	Cornish GC	Perranporth	5.00
1628/CLM	Glasflugel H.201 Standard Libelle	178		2.71	J.N.Cochrane "535"	Lasham	2.00
1629/CLN	Glasflugel H.201 Standard Libelle	175		4.71	J.N.Wardle "142"	Lasham	5.00
1630/CLP	Glasflugel H.201B Standard Libelle	176		2.71	G.D.Sutherland "948"	Booker	3.00
1631/CLQ+	Schempp-Hirth HS.2 Cirrus	99		1.71	K.Bastenfield	Brent Tor	12.00
1632/CLR	Glasflugel H.201B Standard Libelle	173		4.71	D G.Shepherd "284"	Aboyne	6.00
1634/CLT	Schleicher Ka7 Rhonadler	251	D-5529	4.71	R.Spencer	Rhigos	10.99
					t/a The Syndicate		
1636/CLV+	Glasflugel H.201 Standard Libelle	180		3.71	G.B.Monslow	Bidford	5.00
1637/CLW	Glasflugel H.201 Standard Libelle	174		3.71	N.A.Dean & Ptnrs		
	(C/n plate shows "201.779")				"937" Kirton-in-Lindsey		8.00
1638/CLX+	Schleicher K8B	8851		3.71	Midland GC	Long Mynd	12.99
1639/CLY	Hirth Go.III Minimoa	378	PH-390	3.72	Not known	Dunstable	1.79*
			D-5076		(On rebuild 12.95)		
1640/CLZ	Schleicher Ka6E	4056	AGA.2	4.71	H.N.Craven "799"	Pocklington	6.00
1646/CMF+	SZD-32A Foka 5	W-534		7.71	D J Linford	Lasham	4.00
1647/CMG+	Schleicher Ka7 Rhonadler	462	D-8116	7.71	P.M.Williams "Fledermaus" Lasham		2.00
1648/CMH	Glasflugel H.201B Standard Libelle	224		7.71	D.N Greig "165"	North Hill	3.00
1650/CMK+	Schleicher ASK13	13305		8.71	South Wales GC	Usk	12.99

BGA No/Code	Type	C/n	P/I	Date	Owner/operator	Probable Base	CA Expy
1651/CML+	Schleicher K8B	8862		8.71	Vectis GC	Bembridge	3.00
1653/CMN+	Schleicher K8B	8870		8.71	Bristol & Glos GC	Nympsfield	4.00
1655/CMQ	Glasflugel H.201 Standard Libelle	233		8.71	P.Winter & Ptnrs "986"	Ridgewell	4.00
1656/CMR+	Glasflugel H.201 Standard Libelle	225		8.71	J.A.Dandie & Ptnrs	Portmoak	8.00
1657/CMS	Glasflugel H.201 Standard Libelle	234		8.71	D.Manser & Ptnrs "602"	Challock	4.00
1660/CMV	Glasflugel H.201 Standard Libelle	235		8.71	S.E.Evans & Ptnrs "184"	Enstone	4.00
1661/CMW+	Glasflugel H.201B Standard Libelle	242		9.71	A M Dalton	Dunstable	2.00
1662/CMX	Glasflugel H.201 Standard Libelle	232		9.71	W D Johnson "226"	Burn	4.00
1663/(CMY)	Grunau Baby IIIC (Built LSV Fussen)	1	RAFGSA.373 D-1090	1.72	Not known Manor Farm, Glatton (Stored for rebuild 7.95)		*
1664/CMZ+	Schleicher Ka7 Rhonadler	323	D-5589	6.72	Cornish GC	Perranporth	4.00
1668/CND	SZD-9 bis Bocian 1E	P-428	RAFGSA.392	1.72	Angus GC "628"	Drumshade	2.00
1669/CNE	Glasflugel H.201 Standard Libelle	266		1.72	E.T.Melville "525"	Portmoak	11.00
1670/CNF	Glasflugel H.201B Standard Libelle	271		1.72	D.F.Mazingham "709"	Pocklington	4.00
1671/CNG	Glasflugel H.201 Standard Libelle	265		2.72	C.F.Smith & Ptnr "622"	Nympsfield	11.00
1672/CNH	Glasflugel H.201 Standard Libelle	269		2.72	A.D'Otreppe "442"	Lasham	7.00
1673/CNJ+	Glasflugel H.201 Standard Libelle	272		2.72	R.E.Gretton	Crowland	7.00
1674/CNK+	SZD-30 Pirat	B-459		3.72	H.Forshaw & Ptnrs	Rufforth	7.00
1676/CNM+	SZD-9 bis Bocian 1E	P-551		2.72	M.Williamson & Ptnrs	Crowland	5.00
1677/CNN+	Schempp-Hirth HS.4 Standard Cirrus	173		2.72	R.W.Asplin	Camphill	4.00
1678/CNP+	Glasflugel H.201 Standard Libelle	264		3.72	S. & J.McKenzie	Camphill	7.00
1683/CNV	Slingsby T.59F Kestrel 19	1790		6.72	P.H.Fanshawe & E.A.Smith "229"	Snitterfield	2.00
1684/CNW	Slingsby T.59F Kestrel 19	1791		7.72	A.R.Jones "625"	Camphill	2.00
1685/CNX	Slingsby T.59F Kestrel 20	1792		7.72	D.Starer "818"	Dunstable	1.00
1686/CNY	Glasflugel H.201 Standard Libelle	322		9.72	S.B.Marshall & Ptnrs "151"	Portmoak	8.00
1688/CPA	Glasflugel H.201B Standard Libelle	328		9.72	A.T.Hirst & S.Pugh "466"	Booker	4.00
1689/CPB	Slingsby T.59D Kestrel 19	1796		10.72	D.Heslop "885"	North Weald	8.00
1690/CPC+	SZD-32A Foka 5	W-546		3.72	J.Davidson (As "DAL")	Enstone	5.00
1691/CPD	Schleicher ASW17	17026		3.74	E.F.Allsop "292"	Long Mynd	4.00
1692/CPE+	EoN AP.5 Olympia 2B	EoN/0/120	RAFGSA.233	3.72	Not known (W/O Arbroath 10. 9.94; stored 5.97)	Edgehill	8.95*
1693/CPF	Glasflugel H.201 Standard Libelle	267		3.72	J.M.Norman & P.Elvidge "T15"	Pocklington	3.00
1694/CPG+	Schleicher Ka7 Rhonadler	7036	D-4029	4.72	Queens University GC	Bellarena	10.00
1696/CPJ	Schleicher Ka6E	4059	OO-ZDA	4.72	J.Herd & Ptnrs "521"	Pocklington	3.00
1699/CPM+	Glasflugel H.201 Standard Libelle	179		4.72	D.J.Gilder	Aston Down	3.99
1706/CPU	Schempp-Hirth HS.4 Standard Cirrus	194		4.72	J P J.Ketelaar "761"	Feshiebridge	11.99
1707/CPV+	SZD-30 Pirat	B-470		3.72	D.Hale & Ptnrs	Bidford	2.98
1709/CPX+	SZD-30 Pirat	B-460		4.72	J.Murphy	Usk	5.00
1714/CQC	SZD-30 Pirat	B-472		4.72	P.R.Tavener & Ptnrs "601"	Tibenham	7.99
1715/CQD+	Schleicher K8B	419/58	D-5625	4.72	Burn GC	Burn	6.99
1718/CQG+	EoN AP.5 Olympia 2B	EoN/0/044	RAFGSA.206 BGA.542	4.72	L.McKenzie	Sutton Bank	2.00
1720/CQJ	Slingsby T.59A Kestrel 17	1727		5.72	A.Shelton "17K"	Portmoak	7.00
1722/CQL	Schempp-Hirth HS.5 Nimbus 2	11		5.72	M N Erlund "339"	East Kirkby	2.00
1723/CQM	Slingsby T.59F Kestrel 19	1765		5.72	J.A.Knowles "234"	Odiham	5.00
1724/CQN+	Schempp-Hirth HS.4 Standard Cirrus	204G		5.72	M.G.Sankey & Ptnrs	Lasham	3.00
1725/CQP	Schempp-Hirth HS.5 Nimbus 2	4		4.72	D.Caunt & Ptnrs "918"	Booker	1.00
1726/CQQ	Schempp-Hirth HS.5 Nimbus 2	5		4.72	G.L.Barrett "139"	Bidford	8.00
1727/CQR	Schempp-Hirth HS.4 Standard Cirrus	220G		5.72	G.W.Burge & R.N.Kill "703" Sandhill Farm, Shrivenham		7.00
1729/CQT+	Schleicher Ka7 Rhonadler	603	D-5712	6.72	Shenington GC (Stored Kemble 7.97)	Edgehill	7.96*
1732/CQW	SZD-36A Cobra 15	W-572		6.72	C.R.H.Partington "342"	Carlton Moor	7.00
1733/CQX	SZD-30 Pirat	B-483		6.72	The "B" Syndicate "789"	Lleweni Parc	4.00
1734/CQY	Schempp-Hirth HS.4 Standard Cirrus	214		6.72	S.R.Blackmore "D49"	Edgehill	3.00
1736/CRA+	Schleicher Ka7 Rhonadler	7009	???	7.72	Welland GC	Lyveden	5.00
1737/CRB	Glasflugel H.201 Standard Libelle	243		6.72	A.I.Mawer "241"	Winthorpe	5.00
1739/CRD	SZD-36A Cobra 15	W-578		7.72	J.Durman	Pocklington	6.94*
1741/CRF	Birmingham Guild BG-135	001		2.72	C D Stevens "351"	Lee-on-Solent	5.00
1743/CRH	Schempp-Hirth HS.4 Standard Cirrus	233G		8.72	E MacDonald "650"	Portmoak	4.00
1745/CRK	Slingsby T.8 Tutor	930	XE760 VM539	7.72	I.D.Smith (Stored 7.99)	Nympsfield	8.82*
1746/CRL+	Schleicher ASK13	13013	???	8.72	Midland GC	Long Mynd	2.00

BGA No/Code	Type	C/n	P/I	Date	Owner/operator	Probable Base	CA Expy
1747/CRM	Grunau Baby III	1	RAFGSA.361 D-8061	7.72	R.Wasey & Ptnrs "Grumpy"	Sandown	11.96*
1748/CRN	Schempp-Hirth HS.4 Standard Cirrus	234G		8.72	M.G.Woollard "566"	Aston Down	3.00
1750/CRQ+	Glasflugel H.201B Standard Libelle	326		7.72	K.Counsell & Ptnrs	Usk	4.00
1752/CRS	Glasflugel H.201B Standard Libelle	325		8.72	J.E.F.Porter & Ptnrs "707"Booker		7.00
1753/CRT+	Schleicher ASK13	13396		8.72	Bowland Forest GC	Chipping	3.00
1755/CRV+	Glasflugel H.201B Standard Libelle	329		8.72	P.Arthur & Ptnr	Perranporth	5.00
1756/CRW	Glasflugel H.201 Standard Libelle	324		9.72	M.Buick "417"	Nympsfield	3.00
1759/CRZ	Slingsby T.8 Tutor	-	RAFGSA.178	10.72	Not known (Stored 9.96) Chipping		*
1760/CSA	Slingsby T.59F Kestrel 19	1797		11.72	P.L Poole "182"	Parham Park	6.00
1761/CSB+	Slingsby T.59F Kestrel 19	1798		11.72	N.D.Paveley	Pocklington	1.00
1763/CSD	Slingsby T.59D Kestrel 19	1800		12.72	M.J.Silver "53"	Pocklington	6.00
1765/CSF	Slingsby T.59F Kestrel 19	1802		1.73	G.R.Glazebrook "347"	Dunstable	3.00
1766/CSG	Slingsby T.59D Kestrel 19	1804		3.73	A.Swann & D.Williams	Lasham	6.99
	"217" (Mid-air collision with BGA 1943 Bidford 27.7.98)						
1768/CSJ+	Glasflugel H.201B Standard Libelle	372		1.73	B.Searle	Entone	7.00
1769/CSK	Slingsby T.59D Kestrel 20	1806		3.73	H.A. & J.E.Torode "387"(Belgium)		4.99
1770/CSL	Slingsby T.8 Tutor	928	XE758 VF181	10.72	W.D.Baars (The Netherlands)		9.00
1772/CSN	Pilatus B4 PC-11	021		12.72	M.Hine "527"	North Hill	9.00
1773/CSP+	Pilatus B4 PC-11	027		3.73	V.Howells	Chipping	3.00
1775/CSR	Glasflugel H.201 Standard Libelle	368		1.73	W.G.Miller & Ptnrs "808"	North Connel	6.99
1779/CSV	SZD-30 Pirat	B-515		12.72	P.Udell & Ptnrs	Gamston	8.98
1780/CSW+	Pilatus B4 PC-11	022		12.72	I.H.Keyser	Waldershare Park	4.00
1784/CTA+	EoN AP.5 Olympia 2B	EoN/O/146	RAFGSA.285	12.72	P.N.Tolson	Wormingford	9.00
1785/CTB	Schempp-Hirth HS.4 Standard Cirrus	264G		1.73	M.J.Gibbons & Ptnrs "579"	Weston-on-the-Green	3.00
1788/CTE	Schleicher ASW17	17012		1.73	D.Edwards & S.Blackmore "40"	Lasham	2.00
1789/CTF	Schleicher Ka4 Rhonlerche	01	D-3574	1.73	M.Goodman	Winthorpe	9.98
1792/CTJ+	Slingsby T.59D Kestrel 19	1810		3.73	H.B.Walrond & Ptnrs	Rattlesden	4.00
1794/CTL+	Slingsby T.59D Kestrel 19	1812		3.73	P.Codd "116"	Wormingford	4.00
1795/CTM	Slingsby T.59D Kestrel 19	1813		3.73	A S Raffan "401"	Crowland	5.00
1796/CTN+	Slingsby T.59D Kestrel 19	1814		4.73	J.T Goodall	Sutton Bank	1.00
1797/CTP	Slingsby T.59D Kestrel 19	1815		4.73	D.C.Austin "49"	Sutton Bank	6.99
1798/CTQ	Slingsby T.59D Kestrel 20	1816		4.73	K.A.Moules "924"	Bicester	1.00
1799/CTR	Slingsby T.59D Kestrel 19	1817		5.73	D.J.Marpole "402"	Kingston Deverill	2.00
1800/CTS+	EoN AP.5 Olympia 2B	EoN/O/157	RNGSA	1.73	P.J.Thornbury Kingston Deverill		4.00
1801/CTT	Schempp-Hirth HS.4 Standard Cirrus	277G		1.73	S.M.L.Young "873"	Nympsfield	3.00
1802/CTU	Glasflugel H.201 Standard Libelle	371		2.73	J.R.Humpherson "501"	Camphill	4.00
1803/CTV	SZD-30 Pirat	B-528		2.73	B.Fantham	Rhigos	8.00
1804/CTW	SZD-9 bis Bocian 1E	P-598		2.73	Mendip GC "1"	Halesland	8.00
1805/CTX+	SZD-30 Pirat	B-527		2.73	P.Goulding	Crowland	10.00
1807/CTZ+	Schleicher K8B	8035/B5	D-KOCU	4.73	Scottish Gliding Union Ltd	Portmoak	6.00
1809/CUB+	Pilatus B4 PC-11	047		3.73	P.Noonan & D.Wardell	Enstone	6.00
1810/CUC+	Pilatus B4 PC-11	003	HB-1102	5.73	H.M.Pantin & Ptnrs	Dishforth	3.00
1811/CUD	Yorkshire Sailplanes YS-53 Sovereign	02		7.72	D R Bricknell "158"	Saltby	4.00
	(Built from Slingsby T.53B XV951 [1574] w/o 11.4.72)						
1813/CUF	Yorkshire Sailplanes YS-55 Consort	04		11.73	C.G.Taylor & Ptnrs "331"	Sutton Bank	7.00
1816/CUJ	Glasflugel H.201B Standard Libelle	370		2.73	T.G.B.Hobbis & Ptnrs "706"Lasham		3.00
1817/CUK	Glasflugel H.201 Standard Libelle	367		3.73	G.R.Brown "380"	Dunstable	4.00
1818/CUL	Schempp-Hirth HS.4 Standard Cirrus	265G		4.73	L.G.Watts "550/10"	Husbands Bosworth	7.98
1819/CUM+	SZD-30 Pirat	B-534		2.73	T.J.Mottershead	Pocklington	1.00
1821/CUQ	Pilatus B4 PC-11	040		2.73	A.E.Hayes & Ptnrs "633"	Aston Down	11.99
1822/CUS	Schempp-Hirth HS.2 Cirrus VTC	126Y		3.73	G.F.Wearing "842"	Chipping	5.00
1823/CUT	Pilatus B4 PC-11	041		3.73	N.R.Cawte	Gamston	10.95*
	(On repair 1997)						
1829/CUZ+	LET L-13 Blanik	025409		4.73	East Sussex GC	Ringmer	11.98
1830/CVA+	LET L-13 Blanik	025418		3.73	D.Wiseman	Andreas, IoM	6.00
1831/CVB+	LET L-13 Blanik	025419		3.73	Farnborough GC	Odiham	5.00
1832/CVC+	SZD-30 Pirat	B-535		3.73	J.P.Batty	Dunstable	5.00
1834/CVE	Schempp-Hirth HS.2 Cirrus VTC	127Y		3.73	I.M.Stenning "BZ	Gransden Lodge	3.00
1835/CVF+	Schempp-Hirth HS.2 Cirrus VTC	128Y		3.73	I.Hamilton	Chipping	5.00
1836/CVG	Pilatus B4 PC-11	045		3.73	I H Keyser "656"	Waldershare Park	4.99

BGA No/Code	Type	C/n	P/I	Date	Owner/operator	Probable Base	CA Expy
1837/CVH+	Schempp-Hirth SHK	34	N6524A	3.73	M.D.Smith	Parham Park	7.00
1838/CVJ+	Breguet Br.905S Fauvette	37	F-CCJH	6.73	I.Gutsall	Burn	5.00
1839/CVK	Pilatus B4 PC-11	048		3.73	T.M.Perkins "92"	Dunstable	6.99
1840/CVL	Glasflugel H.201B Standard Libelle	369		2.73	N.A.Dean "253" Kirton-in-Lindsey		3.00
1841/CVM	Pilatus B4 PC-11 (powered)	036		3.73	J.A.Mace	Old Sarum	3.00
1842/CVN	SZD-36A Cobra 15	W-608		3.73	N.Bickham "818"	Dunkeswell	9.96*
1843/CVP+	SZD-9 bis Bocian 1E	P-597		3.73	Deeside GC	Aboyne	11.99
1844/CVQ	Glasflugel H.201 Standard Libelle	374		3.73	C.J.Taunton & Ptnrs "428"	Dunstable	4.00
1845/CVR+	SZD-30 Pirat	B-538		3.73	M.Langford Weston-on-the-Green		4.00
1846/CVS+	SZD-36A Cobra 15	W-610		3.73	E.W.Room	Pocklington	6.99
1847/CVT	SZD-36A Cobra 15	W-609		3.73	J.Amor	Ridgewell	1.95*
1849/CVV+	Pilatus B4 PC-11	028		3.73	F.R.Wolff & Ptnrs	Brent Tor	12.00
1850/CVW	Slingsby T.59D Kestrel 19/22	1818		5.73	P.Hogarth "423"	Aston Down	4.00
1851/CVX	Slingsby T.59D Kestrel 19	1823		7.73	Not known "3"	Aston Down	*
	(Crashed Portmoak 6.9.80: wreck stored 7.99)						
1852/CVY	Slingsby T.59D Kestrel 19	1821		7.73	J.Ainsworth "355"	Sleap	6.98*
	(Damaged Upavon 15.6.97)						
1853/CVZ	Slingsby T.59D Kestrel 19	1824		8.73	T.R.F.Gaunt & Ptnrs "269"	Kingston Deverill	3.00
1854/CWA	Slingsby T.59D Kestrel 19	1825		9.73	D.K.Gardiner & Ptnrs "363"	Portmoak	9.00
1855/CWB+	Slingsby T.59D Kestrel 19	1833		1.74	K.Fairness	Milfield	4.00
1857/CWD	Slingsby T.59D Kestrel 19	1835		1.74	A.Kennedy & J.R.Dransfield "998"	Aboyne	2.00
1858/CWE	Glasflugel H.201 Standard Libelle	482		1.74	T.W.S.Stoker "468"	Rufforth	4.00
1859/CWF+	Slingsby T.59D Kestrel 19	1838		2.74	P.Nicholson	Thame	3.00
1860/CWG	Glasflugel H.201 Standard Libelle	391		4.73	K.H.Gregory "322"	Camphill	7.00
1861/CWH+	Schleicher ASK13	13424		4.73	York Gliding Centre	Rufforth	3.00
1862/CWJ+	Schleicher Ka7 Rhonadler	630	D-6057 D-5723	4.73	Wolds GC	Pocklington	6.00
1864/CWL	Schempp-Hirth HS.2 Cirrus VTC	125Y		4.73	J.Richardson	Chipping	1.98*
1866/CWN+	Glasflugel H.201B Standard Libelle	386		4.73	R.B.Petrie	Portmoak	2.00
1869/CWR	Schempp-Hirth HS.2 Cirrus VTC	133Y		4.73	S.T.Bonser "917"	Dunstable	8.00
1870/CWS	Schempp-Hirth HS.2 Cirrus VTC	129Y		4.73	R.W.Cassels & Ptnrs	Ridgewell	5.00
1871/CWT	Glasflugel H.201B Standard Libelle	384		4.73	C.Davison "978"	Camphill	5.00
1873/CWV	Schleicher Rhonlerche II	123	D-8226	4.73	11th Bristol (Headley Park) Scout Troop "Z" (Stored 8.99) Aston Down		5.94*
1875/CWX	Glasflugel H.201 Standard Libelle	36	RAFGSA.132	4.73	C.A.Weyman & Ptnrs Gallows Hill "832"		4.00
1876/CWY	Glasflugel H.201 Standard Libelle	387		4.73	J Dixon "146"	Drumshade	2.00
1877/CWZ+	Glasflugel H.201 Standard Libelle	392		4.73	Derby & Lancs GC	Camphill	9.00
1885/CXH+	SZD-36A Cobra 15	W-619		6.73	C D Street "544"	Lasham	9.00
1886/CXJ	SZD-36A Cobra 15	W-618		6.73	S R Bruce "791"	Portmoak	7.00
1887/CXK+	Glasflugel H.201 Standard Libelle	383		6.73	C.A Turner	Cross Hayes	11.99
1888/CXL+	SZD-30 Pirat	B-548		6.73	R.T.Page & Ptnrs	Wormingford	5.00
1889/CXM	Slingsby T.59D Kestrel 19	1820		7.73	R.P.Beck & Ptnrs "532" Dishforth		4.00
1890/CXN	Yorkshire Sailplanes YS-55 Consort	05		12.73	A.A.Priestley & Ptnrs "508"	Sutton Bank	5.99
1891/CXP	Yorkshire Sailplanes YS-55 Consort	07	BGA.1892	5.76	A.D.Coles	North Hill	10.96*
1897/CXV+	Yorkshire Sailplanes YS-53 Sovereign	03		7.74	C.Wright	Chipping	6.00
1898/CXW	Yorkshire Sailplanes YS-53 Sovereign	1654		3.74	The Tin Bird Syndicate Aboyne		7.93*
	(Wreck stored 5.94)						
1902/CYA	Pilatus B4 PC-11	072		7.73	E.J.Bromwell & Ptnrs North Hill "503"		9.00
1904/CYC+	Pilatus B4 PC-11	029	N47247	7.73	B.Gent & Ptnrs	Ringmer	4.00
	(As "N47247")						
1905/CYD+	SZD-30 Pirat	B-559		7.73	I.Johnstone	Portmoak	7.00
1908/CYG+	Glasflugel H.201 Standard Libelle	441		8.73	M.J Guard	Husbands Bosworth	2.00
1909/CYH+	Slingsby T.41 Skylark 2	995	AGA.4 BGA.801	8.73	B.J.Griffin	Kirton-in-Lindsey	8.99
1910/CYJ+	DFS/49 Grunau Baby 2B	031000	D-6021	8.73	C.Bird	Dunstable	1.90*
	(Built Petera 1943)				(Stored 12.95)		
1911/CYK	Pilatus B4 PC-11	078		8.73	A.M.Walker	Strathaven	9.00
					t/a Pilatus Soaring Syndicate "248"		
1913/CYM	Schempp-Hirth HS.4 Standard Cirrus	48	RAFGSA D-0578	9.73	L.J.Hartfield "299"	Lasham	3.00
1914/CYN	Slingsby T.59D Kestrel 19	JP.054		10.74	S.Cooke & Ptnrs Gransden Lodge "N4"		12.00
	(Built D Jones & T Pentelow)						
1915/CYP	Schempp-Hirth HS.4 Standard Cirrus	369		9.73	O.Stuart-Menteth "982" Cranfield		3.00

BGA No/Code	Type	C/n	P/I	Date	Owner/operator	Probable Base	CA Expy
1916/CYQ	Schempp-Hirth HS.4 Standard Cirrus	364		9.73	D.A.Smith & P.Dunthorne "477"	Nympsfield	2.00
1917/CYR+	LET L-13 Blanik	025610		10.73	Not known	Cranfield	12.90*
	(Damaged nr Bidford 8.7.90; rebuilt using fuselage of BGA.2958 c/n 025817; stored 7.97)						
1919/CYT+	Schempp-Hirth HS.4 Standard Cirrus	357G		9.73	R.Francis	Lleweni Parc	7.99
1925/CYZ+	Schleicher K8B	8882	RAFGSA	9.74	Oxford GC	Weston-on-the-Green	2.00
1929/CZD+	Pilatus B4 PC-11	081		12.73	G.A.Furness	Walney Island	6.00
1930/CZE+	SZD-30 Pirat	S-0114		12.73	L E Ingram	Snitterfield	4.00
1932/CZG+	SZD-30 Pirat	S-0116		12.73	I.Lang	Snitterfield	5.99
1934/CZJ+	SZD-30 Pirat	S-0115		12.73	C.L Groves & Ptnrs	Husbands Bosworth	6.00
1936/CZL	Glasflugel H.201 Standard Libelle	483		1.74	L P Woodage "504"	Dunstable	1.00
1937/CZM+	Munchen Mu-13D-III	10/52	D-1488	9.74	H.Chapple	Bicester	6.00
1938/CZN+	Schleicher ASW15B	15329		3.74	P.Tuppen & Ptnrs	Bembridge	3.00
1940/CZQ+	Slingsby T.59D Kestrel 19	1840		4.74	J.P.Walker & Ptnrs	Husbands Bosworth	5.00
1941/CZR+	Slingsby T.59D Kestrel 19	1842		4.74	R.P.Brisbourne	Rufforth	11.99
1942/CZS+	Slingsby T.59D Kestrel 22	1844		5.74	P.Glennie	Portmoak	3.97*
1943/CZT	Slingsby T.59D Kestrel 19	1848		5.74	G.W.Camp "A3"	Enstone	3.99
1944/CZU	Slingsby T.59D Kestrel 19	1849		6.74	L.Merrett & P.F.Croote	Halesland	5.00
1945/CZV	Slingsby T.59D Kestrel 19	1850		7.74	V.F.G.Tull "415"	Dunstable	6.00
1946/CZW+	Slingsby T.59D Kestrel 20	1846		10.76	C.D Berry "667"	Cranfield	5.00
1949/CZZ	Slingsby T.59D Kestrel 19	1739		6.74	R.M.Grant "900"	Lasham	11.96*
1950/DAA+	SZD-9 bis Bocian 1E	P-639		3.74	Highland GC	Easterton	6.00
1952/DAC	SZD-36A Cobra 15	W-656		3.74	C.D.Peacock	Husbands Bosworth	9.95*
1958/DAJ	Schempp-Hirth HS.5 Nimbus 2	50		3.74	J.D.Jones "14"	Nympsfield	3.00
1960/DAL+	EoN AP.6 Olympia 419	EoN/4/010	RAFGSA.301	4.74	D.M.Judd & Ptnrs	Snitterfield	9.99
1961/DAM	ICA IS-29D	27		4.74	W.T.Barnard "675"	Strathaven	9.00
1962/DAN	SZD-30 Pirat	S-0145		3.74	W.Pottinger & Ptnrs "526"	Ridgewell	4.00
1963/DAP+	SZD-30 Pirat	S-0147		4.74	N.Crawford	Currock Hill	4.00
1964/DAQ+	SZD-36A Cobra 15	W-657		4.74	C.Bigwood & Ptnrs	Lyveden	7.97*
1965/DAR+	Slingsby T.21B	NK	RAFGSA.404	6.74	Nene Valley GC	Upwood	7.00
1966/DAS+	Schempp-Hirth HS.4 Standard Cirrus	378	(BGA.1925)	4.74	A.Hobson & Ptnrs	Burn	3.00
1967/DAT+	SZD-30 Pirat	S-0149		4.74	The Borders GC (Crashed Milfield 1.8.99)	Milfield	5.00
1968/DAU+	SZD-30 Pirat	S-0150		4.74	J.Sentance	Winthorpe	3.00
1969/DAV	SZD-38A Jantar-1	B-608		4.74	R.M.Roberts "240"	Brent Tor	8.00
1970/DAW+	Schleicher Ka6CR	951	RAFGSA D-2025	6.74	R.Lapsley & B.Irwin	Bellarena	3.00
1974/DBA	EoN AP.5 Olympia 2B	EoN/O/156	RNGSA.208	6.74	W.R.Williams "207"	RAF Halton	1.98
1975/DBB+	Slingsby T.51 Dart 17R (Built Greenfly Aviation)	DG/51/01		2.76	S.D.Codd	Crowland	4.00
1976/DBC+	Pilatus B4 PC-11	135		6.74	J.H.France & Ptnrs "851"	Shobdon	12.99
1977/DBD+	SZD-30 Pirat	S-0202		6.74	E W Burgess	Cranfield	4.00
1979/DBF+	Schleicher Ka7 Rhonadler	179	RAFGSA RAFGGA.552/D-5473	6.74	Welland GC	Lyveden	2.00
1980/DBG+	ICA IS-29D	31		6.74	N.D Hughes	Lasham	5.00
1982/DBJ+	Slingsby T.59D Kestrel 19	1856	BGA.1892 BGA.1982	10.74	P L Sanderson "691"	Syerston	5.00
1983/DBK	Slingsby T.59D Kestrel 19	1861		12.74	R.E.Perry & C.Crabb "523"	North Hill	5.00
1986/DBN	Slingsby T.59D Kestrel 19	1857		3.75	A.C.Wright "617"	Sutton Bank	12.99
1987/DBP	Glasflugel H.205 Club Libelle	51		4.75	N.A.White "551"	Rattlesden	4.00
1988/DBQ	Slingsby T.59D Kestrel 19	1863		4.75	P.Ramsden "101"	Rufforth	5.00
1989/DBR	Slingsby T.59D Kestrel 19	1858		4.75	J.G.Bell "95"	Parham Park	3.00
1990/DBS+	Slingsby T.59D Kestrel 19	1864		4.75	J.W.Rice	Kirton-in-Lindsey	5.00
1991/DBT+	Schempp-Hirth Standard Austria S	35	F-CCPQ	7.74	F.J.Tucker "11"	Parham Park	8.00
1993/DBV+	SZD-30 Pirat	S-0227		8.74	M.H.Bryan & Ptnrs	Usk	11.00
1994/DBW+	SZD-9 bis Bocian 1E	P-641		8.74	Sackville GC	Sackville Farm, Riseley	4.99
1995/DBX+	SZD-9 bis Bocian 1E	P-642		8.74	Miss A.G.Veitch t/a Highland Bocian Syndicate	Easterton	11.00
1998/DCA+	SZD-36A Cobra 15	W-686		9.74	M.J.North	Husbands Bosworth	9.98
2000/DCC	Glasflugel H.201B Standard Libelle	585		11.74	J.Warbey & M.Hutchinson "324"	Shobdon	2.00
2002/DCE+	Slingsby T.41 Skylark 2	1003	RAFGGA.540 PH-225	11.74	C.P.Race	Winthorpe	7.00
2003/DCF	Schleicher Ka6CR	6520	RAFGSA.356	11.74	R.Spencer "356"	Burn	7.95*
2004/DCG	Schleicher Ka2B	2	D-7064	12.74	Not known (Stored)	Falgunzeon	*
2005/DCH+	SZD-30 Pirat	S-0315		11.74	Spilsby Soaring	Spilsby	8.96*

BGA No/Code	Type	C/n	P/I	Date	Owner/operator	Probable Base	CA Expy
2006/DCJ	SZD-30 Pirat	S-0316		11.74	N.Jones	North Hill	3.98*
					(Crashed nr North Hill 29.3.97)		
2008/DCL	LET L-13 Blanik	026154		12.74	Enstone Eagles GC	Enstone	8.92*
					(Wreck stored 6.96)		
2010/DCN	Slingsby T.21B	NK	RAFGGA.501	1.75	A.R.Worters	North Connel	7.95*
2013/DCR+	SZD-9 bis Bocian 1E	P-670		1.75	Mendip GC	Halesland	10.96*
					(Crashed Halesland 13.6.96)		
2014/DCS+	Slingsby T.45 Swallow	1538	RAFGGA.544	4.74	H.Dale & Ptnrs	Sutton Bank	6.00
2018/DCW+	Schleicher Ka6CR	1076	D-5228	2.75	Trent Valley GC		
						Kirton-in-Lindsey	7.00
2020/DCY+	Swales SD.3-15V	01		2.75	J.C.Gibson & Ptnrs	Chipping	5.97*
	(Rebuild of incomplete Yorkshire Sailplanes YS-55 Consort c/n 09)						
2021/DCZ+	King-Elliott-Street Osprey	1470		10.75	G.R.Burkert	Lasham	5.00
	(Believed to be converted Slingsby T.51 Dart but c/n conflicts with BGA.1245)						
2022/DDA+	Schempp-Hirth HS.4 Standard Cirrus 532G			2.75	M.J.Woodhead	Parham Park	3.00
2023/DDB+	Schleicher ASK13	13493		2.75	Norfolk GC	Tibenham	4.00
2024/DDC	Slingsby T.21B	1157	RAFGSA.313	3.75	J.Shaw & Ptnrs	Perranporth	6.00
2025/DDD	Schempp-Hirth HS.5 Nimbus 2	84	G-BKPM	3.75	D.D.Copeland	Dunstable	3.00
			BGA.2025		"695"		
2026/DDE+	SZD-38A Jantar-1	B-641		4.75	B.Jones	Bidford	3.98
2030/DDJ+	ICA IS-29D	37		3.75	P.Andrews	Lyveden	7.98*
	(Written-off Lyveden 8.97: to East Surrey College, Redhill as instructional airframe 10.97)						
2031/DDK	SZD-30 Pirat	S-0408	(RNGSA N13)	4.75	Portsmouth Naval GC		
						Lee-on-Solent	9.99
2032/DDL+	Schleicher K8B	218/61	D-5156	4.75	Ouse GC	Rufforth	5.00
2033/DDM	Schempp-Hirth HS.2 Cirrus VTC	164Y		3.75	C.K.Davis & Ptnrs Gransden Lodge		1.00
					"959"		
2034/DDN+	SZD-9 bis Bocian 1E	P-429	RAFGSA.393	3.75	Bath, Wilts & N.Dorset GC		
						Kingston Deverill	5.00
2037/DDR	Schempp-Hirth HS.4 Standard Cirrus 531G			3.75	J.Smith "680"	Pocklington	2.00
2038/DDS	Schleicher ASW15	15009	D-0256	4.75	C.Skeate & Ptnrs "647"	Lasham	3.00
2041/DDV	SZD-38A Jantar-1	B-664		4.75	G.V.McKirdy "536"	Edgehill	5.98*
2042/DDW+	SZD-30 Pirat	S-0433		4.75	M.Dixon & Ptnrs	Parham Park	4.00
2044/DDY+	Schleicher Ka6CR	678	D-8841	4.75	Needwood Forest GC	Cross Hayes	4.00
2047/DEB+	Slingsby T.59D Kestrel 19	1866		10.75	T.Moss "169" Weston-on-the-Green		9.98
2051/DEG+	ICA IS-28B2	48		.	P. & H.Whitehead	Sutton Bank	5.00
2057/DEN	ICA IS-29D	41		4.75	S Struthers "586"	Feshiebridge	10.99
2058/DEP+	Schleicher Ka6CR	6452	AGA...	4.75	C.Lawrence Husbands Bosworth		3.00
			BGA.2058/RAFGSA.350				
2059/DEQ	Glasflugel H.205 Club Libelle	97		4.75	J.A.Holland & Ptnrs		
					"716"	Kingston Deverill	8.98
2064/DEV+	Schleicher Ka6CR	6453	RAFGSA.354	5.75	P.J.Groves & Ptnrs	Long Mynd	5.00
2066/DEX+	LET L-13 Blanik	026348	RAFGSA.R4	6.75	N.Kelly	Talgarth	11.99
			BGA.2066				
2067/DEY+	LET L-13 Blanik	026352	RAFGSA.R12	6.75	Bath, Wilts & N.Dorset GC		
			BGA.2067			Kingston Deverill	7.00
2068/DEZ	ICA IS-29D	43		6.75	R.J.Everett "977"	Sproughton	4.91*
					(Damaged Lewknor 7.3.90: stored 12.95)		
2071/DFC	Schempp-Hirth HS.4 Standard Cirrus 592G			7.75	R.J.Marriott & A.Weatherhead "128"		
						Cranfield	5.00
2073/DFE+	Molino PIK-20	20052		7.75	M.Roff-Jarrett	Parham Park	1.00
2078/DFK+	Molino PIK-20	20039	OH-500	9.75	M.J Fairclough	North Hill	2.00
2079/DFL+	SZD-38A Jantar-1	B-682		9.75	R.J.Sharman	Kenley	4.00
					("245" under wing)		
2081/DFN	Glaser-Dirks DG-100	30		9.75	D.J.Clarke "899"	Wormingford	7.00
2082/DFP+	Aeromere M.100S	029	I-LSUO	9.75	D. & J.Lee	Pocklington	6.98
2084/DFR	Grob G.102 Astir CS	1038		10.75	T.A.Polak "906"	Lasham	3.00
2087/DFU	SZD-38A Jantar-1	B-685		10.75	J.E.New & Ptnrs "30"	Lasham	3.96*
2088/DFV	SZD-38A Jantar-1	B-684		10.75	R.R.Rodwell "164"	Bellarena	7.00
2089/DFW+	SZD-30 Pirat	S-0545		10.75	M.J.Appleby	Strubby	2.00
2090/DFX	SZD-41A Jantar Standard	B-691		10.75	J.C.Tait & Ptnrs "767" Easterton		3.00
2091/DFY+	Schempp-Hirth HS.4 Standard Cirrus 396		AGA...	11.75	G.Lambert Sth Kensington, London		1.93*
					(The Science Museum Flight Gallery 12.97)		
2092/DFZ	Molino PIK-20	20080		11.75	M.J.Leach & J.P.Ashcroft		
					"774" Sandhill Farm, Shrivenham		9.00
2093/DGA+	Schleicher K8B	8587	RAFGSA	11.75	Welland GC	Lyveden	3.00
			BGA.1926/D-....				
2094/DGB+	LET L-13 Blanik	026459		11.75	Black Mountains GC	Bidford	2.96*
	(Rebuilt with fuselage from BGA.2061 pre 1995)				(Damaged Bidford 21.10.95; stored 5.98)		
2097/DGE+	Schempp-Hirth HS.4 Standard Cirrus	75	606	12.75	T.E.Snoddy	Bellarena	7.00
2099/DGG+	Schleicher Ka6E	4061	RAFGSA.263	12.75	N.Holmes & Ptnrs	Long Mynd	5.00

BGA No/Code	Type	C/n	P/I	Date	Owner/operator	Probable Base	CA Expy
2100/DGH+	SZD-30 Pirat	B-533	RNGSA	12.75	E.Lowne	Snitterfield	5.00
			BGA.2100				
2102/DGK+	Schleicher Ka6CR	6287	D-3224	12.75	IBM GC "Betty Blue"	Lasham	6.00
2106/DGP+	LET L-13 Blanik	026560		4.76	J.M.Purves "631"	Rufforth	7.00
2110/DGT	Schleicher Ka2B	181	D-5469	5.76	Not known (Stored)	Falgunzeon	*
2112/DGV	Breguet Br.905S Fauvette	2	HB-632	5.76	T.Cust & Ptnrs	Burn	5.00
2114/DGX	Schempp-Hirth HS.4 Standard Cirrus	75	AGA.3	5.76	G.R.Seaman & Ptnrs	Lasham	5.00
		619	BGA.2114		"610"		
2115/DGY	Schempp-Hirth HS.5 Nimbus 2	105		5.76	J.H.Taylor "195"	Nympsfield	2.00
2117/DHA+	Schleicher K8B	1055	D-8848	5.76	Booker GC	Booker	1.00
	(C/n conflicts with D-8616)		D-5148				
2118/DHB+	SZD-30 Pirat	S-0643		5.76	J.Winsworth	Tibenham	4.00
2119/DHC	SZD-41A Jantar Standard	B-710	(BGA.2109)	5.76	M.C.Burlock "811"	Aston Down	8.00
2123/DHG+	Schleicher Ka6CR	1131	D-5170	5.76	Angus GC	Drumshade	7.00
2124/DHH	Molino PIK-20B	20124		5.76	R.A.Holroyd "116"	Pocklington	5.00
2125/DHJ+	Glaser-Dirks DG-100	48		1.76	H.D.Armitage	Usk	3.00
2126/DHK	Glaser-Dirks DG-100	50		1.76	R.Dell & B.J.Griffin		
					"A30"	Kirton-in-Lindsey	4.00
2127/DHL+	Glaser-Dirks DG-100	52		1.76	K.Adam	Aboyne	7.00
2128/DHM+	Schleicher Ka6E	4124	RAFGSA.26	1.76	J.G.Heard	Seighford	3.00
2129/DHN	Molino PIK-20B	20082		1.76	G J Bass "824"	Challock	6.00
2130/DHP	Slingsby T.45 Swallow	45176		1.76	Dumfries & Galloway GC		
	(Components ex BGA.1041 [1329]: c/n is type/year)					Falgunzeon	10.89*
				(W/O 3.4.64 with parts from BGA.1032; on rebuild 5.95)			
2132/DHR+	Slingsby T.53B	1718		2.76	E.MacDonald	Portmoak	9.00
2134/DHT+	Schleicher Ka6E	4065	???	2.76	I.G Lumley & Ptnrs	Bryngwyn Bach	1.00
2136/DHV+	Molino PIK-20B	20111		3.76	J.D. & G.J.Walker	Booker	5.00
2137/DHW	Schempp-Hirth HS.5 Nimbus 2	106		3.76	A.J.Bauld "951"	Portmoak	2.00
2139/DHY+	Schleicher Ka7 Rhonadler	1137	RAFGSA.266	4.76	G.Whittaker	Chipping	6.00
			D-5162				
2140/DHZ+	SZD-30 Pirat	S-0641		4.76	Peterborough & Spalding GC		
						Crowland	3.00
2141/DJA+	SZD-30 Pirat	S-0642		4.76	Northumbria GC	Milfield	10.00
2142/DJB	Schleicher K8B	8879	(RNGSA.N11)	4.77	Portsmouth Naval GC		
			AGA.17/BGA.2142/RAFGSA.397			Lee-on-Solent	12.99
2144/DJD	Grob G.102 Astir CS	1226		6.76	P.Gascoigne & Ptnrs		
						Kingston Deverill	3.00
2145/DJE+	Schleicher Ka6CR	6412	D-3682	6.76	M.Burton	Shobdon	2.00
2147/DJG	Schleicher Ka2B Rhonschwalbe	231	D-6179	6.76	J.Harmer "K2"	Lasham	5.00
2149/DJJ+	Schleicher ASK18	18029		6.76	Mendip GC	Halesland	3.00
2150/DJK+	Schleicher ASK18	18030		6.76	Booker GC	Booker	5.00
2151/DJL+	SZD-41A Jantar Standard	B-714		6.76	A.M.Cooper	Bryngwyn Bach	2.00
2152/DJM+	SZD-41A Jantar Standard	B-715		6.76	T.E.Betts	Cross Hayes	7.99
2153/DJN	Molino PIK-20B	20140C		7.76	S.L.Cambourne "407"	Lasham	3.00
2154/DJP+	Schleicher K8B	8588	RAFGSA355	7.76	Sackville GC		
						Sackville Farm, Riseley	4.00
2155/DJQ	Grob G.102 Astir CS	1258		7.76	H.Evans & D.J.Jeffries "214" Usk		4.00
2156/DJR	Schleicher Ka6CR	680	D-8423	7.76	J.A.Walker	Thruxton	11.96*
2157/DJS	Schempp-Hirth SHK-1	51	SE-TNF	7.76	S.J.Collins	Nympsfield	5.98
			OY-MFX/HB-898				
2158/DJT+	Schleicher Ka7 Rhonadler	?	RAFGSA	7.76	Enstone Eagles GC	Enstone	8.00
	(Note BGA.4271 also marked "DJT")						
2161/DJW	Manuel Condor	1		7.76	C.V. & R.C.Inwood	Booker	5.98
2162/DJX+	Grob G.102 Astir CS	1259		7.76	D.Cruickshank & Ptnrs	Aboyne	3.00
					"614"		
2164/DJZ	Eiri PIK-20B	20144		7.76	D.S.Puttock "989"	Halesland	8.00
2166/DKB+	Schempp-Hirth Standard Austria S	32	F-CCPR	8.76	J R Parr	Burn	11.99
2167/DKC+	Schleicher K8B	8261	D-1431	8.76	Yorkshire GC	Sutton Bank	12.00
2168/DKD	Glasflugel H.206 Hornet	67	(BGA.2165)	8.76	I.M.Evans "759"	Usk	4.00
2169/DKE+	Schleicher ASK13	13548		8.76	South Wales GC	Usk	1.00
2171/DKG+	Schleicher Ka6CR	6233	D-4327	8.76	C.Nunn & Ptnrs	Wormingford	2.00
2172/DKH	LET L-13 Blanik	026644		8.76	H.E.Birch "769"	Rufforth	6.00
2174/DKK	Schempp-Hirth SHK-1	32	HB-864	8.76	C.Buzzard & D.J.Deacon "884"		
						Husbands Bosworth	5.95*
2175/DKL	Schempp-Hirth HS.5 Nimbus 2	086	D-2111	9.76	G.J.Croll "444"	Snitterfield	3.00
2176/DKM+	Glasflugel H.206 Hornet	49	D-7816	9.76	M.Lee	Rattlesden	4.00
2177/DKN+	Schleicher Ka6CR	6456	D-9358	3.77	D.Lees & Ptnrs	Wormingford	4.98
2179/DKQ+	Glaser-Dirks DG-100G	91G11		9.76	G.Peters	North Hill	2.00
2180/DKR	Grob G.102 Astir CS	1327		9.76	G.D.Crawford Weston-on-the-Green		4.00
					"360"		
2181/DKS	Grob G.102 Astir CS	1330		12.76	C.K.Lewis "788"	Lasham	12.99

BGA No/Code	Type	C/n	P/I	Date	Owner/operator	Probable Base	CA Expy
2182/DKT	Eiri PIK-20B	20155		9.76	G.Barnham "185"	Rufforth	2.00
2183/DKU+	Grob G.102 Astir CS	1326		11.76	G.Jennings	Lasham	3.00
2184/DKV	Grob G.102 Astir CS	1328		9.76	T.J.Ireson		1.99
					"391" Sandhill Farm, Shrivenham		
2185/DKW+	Grob G.102 Astir CS	1329		9.76	D.H.Smith	Edgehill	2.00
2186/DKX	Grob G.102 Astir CS	1331		9.76	L.R. & J.M.Bennett "353"	Booker	3.00
2187/DKY+	Schleicher Ka7 Rhonadler	7187	RAFGSA.342	9.76	Defford Aero Club	Bidford	4.98
	(Stored 8.99)						
2188/DKZ+	Glasflugel H.205 Club Libelle	111	RAFGSA.774	11.76	P.Jackson & C.Parsons	Bidford	5.00
2189/DLA+	Pilatus B4 PC-11	149	RAFGSA	9.76	P.R.Seddon	Chipping	3.00
2190/DLB+	Schleicher ASK18	18040		9.76	Vale of White Horse GC		
					Sandhill Farm, Shrivenham		8.00
2191/DLC	Schleicher ASK13	13549		10.76	Lasham Gliding Society	Lasham	12.99
					"C"		
2192/DLD+	Schleicher K8B	8766	RAFGSA.383	10.76	Shalbourne Soaring Group		
						Rivar Hill	5.00
2193/DLE+	Schleicher Ka6E	4074	AGA.8	10.76	W.P.Grundy	Talgarth	5.00
			RAFGSA				
2195/DLG	Schempp-Hirth HS.4 Standard Cirrus	579	AGA.2	10.76	S.Naylor "596"	Burn	9.00
2196/DLH	Grob G.102 Astir CS77	1646		2.77	B.Bamber & R.Smith "378"	Lasham	4.00
2197/DLJ+	Molino PIK-20B	20157		12.76	M.S Parks	Milfield	6.00
2200/DLM	Grob G.102 Astir CS	1260	(BGA.2163)	11.76	Highland GC "266"	Easterton	2.00
2202/DLP+	Schleicher Ka6CR	6519	RAFGSA.355	11.76	J.R Crosse	Crowland	4.00
2204/DLR+	Scheibe L-Spatz 55	647	BGA.2654	11.76	Dumfries & District GC		
	(Quoted as ex D-3659 but unconfirmed)		BGA.2204/D-5638			Falgunzeon	8.99
2205/DLS+	Schleicher K8B	8650	D-5718	11.76	Devon & Somerset GC	North Hill	1.00
2206/DLT	ICA IS-28B2	32		12.76	A.Woodrow "485"	Tibenham	5.99
2207/DLU	ICA IS-28B2	33	RAFGSA.R92	12.76	Crusaders GC		
			EI-141/BGA.2207		"R92" Kingsfield, Dhekelia		11.99
2209/DLW+	SZD-30 Pirat	B-467	PH-433	12.76	G.Bryce & Ptnrs	North Connel	4.96*
2210/DLX	Slingsby T.45 Swallow	1494	RAFGGA.539	12.76	M.Sanderson	Milfield	5.95*
2211/DLY+	Eiri PIK-20D	20509		1.77	D.C Adlam & Ptnrs	Dunstable	3.00
2212/DLZ	Swales SW.3-15T	03		12.76	R.Harris "456"	Rivar Hill	4.00
2214/DMB	Schleicher K8B	8209	D-4331	1.77	DRA GC "Kate" "831"	Odiham	7.00
2216/DMD	Glaser-Dirks DG-100	75		12.76	B.T.Payne & A.Jenkins "251"		
						Weston-on-the-Green	12.00
2218/DMF+	Schleicher Ka7 Rhonadler	7073	D-4313	1.77	Staffordshire GC	Seighford	7.00
2219/DMG+	Schleicher K8B	8763	RAFGSA.382	1.77	Dorset GC	Gallows Hill	5.00
2220/DMH+	Grob G.102 Astir CS	1511		1.77	Oxford GC	Weston-on-the-Green	4.00
2221/DMJ	Schleicher K8B	8077	PH-290	2.77	Not known (Stored)	Strathaven	*
2222/DMK	Schempp-Hirth SHK	25	D-5401	2.77	M.Oliver "593"	Aston Down	1.00
2223/DML+	Schleicher Ka7 Rhonadler	929	D-6194	2.77	Newark & Notts GC	Winthorpe	3.98
			D-5005				
2224/DMM	Schempp-Hirth HS.5 Nimbus 2	125		2.77	T.E.Linee "338"	Gallows Hill	2.00
2225/DMN+	Glasflugel H.303 Mosquito	20		2.77	A.Crowden	Booker	3.00
2226/DMP	Grob G.102 Astir CS	1239	ZS-GKF	2.77	D.G.Nisbet "233"	Dunstable	3.99
2227/DMQ+	Schleicher Ka6E	4062	RAFGSA.264	2.77	A.R.Bushnell & Ptnr	Crowland	5.00
2228/DMR	Grob G.102 Astir CS	1435		2.77	L.Beale & Ptnrs	Parham Park	3.00
					"511"		
2229/DMS	Glasflugel H.201B Standard Libelle	385	RNGSA	3.77	M.D.White & Ptnrs "259"	Burn	4.00
2231/DMU	Eiri PIK-20D	20524		3.77	A.C.Wanford & Ptnrs		
	(C/n confirmed although duplicates C-GOPN)				"392"	Gransden Lodge	2.00
2232/DMV+	Eiri PIK-20D	20526		3.77	F.S.Parkhill "333"	Crowland	9.00
2234/DMX+	Schleicher ASK13	13567		3.77	Kent GC	Challock	12.99
2235/DMY	Eiri PIK-20D	20532		3.77	G.A.Piper "371"	Parham Park	4.00
2238/DNB	DFS/49 Grunau Baby 2B	2	RAFGSA.380	2.77	P.Underwood	Eaton Bray	*
	(Built Flg.u.Arbeitsg.Hall)		D-8039		(On rebuild 12.95; to be in Luftwaffe c/s)		
2239/DNC	Grob G.102 Astir CS	1428		3.77	A.J.Carpenter	Edgehill	6.99
					"Natural High" "588"		
2240/DND+	Pilatus B4 PC-11AF	136		3.77	R J Happs	Lasham	11.99
2241/DNE+	Grob G.102 Astir CS77	1631		3.77	S P Woolcock	Cranfield	4.00
2242/DNF+	SZD-9 bis Bocian 1D	P-354	HB-657	4.77	M.G.Shaw	Portmoak	4.00
2243/DNG	Schempp-Hirth HS.5 Nimbus 2	126		4.77	A.O.Harkins & A Brown		
					"265"	Gallows Hill	5.00
2245/DNJ+	Schleicher ASK18	18042		4.77	Derby & Lancs GC	Camphill	3.00
2246/DNK	Grob G.102 Astir CS	1434		4.77	745 Syndicate "745"	Wormingford	4.00
2247/DNL+	Glasflugel H.201 Standard Libelle	382	RAFGSA.742	4.77	P.R.Bergson	Thame	3.00
2251/DNQ	Rolladen-Schneider LS-3	3035		1.77	M.Cooper "307"	Challock	3.00
2254/DNT+	SZD-30 Pirat	S-0712		4.77	M.Davidson & Ptnrs	Drumshade	5.00
2255/DNU+	SZD-42-1 Jantar 2	B-783		4.77	C.Rowland & Ptnrs "U2"	Booker	5.00
2256/DNV+	Schleicher ASK13	13568		4.77	Buckminster GC	Saltby	2.00

BGA No/Code	Type	C/n	P/I	Date	Owner/operator	Probable Base	CA Expy
2257/DNW+	Schleicher Ka6CR	829	???	5.77	F G Broom	Rhigos	12.99
2258/DNX+	Schleicher Ka6CR	6094Si	D-5107	5.77	W.R.Schofield	Burn	9.00
2260/DNZ+	Schleicher K8B	8095	???	5.77	North Wales GC	Bryngwyn Bach	5.00
2261/DPA+	Schleicher ASK18	18044		5.77	Norfolk GC	Tibenham	4.99
2264/DPD+	LET L-13 Blanik	026860		5.77	J.L.Whiting	Bidford	3.96*
2267/DPG+	Munchen Mu-13D III	005	D-1327	5.77	G.J.Moore	Dunstable	11.00
2268/DPH	Schempp-Hirth HS.7 Mini Nimbus	009		5.77	J.W.Murdoch "287"	Strathaven	4.00
2269/DPJ+	Grob G.102 Astir CS77	1641		6.77	J.Liddiard & Ptnrs	Lasham	2.00
2270/DPK+	Glasflugel H.303 Mosquito	27		6.77	G.Lawley	Cross Hayes	4.00
2271/DPL	Eiri PIK-20D	20549		6.77	D.W.Standen "437"	Dunstable	7.00
2274/DPP+	Schleicher Ka2B Rhonschwalbe	105	D-1880	6.77	A.L.Roseberry & Ptnrs Aston Down (Stored 8.99)		9.96*
2275/DPQ	Grob G.102 Astir CS77	1632		6.77	D.Patrick	Falgunzeon	4.00
2276/DPR	Scheibe L-Spatz	05	D-1265	6.77	V.W.Jennings	Parham Park	5.00
					t/a Shoreham Soaring Group (As "D-1265") "Sparrowfahrt"		
2278/DPT	Scheibe L-Spatz 55	01	???	7.77	B.V.Smith	Rufforth	7.98
2279/DPU+	EoN AP.5 Olympia 2B	EoN/0/142	RAFGSA.274	7.77	C.H.Thompson	Crowland	10.00
2282/DPX	Schleicher ASW19	19126		7.77	G.L.Boaler & Ptnrs	Nympsfield	3.00
2283/DPY	Grob G.192 Astir CS77	1636		8.77	D S Burton "375"	Lasham	2.00
2284/DPZ+	Slingsby T.34A Sky	822		8.77	N McLaughlin	Saltby	7.00
2285/DQA+	Schleicher Ka6CR	13582		8.77	Essex & Suffolk GC	Wormingford	3.00
2286/DGB	Grob G.102 Astir CS77	1653		8.77	G R Davey "848" Kirton-in-Lindsey		5.00
2287/DQC	Schleicher Ka6CR	6373Si	D-5725	8.77	R.J.Whitaker & I.F.Smith Lasham "572"		3.98
2288/DQD+	Slingsby T.8 Tutor (Built from parts by F.Breeze)	-		8.77	K.Nurcombe	Husbands Bosworth	6.00
2289/DQE	Grob G.102 Astir CS77	1636	(RNGSA.N34)	8.77	Heron GC "480"	RNAS Yeovilton	5.00
2290/DQF	Schleicher Ka6CR	6417	D-5827	9.77	P.James	Saltby	3.00
2291/DQG	Grob G.102 Astir CS77	1649		9.77	Miss A.G.Veitch "770"	Easterton	5.00
2292/DQH	Schmetz Condor IV	V2	D-8538	7.78	M.H.Birch "CONDOR"	Lasham	1.00
2293/DQJ+	Schleicher Ka6CR	228	D-5467	9.77	Lakes GC	Walney Island	1.00
2294/DQK	Schleicher Ka6E (See BGA.2234)	4341	D-0541	9.77	S.Y.Duxbury & R.S.Hawley "542"	Camphill	3.00
2295/DQL+	Schleicher Ka8	509	D-5675	9.77	Aquila GC	Hinton-in-The-Hedges	1.00
2296/DQM	Pilatus B4 PC-11	138	RAFGSA	9.77	A.R.Dearden "196"	Ringmer	9.00
2298/DQP+	Schleicher K8B	1181	???	10.77	Coventry GC	Husbands Bosworth	3.00
2300/DQR	Grob G.102 Astir CS77	1667		10.77	N.R.Warren & Ptnrs "556"	Kingston Deverill	1.00
2301/DQS+	Schleicher Ka6CR	1065	D-5144	10.77	L.Hill	North Hill	3.00
2303/DQU+	Eiri PIK-20D	20579		10.77	A.Duncan	Portmoak	4.00
2306/DQX+	Schleicher Ka7 Rhonadler	743	D-9127	11.77	Scottish Gliding Union Ltd	Portmoak	5.99
2307/DQY	Schleicher K8B	647	D-4375	11.77	Mendip GC	Halesland	8.00
2309/DRA	Schleicher Ka6CR	1118	D-9041	11.77	P Davis "904"	Bidford	7.00
2310/DRB	Glaser-Dirks DG-100	31	PH-532	11.77	J.D.Peck "86"	Bicester	4.00
2312/DRD+	Schleicher Ka6CR	6377Si	D-9080	11.77	Essex & Suffolk GC	Wormingford	3.00
2313/DRE+	Schleicher Ka6CR	6197	D-8558	11.77	J.H.Jowett	North Hill	3.00
2314/DRF+	Schleicher Ka6CR	943	D-8600	11.77	Devon & Somerset GC North Hill (Damaged North Hill 14.7.97)		4.98*
2315/DRG+	Schleicher Ka6CR	6157	D-4090	11.77	W.E.Smith	Gallows Hill	5.99
					t/a Summer Wine Syndicate		
2317/DRJ	Schleicher ASK13	13583		11.77	Lasham Gliding Society Lasham "D"		12.99
2318/DRK+	Grob G.102 Astir CS77	1686		12.77	Cambridge University GC	Gransden Lodge	2.00
2319/DRL+	Scheibe SF-26 Standard	5040	D-7073	12.77	T McKinley	Kirton-in-Lindsey	5.00
2320/DRM+	Schleicher Ka7 Rhonadler	7017	D-4666	12.77	L.Cross & Syndicate	Dunstable	5.00
2321/DRN	Glasflugel H.303 Mosquito	082		12.77	A.Roberts "821"	North Hill	4.00
2322/DRP+	Pilatus B4 PC-11	080	RAFGSA BGA.1927	12.77	H.J.Stone & Ptnrs	Weston-on-the-Green	3.00
2323/DRQ	Grob G.103 Twin Astir	3027		12.77	V.C.Carr & Ptnrs "258"	Sleap	5.00
2324/DRR+	Schleicher Ka2B Rhonschwalbe	49	D-8108	12.77	Dumfries & District GC	Falgunzeon	5.00
2325/DRS+	SZD-9 bis Bocian 1E	P-783		12.77	Mendip GC	Halesland	5.00
2326/DRT	Eiri PIK-20D	20587		1.78	P F Fowler "688"	Sleap	3.00
2327/DRU	Grob G.102 Astir CS77	1685		1.78	A R Wilkinson "344"	Wormingford	3.00
2328/DRV+	Schleicher K8b	8026	D-6169	1.78	Buckminster GC	Saltby	12.98
2329/DRW	Grob G.102 Astir CS	1081	D-3311	1.78	P.A.Brooks "798"	Lasham	5.00
2331/DRY	Schleicher Ka6BR	370	D-5533	1.78	A May	Crowland	7.99

BGA No/Code	Type	C/n	P/I	Date	Owner/operator	Probable Base	CA Expy
2332/DRZ	Schleicher K8B	668	D-4622	1.78	East Sussex GC	Ringmer	7.00
			D-KANB/D-4622				
2333/DSA	Slingsby T.30 Prefect	575	WE985	1.78	R J Sharman	Crowland	2.00
2334/DSB	Schleicher Ka6E	4300	D-0263	1.78	M H Yates	Ridgwell	5.00
2337/DSE	Schempp-Hirth HS.7 Mini Nimbus	36		2.78	G Binnie "227"	Portmoak	1.97*
2338/DSF	Schleicher K8B	8220	D-7114	2.78	Edinburgh University GC	Portmoak	11.00
					"Snoopy"		
2339/DSG	Schleicher Ka6CR	6395	D-5696	2.78	R P Maddocks	Booker	8.00
2340/DSH	Grob G.102 Astir CS77	1698		3.78	R B Petrie "648"	Portmoak	1.00
2341/DSJ	Grob G.103 Twin Astir	3050		2.78	L J Kaye	Shobdon	4.00
2343/DSL	Grob G.103 Twin Astir	3041		3.78	J.G.Hampson "447"	Enstone	5.00
2344/DSM	Fauvel AV.22S	3	F-CCGM	4.78	I.Dunkley	Camphill	8.95*
2345/DSN	Grob G.102 Astir CS77	1698		3.78	J J M Riach "893"	Drumslade	5.00
2346/DSP	Schempp-Hirth HS.7 Mini Nimbus	33		3.78	R.I.Hey & Ptnrs "270"	Nympsfield	3.00
2348/DSR+	Schleicher Ka6CR	970	D-5040	3.78	Cornish GC	Perranporth	5.00
2350/DST	Schleicher ASW20L	20059		3.78	J.E.Gatfield Husbands Bosworth		12.99
					"972"		
2351/DSU+	Grob G.102 Astir CS77	1663		3.78	Bowland Forest GC	Chipping	5.00
2352/DSV	Pilatus B4 PC-11	134	RAFGSA.718	3.78	Staffordshire GC	Seighford	11.95*
			RAFGSA.518		"718"		
2353/DSW	Schempp-Hirth HS.7 Mini Nimbus	37	RNGSA.N33	3.78	S.C.Fear "533"	Crowland	11.99
2354/DSX	Schleicher ASW19	19188		4.78	R.Grundy "877" Kingston Deverill		5.00
2355/DSY+	Schleicher Ka6CR	561	D-5702	4.78	G.Harris	Rufforth	5.00
2357/DTA	Glaser-Dirks DG-200	2-27		4.78	R P Hardcastle "699"	NK	4.00
2359/DTC	Schempp-Hirth HS.6 Janus B	63	RAFGSA.R9	4.78	Dukeries GC	Gamston	5.00
			RAFGSA 16/BGA.2359				
2360/DTD+	Schleicher ASW19	19187		4.78	R.K.Warren	Cross Hayes	4.00
2361/DTE+	Schleicher ASW19	19185		4.78	D.M.Cornish	Gransden Lodge	2.00
2363/DTG	Schempp-Hirth SHK-1	012	D-2034	4.78	M.A.T.Jones & F.A.W.Elliott		
						Rattlesden	4.00
2366/DTK	Glasflugel H.303 Mosquito B	109		4.78	P.France "760"	Usk	5.00
2368/DTM+	Glaser-Dirks DG-200	2-34		4.78	Miss J.Walker & Ptnrs	Lasham	3.00
2369/DTN+	Schleicher K8B	117/58	NK	5.78	K.J.McPhee & Syndicate	Edgehill	11.00
2370/DTP	Schleicher ASW20	20078		5.78	T.S.Hills & Ptnrs "915"	Lasham	1.00
2371/DTQ+	Schleicher ASW20	20054		5.78	D.H.Garrard	Cranfield	4.00
2372/DTR+	EoN AP.6 Olympia 401	EoN/4/005	NEJSGSA.7	5.78	B D Clarke	Ringmer	3.00
			RAFGSA.252/G-APSI				
2373/DTS	CARMAM M.100S Mesange	031	F-CCST	5.78	C.Holmes	Bryngwyn Bach	1.98
2375/DTU+	Schempp-Hirth HS.5 Nimbus 2B	167		5.78	R.E.Wooler	Chipping	4.00
2376/DTV	Glasflugel H.303 Mosquito B	110		5.78	A.J.Watson "704"	Lasham	5.00
2377/DTW+	SZD-30 Pirat	S-0711		5.78	C Kaminskui	North Hill	8.00
2378/DTX	Glasflugel H.303 Mosquito B	111		5.78	K.D.Hook "320"	Portmoak	1.00
2379/DTY	Glasflugel H.303 Mosquito B	112		5.78	R.Ward "766"	Gransden Lodge	4.00
2380/DTZ	Slingsby T.30 Prefect	573	WE983	5.78	C.Hughes "St30"	Nympsfield	12.99
2382/DUB	Glasflugel H.303 Mosquito B	113		5.78	A.G.Reid & Ptnrs "911"	Kenley	4.00
2383/DUC	CARMAM M.100S Mesange	012	F-CCSA	6.78	Not known	Carlton Moor	5.88*
					(Stored 5.94)		
2386/DUF+	Schleicher K8B	8296A	D-5294	6.78	Essex GC	Ridgewell	5.00
2388/DUH+	Scheibe L-Spatz 55	760	NK	6.78	R J Aylesbury	Crowland	6.00
2390/DUK+	Schleicher K8B	752	D-4048	6.78	Bristol & Glos GC	Nympsfield	12.00
2391/DUL	Grob G.102 Astir CS77	1720		6.78	K.J.Screen "642"	Long Mynd	2.00
2394/DUQ+	Glaser-Dirks DG-200	2-43		7.78	D.M.Cottingham	North Hill	3.00
2395/DUR+	Schleicher Ka6CR	6273	OY-DLX	7.78	Rattlesden GC	Rattlesden	5.00
2396/DUS	Schleicher Ka6E	4263	OY-XCB	7.78	M.Toon & C.S.Crocker	Tibenham	5.00
			HB-948		"638"		
2397/DUT	Schleicher ASW20	20089		7.78	T.J.Murphy "T34"	Portmoak	3.00
2400/DUW	DFS 108/49 Grunau Baby 2B	-	VN148	12.77	C.Tonks (North Wales)		*
	(Also allocated BAPC.33)		LN+ST		(On rebuild 1995)		
2401/DUX	Grob G.102 Club Astir	2140		7.78	B.T.Spreckley Le Blanc, France		4.00
					"885"		
2402/DUY	Glaser-Dirks DG-100	24	PH-525	7.78	A.C.Saxton & Ptnrs Carlton Moor		7.00
					"652"		
2405/DVB+	Schleicher ASK13	13596		8.78	Essex & Suffolk GC Wormingford		3.00
	(Components, incl c/n plate, donated to BGA.3493 & possibly discarded parts from crash Dunstable 5.6.82)						
2406/DVC+	Schleicher ASK13	13597		8.78	Southdown GC	Parham Park	3.00
2407/DVD+	LET L-13 Blanik	027021		8.78	Vectis GC	Bembridge	3.00
2408/DVE	Schleicher Ka6E	4226	RAFGSA.379	8.78	M.J.Leach & S.Foggin		
					"879" Sandhill Farm, Shrivenham		2.97*
2410/DVG+	Schleicher Ka6CR	003	D-1916	8.78	R.F.Warren	Ringmer	6.00
	(Built Holzmann-Drespack)						
2411/DVH	Schleicher Ka6E	4117	RAFGSA	8.78	P.Brett "615"	Perranporth	6.00

BGA No/Code	Type	C/n	P/I	Date	Owner/operator	Probable Base	CA Expy
2412/DVJ+	Eiri PIK-20D	20638		8.78	M.C.Hayes "869"	Bidford	3.00
2413/DVK	SZD-48 Jantar Standard 2	W-868		8.78	K.J.Mellor "732"	Gransden Lodge	4.00
2414/DVL	Schleicher ASW19	19222		9.78	P.T Healy & Ptnrs "X96"	Lasham	5.00
2415/DVM+	Glasflugel H.205 Club Libelle	52	RAFGGA.581	9.78	M.J.Gooch	Rattlesden	3.00
2416/DVN+	Eiri PIK-20D	20641		9.78	P.Goulthoorpe	Husbands Bosworth	5.00
2417/DVP	Schleicher ASW19	19220		9.78	E.F.Davies "971"	Booker	4.00
2418/DVQ+	Schleicher K8B	8134	D-0288 D-KICE/D5235	9.78	Staffordshire GC	Seighford	6.99
2419/DVR	Scheibe L-Spatz 55	663	D-1565	9.78	J.Young	Lyveden	6.96*
2420/DVS	Schempp-Hirth HS.4 Standard Cirrus (C/n duplicates VH-GGC)	380	RAFGSA.824	9.78	D.Hands & Ptnr "VS"	Parham Park	2.00
2423/DVV	Schleicher ASW20L	20100		9.78	Mrs A.F.Coppen "810"	Lasham	3.00
2424/DVW	Schleicher ASW20	20099		9.78	Not known "590"	Aston Down	2.85*
	(Damaged in collision with BGA.2618 Lasham 17.8.84; wreck stored 7.99)						
2425/DVX	Schleicher ASK13	13598		9.78	Shenington GC "S13"	Edgehill	12.99
2426/DVY	Schempp-Hirth HS.2 Cirrus	52	OO-ZIR	10.78	G.Martin "272"	Nympsfield	7.00
2427/DVZ	Glasflugel H.303 Mosquito B	133		10.78	B.H.Shaw "Z25"	Husbands Bosworth	4.00
2429/DWB	Glasflugel H.303 Mosquito B (Marked as "BGA.2924")	135		10.78	C.G.Salt & Ptnrs "733"	Lasham	3.00
2430/DWC+	Schleicher Ka6E	4111	AGA.11	10.78	J Osment	Nympsfield	9.00
2432/DWE+	Schleicher Ka7 Rhonadler	7132	D-5427	10.78	UWE GC	RAF Keevil	10.00
2433/DWF+	DFS/49 Grunau Baby 2B (Built RNAY Fleetlands)	-	AGA.16 RNGSA 1-13/VW743	11.78	L.P.Woodage	Dunstable	9.00
2434/DWG+	Schleicher K8B	165/60	D-5750	11.78	Newark & Notts GC	Winthorpe	2.00
2435/DWH+	Schleicher K8B (Built by Gebr. Huber)	1	D-8614 D-8331	11.78	Essex GC	Ridgewell	9.96*
2436/DWJ	Glaser-Dirks DG-200	2-59		11.78	D Evans "191"	Chipping	3.00
2438/DWL	Glasflugel H.303 Mosquito B	141		12.78	A.Stanford & Ptnrs "755"	Husbands Bosworth	9.99
2440/DWN	Schleicher Ka7 Rhonadler	7101	D-5360	12.78	L.R.Merritt	Edgehill	3.00
2441/DWP+	Glasflugel H.303 Mosquito B	136		12.78	Mosquito Syndicate	Bicester	3.00
2442/DWQ+	Grob G.102 Astir CS77	1758		12.78	F.Prime	Gransden Lodge	3.00
2443/DWR	Glasflugel H.303 Mosquito B	134	(BGA.2428)	1.79	C.D.Lovell "P9"	Lasham	2.00
2444/DWS	Eiri PIK-20D	20652		1.79	R. & B.Madelin "728"	Lasham	12.00
2445/DWT	Slingsby T.65A Vega	1898		1.79	A.P.Grimley "886"	Husbands Bosworth	9.00
2446/DWU+	Grob G.102 Astir CS	1201	D-7269	1.79	G.V.McKirdy	Parham Park	5.98
2448/DWW+	Slingsby T.65A Vega	1896		1.79	E.Fitzgerald	Usk	5.00
2451/DWZ+	Schleicher ASW19	19243		2.79	J.A.Stirk & Ptnrs	Burn	4.00
2452/DXA	Glasflugel H.303 Mosquito B	137		2.79	S H Gibson "483"	Dunstable	4.00
2453/DXB	Schleicher ASW20	20142		.	J.Timpany & Ptnrs "81"	Nympsfield	2.00
2455/DXD	Slingsby T.65A Vega	1901		2.79	T.C.Harrington & Ptnrs "132"	Bicester	4.00
2456/DXE+	Slingsby T.65A Vega	1902		2.79	L.M.Astle	Husbands Bosworth	7.99
2457/DXF	Slingsby T.65A Vega	1903		2.79	P.Kitchen "815"	Talgarth	9.00
2458/DXG+	Slingsby T.65A Vega 17L	1906		2.79	M.H.Pope "46"	Bidford	4.00
2459/DXH+	Schleicher Ka6E	4198	RAFGSA.489 D-4093	2.79	B.Hughes	Bicester	2.00
2460/DXJ+	Grob G.102 Astir CS77	1762		3.79	R.Maskell & Ptnrs	Gransden Lodge	12.00
2461/DXK	Centrair ASW20F	20108		3.79	A.Townsend "160"	Booker	6.00
2462/DXL+	Schempp-Hirth HS.4 Standard Cirrus	203G	AGA.1	3.79	P. & A.Gelsthorpe	Lasham	2.00
2463/DXM+	Schleicher Ka7 Rhonadler	626	RAFGGA.551 D-5707	3.79	Vale of Neath GC	Rhigos	8.97*
2464/DXN	Glaser-Dirks DG-200	2-63		3.79	J.A.Johnston "267"	Gransden Lodge	3.00
2465/DXP+	Schleicher K8B	8646A	D-8537	3.79	Stratford-upon-Avon GC	Snitterfield	2.00
2466/DXQ	Schempp-Hirth HS.7 Mini Nimbus C (Build No.MN97)	96		3.79	T.Lamb & P.Hawkins "147"	Weston-on-the-Green	5.00
2467/DXR	Slingsby T.65A Vega	1905		3.79	D.R.Sutton	Sutton Bank	8.94*
2469/DXT	Schempp-Hirth HS.7 Mini Nimbus C	97		3.79	J.M.Beattie "286"	Booker	12.99
2470/DXU+	Slingsby T.59J Kestrel 22	1867	G-BDWZ	3.79	P.J.Bisgood & Ptnrs	Cranfield	3.00
2471/DXV+	Schleicher ASK13	13602		3.79	Cambridge University GC	Gransden Lodge	2.99
2472/DXW	Glasflugel H.303 Mosquito B	142		3.79	P.Newark & Ptnrs "354"	Burn	1.00
2473/DXX	Schleicher ASW19B	19245		3.79	P.F.Whitehead "580"	Bicester	1.00
2474/DXY	Muller Moswey III	?	HB-474	3.79	G.M.Bacon & Ptnrs (As "HB-474")	Gransden Lodge	9.99

BGA No/Code	Type	C/n	P/I	Date	Owner/operator	Probable Base	CA Expy
2477/DYB	Schleicher Ka7 Rhonadler	167/59	D-5775	3.79	South London Gliding Centre		
					(Reported as "DYN") "6"	Kenley	4.00
2478/DYC+	Schleicher Ka6CR	6390	D-1545	3.79	F.J.Smith	Burn	4.00
2479/DYE	Schleicher ASW20L	20143		3.79	T.A.Sage "828"	Dunstable	1.00
2480/DYF	Grob G.102 Astir CS77	1805		3.79	York Gliding Centre	Rufforth	4.00
					"850"		
2481/DYG	Slingsby T.59H Kestrel 22	1868	G-BDZG	3.79	R.E.Gretton & R.L.Darby Crowland		7.00
					"592"		
2482/DYH+	Glaser-Dirks DG-200	2-75		4.79	A.Urwin	Milfield	5.96*
2483/DYJ+	Schleicher Ka6CR	6583	D-5838	4.79	R.M.Morris	Dunstable	6.00
2485/DYL+	CARMAM JP/15-36A Aiglon	37		4.79	M.P.Edwards	Crowland	2.00
2486/DYN+	Schleicher Ka6CR	6129Si	D-8458	4.79	C.N.Harder	Rivar Hill	1.00
	(See BGA.2477)						
2487/DYP	Schleicher Ka6BR	191	OO-ZXL	4.79	D.Ling	Ridgewell	3.98*
			D-5482		"BR" (Crashed Ridgewell 31.5.97)		
2488/DYQ+	Schleicher Ka6CR	6178	D-5328	4.79	Dorset GC	Gallows Hill	8.00
2489/DYR+	Schleicher Ka7 Rhonadler	766	D-5220	4.79	Avon Soaring Centre	Bidford	8.99
2490/DYT	Eiri PIK-20D	20657		4.79	P.J.Hampshire	Parham Park	3.98*
					"537" (Damaged nr Parham 12.4.97)		
2491/DYU	Schempp-Hirth HS.5 Nimbus 2C	181		4.79	A.Pickles "531"	Lasham	6.00
2494/DYX	Schleicher ASW20	20135		4.79	R.Cousins "102"	Challock	4.00
2495/DYZ	Schempp-Hirth HS.5 Nimbus 2C	180		4.79	N.A.Britton "943"	Bidford	4.00
2496/DZA	Slingsby T.65A Vega 17L	1907		4.79	M.P.Garrod	Lasham	1.00
2497/DZB+	Slingsby T.65A Vega	1908		4.79	A.N.Christie	Drumshade	7.00
2498/DZC+	Scheibe L-Spatz 55	642	RAFGGA	4.79	G.A.Ford	Nympsfield	10.98
			D-5629				
2499/DZD	Schleicher ASW19B	19268		4.79	E.J.Silverstone	Llantisilio	6.00
					"573"		
2501/DZF	Schempp-Hirth HS.4 Standard Cirrus 421G	RAFGSA.27		4.79	L.S.Hood "152"	Bicester	3.00
2502/DZG	Schleicher ASW19B	19267		4.79	S.P.Wareham "909"	Gallows Hill	2.00
2504/DZJ	Grob G.102 Club Astir	2230		5.79	J. & R.Acreman "576"	North Hill	4.00
2505/DZK	Schempp-Hirth HS.5 Nimbus 2C	198		5.79	R Hudson "957"	Sutton Bank	2.00
	(Fuselage No.195)						
2507/DZM+	Slingsby T.65A Vega	1909		5.79	D.G.MacArthur	Long Mynd	5.00
2508/DZN	Slingsby T.65A Vega 17L	1910		5.79	D.A.White "990"	Aboyne	7.00
2509/DZP+	Slingsby T.65A Vega	1911		5.79	M.T.Crews	Currock Hill	6.00
2511/DZR+	ICA IS-28B2	87		5.79	Lakes GC	Walney Island	1.00
2512/DZS	SZD-8bis-0 Jaskolka	183	HB-583	5.79	N.A Clark	Parham Park	8.00
2513/DZT	Eiri PIK-20D	20661		5.79	A.C.Garside "106"	Challock	1.00
2514/DZU+	Grob G.102 Astir CS	1076	D-3308	6.79	P.F.Clarke	Booker	1.00
2515/DZV	Scheibe SF-27A Zugvogel V	6065	D-5839	6.79	A.P.Montague "839"	Nympsfield	4.00
2516/DZW+	Schleicher Ka6CR	6628	D-1045	6.79	A.Head	Husbands Bosworth	3.00
2518/DZY	Schleicher ASW19B	19275		6.79	M.C.Fairman & T.Marlow Dunstable		1.00
					"757"		
2522/EAC	Grob G.102 Astir CS77	1803		6.79	B.T.Pratt	Husbands Bosworth	4.00
					"367"		
2523/EAD+	Slingsby T.65A Vega	1912		6.79	P.R.Norrison	Pocklington	6.00
2524/EAE	Schleicher ASW20L	20224		6.79	L.Clayton "107"	Challock	2.00
2525/EAF+	Grob G.102 Astir CS77	1830		6.79	J.Bell	Milfield	7.00
2526/EAG+	Slingsby T.65A Vega	1913		6.79	D.R.Moore	Gransden Lodge	3.00
2527/EAH+	Schleicher Ka6E	4085	D-7542	6.79	M.Lodge	Lasham	7.99
			D-7142				
2528/EAJ	Schempp-Hirth HS.5 Nimbus 2	7	D-0699	6.79	M.Randle "79"	Aston Down	4.00
2529/EAK	Glasflugel H.303 Mosquito B	155		6.79	A.R.L.Parker & Ptnrs Aston Down		2.00
					"594"		
2530/EAL	Schleicher Rhonlerche II	3051/BR	PH-331	7.79	Newcastle & Teesside GC		
					(Stored 5.94)	Carlton Moor	9.91*
2531/EAM+	Schempp-Hirth HS.5 Nimbus 2B	93	D-2787	7.79	P.G.Myers & Syndicate	Chipping	3.00
2535/EAR+	Eiri PIK-20D	NK		7.79	W.Munns	Syerston	12.00
2537/EAT	Eiri PIK-20D	20664		7.79	P.T.Reading & Ptnrs "786" Lasham		4.00
2538/EAU+	Schleicher Ka7 Rhonadler	7092	PH-304	7.79	Welland GC	Upwood	2.00
2539/EAV	Schempp-Hirth HS.7 Mini Nimbus C	136		7.79	W.Cook & K.Porter	Rivar Hill	8.00
2540/EAW+	Grob G.102 Astir CS77	1831		7.79	W.Severn "342"	Cross Hayes	7.00
2543/EAZ+	Schleicher K8B	8138	D-5256	7.79	Shalbourne Soaring Group		
			D-KANO/D-5256 (Crashed Rivar Hill 25.7.97) Rivar Hill					6.98*
2544/EBA+	Slingsby T.65A Vega 17L	1914		7.79	S.M.Smith	Gransden Lodge	5.00
2545/EBB	Grob G.102 Speed Astir IIB	4040		7.79	M.Malcolm & A.F.Grinter		
					"881"	Pocklington	5.00
2546/EBC+	Slingsby T.30B Prefect	583	RAFGSA."33"	7.79	K.R.Reeves	Syerston	4.00
	(Rebuilt with components ex BGA.808 & BGA.1618?) WE993				"Jonathan Livingstone Prefect"		
2547/EBD+	Scheibe Bergfalke IV	5822	D-1005	7.79	Burn GC	Burn	4.98

BGA No/Code	Type	C/n	P/I	Date	Owner/operator	Probable Base	CA Expy
2548/EBE+	Issoire E78 Silene	07		8.79	B.A.Burgess	Husbands Bosworth	9.99
2549/EBF+	Schempp-Hirth HS.7 Mini Nimbus C	138		8.79	P.H.Waite & Ptnrs		
						Sandhill Farm, Shrivenham	3.00
2550/EBG	Eiri PiK-20D	20662		8.79	P.F.Woodcock	Camphill	5.00
	(Assembled from fuselage of BGA.2550 and wings of BGA.2490 1999)						
2552/EBJ	Schleicher ASW19B	19282		8.79	J.D.Hill "h11"	Sutton Bank	12.99
2553/EBK	Schempp-Hirth HS.7 Mini Nimbus C	139	AGA.2	8.79	J.B.Burgoyne	Lyveden	5.00
			BGA.2553		"552"		
2554/EBL+	Schleicher ASK13	13610		8.79	Bristol & Glos GC	Nympsfield	10.99
2555/EBM	Grob G.102 Astir CS77	1843		8.79	D.O.Sephton "807"	Ringmer	4.00
2556/EBN	Centrair ASW20F	20118		8.79	K.W.Blake & Ptnrs "37"	Camphill	7.00
2557/EBP+	Allgaier Geier I	3/4	D-9025	8.79	G.A.Steel & Co	RAF Marham	6.97*
2559/EBR+	Glaser-Dirks DG-200/17	2-89/1706	D-6893	9.79	M.D.Parsons	Lee-on-Solent	6.00
2560/EBS+	Scheibe Zugvogel IIIA	1054	LX-CAF	9.79	I.D.McLeod	Challock	4.00
			D-8363		"Schwarzhornfalke"		
2565/EBX	Schleicher ASW20	20058	D-7973	9.79	J P Davies "644"	Gransden Lodge	7.00
2567/EBZ+	Schleicher ASK13	13614		9.79	Booker GC	Booker	2.00
2568/ECA	Wright Falcon	1		9.79	P.W.Wright	Saltby	8.98
2570/ECC+	Schleicher Ka6CR	60/01	D-5080	9.79	A.Allison & Ptnrs	Burn	4.00
2573/ECF+	Schleicher Ka6CR	856	D-5808	10.79	D.Goldup	Aston Down	7.00
2574/ECG+	Schempp-Hirth SHK	19	D-5359	10.79	M.F.Hardy	Upavon	3.00
			D-1329				
2575/ECH+	Glasflugel H.303 Mosquito B	173		10.79	A.Walker & Ptnrs	Rattlesden	4.00
2576/ECJ+	Slingsby T.65A Vega	1916		10.79	J.E.B.Hart & Ptnrs	Sutton Bank	4.00
2577/ECK+	Slingsby T.65A Vega	1917		10.79	L.Gibson	Milfield	4.97*
2578/ECL+	Slingsby T.65A Vega 17L	1918		10.79	B.H.Bryce-Smith	Gransden Lodge	2.00
2579/ECM+	Slingsby T.65A Vega	1919		10.79	F.L.Wilson	Aston Down	9.99
2580/ECN	Slingsby T.65A Vega 17L	1920		10.79	C.Claxton Syndicate "645"	Booker	3.00
2581/ECP+	Rolladen-Schneider LS-3-17	3426		10.79	M.Collins	Parham Park	3.00
2582/ECQ+	Grob G.102 Astir CS77	1837		10.79	M I Orrey	Tibenham	7.00
2584/ECS	Glasflugel H.303 Mosquito B	166		10.79	R.C.Adams & P.Robinson		
					"955"	Wormingford	3.00
2585/ECT	Glasflugel H.604	2	I-FEVG	10.79	F.K.Russell	Dunstable	3.99
			D-0279		"604"		
2588/ECW+	Schleicher ASK21	21008		11.79	Norfolk GC	Tibenham	10.99
2589/ECX	Schleicher ASW20L	20315		6.80	R.M.Lambert "600"	Feshiebridge	4.00
2590/ECY+	Glasflugel H.201B Standard Libelle	530	RAFGGA.557	11.79	G.Kelly & E.Fry	Bidford	6.00
2591/ECZ+	Schleicher ASK21	21009		4.80	Booker GC	Booker	3.00
2592/EDA	Slingsby T.65A Vega 17L	1888	G-BFYW	11.79	A.R.Worters "647"	Strathaven	5.98
2593/EDB+	CARMAM JP-15-36AR Aiglon	40		11.79	P.J.Martin & Ptnrs	Crowland	3.00
					"494"		
2594/EDC+	Schleicher Ka7 Rhonadler	244	D-8527	12.79	J.C.Shipley	Camphill	6.00
2595/EDD	Schleicher ASW17	17043	D-6865	12.79	S.Mulholland & Ptnrs	Syerston	5.00
					"69"		
2596/EDE	Centrair ASW20F	20128		1.80	G.M.Cumner "750"	Aston Down	5.00
2597/EDF	Schempp-Hirth HS.7 Mini Nimbus C	149		1.80	C.W.Boutcher "530"	Snitterfield	4.00
2598/EDG+	Schleicher Ka6CR	6512	RAFGSA	1.80	S.J.Wood	Cranwell	4.99
2599/EDH+	Glasflugel H.303 Mosquito B	184		1.80	D.G.Cooper	Tibenham	7.00
2600/EDJ+	Glasflugel H.303 Mosquito B	185		1.80	A.J.Leigh & Ptnrs	Camphill	5.00
2601/EDK	Schleicher Ka7	791	D-1633	1.80	York Gliding Centre	Rufforth	1.00
2602/EDL	Focke-Wulf Weihe 50	4	D-0893	1.80	F.K.Russell	Dunstable	10.96*
			HB-555				
2603/EDM+	Glaser-Dirks DG-200	2-98		1.80	A.H.St Pierre	Sutton Bank	3.00
2604/EDN	Glaser-Dirks DG-100G Elan	E12G6		1.80	A.P.Scott & Ptnrs	Currock Hill	6.00
					"820"		
2605/EDP	Glaser-Dirks DG-100G Elan	E19G7		1.80	J.F.Beach & Ptnrs	Nympsfield	3.00
					"448"		
2608/EDS+	Scheibe SF-26 Standard	5038	RAFGGA.???	1.80	I.Davidson	Long Mynd	3.96*
	(Probably ex RAFGGA.548)		D-8454				
2610/EDU+	Schleicher ASK13	13613		1.80	Kent GC	Challock	1.00
2611/EDV	Slingsby T.65A Vega 17L	1893	G-BGCU	2.80	J.L.Clegg "541"	Aston Down	3.00
2612/EDW+	Schleicher ASK21	21010		5.80	London GC	Dunstable	8.00
2613/EDX+	Slingsby T.65D Vega	1928		5.80	M.W.Cater	Husbands Bosworth	4.00
2614/EDY+	Slingsby T.65D Vega	1929		5.80	C.J.Steadman	Husbands Bosworth	4.00
2615/EDZ+	Slingsby T.65C Sport Vega	1931		5.80	R.C.Copley	Chipping	11.00
2616/EEA+	Slingsby T.65C Sport Vega	1932		5.80	Peterborough & Spalding GC		
						Crowland	3.00
2618/EEC+	Schleicher ASW20L	20311	(G-BSTS)	3.80	D.Cushway	Challock	3.00
2619/EED	Schleicher K8B	590	RAGGSA.R91	2.80	Crusaders GC		
			NEJSGSA/BGA.2619/D-5703			Kingsfield, Dhekelia	3.00
2620/EEE+	Schleicher ASW20L	20312		3.80	T E MacFadyen	Aston Down	3.00

BGA No/Code	Type	C/n	P/I	Date	Owner/operator	Probable Base	CA Expy
2621/EEF+	Rolladen-Schneider LS-3-17	3441		3.80	G Nicholas	Rivar Hill	7.99
2622/EEG+	Slingsby T.65C Sport Vega	1922	EI-129 BGA.2622	3.80	G.Harris	Rufforth	9.00
2623/EEH+	Schleicher ASW119	19042	RAFGSA	2.80	K Kiely "166"	Dishforth	4.00
2624/EEJ+	Schleicher ASW20L	20314		9.80	R.R.Stoward	Dunstable	3.00
2625/EEK	Schempp-Hirth HS.5 Nimbus 2C	201		2.80	R.E.Cross "141"	Lasham	12.99
2627/EEM+	Schleicher K8B	8688AB	D-0254	2.80	South Wales GC	Usk	5.00
2628/EEN+	Schempp-Hirth HS.4 Standard Cirrus	75 621	(BGA.2609) RAFGSA 87	2.80	J.Hanlon Weston-on-the-Green		2.00
2629/EEP+	Wassmer WA.26P Squale	36	F-CDSX	3.80	R.H.Parker	Bidford	4.00
2630/EEQ+	Grob G.102 Standard Astir II	5015S	RNGSA.N12	3.80	S.W.Bradford	Dunstable	2.00
2631/EER	Schempp-Hirth HS.7 Mini Nimbus	150		3.80	W.T.Lewis	Perranporth	4.00
2632/EES	Rolladen-Schneider LS-3-17	3248		3.80	R.Illidge & Ptnrs "50"	Camphill	10.00
2634/EEU	Issoire E78 Silene	08		3.80	M.B.Jefferyes & Ptnrs "456"	Ridgewell	8.98
2635/EEV	Centrair ASW20FL	20145		3.80	J.P.Lyell & Ptnr "129"	Lasham	2.00
2636/EEW+	Schleicher Ka6CR	6188	RAFGGA D-6151	3.80	P.E.Lowden	Winthorpe	9.99
2637/EEX+	Rolladen-Schneider LS-3-17	3442		3.80	W A.Dalimer & Ptnr	Aston Down	5.00
2639/EEZ	Rolladen-Schneider LS-3A	3458		3.80	P.Holland "157"	Sutton Bank	12.99
2640/EFA	Schleicher ASW20L	20326		4.80	P.J.Warner "470"	Dunstable	5.00
2641/EFB+	Schempp-Hirth HS.5 Nimbus 2C	216		4.80	N.Revell & Ptnrs	Gamston	6.00
2642/EFC+	Siebert Sie-3	3018	D-0811	4.80	M.S.A.Skinner	Cross Hayes	5.00
2643/EFD+	Schleicher Ka7 Rhonadler	7007	PH-277	7.80	South London Gliding Centre Kenley		1.99
2644/EFE	Centrair ASW20F	20139		5.80	J.A.Quartermaine & Ptnrs "586"	Sutton Bank	2.00
2645/EFF	Schempp-Hirth HS.5 Nimbus 2C	208		4.80	E.R.Duffin & D.L.Jobbins "737"	Rhigos	3.00
2646/EFG+	Schleicher K8B	NK	RAFGGA	4.80	Rattlesden GC	Rattlesden	2.98
2647/EFH	Schleicher ASW20	20308		4.80	M B Judkins "939"	Lasham	4.00
2648/EFJ	Centrair ASW20F	20127		4.80	D.Ball	(Surrey)	6.00
2649/EFK	Centrair ASW20FL	20140		5.80	B.Kerby "543"	Long Mynd	6.00
2650/EFL	Centrair ASW20FL	20133		5.80	D.J.Connolly Kingston Deverill "297"		4.99
2651/EFM+	Schleicher Ka6E	4103	RAFGSA	6.80	G.S.Foster	Parham Park	7.99
2652/EFN+	Scheibe L-Spatz 55	635	D-1617	5.80	E F Weaver	Halton	7.99
2653/EFP	Schleicher K8B	E.01	D-8859	5.80	Not known (Stored 3.95)	Portmoak	7.88*
2655/EFR+	Scheibe L-Spatz	320	RAFGGA	4.80	H. & A.Purser	Cranfield	9.98
2656/EFS	Rolladen-Schneider LS-3	3022	HB-1356	5.80	G.I Boswell "636"	Dunstable	6.99
2657/EFT	Schempp-Hirth HS.5 Nimbus 2B	26	HB-1160	4.80	N.L.Jennings "145"	Lleweni Parc	4.00
2659/EFV	Schleicher ASW20	20041		6.80	A.R McKillen	Bellarena	9.00
2660/EFW+	Slingsby T.65C Sport Vega	1938		7.80	Dukeries GC	Gamston	5.00
2661/EFX	LET L-13 Blanik	026460	AGA.21 RAFGSA.R7/BGA.2095	.80	Enstone Eagles GC	Edgehill	11.94*
			(Crashed Enstone 25.6.94; parts to BGA.3666; wreck stored 6.95)				
2663/EFZ+	Rolladen-Schneider LS-3A	3273		5.80	D.H.Gardner & J.Higgins Aston Down		3.00
2667/EGD	Schleicher ASW17	17028	D-2343	6.80	W.J.Dean "D3"	Booker	7.98
2668/EGE+	Rolladen-Schneider LS-3A	3465		6.80	D.Barker	Nympsfield	1.00
2669/EGF+	Slingsby T.65C Sport Vega	1936		6.80	B.Snook	Old Sarum	1.00
2670/EGG	Slingsby T.65C Sport Vega	1939		6.80	J.Milson "JH"	Usk	5.00
2671/EGH+	Slingsby T.65C Sport Vega	1943		6.80	M.J Davies & Ptnrs	Winthorpe	3.00
2672/EGJ	Slingsby T.65C Sport Vega	1944		6.80	K.J.Towell & Ptnrs "672"	Lasham	3.00
2673/EGK	Schempp-Hirth HS.4 Standard Cirrus	542G	RAFGSA.569 RAFGSA.R2	6.80	I.M.Deans & Ptnrs "569"	Lasham	12.99
2674/EGL+	Schleicher Ka6CR	6330	D-6037	6.80	G.B.Dennis	Halesland	11.97*
			t/a Mendip K6 Syndicate (Damaged North Hill 9.7.97)				
2676/EGN+	Grob G.103 Twin II	3542		7.80	Enstone Eagles GC	Enstone	9.00
2677/EGP	Schleicher ASW20L	20336		7.80	A.W.Gillett & Ptnrs "172"	Nympsfield	2.00
2679/EGR+	Breguet Br.905SA Fauvette	18	F-CCGT	7.80	P.Parker	Tibenham	7.00
2680/EGS	Schempp-Hirth HS.5 Nimbus 2CS	192	D-2111	7.80	P.G.Myers "2"	Chipping	5.00
2681/EGT+	Slingsby T.65D Vega	1933		7.80	D.M.Badley & Ptnrs	Sleap	2.00
2682/EGU+	Slingsby T.65A Vega	1921		7.80	M.N.Bishop	Challock	1.00
2684/EGW	Schempp-Hirth HS.7 Mini Nimbus B (Modified to Mini Nimbus C?)	78	HB-1447	8.80	I F Barnes "844"	Ridgewell	8.00
2685/EGX+	Slingsby T.65C Sport Vega	1937	RAFGSA.R23 BGA.2685	8.80	M.D.Organ Weston-on-the-Green		4.00
2687/EGZ+	Schleicher ASK21	21030		8.80	Needwood Forest GC	Cross Hayes	3.00

BGA No/Code	Type	C/n	P/I	Date	Owner/operator	Probable Base	CA Expy
2688/EHA	Schleicher K8B	136/59	D-5084	8.80	Not known Fairwood Common		*
					(Stored as "D-5084" 1.97)		
2690/EHC+	Eichelsdorfer SB-5B	5017	D-9310	8.80	R.I.Davidson Husbands Bosworth		6.00
2691/EHD	Schleicher ASW20L	20386		10.80	E.A.Arthur & Ptnr	Tibenham	1.00
					"891"		
2692/EHE+	Slingsby T.30B Prefect	582	WE992	10.80	A.P.Stacey	RAF Keevil	3.98
					t/a A.T.C.Syndicate (As "WE992")		
2693/EHF	Caudron C.801	320/4	F-CBTE	5.89	Dutch Aircastle Society		
					Loosdrecht, The Netherlands		4.99
2694/EHG	Slingsby T.65C Sport Vega	1940		10.80	M.J.Vicery & Ptnrs "453"	Lasham	12.99
2695/EHH	Schempp-Hirth Ventus A	07		10.80	P.G.Sheard & A.Stone "V7"	Lasham	2.00
2697/EHK	Rolladen-Schneider LS-4	4068		10.80	S.J.C.Parker "490"	Nympsfield	12.99
2698/EHL	Rolladen-Schneider LS-4	4024		10.80	C.J.Evans "138"	Booker	2.00
2699/EHM+	Schleicher Ka6E	4118	RAFGSA.318	11.80	D.J.Pengally Kingston Deverill		7.00
2700/EHN+	Slingsby T.65C Sport Vega	1942	G-BILH	11.80	G.D.Hayter	Challock	1.00
			BGA.2700				
2701/EHP+	Schempp-Hirth HS.5 Nimbus 2C	234		11.80	L.Kirkham	Seighford	2.00
2702/EHQ	Schleicher ASK21	21035		11.80	University of Surrey GC Lasham		2.00
					"431"		
2704/EHS+	ICA IS-28B2	89		12.80	B.Crowhurst	Crowland	9.99
2705/EHT	Schempp-Hirth HS.5 Nimbus 2C	235		12.80	S.R.Ell "E11"	Camphill	11.99
2706/EHU	Glasflugel H.304	209		12.80	F. & J.M.Townsend "849" Camphill		11.00
2707/EHV	Schleicher ASW20L	20385		12.80	G.S.Neumann & Ptnrs "481" Booker		2.00
2708/EHW+	ICA IS-28B2	86		12.80	M Sanderson	Milfield	11.00
2709/EHX+	DFS/49 Grunau Baby 2B	134	D-1128	12.80	J.A.Knowles "1128"	Odiham	3.98
2710/EHY+	Slingsby T.65D Vega	1941		1.81	R.Spear	Ringmer	10.00
2711/EHZ	Schleicher ASW20L	20388		12.80	D.Hoolahan "413"	Challock	4.00
2712/EJA+	ICA IS-28B2	88		1.81	DRA GC	Odiham	12.00
2713/EJB+	Slingsby T.65C Sport Vega	1945		1.81	I.G.Walker & Ptnrs	Camphill	5.00
2714/EJC+	Slingsby T.65C Sport Vega	1946		2.81	A M.Raper & Ptnrs	Rattlesden	5.00
2715/EJD	Slingsby T.65D Vega 17L	1930		6.81	A.J.French	Booker	5.97*
					"261" (Damaged Dunstable 28.3.97)		
2716/EJE+	Slingsby T.65C Sport Vega	1947		2.81	DRA GC	Odiham	2.00
2717/EJF+	Schleicher K8B	8966	D-2328	1.81	Cambridge University GC		
						Gransden Lodge	11.99
2718/EJG+	Schleicher K8B	01	D-5679	1.81	Kent GC	Challock	2.99
2719/EJH+	Eichelsdorfer SB-5E	5041A	D-5430	1.81	H.J.McEvaddy Husbands Bosworth		6.00
			D-0087				
2720/EJJ	Slingsby T.21B	NK	RAFGSA.120	2.81	N.P.Marriott	Parham Park	3.00
2721/EJK	Centrair ASW20FLP	20172		2.81	A.M.Blackburn "76"	Camphill	5.00
2722/EJL+	Centrair ASW20FL	20183		2.81	R.A.Yates	Bidford	5.00
2725/EJP+	Slingsby T.21B	1131	RAFGSA.238	2.81	Upward Bound Trust	Thame	6.96*
			BGA.846				
2726/EJQ+	Centrair ASW20FL	20184		2.81	G.Falcke & Ptnrs Gransden Lodge		11.99
2727/EJR	Schleicher ASW19B	19334		2.81	Bristol & Glos GC	Nympsfield	3.00
					"193"		
2728/EJS	Slingsby T.65C Sport Vega	1948		2.81	A.D.McLeman "319"	Portmoak	7.00
2729/EJT	Slingsby T.65A Vega	1889	G-VEGA	2.81	W.A.Sanderson "890"	Rattlesden	2.00
			(G-BFZN)		(As "G-VEGA")		
2732/EJW+	Issoire D77 Iris	04		4.81	T.Hurley Husbands Bosworth		2.95*
2734/EJY+	SZD-9 bis Bocian 1D	P-351	D-1587	3.81	The Borders GC	Milfield	5.98
2736/EKA+	Glaser-Dirks DG-200/17	2-128/1730		3.81	M J Lindsey	Tibenham	4.00
2737/EKB	Schempp-Hirth HS.6 Janus C	129		3.81	D.A.Head "710"	Bicester	2.99
2738/EKC+	Schleicher Ka6E	4079	OO-ZDV	4.81	S L Benn	Cranwell	4.00
			OE-0813				
2739/EKD+	Schleicher ASK13	13539	OH-494	4.81	Devon & Somerset GC	North Hill	1.00
2740/EKE	Schleicher ASW20L	20387		4.81	J K Williams "20L"	Ringmer	3.00
2741/EKF+	Grob G.102 Club Astir III	5519C		4.81	Bristol & Glos GC	Nympsfield	3.00
2742/EKG+	Schleicher ASK21	21067	AGA.8	4.81	Wyvern GC	Upavon	11.00
			BGA.2742				
2743/EKH	Schempp-Hirth Ventus B	32		4.81	R Bottomley "714"	Lasham	3.00
2744/EKJ	Schempp-Hirth Ventus B	36		4.81	I.J.Metcalfe "186"	Nympsfield	5.00
2745/EKK+	SZD-48 Jantar Standard 2	W-853		4.81	S.Nutler	Feshie Bridge	9.00
2749/EKP+	Glaser-Dirks DG-100G Elan	E71G46		5.81	P.J.Masson	Lasham	3.00
2751/EKR	Schempp-Hirth HS.5 Nimbus 2C	195	D-4904	5.81	J.W.Evans "117"	Bidford	3.00
2752/EKS+	Scheibe SF-27A Zugvogel V	6096	D-8166	5.81	A.B.Pemberton	Parham Park	2.00
2754/EKU	Schleicher ASW20L	20384		5.81	A.R.Levi & Ptnrs "408"	Rufforth	1.00
2755/EKV+	Rolladen-Schneider LS-4	4102		5.81	M.Ray	Lasham	2.00
2756/EKW	Schempp-Hirth HS.5 Nimbus 2B	111	D-7245	5.81	R.S.Jobar "430"	Lasham	5.00
2757/EKX+	Schleicher Ka6E	4027	D-1221	6.81	A.Coatsworth	Gallows Hill	8.00
					(As "D-1221")		

BGA No/Code	Type	C/n	P/I	Date	Owner/operator	Probable Base	CA Expy
2758/EKY+	Slingsby T.65C Sport Vega	1949		6.81	Essex & Suffolk GC	Wormingford	2.00
2760/ELA+	Schleicher ASW19B	19346		6.81	A.G.Stark	Aboyne	4.00
2762/ELC+	Slingsby T.45 Swallow	1474	AGA. RAFGSA.346	7.81	J.Povall	Dishforth	2.00
2763/ELD+	Slingsby T.65C Sport Vega	1950		8.81	D.J Clark & Ptnrs	Challock	2.00
2764/ELE	Schleicher ASK21	21065		7.81	Midland GC "797"	Long Mynd	3.00
2766/ELG+	Schempp-Hirth Ventus B	46		8.81	H.Forshaw "931"	Burn	4.00
2767/ELH+	Slingsby T.21B	?	RAFGSA.314	7.81	Not known	Enstone	7.91*
	(Possibly ex WB966 [627])		(RAF)		(Stored 3.97)		
2768/ELJ+	Breguet Br.905SA Fauvette	21	F-CCGU	8.81	E.A.Hull	Dunstable	11.00
2769/ELK	Slingsby T.9 King Kite Replica	-		8.83	D.G.Jones Husbands Bosworth		5.99
2770/ELL	Vogt Lo-100 Zwergreiher	25	HB-591	7.81	I.E.Tunstall "LO1"	Syerston	8.99
2772/ELN+	Grob G.102 Astir CS Jeans	2024	???	8.81	J.M.Hughes	Dunstable	3.00
2774/ELQ+	Slingsby T.65D Vega	1934		8.81	J.Bell	Milfield	8.00
2775/ELR	Schempp-Hirth Ventus B	45		8.81	I.D.Smith "188"	Nympsfield	3.00
2776/ELS+	EoN AP.10 460 Srs.1	EoN/S/020	RAFGGA.530	8.81	D.G.Shepherd	Easterton	5.97*
2777/ELT+	Rolladen-Schneider LS-4	4186		9.81	P.D.MaCarthy	Lasham	3.00
2778/ELU	Schleicher ASW20L	20462		9.81	D.W.Lilburn "696"	Aston Down	3.00
2779/ELV+	Scheibe Zugvogel IIIB	1088	F-CCPX	9.81	C.R.W.Hill	Crowland	7.00
2781/ELX+	Schleicher Ka7 Rhonadler	928	D-4023	9.81	Rattlesden GC	Rattlesden	6.00
2782/ELY+	Schleicher Ka6CR	6485Si	D-5172	9.81	P.F Richardson & Ptnrs Bellarena		2.00
2783/ELZ	Schleicher ASW20L	20310		10.81	D.A.Fogden "719"	Booker	2.00
2785/EMB	Rolladen-Schneider LS-4	4185		10.81	L S Hood "352"	Winthorpe	3.00
2788/EME	Glaser-Dirks DG-202/17C	2-176CL18		11.81	F.Boyce "515"Weston-on-the-Green		12.00
2789/EMF	Rolladen-Schneider LS-4	4187		11.81	E.R.Smith & Ptnrs "452" Thruxton		3.00
2790/EMG+	Rolladen Schneider LS-4	4242		5.82	R C Bowsfield	Nympsfield	2.00
2791/EMH+	Schleicher ASK18	18009	D-6872	11.81	Staffordshire GC	Seighford	1.99*
	(Officially regd with c/n 18096)				(W/O in mid-air collision Seighford 2.5.98)		
2792/EMJ+	Slingsby T.65C Sport Vega	1951		1.82	Staffordshire GC	Seighford	4.00
2793/EMK+	Slingsby T.45 Swallow	1514	RAFGGA.545	12.81	A.Povey & Ptnrs	Syerston	5.00
2794/EML	Slingsby T.65A Vega	1892	G-BGCB	12.81	P.W.Williams "218"	North Hill	1.00
2796/EMN+	Slingsby T.65D Vega	1935		1.82	C.D.Sword & Ptnrs	Currock Hill	7.00
2797/EMP+	Slingsby T.65C Sport Vega	1952		2.82	D.R Freehold	Kenley	8.00
2799/EMR+	Slingsby T.65C Sport Vega	1954		2.82	P.Greenway & Ptnrs	Shobdon	7.00
2800/EMS	Slingsby T.65A Vega 17L	1890	G-BGBV	2.82	M.P.Day "T65"	Kenley	9.00
					(As "G-BGBV")		
2801/EMT	Rolladen-Schneider LS-4	4243		12.81	D.B.Eastell "55"	Challock	1.00
2802/EMU	Glaser-Dirks DG-202/17	2-162/1753		1.82	P.B.Gray & Ptnrs "606"	Camphill	4.00
2803/EMV+	Schleicher Ka7 Rhonadler	NK	AGA.13	1.82	Shalbourne Soaring Group		
						Rivar Hill	7.00
2804/EMW	Grunau Baby III	NK	D-1373	7.89	M.T.A.Sands "17"	(France)	9.99
2806/EMY	Rolladen-Schneider LS-4	4189		1.82	N.V.Parry "264"	Nympsfield	3.00
2807/EMZ+	Slingsby T.65A Vega	1891	G-BGCA	2.82	F.S.Smith	Portmoak	4.00
2808/ENA	Rolladen-Schneider LS-4	4191		2.82	J.D.Collins & Ptnr "288" Bidford		5.00
2810/ENC	Schleicher Ka7 Rhonadler	384	D-8111	2.82	I.H.Keyser Waldershare Park		3.00
	(Modified to ASK13 status)				(As "2810")		
2812/ENE	Rolladen-Schneider LS-4	4271		3.82	D.M.Abbey Husbands Bosworth		2.00
					"281"		
2814/ENG+	Focke-Wulf Kranich III	79	D-5420	3.82	P.Davie & Ptnrs	Dunstable	3.00
2816/ENJ	Schempp-Hirth Ventus B	62		3.82	S.J.Boyden "771"	Lasham	6.00
2817/ENK+	Schleicher ASK21	21106		4.82	H Jakeman	Aston Down	3.00
2820/ENN	Schempp-Hirth Nimbus 3	9		4.83	R.Kalin & Ptnrs Gransden Lodge		11.99
					"345"		
2821/ENP	Schempp-Hirth Nimbus 3	10		11.82	L.Bleaken "626"	Aston Down	4.00
2825/ENT	Glasflugel H.304	210		5.82	P.D.Light "902"	Dunstable	4.98
2826/ENU	Glaser-Dirks DG-100G Elan	E108G78		5.82	F.D.Platt "435"	Camphill	3.00
2827/ENV	Schleicher ASW20L	20554		5.82	R.Hone "181"	Booker	5.00
2828/ENW+	Schleicher ASW20L	20567		5.82	A.Hunter	Pocklington	3.00
2830/ENY+	Schleicher ASK13	13606	RAFGSA.R17	6.82	Aquila GC Hinton-in-The-Hedges		4.00
2831/ENZ	Schleicher ASW19B	19366		6.82	O.Pugh	Booker	4.00
2835/EPD+	Schleicher ASK21	21119		8.82	B.Purslow & Ptnrs	Chipping	3.00
2836/EPE+	Schleicher ASW19B	19335	RAFGSA.R18 BGA.2836	6.82	J.Horner	Pocklington	3.00
2837/EPF	Centrair ASW20FLP	20515		7.82	D.J.Howse "323" Gransden Lodge		3.00
2838/EPG	CARMAM M.100S Mesange	3	F-CCPB	7.82	P.Shanahan	Templeton	2.95*
2840/EPJ+	Nord 2000 (Olympia)	10399/69	F-CACX	8.82	B.V.Smith	Dishforth	5.00
2841/EPK	Centrair 101A Pegase	101-012		10.82	742 Syndicate "742"	Bicester	3.00
2843/EPM+	Scheibe SFH-34 Delphin	5115		8.82	Angus GC	Drumshade	3.98
2844/EPN	Breguet Br.905SA Fauvette	11	F-CCIO	8.82	P.F.Woodcock	Camphill	7.95*
2845/EPP	Schleicher ASK13	1609		1.83	Black Mountains GC	Talgarth	4.00
	(Rebuild of PH-368 c/n 13064: c/n is spare fuselage no.)				"T10"		

BGA No/Code	Type	C/n	P/I	Date	Owner/operator	Probable Base	CA Expy
2847/EPR	Hutter H-17	-	(Kenya) PH-269	9.82	D.Shrimpton	Halesland	6.97
2848/EPS	Schleicher ASW20L	20245	RAFGGA.87	7.85	D.Richardson "765"	Booker	4.98
2849/EPT+	Schleicher K8B	?	RAFGGA.504	9.82	Trent Valley GC	Kirton-in-Lindsey	10.00
2850/EPU+	Glaser-Dirks DG-100G Elan	E116G85	(BGA.2833)	10.82	J.E.Rogers "647"	Booker	3.00
2851/EPV+	Schleicher Ka7 Rhonadler	7148	D-5468	10.82	Newark & Notts GC	Winthorpe	2.00
2852/EPW+	Schleicher Ka6CR	6537	(Kenya)	10.82	J.Kitchen	Strubby	2.00
2853/EPX	Schempp-Hirth Ventus B/16.6	107		10.82	W.T.Craig "906"	Saltby	6.00
2855/EPZ	Scheibe Bergfalke II/55	370	D-4012	1.83	G.W.Sturgess	Upavon	8.96*
2856/EQA	Rolladen-Schneider LS-4	4259		10.82	M.R.Fountain "275"	Booker	5.00
2857/EQB+	SZD-30 Pirat	S-0648	D-2702	10.82	R.Firman	Booker	8.00
2859/EQD+	Grob G.102 Astir CS77	1614	PH-570	11.82	D.S.Fenton & Ptnrs	Rhigos	5.00
2860/EQE+	Schleicher ASK13	13627		12.82	Essex GC	Ridgewell	9.00
2861/EQF+	Schleicher ASK13	13626		3.85	Essex GC	Ridgewell	8.00
2862/EQG	Schleicher ASW19B	19265	PH-665	12.82	C.M.Whittington & Ptnrs "239"	Challock	3.00
2864/EQJ	Centrair ASW20FL	20512		1.83	N.S.Roberts "968"	Lasham	3.00
2865/EQK+	Centrair 101A Pegase	101-054		2.83	F.G.Irving & Ptnrs	Lasham	2.00
2866/EQL	Avialsa (Rocheteau) CRA-60 Fauconnet	03K	F-CDNR	1.86	J.James	Saltby	5.99
2867/EQM+	CARMAM M.100S Mesange	81	F-CDKQ	3.83	R.Boyd	Rivar Hill	9.00
2868/EQN	Schempp-Hirth Nimbus 3	31		3.83	A.D.Purnell "340"	Lasham	2.00
2870/EQQ	Schleicher Ka6CR	6541	AGA.24 BGA.1353	4.83	G.H.Costin & Ptnrs "451"	Challock	2.00
2871/EQR+	Schleicher ASK21	21157		3.83	London GC	Dunstable	12.00
2873/EQT	Grob G.103A Twin II Acro	3787-K-65	RAFGSA.R58 BGA.2873	4.83	RAF GSA Centre	RAF Bicester	2.00
2874/EQU+	Pilatus B4 PC-11	201	PH-535	4.83	W.Green & Ptnrs	Chipping	3.00
2877/EQX+	CARMAM M.200 Foehn	54	F-CDKR	4.83	C.A.McLay & Ptnrs	Chipping	4.00
2878/EQY	BAC.VII rep	01		9.91	M.H.Maufe	Brooklands	5.96P*
	(Rebuild of BAC Drone using wings of G-AEJR and new fuselage)						
2879/EQZ+	Schleicher K8B	8113A	D-8763	4.83	Cotswold GC	Aston Down	11.00
2880/ERA	Centrair ASW20FL	20526		4.83	C.C.Pike "283"	Booker	3.00
2881/ERB+	Slingsby T.50 Skylark 4 Special	001		4.83	B.V.Smith	Dishforth	8.00
	(Built C.Almack)						
2887/ERH+	Schleicher ASK21	21147	ZD647 BGA.2887	4.83	Burn GC	Burn	4.00
2888/ERJ	Schleicher ASK21	21148	RAFGSA.R35 ZD648	3.99	Cranwell GC "R35"	Cranwell	3.00
2898/ERU+	Schempp-Hirth Nimbus 3	13	RAFGSA.R26 D-6330	5.83	L.Urbani	Rieti, Italy	6.00
2899/ERV	Rolladen-Schneider LS-4	4257		5.83	R E Francis "854"	Nympsfield	10.00
2900/ERW	Slingsby T.21B	1130	RAFGSA.237 BGA.842	5.83	High Moor GC "The Spruce Goose"	Hafotty Bennett	6.00
2901/ERX	Centrair 101A Pegase	101-058		6.83	V.Sinclair & Ptnrs "180"	Lasham	3.00
2902/ERY+	Slingsby T.59D Kestrel 22	1839	EI-125 D-9253	6.83	R.J.Hart & Ptnr "983"	Crowland	4.00
2903/ERZ	Oberlerchner Mg19a Steinadler	015	OE-0324	6.83	C.Wills	Booker	9.00
2904/ESA+	SZD-9 bis Bocian 1E	P-750		6.83	Coventry GC	Husbands Bosworth	8.00
2905/ESB+	Schleicher ASK21	21176		6.83	A.L.Garfield	Dunstable	2.00
2906/ESC	Rolladen-Schneider LS-4	4261		6.83	J.M.Staley "379"	Bicester	3.00
2907/ESD	Centrair 101A Pegase	101-065		6.83	R.I.Cowderoy "640"	Lasham	3.97*
2908/ESE	Rolladen-Schneider LS-4	4260		6.83	P.C.Fritche "LS4"	Parham Park	2.00
2911/ESH	Centrair 101A Pegase	101-069		7.83	D.M.Byass "118"	Booker	12.99
2912/ESJ+	Schleicher K8B	8730	D-5010	7.83	Bowland Forest GC	Chipping	5.00
2913/ESK	Schleicher Ka2B	697	RAFGSA.594 D-5947	7.83	W.R.Williams	RAF Halton	5.00
2915/ESM	Breguet Br.905SA Fauvette	30	F-CCJA	8.83	A C Jarvis	Parham Park	8.00
2917/ESP+	SZD-48-3 Jantar Standard 3	B-1294		4.84	J.Durman	Pocklington	3.00
2918/ESQ	Glaser-Dirks DG-300 Elan	3E10		4.84	G.Huggins "231" Sandhill Farm, Shrivenham		3.00
2922/ESU+	Schleicher ASK21	21180	RAFGSA.R40 BGA.2922	9.83	Southdown GC	Parham Park	5.00
	(Composite with RAFGSA.R28 c/n 21154)						
2923/ESV+	LET L-13 Blanik	173328	EI-110 IGA 110/G-ATWW	5.84	Herefordshire GC	Shobdon	4.98
2924/ESW	Centrair 101A Pegase	101-068		3.84	A.F.Thomas "590"	Usk	2.00
2925/ESX	Schleicher K8B	.	(ex)	9.83	Wolds GC	Pocklington	12.96*
2926/ESY+	Rolladen-Schneider LS-4	4334		2.84	K.Jenkins & Ptnrs	North Hill	3.00
2928/ETA	Schleicher ASK21	21181		11.83	R W Collings	Husbands Bosworth	4.00
2929/ETB+	Schleicher Ka6E	4365	HB-1021	11.83	A.J.Padgett "A6"	Tibenham	5.00

BGA No/Code	Type	C/n	P/I	Date	Owner/operator	Probable Base	CA Expy
2931/ETD	Schleicher K8B	8923	RAFGSA.R44	1.84	RAFGSA Centre	Bicester	5.00
			RAFGSA.538/RAFGSA.R38/BGA2931				
2932/ETE	Fauvel AV.36C	214	RAFGSA.R53	8.87	J.F.Beringer	RAF Halton	6.98
			D-5353/D-8259		"The Budgie"		
2934/ETG+	Rolladen-Schneider LS-4	4349		12.83	M.W.Rebbeck & Ptnrs	Rattlesden	5.00
2935/ETH+	Schleicher K8B	120	D-5755	4.84	North Wales GC	Bryngwyn Bach	8.00
2936/ETJ	Centrair 101A Pegase	101A-0110		10.84	K.J.Bye "223"	Worminglord	1.00
2937/ETK	SZD-48 Jantar Standard 2	W-876	OY-XJO	2.84	J.A.Cowie "215"	Portmoak	6.00
2938/ETL	Jansson BJ-1B Duster	01		1.85P	I.Beckett	North Hill	3.96*
2939/ETM	Centrair 101 Pegase	101-111		5.84	Booker GC "312"	Booker	3.00
2940/ETN	CARMAM M.100S Mesange	23	F-CCSL	2.84	T.E.Betts	Seighford	8.96*
2941/ETP	Slingsby T.21B	610	WB943	7.84	P.Hepworth	Rufforth	5.00
					t/a Ouse T.21 Syndicate "943" (As "WB943")		
2942/ETQ+	Centrair 101A Pegase	101A-0123		5.84	A R Jennings	Gransden Lodge	4.99
2943/ETR	Schleicher Ka7 Rhonadler	3	D-8339	1.84	Shenington GC "2"	Edgehill	4.00
2944/ETS+	Schleicher ASK13	13635AB		3.84	Upward Bound Trust	Thame	8.00
2946/ETU+	Schleicher Ka7 Rhonadler	?	RAFGSA R.8	4.84	R.Cullum	Strubby	6.00
2947/ETV+	Rolladen-Schneider LS-4	4314	(BGA.2919)	3.84	T.A.Meaker	Kirton-in-Lindsey	3.00
2950/ETY	Rolladen-Schneider LS-4	4368		4.84	R.Harris "249"	Booker	2.00
2951/ETZ	Schleicher ASW20CL	20730		3.84	R.R.Page "20"	Lasham	3.00
2954/EUC+	Schleicher ASK13	13104	AGA.12	4.84	Bristol & Glos GC	Nympsfield	12.99
2955/EUD	Schleicher ASW20C	20734		6.84	D.J.Tagg "56"	Lasham	3.00
2956/EUE+	Scheibe SF-27A Zugvogel V	6106	D-5342	5.84	Newark & Notts GC	Winthorpe	7.00
2957/EUF+	SZD-50-3 Puchacz	B-1090		5.84	D.B.Meeks	Bidford	3.00
					t/a Bidford Gliding Centre		
2958/EUG+	LET L-13 Blanik	025817	RAFGSA.R56	5.84	Avon Soaring Centre	Bidford	5.93*
			RAFGSA.426/BGA.1953				
	(Composite rebuild - fuselage/tail: BGA.1917 [025610], port [025817] & starboard wings (BGA.2028 [026257]))						
2959/EUH	Rolladen-Schneider LS-4	4382		4.84	W.P.Winterton "446"	Parham Park	3.00
2960/EUJ+	Schempp-Hirth Ventus B/16.6	162		4.84	T.Paterson & Ptnrs	Portmoak	11.99
2961/EUK	Centrair ASW20FL	20530		5.84	J.L.Caton "992"	Lasham	2.00
2963/EUM+	Scheibe SF-26A Standard	5039	RAFGSA	5.84	Vale of Neath GC	Rhigos	7.97*
2964/EUN	Slingsby T.21B	588	RAFGSA.R92	4.84	Booker GC	Booker	6.00
			RAFGSA.212/WB925				
2966/EUQ+	Schleicher Ka7 Rhonadler	863	D-4639	5.84	Kent GC	Challock	2.00
2968/EUS	Schempp-Hirth Ventus B/16.6	192		5.84	J.C.Bastin "443"	Rivar Hill	4.00
2969/EUT+	Schleicher Rhonlerche	NK	RAFGSA	5.84	G.De"Orfe & Ptnrs	Gransden Lodge	11.99
2971/EUV+	SZD-42-2 Jantar 2B	B-934		5.84	G.V.McKirdy	Edgehill	5.98
2973/EUX+	Schleicher ASK18	18005	D-3988	5.84	Southdown GC	Parham Park	10.00
2974/EUY	Schleicher ASW20BL	20645		6.84	D.G.Roberts & Ptnrs	Aston Down	3.00
					"88"		
2975/EUZ	Slingsby T.21B	620	WB959	6.84	Dartmoor Gliding Association		
						Brent Tor	9.00
2976/EVA+	Slingsby T.31B	683	WT873	9.84	T.Bull	Parham Park	6.99
2977/EVB+	Schleicher Ka7 Rhonadler	7004	D-5109	6.84	R.Armitage	Waldershare Park	11.00
					t/a Channel GC		
2978/EVC+	CARMAM M.200 Foehn	55	F-CDKT	6.84	W.Young & Ptnrs	Pocklington	3.00
2979/EVD	Rolladen-Schneider LS-3	3024	N63LS	8.84	C.R.Appleyard	Lasham	4.00
			D-7914		"382"		
2980/EVE	Centrair 101A Pegase	101A-0141		6.84	B.M.Chaplin "491"	Lasham	5.00
2981/EVF	Schempp-Hirth Nimbus 3T	15/76	D-KHIJ	3.85	R.A.Foot & Ptnrs "90"	Lasham	2.00
2982/EVG+	Schleicher Ka7 Rhonadler	396	D-0018	7.84	Derby & Lancs GC	Camphill	8.99
2983/EVH+	Schleicher Ka10	10008	HB-791	5.86	J.W Bolt	Brent Tor	5.00
2984/EVJ	Schleicher ASK13	13637AB		7.84	Lasham Gliding Society	Lasham	11.00
					"H"		
2985/EVK+	Grob G.102 Astir CS	1397	PH-546	12.86	D.R.Taylor	Tibenham	6.00
2986/EVL	Grob G.102 Astir CS77	1638	PH-575	8.84	Southdown Aero Services	Lasham	5.00
					"SA1"		
2987/EVM	Centrair 101A Pegase	101A-0157	(RNGSA.N51)	8.84	Culdrose GC	RNAS Culdrose	3.00
2989/EVP	Schleicher ASK13	13638AB		8.84	Lasham Gliding Society	Lasham	11.99
					"K"		
2990/EVQ	Centrair 101A Pegase	101A-0149		8.84	R.J.Dann & Ptnr	Rivar Hill	5.00
					"682"		
2991/EVR	LET L-13 Blanik	172604	G-ASVS	8.84	D.Latimer	Hinton-in-The-Hedges	6.00
			OK-3840				
2992/EVS+	SZD-50-3 Puchacz	B-1091		9.84	Connel GC	North Connel	9.00
2993/EVT+	Scheibe Bergfalke IV	5807	D-0730	9.84	Shalbourne Soaring Society		
						Rivar Hill	8.00
2994/EVU	Raab Doppelraab	515	RAFGSA.666	R	Not known	RAF Bicester	*
	(Built Wolf Hirth 1952)		D-5223		(Frame stored 9.94)		
2995/EVV+	Schleicher ASK23	23004		10.84	Midland GC	Long Mynd	1.00

BGA No/Code	Type	C/n	P/I	Date	Owner/operator	Probable Base	CA Expy
2996/EVW+	Schleicher ASK23	23006		1.85	London GC	Dunstable	12.99
2997/EVX+	Schleicher ASK23	23007		1.85	London GC	Dunstable	11.99
2998/EVY+	Schleicher ASK23	23008		1.85	London GC	Dunstable	10.00
3013/EWP+	Grob G.103A Twin II Acro	33892-K-130	ZE523	11.84	Cambridge University GC		
			BGA.3013			Gransden Lodge	3.00
3015/EWR	Grob G.103A Twin II Acro	33894-K-132	RAFGSA.R70	11.84	Anglia GC "R70"	Wattisham	12.99
			ZE525/BGA.3015				
3064/EYS	Grob G.103A Twin II Acro	33961-K-194	RAFGSA.R71	3.85	Fenland GC	Marham	3.00
			ZE612/BGA.3064				
3076/EZE+	Grob G.103A Twin II Acro	33981-K-214	ZE634	5.85	Oxford GC	Weston-on-the-Green	1.00
			BGA.3076				
3101/FAF	Schleicher ASW20	20214	RAFGSA.271	10.84	M.S.Armstrong	Gallows Hill	5.00
			RAFGSA.R27		"271"		
3103/FAJ	Glaser-Dirks DG-300 Elan	3E50		10.84	B A Brown "790"	Lyveden	3.00
3104/FAK+	Avialsa A.60 Fauconnet	104K	F-CDFG	5.85	I.Gumbrell	Kingston Deverill	5.00
3106/FAM	Schempp-Hirth Nimbus 3/24.5	79		3.85	I.M.Stromberg "115"	Camphill	12.99
3107/FAN	Centrair 101A Pegase	101A-0161		10.84	M Heslop "202"	Parham Park	12.00
3108/FAP	Monnett Monerai	123		5.86P	D.B Rich	Eaglescott	5.99
3109/FAQ	Rolladen-Schneider LS-4	4465		3.85	C.J.Alldis "646"	Bryngwyn Bach	10.00
3110/FAR+	Glasflugel H.205 Club Libelle	58	HB-1262	6.85	G.A.Gair	Kenley	4.00
3112/FAT+	Schleicher ASK13	13528	PH-456	1.85	Dorset GC	Gallows Hill	1.00
3114/FAV+	ICA IS-32A	05		12.84	Black Mountains GC	Talgarth	3.00
3115/FAW	Schempp-Hirth Ventus B/16.6	26	D-6768	2.85	P.Stafford-Allen "333"	Crowland	2.00
3118/FAZ+	Schleicher K8B	8558	D-1043	3.85	Southdown GC "Katie"	Parham Park	1.00
3119/FBA	Schleicher ASW20BL	20665		1.85	R.W.Prestwich "178"	Sleap	12.00
3120/FBB	Schempp-Hirth HS.4 Standard Cirrus	327G	RAFGGA "312"	1.85	M.Andrewartha "822"	Bidford	1.00
3121/FBC+	Schleicher ASW15B	15356	OH-439	5.85	J.M.Dougans "439"	Dunstable	4.00
3122/FBD+	Schleicher ASW15B	15407	OH-445	5.85	R.Pettifer & C.A.McLay	Chipping	5.00
3123/FBE	Rolladen-Schneider LS-6	6028	D-9384	7.85	T.J.Wills "1"	Booker	6.00
3124/FBF	Glaser-Dirks DG-300 Elan	3E9	BGA.2952	1.85	A.L.Garfield "175"	Dunstable	3.00
3125/FBG	SZD-50-3 Puchacz	B-1081		2.85	Not known	Rivar Hill	3.90*
					(Wrecked in gales Booker 25.1.90; stored 5.94)		
3126/FBH	Glaser-Dirks DG-100G Elan	E156G123		4.85	IBM (S.Hants) GC "177"	Lasham	6.00
3127/FBJ+	Schleicher K8B	8221	D-6340	2.85	Bidford GC	Bidford	7.00
3129/FBL	Schleicher Ka2B Rhonschwalbe	373	HB-606	2.85	J.D.Melling	Hall Caine, IoM	5.96*
3130/FBM	Schempp-Hirth Nimbus 3/24.5	73		2.85	T.P.Docherty "727"	Portmoak	12.99
3131/FBN+	Glasflugel H.303 Mosquito B	167	D-6364	5.85	D.R Andrews & Ptnrs	Sleap	2.00
3133/FBQ	Schleicher ASW20BL	20669		4.85	D.W.Gosden "464"	Usk	1.00
3134/FBR	Grob G.102 Astir CS77	1701	SE-TSV	2.88	G.Smith & Ptnrs "773"	Pocklington	4.00
3136/FBT	Schempp-Hirth Ventus BT	218/35		3.85	S.M.Young "488"	Talgarth	5.00
3138/FBV+	Schleicher ASK21	21223		5.85	London GC	Dunstable	1.00
3139/FBW	Glaser-Dirks DG-101G Elan	E174G140		4.85	Surrey & Hants GC "395"	Lasham	3.00
3141/FBY	Schempp-Hirth Discus B	20		4.85	D Latimer "780"	Dunstable	7.00
3142/FBZ	Schleicher Ka6CR	6016	D-4667	5.85	R.Martin & Ptnrs	Booker	1.00
			D-KIMN/D-4667		(As "D-4667")		
3144/FCB+	Centrair 101 Pegase	101-0178	F-CGEA	4.85	N.Stratton	Portmoak	1.00
3145/FCC	Slingsby T.31B	1182	XN243	5.85	D.A.Head & Ptnrs	Bicester	9.00
					(As "XN243")		
3146/FCD	Centrair 101A Pegase B	101A-0207		5.85	G.K.Drury "841"	Challock	3.00
3148/FCF	Slingsby T.21B	MHL.017	WB990	5.85	N.Worrell "993"	Lasham	4.00
3149/FCG	Slingsby T.31B	681	WT871	5.85	J.Desmond	RAF Marham	1.99
					(As "WT871")		
3150/FCH+	CARMAM M.100S Mesange	72	F-CDKD	5.85	P A Pickering	Upwood	1.00
3151/FCJ	Grob G.102 Astir CS	1231	D-4205	5.85	M.Levitt & G.Fellows	Aston Down	2.00
					"571"		
3152/FCK	Schempp-Hirth Ventus B/16.6	241		5.85	L.J.Scott "671"	Bryngwyn Bach	3.00
3153/FCL+	Schleicher K8B	8045E	D-5225	5.85	M.Jackson	Challock	4.98
3154/FCM	Glaser-Dirks DG-300 Elan	3E94		5.85	R.B.Coote "411"	Parham Park	10.00
3155/FCN	Schempp-Hirth HS.4 Standard Cirrus	131	D-0191	6.85	P.Burniss & Syndicate	Nympsfield	12.99
					"920"		
3156/FCP	Rolladen-Schneider LS-6	6030		7.85	E.W.Johnston "721"	Aston Down	2.00
3157/FCQ+	Schleicher K8B	1	RAFGGA...	4.85	M.W.Meagher	Edgehill	3.98
	(Built Bayer)		D-8322 or D-0322?				
3158/FCR	Schleicher Ka6E	4223	OH-375	6.85	R.F.Whitaker & Ptnrs	Parham Park	2.00
			OH-REC		"113"		
3159/FCS	Schempp-Hirth HS.5 Nimbus 2C	233/81	D-5993	7.85	R.W.Hawkins "N2"	Parham Park	12.99
3160/FCT+	Slingsby T.21B	611	WB944	12.86	Upward Bound Trust	Thame	7.99
3162/FCV+	Schleicher ASW20	20076	RAFGSA.R24	6.85	M.J.Davis & Ptnrs	RAF Cosford	3.00
3163/FCW	Schleicher ASK13	13642AB		6.85	Lasham Gliding Society	Lasham	11.00
					"L"		

BGA No/Code	Type	C/n	P/I	Date	Owner/operator	Probable Base	CA Expy
3164/FCX+	Schleicher ASK23	23011		7.85	Midland GC	Long Mynd	1.98*
	(Damaged Long Mynd 26.7.97)						
3165/FCY+	Schleicher ASW15	15122	D-0748	6.85	M.Evershed & Ptnrs	Dunstable	3.00
3166/FCZ	Slingsby T.1 Falcon 1 rep	-		7.85	D.D.Knight & J.Harber RAF Halton		N/E(P)
	(Built Southdown Aero Services)						
3167/FDA	Schleicher ASW15	15050	D-0511	7.85	N W Woodward "7D"	Booker	4.00
3168/FDB+	ICA IS-30	07		9.85	Black Mountains GC	Talgarth	6.00
3169/FDC+	CARMAM JP-15/34 Kit Club	TAH.50/60		3.87	T.A.Hollins	Rufforth	6.00
3170/FDD	Schleicher K8B	8972	AGA.5	7.85	L.D.Young "348"	Rivar Hill	3.00
3171/FDE	Schempp-Hirth Ventus BT	256/53		8.85	P.L.Roberts "510"	Cross Hayes	3.00
3172/FDF+	Grob G.102 Astir CS	1321	D-7338	9.85	P.Andrews	Aston Down	5.00
3173/FDG+	ICA IS-29D2 Club	02		8.85	D.C.Wales		
						Sackville Farm, Riseley	5.00
3177/FDL	Schleicher Ka8	Liz.105/58	D-4650	9.85	G.Millar & Ptnrs	Cranfield	11.95*
3180/FDP	ICA IS-30	08		5.86	C.H.Bolton "996"	Llantisilio	6.00
3181/FDQ+	Slingsby T.31B	710	WT915	9.85	J.F.J.M.Forster "Chris Wills"		
						Maastricht, The Netherlands	8.00
3182/FDR+	Schleicher Ka6CR	6119	D-8456	11.85	P.Hill & R.Grayling		
						Burnford Common	12.99
3184/FDT	Schleicher ASW22	22025	D-7709	10.85	D.P.Taylor	Sutton Bank	5.00
					"W22" (As "BGA.4195" 8.98)		
3185/FDU	Schempp-Hirth Discus B	87		6.86	J.L.Whiting "H5"	Long Mynd	2.00
3186/FDV+	LET L-13 Blanik	173333	D-5826	4.86	T.Wiltshire	East Kirkby	7.98
			D-KOEB/D-5826		(As "D-5826" under wing)		
3187/FDW+	Glaser-Dirks DG-300 Elan	3E143		1.86	N Kelly	Enstone	4.00
3188/FDX+	SZD-48-1 Jantar Standard 2	B-1251	(BGA.2916)	11.85	L.Mathews & Ptnrs	Ringmer	9.00
3189/FDY	Slingsby T21B	MHL.005	WB978	5.99	R.B.Armitage	Waldershare Park	5.00
3191/FEA+	Grob G.103 Twin Astir	3151	RAFGSA.R83	12.85	G.M.Brightman	Edgehill	4.00
			RAFGSA "833"				
3192/FEB	Grob G.102 Club Astir III	5643C		11.85	Surrey & Hants GC "398"	Lasham	3.00
3195/FEE+	Slingsby T.21B	MHL.016	WB989	1.86	K.Schickling		
						Aschaffenburg, Germany	7.00
3196/FEF+	Grob G.102 Astir CS	1164	OY-XGC	2.86	Oxford University GC	Bicester	3.00
3197/FEG	Schempp-Hirth Ventus B/16.6	279		2.86	K.Moorhouse & Ptnr	Rivar Hill	3.00
					"120"		
3198/FEH	Centrair 101A Pegase Club	101A-0268		5.86	Booker GC "318"	Booker	2.00
	(Rebuilt with new fuselage c/n 01304 and original fuselage rebuilt as BGA.3560)						
3199/FEJ	Schempp-Hirth Discus B	76		2.86	D.Geddes "538"	Lasham	12.00
3201/FEL+	Schleicher Ka7 Rhonadler	7231	RAFGGA...	9.86	Burn GC	Burn	11.99
	(See BGA.3231)		D-???				
3203/FEN+	SZD-50-3 Puchacz	B-1326		3.86	Northumbria GC	Currock Hill	6.00
3204/FEP	Schempp-Hirth Ventus BT	284/69		4.86	R.J.Nicholls	Husbands Bosworth	11.99
					"209"		
3205/FEQ	Schleicher ASK13	13650AB		4.86	Lasham Gliding Society	Lasham	12.99
					"M"		
3206/FER	Schempp-Hirth Discus B	75		3.86	D.R.Campbell & Ptnr "370"	Booker	4.00
3207/FES	Schempp-Hirth Discus B	88		4.86	N.G.Storer "564"	Lasham	11.00
3209/FEU	Schleicher ASW22	22030	D-8888	4.86	A.J.French & P.Harvey	Dunstable	11.98
					(Damaged nr Mitcheldean 24.5.97) "89"		
3210/FEV	Glasflugel H.301B Libelle	100	ZS-GFZ	5.86	T.J.Wills	(New Zealand)	9.00
3212/FEX+	Grob G.102 Astir CS77	1660	D-7492	4.86	D.Hartley	Upwood	4.99
3214/FEZ	EoN AP.7 Primary	EoN/P/013	BGA.590??	9.86	G.J.Moore	Brooklands	5.99
	(Reported as ex R13 [c/n EoN/P/037] ex RAFGSA R.13/RAFGSA 113/WP269?)						
3215/FFA+	Schleicher ASK13	13651AB		5.86	Staffordshire GC	Seighford	4.00
3216/FFB	Grob G.102 Astir CS	1123	RAFGSA.R9	5.86	RAF GSA Centre	RAF Bicester	3.00
			RAFGSA.R97/BGA.3216/D-6977 "R9"				
3217/FFC+	Centrair 101A Pegase	101A-0255		5.86	C.A Hitchin	Kingston Deverill	6.00
3221/FFG	Slingsby T.21B	559	WB920	6.86	J.H.Wisselink (As "WB920")		
						Roosendaal, The Netherlands	4.00
3222/FFH+	Schleicher ASW20	20037	D-7947	4.87	J.Hayes "H4"	Dishforth	6.00
3223/FFJ	Grob G.103A Twin II Acro	34075-K-305		6.86	Derby & Lancs GC "623"	Camphill	11.99
3224/FFK	Schempp-Hirth Nimbus 3	87		4.87	Dr.Brennig-James "7"	Booker	5.00
	(see BGA.4149)						
3225/FFL	Slingsby T.21B	MHL.020	WB993	6.87	J.van Os		
						Hilversum, The Netherlands	5.00
3227/FFN+	ICA IS-29D	21	D-9223	8.86	A.Sutton & Ptnrs	Snitterfield	6.00
					"987"		
3228/FFP	Schleicher ASW19B	19317	RAFGSA.R19	6.86	K A Ford "93"	Lasham	3.00
3229/FFQ+	Slingsby T.31B	913	XE800	8.86	I.F.Smith	Booker	9.99
3231/FFS+	Centrair 101A Pegase	101A-0265		6.86	W Murray	Gransden Lodge	2.00
					(As "BGA.3201")		

BGA No/Code	Type	C/n	P/I	Date	Owner/operator	Probable Base	CA Expy
3232/FFT+	Schempp-Hirth Discus B	110		6.86	R.Maskell & Ptnrs	Ridgewell	4.00
3233/FFU+	Glaser-Dirks DG-100G Elan	E200G166		1.87	S.Robinson	Chipping	2.00
3234/FFV+	SZD-51-1 Junior	B-1616	F-WGJA	8.86	Herefordshire GC	Shobdon	7.00
3235/FFW+	Slingsby T21B Sedbergh	1155	XN151	?.86	S.C.Luck	Cranfield	6.00
3236/FFX	Schempp-Hirth Discus B	109		7.86	C.Bainbridge "871"	Wormingford	4.00
3237/FFY+	SZD-51-1 Junior	W-938		11.86	Cornish GC	Perranporth	4.00
3238/FFZ	Slingsby T.21B	MHL.008	WB981	8.86	M.Lake (As "WB981")	Aston Down	6.95*
	(Wfu and wings to BGA.1218 1995; fuselage stored 8.99)						
3239/FGA	Slingsby T.31B	708	WT913	10.86	J.M.Brookes & Ptnrs	Rufforth	7.96*
3240/FGB+	Slingsby T.21B	654	WJ306	8.86	Oxford GC	Weston-on-the-Green	9.00
3241/FGC	Slingsby T.31B	713	WT918	8.86	U.Seegers	(Germany)	4.96*
3244/FGF	Schempp-Hirth Nimbus 3T	25/91		8.86	D.S.Innes "110"	Lasham	2.00
3245/FGG	Slingsby T.21B	665	WG498	9.86	G.A.Ford & Ptnrs	Aston Down	5.00
					(As "WG498")		
3247/FGJ	Schleicher Ka6CR	6634	D-1041	9.86	A.Clark	Booker	7.95*
3248/FGK+	Grob G.102 Astir CS	1323	RAFGSA.R61	9.86	E.Sparrow	Rivar Hill	3.00
			RAFGSA.316				
3250/FGM+	Slingsby T.21B	1160	XN156	7.87	R.B.Petrie	Strathaven	9.00
	(Modified with 330cc engine)						
3252/FGP+	Schleicher ASW19	19121	C-GJXG	11.86	C.Sullivan	Gransden Lodge	2.00
3254/FGR	Schleicher ASK13	13655AB	(RNGSA.N29)	10.86	Portsmouth Naval GC		
	(Built Jubi)					Lee-on-Solent	3.00
3255/FGS	Slingsby T.21B	1161	XN157	10.86	D.W.Cole & Ptnrs	Long Mynd	7.95*
	(Fuselage No.SSK/FF/1745)				(As "XN157")		
3256/FGT+	Glaser-Dirks DG-300 Elan	3E217		3.87	B.J Edwards	Booker	12.00
3257/FGU	Schempp-Hirth HS.4 Standard Cirrus	147	D-0193	4.87	L.E.Ingram "806"	Snitterfield	3.00
3258/FGV+	Schleicher Ka7 Rhonadler	NK	OO-Z..	12.86	Nene Valley GC	Upwood	1.00
	(Hybrid using ex Belgian Ka7 fuselage & wings from Ka2 BGA.2662)						
3259/FGW	Centrair 101A Pegase	101A-0275		6.87	L.P.Smith "701"	Nympsfield	4.00
3261/FGY	Schleicher ASW22	22027	D-3527	1.87	M.Bird "527"	Dunstable	4.00
3262/FGZ+	Schleicher Ka7 Rhonadler	7238	D-5376	1.87	Dartmoor GC "D2"	Brent Tor	10.99
3264/FHB	Slingsby T.21B(T)	MHL.018	WB991	2.87	G.Traves	East Kirkby	2.00
	(Fuji-Robin EC-34PM s/n 82-00391)						
3265/FHC	Slingsby T.21B	MHL.013	WB986	6.87	G.Traves	East Kirkby	7.97
3266/FHD	Schleicher ASW20BL	20694	RAFGGA...	3.87	K.J.Hartley "196"	Bicester	4.00
3267/FHE	Scheibe L-Spatz III	817	LX-CLM	3.87	C.W.Matten & Ptnrs	Culdrose	3.98
3268/FHF+	SZD-51-1 Junior	W-952		3.87	Black Mountains GC	Talgarth	3.00
3269/FHG	Schempp-Hirth HS.7 Mini Nimbus C	140	(BGA.3213)	3.87	R.W.Weaver	Usk	2.00
			ZS-GNI		"187"		
3271/FHJ	Centrair 101A Pegase	101A-0278		5.87	Booker GC "987"	Booker	5.00
3272/FHK+	Slingsby T.31B	695	WT900	4.87	N.Scully & Ptnrs	Dunstable	5.99
					"Tweety"		
3273/FHL	Rolladen-Schneider LS-4	4633		4.87	I.P.Hicks "136"	Cranfield	2.00
3274/FHM	Schleicher ASK13	13662AB		6.87	Lasham Gliding Society	Lasham	4.00
					"P"		
3275/FHN+	Schleicher K8B	NK	RAFGSA.R85	6.87	B.F.Cracknell	Crowland	1.00
			RAFGSA.385/RAFGSA.360				
3277/FHQ	Hols-der-Teufel rep	NK		6.87	M.L.Beach	Brooklands	N/E
	(Built M.L.Beach)				(Sold to Germany c1998)		
3278/FHR	Schempp-Hirth Discus B	152		6.87	P.Tratt & Syndicate	Parham Park	1.00
					"Q5"		
3279/FHS	Schempp-Hirth Ventus CT	326/82		6.87	R.Andrews "154"	Long Mynd	5.00
3280/FHT+	Grob G.102 Astir CS	1234	D-4208	6.87	M.A Taylor	Rattlesden	2.00
3281/FHU+	Schleicher Ka7 Rhonadler	629	RAFGSA.R15	6.87	Dartmoor GC	Brent Tor	3.00
	(Modified to ASK13 standard)		RAFGGA/D-5722				
3282/FHV+	SZD-48-1 Jantar Standard 2	B-1036	D-4516	6.87	R.A.Williams & Ptnrs	Long Mynd	4.00
3283/FHW	Grob G.102 Astir CS	1087	D-6987	6.87	P.W.Roberts "698"	Lasham	2.00
3285/FHY	Scheibe SF-27A Zugvogel V	6045	D-1868	7.87	J.M.Pursey	North Hill	8.00
					"H5" (As "D-1868")		
3286/FHZ+	Schleicher Ka6CR	949	D-4661	8.87	D.Farmilo & Ptnr		
						Husbands Bosworth	2.00
3287/FJA+	Slingsby T.21B	1152	XN148	7.87	East Sussex GC	Ringmer	8.00
3288/FJB+	Slingsby T.21B	MHL.002	WB975	7.87	Angus GC	Drumshade	3.00
3290/FJD+	Slingsby T.21B	MHL.001	WB980	8.87	R.H.Short & Ptnrs	Lyveden	3.00
3291/FJE	Schleicher ASW20BL	20953		7.87	B.Pridal "744"	Booker	11.00
3292/FJF	Slingsby T.21B	586	WB923	9.87	R.L.Hill	Snitterfield	8.00
	(Frame No. SSK/FF 1085)						
3294/FJH+	Grob G.102 Astir CS77	1763	AGA.7	8.87	Shalborne Soaring Society "330"		
						Rivar Hill	4.00
3295/FJJ	Schempp-Hirth Ventus BT	344.93		8.87	R.T.Cole & Ptnrs "134"	Lasham	3.00
3296/FJK+	Centrair 101A Pegase	101-070		4.88	D.J.Ingledew	Lee on Solent	11.00

BGA No/Code	Type	C/n	P/I	Date	Owner/operator	Probable Base	CA Expy
3298/FJM	Rolladen-Schneider LS-4A	4665	D-1431	12.87	G.C.Beardsley & Ptnr "143"	Dunstable	2.00
3299/FJN	Slingsby T.31B	698	WT903	2.88	R.R.Beazer "903"	Camphill	9.00
3301/FJQ+	Schempp-Hirth Ventus CT	104/365		3.88	B.Rood	Hinton-in-The-Hedges	8.00
3302/FJR	Glaser-Dirks DG-300 Club Elan	3E270C2		2.88	G Smith "950"	(France)	3.00
3303/FJS	Glaser-Dirks DG-300 Club Elan	3E271C3		5.88	Yorkshire GC "257"	Sutton Bank	1.00
3304/FJT	Centrair 101A Pegase	101A-0284		2.88	D.M.Smith & A.Marlow "997"	Booker	5.00
3305/FJU	Schleicher K8B	976	OH-240 OH-RTC	11.87	Northumbria GC (As "FJT")	Currock Hill	5.00
3306/FJV	Schleicher ASW15	15109	D-0710	11.87	G.N.Turner & Ptnr "713" Sandhill Farm, Shrivenham		5.00
3307/FJW	Schleicher Ka7	980	OH-241 OH-KKF	?.??	A.J.Pettitt & Syndicate	Rivar Hill	7.00
3308/FJX	Glaser-Dirks DG-300 Elan	3E261		2.88	D.S Jones "728"	North Hill	7.00
3310/FJZ+	Schempp-Hirth SHK	14	D-9330	4.88	R H.Hanna & A. & R.Willis	Bellarena	9.00
3311/FKA+	Schleicher Ka6CR	6239	D-7037 D-5435	2.88	S.T.Dry & B.Davies	Kingston Deverill	4.00
3312/FKB+	Glaser-Dirks DG-600	6-08		10.88	J.A.Watt	Dunstable	4.00
3315/FKE	Schleicher ASW15	15146	D-0794	3.88	D.G.Lloyd & Syndicate "G2"	Bidford	2.00
3317/FKG	Rolladen-Schneider LS-4A	4673		5.88	B.A.Pocock "125"	Kingston Deverill	3.00
3318/FKH+	Schleicher Ka6CR	6343	EI-109 IGA.106	3.88	Ulster GC	Bellarena	6.00
3319/FKJ+	Schleicher K8B	8032	OH-264 OH-RTE	4.88	Aquila GC	Hinton-in-The Hedges	6.00
3320/FKK	Schempp-Hirth Discus B	219		3.88	D.J.Eade "406"	Lasham	3.00
3321/FKL	Schleicher ASW20BL	20954		3.88	J.M.Ley & J.Rollason "152"	Ridgewell	1.00
3322/FKM	Schempp-Hirth Discus B	212		3.88	Surrey & Hants GC "399"	Lasham	1.00
3323/FKN	Schleicher ASH25	25042	(BGA.3491) BGA.3323	7.88	M Bird "13"	Dunstable	11.99
3324/FKP	Slingsby T.21B	632	WB971	2.88	M.Powell (As "WB971")	Booker	4.00
3325/FKQ+	Scheibe SFH-34 Delphin	5119	D-1412	4.88	Bristol & Glos GC	Nympsfield	4.00
3328/FKT+	Schleicher K8B	8382	D-5366	4.88	P.Willock	Lyveden	5.00
3329/FKU	Schleicher Ka6CR	822	D-0025	4.88	D.Robertson (As "FKY")	Camphill	5.00
3330/FKV+	CARMAM M.100S Mesange	60	F-CDDV	5.88	G.G Hunt	Bidford	7.97*
3331/FKW+	Schleicher Ka7 Rhonadler	7145	OH-302 OH-KKJ	4.88	Welland GC	Lyveden	5.00
3332/FKX+ /FKY	Schleicher Ka6CR	6433	D-4316	4.88	D Bartel & Ptnrs (See BGA.3329)	Lasham	5.00
3337/FLC	Glaser-Dirks DG-300 Elan	3E310		9.88	A.R.Milne "808"	Gallows Hill	3.00
3339/FLE	Schempp-Hirth Discus B	207		5.88	Booker GC "314"	Booker	2.00
3340/FLF	Rolladen-Schneider LS-4A	4694		3.88	D.E.Lamb "Z4"	Booker	2.00
3341/FLG	Schleicher ASH25E (Turbo)	25044		6.88	D.S.McKay "A25"	Enstone	4.00
3342/FLH+	Schleicher K8B (Built KK Lehtovaara O/Y)	22	OH-361 OH-RTW	5.88	Aquila GC	Hinton-in-The-Hedges	6.00
3344/FLK+	Schleicher Ka7 Rhonadler	985	D-5047	1.89	Dukeries GC	Gamston	2.00
3345/FLL+	SZD-9 bis Bocian 1D (C/n probably "877")	F-877	OH-336 OH-KBP	7.88	R.G.Wardell-Yerburgh	Kingston Deverill	1.00
3347/FLN	Schleicher ASW24	24011		6.88	D.M.Byass & Ptnrs "161" Dunstable		4.99
	(Written off Booker 6.05.98 & cancelled 28.6.99 - remains to AAIB for tests)						
3348/FLP	Schleicher K8B (Built KK Lehtovaara O/Y)	07	OH-316 OH-RTP	5.88	Bath, Wilts & North Dorset GC (As "FLN" 7.98) Kingston Deverill		2.00
3349/FLQ	Schleicher K8B	8195A	D-8887	8.88	F.J.Glanville	Long Mynd	3.00
3351/FLS+	Schleicher Ka6CR	6180	D-4001	11.88	P.B.Arms	RAF Halton	3.00
3352/FLT+	Glasflugel H.201B Standard Libelle	41	D-0211	12.88	C.Glover	Husbands Bosworth	8.00
3353/FLU	Glasflugel H.201B Standard Libelle	52	D-0298	6.88	C.D.Duthy-James "DJ2"	Talgarth	5.00
3354/FLV	LET L-13 Blanik	173312	D-1335	7.88	North Devon GC "Jenny" "3354"	Eaglescott	5.96*
3355/FLW	Schempp-Hirth HS.4 Standard Cirrus 75	656	F-CEMT	7.88	J.R.Taylor "127"	Perranporth	12.99
3356/FLX+	Glaser-Dirks DG-300 Club Elan	3E304C19		10.88	R.Walker	Rufforth	3.00
3357/FLY	Schleicher ASW24	24012		7.88	I.J.Lewis "983"	North Weald	4.00
3358/FLZ+	Scheibe SF-27A Zugvogel V	6061	D-5378	7.88	R Russon	Long Mynd	2.00
3359/FMA*	Slingsby T.38 Grasshopper	793	WZ797	8.88	Not known (On rebuild 8.98)	Edgehill	8.89

BGA No/Code	Type	C/n	P/I	Date	Owner/operator	Probable Base	CA Expy
3361/FMC	Rolladen-Schneider LS-6B	6184		7.88	B.L.Cooper "68"	Booker	12.99
3362/FMD+	Schleicher Ka7 Rhonadler	343	D-2877	7.88	Not known	Aston Down	12.92*
			HB-603		(Damaged Ringmer 6.5.92: stored 8.99)		
3363/FME+	Schleicher ASW15	15164	D-0825	8.88	T.J.Stanley "927"	Rufforth	1.00
3365/FMG	Schempp-Hirth Discus B	242		8.88	D.R.Zarb "969"	Nympsfield	2.00
3366/FMH	Schleicher ASK13	13673AB		8.88	Lasham Gliding Society "B"	Lasham	1.00
3368/FMK+	Centrair 101 Pegase	101-0293		1.90	A.Bailey	Bidford	6.00
3369/FML+	Schleicher ASW15B	15294	F-CEGR	11.89	A.D.Duke & Ptnrs	Nympsfield	3.99
3370/FMM+	Schleicher Ka6CR	6328	D-1260	10.88	K.E Hebdon	Gamston	7.00
3371/FMN	Schempp-Hirth Ventus CT	123/397		9.88	S C.Kovac "CKF"	Lasham	2.00
3372/FMP	Schleicher ASW24	24023		1.89	A.Hegner "357"	Booker	5.00
3373/FMQ	Schempp-Hirth Discus B	243		10.88	A.L Harris "158"	Nympsfield	3.00
3374/FMR+	Neukom Standard Elfe S-2	05	HB-801	11.88	M.Powell & Ptnrs	Camphill	4.00
3375/FMS	Schleicher ASW15	15061	N111SP	11.88	A.J.Pettit "519"	Lasham	12.99
3376/FMT+	Schempp-Hirth HS.4 Standard Cirrus	249	N2HM	10.89	W.Schmidt	Chipping	3.99
3377/FMU+	Schempp-Hirth HS.4 Standard Cirrus	236	N3LB	7.90	S.A Manktelow	Aston Down	5.00
3380/FMX+	Schleicher ASW24	24014		3.90	D.T.Reilly	North Hill	3.00
3381/FMY	Rolladen-Schneider LS-7	7004	D-1256	12.88	D.F.Holmes "371"	Camphill	5.00
3382/FMZ+	Schleicher Ka7 Rhonadler	7018	D-6035	11.88	Nene Valley GC "2	Upwood	4.00
3383/FNA+	Schleicher K8B	8499	D-5670	11.88	Bowland Forest GC	Chipping	1.00
3385/FNC	Slingsby T.21B	SSK/FF1091	WB9..	11.88	P.Hoffmann (The Netherlands)		5.00
3386/FND+	Schleicher Ka6E	4069	PH-366	11.88	J.M.Smith	North Hill	3.00
3387/FNE+	SZD-38A Jantar-1	B-612	HB-1215	12.88	D.A Salmon & Ptnrs	Camphill	6.00
3388/FNF	Schleicher ASW22B	22053		12.88	T.J.Parker "461"	Dunstable	2.00
3389/FNG	Schleicher ASW24	24015		5.89	G.C.Metcalfe "104"	Lasham	1.00
3390/FNH	Schleicher ASW19	19174	D-7969	2.89	Mrs V.P.Hayley & Ptnrs Ridgewell "A19"		1.00
3392/FNK+	Slingsby T.65A Vega	1897	N9023H	12.88	A.P.Brown	Kenley	4.00
3393/FNL	Schempp-Hirth Discus B	253		11.88	P.A.Holland Kirton-in-Lindsey "705"		3.00
3394/FNM+	Centrair 101B Pegase	101B-0289	F-CGSE	3.89	R.Harrison	Sleap	2.00
3395/FNN	Schempp-Hirth Ventus CT	130/407		12.88	C.A.Marren "109"	Aston Down	10.00
3396/FNP+	Schleicher Ka6CR	567	D-4657	1.89	Notts University GC	Syerston	6.00
3397/FNQ	Schempp-Hirth Discus B	259		12.88	Deeside ASW20 Group "282" Aboyne		5.00
3398/FNR	Schempp-Hirth Discus B	255		3.89	R.Lemin "130"	Nympsfield	2.00
3399/FNS+	Glaser-Dirks DG-300 Club Elan	3E314C23		4.89	R.Arkle	Aboyne	3.00
3400/FNT+	Glaser-Dirks DG-600	6-12		12.88	D.M.Hayes "674"	Rufforth	3.00
3401/FNU	Rolladen-Schneider LS-4A	4732	D-1376	4.89	R J Simpson "190"	Nympsfield	2.00
3403/FNW+	Schleicher Ka6CR	598	HB-634	3.89	Cotswold GC	Aston Down	1.99
					(Crashed nr Aston Down 5.8.98)		
3404/FNX+	Wassmer WA.30 Bijave	84	F-CCTJ	1.89	The Borders GC	Milfield	11.00
3408/FPB+	Schleicher ASW15B	15243	D-2068	12.88	R C Tatlow	Winthorpe	6.00
3410/FPD	Rolladen-Schneider LS-7	7033	D-5178	1.89	P.H.Rackham "973"	Dunstable	12.99
3411/FPE	Schempp-Hirth Ventus CT	131/408		1.89	P.Whitt & N.Francis "238"	Shobdon	3.00
3412/FPF+	Scheibe L-Spatz 55	2720	RAFGGA...	2.89	M.P.Dunlop	Usk	6.99
3414/FPH+	Centrair ASW 20F	20132	F-CFFX	1.89	R.Gibson & Ptnrs	Bidford	3.00
3415/FPJ	Schleicher ASW19	19001	D-1909	1.89	F.W.Pinkerton "459"	Lyveden	5.00
3416/FPK	Glaser-Dirks DG-300 Elan	3E6	D-1233	1.89	G.C.Keall & Ptnrs "Y1" Husbands Bosworth		3.00
3417/FPL	Schempp-Hirth Ventus C	409		1.89	R.V Barrett "242"	Nympsfield	2.00
3418/FPM+	SZD-51-1 Junior	B-1788		3.89	Kent GC	Challock	12.99
3419/FPN	Schleicher ASW20	20376	RAFGGA.545	3.89	E C Wright	Syerston	5.00
			D-8780		"545"		
3420/FPP	Schemmp-Hirth HS.5 Nimbus 2B	142	D-6779	3.89	R.Jones	Walney Island	1.00
			D-2111		"N2"		
3421/FPQ+	Schleicher Ka7 Rhonadler	EB180/61	D-5184	2.89	East Sussex GC	Ringmer	6.99
3424/FPT	Schleicher ASW20	20007	D-7574	2.89	L.Hornsey & Ptnrs "574"	Halton	3.00
3425/FPU+	Schleicher Ka2B Rhonschwalbe	-	HB-698	2.89	T.J.Wilkinson		
	(Built Segelfluggruppe Zwingen)				Sackville Farm, Riseley		3.00
3426/FPV+	Schleicher Ka6E	4123	N29JG	3.89	J.E.Stewart	Bembridge	4.00
			G-AWTP				
3427/FPW	Glaser-Dirks DG-600	6-17		4.89	W.S.Stephen "39"	Aboyne	3.00
3428/FPX+	Schleicher ASK13	13325	F-CDYR	6.89	Booker GC	Booker	5.00
3432/FQB+	Schleicher ASW15B	15340	D-2345	8.89	P.Usborne	Dunstable	10.00
3433/FQC	Glaser-Dirks DG-202/17c	2-178CL19	HB-1645	3.89	A.T.MacDonald "201"	Ridgewell	2.00
3434/FQD+	Schleicher K8B	8289	D-1908	3.89	Kent GC	Challock	12.99
3435/FQE+	Schleicher K8	3	D-6329	4.89	Cotswold GC	Aston Down	7.99
3436/FQF+	Scheibe SF-27A Zugvogel V	6025	D-0009	2.89	S.Maddox	Winthorpe	9.99
3437/FQG	Rolladen-Schneider LS-7	7050	D-1712	6.89	R.W.Spiller "952"	Sutton Bank	6.00

BGA No/Code	Type	C/n	P/I	Date	Owner/operator	Probable Base	CA Expy
3438/FQH	Rolladen-Schneider LS-7	7029	D-1316	4.89	P.J.Lazenby	Rufforth	3.00
3440/FQK+	Grob G.103C Twin III Acro	34123		8.89	P.O'Donald	Gransden Lodge	3.00
3441/FQL	Schleicher Ka6CR	6235	HB-772	3.89	C. & N.Worrell "772"	Lasham	11.00
3442/FQM+	Scheibe SF-27A Zugvogel V	6098	D-9421	2.89	R.D.Noon	Winthorpe	5.00
					(As "D-9421")		
3443/FQN	Schempp-Hirth Ventus B/16.6	141	D-8772	3.89	R.Parsons & Ptnrs	Challock	11.99
			D-KHIB		"479"		
	(Composite rebuild of D-8772 - ex Ventus BT D-KHIB (10/141) - w/o 27.5.85 & possibly HB-1626 (91)						
	as FQN holds build plate "V91")						
3445/FQQ	Glaser-Dirks DG-600	6-11		3.89	M.B.Jefferyes & Ptnr	Ridgewell	6.00
					"656"		
3446/FQR+	Schleicher K8B	8537	PH-349	3.89	Dorset GC	Gallows Hill	11.00
3448/FQT	SZD-48-3 Jantar Standard 3	B-1891	(BGA.3409)	3.90	T H Greenwood		
					"484" Sandhill Farm, Shrivenham		3.00
3449/FQU+	Schleicher Ka7 Rhonadler	1139	D-8614	3.89	J.E.Harber	Halton	4.00
			HB-709				
3450/FQV	CARMAM JP-15/36AR Aiglon	28	F-CETX	3.89	K.H.Withey "P"	Perranporth	4.98
3452/FQX	Schleicher K8B	8037	D-5205	4.89	Burn GC	Burn	1.96*
3453/FQY	Schempp-Hirth Discus B	274		4.89	P.Studer "785"	Nympsfield	2.00
3454/FQZ	Rolladen-Schneider LS-1F	391	F-CEKH	6.89	G.P.Hibberd "L57"	Sleap	3.00
3455/FRA	Rolladen-Schneider LS-6B	6151	D-8081	4.89	P.J.Haseler "32"	Enstone	3.00
3456/FRB	Schempp-Hirth Ventus C	404		3.89	S.R.Nash "758"	Lasham	2.00
3457/FRC	Schempp-Hirth HS.5 Nimbus 2B	151	D-4980	5.89	C.F.Whitbread "988"	Challock	4.00
3458/FRD	Centrair 101A Pegase	101A-0311		4.89	A.Kangars	Husbands Bosworth	12.99
					"JPB" (Reported as "FRG" 7.96)		
3459/FRE+	Schleicher Ka6E	4349	F-CDTL	4.89	D.J.Stewart	Parham Park	6.00
3460/FRF+	Schleicher Ka7 Rhonadler	450/58	D-5653	4.89	P.Roberts & Co	Dunstable	8.00
3461/FRG	Siebert Sie-3	3009	D-0739	4.89	I.R.Taylor & Co	Cross Hayes	4.96*
	(See BGA.3458)						
3462/FRH	Schleicher ASW20CL	20740	D-9229	4.89	J.N.Wilton & Ptnr		
					"634"	Husbands Bosworth	4.00
3463/FRJ	Schempp-Hirth HS.4 Standard Cirrus	103	HB-1041	4.89	P.D.Oswald & Ptnrs "48" Portmoak		2.00
3464/FRK+	Schleicher ASW15B	15214	D-0941	3.89	A.D.Smith	Booker	12.99
3465/FRL	Grob G.102 Astir CS	1373	D-7402	4.89	South Wales GC "609"	Usk	5.00
3466/FRM+	Scheibe SF-27A Zugvogel V	6040	D-3644	4.89	Burn GC	Burn	5.98
3468/FRP	Schempp-Hirth Nimbus 3/24.5	43	N697L	7.89	T.R.Gardner & J.Mardon		
			D-2518		"995"	Aston Down	10.95*
3469/FRQ	Slingsby T.45 Swallow	1420	XT653	4.89	D.Shrimpton	Halesland	6.98
					(As "XT653")		
3470/FRR	Centrair 101A Pegase	101A-0034	(BGA.3451)	4.89	P.A.Lewis	Walney Island	5.00
			F-CFQA		"495" "Scoundrel"		
3471/FRS	Scheibe Zugvogel IIIB	1097	D-2171	4.89	R.J.Dann & N.Kent	Rivar Hill	3.00
			HB-749				
3472/FRT	Schempp-Hirth Ventus CT	137/421		4.89	C.G.Corbett	Dunstable	3.00
	(Reported identity of D-4349 was Type Certificate 04.349)				"170"		
3474/FRV+	Centrair 101A Pegase	101A-0325		10.89	N.J.Robinson	Gransden Lodge	3.00
3475/FRW	Schleicher ASW20L	20202	D-5981	5.89	K.Challinor & Syndicate	Booker	2.00
					"268"		
3476/FRX+	Centrair 101A Pegase	101A-0315		5.89	BBC Gliding Grp	Booker	11.00
3478/FRZ	Schempp-Hirth HS.4 Standard Cirrus	348G	HB-1194	5.89	M.Kent	Lasham	3.00
			D-2172		"H6"		
3479/FSA	Grob G.102 Astir CS	1277	D-7371	4.89	J.Claxton "498"	Dunstable	7.00
3481/FSC*	Slingsby T.38 Grasshopper	751	WZ755	4.90	Not known	Gallows Hill	4.91
					(Stored 5.98)		
3482/FSD	Schleicher ASK13	13367	(RNGSA.N28)	5.89	Portsmouth Naval GC		
			D-0863			Lee-on-Solent	6.00
3483/FSE	Schleicher Ka6CR	6021	D-1946	8.89	G.W.Lobb "964"	North Hill	6.00
3484/FSF+	Schleicher Ka2	120	D-1688	6.89	B.T.Spreckley	Le Blanc, France	10.99
3486/FSH+	Grob G.102 Astir CS Jeans	2090	D-7532	5.89	Buckminster GC	Saltby	11.99
3487/FSJ	Slingsby T.31B	703	WT908	5.89	R.J.Abraham	Dunstable	1.99
					(As "WT908")		
3489/FSL	Schempp-Hirth HS.7 Mini Nimbus	52	HB-1413	6.89	S.C.Waddell "F11"	Booker	2.00
3493/FSQ+	Schleicher ASK13	"13596"		6.89	London GC	Dunstable	1.99
	(Composite containing c/n plate from BGA.2405)						
3494/FSR+	Glaser-Dirks DG-300 Elan	3E343		8.89	E.J.Dent	Nympsfield	11.00
3495/FSS+	Schleicher Ka6E	4019	D-5260	8.89	K.J.Hill & Ptnrs	Lasham	3.00
3496/FST+	Schleicher ASH25E	25073	(BGA.3530)	10.89	K.H.Lloyd & Ptnrs	Aston Down	3.00
			(BGA.3496)				
3497/FSU	Scheibe Zugvogel IIIA	1060	D-9055	6.89	P.W.Williams	Brent Tor	4.00
3498/FSV	Slingsby T.38 Grasshopper	800	WZ819	6.89	P.D.Mann (As "WZ819") RAF Halton		9.97
					(Dismantled 2.99)		

BGA No/Code	Type	C/n	P/I	Date	Owner/operator	Probable Base	CA Expy
3500/FSX	Glaser-Dirks DG-300 Elan	3E344		7.89	C.Hyett "405"	Lasham	1.00
3501/FSY	Schleicher ASH25	25064	D-1578	7.89	B.T.Spreckley Le Blanc, France "162"		11.00
3502/FSZ+	Grob G.102 Astir CS77	1841	D-2908	7.89	D.Gardiner & Ptnr	Aston Down	3.00
3503/FTA+	Schleicher K8B	8702	D-0048	7.89	Lincolnshire GC	Strubby	3.97*
3504/FTB+	Schleicher Ka6CR (Built Bitz)	019	D-8900	7.89	P.J.Blair	Bidford	4.00
3505/FTC	SZD-51-1 Junior	B-1860	(RNGSA.N56)	7.89	Culdrose GC	RNAS Culdrose	3.00
3506/FTD	Schleicher ASW15B	15191	D-0872	8.89	L.G.Callow "205"	Dunstable	8.98
3508/FTF+	Schleicher Ka6CR	6294	D-6081	8.89	A.Sparrow	Rivar Hill	3.00
3509/FTG+	Schleicher Ka7 Rhonadler	535	D-8321	10.89	Angus GC	Drumshade	3.00
3510/FTH+	SZD-50-3 Puchacz	B-1881		8.89	Buckminster GC	Saltby	1.00
3511/FTJ	SZD-48 Jantar Standard 2	W-889	HB-1472	8.89	G.J.Burton & Ptnrs "FTI" Enstone		5.00
3512/FTK	Grob G.102 Astir CS Jeans	2059	OE-5152	10.89	R.Lapsley "518"	Bellarena	4.00
3513/FTL	Schleicher ASW20CL	20751	D-3564	9.89	J.S.Shaw "127"	Dunstable	4.00
3514/FTM	Schleicher K8B	513	D-5708	8.89	West Wales GC	Usk	6.00
3515/FTN	Schleicher K8B	996	D-8539 D-KAEL/D-8539	3.89	Vale of White Horse GC "853" Sandhill Farm, Shrivenham		2.00
3516/FTP	Schleicher ASW20CL	20733	D-3640	1.90	A J Mainwaring "332" Dunstable		3.00
3517/FTQ+	Centrair ASW20FL	20123	F-CFFR	8.89	C.Wilby	Camphill	11.99
3518/FTR+	Grob G.102 Astir CS77	1606	D-4807	10.89	Lakes GC	Walney Island	2.00
3519/FTS+	Glaser-Dirks DG-300 Club Elan	3E349C38		10.89	Southdown GC	Parham Park	12.99
3520/FTT	Slingsby T.21B	589	WB926	9.89	R.Acreman	Gallows Hill	6.00
					(As "WB926")		
3521/FTU+	Schleicher Ka7 Rhonadler	302	HB-599	9.89	Dartmoor GS "Fondue" Brent Tor		3.00
3522/FTV	Rolladen-Schneider LS-7	7073		10.89	D.Hilton & S.White "944" Booker		3.00
3523/FTW	Schempp-Hirth Discus B	292		10.89	N.H.Wall & Ptnrs	Nympsfield	2.00
	(Rebuilt with new fuselage after accident 21.6.91; original fuselage rebuilt as BGA.3879) "230"						
3525/FTY	Rolladen-Schneider LS-7	7075		10.89	A.M.Burgess "753"	Drumshade	3.00
3528/FUB	Schleicher Ka6CR	6007	D-8573	11.89	D.E.Hooper	Eaglescott	7.99
3529/FUD+	SZD-9 bis Bocian 1E	P-689	SP-2807	11.89	Mendip GC	Halesland	8.00
3531/FUF+	Scheibe SF-27A Zugvogel V	6089	D-6068	9.89	East Sussex GC	Ringmer	5.00
3532/FUG	Schleicher ASH25	25074	(BGA.3526)	10.89	J.P.Gorringe & D.S.Hill Lasham "BB"		3.00
3533/FUH	Schempp-Hirth Ventus C	438		10.89	M.A.Gale & Ptnrs Gallows Hill "192"		3.00
3534/FUJ+	Glaser-Dirks DG-300 Elan	3E353		12.89	J.Cook & Ptnrs	Strathaven	2.00
3535/FUL	Schemmp-Hirth Discus B	293		3.90	N.D.Tillett "803"	Dunstable	10.00
3536/FUM+	Schleicher Ka6CR	808	D-6289	3.90	A.C.Marvin	Rufforth	5.00
3537/FUN+	Schleicher ASW20CL	20813	D-3432	4.91	W.H.Parker "432"	Dunstable	3.00
3538/FUP	Schempp-Hirth Discus B	291		10.89	Surrey & Hants GC "397"	Lasham	3.00
3539/FUQ+	Scheibe SF-27A Zugvogel V	6090	D-5196	3.90	G.Elliott & Ptnrs	Ringmer	1.00
3540/FUR	Schempp-Hirth Ventus CT	145/446		3.90	D.S.Towson "256"	Shobdon	4.00
3541/FUS+	SZD-51-1 Junior	B-1912		11.89	Scottish Gliding Union Ltd	Portmoak	6.00
3542/FUT	Glaser-Dirks DG-300 Club Elan	3E350C39		3.90	A.Eltis "Y1"	Gransden Lodge	5.00
3543/FUU+	Glaser-Dirks DG-300 Club Elan	3E360C45		3.90	A.R.MacGregor Kingston Deverill		3.00
3544/FUV	Rolladen-Schneider LS-7	7068		11.89	E.Alston "194"	Brent Tor	12.00
3545/FUW	Slingsby T.31B Cadet TX.3	920	XE807	11.89	D.Shrimpton	Halesland	6.98
					(As "XE807")		
3546/FUY+	SZD-50-3 Puchacz	B-1983		11.89	M.G.Ashton	Eaglescott	4.00
3548/FVA	Schleicher K8B	1051	(RNGSA.N15) D-5117	4.90	Portsmouth Naval GC	Lee-on-Solent	5.00
3549/FVB	Schempp-Hirth Ventus CT	144/445		1.90	M.J.Sesemann "228" Challock		2.00
3550/FVC+	Schleicher ASK13 (Jubi-built)	13682AB		12.89	Devon & Somerset GC North Hill		2.00
3551/FVD+	Scheibe Bergfalke IV	5806	D-0729	12.89	North Wales GC	Bryngwyn Bach	4.99
3552/FVE+	Rolladen-Schneider LS-4	4190	RAFGSA"232" RAFGSA R30/D-4542	1.90	R.J.Rebbeck "232"	Edgehill	5.00
3553/FVF+	Schempp-Hirth HS.5 Nimbus 2C	202	D-2880	3.90	J C Mitchell & J.Wood Chipping		3.00
3554/FVG	Glaser-Dirks DG-600	6-41		12.89	R.G.Tomlinson "660"	Winthorpe	4.00
3555/FVH	Rolladen-Schneider LS-7	7067	(BGA.3527)	12.89	B.R.Forrest & A.Hallum Booker "246"		3.00
3558/FVL+	Scheibe Zugvogel IIIB	1082	D-5224	12.89	F.Hunt	Kirton-in-Lindsey	7.00
3559/FVM	Centrair 101A Pegase	101A-0345		3.90	S.H.North "369"	Yeovilton	5.00
3560/FVN+	Centrair 101A Pegase	101A-0268/2		1.90	G.G.Butter	Snitterfield	6.00
	(Rebuild of BGA.3198 with c/n 10100268)						
3561/FVP+	Centrair 101A Pegase	101A-0350		4.90	J.R.Parry & Ptnr	Long Mynd	3.00
3562/FVQ+	Rolladen-Schneider LS-7	7079		1.90	P.Harvey	Gransden Lodge	11.99
3564/FVS+	Schempp-Hirth HS.4 Standard Cirrus	359G	D-2168	3.90	P.A Clark	Lasham	2.00
3565/FVT	Schempp-Hirth HS.5 Nimbus 2	18	N795	5.90	I.Dunkley "760"	Camphill	7.98
3566/FVU+	Schleicher ASK13	13062	D-1348	4.90	Edinburgh University GC Portmoak		11.99

BGA No/Code	Type	C/n	P/I	Date	Owner/operator	Probable Base	CA Expy
3567/FVV+	Centrair 101A Pegase	101A-0353		4.90	Cambridge University GC		
						Gransden Lodge	3.00
3568/FVW+	Schempp-Hirth Ventus BT	252/51	D-KORN	1.90	I.Champness	Lasham	4.00
3570/FVY+	Scheibe Zugvogel IIIA	1046	D-8323	2.90	S.Ottner & Ptnrs	Rivar Hill	5.99
3571/FVZ	Schleicher Ka6E	4007	D-4104	2.90	R.P.Filipkiewicz "PS"	Booker	4.00
3572/FWA+	Schleicher Ka6CR	6227	D-1062	3.90	N.M.Hill	Weston-on-the-Green	8.00
3573/FWB+	Schleicher ASK13	13224	HB-989	4.90	Cotswold GC	Aston Down	10.00
3574/FWC	Grob G.103C Twin III Acro	34154		4.90	Lasham Gliding Society Ltd		
					"45"	Lasham	3.00
3575/FWD+	Schempp-Hirth Ventus CT	148/468		5.90	R.S.Maxwell-Fendt "888"	Lasham	3.00
3576/FWE+	SZD-50-3 Puchacz	B-1984	(BGA.3547)	2.90	Deeside GC	Aboyne	4.00
3577/FWF	Rolladen-Schneider LS-7	7097		2.90	G.P.Hibberd "618"	Sleap	11.99
3578/FWG+	Centrair 101A Pegase	101A-0252	PH-793	2.90	Devon & Somerset GC	North Hill	2.00
3579/FWH+	Scheibe SF-27A Zugvogel V	6024	D-4733	2.90	R.Sampson	Husbands Bosworth	4.00
3580/FWJ	Rolladen-Schneider LS-7WL	7078		3.90	J.P.Popika "S3"	Gransden Lodge	4.00
3581/FWK	Schempp-Hirth Nimbus 3DT	32		3.90	G.B.Atkinson	Gransden Lodge	7.00
						"29"	
3582/FWL+	Schleicher K8B	106/58	D-7151	2.90	Dukeries GC	Gamston	7.00
					(As "-7151" underwing)		
3583/FWM+	Glaser-Dirks DG-300 Club Elan	3E373C50		6.90	G.J.T.Underwood	Challock	3.00
3584/FWN+	Schleicher ASK13	13285	HB-1023	4.90	Booker GC	Booker	4.00
3585/FWP	Schleicher ASW19B	19262	D-5980	4.90	K.Harris & Ptnrs "980"	Dunstable	3.00
3586/FWQ+	Schleicher ASK21	21460		5.90	Midland GC	Long Mynd	12.99
3587/FWR	Glasflugel H.303 Mosquito	34	N77RL	3.90	S.J.Ferguson "277"	Aston Down	8.99
3588/FWS	Schleicher ASW20C	20765	D-6623	2.90	G.W.Lynch "662"	North Weald	2.00
3589/FWT+	SZD-50-3 Puchacz	B-1988		3.90	Coventry GC	Husbands Bosworth	3.00
3590/FWU	Rolladen-Schneider LS-7	7080		3.90	G.E.Thomas	Husbands Bosworth	4.00
					"768"		
3592/FWW+	Schleicher ASH25E	25093		6.90	A.T.Farmer	Bicester	1.00
3593/FWX	Centrair 101A Pegase	101A-033	F-CFRZ	3.90	R A Adam "B38" Husbands Bosworth		6.00
3594/FWY+	Centrair 101A Pegase	101A-071	F-CFXE	3.90	C.Leeseman & Ptnrs	Lasham	3.00
3595/FWZ+	Schleicher ASW19B	19342	D-2603	4.90	C.Fowler	Camphill	1.00
3596/FXA	Grob G.102 Speed Astir IIB	4083	D-2671	4.90	A.D.Duke "567"	Nympsfield	9.00
3597/FXB	Schleicher K8B	8193/A	D-5597	3.90	R.J.Morris	Brent Tor	5.00
3598/FXC+	Schleicher Ka6E	4268	D-0150	8.90	B.L.Anson	RAF Halton	4.00
3599/FXD	Centrair 101A Pegase	101A-0346	(BGA.3563)	3.90	Coventry GC Husbands Bosworth		10.00
					"285"		
3600/FXE	Rolladen-Schneider LS-7	7090		3.90	J.C.Kingerlee		
					"35"	Weston-on-the-Green	7.00
3601/FXF+	Slingsby T.50 Skylark 4	1455	HB-812	5.90	S.White	Booker	5.00
3602/FXG+	Schempp-Hirth HS.2 Cirrus	23	N1216	8.90	G.F.King	Kingston Deverill	2.00
3603/FXH+	Schleicher Ka7 Rhonadler	353	D-4040	4.90	Vale of Neath GC	Rhigos	8.99
3604/FXJ	Schleicher ASW24	24086		5.90	A.K.Laylee "247"	Booker	2.00
3606/FXL	Schleicher ASH25	25088		4.90	C.R.Simpson & Ptnrs		
					"108"	Husbands Bosworth	2.00
3607/FXM	Schempp-Hirth Discus BT	16/301	D-KHIA	4.90	R.J.H.Fack "173"	Shobdon	11.99
3608/FXN+	CARMAM M.200 Foehn	4	OO-ZNI	4.90	I.Gutzell & Ptnrs	Pocklington	9.99
			(OO-ZXS)/F-CCXS				
3609/FXP+	LET L-23 Super Blanik	907609		7.90	R.O.Windley	Sutton Bank	6.00
					t/a The Blanik Syndicate		
3610/FXQ	Schempp-Hirth Nimbus 3DT	31		4.90	G.O.Wynne & Ptnrs	Lasham	1.00
	(See BGA.3658)				"954"		
3611/FXR	LAK-12 Lietuva	6162		9.90	S R Blackmore "L12"	Enstone	5.00
3612/FXS+	Schleicher Ka6E	4228	D-0073	5.90	R.Woodhouse & B.Wade	Tibenham	6.00
3613/FXT	Centrair 101A Pegase	101A-0056	F-CFQV	4.90	G.Coppola	Viterbo, Italy	11.00
3614/FXU+	Schleicher Ka6E	4071	OH-343	6.90	M E Mann Syndicate	Lasham	3.00
			OH-RSY				
3616/FXW+	Schleicher K8B	8651	D-7203	5.90	South Wales GC	Usk	4.00
			D-KOLA/D-7203				
3617/FXX+	Scheibe L-Spatz 55	756	D-3598	8.91	P.Brown	Ridgewell	6.00
3618/FXY	Schleicher ASW15B	15348	F-CEJL	5.90	V W Jennings "723"	Dunstable	8.00
3620/FYA	SZD-50-3 Puchacz	B-2022		5.90	Cairngorm GC	Feshiebridge	3.00
3621/FYB	Rolladen-Schneider LS-7	7102		5.90	J.T.Hitchcock "779"	Parham	3.00
3622/FYC	Schempp-Hirth Ventus B	83	N90DM	5.90	D.B.Meeks	Sutton Bank	9.99
			F-CEDR/F-WEDR			"A10"	
3623/FYD	Schleicher ASH25	25095		5.90	K.M.H.Wilson "942"	Challock	2.00
3624 FYE	Scheibe Zugvogel IIIB	1067	OY-MHX	5.90	R.J.Hawley	Brent Tor	4.00
			SE-TCE/OY-EFX/D-1814		"94"		
3625/FYF+	Schleicher ASK21	21470		8.90	London GC	Dunstable	6.00
3626/FYG+	Glasflugel H.205 Club Libelle	22	OH-545	5.90	I.H Shattock	Usk	7.00

BGA No/Code	Type	C/n	P/I	Date	Owner/operator	Probable Base	CA Expy
3627/FYH	Rolladen-Schneider LS-4A	4804		7.90	G.W.Craig "224"	Weston-on-the-Green	8.00
3628/FYJ+	Schempp-Hirth HS.4 Standard Cirrus 581G		D-8931	7.90	P.J.Tiller	Pocklington	5.00
3629/FYK	Rolladen-Schneider LS-7	7108		6.90	T J Murphy "34"	Portmoak	3.00
3630/FYL+	SZD-50-3 Puchacz	B-1990		6.90	Deeside GC	Aboyne	4.00
3631/FYM	Schempp-Hirth Discus BT	31/328		6.90	J.A.Denne "326"	Enstone	3.00
3632/FYN	Schempp-Hirth Discus B	179	N75J	7.90	P.Foulger "J3"	Wormingford	3.00
3633/FYP+	LET L-23 Super Blanik	907620		8.90	Needwood Forest GC	Cross Hayes	2.00
3635/FYR+	LET L-23 Super Blanik	917816		7.92	North Wales GC	Llantisilio	6.00
3638/FYU	Glaser-Dirks DG-100 Elan	E111	OY-XMR SE-TYO	6.90	J.L Brigbee "M5"	North Hill	6.00
3639/FYV+	Schleicher ASK21	21468		7.90	Yorkshire GC	Sutton Bank	1.00
3640/FYW	Rolladen-Schneider LS-7	7111		6.90	J.D.Williams "Z7"	Saltby	1.00
3641/FYX	Schempp-Hirth Discus BT	32/333		7.90	M.P.Brockington "208"	Talgarth	5.00
3642/FYY	Schleicher ASK13	13685AB		7.90	Lasham Gliding Society "S"	Lasham	2.00
3643/FYZ	Schleicher ASH25	25097		7.90	M.G.Thick "171"	Sutton Bank	12.99
3644/FZA+	SZD-51-1 Junior	B-1913		7.90	Booker GC	Booker	3.00
3645/FZB	Glasflugel H.201B Standard Libelle	112	OH-388 OH-GLA	7.90	C.Thomas & J.E.Herring "669"	Lasham	5.00
3646/FZC	Schempp-Hirth SHK-1	58	OH-357 OH-SHA	8.91	J.F Mills	Talgarth	6.99
3649/FZF+	SZD-51-1 Junior	B-1861		7.90	Devon & Somerset GC	North Hill	4.00
3650/FZG+	SZD-9 bis Bocian 1D	F-859	SP-2450	9.90	The Borders GC	Milfield	3.00
3651/FZH	Schempp-Hirth Ventus C	455		7.90	G.D.Clack "520"	Rivar Hill	3.00
3653/FZK+	Schempp-Hirth HS.4 Standard Cirrus	81	HB-967	7.90	J.L.Rodgers & Syndicate	Aston Down	8.00
3654/FZL	Schleicher ASW20CL	20764	D-5937	8.90	R.M.Housden "Z6"	Aston Down	8.00
3655/FZM+	Scheibe SF-27A Zugvogel V	6103	D-1772	8.90	D.Thorpe t/a Safety First SG	Camphill	5.00
3656/FZN+	Schleicher ASK13	13045	D-5759	8.90	Black Mountains GC "K13"	Talgarth	8.00
3657/FZP	SZD-51-1 Junior	B-1926	(RNGSA.N16)	8.90	Portsmouth Naval GC	Lee-on-Solent	5.00
3658/FZQ	SZD-50-3 Puchacz	B-2024	(BGA.3637)	8.90	Coventry GC (As "FXQ")	Husbands Bosworth	11.00
3659/FZR+	Schleicher Ka6CR	6136	D-8459	12.90	P.S.Huggins	North Hill	11.00
3660/FZS	LET L-13 Blanik	025609	NEJSGSA.8	8.90	B.J.Shackell & A.Pattemore "L13"	Rivar Hill	4.99
	(Rebuild with parts from BGA.2661)						
3662/FZU	Slingsby T.38 Grasshopper	761	WZ765	8.91	H.Chapple	Berlin	12.96*
	(Probably composite wings ex WZ765 & spare fuselage c/n SSK/FF2069: as "WZ765": to Luftwaffen Museum 1996)						
3663/FZV	Rolladen-Schneider LS-7	7116		12.90	R Roddy "280"	Booker	8.00
3664/FZW+	Glaser-Dirks DG-300 Club Elan	3E378C53		8.90	Mr & Mrs S.Barter	Ringmer	12.99
3665/FZX+	SZD-51-1 Junior	B-1925		9.90	Nene Valley GC	Upwood	3.00
3666/FZY	LET L-33 Solo	940046		3.94	A.W.Cox	Bicester	3.95*
3667/FZZ+	LET L-33 Solo	940220		4.95	D.A Wiseman	Jurby, IoM	4.00
3669/GAB+	LAK-12 Lietuva	6170		1.91	M.Wilshere	Halton	6.00
3670/GAC+	Schleicher Ka6CR	6301	(BGA.3647) D-5572	11.90	York Gliding Centre	Rufforth	2.99
3671/GAD	Rolladen-Schneider LS-3	3032	HB-1363	11.90	M.J.Towler "L5"	Bidford	4.00
3673/GAF	Schleicher ASK21	21152	ZD652 BGA.2892	11.90	Lasham Gliding Society "778"	Lasham	3.00
3674/GAG+	Schleicher ASK21	21143	ZD645 BGA.2885	1.91	Stratford-upon-Avon GC	Snitterfield	3.00
3675/GAH+	Schempp-Hirth HS.4 Standard Cirrus	572	HB-1240	12.90	M.G.Harris	Nympsfield	11.00
3676/GAJ+	Glaser-Dirks DG-300 Club Elan	3E385C56		12.90	M.R Wooley & Ptnrs	Long Mynd	3.00
3677/GAK	LET L-13 Blanik	174522	2-84 (Lithuania)	7.97	North Wales GC	Bryngwyn Bach	8.99
3678/GAL+	Schempp-Hirth HS.4 Standard Cirrus	335	HB-1150	4.91	D.Reynolds & S.Cooke	Aston Down	5.00
3679/GAM+	Schleicher ASK21	21144	ZD646 BGA.2886	11.90	Oxford University GC	Bicester	3.00
3680/GAN+	Glasflugel H.301 Libelle	8	D-4111	12.90	W.J.Dean	Long Mynd	7.00
3681/GAP+	Schempp-Hirth Ventus BT	14/150	OH-774 N416DP	4.91	J.R.Greenwell	Currock Hill	7.00
3682/GAQ	Schleicher Ka7 Rhonadler	3	PH-788 D-5550	4.91	York Gliding Centre "K7"	Rufforth	6.00
3683/GAR	Rolladen-Schneider LS-6C	6205		11.90	A.J.Burton "148"	Shobdon	2.00
3684/GAS+	Schempp-Hirth Ventus CT	157/509		5.91	M W Edwards	Kingston Deverill	4.00
3685/GAT+	Grob G.102 Astir CS	1130	D-4176	11.90	P.J.Bramley	Lasham	2.00
3686/GAU	Glasflugel H.201B Standard Libelle	498	F-CELA	6.93	D.R.Pickett "725"	Crowland	3.00
3687/GAV+	Scheibe SF-27A Zugvogel V	6073	D-5287	11.90	W.Waite	Lleweni Parc	8.00

BGA No/Code	Type	C/n	P/I	Date	Owner/operator	Probable Base	CA Expy
3688/GAW+	Schleicher Ka6CR	61/08	D-6320	12.90	B.D.Floyd	Snitterfield	4.00
3689/GAX	SZD-55-1	551190008		12.90	Rattlesden GC	Rattlesden	2.00
3692/GBA+	Schleicher ASK13	13417	D-2114	12.90	Burn GC	Burn	4.00
3693/GBB+	Schleicher ASK21	21073	D-3239	12.90	B.T.Spreckley	Le Blanc, France	4.00
3695/GBD+	SZD-50-3 Puchacz	B-2028		4.91	Northumbria GC	Currock Hill	5.00
3696/GBE+	Schleicher Ka6CR (Pe)	6133A	D-4085	12.90	J.Swannock	Gamston	6.00
3697/GBF+	Schleicher ASK21	21142	ZD644 BGA.2883	2.91	BBC Gliding Group	Booker	4.00
3698/GBG	Rolladen-Schneider LS-	6214		12.90	M.J.Jordy "676"	Enstone	1.00
3700/GBJ+	Grob G.102 Astir CS	1107	D-4167	1.91	R.S.Stuart	Rhigos	8.00
3701/GBK+	Grob G.102 Astir CS	1461	D-7451	1.91	G R.Jenkins & Ptnrs "Mountain Man"	Lasham	1.00
3702/GBL	Rolladen-Schneider LS-7	7119		11.90	P.B.Walker "720"	Nympsfield	3.00
3703/GBM+	Scheibe SF-27A Zugvogel V	6060	RAFGGA D-5409	1.91	F.C.Sloggett t/a BFMT Syndicate	North Hill	5.00
3704/GBN	Schleicher ASK21	21141	ZD643 BGA.2884	.91	L.W.Evans "843"/"MD"	Wormingford	2.98
3705/GBP+	Schleicher ASK21	21150	ZD650 BGA.2890	.91	London GC (Destroyed by mid-air lightning strike 4.99)	Dunstable	11.99
3706/GBQ	Rolladen-Schneider LS-6	6082	D-3725	.91	A. & P.R.Pentecost "630"	Kingston Deverill	11.00
3707/GBR	Rolladen-Schneider LS-6C	6196	D-3482	11.90	S.Hurd "218"	Dunstable	3.00
3708/GBS	Glaser-Dirks DG-300 Club Elan	3E389C58		.91	Yorkshire GC "206"	Sutton Bank	2.00
3709/GBT	Rolladen-Schneider LS-4A	4355	N220BB N97SL	4.91	S.A.Adlard "690"	Long Mynd	4.95*
3710/GBU	Centrair 101A Pegase	101A-0394		4.91	S.I.Ross "922"	Parham Park	3.99
3711/GBV	Schleicher ASK21	21149	ZD649 BGA.2889	4.91	Wolds GC "649"	Pocklington	3.00
3713/GBX	Schleicher ASW22	22029	D-4325	2.91	E.J.Rogers & Ptnrs "290"	Gransden Lodge	3.00
3714/GBY	Rolladen-Schneider LS-7	7121		1.91	W.J.Morecraft & Ptnrs "425"	Saltby	2.00
3715/GBZ+	Glaser-Dirks DG-500 Elan Trainer	5E34T10		8.91	Needwood Forest GC	Cross Hayes	3.00
3716/GCA+	Schleicher ASW19B	19281	D-3179	3.91	Deeside GC	Aboyne	4.00
3717/GCB	LAK-12 Lietuva	647		3.91	B.Middleton "637"	Dunstable	3.00
3718/GCC+	SZD-51-1 Junior	B-1928		3.91	Coventry GC	Husbands Bosworth	1.00
3719/GCD	Schempp-Hirth HS.4 Standard Cirrus	476	PH-507	2.91	D.B.Brown "507"	Chipping	10.00
3720/GCE	Schleicher ASH25	25105		2.91	C.L.Withall "8"	Dunstable	3.00
3721/GCF+	Schleicher ASK23	23010	AGA.9	2.91	Needwood Forest GC	Cross Hayes	4.00
3722/GCG	Schleicher K8B	8186	D-5227	2.91	Shenington GC "S81"	Edgehill	8.00
3723/GCH	Schleicher ASW15B	15212	PH-438 D-0950	4.91	M.D.Woodman-Smith & Ptnr "438"	Dunstable	4.99
3724/GCJ+	LAK-12 Lietuva (New wings with reconditioned 1982-built fuselage)	626		3.91	P.Crowhurst	Crowland	5.99
3725/GCK+	SZD-50-3 Puchacz	B-2025	(G-BTJV) BGA.3725	3.91	Kent GC	Challock	1.00
3726/GCL+	Grob G.102 Astir CS	1194	D-7311	3.91	D.Draper	Rivar Hill	2.00
3727/GCM	Rolladen-Schneider LS-6C	6216		3.91	M.H.Hardwick "Z29"	Enstone	3.00
3728/GCN	Centrair 101A Pegase	101A-0035	(BGA.3694) F-CFQB	3.91	B.T.Spreckley Le Blanc, France "B35" (Damaged Nympsfield 18.6.95)		3.96*
3729/GCP+	Schleicher Ka6CR	6416	D-6369	5.91	D.Clarke	Burn	4.00
3730/GCQ	Schempp-Hirth HS.2 Cirrus VTC	135Y	D-2945	4.91	P.Jones & Ptnrs "845"	Lasham	5.00
3731/GCR	Schleicher ASW15B	15447	D-6887	3.91	C.J.Anson & Ptnrs "748"	Dunstable	3.00
3732/GCS	Glasflugel H.205 Club Libelle	159	F-CEQL	7.91	N.Stainton "H12"	Bidford	9.99
3733/GCT	Schempp-Hirth Discus B	360		3.91	M.F.Evans "540"	Lasham	2.00
3734/GCU+	SZD-50-3 Puchacz	B-2023	(BGA.3619)	3.91	Buckminster GC	Saltby	4.00
3736/GCX+	Schleicher ASW15	15034	D-0420	5.91	A.S.Edlin	Husbands Bosworth	4.00
3737/GCY	Centrair 101A Pegase	101A-0392		4.91	London GC "908"	Dunstable	11.00
3738/GCZ	Rolladen-Schneider LS-7WL	7130		3.91	S.G.Olender & Ptnr "244" (Spain)		3.00
3739/GDA	Rolladen-Schneider LS-3-17M	3448	RAFGGA.546	5.91	D.J.Moore "546/545"	Aston Down	5.00
3740/GDB+	Schleicher K8B	8152	HB-738	3.91	Welland GC	Lyveden	2.00
3741/GDC+	Slingsby T.38 Grasshopper (Built from spare frame - with c/n SSK/RF.3107)	FF.1795		5.91	F.K.Russell & Ptnrs	Dunstable	5.97*
3742/GDD+	Bolkow Phoebus 17C	836	D-0060	4.91	I.D.McLeod (As "D-0060")	Challock	4.00
3743/GDE+	Schleicher Ka6CR	6570Si	D-5306	4.91	D.N.Jones	Kingston Deverill	5.00
3744/GDF+	Schleicher Ka6BR	389	D-8544	4.91	W.M.Ulyett	Burn	6.00
3747/GDJ	Rolladen-Schneider LS-4A	4832		4.91	A Clark "450"	Aboyne	3.00

BGA No/Code	Type	C/n	P/I	Date	Owner/operator	Probable Base	CA Expy
3748/GDK+	Schleicher K8B	8240	D-5381	4.91	East Sussex GC	Ringmer	4.00
			D-KANU/D-5381				
3750/GDM	Glasflugel H.201B Standard Libelle	597	D-6666	4.91	K.Fear & Syndicate	Crowland	3.00
					"668"		
3751/GDN	Rolladen-Schneider LS-3-17M	3291	D-6932	4.91	S.J Peppler		
					Sandhill Farm, Shrivenham		5.00
					(As "GDS" & "294")		
3752/GDP+	Schleicher ASW19B	19285	D-3160	5.91	W.M.Leutfeld "ED"	Cranfield	4.00
3753/GDQ+	Grob G.102 Astir CS	1145	D-7229	5.91	J.T.Harrison	Camphill	5.00
3754/GDR+	Schempp-Hirth Discus CS	016CS		5.91	R.H.Wright Husbands Bosworth		6.00
	(Built Orlican)						
3755/GDS+	Schleicher ASW15B	15205	D-0902	6.91	G.D.E.Edwards	Dunstable	9.00
	(See BGA.3751)						
3756/GDT	Schleicher ASW24	24120		5.91	D.Bower "T54"	Rufforth	3.00
3757/GDU	Schleicher ASW24	24118		6.91	G.J.Mosore "801"	Dunstable	1.00
3758/GDV+	Schleicher Ka6E	4099	OO-ZWQ	6.91	P.Potter	Snitterfield	5.00
			I-NEST/OE-0807				
3759/GDW+	Scheibe SF-27A Zugvogel V	6116	D-1997	5.91	V Grayson	Challock	6.00
3760/GDX	Schempp-Hirth Discus CS	023CS		7.91	The Soaring Centre		
					"896" Husbands Bosworth		2.00
3761/GDY+	Schleicher ASW15B	15220	D-0947	5.91	J Archer	Bidford	12.99
3762/GDZ	Schleicher ASW24	24116		5.91	I.C.Lees "524"	Pocklington	3.00
3763/GEA+	Schleicher Ka6CR	849	(BGA.3605)	6.91	M Wood	Rufforth	5.00
			D-5801				
3764/GEB+	Grob G.102 Astir CS77	1628	PH-576	6.91	J.O.Lavery	Bellarena	6.00
3767/GEE	Glasflugel H.201B Standard Libelle	94	D-0928	6.91	C.Metcalfe "928"	Gamston	5.00
3768/GEF+	Schleicher Ka6CR	6459	D-1068	5.91	J.B Christie	Nympsfield	7.98
3769/GEG+	Schleicher K8B	689	HB-639	4.91	Newark & Notts GC	Winthorpe	2.00
3770/GEH	Schleicher ASW15B	15276	D-2124	7.91	K.G.Vincent & Ptnrs	Challock	5.00
					"219"		
3772/GEL	SZD-50-3 Puchacz	B-2030	(RNGSA.N23)	5.91	Portsmouth Naval GC		
						Lee-on-Solent	3.00
3773/GEM+	Schleicher Ka6CR	6249	D-8486	6.91	D.Arkley	Rivar Hill	4.00
3774/GEN+	Slingsby T.21B	1154	RAFGGA.550	5.92	A.Harris	RAF Bruggen	4.00
			XN150				
3775/GEP+	Schempp-Hirth HS.4 Standard Cirrus	205G	D-0917	6.91	D.Walker	Gamston	3.00
3777/HAA	Glasflugel H.201B Standard Libelle	356	HB-1090	6.91	T.Mormin & Ptnrs Gransden Lodge		4.00
					"99"		
3778/HAB+	Schleicher Ka6CR	6596	D-1596	1.92	M Greenwood	Rhigos	7.00
3779/HAC+	SZD-50-3 Puchacz	B-2035		6.91	Peterborough & Spalding GC		
						Crowland	5.00
3780/HAD	Glasflugel H.201 Standard Libelle	3	D-8914	7.91	G.S Roe & Ptnrs "429"	Lasham	5.00
3781/HAE+	Glasflugel H.205 Club Libelle	75	D-8687	7.91	J.C Leonard	Bembridge	4.00
3782/HAF	SZD-50-3 Puchacz	B-2031	(RNGSA.N53)	7.91	Culdrose GC	RNAS Culdrose	3.00
3783/HAG+	Schleicher Ka7 Rhonadler	834	D-5795	5.92	Denbigh GC	Lleweni Parc	3.00
3785/HAJ	Schempp-Hirth Ventus C	517		7.91	Surrey & Hants GC "391"	Lasham	2.00
3786/HAK	Slingsby T.31B	844	XA302	8.91	W.Walker (As "XA302")	Syerston	5.96*
3787/HAL+	Schleicher ASK13	13690AB		9.91	Cotswold GC	Aston Down	12.99
3789/HAN	Schempp-Hirth HS.4 Standard Cirrus	130	D-0326	8.91	M.Hastings & Syndicate		
					"278" Weston-on-the-Green		5.00
3790/HAP+	Schleicher Ka6E	4335	HB-985	8.91	C.Delahunt	Long Mynd	8.00
3791/HAQ	Rolladen-Schneider LS-6B	6150	D-8079	9.91	A R Hughes "114" Gransden Lodge		4.00
3792/HAR+	Schleicher K8B	8151	D-8453	9.91	G.Weale	Brent Tor	7.97*
3793/HAS+	SZD-50-3 Puchacz	B-2043		8.91	The Soaring Club		
						Husbands Bosworth	1.00
3794/HAT+	Glaser-Dirks DG-200/17	2-93/1709	D-6843	8.91	D.Simon	Carlton Moor	6.00
3795/HAU+	Grob G.102 Astir CS Jeans	2043	D-3887	9.91	Yorkshire GC	Sutton Bank	3.00
3796/HAV+	Glasflugel H.201B Standard Libelle	40	HB-950	8.91	P.W.Andrews Husbands Bosworth		3.00
3798/HAX+	Schempp-Hirth HS.4 Standard Cirrus	02	ZS-GHZ	10.91	A J Pettit	Rivar Hill	1.00
			ZS-TIM/ZS-GGR/D-0302				
3799/HAY	Rolladen-Schneider LS-7	7154		10.91	N.Leaton & Ptnrs	Challock	7.96*
3801/HBA	Rolladen-Schneider LS-7	7156	D-6041	10.91	P.O'Donald "729" Gransden Lodge		11.00
3802/HBB	Schleicher ASW24	24132		9.91	S.D.Steinberg Gransden Lodge		11.99
					"S1"		
3803/HBC	Rolladen-Schneider LS-6C	6209	D-....	9.91	J.Burry "301"	Lasham	3.00
3804/HBD+	Glaser-Dirks DG-200	2-12	HB-1384	10.91	L.Marshall & Ptnrs	Rattlesden	1.00
3805/HBE	Glaser-Dirks DG-300 Elan	3E237	SE-UFB	5.92	A.W.Cox & Ptnrs "356"	Enstone	9.00
3806/HBF+	Schempp-Hirth HS.5 Nimbus 2C	191	D-3369	10.91	T.Cauldwell		
					Sackville Farm, Riseley		7.00
3807/HBG	Schleicher ASW24	24133		12.91	Imperial College GC "96" Lasham		1.00
3808/HBH	Grob G.103C Twin III	36006		10.91	Imperial College GC "496" Lasham		2.00

BGA No/Code	Type	C/n	P/I	Date	Owner/operator	Probable Base	CA Expy
3809/HBJ	Rolladen-Schneider LS-6C-18	6230		9.91	D.Hill "949"	Edgehill	3.00
3810/HBK+	Grob G.103 Twin Astir	3254-T-31	RAFGGA... D-2389	9.91	R.W.Idle	Burn	5.00
3811/HBL+	Grob G.102 Astir CS77	1626	RAFGSA R78 RAFGSA.778	10.91	J.McCormick	Bidford	4.00
3812/HBM+	Grob G.102 Astir CS77	1633	RAFGSA R65 RAFGSA.R66/RAFGSA.546	12.91	M.Wood	Syerston	6.00
3814/HBP	Glaser-Dirks DG-500/22 Elan	5E36S8		10.91	A.Leigh "522"	Camphill	7.00
3815/HBQ+	Schleicher Ka6CR	6611	D-5616	11.91	H Porter	Snitterfield	5.00
3816/HBR	Schempp-Hirth Nimbus 4T	3/6	(BGA.3784) "PM"	7.92	P S Hawkins	Keiheuvel, Belgium	5.00
3817/HBS+	SZD-41A Jantar Standard	B-852	D-4160	12.91	A.Henderson	Milfield	7.00
3819/HBT+	Grob G.102 Club Astir	2235	PH-675	2.92	G.M.Hall	Winthorpe	3.00
3820/HBU	Centrair ASW20F	20527	F-CFSI	11.91	R.Palmer & R.Mann "605"	Bidford	1.00
3821/HBV	Schempp-Hirth HS.5 Nimbus 2B	143	D-7850	11.91	C.J.Teagle "827"	Sutton Bank	2.00
3822/HBW	Glaser-Dirks DG-300 Club Elan	3E405C64		12.91	P.C.Cannon "829"	Lasham	4.00
3823/HBX+	Slingsby T.45 Swallow	1386	8801M XS650	5.93	C.D.Street & Ptnrs	Lasham	7.00
3824/HBY	Rolladen-Schneider LS-7	7148		11.91	R.C.Bridges "664"	Husbands Bosworth	7.00
3825/HBZ+	Slingsby T.15 Gull III Replica	-		6.92	P.R.Philpot	Chipping	6.00
3826/HCA+	Grob G.103 Twin Astir	3289	D-0094 OO-ZOH/D-3063	12.91	M.Wright "P5"	Rattlesden	4.00
3827/HCB	Schempp-Hirth Nimbus 3DT	47		12.91	P.A.Green "754"	Lasham	4.00
3829/HCC+	SZD-50-3 Puchacz	B-2048		1.92	Heron GC	RNAS Yeovilton	12.99
3830/HCD+	SZD-50-3 Puchacz	B-2049		1.92	Coventry GC	Husbands Bosworth	3.00
3831/HCE	Schleicher ASW19B	19305	D-6527	1.92	N.J.Morgan "346"	Dunstable	1.00
3832/HCF+	SZD-50-3 Puchacz	B-2047		1.92	Shalbourne Soaring Society 	Rivar Hill	1.00
3833/HCG+	Maupin Woodstock One (Built R.Harvey)	NK		10.92	R.Harvey	Swanton Morley	10.99
3834/HCH	Centrair ASW20FP	20178	F-CEUL	3.92	M.P.Eastburn "355"	Saltby	5.00
3835/HCJ+	Grob G.103 Twin II	3709	D-2611	1.92	Peterborough & Spalding GC 	Crowland	6.00
3836/HCK	Slingsby T.21B	623	RAFGGA5.. WB962	1.92	V.Mallon Laarbruch, Germany (As "WB962")		8.00
3837/HCL	Schempp-Hirth Discus B	136	D-4682	3.92	P.E. & R.J.Baker Gransden Lodge "144"		2.00
3838/HCM+	Schleicher Ka7 Rhonadler	498	D-5669	3.92	M.Barnard	Dunstable	8.00
3839/HCN+	CARMAM M.200 Foehn	24	F-CDDR	12.92	J S Shaw	Perranporth	7.99
3840/HCP+	Avialsa A.60 Fauconnet	123K	F-CDLA	3.93	B.H.George	Edgehill	7.95*
3841/HCQ+	Glasflugel H.201B Standard Libelle	197	HB-999	1.92	E.K.Harris	Dunstable	3.00
3842/HCR	SZD-51-1 Junior	B-2003		4.92	Surrey & Hants GC "394"	Lasham	3.00
3843/HCS+	Grob G.102 Astir CS77	1727	RAFGSA.R84 RAFGSA.884	2.92	Buckminster GC	Saltby	4.97*
3845/HCU+	Glaser-Dirks DG-300 Club Elan	3E407C66		2.92	M.S Smith & Ptnrs	Aston Down	5.00
3846/HCV+	Schleicher ASW19B	19084	D-4486	5.93	Miss W.J.Palmer	Dunstable	5.00
3847/HCW+	SZD-51-1 Junior	B-2002	(BGA.3844)	2.92	Deeside GC (As "HCN")	Aboyne	4.00
3848/HCX+	Schleicher ASK21	21541		5.92	Devon & Somerset GC	North Hill	7.00
3849/HCY+	Glaser-Dirks DG-300 Club Elan	3E413C67		5.94	M.A.Thorne	Old Sarum	7.00
3850/HCZ+	Schleicher K8B	8114A	D-4675	2.92	South London Gliding Centre 	Kenley	8.99
3851/HDA+	Pilatus B4 PC-11AF	017	D-0964	3.92	R.C.Mummery	Lasham	7.99
3852/HDB+	SZD-51-1 Junior	B-1997		3.92	Stratford-upon-Avon GC 	Snitterfield	2.00
3853/HDC+	Schleicher ASK13	13308	D-0750	3.93	Bowland Forest GC	Chipping	1.00
3854/HDD	Centrair 101B Pegase	101B-0425		4.92	R.C.Bell "591"	Booker	1.00
3855/HDE+	Pilatus B4 PC-11AF	223	VH-XOZ VH-WQP	4.92	A.J.Hamilton	Aston Down	7.00
3856/HDF	Schempp-Hirth Discus B	404		2.92	T.M.Lipscombe "910"	Lasham	1.00
3858/HDH	Glaser-Dirks DG-202-15 (See BGA.3862)	2-197	???	5.92	R.J.Pirie "991"	Parham Park	4.99
3859/HDJ+	Schleicher ASW20CL	20828	D-8442	3.92	M.Challans & Ptnrs	Booker	2.00
3861/HDL	Schleicher ASW20	20082	D-1617 OH-495	4.92	S.Thackray "137"	Rivar Hill	3.00
3862/HDM	SZD-12A Mucha 100A	448	SP-1987	4.92	T.J.Wilkinson ("HDH") Sackville Farm, Riseley		4.00
3863/HDN+	Schleicher K8B	2	D-8017	3.92	Upward Bound Trust	Thame	9.98
3864/HDP+	SZD-50-3 Puchacz	B-2050	(RNGSA.N36)	3.92	Heron GC	RNAS Yeovilton	6.00
3866/HDR	Glaser-Dirks DG-300 Elan	3E95	RAFGSA R30	3.92	C.J.Cornish "467"	Booker	5.00

BGA No/Code	Type	C/n	P/I	Date	Owner/operator	Probable Base	CA Expy
3868/HDT	Schempp-Hirth Discus BT	76/405		3.92	J.D.J.Glossop & Ptnrs		
					"291"	Gransden Lodge	3.00
3869/HDU+	SZD-51-1 Junior	B-1996		3.92	Cambridge University GC		
						Gransden Lodge	1.00
3870/HDV	Schleicher ASW19B	19345	D-2876	4.92	R.J.Hinley "882"	Camphill	4.00
3871/HDW+	Centrair 101A Pegase	101A-0179	F-CGEE	3.92	T.Head	Husbands Bosworth	6.00
3872/HDX	Rolladen-Schneider LS-7	7161		3.92	P.W.Rodwell "A2"	Crowland	2.00
3873/HDY	Schleicher K8B	8277	D-4094	3.92	M.A Everett	Crowland	4.00
3874/HDZ	Schempp-Hirth Discus CS	078CS		7.92	J.P.Wright & G.Bennett	Challock	3.00
					"W1"		
3875/HEA+	Slingsby T.38 Grasshopper	SSK/FF529	(RAF)	7.92	R.L.McLean	Rufforth	7.00
3876/HEB+	Schleicher Ka6CR	6289	HB-773	5.92	J.W Watt	North Hill	3.00
3877/HEC	SZD-55-1	551191019		5.92	G.P Davis "308"	Aston Down	2.00
3878/HED	Schempp-Hirth Ventus A	17	D-2524	4.92	M.R.Dawson "840"	Hullavington	4.00
3879/HEE	Schempp-Hirth Discus B	292		4.92	Booker GC	Booker	5.00
	(Rebuild of BGA.3523 after accident 21.6.91 but see BGA.4047)				"316"		
3880/HEF+	Glaser-Dirks DG-500 Elan Trainer			5.92	Yorkshire GC	Sutton Bank	3.00
		5E53T20					
3881/HEG+	LAK-12 Lietuva	6206		6.92	R.Kmita & Ptnrs		
						Kirton-in-Lindsey	4.00
3882/HEH	Rolladen-Schneider LS-7WL	7163	D-6078	6.92	R.J.Welford "795"	Gransden Lodge	1.00
3883/HEJ	Schleicher ASW15B	15441	D-6871	5.92	R.Bickerton "687"	Weston on the Gn.	1.00
3884/HEK+	SZD-51-1 Junior	B-2009	BGA.3893	5.94	Cambridge University GC		
			(BGA.3884)			Gransden Lodge	1.00
3885/HEL	Rolladen-Schneider LS-4	4027	D-6431	5.92	G.C.Alison "A9"	Dunstable	2.00
3886/HEM	Schempp-Hirth Discus CS	073CS		5.92	J.H.Nunnerley "473"	Enstone	3.00
3887/HEN	Schempp-Hirth Discus B	422		6.92	A.R.Verity & Ptnrs	Challock	2.00
					"735"		
3888/HEP+	SZD-50-3 Puchacz	B-2057		5.92	Peterborough & Spalding GC		
						Crowland	11.99
3889/HEQ	Schleicher ASW20L	20410	D-6747	6.92	M.Chant "611"	Brent Tor	2.00
3890/HER+	Schleicher ASW19	19240	F-CERR	4.93	B.T.Spreckley	Le Blanc, France	11.00
3891/HES	Centrair 101A Pegase	101A-039	F-CFQF	3.93	B.T.Spreckley	Le Blanc, France	4.00
					"B39"		
3892/HET	Rolladen-Schneider LS-6C	6263		6.92	M P Brooks "335"	Lasham	2.00
3894/HEV+	Schempp-Hirth HS.2 Cirrus	41	OO-ZXY	5.92	D.A Clempson	Portmoak	4.00
			(OO-ZOZ)/D-0104				
3895/HEW	Rolladen-Schneider LS-6C	6250		4.92	R.M.Underhill "486"	Bicester	1.00
3897/HEY	Hutter H-17A	02		6.92	J.M.Lee	Parham Park	5.00
	(Built J.M.Lee - possibly BGA.3661)						
3898/HEZ+	Rolladen-Schneider LS-6C	6264		7.92	J.E.Cruttenden "607"	Lasham	3.00
3899/HFA	Schempp-Hirth Ventus B/16.6	251	RAFGSA.R24	6.92	D.R.Stewart "425"	Winthorpe	6.95*
3900/HFB+	Schleicher Ka6CR	6344Si	D-5825	7.92	S.Tomlinson	Templeton	9.00
3901/HFC	Slingsby T.21B	587	WB924	7.92	M.G Stringer	Dunstable	8.00
	(As "WB924")						
3902/HFD	Grob G.102 Astir CS Jeans	2229	D-5912	6.92	East Sussex GC	Ringmer	8.97*
					"289" (Damaged Kitson Field 15.6.97)		
3903/HFE	Slingsby T.21B	1166	XN187	6.92	A.J.Oultram	Seighford	5.00
	(As "XN187")						
3904/HFF	Schempp-Hirth Standard Cirrus	539	D-8916	2.93	M.S.Morrisroe "870"	Upwood	1.00
3905/HFG	Slingsby T.21B	1165	XN186	6.92	A.M.Thompson	RAF Marham	5.00
3906/HFH+	SZD-50-3 Puchacz	B-2059		8.92	Trent Valley GC		
						Kirton-in-Lindsey	4.00
3907/HFJ+	SZD-42-1 Jantar 2A	B-792	RAFGGA...	4.92	P.Stein	RAF Bruggen	4.00
			OO-ZDE				
3909/HFL	Schleicher ASH25	25147		7.92	T.W.Slater "925/SSC"	Portmoak	2.00
3910/HFM	Rolladen-Schneider LS-6C	6266		7.92	F.J.Shepherd "747"	Booker	6.00
3911/HFN	Wassmer WA-26P Squale	18	F-CDQP	6.92	C.Duthy-James	Talgarth	8.96*
3912/HFP	CARMAM M.100S Mesange	87K	F-CDPQ	6.92	D.Patrick & Ptnr	Falgunzeon	9.96*
3913/HFQ	Rolladen-Schneider LS-6C	6260	(BGA.3908)	6.92	R A Brown "126"	Gamston	3.00
3917/HFU+	SZD-9 bis Bocian 1D	P-334	SP-2038	6.94	T.Wiltshere	(Spilsby)	8.96*
3918/HFV	Schempp-Hirth Ventus B 16.6	204	D-5235	10.92	A.Cliffe "F2"	Camphill	3.00
3919/HFW+	Schleicher K8B	8108	HB-705	9.92	Oxford GC	Weston-on-the-Green	3.00
3920/HFX	Schempp-Hirth Nimbus 4T	12		7.92	R.Jones "82"	Lasham	3.00
3921/HFY	Schempp-Hirth Ventus CT	168/554	(BGA.3916)	7.92	M.Day & D.J.Ellis	Lasham	3.00
			(BGA.3867)		"940"		
3922/HFZ	Abbott-Baynes Scud I Rep	001		R	Brookland Museum	Brooklands	-
					(On display 4.99)		
3923/HGA+	Wassmer WA-26P Squale	43	F-CDUH	3.93	E.C.Murgatroyd		
						Sackville Farm, Riseley	5.99

BGA No/Code	Type	C/n	P/I	Date	Owner/operator	Probable Base	CA Expy
3924/HGB	Grob G.102 Astir CS	1356	D-7386	11.92	P.J.Hollamby & Ptnrs		
	(Rebuilt with wings & components from RAFGGA.507)				"509"	Lee-on-Solent	2.00
3925/HGC+	Schleicher Ka7 Rhonadler	540	D-5689	3.94	T.A.Joint	Lasham	8.00
3928/HGF+	Schleicher ASW15B	15264	D-2128	8.92	I.Thompson	Camphill	4.00
3929/HGG+	Schempp-Hirth HS.4 Standard Cirrus	362	HB-1172	12.92	P.Hodgetts	Seighford	11.99
3930/HGH+	Schleicher ASW19B	19351	D-1199	8.92	A.Wood	Brent Tor	3.00
3931/HGJ	CARMAM M.200 Foehn	33	F-CDHG	9.92	M.Skinner	Cross Hayes	11.95*
3932/HGK+	Schempp-Hirth Discus BT	96/435		10.92	C.T.Skeate	Parham Park	11.99
3933/HGL	Schempp-Hirth Discus B	431		7.92	P.J.Ward "183"	Aston Down	1.00
3934/HGM+	Scheibe SF-27A Zugvogel V	6017	D-9351	9.92	S.Algeo	Lyveden	5.00
3935/HGN	Schempp-Hirth Ventus CT	172/562		9.92	Diamond Sailplanes Ltd		
					"740"	North Hill	8.00
3936/HGP+	Rolladen-Schneider LS-6C	6270		11.92	D.Elrington	Camphill	7.00
3937/HGQ	LAK-12 Lietuva	6208		.94	R.A.M.Lovegrove "637"	Dunstable	6.00
3938/HGR+	LAK-12 Lietuva	6186		3.93	R.G Stevens	Husbands Bosworth	5.00
3939/HGS	Schempp-Hirth Discus B	439		11.92	J.C.Bailey "730"	Challock	11.00
3940/HGT+	FFA Diamant 16.5	40	HB-929	4.94	R.W.Collins	Burn	5.00
3941/HGU+	Avionautica Rio M.100S	048	HB-1038	6.93	R.D.Colman	Old Sarum	5.98
			I-RIKI				
3942/HGV+	Glaser-Dirks DG-500/22 Elan	5E70S11		2.93	B.H.Bryce-Smith	Gransden Lodge	3.00
3943/HGW+	Centrair ASW20F	20102	F-CFFB	1.93	A.M.Smith	Husbands Bosworth	3.00
3944/HGX	LAK-12 Lietuva	6201		5.93	K.Pickering "783"	Parham Park	4.00
3945/HGY	SZD-24C Foka	W-180	SP-2385	12.92	Peterborough & Spalding GC		
						Crowland	5.00
3946/HGZ	Schempp-Hirth Discus BT	95/434		12.92	R.F.Aldous & Ptnrs "502"	Booker	2.00
3947/HHA+	SZD-50-3 Puchacz	B-2058		2.93	Derby & Lancs GC	Camphill	5.00
3949/HHC+	SZD-50-3 Puchacz	B-2080		4.93	Derby & Lancs GC	Camphill	3.00
3950/HHD+	SZD-51-1 Junior	B-2010		3.93	Derby & Lancs GC	Camphill	2.00
3951/HHE+	SZD-51-1 Junior	B-2008		6.93	Derby & Lancs GC	Camphill	2.00
3953/HHG	Slingsby T.31B	705	WT910	1.93	P.Wickwar & Ptnr	Challock	5.97*
					(As "WT910")		
3954/HHH	Rolladen-Schneider LS-6C	6289		12.92	B.R.Wise "963"	Booker	5.00
3955/HHJ+	Glaser-Dirks DG-500/22 Elan	5E71S12		2.93	British Gliding Association		
					"97"	Bicester	12.00
3956/HHK	Schleicher ASW19B	19384	ZD661	3.93	A.J.Peters Syndicate	Lasham	3.00
			BGA.2897		"838"		
3957/HHL+	Schleicher Ka7 Rhonadler	446	OY-XCK	7.93	Lincolnshire GC	Strubby	6.00
			D-5619		"Buttercup"		
3958/HHM+	LAK-12 Lietuva	6195		8.93	R.Parayre	(France)	4.00
3959/HHN	Schempp-Hirth Ventus B/16.6	205	RAFGSA.R27	2.93	N.A.C.Norman	Aboyne	3.00
	(Build No. V-204)				"979"		
3960/HHP	Schempp-Hirth Discus B	399	SE-UKL	2.93	D.J.Knowles "KL"	Camphill	11.00
3961/HHQ	Schempp-Hirth Discus BT	106/453		2.93	J.P.Galloway "977"	Portmoak	1.00
3962/HHR	SZD-55-1	551191020		4.93	R.T.Starling "100"	Nympsfield	2.00
3963/HHS	Schleicher ASW20	20008	SE-TTU	3.93	J.R.Bates "746"	Lasham	3.00
3964/HHT	Rolladen-Schneider LS-6C	6292		7.93	R.C.Bromwich	Kingston Deverill	4.00
					"855"		
3965/HHU	Rolladen-Schneider LS-6C	6296		2.93	P.R.Redshaw "23"	Walney Island	5.00
3967/HHW	LAK-12 Lietuva	6212		3.93	A.J.Dibdin "237"	Dunstable	2.00
3968/HHX	Wassmer WA-26P Squale	14	F-CDQJ	2.93	M.H.Gagg	Long Mynd	2.00
3969/HHY+	Glasflugel H.201B Standard Libelle	119	SE-TIU	3.93	R.Tietma & M.Ainsworth		
						Husbands Bosworth	1.00
3971/HJA+	VFW-Fokker FK-3	0008	D-0409	8.93	M.A Johnson & Ptnrs		
						Sackville Farm, Riseley	3.00
3973/HJC	Rolladen-Schneider LS-6C	6290		3.93	F.J Davis & I.C.Woodhouse		
					"25"	Enstone	1.00
3974/HJD+	Schleicher Ka6E	4141	D-....	2.94	D.Weitzel	Edgehill	2.00
			OH-505/SE-TFM				
3975/HJE	Schleicher K8B	8259	(BGA.3926)	4.93	Denbigh GC	Lleweni Parc	7.00
			RAFGGA.505 (&/or RAFGGA.981?) "505"				
3976/HJF	Rolladen-Schneider LS-6C	6291		4.93	J.L.Bridge "245"	Gransden Lodge	12.99
3978/HJH+	Schempp-Hirth Discus BT	65/391	(N32086)	4.93	P.J.Goulthorpe	Crowland	1.00
			BGA.3978/N224WT		"Z1"		
3979/HJJ	Slingsby T.38 Grasshopper	797	WZ816	R	J.Wilkins		
3980/HJK	Schleicher Ka7 Rhonadler	795	RAFGSA.R5	6.93	Leeds University GC	Rufforth	1.00
			D-5791				
3981/HJL	Schempp-Hirth Discus BT	105/451		5.93	A.R.MacGregor	Kingston Deverill	1.00
					"306"		
3982/HJM+	Hutter H.28-III Replica	ED.02		5.93	E.R.Duffin	Rhigos	6.99
	(Built E.R.Duffin)						
3983/HJN+	Grob Standard Cirrus	440G	HB-1206	6.93	D.F Marlow	Aston Down	5.00

BGA No/Code	Type	C/n	P/I	Date	Owner/operator	Probable Base	CA Expy
3984/HJP	Rolladen-Schneider LS-6C	6303		5.93	T.Stuart "621"	Nympsfield	2.00
3986/HJR	Glasflugel H.201B Standard Libelle	102	SE-TIO	5.95	B Magnani "B9"	Wormingford	3.00
3988/HJT	Centrair ASW20F	20115	F-CFFL	6.93	C.I Roberts & Ptnrs Snitterfield "X16"		6.00
3989/HJU+	Schempp-Hirth Standard Cirrus	134	EC-DNE D-0327	7.93	A M Cooper	Usk	7.00
3990/HJV+	Grob G.102 Astir CS	1007	D-7000	6.93	Cotswold GC	Aston Down	11.00
3991/HJX	Rolladen-Schneider LS-6C	6271		5.93	R.S.Hatwell & M.Haynes "203"	Swanton Morley	1.00
3992/HJY+	Schempp-Hirth Standard Cirrus	459	HB-1207	6.93	W.W Turnbull & Ptnrs	Currock Hill	7.00
3993/HJZ	Schleicher ASW15B	15190	OH-408	5.94	R.R.Beezer "865"	Camphill	7.00
3994/HKA	Schempp-Hirth Discus CS	120CS		5.93	Coventry GC	Husbands Bosworth "135"	2.00
3995/HKB+	Grob G.102 Astir CS77	1658	D-7491	10.93	K.J.McPhee	Kingston Deverill	2.00
3996/HKC+	Grob Standard Cirrus	520G	D-3268	8.93	L.White	Dunstable	5.00
3997/HKD	Grob Standard Cirrus	576G	F-CEMF	7.93	J.A.Clark "C34"	Edgehill	6.00
3999/HKF+	CARMAM JP-15/36AR Aiglon	23	F-CETU	7.93	K. & C.Vincent	Bidford	7.00
4002/HKJ	Penrose Pegasus 2 (Built J.M.Lee)	001		7.93	J.M.Lee	Parham Park	9.98
4003/HKK+	Schleicher K8B	8886	D-0866	1.94	Highland GC	Easterton	3.99
4004/HKL	Schempp-Hirth Discus BT	120/476		2.94	D.P.Knibbs "919"	Seighford	3.00
4005/HKM+	Grob G.102 Astir CS Jeans	2108	D-7636	3.94	D.Simpson	Ridgewell	1.00
4006/HKN+	Centrair 101C Pegase	101-902	N101CR F-WFXB	7.93	J.A.Sutton	Currock Hill	2.99
4007/HKP+	Schleicher ASK23B	23100	D-2935 HB-1935	8.93	Midland GC	Long Mynd	3.00
4008/HKQ	Schempp-Hirth Nimbus 3DT	63		8.93	R.I.Hey & Syndicate "970"	Nympsfield	11.00
4009/HKR+	Jastreb Standard Cirrus G/81	276	OH-663	10.93	J.Evans	Lyveden	7.00
4010/HKS	Jastreb Standard Cirrus G/81	361	SE-TZS	11.93	E.W.Richards	Booker	4.00
4011/HKT+	Schleicher ASW19	19168	D-7958	10.93	A.Birkenshaw & Ptnr	Burn	10.00
	(C/n conflicts with OE-5174 but believed correct)						
4012/HKU	Grob Standard Cirrus	513G	F-CEMA	12.93	T.J Wheeler & Ptnr "C29" Lyveden		3.00
4013/HKV+	Scheibe Zugvogel IIIA	1034	D-8294	10.93	Dartmoor GC	Brent Tor	5.00
4014/HKW+	Marco J-5	009	G-BSBO	6.94	G.K Owen	Usk	9.00
	(Built D.Austin - regd with c/n 001)						
4015/HKX+	Rolladen-Schneider LS-4B	4933		12.93	D.J Hughes	Long Mynd	12.99
4016/HKY	Schempp-Hirth Discus B	461		10.93	J.G Arnold "JA"	Thruxton	2.00
4017/HKZ	CARMAM JP-15/36AR Aiglon	31	F-CFGA	9.93	R.Borthwick "P31"	Milfield	7.00
4019/HLB	Rolladen-Schneider LS-4	4935		4.94	A.W.Edwards "365" Gransden Lodge		6.00
4020/HLC+	Pilatus B4 PC-11	177	SE-UFX OH-455	3.94	C.J Pollard	Wormingford	3.00
4021/HLD	Schempp-Hirth Discus BT	122/479		10.93	C.M.Robinson & Ptnrs "462" (Damaged Parham 7.5.95)	Kenley	10.95*
4024/HLG+	Schleicher ASK21	21596		3.95	London GC	Dunstable	3.00
4025/HLH+	Schleicher K8B	8637	RAFGGA.569 D-5691	2.94	R.Das	Usk	6.00
	(See BGA.4162)						
4027/HLK+	Glasflugel H.301 Libelle	85	SE-TFS	4.95	B.Amos	Booker	3.00
4029/HLM	Schleicher ASW19B	19269	OH-538	2.94	R.A.Colbeck "819"	Booker	2.00
4030/HLN	Schempp-Hirth Discus CS	143CS		1.94	Portsmouth Naval GC "805"	Lee-on-Solent	2.00
4031/HLP+	Schleicher ASK21	21597		3.94	Yorkshire GC	Sutton Bank	3.00
4032/HLQ	Schempp-Hirth Discus B	490		12.93	J.F.Goudie "381"	Portmoak	2.00
4033/HLR	Slingsby T31B	899	XE786	?.9?	D.Thomson	Portmoak	11.00
4034/HLS	Schempp-Hirth Discus B	114	RAFGSA.R11	1.94	C.L.Withall "V5"	Dunstable	1.00
4035/HLT	LAK-12 Lietuva	6190		2.94	Baltic Sailplanes Ltd	Rufforth	2.95*
	(Damaged Rufforth 16.7.94; stored 7.97)						
4036/HLU+	Scheibe SF-27A Zugvogel V	6101	SE-TGP	2.94	G.M.Brightman	Dunstable	2.99
4037/HLV+	Schleicher K8B	8760	SE-UIM D-5005	2.94	M.Cuming "UIM"	Edgehill	1.97*
4038/HLW+	Schleicher ASW19B	19325	D-8799	4.94	F.J.Hayden	Gransden Lodge	3.00
4039/HLX	Schleicher ASH25	25124	D-3988	2.94	P.Pozerskis	Husbands Bosworth "260"	3.00
4040/HLY	Schempp-Hirth Discus CS	161CS		6.94	F.G.Birlison "565"	Aston Down	11.00
4041/HLZ	Schleicher ASW20BL	20951	D-8188	3.94	T Vines "359"	Dunstable	1.00
4042/HMA+	SZD-51-1 Junior	B-2132		3.94	Coventry GC	Husbands Bosworth	11.00
4043/HMB	Glaser-Dirks DG-300 Elan	3E105	D-4676	3.94	J.S.Weston "445"	Bellarena	2.00
4044/HMG+	ICA IS-28B2	353	HA-....	4.94	J.W.Courchee	Tibenham	10.00
4045/HMH	Schleicher K8B	5	D-5735	4.94	Shenington GC "S82"	Edgehill	10.99
	(Officially regd as c/n 2330)						

BGA No/Code	Type	C/n	P/I	Date	Owner/operator	Probable Base	CA Expy
4046/HMK	Rolladen-Schneider LS-6-18W	6324		3.94	A.E.Kay "941"	Booker	12.99
4047/HML	Schempp-Hirth Discus CS	114CS	OO-ZTU	3.94	M.E.Hahnefeld	Parham Park	3.00
	(Composite with wings from BGA.3879)				"38"		
4048/HMM	Glasflugel H.304B	322	SE-UGZ	3.94	I.P.Freestone	Husbands Bosworth	5.00
			D-1005		"D19"		
4050/HMP	Schempp-Hirth Discus B	497		3.94	D.J.Connolly "297"	North Hill	3.00
4051/HMQ	Schempp-Hirth Discus CS	099CS	D-7160	3.94	S.A.Hindley "364"	Edgehill	4.00
4052/HMR	Wassmer WA.30 Bijave	140	F-CCZV	4.94	Bidford GC	Bidford	4.95*
					(As "-CCZV": stored 9.97)		
4053/HMS+	Glaser-Dirks DG-100	40	D-2579	4.94	B.Walton-Knight	Cross Hayes	5.00
4054/HMT	Glasflugel H.303 Mosquito B	153	F-CEDY	3.94	B.T.Spreckley	Le Blanc, France	2.00
					"380"		
4055/HMU+	CARMAM JP-15/36AR Aiglon	22	F-CETT	5.94	J.R.Holmes	Kingston Deverill	3.00
4056/HMV	Schleicher ASK13	13177	(RNGSA.N26)	5.94	Portsmouth Naval GC		
			D-0268			Lee-on-Solent	6.00
4057/HMW+	Scheibe SF-27A Zugvogel V	AB.6111	D-0289	5.94	Surrey Hills GC	Kenley	8.98
					(Written-off)		
4058/HMX	Rolladen-Scheider LS.4B	4230	OO-ZNN	5.94	D.Robson "V19"	Currock Hill	5.00
			F-CEIO				
4059/HMY+	Schempp-Hirth HS.4 Standard Cirrus	121	HB-1034	4.94	C.P.Woodcock & B.J.Thomas		
						Weston-on-the-Green	2.00
4060/HMZ	Federov Me-7 Mechta	M.004		4.94	R.Ellis	Long Mynd	2.96*
					t/a Kenilworth Intl "469"		
4061/HNA+	Glaser-Dirks DG-500/20 Elan	5E128W3		7.94	P.Boneham	Winthorpe	12.98
			(Major components from crash Camphill 12.6.96 stored Rufforth 7.97)					
4062/HNB	Schempp-Hirth HS.6 Janus C	215	D-4149	4.94	C.M.Fox "563"	Lleweni Parc	3.00
4063/HNC+	Schleicher ASW19B	19297	OH-515	4.94	K.C.Morgan	Tibenham	6.00
4064/HND+	Scheibe Zugvogel IIIA	1044	HB-735	5.94	A J.Sadler	Lyveden	4.00
			D-9119				
4065/HNE	Schempp-Hirth HS.5 Nimbus 2B	91	D-2786	5.94	S.Noad & Ptnrs "708"	Challock	6.00
4066/HNF	Schempp-Hirth Duo Discus	11		5.94	Booker GC "315"	Booker	5.00
4067/HNG+	Schleicher K8B	132/59	D-8378	4.94	Bidford GC "8378"	Bidford	5.00
4068/HNH	Schempp-Hirth HS.5 Nimbus 2C	187	D-2830	3.94	A.P.Hatton "599"	Winthorpe	12.99
4069/HNJ+	Schleicher Ka7 Rhonadler	7031	D-1667	5.94	N.J.Orchard-Armitage		
			RAFGGA??/D-6233		"861"	Waldershare Park	3.00
4070/HNK+	SZD-51-1 Junior	B-1496	SP-3299	5.94	Booker GC	Booker	2.00
			(SP-3290)				
4072/HNM	Jastreb Standard Cirrus G/81	360	SE-TZT	7.94	V.L.Brown & Ptnr	Snitterfield	4.00
					"167"		
4073/HNN+	Schempp-Hirth Duo Discus	21		9.94	D.Smith	Aboyne	3.00
4077/HNS	Slingsby T.21B	1164	8942M	6.94	B.Walker	Syerston	8.99
			XN185		(As "XN185")		
4078/HNT	Schleicher ASW15	15167	F-CEAQ	6.94	A.P.Moulang "105"	Challock	4.00
4079/HNU	Schempp-Hirth Nimbus 4DT	3/5	D-KHIA	5.94	D.E.Findon "48"	Bidford	2.00
4080/HNV	Rolladen-Schneider LS-4B	4960		12.94	P.W.Armstrong	Kirton-in-Lindsey	3.00
					"692"		
4081/HNW	Schempp-Hirth Duo Discus	25		11.94	B.A.Bateson & Ptnr	Parham Park	12.00
					"2UP"		
4082/HNX	Rolladen-Schneider LS-4B	4937		7.94	C.S.Crocker "585"	Long Mynd	3.00
4083/HNY+	Centrair 101A Pegase	101A-020		10.95	M.Breen	Booker	10.98
4084/HNZ	Centrair 101A Pegase	101A-032	F-CFRY	7.94	R.H.Partington	Kirton-in-Lindsey	1.00
					"RY"		
4085/HPA	Issoire E78 Silene	4	F-CFEA	R	T.M.Perkins	Dunstable	-
4086/HPB	Hutter H.28 II Replica	-		8.94	D.G.Jones	Husbands Bosworth	8.95P*
4087/HPC+	Schleicher ASW20CL	20787	D-3424	7.94	D.R.Sutton	Pocklington	6.00
4088/HPD	Rolladen-Schneider LS-6C-18	6331	D-1054	10.94	S.G.Sampson "717"	Lasham	2.00
4089/HPE+	Schleicher ASK13	13510	D-3992	10.94	Nottingham University GC		
						Syerston	10.00
4090/HPF	SZD-9 bis Bocian 1E	P-740	OH-508	8.94	Bath, Wilts & North Dorset GC		
					(As "HPH")	Kingston Deverill	10.99
4091/HPG+	Maupin Woodstock	551	VR-HKI	8.94	J.M.Stockwell	Perranporth	9.00
	(Built J.M.Stockwell)						
4092/HPH+	Schempp-Hirth Discus CS	174CS		9.94	M.E.Newland-Smith	Ridgewell	9.00
	(See BGA.4090)				"73"		
4093/HPJ+	Edgley EA.9 Optimist	EA9/001		5.94	Edgley Aeronautics Ltd	Lasham	6.00
4094/HPK	Bibby G.1	1		R	K.Bibby		
4095/HPL	Rolladen-Schneider LS-4B	4959	(BGA.4071)	7.94	P.G.Mellor "655"	Booker	3.00
4096/HPM+	Grob G.102 Astir CS	1072	D-3304	11.94	S.K.Moeller	Lasham	12.99
4098/HPP	Slingsby T.38 Grasshopper	863	XA230	2.95	S.Butler	Gransden Lodge	7.00
4099/HPQ+	Schleicher Ka6CR	6200	D-1933	10.94	E.A.Hull	Dunstable	11.99
4100/HPR+	Schempp-Hirth Discus B	532		2.95	A.S.Decloux	Dunstable	3.00

BGA No/Code	Type	C/n	P/I	Date	Owner/operator	Probable Base	CA Expy
4101/HPS+	Federov Me-7 Mechta	M.005		5.95	R.Ellis	Long Mynd	6.98
					t/a Kenilworth Intl "469"		
4102/HPT+	Federov Me-7 Mechta	M.006		3.96	A E.Griffiths	Long Mynd	12.00
4103/HPU	Glaser-Dirks DG-800S	8-38S9	(BGA.4074)	11.94	R.J.Middleton "848"	Portmoak	2.00
4104/HPV+	Schleicher ASK21	21608		10.94	Scottish Gliding Union Ltd		
						Portmoak	11.00
4105/HPW+	Schleicher ASK21	21609		11.94	Scottish Gliding Union Ltd		
						Portmoak	1.00
4106/HPX	Schempp-Hirth Discus CS	177CS		4.95	P.C.Witmore & M.Whitehead		
					"693"	Gransden Lodge	2.00
4107/HPY	ASC Spirit	EUR.001		5.95	Repclif Avn Ltd	Crewe	6.98
4108/HPZ	ASC Falcon	EUR.002		1.96	Repclif Avn Ltd	Crewe	11.97
4110/HQB	Slingsby T.21B	602	WB935	10.94	C.J.Anson	(Germany)	9.00
	(Officially regd with c/n 1099 which is a corruption of fuselage no.SSK/FF/1099)						
4111/HQC+	Scheibe Bergfalke II/55	322	D-9004	12.94	S.H.Gibson	Bidford	5.99
4112/HQD	Schleicher ASW20	20288	SE-ULA	11.94	D.G.Brain & Ptnrs	Dunstable	3.00
			OH-548		"A20"		
4113/HQE	Schempp-Hirth Duo Discus	29		2.95	D.K.McCarthy "620"	Lasham	1.00
4114/HQF+	CARMAM M.100S Mesange	26	F-CCSO	11.94	R.E.Stokes	Rhigos	6.00
4115/HQG+	LAK-12 Lietuva	6222		4.95	M.Boyle & Ptnrs	Rufforth	5.00
4116/HQH+	Schleicher Ka4 Rhonlerche II	3072/Br	(BGA.4097)	5.95	D.Fulchiron	(France)	8.00
			HB-877				
4117/HQJ	Schempp-Hirth Discus B	336	D-1762	2.95	D.G.Lingafidelter	Dunstable	2.00
					"762"		
4118/HQK	Schleicher ASW20CL	20854	D-3366	1.95	S.D.Minson "S2"	Halesland	2.00
4119/HQL	Rolladen-Schneider LS-6C-18W	6352	D-0794	3.95	B.A.Fairston & A.Stotter		
					"LS6"	Husbands Bosworth	3.00
4120/HQM+	Schempp-Hirth Discus B	44	RAFGSA.R10	1.95	Cambridge University GC		
						Gransden Lodge	3.00
4121/HQN	Schempp-Hirth HS.5 Nimbus 2B	139	D-6494	1.95	D.Peters "D-64"	Burn	3.00
4123/HQR	Schempp-Hirth Discus B	531		4.95	British Gliding Association		
					"19"	Lasham	3.00
4124/HQS+	Grob G.103 Twin Astir	3155	OO-ZEG	2.95	Essex & Suffolk GC	Wormingford	1.00
4125/HQT	Grob G.102 Astir CS77	1678	RAFGGA.561	2.95	D.F.Barley "A77"	Kenley	3.00
4126/HQU+	SZD-9 bis Bocian 1D	F-848	SP-2439	7.97	T.Wiltshere	(Spilsby)	7.98
4127/HQV+	SZD-51-1 Junior	B-2139		3.95	Coventry GC	Husbands Bosworth	11.99
4128/HQW	Schempp-Hirth Discus B	538		3.95	J.E.May "329"	Nympsfield	3.00
4129/HQX+	Schleicher ASW15B	15326	D-2315	3.95	R.Emms	Crowland	3.00
4130/HQY	Schempp-Hirth HS.7 Mini Nimbus C	"328"	D-....	3.95	D.S.Hill "487"	Rivar Hill	3.00
4131/HQZ	Rolladen-Schneider LS-6C-18W	6353	D-1486	3.95	R.E.Jones "U2"	Lasham	2.00
4132/HRA	Grob G.102 Astir CS	1109	(RNGSA.N19)	4.95	Portsmouth Naval GC		
			D-4169			Lee-on-Solent	6.00
4133/HRB+	LAK-12 Lietuva	6223		3.95	J.E.Neville	Portmoak	12.99
4134/HRC	Glaser-Dirks DG-500-20 Elan Trainer			5.95	N.J.Allcoat	Portmoak	4.00
		5E136W5			"390"		
4135/HRD	Slingsby T.21B	634	WB973	3.95	U.Seegers	(Germany)	3.00
4136/HRE+	Schleicher Ka6CR	572	D-9326	4.96	R.J.Playle "932"	Dunstable	4.00
4137/HRF+	Schleicher Ka6E	4272	OO-ZJR	5.95	J.F.Morris	Gransden Lodge	7.00
			D-0165				
4138/HRG+	SZD-51-1 Junior	B-2013		4.95	Scottish Gliding Union Ltd		
						Portmoak	6.00
4139/HRJ	Schleicher K8B	8093Ei	D-5048	4.95	M.Barnard "504"	Turweston	4.99
4140/HRK+	Centrair 101A Pegase	101A-048	F-CFQJ	5.95	I.P Bramley	Dunstable	1.00
4141/HRL+	Schempp-Hirth HS.4 Standard Cirrus	525	D-3099	4.95	M.Harbour	Camphill	4.00
4143/HRN+	Schleicher ASK18	18026	HB-1308	4.95	Stratford-upon-Avon GC		
						Snitterfield	3.00
4144/HRP+	SZD-51-1 Junior	B-1807	SP-3442	5.95	Wolds GC	Pocklington	2.00
4145/HRQ	Schempp-Hirth HS.7 Mini Nimbus C	123	(BGA.4122)	4.95	T.C Wright & Ptnrs	Seighford	4.00
			SE-TVB		"169"		
4146/HRR	Schleicher ASK21	21033	D-7083	2.95	Lakes GC "D70"	Walney Island	1.00
4147/HRS	Schempp-Hirth Discus CS	100CS	D-5100	4.95	M.E.Hughes	Husbands Bosworth	3.00
					"B33"		
4148/HRT+	Schleicher K8B	8390A	D-5599	3.96	Heron GC	RNAS Yeovilton	3.00
			(RNGSA.N..)				
4149/HRU	Centrair ASW20F	20114	F-CFFK	7.95	European Soaring Club		
					"FFK"	Le Blanc, France	4.00
4150/HRV+	SZD-55-1	551195076		11.95	R.W.Southworth	Warsaw, Poland	3.00
4151/HRW	Schempp-Hirth Duo Discus	43		6.95	A.J.Davis "802"	Nympsfield	12.00
4152/HRX	Schempp-Hirth Discus A	545		5.95	P.G.Sheard "P5"	Dunstable	2.00
4153/HRY	Rolladen-Schneider LS-6C-18W	6362		6.95	F.K.Russell "L8"	Dunstable	2.00
4155/HSA	Rolladen-Schneider LS-6C-18W	6361		8.95	D.A.Benton "A1"	Long Mynd	3.00

BGA No/Code	Type	C/n	P/I	Date	Owner/operator	Probable Base	CA Expy
4156/HSB+	Glaser-Dirks DG-300 Elan	3E461		7.95	J S.Foster	Parham Park	3.00
4157/HSC	SZD-50-3 Puchacz	B-2079		8.95	British Gliding Association		
					"99"	Bicester	2.00
4158/HSD	Schempp-Hirth Discus B	258/1	(BGA.4142)	6.95	C.E.Collingham & J.R.Reed		
	(Rebuild of BGA.3406 c/n 258 w/o 26.8.94)				"D15"	Dunstable	3.00
4159/HSE+	Grob G.102 Astir CS77	1635	RAFGSA.R68	9.95	R.G.Tait	Easterton	2.00
			RAFGSA.548				
4161/HSG+	Scheibe SF-27A Zugvogel V	1705/E	D-7827	7.95	Welland GC	Lyveden	7.00
			OE-0827		"7827"		
4162/HSH	Scheibe Zugvogel IIIB	7/1041	D-6558	7.95	J.E.Harman	Lasham	5.00
					(As "HLH") "Brigitta"		
4163/HSJ+	Schempp-Hirth Discus B	546		6.95	K.L.Rowley "D54"	Pocklington	5.00
4164/HSK	Schleicher ASW20CL	20827	D-3499	7.95	T.M.World "933"	Lasham	5.00
4165/HSL	Schempp-Hirth Ventus 2C	1/2	(BGA.4154)	7.95	J.F.D'Arcy "71"	Kenley	3.00
	(Incomplete airframe assembled by Southern Sailplanes)						
4166/HSM+	Schleicher ASK13	13145	D-0168	7.95	Stratford-upon-Avon GC		
						Snitterfield	2.00
4167/HSN+	Schleicher Ka6CR	6218	OO-ZZF	7.95	M.Brennan	Enstone	9.98
			D-8546				
4168/HSP	Schempp-Hirth HS.6 Janus C	112	RAFGSA.R1	R	D.H.Garrard	Gransden Lodge	-
			BGA.2723/D-7013		"385"		
4169/HSQ	Schempp-Hirth Discus B	99	D-2943	8.95	Midland GC "493"	Long Mynd	1.00
4170/HSR	LAK-12 Lietuva	6178		8.95	J.F.Morris & Ptnr		
					"313"	Gransden Lodge	7.00
4171/HSS	Schleicher Ka7 Rhonadler	7015	RAFGSA.R29	8.95	M.Cuming	Edgehill	8.96*
			D-5241				
4173/HSU	Schleicher ASK18	18025	AGA.16	R	R.C.Martin "A17"		
4174/HSV+	Schempp-Hirth HS.4 Standard Cirrus	195	D-0785	3.96	H.Gunther-Heinen	Edgehill	6.99
4175/HSW	Schempp-Hirth Duo Discus	48		8.95	C.R.Simpson " Husbands Bosworth		1.00
					"895"		
4176/HSX+	Scheibe SF-27A Zugvogel V	6031	SE-TDT	9.95	S.D.Jones	Wormingford	4.00
4177/HSY	Pilatus B4 PC-11	050	SE-UFF	9.95	A.L.Dennis "A15"	Walney Island	9.00
			OH-431				
4178/HSZ	Rolladen-Schneider LS-8	8030		9.95	European Soaring Club		
					"197"	Le Blanc, France	12.99
4179/HTA+	Centrair C-201B1 Marianne	201-014	F-CGMM	10.95	E.Crooks	Kirton-in-Lindsey	10.00
4180/HTB	Schempp-Hirth HS.6 Janus A	007	D-3114	7.95	P.J.Gibbs & Ptnrs "TE"	Edgehill	9.99
4181/HTC+	Schleicher ASW15B	15188	OE-0930	10.95	N.A.Page	Camphill	1.00
4182/HTD	Grob G.102 Astir CS	1012	D-6508	1.96	G.V McKirdy	Edgehill	4.00
					"VMC (As "D-6508")		
4183/HTE+	Grob G.102 Astir CS77	1716	RAFGSA.R82	11.95	J.R.Whittington	Challock	1.00
			RAFGSA.882				
4184/HTF+	LAK-12 Lietuva	6180		5.96	D.Stidwell	Cross Hayes	5.00
4185/HTG+	Grob G.102 Astir CS	1510	RAFGSA.R59	10.95	Trent Valley GC		
			RAFGSA.R69/RAFGSA.519			Kirton-in-Lindsey	1.00
4186/HTH	Schempp-Hirth Janus CT	185/2	N137DB	10.95	S.A.Adlard "C4"	Long Mynd	5.00
			D-KHIE		(Cambridge Aero Instruments Research vehicle)		
4187/HTJ+	Schleicher ASK13	13125	D-6048	12.95	Ulster GC	Bellarena	2.00
4189/HTL	Rolladen-Schneider LS-8-18	8038	D-3156	10.95	A. & L.Wells "LS"	Bidford	12.99
4190/HTM	Rolladen-Schneider LS-8-18	8036		10.95	T.J.Scott "Z8"	Booker	4.00
4191/HTN	Schleicher ASW22	22013	ZS-GLN	4.96	S.Bates "S22"	Edgehill	3.00
4192/HTP	Rolladen-Schneider LS-8-18	8039	D-3175	11.95	R.A.Browne "L58"	Crowland	12.99
4193/HTQ	Rolladen-Schneider LS-8-18	8037	D-2993	11.95	P.G. & S.J.Crabb		
					"C64" Sandhill Farm, Shrivenham		9.00
4194/HTR+	Grob G.102 Astir CS	1190	D-7307	11.95	I.Wright	Kingston Deverill	2.00
4195/HTS	Rolladen-Schneider LS-8-18	8040		11.95	R.A.Cheetham	Dunstable	10.00
	(See BGA.3184)				"E1"		
4196/HTT+	Schleicher ASW20CL	20627	D-2410	11.95	G.D Clack	Lasham	3.00
4197/HTU+	Schempp-Hirth HS.2 Cirrus	88	D-0478	12.95	S.Kochanowski	Lasham	5.00
4198/HTV+	Schleicher ASK21	21624	D-8355	3.96	Cambridge University GC		
						Gransden Lodge	2.00
4199/HTW+	Pottier JP15-34 Kit Club	50-39	F-CFGF	12.95	R.P Halton	Bidford	3.99
4200/HTX	Schleicher ASW20	20239	D-3180	3.96	C.B.Starkey "900"	Lasham	2.00
4201/HTY+	LET L-13 Blanik	026318	LY-GDT	4.96	North Devon GC	Eaglescott	5.00
			DOSAAF				
4202/HTZ	Bolkow Phoebus 17C	908	OO-ZDJ	12.95	A.de Tourtoulon	Wormingford	3.00
			BGA.1573		"833"		
4203/HUA+	Schleicher ASW19	19091	D-3840	12.95	M.T Davenport	Lasham	3.99
4204/HUB+	SZD-48-3 Jantar Standard	B-1527	DOSAAF	3.96	C.F.Sermanni	(Lochwinnoch)	3.00
4205/HUC+	Schempp-Hirth Janus CE	170	(BGA.4188)	2.96	C.W.Price	Wormingford	12.99
			D-3189				

BGA No/Code	Type	C/n	P/I	Date	Owner/operator	Probable Base	CA Expy
4206/HUD+	Schleicher ASK13	13018	D-9203	2.96	London GC	Dunstable	11.00
4207/HUE	Schleicher ASW27	27022		10.96	E.H.Downham "N5"	Dunstable	3.00
4208/HUF+	Schleicher ASK13	13109	OO-ZWE	3.96	London GC	Dunstable	8.00
4209/HUG+	Rolladen-Schneider LS-8-18	8047	D-3472	3.96	A.O'Regan	Sutton Bank	6.98
					(to ZS-GUY 27.8.98 - same owner)		
4210/HUH	Schempp-Hirth HS.6 Janus	15	D-3116	5.96	B.A.Fairston	Husbands Bosworth	6.00
					"D31"		
4211/HUJ+	Centrair ASW20F	20170	F-CFLY	3.96	S.Lee	Rattlesden	6.00
4212/HUK+	Schleicher Ka6CR	6385	SE-TCN	4.96	T.J Donovan & Ptnr	Lyveden	4.00
4213/HUL	Schempp-Hirth HS.2 Cirrus	V3	HB-900	2.96	I.Ashton & Ptnrs "624"	Chipping	5.00
4214/HUM	Rolladen-Schneider LS-6C	6267	OO-ZXS	3.96	A.Hall	Lasham	12.99
			D-4350		"241"		
4215/HUN+	Grob G.102 Astir CS Jeans	2089	D-7531	2.96	D P.Manchett	Lleweni Parc	11.00
4216/HUP	Schempp-Hirth Ventus 2CT	4/11		2.96	C G Corbett "170"	Tibenham	11.99
4217/HUQ	Federov Me-7 Mechta	007		6.96	J S Fielden	Brent Tor	8.99
4218/HUR+	Schempp-Hirth HS.2 Cirrus	12	HB-927	4.96	D G Slocombe	Burn	5.00
4219/HUS+	Scheibe SF-27A Zugvogel V	6010	D-1035	8.97	C J Palmer	Booker	8.00
4220/HUT+	Centrair ASW20F	20187	F-CEUQ	4.96	G.A MacFadyen	Nympsfield	11.99
4221/HUU+	Schleicher ASK13	13527AB	D-7506	4.96	Upward Bound Trust	Thame	8.00
			D-8945				
4222/HUV	Rolladen-Schneider LS-8-18	8056	D-3823	4.96	C.P.Jeffery "64"	Gransden Lodge	3.00
4223/HUW	Rolladen-Schneider LS-8A	8058		3.96	B.T.Spreckley	Le Blanc, France	11.00
					"S8"		
4224/HUX	Schempp-Hirth Ventus 2C	7/12		3.96	E.R.Lysakowski "58"	Lasham	3.99
4225/HUY+	Schempp-Hirth Ventus CT	84/329	D-KILZ	4.96	M A Challans "880"	Lasham	12.99
4226/HUZ	Schempp-Hirth Discus BT	158/559		3.96	J.Lynchenhaun "200"	Lleweni Parc	2.00
4227/HVA+	SZD-59 Acro	B-2169		5.96	C.Williams	Lasham	5.00
4228/HVB	Slingsby T.31B	850	(BGA.3249)	4.96	M.Hoogenbosch		5.00
			XA308			Maastrict, The Netherlands	
4229/HVC	Slingsby T.38 Grasshopper	766	WZ770	R	J.Forster	(The Netherlands)	
4230/HVD	SZD-55-1	551193052		4.96	Anglo-Polish Sailplanes Ltd		
					"304"	Booker	4.00
4231/HVE	Schempp-Hirth Ventus 2CT	8/19	D-KHIA	3.96	Glyndwr Soaring Club		
					"W54"	Lleweni Parc	5.00
4232/HVF	Rolladen-Schneider LS-8-18	8059	D-1683	4.96	M.D.Wells "321"	Bidford	4.00
4233/HVG	Schleicher ASK21	21062	D-2606	4.96	Rattlesden GC "RP1"	Rattlesden	2.00
4234/HVH+	Pilatus B4 PC-11	067	D-2156	5.96	C.Cain	Lasham	6.00
4235/HVJ	Scheibe SF-27A Zugvogel V	6012	OE-0762	6.96	C.Bleaden	Kirton-in-Lindsey	7.00
					"962"		
4236/HVK+	Grob G.102 Astir CS	1161	D-4182	4.96	F.R.Panter	Tibenham	3.00
4237/HVL	Rolladen-Schneider LS-8-18	8060		4.96	D.W Allison "LS8"	RAF Wyton	1.00
4238/HVM	Glaser-Dirks DG-300 Elan	3E177	D-4314	5.96	Surrey & Hants GC "393"	Lasham	2.00
4240/HVP	Schleicher ASW20	20374	D-1961	5.96	E.J.Smallbone	Lasham	2.00
			BGA.4076/EC-DLN		"930"		
4241/HVQ+	Schleicher ASK13	13251	D-0605	4.96	R.R Brown	Edgehill	3.00
4242/HVR+	Schempp-Hirth Discus B	560		5.96	Yorkshire Gliding Club (Pty) Ltd		
						Sutton Bank	4.00
4244/HVT	Schempp-Hirth Ventus 2B	37		5.96	P.R.Jones "210"	Booker	2.00
4245/HVU	Rolladen-Schneider LS-8A	8066		4.96	S.J.Crabb		
					"C65" Sandhill Farm, Shrivenham		11.00
4246/HVV+	Rolladen-Schneider LS-4B	41009		1.97	A.Bardgett	Currock Hill	1.00
4247/HVW+	Schleicher ASK13	13431	D-2140	6.96	Rattlesden GC	Rattlesden	4.00
4248/HVX+	Centrair ASW20F	20528	F-CFSJ	6.96	A.S Goldsmith	Camphill	6.99
4249/HVY	Schempp-Hirth Ventus 2C	9/21		5.96	R.Ashurst "584"	Lasham	1.00
4250/HVZ+	Schempp-Hirth HS.4 Standard Cirrus	567G	HB-1269	6.96	M. & J.Miles		
						Hinton-in-the-Hedges	3.00
4251/HWA	Schempp-Hirth Ventus 2C	8/20		6.96	C.Garton "31"	Lasham	10.00
4252/HWB	Schempp-Hirth Duo Discus	84		5.96	Lasham Gliding Society	Lasham	3.00
					"775" "The Blubberbuss"		
4253/HWC	Glasflugel H.201B Standard Libelle	310	HB-1076	7.96	J.C.Rogers "L18"	Winthorpe	3.00
4254/HWD+	Schempp-Hirth HS.4 Standard Cirrus	97	HB-987	6.96	M.A.Edmonds		
						Sandhill Farm, Shrivenham	1.99
4255/HWE+	Schleicher K8B	1151	HB-700	5.96	J.P.Brady	Brent Tor	2.00
4256/HWF+	Jastreb Standard Cirrus G/81	281	SE-TZC	6.96	G.Earle "ZC"	Booker	6.00
4257/HWG+	Glasflugel H.201B Standard Libelle	259	HB-1051	6.96	M.R Fox	Pocklington	6.00
4258/HWH	Schempp-Hirth Ventus CT	182/599	RAFGGA.506	7.96	H.R.Browning "712"	Lasham	11.00
4260/HWK	Grob G.104 Speed Astir IIB	4070	OO-ZVQ	7.96	P.Gilbert	Tours, France	7.97*
			LX-CRT				
4261/HWL	Rolladen-Schneider LS-8A	8076		6.96	M.Coffee "84"	Bidford	3.00
4262/HWM	Rolladen-Schneider LS-8A	8079		7.96	B.C.Marsh "D7"	Bidford	3.00
4263/HWN	Schempp-Hirth Nimbus 3T	8/60	D-KHIF	7.96	H.N.Lenz "598"	Lasham	7.00

BGA No/Code	Type	C/n	P/I	Date	Owner/operator	Probable Base	CA Expy
4264/HWP+	Glaser-Dirks DG-100G Elan	E24G13	D-3772	7.96	C.A.Sheldon	Pocklington	7.00
4265/HWQ+	Scheibe L-Spatz 55	607	D-6195	7.96	A.Gruber	Usk	8.00
4266/HWR	Rolladen-Schneider LS-3A	3098	D-3902	7.96	G.L.Askew & Ptnr "M1"	Seighford	7.97
4267/HWS	Rolladen-Schneider LS-8-18	8080		2.97	E.A.Coles "75"	Dunstable	1.00
4268/HWT	Schleicher K8B	8780	HB-958	7.96	Shenington GC "S83"	Edgehill	8.00
4270/HWV	Schempp-Hirth Discus B	"561"		8.96	N.J Passmore	Parham Park	5.00
	(Rebuild fuselage AGA.4 c/n 206 & new wings)				"526"		
	(Quoted c/n incorrect as 561 is D-KVKA - note Discus RAFGGA.561 is BGA4318)						
4271/HWW	Grob G.103 Twin II Acro	3658-K-27	OE-5285	8.96	T.Gage "DJT"	Lasham	3.00
4272/HWX	SZD-59 Acro	B-2170		9.96	Anglo-Polish Sailplanes Ltd		
						Booker	8.00
4273/HWY	Jastreb Standard Cirrus VTC G/81	359	LN-GAL	9.96	S.R.Kronfield "168"	Booker	9.97
4274/HWZ+	Schleicher ASW19B	19316	HB-1524	9.96	D.Housky	Winthorpe	3.00
4275/HXA+	Scheibe Zugvogel IIIB	1107	D-2005	3.97	B W Millar	Portmoak	3.00
4276/HXB+	Grob G.102 Astir CS77	1819	D-6755	9.96	K.S.Wells	Crowland	9.00
4278/HXC	Rolladen-Schneider LS-8A	8094		2.97	S.M.Smith "M8"	Gransden Lodge	2.00
4279/HXD+	Schleicher ASW27	27030		3.97	M.Jerman	Wormingford	2.00
4280/HXE	Schleicher ASW19B	19053	D-6699	9.96	M.Lloyd-Owen "Y4"	Lasham	11.00
4283/HXH+	Schempp-Hirth Discus B	573	BGA.4375	6.98	Deeside GC	Aboyne	5.00
			(BGA.4283)				
4284/HXJ+	Schleicher ASK13	13216	D-0417	11.96	Cotswold GC	Aston Down	11.00
4286/HXL	Letov LF-107 Lunak	39	OK-0927	11.96	G.Saw (As "OK-0927")	Booker	12.99
4287/HXM+	Grob G.102 Astir CS	1272	D-7367	11.96	D.P.Compston	Bicester	2.00
4288/HXN	Rolladen-Schneider LS-8A	8095		1.97	J.L Birch "57"	Dunstable	2.00
4289/HXP	Schleicher ASK13	13023	D-3656	11.96	Vale of White Horse GC		
					"856" Sandhill Farm, Shrivenham		2.00
4290/HXQ	Schleicher ASH25B	25187	OH-874	11.96	R.A Cheetham "156"	Rufforth	11.00
4291/HXR	Schempp-Hirth Ventus CT	88/333	D-KESH	2.97	W.A'Court "560"	Lasham	4.00
4292/HXS	Schempp-Hirth Ventus 2CT	10/41		11.96	I.R.Cook "V11"	Thruxton	3.00
4293/HXT	Rolladen-Schneider LS-4A	4325	ZS-GNV	3.97	B.T.Spreckley Le Blanc, France		4.00
					"LS4"		
4294/HXU+	Schleicher ASW19B	19359	SE-TXN	4.97	G A Chalmers	Drumshade	4.00
4295/HXV+	Schleicher ASK13	13080	D-5462	12.96	Aquila GC Hinton-in-The-Hedges		12.00
4296/HXW	Rolladen-Schneider LS-8A	8097		3.97	W.Aspland "325"	Dunstable	3.00
4297/HXX+	Schempp-Hirth HS.4 Standard Cirrus 154G		D-0363	1.97	E J Winning	Templeton	2.00
	(Built Grob)						
4298/HXY+	Grob G.102 Astir Jeans	1781	D-7689	12.96	I.Worten	Bidford	2.00
4299/HXZ	Rolladen-Schneider LS-4	4249	SE-TXF	3.97	E.J.Foggin		
					"S5" Sandhill Farm, Shrivenham		3.00
4300/HYA	Rolladen-Schneider LS-6	"634B"		2.97	R.H.Dixon "DD"	Parham Park	3.00
4301/HYB	Schempp-Hirth Discus B	140	D-4684	4.97	T.P.Browning "T5"	Lasham	1.00
4302/HYC+	Eichelsdorfer SB-5E Sperber	5042	D-2009	3.97	H.Hughson	RAF Bruggen	6.00
	(Built Akaflieg Braunschweig)		BGA.3447/RAFGGA/D-2009 (As "D-2009")				
4303/HYD+	Schleicher ASW24	24039	OE-5460	2.97	P J.Metcalfe	Lasham	3.00
4304/HYE+	Glaser-Dirks DG-505 Elan Orion	5E167X22		12.96	Bristol & Glos GC	Nympsfield	1.00
					"913"		
4305/HYF	Rolladen-Schneider LS-8-18	8106		3.97	K.M.Barker "KM"	Nympsfield	3.00
4307/HYH+	Rolladen-Schneider LS-3-17	3186	D-6650	1.97	J.Lamb	Bellarena	4.00
4308/HYJ+	Schleicher ASK21	21066	D-2724	1.97	Highland GC	Easterton	3.00
4309/HYK+	Centrair ASW20FLP	20176	F-CEUN	9.97	J.C.Riddell	Rufforth	10.99
4310/HYL	Schempp-Hirth Ventus 2A	44		5.97	A J Stone "K4"	Booker	1.00
4311/HYM	DWLKK PW-5 Smyk	17.06.020		1.97	T.Joint	Lasham	11.99
					"PW5" "Iceman"		
4312/HYN	Schleicher K8B	8310A	D-1018	11.97	G.Brook	Crowland	1.00
4313/HYP+	SZD-50-3 Puchacz	B-2082		2.97	Rattlesden GC	Rattlesden	4.00
4314/HYQ	Grob G.102 Astir CS	1332	AGA.6	R			
4315/HYR	Schleicher ASW27	27013	D-8733	3.97	A.R.Hutchings "432"	Dunstable	3.00
4316/HYS	Schleicher ASK21	21519	RAFGGA.514	?.9?	AGA "A14"	Wattisham	6.00
4317/HYT+	Schleicher ASK21	21568	AGA.20	?.9?	Wyvern GC	Upavon	1.00
			RAFGGA.515		"A16"		
4318/HYU	Schempp-Hirth Discus CS	192CS	RAFGSA.R61	?.9?	Anglia GC	Wattisham	6.00
			RAFGGA.561		"A61"		
4319/HYV	Schleicher K8B	558	RAFGGA.558	R			
4320/HYW+	Schleicher K8B	8163A	D-5316	3.97	Lincs GC	Strubby	5.00
			D-3202				
4321/HYX+	Schleicher K8B	686	D-5742		Oxford University GC	Bicester	4.00
					("5742" under wing)		
4322/HYY	Schempp-Hirth Nimbus 3DT	21	RAFGSA.R26	3.97	N.J.Wright	Bidford 3.00	
			D-KAFA/D-5847		"A26"		
4323/HYZ	Rolladen-Schneider LS-8-18	8104		4.97	P J Coward "L88"	Crowland	1.00
4324/HZA	Schempp-Hirth Nimbus 3/24.5	94	SE-UFO	4.97	C.J.Short "376"	Lasham	4.00

BGA No/Code	Type	C/n	P/I	Date	Owner/operator	Probable Base	CA Expy
4325/HZB	DWLKK PW-5 Smyk	17.06.021		2.97	J.D.Scott "JS1" Gransden Lodge		2.00
4326/HZC	Grob G.102 Astir CS	1092	D-6991	3.97	G.S.Roe "216"	Lasham	1.00
4327/HZD+	Schleicher ASW15B	15327	D-2191	3.97	C.P.Ellison	Rivar Hill	1.00
4328/HZE	Schempp-Hirth Discus CS	121CS	D-6946	3.97	A.D.Irving "T3"	Kenley	3.00
4329/HZF	Centrair 101A Pegase	101A-0262	PH-796	5.97	B.R.George "G7" Gransden Lodge		3.00
4330/HZG	Rolladen-Schneider LS-8-18	8118		3.97	N.G.Hackett Husbands Bosworth "X7"		4.00
4331 HZH+	Schleicher Ka6CR	6461	HB-836	5.97	M.E.de Torre	Gamston	7.00
4332/HZJ+	Schempp-Hirth HS.4 Standard Cirrus	23	HB-981	3.97	A.B.Stokes	Enstone	1.00
4333/HZK+	Not allotted						
4334/HZL+	Schempp-Hirth HS.4 Standard Cirrus	304	D-2060	4.97	P.Conran (London SW18)		1.00
4335/HZM	Rolladen-Schneider LS-4A	4762	D-1394	4.97	P G Dowse "U1"	Edgehill	2.00
4336/HZN	Schleicher Ka2B Rhonschwalbe	195	D-6173	3.97	D.E.Lamb (As "D-6173")	Booker	4.00
4337/HZP	Rolladen-Schneider LS-8A	8117		3.97	S.J.Redman "56" Gransden Lodge		4.00
4338/HZQ	Schleicher ASW27	27018	D-4499	3.97	M.D.Rogers "K5"	Dunstable	2.00
4339/HZR+	Schleicher ASK21	21079	D-4491	5.97	A.Roseberry	Aston Down	3.00
4340/HZS	Schempp-Hirth Ventus 2A	43		3.97	A.E.Kay "K1" Weston-on-the-Green		2.00
4341/HZT	Centrair ASW20F	20150	F-CFLL	8.97	T.J.Banks "X50"	Ringmer	9.00
4342/HZU	Schempp-Hirth HS.4 Standard Cirrus	366	HB-1258 N71KW	4.97	D.R.Piercy "B11"	Winthorpe	11.99
4343/HZV	Schempp-Hirth HS.4 Standard Cirrus	305	HB-1457 D-2061	4.97	P.Cox "P61"	Enstone	2.00
4344/HZW	Schempp-Hirth Nimbus 3T	22/88	D-KILO	6.97	J.Ellis "112"	Sutton Bank	2.00
4345/HZX	Schleicher K8B	8257	D-8476	4.97	G.E.W.Woodward "476"	Upwood	4.00
4346/HZY	Rolladen-Schneider LS-4A	4479	D-3458	4.97	N.P.Wedi "EN"	Booker	2.00
4347/HZZ	Schleicher ASW20L	20273	N727AM	4.97	P.E.Rice "LD"	Wormingford	5.00
4348/JAA+	Schempp-Hirth HS.6 Janus B	163	D-3147	4.97	A.A.Baker	Lasham	12.00
4349/JAB+	Glaser-Dirks DG-300 Elan	3E320	OY-XTC	4.97	P.B.Jones	Lasham	4.00
4350/JAC	Schempp-Hirth Duo Discus	128		5.97	British Gliding Association "98"	Bicester	3.00
4351/JAD+	Schleicher ASK21	21659		10.97	Borders GC	Milfield	9.00
4352/JAE	Glaser-Dirks DG-200/17C	2-62	HB-1443	4.97	S.A.White Hinton-in-The-Hedges "N8"		2.00
4353/JAF	Schempp-Hirth Ventus 2B	33	(BGA.4306)	4.97	M.J.Young "V57" Gransden Lodge		3.00
4354/JAG+	Schleicher ASW20L	20136	HB-1474	7.97	654 Syndicate "654" Currock Hill		6.00
4355/JAH	Schempp-Hirth Discus B	572		5.97	K.Neave "921"	Nympsfield	5.00
4356/JAJ	Glaser-Dirks DG-202/17	2-150/1744	D-4154	5.97	T.R Dews Kingston Deverill		3.99
4357/JAK	Schleicher Ka6E	4301	F-CDRJ	R	"916"		
4358/JAL+	Schleicher Ka6E	4360	F-CDTX	6.97	N.Gilkes	Lasham	12.00
4359/JAM	Schleicher ASW15B	15353	D-2360	5.97	T.J.Beckwith "777" Sackville Farm, Riseley		1.00
4360/JAN+	Schempp-Hirth Discus B	575		10.97	Wolds GC	Pocklington	11.00
4361/JAP	Slingsby T.38 Grasshopper	779	WZ783	R			
4362/JAQ+	Schempp-Hirth Discus B	190	D-0960	6.97	P.D.Duffin "823"	Wormingford	4.00
4363/JAR	Schempp-Hirth Discus BT	83/417	D-KHEI	5.97	C.J.Partridge "P3"	Lasham	2.00
4364/JAS	Glasflugel H.201 Standard Libelle	109	SE-TIS	5.97	M.D.Wells "7Q"	Enstone	5.98
4365/JAT+	Schleicher K8B	8150	D-4390	6.97	Wolds GC	Pocklington	6.00
4366/JAU	Slingsby T.21B	585	WB922	5.97	J.Priddle Kingston Deverill (As "WB922")		6.00
4367/JAV+	Schleicher ASK21	21662		11.97	Wolds GC	Pocklington	11.00
4368/JAW	Glaser-Dirks DG-200/17	2-180/1759	D-5618	6.97	J.Walker "M4"	Lasham	1.00
4369/JAX+	Schleicher ASK21	21665		1.98	Wolds GC	Pocklington	1.00
4370/JAY	Schleicher ASW20	20034	D-7941	6.97	D.A.Smith "123"Kingston Deverill		5.00
4371/JAZ+	Grob G.102 Astir Jeans	2073	D-7586	8.97	Bath, Wilts & Dorset GC Kingston Deverill		8.00
4372/JBA+	Slingsby T.38 Grasshopper	1262	XP463	6.98	J A Northern & Pntr	Challock	8.00
	(Assembled from components; p/i is starboard wing only)						
4373/JBB	Rolladen-Schneider LS-8	8003	D-8023	8.97	R F Thirkell "B3"	Lasham	12.00
4374/JBC	Schempp-Hirth Ventus 2CT	15/61		6.97	B.A.Bateson "2B"	Ringmer	5.00
4375/JBD					See BGA.4283		
4376/JBE	ISF Mistral C	MC.020/79	OY-XLX PH-667	7.97	H.H.Crowther "LX"	Aston Down	6.00
4377/JBF	Glasfugel H.201 Standard Libelle	246	F-CDPV	7.97	L Coles	Booker	4.00
4378/JBG	Schempp-Hirth Ventus B	135	OE-5315	7.97	W.R.Longstaff "U9"	Easterton	5.99
4379/JBH	Eiri PIK-20D	20621	OH-529	7.97	537 Syndicate "537"	Parham Park	1.00
4380/JBJ	Jastreb Standard Cirrus G/81	280	SE-TZD	7.97	T.Rendell "G81"	Lasham	7.00
4381/JBK	Schleicher ASW19B	19204	D-4099 PH-602	11.97	R.E.Robertson "L3"	Booker	12.99
4383/JBM	Schleicher ASK21	21089	D-6391	7.97	Staffs GC	Seighford	7.00
4384/JBN	Schempp-Hirth Discus B	94	D-7175	R	"S21"		
4385/JBP	Rolladen-Schneider LS-6-18W	6378		7.97	I.C.Baker "B21"	Nympsfield	6.00

BGA No/Code	Type	C/n	P/I	Date	Owner/operator	Probable Base	CA Expy
4386/JBQ	Rolladen-Schneider LS-8-18	8148		9.97	L.Hill "LH7"	North Hill	9.00
4387/JBR	Schempp-Hirth Discus B	90	F-CGGD	8.97	A.A.Baker	Odiham	10.00
			F-WGGD		"AB"		
4388/JBS+	LAK-12 Lietuva	6115	???	8.97	I.G.Smith & Ptnrs	Ringmer	3.00
4389/JBT+	Schleicher ASW19	19075	D-4477	8.97	Aquila GC Hinton-in-The-Hedges		1.00
4390/JBU	Rolladen-Schneider LS-6-18W	6350	D-0462	9.97	J.Gorringe "HL"	Lasham	9.99
4391/JBV	Monnett Monerai	-		7.97	B.Nibett	Keevil	7.98
	(Built J.Foxson/B.Nibett)						
4392/JBW	Schempp-Hirth Discus BT	34/337	D-KBJR	8.97	N.C.Pringle "710"	Lasham	7.00
4393/JBX+	Rolladen-Schneider LS-4A	4293	D-9111	4.98	P Lee & Pntr	Aston Down	3.00
4394/JBY+	LAK-12 Lietuva	6185		8.97	Baltic Sailplanes Ltd		
						Husbands Bosworth	8.99
4395/JBZ+	Grob G.102 Astir CS	1492	D-4794	8.97	K.R.Bryer	Nympsfield	9.00
4396/JCA+	Schleicher ASW15B	15202	(BGA.4049)	9.97	R.H. & A.Moss	Nympsfield	9.00
			OH-410				
4397/JCB+	Rolladen-Schneider LS-6C-18WL	6234	D-6116	4.98	K Nicholson	Dunstable	4.99
4399/JCD	Schleicher ASW24	24101	D-6091	10.97	M.D.Evershed "H5"	Crowland	2.00
4400/JCE	Schempp-Hirth Ventus BT	46/240	D-KFMS	9.97	A.G.Reid "911"	Kenley	9.00
4401/JCF+	Grob G.102 Astir CS77	1705	PH-1012	9.97	Northumbria GC	Currock Hill	10.00
			D-7634				
4402/JCG+	DWLKK PW-5 Smyk	17.09.003		9.97	V.H.Spencer	Dunstable	11.99
4403/JCH+	MDM-1 Fox	218		.97	C.Cain	Lasham	7.00
4404/JCJ	Grob Standard Cirrus	434G	SE-TNC	5.98	M R Garwood "C7"	Crowland	6.00
4405/JCK	Schempp-Hirth Discus BT	92/430	D-KIDE	10.97	D.Coppin "DC"	Lasham	10.99
4406/JCL	Rolladen-Schneider LS-8-18	8147		10.97	T.W.Slater "T2"	Aboyne	12.00
4407/JCM	Schleicher ASW27	27064		12.97	M.Clayton "W27"	Bidford	2.00
4408/JCN+	Schempp-Hirth HS.4 Standard Cirrus	646	D-7247	10.97	P.W.Reavell	Camphill	10.99
4409/JCP	Rolladen-Schneider LS-8-18	8146		10.97	A.J.Emck "36"	Lasham	11.99
4410/JCQ	Schleicher ASW19B	19086	PH-562	12.97	A.J.Preston "W19"	Dunstable	12.99
4411/JCR+	Grob G.102 Astir CS	1181	OE-5188	10.97	B Harrison Kingston Deverill		10.00
4412/JCS	Slingsby T.31B	693	BGA.3284	10.97	M.Steiner	(Germany)	3.00
			WT898		(As "WT898")		
4413/JCT	Schempp-Hirth Nimbus 4T	7/21	D-KKKL	10.97	D S Innes "176"	Lasham	11.99
4414/JCU	Schempp-Hirth HS.4 Standard Cirrus	75	D-6604	10.97	N.Swinton	Halton	11.00
		688			"616"		
4415/JCV	Schleicher ASH25E	25069	D-KAIM	11.97	B.R.George "IM" Gransden Lodge		3.00
4416/JCW+	Grob G.102 Astir CS77	1612	PH-573	10.97	C.R.Phipps	Bryngwyn Bach	1.00
4417/JCX+	Schempp-Hirth Discus bT	93/432	D-KJOB	10.97	J.E.Bowman	Bidford	11.00
4418/JCY	Rolladen-Schneider LS-8-18	8171		12.97	M.C.Foreman "F3"	Lasham	12.00
4419/JCZ+	Schleicher Ka6CR	6108	D-7152	11.97	N.W.Hanney Kingston Deverill		2.00
4420/JDA	Schempp-Hirth Nimbus 3/24.5	8	D-1788	11.97	G.R.Ross "GR"	Lasham	1.00
4421/JDB	Slingsby T.38 Grasshopper	809	WZ828	11.97	H.Chapple (As "WZ828")	Bicester	12.99
4422/JDC	Schleicher ASW27	27010	D-6209	12.97	P.J.Henderson "A27"	Challock	11.99
4423/JDD+	Glaser-Dirks DG-200/17C	2-171/CL17	PH-717	12.97	J.Richardson	Chipping	1.00
4424/JDE	Rolladen-Schneider LS-8-18	8151		5.98	I M Evans "EZ"	Shobdon	5.00
4425/JDF	Schleicher ASH25E	25150	D-KPAS	11.97	J.E.Cruttenden "907"	Lasham	11.99
4426/JDG	Rolladen-Schneider LS-6B	6145	D-5675	2.98	A Jelden "KW"	Booker	2.00
4427/JDH	Rolladen-Schneider LS-6C-18W	6287	D-9128	2.98	K H Dietrich "2F"	(Germany)	2.00
4428/JDJ	Rolladen-Schneider LS-3	3010	D-7729	11.97	J.C.Burdett	Chipping	11.00
4429/JDK	Rolladen-Schneider LS-8-18	8153		3.98	K Nicholson Verbier, Switzerland		3.00
					"SK1"		
4430/JDL	Schempp-Hirth Discus bT	165/578		4.98	S Robinson "SR"	Chipping	3.00
4431/JDM	Schleicher ASW15B	15280	F-CEGL	1.98	D C Blyth	Tibenham	3.00
4432/JDN+	Glaser-Dirks DG-505	5E180X31		3.98	Devon & Somerset GC	North Hill	3.00
4433/JDP+	Glaser-Dirks DG-200/17	2-136/1734	D-0152	12.97	J.J.Benton	Camphill	1.00
4434/JDQ+	Schleicher ASW19	19106	D-3862	2.99	P Winder	Lasham	2.00
4435/JDR	Schleicher ASW15A	15053	D-6910	2.98	L Whitaker	Booker	4.00
4436/JDS+	Schempp-Hirth HS.4 Standard Cirrus	75	D-4057	3.98	Burn GC	Burn	5.00
		638	OY-XCZ				
4437/JDT	Rolladen-Schneider LS-8	8172		1.98	R.J.Rebbeck "232"	Dunstable	12.99
4438/JDU+	LET L-13 Blanik	026303	D-8919	12.97	Herefordshire GC	Shobdon	12.99
4439/JDV+	Glaser-Dirks DG-303	3E481A24		3.98	I N Busby	Booker	3.00
4440/JDW+	DWLKK PW-5 Smyk	17.09.018		12.97	G.Pledger	Currock Hill	12.99
4441/JDX+	Wassmer WA-28F Espadon	101	F-CDZU	12.97	S.S.Turner	Upwood	3.00
4442/JDY	Rolladen-Schneider LS-8	8173		2.98	J Gorringe "P2"	Booker	4.00
4443/JDZ	Schempp-Hirth Nimbus 4T	18	D-KOLF	1.98	T P Browning "111"	Lasham	2.00
4444/JEA	Rolladen-Schneider LS-8-18	8159	D-2411	3.98	R I Davidson Husbands Bosworth		4.00
					"D4"		
4445/JEB+	Schleicher ASW24	24172	D-9344	2.98	M.A.& J.Taylor	Rattlesden	11.99
4446/JEC+	SZD-50-3 Puchacz	B-2197		4.98	Cambridge University GC		
						Gransden Lodge	3.00

BGA No/Code	Type	C/n	P/I	Date	Owner/operator	Probable Base	CA Expy
4447/JED	Schleicher ASW15B	15427	D-3976	1.98	P.R.Williams	Lyveden	2.00
4448/JEE	Schleicher ASW20L	20073	(BGA.4456)	2.98	C.J.Bailey	Wormingford	2.00
			D-7666				
4449/JEF	Schempp-Hirth Ventus CT	126/400	D-KFWH	1.98	M.R.Emmett "M2"	Booker	10.00
4450/JEG	Rolladen-Schneider LS-8-18	8150		1.98	H.Luxton "685"	Booker	2.00
4451/JEH	Glasflugel H.303 Mosquito B	172	OY-XKE	2.98	M.J.Stephens "KE"	Booker	3.00
	(As "OY-XKE" under wing)						
4452/JEJ	Rolladen-Schneider LS-7WL	7074	OE-5477	3.98	I.Mountain "F1"	Dunstable	3.00
4453/JEK	Grob G.102 Astir CS	1374	(BGA.4398)	8.99	S.R.Allen	Thame	8.00
			D-7403				
4454/JEL	Schleicher ASW24	24044	PH-866	2.98	M.Dawson"W2"	Keevil	2.00
4455/JEM	Schempp-Hirth Duo Discus	146	-	3.98	H.Kindell "570"	Lasham	2.00
4456/JEN	Schleicher ASW20L	20073			See BGA.4448		
4457/JEP+	Rolladen-Schneider LS-4B	41021		3.99	C.F.Carter	Long Mynd	3.00
4458/JEQ	Schempp-Hirth Nimbus 3D	1/6	OO-ZOZ	2.98	M.Pocock "OZ"	Rivar Hill	1.00
			HB-1921/D-7695				
4459/JER	Schempp-Hirth Standard Cirrus	654	D-6475	4.98	J.Hoskins "JH"	Thruxton	2.00
			OO-ZBM				
4460/JES	Schleicher ASW19	19119	SE-TTV	3.98	M.Dale "V4"	Sutton Bank	3.00
4461/JET+	Schempp-Hirth Ventus CT	161	RAFGSA.R38	2.98	B.Bryce-Smith	Gransden Lodge	2.00
4462/JEU+	Glasflugel H201 Standard Libelle	55	SE-TIC	4.98	D.Johns	Bidford	3.00
4463/JEV+	Schempp-Hirth Standard Cirrus B	650	OE-5072	2.98	M.White	Camphill	2.00
4464/JEW	Schleicher Ka6CR	6493	D-4116	2.98	J.McLaughlin "D42"	Sleap	2.00
4465/JEX	Schempp-Hirth Ventus 2A	64	-	3.98	D.Watt "DW"	Bicester	2.00
4466/JEY	Schempp-Hirth Standard Cirrus	456G	D-3255	3.98	R.Lockett"T7"	North Weald	3.00
4467/JEZ	Glaser-Dirks DG-100	3	PH-792	3.98	G.Dale "274"	Lasham	3.00
			D-3721				
4468/JFA+	Schempp-Hirth Standard Cirrus	225	D-0974	4.98	M.Sheahan,	Lasham	2.00
4469/JFB	Rolladen-Schneider LS-8-18	8152		3.98	I.Freestone "S6"	Lyveden	3.00
4470/JFC	Schempp-Hirth Discus CS	054CS	RAFGSA.R55	3.98	Bannerdown GC "R55"	Keevil	4.00
4471/JFD	Grob G.102 Astir CS	1429	RAFGSA.742	3.98	RAFGSA Centre "R8"	Bicester	10.00
			D-7425				
4472/JFE	Schempp-Hirth Janus CE	299	RAFGSA.R16	3.98	RAFGSA Centre "16"	Bicester	3.00
4473/JFF	Schempp-Hirth Duo Discus	131	RAFGSA.R26	3.98	RAFGSA Centre "26"	Bicester	1.00
4474/JFG	Schempp-Hirth Discus b	254	RAFGSA.R15	3.98	RAFGSA Centre "R15"	Bicester	3.99
					(To BGA.4623 12.98)		
4475/JFH	Schempp-Hirth Duo Discus	118	RAFGSA R1	3.98	RAFGSA Centre "R1"	Bicester	3.00
4476/JFJ+	Schleicher ASW20CL	20830	D-8307	4.98	W.R.Mills	Usk	3.00
			F-CGCS				
4477/JFK+	Schleicher ASW20L	20201	D-5979	4.98	S.Housden	Nympsfield	4.00
4478/JFL	Rolladen-Schneider LS-8-18	8178	-	3.98	G.Smith "42"	Dunstable	1.00
4479/JFM	Schleicher ASK13	13222	D-0396	3.98	Newark & Notts GC	Winthorpe	3.00
4480/JFN	Schleicher ASH25E	25060	D-KCOH	6.98	R.Baker "OH"	Cranfield	3.00
4481/JFP	Schempp-Hirth Ventus A	19	PH-707	3.98	S.Harris "HB"	(London)	2.00
4482/JFQ	Schempp-Hirth Nimbus 4DT	9/40	-	5.98	J.Delafield "66"	Bicester	5.00
4483/JFR	Schempp-Hirth Ventus cT	170	RAFGSA.R24	12.97	RAFGSA Centre "221"	Bicester	1.00
4484/JFS	Schempp-Hirth Ventus cT	147	RAFGSA.R28	7.98	M.J.Towler "528"	Snitterfield	7.00
4485/JFT+	Schleicher K8B	8451	D-1883	3.98	South London Gliding Centre		
						Kenley	4.00
4486/JFU+	Schleicher ASW19	19038	D-4531	3.98	East Sussex GC	Ringmer	2.00
4487/JFV	Schleicher ASK21	21675	-	6.98	Scottish GU "WA1"	Portmoak	6.00
4488/JFW+	LAK-12 Lietuva	6192	LX-CDM	4.98	A.Hatfield	Crowland	4.00
4489/JFX	Rolladen-Schneider LS-8A	8174		3.98	D.Campbell "370"	Booker	4.00
4490/JFY	Federov Me-7b	8		10.98	D.Adams	Rivar Hill	10.99
4491/JFZ	Federov Me-7b	9		10.98	M.Powell-Brett	Long Mynd	11.00
4492/JGA	Federov Me-7b	10	-	10.98	M.Wilkinson	Challock	11.00
4493/JGB	Schleicher K8B	AB.02	D-8868	5.98	Cambridge UGC	Gransden Lodge	4.00
					"CU"		
4494/JGC	Rolladen-Schneider LS-6A	6031	D-6699	4.98	Gliding Expeditions Ltd		
			PH-763		"CC"	Les Ages, France	4.00
4495/JGD+	Schleicher K8B	8214A-SH	D-??..	4.98	R.E.Pettifer	Chipping	3.00
4496/JGE	Schleicher ASK21	21068	RAFGSA.R21	2.98	N.Wall "R21"	Long Mynd	6.00
4497/JGF+	Neukom Elfe S4D	416	BGA.3316	5.98	C.Inwood	Lasham	5.00
			D-4820				
4498/JGG+	Schleicher ASW15B	15332	D-2325	4.98	L.Groves	Ringmer	2.00
4499/JGH+	Schempp-Hirth Nimbus 2C	188	OO-ZZM	4.98	D.Prosolek	Gamston	4.00
			D-2834				
4500/JGJ+	Schleicher ASK21	21039	RAFGSA.R22	4.98	Midland GC	Long Mynd	5.00
4501/JGK	Molino Pik-20D	20571	OO-ZDL	4.98	R.Cassidy	Milfield	4.00
			D-6707		"ZDL"		
4502/JGL	Schempp-Hirth Discus CS	148CS	RAFGSA.R27	4.98	Chilterns GC "27"	Halton	3.99

BGA No/Code	Type	C/n	P/I	Date	Owner/operator	Probable Base	CA Expy
4503/JGM	Schempp-Hirth Discus CS	36CS	RAFGSA.R53	4.98	Chilterns GC "R53"	Halton	11.99
4504/JGN	Schempp-Hirth Standard Cirrus	554	D-8674	4.98	F.Wilson	Pocklington	5.00
4505/JGP	Schempp-Hirth Ventus 2cT	3/10	N200EE	4.98	C.Morris "E8"	Bidford	3.00
			D-KHIA				
4506/JGQ+	LET L-13 Blanik	026224	HB-1282	6.98	Joint Aviation Services	Lasham	6.00
4507/JGR	Schempp-Hirth Discus bT	10/275	D-KGPS	5.98	J.Horne "BT"	Wormingford	5.00
			D-5461				
4508/JGS	Rolladen-Schneider LS-8-18	8180	-	5.98	G Stingemore "X1"	Shobdon	3.00
4509/JGT+	Scheibe SF27	6021	D-1126	4.98	South London Gliding Centre		
						Kenley	4.99
4510/JGU	Schempp-Hirth Mini Nimbus	69	HB-1427	5.98	P.Etherington Husbands Bosworth		5.00
4511/LGC+	Schempp-Hirth Duo Discus	173	D-4020	R			
4512/JGW+	Schleicher ASK13	13146	D-0169	5.98	Newark & Notts GC.	Winthorpe	2.00
4513/JGX+	Schleicher K8B	753	D-1878	5.98	J.Fisher	Andreas	4.00
4514/JGY	Schempp-Hirth Standard Cirrus	333	SE-TMU	5.98	P.Chapman "C3" Husbands Bosworth		5.00
4515/JGZ	Glasflugel H-201 Standard Libelle	193	D-0697	5.98	J.Edwards	Pocklington	5.00
4516/JHA	Schempp-Hirth Standard Cirrus	645	D-4240	5.98	J.Lee	Pocklington	5.99
4517/JHB+	Scheibe L-Spatz 55	552	D-1618	8.98	A.Gruber	Rhigos	7.00
4518/JHC+	Schleicher ASW19B	19304	OO-ZBN	8.98	Scottish GU	Portmoak	8.00
4519/JHD+	Schleicher Ka6E	4307	OY-XGS	5.98	P.Francon-Smith	Crowland	5.00
			D-0272		"Y1" &"OY-XGS"		
4520/JHE	Grob G.102 Astir CS Jeans	2189	CS-PBI	5.98	AC de Portugal	Lisbon	2.00
			BGA3977/D-7764				
4521/JHF	Schempp-Hirth Nimbus 4T	30		5.98	G.Kerstjens "VW"	(Belgium)	5.00
4522/JHG	Grob G.102 Astir CS	1084	D-6984	5.98	J.Pack "BIT"	The Park	2.00
4523/JHH+	Schempp-Hirth Standard Cirrus	349G	D-3006	5.98	R.L.Fox	Rufforth	5.00
4524/JHJ	Glasflugel H-201 Standard Libelle	495	HB-1187	R			
4525/JHK+	Schleicher K8B	558	AGA.21	8.98	AGA Kestrel GC	Odiham	8.99
			BGA4319/RAFGSA.558		"A55"		
4526/JHL+	Schleicher Ka6E	4073	SE-TFB	6.98	N.J.Banks	Tibenham	5.00
4527/JHM+	Schempp-Hirth Discus b	373	???	6.98	J.May	Camphill	6.00
4528/JHN+	Grob G.102 Astir Jeans CS	2110	D-7638	5.98	B.Niblett Kingston Deverill		2.00
4529/JHP+	Valentin Mistral C	MC048-82	D-4948	6.98	D.J.Ingledew	(Hamble)	4.00
4530/JHQ	Schleicher ASK18	18021	RAFGSA.R43	9.98	RAFGSA Centre	Bicester 9.99	
			RAFGSA.713/RAFGSA.113 "R43"				
4531/JHR	Centrair Alliance SNC-34c	34026	-	6.98	Nevyn International	Bicester	6.00
					"A34"		
4532/JHS	Schleicher ASW19B	19047	D-6716	3.99	D.L.Jobbins	Usk	3.00
4533/JHT	Schempp-Hirth Discus 2A	2	- ? -	5.98	W.Murray "D2"	Membury	5.00
4534/JHU	Rolladen-Schneider LS-8-18	8197		7.98	S.Thompson "OP8"	Parham Park	7.00
4535/JHV	Schempp-Hirth Discus b	265	RAFGGA547	5.98	RAFGSA Phoenix GC	RAF Bruggen	5.99
			RAFGGA500		"547"		
4536/JHW+	Glaser-Dirks DG-200	2-19	HB-1400	6.98	P.I.Fenner	Lasham	6.00
4537/JHX+	Bolkow Phoebus C	930	OO-ZYN	6.98	M.Dunlop	Usk	6.00
			F-CDON				
4538/JHY	Rolladen-Schneider LS-8-18	8181	D-9988	7.98	L.E.N.Tanner "LT"	Aboyne	6.00
4539/JHZ	Schleicher ASW20	20313	D-6532	6.98	S.Hughes "G41"	Camphill	5.00
4540/JJA	Schempp-Hirth Cirrus	13	D-8114	7.98	P.Tolson "A71"	Saltby	7.99
4541/JJB	Rolladen-Schneider LS-4	4542	D-2397	6.98	M.Tomlinson "615"	Rhigos	6.00
4542/JJC+	Schleicher ASK13	13661AB	D-1503	7.98	East Sussex GC	Ringmer	7.00
4543/JJD	Schempp-Hirth Discus bT	5/262	D-KIHS	7.98	D.Wilson "SUF" & "K11"	Burn	6.00
4544/JJE	Schempp-Hirth Discus b	379	OE-5530	7.98	N.Braithwaite "J01"	Long Mynd	11.00
4545/JJF	Schleicher ASW20	27086	-	6.98	G.Read "G1"	Booker	12.99
4546/JJG+	Schempp-Hirth Nimbus 4T	3	D-KIXL	7.98	P.G.Sheard "V1"	Dunstable	7.00
4547/JJH	Glaser-Dirks DG-800S	8-137S30		4.99	W.R.Brown "899"Husbands Bosworth		4.00
4548/JJJ+	Schempp-Hirth Standard Cirrus	284	D-2946	7.98	R.Stevens (As "2946")	Bidford	5.00
4549/JJK	Rolladen-Schneider LS-8	8199		8.98	K.Payne "K8"	Husbands Bosworth	7.00
4550/JJL	Schleicher ASW19B	19302	D-4227	4.99	Newark & Notts GC		
					"D-42"	Winthorpe	4.00
4551/JJM	Schempp-Hirth Standard Cirrus	403G	D-2933	7.98	B.Dakin Husbands Bosworth		7.00
4552/JJN	Slingsby T.38	1267	XP490	7.98	Swanton Morley Collection		
	(Rear fuselage no SSK/RF/2067)				(As "XP490") Swanton Morley		7.99
4553/JJP	Schempp-Hirth Duo Discus	180	-	7.98	R.Fack "494"	Long Mynd	5.00
4554/JJQ+	SZD-51-1 Junior	B-2191		7.98	Norfolk GC	Tibenham	9.00
4555/JJR	Schleicher ASK21	21054	RAFGSA.R73	8.98	RAFGSA Centre	Bicester	2.00
			RAFGGA.513		"R73"		
4556/JJS	Slingsby T.38	873	XA240	R			
4557/JJT	Schleicher ASW27	27070	D-6209	8.98	P.Wells "Z1"	Booker	7.00
4558/JJU	Rolladen-Schneider LS-8a	8200		8.98	P.Harvey "H2"	Cranfield	2.00
4559/JJV+	Schleicher Ka6CR	1001	D-1719	8.98	L.Simpson	Long Mynd	10.00
4561/JJX+	Schleicher ASW15B	15323	D-2312	9.98	T.Davis	Portmoak	9.00

BGA No/Code	Type	C/n	P/I	Date	Owner/operator	Probable Base	CA Expy
4562/JJY+	Schempp-Hirth Ventus bT	273/61	PH-981 D-KMIH	9.98	A.J.Leigh	Camphill	3.00
4563/JJZ	Schempp-Hirth Discus bT	156/556	OO-ZQX	9.98	B.Walker "BW"	Nympsfield	3.00
4564/JKA+	Schleicher ASK21	21059	D-8835	10.98	E Sussex GC	Ringmer	10.99
4565/JKB+	DWLKK PW-5	17.10.008	CS-PBN	9.98	J.Gibson	Chipping	9.00
4566/JKC+	MDM-1 Fox	224	SP-P632	9.98	G.Westgate & Ptnr	Ringmer	9.00
4567/JKD	Rolladen-Schneider LS-8-18	8215		10.98	R.Large "P1"	Lyveden	10.00
4568/JKE	DWLKK PW-5	17.11.025		10.98	Burn GC	Burn	10.00
4569/JKF+	Glaser-Dirks DG-200	2-35	D-6069	10.98	R.Hutchinson	Sutton Bank	10.00
4570/JKG	Schleicher ASK18	18021	RAFGSA.R43	3.99	RAFGSA Centre "R48"	Bicester	3.00
4571/JKH	Schempp-Hirth Ventus cT	174	RAFGSA.R30	10.98	RAFGSA Centre "R30"	Bicester	11.00
4572/JKJ	Schleicher ASK21	21679	(RAFGSA.R21)	10.98	RAFGSA Centre "R21"	Bicester	10.00
4573/JKK	Schleicher ASK21	21182	AGA.11	10.98	AGA Kestrel GC "A7"	Odiham	11.00
4574/JKL	Rolladen-Schneider LS-8	8218		4.99	R.Welford	Gransden Lodge	4.00
4575/JKM	Glaser-Dirks DG-202-17M	2-148/1746	D-4155	10.98	A.Brown "Z10"	Strathaven	10.99
4576/JKN	Rolladen-Schneider LS-8-18	8214		10.98	D.Booth "790"	Crowland	10.00
4577/JKP	Rolladen-Schneider LS-4B	41000	PH-1089	12.98	M Hope "PH1"	Booker	12.99
4578/JKQ	Schleicher ASK21	21098	RAFGSA.R20	1.99	RAFGSA Bannerdown GC "R20" Keevil		1.00
4579/JKR	Schempp-Hirth Discus B	151	RAFGSA.R12	11.98	RAFGSA Bannerdown GC "R12" Keevil		11.99
4580/JKS	Schleicher ASW19B	19362	D-1273	11.98	P Tavener "S19"	Tibenham	11.99
4581/JKT	Schleicher ASK13	13615	RAFGSA.R7	8.99	Clevelands GC	Dishforth	8.00
4582/JKU	Schleicher ASK18	18022	RAFGSA.R33	6.99	Clevelands GC "R33"	Dishforth	6.00
4583/JKV	Grob G103 Twin II Astir	34042-K-273	RAFGSA.R52	5.99	Clevelands GC "R52"	Dishforth	5.00
4584/JKW	Grob G.102 Astir CS 77	1666	RAFGSA.R60	1.99	Clevelands GC "R60"	Dishforth	1.00
4585/JKX	Schempp-Hirth Discus B	247	RAFGSA.R17	8.99	Clevelands GC "R17"	Dishforth	8.00
4586/JKY	Schempp-Hirth Ventus cT	181	RAFGSA.R24	11.98	A.W.Duerden "24"	Chipping	11.99
4587/JKZ	Schleicher ASK21	21123	RAFGSA.R25	12.98	RAFGSA Centre "R25"	Bicester	12.00
4588/JLA+	Schempp-Hirth Ventus 2cT	26/94	PH-1129	11.98	C.Neighbour	Camphill	11.00
4589/JLB	Schempp-Hirth Ventus 2A	74		11.98	R.Knight "70"	Milfield	11.00
4590/JLC	Schempp-Hirth Discus CS	193CS	RAFGSA.R10	11.98	RAFGSA Centre "R10"	Bicester	11.00
4592/JLE	Schleicher ASK13	13245	RAFGSA.R90 NEJSGSA.1	10.98	RAFGSA Crusaders GC "R90" Kingsfield, Dhekelia		10.00
4593/JLF+	Schleicher ASK13	13150	AGA.14	12.98	Wyvern GC	Upavon	12.00
4594/JLG	SZD-51-1 Junior	B.1933	AGA.5	2.99	Wyvern GC	Upavon	2.00
4595/JLH	Rolladen-Schneider LS-4	4256	AGA.1	3.99	Wyvern GC	Upavon	3.00
4596/JLJ	Rolladen-Schneider LS-4B	4997	AGA.2	12.98	Wyvern GC "A8"	Upavon	12.99
4597/JLK	Rolladen-Schneider LS-7	7112	AGA.3	4.99	Wyvern GC	Upavon	4.00
4598/JLL	Schleicher ASK13	13144	HB-952	11.98	Portsmouth Naval GC "N25"	Lee-on-Solent	11.99
4599/JLM	Schempp-Hirth HS.6 Janus C	210	RAFGSA.R2	5.99	Cranwell GC "R2"	Cranwell	11.00
4600/JLN	Rolladen-Schneider LS-8-18	8169	RAFGSA.R4	3.99	Buckminster GC "R4"	Saltby	3.00
4601/JLP	Schempp-Hirth Discus CS	034CS	RAFGSA.R39	4.99	Cranwell GC "R39"	Cranwell	4.00
4602/JLQ	Schleicher ASK13	13608	RAFGSA.R40 RAFGSA.R4	4.99	Cranwell GC "R40"	Cranwell	4.00
4603/JLR	Grob G.102 Astir CS	1509	RAFGSA.R57	2.99	Cranwell GC "R57"	Cranwell	2.00
4604/JLS	Schleicher K8B	8950	RAFGSA.R75	3.99	Cranwell GC "R75"	Cranwell	3.00
4605/JLT	Schleicher Ka6E	4115	D-6082	11.98	M.Thompson	Husbands Bosworth	12.00
4606/JLU	Schempp-Hirth Ventus cT	37		3.99	J.C.Mitchell "11"	Chipping	3.00
4607/JLV+	Schleicher Ka6E	4192	OY-XEU D-4424	1.99	M.S.Neal	Crowland	1.00
4608/JLW	Schempp-Hirth Discus CS (C/n also reported as 133/1991)	033CS	RAFGSA.R87	12.98	RAFGSA Centre "87"	Bicester	12.99
4609/JLX+	Grob Standard Cirrus	279G	OO-ZGL D-1985	11.98	M.Fisher	Edgehill	11.99
4610/JLY	Schleicher ASW27	27111		6.99	P.C.Piggott	Husbands Bosworth	6.00
4611/JLZ	Grob G.103A Twin II Astir	3633-K-15	D-7912	12.98	T.Dews "21"	Kingston Deverill	12.99
4612/JMA	Schleicher ASK18	18038	RAFGSA.R36 RAFGSA.236	6.99	RAFGSA Centre "R36"	Bicester	6.00
4613/JMB	Rolladen-Schneider LS-8	8130	RAFGSA.R5	2.99	RAFGSA Centre "R5"	Bicester	2.00
4614/JMC+	Schleicher ASK21	21681	(RAFGSA.R22)	12.98	RAFGSA "R22"	Bicester	12.00
4615/JMD	Schempp-Hirth Discus b	241	RAFGSA.R23	4.99	R.C.Oliver "P23"	Kenley	4.00
4616/JME	Schleicher Ka7	5	D-8867	12.98	W.Masterson	(Jamaica)	12.99
4617/JMF	Rolladen-Schneider LS-8-18	8232		R	P.Onn		
4618/JMG	SZD-51-1 Junior	B.2192		4.99	Kent GC	Challock	4.00
4619/JMH+	Schempp-Hirth Standard Cirrus	571	HB-1263	12.98	M.Fryer	Rufforth	12.99
4620/JMJ	Schleicher ASK13	13616	RAFGSA.R46	9.99	Fenland GC "R46"	Marham	9.00
4621/JMK	Schleicher ASK18	18023	RAFGSA.R49	1.99	Fenland GC "R49"	Marham	1.00
4622/JML	Grob G.102 Astir CS 77	1718	RAFGSA.R63	1.99	Fenland GC "R63"	Marham	1.00
4623/JMM+	Schempp-Hirth Discus b	254	BGA.4474 RAFGSA.R15	12.98	P.Crabb "R15"	Crowland	12.99

BGA No/Code	Type	C/n	P/I	Date	Owner/operator	Probable Base	CA Expy
4624/JMN+	Schempp-Hirth Nimbus 2B	38	D-1129 HB-1159	12.98	M.Holroyd	Pocklington	12.00
4625/JMO	Rolladen-Schneider LS-8-18	8225		12.98	J Langrick "781"	Husbands Bosworth	12.99
4626/JMP+	Schleicher ASK13	13446	D-2984	1.99	East Sussex GC	Ringmer	1.00
4627/JMQ	Schleicher ASW20L	20499	F-CADB	1.99	S.G.Back "KR"	Crowland	1.00
4628/JMR	Rolladen-Schneider LS8-18	8198	D-0280	12.98	D.Williams "628"	Lasham	12.99
4629/JMS	Schleicher ASK21	21212	RAFGGA.521	11.98	Phoenix GC	RAF Bruggen	11.99
4630/JMT	Rolladen-Schneider LS-8-18	8223		2.99	J.Burry "301"	Lasham	11.00
4631/JMU	Rolladen-Schneider LS-8	8246		3.99	R.Payne "140"	Nympsfield	3.00
4632/JMV	Schempp-Hirth HS.5 Nimbus 2C	179	D-6738	1.99	K.R.Walton "EW"	Lasham	1.00
4633/JMW	Schleicher ASK13	13688AB	RAFGGA.567	1.99	Bannerdown GC "R59"	Keevil	1.00
4634/JMX	Schleicher ASK13	13107	RAFGSA.R86 RAFGSA.386	2.99	Fulmar GC "R86"	Kinloss	2.00
4635/JMY	SZD-51-1 Junior	W-959	OO-ZRH	3.99	Highland GC	Easterton	3.00
4636/JMZ	Schleicher ASK13	13099	RAFGSA.R37	1.99	Wrekin GC "R37"	Cosford	1.00
4637/JNA	Grob G.102 Astir CS Jeans	2160	D-4556	2.99	Shenington GC	Edgehill	2.00
4638/JNB	Rolladen-Schneider LS-8A	8227		2.99	P.M.Shelton "D1"	Cross Hayes	2.00
4639/JNC	Schempp-Hirth Standard Cirrus	322	HB-1157	2.99	S.M.Veness	Bicester	2.00
4640/JND	Slingsby T38 Grasshopper	SSK/OW2987	ex -	R	S.Williams		
4641/JNE	Schempp-Hirth Discus 2	18		2.99	M.H.Clegg "561"	Bruggen	2.00
4642/JNF	Schempp-Hirth Discus 2A	12		2.99	A.J.Davis "80"	Nympsfield	2.00
4643/JNG	Glasflugel H.201B Standard Libell	6	SE-TFU	3.99	P.K.Spencer	Edgehill	3.00
4644/JNH	Schleicher ASW27	27102		3.99	E.Drew "E3"	Crowland	3.00
4645/JNJ	Rolladen-Schneider LS-8-18	8226		2.99	J.D.Spencer "601"	Dunstable	2.00
4646/JNK	Rolladen-Schneider LS-8-18	8244		2.99	M.J.Jordy "676"	Enstone	2.00
4647/JNL+	Schempp-Hirth HS.6 Janus B	25	HB-1313	2.99	D.M.Ruttle	Saltby	2.00
4648/JNM	Rolladen-Schneider LS-8A	8232	(BGA.4617)	3.99	P.Onn "P4"	Dunstable	3.00
4649/JNN+	Schleicher K-8B	8744	D-8583	3.99	Buckminster GC	Saltby	3.00
4650/JNP	Rolladen-Schnieder LS-6B	6109	D-5853	R	P.Fink		
4651/JNQ	Glaser-Dirks DG-300 Elan	3E-341	SE-UHO	4.99	F.C.Roles	Camphill	4.00
4652/JNR+	Glasflugel H.303 Mosquito B	159	D-5908	3.99	I.Agutter	Wormingford	3.00
4653/JNS	Schleicher ASW27	27103		3.99	B.H.Owen "Z2"	Lasham	12.00
4654/JNT	Schleicher ASW19B	19371	D-2233	4.99	S.Cheshire "SC"	Booker	4.00
4655/JNU	Rolladen-Schneider LS-6C	6345	RAFGSA.R69 RAFGGA.553/D-8037	3.99	Chilterns GC "R69"	Halton	3.00
4656/JNV	Schleicher ASW22BL	22079		4.99	R.A.Cheetham "E2"	Dunstable	4.00
4657/JNW	Rolladen-Schneider LS-8	8217		3.99	A.J.Limb "L4"	Husbands Bosworth	3.00
4658/JNX	LET L-13 Blanik	027408	OK-2712	5.99	Vectis GC	Bembridge	5.00
4659/JNY	Schempp-Hirth Discus 2B	17		3.99	D.H.Conway "CZ"	(Malmesbury)	3.00
4660/JNZ	Glaser-Dirks DG-100G Elan	70	(D-7324) HB-1234	3.99	R.C.Martin "813"	Farnborough	3.00
4661/JPA	Schempp-Hirth Duo Discus	201		3.99	The Soaring Centre "HB1"	Husbands Bosworth	3.00
4662/JPB	Schleicher ASK23	23005	AGA.18	4.99	Kestrel GC "A5"	Odiham	4.00
4663/JPC	Schleicher ASK13	13256	RAFGSA.R51	3.99	Anglia GC "R52"	Wattisham	3.00
4664/JPD	Schempp-Hirth Ventus 2CT	39		3.99	A.Hearne "V2T"	Challock	3.00
4665/JPE	Rolladen-Schneider LS-1f	488	F-CESC	5.99	A.A.Darlington "L77"	(Chippenham)	5.00
4666/JPF+	Glaser-Dirks DG-100	22	D-3735	5.99	H.G.Burkett	(Southampton)	5.00
4667/JPG	Schempp-Hirth Ventus 2CT	2		4.99	P.Naegeli "520"	Rivar Hill	4.00
4668/JPH	Rolladen-Schneider LS-8-18	8259		7.99	J.P.Ben-David "CB"	Lasham	7.00
4669/JPJ	Grob G.104 Speed Astir IIB	4089	OE-5352	4.99	K.Sleigh "SA"	Rattlesden	4.00
4670/JPK	Slingsby T.34 Sky	672	RAFGSA.876 XA876/G-672	5.99	J.Tournier	Booker	5.00
4671/JPL	Rolladen-Schneider LS-8-18	8249		4.99	I.Reekie "RW"	(Aylesbury)	4.00
4672/JPM+	Grob G.102 Astir CS Jeans	2209	D-3825	5.99	J.Thorpe	Cross Hayes	5.00
4673/JPN	Schleicher ASW27	27117		6.99	M.Strathern "280"	Nympsfield	6.00
4674/JPP+	Schempp-Hirth Discus B	206	AGA.4	4.99	Kestrel GC "388"	Odiham	4.00
4675/JPQ	Schleicher ASK18	18002	RAFGSA.R32 RAFGSA.213/D-3978	5.99	Fulmar GC	Kinloss	5.00
4676/JPR	Rolladen-Schneider LS-8-18	8245		4.99	D.M.Byass "161"	Dunstable	4.00
4677/JPS	Schleicher ASW27	27108		5.99	C.C.Lyttleton "CL"	Dunstable	5.00
4678/JPT+	Schleicher ASW27	27113		10.99	R&W Willis-Fleming	North Hill	10.00
4679/JPU	Schempp-Hirth Discus CS	257CS		4.99	K.Armitage "TL2"	Camphill	4.00
4680/JPV	Schleicher ASK13	13312	RAFGSA.R88 RAFGSA.186	5.99	RAFGSA Centre "R88"	Bicester	5.00
4681/JPW+	Glaser-Dirks DG-200	2-48	D-2201	5.99	J.P.Goodison	Burn	5.00
4682/JPX	Schleicher ASW15	15160	D-0823	5.99	P.Seymour	Cranfield	5.00
4683/JPY	Schleicher ASK13	13653AB	RAFGGA.509	5.99	Phoenix GC "R59"	Bruggen	5.00
4684/JPZ	Schleicher ASK18	18027	RAFGSA.563	4.99	Phoenix GC	Bruggen	4.00

BGA No/Code	Type	C/n	P/I	Date	Owner/operator	Probable Base	CA Expy
4685/JQA	Schempp-Hirth Discus B	265	RAFGGA.547 RAFGGA.500	4.99	Phoenix GC "547" Bruggen		4.00
4686/JQB	Schleicher K8B	8880	RAFGGA.R98 RAFGSA.398	5.99	A.J.Taylor & Ptnrs Lee on Solent		5.00
4687/JQC	Schempp-Hirth Discus bT	127/488	D-KITT (3)	5.99	J.C.Taggart "JT"	Bellarena	5.00
4688/JQD	Rolladen-Schneider LS-8A	8224		5.99	Fenland GC "R3"	Marham	5.00
4689/JQE+	Schempp-Hirth HS4 Standard Cirrus 75 25		OO-ZRS D-0483	6.99	P.Francon-Smith	(Stamford)	6.00
4690/JQF	Glaser-Dirks DG-505 Elan Orion	5E194X38		6.99	Scottish GU "SGC"	Portmoak	6.00
4691/JQG	Grob G.103 Twin Astir	33946-K-197	RAFGSA.R50	5.99	Fulmar GC "R50"	Kinloss	5.00
4692/JQH	LAK-12 Lietuva	6188		5.99	A.Pozerskis Husbands Bosworth		5.00
4693/JQJ+	Schleicher K8B	8795	RAFGSA.R47 BGA.1564	5.99	Staffordshire GC	Seighford	5.00
4694/JQK	Schempp-Hirth Discus CS	075CS	RAFGGA.501	5.99	Phoenix GC "501"	Bruggen	5.00
4695/JQL	Schempp-Hirth Ventus 2A	79		5.99	S.G.Jones "110"	Membury	5.00
4696/JQM	Schleicher ASW-27	27114		6.99	A.Hegner "Z9"	Camphill	6.00
4697/JQN	Grob G.102 Astir CS 77	1634	RAFGSA.R67 RAFGGA.547	6.99	RAFGSA Centre	Bicester	6.00
4698/JQP	Centrair 101A Pegase	101-066	F-CFQY	6.99	K.J.Sleigh	Rattlesden	6.00
4699/JQQ	Schempp-Hirth Duo Discus	227		R	H.Reid		
4700/JQR+	Schempp-Hirth Ventus 2cT	49/...		10.99	M.C.Costin	Crowland	10.00
4701/JQS+	Schempp-Hirth (Grob) Standard Cirrus	251C	D-1147	6.99	M.Charlton	(Amble)	6.00
4702/JQT+	Grob G.102 Astir CS Jeans	2076	D-7589	6.99	Southdown GC	Parham Park	6.00
4703/JQU	LAK-17A	102		6.99	A Pozerskis Husbands Bosworth "L17"		6.00
4704/JQV	Schleicher ASW27	27112		7.99	I.N.Lingham "Z12"	Booker	7.00
4705/JQW+	Schempp-Hirth HS.2 Cirrus 18	47	D-0186	7.99	G.E.Smith	Parham Park	7.00
4706/JQX+	Schleicher ASK21	21702		9.99	Southdown GC	Parham Park	9.00
4707/JQY	Slingsby T.21 Sedbergh	666	RAFGSA.R92 NEJSGSA.4/WG499	6.99	Crusaders GC Kingsfield, Dhekelia		6.00
4708/JQZ+	Schleicher K8B	8854	RAFGSA.R42 RAFGSA.323	7.99	Bowland Forest GC	Chipping	7.00
4709/JRA..	Rolladen-Schneider LS-8-18	8263		7.99	S.R.Ell "E11"	Sutton Bank	7.00
4710/JRB	Schleicher ASW19B	19227	D-2713	7.99	K.F.Bell "S33"	Lasham	7.00
4711/JRC+	Glaser-Dirks DG300 Club Elan	3E-20	HB-1718	8.99	D.P.Sillett	Rattlesden	8.00
4712/JRD	Grob G102 Astir CS	1487	RAFGSA.R18 RAFGSA.540/D-4791	6.99	RAFGSA Centre "R18"	Bicester	6.00
4713/JRE	Schleicher ASW-15	15048	LN-GGL	8.99	J.D.Pride "JP"	Long Mynd	8.00
4714/JRF+	SZD-50-3 Puchacz	B-1395	OO-ZTX	8.99	Derby & Lancs GC	Camphill	8.00
4715/JRG+	Schempp-Hirth Standard Cirrus	146	D-0297	8.99	R.Sinden	Talgarth	8.00
4716/JRH	Schleicher ASW27	27118		8.99	P.C.Jarvis "T27"	Booker	8.00
4717/JRJ+	SZD-50-3 Puchacz	503199327		8.99	Bidford GC	Bidford	8.00
4718/JRK	Rolladen-Schneider LS-8-18	8267		9.99	D.King "618"	Snitterfield	9.00
4719/JRL	Glaser-Dirks DG-100G Elan	E185G151	D-1246	R	W.Venner		
4720/JRM+	Grob G102 Astir CS	1332	AGA.6 BGA.4314	9.99	Chilterns G	Halton	9.00
4721/JRN	Glaser-Dirks DG-202/17C	2-118CL01	D-7267	9.99	T.G.Roberts	Lasham	9.00
4722/JRP	Grob G102 Astir CS Jeans	2244	D-5951	9.99	Borders GC	Milfield	9.00
4723/JRQ	Neukom Elfe PM3	001	N6351U N63514/HB-526	11.99	G.Mclean	Seighford	11.00
4724/JRR	Schempp-Hirth Discus bT	50/367	PH-1087 D-KBHM	R	C.Lear		
4725/JRS	Valentin Mistral C	MC021/79	D-4921	R	A.Towse		
4726/JRT	Schempp-Hirth Standard Cirrus	99	D-0734	10.99	S.Hutchinson Husbands Bosworth		10.00
4727/JRU	Schleicher ASW24	24168	D-7085	R	M.Bull		
4728/JRV	Schleicher ASW19B	19233	D-2644	10.99	M.Roome "B19"	Lasham	10.00
4729/JRW.	Grob G103A Twin II Acro	34040-K-271	RAFGGA.556	10.99	RAFGSA Centre "R95"	Bicester	10.00
4730/JRX	Schleicher ASK13	13375	RAFGSA.R41	10.99	Chilterns GC	Halton	10.00
4731/JRY	Edgely EA-9	008		R			
4732/JRZ	Colditz Cock rep (Built M.Francis)	--		R	M.Francis	Camphill	
4733/JSA	Scheibe SF-27MB	6303	D-KIBE	R	M.Davies		
4734/JSB	Rolladen-Schneider LS-4	4424	D-4541	R	V.Melzer		
4735/JSC	Schempp-Hirth Numbus 3dT	10	F-CFUE	11.99	D.P.Taylor & P.J.Teagle "827"	Sutton Bank	11.00
4736/JSD	Grob G102 Astir CS	1133	RAFGSA.R77	R	RAFGSA "R77"		
4737/JSE	Schempp-Hirth Discus b	365	PH-918	R	A.Dartington "296"	Lasham	
4738/JSF	Rolladen-Schneider LS-1f	383	LN-GGG SE-TOU	R	R.Johnson		
4739/JSG	Schleicher Ka6E	4248	D-0090	R	J.S.Halford		

BGA No/Code	Type	C/n	P/I	Date	Owner/operator	Probable Base	CA Expy
4740/JSH	Grob G102 Astir IIIB	5504CB	D-6470	11.99	Surrey & Hants GC "396"	Lasham	11.00
4741/JSJ	Rolladen-Schneider LS-7WL	7058	(ex ?)	10.99	T.Moyes "7X"	Camphill	10.00
4742/JSK+	Grob G102 Astir CS	1521	D-7455	11.99	J.Bolt	North Hill	11.00
4743/JSL+	Schempp-Hirth Ventus cT	121		11.99	B.Ingles	Bidford	11.00
4744/JSM	Glaser-Dirks DG100G	84G5	HB-1335	R	A.Burger - see BGA.4759		
4745/JSN	Schleicher K8B	8916	RAFGSA.R45 RAFGSA.245	11.99	Chilterns GC "R45"	Halton	11.00
4746/JSP	Slingsby T.31B	909	XE796.	R			
4747/JSQ	Rolladen-Schneider LS-8-18	8301		R			
4748/JSR	SZD-50-3 Puchacz	B-1386	OY-XRV SP-3283	R	Bidford GC	Bidford	
4749/JSS	Schleicher ASW27B	27121		12.99	J.H.Belk "JB"	Dunstable	12.00
4750/JST	Rolladen-Schneider LS-1c	86	OO-ZPA D-0766	R	L.Gerrard		
4751/JSU	Rolladen-Schneider LS-8-18	8297		R	J.Bell		
4752/JSV	Schleicher ASK13	13127	RAFGSA.R80 BGA.1509	1.00	RAFGSA Centre "R80"	Bicester	1.01
4753/JSW	Rolladen-Schneider LS-4	4262	- ? -	R	B.Spreckley	(France)	
4754/JSX	Glaser-Dirks DG-505 Orion	5E200X44..		R	Oxford GC	Weston on the Green	
4755/JSY	Pilatus B4 PC-11	127	D-3055 PH-578	1.00	A.de Tourboulon & Ptnr.	Wormingford	1.01
4756/JSZ	Schleicher ASK-18	18012	?	R	K.Sleigh		
4757/JTA	Colditz Cock rep (Built Southdown Aero Services)	SA3		R	Southdown Aero Services	Lasham	
4758/JTB	Schleicher ASW24	24017	D-3465	R	P Goodwin		
4759/JTC	Glaser-Dirks DG-100G	84G5	(BGA.4744) HB-1335	R	A.Burger		
4760/JTD	Rolladen-Schneider LS-6-18W	6371		R	C.Mayhew		
4761/JTE	Schempp-Hirth Standard Cirrus	470G	D-3718	R	G.Reeves		

PART 2 - RAF GLIDING & SOARING ASSOCIATION

In 1998 it was decided that the BGA would take responsibilty for the certification of all Service gliders. This meant that the specific Service registers would be disbanded and, in future, all gliders would adopt BGA references. The notes below indicate that the process is now complete. For the record we include all the Service registers this year but they will no longer feature in future editions.

Note that RAFGSA 'R' numbers are now regarded as BGA Competition Numbers and several have been re-issued to gliders with BGA Certificates of Airworthiness but which have not previously held RAFGSA identities.

RAFGSA No.	Type	C/n	P/I	Owner/operator	Probable Base/Notes	
R1	Schempp-Hirth Duo Discus	118		RAFGSA Centre	Bicester	To BGA.4475
R2*	Schempp-Hirth HS.6 Janus C	210		Cranwell GC	Cranwell	To BGA.4599
R3	Schleicher ASK13	13599		RAFGSA Centre	Bicester	To BGA.4688
R4	Rolladen-Schneider LS-8-18	8169		Cranwell GC	Cranwell	To BGA.4600
R5	Rolladen-Schneider LS-8-18	8130		Four Counties GC	Syerston	To BGA.4613
R6*	Schempp-Hirth Discus B	175		Wrekin GC	Cosford	
R7*	Schleicher ASK13	13615		Clevelands GC	Dishforth	To BGA.4581
R8	Grob G.102 Astir CS	1379	OY-XGE	RAFGSA Centre	Bicester	To BGA.4471
R9	Schempp-Hirth HS.6 Janus B	63	RAFGSA.16 BGA.2359	Not known		To BGA.2359
R9	Grob G.102 Astir CS	1123	RAFGSA R97 BGA.3216/D-	Four Counties GC 6977	Syerston	To BGA.3216
R10*	Schempp-Hirth Discus CS	193CS		RAFGSA Centre	Bicester	To BGA.4590
R12*	Schempp-Hirth Discus B	151		Bannerdown GC	Keevil	To BGA.4579
R15*	Schempp-Hirth Discus B	254	(BGA.4474)	RAFGSA Centre	Bicester	To BGA.4623
R16	Schempp-Hirth Janus CE	21/299		RAFGSA Centre "16"	Bicester	To BGA.4472
R17*	Schempp-Hirth Discus B	247		Clevelands GC	Dishforth	To BGA.4585
R18	Grob G.102 Astir	1487	RAFGGA.540 D-7425	Two Rivers GC	Bruggen....	To BGA.4712
R20	Schleicher ASK21	21098		Bannerdown GC	Keevil	To BGA.4578
R21	Schleicher ASK21	21068		(Sold during 1998)		To BGA.4496
R21	Schleicher ASK21	21679		RAFGSA Centre	Bicester	To BGA.4572
R22	Schleicher ASK21	21039		(Sold during 1998)		To BGA.4500
R22	Schleicher ASK21	21681		RAFGSA Centre	Bicester	To BGA.4614
R23*	Schempp-Hirth Discus B	241		RAFGSA Centre	Bicester	To BGA.4615
R24	Schempp-Hirth Ventus cT	170/560		(Sold during 1998)		To BGA.4483
R24	Schempp-Hirth Ventus cT	181/597	RAFGGA.557	Clevelands GC "24"	Dishforth	To BGA.4586
R25	Schleicher ASK21	21123		RAFGSA Centre	Bicester	To BGA.4587
R26	Schempp-Hirth Duo Discus	131		RAFGSA Centre "26"	Bicester	To BGA.4473
R27	Schempp-Hirth Discus CS	148CS		Chilterns GC "27"	Halton	To BGA.4502
R28*	Schempp-Hirth Ventus CT	147/456		Cranwell GC	Cranwell	To BGA.4484
R30	Schempp-Hirth Ventus CT	174/566		RAFGSA Centre	Bicester	To BGA.4571
R31	Schleicher ASK13	13609	BGA.2533	Fulmar GC	Kinloss	
R32	Schleicher ASK18	18002	RAFGSA.213 D-3978	Fulmar GC	Kinloss....	To BGA.4675
R33	Schleicher ASK18	18022	RAFGSA.223	Clevelands GC	Dishforth	To BGA.4582
R34	Schleicher ASK13	13542	F-CERF	Chilterns GC "34"	Halton	
R35	Schleicher ASK21	21148	ZD648	Cranwell GC	Cranwell	To BGA.2888
R36	Schleicher ASK18	18038	RAFGSA.236	Four Counties GC	Syerston	To BGA.4612
R37	Schleicher ASK13	13099	RAFGSA.378	Wrekin GC	Cosford...	To BGA.4636
R38	Schempp-Hirth Ventus CT	161/521		(Sold during 1988)		To BGA.4461
R39	Schempp-Hirth Discus CS	034CS		Cranwell GC	Cranwell	To BGA.4601
R40	Schleicher ASK13	13608	RAFGSA.R4	Cranwell GC	Cranwell	To BGA.4602
R41	Schleicher ASK13	13375	RAFGSA.241?	Chilterns GC	Halton	To BGA.4730
R42	Schleicher K8B	8854	RAFGSA.323	Anglia GC	Wattisham.	To BGA.4708
R43	Schleicher ASK18	18021	RAFGSA.713 RAFGSA.113	RAFGSA Centre	Bicester	To BGA.4570
R44	Schleicher K8B	8923	RAFGSA.538 RAFGSA.R38/BGA.2931	Bannerdown GC	Keevil	To BGA.2931
R45	Schleicher K8B	8916	RAFGSA.245	Chilterns GC	Halton	To BGA.4745
R46	Schleicher ASK13	13616	RAFGSA.R16	Fenlands GC	Marham	To BGA.4620
R47	Schleicher K8B	8795	BGA.1564	Chilterns GC	Halton	To BGA.4693
R48	Schleicher ASK18	18036	RAFGSA.448	RAFGSA Centre	Bicester..	
	(Composite rebuild 1986/89 of crashed c/n 18036 plus possibly R43)					
R49	Schleicher ASK18	18023	RAFGSA.318	Fenlands GC	Marham	To BGA.4621
R50	Grob G.103A Twin II Acro	33964-K-197		Fulmar GC	Kinloss	To BGA.4691

RAFGSA No.	Type	C/n	P/I	Owner/operator		Probable Base/Notes	
R51	Schleicher ASK13	13256		Anglia GC		Wattisham	To BGA.4663
R52	Grob G.103A Twin II Acro	34042-K-273		Clevelands GC		Dishforth	To BGA.4583
R53	Schempp-Hirth Discus CS	036CS		Chilterns GC		Halton	To BGA.4503
R55	Schempp-Hirth Discus CS	054CS		Fenlands GC		Marham	To BGA.4470
R57	Grob G.102 Astir CS	1509	RAFGSA.507	Cranwell GC		Cranwell	To BGA.4603
R58	Grob G.103A Twin II Acro	3787-K-65	BGA.2873	Four Counties GC		Syerston	To BGA.2873
R60	Grob G.102 Astir CS77	1666	RAFGSA.560	Clevelands GC		Dishforth	To BGA.4584
R61	Schempp-Hirth Discus CS	192CS	RAFGSA.561	Anglia GC		Wattisham	To BGA.4318
R63	Grob G.102 Astir CS77	1718	RAFGSA.883	Fenland GC		Marham	To BGA.4622
R67	Grob G.102 Astir CS77	1634	RAFGSA.547	Anglia GC		Wattisham	To BGA.4697
R69	Rolladen-Schneider LS-6-18W	6345	RAFGSA.553 RAFGSA.R69/D-8037	Phoenix GC		Bruggen	To BGA.4655
R70	Grob G.103A Twin II Acro	33894-K-132	ZE525 BGA.3015	Anglia GC		Wattisham	To BGA.3015
R71	Grob G.103A Twin II Acro	33961-K-194	ZE612	Fenlands GC		Marham	To BGA.3064
R73	Schleicher ASK21	21054	RAFGGA.513	RAFGSA Centre		Bicester	To BGA.4555
R75	Schleicher K8B	8950	RAFGSA.285	Cranwell GC		Cranwell	To BGA.4604
R77	Grob G.102 Astir CS	1133	D-4177	Wrekin GC		Cosford	To BGA.4736
R80	Schleicher ASK13	13127	BGA.1509	Bannerdown GC		Keevil	To BGA.4752
R83	Schleicher ASK13	13035	BGA.1427	Four Counties GC		Syerston	To BGA.1427
R86	Scleicher ASK13	13312	RAFGSA.386	Fulmar GC		Kinloss	To BGA.4634
R87*	Schempp-Hirth Discus CS	033CS		RAFGSA Centre "87"		Bicester	To BGA.4608
R88	Schleicher ASK13	13312	RAFGSA.R88 RAFGSA.186	Wrekin GC		Cosford	To BGA.4680
R90	Schleicher ASK13	13245	NEJSGSA.1	Crusaders GC	Kingsfield, Dhekelia		To BGA.4592
R91	Schleicher K8B	590	NEJSGSA BGA.2619/D-5703	Crusaders GC	Kingsfield, Dhekelia		To BGA.2619
R92	Slingsby T.21B	666	NEJSGSA.4 WG499	Crusaders GC	Kingsfield, Dhekelia		To BGA.4707
R93	ICA-Brasov IS-28B	33	EI-141 BGA.2207	Crusaders GC	Kingsfield, Dhekelia		To BGA.2207
R95	Schleicher K8B	8778	RAFGSA.395	Wrekin GC		Cosford	
	(Composite with RAFGSA.R96 c/n 8806 ex RAFGSA.396; c/n officially quoted as 8878, but this is D-0848)						
R97	Grob G.102 Astir CS	1123	BGA.3216 D-6977	Bannerdown GC		Keevil	To BGA.3216
R98	Schleicher K8B	8880	RAFGSA.398	Fenlands GC		Marham	To BGA.4686
R99	Slingsby T.45 Swallow	1387	NEJSGSA.3 XS651	Crusaders GC	Kingsfield, Dhekelia		

PART 3 - RAF GERMANY GLIDING & SOARING ASSOCIATION

RAFGGA No.	Type	C/n	P/I	Owner/operator		Probable Base/Notes
RAFGGA.312	Glaser-Dirks DG-300 Elan	?		Two Rivers GC	Laarbruch	Fate not known
RAFGGA.501	Schempp-Hirth Discus CS	075CS		Two Rivers GC	Laarbruch	To BGA.4694
RAFGGA.502	Scheibe L-Spatz 55	-		A.Taylor	West Raynham (Stored 11.93)	
	(Identity unconfirmed: ex RAF Bruggen)					
RAFGGA.509	Schleicher ASK13	13653		Phoenix GC	Bruggen...	To RAFGSA.R59/BGA.4683
RAFGGA.513	Schleicher ASK21	21054			Bicester	To RAFGSA.R73/BGA.4555
RAFGGA.514	Schleicher ASK21	21519				To BGA.4316
RAFGGA.515	Schleicher ASK21	21568				To BGA.4317
RAFGGA.521	Schleicher ASK21	21212		Phoenix GC	Bruggen	To BGA.4629
RAFGGA.540	Grob G.102 Astir CS	1487	D-4791	Two Rivers GC	Laarbruch	To RAFGSA.R18/BGA.4712
RAFGGA.547	Schempp-Hirth Discus B	265	RAFGGA.500	Phoenix GC	Bruggen	To BGA.4685
RAFGGA.556	Grob G.103A Twin II Acro	34040-K-271		Two Rivers GC	Laarbruch	To BGA.4729
RAFGGA.558	Schleicher K8B.......	558		British Forces GC	Achmer	To AGA.21/BGA.4319
RAFGGA.561	Schempp-Hirth Discus CS	192CS		British Forces GC	Achmer	To RAFGSA.R61/BGA.4318
RAFGGA.562	Schleicher K8B	?		Two Rivers GC	Laarbruch	Fate not known
RAFGGA.563	Schleicher ASK18	18027		Phoenix GC	Bruggen....	To BGA.4684
RAFGGA.567	Schleicher ASK13	13688AB		Two Rivers GC	Laarbruch	To BGA.4633/'R59'
RAFGGA.591	Schleicher Ka.4 Rhonlerche II	209	D-0359 F-C...	Museum of Flight/Royal Museum of Scotland East Fortune (On display 3.96)		

PART 4 – RN GLIDING & SOARING ASSOCIATION

There are three clubs in the RNGSA as follows:

1...Portsmouth Naval Gliding Club, Lee-on-Solent
```
RNGSA.N11  Schleicher K8B           BGA.2142
      N13  SZD-30 Pirat             BGA.2031
      .N15 Schleicher K8B           BGA.3548
      .N16 SZD-51-1 Junior          BGA.3657
      .N19 Grob G.102 Astir CS      BGA.4132
      .N21 Slingsby T.21B           BGA. 673
      .N23 SZD-50-3 Puchacz         BGA.3772
      .N25 Schleicher ASK-13        BGA.4598
      .N26 Schleicher ASK13         BGA.4056
      N27  Schleicher Ka7 Rhonadler BGA.1157
      .N28 Schleicher ASK13         BGA.3482
      .N29 Schleicher ASK13         BGA.3254
      .N.. Schempp-Hirth Discus CS  BGA.4030 "805"
```

2. Heron Gliding Club, RNAS Yeovilton
```
RNGSA.N31  Slingsby T.49B Capstan   BGA.1134
      .N34 Grob G.102 Astir CS77    BGA.2289  "480"
      .N36 SZD-50-3 Puchacz         BGA.3864  "HDP"
      .N.. Schleicher K8B           BGA.4148
```

3. Culdrose Gliding Club, RNAS Culdrose/Predannack
```
RNGSA.N51  Centrair 101A Pegase     BGA.2987
      .N52 SZD-30 Pirat             BGA.1551
      .N53 SZD-50-3 Puchacz         BGA.3782
      .N54 Slingsby T.49B Capstan   BGA.1360
      .N55 Slingsby T.49B Capstan   BGA.1118
      .N56 SZD-51-1 Junior          BGA.3505
```

PART 5 – ARMY GLIDING ASSOCIATION

AGA No.	Type	C/n	P/I	Owner/operator		Probable Base/Notes
AGA. 1	Rolladen-Schneider LS-4	4256		Wyvern GC "412"	Upavon	To BGA.4595
AGA. 2	Rolladen-Schneider LS-4B	4997		Wyvern GC "A8"	Upavon	To BGA.4596
AGA. 3	Rolladen-Schneider LS-7	7112		Wyvern GC "12"	Upavon	To BGA.4597
AGA. 4	Schempp-Hirth Discus B	206		Wyvern GC "388"	Upavon	To BGA.4720
AGA. 5	SZD-51-1 Junior	B-1933	(BGA.3699)	Wyvern GC "A6"	Upavon	To BGA.4594
AGA. 6	Grob G.102 Astir CS	1332		Sold		To BGA.4314
AGA. 8	Schleicher ASK21	21067	BGA.2742	Wyvern GC "EKG"	Upavon	To BGA.2742
AGA.11	Schleicher ASK21	21182		Kestrel GC "A7"	Odiham	To BGA.4573
AGA.14	Schleicher ASK13	13150		Wyvern GC "A2"	Upavon	To BGA.4593
AGA.15	Schleicher ASK13	13591	BGA.2385	Kestrel GC "A1"	Odiham	
AGA.18	Schleicher ASK23	23005		Kestrel GC "A5"	Odiham	To BGA.4662
AGA.20	Schleicher ASK-21	21568	RAFGGA.515 BGA.4317	Wyvern GC "A16"	Upavon	To BGA.4317
AGA.21	Schleicher K-8B	558	RAFGGA.558	Kestrel GC "A55"	Odiham	To BGA.4525

..@ AGA.4 was badly damaged after spinning-in nr Reading 14.5.95 and was rebuilt with new fuselage.
The remains of AGA.4 were rebuilt with wings from Discus B c/n 561 as BGA.4270.

PART 6 - IRISH GLIDING ASSOCIATION

The Irish Gliding Association's registration system is similar to that adopted by the British Glider Association although, latterly, the "IGA" prefix has given way to "EI" as the prime means of identification. Consequently, a number of existing older gliders were re-registered. The IGA listing has been up-dated from Air-Britain sources but the C of A status is at 31 January 1997. Thanks to Richard Cawsey for the changes this year.

Regn	Type	C/n	P/I	Date	Owner/operator	Probable Base	CA Expy
IGA.6*	Slingsby T.8 Tutor	-	IAC.6	.56	Eyre Square Shopping Centre		
			VM657		(Noted 5.99)	Galway City	
EI-100	SZD-12A Mucha 100A	494	OY-XAN	.95	J.Finnan & M.O'Reilly	Gowran Grange	1. 7.97
EI-102	Slingsby T.26 Kite 2	?	IGA.102	.54	Dublin GC	Gowran Grange	--
			IAC.102/BGA...		(Stored 5.99)		
EI-105	Schleicher Ka7 Rhonadler	775	IGA.7	.60	Dublin GC	Gowran Grange	14. 6.97
					(Noted 5.99)		
EI-108	Schleicher K8B	8486		.65	Dublin GC "08"	Gowran Grange	13. 4.97
	(Logbook shows c/n 8468)				(Flying 5.99)		
EI-111	Schleicher Ka6CR	6565	IGA.9	.67	Not known	Gowran Grange	30. 3.97
					(Noted 5.99) "11"		
EI-112	Schleicher ASK13	13131		.69	Dublin GC	Gowran Grange	9. 3.97
					(Flying 5.99)		
EI-113	Schleicher ASK13	13189		.69	Clonmel GC	Kilkenny	17. 7.97
EI-115	EoN AP.5 Olympia 2B	EoN/0/155	BGA.1097	.70	S Cashin	Gowran Grange	
					(On rebuild 4.96)		
EI-118	EoN AP.8 Baby	EoN/B/001	BGA.608	.73	B.Douglas	Gowran Grange	
			RAFGSA.217/BGA.608/G-ALLU/BGA.608 (Stored 6.95)				
EI-120	LET L-13 Blanik	175205	RAFGSA	.75	Not known	Gowran Grange	
			BGA.1730		(Noted 5.99)		
EI-121	Pilatus B4 PC11AF	199		.77	Clonmel GC (Stored 6.95)	Kilkenny	
EI-124	Grob G.102 Astir Standard CS 77		D-....	.80	Nutgrove Shopping Centre		
		1761			(Noted 5.99)	Churchtown, Dublin	
EI-127	Schleicher Ka6CR	662	PH-259	.	(Current 1993)		
EI-128	Schleicher Ka6CR	6649	D-1393	.	Dublin GC	Gowran Grange	
					(Noted 5.99)		
EI-130	Scheibe L-Spatz	200	BGA.2199	.	J.J.Sullivan	Gowran Grange	
			D-4707		"White Cloud"		
EI-132	Schleicher ASW17	17031	D-2365	.	Not known "TK"	Gowran Grange	17. 6.97
EI-133	Schleicher K8B	8557	D-8517	.91	Dublin GC	Gowran Grange	14. 6.97
			D-9367		(Noted 5.99) "33"		
EI-134	Schleicher ASW15B	15249	D-1087	.91	Not known "34"	Gowran Grange	7. 5.97
EI-135	Slingsby T.38 Grasshopper	758	WZ762	.91	Not known	Gowran Grange	
					(Wings from WZ756 or WZ768; stored as "WZ762" 5.99)		
EI-136	Schleicher ASK18	18007	BGA.2945	.91	Dublin GC	Gowran Grange	30. 7.97
			D-6868		(Flying 5.99)		
EI-137	Rolladen-Schneider LS3-17	3308	D-3521	.92	Not known	Gowran Grange	1. 3.97
EI-138	Schempp-Hirth Discus CS	089CS		.92	B.Ramseyer "BR"	Gowran Grange	
EI-139	Slingsby T.31B	902	BGA.3485	.93	P.Bedford Syndicate	Gowran Grange	2. 8.97
			G-BOKG/XE789				
EI-140	SZD-12A Mucha 100A	491	HB-647	.93	D.Mongey	Gowran Grange	
EI-142	Scheibe SF-27A Zugvogel V	6049	(EI-144)	.94	Not known	Gowran Grange	19. 7.97
			D-1444				
EI-143	Schleicher ASK13	13112	BGA.1501	.94	Dublin GC	Gowran Grange	
					(Flying 5.99)		
EI-145	Glaser-Dirks DG-200	2-88	PH-930	.95	Not known	Gowran Grange	
					(Noted 5.99)		
EI-146	Scheibe Zugvogel IIIB	1085	D-4096	.96	N Shortt & T Daly "TK"	Gowran Grange	
					(Noted 5.99)		
EI-147	Glaser-Dirks DG-200	2-22	D-6760	.97	Not known	Gowran Grange	

SECTION 8

PART 1 - ALPHABETICAL TYPE INDEX (UK & IRELAND)

Herewith a summary of BGA No/Code tie-ups but note the letters I and O are not used (except for JMO).

BGA No.	Code	BGA No.	Code
101- 230	None	3535–3545	FUL–FUW
231- 246	AAA–AAR	3546-3735	FUY–GCV
247- 605	AAT-ARR	3736-3770	GCX–GEQ
606- 628	ART–ASR	3771-3776	GEK–GEQ
629- 806	AST–BAC	3777–3817	HAA–HBS
807- 1245	BAE–BUL	3818	Not used
1246–1380	BUN-CAC	3819–3827	HBT–HCB
1381–1681	CAG–CNS	3828	Not used
1682–1819	CNU–CUM	3829–3990	HCC–HJV
1820–1821	CUP–CUQ	3991–4043	HJX–HMB
1822–2048	CUS–DEC	4044–4045	HMG–HMH
2049–2391	DEE–DUL	4046–4122	HMK–HQP
2392–2478	DUN–DYC	4123–4138	HQR–HRG
2479–2485	DYE–DYL	4139–4276	HRJ–HXB
2486–2489	DYN–DYR	4277	Not used
2490–2494	DYT–DYX	4278–4624	HXC–JMN
2495–3101	DYZ–FAF	4625	JMO
3102–3528	FAH–FUB	4626–4708	JMP–JQZ
3529–3534	FUD–FUJ		

A
BBOTT-BAYNES

SCUD I: HFZ *SCUD II:* AAA *SCUD III:* ACF AVA
AEROMERE - see CARMAM
ALLGAIER GEIER: EBP
ASC
FALCON: HPZ *SPIRIT:* HPY
AVIA
40P: AUW
AVIALSA - see SCHEIBE
AVIONAUTICA RIO - see CARMAM

B
AC *VII rep:* EQY

BIBBY *G.1:* HPK
BIRMINGHAM GUILD - see SWALES & YORKSHIRE SAILPLANES
BG.135: CRF CUF CXN CXP DCY DLZ
BOLKOW *PHOEBUS C:* CGX CHC CHJ CJB CJJ CKC GDD HTZ JHX
BREGUET *905 FAUVETTE:* CVJ DGV EGR ELJ EPN ESM

C
ARMAM - see AEROMERE/AVIONAUTICA RIO

M.100S MESANGE: CBR CLU DFP DTS DUC EPG EQM ETN FCH FKV HFP HGU HQF *M.200 FOEHN:* EQX EVC FXN HCN HGJ
JP.15/34 KIT-CLUB/15/36A AIGLON: DYL EDB FDC FQV HKF HKZ HMU HTW
CAUDRON *C.801:* EHF
CENTRAIR - see SCHLEICHER
101 PEGASE: EPK EQK ERX ESD ESH ESW ETJ ETM ETQ EVE EVM EVQ FAN FCB FCD FEH FFC FFS FGW FHJ FJK FJT FMK FNM FRD FRR FRV FRX
FVM FVN FVP FVV FWG FWX FWY FXD FXT GBU GCN GCY HDD HDW HES HKN HNY HNZ HRK HZF JQP *201 MARIANNE:* HTA *ALLIANCE SNC-34:* JHR
CHARD - see KING-ELLIOTT-STREET
COLDITZ *COCK REP:* JRZ JTA (Both are unrelated designs)

D
ES -see GRUNAU/EoN/NORD and including FOCKE-WULF WEIHE/SCHLEICHER production
KRANICH: BGT BQJ *OLYMPIA-MEISE:* AKD *108-68 WEIHE:* AKC BKC BNC BTV BWR EDL
DWLKK *PW-5 SMYK:* HYM HZB JCG JDW JKB JKE

EDGLEY *EA.9:* HPJ JRY

EICHELSDORFER *SB.5:* EHC EJH HYC
EIRI *PIK-20:* DFE DFK DFZ DHH DHN DHV DJN DJZ DKT DLJ DLY DMU DMV DMY DPL DQU DRT DVJ DVN DWS DYT DZT EAR EAT EBG JBH JGK

EoN: see DFS/NORD
 AP.5 OLYMPIA: AMK AMP AMR AMT AMW ANW APC APV AUU AVD AWU AZR AZT BBH BCK BEL BGR BGX BHC BJC BKK BKL BKS BKU BKX BLN BLP BLQ
 BLS BNG BPL BQQ BRL BWX CAF CAK CBS CGU CHK CPE CQG CTA CTS DBA DPU EI-115
 AP.6 OLYMPIA 401/403/419: BLJ BLK BVW DAL DTR   *AP.7 PRIMARY/ETON TX.1:* AQQ AQY AQZ CLJ FEZ   *AP.8 BABY:* ASS AST G-ALRH EI-118
 AP.10 460/463/465: BQM BQS BQT BRK BRQ BSQ BTG BTN BTQ BUG BUH BUK BUV BVN BWB BWE BWG BWU BXC BXY BYE BZB BZR BZS BZV BZW CAP
 CAN CAT CBV ELS

FAUVEL
 AV.22S: DSM   *AV.36C:* ETE
FEDEROV *Me-7 MECHTA:* HMZ HPS HPT HUQ JFY JFZ JGA
FFA *DIAMANT:* CDG CDW CGM CGS HGT
FOCKE-WULF - see DFS WEIHE
 KRANICH III: ENG

GINN-LESNIAK *KESTREL:* CJC
GLASER-DIRKS
 DG-100/DG-101: DFN DHJ DHK DHL DKQ DMD DRB DUY EDN EDP EKP ENU EPU FBH FBW FFU FYU HMS HWP JEZ JNZ JPF JRL JSM JTC
 DG.200/DG.202: DTA DTM DUQ DWJ DXN DYH EBR EDM EKA EME EMU EQP FQC HAT HBD HDH JAE JAJ JAW JDD JDP JHW JKF JKM JPW JRN EI-145
 EI-147
 DG.300/DG.303 ELAN: ESQ FAJ FBF FCM FDW FGT FJR FJS FJX FLC FLX FNS FPK FSR FSX FTS FUJ FUT FUU FWM FZW GAJ GBS HBE HBW HCU
 HCY HDR HMB HSB HVM JAB JDV JNQ JRC GGA.312   *DG-500/DG-505 ELAN:* GBZ HBP HEF HGV HHJ HNA HRC HYE JDN JQF JSX
 DG-600: FKB FNT FPW FQQ FVG   *DG-800:* HPU JBL JJH
GLASFLUGEL
 H.201 STANDARD LIBELLE: CFS CFX CFY CKF CKY CLM CLN CLP CLR CLV CLW CMH CMQ CMR CMS CMV CMW CMX CNE CNF CNG CNH CNJ CNP CNY
 CPA CPF CPM CRB CRQ CRS CRV CRW CSJ CSR CTU CUJ CUK CVL CVQ CWE CWG CWN CWT CWX CWY CWZ CXK CYG CZL DCC DMS DNL ECY FLT FLU
 GAU GDM GEE HAA HAD HAV HCQ HHY HJR HWC HWG JAS JBF JEU JGZ JHJ JNG
 H.205 CLUB LIBELLE: DBP DEQ DKZ DVM FAR FYG GCS HAE   *H.206 HORNET:* DKD DKM   *H.301 LIBELLE:* FEV GAN HLK
 H.303 MOSQUITO: DMN DPK DRN DTK DTV DTX DTY DUB DVZ DWB DWL DWO DWR DXA DXW EAK ECH ECS EDH EDJ FBN FWR HMT JEH JNR
 H.304: EHU ENT HMM   *H.604:* ECT
GROB - see SCHEMPP-HIRTH
 G.102/G.104 (SPEED) ASTIR: DFR DJD DJQ DJX DKR DKS DKU DKV DKW DKX DLH DLM DMH DMP DMR DNC DNE DNK DPJ DPQ DPY DQB DQE DQG DQR
 DRK DRU DRW DSH DSN DSU DUL DUX DWQ DWU DXJ DYF DZJ DZU EAC EAF EAW EBB EBM ECQ EEQ EKF ELN EQD EVK EVL FBR FCJ FDF FEB FEF
 FEX FFB FGK FHT FHW FJH FRL FSA FSH FSZ FTK FTR FXA GAT GBJ GBK GCL GDQ GEB HAU HBL HBM HBT HCS HFD HGB HJV HKB HKM HPM HQT
 HRA HSE HTD HTE HTG HTR HUN HVK HWK HXB HXM HXY HYQ HZC JAZ JBZ JCF JCR JCW JEK JFD JHE JHG JHN JKW JLR JML JNA JPJ JPM JQN
 JQT JRD JRM JRP JSD JSH JSK R8 R19 R97 EI-124
 G.103 TWIN ASTIR/ACRO: DRQ DSJ DSL EGN EQT EWP EWR EYS EZE FEA FFJ FQK FWC HBH HBK HCA HCJ HQS HWW JKV JLZ JQG JRW R70
GRUNAU (including DFS/FOKKER/HAWKRIDGE production)
 BABY: ABZ AQN ASC BTD CBK CMY CRM CYJ DNB DUW DWF EHX EMW HJB D-8006 D-3-340

HAWKRIDGE *DAGLING:* ALX ALZ
HIRTH *Go.III MINIMOA:* CLY
HOLS-DER-TEUFEL *REP:* FHQ
HUTTER
 H.17: ALW EPR HEY   *H.28:* HJM HPB

ICA
 IS-28B2: DEG DLT DLU DZR EHS EHW EJA HMG R93   *IS-29D:* DAM DBG DDJ DEN DEZ FDG FFN   *IS-30:* FDB FDP   *IS-32A:* FAV
ISF *MISTRAL C:* JBE JRS
ISSOIRE
 D77 IRIS: EET EJW   *E78 SILENE:* EBE EEU HPA

JANSSON *BJ-1B DUSTER:* ETL
JASTREB - see SCHEMPP-HIRTH

KING-ELLIOTT-STREET *OSPREY:* DCZ

LAK

LAK-12 LIETUVA: FXR GAB GCB GCJ HEG HGQ HGR HGX HHM HHW HLT HQG HRB HSR HTF JBS JBY JFW JQH   *LAK-17:* JQU
LANAVERRE - see SCHEMPP-HIRTH
LET
L-13 BLANIK: BVY BXR BXV BXW CAW CFD CUZ CVA CVB CYR DCL DEX DEY DGB DGP DKH DPD DVD EFX ESV EUG EVR FDV FLV FZS GAK HTY JDU
JGQ JNX EI-120   *L-23 SUPER BLANIK:* FXP FYP FYR   *L-33 SOLO:* FZY FZZ
LETOV *LF-107 LUNAK:* HXL

MANUEL

CONDOR: DJW   *WILLOW WREN:* BGA.162
MARCO *J-5:* HKW
MAUPIN *WOODSTOCK:* HCG HPG
MDM *MDM-1 FOX:* JCH JKC
MOLINO - see EIRI
MONNETT *MONERAI:* FAP JBV
MULLER *MOSWEY III:* DXY
MUNCHEN *MU-13D:* CZM DPG

NEUKOM

STANDARD ELFE S-2: FMR JGF   *ELFE PM3:* JRQ
NORD see EoN:
 2000: EPJ
OBERLERCHNER see SCHEMPP-HIRTH
 Mg19a STEINADLER: ERZ

PENROSE *PEGASUS:* HKJ

PIK see EIRI
 PIK-16C VASAMA: CGV
PILATUS *B4 PC-11:* CSN CSP CSW CUB CUC CUQ CUT CVG CVK CVM CVV CYA CYC CYK CZD DBC DLA DND DQM DRP DSV EQU HDA HDE HLC HSY HVH
JSY EI-121
POTTIER - see CARMAM

RAAB *DOPPELRAAB:* EVU

ROLLADEN-SCHNEIDER
LS1F: FQZ JPE JSF JST   *LS3:* DNQ ECP EEF EES EEX EEZ EFS EFZ EGE EVD GAD GDA GDN HWR HYH JDJ EI-137
LS4: EHK EHL EKV ELT EMB EMF EMG EMT EMY ENA ENE EQA ERV ESC ESE ESY ETG ETV ETY EUH FAQ FHL FJM FKG FLF FNU FVE FYH GBT GDJ
HEL HKX HLB HMX HNV HNX HPL HVV HXF HXT HXZ HZM HZY JBX JEP JJB JKP JLH JLJ JSB JSW
LS6: FBE FCP FMC FRA GAR GBG GBQ GBR GCM HAQ HBC HBJ HET HEW HEZ HFM HFQ HGP HHH HHT HHU HJC HJF HJP HJX HMK HPD HQL HQZ HRY
HSA HUM HYA JBP JBQ JBU JCB JDG JDH JGC JNP JNU JTD
LS7: FMY FPD FQG FQH FTV FTY FUV FVH FVQ FWF FWJ FWU FXE FYB FYK FYW FZV GBL GBY GCZ HAY HBA HBY HDX HEH JEJ JLK JSJ
LS8: HSZ HTL HTM HTP HTQ HTS HUG HUV HUW HVF HVL HVU HWL HWM HWS HXC HXN HXW HYF HYZ HZG HZP JBB JCL JCP JCY JDE JDK JDT JDY
JEA JEG JFB JFL JFX JGS JHU JHY JJK JJU JKD JKL JKN JLN JMB JMF JMO JMR JMT JMU JMW JNB JNJ JNK JNM JNW JPH JPL JPR JQD JRA
JRK JSQ JSU

SCHEIBE (including AVIALSA/ROCHETEAU production)

BERGFALKE: CDR CEV EBD EPZ EVT FVD HQC
L-SPATZ: DLR DPR DPT DUH DVR DZC EFN EFR EQL FAK FHE FPF FXX HCP HWQ JHB GGA.502 EI-130
ZUGVOGEL III: EBS ELV FRS FSU FVL FVY HKV HND HSH HXA EI-146   *SF-26 STANDARD:* DRL EDS EUM
SF-27A ZUGVOGEL V: DZV EKS EUE FHY FLZ FQF FQM FRM FUF FUQ FWH FZM GAV GBM GDW HGM HLU HMW HSG HSX HUS HVJ JSA EI-142
SFH-34 DELPHIN: EPM FKQ
SCHEMPP-HIRTH (including GROB/JASTREB/OBERLERCHNER production)
STANDARD AUSTRIA: BPN DBT DKB
SHK/SHK-1: CAQ CAR CBU CCB CGT CGZ CJK CJL CJN CLG CVH DJS DKK DMK DTG ECG FJZ FZC
HS.2 CIRRUS/CIRRUS VTC: CDH CEA CEC CFK CGY CJR CLQ CUS CVE CVF CWL CWR CWS DDM DVY FXG GCQ HEV HTU HUL HUR JJA JQW

HS.4 STANDARD CIRRUS: CKZ CLA CLH CNN CPU CQN CQR CQY CRH CRN CTB CTT CUL CYM CYP CYQ CYT DAS DDA DDR DFC DFY DGE DGX DLG DVS DXL DZF EEN EGK FBB FCN FGU FLW FMT FMU FRJ FRZ FVS FYJ FZK GAH GAL GCD GEP HAN HAX HFF HGG HJN HJU HJY HKC HKD HKR HKS HKU HMY HNM HRL HSV HVZ HWD HWF HWY HXX HZJ HZL HZU HZV JBJ JCJ JCN JCU JDS JER JEV JEY JFA JGN JGY JHA JHH JJJ JJM JLX JMH JNC JQS JRG JRT JTE

HS.5 NIMBUS 2: CQL CQP CQQ DAJ DDD DGY DHW DKL DMM DNG DTU DYU DYZ DZK EAJ EAM EEK EFB EFF EFT EGS EHP EHT EKR EKW FCS FPP FRⅡ FVF FVT HBF HBV HNE HNH HQN JGH JMN JMV JQE G-BKPM   _HS.6 JANUS:_ DTC EKB HNB HSP HTB HTH HUC HUH JAA JFE JLM JNL

HS.7 MINI NIMBUS: DPH DSE DSP DSW DXQ DXT EAV EBF EBK EDF EER EGW FHG FSL HQY HRQ JGU

NIMBUS 3/4: ENN ENP EQN ERU EVF FAM FBM FFK FGF FRP FWK FXQ HBR HCB HFX HKQ HNU HWN HYY HZA HZW JCT JDA JDZ JEQ JFQ JHF JJG JSC

DISCUS A/B/CS: FBY FDU FEJ FER FES FFT FFX FHR FKK FKM FLE FMG FMQ FNL FNQ FNR FQY FTW FUL FUP FXM FYM FYN FYX GCT GDR GDX HCⅡ HDF HDT HDZ HEE HEM HEN HGK HGL HGS HGZ HHP HHQ HJH HJL HKA HKL HKY HLD HLN HLQ HLS HLY HML HMP HMQ HPH HPR HPX HQJ HQM HQR HQW HRS HRX HSD HSJ HSQ HUZ HVR HWV HXH HYB HYU HZE JAH JAN JAQ JAR JBD JBN JBR JBW JCK JCX JDL JFC JFG JGL JGM JGR JHM JHT JHV JJD JJE JJZ JKR JKX JLC JLP JLW JMD JMM JPP JPU JQA JQC JQK JRR JSE R6 EI-138   _DISCUS 2:_ JNE JNF JNY

DUO DISCUS: HNF HNN HNW HQE HRW HSW HWB JAC JEM JFF JFU JGV JJP JPA JQQ

VENTUS A/B/C: EHH EKH EKJ ELG ELR ENJ EPX EUJ EUS FAW FBT FCK FDE FEG FEP FHS FJJ FJQ FMN FNN FPE FPL FQN FRB FRT FUH FUR FVB FVW FWD FYC FZH GAP GAS HAJ HED HFA HFV HFY HGN HHN HUY HVE HWH HXR HYG JBG JCE JEF JET JFP JFR JFS JJY JKH JKY JLA JLU JSL

VENTUS 2: HSL HUP HUX HVE HVT HVY HWA HXS HYL HZS JAF JBC JEX JGP JLB JLU JPD JPG JQL JQR

<u>SCHLEICHER</u> (including <u>CENTRAIR</u> production)

RHONBUSSARD: AEM   _RHONSPERBER:_ ABG

Ka2B RHONSCHWALBE: DCG DGT DJG DPP DRR ESK FBL FPU FSF HZN   _Ka4 RHONLERCHE II:_ CTF CWV EAL EUT HQH GGA.591

Ka6/BR/CR (RHONSEGLER): BKJ BKW BND BNH BQL BTJ BTM BUZ BVR BVX BVZ BWC BXT BYL BYM BYU BZQ BZX CBM CBY CCJ CJY DAW DCF DCW DDY DEP DEV DGK DHG DJE DJR DKG DKN DLP DNW DNX DQC DQF DQJ DQS DRA DRD DRE DRF DRG DRY DSG DSR DSY DUR DVG DYC DYJ DYN DYP DYQ DZW ECC ECF EDG EEW EGL ELY EPW EQQ FBZ FDR FGJ FHZ FKA FKH FKU FKX FLS FMM FNP FNW FQL FSE FTB FTF FUB FUM FWA FZR GAC GAW GBE GCP GDE GDF GEA GEF GEM HAB HBQ HEB HFB HPQ HRE HSM HUK HZH JCZ JEW JJV EI-111 127 128

_Ka6E:_ BYX CAC CAE CAG CAS CCA CCD CCG CCL CCR CCU CCV CDA CDB CDD CDF CDV CDZ CED CEG CEL CEM CEQ CEW CEY CFL CGB CGD CGE CGK CGN CHB CHZ CKL CLZ CPJ DGG DHM DHT DLE DMQ DQK DSB DUS DVE DVH DWC DXH EAH EFM EHM EKC EKX ETB FCR FND FPV FRE FSS FVZ FXC FXS FXU GDV HAP HJD HRF JAK JAL JHD JHL JLT JLV JSG

Ka7 RHONADLER: BFP BKN BQK BQU BRM BVB CFC CLF CLK CLT CMG CMZ CPG CQT CRA CWJ DBF DHY DJT DKY DMF DML DQX DRM DWE DWN DXM DYⅡ DYR EAU EDC EDK EFD ELX EMV ENC EPV ETR ETU EUQ EVB EVG FEL FGV FGZ FHU FJW FKW FLK FMD FMZ FPQ FQU FRF FTG FTU FXH GAQ HAG HCM HGC HHL HJK HNJ HSS JME EI-105

_K8B:_ CDC CDK CFF CGH CGJ CHU CLF CJM CKW CLX CML CMN CQD CTZ CYZ DDL DFQ DGA DHA DJB DJP DKC DLD DLS DMB DMG DMJ DNZ DQL DQP DQY DRV DRZ DSF DTN DUF DUK DVQ DWG DWH DXP EAZ EED EEM EFG EFP EHA EJF EJG EPT EQZ ESJ ESX ETD FAZ FBJ FCL FCQ FDD FDL FHN FJU FKJ FKT FLH FLP FLQ FNA FQD FQE FQR FQX FTA FTM FTN FVA FWL FXB FXW GCG GDB GDK GEG HAR HCZ HDN HDY HFW HJE HKK HLH HLV HMH HNG HRJ HRT HWE HWT HYN HYV HYW HYX HZX JAT JFT JGB JGD JGX JHK JLS JNN JQB JQJ JQZ JSN R95 GGA.562 NEJSGSA?? EI-108 EI-133   _Ka10:_ EVH

ASK13: CAV CBW CCC CCE CCF CCM CCP CCT CCW CCX CCY CCZ CDJ CEJ CEX CFA CFB CFG CFM CGQ CGR CHW CJD CKR CKU CKV CMK CRL CRT CWⅡ DDB DKE DLC DMX DNV DQA DRJ DVB DVC DVX DXV EBL EBZ EDU EKD ENY EPP EQE EQF ETS EUC EVJ EVP FAT FCW FEQ FFA FGR FHM FHU FMH FPX FSD FSQ FVC FVU FWB FWN FYV FZN GBA HAL HDC HMV HPE HSM HTJ HUD HUF HUU HVQ HVW HXJ HXP HXV JFM JGW JJC JKT JLE JLF JLL JLQ JMJ JMP JMW JMX JMZ JPC JPV JPY JRX JSV R3 R31 R34 AGA.15 EI-112 EI-113 EI-143

ASW15: CHT CJP CKP CZN DDS FBC FBD FCY FDA FJV FKE FME FML FMS FPB FQB FRK FTD FXY GCH GCR GCX GDS GDY GEH HEJ HGF HJZ HNT HQⅡ HTC HZD JAM JCA JDM JDR JED JGG JJX JPX JRE EI-134   _ASW17:_ CPD CTE EDD EGD EI-132

ASK18: DJJ DJK DLB DNJ DPA EMH EUX HRN HSU JHQ JKG JKU JMA JMK JPQ JPZ JSZ R48 EI-136

ASW19: DPX DSX DTD DTE DVL DVP DWZ DXX DZD DZG DZY EBJ EEH EJR ELA ENZ EPE EQG FFP FGP FNH FPJ FWP FWZ GCA GDP HCE HCV HDV HEⅡ HGH HHK HKT HLM HLW HNC HUA HWZ HXE HXU JBK JBT JCQ JDQ JES JFU JHC JHS JJL JKS JNT JRB JRV

ASW20: DST DTP DTQ DUT DVV DVW DXB DYE DYX EAE EBN EBX ECX EDE EEC EEE EEJ EEV EFA EFE EFH EFJ EFK EFL EFV EGP EHD EHV EHZ EJK EJL EJQ EKE EKU ELU ELZ ENV ENW EPF EPS EQJ ERA ETZ EUB EUD EUK EUY FAF FBA FBQ FCV FFH FHD FJE FKL FPH FPN FPT FRH FRW FTL FTP FTQ FUN FWS FZL HBU HCH HDJ HDL HEQ HGW HHS HJT HLZ HPC HQD HQK HRU HSK HTT HTX HUJ HUT HVP HVX HYK HZT HZZ JAG JAY JEE JEN JFJ JFK JHZ JMQ

ASK21: ECW ECZ EDW EGZ EHQ EKG ELE ENK EPD EQR ERH ERJ ESB ESU ETA FBV FWQ FYF FYV GAF GAG GAM GBB GBF GBN GBP GBV HCX HLG HLFⅡ HPV HPW HRR HTV HVG HYJ HYS HYT HZR JAD JAV JAX JBM JFV JGE JGJ JJR JKA JKJ JKQ JKZ JMC JMS JQX

ASW22: FDT FEU FGY FNF GBX HTN JNV   _ASK23:_ EVV EVW EVX EVY FCX GCF HKP JPB

ASW24/E: FLN FLY FMP FMX FNG FXJ GDT GDU GDZ HBB HBG HYD JCD JEB JEL JRU JTC

ASH25: FKN FLG FST FSY FUG FWW FXL FYD FYZ GCE HFL HLX HXQ JCV JDF JFN

ASW27: HUE HXD HYR HZQ JCM JDC JJF JJT JLY JNH JNS JPN JPS JPT JQM JQV JRH JSS

<u>SCHMETZ</u> _CONDOR:_ DQH

<u>SCOTT</u> _VIKING:_ AHU

<u>SHENSTONE</u> _HARBINGER:_ BNA

<u>SHORT</u> _NIMBUS:_ ALA

<u>SIEBERT</u> _SIE 3:_ EFC FRG

<u>SLINGSBY</u> (including <u>YORKSHIRE SAILPLANES</u> production)

T.1 FALCON 1: ABN FCZ   _T.6 KITE 1:_ AAF AAX ACH ADJ AGW AHC   _T.7 CADET:_ AWZ BQE

T.8 TUTOR: AJW AKW ALR AZK AZQ BAA BBG BCB BCH BDW BEF CRK CRZ CSL DQD IGA.6   _T.9 KING KITE REP:_ ELK

T.12 GULL I: AGE BED   _T.13 PETREL:_ AHW ATR   _T.15 GULL III:_ ATH HBZ

_T.21:_ AQE AQG AQH ARM ASB ATK AUG AUJ AUP AWD AZC BCF BCU BDA BDM BFD BFY BGB BGG BGP BGY BJF BJV BMQ BMU BQF BTH BUW BXK BYY BZA CEK DAR DCN DDC EJJ EJP ELH ERW ETP EUN EUZ FCF FCT FDY FEE FFG FFL FFW FFZ FGB FGG FGM FGS FHB FHC FJA FJB FJD FJF FKP FNC FTT GEN HCK HFC HFE HFG HNS HQB HRD JAU JQY   _T.25 GULL 4:_ APZ   _T.26 KITE 2:_ AUD AVF EI-102

T.30B PREFECT: ARK ASN AVT AZF BAN BQP CKJ DSA DTZ EBC EHE

_T.31B:_ BZY CHQ EVA FCC FCG FDQ FFQ FGA FGC FHK FJN FSJ FUW HAK HHG HLR HVB JCS JSP EI-139

T.34 SKY: AVB AVC AVL AVQ DPZ JPK   _T.38 GRASSHOPPER:_ FMA FSV GDC HEA HJJ HPP HVC JAP JBA JDB JJN JJS JND EI-135

T.41 SKYLARK 2: 724 AWX AXB AXP AXR AXU AYD AYY AZP AZY BAH BAM BAV BAZ BBA BBU BCX BDY BEA BFL CCS CHE CYH DCE

T.42 EAGLE: AXJ AZA BAY BBB BBQ BDF

T.43 SKYLARK 3: AXD AXE AXL AYF AYH BAC BAW BBT BCM BCP BCS BCV BCW BER BET BEX BEZ BFC BFE BFG BGD BGH BGL BHQ BHT BJB BJK BJW BKE BUT
T.45 SWALLOW: BCY BDR BEM BEY BFB BHV BJP BJY BJZ BKP BLU BML BNS BNU BPX BRC BRE BRG BSX BTA BVF BWK BXP BYB BYJ BYK BZL BZM CAX CHY DCS DHP DLX ELC EMK FRQ HBX R99
T.49 CAPSTAN: BJQ BNR BPD BPS BPT BPU BPV BPW BRA BRW BSE BSK BSS BST BUC BUR BZG
T.50 SKYLARK 4: BKA BLA BLE BLH BLW BLZ BMW BMX BMY BNE BNK BNM BNN BNP BNQ BPA BPB BPC BPE BPG BPJ BPK BPZ BQZ BSC BSG BSH BSR BSY BSZ BTK BUE ERB FXF
T.51 DART: BRB BRD BRT BRU BRY BSA BSL BSM BSV BSW BUF BUL BUP BVC BVE BVH BVJ BVL BVM BWJ BWM BWP BWQ BWS BWT BXE BXG BXH BXL BXM BYA BYC BYG BZC BZF BZH BZJ CAZ CBA DBB   *T.53:* CUD CXV CXW DHR
T.59 KESTREL: CFT CNV CNW CNX CPB CQJ CQM CSA CSB CSD CSF CSG CSK CTJ CTL CTM CTN CTP CTQ CTR CVW CVX CVY CVZ CWA CWB CWD CWF CXM CYN CZQ CZR CZS CZT CZU CZV CZW CZZ DBJ DBK DBN DBQ DBR DBS DEB DXU DYG ERY
T.65 VEGA: DWT DWW DXD DXE DXF DXG DXR DZA DZB DZM DZN DZP EAD EAG EBA ECJ ECK ECL ECM ECN EDA EDV EDX EDY EDZ EEA EEG EFW EGF EGG EGH EGJ EGT EGU EGX EHG EHN EHY EJB EJC EJD EJE EJS EJT EKY ELD ELQ EMJ EML EMN EMP EMR EMS EMZ FNK
STANDARD AUSTRIA - see SCHEMPP-HIRTH
SWALES - see BIRMINGHAM GUILD
SZD
SZD-8 JASKOLKA: DZS
SZD-9 BOCIAN: BJD BMM BVS CCN CEB CHF CKN CND CNM CTW CVP DAA DBW DBX DCR DDN DNF DRS EJY ESA FLL FUD FZG HFU HPF HQU
SZD-12A MUCHA: HDM EI-100 EI-140   *SZD-24/SZD-32 FOKA:* BZP BZZ CBP CMF CPC HGY
SZD-30 PIRAT: CBN CDX CEN CHG CHL CKD CNK CPV CPX CQC CQX CSV CTV CTX CUM CVC CVR CXL CYD CZE CZG CZJ DAN DAP DAT DAU DBD DBV DCH DCJ DDK DDW DFW DGH DHB DHZ DJA DLW DNT DTW EQB FKD
SZD-36A COBRA 15: CQW CRD CVN CVS CVT CXH CXJ DAC DAQ DCA   *SZD-38A JANTAR-1:* DAV DDE DDV DFL DFU DFV FNE
SZD-41A/SZD-48 JANTAR-STANDARD: DFX DHC DJL DJM DVK EKK ESP ETK FDX FHV FQT FTJ HBS HUB   *SZD-42 JANTAR-2:* DNU EUV HFJ
SZD-50-3 PUCHACZ: EUF EVS FBG FEN FTH FUY FWE FWT FYA FYL FZQ GBD GCK GCU GEL HAC HAF HAS HCC HCD HCF HDP HEP HFH HHA HHC HSC HYP JEC JRF JRJ JSR G-BTJV
SZD-51-1 JUNIOR: FFV FFY FHF FPM FTC FUS FZA FZF FZP FZX GCC HCR HCW HDB HDU HEK HHD HHE HMA HNK HQV HRG HRP JJQ JLG JMG JMY
SZD-55: GAX HEC HHR HRV HVD   *SZD-59 ACCRO:* HVA HWX

V

FW-FOKKER *FK-3:* HJA
VALENTIN *MISTRAL:* JHP
VOGT *LO-100 ZWERGREIHER:* ELL

W

ASSMER

WA21 JAVELOT II: CJG   *WA22 SUPER JAVELOT:* CEH   *WA26P SQUALE:* EEP HFN HGA HHX   *WA28F ESPADON:* JDX
WA30 BIJAVE: FNX HMR
WRIGHT *FALCON:* ECA

Y

ORKSHIRE SAILPLANES - see BIRMINGHAM GUILD/SLINGSBY

Z

LIN *24 KRAJANEK:* ATV

PART 2 - BGA COMPETITION NUMBERS & (TAIL) CODES

BGA Competition Numbers are issued to members/pilots and not to individual gliders but, beware, they change frequently. There is no formal list of Competition Numbers and little control over other gliders wearing similar or past numbers, or other (tail) codes- see below. The listing is a composite based on BGA information and reported sightings. Competition Numbers marked with an asterisk indicate where gliders have been noted with the numbers shown. In some cases because joint (syndicate) ownership is common this means that the Competition Number belongs to a member of a syndicate other than the one whose name appears as owner in the BGA's records. The member's name/glider type is shown where the glider concerned is not identified. This sub-section now includes the separate Alpha-Numeric (tail)-code listing.

No.	BGA No.	No.	BGA No.	No.	BGA No.	No.	BGA No.	No.	BGA No.
1	1144*	1	1804*	1	3123	2	869*	2	2680
2	2943*	2	3382*	3	(J.D.Bally)	3	1851*	4	G-STEN
5	1381	6	(G.H.Herringshaw)	6	2477*	7	3224	8	3720
9	1317	10	1818	11	(P.Potgeiter)	11	4606*	11	1991
12	4597	13	3323	14	1958	15	(G.D.Ackroyd)*	16	4472
17	2804	18	1475	19	4123	20	(J.S.Langberg)	20	2951*
21	4611	22	(T.S.Zealley)	23	3965	24	4586	25	3973
26	4473	27	4502	28	(D.S.McKay)	29	(J.D.J.Glossop)	29	3581*
30	2087	31	4251	32	3455	33	778	34	2397*
34	3629	35	3600	36	4409	37	(S.P.Robertshaw)	37	2556*
38	(N.P.Marriott)	38	4047*	39	3427	40	(B.Fitchett)	40	1788*
41	(R.Rutherford)	42	4478	43	(R.M.Grant)	44	(T.B.Sargeant)	45	3574
46	2458	47	1435	48	3463*	48	4079	49	1797
50	2632	51	(J.K.G.Pack)	52	(Army GA)*	53	1763	54	(R.Jones)
55	2801	56	4337	57	(M.J.Young)	57	4288*	58	4224*
58	(J.F.D'Arcy)	59	(B.T.Spreckley)	60	G-BPMH*	61	1262*	62	1514
63	(S.G.Olender)	64	(C.P.Jeffery)	65	(A.K.Lincoln)	66	4482	67	1052
68	3361	69	(E.C.Wright)	69	2595*	70	4589	71	4165
72	(S.Sturland)*	73	4092	74	2224	75	4267	76	2721
77	1377	78	2345	79	2528	80	4642	81	2453*
81	(J.R.Upton)	82	3920	83	3680	83	1584*	84	4261
85	(D.J.Robertson)	86	2310	87		88	2974	89	3209*
89	(J.A.K.Millar)	90	2981	91	(R.K.Hendra)	92	1839	93	3228
94	3624*	94	(S.A.White LS.7)*	95	1989	96	3807	97	3955
98	2692*	99	4157*	99	3777*	100	3962	101	1988
102	2494	102	2494	103	(C.J.Mayhew)	104	3389	105	4078
106	2513	107	2524*	107	(G.O.Avis)	108	3606	109	3395
110	3244	110	4695	111	(T.A.Joint)	111	4443	112	4344
112	G-SOOM*	113	(R.F.Whittaker)	113	3158*	114	(A.R.Hughes)	114	3791
115	3106	116	1794*	116	2124	117	1386*	117	2751
118	2911	119	(E.W.Richards)	120	3197	121	1316	122	(A.S.Decloux)
123	4370	124	1530	125	(S.R.Grzeskowiak)	125	3317*	126	3913*
127	3355	128	2071	129	2635	130	3398	131	(W.J.Dean)
132	2455	134	(A.D.W.Mattin)	134	3295*	135	3994	136	793*
136	3273	137	(S.J.Parsonage)	137	3861*	138	2698	139	1726*
140	4631	141	2625	142	1629	143	3298	144	3837
145	2657	146	1876	146	1876	147	2466	148	3683
150	1269*	150	(J.S.McCullagh)	151	1686	152	2501	152	3321*
153	1528	154	3279	155	(W.R.Davis)	156	(J.M.Airey)	157	2639
158	1811*	158	2869*	158	3373	159	(I.Johnston)	160	2461
161	(J.A.McCoshim)	161	929*	161	4676	162	(B.H.Owen)	162	3501*
163	(C.R.Dearman)	163	1089*	163	1299*	164	2088	165	(D.N.Greig)
165	1648*	166	(K.Kiely)	167	4072	168	4273	169	4145
169	(C.Buzzard)	170	3472*	170	4216	171	3643	172	2677
172	(G.D.Morris)	173	3607	174	(Mendip GC)	175	3124	176	4413
177	1493*	177	3126	178	3119	180	2901*	180	(A.Jacobs)
181	2827	182	1293*	182	1760	183	3933	184	1660
185	2182*	185	(K.G.Reid)	186	2744	187	3263	188	2775
189	2371	190	3401	191	2436	192	3533*	193	2727
194	3544	195	2115	196	2296*	196	3266	197	(P.M.Jessop)
197	4178*	198	1015	199	(J.P.C.Fuchs)	200	4226	201	(C.J.Lowrie)*
201	3433*	202	3107	203	3991	204	(M.A.Taylor)	205	3506*
205	(J.L.Birch)	206	3708	207	1974	208	3641	209	3204
210	4244	211	(G.A.Childs)	211	1222*	212	(Chilterns GC)	213	(K.S.Matcham)
214	2155*	214	(N.S.Jones)	215	(M.H.Jones & Ptnrs)	215	2937*	216	4326*
217	2960*	217	(R.J.Clement)	218	2794*	218	3707	219	3770*
219	(C.J.Ireland)	221	4483*	221	(P.J.Stratten)	222	1579	223	2936
224	3627	225	1336	226	1662	227	2337*	227	(A.T.Farmer)
228	1047*	228	3549	229	1683	230	3523	231	2918

No.	BGA No	No.	BGA No.	No.	BGA No.	No.	BGA No.	No.	BGA No.
232	3552	232	4437	232	4437	233	(J.A.Stephens)*	233	2226*
234	1723	235	(D.Briggs)	236	3717	237	3967	238	3411
238	3411	239	2862	240	1969	241	1737*	241	4214
242	3417	243	(J.A.McCoshim)*	244	3738	245	2079*	245	3976
246	3555	247	3604	248	1911	249	2950*	249	(J.A.Johnston)
251	2216	252	1624	253	1840	254	(D.A.Smith)*	255	1116
256	3540	257	3303	258	(B.D.Bate)	258	2323*	259	2229
260	4039	269	1853	261	2715*	262	(D.Allison/LS.8)	263	(R.N.Turner)
264	2806	265	2243	266	2200	267	2464	268	3475*
268	(G.K.Payne)	270	2346	271	3101	271	1513*	272	2426
273	(J.H.Fox)	274	4467	275	2856	276	(C.D.Lovell)*	277	3587
278	3789	280	4673	280	3663*	281	2812	282	(R.Henderson)
282	3397*	283	(D.J.Maynard)	283	2880*	284	1632	285	3599
286	2469	287	2268	288	2808	290	3713		
291	3868	292	(A.S.Edlin)	293	(D.E.Lamb)*	294	(S.C.Foggin)		
294	3751*	295	(R.M.Hitchin)	296	4737	297	4050		
297	2650*	298	(M.B.Hill)*	299	1913	300	(A.D.Evans)		
300	4630	301	3803*	303	(S.G.Olender)	303	1470*	304	4230
306	3981	307	2251	308	3877	309	(G.F.Fisher)	309	1533*
310	(S.Sheard)	311	1359	312	2939	313	4170	314	3339
315	4066	316	3879	318	3198	319	2728	320	2788*
321	4232	322	1860*	393	4238	323	2837		
324	2000	325	(P.F.Brice)	325	4296*	326	3631	327	1043
328	(J.T.Phillips)*	329	4128	330	3294*	331	1813	332	3516
333	3115	334	2327	335	3892	336	(A.B.Adams)*	337	1543*
338	(S.M.Turner)*	339	1722	340	2868	341	(C.J.Cornish)*	342	1732
342	2540*	343	1412*	345	2820	346	(G.G.Pursey)	346	3831*
347	1765	348	3170*	350	1348	351	1741	352	2785
352	1331*	353	2186	354	2472	355	1852*	355	3834
356	2003*	356	3805	357	(M.P.Brooks)	357	1397*	357	1568*
357	3372*	358	(K.J.Sleigh-Ives)*	359	4041	360	2180	361	(J.F.Beringer)
362	1362*	362	1420*	363	1854	364	4051	365	4019
366	1240	367	2522	368	1220*	369	3559	370	3206
370	4489	371	2235*	371	3381	372	1393		
373	1428*	374	(A.D.Hyslop)*	375	2283	376	4324		
377	(F.B.Jeynes)	377	1290*	378	2196	379	2906		
380	(P.J.Kite)	380	1817*	380	4054*	381	4032		
382	2979*	385	4168	386	G-ORIG	387	1769*	388	4674
389	(D.Peters)*	390	4134	391	724	391	2184*	391	3785
392	2231	394	3842	395	3139	396	4740	397	3538
398	3192	399	3322	400	(R.L.McLean)*	401	1795	402	1799
403	(J.A.Ayers)*	403	G-BSOM*	404	1268	405	3500	406	1361*
406	3320	407	2153	408	2754	411	3154		
412	AGA.1	413	2711	414	3339	415	1945	416	(H.T.Morris)*
417	1756	418	(J.C.M.Docherty)*	418	1524*	419	(M.L.Boxall)	420	(G.E.McAndrew)*
421	G-BNCN*	421	(A.C.E.van Gontard)	422	1392	423	1850		
424	(K.M.Davis) *	424	1284*	425	3899*	425	3714		
426	(J.E.Evason)*	427	(G.B.Brown)	428	1844	429	(C.M.Elsden)		
429	3780*	430	2756	431	2702*	432	4315		
432	3537	433	(D.C.Unwin)	433	2193*	434	4428	434	G-OAPW*
435	2826	436	(C.P.Long)	437	(W.A.Coates)	437	2271*	438	3723*
439	3121*	440	2282*	441	(F.C.Roles)	442	1672	443	2968
444	2175	445	4043	446	2959	447	(S.E.Evans)*	447	2343*
448	2605	449	1538	450	3747	451	(D.N.Griffiths)		
451	2870*	452	2789	453	1368*	453	2694		
454	(B.H.Owen)	456	2212*	456	2634	457	(G.P.Hibberd)*		
458	1487	459	3415	460	(N Wales GC)*	461	3388		
462	4021*	463	1201*	464	3133	465	1288	466	1688*
466	(K.Hampson)	467	(R.Starmer)	467	3866*	468	1858	469	4060*
469	4101*	470	2640	471	1369	472	(C.J.Davies)*	473	(J.H.Nunnerley)
474	1574	475	3886	476	4345	477	1916	478	(P.McLean)*
479	3443	480	(R.Boddy)	480	2289*	481	2707	483	(K.S.Whiteley)
483	2452*	484	3448	485	2206*	486	3895	487	4130
488	3136	490	2697*	491	2980	492	G-BRRG		
493	4169	494	2593	494	4553	495	3470	496	3808
498	3479	499	(D.P.Taylor)	500	(J.S.Halford)	501	(A.B.Dickinson)	501	1802*
502	3946	503	1902	504	1936	505	3975*	505	(R.W.Harding)
506	RAFGSA.506	507	(B.van Woerden)	507	3719*	508	1890	509	3924
510	3171	511	(J.C.Ennis)	511	2228*	512	(A.K.Mitchell)	513	(D.B.Almey)*
514	(I.P.Freestone)	515	2788	517	1298	517	2123*	518	3512*

No.	BGA No	No.	BGA No	No.	BGA No.	No.	BGA No.	No.	BGA No.
518	(T.Busby)	519	3375*	519	(A.F.Brind)	520	4667		
520	3651*	521	1696*	521	(C.M.Greaves)	522	(W.Young)		
522	3814	523	1983*	524	3762	525	(J.Fisher)		
525	1669	526	(J.R.Martindale)	526	4270*	526	1962*		
527	3261*	527	(P.Shrosbree)	527	1772*	528	4484	529	(J.A.Tanner)
530	(A.A.A.Maitland)	530	2597*	531	2491	532	1889	533	2353
535	1628*	536	(M.D.White)*	536	2041*	537	2490*	537	4379
538	3199	539	(I.B.Kennedy)	540	3733	541	2611	542	2294
543	(D.C.Phillips)	543	2649*	544	1885*	545	3419*	545	3739*
545	(C.V.J.Heames)	546	3739*	547	4535	549	867	550	1818
551	1987	552		552	2553	553	(Phoenix GC)*	555	(R.S.Maxwell-Fendt)
556	2300	557	(RAFGSA)	558	(K.S.Smith)	560	4291	561	4641
562	2057	563	4062	564	3207	565	4040	566	1748
567	3596	568	2301*	569	2673	570	4455	571	1127*
571	3151	572	(I.F.Smith)	572	2287*	573	(J.M.Anderson)	573	2499
574	3424	575	(P.P.Brightman)*	576	2504*	577	1546	579	1785
580	2473	581	(P.S.Worth)	584	4249	585	4082	586	2644
588	2239*	590	2924	591	3854*	591	(Scottish GU)	592	2481
593	2222	594	2529	595	(S.W.Bennett)	596	2195	597	1198
598	4263*	599	4068	600	916	601	4645	601	1714*
602	1657	604	2585	605	3820	606	2802	607	3898
608	(D.S.Taylor)*	609	3465	610	2114	611	(R.S.Johns)	612	3542
613	(D.King)	614	2162	615	2411	615	4541	616	4414
617	1986	618	3577*	618	4718	619	1436*		
619	1456	620	4113	621	3984	622	1671		
623	3223*	624	4213	625	(S.R.Watson)	625	1684*		
626	2821	628	1668*	628	4628	628	(D.Williams)	629	(B.A.Jones)*
630	3706	633	(R.J.Large)*	633	1821*	634	3462	636	(R.A.Holroyd)
636	2656*	637	(J.Dalrymple-Smith)	637	3917*	638	2396	639	2497*
640	2907*	642	(W.J.Tolley)	644	2565	645	(D.G.Tanner)	645	2580*
646	3109	647	2038*	647	2592*	648	2850*	648	2340
649	3711	650	1743	652	(M.A.Fellis)	652	2402*	653	1104*
654	(R.Strange)*	655	4095	656	1836*	656	3445	658	ZD658 "YX"
659	ZD659 "YY"	660	3554	661	(E.MacDonald)	662	(P.C.Gill)	662	3588*
663	663*	664	(R.A.Johnson)	664	3824	665	(J.B.Dalton)	666	3800
667	(T.J.Scott)*	668	3750	669	3645	670	(D.J.Hill/Ventus)	671	3152
672	2672*	673	(D.W.Lilburn)*	674	3400	675	1961	676	4646
677	(K.Fairness)	678	(H.M.Pantin)	679	1401	680	2037*	681	(M.P.Weaver)*
682	2990	683	1454	684	(S.C.Fear)	685	4450	686	(S.J.Jenkins)
686	1312*	687	3883	688	(L.Dent)	688	2326*	690	3709*
691	1982	692	4080	693	4106	695	2025	696	(E.R.Walker)
696	2778*	698	3283	699	2357	700	(S.J.McNeil)*	701	3259
702	1400	703	1727*	703	(M.R.Parker)	704	2376	705	3393
706	1816	707	(G.J.Lyons)	707	1752*	708	(R.G.Green)*	708	4065*
709	1670	710	2737*	710	4392	711	(M.Chant)		
712	4258	713	3306	714	2743	715	1383	716	2059*
717	4088	718	2352*	719	2783	720	3702	721	3156
723	3618	724	1616	725	3686	727	3130	728	2444*
728	3308	729	3801	730	3939	732	2413	733	2429
734	(F.G.Bradney)	735	3887	737	2645	739	1088	740	3935
741	1121	742	2841*	742	(E.K.Stephenson)	742		743	1615*
744	3291	745	2246	746	3963*	747	3910	748	(J.Hodgkinson)
748	3731*	750	2596	753	3525	754	3827*	755	2438*
757	2518	758	(J.Nash)	758	3456*	759	(J.M.Hall)	759	2168*
760	985*	761	2366	761	1706	762	4117		
764	(J.F.Morris)*	764	1570*	765	2848*	766	2379	767	2090
768	3590	769	(M.Tolson)	769	2172*	770	2291	771	(C.E.Wick)
771	2816*	772	3441	773	3134	774	2092	775	4252
776	(N.J.Leaton)*	777	(C.Paylor)	777	4359*	778	3673	779	3621
780	3141	781	1308*	781	4625	782	(B.R.Bartlett)*	783	3944
784	(P.M.Shelton)*	785	3453	786	2537*	787	(C.J.Bailey)	788	2181
789	(S.J.Wright)	789	1088*	789	1733*	790	3103*	790	4576
791	1886	795	3882	797	2764	798	2329	799	1640*
800	G-LEES	801	3757	802	4151	803	3535		
805	4030	806	3257	807	2555	808	1775*	809	1123*
810	2423*	810	(G.J.Hinder)	811	2119	812	1391	813	4660
814	1476	815	2457*	818	1685	818	1842*	819	4029
820	2604*	820	(S.M.Hall)	821	2321	822	3120	823	2129*
823	4362	824	2129	826	(P.F.Croote)*	827	4735	827	3821*

No.	BGA No	No.	BGA No.	No.	BGA No.	No.	BGA No.	No.	BGA No.
828	2479	829	3822	830	(A.C.Robertson)	831	2214*	832	1875
833	4202	837	1247	838	3956	839	2515	840	(S.J.Ayres)
840	3878*	841	3146	842	1822	843	3704	844	2684*
844	(G.R.Davey)	845	(M.K.Field)	845	3730*	846	1562		
848	2286*	848	4103	849	2706	850	2480*	851	1976*
853	3515	854	2899	855	3964	856	4289	857	(M.Uphill)
858	1689	859	1136*	861	1295	861	4069*	862	1519
864	(J.C.Rogers)*	865	3993	866	(H.S.Franks)*	867	(F.G.Wilson)	868	(D.F.Teasdel)*
869	2412	870	3904	871	3236	873	(C.Osgood)	873	1801*
875	(R.B.Christy)*	876	(See Note)	877	2354	878	1433*	879	2408
880	4225	881	2545	882	3870	883	G-ORTM*	884	2174*
885	2401	886	2445	887	3349	888	3575	890	2729
891	2691	893	2345	895	4175	896	3760	898	(I.W.Paterson)*
899	2081*	900	1949*	900	4200	901	(C.D.Stainer)	902	2825
903	3299*	904	(T.T.Caswell)*	904	2309*	905	1419*	906	2084*
906	2853	907	4425	908		909	2502	910	3856
911	4400	911	2382	912	(F.B.Reilly)	913	1536	913	4304*
914	(J.Archer)	915	2370	916	(P.I.Fenner)	916	4356*	917	(A.I.Galbraith)
917	1869*	918	1725	919	4004	920	(K.Neave)	920	3155*
921	4355	922	3710*	924	1798	925	(Scottish GA)	925	3909*
927	3363	928	3767	929	G-MOAK	930	4240	931	(R.L.Fox)*
931	2766*	932	4136*	933	4164	935	(G.W.Lynch)*	937	(J.Williams)
937	1637*	939	2647	940	3921	941	(R.J.Smith)	941	4046*
942	(C.C.Lyttelton)	942	3623*	943	2495	943	2941*	944	3522
948	1630	949	(G.J.Lyons)	949	3809*	950	3302	951	(D.Hatton)
951	2137*	952	(D.W.Smith)	952	3437*	954	(P.J.Pengelly)	954	3610*
955	2584	957	2505	959	2033	960	(C.J.Nicholas)	961	1598
962	4235*	963	3954	964	3483*	966	(G.Martin)*	968	(R.Grey)
968	2864*	969	3365	970	(P.Harper-Little)	970	4008*	971	2417
972	2350	973	3410	974	ZD974 "SY"	975	ZD975 "SZ"	976	(P.L.Bisgood)*
977	2068*	977	3961	978	1871	979	3959	980	(A.G.Kefford)
980	3585*	982	1915	983	3357*	983	2902.	985	(S.E.Crozier)
986	1655	987	(Booker GC)	987	3227*	987	3271*	988	3457
989	2164	990	2508	991	3858*	991	(G.D.Coppin)	992	2961
993	3148	994	1380	995	3468*	996	3180*	997	3304
998	(A.J.Clarke)*	998	1857*						

ALPHA/NUMERIC (TAIL) CODES

Code	BGA No	Code	BGA No.	Code	BGA No.	Code	BGA No.	Code	BGA No.
2B	4374	2CS	(P.G.Myers)	2F	4427	2UP	(R.A.Walker)	2UP	4081*
3D	(J.W.Davidson)	5UE	..(S.K.Armstrong)	7D	3167*	7H	4377	7Q	4364*
7X	4741	17K	1720	20L	2740..........	96X	(P.Henly)*	A1	4155
A2	(P.W.Rodwell)	A2	3872	A3	(P.R.Freeman)	A3	1943*	A5	4662
A6	2929*	A6	4594	A7	4573	A8	4596	A9	3885
A10	3622	A11	(Army GA)	A14	4316	A15	4177	A16	4317
A17	4173*	A19	3390	A20	(P.Stammell)	A20	4112*	A25	(G.W.Lynch)
A25	3341*								
A26	4322	A27	4422	A30	2126	A34	4531	A55	4525
A61	4318	A77	4125	A98	3438	AB	4387	AT	(M.Wright)
AV8	(M.Wright)	B	1031*	B	3366	B1	1500*	B1	(M.Griffiths)
B2	4385	B3	4373	B4	(N.A.Scully)	B9	(B.O.Marcham)	B9	3986*
B11	4342	B19	4728	B21	4385*	B33	4147	B35	3728*
B38	(I.R.Stanley)..	B38	3593*	B39		B96	1283	BB	3532
BR	2487*	BS	(S.J.C.Parker)	BT	(J.A.Horne)	BW	4563	BZ	1834
C	2191	C1	(J.B.Christey)*	C3	(P.A.Chapman)	C4	4186	C7	4404
C8	(C.Bradley)	C29	(C.R.Greengrass)	C29	4012*	C34	3997	C64	4193
CB	4668	CC	(B.T.Spreckley)	CKF	3371*	CL	4677	CU	(Camb Univ GC)
CW	(C.C.Watt)	CZ	4659	D	2317	D2	(I.D.Smith)	D3	2667
D4	(D.J.Westwood)	D4	4444*	D7	4262	D15	4158	D19	4048
D31	4210	D41	(J.McLaughlan)	D42	4464	D49	1734	D54	(K.L.Rowley)
D64	4121	D70	4146	DC	4405	DD	4300	DR7	(D.M.Ruttle)
DV8	(P.E.Thelwall)	DW	4465	E	285*	E1	4195	E2	4656
E3	4644	E8	4505	E11	2705	E11	4709	E60	3565
E60	(I.Dunkley)*	ED	3752*	EN	4346	ET	(P.N.Tolson)	EU	(J.Lee)
EW	(K.R.Walton)	EW	4632	EZ	4424	F	400*	F1	(A.J.Clarke)
F1	4452*	F2	(D.P.Francis)	F2	3918*	F3	4418	F4	1367
F11	3489	F15	(I.Mountain)	FK	(B.T.Spreckley)	FFK	4149*	FTI	3511*

Code	BGA No	Code	BGA No.	Code	BGA No.	Code	BGA No.	Code	BGA No.
G	698*	G1	(G.F.Read)	G1	4545	G2	3315	G3	(I.D.Smith)*
G7	4329	G41	4539	G46	698	G81	4380*		
G81	(G.Macdonald)	GR	4420	GS	(G.E.Smith)	H	2984		
H2	4558	H4	3222	H5	3185	H5	4399*		
H6	3478*	H8	(D.J.Howse)	H11	2552	H12	3732		
H17	490*	H20	(J.L.Whiting)	H23	1189	HB	(S.J.Harris)	HB1	4661
HCN	3847*	HF5	(H.Smith)	HH5	(D.L.Jobbins)	HL	4390	IM	(E.J.Rogers)
IM	4415*	IV	(S.A.Adlard)	J2	(D.Chalmers-Brown)	J3	3632	J4	(P.G.Sheard)
JA	4016	JB	4749	JD	1483	JH	4459	JH	2670
JM	(J.F.Morris)	JT	4687	JP	4713	J01	(N.Braithwaite)	JS1	4325
K	2989	K1	4340	K2	2147	K4	4310	K5	4338
K7	3682*	K8	4549	K8	(K.W.Payne)	K9	(C.T.Williams)	K11	(D.Wilson)
K13	3656	K18	(I.L.Pattingale)	K21	(N.Wall)	KE	4451	KL	3960
KM	4305	KR	4627	KW	4426	L	3163	L1	(R.M.Davies)
L2	(M.D.Allan)	L3	4381	L4	4657	L5	(P.B.Turner)	L5	3671*
L8	4153	L12	3611	L13	3660	L17	4703	L18	4253
L51	(G.M.Ariss)	L57	3454	L58	4192	L77	4665	L88	4323
L88	(P J Coward)	L99	1438*	L01	2770	LD	4347	LE5	(L.Clark)*
LH7	4386	LS	4189	LS4	2908	LS4	4293*	LS6	4119
LS8	4237	LT	4538	LX	4376*	M	3205	M1	4266*
M2	4449	M3	1035*	M4	4368	M5	3638	M4	4368
M5	3638	M7	(M.D.Evans)	M8	4278	M25	(R.J.Baker)	MB	(M.Bull)
MD	3704*	MF	(M.R.Fountain)	N2	3159	N2	3420*	N4	1914
N5	4207	N6	(S.Kerby)	N8	4352	N11	2142	N13	2031
N16	3657	N21	(K.W.Morton)	N23	3772	N25	4598	N27	1157
N29	3254	N31	1134	N51	2987	N52	1551	N54	1360
N56..3505		OP8	(S.C.Thompson)	OZ	(R.Lynch)	OZ	4458*	P	3274
P	3450*	P1	4567	P1	4567	P2	(P.O.Paterson)	P2	4442*
P3	4363	P4	4648	P5	(G.Bird)	P5	3826*	P5	4152*
P9	2443	P23	4615	P31	4017*	P61	4343	PM	3816
PH1	4577	PM3	4723	PN	(P.C.Naegeli)	PS	3571*	PW5	4311
PT	(P.W.Roberts)	Q5	3278	R1	4475	R2	4599	R3	RAFGSA
R4	4600	R5	4613	R6	RAFGSA	R8	4471	R9	3216
R10	4590	R12	4579	R15	4623	R17	4585	R18	4712
R19	RAFGSA	R20	4578*	R21	4572	R22	4614	R25	4587
R30	4571	R33	4582*	R35	2888*	R36	4612*	R37	4636
R38	4461	R39	4601	R48	4570	R49	4621	R52	4583*
R53	4503	R55	4470	R57	4603	R60	4584	R63	4622
R67	4697	R69	4655	R70	3015	R71	RAFGSA	R73	4555
R75	4604*	R77	4736	R80	4752*	R87	4608	R90	4592
R92	2207*	R97	RAFGSA Centre*						
RP1	4233	RW	4671	RY	4084	S	3642		
S1	(S.J.Harland)	S1	3802*	S2	4118	S3	3580	S4	4293
S5	4299*	S5	(G.N.Turner)	S6	4469	S7	2943	S8	4223
S13	2425	S14	1572	S19	4580	S21	4383	S22	(J.B.Gidding)
S22	4191	S27	(B.A.Fairston)	S30	2380	S32	(M.P.Wakem)*	S33	4710
S70	(S.Edwards)	S82	4045	S83	4268	SA	4669	SA1	2986
SA2	(Southdown AS)	SB8	(J.E.Bowman)*	SC	4654	SK1	4429	SR	4430*
SY	ZD974	SZ	ZD975	SGC	4690	SSC	3909*	T1	(P.H.Turner)
T1	G-OPHT*	T2	4406	T3	4328	T4	(N.D.Tillett)	T5	4301
T7	4466	T8	(P.G.Wright)	T10	2845	T15	1693	T21	948*
T27	4716	T30	625	T34	2397*	T34	(E.T.Murphy)	T42	(P.A.Green)
T42	614*	T45	873	T49	(J.A.Clark)	T49	1203*	T51	1164
T54	3756*	T65	2800	TE	4180	TL2	(S.J.Armitage)	TL2	4679*
U1	4335	U2	2255*	U2	4131	U9	4378	UIM	4037*
V1	4546	V2	(S.R.Jones)	V2C	(P.McLean)	V2T	4664	V3	(P.G.Sheard)
V4	4460	V5	4034	V7	2695*	V7	(J.A.White)	V11	4292
V19	4058	V57	4353	VB	4334	VMC	4182*	V	2420*
W1	3874	W2	4454	W8	(R.J.Welford)	W19	(A.J.Preston)	W19	4410*
W27	4407	W54	4231	WA1	(Scottish GU)	X1	4508	X2	(R.Arkle)
X5	(L.Gerrard)	X7	4330	X15	(R.Arkle)	X16	3988*	X16	(A.S.Edlin)*
X32	(A.J.O'Regan)	X50	4341	X70	(R.S.Lee)	X96	2414	XY	(See Note)
Y1	(M.A.Edmonds)	Y1	3416*	Y4	4280	Z	1873	Z1	3978*
Z1	4557	Z2	4653	Z3	(P.M.Wells)	Z4	3340	Z5	(E.W.Johnston)*
Z6	(A J.Preston)*	Z6	3654*	Z7	3640	Z8	4190	Z9	4696
Z10	4575	Z11	1374*	Z12	4704	Z22	(S.M.Veness)	Z25	2427
Z29	3727	ZC	4256	8378	4067	WB981	3238		

NOTES: (i)   Codes "SY" to "ZZ" are allocated to the Air Cadets Central Gliding School.
       (ii) There remain a few gliders which wear foreign identities but without nationality mark, namely:
             CCZV = BGA.4052, 1128 = BGA.2709, 3354 = BGA.3354, 7151 = BGA.3582 and 7827 = BGA.4161.
       (iii) Some imported, or ex British civil, gliders still carry their previous marks. Known examples include:

G-ALLF = BGA.599   HB-474 = BGA.2474   XA240 = BGA.4556
G-ALRD = BGA.416   N47247 = BGA.1904   XA302 = BGA.3786
G-ALRH = BGA.629   OK-0927 = BGA.4286   XE807 = BGA.3545
G-ALRK = BGA.490   OK-8592 = BGA.655   XN157 = BGA.3255
G-APWL = BGA.1172   TS291 = BGA.852   XN185 = BGA.4077
G-ATRA = BGA.1325   VM637 = BGA.895   XN187 = BGA.3903
G-BGBV = BGA.2800   VM687 = BGA.794   XN243 = BGA.3145
D-0060 = BGA.3742   WB920 = BGA.3221   XP490 = BGA.4552
D-1221 = BGA.2757   WB922 = BGA.4366   XP463 = BGA.4372
D-1868 = BGA.3285   WB924 = BGA.3901   XS652 = BGA.1107
D-2009 = BGA.4302   WB926 = BGA.3520
D-4667 = BGA.3142   WB943 = BGA.2941
D-5084 = BGA.2688   WB962 = BGA.3836
D-5826 = BGA.3186   WB971 = BGA.3324
D-6173 = BGA.4336   WB981 = BGA.1218
D-6508 = BGA.4182   WE992 = BGA.2692
D-8006 = See Note (iv) WT871 = BGA.3149
D-9421 = BGA.3442   WT898 = BGA.4412
D-3-340 = See Note (v) WT908 = BGA.3487
D-11-3224 = BGA.1147   WT910 = BGA.3953
G285 = BGA.285   WZ819 = BGA.3498
G498 = BGA.3245   WZ828 = BGA.4421

       (iv) D-8006 - Grunau Baby II, coded "XY", was last seen 10.94. The BGA number, if allocated, is not known.
       (v)   "D-3-340" - Grunau Baby was last seen 3.96. No identity is known.
       (vi) FDM - Last reported 8.97, identity not known.

SECTION 9

VHF RADIO FREQUENCIES

Private airstrips are only included in this list if details are commonly available in other published guides. Readers are reminded that all airstrips and many airfields are on STRICTLY PRIVATE property and reference to them here or in the main text of the Registers does not convey any public right of entry. In every case prior permission is required. For further details, including contact telephone numbers if seeking authority or permission to visit, readers are directed to the excellent annual POOLEY'S FLIGHT GUIDE and also to Brian Lockyears' very informative "FARM 'STRIPS' & PRIVATE AIRFIELDS FLIGHT GUIDE". To assist I have adopted the latter's nomenclatures for the Probable Base column in SECTIONS 1 & 2.

UNITED KINGDOM: Note: A-G=Air to Ground Communication & ATIS=Automatic Terminal Information Service.

LOCATION	TOWER/AFIS/A-G	GROUND	APPROACH	AREA RADAR	ATIS
ABERDEEN	118.10	121.70	120.40	188.30	121.85
ABERPORTH	122.15				
ALDERNEY	125.35		128.65		
ANDREWSFIELD	130.55				
ASHCROFT FARM/ WINSFORD	122.525				
AVIEMORE	130.10				
BAGBY	123.25		125.00/127.75		
BALDONNEL	123.50		122.00	129.70/122.3	
BARRA	118.075/130.65				
BARROW	123.20				
CHARITY FARM/ BAXTERLEY	120.30				
BECCLES	134.60				
BELFAST CITY	130.75		130.85	134.80	
BELFAST/ ALDERGROVE	118.30	121.75	120.00	120.90	128.20
BELLE VUE/ BARNSTAPLE	123.575				
BEMBRIDGE	123.25				
BENBECULA	119.20				
BERWICK-ON-TWEED/ WINFIELD	123.50				
LINLEY HILL/ BEVERLEY	123.05				
BIDEFORD	122.95				
BIGGIN HILL	134.80		129.40		121.875
BIRMINGHAM	118.30	121.80	118.05		126.275
BLACKBUSHE	122.30				
BLACKPOOL	118.40/135.95	119.95			121.75
BODMIN	122.70				
BOOKER	126.55	121.775			
BOSHIP/HAILSHAM	129.825				
BOUGHTON/ KINGS LYNN			124.15		
BOURN	129.80				
BOURNE PARK/ ANDOVER				126.70	
BOURNEMOUTH	125.60	121.70	119.625	118.65	121.95
BRAINTREE	130.775				
BREIDDEN/ WELSHPOOL	130.425				
BREIGHTON	129.80				
BRISTOL	133.85		128.55	124.35	126.025
BRITTAS BAY	118.25				
BROOK FARM/ GARSTANG	129.825				
BROUGH	130.55				
BURNHAM/ KINGS LYNN				124.15	
CAERNARFON	122.25				
CAMBRIDGE	122.20		123.60	130.75	
CAMPBELTOWN	125.90				

LOCATION	TOWER/AFIS/A-G	GROUND	APPROACH	AREA RADAR	ATIS
CARDIFF	125.00		125.85	124.10	119.475
CARDIFF/ TREMORFA HELIPORT	129.90				
CARK	129.90				
CARLISLE			123.60		
CASTLE BYTHAM/ GRANTHAM				130.20	
CHATTERIS	129.90				
CHESTER	124.95		123.35	130.25	
CHILBOLTON				126.70	
CHILTERN PARK				120.90	
CITY OF DERRY/ EGLINTON	134.15		123.65		
CLACTON	135.40				
CLENCH COMMON/ MARLBOROUGH	129.825				
CLOUGH FARM/ SKEGNESS				120.80/127.35	
COMPTON ABBAS	122.70			126.70/127.35	
CONINGTON	129.725				
COVENTRY	124.80	121.70	119.25	122.00	126.05
CRANFIELD	134.925		122.85		121.875
CROFT FARM/ DEFFORD	119.10				
CROFT/SKEGNESS				129.80	
CROMER/NORTHREPPS	129.825				
CROSLAND MOOR/ HUDDERSFIELD	122.20				
CROWFIELD	122.775		125.80		
CROWLAND	130.10/130.40				
CUMBERNAULD	120.60				
CURROCK HILL	130.10				
DEANLAND	129.725				
DEENETHORPE	127.575				
DENHAM	130.725				
DERBY/EGGINTON	118.35				
DISHFORTH	122.10				
DRAYTON ST LEONARD				120.90	
DUNDEE	122.90		122.90		
DUNKESWELL	123.475				
DUXFORD	122.075				
EAGLESCOTT	123.00				
EARLS COLNE	122.425				
EAST FORTUNE	129.825				
EAST MIDLANDS	124.00	121.90	119.65	120.125	128.225
EDINBURGH	118.70	121.75	121.20	128.975	132.075
ELSTREE	122.40				
ENNISKILLEN	123.20				
ENSTONE	129.875				
ERROL	129.9			122.90/126.50	
ESHOTT	129.825				
ETTINGTON	124.025				
EXETER	119.80		128.15	119.05	
FADMOOR	123.30				
FAIR ISLE	118.025				
FAIROAKS	123.425				
FARNBOROUGH	122.50		134.35	125.25	
FELIXKIRK				127.75	
FELTHORPE	123.50				
FENLAND	122.925				
FESHIE BRIDGE	130.10				
FILTON	132.35/134.50		122.725	127.975	
FULL SUTTON	132.325				
GAMSTON	130.475				
GARSTON FARM/ MARSHFIELD				122.10	

LOCATION	TOWER/AFIS/A-G	GROUND	APPROACH	AREA RADAR	ATIS
GARTON/HULL	122.075				
GLASGOW	118.80	121.70	119.10	119.30/121.30	129.575
GLENROTHES	130.45				
GLOUCESTERSHIRE	122.90		125.65	120.975	129.575
GOODWOOD	122.45				
GOODWOOD RACECOURSE	130.50				
GRAVELEY				129.55	
GREAT MASSINGHAM			124.15		
GREAT ORTON	129.825				
GREAT YARMOUTH	123.40				
GREEN FARM/ COMBROOK	124.025				
GRIMSBY/CUXWOLD	122.35				
GROVE FARM/ RETFORD				127.35	
GUERNSEY	119.95	121.80	128.65	118.90/124.50	
HALFPENNY GREEN	123.00				
HALTON	130.425				
HAVERFORDWEST	122.20				
HAYES	123.65				
HENLOW	121.10				
HENSTRIDGE	130.25				
HETHEL					
HILCOTE HELIPORT	122.95				
HINTON-IN-THE- HEDGES	119.45				
HITCHEN/ RUSH GREEN			129.55		
HUCKNALL	130.80				
HULL/MOUNT AIREY	123.65				
HUMBERSIDE	118.55		124.675	123.15	124.125
HUSBANDS BOSWORTH	129.975				
INCE	129.825				
INVERNESS	122.60				
ISLAY/PORT ELLEN	123.15				
ISLE OF MAN	118.90		120.85	118.20/125.30	
JERICHO FARM/ LAMBLEY	123.05				
JERSEY	119.45	121.90	120.30	118.55/125.20	129.725
KEMBLE	118.90				
KINGSMUIR			126.50		
KINLOSS	122.10				
KIRKBRIDE	129.825		123.60		
KIRKBYMOORSIDE	129.9				
KIRKWALL/ GRIMSETTER	118.30				
LAMB HOLM	129.825				
LANDS END/ST.JUST	130.70				
LANGAR	129.90				
LASHAM	129.90		125.25		
LASHENDEN/ HEADCORN	122.00				
LEEDS HELIPORT	129.75				
LEEDS-BRADFORD	120.30		123.75	121.05	118.025
LEEMING	122.10		127.75		
LEE-ON-SOLENT	132.65				
LEICESTER	122.125				
LEITH HELIPORT	122.25				
LEUCHARS	122.10	120.80	126.50	123.20	
LINTON-ON-OUSE	122.10		129.15		
LIPPETTS HILL	130.475				
LISKEARD HELIPORT	129.90				
LITTLE CHASE FM/ KENILWORTH			118.05		126.675
LITTLE GRANSDEN	130.85				
LITTLE STAUGHTON	123.925				

LOCATION	TOWER/AFIS/A-G	GROUND	APPROACH	AREA RADAR	ATIS
LIVERPOOL	118.10		119.85	118.45	
LLANBEDR	122.50				
LODGE ROAD/ TATTERSHALL THORPE			120.80/127.35		
LONDON (GATWICK)	124.225	121.815/121.95	126.825	118.95	136.525
LONDON (HEATHROW)	118.50/118.70	121.90/121.975	119.725		123.90
LONDON (STANSTED)	123.80	121.725	120.625	126.95	127.175
LONDON (WESTLAND)	122.90				
LONDON CITY	118.075		132.70	128.025	127.95
LONDONDERRY	134.15		123.625		
LONG STRATTON	122.95				
LONG STRATTON	122.95				
LOSSIEMOUTH	118.90		119.35		
LUTON	132.55	121.75	129.55	126.725	120.575
LYDD	120.70				
LYNEHAM	119.225	129.475		123.40	
MACHRIHANISH/ CAMPBELTOWN	122.10/125.90				
MANCHESTER	118.625 APP	121.70	119.40	121.35	128.175
MANCHESTER/BARTON	122.70				
MANSTON	119.925		129.45	118.52	
MANTON				123.40	
MARSHLAND/WISBECH	130.375				
MARSTON MOOR	122.975				
MAYPOLE FARM/ HERNE BAY			126.35		
MIDDLE WALLOP	118.275		118.275		
MILDEN/IPSWICH				125.80	
MILTON	122.10/122/30			130.20	
MONA	122.00				
MOUNT AIREY/HULL	123.65/124.675				
NETHERTHORPE	123.275				
NETHERTHORPE	123.275/128.525				
NEWARK/ STUBTON PARK	119.425				
NEWCASTLE	119.70		124.375	118.50	
NEWQUAY	123.40		125.55	126.50	
NEWTON	119.125				
NEWTOWNARDS	123.50				
NORTH COATES	120.15		122.175		
NORTH WEALD	123.525/129.975				
NORTHAMPTON	122.70				
NORTHOLT	124.975		126.450	130.350	
NORWICH	124.25		119.350	128.325	128.625
NOTTINGHAM	122.80				
NUTHAMPSTEAD				120.625	
OAKSEY PARK	122.775				
OBAN	122.775				
ODIHAM	122.10				
OLD BUCKENHAM	124.40				
OLD SARUM	123.20		126.70		
OLD WARDEN	123.05				
OTHERTON	129.825				
OXFORD	118.875	121.95	125.325		121.75
PANSHANGER	120.25				
PEAR TREE FARM/ KNUTSFORD			119.40		
PEMBREY	124.40				
PENZANCE HELIPORT	118.10				
PEPLOW				120.775	
PERRANPORTH	119.75/130.10			126.50	
PERTH	119.80				
PETERHEAD	122.375				
PLOCKTON	122.375				
PLYMOUTH	118.150		133.55		
POCKLINGTON	130.10				

LOCATION	TOWER/AFIS/A-G	GROUND	APPROACH	AREA RADAR	ATIS
POPHAM	129.80				
POPLAR HALL FARM/ ELMSETT	130.90				
PRESTWICK	118.15		120.55	119.45	127.125
RAYNE HALL FARM/ BRAINTREE	130.775				
REDHILL	120.275				
REDNAL	118.175				
RINGMER	129.90				
ROCHESTER	122.25				
RODDIDGE/FRADLEY	129.825				
RUSH GREEN	122.35				
SALTBY				130.20	
SANDOWN/IoW	123.50				
SANDTOFT	130.425			127.35	
SCARBOROUGH	130.125				
SCATSTA	123.60		123.60	122.40	
SCILLY ISLES/ ST.MARYS	123.15		123.15		
SEETHING	122.60				
SEIGHFORD	129.90				
SHAWBURY	122.10			120.775	
SHEFFIELD CITY	128.525		128.525		128.525
SHENINGTON	129.9				
SHERBURN-IN-ELMET	122.60				
SHIPDHAM	119.55				
SHOBDON	123.50				
SHOREHAM	123.15		123.15		132.40
SIBSON	122.30			130.20	
SILVERSTONE	121.07				
SKEGNESS	132.425				
SLEAP	122.45			120.775	
SOUTH BURLINGHAM			119.35		
SOUTHAMPTON	118.20		128.85	120.225	
SOUTHEND	127.725		128.95		121.80
SPANHOE			130.20/122.10		
ST MICHAELS	129.825				
STAPLEFORD	122.80				
STORNOWAY	123.50				
STOW/LINCOLN				127.35	
STRATHALLAN	129.90				
STRUBBY HELIPORT	122.375/130.1				
STURGATE	130.30				
SUMBURGH	118.25		123.15		125.85
SWANSEA	119.70				
SWANTON MORLEY	123.50				
SWINDON/DRAYCOTT	118.425				
SWINDON/REDLANDS	129.825				
TALYBONT	129.825		134.35/122.50		
TATENHILL	124.075				
TEESSIDE	119.80		118.85	128.85	136.2
THIRSK/ SUTTON BANK	130.40				
THRUXTON	130.45				
TIBENHAM	129.975				
TILSTOCK	129.90				
TIREE	122.70				
TOPCLIFFE	130.825		125.00		
TOWER FARM/ WOOLLASTON	122.70				
TRURO	129.80				
TURWESTON	122.175				
UNST	130.350				
UPFIELD FARM/NEWPORT	130.40				
VALLEY	122.10		134.35		
WADDINGTON	122.10		127.35		

LOCATION	TOWER/AFIS/A-G	GROUND	APPROACH	AREA RADAR	ATIS
WADSWICK/CORSHAM	123.10				
WALEY FARM/ CONINGSBY			120.80		
WALTON WOOD/ PONTEFRACT	123.625				
WARTON	130.80		124.45	129.725	
WATTISHAM	122.10			123.30/124.925	
WELLESBOURNE MOUNTFORD	124.025				
WELSHPOOL	123.25				
WEST FREUGH	122.55		130.05	130.725	
WESTON-ON-THE- GREEN	133.65				
WESTONZOYLAND	129.825			127.35	
WHITCHURCH	122.075				
WHITE WALTHAM	122.60				
WICK	119.70/130.575		119.70		
WICKENBY	122.45			127.35	
WIGTOWN	123.05				
WOLD NEWTON	130.125				
WOODFORD	120.70		120.70	130.05	
WOODVALE	119.75		121.00		
WROUGHTON	123.225				
YARNSCOMBE/ BELLE VUE	123.575				
YEOVIL	125.40		130.80		
YEOVILTON	122.10		127.35		
YORK/RUFFORTH	129.975				

IRELAND

LOCATION	TOWER/AFIS/A-G	GROUND	APPROACH	AREA RADAR	ATIS
ABBEYSHRULE	122.60				
BALLARENA	130.10				
BANTRY	122.40				
BELMULLET	123.60				
BIRR	122.95				
CASTLEBAR	122.60				
CASTLEFORBES	130.50				
CLONBOLLOGUE	128.55				
CONNAUGHT/KNOCK	130.70	121.90			
CONNEMARA	123.00				
COONAGH	129.90				
CORK	119.30	121.80	119.90	119.90	120.925
DONEGAL	129.80				
DUBLIN	118.60	121.80	121.10	124.65/129.175	124.525
GALWAY/CARNMORE	122.50	122.20			
GORMANSTOWN	122.70				
GOWRAN GRANGE	130.40				
INISHEER	123.00				
INISHMAAN	123.00				
INISHMORE	123.00				
KERRY/FARRANFORE	123.325				
KILKENNY	122.90/130.40				
KILRUSH	123.45				
NEWCASTLE	122.525				
PUNCHESTOWN	130.40				
SHANNON	118.70	121.80	121.40	124.70/127.50	130.95
SLIGO/STRANDHILL	122.10				
SPANISH POINT	123.30				
TRIM	123.30				
WATERFORD/PORTLAW	129.85			124.70	
WESTON	122.40				

AIR-BRITAIN SALES

Companion publications to the United Kingdom and Ireland Aircraft Registers are also available by post-free mail order from

Air-Britain Sales Department (Dept UK00)
19 Kent Road, Grays
ESSEX RM17 6DE

VISA/MASTERCARD/DELTA/SWITCH accepted - please give full details of card number and expiry date.

EUROPEAN REGISTERS HANDBOOK 2000   £18.00 (Members)   £22.50 (Non-members)

Current registers of over 40 Western and Eastern European countries plus Middle East.

AIRLINE FLEETS 2000   £16.00 (Members)   £19.50 (Non-members)

Over 1600 fleets listed plus leasing companies and "airliners in limbo".

BUSINESS JETS INTERNATIONAL 2000   £13.00 (Members)   £16.(Non-members) - Hard-Back
                                          £12.00 (Members)   £15 (Non-members) - Soft-Back

Complete production lists of all purpose-built business jets with full 20,000+ cross-reference.

TURBOPROP AIRLINERS AND MILITARY TRANSPORTS OF THE WORLD 2000   £To be announced

Detailed production lists of 80 turboprop airliner types including Eastern Europeans and military transports with full cross-reference index.

JET AIRLINERS OF THE WORLD 1949-2000   £To be announced

Including military transport, reconnaissance and surveillance types and variants. Detailed production lists of nearly 100 jet airliner types with expanded coverage on Soviet built types and purely military jet transports with full cross-reference index containing over 45,000 registrations and serials.

THE BRITISH CIVIL AIRCRAFT REGISTERS 1919-1999   £30.00 (Members)   £37.50.(Non-members)
Contains details of all known UK & Ireland registrations allotted with information on type/mode, c/ns, previous identities, original registration dates and subsequent identitiies or fate. Covers K100-K175, G-EAAA-G-EBZZ & G-AAAA-ZZZZ series including microlight registrations plus 1919-1929 Commonwealth usage of G-AU, G-CA, G-CY, G-IA, G-NZ & G-UA batches, 49,000 entries, 912 pages.

BOEING 707/720/C-135   £29,50 (Members)   £37.00 (Non-members)
Full production histories, airline and air force operators, almost 500 pages, 200 colour & nearly 100 b&w photos.

MILITARY TITLES: Air-Britain also publishes a comprehensive range of military titles:

RAF Serial Registers
Detailed RAF Type "Files"
Squadron Histories
Royal Navy Aircraft Histories.

IMPORTANT NOTE - Members receive substantial discounts on all of the above Air-Britain publications.

For details of membership - see overleaf.